# Periodic Table of the Elements

Key:

Uranium
92
U
238.0289
— Atomic number
— Symbol
— Atomic weight

Legend:
- MAIN GROUP METALS
- TRANSITION METALS
- METALLOIDS
- NONMETALS

| Group | | |
|---|---|---|
| 1A (1) | 2A (2) | |

**Period 1**
- Hydrogen 1 H 1.0079
- Helium 2 He 4.0026

**Period 2**
- Lithium 3 Li 6.941
- Beryllium 4 Be 9.0122
- Boron 5 B 10.811
- Carbon 6 C 12.011
- Nitrogen 7 N 14.0067
- Oxygen 8 O 15.9994
- Fluorine 9 F 18.9984
- Neon 10 Ne 20.1797

**Period 3**
- Sodium 11 Na 22.9898
- Magnesium 12 Mg 24.3050
- Aluminum 13 Al 26.9815
- Silicon 14 Si 28.0855
- Phosphorus 15 P 30.9738
- Sulfur 16 S 32.066
- Chlorine 17 Cl 35.4527
- Argon 18 Ar 39.948

**Period 4**
- Potassium 19 K 39.0983
- Calcium 20 Ca 40.078
- Scandium 21 Sc 44.9559
- Titanium 22 Ti 47.867
- Vanadium 23 V 50.9415
- Chromium 24 Cr 51.9961
- Manganese 25 Mn 54.9380
- Iron 26 Fe 55.845
- Cobalt 27 Co 58.9332
- Nickel 28 Ni 58.6934
- Copper 29 Cu 63.546
- Zinc 30 Zn 65.38
- Gallium 31 Ga 69.723
- Germanium 32 Ge 72.61
- Arsenic 33 As 74.9216
- Selenium 34 Se 78.96
- Bromine 35 Br 79.904
- Krypton 36 Kr 83.80

**Period 5**
- Rubidium 37 Rb 85.4678
- Strontium 38 Sr 87.62
- Yttrium 39 Y 88.9059
- Zirconium 40 Zr 91.224
- Niobium 41 Nb 92.9064
- Molybdenum 42 Mo 95.96
- Technetium 43 Tc (97.907)
- Ruthenium 44 Ru 101.07
- Rhodium 45 Rh 102.9055
- Palladium 46 Pd 106.42
- Silver 47 Ag 107.8682
- Cadmium 48 Cd 112.411
- Indium 49 In 114.818
- Tin 50 Sn 118.710
- Antimony 51 Sb 121.760
- Tellurium 52 Te 127.60
- Iodine 53 I 126.9045
- Xenon 54 Xe 131.29

**Period 6**
- Cesium 55 Cs 132.9055
- Barium 56 Ba 137.327
- Lanthanum 57 La 138.9055
- Hafnium 72 Hf 178.49
- Tantalum 73 Ta 180.9479
- Tungsten 74 W 183.84
- Rhenium 75 Re 186.207
- Osmium 76 Os 190.23
- Iridium 77 Ir 192.22
- Platinum 78 Pt 195.084
- Gold 79 Au 196.9666
- Mercury 80 Hg 200.59
- Thallium 81 Tl 204.3833
- Lead 82 Pb 207.2
- Bismuth 83 Bi 208.9804
- Polonium 84 Po (208.98)
- Astatine 85 At (209.99)
- Radon 86 Rn (222.02)

**Period 7**
- Francium 87 Fr (223.02)
- Radium 88 Ra (226.0254)
- Actinium 89 Ac (227.0278)
- Rutherfordium 104 Rf (267)
- Dubnium 105 Db (268)
- Seaborgium 106 Sg (271)
- Bohrium 107 Bh (272)
- Hassium 108 Hs (270)
- Meitnerium 109 Mt (276)
- Darmstadtium 110 Ds (281)
- Roentgenium 111 Rg (280)
- Copernicium 112 Cn (285)
- Ununtrium 113 Uut Discovered 2004
- Ununquadium 114 Uuq Discovered 1999
- Ununpentium 115 Uup Discovered 2004
- Ununhexium 116 Uuh Discovered 1999
- Ununseptium 117 Uus Discovered 2010
- Ununoctium 118 Uuo Discovered 2002

**Group labels (transition metals):**
3B (3), 4B (4), 5B (5), 6B (6), 7B (7), 8B (8)(9)(10), 1B (11), 2B (12)

3A (13), 4A (14), 5A (15), 6A (16), 7A (17), 8A (18)

**Lanthanides**
- Cerium 58 Ce 140.116
- Praseodymium 59 Pr 140.9076
- Neodymium 60 Nd 144.242
- Promethium 61 Pm (144.91)
- Samarium 62 Sm 150.36
- Europium 63 Eu 151.964
- Gadolinium 64 Gd 157.25
- Terbium 65 Tb 158.9254
- Dysprosium 66 Dy 162.50
- Holmium 67 Ho 164.9303
- Erbium 68 Er 167.26
- Thulium 69 Tm 168.9342
- Ytterbium 70 Yb 173.054
- Lutetium 71 Lu 174.9668

**Actinides**
- Thorium 90 Th 232.0381
- Protactinium 91 Pa 231.0359
- Uranium 92 U 238.0289
- Neptunium 93 Np (237.0482)
- Plutonium 94 Pu (244.664)
- Americium 95 Am (243.061)
- Curium 96 Cm (247.07)
- Berkelium 97 Bk (247.07)
- Californium 98 Cf (251.08)
- Einsteinium 99 Es (252.08)
- Fermium 100 Fm (257.10)
- Mendelevium 101 Md (258.10)
- Nobelium 102 No (259.10)
- Lawrencium 103 Lr (262.11)

Note: Atomic masses are 2007 IUPAC values (up to four decimal places). Numbers in parentheses are atomic masses or mass numbers of the most stable isotope of an element.

Standard Colors for Atoms in Molecular Models:
- carbon atoms
- hydrogen atoms
- oxygen atoms
- nitrogen atoms
- chlorine atoms

EIGHTH EDITION
AP* EDITION

# CHEMISTRY
## & Chemical Reactivity

### John C. Kotz

State University of New York
College at Oneonta

### Paul M. Treichel

University of Wisconsin–Madison

### John R. Townsend

West Chester University of Pennsylvania

BROOKS/COLE
CENGAGE Learning™

Australia • Brazil • Japan • Korea • Mexico • Singapore • Spain • United Kingdom • United States

**BROOKS/COLE**
CENGAGE Learning™

*Chemistry & Chemical Reactivity,* **Eighth Edition**
**AP\* edition**
John C. Kotz, Paul M. Treichel, John R. Townsend

Publisher: Mary Finch

Executive Editor: Lisa Lockwood

Senior Developmental Editor: Peter McGahey

Assistant Editor: Elizabeth Woods

Editorial Assistant: Krista Mastroianni

VP, Director, Advanced and Elective Products Program: Alison Zetterquist

Editorial Coordinator, Advanced and Elective Products Program: Jean Woy

Senior Media Editor: Lisa Weber

Media Editor: Stephanie Van Camp

Senior Marketing Manager: Nicole Hamm

Marketing Coordinator: Julie Stefani

Marketing Communications Manager: Linda Yip

Content Project Manager: Teresa L. Trego

Design Director: Rob Hugel

Art Director: John Walker

Print Buyer: Rebecca Cross

Rights Acquisitions Specialist: Dean Dauphinais

Production Service: Graphic World Inc.

Text Designer: Jeanne Calabrese

Art Editor: Patrick Harman

Photo Researcher: Scott Rosen

Text Researcher: Sue Howard

Copy Editor: Graphic World Inc.

Illustrator: Patrick Harman/Graphic World Inc.

OWL producers: Stephen Battisti, Cindy Stein, David Hart (Center for Educational Software Development, University of Massachusetts, Amherst)

Cover Designer: Riezebos Holzbaur/Tim Heraldo

Cover Image: Joanna Aizenberg Rights-Managed

Compositor: Graphic World Inc.

Library of Congress Control Number: 2010938984

ISBN-13: 978-1-1114-2704-7

ISBN-10: 1-1114-2704-6

**Brooks/Cole**
20 Davis Drive
Belmont, CA 94002-3098
USA

Cengage Learning is a leading provider of customized learning solutions with office locations around the globe, including Singapore, the United Kingdom, Australia, Mexico, Brazil, and Japan. Locate your local office at **www.cengage.com/global**

Cengage Learning products are represented in Canada by Nelson Education, Ltd.

To learn more about Brooks/Cole, visit **www.cengage.com/brookscole**

Purchase any of our products at our preferred online store **www.CengageBrain.com**

\*AP and Advanced Placement Program are registered trademarks of the College Entrance Examination Board, which was not involved in the production of, and does not endorse, this product.

Printed in the United States of America
1  2  3  4  5  6  7  14  13  12  11

# BRIEF CONTENTS

# CONTENTS

# Go Chemistry Modules  go Chemistry

Go Chemistry® modules are mini video lectures prepared by the book author, John C. Kotz, that may include animations, problems, or eFlashcards for quick review of key concepts. They play on video iPods, iPhones, iPads, personal video players, and iTunes and are correlated to the text by annotations in the margin. If you are using OWL, Go Chemistry is included in the Cengage *YouBook*. You can download two sample modules and purchase modules individually or as a set at **www.cengagebrain.com** (ISBN 0-495-38228-0). Ask your sales representative about available discounts.

# Go Chemistry Modules [go Chemistry]

Go Chemistry® modules are mini video lectures prepared by the book author, John C. Kotz, that may include animations, problems, or eFlashcards for quick review of key concepts. They play on video iPods, iPhones, iPads, personal video players, and iTunes and are correlated to the text by annotations in the margin. If you are using OWL, Go Chemistry is included in the Cengage *YouBook*. You can download two sample modules and purchase modules individually or as a set at **www.cengagebrain.com** (ISBN 0-495-38228-0). Ask your sales representative about available discounts.

| Chapter 1 | Basic Concepts of Chemistry | Module 1 | The Periodic Table |
|---|---|---|---|
| Chapter 2 | Atoms, Molecules, and Ions | Module 2 | Predicting Ion Charges |
| | | Module 3 | Names to Formulas of Ionic Compounds |
| | | Module 4 | The Mole |
| Chapter 3 | Chemical Reactions | Module 5 | Predicting the Water Solubility of Ionic Compounds |
| | | Module 6 | Writing Net Ionic Equations |
| Chapter 4 | Stoichiometry: Quantitative Information about Chemical Reactions | Module 7 | Simple Stoichiometry |
| | | Module 8a | Stoichiometry and Limiting Reactants (Part 1) |
| | | Module 8b | Stoichiometry and Limiting Reactants (Part 2) |
| | | Module 9a | pH (Part 1) |
| | | Module 9b | pH (Part 2) |
| Chapter 5 | Principles of Chemical Reactivity: Energy and Chemical Reactions | Module 10 | Thermochemistry and Hess's Law |
| Chapter 7 | The Structure of Atoms and Periodic Trends | Module 11 | Periodic Trends |
| Chapter 8 | Bonding and Molecular Structure | Module 12 | Drawing Lewis Electron Dot Structures |
| | | Module 13 | Molecular Polarity |
| Chapter 9 | Bonding and Molecular Structure: Orbital Hybridization and Molecular Orbitals | Module 14 | Hybrid Atomic Orbitals |
| Chapter 10 | Carbon: Not Just Another Element | Module 15 | Naming Organic Compounds |
| Chapter 11 | Gases and Their Properties | Module 16 | Gas Laws and the Kinetic Molecular Theory |
| Chapter 12 | Intermolecular Forces and Liquids | Module 17 | Intermolecular Forces |
| Chapter 13 | The Chemistry of Solids | Module 18 | The Solid State |
| Chapter 14 | Solutions and Their Behavior | Module 19 | Colligative Properties |
| Chapter 15 | Chemical Kinetics: The Rates of Chemical Reactions | Module 20 | Chemical Kinetics |
| Chapter 16 | Principles of Chemical Reactivity: Equilibria | Module 21 | Chemical Equilibrium |
| Chapter 17 | Principles of Chemical Reactivity: The Chemistry of Acids and Bases | Module 22 | Equilibrium: pH of a Weak Acid |
| Chapter 18 | Principles of Chemical Reactivity: Other Aspects of Aqueous Equilibria | Module 23 | Understanding Acid–Base Buffers |
| Chapter 19 | Principles of Chemical Reactivity: Entropy and Free Energy | Module 24 | Gibbs Free Energy and Equilibrium |
| Chapter 20 | Principles of Chemical Reactivity: Electron Transfer Reactions | Module 25 | Oxidation–Reduction Reactions |

The authors of this book have many years of experience teaching general chemistry and other areas of chemistry at the college level. Although we have been at different institutions, both large and small, during our careers, we share several goals. One is to provide a broad overview of the principles of chemistry, the reactivity of the chemical elements and their compounds, and the applications of chemistry. To reach that goal with our students, we have tried to show the close relation between the observations chemists make of chemical and physical changes in the laboratory and in nature and the way these changes are viewed at the atomic and molecular level.

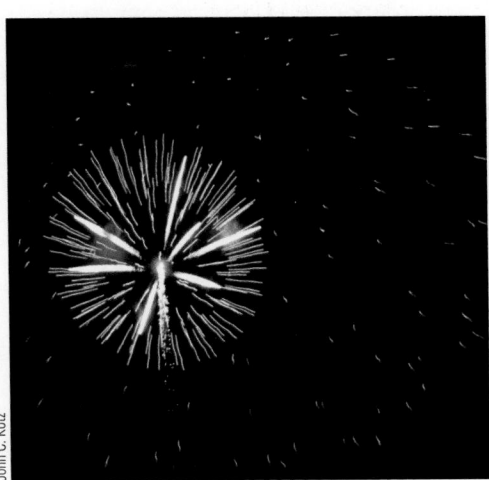

John C. Kotz

Another of our goals has been to convey a sense that chemistry not only has a lively history but is also dynamic, with important new developments occurring every year. Furthermore, we want to provide some insight into the chemical aspects of the world around us. Indeed, a major objective of this book is to provide the tools needed for you to function as a chemically literate citizen. Learning about the chemical world is just as important as understanding some basic mathematics and biology and as important as having an appreciation for history, music, and literature. For example, you should know what materials are important to our economy, some of the reactions in plants and animals and in our environment, and the role that chemists play in protecting the environment. In this regard, one growing area of chemistry, highlighted throughout this edition, is "green" or sustainable chemistry.

These goals have been translated into *Chemistry & Chemical Reactivity*, a book that has been used by more than 1 million students in its first seven editions. The first edition had a copyright date of 1987, and the copyright date for this edition is 2012. So, **this is the 25th anniversary of the book**. It is its silver (Ag) anniversary!

Looking back over the previous editions, we can see how the book has changed. There have been many new and exciting additions to the content of the book. In addition, there have been significant advances in the technology of communicating information, and we have tried to take advantage of those new approaches. A desire to make the book even better for our students has been the impetus behind the preparation of each new edition. With this edition, you will see a new approach to problem solving, new ways to describe contemporary uses of chemistry, new technologies, and improved integration with existing technologies.

## Emerging Developments in Content Usage and Delivery: OWL, Go Chemistry®, and the Cengage *YouBook*

Our ongoing challenge as authors and educators is to use multimedia to engage students and to help them reach a higher level of conceptual understanding. More than 15 years ago we incorporated electronic media into this text with the first edition of our *Interactive General Chemistry* CD, a learning tool used by thousands of students worldwide.

As technology has advanced, we have made major changes in our integrated media program. Through several editions we redesigned the media so that students can interact with simulations, tutorials, active figures, and end-of-chapter questions, first through the *Interactive General Chemistry* CD and then with **OWL (Online Web Learning)**. OWL, which was developed at the University of Massachusetts, has been used by hundreds of thousands of students in the past few years.

More recently, we developed and integrated **Go Chemistry** tutorial videos into the seventh edition and more fully into this new edition. These tutorials are 5- to 10-minute mini lectures on topics such as solving equilibrium problems, features of the periodic table, naming compounds, polar molecules, writing net ionic equations, and identifying intermolecular forces.

## What's New in This Edition

1. All **Example problems** in the book illustrate a **NEW approach to problem solving**. Each Example problem is broken down into the following categories: Problem, What Do You Know?, Strategy, Solution, Think About Your Answer, and Check Your Understanding. The "Check Your Understanding" questions are largely a revision of the Exercises from previous editions. Being included in the Example format should make them a more useful tool.

2. **NEW Interactive Examples in OWL** allow students to work approximately 70 examples from the book multiple times in slightly different versions to encourage thinking their way through the example instead of passively reading through to the solution.

3. At the end of almost every section in a chapter there are **NEW multiple choice Review & Check questions**. These are meant to be done in a few minutes to check the understanding of the section. In the Cengage *YouBook* these questions are interactive quizzes with feedback. (These questions could also be used in class by instructors to assess student understanding through electronic student response systems.)

4. **Strategy Maps** are a **NEW** feature of this edition. There are approximately 60 maps accompanying Example problems throughout the book. These are visual representations of the pathways to solving problems.

5. Except for Chapter 1, each chapter has **NEW extended Study Questions called *Applying Chemical Principles***. These help students apply principles learned across several chapters to real-world problems. Topics include the discovery of the noble gases, the discovery of elements on the sun, antacids, gunpowder, the rare earth elements, dating meteorites, and lighter-than-air ships.

**General Strategy Map**

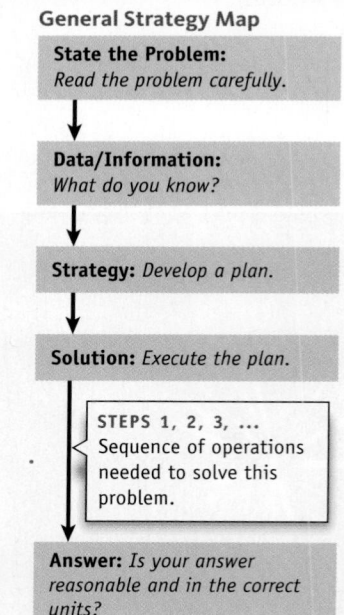

State the Problem:
*Read the problem carefully.*

Data/Information:
*What do you know?*

Strategy: *Develop a plan.*

Solution: *Execute the plan.*

STEPS 1, 2, 3, …
Sequence of operations needed to solve this problem.

Answer: *Is your answer reasonable and in the correct units?*

6. There are 2210 end-of-chapter **Study Questions** in the book in addition to the Check Your Understanding, Review & Check, and Applying Chemical Principles questions. Over 1900 of these questions are available in OWL, more than double the number of questions available in OWL in the previous edition.

7. Another **NEW** feature is a discussion of the Principles of **Green Chemistry** are noted in Chapter 1. This is followed by 10 articles on green chemistry throughout the book. See, for example, an explanation of atom economy (page 168), the synthesis of ibuprofen (page 385), and lithium and green cars (page 586). The development of this NEW feature was assisted by Professor Michael Cann of the University of Scranton, a green chemistry authority.

8. This edition of the book is also available as a Cengage *YouBook*, a digital textbook. This includes all the same content as the print book, but it also has clickable videos, animations, Guided Tours of figures with

tutorials, three-dimensional molecular models, and quick quiz Review & Check questions. Those who choose the Cengage *YouBook* will also have access to strategy maps with audio/video explanations done by one of the authors or by Salman Khan, who has published hundreds of video tutorials on the Internet in many areas of science.

9. The **Interchapters** on energy, biochemistry, materials chemistry, and the environment have been revised to bring them up to date with the latest developments.

10. There are 10 **NEW chapter opening stories**. See, for example, essays on gold (page 1), energy and diet (page 208), rubies and sapphires (page 300), chocolate (page 438), and green cars (page 582).

11. A total of **17 NEW Case Studies** have been added. These include the story of Ötzi, the Iceman of the Alps (page 58); free radicals and hair dye (page 363); methane hydrates and the Gulf of Mexico oil spill (page 538); a pet food catastrophe (page 565); and exploding lakes and Diet Cokes (page 629).

12. *Reorganization/addition/revision of material:*
    - A short introduction to energy has been moved from Chapter 5 to Chapter 1, and the units used in thermochemistry are introduced in the *Let's Review* portion of Chapter 1. This will assist instructors who wish to use this book in an "atoms-first" approach.
    - The material on metallic bonding and semiconductors has been moved from the materials interchapter into the chapter on solid-state chemistry (Chapter 13).
    - A short discussion on activities has been added to the equilibrium chapter (Chapter 16).
    - Many of the illustrations have been updated and/or redone.
    - New Study Questions have been added to a number of the chapters.

In addition, an entirely new *digital textbook—the* Cengage *YouBook*—has been developed for this edition. The Cengage *YouBook* is a fully electronic, full-color version of the book with extensive interactivity. You can use it with your desktop or laptop computer, to read the text, access useful databases, watch videos of chemical reactions, take a Guided Tour of a book figure, and much more.

## Audience for *Chemistry & Chemical Reactivity* and OWL

The textbook (both as a printed book and the Cengage *YouBook* digital version) and OWL are designed for introductory courses in chemistry for students interested in further study in science, whether that science is chemistry, biology, engineering, geology, physics, or related subjects. Our assumption is that students beginning this course have had some preparation in algebra and in general science. Although undeniably helpful, a previous exposure to chemistry is neither assumed nor required.

## Philosophy and Approach of the *Chemistry & Chemical Reactivity* Program

We have had several major, but not independent, objectives since the first edition of the book. The first was to write a book that students would enjoy reading and that would offer, at a reasonable level of rigor, chemistry and chemical principles in a format and organization typical of courses today. Second, we wanted to convey the utility and importance of chemistry by introducing the properties of the elements, their compounds, and their reactions as early as possible and by focusing the discussion as much as possible on these subjects. Finally, with the **Go Chemistry** modules and complete integration of *OWL*, we have incorporated electronic tools to bring students to a higher level of conceptual understanding.

Flame colors by salts of boron, sodium, and strontium.

© Cengage Learning/Charles D. Winters

The American Chemical Society has been urging educators to put "chemistry" back into introductory chemistry courses. We agree wholeheartedly. Therefore, we have tried to describe the elements, their compounds, and their reactions as early and as often as possible by:

- Bringing **material on the properties of elements and compounds** as early as possible into the Examples and Study Questions (and especially the *Applying Chemical Principles* questions) and to introduce new principles using realistic chemical situations.
- Using numerous **color photographs** of the elements and common compounds, of chemical reactions, and of common laboratory operations and industrial processes.
- Introducing each chapter with a **problem in practical chemistry**—for example, a short discussion of the energy in common foods or the source of lithium in car batteries—that is relevant to the chapter.
- Using numerous *Case Studies* and introducing new *Applying Chemical Principles* study questions that delve into practical chemistry.

## AP* Features

- A *correlation guide* of topics for the Chemistry AP* Course to pages in the text.
- Sections on *Preparing For and Taking the AP* Exam*, which offer strategies, examples of question types,

and helpful tips for mastering the AP* Exam in Chemistry.

## General Organization of the Book

*Chemistry & Chemical Reactivity* has two broad themes: *Chemical Reactivity* and *Bonding and Molecular Structure*. The chapters on *Principles of Reactivity* introduce the factors that lead chemical reactions to be successful in converting reactants to products. Under this topic there is a discussion of common types of reactions, the energy involved in reactions, and the factors that affect the speed of a reaction. One reason for the enormous advances in chemistry and molecular biology in the last several decades has been an understanding of molecular structure. Therefore, sections of the book on *Principles of Bonding and Molecular Structure* lay the groundwork for understanding these developments. Particular attention is paid to an understanding of the structural aspects of such biologically important molecules as DNA.

## Flexibility of Chapter Organization

A glance at the introductory chemistry texts currently available shows that there is a generally common order of topics used by educators. With only minor variations, we have followed that order. That is not to say that the chapters in our book cannot be used in some other order. We have written this book to be as flexible as possible. An example is the **flexibility of covering the behavior of gases** (Chapter 11). It has been placed with chapters on liquids, solids, and solutions (Chapters 12–14) because it logically fits with those topics. However, it can easily be read and understood after covering only the first four chapters of the book.

Similarly, chapters on atomic and molecular structure (Chapters 6–9) could be used in an **atoms-first approach** before the chapters on stoichiometry and common reactions (Chapters 3 and 4). To facilitate this, we have moved an introduction to energy and its units to Chapter 1.

Also, the chapters on chemical equilibria (Chapters 16–18) can be covered before those on solutions and kinetics (Chapters 14 and 15).

Organic chemistry (Chapter 10) is often left to one of the final chapters in chemistry textbooks. However, we believe the importance of organic compounds in biochemistry and in consumer products means that material should be presented earlier in the sequence of chapters. Therefore, it follows the chapters on structure and bonding because organic chemistry illustrates the application of models of chemical bonding and molecular structure. However, one can use the remainder of the book without including this chapter.

The order of topics in the text was also devised to introduce as early as possible the background required for the laboratory experiments usually performed in introductory chemistry courses. For this reason, chapters on chemical and physical properties, common reaction types, and stoichiometry begin the book. In addition, because an understanding of energy is so important in the study of chemistry, energy and its units are introduced in Chapter 1 and thermochemistry is introduced in Chapter 5.

Crystals of fluorite, $CaF_2$.

## Interchapters

In addition to the regular chapters, uses and applications of chemistry are described in more detail in supplemental chapters on *The Chemistry of Fuels and Energy Sources; Milestones in the Development of Chemistry and the Modern View of Atoms and Molecules; The Chemistry of Life: Biochemistry; The Chemistry of Modern Materials;* and *The Chemistry of the Environment.*

## Organization and Purposes of the Sections of the Book

### Part One: The Basic Tools of Chemistry

The basic ideas and methods that are the basis of all chemistry are introduced in Part One. Chapter 1 defines important terms, and the accompanying *Let's Review* section reviews units and mathematical methods. Chapter 2 introduces atoms, molecules, and ions, and the most important organizational device in chemistry, the periodic table. In Chapters 3 and 4 we begin to discuss the principles of chemical reactivity and to introduce the numerical methods used by chemists to extract quantitative information from chemical reactions. Chapter 5 is an introduction to the energy involved in chemical processes. The supplemental chapter *The Chemistry of Fuels and Energy Sources* follows Chapter 5 and uses the concepts developed in the preceding chapters.

### Part Two: The Structure of Atoms and Molecules

The goal of this section is to outline the current theories of the arrangement of electrons in atoms (Chapters 6 and 7). This discussion is tied closely to the arrangement of elements in the periodic table and to periodic properties. In Chapter 8 we discuss the details of chemical bonding and the properties of these bonds. In addition, we show how to derive the three-dimensional structure of simple molecules. Finally, Chapter 9 considers the major theories of chemical bonding in more detail.

This part of the book is completed with a discussion of organic chemistry (Chapter 10), primarily from a structural point of view.

This section includes the interchapter on *Milestones in the Development of Chemistry and the Modern View of Atoms and Molecules.* It also includes *The Chemistry of Life: Biochemistry* to provide an overview of some of the most important aspects of biochemistry.

### Part Three: States of Matter

The behavior of the three states of matter—gases, liquids, and solids—is described in Chapters 11–13. The discussion of liquids and solids is tied to gases through the description of intermolecular forces in Chapter 12, with particular attention given to liquid and solid water. In Chapter 14 we describe the properties of solutions, intimate mixtures of gases, liquids, and solids.

Designing and making new materials with useful properties is one of the most exciting areas of modern chemistry. Therefore, this section includes the interchapter *The Chemistry of Modern Materials.*

### Part Four: The Control of Chemical Reactions

This section is wholly concerned with the *Principles of Reactivity.* Chapter 15 examines the rates of chemical processes and the factors controlling these rates. Next, we move to Chapters 16–18, which describe chemical reactions at equilibrium. After an introduction to equilibrium in Chapter 16, we highlight the reactions involving acids and bases in water (Chapters 17 and 18) and reactions leading to slightly soluble salts (Chapter 18). To tie together the discussion of chemical equilibria, we again explore thermodynamics in Chapter 19. As a final topic in this section we describe in Chapter 20 chemical reactions involving the transfer of electrons and the use of these reactions in electrochemical cells.

*The Chemistry of the Environment* supplemental chapter is at the end of Part Four. This chapter uses ideas from kinetics and chemical equilibria, in particular, as well as principles described in earlier chapters in the book.

### Part Five: The Chemistry of the Elements and Their Compounds

Although the chemistry of the various elements is described throughout the book, Part Five considers this topic in a more systematic way. Chapter 21 is devoted to the chemistry of the main group elements, whereas Chapter 22 is a discussion of the transition elements and their compounds. Finally, Chapter 23 is a brief discussion of nuclear chemistry.

## Features of the Book

Several years ago a student of one of the authors, now an accountant, shared an interesting perspective with us. He said that, while general chemistry was one of his hardest subjects, it was also the most useful course he had taken because it taught him how to solve problems. We were gratified by this perspective. We have always thought that, for many students, an important goal in general chemistry was not only to teach students chemistry but also to help them learn critical thinking and problem-solving skills. Many of the features of the book are meant to support those goals.

## Problem-Solving Approach: Organization and Strategy Maps

Worked-out examples are an essential part of each chapter. To better assist students in following the logic of a solution, these problems are now organized around the following outline:

**PROBLEM**

    This is the statement of the problem.

**WHAT DO YOU KNOW?**

    You outline what information you have and begin to think about a solution.

**STRATEGY**

    You combine the information available with the objective to devise a pathway to solution.

**SOLUTION**

    You work through the steps, both logical and mathematical, to the answer.

**THINK ABOUT YOUR ANSWER**

    You ask if the answer is reasonable or what it means.

**CHECK YOUR UNDERSTANDING**

    This is a similar problem for you to try. Solutions to the problems are in Appendix O.

For many problems, a **strategy map** can be a useful tool in solving the problem. For example, on pages 42–44, we ask how thick the oil layer would be if you spread a given mass of oil on the surface of water in a dish. The density of the oil is also given. To help see the logic of the problem, the Example is accompanied by the strategy map given here.

There are approximately 60 strategy maps in the book accompanying Example problems. Many of the strategy maps in the Cengage *YouBook* digital textbook are accompanied by an audio explanation.

**Strategy Map** for Example 5

**PROBLEM**

*How thick* will an oil layer be when a **given mass** covers a **given area**?

**DATA/INFORMATION**

**Mass** and **density** of the oil and **diameter** of the circular surface to be covered.

STEP 1. Calculate the **volume** of oil from **mass** and **density**.

**Volume** of oil in **cm³**

STEP 2. Calculate the **surface area** from the **diameter**.

**Area** to be covered in **cm²**

STEP 3. Divide the oil **volume** by the **surface area** to calculate the thickness in **cm**.

**Thickness** of oil layer in **cm**.

## Review & Check: New Quick Review Questions

We have also added new, multiple choice questions at the end of almost every section. Students can check their understanding of the section by attempting these brief questions. Answers to the questions are in Appendix P. In the Cengage *YouBook* digital textbook the questions are clickable so you can quickly check to see if you know the correct answer.

## Chapter Goals/Revisited

The learning goals for each chapter are listed on the first page of each chapter and then are revisited on the last page. There the revisited goals are given in more detail. These goals are of great use in studying. Students can go through the goals and ask themselves if they have met each one. Furthermore, specific end-of-chapter Study Questions are listed that help students determine if they have met those goals.

## End-of-Chapter Study Questions

There are 50 to over 100 Study Questions for each chapter. They are grouped as follows:

**Practicing Skills**

    These questions are grouped by the topic covered by the questions.

**General Questions**

    There is no indication regarding the type of question.

**In the Laboratory**

    These are problems that may be encountered in a laboratory experiment on the chapter material.

**Summary and Conceptual Questions**

    These questions use concepts from the current chapter as well as preceding chapters.

**Applying Chemical Principles**

    These questions are preceded by a short description giving the background necessary to address the problem.

Study Questions have been available in the OWL Online Web Learning system for the last two editions. In this edition, we have more than doubled the number available. The OWL system now has over 1900 of the roughly 2200 Study Questions in the book.

Finally, note that some questions are marked with a small red triangle (▲). These are meant to be somewhat more challenging than other questions.

## Boxed Essays

As in the seventh edition, we continue to include boxed essays titled *A Closer Look* (for a more in-depth look at relevant material), and *Problem Solving Tips*. We have added or revised a number of the *Case Studies*, some of which deal with "green" or sustainable chemistry.

## A Word About the Cengage *YouBook*

The Cengage *YouBook* is an interactive digital version of the complete book and retains the paging integrity of the printed textbook. Either the digital version or the printed version of the book can be used in class.

The Cengage *YouBook* has clickable videos of reactions, Guided Tours of book figures, three-dimensional molecular models, searchable databases of chemical information, and the end-of-section Review & Check questions have clickable answers.

A unique feature of the Cengage *YouBook* is the **audio versions of the strategy maps**. For many of the maps in the book, one of the book authors will give a step-by-step audio explanation of the Example problem and explain some of the details of the strategy and solution.

Some of the audio strategy maps have been done by Salman Khan, who has recently been recognized around the world for his online tutorials, not only in chemistry but also in biology, linear algebra, geometry, trigonometry, statistics, pre-calculus, economics, money and banking, finance, and others. The web address for these tutorials is

www.khanacademy.org

All of Khan's tutorials are free and are on YouTube. The Cengage *YouBook* will link to those videos that Mr. Khan has done specifically for *Chemistry & Chemical Reactivity*. However, students should also explore all of the others for chemistry and for other areas of interest.

## Changes for the Eighth Edition

Significant additions to the book, such as a new problem-solving format, strategy maps, essays on green chemistry, and *Applying Chemical Principles* problems, have been outlined in the section on "What's New." In addition, we have produced many new photos and new illustrations and have continually tried to improve the writing throughout. The following chapter-by-chapter listing indicates more specific changes from the seventh edition of the book to this edition.

### Chapter 1 Basic Concepts of Chemistry

- New opening story: Gold!
- New opening section: we now outline the forensic investigation of the Iceman of the Alps.
- New *Closer Look:* Careers in Chemistry. Features a former student who is now a forensic chemist.
- New Section 1.2, Sustainability and Green Chemistry. Green chemistry is a theme used throughout the book.
- New *Closer Look:* Principles of Green Chemistry.
- New *Closer Look:* Element Names and Symbols.
- New Section 1.8: Energy: Some Basic Principles. Introduction to energy moved into this chapter from Chapter 5.

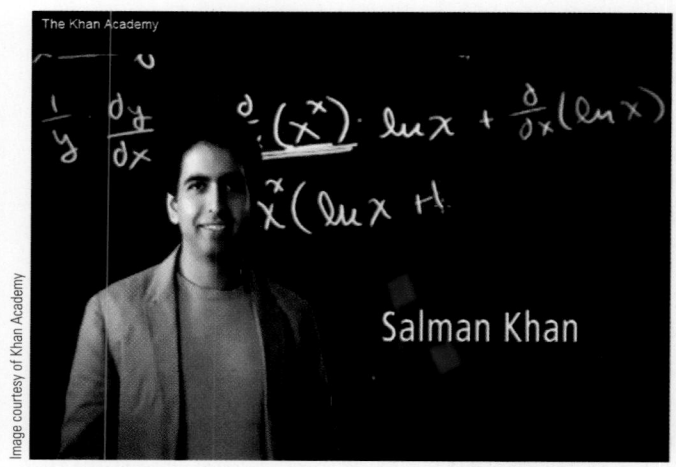

The Khan Academy

Salman Khan

Image courtesy of Khan Academy

**Salman Khan of the Khan Academy.**

- New *Case Study:* $CO_2$ in the Oceans.
- Twelve new or revised Study Questions (out of 46).

### Let's Review: The Tools of Quantitative Chemistry

- New: Energy units introduced. (This was in Chapter 5 in the seventh edition.)
- Strategy maps introduced into the book for the first time.
- Six new or revised Study Questions (out of 67).

### Chapter 2 Atoms, Molecules, and Ions

- New *Case Study:* Using Isotopes: Ötzi, the Iceman of the Alps.
- New *Case Study:* Mummies, Bangladesh, and the Formula of Compound 606.
- Fourteen new Study Questions (out of 165).
- *Applying Chemical Principles:* Argon—An Amazing Discovery.

### Chapter 3 Chemical Reactions

- New figure (Figure 3.9) to predict the species present in aqueous solution.
- Updated *Closer Look:* Sulfuric Acid.
- Twelve new Study Questions (out of 93).
- *Applying Chemical Principles:* Superconductors.

### Chapter 4 Stoichiometry: Quantitative Information about Chemical Reactions

- New opening story: The Chemistry of Pyrotechnics.
- New *Case Study:* Green Chemistry and Atom Economy.
- Three new Study Questions (out of 139).
- *Applying Chemical Principles:* Antacids.

### Chapter 5 Principles of Chemical Reactivity: Energy and Chemical Reactions

- New opening story: Energy and Your Diet.
- Section on basic principles of heat (pp. 209–211 in seventh edition) moved to Chapter 1 Let's Review.
- Ten new Study Questions (out of 110).
- *Applying Chemical Principles:* Gunpowder.

A device used to ignite gas burners. Depends on rare earth elements.

## Chapter 6 The Structure of Atoms

- New opening story: Fireworks.
- Boxed essay on orbitals rewritten and slightly expanded.
- Section on introduction to wave mechanics rewritten.
- Three new Study Questions (out of 84).
- *Applying Chemical Principles:* Chemistry of the Sun.

## Chapter 7 The Structure of Atoms and Periodic Trends

- New opening story: Rubies and Sapphires—Pretty Stones.
- Rewritten discussion of effective nuclear charge with new figures.
- Expanded discussion of configurations of transition metal electron configurations, especially Cr and Cu.
- New *Closer Look:* Orbital Energies, $Z^*$, and Electron Configurations.
- Clarified relation of electron attachment enthalpy and electron affinity.
- *Applying Chemical Principles:* The Not-So-Rare Earths.

## Chapter 8 Bonding and Molecular Structure

- New *Closer Look:* A Scientific Controversy—Are There Double Bonds in Sulfate and Phosphate Ions?
- New *Case Study:* Hydroxyl Radicals, Atmospheric Chemistry, and Hair Dyes.
- Electrostatic potential maps were introduced in the seventh edition. We have slightly enlarged the use of these figures for this edition and are using the industry standard software to create them.
- New *Case Study:* Ibuprofen, A Study in Green Chemistry.
- Eleven new or revised Study Questions (out of 96).

- *Applying Chemical Principles:* Linus Pauling and Electronegativity.

## Chapter 9 Bonding and Molecular Structure: Orbital Hybridization and Molecular Orbitals

- Updated discussion of molecular orbital theory.
- New *Case Study:* Green Chemistry, Safe Dyes, and Molecular Orbitals.
- New *Closer Look:* Three-Center Bonds and Hybrid Orbitals with *d* Orbitals.
- Thirteen new or revised Study Questions (out of 80).
- *Applying Chemical Principles:* Probing Molecules with Photoelectron Spectroscopy.

## Chapter 10 Carbon: Not Just Another Element

- New opening story: The Food of the Gods.
- New *Case Study:* An Awakening with L-DOPA.
- New *Closer Look:* Copolymers and Engineering Plastics for Lego Bricks and Tattoos.
- New *Closer Look:* Green Chemistry: Recycling PET.
- New *Case Study:* Green Adhesives.
- Deleted boxed essays on fats and oils, biofuels, dyes, and "super diapers," but some information on fats and oils was incorporated into the biochemistry interchapter.
- Fifteen new or revised Study Questions (out of 109).
- *Applying Chemical Principles:* Biodiesel—An Attractive Fuel for the Future?

## Chapter 11 Gases and Their Properties

- New *Closer Look:* SCUBA Diving—An Application of the Gas Laws.
- New *Case Study:* What to Do with All of That $CO_2$? More on Green Chemistry.
- Six new or rewritten Study Questions (out of 108).
- *Applying Chemical Principles:* The Goodyear Blimp.

**White phosphorus.**

### Chapter 12 Intermolecular Forces and Liquids

- New opening story: Geckos Can Climb Up der Waals.
- New *Case Study:* Hydrogen Bonding & Methane Hydrates: Opportunities and Problems. This is about the 2010 oil release in the Gulf of Mexico.
- New *Case Study:* A Pet Food Catastrophe.
- New *Closer Look:* Supercritical $CO_2$ and Green Chemistry.
- Seven new or rewritten Study Questions (out of 67).
- *Applying Chemical Principles:* Chromatography.

### Chapter 13 The Chemistry of Solids

- New opening story: Lithium and "Green Cars."
- New *Case Study:* High-Strength Steels and Unit Cells.
- New Section 13.3, Bonding in Metals and Semiconductors. This was moved to Chapter 13 from the Interchapter on materials.
- New *Case Study:* Graphene—The Hottest New Network Solid.
- Eighteen new or rewritten Study Questions (out of 62).
- *Applying Chemical Principles:* Tin Disease.

### Chapter 14 Solutions and Their Behavior

- New opening story: Survival at Sea.
- New *Case Study:* Exploding Lakes and Diet Cokes.
- New *Closer Look:* Reverse Osmosis for Pure Water.
- Four new or rewritten Study Questions (out of 106).
- *Applying Chemical Principles:* Distillation.

### Chapter 15 Chemical Kinetics: The Rates of Chemical Reactions

- Four new Study Questions (out of 88).
- *Applying Chemical Principles:* Kinetics and Mechanisms: A 70-Year-Old Mystery Solved.

### Chapter 16 Principles of Chemical Reactivity: Equilibria

- New *Closer Look:* Activities and Units of $K$.
- Eight new or rewritten Study Questions (out of 72).
- *Applying Chemical Principles:* Trivalent Carbon.

### Chapter 17 Principles of Chemical Reactivity: The Chemistry of Acids and Bases

- New *Case Study:* Would You Like Some Belladonna Juice in Your Drink?
- Rearranged the sections on Polyprotic Acids and Bases (Section 17.9) and Molecular Structure, Bonding, and Acid–Base Behavior (Section 17.10).
- Some of the 121 Study Questions were reorganized.
- *Applying Chemical Principles:* The Leveling Effect, Nonaqueous Solvents, and Superacids.

### Chapter 18 Principles of Chemical Reactivity: Other Aspects of Aqueous Equilibria

- New opening story: Nature's Acids.
- New *Case Study:* Chemical Equilibria in the Oceans.
- Several new and modified Study Questions (out of 112).
- *Applying Chemical Principles:* Everything That Glitters. . . .

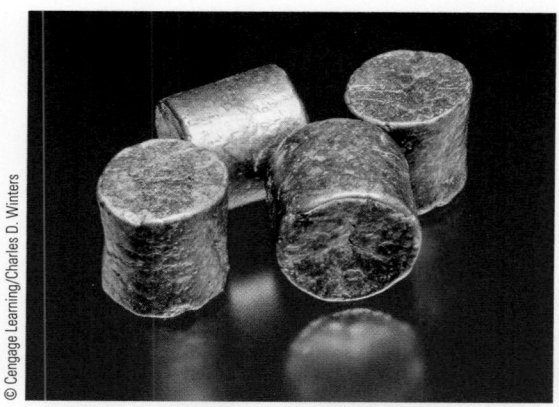

Samples of cobalt metal.

### Chapter 19 Principles of Chemical Reactivity: Entropy and Free Energy

- New opening story: Hydrogen for the Future?
- Given the key role of thermodynamics in chemistry, this chapter was carefully revised. Sections on free energy were reorganized.
- Three modified or new Study Questions (out of 84).
- *Applying Chemical Principles:* Are Diamonds Forever?

### Chapter 20 Principles of Chemical Reactivity: Electron Transfer Reactions

- New opening story: Battery Power.
- Problem Solving Tip on balancing equations for reactions in basic solution was revised.
- Fourteen new Study Questions (out of 103).
- *Applying Chemical Principles:* Sacrifice!

### Chapter 21 The Chemistry of the Main Group Elements

- Six new Study Questions (out of 106).
- *Applying Chemical Principles:* van Arkel Triangles and Bonding.

### Chapter 22 The Chemistry of the Transition Elements

- *Applying Chemical Principles:* Green Catalysts.

### Chapter 23 Nuclear Chemistry

- The *Closer Look:* The Search for New Elements was updated with the newest discoveries.
- Study Questions were reorganized.
- *Applying Chemical Principles:* The Age of Meteorites.

## Alternate Versions
### Cengage *YouBook* with OWL

The Cengage *YouBook* is a Flash-based, interactive, and customizable eBook version available with OWL. The teacher text edit feature allows for modification of the narrative by adding notes, re-ordering entire sections and chapters, and hiding content. Additional assets include animated figures, video clips, and student highlighting and note tools. See the OWL description below for more details.

## Supporting Materials

### ◔WL
### OWL for General Chemistry

**Instant Access OWL with Cengage *YouBook* (6 months)**
**ISBN-10: 1-111-30524-2; ISBN-13: 978-1-111-30524-6**

**Instant Access OWL with Cengage *YouBook* (24 months)**
**ISBN-10: 1-111-30521-8; ISBN-13: 978-1-111-30521-5**

By Roberta Day and Beatrice Botch of the University of Massachusetts, Amherst, and William Vining of the State University of New York at Oneonta.

**OWL** Online Web Learning offers more assignable, gradable content (including end-of-chapter questions specific to this textbook) and more reliability and flexibility than any other system. OWL's powerful course management tools allow teachers to control due dates, number of attempts, and whether students see answers or receive feedback on how to solve problems. OWL includes the Cengage *YouBook*, a Flash-based eBook that is interactive and customizable. It features a text edit tool that allows teachers to modify the textbook narrative as needed. With the Cengage *YouBook*, teachers can quickly re-order entire sections and chapters or hide any content they don't teach to create an eBook that perfectly matches their syllabus. Teachers can further customize the Cengage *YouBook* by publishing web links. Additional media assets include animated figures, video clips, highlighting, notes, and more.

Developed by chemistry instructors for teaching chemistry, OWL is the only system specifically designed to support **mastery learning**, where students work as long as they need to master each chemical concept and skill. OWL has already helped hundreds of thousands of students master chemistry through a wide range of assignment types, including tutorials, interactive simulations, and algorithmically generated homework questions that provide instant, answer-specific feedback.

OWL is continually enhanced with online learning tools to address the various learning styles of today's students such as:

- **Quick Prep** review courses that help students learn essential skills to succeed in General and Organic Chemistry
- **Jmol** molecular visualization program for rotating molecules and measuring bond distances and angles
- **Go Chemistry**® mini video lectures on key concepts that students can play on their computers or download to their video iPods, smart phones, or personal video players
- For this text, OWL includes **How Do I Solve It** problem-solving exercises, new **Interactive Example** assignments, as well as parameterized end-of-chapter questions and **Student Self Assessment** questions

In addition, when you become an OWL user, you can expect service that goes far beyond the ordinary.

For more information about available discounts or to see a demo, please contact your sales representative or visit us at **www.cengage.com/owl**.

### FOR THE TEACHER

Supporting teacher materials are available to qualified adopters. Please consult your sales representative for details. Visit **login.cengage.com** and search for this book to access the Instructor's Companion Site, where you can

- See samples of materials
- Request a sample copy
- Download digital files of the ExamView test bank and other helpful materials for instructors and students

### PowerLecture CD/DVD Package with JoinIn® and ExamView®

**ISBN-10: 1-111-42719-4; ISBN-13: 978-1-111-42719-1**

This digital library and presentation tool that includes:

- **PowerPoint® lecture slides**, written specially for *Chemistry & Chemical Reactivity*, which teachers can customize by importing their own lecture slides or other materials.
- Image libraries that contain **digital files for all text art, most photographs, all numbered tables, and multimedia animations** in a variety of digital formats. These files can be used to print transparencies, create your own PowerPoint slides, and supplement your lectures.
- Digital files of the complete **Instructor's Resource Manual** and **ExamView test bank.**
- Sample chapters from the **Student Solutions Manual** and **Study Guide.**
- **ExamView testing software** that enables you to create, deliver, and customize tests using the more than 1250 test bank questions written specifically for this text by David Treichel, Nebraska Wesleyan University.
- **JoinIn student response (clicker) questions** written for this book for use with the classroom response system of the instructor's choice.

### Instructor's Companion Site

Go to **login.cengage.com** and search for this book to access the Instructor's Companion site, which has resources such as a Blackboard version of ExamView.

### Instructor's Resource Manual

by John Vincent, The University of Alabama

**ISBN-10: 1-111-42697-X; ISBN-13: 978-1-111-42697-2**

Available both on the PowerLecture Instructor's Resource DVD and in print, this comprehensive resource contains worked-out solutions to *all* end-of-chapter Study Questions and features ideas for instructors on how to fully utilize resources and technology in their courses. It provides questions for electronic response (clicker) systems, suggests classroom demonstrations, and emphasizes good and innovative teaching practices.

## Transparencies

**ISBN-10: 1-111-57489-8; ISBN-13: 978-1-111-57489-5**

A collection of 150 full-color transparencies of key images selected from the text by the authors. The PowerLecture Instructor's Resource DVD also gives instructors access to all text art and many photos to help in preparing transparencies for material not present in this set.

## AP* Teacher's Guide

by Linda Wood, Lowndes High School

**ISBN-10: 1-111-42705-4; ISBN-13: 978-1-111-42705-4**

A complete, printed guide for the AP instructor, featuring chapter outlines, lessons plans with helpful pointers and suggested in-text exercises, and estimated lecture schedules. It complements the core text and assists both the seasoned and the new AP teacher.

## Instructor's Manual for Experimental Chemistry in the AP* Laboratory

This detailed manual includes tips on set-up performance of all 30 experiments and solutions to problems for the AP instructor to accompany *Experimental Chemistry in the AP Laboratory*. It is downloadable in both Word and PDF format from the Instructor's Companion Site.

## FOR THE STUDENT

### Visit CengageBrain.com

At **www.cengagebrain.com** you can access additional course materials as well as purchase Cengage products, including those listed below. Search by ISBN using the list below or find this textbook's ISBN on the back cover of your book. Teachers can log in at **login.cengage.com.**

### Student Companion Site

This site includes a glossary, flashcards, an interactive periodic table, and samples of the Study Guide and Student Solutions Manual, which are all accessible from **www.cengagebrain.com.**

## ♥OWL

## Quick Prep for General Chemistry

**Instant Access OWL Quick Prep for General Chemistry (90 days)**

**ISBN-10: 0-495-56030-8; ISBN-13: 978-0-495-56030-2**

Quick Prep is a self-paced online short course that helps students succeed in general chemistry. Students who completed Quick Prep through an organized class or self-study averaged almost a full letter grade higher in their subsequent general chemistry course than those who did not. Intended to be taken prior to the start of the semester, Quick Prep is appropriate for both underprepared students and for students who seek a review of basic skills and concepts. Quick Prep features an assessment quiz to focus students on the concepts they need to study to be prepared for general chemistry. Quick Prep is approximately 20 hours of instruction delivered through OWL with no textbook required and can be completed at any time in the student's schedule. Teachers can package a printed access card for Quick Prep with the textbook or students can purchase instant access at **www.cengagebrain.com.** To view an OWL Quick Prep demonstration and for more information, visit **www.cengage.com/chemistry/quickprep** or contact your sales representative about available discounts.

**go Chemistry**

## Go Chemistry® for General Chemistry

**ISBN-10: 0-495-38228-0; ISBN-13: 978-0-495-38228-7**

Pressed for time? Miss a lecture? Need more review? Go Chemistry for General Chemistry is a set of 27 downloadable mini video lectures, available for purchase separately. Developed by one of this book's authors, Go Chemistry helps you quickly review essential topics—whenever and wherever you want! Each video contains animations and problems and can be downloaded to your computer desktop or portable video player (e.g., iPod or iPhone) for convenient self-study and exam review. Selected Go Chemistry videos have e-Flashcards to briefly introduce a key concept and then test student understanding with a series of questions. The Cengage *YouBook* in OWL contains Go Chemistry. Teachers can package a printed access card for Go Chemistry with the textbook. Students can enter the ISBN above at **www.cengagebrain.com** to download two free videos or to purchase instant access to the 27-video set or individual videos. Ask your sales representative about available discounts.

## CengageBrain.com App

Now students can prepare for class anytime and anywhere using the CengageBrain.com application developed specifically for the Apple iPhone® and iPod touch®, which allows students to access free study materials—book-specific quizzes, flashcards, related Cengage Learning materials and more—so they can study the way they want, when they want to . . . even on the go. For more information about this complimentary application, please visit **www.cengagebrain.com.** Available on the iTunes App Store.

## Student Solutions Manual

by Alton J. Banks, North Carolina State University

**ISBN-10: 1-111-42698-8; ISBN-13: 978-1-111-42698-9**

Improve your performance at exam time with this manual's detailed solutions to the blue-numbered end-of-chapter Study Questions found in the text. This comprehensive guide helps you develop a deeper intuitive understanding of chapter material through constant reinforcement and practice. Solutions match the problem-solving strategies used in the text. Sample chapters are available for review on the PowerLecture Instructor's DVD and on the student companion website, which is accessible from **www.cengagebrain.com**. Ask your sales representative about available discounts.

## Study Guide

by Michael J. Moran and John R. Townsend, West Chester University of Pennsylvania

**ISBN-10: 1-111-42699-6; ISBN-13: 978-1-111-42699-6**

With learning tools explicitly linked to the Chapter Goals introduced in each chapter, this guide helps ensure that you are well prepared for class and exams. It includes chapter overviews, key terms and definitions, expanded commentary, study tips, worked-out examples, and direct references back to the text. Sample chapters are available for review on the student companion website, which is accessible from **www.cengagebrain.com**. Ask your sales representative about available discounts.

## Fast Track to a 5: Preparing for the AP* Examination

by Sheldon Knoespel, Michigan State University

**ISBN-10: 0-840-06944-8; ISBN-13: 978-0-8400-6944-3**

Fast Track to a 5 will help students prepare for the AP* exam quickly, efficiently, and effectively. This comprehensive test-prep resource provides a diagnostic pretest to assess prior knowledge, test-taking strategies, in-depth review and reinforcement of key concepts, and full-length practice exams, all cross-referenced to *Chemistry & Chemical Reactivity 8e*. Available for purchase either with the text or separately.

## Essential Math for Chemistry Students, Second Edition

by David W. Ball, Cleveland State University

**ISBN-10: 0-495-01327-7; ISBN-13: 978-0-495-01327-3**

This short book is intended to help you gain confidence and competency in the essential math skills you need to succeed in general chemistry. Each chapter focuses on a specific type of skill and has worked-out examples to show how these skills translate to chemical problem solving. The book includes references to the OWL learning system where you can access online algebra skills exercises. Ask your sales representative about available discounts.

## Survival Guide for General Chemistry with Math Review, Second Edition

by Charles H. Atwood, University of Georgia

**ISBN-10: 0-495-38751-7; ISBN-13: 978-0-495-38751-0**

Intended to help you practice for exams, this survival guide shows you how to solve difficult problems by dissecting them into manageable chunks. The guide includes three levels of proficiency questions—A, B, and minimal—to quickly build confidence as you master the knowledge you need to succeed in your course. Ask your sales representative about available discounts.

## Experimental Chemistry in the AP* Laboratory

by John Little, Saint Mary's High School

**ISBN-10: 1-111-42761-5; ISBN-13: 978-1-111-42761-0**

This lab manual features thirty experiments designed to illustrate and challenge the key chemical concepts from atomic structure to gas laws. These experiments are specifically created for the AP Chemistry student to provide a visual and tactile laboratory experience. Ask your sales representative about available discounts.

## Signature Labs . . . for the Customized Laboratory

Signature Labs is Cengage Learning's digital library of tried-and-true labs that help you take the guesswork out of running your chemistry laboratory. Select just the experiments you want from hundreds of options and approaches. Provide your students with only the experiments they will conduct and know you will get the results you seek. Visit **www.signaturelabs.com** to begin building your manual today. Ask your sales representative about available discounts.

# ACKNOWLEDGMENTS

Preparing this new edition of *Chemistry & Chemical Reactivity* took over two years of continuous effort. As in our work on the first seven editions, we have had the support and encouragement of our families and of wonderful friends, colleagues, and students.

## A Special Acknowledgment: John Vondeling

The publication of this book, with its copyright of 2012, marks its 25th anniversary. The first edition had a copyright date of 1987 and was the result of a collaboration with our publisher, the late John Vondeling of Saunders College Publishing. John literally invented many of the practices now considered standard among companies publishing college science textbooks. He was responsible for publishing some of the classic textbooks in chemistry, physics, and astronomy. The success of this book in its various editions owes much to John. It may not have become a reality without his confidence that it would be a worthwhile addition to the library of science texts. He was also a good friend, and we miss his humanity, his sense of humor, and his colorful personality.

## CENGAGE LEARNING Brooks/Cole

The seventh edition of this book was published by the Brooks/Cole group of Cengage Learning, and we continue with the same excellent team we have had in place for the previous several years.

The seventh edition of the book was very successful, in large part owing to the work of Lisa Lockwood as our executive editor. She has an excellent sense of the market and has helped guide the new edition.

Peter McGahey has been our the Development Editor since he joined us to work on the fifth edition. Peter is blessed with energy, creativity, enthusiasm, intelligence, and good humor. He is a trusted friend and confidant who cheerfully answers our many questions during almost-daily phone calls.

No book can be successful without proper marketing. Nicole Hamm was a great help in marketing the seventh edition, and she is back in that role for this edition. She is knowledgeable about the market and has worked tirelessly to bring the book to everyone's attention.

Our team at Brooks/Cole is completed with Teresa Trego, Production Manager; Lisa Weber and Stephanie VanCamp, Media Editors; Julie Stefani, Marketing Coordinator; and Elizabeth Woods, Assistant Editor. Schedules are very demanding in textbook publishing, and Teresa has helped to keep us on schedule. We certainly appreciate her organizational skills. Lisa was involved in the development of the Go Chemistry modules and our expanded use of OWL. Stephanie handles the Cengage *YouBook*, and Liz also oversees the development of the ancillaries, such as the PowerPoint notes that accompany text.

Megan Greiner of Graphic World Inc. guided the book through its almost year-long production, and Andy Vosburgh of that company was enormously helpful in getting us through the use of new software. Scott Rosen of the Bill Smith Studio directed the photo research for the book and was successful in filling our sometimes offbeat requests for particular photos.

## Photography, Art, and Design

Most of the color photographs for this edition were beautifully created by Charles D. Winters. He produced several dozen new images for this book, always with a creative eye. Charlie's work gets better with each edition. We have worked with Charlie for more than 20 years and have become close friends. We listen to his jokes, both new and old—and always forget them.

When the fifth edition was being planned, we brought in Patrick Harman as a member of the team. Pat designed the first edition of our *Interactive General Chemistry* CD (published in the 1990s), and we believe its success is in no small way connected to his design skill. For the fifth, sixth, and seventh editions of the book, Pat went over almost every figure, and almost every word, to bring a fresh perspective to ways to communicate chemistry. Once again he has worked on designing and producing new illustrations for this edition, and his creativity is obvious in their clarity. In addition, he has been an enormous help in designing and producing media for the *YouBook*. Pat has also become a good friend, and we share interests not only in books but in music.

## Other Collaborators

We have been fortunate to have a number of other colleagues who have played valuable roles in this project.

- Bill Vining (State University of New York, Oneonta) was a co-author of the *Interactive GeneralChemistry* CD and has authored many of the media assets in OWL. He has been a friend for many years and recently took the place of one of the authors on the faculty at SUNY–Oneonta. Bill has again applied his considerable energy and creativity in preparing many more OWL questions with tutorials and some of the assets in the Cengage *YouBook*.

- Barbara Stewart (University of Maine) authored the new Interactive Examples in OWL.

- Alton Banks (North Carolina State University) has also been involved for a number of editions preparing the *Student Solutions Manual*. Alton has been very helpful in ensuring the accuracy of the Study Question answers in the book, as well as in their respective manuals.

- Michael Moran (West Chester University) has again updated and revised the *Study Guide* for this text. Our textbook has had a history of excellent study guides, and this manual follows that tradition.

- Jay Freedman was the development editor for the first edition of the book and played an important role in its success. For several editions of the book Jay has also done a masterful job compiling the index/glossary for this edition.

- Donnie Byers (Johnson County Community College) has been a long-time user of the book and a member of our Advisory Board. For this edition she coordinated the revisions of the end-of-chapter changes for the international edition.

- David Treichel (Nebraska Wesleyan University) wrote the *Applying Chemical Principles* problems, did the accuracy review, and developed the test bank.

- John Vincent (The University of Alabama–Tuscaloosa) wrote the *Instructor's Resource Manual*, did several reviews, and did an accuracy review.

- Barbara Mowrey, York College of Pennsylvania, also was an accuracy reviewer of the page proofs.

- Michael C. Cann (University of Scranton) helped identify ways in which green chemistry content could be incorporated.

- Salman Khan worked with us on developing audio/video tutorials of some of the book's Example problems. He is making significant contributions to education in the United States and elsewhere. See his website (**www.khanacademy.org**) for the extensive list of free tutorials he has done in all fields of science as well as in mathematics, economics, and finance.

- John Emsley (University of Cambridge) wrote the interchapter on the history of the development of chemistry.

- Jeffrey J. Keaffaber (University of Florida) wrote the Case Study *A Healthy Aquarium and the Nitrogen Cycle* in Chapter 21.

- Eric Scerri (University of California, Los Angeles) wrote the *A Closer Look: The Story of the Periodic Table* in Chapter 2.

## Reviewers for the Eighth Edition

As we began to develop the new edition we had helpful input from the following reviewers:

- Gerald M. Korenowski, Rensselaer Polytechnic Institute

- Robert LaDuca, Michigan State University

- Jeffrey Mack, California State University, Sacramento

- Armando Rivera, East Los Angeles College

- Daniel Williams, Kennesaw State University

- Steven Wood, Brigham Young University

- Roger A. Hinrichs, Weill Cornell Medical College in Qatar, reviewed the energy interchapter

- Leonard Interrante, Rensselaer Polytechnic Institute, reviewed the materials interchapter

- Trudy E. Thomas-Smith, SUNY College at Oneonta, reviewed the environment interchapter

- John Vincent, The University of Alabama, reviewed the environment interchapter

## Advisory Board for the Eighth Edition

As the new edition was being planned, this board listened to some of our ideas and made other suggestions. We hope to continue our association with these energetic and creative chemical educators.

- Donnie Byers, Johnson County Community College

- Elizabeth Dorland, Washington University of St. Louis

- Michael Finnegan, Washington State University

- Greg Gellene, Texas Tech University

- Milton Johnson, University of South Florida

- Jeffrey Mack, California State University, Sacramento

- Sara McIntosh, Rensselaer Polytechnic Institute

- MaryKay Orgill, University of Nevada, Las Vegas

- Don Siegel, Rutgers University

- Eric Simanek, Texas A&M University

## Reviewers for the Seventh Edition

- Gerald M. Korenowski, Rensselaer Polytechnic Institute

- Robert L. LaDuca, Michigan State University

- Jeffrey Alan Mack, California State University, Sacramento

- Armando M. Rivera-Figueroa, East Los Angeles College

- Daniel J. Williams, Kennesaw State University

- Steven G. Wood, Brigham Young University

- Roger A. Hinrichs, Weill Cornell Medical College in Qatar (reviewed the Energy interchapter)

- Leonard Fine, Columbia University (reviewed the Materials interchapter)

## Advisory Board for the Seventh Edition

As the seventh edition was being planned, this board listened to some of our ideas and made other suggestions. We hope to continue our association with these energetic and creative chemical educators.

- Donnie Byers, Johnson County Community College

- Sharon Fetzer Gislason, University of Illinois, Chicago

- Adrian George, University of Nebraska

- George Grant, Tidewater Community College, Virginia Beach Campus

- Michael Hampton, University of Central Florida

- Milton Johnston, University of South Florida

- Jeffrey Alan Mack, California State University, Sacramento

- William Broderick, Montana State University

- Shane Street, University of Alabama

- Martin Valla, University of Florida

**John C. Kotz**, a State University of New York Distinguished Teaching Professor, Emeritus, at the College at Oneonta, was educated at Washington and Lee University and Cornell University. He held National Institutes of Health post-doctoral appointments at the University of Manchester Institute for Science and Technology in England and at Indiana University. He has coauthored three text-books in several editions (*Inorganic Chemistry, Chemistry & Chemical Reactivity,* and *The Chemical World*) and the *General ChemistryNow CD.* His research in inorganic chemistry and electrochemistry also has been published. He was a Fulbright Lecturer and Research Scholar in Portugal in 1979 and a Visiting Professor there in 1992. He was also a Visiting Professor at the Institute for Chemical Education (University of Wisconsin, 1991–1992), at Auckland University in New Zealand (1999), and at Potchefstroom University in South Africa in 2006. He has been an invited speaker on chemical education at conferences in South Africa, New Zealand, and Brazil. He also served four years as a mentor for the U.S. National Chemistry Olympiad Team. He has received several awards, among them a State University of New York Chancellor's Award (1979), a National Catalyst Award for Excellence in Teaching (1992), the Estee Lecturership at the University of South Dakota (1998), the Visiting Scientist Award from the Western Connecticut Section of the American Chemical Society (1999), the Distinguished Education Award from the Binghamton (NY) Section of the American Chemical Society (2001), the SUNY Award for Research and Scholarship (2005), and the Squibb Lectureship in Chemistry at the University of North Carolina-Asheville (2007). He may be contacted by email at kotzjc@oneonta.edu.

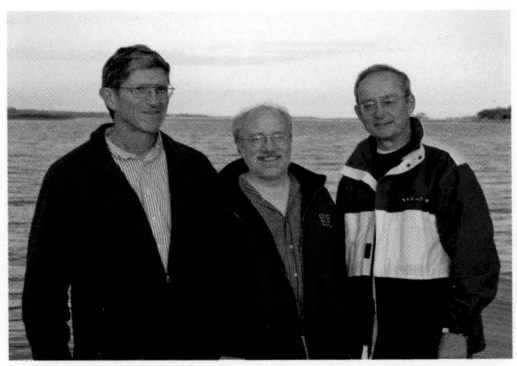

Left to right: Paul Treichel, John Townsend, and John Kotz.

**Paul M. Treichel**, received his B.S. degree from the University of Wisconsin in 1958 and a Ph.D. from Harvard University in 1962. After a year of postdoctoral study in London, he assumed a faculty position at the University of Wisconsin–Madison. He served as department chair from 1986 through 1995 and was awarded a Helfaer Professorship in 1996. He has held visiting faculty positions in South Africa (1975) and in Japan (1995). Retiring after 44 years as a faculty member in 2007, he is currently Emeritus Professor of Chemistry. During his faculty career he taught courses in general chemistry, inorganic chemistry, organometallic chemistry, and scientific ethics. Professor Treichel's research in organometallic and metal cluster chemistry and in mass spectrometry, aided by 75 graduate and under-graduate students, has led to more than 170 papers in scientific journals. He may be contacted by email at treichel@chem.wisc.edu.

**John R. Townsend**, Professor of Chemistry at West Chester University of Pennsylvania, completed his B.A. in Chemistry as well as the Approved Program for Teacher Certification in Chemistry at the University of Delaware. After a career teaching high school science and mathe-matics, he earned his M.S. and Ph.D. in biophysical chemistry at Cornell University, where he also received the DuPont Teaching Award for his work as a teaching assistant. After teaching at Bloomsburg University, he joined the faculty at West Chester University, where he coordinates the chemistry education program for pro-spective high school teachers and the general chemistry lecture program for science majors. He has been the university supervisor for more than 50 prospective high school chemistry teachers during their student teaching semester. His research interests are in the fields of chem-ical education and biochemistry. He may be contacted by email at jtownsend@wcupa.edu.

The cover photograph, titled "Save Our Earth, Let's Go Green," is from the research of Professor Joanna Aizenberg, Boaz Pokroy, and Sung Hoon Kang. Professor Aizenberg holds a joint appointment at Harvard University in the Department of Chemistry and Chemical Biology and the Department of Materials Science. This electron microscope photograph, showing hairlike fibers of epoxy resin assembling around a 2-$\mu$m polystyrene sphere, was the first place winner in the 2009 International Science and Engineering Visualization Challenge sponsored by *Science* magazine.

For this study, these scientists created a regular array of hairlike epoxy fibers, anchored at one end to a horizontal base. In water and other solvents, these epoxy pillars stand straight up and do not interact with each other. As the solvent evaporates, however, the fibers self-organize, clumping together in a helical pattern, a result of the attractive intermolecular forces in a process called capillary action. If polystyrene spheres are suspended in the liquid, the fibers wind around the sphere. Aizenberg said her group is now trying to make the process reversible, which would allow its possible use in drug release or self-cleaning materials. For example, she envisions polymer fingers that grab dust particles or floating

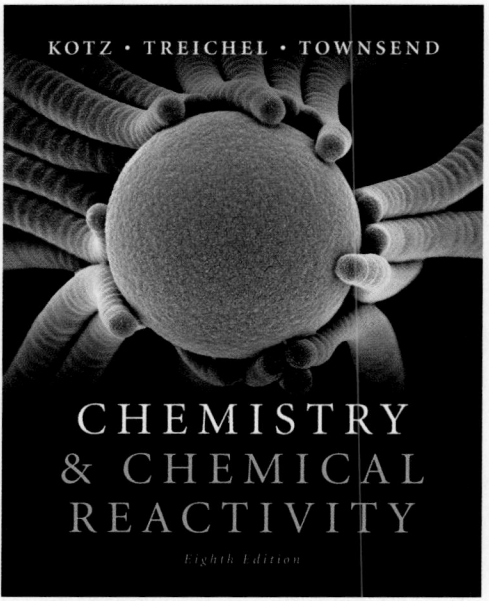

KOTZ • TREICHEL • TOWNSEND

© Cengage Learning

CHEMISTRY
& CHEMICAL
REACTIVITY

*Eighth Edition*

bacteria, later to release them so the contaminants can be washed away.

Aizenberg said the image "also brings to mind our collaborative effort to hold up the planet and keep it running." The judges in the photo competition liked both the image and the message. We also liked this photo because it portrays a dynamic research area and the importance of chemistry in the broader arena of science.

Regarding her research in general, Aizenberg said "We try to identify biological systems that have unusual structures that are naturally optimized to make extremely sophisticated, efficient, and highly potent devices and materials." Then the group uses the underlying biological design "to fabricate a new generation of self-assembling and adaptive materials based on biological architectures."

You will encounter further research of Professor Aizenberg on sea sponges in the Let's Review section of Chapter 1. See Chapter 10 for more information on the polymers involved, and see Chapter 12 for a discussion on intermolecular forces. The image originally appeared in *Science*, 19 February 2010 (Vol. 327. no. 5968, pp. 954–955). The website for Professor Aizenberg's research is **www.seas.harvard.edu/aizenberg_lab**.

**Correlation to AP* Course**

| TOPICS | Page Numbers |
|---|---|
| **I.  Structure of Matter (20%)** | |
| **A.  Atomic theory and atomic structure** | |
| 1.  Evidence for the atomic theory | 51–61, 335–343 |
| 2.  Atomic masses; determination by chemical and physical means | 52–56 |
| 3.  Atomic number and mass number; isotopes | 52–57, 60–61, 93 |
| 4.  Electron energy levels: atomic spectra, quantum numbers, atomic orbitals | 267–289, 301–315 |
| 5.  Periodic relationships including, for example, atomic radii, ionization energies, electron affinities, oxidation states | 58–66, 315–323 |
| **B.  Chemical bonding** | |
| 1.  Binding forces | |
| a.  Types: ionic, covalent, metallic, hydrogen bonding, van der Waals (including London dispersion forces) | 78–79, 345–346, 550–564, 594–596 |
| b.  Relationships to states, structure, and properties of matter | 550–569, 571–573 |
| c.  Polarity of bonds, electronegativities | 371–374 |
| 2.  Molecular models | |
| a.  Lewis structures | 348–363 |
| b.  Valence bond: hybridization of orbitals, resonance, sigma and pi bonds | 356–359, 402–416 |
| c.  VSEPR | 364–370 |
| 3.  Geometry of molecules and ions, structural isomerism of simple organic molecules and coordination complexes; dipole moments of molecules; relation of properties to structure | 364–370, 375–381, 1034–1036 |
| **C.  Nuclear chemistry: nuclear equations, half-lives, and radioactivity; chemical applications** | 1059–1081 |
| **II.  States of Matter (20%)** | |
| **A.  Gases** | |
| 1.  Laws of ideal gases | |
| a.  Equation of state for an ideal gas | 510–521 |
| b.  Partial pressures | 524–527 |
| 2.  Kinetic-molecular theory | |
| a.  Interpretation of ideal gas laws on the basis of this theory | 527–531 |
| b.  Avogadro's hypothesis and the mole concept | 516–517 |
| c.  Dependence of kinetic energy of molecules on temperature | 7, 529–530 |
| d.  Deviations from ideal gas laws | 534–535 |
| **B.  Liquids and solids** | |
| 1.  Liquids and solids from the kinetic-molecular viewpoint | 7, 564 |
| 2.  Phase diagrams of one-component systems | 606–607 |
| 3.  Changes of state, including critical points and triple points | 571–572, 602–607 |
| 4.  Structure of solids; lattice energies | 583–601 |
| **C.  Solutions** | |
| 1.  Types of solutions and factors affecting solubility | 119–123, 617–629 |
| 2.  Methods of expressing concentration (The use of normalities is not tested.) | 173–178, 618–620 |
| 3.  Raoult's law and colligative properties (nonvolatile solutes); osmosis | 630–642 |
| 4.  Non-ideal behavior (qualitative aspects) | 630, 641 |

See *AP* General Chemistry Lab* for *'Chemistry and Chemical Reactivity, 8th Edition'*

*AP and Advanced Placement are registered trademarks of the College Entrance Examination Board, which was not involved in the production of and does not endorse this product.

| TOPICS | Page Numbers |
|---|---|
| **IV. Descriptive Chemistry (10%–15%)** | |
| A. Chemical reactivity and products of chemical reactions | 123–146 |
| B. Relationships in the periodic table: horizontal, vertical, and diagonal with examples from alkali metals, alkaline earth metals, halogens, and the first series of transition elements | 962–1006, 1018–1023 |
| C. Introduction to organic chemistry: hydrocarbons and functional groups (structure, nomenclature, chemical properties). Physical and chemical properties of simple organic compounds should also be included as exemplary material for the study of other areas, such as bonding, equilibria involving weak acids, kinetics, colligative properties, and stoichiometric determinations of empirical and molecular formulas. | 323–326, 439–472 |
| **V. Laboratory (5%–10%)** | |

## Preparing for the AP* Chemistry Examination

Advanced Placement can be exhilarating. Whether you are taking an AP course at your school or working independently, the stage is set for a great intellectual experience.

But sometime after New Year's Day, when the examination begins to loom on a very real horizon, Advanced Placement can seem downright intimidating—in fact, even adults long out of high school refuse the opportunity to take the examination for a lark. If you dread taking the test, you are in good company.

The best way to deal with an AP examination is to master it, not let it master you. If you can think of these examinations as a way to show off how much chemistry you know, you have a leg up. Attitude *does* help. If you are not one of those students, there is still a lot you can do to sideline your anxiety. This book is designed to put you on a fast track. Focused review and practice time will help you master the examination so that you can walk in with confidence and score a 5.

### What's in the *Chemistry & Chemical Reactivity* Textbook That Will Help Your Preparation

As you work your way through the textbook, there are some features that will assist you in getting the most out of the textbook:

- Pay particular attention to the Problem Solving Tips found in most chapters. These tips provide useful information, which serves as a good review of key concepts as well as useful problem-solving strategies.
- Make certain you carefully study the Examples with solutions in each chapter. These will often give you a guide to help develop your problem-solving skills.
- Read the Chapter Goals Revisited section that highlights the material presented in the chapter as a means to double check your understanding before you proceed.
- Answer the Study Questions at the end of each chapter as a measure of your understanding. This will give you instant feedback as to how much of the chapter you may need to study again.
- Working in small groups, answer the Study Questions at the end of each chapter that are designated as "more challenging" by the red solid triangle icon ▲. This is an excellent opportunity to gauge your level of understanding and to receive assistance from your classmates.
- Do as many Summary and Conceptual Questions as you can. These problems are intended to incorporate many different concepts into the solution. Problems like this are particularly good practice for the free-response portion of the AP* exam.
- Note that each chapter begins with an introduction on a topic related to the material presented in that chapter, along with a series of questions. Spend some time answering these questions as they not only reinforce the material in the chapter but are also good practice for the free-response questions on the AP exam.
- In this edition, the authors have added Strategy Maps to accompany many of the Example Problems in the text. The maps are visual representations of pathways to solve problems.
- All of the Example problems in this edition illustrate a new approach to problem solving. Each Example problem is broken down into the following categories: Problem, What Do You Know?, Strategy, Solution, Think About your Answer, and Check Your Understanding.

* AP and Advanced Placement Program are registered trademarks of the College Entrance Examination Board, which was not involved in the production of, and does not endorse, this product.

Being successful in chemistry usually involves careful reading of the textbook and working as many different types of problems as possible. The successful student is not one who just memorizes a bunch of facts but one who is able to begin to tie the various facts and concepts together in the understanding of a new problem. Chemistry is like a lot of subjects in that an understanding of new material often depends on an understanding of previous concepts.

## Before the Examination

By February, long before the exam, you need to make sure that you are registered to take the test. Many schools take care of the paperwork and handle the fees for their AP students, but check with your teacher or the AP coordinator to make sure that you are on the list. This is especially important if you have a documented disability and need test accommodations. If you are studying AP independently, call AP Services at the College Board for the name of the local AP coordinator, who will help you through the registration process.

The evening before the exam is not a great time for partying. Nor is it a great time for cramming. If you like, look over class notes or drift through your textbook, concentrating on the broad outlines, not the small details, of the course.

The evening before the exam *is* a great time to get your things together for the next day. Sharpen a fistful of no. 2 pencils with good erasers; bring a scientific calculator with fresh batteries. You may bring a programmable calculator; the memory will not be erased or cleared by the test administrator. It must not have a typewriter-style keyboard. Wind your watch, and turn off the alarm if it has one; get a piece of fruit or a snack bar and a bottle of water for the break. Make sure you have your Social Security number and whatever photo identification and admission ticket are required. Then relax. And get a good night's sleep.

On the day of the examination, it is wise not to skip breakfast—studies show that students who eat a hot breakfast before testing get higher grades. Be careful not to drink a lot of liquid, thereby necessitating a trip to the bathroom during the exam. Breakfast will give you the energy you need to power you through the exam—and more. You do not want to be distracted by a growling stomach or hunger pangs. You will spend some time waiting while everyone is seated in the assigned room for the appropriate exam before the test has even begun. With a short break between Section I and Section II, the AP Chemistry exam lasts for more than two and a half hours. So be prepared for a long morning.

Be sure to wear comfortable clothes, taking along a sweater in case the heating or air-conditioning is erratic. Be sure, too, to wear clothes you like—everyone performs better when they think they look better—and by all means, wear your lucky socks.

You have been on the fast track. Now go get a 5!

## Taking The AP* Chemistry Examination

The AP Chemistry examination consists of two sections: Section I has 75 multiple-choice questions; Section II has 6 free-response questions. You will have 90 minutes for the multiple-choice portion. You will not be allowed to use a calculator for the multiple-choice questions. The questions are collected, and you will be given a short break. You then have 95 minutes for the free-response section, which is broken into two portions.

You will be allowed to use a calculator in Part A, with a time limit of 55 minutes. All three questions in Part A are mandatory, with the first question involving an equilibrium problem and the next two questions based on a variety of topics, including a laboratory-based question. Each of these questions will be weighted equally at

20% of the overall Section II score. Time will be called at 55 minutes, at which time calculators must be put away for the remaining 40 minutes.

In Part B, you will be asked to answer three questions. Question 4, which is worth 10% of Section II, will ask you to write the balanced chemical equation for three separate chemical reactions and then answer one related question about each reaction. You will then answer two mandatory essays, one of which may be lab-based if a lab-based question was not asked in Part A. Each of the two questions in Part B is weighted equally, accounting for 15% of the Section II score.

The table on the next page summarizes each part of the AP Chemistry examination.

## Strategies for the Multiple-Choice Section

Here are some rules of thumb to help you work your way through the multiple-choice questions:

There are five possible answers for each question. Each correct answer is worth 1 point; by a recent change in AP scoring (effective with the 2011 exam), you will no longer lose points for an incorrect answer. Therefore, it is worthwhile to answer every question, even if you have to guess. Because there are five possible answers for each question, you have at least a 20% chance of guessing correctly. If you can eliminate even just one response, it will always improve your chances of guessing correctly.

**Read the question carefully** Pressured for time, many students make the mistake of reading the questions too quickly or merely skimming them. By reading a question carefully, you may already have some idea about the correct answer. You can then look for it in the responses. Careful reading is especially important in EXCEPT questions.

**Eliminate any answer you know is wrong** You can write on the multiple-choice question test book. As you read through the responses, draw a line through any answer you know is wrong.

**AP\* Chemistry Exam–Distribution of Questions**

| Weighting | | Possible Topics | Time Allowed |
|---|---|---|---|
| **Section I** | 50% | Multiple choice | 90 minutes |
| **Section II** | 50% | | |
| **Part A (all mandatory)** | | | 55 minutes |
| Question 1 | | Equilibrium | |
| Questions 2 and 3 | | Thermochemistry, thermodynamics, kinetics, stoichiometry, redox, or laboratory-based | |
| **Part B (all mandatory)** | | | 40 minutes |
| Question 4 | | Reactions (three balanced equations with related second question for each one) | |
| Question 5 | | Essay—gases, states of matter, kinetics, redox, thermochemistry, electrochemistry, periodicity, or lab-based | |
| Question 6 | | Essay/minor calculations—same topics as those listed for Question 5 | |

**Read all of the possible answers, then choose the most accurate response** AP examinations are written to test your precise knowledge of a subject. Some of the responses may be partially correct, but there will only be one response that is completely true.

**Avoid absolute responses** These answers often include the words "always" or "never." For example, the statement "all chlorides are always soluble in water" is incorrect because compounds such as silver chloride and lead(II) chloride are insoluble in water.

**Mark tough questions** If you are stuck on a question, mark it in the margin of the question book. Then go back and work on the questions you skipped. Leave yourself enough time to fill in answers—even guesses—on all unanswered items before the time expires.

## Types of Multiple-Choice Questions

There are various kinds of multiple-choice questions. Here are some suggestions for approaching each kind:

**Classic/Best Answer Questions** This is the most common type of multiple-choice question. It simply requires you to read the question and select the most correct answer. For example:

1. Which of the following molecules is tetrahedral in shape?

    (A) $NH_3$
    (B) $H_2O$
    (C) $CH_4$
    (D) $SF_4$
    (E) $XeF_4$

**Answer:** (C). Eliminate (A) and (B) because these do not have 4 atoms attached as in a tetrahedrally-shaped molecule. On your booklet or scratch paper, draw the Lewis structures for the remaining molecules. A molecule with tetrahedral shape has four atoms attached and no lone pairs. (D) and (E) have lone pairs.

**Classification Set** In this type of question, there is a list of five lettered headings consisting of possible answers followed by a list of numbered phrases. You must select the heading that is most closely related to each numbered phrase. Headings may be used once, more than once, or not at all.

Questions 1–3 refer to 0.10 M solutions.

    (A) $NH_3$, ammonia
    (B) NaOH, sodium hydroxide
    (C) $CH_3COOH$, acetic acid
    (D) $NaNO_3$, sodium nitrate
    (E) $CH_3COOK$, potassium acetate

1. Has a pH equal to 7.0.
2. Has a pH less than 7.0.
3. Can be mixed with 0.10 M sodium acetate to make a buffer.

For the classification set, answer each question one at a time. Some of the answers can be used more than once or not at all. Begin by knowing what is meant by each phrase in questions 1 through 3. For example, what is a buffer made of?

1.  Look for a neutral solution because the pH equals 7. Salts that have parent acids that are strong will be neutral because their conjugate base will be too weak to undergo hydrolysis. $NO_3^-$ is the conjugate base of the strong acid $HNO_3$. Answer is (D).
2.  Look for an acid or the conjugate acid of a weak base because the pH is less than 7. Answer is (C).
3.  A buffer is made of a weak acid and its conjugate base (or a weak base and its conjugate acid). Sodium acetate contains acetate, which is the conjugate base of the weak acid acetic acid. Answer is (C).

**List and Group Questions**  In this type of question, there is a list of possible answers, and you must select the answer that contains the correct group of responses.

1.  The concentration of a solution can be determined by which of the following method(s)?

    I.   Titration with a solution of known concentration
    II.  Calorimetry
    III. Spectrometric/colorimetric

    (A) I only
    (B) II only
    (C) III only
    (D) I and II only
    (E) I and III only
    (F) I, II, and III

**Answer:**  (E). To approach the question, draw a line through choice II because calorimetry is used to determine the change in enthalpy of a reaction. Continue to cross out items that are wrong and the responses that contain them. Draw a line through II and answers (D) and (F), which both contain choice II. Now you have narrowed down the possible responses.

**Non-Calculator Computations**  These questions require computations without the use of a calculator. Simple mathematics or the choice of the correct algebraic setup will be involved.

> **Example:**  A weak acid, HA, has a $K_a$ value of $1.0 \times 10^{-6}$. Calculate the pH after the complete reaction of 40.0 mL of 0.0100 $M$ HA with 10.0 mL of 0.0200 $M$ NaOH.
>
> (A) 2.0
> (B) 6.0
> (C) 7.0
> (D) 8.0
> (E) 14.0

To answer this question, you must consider at what point in the titration the question is referring to. Because the base, NaOH, is twice as concentrated as the acid, HA, it will take half as much NaOH to reach the equivalence point, or 20.0 mL. We are not at the equivalence point. Half the amount of the NaOH, 10.0 mL, needed to reach the equivalence point has been added. Halfway to the equivalence point, the pH equals the $pK_a$ which equals $-\log(K_a)$ or 6.0. Answer is (B).

**Example:** $2C(s) + O_2(g) \rightarrow 2CO(g)$

Into a 3.0-L container at 25° C are placed 1.2 g of carbon, graphite, and 3.2 g oxygen gas.

If the carbon and the oxygen react completely to form $CO(g)$, what will be the final pressure in the container at 25° C?

(A) $\dfrac{0.05(0.082)(298)}{3.0}$ atm

(B) $\dfrac{0.10(0.082)(25)}{3.0}$ atm

(C) $\dfrac{0.15(0.082)(298)}{3.0}$ atm

(D) $\dfrac{0.20(0.082)(298)}{3.0}$ atm

(E) $\dfrac{0.10(0.082)(298)}{3.0}$ atm

To answer this question, 1.2 g of carbon is 0.10 mol of carbon (1 mole of carbon equals 12 g). Similarly, 3.2 g of $O_2$ is 0.10 mol of $O_2$. The limiting reactant is carbon producing 0.10 mol of CO. $O_2$ is present in excess. (0.10 mol of CO requires 0.05 mol of $O_2$ leaving 0.05 mol of $O_2$.) When the reaction is complete, there is 0.10 mol CO + 0.05 mol $O_2$ left, which equals 0.15 mol total. Answer is (C).

## Strategies for the Free-Response Section

Section II of the AP exam comes with a periodic table, a table of standard reduction potentials, $E^0_{red}$, and a table of equations and constants.

Scan all of the questions in the section you are working in and mark those that you know you can answer correctly. Do these problems first.

You will be provided with an answer booklet, as well as an insert that contains the same questions as the answer booklet but without the spaces. You can remove the insert for reference. All of your work and answers for each problem must be shown in the answer booklet. No credit will be given for work shown on the insert, but you may write on it.

Show all of your work. Partial credit will be awarded for problems if the correct work is shown but the answer is not present or is incorrect. In problems involving calculations, circle your final answer.

Cross out incorrect answers with an "X" rather than spending time erasing.

Be clear, neat, and organized in your work. If a grader cannot clearly understand your work, you may not receive full credit.

Some free-response questions have four parts: a, b, c, and d. Attempt to solve each part. Even if your answer to "a" is incorrect, you still may be awarded points for the remaining parts of the question if the work is correct for those parts.

Units are important in your answer. Keeping track of your units throughout calculations and performing unit cancellation where possible will help guide you to your answer. Points will be deducted for missing or incorrect units in the answer.

You do not need to work the questions in order. Make sure you put the number of the question in the corner of each page of your essay booklet. In addition, questions are sometimes broken into parts, such as (a) and (b). When this is the case, label each part of your response.

## Strategies for Answering Essay Questions

Essay questions will ask you to explain, compare, and predict. Minor calculations, showing mathematical relationships, or drawing graphs or structures, may also be involved. These are not usually traditional essay questions. Most do not require an introduction, conclusion, or even a thesis. Many of these questions may be written in a bulleted or short-answer format. Although this may sound easier than writing a traditional essay, it is important that you know the material very well because these are targeted questions. Examination readers want specifics. They are looking for accurate information presented in clear, concise prose. You cannot mask vague information with elegant prose.

To be successful in writing essays for the AP Chemistry exam, be sure to get straight to the answer and use key terms in your explanations. Sometimes, if you ramble on and on, you might accidentally state an incorrect fact. Points will be deducted for incorrect or extraneous information.

Techniques to write essays include chart format, bullet format, and outline format. None of these styles requires that you write complete sentences. In each of these styles, restate the question in simple terms, using your own words. Restate each part (a, b, and so on) separately, not together. In your restatement and response, underline key words or concepts.

**Fill in a chart to answer the question.** This style is helpful in answering questions about electronic and molecular structure. This method is also used in the example on identification of the set of four quantum numbers for each electron in an element in this chapter.

**In bullet format, make a list**, using a bullet (■) for each new concept. Leave room between concepts because you may want to come back later to fill them in.

**Outline format** is more traditional, using Roman numerals, letters, etc. This takes more time to organize ideas, but it does show progression of ideas in a logical sequence. As in the bulleted format, leave room between concepts because you may want to come back later to fill them in.

Lastly, **the freestyle method** sometimes results in rambling and incomplete answers. Writing in paragraphs does not allow room for additional ideas to be added.

## Scoring for Free-Response Questions
### Section II—Part A

Question number one is usually a multistep equilibrium problem.

### Sample Problem #1 (Weighted 20% of Part II)

1.  Answer the following questions related to the equilibrium of benzoic acid, $HC_7H_5O_2$.

    (A) A sample of 0.100 M benzoic acid, $HC_7H_5O_2$, ionizes by 2.5%. Calculate the equilibrium constant, $K_a$, for benzoic acid.

    (B) A 30.0 mL sample of 0.100 M $HC_7H_5O_2$ (aq) is titrated with 5.0 mL of 0.20 M KOH (aq). Calculate the pH of the resulting solution after the base has been added.

    (C) A 30.0 mL sample of 0.100 M $HC_7H_5O_2$ (aq) is titrated with 7.5 mL of 0.20 M KOH (aq). Calculate the pH of the resulting solution after the base has been added.

    (D) A 30.0 mL sample of 0.100 M $HC_7H_5O_2$ (aq) is titrated with 15.0 mL of 0.20 M KOH (aq). Calculate the pH of the resulting solution after the base has been added.

    (E) A 30.0 mL sample of 0.100 M $HC_7H_5O_2$ (aq) is titrated with 20.0 mL of 0.20 M KOH (aq). Calculate the pH of the resulting solution after the base has been added.

    (F) What mass of sodium benzoate, $NaC_7H_5O_2$, must be added to 100.0 mL of 0.100 M $HC_7H_5O_2$ (aq) to make a buffer with a pH equal to 5.00? Assume no volume change (molar mass of $NaC_7H_5O_2$ = 144 g/mol).

## Scoring Guidelines–Sample Problem 1

(A)  $\dfrac{x}{0.100} \times 100\% = 2.5\%; x = 0.0025$

1 point for correct<br>significant figures

|   | $HC_7H_5O_2$ | $\rightleftharpoons$ | $H^+$ | $+$ | $C_7H_5O_2^-$ |
|---|---|---|---|---|---|
| I | 0.100 | | 0 | | 0 |
| C | $-x$ | | $x$ | | $x$ |
| E | $0.100 - x$ | | $x$ | | $x$ |

1 point for the cor-<br>rect value of $x$

$K_a = \dfrac{[H^+]\,[C_7H_5O_2^-]}{[HC_7H_5O_2]} = \dfrac{x^2}{0.10 - x} =$

1 point for correct<br>value of $K_a$

$\dfrac{(0.0025)^2}{0.100 - 0.0025} = \dfrac{6.25 \times 10^{-6}}{0.098} = 6.4 \times 10^{-5}$

(B)

|   | $HC_7H_5O_2$ | $\rightleftharpoons$ | $H^+$ | $+$ | $C_7H_5O_2^-$ |
|---|---|---|---|---|---|
| initial mol | 0.0030 | | 0 | | 0 |
| Add $OH^-$ | $-0.0010$ | | 0 | | $+0.0010$ |
| new | | | | | |
| initial mol | <u>0.0020</u> | | 0 | | <u>0.0010</u> |
| I | 0.0350 L | | | | 0.0350L |
| | 0.057 M | | 0 | | 0.029 M |
| C | $-x$ | | $+x$ | | $+x$ |
| E | $0.057 - x$ | | $x$ | | $0.029 + x$ |
| | $0.057 - x$ | | | | |

1 point for correct<br>calculation of moles<br>or molarity of<br>$HC_7H_5O_2$ and $C_7H_5O_2^-$

$6.4 \times 10^{-5} = \dfrac{[H^+]\,(0.029 + x)}{0.057 + x} \approx \dfrac{[H^+]0.029}{0.057}$

$1.3 \times 10^{-4} M = [H^+]\ pH = -\log[H^+] = 3.89$

1 point for correct pH

Alternately, you can use the Henderson–Hasselbach equation. Volume cancels.

$pH = pK_a + \log\left[\dfrac{0.0010\,\text{mol}}{0.0020\ \text{mol}}\right] = 4.19 + (-.30) = 3.89$

(C)  0.00750 L $\times$ 0.200 mol/L =
0.0015 mol $OH^-$ = moles $C_7H_5O_2^-$
Initial moles of acid = 0.0030 mol
Half of the acid has been neutralized; $pH = pK_a = 4.19$

1 point for calcula-<br>tion of mol $OH^-$ =<br>moles $C_7H_5O_2^-$<br>1 point for correct pH

(D)  0.015 L $\times$ 0.20 mol / L = 0.0030 mol $OH^-$
mol acid = mol $OH^-$
equivalence point only $C_5H_7O_2^-$ present
0.0030 mol/0.045 L = 0.067 M

|   | $C_5H_7O_2^- + H_2O$ | $\rightleftharpoons$ | $OH^-$ | $+$ | $HC_5H_7O_2$ |
|---|---|---|---|---|---|
| I | 0.67 M | | 0 | | 0 |
| C | $-x$ | | $+x$ | | $+x$ |
| E | $0.067 - x$ | | $x$ | | $x$ |

$K_b = \dfrac{K_w}{K_a} = \dfrac{1.0 \times 10^{-14}}{6.4 \times 10^{-5}} = 1.6 \times 10^{-10}$

1 point for correct $K_b$<br>value

$K_b = \dfrac{[OH^-][HC_7H_5O_2]}{[C_7H_5O_2^-]} = \dfrac{x^2}{0.067 - x} \sim \dfrac{x^2}{0.067}$

$x = [(1.6 \times 10^{-10})(0.67)\,]^{\frac{1}{2}} = 3.3 \times 10^{-6} M\ OH^-$
$pOH = 5.48 ; pH = 14.00 - 5.48 = 8.52$

1 point for correct pH

(E) 0.0300 L × 0.10 mol/L =0.0030 mol $HC_5H_7O_2$

0.0200 L × 0.20 mol/L = 0.0040 mol $OH^-$

Excess $OH^-$ = 0.0040 mol − 0.0030 mol/0.0500 L = 0.020 M $OH^-$

pOH = 1.70 ; pH = 14 − pOH = 12.30

*1 point for correct molarity of excess ion*

*1 point for correct pH; alternatively, can solve using $K_w = [H^+][OH^-]$, solve for $H^+$, then pH.*

(F) pH = $pK_a$ + log ($[C_7H_5O_2^-]/[HC_7H_5O_2]$)

5.00 = 4.19 + log ($[mol\ C_7H_5O_2^-]/[0.010\ mol]$)

0.81 = log($[mol\ C_7H_5O_2^-]/[0.010\ mol]$)

antilog 0.81 = (mol $C_7H_5O_2^-$)/0.010 mol

0.065 = mol $C_7H_5O_2^-$

Mass of $NaC_7H_5O_2$ = 0.065 × 144 g/mol = 9.4 g

*1 point for correct values for $pK_a$ and mol of acid*

*1 point for correct answer*

**Sample Problem #2 or #3**

You will work two problems here, each worth 20% of Part II.

$$C_2H_4(g) + 3\ O_2(g) \rightarrow 2\ CO_2(g) + 2H_2O(g)$$

Information about the substances involved in the reaction presented above is tabulated below.

| Substance | S0(J/mol · K) | ΔGof(kJ/mol) |
|---|---|---|
| $C_2H_4(g)$ | ? | 68 |
| $O_2(g)$ | 205 | 0 |
| $CO_2(g)$ | 213.6 | −394 |
| $H_2O(g)$ | 189 | −229 |

| Bond | Bond Energy (kJ/mol) |
|---|---|
| O—H | 467 |
| O—O | 146 |
| O=O | 495 |
| C—H | 413 |
| C—C | 347 |
| C=C | 614 |
| C≡C | 839 |
| C—O | 358 |
| C=O | 799 |

(a) Calculate the value for the standard free energy change, ΔG°, at 25° C for the reaction. What does the sign of ΔG° indicate about the reaction?
(b) Calculate the value for the standard enthalpy change, ΔH°, at 25° C for the reaction. What does the sign of ΔH° indicate about the reaction?
(c) Calculate the value for the standard entropy change, ΔS°, at 25° C for the reaction. What does the sign of ΔS° indicate about the reaction?
(d) Calculate the value for the absolute entropy of $C_2H_4(g)$ at 25° C.

## Scoring Guidelines—Sample Problem #2 or #3

(A) $\Delta G° = 2(-394) + 2(-229) - 68 =$
$-1314$ kJ/mol.

1 point for correct value of
$\Delta G°$

(B)

1 point for meaning of sign
1 point for correct Lewis structures of reactants and products

**Bonds Broken**

4 C—H 4(413)
1 C=C 1(614)
3 O=O 3(495)
+3751 kJ

**Bonds Formed**

4 C=O 4(799)
4 O—H 4(467)
−5064 kJ

$\Delta H° = 3751$ kJ $+ -5064$ kJ $= -1313$ kJ

The reaction is exothermic since $\Delta H°$ is negative.

1 point for correct value
of $\Delta H°$

(C) $\Delta G° = \Delta H° - T\Delta S°$ ; $\Delta S° = (\Delta H° - \Delta G°) / T$

1 point for meaning of sign

$\Delta S° = -1313 - (-1314$ kJ$) / 298$ K
$= 0.0034$ kJ/K

1 point for correct value
of $\Delta S°$

A positive sign of change in entropy indicates that
entropy is increasing in the reaction.

1 point for meaning of sign

Here, it barely
changes.

(D) $\Delta S° = 2S°_{CO_2} + 2 S°_{H_2O} - (S°_{C_2H_4} + 3S°_{O_2})$

$S°_{C_2H_4} = 2 S°_{CO_2} + 2 S°_{H_2O} - 3 S°_{O_2} - \Delta S°$

$= 2 (213.6) + 2 (189) - 3(205) - 3.4$

$= 187$ J/K

1 point for value of absolute
$S°$

## Sample Problem #4 Reactions—Weighted 10%

You will be given three chemical reactions to balance, and then you must answer a
second question about each reaction. Solutions are aqueous unless otherwise indicated. In all cases, a reaction occurs. If a substance is extensively ionized, such as a
strong acid or a completely soluble compound, write it as separate ions. Be sure to
cancel out spectator ions or molecules that are unchanged by the reaction.

Each reaction is worth 4 points: 1 point for the correct reactants, 2 points for
correct product(s), and 1 point for a correctly balanced equation. For the follow-up
question, 1 point will be awarded.

1. (i) Equal volumes of equimolar solutions of sodium
hydroxide and acetic acid are mixed.
(ii) Identify a conjugate acid-base pair in the reaction.

(i) $CH_3COOH + OH^- \rightarrow HOH + CH_3COO^-$

1 point for correct reactants
2 points for correct products
Only 1 product point is
awarded if water is written
as $H^+ + OH^-$ or if
$CH_3COONa$ is written as one
of the products

(ii) $CH_3COOH$ (acid) and $CH_3COO^-$ (base) OR $OH^-$
(base) and HOH (acid)

1 point for correct identification of either pair

**Sample Problem #5—Weighted 15%**

This mandatory essay could be a lab-based question. There are 22 recommended experiments suggested by the College Board. The question usually asks you to describe a laboratory procedure for one of these experiments or analyze sources of errors. Your response is graded for its accuracy and relevance. You should be clear and well-organized when answering.

A student is instructed to identify an unknown solid by conducting four qualitative laboratory tests. The solid substance could either be potassium carbonate, $K_2CO_3$, or benzoic acid, $C_6H_5COOH$. Describe each of the four possible lab tests that can be performed. For each test, identify the observations for both potassium carbonate, $K_2CO_3$, and benzoic acid, $C_6H_5COOH$.

| | |
|---|---|
| 1) Perform a flame test. The potassium ion in $K_2CO_3$ will burn a characteristic lavender color. The flame resulting from burning $C_6H_5COOH$ will not be lavender. | 1 point for identification of test 1 point for listing observations for both possible substances |
| 2) Dissolve solid in water and perform a conductivity test. Potassium carbonate is a strong electrolyte and the bulb on the tester will be brightly lit. If the unknown is $C_6H_5COOH$, the bulb will barely be lit since benzoic acid is a weak acid, so it is also a weak conductor of electricity. | 1 point for identification of test 1 point for listing observations for both possible substances |
| 3) Dissolve solid in water and measure the pH. A basic pH ($>7$) reveals that the unknown is $K_2CO_3$. An acidic pH identifies the unknown as $C_6H_5COOH$. | 1 point for identification of test 1 point for listing observations for both possible substances |
| 4) Add an acid like HCl, which contains a source of hydrogen ion. If the unknown is $K_2CO_3$, the mixture will bubble (release gas). If the unknown is $C_6H_5COOH$, there will be no bubbles. | 1 point for identification of test 1 point for listing observations for both possible substances |

**Sample Problem #6—Weighted 15%**

This problem usually combines chemical calculations with essay writing. Questions of the type mentioned in Sample Problem #7 have also been found here.

$$A(g) + 2\ B(g) \rightarrow C(g) + D(g)$$

Consider the equation above:

(a) Using the table below, calculate the value of $\Delta H^\circ$ for the reaction at 25° C. Show all of your work.

$\Delta H^\circ_f$ (kJ/mol)

| | |
|---|---|
| A | $-1275$ |
| B | $-166$ |
| C | $-393$ |
| D | $-286$ |

(b) Sketch the potential energy diagram for the reaction above. Label the activation energy for the forward reaction.

(c) Explain how the magnitude of the standard entropy of the reaction, $\Delta S^\circ$, will change for the reaction at 25°C.

(d) Predict the sign of the standard free energy change, $\Delta G^\circ$, using your answers to parts (a) and (c).

(e) Write the rate law for the reaction using the information in the table below. Explain how you obtained your result.

| Trial # | Initial [A] (mol/L) | Initial [B] (mol/L) | Initial Rate of Formation of C (mol L$^{-1}$s$^{-1}$) |
|---|---|---|---|
| 1 | 0.10 | 0.10 | 0.20 |
| 2 | 0.20 | 0.10 | 0.40 |
| 3 | 0.40 | 0.20 | 6.4 |

(a) $\Delta H° = [-393 + -286] - [-1275 + 2(-166)] = -679 - (-1607) = 928$ kJ

**1 point for correct value of $\Delta H°$**

(b)

**1 point for showing that energy of products > energy of reactants**

**1 point for labeling the activation energy**

(c) The standard entropy change will decrease because the moles of gas decrease from reactants to products (3 mol → 2 mol).

**1 point: must say why entropy decreases**

(d) $\Delta G° = \Delta H° - T \Delta S°$
= positive − (negative) = positive $\Delta G°$
therefore the reaction is nonspontaneous at all temperatures.

**1 point for determination of order in A: must show work**

(e) $\dfrac{\text{Rate 2}}{\text{Rate 1}} = \dfrac{k[A]^x[B]^y}{k[A]^x[B]^y}$

$= \dfrac{k[0.20]^x \cancel{[0.10]^y}}{k[0.10]^x \cancel{[0.10]^y}} = \dfrac{0.40}{0.20}$

$= 2^x = 2; \ x = 1$

$\dfrac{\text{Rate 3}}{\text{Rate 2}} = \dfrac{k[A]^x[B]^y}{k[A]^x[B]^y}$

$\dfrac{k[0.40]^x[0.20]^y}{k[0.20]^x[0.10]^y} = \dfrac{6.4}{0.40}$

$= 2^x \times 2^y = 16$
$= 2^1 \times 2^y = 16; \ 2^y = 8; \ y = 3$

**1 point for determination of order in B: must show work**

## Another Possible Sample Problem #6

This essay usually asks you to explain chemical phenomena.

Use appropriate chemical principles to account for the following observation. Your answer must include references to both substances.

(a) At 25° C and 1.0 atm, ethane ($C_2H_6$) is a gas, and ethanol ($CH_3CH_2OH$) is a liquid.

There are usually three more questions, parts (b), (c), and (d), which may or may not be related to (a) or each other, but all are scored in a similar way to (a) below.

(a)  Ethane, $C_2H_6$, has London dispersion forces. Ethanol, $CH_3CH_2OH$, has hydrogen bonding. Hydrogen bonding is stronger than London dispersion forces.

1 point for indicating the correct intermolecular force for each molecule

1 point for indicating that hydrogen bonding is stronger than dispersion forces

# 1    Basic Concepts of Chemistry

Image copyright Tomislav Forgo, 2010. Used under license from Shutterstock.com

## Gold!

Gold has been prized by humans for centuries to adorn bodies and serve as currency. It is extracted from the earth all over the world, and the oceans are estimated to contain more than 10 million tons. Wars have been, and are being, fought over it, and humans have been enslaved to mine it.

Gold is prized not only because it is beautiful, but because it is unaffected by air, water, alkalis, and acids (except for *aqua regia,* a mixture of hydrochloric and nitric acids). These properties have made gold much valued as jewelry, which in fact consumes about 75% of the gold on the market. But a large fraction, more than 60 tons a year, is also used in dentistry. And of course some gold is used in architecture. For example, the dome of St. Isaac's Cathedral in St. Petersburg, Russia, is covered with 220 pounds of gold in wafer-thin sheets.

A few years ago a young chemist in Vienna, Austria wanted to see just how permanent the gold was in his wedding band. The ring was 18-carat gold (which means it was 75% gold and 25% other metals, probably copper and silver). One week after his wedding day he took off the ring, cleaned it carefully, and weighed it. It had a mass of 5.58387 g. He weighed it weekly from then on, and after 1 year it had lost 6.15 mg just from normal wear and tear. He found that the activities that took the greatest toll on the gold were vacationing on a sandy beach and gardening. Even clapping his hands at a rock concert led to the loss of 0.17 mg, greater than the average weekly loss of 0.12 mg.

He has calculated that if all of the married couples in his city of Vienna lost the same amount of gold from their wedding bands as he did, the loss would amount to about 2.2 kg per year. At 2010 gold prices ($1140 per troy ounce; $36 per gram), about $81,000 worth of gold "disappears" in Vienna each year.

## Questions:

1. Assume there are 56 million married couples in the United States, and each person has an 18-carat gold ring. How much gold is lost by all the wedding rings in the United States in 1 year (in units of grams)? Assuming the 2010 price listed, what is the lost gold worth?
2. 18-carat gold is 25% copper and silver. What are the symbols of those elements?
3. Gold melts at 1064 °C. What is that temperature in kelvins?
4. The density of gold is 19.3 $g/cm^3$.
   (a) Use one of the periodic tables on the Internet (such as www.ptable.com) to find out if gold is the most dense of all of the known elements.
   (b) If a wedding band is 18-carat gold and has a mass of 5.58 g, what volume of gold is contained within the ring?

**Answers to these questions are available in Appendix N.**

## CHAPTER OUTLINE

## CHAPTER GOALS

*See Chapter Goals Revisited (page 19) for Study Questions keyed to these goals.*

- Understand the differences between hypotheses, laws, and theories.

- Be aware of the principles of green chemistry.

- Apply the kinetic-molecular theory to the properties of matter.

- Classify matter.

- Recognize elements, atoms, compounds, and molecules.

- Identify physical and chemical properties and changes.

- Describe various forms of energy.

In 1991 a hiker in the Alps on the Swiss-Italian border found a well-preserved human body. Although it was first thought to be a person who had recently died, a number of scientific studies over more than a decade concluded the man had lived 53 centuries ago and was about 46 years old when he died. He became known as Ötzi the Iceman.

The discovery of the Iceman's body, the oldest natural human mummy, set off innumerable scientific studies that brought together chemists, biologists, anthropologists, paleontologists, and others from all over the world. Following these studies gives us a marvelous view of how science is done. Among the many discoveries made about the Iceman were the following:

- Some investigators looked for food residues in the Iceman's intestines. In addition to finding a few particles of grain, they located tiny flakes of mica believed to come from stones used to grind the grain the man ate. They analyzed these flakes (using argon isotopes, page 58) and found their composition was like that of mica in a small area south of the Alps, thus establishing where the man lived in his later years.

**OWL**

Sign in to OWL at **www.cengage.com/owl** to view tutorials and simulations, develop problem-solving skills, and complete online homework assigned by your professor.

**go Chemistry**

Download mini lecture videos for key concept review and exam prep from OWL or purchase them from **www.cengagebrain.com**

**(a)** The Iceman before the body was removed from the ice within which he had been frozen for almost 53 centuries.

**(b)** The body of the Iceman now lies in the Archaeological Museum of South Tyrol in Bolzano, Italy.

**Ötzi, the Iceman.** The name "Ötzi" comes from the Ötz valley, the region of Europe (on the Austrian-Italian border) where the man was found.

- High levels of copper and arsenic were found in the Iceman's hair. These observations, combined with the discovery that his ax was nearly pure copper, led the investigators to conclude he had been involved in copper smelting.
- One fingernail was still present on his body. Amazingly, scientists could conclude from its appearance that he had been sick three times in the 6 months before he died and his last illness had lasted for 2 weeks.
- Australian scientists took samples of blood residues from his stone-tipped knife, his arrows, and his coat. Using techniques developed to study ancient DNA, they found the blood came from four different individuals. In fact, the blood on one arrow tip was from two different individuals, suggesting that the man had killed two different people. Perhaps he had killed one person, retrieved the arrow, and used it to kill another.

The many different methods used to reveal the life of the Iceman and his environment are used by scientists around the world, including present-day forensic scientists to study accidents and crimes. As you study chemistry and the chemical principles in this book, keep in mind that many areas of science depend on chemistry and that many different careers in the sciences are available. As one example of a scientific career, you can read on page 4 about the experience in forensic chemistry of a former student of one of the authors.

## 1.1    Chemistry and Its Methods

Chemistry is about change. It was once only about changing one natural substance into another—wood and oil burn, grape juice turns into wine, and cinnabar (Figure 1.1), a red mineral from the earth, ultimately changes into shiny quicksilver (mercury) upon heating. The emphasis was largely on finding a recipe to carry out the desired transformation with little understanding of the underlying structure of the materials or explanations for why particular changes occurred. Chemistry is still about change, but now chemists focus on the change of one pure substance, whether natural or synthetic, into another and on understanding that change (Figure 1.2). As you will see, in modern chemistry, we now picture an exciting world of submicroscopic atoms and molecules interacting with each other. We have also developed ways to predict whether or not a particular reaction may occur.

Although chemistry is endlessly fascinating—at least to chemists—why should you study chemistry? Each person probably has a different answer, but many students take a chemistry course because someone else has decided it is an

**FIGURE 1.1** Cinnabar and mercury.

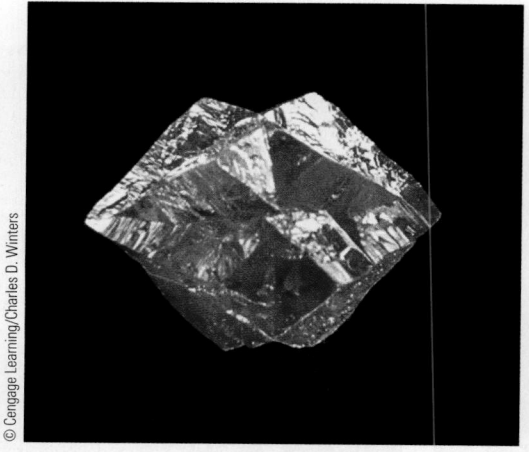

**(a)** The red crystals of cinnabar are the chemical compound mercury(II) sulfide.

**(b)** Heating cinnabar in air changes it into orange mercury(II) oxide, which, on further heating, decomposes to the elements mercury (the droplets seen on the inside of the test tube wall) and oxygen gas.

Solid sodium, Na

Chlorine gas, Cl$_2$

Photos: © Cengage Learning/Charles D. Winters

Sodium chloride solid, NaCl

**FIGURE 1.2  Forming a chemical compound.** Sodium chloride, table salt, can be made by combining sodium metal (Na) and yellow chlorine gas (Cl$_2$). The result is a crystalline solid, common salt. (The tiny spheres show how the atoms are arranged in the substances. In the case of the salt crystal, the spheres represent electrically charged sodium and chlorine ions.)

important part of preparing for a particular career. Chemistry is especially useful because it is central to our understanding of disciplines as diverse as biology, geology, materials science, medicine, physics, and some branches of engineering. In addition, chemistry plays a major role in the economy of developed nations, and chemistry and chemicals affect our daily lives in a wide variety of ways. Furthermore, a course in chemistry can help you see how a scientist thinks about the world and how to solve problems. The knowledge and skills developed in such a course will benefit you in many career paths and will help you become a better informed citizen in a world that is becoming technologically more complex— and more interesting.

## Hypotheses, Laws, and Theories

As scientists we study questions of our own choosing or ones that someone else poses in the hope of finding an answer or discovering some useful information. When the Iceman was discovered, there were many questions that scientists could try to answer, such as where he was from. They knew he was likely from an area on the border of what is now Austria and Italy. As you will learn later (page 58), the type of oxygen present in water differs slightly from place to place, so testing the oxygen in the Iceman's body might help locate his home. That is, the scientists formed a **hypothesis**, a tentative explanation or prediction based on experimental observations.

After formulating one or more hypotheses, scientists perform experiments designed to give results that confirm or invalidate these hypotheses. In chemistry this usually requires that both quantitative and qualitative information be collected. **Quantitative** information is numerical data, such as the temperature at which a chemical substance melts or its mass (Figure 1.3). **Qualitative** information, in contrast, consists of nonnumerical observations, such as the color of a substance or its physical appearance.

In the case of the Iceman, scientists have assembled a great deal of qualitative and quantitative information on his body, his clothing, and his weapons. Among this was information from recent studies on his tooth enamel and bones. Different oxygen isotopes in these body parts showed that the Iceman must have consumed water from a relatively small location within what is now Italy (page 58). The mystery of his place of origin was solved.

## A CLOSER LOOK

# Careers in Chemistry

Your course in general chemistry is just the beginning, and this may be the time when you are just starting to have a sense of your future career direction. This course may interest you in learning even more about chemistry as you prepare for a career in chemistry, but it may also serve as one of the first steps to prepare you for a career in other areas of science, medicine, engineering, or even one as seemingly far from chemistry as finance. One area of science that draws on many others is forensic science, and the photo here is of Caitlin Kilcoin, a forensic chemist and former student of one of this book's authors.

While taking General Chemistry, Ms. Kilcoin became interested in forensic chemistry, so, after her undergraduate studies, she earned a M.S. degree in forensic science at Virginia Commonwealth University in Richmond, Virginia. As part of that program she worked as an intern in Las Vegas, Nevada.

After finishing her advanced degree, she began working for the Department of General Services of the State of Virginia in the Chemical Terrorism Unit. There she worked under the Food Emergency Response Network, a program established by the Food and Drug Administration. This work involved testing food samples from customs agencies

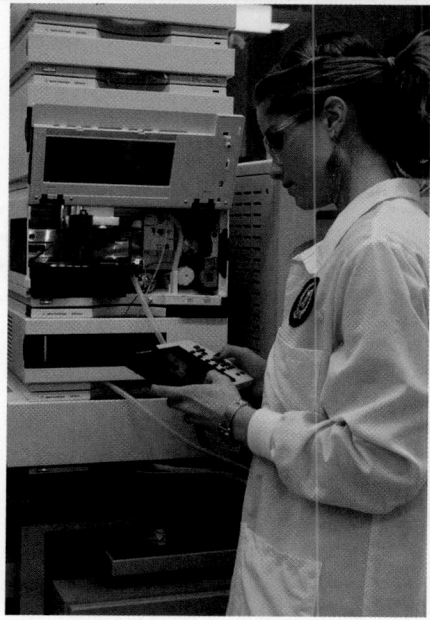

Caitlin Kilcoin, forensic chemist and former student of one of this book's authors.

during the time when companies in China were found to be contaminating food stuffs with the chemical compound melamine (▶ Chpater 12, page 565). Another aspect of

that work was testing food for other toxins. In addition, her laboratory was responsible for testing unknown samples that were submitted as evidence in legal cases. These included suspicious powders, adulterated food samples, and sometimes arson samples.

Ms. Kilcoin told us that deciding that you would like to work in the field of chemistry is the easy part. Where it becomes more involved is defining exactly which path you want to take within the field. "But you should take time to figure out whether you're the type of person who likes to have an established set of procedures or one who likes the research aspect of chemistry and is not afraid of the unknowns." Either way, she stresses the importance of obtaining an advanced degree. Within a highly competitive field, this degree will help you stand out among other applicants. "As a chemist working in the field, I found that I always need to be prepared for the unexpected. Just when I think that people can't get any more outlandish in their criminal attempts, another sample is submitted to the lab for analysis that tops the one before it. The best part is that they probably always think they're going to get away with it. However, I think science has proven that that is not always the case."

The analysis using oxygen isotopes to determine the Iceman's home can only be done because it is well known that oxygen isotopes in water vary with altitude in predictable ways. That is, the variation in isotope composition with location can be deemed a law of science. After numerous experiments by many scientists over an extended period of time, an hypothesis may become a **law**—a concise verbal or mathematical statement of a behavior or a relation that seems always to be the same under the same conditions.

We base much of what we do in science on laws because they help us predict what may occur under a new set of circumstances. For example, we know from experience

**FIGURE 1.3 Qualitative and quantitative observations.** A new substance is formed by mixing two known substances in solution, and several observations can be made. *Qualitative* observations: Before mixing, one solution is light green and the other is colorless. After mixing, the solution is colorless but there is now a bright red solid in the beaker. *Quantitative* observations: 100 mL of one solution is mixed with 10 mL of the other. Although not shown here, the mass of the solid after mixing is 3.6 g.

that if the chemical element sodium comes in contact with water, a violent reaction occurs and new substances are formed (Figure 1.4), and we know that the mass of the substances produced in the reaction is exactly the same as the mass of sodium and water used in the reaction. That is, *mass is always conserved in chemical reactions.*

Once enough reproducible experiments have been conducted and experimental results have been generalized as a law or general rule, it may be possible to conceive a theory to explain the observation. A **theory** is a well-tested, unifying principle that explains a body of facts and the laws based on them. It is capable of suggesting new hypotheses that can be tested experimentally.

Sometimes nonscientists use the word *theory* to imply that someone has made a guess and that an idea is not yet substantiated. But, to scientists, a theory is based on carefully determined and reproducible evidence. Theories are the cornerstone of our understanding of the natural world at any given time. Remember, though, that theories are inventions of the human mind. Theories can and do change as new facts are uncovered.

**FIGURE 1.4** The metallic element sodium reacts with water.

## Goals of Science

The sciences, including chemistry, have several goals. Two of these are prediction and control. We do experiments and seek generalities because we want to be able to predict what may occur under other sets of circumstances. We also want to know how we might control the outcome of a chemical reaction or process.

Two further goals are understanding and explaining. We know, for example, that certain elements such as sodium will react vigorously with water. But why should this be true? To explain and understand this, we turn to theories such as those developed in Chapters 7 and 8.

## Dilemmas and Integrity in Science

You may think research in science is straightforward: Do experiments, collect information, and draw a conclusion. But, research is seldom that easy. Frustrations and disappointments are common enough, and results can be inconclusive. Experiments sometimes contain some level of uncertainty, and spurious or contradictory data can be collected. For example, suppose you do an experiment expecting to find a direct relation between two experimental quantities. You collect six data sets. When plotted on a graph, four of the sets lie on a straight line, but two others lie far away from the line. Should you ignore the last two points? Or should you do more experiments when you know the time they take will mean someone else could publish their results first and thus get the credit for a new scientific principle? Or should you consider that the two points not on the line might indicate that your original hypothesis is wrong and that you will have to abandon a favorite idea you have worked on for a year? Scientists have a responsibility to remain objective in these situations, but sometimes it is hard to do.

It is important to remember that scientists are human and therefore subject to the same moral pressures and dilemmas as any other person. To help ensure integrity in science, some simple principles have emerged over time that guide scientific practice:

- Experimental results should be reproducible. Furthermore, these results should be reported in the scientific literature in sufficient detail that they can be used or reproduced by others.
- Conclusions should be reasonable and unbiased.
- Credit should be given where it is due.

## 1.2    Sustainability and Green Chemistry

The world's population is about 6.8 billion people, with about 7 million added every month. Each of these new persons needs shelter, food, and medical care, and each uses increasingly scarce resources like fresh water and energy. And each produces

**A CLOSER LOOK**

## Principles of Green Chemistry

Paul Anastas and John Warner enunciated the principles of green chemistry in their book *Green Chemistry: Theory and Practice* (Oxford, 1998). Among these are the ones stated below. As you read *Chemistry & Chemical Reactivity*, we will remind you of these principles, and others, and how they can be applied.

- "It is better to prevent waste than to treat or clean up waste after it is formed."
- New pharmaceuticals or consumer chemicals are synthesized, that is, made, by a large number of chemical processes. Therefore, "synthetic methods should be designed to maximize the incorporation of all materials used in the final product."
- Where possible, synthetic methods "should be designed to use and generate substances that possess little or no toxicity to human health or the environment."

- "Chemical products should be designed to [function effectively] while still reducing toxicity."
- "Energy requirements should be recognized for their environmental and economic impacts and should be minimized. Synthetic methods should be conducted at ambient temperature and pressure."
- Raw materials "should be renewable whenever technically and economically practical."
- "Chemical products should be designed so that at the end of their function, they do not persist in the environment or break down into dangerous products."
- Substances used in a chemical process should be chosen to minimize the potential for chemical accidents, including releases, explosions, and fires.

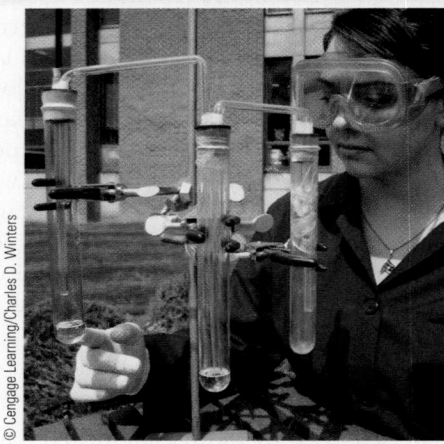

**A student performs a "green" synthesis.** In this experiment a chemical compound is made using a new method that avoids toxic chemicals.

by-products in the act of living and working that can affect our environment. With such a large population, these individual effects can add up to cause large consequences for our planet. The focus of scientists, planners, and politicians is increasingly turning to a concept of "sustainable development."

James Cusumano, a chemist and former president of a chemical company, said that "On one hand, society, governments, and industry seek economic growth to create greater value, new jobs, and a more enjoyable and fulfilling lifestyle. Yet, on the other, regulators, environmentalists, and citizens of the globe demand that we do so with *sustainable development*—meeting today's global economic and environmental needs while preserving the options of future generations to meet theirs. How do nations resolve these potentially conflicting goals?" This is even more true now than it was in 1995 when Dr. Cusumano made this statement in the *Journal of Chemical Education.*

Much of the increase in life expectancy and quality of life, at least in the developed world, is derived from advances in science. But we have paid an environmental price for it, with increases in gases such as nitrogen oxides and sulfur oxides in the atmosphere, acid rain falling in many parts of the world, and waste pharmaceuticals entering the water supply. Among many others, chemists are seeking answers to this dilemma, and one response has been to practice *green chemistry.*

This concept of green chemistry began to take root more than 10 years ago and is now beginning to lead to new ways of doing things and to lower pollutant levels. By the time you finish this book, you will have been introduced to most, if not all, the underlying principles of green chemistry. As you can see in "A Closer Look: Principles of Green Chemistry," they are simple ideas. The challenge is to put them into practice.

## 1.3 Classifying Matter

This chapter begins our discussion of how chemists think about science in general and about matter in particular. After looking at a way to classify matter, we will turn to some basic ideas about elements, atoms, compounds, and molecules and describe how chemists characterize these building blocks of matter.

## States of Matter and Kinetic-Molecular Theory

An easily observed property of matter is its **state**—that is, whether a substance is a solid, liquid, or gas (Figure 1.5). You recognize a material as a solid because it has a rigid shape and a fixed volume that changes little as temperature and pressure change. Like solids, liquids have a fixed volume, but a liquid is fluid—it takes on the shape of its container and has no definite shape of its own. Gases are fluid as well, but the volume of a gas is determined by the size of its container. The volume of a gas varies more than the volume of a liquid with changes in temperature and pressure.

At low enough temperatures, virtually all matter is found in the solid state. As the temperature is raised, solids usually melt to form liquids. Eventually, if the temperature is high enough, liquids evaporate to form gases. Volume changes typically accompany changes in state. For a given mass of material, there is usually a small increase in volume on melting—water being a significant exception—and then a large increase in volume occurs upon evaporation.

The **kinetic-molecular theory of matter** helps us interpret the properties of solids, liquids, and gases. According to this theory, all matter consists of extremely tiny particles (atoms, molecules, or ions) that are in constant motion.

- In solids these particles are packed closely together, usually in a regular array. The particles vibrate back and forth about their average positions, but seldom do particles in a solid squeeze past their immediate neighbors to come into contact with a new set of particles.
- The particles in liquids are arranged randomly rather than in the regular patterns found in solids. Liquids and gases are fluid because the particles are not confined to specific locations and can move past one another.
- Under normal conditions, the particles in a gas are far apart. Gas molecules move extremely rapidly and are not constrained by their neighbors. The molecules of a gas fly about, colliding with one another and with the container walls. This random motion allows gas molecules to fill their container, so the volume of the gas sample is the volume of the container.

An important aspect of the kinetic-molecular theory is that the higher the temperature, the faster the particles move. The energy of motion of the particles (their **kinetic energy**, page 16) acts to overcome the forces of attraction between particles. A solid melts to form a liquid when the temperature of the solid is raised to the point at which the particles vibrate fast enough and far enough to push one another out of the way and move out of their regularly spaced positions. As the temperature increases even more, the particles move even faster until finally they can escape the clutches of their comrades and enter the gaseous state. *Increasing temperature corresponds to faster and faster motions of atoms and molecules,* a general rule you will find useful in many future discussions.

● **Water—Changes in Volume on Freezing.** Water is an exception to the general statement that a given mass of a substance has a smaller volume as a solid than as a liquid. Water is unique in that, for a given mass, the volume *increases* on changing from a liquid to a solid, that is, its density decreases. (See Table 1.2 on page 13.)

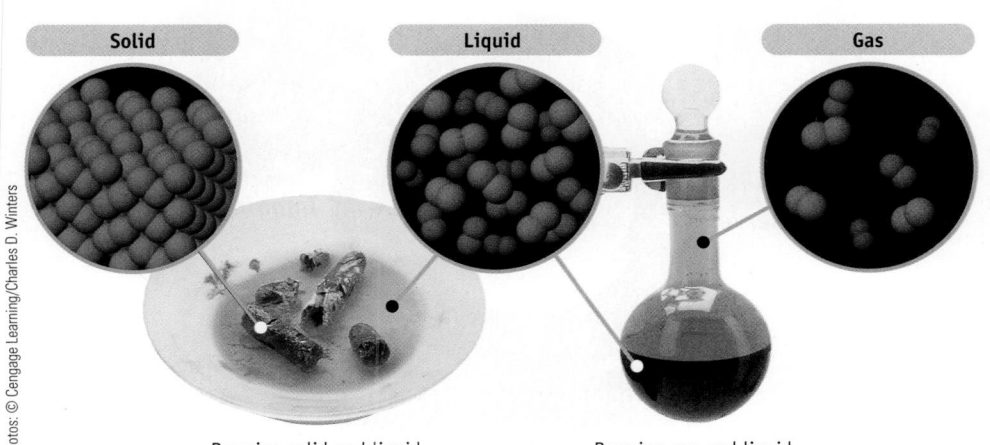

Photos: © Cengage Learning/Charles D. Winters

Solid          Liquid          Gas

Bromine solid and liquid          Bromine gas and liquid

**FIGURE 1.5 States of matter—solid, liquid, and gas.** Elemental bromine exists in all three states near room temperature. The tiny spheres represent bromine (Br) atoms. In elemental bromine, two Br atoms join to form a $Br_2$ molecule. (▶ Chapter 2.)

## Matter at the Macroscopic and Particulate Levels

The characteristic properties of gases, liquids, and solids are observed by the un-aided human senses. They are determined using samples of matter large enough to be seen, measured, and handled. Using such samples, we can determine, for ex-ample, what the color of a substance is, whether it dissolves in water, whether it conducts electricity, and if it reacts with oxygen. Observations such as these gener-ally take place in the **macroscopic** world of chemistry (Figure 1.6). This is the world of experiments and observations.

Now let us move to the level of atoms, molecules, and ions—a world of chem-istry we cannot see. Take a macroscopic sample of material and divide it, again and again, past the point where the amount of sample can be seen by the naked eye, past the point where it can be seen using an optical microscope. Eventually you reach the level of individual particles that make up all matter, a level that chemists refer to as the **submicroscopic** or **particulate** world of atoms and molecules (Fig-ures 1.5 and 1.6).

Chemists are interested in the structure of matter at the particulate level. At-oms, molecules, and ions cannot be "seen" in the same way that one views the mac-roscopic world, but they are no less real. Chemists imagine what atoms must look like and how they might fit together to form molecules. They create models to rep-resent atoms and molecules (Figures 1.5 and 1.6)—where tiny spheres are used to represent atoms—and then use these models to think about chemistry and to ex-plain the observations they have made about the macroscopic world.

It has been said that chemists carry out experiments at the macroscopic level, but they think about chemistry at the particulate level. They then write down their observations as "symbols," the formulas (such as $H_2O$ for water or $NH_3$ for ammonia molecules) and drawings that signify the elements and compounds involved. This is a useful perspective that will help you as you study chemistry. Indeed, one of our goals is to help you make the connections in your own mind among the symbolic, particulate, and macroscopic worlds of chemistry.

## Pure Substances

A chemist looks at a glass of drinking water and sees a liquid. This liquid could be the pure chemical compound water. More likely, though, the liquid is a homoge-neous mixture of water and dissolved substances—that is, a **solution**. Specifically, we can classify a sample of matter as being either a pure substance or a mixture (Figure 1.7).

A pure substance has a set of unique properties by which it can be recog-nized. Pure water, for example, is colorless and odorless. If you want to identify a

**FIGURE 1.6 Levels of matter.**
We observe chemical and physical processes at the macroscopic level. To understand or illustrate these processes, scientists often imagine what has occurred at the particulate atomic and molecular levels and write symbols to represent these observa-tions. A beaker of boiling water can be visualized at the particulate level as rapidly moving $H_2O$ molecules. The process is symbolized by the chemical equation $H_2O$ (liquid) $\rightarrow$ $H_2O$ (gas).

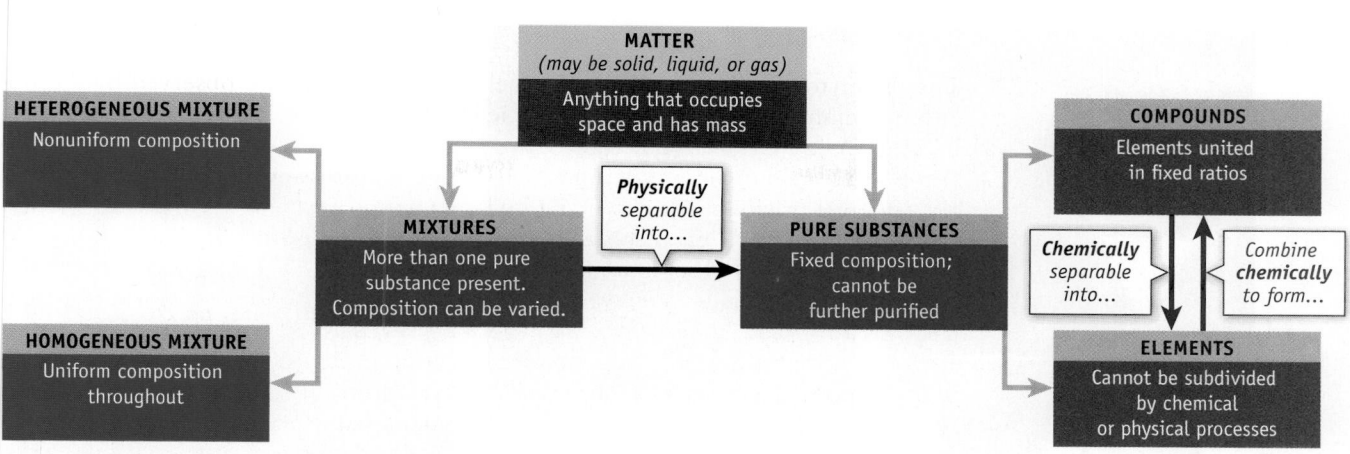

**FIGURE 1.7** Classifying matter.

substance conclusively as water, you would have to examine its properties carefully and compare them against the known properties of pure water. Melting point and boiling point serve the purpose well here. If you could show that the substance melts at 0 °C and boils at 100 °C at atmospheric pressure, you can be certain it is water. No other known substance melts and boils at precisely these temperatures.

A second feature of a pure substance is that it cannot be separated into two or more different species by any physical technique at ordinary temperatures. If it could be separated, our sample would be classified as a mixture.

## Mixtures: Homogeneous and Heterogeneous

A mixture consists of two or more pure substances that can be separated by physical techniques. Sand on the beach is a **heterogeneous** mixture of solids and liquids (Figure 1.8a), a mixture in which the uneven texture of the material can be detected. However, there are heterogeneous mixtures that may appear completely uniform but on closer examination are not (Figure 1.8b). Milk, for example, appears smooth in texture to the unaided eye, but magnification would reveal fat and protein globules within the liquid. In a heterogeneous mixture the properties in one region are different from those in another region.

**(a)** A sample of beach sand is clearly heterogeneous. Each particle of sand and shells can be seen with the naked eye, and the sand and other particles can be separated.

**(b)** A sample of milk may look homogeneous, but examination with an optical microscope shows it is, in fact, a heterogeneous mixture of liquids and suspended particles (fat globules).

**(c)** A homogeneous mixture, here consisting of salt in water. The model shows that salt in water consists of separate, electrically charged particles (ions), but the particles cannot be seen with an optical microscope.

**FIGURE 1.8** **Heterogeneous and homogeneous mixtures.**

**(a)** A laboratory setup. A beaker full of muddy water is passed through a paper filter, and the mud and dirt are removed.

**(b)** A water treatment plant uses filtration to remove suspended particles from the water.

**FIGURE 1.9** Purifying a heterogeneous mixture by filtration.

A **homogeneous** mixture consists of two or more substances in the same phase (Figure 1.8c). No amount of optical magnification will reveal a homogeneous mixture to have different properties in different regions. Homogeneous mixtures are often called **solutions**. Common examples include air (mostly a mixture of nitrogen and oxygen gases), gasoline (a mixture of carbon- and hydrogen-containing compounds called *hydrocarbons),* and a soft drink in an unopened container.

When a mixture is separated into its pure components, the components are said to be **purified**. Efforts at separation are often not complete in a single step, however, and repetition almost always gives an increasingly pure substance. For example, soil particles can be separated from water by filtration (Figure 1.9). When the mixture is passed through a filter, many of the particles are removed. Repeated filtrations will give water a higher and higher state of purity. This purification process uses a property of the mixture, its clarity, to measure the extent of purification. When a perfectly clear sample of water is obtained, all of the soil particles are assumed to have been removed.

## 1.4 Elements

**Module 1: The Periodic Table** covers concepts in this section.

Passing an electric current through water can decompose it to gaseous hydrogen and oxygen (Figure 1.10a). Substances like hydrogen and oxygen that are composed of *only one type of atom* are classified as **elements**. Currently 118 elements are known. Of these, only about 90—some of which are illustrated in Figure 1.10—are found in nature. The remainder have been created by scientists. *Names and symbols for each element are listed in the tables at the front and back of this book.* Carbon (C), sulfur (S), iron (Fe), copper (Cu), silver (Ag), tin (Sn), gold (Au), mercury (Hg), and lead (Pb) were known to the early Greeks and Romans and to the alchemists of ancient China, the Arab world, and medieval Europe. However, many other elements—such as aluminum (Al), silicon (Si), iodine (I), and helium (He)—were not discovered until the 18th and 19th centuries. Finally, scientists in the 20th and 21st centuries have made elements that do not exist in nature, such as technetium (Tc), plutonium (Pu), and americium (Am).

The table inside the front cover of this book, in which the symbol and other information for the elements are enclosed in a box, is called the **periodic table**. We will describe this important tool of chemistry in more detail beginning in Chapter 2.

An **atom** is the smallest particle of an element that retains the characteristic chemical properties of that element. Modern chemistry is based on an understanding and exploration of nature at the atomic level (▶ Chapters 6 and 7).

## A CLOSER LOOK

# Element Names and Symbols

The stories behind some of the names of the elements are fascinating. Many obviously have names and symbols with Latin or Greek

**Nicolaus Copernicus (1473–1543).** The most recently named element, 112, was named for Copernicus.

Erich Lessing/Art Resource, NY

origins. Examples include helium (He), from the Greek word *helios* meaning "sun," and lead, whose symbol, Pb, comes from the Latin word for "heavy," *plumbum*. More recently discovered elements have been named for their place of discovery or place of significance. Examples include americium (Am), californium (Cf), scandium (Sc), europium (Eu), francium (Fr), polonium (Po), and many others.

A number of elements are named for their discoverers or famous scientists: curium (Cm), einsteinium (Es), fermium (Fm), mendeleevium (Md), nobelium (No), seaborgium (Sg), and meitnerium (Mt), among others. The most recently named element, element 112, was given its official name, copernicium (Cn), only in 2010. It was named after Nicolaus Copernicus (1473–1543), who first proposed that Earth and the

other planets orbited the sun. Some say his work was the beginning of the scientific revolution.

What do you suppose is the origin of the names of the elements uranium, plutonium, and neptunium?

When writing the symbol for an element notice that only the first letter of an element's symbol is capitalized. For example, cobalt is Co, not CO. The notation CO represents the chemical compound carbon monoxide. Also note that the element name is not capitalized, except at the beginning of a sentence.

To learn more about element names and the periodic table, there are several excellent references on the Internet.
- www.ptable.com
- www.pubs.acs.org/cen/80th/elements.html

---

**REVIEW & CHECK FOR SECTION 1.4**

Using the periodic table inside the front cover of this book:

1.  What is the symbol for the element sodium?

    (a)  S            (b)  Na            (c)  So            (d)  Sm

2.  What is the name of the element with the symbol Si?

    (a)  silver        (b)  sulfur        (c)  selenium        (d)  silicon

● **Review and Check** At the end of almost all sections of each chapter there will be a set of multiple-choice questions to check your understanding. Answers to these questions are in Appendix P. In the YouBook version, you can click on an answer.

Oxygen—gas    Hydrogen—gas    Mercury—liquid    Powdered sulfur—solid    Copper wire—solid    Iron chips—solid    Aluminum—solid    Water—liquid

Photos: © Cengage Learning/Charles D. Winters

**(a)**                                **(b)**

**FIGURE 1.10 Elements. (a)** Passing an electric current through water produces the elements hydrogen (test tube on the right) and oxygen (test tube on the left). **(b)** Chemical elements can often be distinguished by their color and their state at room temperature.

**(a)** The material in the dish is a mixture of iron chips and sulfur. The iron can be removed easily by using a magnet.

**(b)** Iron pyrite is a chemical compound composed of iron and sulfur. It is often found in nature as perfect, golden cubes.

**FIGURE 1.11** Mixtures and compounds.

## 1.5    Compounds

A pure substance like sugar, salt, or water, which is composed of two or more different elements held together by **chemical bonds**, is referred to as a **chemical compound**. Even though only 118 elements are known, there appears to be no limit to the number of compounds that can be made from those elements. More than 54 million compounds are now known, with many thousands added to the list each year.

When elements become part of a compound, their original properties, such as their color, hardness, and melting point, are replaced by the characteristic properties of the compound. Consider common table salt (sodium chloride), which is composed of two elements (see Figure 1.2):

- Sodium is a shiny metal that reacts violently with water. Its solid state structure has sodium atoms tightly packed together.
- Chlorine is a light yellow gas that has a distinctive, suffocating odor and is a powerful irritant to lungs and other tissues. The element is composed of $Cl_2$ molecules in which two chlorine atoms are tightly bound together.
- Sodium chloride, or common salt (NaCl), is a colorless, crystalline solid composed of sodium and chlorine ions bound tightly together. Its properties are completely unlike those of the two elements from which it is made.

It is important to distinguish between a mixture of elements and a chemical compound of two or more elements. Pure metallic iron and yellow, powdered sulfur (Figure 1.11a) can be mixed in varying proportions. In the chemical compound iron pyrite (Figure 1.11b), however, there is no variation in composition. Not only does iron pyrite exhibit properties peculiar to itself and different from those of either iron or sulfur, or a mixture of these two elements, but it also has a definite percentage composition by mass (46.55% Fe and 53.45% S). Thus, two major differences exist between a mixture and a pure compound: A compound has distinctly different characteristics from its parent elements, and it has a definite percentage composition (by mass) of its combining elements.

Some compounds—such as table salt, NaCl—are composed of **ions**, which are electrically charged atoms or groups of atoms (▶ Chapter 2). Other compounds—such as water and sugar—consist of **molecules**, the smallest discrete units that retain the composition and chemical characteristics of the compound.

The composition of any compound is represented by its **chemical formula**. In the formula for water, $H_2O$, for example, the symbol for hydrogen, H, is followed by a subscript 2, indicating that two atoms of hydrogen occur in a single water molecule. The symbol for oxygen appears without a subscript, indicating that one oxygen atom occurs in the molecule.

As you shall see throughout this book, molecules can be represented with models that depict their composition and structure. Figure 1.12 illustrates the names, formulas, and models of the structures of a few common molecular compounds.

| NAME | Water | Methane | Ammonia | Carbon dioxide |
|---|---|---|---|---|
| FORMULA | $H_2O$ | $CH_4$ | $NH_3$ | $CO_2$ |
| MODEL | | | | |

**FIGURE 1.12 Names, formulas, and models of some common molecular compounds.** Models of molecules appear throughout this book. In such models, C atoms are gray, H atoms are white, N atoms are blue, and O atoms are red.

**FIGURE 1.13 Physical properties.** An ice cube and a piece of lead can be differentiated easily by their physical properties (such as density, color, and melting point).

## 1.6 Physical Properties

You recognize your friends by their physical appearance: their height and weight and the color of their eyes and hair. The same is true of chemical substances. You can tell the difference between an ice cube and a cube of lead of the same size not only because of their appearance (one is clear and colorless, and the other is a lustrous metal) (Figure 1.13) but also because one is more dense (lead) than the other (ice). Properties such as these, which can be observed and measured without changing the composition of a substance, are called **physical properties**. The chemical elements in Figure 1.10, for example, clearly differ in terms of their color, appearance, and state (solid, liquid, or gas). Physical properties allow us to classify and identify substances. Table 1.1 lists a few physical properties of matter that chemists commonly use.

**Density**, the ratio of the mass of an object to its volume, is a physical property useful for identifying substances.

$$\text{Density} = \frac{\text{mass}}{\text{volume}} \tag{1.1}$$

For example, you can readily tell the difference between an ice cube and a cube of lead of identical size because lead has a high density, 11.35 g/cm³ (11.35 grams per cubic centimeter), whereas ice has a density slightly less than 0.917 g/cm³. An ice cube with a volume of 16.0 cm³ has a mass of 14.7 g, whereas a cube of lead with the same volume has a mass of 182 g.

The **temperature** of a sample of matter often affects the numerical values of its properties. Density is a particularly important example. Although the change in water density with temperature seems small (Table 1.2), it affects our environment profoundly. For example, as the water in a lake cools, the density of the water

● **Units of Density** As described on page 25 the decimal system of units in the sciences is called the Systemé International d'Unites; often referred to as SI units. The SI unit of mass is the kilogram and the SI unit of length is the meter. Therefore, the SI unit of density is kg/m³. In chemistry, the more commonly used unit is g/cm³. To convert from kg/m³ to g/cm³, divide by 1000.

● **Calculations Involving Density and Mathematics Review** See *Let's Review* beginning on page 24 for a review of some of the mathematics used in introductory chemistry.

● **Temperature Scales** Scientists use the Celsius (°C) and Kelvin scales (K) for temperature. (▶ page 26.)

Table 1.1 **Some Physical Properties**

| Property | Using the Property to Distinguish Substances |
|---|---|
| Color | Is the substance colored or colorless? What is the color, and what is its intensity? |
| State of matter | Is it a solid, liquid, or gas? If it is a solid, what is the shape of the particles? |
| Melting point | At what temperature does a solid melt? |
| Boiling point | At what temperature does a liquid boil? |
| Density | What is the substance's density (mass per unit volume)? |
| Solubility | What mass of substance can dissolve in a given volume of water or other solvent? |
| Electric conductivity | Does the substance conduct electricity? |
| Malleability | How easily can a solid be deformed? |
| Ductility | How easily can a solid be drawn into a wire? |
| Viscosity | How easily will a liquid flow? |

Table 1.2 **Temperature Dependence of Water Density**

| Temperature (°C) | Density of Water (g/cm³) |
|---|---|
| 0 (ice) | 0.917 |
| 0 (liq water) | 0.99984 |
| 2 | 0.99994 |
| 4 | 0.99997 |
| 10 | 0.99970 |
| 25 | 0.99707 |
| 100 | 0.95836 |

**FIGURE 1.14 Temperature dependence of physical properties. (a)** *Change in density with temperature.* Ice cubes were placed in the right side of the tank and blue dye in the left side. The water beneath the ice is cooler and denser than the surrounding water, so it sinks. The convection current created by this movement of water is traced by the dye movement as the denser, cooler water sinks. **(b)** *Temperature and calibration.* Laboratory glassware is calibrated for specific temperatures. The pipet will deliver and the volumetric flask will contain the specified volume at the indicated temperature.

(a)                                    (b)

increases and the denser water sinks (Figure 1.14a). This continues until the water temperature reaches 3.98 °C, the point at which water has its maximum density (0.999973 g/cm³). If the water temperature drops further, the density decreases slightly and the colder water floats on top of water at 3.98 °C. If water is cooled below about 0 °C, solid ice forms. Water is unique among substances in the universe: Its solid form is less dense than its liquid form, so ice floats on water.

The volume of a given mass of liquid changes with temperature, so its density does as well. This is the reason laboratory glassware used to measure precise volumes of solutions always specifies the temperature at which it was calibrated (Figure 1.14b).

## Extensive and Intensive Properties

**Extensive properties** depend on the amount of a substance present. The mass and volume of the samples of elements in Figure 1.10, or the amount of energy transferred as heat from burning gasoline, are extensive properties, for example.

In contrast, **intensive properties** do *not* depend on the amount of substance. A sample of ice will melt at 0 °C, no matter whether you have an ice cube or an iceberg.

The mass and volume of an object are extensive properties because they depend on the amount of sample present. Interestingly, the density of the object, the quotient of mass and volume, is an intensive property. The density of gold, for example, is the same (19.3 g/cm³ at 20 °C) whether you have a flake of pure gold or a solid gold ring.

Intensive properties are often useful in identifying a material. For example, the temperature at which a material melts (its melting point) is often so characteristic that it can be used to identify the solid (Figure 1.15).

**FIGURE 1.15 A physical property used to distinguish compounds.** Aspirin and naphthalene both are white solids at 25 °C. One way to tell them apart is by a difference in physical properties. At the temperature of boiling water, 100 °C, naphthalene is a liquid (left), whereas aspirin is a solid (right).

Naphthalene is a white solid at 25 °C but has a melting point of 80.2 °C.

Aspirin is a white solid at 25 °C. It has a melting point of 135 °C.

**REVIEW & CHECK FOR SECTION 1.6**

1.  Which of the following is NOT a physical property?

    (a)  liquid nitrogen boils at $-196\ ^\circ C$

    (b)  sugar dissolves in water

    (c)  gasoline burns in air

    (d)  gold melts at $1064\ ^\circ C$

    (e)  a copper compound is blue

2.  A piece of a polypropylene rope (used for water skiing) floats on water, whereas a tere-phthalate polymer from a soda bottle sinks in water. What is the order of increasing density of these substances?

    (a)  water < polypropylene < soda bottle plastic

    (b)  polypropylene < water < soda bottle plastic

    (c)  polypropylene < soda bottle plastic < water

    (d)  soda bottle plastic < polypropylene < water

    (e)  soda bottle plastic < water < polypropylene

3.  Which of the following is an extensive property of mercury (see Figure 1.10)?

    (a)  shiny surface

    (b)  melts at 234.22 K

    (c)  density = 13.6 g/cm$^3$

    (d)  volume = 13.6 cm$^3$

## 1.7  Physical and Chemical Changes

Changes in physical properties are called **physical changes**. In a physical change the identity of a substance is preserved even though it may have changed its physical state or the gross size and shape of its pieces. A physical change does not result in a new chemical substance being produced. The substances (atoms, molecules, or ions) present before and after the change are the same. An example of a physical change is the melting of a solid (Figure 1.15). In the case of ice melting, the molecules present both before and after the change are $H_2O$ molecules. Their chemical identity has not changed; they are now simply able to flow past one another in the liquid state instead of being locked in position in the solid.

A physical property of hydrogen gas ($H_2$) is its low density, so a balloon filled with $H_2$ floats in air (Figure 1.16). Suppose, however, that a lighted candle is brought up to the balloon. When the heat causes the skin of the balloon to rupture, the hydrogen combines with the oxygen ($O_2$) in the air, and the heat of the candle sets off a chemical reaction, producing water, $H_2O$. This reaction is an example of a

$O_2$ (gas)    $2\ H_2$ (gas)    $2\ H_2O$(gas)

**(a)**    **(b)**

Photos © Cengage Learning/ Charles D. Winters

**FIGURE 1.16  A chemical change—the reaction of hydrogen and oxygen. (a)** A balloon filled with molecules of hydrogen gas and surrounded by molecules of oxygen in the air. (The balloon floats in air because gaseous hydrogen is less dense than air.) **(b)** When ignited with a burning candle, $H_2$ and $O_2$ react to form water, $H_2O$.

**chemical change**, in which one or more substances (the **reactants**) are transformed into one or more different substances (the **products**).

A chemical change at the particulate level is illustrated by the reaction of hydrogen and oxygen molecules to form water molecules.

$$2 \ H_2(gas) + O_2(gas) \longrightarrow 2 \ H_2O(gas)$$

Reactants          Products

The representation of the change using chemical formulas is called a **chemical equation**. It shows that the substances on the left (the reactants) produce the substances on the right (the products). As this equation shows, there are four atoms of H and two atoms of O before *and* after the reaction, but the molecules before the reaction are different from those after the reaction.

A **chemical property** indicates whether and sometimes how readily a material undergoes a chemical change with another material. For example, a chemical property of hydrogen gas is that it reacts vigorously with oxygen gas.

---

**REVIEW & CHECK FOR SECTION 1.7**

When camping in the mountains, you boil a pot of water on a campfire to make tea. Which of the following is a chemical change?

(a)   The water boils.

(b)   The campfire wood burns.

(c)   The tea dissolves in the hot water.

(d)   The pot melts from the heat of the fire.

---

## 1.8 Energy: Some Basic Principles

● **Units of Energy** Energy in chemistry is measured in units of joules. See *Let's Review* (page 24) and Chapter 5 for calculations involving energy units.

Energy, which is a crucial part of many chemical and physical changes, is defined as the capacity to do work. You do work against the force of gravity when carrying yourself and hiking equipment up a mountain. The energy to do this is provided by the food you have eaten. Food is a source of chemical energy—energy stored in chemical compounds and released when the compounds undergo the chemical reactions of metabolism in your body. Chemical reactions almost always either release or absorb energy.

Energy can be classified as kinetic or potential. **Kinetic energy** is energy associated with motion, such as:

- The motion of atoms, molecules, or ions at the submicroscopic (particulate) level (*thermal energy*). All matter has thermal energy.
- The motion of macroscopic objects such as a moving tennis ball or automobile (*mechanical energy*).
- The movement of electrons in a conductor (*electrical energy*).
- The compression and expansion of the spaces between molecules in the transmission of sound (*acoustic energy*).

**Potential energy** results from an object's position and includes:

- Energy possessed by a ball held above the floor and by water at the top of a water wheel (*gravitational energy*) (Figure 1.17a).
- Energy stored in an extended spring.
- Energy stored in fuels (*chemical energy*) (Figure 1.17b). Almost all chemical reactions involve a change in chemical energy.
- Energy associated with the separation of two electrical charges (*electrostatic energy*) (Figure 1.17c).

# CO₂ in the Oceans

"Over the past 200 years, the oceans have absorbed approximately 550 billion tons of $CO_2$ from the atmosphere, or about a third of the total amount of anthropogenic emissions over that period." This amounts to about 22 million tons *per day*. This statement was made by R. A. Feely, a scientist at the National Oceanographic and Atmospheric Administration, in connection with studies on the effects of carbon dioxide on ocean chemistry.

The amount of $CO_2$ dissolved in the oceans is of great concern and interest to oceanographers because it affects the pH of the water, that is, its level of acidity. This in turn can affect the growth of marine systems such as corals and sea urchins and microscopic coccolithophores (single-cell phytoplankton).

**Sea urchins.** The growth of spines by sea urchins depends on the level of $CO_2$ in the water. (left) Normal growth at the current $CO_2$ level in the ocean (400 ppm). (right) Growth at a level of 2850 ppm (an extreme level used for lab studies).

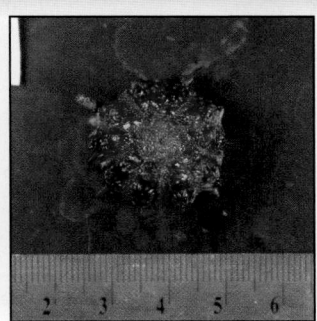

Image courtesy of Justin B. Ries, Department of Marine Sciences, University of North Carolina at Chapel Hill

Image copyright David Mckee, 2010. Used under license from Shutterstock.com

**Clown fish**. The larvae of the clown fish are affected by high levels of $CO_2$ in the ocean.

Recent studies have indicated that, in water with a high $CO_2$ content, the spines of sea urchins are greatly impaired, the larvae of orange clown fish lose their homing ability, and the concentrations of calcium, copper, manganese, and iron in sea water are affected, sometimes drastically.

## Questions:

1. Much has been written about $CO_2$. What is its name?
2. Give the symbols for the four metals mentioned in this article.
3. Of the four metals mentioned here, which is the most dense? The least dense? (Use an Internet tool such as www.ptable.com to find this information.)
4. The spines of the sea urchin, corals, and coccolithophores all are built on the compound $CaCO_3$. What elements are involved in this compound? Do you know its name?

**Answers to these questions are available in Appendix N.**

## Reference:

"Off-Balance Ocean: Acidification from absorbing atmospheric $CO_2$ is changing the ocean's chemistry," Rachel Petkewich, *Chemical and Engineering News*, February 23, 2009, page 56.

Bruce Roberts/Photo Researchers, Inc.

NASA/Glenn Research Center (GRC)

Image copyright Andriano, 2010. Used under license from Shutterstock.com

**(a)** Water at the top of a water wheel represents stored, or potential, energy. As water flows over the wheel, its potential energy is converted to mechanical energy.

**(b)** Chemical potential energy of the fuel and oxygen is converted to thermal and mechanical energy in a jet engine.

**(c)** Lightning converts electrostatic energy into radiant and thermal energy.

**FIGURE 1.17** Energy and its conversion.

Potential energy
(energy of position)

Kinetic energy
(energy of motion)

Heat and work
(thermal and
mechanical energy)

**FIGURE 1.18** The law of energy conservation. The diver's potential energy is converted to kinetic energy, which is then transferred to the water, illustrating the law of conservation of energy.

Potential energy and kinetic energy can be interconverted. For example, as water falls over a waterfall, its potential energy is converted into kinetic energy. Similarly, kinetic energy can be converted into potential energy: The kinetic energy of falling water can turn a turbine to produce electricity, which can then be used to convert water into $H_2$ and $O_2$ by electrolysis. Hydrogen gas contains stored chemical potential energy because it can be burned to produce heat and light or electricity.

## Conservation of Energy

Standing on a diving board, you have considerable potential energy because of your position above the water. Once you dive off the board, some of that potential energy is converted into kinetic energy (Figure 1.18). During the dive, the force of gravity accelerates your body so that it moves faster and faster. Your kinetic energy increases and your potential energy decreases. At the moment you hit the water, your velocity is abruptly reduced and much of your kinetic energy is transferred to the water as your body moves it aside. Eventually you float to the surface, and the water becomes still again. If you could see them, however, you would find that the water molecules are moving a little faster in the vicinity of your entry into the water; that is, the kinetic energy of the water molecules is slightly higher.

This series of energy conversions illustrates the **law of conservation of energy**, which states that *energy can neither be created nor destroyed*. Or, to state this law differently, *the total energy of the universe is constant*. The law of conservation of energy summarizes the results of many experiments in which the amounts of energy transferred have been measured and in which the total energy content has been found to be the same before and after an event.

Let us examine this law in the case of a chemical reaction, the reaction of hydrogen and oxygen to form water (see Figure 1.16). In this reaction, the reactants (hydrogen and oxygen) have a certain amount of energy associated with them. When they react, some of this energy is released to the surroundings. If we were to add up all of the energy present before the reaction and all of the energy present after the reaction, we would find that the energy has only been redistributed; the total amount of energy in the universe has remained constant. Energy has been conserved.

---

**REVIEW & CHECK FOR SECTION 1.8**

1. Which of the following has the highest thermal energy?

   (a) 1.0 g of ice at 0 °C

   (b) 1.0 g of liquid water at 25 °C

   (c) 1.0 g of liquid water at 100 °C

   (d) 1.0 g of water vapor at 100 °C

2. Which of the following is an incorrect statement?

   (a) A mixture of $H_2$ and $O_2$ has lower chemical potential energy than $H_2O$.

   (b) Input of energy is required to split a $H_2$ molecule into two H atoms.

   (c) Water at 30 °C has a higher thermal energy than the same amount of water at 20 °C.

   (d) In the reaction of $H_2O$ and Na (see Figure 1.4), chemical potential energy is converted to thermal energy.

## CHAPTER GOALS REVISITED

*Now that you have studied this chapter, you should ask whether you have met the chapter goals. In particular, you should be able to*

### Understand the differences between hypotheses, laws, and theories
a.   Recognize the difference between a hypothesis and a theory and how laws are established (Section 1.1).

### Be aware of the principles of green chemistry (Section 1.2)

### Apply the kinetic-molecular theory to the properties of matter
a.   Understand the basic ideas of the kinetic-molecular theory (Section 1.3).

### Classify matter
a.   Recognize the different states of matter (solids, liquids, and gases) and give their characteristics (Section 1.3). **Study Question: 31.**
b.   Appreciate the difference between pure substances and mixtures and the difference between homogeneous and heterogeneous mixtures (Section 1.3). **Study Questions: 21, 29, 30.**
c.   Recognize the importance of representing matter at the macroscopic level and at the particulate level (Section 1.3). **Study Questions: 25, 26.**

### Recognize elements, atoms, compounds, and molecules
a.   Identify the name or symbol for an element, given its symbol or name, respectively (Section 1.4). **Study Questions: 1–4, and Go Chemistry Module 1.**
b.   Use the terms *atom, element, molecule, and compound* correctly (Sections 1.4 and 1.5). **Study Questions: 5, 6.**

### Identify physical and chemical properties and changes
a.   List commonly used physical properties of matter (Sections 1.5 and 1.6).
b.   Identify several physical and chemical properties of common substances (Sections 1.5–1.7). **Study Questions: 7–10, 17, 18, 20.**
c.   Relate density to the volume and mass of a substance (Section 1.6). **Study Questions: 15, 16, 27, 28, 33, 35, 39, 42, 43.**
d.   Explain the difference between chemical and physical changes (Section 1.7). **Study Questions: 8, 23, 24, 45.**
e.   Understand the difference between extensive and intensive properties and give examples of them (Section 1.6). **Study Questions: 15, 16.**

### Describe various forms of energy
a.   Identify types of potential and kinetic energy (Section 1.8). **Study Question: 13.**
b.   Recognize and apply the law of conservation of energy (Section 1.8).

 and

Sign in at **www.cengage.com/owl** to:
- View tutorials and simulations, develop problem-solving skills, and complete online homework assigned by your professor.
- For quick review and exam prep, download Go Chemistry mini lecture modules from OWL (or purchase them at **www.cengagebrain.com**)

Access **How Do I Solve It?** tutorials on how to approach problem solving using concepts in this chapter.

## Key Equation

**Equation 1.1 (page 13)** Density: In chemistry the common unit of density is $g/cm^3$, whereas $kg/m^3$ is commonly used in geology and oceanography.

$$\text{Density} = \frac{\text{mass}}{\text{volume}}$$

# Study Questions

## Practicing Skills

### Matter: Elements and Atoms, Compounds, and Molecules

1. Give the name of each of the following elements:
   (a) C        (c) Cl       (e) Mg
   (b) K        (d) P        (f) Ni

2. Give the name of each of the following elements:
   (a) Mn       (c) Na       (e) Xe
   (b) Cu       (d) Br       (f) Fe

3. Give the symbol for each of the following elements:
   (a) barium   (c) chromium   (e) arsenic
   (b) titanium (d) lead       (f) zinc

4. Give the symbol for each of the following elements:
   (a) silver    (c) plutonium   (e) technetium
   (b) aluminum  (d) tin         (f) krypton

5. In each of the following pairs, decide which is an element and which is a compound.
   (a) Na or NaCl
   (b) sugar or carbon
   (c) gold or gold chloride

6. In each of the following pairs, decide which is an element and which is a compound.
   (a) $Pt(NH_3)_2Cl_2$ or Pt
   (b) copper or copper(II) oxide
   (c) silicon or sand

### Physical and Chemical Properties

7. In each case, decide if the underlined property is a physical or chemical property.
   (a) The color of elemental bromine is <u>orange-red</u>.
   (b) Iron <u>turns to rust</u> in the presence of air and water.
   (c) Hydrogen can <u>explode</u> when ignited in air (Figure 1.16).
   (d) The <u>density</u> of titanium metal is 4.5 g/cm³.
   (e) Tin metal <u>melts</u> at 505 K.
   (f) Chlorophyll, a plant pigment, is <u>green</u>.

8. In each case, decide if the change is a chemical or physical change.
   (a) A cup of household bleach changes the color of your favorite T-shirt from purple to pink.
   (b) Water vapor in your exhaled breath condenses in the air on a cold day.
   (c) Plants use carbon dioxide from the air to make sugar.
   (d) Butter melts when placed in the sun.

9. Which part of the description of a compound or element refers to its physical properties and which to its chemical properties?
   (a) The colorless liquid ethanol burns in air.
   (b) The shiny metal aluminum reacts readily with orange-red bromine.

10. Which part of the description of a compound or element refers to its physical properties and which to its chemical properties?
    (a) Calcium carbonate is a white solid with a density of 2.71 g/cm³. It reacts readily with an acid to produce gaseous carbon dioxide.
    (b) Gray, powdered zinc metal reacts with purple iodine to give a white compound.

## Energy

11. The flashlight in the photo does not use batteries. Instead, you move a lever, which turns a geared mechanism and finally results in light from the bulb. What type of energy is used to move the lever? What type or types of energy are produced?

**A hand-operated flashlight.**

12. A solar panel is pictured in the photo. When light shines on the panel, it generates an electric current that can be used to recharge the batteries in an electric car. What types of energy are involved in this setup?

**A solar panel.**

13. Determine which of the following represent potential energy and which represent kinetic energy.
    (a) thermal energy
    (b) gravitational energy
    (c) chemical energy
    (d) electrostatic energy

**14.** Determine whether kinetic energy is being converted to potential energy, or vice versa, in the following processes.
   (a) Water cascades downward in a waterfall.
   (b) Electrolysis of water produces $H_2$ and $O_2$.
   (c) An electric current is generated by a chemical reaction in a battery.
   (d) Water boils when heated on a gas stove.

## General Questions

*These questions are not designated as to type or location in the chapter. They may combine several concepts.*

**15.** A piece of turquoise is a blue-green solid; it has a density of $2.65 \text{ g/cm}^3$ and a mass of $2.5$ g.
   (a) Which of these observations are qualitative and which are quantitative?
   (b) Which of the observations are extensive and which are intensive?
   (c) What is the volume of the piece of turquoise?

**16.** Iron pyrite (fool's gold, Figure 1.11) has a shiny golden metallic appearance. Crystals are often in the form of perfect cubes. A cube 0.40 cm on each side has a mass of 0.064 g.
   (a) Which of these observations are qualitative and which are quantitative?
   (b) Which of the observations are extensive and which are intensive?
   (c) What is the density of the sample of iron pyrite?

**17.** Which observations below describe chemical properties?
   (a) Sugar is soluble in water.
   (b) Water boils at 100 °C.
   (c) Ultraviolet light converts $O_3$ (ozone) to $O_2$ (oxygen).
   (d) Ice is less dense than water.

**18.** Which observations below describe chemical properties?
   (a) Sodium metal reacts violently with water.
   (b) $CO_2$ does not support combustion.
   (c) Chlorine is a green gas.
   (d) Heat is required to melt ice.

**19.** The mineral fluorite contains the elements calcium and fluorine and can have various colors, including blue, violet, green, and yellow.

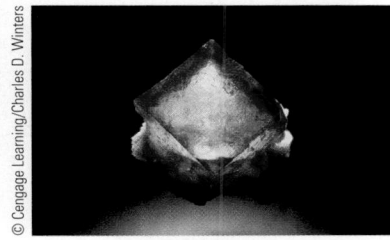

© Cengage Learning/Charles D. Winters

**The mineral fluorite, calcium fluoride.**

   (a) What are the symbols of these elements?
   (b) How would you describe the shape of the fluorite crystals in the photo? What can this tell us about the arrangement of the particles (ions) inside the crystal?

**20.** Azurite, a blue, crystalline mineral, is composed of copper, carbon, and oxygen.

© Cengage Learning/Charles D. Winters

**Azurite is a deep blue crystalline mineral. It is surrounded by copper pellets and powdered carbon (in the dish).**

   (a) What are the symbols of the three elements that combine to make the mineral azurite?
   (b) Based on the photo, describe some of the physical properties of the elements and the mineral. Are any the same? Are any properties different?

**21.** Small chips of iron are mixed with sand (see photo). Is this a homogeneous or heterogeneous mixture? Suggest a way to separate the iron from the sand.

© Cengage Learning/Charles D. Winters

**Chips of iron mixed with sand.**

**22.** You have a solution of NaCl dissolved in water. Describe a method by which these two compounds could be separated.

**23.** Identify the following as either physical changes or chemical changes.
   (a) Dry ice (solid $CO_2$) sublimes (converts directly from solid to gas phase).
   (b) Mercury's density decreases as the temperature increases.
   (c) Energy is given off as heat when natural gas (mostly methane, $CH_4$) burns.
   (d) NaCl dissolves in water.

**24.** Identify the following as either physical changes or chemical changes.
   (a) The desalination of sea water (separation of pure water from dissolved salts).
   (b) The formation of $SO_2$ (an air pollutant) when coal containing sulfur is burned.
   (c) Silver tarnishes.
   (d) Iron is heated to red heat.

**25.** In Figure 1.2 you see a piece of salt and a representation of its internal structure. Which is the macroscopic view and which is the particulate view? How are the macroscopic and particulate views related?

26. In Figure 1.5 you see macroscopic and particulate views of the element bromine. Which are the macroscopic views and which are the particulate views? Describe how the particulate views explain properties of this element related to the state of matter.

27. Carbon tetrachloride, $CCl_4$, a common liquid compound, has a density of 1.58 g/cm³. If you place a piece of a plastic soda bottle ($d = 1.37$ g/cm³) and a piece of aluminum ($d = 2.70$ g/cm³) in liquid $CCl_4$, will the plastic and aluminum float or sink?

28. The following photo shows copper balls, immersed in water, floating on top of mercury. What are the liquids and solids in this photo? Which substance is most dense? Which is least dense?

**Water, copper, and mercury.**

29. Categorize each of the following as an element, a compound, or a mixture.
    (a) sterling silver
    (b) carbonated mineral water
    (c) tungsten
    (d) aspirin

30. Categorize each of the following as an element, a compound, or a mixture.
    (a) air         (c) brass
    (b) fluorite    (d) 18-carat gold

31. ▲ Make a drawing, based on the kinetic-molecular theory and the ideas about atoms and molecules presented in this chapter, of the arrangement of particles in each of the cases listed here. For each case, draw 10 particles of each substance. It is acceptable for your diagram to be two dimensional. Represent each atom as a circle, and distinguish each different kind of atom by shading.
    (a) a sample of solid iron (which consists of iron atoms)
    (b) a sample of *liquid* water (which consists of $H_2O$ molecules)
    (c) a sample of water *vapor*

32. ▲ Make a drawing, based on the kinetic-molecular theory and the ideas about atoms and molecules presented in this chapter, of the arrangement of particles in each of the cases listed here. For each case, draw 10 particles of each substance. It is acceptable for your diagram to be two dimensional. Represent each atom as a circle, and distinguish each different kind of atom by shading.
    (a) a homogeneous mixture of water vapor and helium gas (which consists of helium atoms)
    (b) a heterogeneous mixture consisting of liquid water and solid aluminum; show a region of the sample that includes both substances
    (c) a sample of brass (which is a homogeneous solid mixture of copper and zinc)

33. Hexane ($C_6H_{14}$, density = 0.766 g/cm³), perfluorohexane ($C_6F_{14}$, density = 1.669 g/cm³), and water are immiscible liquids; that is, they do not dissolve in one another. You place 10 mL of each in a graduated cylinder, along with pieces of high-density polyethylene (HDPE, density = 0.97 g/cm³), polyvinyl chloride (PVC, density = 1.36 g/cm³), and Teflon (density = 2.3 g/cm³). None of these common plastics dissolves in these liquids. Describe what you expect to see.

34. ▲ You have a sample of a white crystalline substance from your kitchen. You know that it is either salt or sugar. Although you could decide by taste, suggest another property that you could use to decide. (*Hint:* You may use the World Wide Web or a handbook of chemistry in the library to find some information.)

35. You can figure out whether a substance floats or sinks if you know its density and the density of the liquid. In which of the liquids listed below will high-density polyethylene (HDPE) float? (HDPE, a common plastic, has a density of 0.97 g/cm³. It does not dissolve in any of these liquids.)

| Substance | Density (g/cm³) | Properties, Uses |
|---|---|---|
| Ethylene glycol | 1.1088 | Toxic; major component of automobile antifreeze |
| Water | 0.9997 | |
| Ethanol | 0.7893 | Alcohol in alcoholic beverages |
| Methanol | 0.7914 | Toxic; gasoline additive to prevent gas line freezing |
| Acetic acid | 1.0492 | Component of vinegar |
| Glycerol | 1.2613 | Solvent used in home care products |

36. Milk in a glass bottle was placed in the freezing compartment of a refrigerator overnight. By morning, a column of frozen milk emerged from the bottle. Explain this observation.

**Frozen milk in a glass bottle.**

37. You are given a sample of a silvery metal. What information could you use to prove the metal is silver?

38. Describe an experimental method that can be used to determine the density of an irregularly shaped piece of metal.

39. Diabetes can alter the density of urine, so urine density can be used as a diagnostic tool. Diabetics can excrete too much sugar or excrete too much water. What do you predict will happen to the density of urine under each of these conditions? (*Hint:* Water containing dissolved sugar is more dense than pure water.)

40. Suggest a way to determine if the colorless liquid in a beaker is water. How could you discover if there is salt dissolved in the water?

41. The following photo shows the element potassium reacting with water to form the element hydrogen, a gas, and a solution of the compound potassium hydroxide.

**Potassium reacting with water to produce hydrogen gas and potassium hydroxide.**

   (a) What states of matter are involved in the reaction?
   (b) Is the observed change chemical or physical?
   (c) What are the reactants in this reaction, and what are the products?
   (d) What qualitative observations can be made concerning this reaction?

42. Three liquids of different densities are mixed. Because they are not miscible (do not form a homogeneous solution with one another), they form discrete layers, one on top of the other. Sketch the result of mixing carbon tetrachloride ($CCl_4$, $d = 1.58$ g/cm$^3$), mercury ($d = 13.546$ g/cm$^3$), and water ($d = 1.00$ g/cm$^3$).

43. Four balloons are each filled with a different gas, each having a different density:

   helium, $d = 0.164$ g/L          neon, $d = 0.825$ g/L

   argon, $d = 1.633$ g/L          krypton, $d = 4.425$ g/L

   If the density of dry air is 1.12 g/L, which balloon or balloons float in air?

44. A copper-colored metal is found to conduct an electric current. Can you say with certainty that it is copper? Why or why not? Suggest additional information that could provide unequivocal confirmation that it is copper.

45. The photo below shows elemental iodine dissolving in ethanol to give a solution. Is this a physical or chemical change?

**Elemental iodine dissolving in ethanol.**

46. ▲ You want to determine the density of a compound but have only a tiny crystal, and it would be difficult to measure mass and volume accurately. There is another way to determine density, however, called the *flotation method*. If you placed the crystal in a liquid whose density is precisely that of the substance, it would be suspended in the liquid, neither sinking to the bottom of the beaker nor floating to the surface. However, for such an experiment you would need to have a liquid with the precise density of the crystal. You can accomplish this by mixing two liquids of different densities to create a liquid having the desired density.
   (a) Consider the following: you mix 10.0 mL of $CHCl_3$ ($d = 1.492$ g/mL) and 5.0 mL of $CHBr_3$ ($d = 2.890$ g/mL), giving 15.0 mL of solution. What is the density of this mixture?
   (b) Suppose now that you wanted to determine the density of a small yellow crystal to confirm that it is sulfur. From the literature, you know that sulfur has a density of 2.07 g/cm$^3$. How would you prepare 20.0 mL of the liquid mixture having that density from pure samples of $CHCl_3$ and $CHBr_3$? (*Note:* 1 mL = 1 cm$^3$.)

# Let's Review

# The Tools of Quantitative Chemistry

John C. Katz

**Copper** Copper (Cu) is the 26th most abundant element in the Earth's crust (not too different from its near neighbors nickel and zinc in the periodic table). Copper and its minerals are widely distributed, and obtaining the metal from its ores is relatively easy. As a result, elemental copper is used around the world for many useful items, from cooking pots to electric wires. The photo (above left) shows large copper pots on sale in a market in southwestern China.

Pure copper (often called *native copper*) is found in nature, but more commonly it is found combined with other elements in minerals such as cuprite, azurite, or malachite. Copper metal is relatively soft but, when combined in a ratio of about 2 to 1 with tin, it forms bronze. Bronze was important in early civilizations and gave its name to an epoch of human development, the Bronze Age, which started around 3000 BC and lasted until about 1000 BC. (The Iceman you learned about on page 1 lived just before the Bronze Age and had an ax made of copper.) The development of bronze was significant because bronze is stronger than copper and can be shaped into a sharper edge. This improved the cutting edges of plows and weapons, thus giving cultures that possessed bronze advantages over those that did not.

Copper is now used in electric wiring because it is a good conductor of electricity, and it is used in cooking pots because it conducts heat well. It is also described as one of the "coinage metals" (along with silver and gold) because it has been used in coins for centuries. And most gold jewelry is a mixture of gold with some copper.

Compounds of copper are common, and copper is one of the eight essential metals in our bodies, where it is needed for some enzymes to use oxygen more effectively. Fortunately, it is found in common foods (in meats such as lamb, duck, pork, and beef, and in nuts such as almonds and walnuts). The average person has about 72 mg of copper in his or her body.

The figure (above right) shows what happens as we zoom into copper at the particulate level. We begin to see atoms arranged in a regular array, or *lattice*, as chemists call it. Zooming in even closer, we see the smallest repeating unit of the crystal.

You can learn more about copper and its properties by answering Study Questions 60 and 61 at the end of this *Let's Review* section.

A t its core, chemistry is a quantitative science. Chemists make measurements of, among other things, size, mass, volume, time, and temperature. Scientists then manipulate that information to search for relationships among properties and to provide insight into the molecular basis of matter.

This section reviews the units used in chemistry, briefly describes the proper treatment of numerical data, and reviews some mathematical skills you will need in chemical calculations. After studying this section you should be able to:

- Use the common units for measurements in chemistry and make unit conversions (such as from liters to milliliters).
- Express and use numbers in exponential or scientific notation.
- Incorporate quantitative information into an algebraic expression and solve that expression.
- Read information from graphs.
- Prepare and interpret graphs of numerical information, and, if a graph produces a straight line, find the slope and equation of the line.
- Recognize and express uncertainties in measurements.

## 1 Units of Measurement

Doing chemistry requires observing chemical reactions and physical changes. We make qualitative observations—such as changes in color or the evolution of heat— and quantitative measurements of temperature, time, volume, mass, and length or size. To record and report measurements, the scientific community has chosen a modified version of the **metric system**. This decimal system, used internationally in science, is called the Système International d'Unités (International System of Units), abbreviated **SI**.

All SI units are derived from base units, and these are listed in Table 1. Larger and smaller quantities are expressed by using appropriate prefixes with the base unit (Table 2). The nanometer (nm), for example, is 1 billionth of a meter. That is, it is equivalent to $1 \times 10^{-9}$ m (meter). Dimensions on the nanometer scale are common in chemistry and biology because, for example, a typical molecule is about 1 nm across and a bacterium is about 1000 nm in length. The prefix *nano-* is also used in the name for a new area of science, *nanotechnology*, which involves the synthesis and study of materials having this tiny size.

### Temperature Scales

Two temperature scales are commonly used in scientific work: Celsius and Kelvin (Figure 1). The Celsius scale is generally used worldwide for measurements in the laboratory. When calculations incorporate temperature data, however, the Kelvin scale must almost always be used.

Table 1 **The Seven SI Base Units**

| Measured Property | Name of Unit | Abbreviation |
|---|---|---|
| Mass | Kilogram | kg |
| Length | Meter | m |
| Time | Second | s |
| Temperature | Kelvin | K |
| Amount of substance | Mole | mol |
| Electric current | Ampere | A |
| Luminous intensity | Candela | cd |

• **The Kilogram, a New Standard Needed?** Unlike the second and the meter, the kilogram is defined by a physical object: a block of platinum-iridium alloy in a building in Paris, France. The block has been mysteriously losing mass, so there is great interest in the scientific community to find a better way to define the kilogram. One suggestion is that it be defined as the mass of $5.0184515 \times 10^{25}$ atoms of the carbon-12 isotope.

● **Common Conversion Factors**

1000 g = 1 kg
$1 \times 10^9$ nm = 1 m
10 mm = 1 cm
100 cm = 10 dm = 1 m
1000 m = 1 km

Conversion factors for SI units are given in Appendix C and inside the back cover of this book.

**Table 2  Selected Prefixes Used in the Metric System**

| Prefix | Abbreviation | Meaning | Example |
|--------|--------------|---------|---------|
| Giga- | G | $10^9$ (billion) | 1 gigahertz = $1 \times 10^9$ Hz |
| Mega- | M | $10^6$ (million) | 1 megaton = $1 \times 10^6$ tons |
| Kilo- | k | $10^3$ (thousand) | 1 kilogram (kg) = $1 \times 10^3$ g |
| Deci- | d | $10^{-1}$ (tenth) | 1 decimeter (dm) = $1 \times 10^{-1}$ m |
| Centi- | c | $10^{-2}$ (one hundredth) | 1 centimeter (cm) = $1 \times 10^{-2}$ m |
| Milli- | m | $10^{-3}$ (one thousandth) | 1 millimeter (mm) = $1 \times 10^{-3}$ m |
| Micro- | $\mu$ | $10^{-6}$ (one millionth) | 1 micrometer (µm) = $1 \times 10^{-6}$ m |
| Nano- | n | $10^{-9}$ (one billionth) | 1 nanometer (nm) = $1 \times 10^{-9}$ m |
| Pico- | p | $10^{-12}$ | 1 picometer (pm) = $1 \times 10^{-12}$ m |
| Femto- | f | $10^{-15}$ | 1 femtometer (fm) = $1 \times 10^{-15}$ m |

● **Lord Kelvin**
William Thomson (1824–1907), known as Lord Kelvin, was a professor of natural philosophy at the University in Glasgow, Scotland, from 1846 to 1899. He was best known for his study of heat and work, from which came the concept of the absolute temperature scale.

E. F. Smith Collection/Van Pelt Library/University of Pennsylvania

### The Celsius Temperature Scale

The size of the Celsius degree is defined by assigning zero as the freezing point of pure water (0 °C) and 100 as its boiling point (100 °C). You may recognize that a comfortable room temperature is around 20 °C and your normal body temperature is 37 °C. We find that the warmest water we can stand to immerse a finger in is about 60 °C.

### The Kelvin Temperature Scale

William Thomson, known as Lord Kelvin (1824–1907), first suggested the temperature scale that now bears his name. The Kelvin scale uses the same size unit as the Celsius scale, but it assigns zero as the lowest temperature that can be achieved, a point called **absolute zero**. Many experiments have found that this limiting temperature is −273.15 °C (−459.67 °F). *Kelvin units and Celsius degrees are the same size.*

**FIGURE 1** Comparison of Fahrenheit, Celsius, and Kelvin scales. The reference, or starting point, for the Kelvin scale is absolute zero (0 K = −273.15 °C), which has been shown theoretically and experimentally to be the lowest possible temperature.

Thus, the freezing point of water is reached at 273.15 K; that is, 0 °C = 273.15 K. The boiling point of pure water is 373.15 K. Temperatures in Celsius degrees are readily converted to kelvins, and vice versa, using the relation

$$T \ (K) = \frac{1 \ K}{1 \ °C} \ (T \ °C + 273.15 \ °C) \tag{1}$$

Thus, a common room temperature of 23.5 °C is

$$T \ (K) = \frac{1 \ K}{1 \ °C} \ (23.5 \ °C + 273.15 \ °C) = 296.7 \ K$$

There are two important things to notice here:

- Converting from degrees Celsius to kelvins simply requires adding 273.15 to the temperature in Celsius, and converting from kelvins to degrees Celsius requires subtracting 273.15 from the value in kelvins.
- The degree symbol (°) is not used with Kelvin temperatures. The name of the unit on this scale is the *kelvin* (not capitalized), and such temperatures are designated with a capital K.

● **Temperature Conversions and Significant Figures**  When converting 23.5 °C to kelvins, adding 273.15 gives 296.65. However, the rules of "significant figures" (page 37) tell us that the sum or difference of two numbers can have no more decimal places than the number with the fewest decimal places. Thus, we round the answer to 296.7 K, a number with one decimal place.

## Length, Volume, and Mass

The meter is the standard unit of *length*, but objects observed in chemistry are frequently smaller than 1 meter. Measurements are often reported in units of centimeters (cm), millimeters (mm), or micrometers ($\mu$m) (Figure 2), and objects on the atomic and molecular scale have dimensions of nanometers (nm; 1 nm = $1 \times 10^{-9}$ m) or picometers (pm; 1 pm = $1 \times 10^{-12}$ m) (Figure 3).

To illustrate the range of dimensions used in science, let us look at a recent study of the glassy skeleton of a sea sponge. The sea sponge in Figure 2a is about 20 cm long and a few centimeters in diameter. A closer look (Figure 2b) shows more detail of the lattice-like structure. Scientists at Bell Laboratories found that each strand of the lattice is a ceramic-fiber composite of silica ($SiO_2$) and protein less than 100 $\mu$m in diameter (Figure 2c). These strands are composed of "spicules," which, at the nanoscale level, consist of silica nanoparticles just a few nanometers in diameter (Figure 2d).

Photos courtesy of Joanna Aizenberg, Bell Laboratories. Reference: J. Aizenberg, et al.. Science, Vol 309, pages 275–278, 2005.

(a) Photograph of the glassy skeleton of a sea sponge, *Euplectella*. Scale bar = 5 cm.

(b) Fragment of the structure showing the square grid of the lattice with diagonal supports. Scale bar = 1 mm.

(c) Scanning electron microscope (SEM) image of a single strand showing its ceramic-composite structure. Scale bar = 20 $\mu$m.

(d) SEM image of the surface of a strand showing that is it composed of nanoscale spheres of hydrated silica. Scale bar = 500 nm.

**FIGURE 2  Dimensions in chemistry and biology.** These photos are from the research of Professor Joanna Aizenberg, now at Harvard University. Another image from her research on new materials is featured on the cover of this book.

**FIGURE 3 Dimensions in the molecular world.** Dimensions on the molecular scale are often given in terms of nanometers (1 nm = $1 \times 10^{-9}$ m) or picometers (1 pm = $1 \times 10^{-12}$ m). Here, the distance between C atoms in diamond is 0.154 nm or 154 pm. An older but often-used non-SI unit is the Ångstrom unit (Å), where 1 Å = $1.0 \times 10^{-10}$ m. The C–C distance in diamond would be 1.54 Å.

The distance between turns of the DNA helix is 3.4 nm.

3.4 nm

0.154 nm

A portion of the diamond structure

## EXAMPLE 1 Distances on the Molecular Scale

**Problem** The distance between an O atom and an H atom in a water molecule is 95.8 pm. What is this distance in nanometers (nm)?

**What Do You Know?** You know the interatomic O–H distance and the relationships of the metric units.

95.8 pm

**Strategy** You can solve this problem by knowing the relationship or conversion factor between the units in the information you are given (picometers) and the desired units (meters or nanometers). (For more about conversion factors and their use in problem solving, see page 39.) There is no conversion factor given in Table 2 to change nanometers to picometers directly, but relationships are listed between meters and picometers and between meters and nanometers. Therefore, we first convert picometers to meters, and then we convert meters to nanometers.

$$\text{picometers} \xrightarrow{\;x\; ^{m}/_{pm}\;} \text{meters} \xrightarrow{\;y\; ^{nm}/_{m}\;} \text{nanometers}$$

**Solution** Using the appropriate conversion factors (1 pm = $1 \times 10^{-12}$ m and 1 nm = $1 \times 10^{-9}$ m), we have

$$95.8 \text{ pm} \times \frac{1 \times 10^{-12} \text{ m}}{1 \text{ pm}} = 9.58 \times 10^{-11} \text{ m}$$

$$9.58 \times 10^{-11} \text{ m} \times \frac{1 \text{ nm}}{1 \times 10^{-9} \text{ m}} = 9.58 \times 10^{-2} \text{ nm} \text{ or } 0.0958 \text{ nm}$$

**Think about Your Answer** A nanometer is a larger unit than a picometer, so the same distance expressed in nanometers should have a smaller numerical value. Our answer is in line with this. Notice how the units cancel to leave an answer whose unit is that of the numerator of the conversion factor. The process of using units to guide a calculation is called *dimensional analysis*. It is explored further on pages 39–41.

### Check Your Understanding

The C–C distance in diamond (Figure 3) is 0.154 nm. What is this distance in picometers (pm)? In centimeters (cm)?

## Energy and Food

The U.S. Food and Drug Administration (FDA) mandates that nutritional data, including energy content, be included on almost all packaged food. The Nutrition Labeling and Education Act of 1990 requires that the total energy from protein, carbohydrates, fat, and alcohol be specified. How is this determined? Initially, the method used was calorimetry. In this method (described in Section 5.6), a food product is burned, and the energy transferred as heat in the combustion is measured. Now, however, energy contents are estimated using the Atwater system. This specifies the following average values for energy sources in foods:

1 g protein = 4 kcal (17 kJ)
1 g carbohydrate = 4 kcal (17 kJ)
1 g fat = 9 kcal (38 kJ)
1 g alcohol = 7 kcal (29 kJ)

Because carbohydrates may include some indigestible fiber, the mass of fiber is subtracted from the mass of carbohydrate when calculating the energy from carbohydrates.

As an example, one serving of cashew nuts (about 28 g) has

14 g fat = 126 kcal
6 g protein = 24 kcal
7 g carbohydrates − 1 g fiber = 24 kcal
Total = 174 kcal (728 kJ)

A value of 170 kcal is reported on the package.

You can find data on more than 6000 foods at the Nutrient Data Laboratory website (www.ars.usda.gov/ba/bhnrc/ndl).

**Nutrition Facts**
Serving Size 1 cup (30g)
　　Children Under 4 - ¾ cup (20g)
Servings Per Container About 19
　　Children Under 4 - About 28

| Amount Per Serving | Cheerios | with ½ cup skim milk | Cereal for Children Under 4 |
|---|---|---|---|
| **Calories** | 110 | 150 | 70 |
| Calories from Fat | 15 | 20 | 10 |

| | % Daily Value** | | |
|---|---|---|---|
| **Total Fat** 2g* | 3% | 3% | 1g |
| Saturated Fat 0g | 0% | 3% | 0g |
| Polyunsaturated Fat 0.5g | | | 0g |
| Monounsaturated Fat 0.5g | | | 0g |
| **Cholesterol** 0mg | 0% | 1% | 0mg |
| **Sodium** 210mg | 9% | 12% | 140mg |
| **Potassium** 200mg | 6% | 12% | 130mg |

**Energy and food labels.** All packaged foods must have labels specifying nutritional values, with energy given in Calories (where 1 Cal = 1 kilocalorie).

---

Chemists often use glassware such as beakers, flasks, pipets, graduated cylinders, and burets, which are marked in volume units (Figure 4). The SI unit of volume is the cubic meter ($m^3$), which is too large for everyday laboratory use. Chemists usually use the liter (L) or the milliliter (mL) for volume measurements. One liter is equivalent to the volume of a cube with sides equal to 10 cm [$V = (0.1\ m)^3 = 0.001\ m^3$].

$$1\ liter\ (L) = 1000\ cm^3 = 1000\ mL = 0.001\ m^3$$

Because there are exactly 1000 mL (= 1000 $cm^3$) in a liter, this means that

$$1\ mL = 0.001\ L = 1\ cm^3$$

The units *milliliter and cubic centimeter* (or "cc") *are interchangeable.* Therefore, a flask that contains exactly 125 mL has a volume of 125 $cm^3$.

Although not widely used in the United States, the cubic decimeter ($dm^3$) is a common unit in the rest of the world. A length of 10 cm is called a decimeter (dm). Because a cube 10 cm on a side defines a volume of 1 liter, *a liter is equivalent to a cubic decimeter:* $1\ L = 1\ dm^3$. Products in Europe, Africa, and other parts of the world are often sold by the cubic decimeter.

The *deciliter, dL,* which is exactly equivalent to 0.100 L or 100 mL, is widely used in medicine. For example, standards for concentrations of environmental contaminants are often set as a certain mass per deciliter. The state of Massachusetts recommends that children with more than 10 micrograms ($10 \times 10^{-6}$ g) of lead per deciliter of blood undergo further testing for lead poisoning.

Finally, when chemists prepare chemicals for reactions, they often take given masses of materials. The *mass* of a body is the fundamental measure of the quantity of matter, and the SI unit of mass is the kilogram (kg). Smaller masses are expressed in grams (g) or milligrams (mg).

$$1\ kg = 1000\ g\ and\ 1\ g = 1000\ mg$$

## Energy Units

When expressing energy quantities, most chemists (and much of the world outside the United States) use the **joule** (J), the SI unit. The joule is related directly to the units used for mechanical energy: 1 J equals 1 kg · $m^2/s^2$. Because the joule is inconveniently small for most uses in chemistry, the kilojoule (kJ), equivalent to 1000 joules, is often the unit of choice.

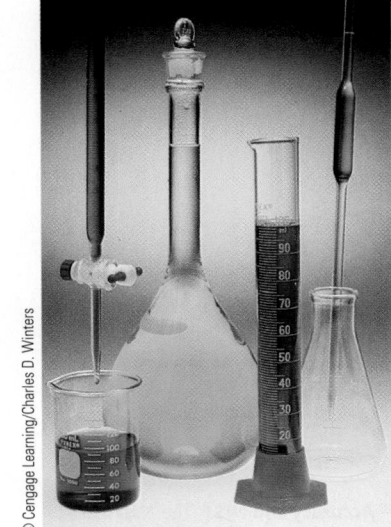

© Cengage Learning/Charles D. Winters

**FIGURE 4 Some common laboratory glassware.** Volumes are marked in units of milliliters (mL). Remember that 1 mL is equivalent to 1 $cm^3$.

● **James Joule** The joule is named for James P. Joule (1818–1889), the son of a wealthy brewer in Manchester, England. The family wealth and a workshop in the brewery gave Joule the opportunity to pursue scientific studies. Among the topics that Joule studied was the issue of whether heat was a massless fluid. Scientists at that time referred to this idea as the caloric hypothesis. Joule's careful experiments showed that heat and mechanical work are related, providing evidence that heat is not a fluid.

Oesper Collection in the History of Chemistry/University of Cincinnati

● **Review & Check** Answers to the Review & Check questions are in Appendix P. In the Cengage *YouBook*, click on an answer to see if you are correct.

To give you some feeling for joules, suppose you drop a six-pack of soft-drink cans, each full of liquid, on your foot. Although you probably will not take time to calculate the kinetic energy at the moment of impact, it is between 4 J and 10 J.

The calorie (cal) is an older energy unit. It is defined as the energy transferred as heat that is required to raise the temperature of 1.00 g of pure liquid water from 14.5 °C to 15.5 °C. A kilocalorie (kcal) is equivalent to 1000 calories. The conversion factor relating joules and calories is

$$\text{1 calorie (cal)} = \text{4.184 joules (J)}$$

The dietary Calorie (with a capital C) is often used in the United States to represent the energy content of foods. The dietary Calorie (Cal) is equivalent to the kilocalorie or 1000 calories. Thus, a breakfast cereal that gives you 100.0 Calories of nutritional energy per serving provides 100.0 kcal or 418.4 kJ.

---

### REVIEW & CHECK FOR SECTION 1

1.  Liquid nitrogen boils at 77 K. What is this temperature in Celsius degrees?

    (a)  350 °C          (b)  −196 °C          (c)  77 °C          (d)  −109 °C

2.  A square platinum sheet has sides 2.50 cm long and a thickness of 0.25 mm. What is the volume of the platinum sheet (in $cm^3$)?

    (a)  16 $cm^3$          (b)  630 $cm^3$          (c)  0.16 $cm^3$          (d)  160 $cm^3$

3.  A standard wine bottle has a volume of 750. mL. What volume, in liters, does this represent?

    (a)  0.750 L          (b)  0.00750 L          (c)  7.50 L          (d)  75.0 L

4.  One U.S. gallon is equivalent to 3.7865 L. What is the volume in liters of a 2.0-quart carton of milk? (There are 4 quarts in a gallon.)

    (a)  19 L          (b)  3.8 L          (c)  1.9 L          (d)  0.95 L

5.  A circulated U.S. quarter has a mass of 5.59 g. Express this mass in milligrams.

    (a)  $5.59 \times 10^3$ mg          (b)  5.59 mg          (c)  55.9 mg          (d)  559 mg

6.  An environmental study of a river found a pesticide present to the extent of 0.02 microgram per liter of water. Express this amount in grams per liter.

    (a)  2 g/L          (b)  0.02 g/L          (c)  $2 \times 10^3$ g/L          (d)  $2 \times 10^{-8}$ g/L

7.  The label on a cereal box indicates that one serving (with skim milk) provides 251 Cal. What is this energy in kilojoules (kJ)?

    (a)  251 kJ          (b)  59.8 kJ          (c)  1050 kJ          (d)  4380 kJ

---

## 2    Making Measurements: Precision, Accuracy, Experimental Error, and Standard Deviation

The **precision** of a measurement indicates how well several determinations of the same quantity agree. This is illustrated by the results of throwing darts at a target. In Figure 5a, the dart thrower was apparently not skillful, and the precision of the dart's placement on the target is low. In Figures 5b and 5c, the darts are clustered together, indicating much better consistency on the part of the thrower—that is, greater precision.

**Accuracy** is the agreement of a measurement with the accepted value of the quantity. Figure 5c shows that our thrower was accurate as well as precise—the average of all shots is close to the targeted position, the bull's eye.

Figure 5b shows it is possible to be precise without being accurate—the thrower has consistently missed the bull's eye, although all the darts are clustered precisely around one point on the target. This is analogous to an experiment with some flaw

● **Accuracy and NIST** The National Institute of Standards and Technology (NIST) is an important resource for the standards used in science. Comparison with NIST data is a test of the accuracy of the measurement (see www.nist.gov).

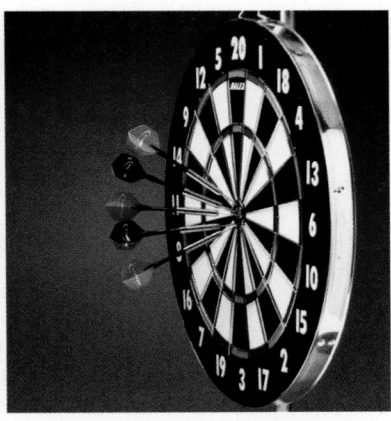

**(a)** Poor precision and poor accuracy     **(b)** Good precision and poor accuracy     **(c)** Good precision and good accuracy

**FIGURE 5** Precision and accuracy.

(either in design or in a measuring device) that causes all results to differ from the correct value by the same amount.

The accuracy of a result in the laboratory is often expressed in terms of percent error, whereas the precision is expressed as a standard deviation.

## Experimental Error

If you measure a quantity in the laboratory, you may be required to report the error in the result, the difference between your result and the accepted value,

$$\text{Error in measurement} = \text{experimentally determined value} - \text{accepted value}$$

or the **percent error.**

$$\text{Percent error} = \frac{\text{error in measurement}}{\text{accepted value}} \times 100\%$$

● **Percent Error** Percent error can be positive or negative, indicating whether the experimental value is too high or too low compared to the accepted value. In Example 2, Student B's percent error is −0.2%, indicating it is 0.2% lower than the accepted value.

## EXAMPLE 2  Precision, Accuracy, and Error

**Problem** A coin has an "accepted" diameter of 28.054 mm. In an experiment, two students measure this diameter. Student A makes four measurements of the diameter of the coin using a precision tool called a micrometer. Student B measures the same coin using a simple plastic ruler. The two students report the following results:

| Student A | Student B |
|-----------|-----------|
| 28.246 mm | 27.9 mm   |
| 28.244    | 28.0      |
| 28.246    | 27.8      |
| 28.248    | 28.1      |

What is the average diameter and percent error obtained in each case? Which student's data are more accurate?

**What Do You Know?** You know the data collected by the two students and want to compare them with the "accepted" value by calculating the percent error.

**Strategy** For each set of values, we calculate the average of the results and then compare this average with 28.054 mm.

**Solution** The average for each set of data is obtained by summing the four values and dividing by 4.

Average value for Student A = 28.246 mm
Average value for Student B = 28.0 mm

Although Student A has four results very close to one another (and so of high precision), Student A's result is less accurate than that of Student B. The average diameter for Student A differs from the "accepted" value by 0.192 mm and has a percent error of 0.684%:

$$\text{Percent error} = \frac{28.246 \text{ mm} - 28.054 \text{ mm}}{28.054 \text{ mm}} \times 100\% = \boxed{0.684\%}$$

Student B's measurement has a percent error of only about $\boxed{-0.2\%}$.

**Think about Your Answer** Although Student A had less accurate results than Student B, they were more precise; the standard deviation for Student A is $2 \times 10^{-3}$ (calculated as described below), in contrast to Student B's larger value (standard deviation = 0.14). Possible reasons for the error in Student A's result are incorrect use of the micrometer or a flaw in the instrument.

---

**Check Your Understanding**

Two students measured the freezing point of an unknown liquid. Student A used an ordinary laboratory thermometer calibrated in 0.1 °C units. Student B used a thermometer certified by NIST (National Institute of Standards and Technology) and calibrated in 0.01 °C units. Their results were as follows:

**Student A:**  −0.3 °C, 0.2 °C, 0.0 °C, −0.3 °C

**Student B:**  −0.02 °C, +0.02 °C, 0.00 °C, +0.04 °C

Calculate the average value for A and B and, knowing the liquid was water (and using kelvins for temperature), calculate the percent error for each student. Which student has the smaller error?

---

## Standard Deviation

Laboratory measurements can be in error for two basic reasons. First, "determinate" errors are caused by faulty instruments or human errors such as incorrect record keeping. Second, so-called indeterminate errors arise from uncertainties in a measurement where the cause is not known and cannot be controlled by the lab worker. One way to judge the indeterminate error in a result is to calculate the standard deviation.

The **standard deviation** of a series of measurements is *equal to the square root of the sum of the squares of the deviations for each measurement from the average, divided by one less than the number of measurements*. It has a precise statistical significance: Assuming a large number of measurements is used to calculate the average, 68% of the values collected are expected to be within one standard deviation of the value determined, and 95% are within two standard deviations.

Suppose you carefully measured the mass of water delivered by a 10-mL pipet. (A pipet containing a green solution is shown in Figure 4.) For five attempts at the measurement (shown in column 2 of the following table), the standard deviation is found as follows. First, the average of the measurements is calculated (here, 9.984). Next, the deviation of each individual measurement from this value is determined (column 3). These values are squared, giving the values in column 4, and the sum of these values is determined. The standard deviation is then calculated by dividing this sum by the number of determinations minus 1 (= 4) and taking the square root of the result.

| Determination | Measured Mass (g) | Difference between Measurement and Average (g) | Square of Difference |
|:---:|:---:|:---:|:---:|
| 1 | 9.990 | 0.006 | $4 \times 10^{-5}$ |
| 2 | 9.993 | 0.009 | $8 \times 10^{-5}$ |
| 3 | 9.973 | −0.011 | $12 \times 10^{-5}$ |
| 4 | 9.980 | −0.004 | $2 \times 10^{-5}$ |
| 5 | 9.982 | −0.002 | $0.4 \times 10^{-5}$ |

$$\text{Average mass} = 9.984 \text{ g}$$

$$\text{Sum of squares of differences} = 26 \times 10^{-5}$$

$$\text{Standard deviation} = \sqrt{\frac{26 \times 10^{-5}}{4}} = 0.008$$

Based on this calculation, it would be appropriate to represent the measured mass as $9.984 \pm 0.008$ g. This would tell a reader that if this experiment were repeated, a majority of the values would fall in the range from 9.976 g to 9.992 g.

---

**REVIEW & CHECK FOR SECTION 2**

Two students were assigned to determine the mass of a sample of an unknown liquid. Student A used an ordinary laboratory balance that could determine mass to $\pm 0.01$ g. Student B used an analytical balance that could measure mass to $\pm 0.1$ mg. Each made four measurements, giving the following results:

Student A:    8.19 g, 8.22 g, 8.21 g, 8.25 g

Student B:    8.2210 g, 8.2210 g, 8.2209 g, 8.2210 g

1.  What is the standard deviation for Student A?

    (a)   0.2 g          (b)   0.02 g          (c)   0.03 g          (d)   0.04 g

2.  Which student is more precise?

    (a)   A          (b)   B

---

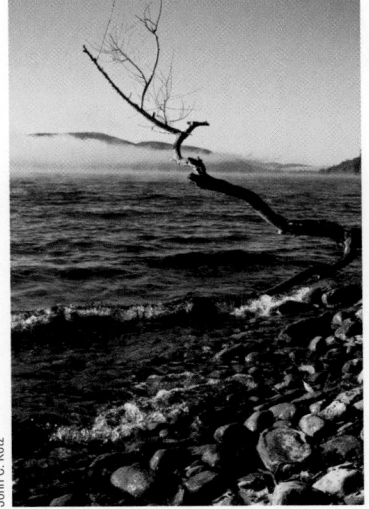

**FIGURE 6** **Lake Otsego.** Cooperstown, NY, is located by this beautiful lake.

# 3   Mathematics of Chemistry

## Exponential or Scientific Notation

Lake Otsego in northern New York is also called *Glimmerglass,* a name suggested by James Fenimore Cooper (1789–1851), the great American author and an early resident of the village now known as Cooperstown. Extensive environmental studies have been done along this lake (Figure 6), and some quantitative information useful to chemists, biologists, and geologists is given in the following table:

| Lake Otsego Characteristics | Quantitative Information |
| --- | --- |
| Area | $2.33 \times 10^7$ m$^2$ |
| Maximum depth | 505 m |
| Dissolved solids in lake water | $2 \times 10^2$ mg/L |
| Average rainfall in the lake basin | $1.02 \times 10^2$ cm/year |
| Average snowfall in the lake basin | 198 cm/year |

All of the data collected are in metric units. However, some data are expressed in **fixed notation** (505 m, 198 cm/year), whereas other data are expressed in **exponential**, or **scientific**, **notation** ($2.33 \times 10^7$ m$^2$). Scientific notation is a way of presenting very large or very small numbers in a compact and consistent form that simplifies calculations. Because of its convenience, scientific notation is widely used in sciences such as chemistry, physics, engineering, and astronomy (Figure 7).

In scientific notation a number is expressed as the product of two numbers: $N \times 10^n$. N is the *digit term* and is a number between 1 and 9.9999. . . . The second number, $10^n$, the *exponential term*, is some integer power of 10. For example, 1234 is written in scientific notation as $1.234 \times 10^3$, or 1.234 multiplied by 10 three times:

$$1234 = 1.234 \times 10^1 \times 10^1 \times 10^1 = 1.234 \times 10^3$$

**FIGURE 7** **Exponential numbers in astronomy.** The spiral galaxy M-83 is $3.0 \times 10^6$ parsecs away from Earth and has a diameter of $9.0 \times 10^3$ parsecs. One parsec (pc), a unit used in astronomy, is equivalent to 206265 AU (astronomical units), where 1 AU is $1.496 \times 10^8$ km. What is the distance between Earth and M-83 in kilometers (km)?

Conversely, a number less than 1, such as 0.01234, is written as $1.234 \times 10^{-2}$. This notation tells us that 1.234 should be divided twice by 10 to obtain 0.01234:

$$0.01234 = \frac{1.234}{10^1 \times 10^1} = 1.234 \times 10^{-1} \times 10^{-1} = 1.234 \times 10^{-2}$$

When converting a number to scientific notation, notice that the exponent $n$ is positive if the number is greater than 1 and negative if the number is less than 1. The value of $n$ is the number of places by which the decimal is shifted to obtain the number in scientific notation:

$$1\,2\,3\,4\,5. = 1.2345 \times 10^4$$

(a) Decimal shifted four places to the left. Therefore, $n$ is positive and equal to 4.

$$0.0\,0\,0\,1\,2 = 1.2 \times 10^{-3}$$

(b) Decimal shifted three places to the right. Therefore, $n$ is negative and equal to 3.

If you wish to convert a number in scientific notation to one using fixed notation (that is, not using powers of 10), the procedure is reversed:

$$6\,.\,2\,7\,3 \times 10^2 = 627.3$$

(a) Decimal point moved two places to the right because $n$ is positive and equal to 2.

$$0\,0\,6.273 \times 10^{-3} = 0.006273$$

(b) Decimal point shifted three places to the left because $n$ is negative and equal to 3.

Two final points should be made concerning scientific notation. First, be aware that calculators and computers often express a number such as $1.23 \times 10^3$ as 1.23E3 or $6.45 \times 10^{-5}$ as 6.45E-5. Second, some electronic calculators can readily convert numbers in fixed notation to scientific notation. If you have such a calculator, you may be able to do this by pressing the EE or EXP key and then the "=" key (but check your calculator manual to learn how your device operates).

In chemistry, you will often have to use numbers in exponential notation in mathematical operations. The following five operations are important:

● **Comparing the Earth and a Plant Cell—Powers of 10**
Earth = 12,760,000 meters wide
= 12.76 million meters
= $1.276 \times 10^7$ meters
Plant cell = 0.00001276 meter wide
= 12.76 millionths of a meter
= $1.276 \times 10^{-5}$ meters

• *Adding and Subtracting Numbers Expressed in Scientific Notation*
When adding or subtracting two numbers, first convert them to the same powers of 10. The digit terms are then added or subtracted as appropriate:

$$(1.234 \times 10^{-3}) + (5.623 \times 10^{-2}) = (0.1234 \times 10^{-2}) + (5.623 \times 10^{-2})$$

$$= 5.746 \times 10^{-2}$$

• *Multiplication of Numbers Expressed in Scientific Notation*
The digit terms are multiplied in the usual manner, and the exponents are added. The result is expressed with a digit term with only one nonzero digit to the left of the decimal place:

$$(6.0 \times 10^{23}) \times (2.0 \times 10^{-2}) = (6.0)(2.0 \times 10^{23-2}) = 12 \times 10^{21} = 1.2 \times 10^{22}$$

• *Division of Numbers Expressed in Scientific Notation*
The digit terms are divided in the usual manner, and the exponents are subtracted. The quotient is written with one nonzero digit to the left of the decimal in the digit term:

$$\frac{7.60 \times 10^3}{1.23 \times 10^2} = \frac{7.60}{1.23} \times 10^{3-2} = 6.18 \times 10^1$$

You will be performing a number of calculations in general chemistry, most of them using a calculator. Many different types of calculators are available, but this problem-solving tip describes several of the kinds of operations you will need to perform on a typical calculator. Be sure to consult your calculator manual for specific instructions to enter scientific notation and to find powers and roots of numbers.

**1. Scientific Notation**
When entering a number such as $1.23 \times 10^{-4}$ into your calculator, you first enter 1.23 and then press a key marked EE or EXP (or something similar). This enters the "$\times 10$" portion of the notation for you. You then complete the entry by keying in the exponent of the number, 4. (To change the exponent from $+4$ to $-4$, press the "$+/-$" key.)

A common error made by students is to enter 1.23, press the multiply key ($\times$), and

# Using Your Calculator

then key in 10 before finishing by pressing EE or EXP followed by $-4$. This gives you an entry that is 10 times too large.

**2. Powers of Numbers**
Electronic calculators often offer two methods of raising a number to a power. To square a number, enter the number and then press the $x^2$ key. To raise a number to any power, use the $y^x$ (or similar key such as ^). For example, to raise $1.42 \times 10^2$ to the fourth power:

1. Enter $1.42 \times 10^2$.
2. Press $y^x$.
3. Enter 4 (this should appear on the display).
4. Press =, and $4.0659 \times 10^8$ appears on the display.

**3. Roots of Numbers**
A general procedure for finding any root is to use the $y^x$ key. For a square root, x is 0.5 (or

1/2), whereas x is 0.3333 (or 1/3) for a cube root, 0.25 (or 1/4) for a fourth root, and so on. For example, to find the fourth root of $5.6 \times 10^{-10}$:

1. Enter the number.
2. Press the $y^x$ key.
3. Enter the desired root. Because we want the fourth root, enter 0.25.
4. Press =. The answer here is $4.9 \times 10^{-3}$.

To make sure you are using your calculator correctly, try these sample calculations:

1. $(6.02 \times 10^{23})(2.26 \times 10^{-5})/367$
   (Answer $= 3.71 \times 10^{16}$)
2. $(4.32 \times 10^{-3})^3$
   (Answer $= 8.06 \times 10^{-8}$)
3. $(4.32 \times 10^{-3})^{1/3}$
   (Answer $= 0.163$)

- *Powers of Numbers Expressed in Scientific Notation*
  When raising a number in exponential notation to a power, treat the digit term in the usual manner. The exponent is then multiplied by the number indicating the power:

$$(5.28 \times 10^3)^2 = (5.28)^2 \times 10^{3 \times 2} = 27.9 \times 10^6 = 2.79 \times 10^7$$

- *Roots of Numbers Expressed in Scientific Notation*
  Unless you use an electronic calculator, the number must first be put into a form in which the exponent is exactly divisible by the root. For example, for a square root, the exponent should be divisible by 2. The root of the digit term is found in the usual way, and the exponent is divided by the desired root:

$$\sqrt{3.6 \times 10^7} = \sqrt{36 \times 10^6} = \sqrt{36} \times \sqrt{10^6} = 6.0 \times 10^3$$

## Significant Figures

In most experiments, several kinds of measurements must be made, and some can be made more precisely than others. It is common sense that a result calculated from experimental data can be no more precise than the least precise piece of information that went into the calculation. This is where the rules for significant figures come in. **Significant figures** are the digits in a measured quantity that were observed with the measuring device.

### Determining Significant Figures

Suppose we place a new U.S. dime on the pan of a standard laboratory balance such as the one pictured in Figure 8 and observe a mass of 2.265 g. This number has four significant figures or digits because all four numbers are observed. However, you will learn from experience that the final digit (5) is somewhat uncertain because you may notice the balance readings can change slightly and give masses of 2.264, 2.265, and 2.266, with the mass of 2.265 observed most of the time. Thus,

© Cengage Learning/Charles D. Winters

**FIGURE 8 Standard laboratory balance and significant figures.** Such balances can determine the mass of an object to the nearest milligram. Thus, an object may have a mass of 13.456 g (13456 mg, five significant figures), 0.123 g (123 mg, three significant figures), or 0.072 g (72 mg, two significant figures).

2.50 cm

13.56 g

6.45 cm

3.1 mm

**FIGURE 9** Data used to determine the density of a metal.

of the four significant digits (2.265) the last (5) is uncertain. In general, *in a number representing a scientific measurement, the last digit to the right is taken to be inexact.* Unless stated otherwise, it is common practice to assign an uncertainty of ±1 to the last significant digit.

Suppose you want to calculate the density of a piece of metal (Figure 9). The mass and dimensions were determined by standard laboratory techniques. Most of these data have two digits to the right of the decimal, but they have different numbers of significant figures.

| Measurement | Data Collected | Significant Figures |
|---|---|---|
| Mass of metal | 13.56 g | 4 |
| Length | 6.45 cm | 3 |
| Width | 2.50 cm | 3 |
| Thickness | 3.1 mm = 0.31 cm | 2 |

The quantity 0.31 cm has two significant figures. The 3 in 0.31 is exactly known, but the 1 is uncertain. That is, the thickness of the metal piece may have been as small as 0.30 cm or as large as 0.32 cm, but it is most likely 0.31 cm. In the case of the width of the piece, you found it to be 2.50 cm, where 2.5 is known with certainty, but the final 0 is uncertain. There are three significant figures in 2.50.

When you read a number in a problem or collect data in the laboratory (Figure 10), how do you determine which digits are significant?

First, is the number an exact number or a measured quantity? If it is an exact number, you don't have to worry about the number of significant figures. For example, there are exactly 100 cm in 1 m. We could add as many zeros after the decimal place as we want, and the expression would still be true. Using this number in a calculation will not affect how many significant figures you can report in your answer.

If, however, the number is a measured value, you must take into account significant figures. The number of significant figures in our data above is clear, with the possible exception of 0.31 and 2.50. Are the zeroes significant?

1. *Zeroes between two other significant digits are significant.* For example, the zero in 103 is significant.

The 10-mL graduated cylinder is marked in 0.1-mL increments. Graduated cylinders are not considered precision glassware, so, at best, you can expect no more than two significant figures when reading a volume.

A 50-mL buret is marked in 0.10-mL increments, but it may be read with greater precision (0.01 mL).

A volumetric flask is meant to be filled to the mark on the neck. For a 250-mL flask, the volume is known to the nearest 0.12 mL, so the flask contains 250.0 ± 0.1 mL when full to the mark (four significant figures).

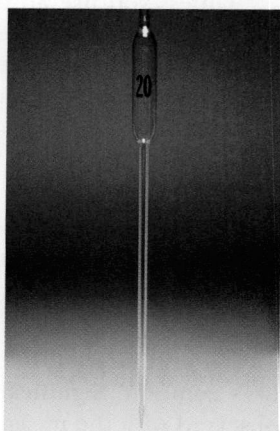

A pipet is like a volumetric flask in that it is filled to the mark on its neck. For a 20-mL pipet the volume is known to the nearest 0.02 mL.

**FIGURE 10** Glassware and significant figures.

2. *Zeroes to the right of a nonzero number, and also to the right of a decimal place, are significant.* For example, in the number 2.50 cm, the zero is significant.

3. *Zeroes that are placeholders are not significant.* There are two types of numbers that fall under this rule.

(a) The first are decimal numbers with zeroes that occur *before* the first nonzero digit. For example, in 0.0013, only the 1 and the 3 are significant; the zeroes are not. This number has two significant figures.

(b) The second are *numbers with trailing zeroes* that must be there to indicate the magnitude of the number. For example, the zeroes in the number 13,000 may or may not be significant; it depends on whether they were measured or not. To avoid confusion with regard to such numbers, *we shall assume in this book that trailing zeroes are significant when there is a decimal point to the right of the last zero.* Thus, we would say that 13,000 has only two significant figures but that 13,000. has five. We suggest that the best way to be unambiguous when writing numbers with trailing zeroes is to use scientific notation. For example $1.300 \times 10^4$ clearly indicates four significant figures, whereas $1.3 \times 10^4$ indicates two and $1.3000 \times 10^4$ indicates five.

## Using Significant Figures in Calculations

When doing calculations using measured quantities, we follow some basic rules so that the results reflect the precision of all the measurements that go into the calculations. *The rules used for significant figures in this book are as follows:*

**Rule 1.** When adding or subtracting numbers, the number of decimal places in the answer is equal to the number of decimal places in the number with the fewest digits after the decimal.

| | |
|---|---|
| 0.122 | decimal places |
| + 1.9 | 1 decimal place |
| +10.925 | 3 decimal places |
| 12.945 | 3 decimal places |

The sum should be reported as 12.9, a number with one decimal place, because 1.9 has only one decimal place.

**Rule 2.** In multiplication or division, the number of significant figures in the answer is determined by the quantity with the fewest significant figures.

$$\frac{0.01208}{0.0236} = 0.512, \text{ or in scientific notation, } 5.12 \times 10^{-1}$$

Because 0.0236 has only three significant digits, while 0.01208 has four, the answer should have three significant digits.

**Rule 3.** When a number is rounded off, the last digit to be retained is increased by one only if the following digit is 5 or greater.

| Full Number | Number Rounded to Three Significant Digits |
|---|---|
| 12.696 | 12.7 |
| 16.349 | 16.3 |
| 18.35 | 18.4 |
| 18.351 | 18.4 |

● **Zeroes and Common Laboratory Mistakes** We often see students find the mass of a chemical on a balance and fail to write down trailing zeroes. For example, if you find the mass is 2.340 g, the final zero is significant and must be reported as part of the measured value. The number 2.34 g has only three significant figures and implies the 4 is uncertain, when in fact the balance reading indicated the 4 is certain.

● **Calculations and Significant Figures** Keep in mind that there is one rule for addition/subtraction and another rule for multiplication/division. A common error that students make is to learn only one rule and use it in all circumstances.

Now let us apply these rules to calculate the density of the piece of metal in Figure 9.

$$\text{Length} \times \text{width} \times \text{thickness} = \text{volume}$$

$$6.45 \text{ cm} \times 2.50 \text{ cm} \times 0.31 \text{ cm} = 5.0 \text{ cm}^3$$

$$\text{Density} = \frac{\text{mass (g)}}{\text{volume (cm}^3)} = \frac{13.56 \text{ g}}{5.0 \text{ cm}^3} = 2.7 \text{ g/cm}^3$$

The calculated density has two significant figures because *a calculated result can be no more precise than the least precise data used,* and here the thickness has only two significant figures.

One last word on significant figures and calculations: When working problems, you should do the calculation with all the digits allowed by your calculator and round off only at the end of the calculation. *Rounding off in the middle of a calculation can introduce errors.*

### EXAMPLE 3    Using Significant Figures

**Problem**  An example of a calculation you will do later in the book (▶Chapter 11) is

$$\text{Volume of gas (L)} = \frac{(0.120)(0.08206)(273.15 + 23)}{(230/760.0)}$$

Calculate the final answer to the correct number of significant figures.

**What Do You Know?**  You know the rules for determining the number of significant figures for each number in the equation.

**Strategy**  First decide on the number of significant figures represented by each number and then apply Rules 1–3.

**Solution**

| Number | Number of Significant Figures | Comments |
|---|---|---|
| 0.120 | 3 | The trailing 0 is significant. |
| 0.08206 | 4 | The first 0 to the immediate right of the decimal is not significant. |
| 273.15 + 23 = 296 | 3 | 23 has no decimal places, so the sum can have none. |
| 230/760.0 = 0.30 | 2 | 230 has two significant figures because the last zero is not significant. In contrast, there is a decimal point in 760.0, so there are four significant digits. The quotient will have only two significant digits. |

Multiplication and division gives 9.63 L. However, analysis shows that one of the pieces of information is known to only two significant figures. Therefore, we should report the volume of gas as 9.6 L, a number with two significant figures.

**Think about Your Answer**  Be careful when you add or subtract two numbers because it is easy to make significant figure errors when doing so.

---

**Check Your Understanding**

What is the result of the following calculation?

$$x = \frac{(110.7 - 64)}{(0.056)(0.00216)}$$

**REVIEW & CHECK FOR SECTION 3**

1. How many significant figures are indicated by $2.33 \times 10^3$?
   (a) 1    (b) 2    (c) 3    (d) 4

2. How many significant figures are indicated by 200?
   (a) 1    (b) 2    (c) 3

3. What is the sum of 10.26 g and 0.063 g?
   (a) 10.323 g    (b) 10.32 g    (c) 10.3 g    (d) 10. g

4. What is the product of 10.26 cm and 0.063 cm?
   (a) 0.6464 cm²    (b) 0.646 cm²    (c) 0.65 cm²    (d) 0.6 cm²

# 4  Problem Solving by Dimensional Analysis

Figure 9 illustrated the data that were collected to determine the density of a piece of metal. The thickness was measured in millimeters, whereas the length and width were measured in centimeters. To find the volume of the sample in cubic centimeters, we first had to have the length, width, and thickness in the same units, so we converted the thickness to centimeters.

$$3.1 \text{ mm} \times \frac{1 \text{ cm}}{10 \text{ mm}} = 0.31 \text{ cm}$$

Here, we multiplied the number we wished to convert (3.1 mm) by a *conversion factor* (1 cm/10 mm) to produce the result in the desired unit (0.31 cm). Notice that units are treated like numbers. Because the unit "mm" was in both the numerator and the denominator, dividing one by the other leaves a quotient of 1. The units are said to "cancel out." This leaves the answer in centimeters, the desired unit.

This approach to problem solving is often called **dimensional analysis** (or sometimes the **factor-label method**). It is a general problem-solving approach that uses the dimensions or units of each value to guide us through calculations.

A **conversion factor** expresses the equivalence of a measurement in two different units (1 cm ≡ 10 mm; 1 g ≡ 1000 mg; 12 eggs ≡ 1 dozen; 12 inches ≡ 1 foot). Because the numerator and the denominator describe the same quantity, the conversion factor is equivalent to the number 1. Therefore, multiplication by this factor does not change the measured quantity, only its units. A conversion factor is always written so that it has the form "new units divided by units of original number."

Number in original unit $\left[\dfrac{\text{new unit}}{\text{original unit}}\right]$ = new number in new unit

Quantity to express in new units    Conversion factor    Quantity now expressed in new units

● **Using Conversion Factors and Doing Calculations** As you work problems in this book and read Example problems, notice that proceeding from given information to an answer very often involves a series of multiplications. That is, we multiply the given data by a conversion factor, multiply the answer of that step by another factor, and so on, to the answer.

## EXAMPLE 4  Using Conversion Factors and Dimensional Analysis

**Problem** Oceanographers often express the density of sea water in units of kilograms per cubic meter. If the density of sea water is 1.025 g/cm³ at 15 °C, what is its density in kilograms per cubic meter?

**What Do You Know?** You know the density in a unit involving mass in grams and volume in cubic centimeters. Each of these has to be changed to its equivalent in kilograms and cubic meters, respectively.

● **Who Is Right—You or the Book?**

If your answer to a problem in this book does not quite agree with the answers in Appendix N through Q, the discrepancy may be the result of rounding the answer after each step and then using that rounded answer in the next step. This book follows these conventions:

(a) Final answers to numerical problems result from retaining several digits more than the number required by significant figures throughout the calculation and rounding only at the end.

(b) In Example problems, the answer to each step is given to the correct number of significant figures for that step, but more digits are carried to the next step. The number of significant figures in the final answer is dictated by the number of significant figures in the original data.

**Strategy** To simplify this problem, break it into three steps. First, change the mass in grams to kilograms. Next, convert the volume in cubic centimeters to cubic meters. Finally, calculate the density by dividing the mass in kilograms by the volume in cubic meters.

**Solution** First convert the mass in grams to a mass in kilograms.

$$1.025 \text{ g} \times \frac{1 \text{ kg}}{1000 \text{ g}} = 1.025 \times 10^{-3} \text{ kg}$$

No conversion factor is available in one of our tables to directly change units of cubic centimeters to cubic meters. You can find one, however, by cubing (raising to the third power) the relation between the meter and the centimeter:

$$1 \text{ cm}^3 \times \left(\frac{1 \text{ m}}{100 \text{ cm}}\right)^3 = 1 \text{ cm}^3 \times \left(\frac{1 \text{ m}^3}{1 \times 10^6 \text{ cm}^3}\right) = 1 \times 10^{-6} \text{ m}^3$$

Therefore, the density of sea water is

$$\text{Density} = \frac{1.025 \times 10^{-3} \text{ kg}}{1 \times 10^{-6} \text{ m}^3} = \boxed{1025 \text{ kg/m}^3}$$

**Think about Your Answer** Densities in units of kg/m³ can often be large numbers. For example, the density of platinum is 21,450 kg/m³, but dry air has a density of only 1.204 kg/m³.

**Check Your Understanding**

The density of gold is 19,320 kg/m³. What is this density in g/cm³?

---

# Out of Gas!

On July 23, 1983, a new Boeing 767 jet aircraft was flying at 26,000 ft from Montreal to Edmonton as Air Canada Flight 143. Warning buzzers sounded in the cockpit. One of the world's largest planes was now a glider—the plane had run out of fuel!

How did this modern airplane, having the latest technology, run out of fuel? A simple mistake had been made in calculating the amount of fuel required for the flight!

Like all Boeing 767s, this plane had a sophisticated fuel gauge, but it was not working properly. The plane was still allowed to fly, however, because there is an alternative method of determining the quantity of fuel in the tanks. Mechanics can use a stick, much like the oil dipstick in an automobile engine, to measure the fuel level in each of the three tanks. The mechanics in Montreal read the dipsticks, which were calibrated in centimeters, and translated those readings to a volume in liters. According to this, the plane had a total of 7682 L of fuel.

Pilots always calculate fuel quantities in units of mass because they need to know the total mass of the plane before take-off. Air Canada pilots had always calculated the quantity of fuel in pounds, but the new 767's fuel consumption was given in kilograms. The pilots knew that 22,300 kg of fuel was required for the trip. If 7682 L of fuel

remained in the tanks, how much had to be added? This involved using the fuel's density to convert 7682 L to a mass in kilograms. The mass of fuel to be added could then be calculated, and that mass converted to a volume of fuel to be added.

The First Officer of the plane asked a mechanic for the conversion factor to do the volume-to-mass conversion, and the mechanic replied "1.77." Using that number, the First Officer and the mechanics calculated that 4917 L of fuel should be added. But later calculations showed that this is only about one fourth of the required amount of fuel! Why? Because no one thought about the units of the number 1.77. They realized later that 1.77 has units of pounds per liter and not kilograms per liter.

Out of fuel, the plane could not make it to Winnipeg, so controllers directed them to the town of Gimli and to a small airport abandoned by the Royal Canadian Air Force. After gliding for almost 30 minutes, the plane approached the Gimli runway. The runway, however, had been converted to a race course for cars, and a race was underway. Furthermore, a steel barrier had been erected across the runway. Nonetheless, the pilot managed to touch down very near the end of the runway. The plane sped down the concrete strip; the nose wheel collapsed; several tires blew—and

the plane skidded safely to a stop just before the barrier. The Gimli glider had made it! And somewhere an aircraft mechanic is paying more attention to units on numbers.

**Questions:**

1. What is the fuel density in units of kg/L?
2. What mass and what volume of fuel should have been loaded? (1 lb = 453.6 g) (See Study Question 62, page 49.)

**Answers to these questions are available in Appendix N.**

© Wayne Glowacki/Winnipeg Free Press, July 23, 1987, reproduced with permission.

**The Gimli glider.** After running out of fuel, Air Canada Flight 143 glided 29 minutes before landing on an abandoned airstrip at Gimli, Manitoba, near Winnipeg.

# 5    Graphs and Graphing

In a number of instances in this text, graphs are used when analyzing experimental data with a goal of obtaining a mathematical equation that may help us predict new results. The procedure used will often result in a straight line, which has the equation

$$y = mx + b$$

In this equation, $y$ is usually referred to as the dependent variable; its value is determined from (that is, is dependent on) the values of $x$, $m$, and $b$. In this equation, $x$ is called the independent variable, and $m$ is the slope of the line. The parameter $b$ is the $y$-intercept—that is, the value of $y$ when $x = 0$. Let us use an example to investigate two things: (1) how to construct a graph from a set of data points and (2) how to derive an equation for the line generated by the data.

A set of data points to be graphed is presented in Figure 11. We first mark off each axis in increments of the values of $x$ and $y$. Here, our $x$-data are within the range from $-2$ to 4, so the $x$-axis is marked off in increments of 1 unit. The $y$-data fall within the range from 0 to 2.5, so we mark off the $y$-axis in increments of 0.5. Each data point is marked as a circle on the graph.

After plotting the points on the graph (round circles), we draw a straight line that comes as close as possible to representing the trend in the data. (Do not just connect the dots!) Because there is always some inaccuracy in experimental data, the straight line we draw is unlikely to pass exactly through every point.

To identify the specific equation corresponding to our data, we must determine the $y$-intercept *(b)* and slope *(m)* for the equation $y = mx + b$. The $y$-intercept is the point at which $x = 0$ and thus is the point where the line intersects the $y$-axis. (In Figure 11, $y = 1.87$ when $x = 0$). The slope is determined by selecting two points *on the line* (marked with squares in Figure 11) and calculating the difference in values

● **Determining the Slope with a Computer Program—Least-Squares Analysis** Generally, the easiest method of determining the slope and intercept of a straight line (and thus the line's equation) is to use a program such as Microsoft Excel or Apple's Numbers. These programs perform a "least-squares" or "linear regression" analysis and give the best straight line based on the data. (This line is referred to in Excel or Numbers as a trendline.)

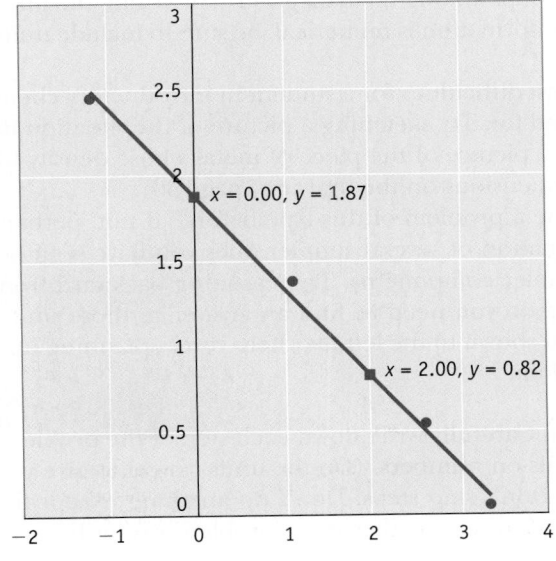

| **Experimental data** | |
| --- | --- |
| $x$ | $y$ |
| 3.35 | 0.0565 |
| 2.59 | 0.520 |
| 1.08 | 1.38 |
| $-1.19$ | 2.45 |

Using the points marked with a square, the slope of the line is:

$$\text{Slope} = \frac{\Delta y}{\Delta x} = \frac{0.82 - 1.87}{2.00 - 0.00} = -0.525$$

**FIGURE 11** Plotting data. Data for the variable $x$ are plotted on the horizontal axis (abscissa), and data for $y$ are plotted on the vertical axis (ordinate). The slope of the line, $m$ in the equation $y = mx + b$, is given by $\Delta y/\Delta x$. The intercept of the line with the $y$-axis (when $x = 0$) is $b$ in the equation. Using Microsoft Excel with these data and doing a linear regression analysis, we find $y = -0.525x + 1.87$.

of $y$ ($\Delta y = y_2 - y_1$) and $x$ ($\Delta x = x_2 - x_1$). The slope of the line is then the ratio of these differences, $m = \Delta y/\Delta x$. Here, the slope has the value $-0.525$. With the slope and intercept now known, we can write the equation for the line

$$y = -0.525x + 1.87$$

and we can use this equation to calculate $y$-values for points that are not part of our original set of $x$–$y$ data. For example, when $x = 1.50$, we find $y = 1.08$.

---

**REVIEW & CHECK FOR SECTION 5**

To find the mass of 32 jelly beans, we weighed several samples of beans.

| Number of Beans | Mass (g) |
|---|---|
| 5 | 12.82 |
| 11 | 27.14 |
| 16 | 39.30 |
| 24 | 59.04 |

Plot these data with the number of beans on the horizontal or $x$-axis and the mass of beans on the vertical or $y$-axis.

1.   What is the approximate slope of the line?

   (a)  2.4          (b)  0.42          (c)  3.2          (d)  4.8

2.   Use your graph or equation of a straight line to calculate the mass of 32 jelly beans.

   (a)  150 g          (b)  100 g          (c)  13 g          (d)  78 g

---

# 6   Problem Solving and Chemical Arithmetic

Some of the calculations in chemistry can be complex. Students frequently find it helpful to follow a definite plan of attack as illustrated in examples throughout this book.

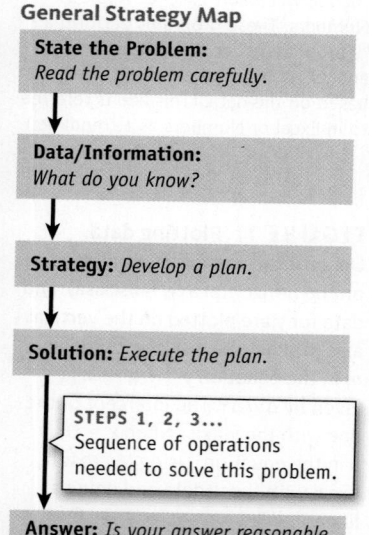

**General Strategy Map**

State the Problem:
*Read the problem carefully.*

↓

Data/Information:
*What do you know?*

↓

Strategy: *Develop a plan.*

↓

Solution: *Execute the plan.*

STEPS 1, 2, 3...
Sequence of operations
needed to solve this problem.

Answer: *Is your answer reasonable
and in the correct units?*

● **Strategy Maps** Many Example problems in this book are accompanied by a Strategy Map that outlines a route to a solution. In the YouBook many of these maps are accompanied by an audio/video explanation and a tutorial.

**Step 1:  State the Problem.** Read it carefully—and then read it again.

**Step 2:  What Do You Know?** Determine specifically what you are trying to determine and what information you are given. What key principles are involved? What information is known or not known? What information might be there just to place the question in the context of chemistry? Organize the information to see what is required and to discover the relationships among the data given. Try writing the information down in table form. If the information is numerical, be sure to include units.

**Step 3:  Strategy.** One of the greatest difficulties for a student in introductory chemistry is picturing what is being asked for. Try sketching a picture of the situation involved. For example, we sketched a picture of the piece of metal whose density we wanted to calculate and put the dimensions on the drawing (page 36).

   Develop a plan. Have you done a problem of this type before? If not, perhaps the problem is really just a combination of several simpler ones you have seen before. Break it down into those simpler components. Try reasoning backward from the units of the answer. What data do you need to find an answer in those units? Drawing a strategy map such as that shown to the left may help you in planning how you will go about solving the problem.

**Step 4:  Solution.** Execute the plan. Carefully write down each step of the problem, being sure to keep track of the units on numbers. (Do the units cancel to give you the answer in the desired units?) Don't skip steps. Don't do anything except the simplest steps in your head. Students often say they got a problem wrong because they "made a stupid mistake." Your instructors—and book authors—also make them, and it is usually because they don't take the time to write down the steps of the problem clearly.

**Step 5: Think about Your Answer.** Ask yourself whether the answer is reasonable and if you obtained an answer in the correct units.

**Step 6: Check Your Understanding.** In this text each Example is followed by another problem for you to try. (The solutions to those questions are in Appendix O.) When doing homework Study Questions, try one of the simpler *Practicing Skills* questions to see if you understand the basic ideas.

The steps we outline for problem solving are ones that many students have found to be successful, so try to consciously follow this scheme. But also be flexible. The "What Do You Know?" and "Strategy" steps often blend into a single set of ideas.

## ⚛WL   INTERACTIVE EXAMPLE 5   Problem Solving

**Problem** A mineral oil has a density of 0.875 $g/cm^3$. Suppose you spread 0.75 g of this oil over the surface of water in a large dish with an inner diameter of 21.6 cm. How thick is the oil layer? Express the thickness in centimeters.

**What Do You Know?** You know the mass and density of the oil and the diameter of the surface to be covered.

**Strategy** It is often useful to begin solving such problems by sketching a picture of the situation.

This helps you recognize that the solution to the problem is to find the volume of the oil on the water. If you know the volume, then you can find the thickness because

$$\text{Volume of oil layer} = (\text{thickness of layer}) \times (\text{area of oil layer})$$

So, you need two things: (1) the volume of the oil layer and (2) the area of the layer. The volume can be found using the mass and density of the oil. The area can be found because the oil will form a circle, which has an area equal to $\pi \times r^2$ (where r is the radius of the dish).

**Solution** First, calculate the volume of oil. The mass of the oil layer is known, so combining the mass of oil with its density gives the volume of the oil used:

$$0.75 \ \cancel{g} \times \frac{1 \ cm^3}{0.875 \ \cancel{g}} = 0.86 \ cm^3$$

Next, calculate the area of the oil layer. The oil is spread over a circular surface, whose area is given by

$$\text{Area} = \pi \times (\text{radius})^2$$

The radius of the oil layer is half its diameter (= 21.6 cm) or 10.8 cm, so

$$\text{Area of oil layer} = (3.142)(10.8 \ cm)^2 = 366 \ cm^2$$

With the volume and the area of the oil layer known, the thickness can be calculated.

$$\text{Thickness} = \frac{\text{volume}}{\text{area}} = \frac{0.86 \ cm^3}{366 \ cm^2} = \boxed{0.0023 \ cm}$$

**Strategy Map for Example 5**

**PROBLEM**
*How thick* will an oil layer be when a **given mass** covers a **given area**?

↓

**DATA/INFORMATION**
**Mass** and **density** of the oil and **diameter** of the circular surface to be covered.

↓

STEP 1. Calculate the **volume** of oil from **mass** and **density**.

↓

**Volume** of oil in **cm³**

↓

STEP 2. Calculate the **surface area** from the **diameter**.

↓

**Area** to be covered in **cm²**

↓

STEP 3. Divide the oil **volume** by the **surface area** to calculate the thickness in **cm**.

↓

**Thickness** of oil layer in **cm**

**Think about Your Answer** In the volume calculation, the calculator shows 0.857143.... The quotient should have two significant figures because 0.75 has two significant figures, so the result of this step is 0.86 cm³. In the area calculation, the calculator shows 366.435.... The answer to this step should have three significant figures because 10.8 has three. When these interim results are combined in calculating thickness, however, the final result can have only two significant figures. Remember that premature rounding can lead to errors.

**Check Your Understanding**

A particular paint has a density of 0.914 g/cm³. You need to cover a wall that is 7.6 m long and 2.74 m high with a paint layer 0.13 mm thick. What volume of paint (in liters) is required? What is the mass (in grams) of the paint layer?

---

**REVIEW & CHECK FOR SECTION 6**

A spool of copper wire has a mass of 4.26 kg. How long is the wire in the spool if the wire has a diameter of 2.2 mm? (The density of copper is 8.96 g/cm³.)

(a)  280 m          (b)  220 m                    (c)  130 m                    (d)  14 m

---

## Study Questions

⚫WL Interactive versions of these questions are assignable in OWL.

▲ denotes challenging questions.

Blue-numbered questions have answers in Appendix R and fully worked solutions in the *Student Solutions Manual*.

## Practicing Skills

### Temperature Scales

1. Many laboratories use 25 °C as a standard temperature. What is this temperature in kelvins?

2. The temperature on the surface of the sun is $5.5 \times 10^3$ °C. What is this temperature in kelvins?

3. Make the following temperature conversions:

   | °C | K |
   |------|------|
   | (a) 16 | _____ |
   | (b) _____ | 370 |
   | (c) 40 | _____ |

4. Make the following temperature conversions:

   | °C | K |
   |------|------|
   | (a) _____ | 77 |
   | (b) 63 | _____ |
   | (c) _____ | 1450 |

### Length, Volume, Mass, and Density
*(See Example 1.)*

5. A marathon distance race covers a distance of 42.195 km. What is this distance in meters? In miles?

6. The average lead pencil, new and unused, is 19 cm long. What is its length in millimeters? In meters?

7. A standard U.S. postage stamp is 2.5 cm long and 2.1 cm wide. What is the area of the stamp in square centimeters? In square meters?

8. A compact disc has a diameter of 11.8 cm. What is the surface area of the disc in square centimeters? In square meters? [Area of a circle = $(\pi)(\text{radius})^2$]

9. A typical laboratory beaker has a volume of 250. mL. What is its volume in cubic centimeters? In liters? In cubic meters? In cubic decimeters?

10. Some soft drinks are sold in bottles with a volume of 1.5 L. What is this volume in milliliters? In cubic centimeters? In cubic decimeters?

11. A book has a mass of 2.52 kg. What is this mass in grams?

12. A new U.S. dime has a mass of 2.265 g. What is its mass in kilograms? In milligrams?

13. ▲ Ethylene glycol, $C_2H_6O_2$, is an ingredient of automobile antifreeze. Its density is 1.11 g/cm³ at 20 °C. If you need 500. mL of this liquid, what mass of the compound, in grams, is required?

14. ▲ A piece of silver metal has a mass of 2.365 g. If the density of silver is 10.5 g/cm³, what is the volume of the silver?

15. You can identify a metal by carefully determining its density ($d$). An unknown piece of metal, with a mass of 2.361 g, is 2.35 cm long, 1.34 cm wide, and 1.05 mm thick. Which of the following is the element?
(a) nickel, $d = 8.91$ g/cm³
(b) titanium, $d = 4.50$ g/cm³
(c) zinc, $d = 7.14$ g/cm³
(d) tin, $d = 7.23$ g/cm³

16. Which occupies a larger volume, 600 g of water (with a density of 0.995 g/cm³) or 600 g of lead (with a density of 11.35 g/cm³)?

## Energy Units

17. You are on a diet that calls for eating no more than 1200 Cal/day. What is this energy in joules?

18. A 2-in. piece of chocolate cake with frosting provides 1670 kJ of energy. What is this in dietary Calories (Cal)?

19. One food product has an energy content of 170 kcal per serving, and another has 280 kJ per serving. Which food provides the greater energy per serving?

20. Which provides the greater energy per serving, a raw apple or a raw apricot? Go to the USDA Nutrient Database on the World Wide Web (www.ars.usda.gov/Services/docs.htm?docid=18878) for the information. Report the energy content of the fruit in kcal and kJ.

## Accuracy, Precision, Error, and Standard Deviation
(See Example 2.)

21. You and your lab partner are asked to determine the density of an aluminum bar. The mass is known accurately (to four significant figures). You use a simple metric ruler to measure its dimensions and obtain the results for Method A. Your partner uses a precision micrometer and obtains the results for Method B.

| Method A (g/cm³) | Method B (g/cm³) |
|---|---|
| 2.2 | 2.703 |
| 2.3 | 2.701 |
| 2.7 | 2.705 |
| 2.4 | 5.811 |

The accepted density of aluminum is 2.702 g/cm³.
(a) Calculate the average density for each method. Should all the experimental results be included in your calculations? If not, justify any omissions.
(b) Calculate the percent error for each method's average value.
(c) Calculate the standard deviation for each set of data.
(d) Which method's average value is more precise? Which method is more accurate?

22. The accepted value of the melting point of pure aspirin is 135 °C. Trying to verify that value, you obtain 134 °C, 136 °C, 133 °C, and 138 °C in four separate trials. Your partner finds 138 °C, 137 °C, 138 °C, and 138 °C.
(a) Calculate the average value and percent error for your data and your partner's data.
(b) Which of you is more precise? More accurate?

## Exponential Notation and Significant Figures
(See Example 3.)

23. Express the following numbers in exponential or scientific notation, and give the number of significant figures in each.
(a) 0.054 g       (c) 0.000792 g
(b) 5462 g        (d) 1600 mL

24. Express the following numbers in fixed notation (e.g., $1.23 \times 10^2 = 123$), and give the number of significant figures in each.
(a) $1.623 \times 10^3$   (c) $6.32 \times 10^{-2}$
(b) $2.57 \times 10^{-4}$  (d) $3.404 \times 10^3$

25. Carry out the following operations. Provide the answer with the correct number of significant figures.
(a) $(1.52)(6.21 \times 10^{-3})$
(b) $(6.217 \times 10^3) - (5.23 \times 10^2)$
(c) $(6.217 \times 10^3) \div (5.23 \times 10^2)$
(d) $(0.0546)(16.0000)\left[\dfrac{7.779}{55.85}\right]$

26. Carry out the following operations. Provide the answer with the correct number of significant figures.
(a) $(6.25 \times 10^2)^3$
(b) $\sqrt{2.35 \times 10^{-3}}$
(c) $(2.35 \times 10^{-3})^{1/3}$
(d) $(1.68)\left[\dfrac{23.56 - 2.3}{1.248 \times 10^3}\right]$

## Graphing

27. To determine the average mass of a popcorn kernel, you collect the following data:

| Number of kernels | Mass (g) |
|---|---|
| 5 | 0.836 |
| 12 | 2.162 |
| 35 | 5.801 |

Plot the data with number of kernels on the x-axis and mass on the y-axis. Draw the best straight line using the points on the graph (or do a least-squares or linear regression analysis using a computer program), and then write the equation for the resulting straight line. What is the slope of the line? What does the slope of the line signify about the mass of a popcorn kernel? What is the mass of 20 popcorn kernels? How many kernels are there in a handful of popcorn with a mass of 20.88 g?

**28.** Use the graph below to answer the following questions:
(a) What is the value of $x$ when $y = 4.0$?
(b) What is the value of $y$ when $x = 0.30$?
(c) What are the slope and the $y$-intercept of the line?
(d) What is the value of $y$ when $x = 1.0$?

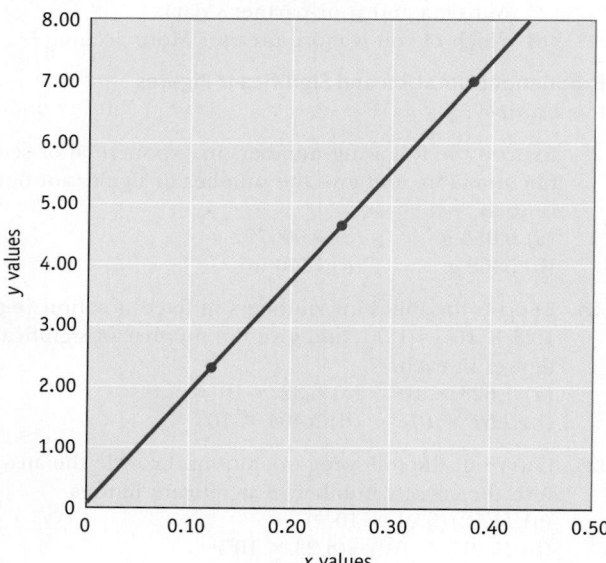

**29.** Use the graph below to answer the following questions.
(a) Derive the equation for the straight line, $y = mx + b$.
(b) What is the value of $y$ when $x = 6.0$?

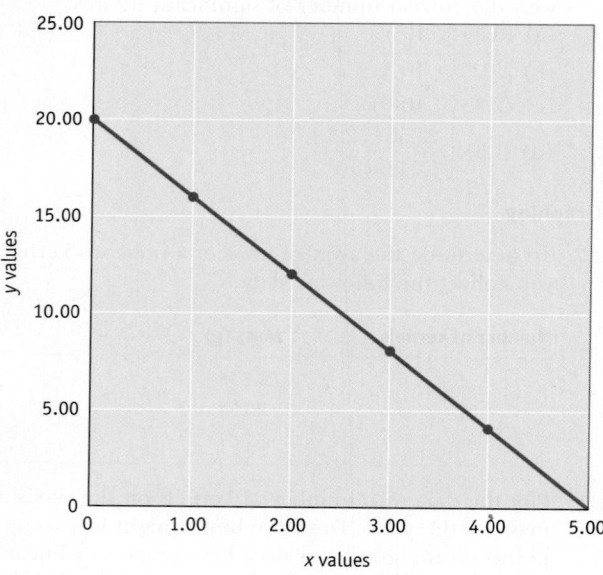

**30.** The following data were collected in an experiment to determine how an enzyme works in a biochemical reaction.

| Amount of $H_2O_2$ | Reaction Speed (amount/second) |
| --- | --- |
| 1.96 | $4.75 \times 10^{-5}$ |
| 1.31 | $4.03 \times 10^{-5}$ |
| 0.98 | $3.51 \times 10^{-5}$ |
| 0.65 | $2.52 \times 10^{-5}$ |
| 0.33 | $1.44 \times 10^{-5}$ |
| 0.16 | $0.585 \times 10^{-5}$ |

(a) Plot these data as 1/amount on the $y$-axis and 1/speed on the $x$-axis. Draw the best straight line to fit these data points.
(b) Determine the equation for the data, and give the values of the $y$-intercept and the slope. (*Note:* In biochemistry this is known as a Lineweaver-Burk plot, and the $y$-intercept is related to the maximum speed of the reaction.)

**Solving Equations**

**31.** Solve the following equation for the unknown value, $C$.
$$(0.502)(123) = (750.)C$$

**32.** Solve the following equation for the unknown value, $n$.
$$(2.34)(15.6) = n(0.0821)(273)$$

**33.** Solve the following equation for the unknown value, $T$.
$$(4.184)(244)(T - 292.0) + (0.449)(88.5)(T - 369.0) = 0$$

**34.** Solve the following equation for the unknown value, $n$.
$$-246.0 = 1312\left[\frac{1}{2^2} - \frac{1}{n^2}\right]$$

# General Questions

*These questions are not designated as to type or location in the chapter. They may combine several concepts.*

**35.** Molecular distances are usually given in nanometers (1 nm = $1 \times 10^{-9}$ m) or in picometers (1 pm = $1 \times 10^{-12}$ m). However, the angstrom (Å) unit is sometimes used, where 1 Å = $1 \times 10^{-10}$ m. (The angstrom unit is not an SI unit.) If the distance between the Pt atom and the N atom in the cancer chemotherapy drug cisplatin is 1.97 Å, what is this distance in nanometers? In picometers?

**Cisplatin.**

**36.** The separation between carbon atoms in diamond is 0.154 nm. What is their separation in meters? In picometers (pm)? In Angstroms (Å)?

**A portion of the diamond structure.**

37. A red blood cell has a diameter of 7.5 $\mu$m (micrometers). What is this dimension in (a) meters, (b) nanometers, and (c) picometers?

38. The platinum-containing cancer drug cisplatin (Study Question 35) contains 65.0 mass-percent of the metal. If you have 1.53 g of the compound, what mass of platinum (in grams) is contained in this sample?

39. The anesthetic procaine hydrochloride is often used to deaden pain during dental surgery. The compound is packaged as a 10.% solution (by mass; $d = 1.0$ g/mL) in water. If your dentist injects 0.50 mL of the solution, what mass of procaine hydrochloride (in milligrams) is injected?

40. You need a cube of aluminum with a mass of 7.6 g. What must be the length of the cube's edge (in cm)? (The density of aluminum is 2.698 g/cm³.)

41. You have a 250.0-mL graduated cylinder containing some water. You drop three marbles with a total mass of 95.2 g into the water. What is the average density of a marble?

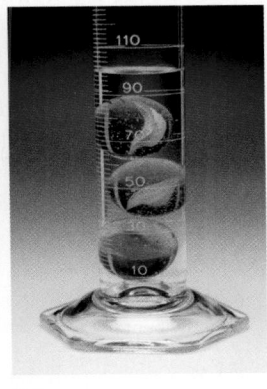

**(a)**                **(b)**

**Determining density.** (a) A graduated cylinder with 61 mL of water. (b) Three marbles are added to the cylinder.

42. You have a white crystalline solid, known to be one of the potassium compounds listed below. To determine which, you measure its density. You measure out 18.82 g and transfer it to a graduated cylinder containing kerosene (in which these compounds will not dissolve). The level of liquid kerosene rises from 8.5 mL to 15.3 mL. Calculate the density of the solid, and identify the compound from the following list.
    (a) KF, $d = 2.48$ g/cm³
    (b) KCl, $d = 1.98$ g/cm³
    (c) KBr, $d = 2.75$ g/cm³
    (d) KI, $d = 3.13$ g/cm³

43. ▲ The smallest repeating unit of a crystal of common salt is a cube (called a unit cell) with an edge length of 0.563 nm.

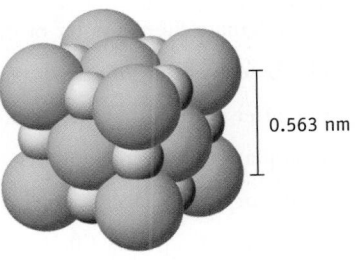

0.563 nm

**Sodium chloride, NaCl.**

(a) What is the volume of this cube in cubic nanometers? In cubic centimeters?
(b) The density of NaCl is 2.17 g/cm³. What is the mass of this smallest repeating unit ("unit cell")?
(c) Each repeating unit is composed of four NaCl units. What is the mass of one NaCl formula unit?

44. Diamond has a density of 3.513 g/cm³. The mass of diamonds is often measured in "carats," where 1 carat equals 0.200 g. What is the volume (in cubic centimeters) of a 1.50-carat diamond?

45. The element gallium has a melting point of 29.8 °C. If you held a sample of gallium in your hand, should it melt? Explain briefly.

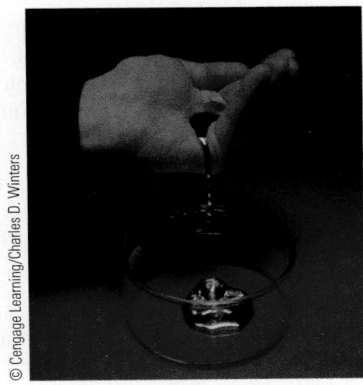

**Gallium metal.**

46. ▲ The density of pure water at various temperatures is given below.

| T(°C) | d (g/cm³) |
|---|---|
| 4 | 0.99997 |
| 15 | 0.99913 |
| 25 | 0.99707 |
| 35 | 0.99406 |

Suppose your laboratory partner tells you the density of water at 20 °C is 0.99910 g/cm³. Is this a reasonable number? Why or why not?

47. When you heat popcorn, it pops because it loses water explosively. Assume a kernel of corn, with a mass of 0.125 g, has a mass of only 0.106 g after popping.
    (a) What percentage of its mass did the kernel lose on popping?
    (b) Popcorn is sold by the pound in the United States. Using 0.125 g as the average mass of a popcorn kernel, how many kernels are there in a pound of popcorn? (1 lb = 453.6 g)

48. ▲ The aluminum in a package containing 75 ft² of kitchen foil weighs approximately 12 ounces. Aluminum has a density of 2.70 g/cm³. What is the approximate thickness of the aluminum foil in millimeters? (1 ounce = 28.4 g)

49. ▲ Fluoridation of city water supplies has been practiced in the United States for several decades. It is done by continuously adding sodium fluoride to water as it comes from a reservoir. Assume you live in a

medium-sized city of 150,000 people and that 660 L (170 gal) of water is used per person per day. What mass of sodium fluoride (in kilograms) must be added to the water supply each year (365 days) to have the required fluoride concentration of 1 ppm (part per million)—that is, 1 kilogram of fluoride per 1 million kilograms of water? (Sodium fluoride is 45.0% fluoride, and water has a density of 1.00 g/cm³.)

50. ▲ About two centuries ago, Benjamin Franklin showed that 1 teaspoon of oil would cover about 0.5 acre of still water. If you know that $1.0 \times 10^4$ m² = 2.47 acres and that there is approximately 5 cm³ in a teaspoon, what is the thickness of the layer of oil? How might this thickness be related to the sizes of molecules?

51. ▲ Automobile batteries are filled with an aqueous solution of sulfuric acid. What is the mass of the acid (in grams) in 500. mL of the battery acid solution if the density of the solution is 1.285 g/cm³ and the solution is 38.08% sulfuric acid by mass?

52. A 26-meter-tall statue of Buddha in Tibet is covered with 279 kg of gold. If the gold was applied to a thickness of 0.0015 mm, what surface area is covered (in square meters)? (Gold density = 19.3 g/cm³)

53. At 25 °C, the density of water is 0.997 g/cm³, whereas the density of ice at −10 °C is 0.917 g/cm³.
   (a) If a soft-drink can (volume = 250. mL) is filled completely with pure water at 25 °C and then frozen at −10 °C, what volume does the ice occupy?
   (b) Can the ice be contained within the can?

54. Suppose your bedroom is 18 ft long and 15 ft wide, and the distance from floor to ceiling is 8 ft 6 in. You need to know the volume of the room in metric units for some scientific calculations.
   (a) What is the room's volume in cubic meters? In liters?
   (b) What is the mass of air in the room in kilograms? In pounds? (Assume the density of air is 1.2 g/L and that the room is empty of furniture.)

55. A spherical steel ball has a mass of 3.475 g and a diameter of 9.40 mm. What is the density of the steel? [The volume of a sphere = $(4/3)\pi r^3$ where $r$ = radius.]

56. ▲ You are asked to identify an unknown liquid that is known to be one of the liquids listed below. You pipet a 3.50-mL sample into a beaker. The empty beaker had a mass of 12.20 g, and the beaker plus the liquid weighed 16.08 g.

| Substance | Density at 25 °C (g/cm³) |
|---|---|
| Ethylene glycol | 1.1088 (major component of automobile antifreeze) |
| Water | 0.9971 |
| Ethanol | 0.7893 (alcohol in alcoholic beverages) |
| Acetic acid | 1.0492 (active component of vinegar) |
| Glycerol | 1.2613 (solvent used in home care products) |

   (a) Calculate the density and identify the unknown.
   (b) If you were able to measure the volume to only two significant figures (that is, 3.5 mL, not 3.50 mL), will the results be sufficiently accurate to identify the unknown? Explain.

57. ▲ You have an irregularly shaped piece of an unknown metal. To identify it, you determine its density and then compare this value with known values that you look up in the chemistry library. The mass of the metal is 74.122 g. Because of the irregular shape, you measure the volume by submerging the metal in water in a graduated cylinder. When you do this, the water level in the cylinder rises from 28.2 mL to 36.7 mL.
   (a) What is the density of the metal? (Use the correct number of significant figures in your answer.)
   (b) The unknown is one of the seven metals listed below. Is it possible to identify the metal based on the density you have calculated? Explain.

| Metal | Density (g/cm³) | Metal | Density (g/cm³) |
|---|---|---|---|
| Zinc | 7.13 | Nickel | 8.90 |
| Iron | 7.87 | Copper | 8.96 |
| Cadmium | 8.65 | Silver | 10.50 |
| Cobalt | 8.90 | | |

58. ▲ There are five hydrocarbon compounds (compounds of C and H) that have the formula $C_6H_{14}$. (These are isomers; they differ in the way that C and H atoms are attached. ▶ Chapter 10.) All are liquids at room temperature but have slightly different densities.

| Hydrocarbon | Density (g/mL) |
|---|---|
| Hexane | 0.6600 |
| 2,3-Dimethylbutane | 0.6616 |
| 1-Methylpentane | 0.6532 |
| 2,2-Dimethylbutane | 0.6485 |
| 2-Methylpentane | 0.6645 |

   (a) You have a pure sample of one of these hydrocarbons, and to identify it you decide to measure its density. You determine that a 5.0-mL sample (measured in a graduated cylinder) has a mass of 3.2745 g (measured on an analytical balance.) Assume that the accuracy of the values for mass and volume is plus or minus one (±1) in the last significant figure. What is the density of the liquid?
   (b) Can you identify the unknown hydrocarbon based on your experiment?
   (c) Can you eliminate any of the five possibilities based on the data? If so, which one(s)?
   (d) You need a more accurate volume measurement to solve this problem, and you redetermine the volume to be 4.93 mL. Based on these new data, what is the unknown compound?

59. ▲ Suppose you have a cylindrical glass tube with a thin capillary opening, and you wish to determine the diameter of the capillary. You can do this experimentally by weighing a piece of the tubing before and after filling a portion of the capillary with mercury. Using the following information, calculate the diameter of the capillary.

Mass of tube before adding mercury = 3.263 g

Mass of tube after adding mercury = 3.416 g

Length of capillary filled with mercury = 16.75 mm

Density of mercury = 13.546 g/cm³

Volume of cylindrical capillary filled with mercury = $(\pi)(\text{radius})^2(\text{length})$

**60. COPPER:** Copper has a density of 8.96 g/cm³. An ingot of copper with a mass of 57 kg (126 lb) is drawn into wire with a diameter of 9.50 mm. What length of wire (in meters) can be produced? [Volume of wire = $(\pi)(\text{radius})^2(\text{length})$]

**61. ▲ COPPER:** See the illustration of the copper lattice on page 24.
  (a) Suppose you have a cube of copper metal that is 0.236 cm on a side with a mass of 0.1206 g. If you know that each copper atom (radius = 128 pm) has a mass of $1.055 \times 10^{-22}$ g (you will learn in Chapter 2 how to find the mass of one atom), how many atoms are there in this cube? What fraction of the cube is filled with atoms? (Or conversely, how much of the lattice is empty space?) Why is there "empty" space in the lattice?
  (b) Now look at the smallest, repeating unit of the crystal lattice of copper. Knowing that an edge of this cube is 361.47 pm and the density of copper is 8.960 g/cm³, calculate the number of copper atoms in this smallest, repeating unit.

**62. ▲ CASE STUDY:** In July 1983, an Air Canada Boeing 767 ran out of fuel over central Canada on a trip from Montreal to Edmonton. (The plane glided safely to a landing at an abandoned airstrip.) The pilots knew that 22,300 kg of fuel was required for the trip, and they knew that 7682 L of fuel was already in the tank. The ground crew added 4916 L of fuel, which was only about one fourth of what was required. The crew members used a factor of 1.77 for the fuel density—the problem is that 1.77 has units of pounds per liter and not kilograms per liter! What is the fuel density in units of kg/L? What mass and what volume of fuel should have been loaded? (1 lb = 453.6 g)

## In the Laboratory

**63.** A sample of unknown metal is placed in a graduated cylinder containing water. The mass of the sample is 37.5 g, and the water levels before and after adding the sample to the cylinder are as shown in the figure. Which metal in the following list is most likely the sample? (*d* is the density of the metal.)
  (a) Mg, *d* = 1.74 g/cm³     (d) Al, *d* = 2.70 g/cm³
  (b) Fe, *d* = 7.87 g/cm³     (e) Cu, *d* = 8.96 g/cm³
  (c) Ag, *d* = 10.5 g/cm³     (f) Pb, *d* = 11.3 g/cm³

Graduated cylinders with unknown metal *(right)*.

**64.** Iron pyrite is often called "fool's gold" because it looks like gold (see page 12). Suppose you have a solid that looks like gold, but you believe it to be fool's gold. The sample has a mass of 23.5 g. When the sample is lowered into the water in a graduated cylinder (see Study Question 63), the water level rises from 47.5 mL to 52.2 mL. Is the sample fool's gold (*d* = 5.00 g/cm³) or "real" gold (*d* = 19.3 g/cm³)?

**65.** You can analyze for a copper compound in water using an instrument called a spectrophotometer. [A spectrophotometer is a scientific instrument that measures the amount of light (of a given wavelength) that is absorbed by the solution.] The amount of light absorbed at a given wavelength of light (A) depends directly on the mass of compound per liter of solution. To calibrate the spectrophotometer, you collect the following data:

| Absorbance (A) | Mass per Liter of Copper Compound (g/L) |
|---|---|
| 0.000 | 0.000 |
| 0.257 | $1.029 \times 10^{-3}$ |
| 0.518 | $2.058 \times 10^{-3}$ |
| 0.771 | $3.087 \times 10^{-3}$ |
| 1.021 | $4.116 \times 10^{-3}$ |

Plot the absorbance (A) against the mass of copper compound per liter (g/L), and find the slope (*m*) and intercept (*b*) (assuming that A is *y* and the amount in solution is *x* in the equation for a straight line, $y = mx + b$). What is the mass of copper compound in the solution in g/L and mg/mL when the absorbance is 0.635?

**66.** A gas chromatograph is calibrated for the analysis of isooctane (a major gasoline component) using the following data:

| Percent Isooctane (x-data) | Instrument Response (y-data) |
|---|---|
| 0.352 | 1.09 |
| 0.803 | 1.78 |
| 1.08 | 2.60 |
| 1.38 | 3.03 |
| 1.75 | 4.01 |

If the instrument response is 2.75, what percentage of isooctane is present? (Data are taken from *Analytical Chemistry, An Introduction,* by D.A. Skoog, D.M. West, F.J. Holler, and S.R. Crouch, Cengage Learning, Brooks/Cole, Belmont, CA, 7th Edition, 2000.)

**67.** A general chemistry class carried out an experiment to determine the percentage (by mass) of acetic acid in vinegar. Ten students reported the following values: 5.22%, 5.28%, 5.22%, 5.30%, 5.19%, 5.23%, 5.33%, 5.26%, 5.15%, 5.22%. Determine the average value and the standard deviation from these data. How many of these results fell within one standard deviation of this average value?

# 2   Atoms, Molecules, and Ions

TABELLE II.

| REIHEN | GRUPPE I. — R²O | GRUPPE II. — RO | GRUPPE III. — R²O³ | GRUPPE IV. RH⁴ RO² | GRUPPE V. RH³ R²O⁵ | GRUPPE VI. RH² RO³ | GRUPPE VII. RH R²O⁷ | GRUPPE VIII. — RO⁴ |
|---|---|---|---|---|---|---|---|---|
| 1 | H=1 | | | | | | | |
| 2 | Li=7 | Be=9,4 | B=11 | C=12 | N=14 | O=16 | F=19 | |
| 3 | Na=23 | Mg=24 | Al=27,3 | Si=28 | P=31 | S=32 | Cl=35,5 | |
| 4 | K=39 | Ca=40 | — =44 | Ti=48 | V=51 | Cr=52 | Mn=55 | Fe=56, Co=59, Ni=59, Cu=63. |
| 5 | (Cu=63) | Zn=65 | — =68 | — =72 | As=75 | Se=78 | Br=80 | |
| 6 | Rb=85 | Sr=87 | ?Yt=88 | Zr=90 | Nb=94 | Mo=96 | — =100 | Ru=104, Rh=104, Pd=106, Ag=108. |
| 7 | (Ag=108) | Cd=112 | In=113 | Sn=118 | Sb=122 | Te=125 | J=127 | |
| 8 | Cs=133 | Ba=137 | ?Di=138 | ?Ce=140 | | | | — — — — |
| 9 | (—) | — | — | — | — | — | — | |
| 10 | — | — | ?Er=178 | ?La=180 | Ta=182 | W=184 | — | Os=195, Ir=197, Pt=198, Au=199. |
| 11 | (Au=199) | Hg=200 | Tl=204 | Pb=207 | Bi=208 | — | — | |
| 12 | — | — | — | Th=231 | — | U=240 | — | — — — — |

Photos © Cengage Learning/Charles D. Winters

## The Periodic Table, the Central Icon of Chemistry

Nineteenth-century chemists such as Newlands, Chancourtois, Mayer, and others devised ways to organize the chemistry of the elements with varying degrees of success. However, it was Dmitri Mendeleev in 1870 who first truly recognized the periodicity of the chemistry of the elements, who proposed the first periodic table, and who used this to predict the existence of yet-unknown elements.

Mendeleev placed the elements in a table in order of increasing atomic weight. In doing so Li, Be, B, C, N, O, and F became the first row of the table. The next element then known, sodium (Na), had properties quite similar to those of lithium (Li), so Na began the next row of the table. As additional elements were added in order of increasing atomic weight, elements with similar properties fell in columns or groups.

If you compare the periodic table published by Mendeleev in 1871 (shown here) with the table in the front of this book, you will see that many elements are missing in the 1871 table. Mendeleev's genius was that he recognized there must be yet-undiscovered elements, so he left a place for them in the table (marking the empty places with a —). For example, Mendeleev concluded that "Gruppe IV" was missing an element between silicon (Si) and tin (Sn) and marked its position as "— = 72." He called the missing element *eka-silicon* and predicted the element would have an atomic weight of 72 and a density of 5.5 g/cm³. Based on this and other predictions, chemists knew what to look for in mineral samples, and soon many of the missing elements were discovered.

### Questions:

1. What is eka-silicon, and how close were Mendeleev's predictions to the actual values for this element?
2. How many of the missing elements can you identify?

**Answers to these questions are available in Appendix N.**

## CHAPTER GOALS

*See Chapter Goals Revisited (page 96) for Study Questions keyed to these goals.*

- Describe atomic structure and define atomic number and mass number.

- Understand the nature of isotopes and calculate atomic masses from isotopic masses and abundances.

- Know the terminology of the periodic table.

- Interpret, predict, and write formulas for ionic and molecular compounds.

- Name ionic and molecular compounds.

- Understand some properties of ionic compounds.

- Explain the concept of the mole and use molar mass in calculations.

- Derive compound formulas from experimental data.

The chemical elements are forged in stars and, from these elements, molecules such as water and ammonia are made in outer space. These simple molecules and much more complex ones such as DNA and hemoglobin are found on earth. To comprehend the burgeoning fields of molecular biology as well as all modern chemistry, we have to understand the nature of the chemical elements and the properties and structures of molecules. This chapter begins our exploration of the chemistry of the elements, the building blocks of chemistry, and the compounds they form.

### 2.1 Atomic Structure—Protons, Electrons, and Neutrons

Around 1900 a series of experiments done by scientists in England such as Sir Joseph John Thomson (1856–1940) and Ernest Rutherford (1871–1937) established a model of the atom that is still the basis of modern atomic theory. Atoms themselves are made of subatomic particles, three of which are important in chemistry: electrically positive protons, electrically negative electrons, and, in all except one type of hydrogen atom, electrically neutral neutrons. The model places the more massive protons and neutrons in a very small nucleus (Figure 2.1), which contains all the positive charge and almost all the mass of an atom. Electrons, with a much smaller mass than protons or neutrons, surround the nucleus and occupy most of the volume. In a neutral atom, the number of electrons equals the number of protons.

The chemical properties of elements and molecules depend largely on the electrons in atoms. We shall look more carefully at their arrangement and how they influence atomic properties in Chapters 6 and 7. In this chapter, however, we first want to describe how the composition of the atom relates to its mass and then to the mass of compounds. This is crucial information when we consider the quantitative aspects of chemical reactions in later chapters.

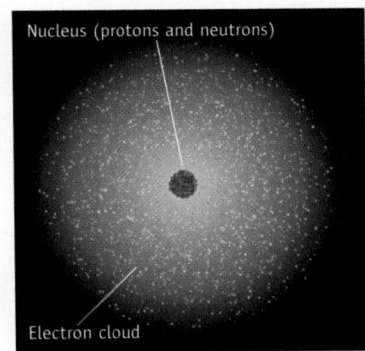

**FIGURE 2.1 The structure of the atom.** All atoms contain a nucleus with one or more protons (positive electric charge) and, except for one type of H atom, neutrons (no charge). Electrons (negative electric charge) are found in space as a "cloud" around the nucleus. In an electrically neutral atom, the number of electrons equals the number of protons. Note that this figure is not drawn to scale. If the nucleus were really the size depicted here, the electron cloud would extend over 200 m. The atom is mostly empty space!

## 2.2   Atomic Number and Atomic Mass

### Atomic Number

*All atoms of a given element have the same number of protons in the nucleus.* Hydrogen is the simplest element, with one nuclear proton. All helium atoms have two protons, all lithium atoms have three protons, and all beryllium atoms have four protons. The number of protons in the nucleus of an element is given by its **atomic number**, which is generally indicated by the symbol **Z**.

Currently known elements are listed in the periodic table inside the front cover of this book and on the list inside the back cover. The integer number at the top of the box for each element in the periodic table is its atomic number. A sodium atom (Na), for example, has an atomic number of 11, so its nucleus contains 11 protons. A uranium atom (U) has 92 nuclear protons and $Z = 92$.

### Relative Atomic Mass and the Atomic Mass Unit

With the quantitative work of the great French chemist Antoine Laurent Lavoisier (1743–1794), chemistry began to change from medieval alchemy to a modern field of study (page 112). As 18th- and 19th-century chemists tried to understand how the elements combined, they carried out increasingly quantitative studies aimed at learning, for example, how much of one element would combine with another. Based on this work, they learned that the substances they produced had a constant composition, so they could define the relative masses of elements that would combine to produce a new substance. At the beginning of the 19th century, John Dalton (1766–1844) suggested that the combinations of elements involve atoms and proposed a relative scale of atom masses. Apparently for simplicity, Dalton chose a mass of 1 for hydrogen on which to base his scale.

The atomic mass scale has changed since 1800, but like the 19th-century chemists, we still use *relative* masses with the standard today being carbon. A carbon atom having six protons and six neutrons in the nucleus is assigned a mass value of exactly 12. From chemical experiments and physical measurements, we know an oxygen atom having eight protons and eight neutrons has 1.33291 times the mass of carbon, so it has a relative mass of 15.9949. Masses of atoms of other elements are assigned in a similar manner.

Masses of fundamental atomic particles are often expressed in **atomic mass units (u)**. *One atomic mass unit, 1 u, is one-twelfth of the mass of an atom of carbon with six protons and six neutrons.* Thus, such a carbon atom has a mass of exactly 12 u. The atomic mass unit can be related to other units of mass using the conversion factor 1 atomic mass unit (u) = $1.661 \times 10^{-24}$ g.

### Mass Number

Because proton and neutron masses are so close to 1 u, while the mass of an electron is only about 1/2000 of this value (Table 2.1), the approximate mass of an atom can be estimated if the number of neutrons and protons is known. The sum of the number of protons and neutrons for an atom is called its **mass number** and is given the symbol *A*.

$$A = \text{mass number} = \text{number of protons} + \text{number of neutrons}$$

For example, a sodium atom, which has 11 protons and 12 neutrons in its nucleus, has a mass number of 23 ($A = 11$ p + 12 n). The most common atom of uranium has 92 protons and 146 neutrons, and a mass number of $A = 238$. Using this information, we often symbolize atoms with the following notation:

$$\text{Mass number} \rightarrow \,^{A}_{Z}\text{X} \leftarrow \text{Element symbol}$$
$$\text{Atomic number} \rightarrow$$

The subscript *Z* is optional because the element's symbol tells us what the atomic number must be. For example, the atoms described previously have

---

Copper

29 ⋯⋯⋯Atomic number

**Cu** ⋯⋯⋯Symbol

---

● **Historical Perspective on the Development of Our Understanding of Atomic Structure** A brief history of important experiments and the scientists involved in developing the modern view of the atom is on pages 334–343.

---

● **How Small Is an Atom?** The radius of the typical atom is between 30 and 300 pm ($3 \times 10^{-11}$ m to $3 \times 10^{-10}$ m). To get a feeling for the incredible smallness of an atom, consider that 1 cm³ contains about three times as many atoms as the Atlantic Ocean contains teaspoons of water.

**Table 2.1 Properties of Subatomic Particles***

| Particle | Mass | | Charge | Symbol |
| | Grams | Atomic Mass Units | | |
| --- | --- | --- | --- | --- |
| Electron | $9.109383 \times 10^{-28}$ | 0.0005485799 | 1− | $_{-1}^{0}e$ or $e^-$ |
| Proton | $1.672622 \times 10^{-24}$ | 1.007276 | 1+ | $_{1}^{1}p$ or $p^+$ |
| Neutron | $1.674927 \times 10^{-24}$ | 1.008665 | 0 | $_{0}^{1}n$ or $n$ |

*These values and others in the book are taken from the National Institute of Standards and Technology website at http://physics.nist.gov/cuu/Constants/index.html

the symbols $_{11}^{23}Na$ or $_{92}^{238}U$, or just $^{23}Na$ or $^{238}U$. In words, we say "sodium-23" or "uranium-238."

## EXAMPLE 2.1 Atomic Composition

**Problem** What is the composition of an atom of phosphorus with 16 neutrons? What is its mass number? What is the symbol for such an atom? If the atom has an actual mass of 30.9738 u, what is its mass in grams? Finally, what is the mass of this phosphorus atom relative to the mass of a carbon atom with a mass number of 12?

**What Do You Know?** You know the name of the element and the number of neutrons. You also know the actual mass, so you can determine its mass relative to carbon-12.

**Strategy** The symbol for phosphorus is P. You can look up the atomic number (which equals the number of protons) for this element on the periodic table. The mass number is the sum of the number of protons and neutrons. The mass of the atom in grams can be obtained from the mass in atomic mass units using the conversion factor $1 u = 1.661 \times 10^{-24}$ g. The relative mass of an atom of P compared to $^{12}C$ can be determined by dividing the mass of the P atom in atomic mass units by the mass of a $^{12}C$ atom, 12.0000 u.

**Solution** A phosphorus atom has 15 protons and, because it is electrically neutral, also has 15 electrons. A phosphorus atom with 16 neutrons has a mass number of 31.

$$\text{Mass number} = \text{number of protons} + \text{number of neutrons} = 15 + 16 = 31$$

The atom's complete symbol is $_{15}^{31}P$.

$$\text{Mass of one } ^{31}P \text{ atom} = (30.9738 \text{ u}) \times (1.661 \times 10^{-24} \text{ g/u}) = 5.145 \times 10^{-23} \text{ g}$$

Mass of $^{31}P$ relative to the mass of an atom of $^{12}C$: 30.9738/12.0000 = 2.58115

**Think about Your Answer** Because phosphorus has an atomic number greater than carbon's, you expect its relative mass to be greater than 12.

---

**Check Your Understanding**

1. What is the mass number of an iron atom with 30 neutrons?

2. A nickel atom with 32 neutrons has a mass of 59.930788 u. What is its mass in grams?

3. How many protons, neutrons, and electrons are in a $^{64}Zn$ atom?

---

**REVIEW & CHECK FOR SECTION 2.2**

1. The mass of an atom of manganese is 54.9380 u. How many neutrons are contained in one atom of this element?

   (a) 25          (b) 30          (c) 29          (d) 55

2. An atom contains 12 neutrons and has a mass number of 23. Identify the element.

   (a) C          (b) Mg          (c) Na          (d) Cl

Solid H₂O

Liquid H₂O

Solid D₂O

© Cengage Learning/Charles D. Winters

**FIGURE 2.2 Ice made from "heavy water."** Water containing ordinary hydrogen ($^1_1$H, protium) forms a solid that is less dense ($d = 0.917$ g/cm³ at 0 °C) than liquid $H_2O$ ($d = 0.997$ g/cm³ at 25 °C), so it floats in the liquid. (Water is unique in this regard. The solid phase of virtually all other substances sinks in the liquid phase of that substance.) Similarly, "heavy ice" ($D_2O$, deuterium oxide) floats in "heavy water." $D_2O$-ice is denser than liquid $H_2O$, however, so cubes made of $D_2O$ sink in liquid $H_2O$.

## 2.3 Isotopes

In only a few instances (for example, aluminum, fluorine, and phosphorus) do all atoms in a naturally occurring sample of a given element have the same mass. Most elements consist of atoms having several different mass numbers. For example, there are two kinds of boron atoms, one with a mass of about 10 ($^{10}$B) and a second with a mass of about 11 ($^{11}$B). Atoms of tin can have any of 10 different masses. Atoms with the same atomic number but different mass numbers are called **isotopes**.

All atoms of an element have the same number of protons—five in the case of boron. To have different masses, isotopes must have different numbers of neutrons. The nucleus of a $^{10}$B atom ($Z = 5$) contains five protons and five neutrons, whereas the nucleus of a $^{11}$B atom contains five protons and six neutrons.

Scientists often refer to a particular isotope by giving its mass number (for example, uranium-238, $^{238}$U), but the isotopes of hydrogen are so important that they have special names and symbols. All hydrogen atoms have one proton. When that is the only nuclear particle, the isotope is called *protium*, or just "hydrogen." The isotope of hydrogen with one neutron, $^2_1$H, is called *deuterium*, or "heavy hydrogen" (symbol = D). The nucleus of radioactive hydrogen-3, $^3_1$H, or *tritium* (symbol = T), contains one proton and two neutrons.

The substitution of one isotope of an element for another isotope of the same element in a compound sometimes can have an interesting effect (Figure 2.2). This is especially true when deuterium is substituted for hydrogen because the mass of deuterium is double that of hydrogen.

### Isotope Abundance

A sample of water from a stream or lake will consist almost entirely of $H_2O$ where the H atoms are the $^1$H isotope. A few molecules, however, will have deuterium ($^2$H) substituted for $^1$H. We can predict this outcome because we know that 99.985% of all hydrogen atoms on earth are $^1$H atoms. That is, the abundance of $^1$H atoms is 99.985%.

$$\text{Percent abundance} = \frac{\text{number of atoms of a given isotope}}{\text{total number of atoms of all isotopes of that element}} \times 100\% \quad \textbf{(2.1)}$$

The remainder of naturally occurring hydrogen is deuterium, whose abundance is only 0.015% of the total hydrogen atoms. Tritium, the radioactive $^3$H isotope, occurs naturally in only trace amounts.

Consider again the two isotopes of boron. The boron-10 isotope has an abundance of 19.91%; the abundance of boron-11 is 80.09%. Thus, if you could count out 10,000 boron atoms from an "average" natural sample, 1991 of them would be boron-10 atoms and 8009 of them would be boron-11 atoms.

### Determining Atomic Mass and Isotope Abundance

● **Atomic Masses of Some Isotopes**

| Atom | Atomic Mass (u) |
|---|---|
| $^4$He | 4.0092603 |
| $^{13}$C | 13.003355 |
| $^{16}$O | 15.994915 |
| $^{58}$Ni | 57.935346 |
| $^{60}$Ni | 59.930788 |
| $^{79}$Br | 78.918336 |
| $^{81}$Br | 80.916289 |
| $^{197}$Au | 196.966543 |
| $^{238}$U | 238.050784 |

● **Isotopic Masses and the Mass Defect** Actual masses of atoms are always less than the sum of the masses of the subatomic particles composing that atom. This is called the *mass defect* and the reason for it is discussed in Chapter 23.

The masses of isotopes and their abundances are determined experimentally using a mass spectrometer (Figure 2.3). A gaseous sample of an element is introduced into the evacuated chamber of the spectrometer, and the atoms or molecules of the sample are converted to positively charged particles (called *ions*). The cloud of ions forms a beam as they are attracted to negatively charged plates within the instrument. As the ions stream toward the negatively charged detector, they fly through a magnetic field, which causes the paths of the ions to be deflected. The extent of deflection depends on particle mass: The less massive ions are deflected more, and the more massive ions are deflected less. The ions, now separated by mass, are detected at the end of the chamber. Chemists using modern instruments can measure isotopic masses to as many as nine significant figures.

Except for carbon-12, whose mass is defined to be exactly 12 u, isotopic masses do not have integer values. However, the isotopic masses are always very close to the mass numbers for the isotope. For example, the mass of an atom of boron-11 ($^{11}$B, 5 protons and 6 neutrons) is 11.0093 u, and the mass of an atom of iron-58 ($^{58}$Fe, 26 protons and 32 neutrons) is 57.9333 u.

**1.** A sample is introduced as a vapor into the ionization chamber.

There it is bombarded with high-energy electrons that strip electrons from the atoms or molecules of the sample.

**2.** The resulting positive particles are accelerated by a series of negatively charged accelerator plates into an analyzing chamber.

**3.** This chamber is in a magnetic field, which is perpendicular to the direction of the beam of charged particles.

The magnetic field causes the beam to curve. The radius of curvature depends on the mass and charge of the particles (as well as the accelerating voltage and strength of the magnetic field).

**4.** Here, particles of $^{21}Ne^+$ are focused on the detector, whereas beams of ions of $^{20}Ne^+$ and $^{22}Ne^+$ (of lighter or heavier mass) experience greater and lesser curvature, respectively, and so fail to be detected.

By changing the magnetic field, charged particles of different masses can be focused on the detector to generate the observed spectrum.

**FIGURE 2.3  Mass spectrometer.** A mass spectrometer will separate ions of different mass and charge in a gaseous sample of ions. The instrument allows the researcher to determine the accurate mass of each ion, whether the ions are composed of individual atoms, molecules, or molecular fragments.

---

**REVIEW & CHECK FOR SECTION 2.3**

Silver has two isotopes, one with 60 neutrons (percent abundance = 51.839%) and the other with 62 neutrons. What is the symbol of the isotope with 62 neutrons, and what is its percent abundance?

(a)  $^{107}_{47}Ag$, 51.839%      (b)  $^{107}_{47}Ag$, 48.161%      (c)  $^{109}_{47}Ag$, 51.839%      (d)  $^{109}_{47}Ag$, 48.161%

---

## 2.4  Atomic Weight

Every sample of boron has some atoms with a mass of 10.0129 u and others with a mass of 11.0093 u. The **atomic weight** of the element, the average mass of a representative sample of boron atoms, is somewhere between these values. For boron, for example, the atomic weight is 10.81. If isotope masses and abundances are known, the atomic weight of an element can be calculated using Equation 2.2.

● **Atomic Mass, Relative Atomic Mass, and Atomic Weight** The atomic mass is the mass of an atom at rest. The relative atomic mass, also known as the atomic weight or average atomic weight, is the average of the atomic masses of all of the element's isotopes. The term *atomic weight* is slowly being phased out in favor of "relative atomic mass."

$$\text{Atomic weight} = \left(\frac{\% \text{ abundance isotope 1}}{100}\right)(\text{mass of isotope 1})$$
$$+ \left(\frac{\% \text{ abundance isotope 2}}{100}\right)(\text{mass of isotope 2}) + \ldots$$

(2.2)

For boron with two isotopes ($^{10}B$, 19.91% abundant; $^{11}B$, 80.09% abundant), we find

$$\text{Atomic weight} = \left(\frac{19.91}{100}\right) \times 10.0129 + \left(\frac{80.09}{100}\right) \times 11.0093 = 10.81$$

Equation 2.2 gives an average mass, weighted in terms of the abundance of each isotope for the element. As illustrated by the data in Table 2.2, *the atomic weight of an element is always closer to the mass of the most abundant isotope or isotopes.*

**Table 2.2  Isotope Abundance and Atomic Weight**

| Element | Symbol | Atomic Weight | Mass Number | Isotopic Mass | Natural Abundance (%) |
|---------|--------|---------------|-------------|---------------|-----------------------|
| Hydrogen | H | 1.00794 | 1 | 1.0078 | 99.985 |
|  | D* |  | 2 | 2.0141 | 0.015 |
|  | T† |  | 3 | 3.0161 | 0 |
| Boron | B | 10.811 | 10 | 10.0129 | 19.91 |
|  |  |  | 11 | 11.0093 | 80.09 |
| Neon | Ne | 20.1797 | 20 | 19.9924 | 90.48 |
|  |  |  | 21 | 20.9938 | 0.27 |
|  |  |  | 22 | 21.9914 | 9.25 |
| Magnesium | Mg | 24.3050 | 24 | 23.9850 | 78.99 |
|  |  |  | 25 | 24.9858 | 10.00 |
|  |  |  | 26 | 25.9826 | 11.01 |

*D = deuterium; †T = tritium, radioactive.

The atomic weight of each stable element is given in the periodic table inside the front cover of this book. In the periodic table, each element's box contains the atomic number, the element symbol, and the atomic weight. For unstable (radioactive) elements, the atomic weight or mass number of the most stable isotope is given in parentheses.

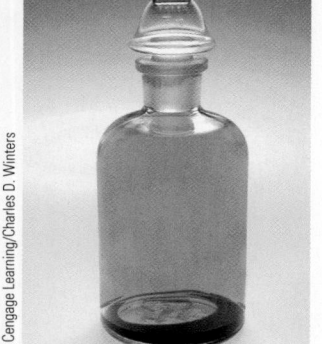

**Elemental bromine.** Bromine is a deep orange-red, volatile liquid at room temperature. It consists of $Br_2$ molecules in which two bromine atoms are chemically bonded together. There are two, stable, naturally occurring isotopes of bromine atoms: $^{79}Br$ (50.69% abundance) and $^{81}Br$ (49.31% abundance).

## EXAMPLE 2.2    Calculating Atomic Weight from Isotope Abundance

**Problem**  Bromine has two naturally occurring isotopes. One has a mass of 78.918338 u and an abundance of 50.69%. The other isotope has a mass of 80.916291 u and an abundance of 49.31%. Calculate the atomic weight of bromine.

**What Do You Know?**  You know the mass and abundance of each of the two isotopes.

**Strategy**  The atomic weight of any element is the weighted average of the masses of the isotopes in a representative sample. To calculate the atomic weight, multiply the mass of each isotope by its percent abundance divided by 100 (Equation 2.2).

**Solution**

Atomic weight of bromine = (50.69/100)(78.918338) + (49.31/100)(80.916291) = 79.90 u

**Think about Your Answer**  You can quickly estimate the atomic weight from the data given. There are two isotopes, mass numbers of 79 and 81, in approximately equal abundance. From this, we would expect the average mass to be about 80, midway between the two mass numbers. The calculation bears this out.

**Check Your Understanding**

Verify that the atomic weight of chlorine is 35.45, given the following information:

$^{35}Cl$ mass = 34.96885; percent abundance = 75.77%

$^{37}Cl$ mass = 36.96590; percent abundance = 24.23%

## EXAMPLE 2.3    Calculating Isotopic Abundances

**Problem**  Antimony, Sb, has two stable isotopes: $^{121}Sb$, 120.904 u, and $^{123}Sb$, 122.904 u. What are the relative abundances of these isotopes?

**What Do You Know?** You know the masses of the two isotopes of the element and know their weighted average, the atomic weight, is 121.760 u (see the periodic table).

**Strategy** You can predict that the lighter isotope ($^{121}$Sb) must be the more abundant because the atomic weight is closer to 121 than to 123. To calculate the abundances recognize there are two unknown but related quantities, and you can write the following expression (where the fractional abundance of an isotope is the percent abundance of the isotope divided by 100)

**A sample of the metalloid antimony.** The element has two stable isotopes, $^{121}$Sb and $^{123}$Sb.

$$\text{Atomic weight} = 121.760$$

$$= (\text{fractional abundance of } ^{121}\text{Sb})(120.904) +$$

$$(\text{fractional abundance of } ^{123}\text{Sb})(122.904)$$

or

$$121.760 = x(120.904) + y(122.904)$$

where $x$ = fractional abundance of $^{121}$Sb and $y$ = fractional abundance of $^{123}$Sb. Because you know that the fractional abundances of the isotopes must equal 1, $x + y = 1$, and you can solve the equations simultaneously for $x$ and $y$.

**Solution** Because y = fractional abundance of $^{123}$Sb = $1 - x$, you can make a substitution for $y$.

$$121.760 = x(120.904) + (1 - x)(122.904)$$

Expanding this equation, you have

$$121.760 = 120.904x + 122.904 - 122.904x$$

Finally, solving for $x$, you find

$$121.760 - 122.904 = (120.904 - 122.904)x$$

$$x = 0.5720$$

The fractional abundance of $^{121}$Sb is 0.5720 and its percent abundance is 57.20%. This means that the percent abundance of $^{123}$Sb must be 42.80%.

**Think about Your Answer** The result confirms your initial inference that the lighter isotope is the more abundant of the two.

---

**Check Your Understanding**

Neon has three stable isotopes, one with a small abundance. What are the abundances of the other two isotopes?

$^{20}$Ne, mass = 19.992435; percent abundance = ?

$^{21}$Ne, mass = 20.993843; percent abundance = 0.27%

$^{22}$Ne, mass = 21.991383; percent abundance = ?

---

**REVIEW & CHECK FOR SECTION 2.4**

1.  Which is the more abundant isotope of copper, $^{63}$Cu or $^{65}$Cu?

    (a)  $^{63}$Cu          (b)  $^{65}$Cu

2.  Which of the following is closest to the observed abundance of $^{71}$Ga, one of two stable gallium isotopes ($^{69}$Ga and $^{71}$Ga)?

    (a)  60%          (b)  40%          (c)  20%          (d)  70%

# Using Isotopes: Ötzi, the Iceman of the Alps

In 1991 a hiker in the Alps on the Austrian-Italian border found the well-preserved remains of an approximately 46-year-old man, now nick-named "The Iceman," who lived about 5200 years ago (page 1). Studies using isotopes of oxygen, strontium, lead, and argon, among others, have helped scientists paint a detailed picture of the man and his life.

The $^{18}O$ isotope of oxygen can give information on the latitude and altitude in which a person was born and raised. Oxygen in biominerals such as teeth and bones comes primarily from ingested water. The important fact is that there is a variation in the amount of $^{18}O$ water ($H_2^{18}O$) that depends on how far inland the watershed is found and on its altitude. As rain clouds move inland, water based on $^{18}O$ will be "rained out" before $H_2^{16}O$. The lakes and rivers on the northern side of the Alps are known to have a lower $^{18}O$ content than those on the southern side of the mountains. On the northern side precipitation originates in the cooler, and more distant, Atlantic Ocean. On the southern side, the precipitation comes from the closer and warmer Mediterranean Sea. The $^{18}O$ content of the teeth and bones of the Iceman was found to be relatively high and characteristic of the watershed south of the Alps. He had clearly been born and raised in that area.

The relative abundance of isotopes of heavier elements also varies slightly from place to place and in their incorporation into different minerals. Strontium, a member of Group 2A along with calcium, is incorporated into teeth and bones. The ratio of strontium isotopes, $^{87}Sr/^{86}Sr$, and of lead isotopes, $^{206}Pb/^{204}Pb$, in the Iceman's teeth and bones was characteristic of soils from a narrow region of Italy south of the Alps, which established more clearly where he was born and lived of his life.

The investigators also looked for food residues in the Iceman's intestines. Although a few grains of cereal were found, they also located tiny flakes of mica believed to have broken off stones used to grind grain and that were therefore eaten when the man ate the grain. They analyzed these flakes using argon isotopes, $^{40}Ar$ and $^{39}Ar$, and found their signature was like that of mica in an area south of the Alps, thus establishing where he lived in his later years.

The overall result of the many isotope studies showed that the Iceman lived thousands of years ago in a small area about 10–20 kilometers west of Merano in northern Italy.

For details of the isotope studies, see W. Müller, et al., *Science*, Volume 302, October 13, 2003, pages 862–866.

**Ötzi the Iceman.** A well-preserved mummy of a man who lived in northern Italy about 5000 years ago.

**Questions:**

1. How many neutrons are there in atoms of $^{18}O$? In each of the two isotopes of lead?

2. $^{14}C$ is a radioactive isotope of carbon that occurs in trace amounts in all living materials. How many neutrons are in a $^{14}C$ atom?

3. The ratio $^{87}Sr/^{86}Sr$ in the Iceman study was in the range of 0.72. How does this compare with the ratio calculated from average abundances ($^{87}Sr = 7.00\%$ and $^{86}Sr = 9.86\%$)?

**Answers to these questions are available in Appendix N.**

---

## 2.5 The Periodic Table

- **About the Periodic Table** For more information on the periodic table we recommend the following:
  - American Chemical Society (pubs.acs.org/cen/80th/elements.html).
  - www.ptable.com
  - J. Emsley: *Nature's Building Blocks— An A–Z Guide to the Elements*, New York, Oxford University Press, 2001.
  - E. Scerri, *The Periodic Table*, New York, Oxford University Press, 2007.

The periodic table of elements is one of the most useful tools in chemistry. Not only does it contain a wealth of information, but it can also be used to organize many of the ideas of chemistry. It is important to become familiar with its main features and terminology.

### Developing the Periodic Table

Although the arrangement of elements in the periodic table is now understood on the basis of atomic structure [▶ Chapters 6 and 7], the table was originally developed from many experimental observations of the chemical and physical properties of elements and is the result of the ideas of a number of chemists in the 18th and 19th centuries.

In 1869, at the University of St. Petersburg in Russia, Dmitri Ivanovitch Mendeleev (1834–1907) was pondering the properties of the elements as he wrote a textbook on chemistry. On studying the chemical and physical properties of the elements, he realized that, if the elements were arranged in order of increasing atomic mass, elements with similar properties appeared in a regular pattern. That is, he saw a **periodicity** or periodic repetition of the properties of elements. Mendeleev organized the known elements into a table by lining them up in horizontal rows in order of increasing atomic mass (page 50). Every time he came to an element with properties similar to one already in the row, he started a new row. For example, the elements Li, Be, B, C, N, O, and F were in a row. Sodium was the next element then

**Module 1: The Periodic Table** covers concepts in this section.

# The Story of the Periodic Table

*by Eric R. Scerri, UCLA*

Dmitri Mendeleev was probably the greatest scientist produced by Russia. The youngest of 14 children, he was taken by his mother on a long journey, on foot, in order to enroll him into a university. However, several attempts initially proved futile because, as a Siberian, Mendeleev was barred from attending certain institutions. His mother did succeed in enrolling him in a teacher training college, thus giving Mendeleev a lasting interest in science education, which contributed to his eventual discovery of the periodic system that essentially simplified the subject of inorganic chemistry.

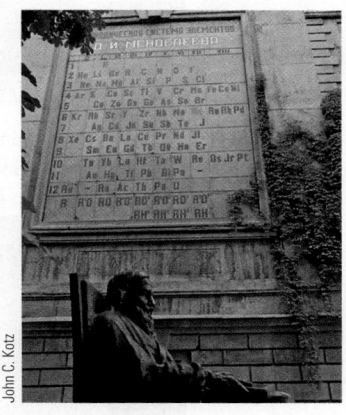

**Statue of Dmitri Mendeleev and a periodic table.** This statue and mural are at the Institute of Metrology in St. Petersburg, Russia.

*John C. Kotz*

After completing a doctorate, Mendeleev headed to Germany for a postdoctoral fellowship and then returned to Russia, where he set about writing a book aimed at summarizing all of inorganic chemistry. It was while writing this book that he identified the organizing principle with which he is now invariably connected—the periodic system of the elements.

More correctly, though, the periodic system was developed by Mendeleev, as well as five other scientists, over a period of about 10 years, after the Italian chemist Cannizzaro had published a consistent set of atomic weights in 1860. It appears that Mendeleev was unaware of the work of several of his co-discoverers, however.

In essence, the periodic table groups together sets of elements with similar properties into vertical columns. The underlying idea is that if the elements are arranged in order of increasing atomic weights, there are approximate repetitions in their chemical properties after certain intervals. As a result of the existence of the periodic table, students and even professors of chemistry were no longer obliged to learn the properties of all the elements in a disorganized fashion. Instead, they could concentrate on the properties of representative members of the eight columns or groups in the early short-form periodic table, from which they could predict properties of other group members.

Mendeleev is justly regarded as the leading discoverer of the periodic table since he continued to champion the finding and drew out its consequences to a far greater extent than any of his contemporaries. First, he accommodated the 65 or so elements that were known at the time into a coherent scheme based on ascending order of atomic weight while also reflecting chemical and physical similarities. Next, he noticed gaps in his system, which he reasoned would eventually be filled by elements that had not yet been discovered. In addition, by judicious interpolation between the properties of known elements, Mendeleev predicted the nature of a number of completely new elements. Within a period of about 20 years, three of these elements—subsequently called gallium, scandium, and germanium—were isolated and found to have almost the exact properties that Mendeleev had predicted.

What is not well known is that about half of the elements that Mendeleev predicted were never found. But given the dramatic success of his early predictions, these later lapses have largely been forgotten.

**Eric Scerri,** *The Periodic Table: Its Story and Its Significance,* Oxford University Press, New York, 2007.

---

known; because its properties closely resembled those of Li, Mendeleev started a new row. As more and more elements were added to the table, new rows were begun, and elements with similar properties (such as Li, Na, and K) were placed in the same vertical column.

An important feature of Mendeleev's table—and a mark of his genius—was that he left an empty space in a column when he believed an element was not known but should exist and have properties similar to the elements above and below it in his table. He deduced that these spaces would be filled by undiscovered elements. For example, he left a space between Si (silicon) and Sn (tin) in Group 4A for an element he called *eka-silicon.* Based on the progression of properties in this group, Mendeleev was able to predict the properties of the missing element. With the discovery of germanium (Ge) in 1886, Mendeleev's prediction was confirmed.

In Mendeleev's table the elements were ordered by increasing mass. A glance at a modern table, however, shows that, if some elements (such as Ni and Co, Ar and K, and Te and I) were ordered by mass and not chemical and physical properties, they would be reversed in their order of appearance. Mendeleev recognized these discrepancies and simply assumed the atomic masses known at that time were inaccurate—not a bad assumption based on the analytical methods then in use. In fact, his order is correct and what was wrong was his assumption that element properties were a function of their mass.

● **Mendeleev and Atomic Numbers** Mendeleev developed the periodic table based on atomic masses. The concept of atomic numbers was not known until after the development of the structure of the atom in the early 20th century.

In 1913 H. G. J. Moseley (1887–1915), a young English scientist working with Ernest Rutherford (1871–1937), bombarded many different metals with electrons in a cathode-ray tube (page 340) and examined the x-rays emitted in the process. Moseley realized the wavelength of the x-rays emitted by a given element was related in a precise manner to the positive charge in the nucleus of the atoms of

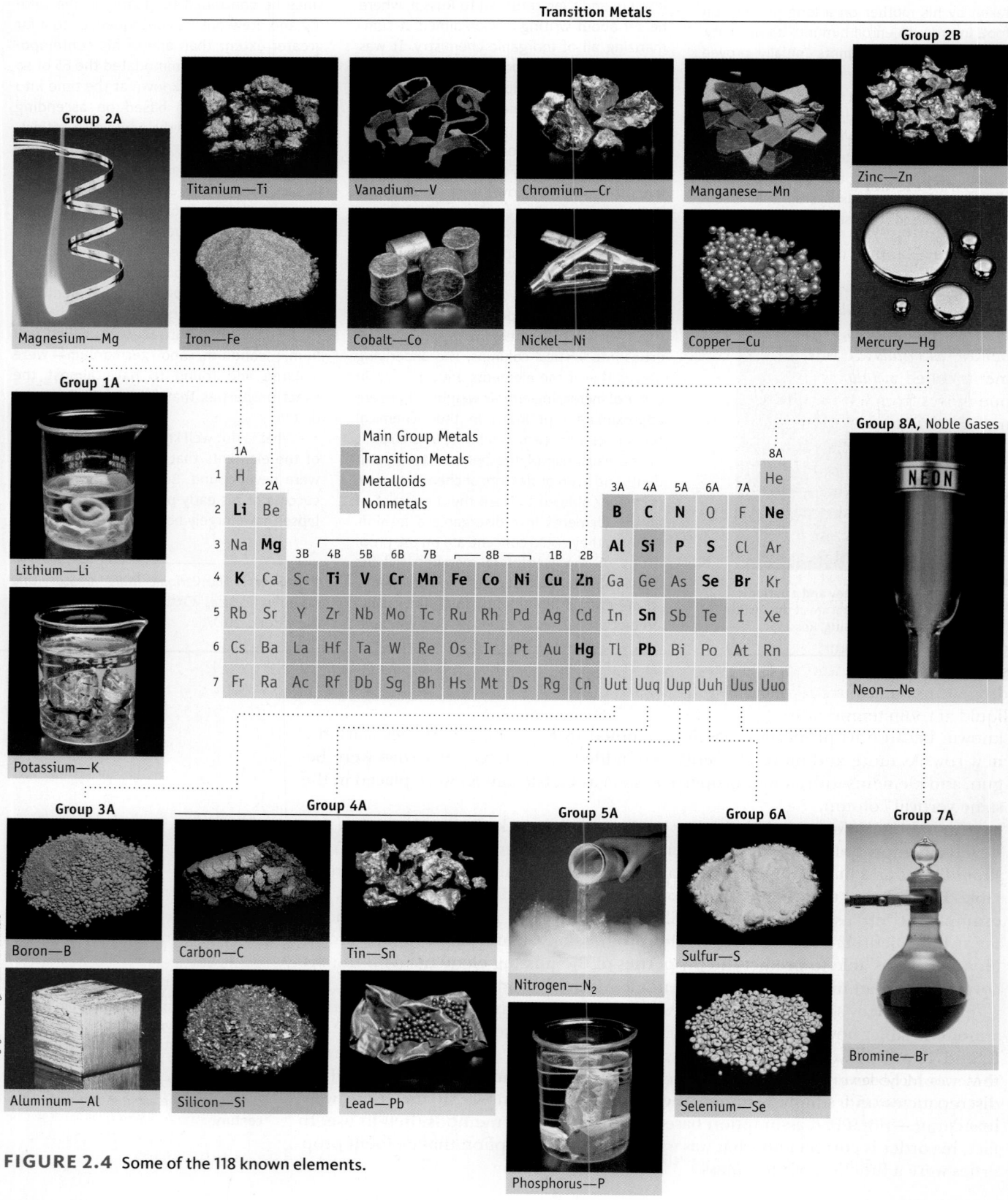

**FIGURE 2.4** Some of the 118 known elements.

the element and that this provided a way to experimentally determine the atomic number of a given element. Indeed, once atomic numbers could be determined, chemists recognized that organizing the elements in a table by increasing atomic number corrected the inconsistencies in Mendeleev's table. The **law of chemical periodicity** is now stated as *the properties of the elements are periodic functions of atomic number.*

## Features of the Periodic Table

The main organizational features of the periodic table are the following:

- Elements are arranged so that those with similar chemical and physical properties lie in vertical columns called **groups** or **families**. The periodic table commonly used in the United States has groups numbered 1 through 8, with each number followed by the letter A or B. The A groups are often called the **main group elements** and the B groups are the **transition elements**.
- The horizontal rows of the table are called **periods**, and they are numbered beginning with 1 for the period containing only H and He. For example, sodium, Na, in Group 1A, is the first element in the third period. Mercury, Hg, in Group 2B, is in the sixth period (or sixth row).

The periodic table can be divided into several regions according to the properties of the elements. On the table inside the front cover of this book, elements that behave as *metals* are indicated in purple, *nonmetals* are indicated in yellow, and elements called *metalloids* appear in green. Elements gradually become less metallic as one moves from left to right across a period, and the metalloids lie along the metal-nonmetal boundary. Some elements are shown in Figure 2.4.

You are probably familiar with many properties of **metals** from your own experience (Figure 2.5a). At room temperature and normal atmospheric pressure metals are solids (except for mercury), can conduct electricity, are usually ductile (can be drawn into wires) and malleable (can be rolled into sheets), and can form alloys (mixtures of one or more metals in another metal). Iron (Fe) and aluminum (Al) are used in automobile parts because of their ductility, malleability, and low cost relative to other metals. Copper (Cu) is used in electric wiring because it conducts electricity better than most other metals.

The **nonmetals** lie to the right of a diagonal line that stretches from B to Te in the periodic table and have a wide variety of properties. Some are solids (carbon, sulfur, phosphorus, and iodine). Five elements are gases at room temperature (hydrogen, oxygen, nitrogen, fluorine, and chlorine). One nonmetal, bromine, is a liquid at room temperature (Figure 2.5b). With the exception of carbon in the form

Periods

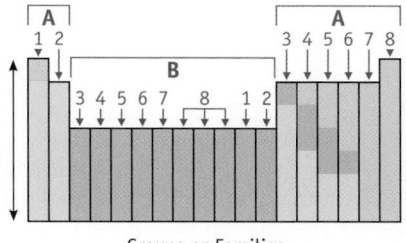

Groups or Families

**● Periods and Groups in the Periodic Table** One way to designate periodic groups is to number them 1 through 18 from left to right. This method is generally used outside the United States. The system predominant in the United States labels main group elements as Groups 1A–8A and transition elements as Groups 1B–8B. This book uses the A/B system.

☐ Main Group Metals    ☐ Metalloids
☐ Transition Metals    ☐ Nonmetals

**(a) Metals** Molybdenum (Mo, wire), bismuth (Bi, center object), and copper (Cu) are metals. Metals can be generally drawn into wires and conduct electricity.

**FIGURE 2.5 Metals, nonmetals, and metalloids.**

**(b) Nonmetals** Only about 18 elements can be classified as nonmetals. Here are orange-red liquid bromine and purple solid iodine.

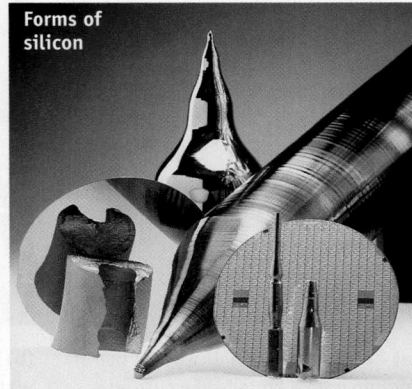

**(c) Metalloids** Only 6 elements are generally classified as metalloids or semimetals. This photograph shows solid silicon in various forms, including a wafer that holds printed electronic circuits.

of graphite, nonmetals do not conduct electricity, which is one of the main features that distinguishes them from metals.

The elements next to the diagonal line from boron (B) to tellurium (Te) have properties that make them difficult to classify as metals or nonmetals. Chemists call them **metalloids** or, sometimes, **semimetals** (Figure 2.5c). You should know, however, that chemists often disagree about which elements fit into this category. We will define a metalloid as an element that has some of the physical characteristics of a metal but some of the chemical characteristics of a nonmetal; we include only B, Si, Ge, As, Sb, and Te in this category. This definition reflects the ambiguity in the behavior of these elements. Antimony (Sb), for example, conducts electricity as well as many elements that are true metals. Its chemistry, however, resembles that of a nonmetal such as phosphorus.

## A Brief Overview of the Periodic Table and the Chemical Elements

● **Alkali and Alkaline** The word *alkali* comes from the Arabic language. Ancient Arabian chemists discovered that ashes of certain plants, which they called al-qali, gave water solutions that felt slippery and burned the skin. These ashes contain compounds of Group 1A elements that produce alkaline (basic) solutions.

Elements in the leftmost column, **Group 1A**, are known as the **alkali metals** (except H). All the alkali metals are solids at room temperature and all are reactive. For example, they react with water to produce hydrogen and alkaline solutions (Figure 2.6). Because of their reactivity, these metals are only found in nature combined in compounds (such as NaCl) (◄ Figure 1.2), never as free elements.

The second group in the periodic table, **Group 2A**, is also composed entirely of metals that occur naturally only in compounds. Except for beryllium (Be), these elements react with water to produce alkaline solutions, and most of their oxides (such as lime, CaO) form alkaline solutions; hence, they are known as the **alkaline earth metals**. Magnesium (Mg) and calcium (Ca) are the seventh and fifth most abundant elements in the earth's crust, respectively (Table 2.3). Calcium, one of the important elements in teeth and bones, occurs naturally in vast limestone deposits. Calcium carbonate ($CaCO_3$) is the chief constituent of limestone and of corals, sea shells, marble, and chalk. Radium (Ra), the heaviest alkaline earth element, is radioactive and is used to treat some cancers by radiation.

● **Placing H in the Periodic Table** Where to place H? Tables often show it in Group 1A even though it is clearly not an alkali metal. However, in its reactions it forms a 1+ ion just like the alkali metals. For this reason, H is often placed in Group 1A.

Aluminum, an element of great commercial importance, is in **Group 3A** (Figure 2.4). This element and three others of Group 3A (gallium, indium, and thallium) are metals, whereas boron (B) is a metalloid. Aluminum (Al) is the most

**(a) Cutting sodium** Cutting a bar of sodium with a knife is like cutting a stick of cold butter.

**(b) Potassium reacts with water.** When an alkali metal such as potassium is treated with water, a vigorous reaction occurs, giving an alkaline solution and hydrogen gas, which burns in air.

**FIGURE 2.6** Properties of the alkali metals.

**Table 2.3 The 10 Most Abundant Elements in the Earth's Crust**

| Rank | Element | Abundance (ppm)* |
|---|---|---|
| 1 | Oxygen | 474,000 |
| 2 | Silicon | 277,000 |
| 3 | Aluminum | 82,000 |
| 4 | Iron | 41,000 |
| 5 | Calcium | 41,000 |
| 6 | Sodium | 23,000 |
| 7 | Magnesium | 23,000 |
| 8 | Potassium | 21,000 |
| 9 | Titanium | 5,600 |
| 10 | Hydrogen | 1,520 |

*ppm = parts per million = g per 1000 kg.

Photos © Cengage Learning/Charles D. Winters

abundant metal in the earth's crust at 8.2% by mass. It is exceeded in abundance only by the nonmetal oxygen and metalloid silicon. Not surprisingly, these three elements are found combined in common materials such as clays and minerals. Boron occurs in the mineral borax, a compound used as a cleaning agent, antiseptic, and flux for metal work.

As a metalloid, boron has a different chemistry than the other elements of Group 3A, all of which are metals. Nonetheless, all form compounds with analogous formulas such as $BCl_3$ and $AlCl_3$, and this similarity marks them as members of the same periodic group.

Thus far all the elements we have described, except boron, have been metals. Beginning with **Group 4A**, however, the groups contain more and more nonmetals. In Group 4A there is a nonmetal, carbon (C), two metalloids, silicon (Si) and germanium (Ge), and two metals, tin (Sn) and lead (Pb) (Figure 2.4). Because of the change from nonmetallic to metallic behavior, more variation occurs in the properties of the elements of this group than in most others. Nonetheless, there are similarities. For example, these elements form compounds with analogous formulas such as $CO_2$, $SiO_2$, $GeO_2$, and $PbO_2$.

Carbon is the basis for the great variety of chemical compounds that make up living things. It is also found in Earth's atmosphere as $CO_2$, on the surface of the Earth in carbonates like limestone and coral (calcium carbonate, $CaCO_3$), and in coal, petroleum, and natural gas—the fossil fuels.

One interesting aspect of the chemistry of the nonmetals is that a particular element can often exist in several different and distinct forms, called **allotropes**, each having its own properties. Carbon has many allotropes, the best known of which are graphite and diamond. Graphite consists of flat sheets in which each carbon atom is connected to three others (Figure 2.7a). Because the sheets of carbon atoms cling only weakly to one another, one layer can slip easily over another. This explains why graphite is soft, is a good lubricant, and is used in pencil lead. [Pencil "lead" is not the element lead (Pb) but a composite of clay and graphite that leaves a trail of graphite on the page as you write.]

In diamond each carbon atom is connected to four others at the corners of a tetrahedron, and this extends throughout the solid (Figure 2.7b). This structure

**Liquid gallium.** Bromine and mercury are the only elements that are liquids under ambient conditions. Gallium (melting point = 29.8 °C) and cesium (melting point = 28.4 °C) melt slightly above room temperature. Here gallium melts when held in the hand.

**(a) Graphite**. Graphite consists of layers of carbon atoms. Each carbon atom is linked to three others to form a sheet of six-member, hexagonal rings.

**(b) Diamond**. In diamond the carbon atoms are also arranged in six-member rings, but the rings are not planar because each C atom is connected tetrahedrally to four other C atoms.

**(c) Buckyballs**. A member of the family called buckminsterfullerenes, $C_{60}$ is an allotrope of carbon. Sixty carbon atoms are arranged in a spherical cage that resembles a hollow soccer ball. Notice that each six-member ring shares an edge with three other six-member rings and three five-member rings. Chemists call this molecule a "buckyball." $C_{60}$ is a black powder; it is shown here in the tip of a pointed glass tube.

**FIGURE 2.7  The allotropes of carbon.**

**FIGURE 2.8 Compounds containing silicon.** Ordinary clay, sand, and many gemstones are based on compounds of silicon and oxygen. Here clear, colorless quartz and dark purple amethyst lie in a bed of sand. All are silicon dioxide, $SiO_2$. The different colors are due to impurities.

causes diamonds to be extremely hard, denser than graphite ($d = 3.51$ g/cm$^3$ for diamond versus $d = 2.22$ g/cm$^3$ for graphite), and chemically less reactive. Because diamonds are not only hard but are excellent conductors of heat, they are used on the tips of metal- and rock-cutting tools.

In the late 1980s another form of carbon was identified as a component of black soot, the stuff that collects when carbon-containing materials are burned in a deficiency of oxygen. This substance is made up of molecules with 60 carbon atoms arranged as a spherical "cage" (Figure 2.7c). You may recognize that the surface is made up of five- and six-member rings and resembles a hollow soccer ball. The shape also reminded its discoverers of an architectural dome conceived several decades ago by the American philosopher and engineer, R. Buckminster Fuller. This led to the official name of the allotrope, buckminsterfullerene, although chemists often simply call these molecules "buckyballs."

Oxides of silicon are the basis of many minerals such as clay, quartz, and beautiful gemstones like amethyst (Figure 2.8). Tin and lead have been known for centuries because they are easily smelted from their ores. Tin alloyed with copper makes bronze, which was used in ancient times in utensils and weapons. Lead has been used in water pipes and paint, even though the element is toxic to humans.

Nitrogen in **Group 5A** occurs naturally in the form of the diatomic molecule $N_2$ (Figures 2.9) and makes up about three-fourths of earth's atmosphere. It is also incorporated in biochemically important substances such as chlorophyll, proteins, and DNA. Scientists have long sought ways to make compounds from atmospheric nitrogen, a process referred to as "nitrogen fixation." Nature accomplishes this easily in some prokaryotic organisms, but severe conditions (high temperatures, for example) must be used in the laboratory and in industry to cause $N_2$ to react with other elements (such as $H_2$ to make ammonia, $NH_3$, which is widely used as a fertilizer).

Phosphorus is also essential to life. It is an important constituent in bones, teeth, and DNA. The element glows in the dark if it is in the air (owing to its reaction with $O_2$), and its name, based on Greek words meaning "light-bearing," reflects this. This element also has several allotropes, the most important being white (Figure 2.4) and red phosphorus. Both forms of phosphorus are used commercially. White phosphorus ignites spontaneously in air, so it is normally stored under water. When it does react with air, it forms $P_4O_{10}$, which can react with water to form phosphoric acid ($H_3PO_4$), a compound used in food products such as soft drinks. Red phosphorus is used in the striking strips on match books. When a match is struck, potassium chlorate in the match head mixes with some red phosphorus on the striking strip, and the friction is enough to ignite this mixture.

As with Group 4A, we again see nonmetals (N and P), metalloids (As and Sb), and a metal (Bi, Figure 2.5a) in Group 5A. In spite of these variations, they also form analogous compounds such as the oxides $N_2O_5$, $P_4O_{10}$ and $As_2O_5$.

Oxygen, which constitutes about 20% of earth's atmosphere and which combines readily with most other elements, is at the top of **Group 6A**. Most of the energy that powers life on earth is derived from reactions in which oxygen combines with other substances.

Sulfur has been known in elemental form since ancient times as brimstone or "burning stone" (Figure 2.10). Sulfur, selenium, and tellurium are often referred to collectively as *chalcogens* (from the Greek word, *khalkos*, for copper) because most copper ores contain these elements. Their compounds can be foul-smelling and poisonous; nevertheless, sulfur and selenium are essential components of the

**FIGURE 2.9 Elements that Exist as Diatomic or Triatomic Molecules.** Seven of the known elements exist as diatomic, or two-atom, molecules. Oxygen has an additional allotrope, ozone, with three O atoms in each molecule.

human diet. By far the most important compound of sulfur is sulfuric acid ($H_2SO_4$), which is manufactured in larger amounts than any other compound.

As in Group 5A, the second- and third-period elements of Group 6A have different structures. Like nitrogen, oxygen is also a diatomic molecule (Figure 2.9). Unlike nitrogen, however, oxygen has an allotrope, the triatomic molecule ozone, $O_3$. Sulfur, which can be found in nature as a yellow solid, has many allotropes, the most common of which consists of eight-member, crown-shaped rings of sulfur atoms (Figure 2.10).

Polonium, the radioactive element in Group 6A, was isolated in 1898 by Marie and Pierre Curie, who separated a small amount from tons of a uranium-containing ore and named it for Madame Curie's native country, Poland.

In Group 6A we once again observe a variation of properties. Oxygen, sulfur, and selenium are nonmetals, tellurium is a metalloid, and polonium is a metal. Nonetheless, there is a family resemblance in their chemistries. All of oxygen's fellow group members form oxygen-containing compounds ($SO_2$, $SeO_2$, and $TeO_2$), and all form sodium-containing compounds ($Na_2O$, $Na_2S$, $Na_2Se$, and $Na_2Te$).

At the far right of the periodic table are two groups composed entirely of nonmetals. The **Group 7A** elements—fluorine, chlorine, bromine, iodine, and radioactive astatine—are nonmetals and all exist as diatomic molecules (Figure 2.9). At room temperature fluorine ($F_2$) and chlorine ($Cl_2$) are gases. Bromine ($Br_2$) is a liquid and iodine ($I_2$) is a solid, but bromine and iodine vapor are clearly visible over the liquid or solid (Figure 2.5b).

The Group 7A elements are among the most reactive of all elements, and all combine violently with alkali metals to form salts such as table salt, NaCl (◄ Figure 1.2). The name for this group, the **halogens**, comes from the Greek words *hals*, meaning "salt," and *genes*, for "forming." The halogens react not only with metals but also with most nonmetals.

The **Group 8A** elements—helium, neon, argon, krypton, xenon, and radioactive radon—are the least reactive elements (Figure 2.11). All are gases, and none is abundant on Earth or in the Earth's atmosphere (although argon is the third most abundant gas in dry air at 0.9%). Because of this, they were not discovered until the end of the 19th century (see page 109). Helium, the second most abundant element in the universe after hydrogen, was detected in the sun in 1868 by analysis of the solar spectrum but was not found on Earth until 1895. (The name of the element comes from the Greek word for the sun, *helios*.)

It was long believed that none of the Group 8A elements would combine chemically with any other element. However, in 1962, a compound of xenon and fluorine ($XeF_4$) was first prepared, and this opened the way to the preparation of a number of other such compounds. A common name for this group, the **noble gases**, denotes their general lack of reactivity. For the same reason they are sometimes called the *inert gases* or, because of their low abundance, the *rare gases*.

© Cengage Learning/Charles D. Winters

**FIGURE 2.10 Sulfur.** The most common allotrope of sulfur consists of S atoms arranged in eight-member, crown-shaped rings.

● **Special Group Names** Some groups have common and widely used names (see Figure 2.4).

Group 1A: Alkali metals

Group 2A: Alkaline earth metals

Group 7A: Halogens

Group 8A: Noble gases

© Cengage Learning/Charles D. Winters

**FIGURE 2.11 The noble gases.** This kit is sold for detecting the presence of radioactive radon in the home. Neon gas is used in advertising signs, and xenon-containing headlights are increasingly popular on automobiles.

**Lanthanides.** If you use a Bunsen burner in the lab, you may light it with a "flint" lighter. The flints are composed of iron and "mischmetal," a mixture of lanthanide elements, chiefly Ce, La, Pr, and Nd with traces of other lanthanides. (The word *mischmetal* comes from the German for "mixed metals.") It is produced by the electrolysis of a mixture of lanthanide oxides.

Stretching between Groups 2A and 3A is a series of elements called the **transition elements**. These fill the B-groups (1B through 8B) in the fourth through the seventh periods in the center of the periodic table. All are metals (Figure 2.4), and 13 of them are in the top 30 elements in terms of abundance in the earth's crust (Table 2.3). Most occur naturally in combination with other elements, but a few—copper (Cu), silver (Ag), gold (Au), and platinum (Pt)—are much less reactive and so can be found in nature as pure elements.

Virtually all of the transition elements have commercial uses. They are used as structural materials (iron, titanium, chromium, copper); in paints (titanium, chromium); in the catalytic converters in automobile exhaust systems (platinum and rhodium); in coins (copper, nickel, zinc); and in batteries (manganese, nickel, zinc, cadmium, mercury).

A number of the transition elements play important biological roles. For example, iron, a relatively abundant element (Table 2.3), is the central element in the chemistry of hemoglobin, the oxygen-carrying component of blood.

Two rows at the bottom of the table accommodate the **lanthanides** [the series of elements between the elements lanthanum ($Z = 57$) and hafnium ($Z = 72$)] and the **actinides** [the series of elements between actinium ($Z = 89$) and rutherfordium ($Z = 104$)]. Some lanthanide compounds are used in color television picture tubes, uranium ($Z = 92$) is the fuel for atomic power plants, and americium ($Z = 95$) is used in smoke detectors.

---

**REVIEW & CHECK FOR SECTION 2.5**

1.  Which of the following elements is a metalloid?

    (a)  Ge          (b)  S          (c)  Be          (d)  Al

2.  What is the symbol for the element in the third period and the fourth group?

    (a)  Si          (b)  Sc          (c)  V          (d)  N

3.  What is the most abundant element in the Earth's crust?

    (a)  Fe          (b)  C          (c)  O          (d)  N

4.  What is the name given to elements that exist in different forms, such as graphite, diamond, and buckyballs?

    (a)  isotopes          (b)  isomers          (c)  allotropes          (d)  nonmetals

---

## 2.6    Molecules, Compounds, and Formulas

A molecule is the smallest identifiable unit into which some pure substances like sugar and water can be divided and still retain the composition and chemical properties of the substance. Such substances are composed of identical molecules consisting of two or more atoms bound firmly together. For example, atoms of aluminum, Al, combine with molecules of bromine, $Br_2$, to produce a molecule of the compound aluminum bromide, $Al_2Br_6$ (Figure 2.12).

$$2\ Al(s) + 3\ Br_2(\ell) \rightarrow Al_2Br_6(s)$$

aluminum + bromine → aluminum bromide

To describe this chemical change (or chemical reaction) on paper, the composition of each element and compound is represented by a symbol or formula. Here one molecule of $Al_2Br_6$ is composed of two Al atoms and six Br atoms.

### Formulas

For molecules more complicated than water, there is often more than one way to write the formula. For example, the formula of ethanol (also called ethyl alcohol) can be represented as $C_2H_6O$ (Figure 2.13). This **molecular formula** describes the

Photos © Cengage Learning/
Charles D. Winters

**(a)** Solid aluminum and (in the beaker) liquid bromine.

**(b)** When the aluminum is added to the bromine, a vigorous chemical reaction occurs.

**(c)** The reaction produces white, solid aluminum bromide, $Al_2Br_6$.

**FIGURE 2.12  Reaction of the elements aluminum and bromine.**

composition of ethanol molecules—two carbon atoms, six hydrogen atoms, and one atom of oxygen occur per molecule—but it gives us no structural information. Structural information—how the atoms are connected and how the molecule fills space—is important, however, because it helps us understand how a molecule can interact with other molecules, which is the essence of chemistry.

To provide some structural information, it is useful to write a **condensed formula**, which indicates how certain atoms are grouped together. For example, the condensed formula of ethanol, $CH_3CH_2OH$ (Figure 2.13), informs us that the molecule consists of three "groups": a $CH_3$ group, a $CH_2$ group, and an OH group. Writing the formula as $CH_3CH_2OH$ also shows that the compound is not dimethyl ether, $CH_3OCH_3$, a compound with the same molecular formula but with a different structure and distinctly different properties.

That ethanol and dimethyl ether are different molecules is further apparent from their **structural formulas** (Figure 2.13). This type of formula gives us an even higher level of structural detail, showing how all of the atoms are attached within a molecule. The lines between atoms represent the chemical bonds that hold atoms together in this molecule [▶ Chapter 8].

● **Writing Formulas** When writing molecular formulas of organic compounds (compounds with C, H, and other elements) the convention is to write C first, then H, and finally other elements in alphabetical order. For example, acrylonitrile, a compound used to make consumer plastics, has the condensed formula $CH_2CHCN$. Its molecular formula would be $C_3H_3N$.

| NAME | MOLECULAR FORMULA | CONDENSED FORMULA | STRUCTURAL FORMULA | MOLECULAR MODEL |
|------|-------------------|-------------------|--------------------|-----------------|
| Ethanol | $C_2H_6O$ | $CH_3CH_2OH$ | | |
| Dimethyl ether | $C_2H_6O$ | $CH_3OCH_3$ | | |

● **Standard Colors for Atoms in Molecular Models** The colors listed here are used for molecular models in this book and are generally used by chemists.

carbon atoms

hydrogen atoms

oxygen atoms

nitrogen atoms

chlorine atoms

**FIGURE 2.13  Four approaches to showing molecular formulas.** Here the two molecules have the same molecular formula. However, once they are written as condensed or structural formulas, or illustrated with a molecular model, it is clear that these molecules are different.

**FIGURE 2.14 Ice.** Snowflakes are six-sided structures, reflecting the underlying structure of ice. Ice consists of six-sided rings formed by water molecules, in which each side of a ring consists of two O atoms and an H atom.

## Molecular Models

Molecular structures are often beautiful in the same sense that art is beautiful, and there is something intrinsically beautiful about the pattern created by water molecules assembled in ice (Figure 2.14).

More important, however, is the fact that the physical and chemical properties of a molecular compound are often closely related to its structure. For example, two well-known features of ice are related to its structure. The first is the shape of ice crystals: The sixfold symmetry of macroscopic ice crystals also appears at the particulate level in the form of six-sided rings of hydrogen and oxygen atoms. The second is water's unique property of being less dense when it is solid than when it is liquid. The lower density of ice, which has enormous consequences for earth's climate, results from the fact that molecules of water are not packed together tightly in ice.

Because molecules are three dimensional, it is often difficult to represent their shapes on paper. Certain conventions have been developed, however, that help represent three-dimensional structures on two-dimensional surfaces. Simple perspective drawings are often used (Figure 2.15).

Several kinds of molecular models exist. In the **ball-and-stick model**, spheres, usually in different colors, represent the atoms, and sticks represent the bonds holding them together. These models make it easy to see how atoms are attached to one another. Molecules can also be represented using **space-filling models**. These models are more realistic because they offer a better representation of relative sizes of atoms and their proximity to each other when in a molecule. A disadvantage of pictures of space-filling models is that atoms can often be hidden from view.

Simple perspective
drawing

Plastic model

Ball-and-stick model

Space-filling model

All visualizing techniques
represent the same molecule.

**FIGURE 2.15** Ways of depicting a molecule, here the methane ($CH_4$) molecule.

**REVIEW & CHECK FOR SECTION 2.6**

Cysteine, whose molecular model and structural formula are illustrated here, is an important amino acid and a constituent of many living things. What is its molecular formula?

Molecular model          Structural formula

(a)  $C_3H_6O_2S$          (b)  $C_3H_7NO_2S$          (c)  $C_3H_7N_2OS$          (d)  $C_3H_7NO_2$

## 2.7  Ionic Compounds: Formulas, Names, and Properties

The compounds you have encountered so far in this chapter are **molecular compounds**—that is, compounds that consist of discrete molecules at the particulate level. **Ionic compounds** constitute another major class of compounds. They consist of **ions**, atoms, or groups of atoms that bear a positive or negative electric charge. Many familiar compounds are composed of ions (Figure 2.16). Table salt, or sodium chloride (NaCl), and lime (CaO) are just two. To be able to recognize ionic compounds and to write formulas for these compounds, it is important to know the formulas and charges of common ions. You also need to know the names of ions and be able to name the compounds they form.

**go Chemistry**

**Modules 2: Predicting Ion Charges and 3: Names to Formulas of Ionic Compounds** cover concepts in this section.

### Ions

Atoms of many elements can gain or lose electrons in the course of a chemical reaction. To be able to predict the outcome of chemical reactions [▶ Chapter 3], you need to know whether an element will likely gain or lose electrons and, if so, how many.

### Cations

If an atom loses an electron (which is transferred to an atom of another element in the course of a reaction), the atom now has one fewer negative electrons than it has positive protons in the nucleus. The result is a positively charged ion called a **cation**

**FIGURE 2.16** Some common ionic compounds.

| Common Name | Name | Formula | Ions Involved |
|---|---|---|---|
| Calcite | Calcium carbonate | $CaCO_3$ | $Ca^{2+}$, $CO_3^{2-}$ |
| Fluorite | Calcium fluoride | $CaF_2$ | $Ca^{2+}$, $F^-$ |
| Gypsum | Calcium sulfate dihydrate | $CaSO_4 \cdot 2\,H_2O$ | $Ca^{2+}$, $SO_4^{2-}$ |
| Hematite | Iron(III) oxide | $Fe_2O_3$ | $Fe^{3+}$, $O^{2-}$ |
| Orpiment | Arsenic sulfide | $As_2S_3$ | $As^{3+}$, $S^{2-}$ |

Hematite, $Fe_2O_3$      Calcite, $CaCO_3$

Gypsum, $CaSO_4 \cdot 2\,H_2O$      Fluorite, $CaF_2$      Orpiment, $As_2S_3$

© Cengage Learning/Charles D. Winters

**FIGURE 2.17 Ions.** A lithium-6 atom is electrically neutral because the number of positive charges (three protons) and negative charges (three electrons) are the same. When it loses one electron, it has one more positive charge than negative charge, so it has a net charge of 1+. We symbolize the resulting lithium cation as Li$^+$. A fluorine atom is also electrically neutral, having nine protons and nine electrons. A fluorine atom can acquire an electron to produce an F$^-$ anion. This anion has one more electron than it has protons, so it has a net charge of 1−.

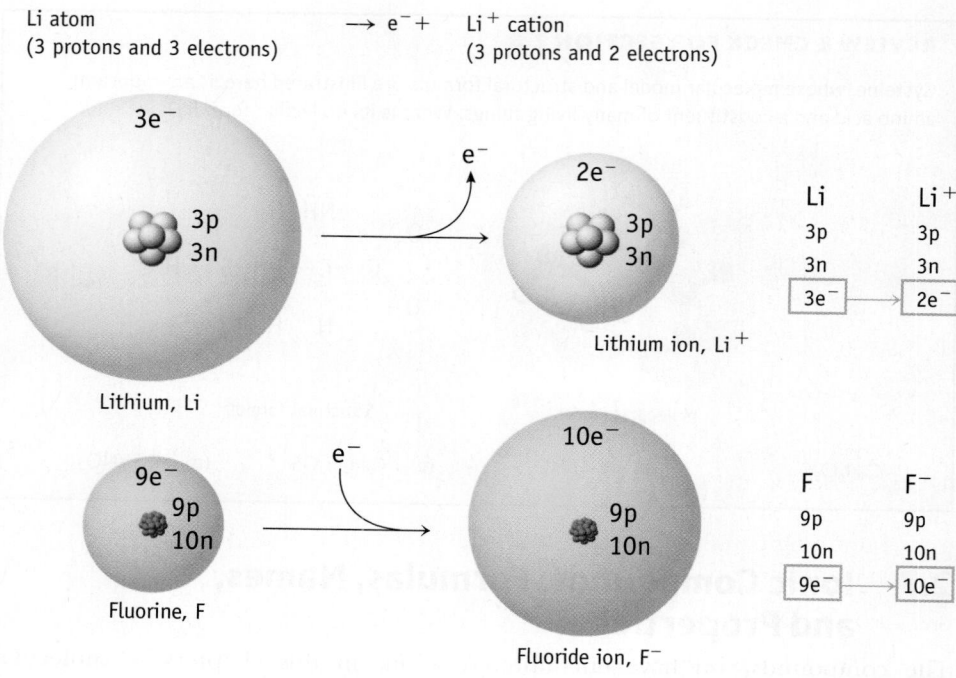

(Figure 2.17). (The name is pronounced "cat´-i-on.") Because it has an excess of one positive charge, we write the cation's symbol as, for example, Li$^+$:

$$\text{Li atom} \;\longrightarrow\; \text{e}^- \;+\; \text{Li}^+ \text{ cation}$$

(3 protons and 3 electrons)      (3 protons and 2 electrons)

### Anions

Conversely, if an atom gains one or more electrons, there is now one or more negatively charged electrons than protons. The result is an **anion** (pronounced "ann´-i-on") (Figure 2.17).

$$\text{O atom} + 2\,\text{e}^- \;\longrightarrow\; \text{O}^{2-} \text{ anion}$$

(8 protons and 8 electrons)      (8 protons and 10 electrons)

Here the O atom has gained two electrons, so we write the anion's symbol as O$^{2-}$.

How do you know whether an atom is likely to form a cation or an anion? It depends on whether the element is a metal or a nonmetal.

- Metals generally lose electrons in their reactions to form cations.
- Nonmetals frequently gain one or more electrons to form anions in their reactions.

### Monatomic Ions

Monatomic ions are single atoms that have lost or gained electrons. As indicated in Figure 2.18, *metals typically lose electrons to form monatomic cations, and nonmetals typically gain electrons to form monatomic anions.*

How can you predict the number of electrons gained or lost? Like lithium in Figure 2.18, *metals of Groups 1A–3A form positive ions having a charge equal to the group number of the metal.*

| Group | Metal Atom | Electron Change | | Resulting Metal Cation |
|-------|-----------|-----------------|---|------------------------|
| 1A | Na (11 protons, 11 electrons) | −1 | → | Na$^+$ (11 protons, 10 electrons) |
| 2A | Ca (20 protons, 20 electrons) | −2 | → | Ca$^{2+}$ (20 protons, 18 electrons) |
| 3A | Al (13 protons, 13 electrons) | −3 | → | Al$^{3+}$ (13 protons, 10 electrons) |

Transition metals (B-group elements) also form cations. Unlike the A-group metals, however, no easily predictable pattern of behavior occurs for transition metal cations. In addition, transition metals often form several different ions. An iron-containing compound, for example, may contain either $Fe^{2+}$ or $Fe^{3+}$ ions. Indeed, 2+ and 3+ ions are typical of many transition metals (Figure 2.18).

● **Writing Ion Formulas** When writing the formula of an ion, the charge on the ion must be included.

| Group | Metal Atom | Electron Change | | Resulting Metal Cation |
|---|---|---|---|---|
| 7B | Mn (25 protons, 25 electrons) | −2 | → | $Mn^{2+}$ (25 protons, 23 electrons) |
| 8B | Fe (26 protons, 26 electrons) | −2 | → | $Fe^{2+}$ (26 protons, 24 electrons) |
| 8B | Fe (26 protons, 26 electrons) | −3 | → | $Fe^{3+}$ (26 protons, 23 electrons) |

*Nonmetals often form ions having a negative charge equal to the group number of the element minus 8.* For example, nitrogen is in Group 5A, so it forms an ion having a 3− charge because a nitrogen atom can gain three electrons.

| Group | Nonmetal Atom | Electron Change | | Resulting Nonmetal Anion |
|---|---|---|---|---|
| 5A | N (7 protons, 7 electrons) | +3 | → | $N^{3-}$ (7 protons, 10 electrons) Charge = 5 − 8 = −3 |
| 6A | S (16 protons, 16 electrons) | +2 | → | $S^{2-}$ (16 protons, 18 electrons) Charge = 6 − 8 = −2 |
| 7A | Br (35 protons, 35 electrons) | +1 | → | $Br^-$ (35 protons, 36 electrons) Charge = 7 − 8 = −1 |

Notice that hydrogen appears at two locations in Figure 2.18. The H atom can either lose or gain electrons, depending on the other atoms it encounters.

Electron lost: H (1 proton, 1 electron) → $H^+$ (1 proton, 0 electrons) + $e^-$

Electron gained: H (1 proton, 1 electron) + $e^-$ → $H^-$ (1 proton, 2 electrons)

Finally, the noble gases *very* rarely form monatomic cations and never form monatomic anions in chemical reactions.

## Ion Charges and the Periodic Table

The metals of Groups 1A, 2A, and 3A form ions having 1+, 2+, and 3+ charges (Figure 2.18); that is, their atoms lose one, two, or three electrons, respectively. *For Group 1A and 2A metals and aluminum, the number of electrons remaining on the cation is the same as the number of electrons in an atom of the noble gas that precedes it in the periodic table.* For example, $Mg^{2+}$ has 10 electrons, the same number as in an atom of the noble gas neon (atomic number 10).

An atom of a nonmetal near the right side of the periodic table would have to lose a great many electrons to achieve the same number as a noble gas atom of lower atomic number. (For instance, Cl, whose atomic number is 17, would have to lose 7 electrons to have the same number of electrons as Ne.) If a nonmetal atom were to gain just a few electrons, however, it would have the same number as a noble gas

Group 1A, 2A, 3A metals form $M^{n+}$ cations where $n$ = group number.

**Main group metals.**

Photos © Cengage Learning/
Charles D. Winters

**Calcite, CaCO₃**
**Calcium carbonate**

**Apatite, Ca₅F(PO₄)₃**
**Calcium fluorophosphate**

**Celestite, SrSO₄**
**Strontium sulfate**

**FIGURE 2.19** Common ionic compounds based on polyatomic ions.

atom of higher atomic number. For example, an oxygen atom has eight electrons. By gaining two electrons per atom it forms $O^{2-}$, which has 10 electrons, the same number as neon. *Anions having the same number of electrons as the noble gas atom succeeding it in the periodic table are commonly observed in chemical compounds.*

### Polyatomic Ions

Polyatomic ions are made up of two or more atoms, and the collection has an electric charge (Figure 2.19 and Table 2.4). For example, carbonate ion, $CO_3^{2-}$, a common polyatomic anion, consists of one C atom and three O atoms. The ion has two

**Table 2.4  Formulas and Names of Some Common Polyatomic Ions**

| Formula | Name | Formula | Name |
|---|---|---|---|
| **Cation: Positive Ion** | | | |
| $NH_4^+$ | Ammonium ion | | |
| **Anions: Negative Ions** | | | |
| **Based on a Group 4A element** | | **Based on a Group 7A element** | |
| $CN^-$ | Cyanide ion | $ClO^-$ | Hypochlorite ion |
| $CH_3CO_2^-$ | Acetate ion | $ClO_2^-$ | Chlorite ion |
| $CO_3^{2-}$ | Carbonate ion | $ClO_3^-$ | Chlorate ion |
| $HCO_3^-$ | Hydrogen carbonate ion (or bicarbonate ion) | $ClO_4^-$ | Perchlorate ion |
| $C_2O_4^{2-}$ | Oxalate ion | | |
| **Based on a Group 5A element** | | **Based on a transition metal** | |
| $NO_2^-$ | Nitrite ion | $CrO_4^{2-}$ | Chromate ion |
| $NO_3^-$ | Nitrate ion | $Cr_2O_7^{2-}$ | Dichromate ion |
| $PO_4^{3-}$ | Phosphate ion | $MnO_4^-$ | Permanganate ion |
| $HPO_4^{2-}$ | Hydrogen phosphate ion | | |
| $H_2PO_4^-$ | Dihydrogen phosphate ion | | |
| **Based on a Group 6A element** | | | |
| $OH^-$ | Hydroxide ion | | |
| $SO_3^{2-}$ | Sulfite ion | | |
| $SO_4^{2-}$ | Sulfate ion | | |
| $HSO_4^-$ | Hydrogen sulfate ion (or bisulfate ion) | | |

units of negative charge because there are two more electrons (a total of 32) in the ion than there are protons (a total of 30) in the nuclei of one C atom and three O atoms.

The ammonium ion, $NH_4^+$, is a common polyatomic cation. In this case, four H atoms surround an N atom, and the ion has a 1+ electric charge. This ion has 10 electrons, but there are 11 positively charged protons in the nuclei of the N and H atoms (seven and one each, respectively).

## Formulas of Ionic Compounds

Compounds are electrically neutral; that is, they have no net electric charge. Thus, in an ionic compound the numbers of positive and negative ions must be such that the positive and negative charges balance. In sodium chloride, the sodium ion has a 1+ charge ($Na^+$) and the chloride ion has a 1− charge ($Cl^-$). These ions must be present in a 1 : 1 ratio, and so the formula is NaCl.

The gemstone ruby is largely the compound formed from aluminum ions ($Al^{3+}$) and oxide ions ($O^{2-}$) (but the color comes from a trace of $Cr^{3+}$ ions.) Here the ions have positive and negative charges that are of different absolute value. To have a compound with the same number of positive and negative charges, two $Al^{3+}$ ions [total charge = $2 \times (3+) = 6+$] must combine with three $O^{2-}$ ions [total charge = $3 \times (2-) = 6-$] to give a formula of $Al_2O_3$.

Calcium is a Group 2A metal, and it forms a cation having a 2+ charge. It can combine with a variety of anions to form ionic compounds such as those in the following table:

**Ruby, $Al_2O_3$.** Gems called *rubies* are largely composed of $Al^{3+}$ and $O^{2-}$ ions with a trace of $Cr^{3+}$ ion. It is the chromium(III) ions that give the gem its color.

| Compound | Ion Combination | Overall Charge on Compound |
|---|---|---|
| $CaCl_2$ | $Ca^{2+} + 2\,Cl^-$ | $(2+) + 2 \times (1-) = 0$ |
| $CaCO_3$ | $Ca^{2+} + CO_3^{2-}$ | $(2+) + (2-) = 0$ |
| $Ca_3(PO_4)_2$ | $3\,Ca^{2+} + 2\,PO_4^{3-}$ | $3 \times (2+) + 2 \times (3-) = 0$ |

In writing formulas of ionic compounds, the convention is that *the symbol of the cation is given first, followed by the anion symbol.* Also notice the use of parentheses when more than one polyatomic ion of a given kind is present [as in $Ca_3(PO_4)_2$]. (None, however, are used when only one polyatomic ion is present, as in $CaCO_3$.)

● **Balancing Ion Charges in Formulas**
Aluminum, a metal in Group 3A, loses three electrons to form the $Al^{3+}$ cation. Oxygen, a nonmetal in Group 6A, gains two electrons to form an $O^{2-}$ anion. Notice that in the compound formed from these ions the charge on the cation is the subscript on the anion, and vice versa.

$$2\,Al^{3+} + 3\,O^{2-} \rightarrow Al_2O_3$$

This often works well, but be careful. The subscripts of $Ti^{4+}$ and $O^{2-}$ are reduced to the simplest ratio in $TiO_2$ (1 Ti to 2 O, rather than 2 Ti to 4 O).

$$Ti^{4+} + 2\,O^{2-} \rightarrow TiO_2$$

### EXAMPLE 2.4    Ionic Compound Formulas

**Problem** For each of the following ionic compounds, write the symbols for the ions present and give the relative number of each: (a) $Li_2CO_3$, and (b) $Fe_2(SO_4)_3$.

**What Do You Know?** You know the formulas of the ionic compounds, the predicted charges on monatomic ions (Figure 2.18), and the formulas and charges of polyatomic ions (Table 2.4).

**Strategy** Divide the formula of the compound into the cations and anions. To accomplish this you will have to recognize, and remember, the composition and charges of common ions.

**Solution**

(a) $Li_2CO_3$ is composed of two lithium ions, $Li^+$, for each carbonate ion, $CO_3^{2-}$. Li is a Group 1A element and always has a 1+ charge in its compounds. Because the two 1+ charges balance the negative charge of the carbonate ion, the latter must be 2−.

(b) $Fe_2(SO_4)_3$ contains two iron(III) ions, $Fe^{3+}$, for every three sulfate ions, $SO_4^{2-}$. The way to recognize this is to recall that sulfate has a 2− charge. Because three sulfate ions are present (with a total charge of 6−), the two iron cations must have a total charge of 6+. This is possible only if each iron cation has a charge of 3+.

**Think about Your Answer** The charges predicted are in line with those in Figure 2.18 and Table 2.4. Remember that the formula for an ion must include its composition and its charge. Formulas for ionic compounds are always written with the cation first and then the anion, but ion charges are not included.

**Check Your Understanding**

(a) Give the number and identity of the constituent ions in each of the following ionic compounds: $NaF$, $Cu(NO_3)_2$, and $NaCH_3CO_2$.

(b) Iron, a transition metal, forms ions having 2+ and 3+ charges. Write the formulas of the compounds formed between chloride ions and these two different iron cations.

---

## EXAMPLE 2.5     Ionic Compound Formulas

**Problem** Write formulas for ionic compounds composed of an aluminum cation and each of the following anions: (a) fluoride ion, (b) sulfide ion, and (c) nitrate ion.

**What Do You Know?** You know the names of the ions involved, the predicted charges on monatomic ions (Figure 2.18), and the names of polyatomic ions (Table 2.4).

**Strategy** First decide on the formula of the Al cation and the formula of each anion. Combine the Al cation with each type of anion to form electrically neutral compounds.

**Solution** An aluminum cation is predicted to have a charge of 3+ because Al is a metal in Group 3A.

(a) Fluorine is a Group 7A element. The charge of the fluoride ion is predicted to be 1− (from $7 - 8 = 1-$). Therefore, we need 3 $F^-$ ions to combine with one $Al^{3+}$. The formula of the compound is $AlF_3$.

(b) Sulfur is a nonmetal in Group 6A, so it forms a 2− anion. Thus, we need to combine two $Al^{3+}$ ions [total charge is $6+ = 2 \times (3+)$] with three $S^{2-}$ ions [total charge is $6- = 3 \times (2-)$]. The compound has the formula $Al_2S_3$.

(c) The nitrate ion has the formula $NO_3^-$ (see Table 2.4). The answer here is therefore similar to the $AlF_3$ case, and the compound has the formula $Al(NO_3)_3$. Here we place parentheses around $NO_3$ to show that three polyatomic $NO_3^-$ ions are involved.

**Think about Your Answer** The most common error students make is not knowing the correct charge on an ion.

---

**Check Your Understanding**

Write the formulas of all neutral ionic compounds that can be formed by combining the cations $Na^+$ and $Ba^{2+}$ with the anions $S^{2-}$ and $PO_4^{3-}$.

---

# Names of Ions

## Naming Positive Ions (Cations)

With a few exceptions (such as $NH_4^+$), the positive ions described in this text are metal ions. Positive ions are named by the following rules:

1. For a monatomic positive ion (that is, a metal cation) the name is that of the metal plus the word "cation." For example, we have already referred to $Al^{3+}$ as the aluminum cation.

2. Some cases occur, especially in the transition series, in which a metal can form more than one type of positive ion. In these cases the charge of the ion is indicated by a Roman numeral in parentheses immediately following the ion's name. For example, $Co^{2+}$ is the cobalt(II) cation, and $Co^{3+}$ is the cobalt(III) cation.

Finally, you will encounter the ammonium cation, $NH_4^+$, many times in this book and in the laboratory. Do not confuse the ammonium cation with the ammonia molecule, $NH_3$, which has no electric charge and one less H atom.

● **"-ous" and "-ic" Endings** An older naming system for metal ions uses the ending -ous for the ion of lower charge and -ic for the ion of higher charge. For example, there are cobaltous ($Co^{2+}$) and cobaltic ($Co^{3+}$) ions. In addition, this older system sometimes uses the root of the Latin name of some elements in the names of their ions. For example, the Latin name for iron is *ferrum*, and this system calls the iron cations the ferrous ($Fe^{2+}$) and ferric ($Fe^{3+}$) ions. We do not use this system in this book, but some chemical manufacturers continue to use it.

## Naming Negative Ions (Anions)

There are two types of negative ions: those having only one atom (*monatomic*) and those having several atoms (*polyatomic*).

1. A monatomic negative ion is named by adding -*ide* to the stem of the name of the nonmetal element from which the ion is derived (Figure 2.20). The anions of the Group 7A elements, the halogens, are known as the fluoride, chloride, bromide, and iodide ions and as a group are called **halide ions**.

2. Polyatomic negative ions are common, especially those containing oxygen (called **oxoanions**). The names of some of the most common oxoanions are given in Table 2.4. Although most of these names must simply be learned, some guidelines can help. For example, consider the following pairs of ions:

$NO_3^-$ is the nitrate ion, whereas $NO_2^-$ is the nitrite ion.

$SO_4^{2-}$ is the sulfate ion, whereas $SO_3^{2-}$ is the sulfite ion.

The oxoanion having the greater number of oxygen atoms is given the suffix -*ate*, and the oxoanion having the smaller number of oxygen atoms has the suffix -*ite*. For a series of oxoanions having more than two members, the ion with the largest number of oxygen atoms has the prefix *per*- and the suffix -*ate*. The ion having the smallest number of oxygen atoms has the prefix *hypo*- and the suffix -*ite*. The chlorine oxoanions are the most commonly encountered example.

| | |
|---|---|
| $ClO_4^-$ | *Perchlorate* ion |
| $ClO_3^-$ | *Chlorate* ion |
| $ClO_2^-$ | *Chlorite* ion |
| $ClO^-$ | *Hypochlorite* ion |

Oxoanions that contain hydrogen are named by adding the word "hydrogen" before the name of the oxoanion. If two hydrogens are in the anion, we say "dihydrogen." Many hydrogen-containing oxoanions have common names that are used as well. For example, the hydrogen carbonate ion, $HCO_3^-$, is called the bicarbonate ion.

| Ion | Systematic Name | Common Name |
|---|---|---|
| $HPO_4^{2-}$ | Hydrogen phosphate ion | |
| $H_2PO_4^-$ | Dihydrogen phosphate ion | |
| $HCO_3^-$ | Hydrogen carbonate ion | Bicarbonate ion |
| $HSO_4^-$ | Hydrogen sulfate ion | Bisulfate ion |
| $HSO_3^-$ | Hydrogen sulfite ion | Bisulfite ion |

## Names of Ionic Compounds

The name of an ionic compound is built from the names of the positive and negative ions in the compound. The name of the positive cation is given first, followed by the name of the negative anion. Examples of ionic compound names are given below.

| Ionic Compound | Ions Involved | Name |
|---|---|---|
| $CaBr_2$ | $Ca^{2+}$ and 2 $Br^-$ | Calcium bromide |
| $NaHSO_4$ | $Na^+$ and $HSO_4^-$ | Sodium hydrogen sulfate |
| $(NH_4)_2CO_3$ | 2 $NH_4^+$ and $CO_3^{2-}$ | Ammonium carbonate |
| $Mg(OH)_2$ | $Mg^{2+}$ and 2 $OH^-$ | Magnesium hydroxide |
| $TiCl_2$ | $Ti^{2+}$ and 2 $Cl^-$ | Titanium(II) chloride |
| $Co_2O_3$ | 2 $Co^{3+}$ and 3 $O^{2-}$ | Cobalt(III) oxide |

**FIGURE 2.20** Names and charges of some common monatomic ions.

● **Naming Oxoanions**

● **Names of Compounds Containing Transition Metal Cations** Be sure to notice that the charge on a transition metal cation is indicated by a Roman numeral and is included in the name.

**PROBLEM SOLVING TIP 2.1**

Writing formulas for ionic compounds takes practice, and it requires that you know the formulas and charges of the most common ions. The charges on monatomic ions are often evident from the position of the element in the periodic table, but you simply have to remember the formula and charges of polyatomic ions, especially the most common ones such as nitrate, sulfate, carbonate, phosphate, and acetate.

## Formulas for Ions and Ionic Compounds

If you cannot remember the formula of a polyatomic ion or if you encounter an ion you have not seen before, you may be able to figure out its formula. For example, suppose you are told that $NaCHO_2$ is sodium formate. You know that the sodium ion is $Na^+$, so the formate ion must be the remaining portion of the compound; it must have a charge of 1− to balance the 1+ charge on the sodium ion. Thus, the formate ion must be $CHO_2^-$.

Finally, when writing the formulas of ions, you *must* include the charge on the ion (except in the formula of an ionic compound). Writing Na when you mean sodium ion is incorrect. There is a vast difference in the properties of the element sodium (Na) and those of its ion ($Na^+$).

## Properties of Ionic Compounds

When a particle having a negative electric charge is brought near another particle having a positive electric charge, there is a force of attraction between them (Figure 2.21). In contrast, there is a repulsive force when two particles with the same charge—both positive or both negative—are brought together. These forces are called **electrostatic forces**, and the force of attraction (or repulsion) between ions is given by **Coulomb's law** (Equation 2.3):

$$\text{Force} = -k\,\frac{(n^+e)(n^-e)}{d^2}$$

charge on + and − ions ⟶ charge on electron
proportionality constant ⟶ distance between ions

(2.3)

where, for example, $n^+$ is +3 for $Al^{3+}$ and $n^-$ is −2 for $O^{2-}$. Based on Coulomb's law, the force of attraction between oppositely charged ions increases

- as the ion charges ($n^+$ and $n^-$) increase. Thus, the attraction between ions having charges of 2+ and 2− is greater than that between ions having 1+ and 1− charges (Figure 2.21).
- as the distance between the ions becomes smaller (Figure 2.21).

Ionic compounds do not consist of simple pairs or small groups of positive and negative ions. The simplest ratio of cations to anions in an ionic compound is represented by its formula, but an ionic solid consists of millions upon millions of ions arranged in an extended three-dimensional network called a **crystal lattice**. A

**(a)** Ions such as $Li^+$ and $F^-$ are held together by an electrostatic force. Here a lithium ion is attracted to a fluoride ion, and the distance between the nuclei of the two ions is *d*.

**(b)** Forces of attraction between ions of opposite charge increase with increasing ion charge and decrease with increasing distance (*d*).

**FIGURE 2.21** Coulomb's law and electrostatic forces.

**PROBLEM SOLVING TIP 2.2**

Students often ask how to know whether a compound is ionic. Here are some useful guidelines.

1. Most metal-containing compounds are ionic. So, if a metal atom appears in the formula of a compound and especially when it is the element listed first, a good first guess is that it is ionic. (There are interesting exceptions, but few come up in introductory chemistry.) It is helpful in this regard to recall trends in metallic

## Is a Compound Ionic?

behavior: All elements to the left of a diagonal line running from boron to tellurium in the periodic table are metallic.

2. If there is no metal in the formula, it is likely that the compound is not ionic. The exceptions here are compounds composed of polyatomic cations based on nonmetals (e.g., $NH_4Cl$ or $NH_4NO_3$).

3. Learn to recognize the formulas of polyatomic ions (see Table 2.4). Chemists write the formula of ammonium nitrate as

$NH_4NO_3$ (not as $N_2H_4O_3$) to alert others to the fact that it is an ionic compound composed of the common polyatomic ions $NH_4^+$ and $NO_3^-$.

As an example of these guidelines, you can be sure that $MgBr_2$ ($Mg^{2+}$ with $Br^-$) and $K_2S$ ($K^+$ with $S^{2-}$) are ionic compounds. On the other hand, the compound $CCl_4$, formed from two nonmetals, C and Cl, is not ionic.

portion of the lattice for NaCl, illustrated in Figure 2.22, represents a common way of arranging ions for compounds that have a 1:1 ratio of cations to anions.

Ionic compounds have characteristic properties that can be understood in terms of the charges of the ions and their arrangement in the lattice. Because each ion is surrounded by oppositely charged nearest neighbors, it is held tightly in its allotted location. At room temperature each ion can move just a bit around its average position, but considerable energy must be added before an ion can escape the attraction of its neighboring ions. Only if enough energy is added will the lattice structure collapse and the substance melt. Greater attractive forces mean that ever more energy—and higher and higher temperatures—is required to cause melting. Thus, $Al_2O_3$, a solid composed of $Al^{3+}$ and $O^{2-}$ ions, melts at a much higher temperature (2072 °C) than NaCl (801 °C), a solid composed of $Na^+$ and $Cl^-$ ions.

Most ionic compounds are "hard" solids. That is, the solids are not pliable or soft. The reason for this characteristic is again related to the lattice of ions. The nearest neighbors of a cation in a lattice are anions, and the force of attraction makes the lattice rigid. However, a blow with a hammer can cause the lattice to break cleanly along a sharp boundary. The hammer blow displaces layers of ions just enough to cause ions of like charge to become nearest neighbors, and the repulsion between these like-charged ions forces the lattice apart (Figure 2.23).

© Cengage Learning/Charles D. Winters

**FIGURE 2.22** Sodium chloride. A crystal of NaCl consists of an extended lattice of sodium ions and chloride ions in a 1:1 ratio.

**FIGURE 2.23** Ionic solids.

© Cengage Learning/Charles D. Winters

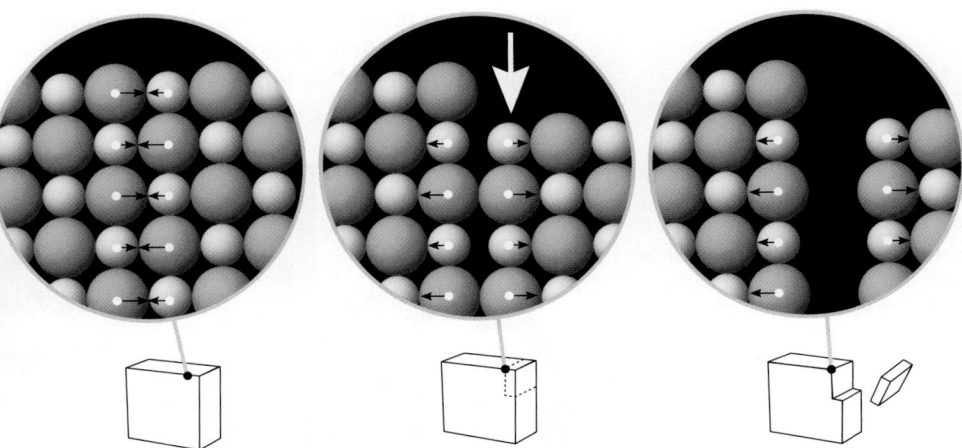

**(a)** An ionic solid is normally rigid owing to the forces of attraction between oppositely charged ions. When struck sharply, however, the crystal can cleave cleanly.

**(b)** When a crystal is struck, layers of ions move slightly, and ions of like charge become nearest neighbors. Repulsions between ions of similar charge cause the crystal to cleave.

**REVIEW & CHECK FOR SECTION 2.7**

1. What is the most likely charge on an ion of barium?

   (a) 2−        (b) 2+        (c) 3+        (d) 1−

2. When gallium forms an ion, it

   (a) loses 3 electrons        (c) loses 2 electrons

   (b) gains 3 electrons        (d) gains 2 electrons

3. The name of the compound $(NH_4)_2S$ is

   (a) nitrohydrogen sulfide        (c) ammonium sulfur

   (b) ammonium sulfide        (d) ammonia sulfide

4. The formula of barium acetate is

   (a) $Ba(CH_3CO_2)_2$        (c) $BaMnO_4$

   (b) $BaCH_3CO_2$        (d) $BaCO_3$

5. The name of the compound with the formula $V_2O_3$ is

   (a) vanadium(III) oxide        (c) divanadium trioxide

   (b) vanadium oxide        (d) vanadium trioxide

6. Which should have the higher melting point, MgO or NaCl?

   (a) MgO        (b) NaCl

# 2.8 Molecular Compounds: Formulas and Names

Many familiar compounds are not ionic, they are molecular: the water you drink, the sugar in your coffee or tea, or the aspirin you take for a headache.

Ionic compounds are generally solids, whereas molecular compounds can range from gases to liquids to solids at ordinary temperatures (Figure 2.24). As size and molecular complexity increase, compounds generally exist as solids. We will explore some of the underlying causes of these general observations in Chapter 12.

Some molecular compounds have complicated formulas that you cannot, at this stage, predict or even decide if they are correct. However, there are many simple compounds you will encounter often, and you should understand how to name them and, in many cases, know their formulas.

Let us look first at molecules formed from combinations of two nonmetals. These "two-element" or **binary compounds** of nonmetals can be named in a systematic way.

**FIGURE 2.24 Molecular compounds.** Ionic compounds are generally solids at room temperature. In contrast, molecular compounds can be gases, liquids, or solids. The molecular models are of caffeine (in coffee), water, and citric acid (in lemons).

Hydrogen forms binary compounds with all of the nonmetals except the noble gases. For compounds of oxygen, sulfur, and the halogens, the H atom is generally written first in the formula and is named first. The other nonmetal is named as if it were a negative ion.

| Compound | Name |
|---|---|
| HF | Hydrogen fluoride |
| HCl | Hydrogen chloride |
| $H_2S$ | Hydrogen sulfide |

Although there are exceptions, *most binary molecular compounds are a combination of nonmetallic elements from Groups 4A–7A with one another or with hydrogen.* The formula is generally written by putting the elements in order of increasing group number. When naming the compound, the number of atoms of a given type in the compound is designated with a prefix, such as "di-," "tri-," "tetra-," "penta-," and so on.

| Compound | Systematic Name |
|---|---|
| $NF_3$ | Nitrogen trifluoride |
| NO | Nitrogen monoxide |
| $NO_2$ | Nitrogen dioxide |
| $N_2O$ | Dinitrogen monoxide |
| $N_2O_4$ | Dinitrogen tetraoxide |
| $PCl_3$ | Phosphorus trichloride |
| $PCl_5$ | Phosphorus pentachloride |
| $SF_6$ | Sulfur hexafluoride |
| $S_2F_{10}$ | Disulfur decafluoride |

Finally, many of the binary compounds of nonmetals were discovered years ago and have common names.

| Compound | Common Name | Compound | Common Name |
|---|---|---|---|
| $CH_4$ | Methane | $N_2H_4$ | Hydrazine |
| $C_2H_6$ | Ethane | $PH_3$ | Phosphine |
| $C_3H_8$ | Propane | NO | Nitric oxide |
| $C_4H_{10}$ | Butane | $N_2O$ | Nitrous oxide ("laughing gas") |
| $NH_3$ | Ammonia | $H_2O$ | Water |

● **Formulas of Binary Nonmetal Compounds Containing Hydrogen** Simple hydrocarbons (compounds of C and H) such as methane ($CH_4$) and ethane ($C_2H_6$) have formulas written with H following C, and the formulas of ammonia and hydrazine have H following N. Water and the hydrogen halides, however, have the H atom preceding O or the halogen atom. Tradition is the only explanation for such irregularities in writing formulas.

● **Hydrocarbons** Compounds such as methane, ethane, propane, and butane belong to a class of hydrocarbons called *alkanes*.

methane, $CH_4$

propane, $C_3H_8$

ethane, $C_2H_6$

butane, $C_4H_{10}$

---

**REVIEW & CHECK FOR SECTION 2.8**

1.  What is the formula for dioxygen difluoride?

    (a)  $O_2F_2$        (b)  OF        (c)  $O_2F$        (d)  $OF_2$

2.  Compound names and formulas are listed below. Which name is incorrect?

    (a)  carbon disulfide, $CS_2$        (c)  boron trifluoride, $BF_3$

    (b)  nitrogen pentaoxide, $N_2O_5$        (d)  sulfur tetrafluoride, $SF_4$

3.  The name of the compound with the formula $N_2F_4$ is

    (a)  nitrogen fluoride        (c)  dinitrogen tetrafluoride

    (b)  dinitrogen fluoride        (d)  nitrogen tetrafluoride

4.  The name of the compound with the formula $P_4O_{10}$ is

    (a)  phosphorus oxide        (c)  tetraphosphorus oxide

    (b)  tetraphosphorus decaoxide        (d)  phosphorus decaoxide

## 2.9 Atoms, Molecules, and the Mole

One of the most exciting aspects of chemical research is the discovery of some new substance, and part of this process of discovery involves quantitative experiments. When two chemicals react with each other, we want to know how many atoms or molecules of each are used so that formulas can be established for the reaction's products. To do so, we need some method of counting atoms and molecules. That is, we must discover a way of connecting the macroscopic world, the world we can see, with the particulate world of atoms, molecules, and ions. The solution to this problem is to define a unit of matter that contains a known number of particles. That chemical unit is the mole.

The **mole** (abbreviated mol) is the SI base unit for measuring an *amount of a substance* (◀ Table 1, page 25) and is defined as follows:

> A **mole** is the amount of a substance that contains as many elementary entities (atoms, molecules, or other particles) as there are atoms in exactly 12 g of the carbon-12 isotope.

The key to understanding the concept of the mole is recognizing that *one mole always contains the same number of particles, no matter what the substance.* One mole of sodium contains the same number of atoms as one mole of iron and the same as the number of molecules in one mole of water. How many particles? Many, many experiments over the years have established that number as

$$1 \text{ mole} = 6.0221415 \times 10^{23} \text{ particles}$$

This value is known as **Avogadro's number** (symbolized by $N_A$) in honor of Amedeo Avogadro, an Italian lawyer and physicist (1776–1856) who conceived the basic idea (but never determined the number).

• **The "Mole"** The term *mole* was introduced about 1895 by Wilhelm Ostwald (1853–1932), who derived the term from the Latin word *moles*, meaning a "heap" or a "pile."

### Atoms and Molar Mass

The mass in grams of one mole of any element ($6.0221415 \times 10^{23}$ atoms of that element) is the **molar mass** of that element. Molar mass is conventionally abbreviated with a capital italicized $M$ and has units of grams per mole (g/mol). *An element's molar mass is the amount in grams numerically equal to its atomic weight.* Using sodium and lead as examples,

Molar mass of sodium (Na) = mass of 1.000 mol of Na atoms

= 22.99 g/mol

= mass of $6.022 \times 10^{23}$ Na atoms

Molar mass of lead (Pb) = mass of 1.000 mol of Pb atoms

= 207.2 g/mol

= mass of $6.022 \times 10^{23}$ Pb atoms

• **A Difference Between the Terms** *Amount* **and** *Quantity* The terms "amount" and "quantity" are used in a specific sense by chemists. The amount of a substance is the number of moles of that substance. In contrast, quantity refers, for example, to the mass or volume of the substance. See W. G. Davies and J. W. Moore. *Journal of Chemical Education*, Vol. 57, p. 303, 1980. See also http://physics.nist.gov

Figure 2.25 shows the relative sizes of a mole of some common elements. Although each of these "piles of atoms" has a different volume and different mass, each contains $6.022 \times 10^{23}$ atoms.

*The mole concept is the cornerstone of quantitative chemistry.* It is essential to be able to convert from moles to mass and from mass to moles. Dimensional analysis, which is described in Let's Review, page 39, shows that this can be done in the following way:

| MASS ⟷ MOLES CONVERSION | |
|---|---|
| *Moles to Mass* | *Mass to Moles* |
| Moles $\times \dfrac{\text{grams}}{1 \text{ mol}}$ = grams | Grams $\times \dfrac{1 \text{ mol}}{\text{grams}}$ = moles |
| ↑ molar mass | ↑ 1/molar mass |

**FIGURE 2.25** **One mole of common elements.** (*Left to right*) Sulfur powder, magnesium chips, tin, and silicon. (*Above*) Copper beads.

Copper
63.546 g

Sulfur
32.066 g

Magnesium
24.305 g

Tin
118.71 g

Silicon
28.086 g

© Cengage Learning/Charles D. Winters

For example, what mass, in grams, is represented by 0.35 mol of aluminum? Using the molar mass of aluminum (27.0 g/mol), you can determine that 0.35 mol of Al has a mass of 9.5 g.

$$0.35 \text{ mol Al} \times \frac{27.0 \text{ g Al}}{1 \text{ mol Al}} = 9.5 \text{ g Al}$$

Molar masses of the elements are generally known to at least four significant figures. The convention followed in calculations in this book is to use a value of the molar mass with at least one more significant figure than in any other number in the problem. For example, if you weigh out 16.5 g of carbon, you use 12.01 g/mol for the molar mass of C to find the amount of carbon present.

$$16.5 \text{ g C} \times \frac{1 \text{ mol C}}{12.01 \text{ g C}} = 1.37 \text{ mol C}$$

↑
Note that four significant figures are used in the molar mass, but there are three in the sample mass.

Using one more significant figure for the molar mass means the accuracy of this value will not affect the accuracy of the result.

---

**A CLOSER LOOK**

## Amedeo Avogadro and His Number

Amedeo Avogadro, conte di Quaregna, (1776–1856) was an Italian nobleman and a lawyer. In about 1800, he turned to science and was the first professor of mathematical physics in Italy.

Avogadro did not himself propose the notion of a fixed number of particles in a chemical unit. Rather, the number was named in his honor because he had performed experiments in the 19th century that laid the groundwork for the concept.

Just how large is Avogadro's number? One mol of unpopped popcorn kernels would cover the continental United States to a depth of about 9 miles. One mole of pennies divided equally among every man, woman, and child in the United States would allow each person to pay off the national debt ($11.6 trillion or $11.6 \times 10^{12}$ dollars) and there would still be about $8 trillion left over per person! A mole of pennies does not go as far as it used to!

Is the number a unique value like π? No. It is fixed by the definition of the mole as exactly 12 g of carbon-12. If one mole of carbon were defined to have some other mass, then Avogadro's number would have a different value.

E. F. Smith Collection/
Van Pelt Library/
University of Pennsylvania

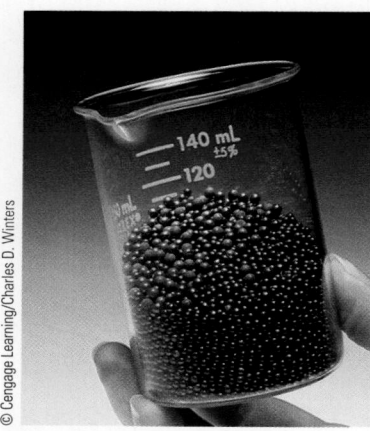

© Cengage Learning/Charles D. Winters

**Lead.** A 150-mL beaker containing 2.50 mol or 518 g of lead.

## EXAMPLE 2.6  Mass, Moles, and Atoms

**Problem** Consider two elements in the same vertical column of the periodic table, lead and tin.

(a)  What mass of lead, in grams, is equivalent to 2.50 mol of lead (Pb)?

(b)  What amount of tin, in moles, is represented by 36.6 g of tin (Sn)? How many atoms of tin are in the sample?

**What Do You Know?** You know the amount of lead and the mass of tin. You also know, from the periodic table in the front of the book, the molar masses of lead (207.2 g/mol) and tin (118.7 g/mol). For part (b) Avogadro's number is needed (and is given in the text and inside the back cover of the book).

**Strategy** The molar mass is the quantity in grams numerically equal to the atomic weight of the element.

Part (a)  Multiply the amount of Pb by the molar mass.

Part (b)  Multiply the mass of tin by (1/molar mass). To determine the number of atoms, multiply the amount of tin by Avogadro's number.

**Solution**

(a)  Convert the amount of lead in moles to mass in grams.

$$2.50 \text{ mol Pb} \times \frac{207.2 \text{ g}}{1 \text{ mol Pb}} = \boxed{518 \text{ g Pb}}$$

(b)  Convert the mass of tin to the amount in moles,

$$36.6 \text{ g Sn} \times \frac{1 \text{ mol Sn}}{118.7 \text{ g Sn}} = \boxed{0.308 \text{ mol Sn}}$$

and then use Avogadro's number to find the number of atoms in the sample.

$$0.308 \text{ mol Sn} \times \frac{6.022 \times 10^{23} \text{ atoms Sn}}{1 \text{ mol Sn}} = \boxed{1.86 \times 10^{23} \text{ atoms Sn}}$$

**Think about Your Answer** To find a mass from an amount of substance, use the conversion factor (mass/mol) (= molar mass). To find the amount from mass of a substance, use the conversion factor (mol/mass) (= 1/molar mass). You can sometimes catch a mistake in setting up a conversion factor upside down if you think about your answers. For example, if we had made this mistake in part b, we would have calculated that there was less than one atom in 0.308 mol of Sn, clearly an unreasonable answer.

**Check Your Understanding**

The density of gold, Au, is 19.32 g/cm³. What is the volume (in cubic centimeters) of a piece of gold that contains $2.6 \times 10^{24}$ atoms? If the piece of metal is a square with a thickness of 0.10 cm, what is the length (in centimeters) of one side of the piece?

© Cengage Learning/Charles D. Winters

**Tin.** A sample of tin having a mass of 36.6 g (or $1.86 \times 10^{23}$ atoms).

## Molecules, Compounds, and Molar Mass

The formula of a compound tells you the type of atoms or ions in the compound and the relative number of each. For example, one molecule of methane, $CH_4$, is made up of one atom of C and four atoms of H. But suppose you have Avogadro's number of C atoms ($6.022 \times 10^{23}$) combined with the proper number of H atoms. For $CH_4$ this means there are $4 \times 6.022 \times 10^{23}$ H atoms per mole of C atoms. What masses of atoms are combined, and what is the mass of this many $CH_4$ molecules?

| C | + | 4 H | $\longrightarrow$ | CH₄ |
|---|---|---|---|---|
| $6.022 \times 10^{23}$ C atoms | | $4 \times 6.022 \times 10^{23}$ H atoms | | $6.022 \times 10^{23}$ CH₄ molecules |
| = 1.000 mol of C | | = 4.000 mol of H atoms | | = 1.000 mol of CH₄ molecules |
| = 12.01 g of C atoms | | = 4.032 g of H atoms | | = 16.04 g of CH₄ molecules |

Because we know the number of moles of C and H atoms, we can calculate the masses of carbon and hydrogen that combine to form $CH_4$. It follows that the mass of $CH_4$ is the sum of these masses. That is, 1 mol of $CH_4$ has a mass equal to the mass of 1 mol of C atoms (12.01 g) plus 4 mol of H atoms (4.032 g). Thus, the *molar mass, M,* of $CH_4$ is 16.04 g/mol. The molar masses of some substances are:

**Molar and Molecular Masses**

| Substance | Molar Mass, $M$ (g/mol) | Average Mass of One Molecule (g/molecule) |
|---|---|---|
| $O_2$ | 32.00 | $5.314 \times 10^{-23}$ |
| $NH_3$ | 17.03 | $2.828 \times 10^{-23}$ |
| $H_2O$ | 18.02 | $2.992 \times 10^{-23}$ |
| $NH_2CH_2CO_2H$ (glycine) | 75.07 | $1.247 \times 10^{-22}$ |

Ionic compounds such as NaCl do not exist as individual molecules. Thus, for ionic compounds we write the simplest formula that shows the relative number of each kind of atom in a "formula unit" of the compound, and the molar mass is calculated from this formula ($M$ for NaCl = 58.44 g/mol). To differentiate substances like NaCl that do not contain molecules, chemists sometimes refer to their *formula weight* instead of their molar mass.

Figure 2.26 illustrates 1-mol quantities of several common compounds. To find the molar mass of any compound, you need only to add up the atomic masses for each element in the compound, taking into account any subscripts on elements. As an example, let us find the molar mass of aspirin, $C_9H_8O_4$. In one mole of aspirin there are 9 mol of carbon atoms, 8 mol of hydrogen atoms, and 4 mol of oxygen atoms, which add up to 180.2 g/mol of aspirin.

$$\text{Mass of C in 1 mol } C_9H_8O_4 = 9 \text{ mol C} \times \frac{12.01 \text{ g C}}{1 \text{ mol C}} = 108.1 \text{ g C}$$

$$\text{Mass of H in 1 mol } C_9H_8O_4 = 8 \text{ mol H} \times \frac{1.008 \text{ g H}}{1 \text{ mol H}} = 8.064 \text{ g H}$$

$$\text{Mass of O in 1 mol } C_9H_8O_4 = 4 \text{ mol O} \times \frac{16.00 \text{ g O}}{1 \text{ mol O}} = 64.00 \text{ g O}$$

$$\text{Total mass of 1 mol of } C_9H_8O_4 = \text{molar mass of } C_9H_8O_4 = 180.2 \text{ g}$$

© Cengage Learning/Charles D. Winters

Aspirin, $C_9H_8O_4$
180.2 g/mol

Copper(II) chloride dihydrate, $CuCl_2 \cdot 2\ H_2O$
170.5 g/mol

Iron(III) oxide, $Fe_2O_3$
159.7 g/mol

$H_2O$
18.02 g/mol

**FIGURE 2.26 One-mole quantities of some compounds.** The second compound, $CuCl_2 \cdot 2H_2O$, is called a *hydrated compound* because water is associated with the $CuCl_2$ (see page 94). Thus, one "formula unit" consists of one $Cu^{2+}$ ion, two $Cl^-$ ions, and two water molecules. The molar mass is the sum of the mass of 1 mol of Cu, 2 mol of Cl, and 2 mol of $H_2O$.

● **Aspirin Formula** Aspirin has the molecular formula $C_9H_8O_4$ and a molar mass of 180.2 g/mol. Aspirin is the common name of the compound acetylsalicylic acid.

As was the case with elements, it is important to be able to convert between amounts (moles) and mass (grams). For example, if you take 325 mg (0.325 g) of aspirin in one tablet, what amount of the compound have you ingested? Based on a molar mass of 180.2 g/mol, there is 0.00180 mol of aspirin per tablet.

$$0.325 \text{ g aspirin} \times \frac{1 \text{ mol aspirin}}{180.2 \text{ g aspirin}} = 0.00180 \text{ mol aspirin}$$

Using the molar mass of a compound it is possible to determine the number of molecules in any sample from the sample mass and to determine the mass of one molecule. For example, the number of aspirin molecules in one tablet is

$$0.00180 \text{ mol aspirin} \times \frac{6.022 \times 10^{23} \text{ molecules}}{1 \text{ mol aspirin}} = 1.08 \times 10^{21} \text{ molecules}$$

and the mass of one molecule is

$$\frac{180.2 \text{ g aspirin}}{1 \text{ mol aspirin}} \times \frac{1 \text{ mol aspirin}}{6.022 \times 10^{23} \text{ molecules}} = 2.99 \times 10^{-22} \text{ g/molecule}$$

### ⓌWL  INTERACTIVE EXAMPLE 2.7   Molar Mass and Moles

**Problem**  You have 16.5 g of oxalic acid, $H_2C_2O_4$.

(a)   What amount is represented by 16.5 g of oxalic acid?

(b)   How many molecules of oxalic acid are in 16.5 g?

(c)   How many atoms of carbon are in 16.5 g of oxalic acid?

**What Do You Know?**  You know the mass and formula of oxalic acid. The molar mass of the compound can be calculated based on the formula.

**Strategy**  The strategy is outlined in the strategy map.

- The molar mass is the sum of the masses of the component atoms.

- Part (a) Use the molar mass to convert mass to amount.

- Part (b) Use Avogadro's number to calculate the number of molecules from the amount.

- Part (c) From the formula you know there are two atoms of carbon in each molecule.

**Solution**

(a)   *Moles represented by 16.5 g*

Let us first calculate the molar mass of oxalic acid:

$$2 \text{ mol C per mol } H_2C_2O_4 \times \frac{12.01 \text{ g C}}{1 \text{ mol C}} = 24.02 \text{ g C per mol } H_2C_2O_4$$

$$2 \text{ mol H per mol } H_2C_2O_4 \times \frac{1.008 \text{ g H}}{1 \text{ mol H}} = 2.016 \text{ g H per mol } H_2C_2O_4$$

$$4 \text{ mol O per mol } H_2C_2O_4 \times \frac{16.00 \text{ g O}}{1 \text{ mol O}} = 64.00 \text{ g O per mol } H_2C_2O_4$$

Molar mass of $H_2C_2O_4$ = 90.04 g per mol $H_2C_2O_4$

Now calculate the amount in moles. The molar mass (expressed here in units of 1 mol/90.04 g) is used in all mass-mole conversions.

$$16.5 \text{ g } H_2C_2O_4 \times \frac{1 \text{ mol}}{90.04 \text{ g } H_2C_2O_4} = \boxed{0.183 \text{ mol } H_2C_2O_4}$$

**Strategy Map 2.7**

> **PROBLEM**
>
> Find **amount of oxalic acid** in a given mass. Then find **number of molecules** and **number of C atoms** in the sample.

↓

> **DATA/INFORMATION KNOWN**
>
> ● **Mass** of sample
> ● **Formula** of compound
> ● **Avogadro's number**

> STEP 1. Calculate **molar mass** of oxalic acid.

**Molar mass** of oxalic acid **(g/mol)**

> STEP 2. Use molar mass to calculate **amount** (multiply mass by 1/molar mass).

**Amount (mol)** of oxalic acid

> STEP 3. Multiply by **Avogadro's number**.

**Number** of molecules

> STEP 4. Multiply by number of **C atoms** per molecule.

**Number** of C atoms in sample

(b)   *Number of molecules*

Use Avogadro's number to find the number of oxalic acid molecules in 0.183 mol of $H_2C_2O_4$.

$$0.183 \text{ mol} \times \frac{6.022 \times 10^{23} \text{ molecules}}{1 \text{ mol}} = \boxed{1.10 \times 10^{23} \text{ molecules}}$$

(c)   *Number of C atoms*

Because each molecule contains two carbon atoms, the number of carbon atoms in 16.5 g of the acid is

$$1.10 \times 10^{23} \text{ molecules} \times \frac{2 \text{ C atoms}}{1 \text{ molecule}} = \boxed{2.21 \times 10^{23} \text{ C atoms}}$$

**Think about Your Answer**  The mass of oxalic acid was 16.5 g, much less than the mass of a mole, so check to make sure your answer reflects this. The number of molecules of the acid should be many fewer than in one mole of molecules.

---

**Check Your Understanding**

If you have 454 g of citric acid ($H_3C_6H_5O_7$), what amount (moles) does this represent? How many molecules? How many atoms of carbon?

---

**REVIEW & CHECK FOR SECTION 2.9**

1.   What is the molar mass of calcium nitrate?

   (a)   150.08 g/mol              (c)   164.09 g/mol

   (b)   102.08 g/mol              (d)   68.09 g/mol

2.   Which of the following contains the largest number of molecules?

   (a)   24 g of $O_2$      (b)   4.0 g of $H_2$      (c)   19 g of $F_2$      (d)   28 g of $N_2$

3.   Which of the following has the largest mass?

   (a)   0.50 mol Na      (b)   0.20 mol K      (c)   0.40 mol Ca      (d)   0.60 mol Mg

4.   Which quantity represents the largest amount (moles) of the indicated substance?

   (a)   $6.02 \times 10^{23}$ molecules of $H_2O$          (c)   $3.01 \times 10^{23}$ molecules of $Br_2$

   (b)   22 g of $CO_2$                                      (d)   30 g of HF

5.   How many atoms of oxygen are contained in 16 g of $O_2$?

   (a)   $6.0 \times 10^{23}$ atoms of O                     (c)   $1.5 \times 10^{23}$ atoms of O

   (b)   $3.0 \times 10^{23}$ atoms of O                     (d)   $1.2 \times 10^{24}$ atoms of O

---

## 2.10  Describing Compound Formulas

Given a sample of an unknown compound, how can its formula be determined? The answer lies in *chemical analysis*, a major branch of chemistry that deals with the determination of formulas and structures.

### Percent Composition

Any sample of a pure compound always consists of the same elements combined in the same proportion by mass. This means molecular composition can be expressed in at least three ways:

1.   in terms of the number of atoms of each type per molecule or per formula unit—that is, by giving the formula of the compound
2.   in terms of the mass of each element per mole of compound

3. in terms of the mass of each element in the compound relative to the total mass of the compound—that is, as a mass percent

Suppose you have 1.0000 mol of $NH_3$ or 17.031 g. This mass of $NH_3$ is composed of 14.007 g of N (1.0000 mol) and 3.0237 g of H (3.0000 mol). If you compare the mass of N to the total mass of compound, 82.246% of the total mass is N (and 17.755% is H).

$$\text{Mass of N per mole of NH}_3 = \frac{1 \text{ mol N}}{1 \text{ mol NH}_3} \times \frac{14.007 \text{ g N}}{1 \text{ mol N}} = 14.007 \text{ g N/1 mol NH}_3$$

$$\text{Mass percent N in NH}_3 = \frac{\text{mass of N in 1 mol NH}_3}{\text{mass of 1 mol NH}_3} \times 100\%$$

$$= \frac{14.007 \text{ g N}}{17.031 \text{ g NH}_3} \times 100\%$$

$$= 82.244\% \text{ (or 82.244 g N in 100.000 g NH}_3)$$

$$\text{Mass of H per mole of NH}_3 = \frac{3 \text{ mol H}}{1 \text{ mol NH}_3} \times \frac{1.0079 \text{ g H}}{1 \text{ mol H}}$$

$$= 3.0237 \text{ g H/1 mol NH}_3$$

$$\text{Mass percent H in NH}_3 = \frac{\text{mass of H in 1 mol NH}_3}{\text{mass of 1 mol NH}_3} \times 100\%$$

$$= \frac{3.0237 \text{ g H}}{17.031 \text{ g NH}_3} \times 100\%$$

$$= 17.755\% \text{ (or 17.755 g H in 100.000 g NH}_3)$$

● **Molecular Composition** Molecular composition can be expressed as a percent (mass of an element in a 100-g sample × 100%). For example, $NH_3$ is 82.244% N. Therefore, it has 82.244 g of N in 100.000 g of compound.

82.244% of $NH_3$ mass is **nitrogen**.

17.755% of $NH_3$ mass is **hydrogen**.

These values represent the mass percent of each element, or percent composition by mass. They tell you that in a 100.00-g sample there are 82.244 g of N and 17.755 g of H.

## EXAMPLE 2.8 Using Percent Composition

**Problem** What is the mass percent of each element in propane, $C_3H_8$? What mass of carbon is contained in 454 g of propane?

**What Do You Know?** You know the formula of propane. You will need the atomic weights of C and H to calculate the mass percent of each element.

**Strategy**

- Calculate the molar mass of propane.

- From the formula, you know there are 3 moles of C and 8 moles of H per mole of $C_3H_8$. Determine the mass of C and H represented by these amounts. The percent of each element is the mass of the element divided by the molar mass.

- The mass of C in 454 g of $C_3H_8$ is obtained by multiplying this mass by the % C/100, (that is, by the decimal fraction of C in the compound).

**Solution**

(a) The molar mass of $C_3H_8$ is 44.097 g/mol.

(b) Mass percent of C and H in $C_3H_8$:

$$\frac{3 \text{ mol C}}{1 \text{ mol C}_3H_8} \times \frac{12.01 \text{ g C}}{1 \text{ mol C}} = 36.03 \text{ g C/1 mol C}_3H_8$$

$$\text{Mass percent of C in C}_3H_8 = \frac{36.03 \text{ g C}}{44.097 \text{ g C}_3H_8} \times 100\% = \boxed{81.71\% \text{ C}}$$

$$\frac{8 \text{ mol H}}{1 \text{ mol C}_3H_8} \times \frac{1.008 \text{ g H}}{1 \text{ mol H}} = 8.064 \text{ g H/1 mol C}_3H_8$$

$$\text{Mass percent of H in C}_3H_8 = \frac{8.064 \text{ g H}}{44.097 \text{ g C}_3H_8} \times 100\% = \boxed{18.29\% \text{ H}}$$

(c)   Mass of C in 454 g of $C_3H_8$:

$$454 \text{ g } C_3H_8 \times \frac{81.71 \text{ g C}}{100.0 \text{ g } C_3H_8} = \boxed{371 \text{ g C}}$$

**Think about Your Answer**  Once you know the percent C in the sample, you could calculate the percent H from it using the formula %H = 100% − %C.

**Check Your Understanding**

1.   Express the composition of ammonium carbonate, $(NH_4)_2CO_3$, in terms of the mass of each element in 1.00 mol of compound and the mass percent of each element.

2.   What is the mass of carbon in 454 g of octane, $C_8H_{18}$?

## Empirical and Molecular Formulas from Percent Composition

Now let us consider the reverse of the procedure just described: using relative mass or percent composition data to find a molecular formula. Suppose you know the identity of the elements in a sample and have determined the mass of each element in a given mass of compound by chemical analysis [▶ Section 4.4]. You can then calculate the relative amount (moles) of each element, which is also the relative number of atoms of each element in the formula of the compound. For example, for a compound composed of atoms of A and B, the steps from percent composition to a formula are as follows:

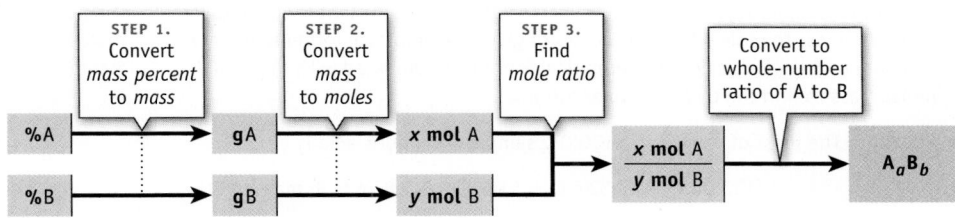

As an example, let us derive the formula for hydrazine, a compound used to remove oxygen from water in heating and cooling systems. It is composed of 87.42% N and 12.58% H and is a close relative of ammonia.

**Step 1:** *Convert mass percent to mass.* The mass percentages of N and H in hydrazine tell us there are 87.42 g of N and 12.58 g of H in a 100.00-g sample.

**Step 2:** *Convert the mass of each element to moles.* The amount of each element in the 100.00-g sample is

$$87.42 \text{ g N} \times \frac{1 \text{ mol N}}{14.007 \text{ g N}} = 6.241 \text{ mol N}$$

$$12.58 \text{ g H} \times \frac{1 \text{ mol H}}{1.0079 \text{ g H}} = 12.48 \text{ mol H}$$

**Step 3:** *Find the mole ratio of elements.* Use the amount (moles) of each element in the 100.00-g of sample to find the amount of one element relative to the other. To do this divide the larger amount by the smaller amount. For hydrazine, this ratio is 2 mol of H to 1 mol of N,

$$\frac{12.48 \text{ mol H}}{6.241 \text{ mol N}} = \frac{2.00 \text{ mol H}}{1.00 \text{ mol N}} \longrightarrow NH_2$$

showing that there are 2 mol of H atoms for every 1 mol of N atoms in hydrazine. Thus, in one molecule, two atoms of H occur for every atom of N; that is, the formula is $NH_2$. This simplest, whole-number atom ratio of atoms in a formula is called the **empirical formula**.

● **Deriving a Formula**  Percent composition gives the mass of an element in 100 g of a sample. However, in deriving a formula, any amount of sample is appropriate if you know the mass of each element in that sample mass.

Percent composition data allow us to calculate the atom ratios in a compound. A *molecular formula*, however, must convey two pieces of information: (1) the relative numbers of atoms of each element in a molecule (the atom ratios) and (2) the total number of atoms in the molecule. For hydrazine there are twice as many H atoms as N atoms, so the molecular formula could be $NH_2$. Recognize, however, that percent composition data give only the simplest possible ratio of atoms in a molecule. The empirical formula of hydrazine is $NH_2$, but the true molecular formula could be $NH_2$, $N_2H_4$, $N_3H_6$, $N_4H_8$, or any other formula having a 1:2 ratio of N to H.

To determine the molecular formula from the empirical formula, the molar mass must be obtained from experiment. For example, experiments show that the molar mass of hydrazine is 32.0 g/mol, twice the formula mass of $NH_2$, which is 16.0 g/mol. Thus, the molecular formula of hydrazine is two times the empirical formula of $NH_2$, that is, $N_2H_4$.

## ʊWL INTERACTIVE EXAMPLE 2.9 Calculating a Formula from Percent Composition

**Problem** Many soft drinks contain sodium benzoate as a preservative. When you consume the sodium benzoate, it reacts with the amino acid glycine in your body to form hippuric acid, which is then excreted in the urine. Hippuric acid has a molar mass of 179.17 g/mol and is 60.33% C, 5.06% H, and 7.82% N; the remainder is oxygen. What are the empirical and molecular formulas of hippuric acid?

**What Do You Know?** You know the mass percent of C, H, and N. The mass percent of oxygen is not known but is obtained by difference. You also know the molar mass and will need atomic weights of these four elements for the calculation.

**Strategy** Assume the mass percent of each element is equivalent to its mass in grams, and convert each mass to moles. The ratio of moles gives the empirical formula. The mass of a mole of compound having the calculated empirical formula is compared with the actual, experimental molar mass to find the true molecular formula.

**Solution** The mass of oxygen in a 100.0-g sample of hippuric acid is

$$100.00 \text{ g} = 60.33 \text{ g C} + 5.06 \text{ g H} + 7.82 \text{ g N} + \text{mass of O}$$

$$\text{Mass of O} = 26.79 \text{ g O}$$

The amount of each element is

$$60.33 \text{ g C} \times \frac{1 \text{ mol C}}{12.011 \text{ g C}} = 5.023 \text{ mol C}$$

$$5.06 \text{ g H} \times \frac{1 \text{ mol H}}{1.008 \text{ g H}} = 5.02 \text{ mol H}$$

$$7.82 \text{ g N} \times \frac{1 \text{ mol N}}{14.01 \text{ g N}} = 0.558 \text{ mol N}$$

$$26.79 \text{ g O} \times \frac{1 \text{ mol O}}{15.999 \text{ g O}} = 1.674 \text{ mol O}$$

To find the mole ratio, the best approach is to base the ratios on the smallest number of moles present—in this case, nitrogen.

$$\frac{\text{mol C}}{\text{mol N}} = \frac{5.023 \text{ mol C}}{0.558 \text{ mol N}} = \frac{9.00 \text{ mol C}}{1.00 \text{ mol N}} = 9 \text{ mol C}/1 \text{ mol N}$$

$$\frac{\text{mol H}}{\text{mol N}} = \frac{5.02 \text{ mol C}}{0.558 \text{ mol N}} = \frac{9.00 \text{ mol C}}{1.00 \text{ mol N}} = 9 \text{ mol H}/1 \text{ mol N}$$

$$\frac{\text{mol O}}{\text{mol N}} = \frac{1.674 \text{ mol O}}{0.558 \text{ mol N}} = \frac{3.00 \text{ mol O}}{1.00 \text{ mol N}} = 3 \text{ mol O}/1 \text{ mol N}$$

Now we know there are 9 mol of C, 9 mol of H, and 3 mol of O per 1 mol of N. Thus, the empirical formula is $C_9H_9NO_3$.

The experimentally determined molar mass of hippuric acid is 179.17 g/mol. This is the same as the empirical formula weight, so the molecular formula is $C_9H_9NO_3$.

---

**Strategy Map 2.9**

**PROBLEM**

Determine **empirical** and **molecular formulas** based on *known composition* and *known molar mass*.

↓

**DATA/INFORMATION KNOWN**

- Molar mass
- Percent composition

**STEP 1.** Assume each **atom %** is equivalent to **mass in grams** in **100 g** sample.

**Mass** of each element in a **100 g** sample of the compound

**STEP 2.** Use **atomic weight** of each element to calculate **amount** of each element in 100 g sample (multiply **mass** by **mol/g**).

**Amount (mol)** of each element in **100 g** sample

**STEP 3.** Divide the *amount of each element* by the *amount of the element present* **in the least amount**.

**Whole-number ratio** of the *amount of each element* to the *amount of element present in the least amount* = **empirical formula**

**STEP 4.** Divide *known* **molar mass** by **empirical formula mass**.

**Molecular formula**

**Think about Your Answer** There is another approach to finding the molecular formula here. Knowing the percent composition of hippuric acid and its molar mass, you could calculate that in 179.17 g of hippuric acid there are 108.06 g of C (8.997 mol of C), 9.06 g of H (8.99 mol of H), 14.01 g N (1.000 mol N), and 48.00 g of O (3 mol of O). This gives us a molecular formula of $C_9H_9NO_3$. However, you must recognize that *this approach can only be used when you know* **both** the percent composition and the molar mass.

**Check Your Understanding**

1.   What is the empirical formula of naphthalene, $C_{10}H_8$?

2.   The empirical formula of acetic acid is $CH_2O$. If its molar mass is 60.05 g/mol, what is the molecular formula of acetic acid?

3.   Isoprene is a liquid compound that can be polymerized to form natural rubber. It is composed of 88.17% carbon and 11.83% hydrogen. Its molar mass is 68.11 g/mol. What are its empirical and molecular formulas?

4.   Camphor is found in camphor wood, much prized for its wonderful odor. It is composed of 78.90% carbon and 10.59% hydrogen. The remainder is oxygen. What is its empirical formula?

**Hippuric Acid, $C_9H_9NO_3$** This substance, which can be isolated as white crystals, is found in the urine of humans and of herbivorous animals.

## Determining a Formula from Mass Data

The composition of a compound in terms of mass percent gives us the mass of each element in a 100.0-g sample. In the laboratory we often collect information on the composition of compounds slightly differently. We can

1.   Combine known masses of elements to give a sample of the compound of known mass. Element masses can be converted to amounts (moles), and the ratio of amounts gives the combining ratio of atoms—that is, the empirical formula. This approach is described in Example 2.10.

2.   Decompose a known mass of an unknown compound into "pieces" of known composition. If the masses of the "pieces" can be determined, the ratio of moles of the "pieces" gives the formula. An example is a decomposition such as

$$Ni(CO)_4(\ell) \rightarrow Ni(s) + 4\ CO(g)$$

The masses of Ni and CO can be converted to moles, whose 1:4 ratio would reveal the formula of the compound. We will describe this approach in Chapter 4.

### ⬥WL   INTERACTIVE EXAMPLE 2.10   Formula of a Compound from Combining Masses

**Problem** Oxides of virtually every element are known. Bromine, for example, forms several oxides when treated with ozone. Suppose you allow 1.250 g of bromine, $Br_2$, to react with ozone and obtain 1.876 g of $Br_xO_y$. What is the formula of the product?

**What Do You Know?** You know that you begin with a given mass of bromine and that all of the bromine becomes part of bromine oxide of unknown formula. You also know the mass of the product, and because you know the mass of Br in this product, you can determine the mass of O in the product.

**Strategy**

*   The mass of oxygen is determined as the difference between the product mass and the mass of bromine used.

*   Calculate the amounts of Br and O from the masses of each element.

*   Find the lowest whole number ratio between the moles of Br and moles of O. This defines the empirical formula.

**Strategy Map 2.10**

**PROBLEM**
Determine **empirical formula** based on *masses of combining elements*.

⬇

**DATA/INFORMATION KNOWN**
*   Mass of one element in binary compound
*   Mass of product

**STEP 1.** Find *mass of second element* by **difference**.

⬇

**Mass of each element** in a sample of the compound

**STEP 2.** Use **atomic weight** of each element to calculate **amount** of each element in sample (multiply mass by mol/g).

⬇

**Amount (mol)** of each element in sample

**STEP 3.** Divide the *amount of each element* by the *amount of the element present* **in the least amount**.

⬇

**Whole-number ratio** of the *amount of each element* to the *amount of element present in the least amount* = **empirical formula**

• The experimental data available to find a formula may be in the form of percent composition or the masses of elements combined in some mass of compound. No matter what the starting point, the first step is always to convert masses of elements to moles.

• Be sure to use *at least* three significant figures when calculating empirical formulas. Using fewer significant figures can give a misleading result.

## Finding Empirical and Molecular Formulas

• When finding atom ratios, always divide the larger number of moles by the smaller one.

• Empirical and molecular formulas can differ for molecular compounds. In contrast, there is no "molecular" formula for an ionic compound; all that can be recorded is the empirical formula.

• Determining the molecular formula of a compound after calculating the empirical formula requires knowing the molar mass.

• When *both* the percent composition and the molar mass are known for a compound, the alternative method mentioned in *Think about Your Answer* in Example 2.9 could be used.

**Solution**  You already know the mass of bromine in the compound, so you can calculate the mass of oxygen in the compound by subtracting the mass of bromine from the mass of the product.

$$1.876 \text{ g product} - 1.250 \text{ g Br}_2 = 0.626 \text{ g O}$$

Next, calculate the amount of each reactant. Notice that, although $Br_2$ was the reactant, we need to know the amount of Br in the product.

$$1.250 \text{ g Br}_2 \times \frac{1 \text{ mol Br}_2}{159.81 \text{ g}} = 0.007822 \text{ mol Br}_2$$

$$0.007822 \text{ mol Br}_2 \times \frac{2 \text{ mol Br}}{1 \text{ mol Br}_2} = 0.01564 \text{ mol Br}$$

$$0.626 \text{ g O} \times \frac{1 \text{ mol O}}{16.00 \text{ g O}} = 0.0391 \text{ mol O}$$

Find the ratio of moles of O to moles of Br:

$$\text{Mole ratio} = \frac{0.0391 \text{ mol O}}{0.01564 \text{ mol Br}} = \frac{2.50 \text{ mol O}}{1.00 \text{ mol O}}$$

The atom ratio is 2.5 mol O/1.0 mol Br. However, atoms combine in the ratio of small whole numbers, so we double this to give a ratio of 5 mol O to 2 mol Br. Thus, the product is dibromine pentaoxide, $Br_2O_5$.

**Think about Your Answer**  The whole number ratio of 5:2 was found by realizing that 2.5 = 2 1/2 = 5/2. This problem rests on the principle of the conservation of matter. All of the bromine used in the reaction is part of the product.

---

**Check Your Understanding**

Gallium oxide, $Ga_xO_y$, forms when gallium is combined with oxygen. Suppose you allow 1.25 g of gallium (Ga) to react with oxygen and obtain 1.68 g of $Ga_xO_y$. What is the formula of the product?

---

## EXAMPLE 2.11    Determining a Formula from Mass Data

**Problem**  Tin metal (Sn) and purple iodine ($I_2$) combine to form orange, solid tin iodide with an unknown formula.

$$\text{Sn metal} + \text{solid } I_2 \quad \rightarrow \quad \text{solid } Sn_xI_y$$

Weighed quantities of Sn and $I_2$ are combined, where the quantity of Sn is more than is needed to react with all of the iodine. After $Sn_xI_y$ has been formed, it is isolated by filtration. The mass of excess tin is also determined. The following data were collected:

| | |
|---|---|
| Mass of tin (Sn) in the original mixture | 1.056 g |
| Mass of iodine ($I_2$) in the original mixture | 1.947 g |
| Mass of tin (Sn) recovered after reaction | 0.601 g |

What is the empirical formula of the tin iodide obtained?

**(a)** Weighed samples of tin (left) and iodine (right).

**(b)** The tin and iodine are heated in a solvent.

**(c)** The hot reaction mixture is filtered to recover unreacted tin.

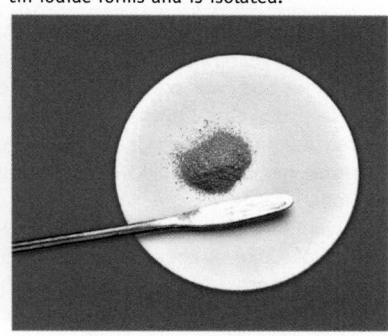

**(d)** When the solvent cools, solid, orange tin iodide forms and is isolated.

**Determining a formula.** The formula of a compound composed of tin and iodine can be determined by finding the mass of iodine that combines with a given mass of tin.

**What Do You Know?** You know the mass of iodine used in the reaction. The mass of tin used in this reaction is needed, and it can be determined from the mass information given. You need the atomic weights of tin and iodine.

**Strategy**

- The mass of tin consumed in the reaction is determined by subtracting the mass of tin recovered from the initial mass of tin.

- Calculate the amounts of Sn and I from the masses of each element.

- Find the lowest whole number ratio between the moles of Sn and moles of I. This defines the empirical formula.

**Solution** First, let us find the mass of tin that combined with iodine:

| | |
|---|---|
| Mass of Sn in original mixture | 1.056 g |
| Mass of Sn recovered | − 0.601 g |
| Mass of Sn combined with 1.947 g $I_2$ | 0.455 g |

Now convert the mass of tin to the amount of tin.

$$0.455 \text{ g Sn} \times \frac{1 \text{ mol Sn}}{118.7 \text{ g Sn}} = 0.00383 \text{ mol Sn}$$

No $I_2$ was recovered; it all reacted with Sn. Therefore, 0.00383 mol of Sn combined with 1.947 g of $I_2$. Because we want to know the amount of I that combined with 0.00383 mol of Sn, we calculate the amount of I from the mass of $I_2$.

$$1.947 \text{ g } I_2 \times \frac{1 \text{ mol } I_2}{253.81 \text{ g } I_2} \times \frac{2 \text{ mol I}}{1 \text{ mol } I_2} = 0.01534 \text{ mol I}$$

Finally, we find the ratio of moles.

$$\frac{\text{mol I}}{\text{mol Sn}} = \frac{0.01534 \text{ mol I}}{0.00383 \text{ mol Sn}} = \frac{4.01 \text{ mol I}}{1.00 \text{ mol Sn}} = \frac{4 \text{ mol I}}{1 \text{ mol Sn}}$$

There are four times as many moles of I as moles of Sn in the sample. Therefore, there are four times as many atoms of I as atoms of Sn per formula unit. The empirical formula is $SnI_4$.

**Think about Your Answer** This is very similar to Example 2.10.

**Check Your Understanding**

Analysis shows that 0.586 g of potassium metal combines with 0.480 g of $O_2$ gas to give a white solid having a formula of $K_xO_y$. What is the empirical formula of the compound?

# Mummies, Bangladesh, and the Formula of Compound 606

The Iceman of the Alps lived over 5000 years ago (page 58), but his body was preserved in the ice for thousands of years. Other civilizations deliberately mummified their dead, and one curious case has been studied by archeologists for some years.

Over 6800 years ago, in what is now the nation of Chile, a child died at an age of about 6 months. After removing the head and internal organs, someone modeled a head of clay and placed it on the torso. The cause of death for this child, and of others whose mummified remains have been found in this region, was apparently arsenic poisoning.

Arsenic occurs naturally in geological formations in many parts of the world, including the mountains of Chile. Rain and snowmelt flow from the mountains, carrying dissolved minerals, among them arsenic-containing salts. In one region of Chile, a

region in which the mummies were found, the river water has 860 mg of arsenic per liter, 86 times the World Health Organization's guideline.

Another region of the world greatly affected by arsenic salts in the ground water is Bangladesh. Here the arsenic is carried from the mountains of Tibet into the flood plains of Bangladesh by the great Brahmaputra River. Enormous efforts have been made to alleviate the problem with some success.

The practice in medicine for some centuries has been to find compounds that are toxic to certain organisms but not so toxic that the patient is harmed. In the early part of the 20th century, Paul Ehrlich set out to find just such a compound that would cure syphilis, a venereal disease that was rampant at the time. He screened hundreds of compounds, and found that his 606th compound was effective: an arsenic-containing drug now called salvarsan. It was used for some years for syphilis treatment until penicillin was discovered in the 1930s.

Salvarsan was a forerunner of the modern drug industry. Interestingly, what chemists long thought to be a single compound was in fact a mixture of compounds. Question 2 below will lead you to the molecular formula for both of them.

For more about arsenic and its effect in the environment, see H. Pringle, *Science*, 29 May 2009, Volume 324, page 1130 and Y. Bhattacharjee, *Science*, 23 March 2007, Volume 315, page 1659.

**The hands of a woman in Bangladesh.** The spots are the symptom of arsenocosis caused by ingesting arsenic-containing water.

**A sample of orpiment, a common arsenic-containing mineral ($As_2S_3$).** The name of the element is thought to come from the Greek word for this mineral, which was long favored by 17th century Dutch painters as a pigment.

## Questions:

1. Enargite is an arsenic-containing ore. It has 19.024% As, 48.407% Cu, and 32.569% S. What is the empirical formula of the ore?

2. Salvarsan was long thought to be a single substance. Recently, however, a mass spectrometry study of the compound shows it to be a mixture of two molecules with the same empirical formula. Each has the composition 39.37% C, 3.304% H, 8.741% O, 7.652% N, and 40.932% As. One has a molar of mass of 549 g/mol and the other has a molar mass of 915 g/mol. What are the molecular formulas of the compounds?

**Answers to these questions are available in Appendix N.**

## Determining a Formula by Mass Spectrometry

We have described chemical methods of determining a molecular formula, but there are many instrumental methods as well. One of them is *mass spectrometry* (Figure 2.27). We introduced this technique earlier when discussing the existence of isotopes and their relative abundance (Figure 2.3). If a compound can be turned into a vapor, the vapor can be passed through an electron beam in a mass spectrometer where high energy electrons collide with the gas phase molecules. These high-energy collisions cause the molecule to lose electrons and turn the molecules into positive ions. These ions usually break apart or fragment into smaller pieces. As illustrated in Figure 2.27 the cation created from ethanol ($CH_3CH_2OH^+$) fragments (losing an H atom) to give another cation ($CH_3CH_2O^+$), which further fragments. A mass spectrometer detects and records the masses of the different particles. Analysis of the spectrum can help identify a compound and can give an accurate molar mass.

**A CLOSER LOOK**

# Mass Spectrometry, Molar Mass, and Isotopes

Bromobenzene, $C_6H_5Br$, has a molar mass of 157.010 g/mol. Why, then, are there two prominent lines at mass-to-charge ratios ($m/Z$) of 156 and 158 in the mass spectrum of the compound (when $Z = +1$)? The answer shows us the influence of isotopes on molar mass.

Bromine has two, naturally occurring isotopes, $^{79}Br$ and $^{81}Br$. They are 50.7% and 49.3% abundant, respectively. What is the mass of $C_6H_5Br$ based on each isotope? If we use the most abundant isotopes of C and H ($^{12}C$ and $^{1}H$), the mass of the molecule having the $^{79}Br$ isotope, $C_6H_5{}^{79}Br$, is 156. The mass of the molecule containing the $^{81}Br$ isotope, $C_6H_5{}^{81}Br$, is 158.

The calculated molar mass of bromobenzene is 157.010, a value derived from the atomic masses of the elements. The molar mass reflects the abundances of all of the isotopes. In contrast, the mass spectrum has a line for each possible combination of isotopes. This also explains why there are also small lines at the mass-to-charge ratios of 157 and 159. They arise from various combinations of $^{1}H$, $^{12}C$, $^{13}C$, $^{79}Br$, and $^{81}Br$ atoms. In fact careful analysis of such patterns can identify a molecule unambiguously.

Bromobenzene mass spectrum

$$158 = (^{12}C)_6(^1H)_5{}^{81}Br^+$$

$$156 = (^{12}C)_6(^1H)_5{}^{79}Br^+$$

$CH_2OH^+$
($m/Z = 31$ u)

$C_2H_5{}^+$
($m/Z = 29$ u)

$CH_3{}^+$
($m/Z = 15$ u)

$CH_3CH_2O^+$
($m/Z = 45$ u)

$CH_3CH_2OH^+$
($m/Z = 46$ u)

**FIGURE 2.27 Mass spectrum of ethanol, $CH_3CH_2OH$.** A prominent peak or line in the spectrum is the "parent" ion ($CH_3CH_2OH^+$) at mass 46. (The parent ion is the heaviest ion observed.) The mass designated by the peak for the parent ion confirms the formula of the molecule. Other peaks are for "fragment" ions. This pattern of lines can provide further, unambiguous evidence of the formula of the compound. (The horizontal axis is the mass-to-charge ratio of a given ion. Because almost all observed ions have a charge of $Z = +1$, the value observed is the mass of the ion.) (See "A Closer Look: Mass Spectrometry, Molar Mass, and Isotopes.")

---

**REVIEW & CHECK FOR SECTION 2.10**

1.    Which of the following hydrocarbons has the highest percentage of carbon?

(a)   methane, $CH_4$                (c)   propane, $C_3H_8$

(b)   ethane, $C_2H_6$               (d)   butane, $C_4H_{10}$

2.  Which of the following organic compounds has the highest percentage of carbon?

    (a)  benzene, $C_6H_6$

    (b)  ethane, $C_2H_6$

    (c)  ethanol, $C_2H_5OH$

    (d)  acetic acid, $CH_3CO_2H$

3.  An organic compound has an empirical formula $CH_2O$ and a molar mass of 180 g/mol. What is its molecular formula?

    (a)  $CH_2O$

    (b)  $C_6H_{12}O_6$

    (c)  $C_2H_4O_2$

    (d)  $C_5H_{10}O_5$

4.  Eugenol is the major component in oil of cloves. It has a molar mass of 164.2 g/mol and is 73.14% C and 7.37% H; the remainder is oxygen. What are the empirical and molecular formulas of eugenol?

    (a)  $C_5H_6O$, $C_5H_6O$

    (b)  $C_5H_6O$, $C_{10}H_{12}O_2$

    (c)  $C_6H_5O$, $C_{12}H_{10}O_2$

    (d)  $C_3H_6O$, $C_6H_{12}O_2$

**FIGURE 2.28 Gypsum wallboard.** Gypsum is hydrated calcium sulfate, $CaSO_4 \cdot 2H_2O$.

## 2.11 Hydrated Compounds

If ionic compounds are prepared in water solution and then isolated as solids, the crystals often have molecules of water trapped in the lattice. Compounds in which molecules of water are associated with the ions of the compound are called **hydrated compounds**. The beautiful blue copper(II) compound in Figure 2.26, for example, has a formula that is conventionally written as $CuCl_2 \cdot 2 H_2O$. The dot between $CuCl_2$ and $2 H_2O$ indicates that 2 mol of water are associated with every mole of $CuCl_2$; it is equivalent to writing the formula as $CuCl_2(H_2O)_2$. The name of the compound, copper(II) chloride dihydrate, reflects the presence of 2 mol of water per mole of $CuCl_2$. The molar mass of $CuCl_2 \cdot 2 H_2O$ is 134.5 g/mol (for $CuCl_2$) plus 36.0 g/mol (for $2 H_2O$) for a total molar mass of 170.5 g/mol.

Hydrated compounds are common. The walls of your home may be covered with wallboard, or "plaster board" (Figure 2.28) These sheets contain hydrated calcium sulfate, or gypsum ($CaSO_4 \cdot 2 H_2O$), as well as unhydrated $CaSO_4$, sandwiched between paper. Gypsum is a mineral that can be mined. Now, however, it is more commonly obtained as a byproduct in the manufacture of hydrofluoric acid and phosphoric acid.

If gypsum is heated between 120 and 180 °C, the water is partly driven off to give $CaSO_4 \cdot \frac{1}{2} H_2O$, a compound commonly called "plaster of Paris." If you have ever broken an arm or leg and had to have a cast, the cast may have been made of this

**FIGURE 2.29 Dehydrating hydrated cobalt(II) chloride, $CoCl_2 \cdot 6H_2O$.** $CoCl_2 \cdot 6H_2O$ also makes a good "invisible ink." A solution of cobalt(II) chloride in water is red, but if you write on paper with the solution it cannot be seen. When the paper is warmed, however, the cobalt compound dehydrates to give the deep blue anhydrous compound, and the writing becomes visible.

Cobalt(II) chloride hexahydrate [$CoCl_2 \cdot 6H_2O$] is a deep red compound.

When it is heated, the compound loses the water of hydration and forms the deep blue compound $CoCl_2$.

compound. It is an effective casting material because, when added to water, it forms a thick slurry that can be poured into a mold or spread out over a part of the body. As it takes on more water, the material increases in volume and forms a hard, inflexible solid. These properties also make plaster of Paris a useful material for artists, because the expanding compound fills a mold completely and makes a high-quality reproduction.

Hydrated cobalt(II) chloride is the red solid in Figure 2.29. When heated it turns purple and then deep blue as it loses water to form anhydrous $CoCl_2$; "anhydrous" means a substance without water. On exposure to moist air, anhydrous $CoCl_2$ takes up water and is converted back into the red hydrated compound. It is this property that allows crystals of the blue compound to be used as a humidity indicator. You may have seen them in a small bag packed with a piece of electronic equipment.

There is no simple way to predict how much water will be present in a hydrated compound, so it must be determined experimentally. Such an experiment may involve heating the hydrated material so that all the water is released from the solid and evaporated. Only the anhydrous compound is left. The formula of hydrated copper(II) sulfate, commonly known as "blue vitriol," is determined in this manner in Example 2.12.

White $CuSO_4$

Blue $CuSO_4 \cdot 5\ H_2O$

**FIGURE 2.30 Heating a hydrated compound.** The formula of a hydrated compound can be determined by heating a weighed sample enough to cause the compound to release its water of hydration. Knowing the mass of the hydrated compound before heating and the mass of the anhydrous compound after heating, we can determine the mass of water in the original sample.

---

**◉WL INTERACTIVE EXAMPLE 2.12** Determining the Formula
of a Hydrated Compound

**Problem** You want to know the value of $x$ in blue, hydrated copper(II) sulfate, $CuSO_4 \cdot x\ H_2O$, that is, the number of water molecules for each unit of $CuSO_4$. In the laboratory you weigh out 1.023 g of the solid. After heating the solid thoroughly in a porcelain crucible (Figure 2.30), 0.654 g of nearly white, anhydrous copper(II) sulfate, $CuSO_4$, remains.

$$1.023\ \text{g}\ CuSO_4 \cdot x\ H_2O + \text{heat} \rightarrow 0.654\ \text{g}\ CuSO_4 + ?\ \text{g}\ H_2O$$

**What Do You Know?** You know the mass of the copper sulfate sample including water (before heating) and with no water (after heating). Therefore, you know the mass of water in the sample and the mass of $CuSO_4$.

**Strategy** To find $x$ you need to know the amount of $H_2O$ per mole $CuSO_4$.

- Determine the mass of water released on heating the hydrated compound.

- Calculate the amount (moles) of $CuSO_4$ and $H_2O$ from their masses and molar masses.

- Determine the smallest whole number ratio (amount $H_2O$/amount $CuSO_4$).

**Solution** Find the mass of water.

| | |
|---|---|
| Mass of hydrated compound | 1.023 g |
| − Mass of anhydrous compound, $CuSO_4$ | −0.654 |
| Mass of water | 0.369 g |

Next convert the masses of $CuSO_4$ and $H_2O$ to moles.

$$0.369\ \text{g}\ H_2O \times \frac{1\ \text{mol}\ H_2O}{18.02\ \text{g}\ H_2O} = 0.0205\ \text{mol}\ H_2O$$

$$0.654\ \text{g}\ CuSO_4 \times \frac{1\ \text{mol}\ CuSO_4}{159.6\ \text{g}\ CuSO_4} = 0.00410\ \text{mol}\ CuSO_4$$

The value of $x$ is determined from the mole ratio.

$$\frac{0.0205\ \text{mol}\ H_2O}{0.00410\ \text{mol}\ CuSO_4} = \frac{5.00\ \text{mol}\ H_2O}{1.00\ \text{mol}\ CuSO_4}$$

The water-to-$CuSO_4$ ratio is 5∶1, so the formula of the hydrated compound is $CuSO_4 \cdot 5\ H_2O$. Its name is copper(II) sulfate pentahydrate.

**Strategy Map 2.12**

**PROBLEM**

Determine **formula of hydrated salt** based on *masses of water and dehydrated salt.*

↓

**DATA/INFORMATION KNOWN**

- Mass of sample before and after heating to dehydrate

**STEP 1.** Find *masses of salt and water* by **difference.**

↓

**Mass of salt and water** in a sample of the hydrated compound

**STEP 2.** Use **molar mass** of salt and water to calculate **amount** of each in sample (multiply **mass** by **mol/g**).

↓

**Amount (mol)** of salt and water in sample

**STEP 3.** Divide the *amount of water* by the *amount of the dehydrated salt.*

↓

**Formula** = *ratio of the amount of water to the amount of salt* in dehydrated sample

**Think about Your Answer** The ratio of the amount of water to the amount of $CuSO_4$ is a whole number. This is almost always the case with hydrated compounds.

**Check Your Understanding**

Hydrated nickel(II) chloride is a beautiful green, crystalline compound. When heated strongly, the compound is dehydrated. If 0.235 g of $NiCl_2 \cdot x\ H_2O$ gives 0.128 g of $NiCl_2$ on heating, what is the value of $x$?

---

**REVIEW & CHECK FOR SECTION 2.11**

Epsom salt is $MgSO_4 \cdot 7H_2O$. When heated to 70 to 80 °C it loses some, but not all, of its water of hydration. Suppose you heat 2.465 g of Epsom salt to 75 °C and find that the mass is now only 1.744 g. What is the formula of the slightly dehydrated salt?

(a)  $MgSO_4 \cdot 6H_2O$

(b)  $MgSO_4 \cdot 5H_2O$

(c)  $MgSO_4 \cdot 4H_2O$

(d)  $MgSO_4 \cdot 3H_2O$

---

Sign in at **www.cengage.com/owl** to:
- View tutorials and simulations, develop problem-solving skills, and complete online homework assigned by your professor.
- For quick review and exam prep, download Go Chemistry mini lecture modules from OWL (or purchase them at **www.cengagebrain.com**)

❓ Access **How Do I Solve It?** tutorials on how to approach problem solving using concepts in this chapter.

# CHAPTER GOALS REVISITED

*Now that you have studied this chapter, you should ask whether you have met the chapter goals. In particular, you should be able to*

### Describe atomic structure and define atomic number and mass number

a.  Describe electrons, protons, and neutrons, and the general structure of the atom (Section 2.1). **Study Questions: 1, 7.**

b.  Understand the relative mass scale and the atomic mass unit (Section 2.2).

### Understand the nature of isotopes and calculate atomic masses from isotopic masses and abundances

a.  Define isotope and give the mass number and number of neutrons for a specific isotope (Sections 2.2 and 2.3). **Study Questions: 5, 6, 8, 14, 97.**

b.  Do calculations that relate the atomic weight (atomic mass) of an element and isotopic abundances and masses (Section 2.4). **Study Questions: 16–18, 98, 158.**

### Know the terminology of the periodic table

a.  Identify the periodic table locations of groups, periods, metals, metalloids, nonmetals, alkali metals, alkaline earth metals, halogens, noble gases, and the transition elements (Section 2.5). **Study Questions: 24, 25, 29, 103, and Go Chemistry Module 1.**

b.  State similarities and differences in properties of some of the common elements of a group (Section 2.5). **Study Questions: 28, 30.**

### Interpret, predict, and write formulas for ionic and molecular compounds

a.  Recognize and interpret molecular formulas, condensed formulas, and structural formulas (Section 2.6). **Study Questions: 31, 33.**

b.  Recognize that metal atoms commonly lose one or more electrons to form positive ions, called cations, and nonmetal atoms often gain electrons to form negative ions, called anions (Figure 2.17).

c.  Predict the charge on a metal cation: for Groups 1A, 2A, and 3A ions, the charge is equal to the group number in which the element is found in the periodic table ($M^{n+}$, $n$ = Group number) (Section 2.7); for transition metal cations, the charges are often 2+ or 3+, but other charges are observed. **Study Questions: 35, 37, 43, and Go Chemistry Module 2.**

d.  Recognize that the negative charge on a single-atom or monatomic anion, $X^{n-}$, is given by $n =$ Group number $- 8$ (Section 2.7). **Study Questions: 37, 40.**
e.  Write formulas for ionic compounds by combining ions in the proper ratio to give no overall charge (Section 2.7). **Study Questions: 41, 43, 45, 47.**

### Name ionic and molecular compounds

a.  Give the names or formulas of polyatomic ions, knowing their formulas or names, respectively (Table 2.4 and Section 2.7). **Study Questions: 37, 38.**
b.  Name ionic compounds and simple binary compounds of the nonmetals (Sections 2.7 and 2.8). **Study Questions: 49, 57–60, 128, and Go Chemistry Module 3.**

### Understand some properties of ionic compounds

a.  Understand the importance of Coulomb's law (Equation 2.3), which describes the electrostatic forces of attraction and repulsion of ions. Coulomb's law states that the force of attraction between oppositely charged species increases with electric charge and with decreasing distance between the species (Section 2.7). **Study Question: 56.**

### Explain the concept of the mole and use molar mass in calculations

a.  Understand that the molar mass of an element is the mass in grams of Avogadro's number of atoms of that element (Section 2.9). **Study Questions: 61, 62, 65, 105, and Go Chemistry Module 4.**
b.  Know how to use the molar mass of an element and Avogadro's number in calculations (Section 2.9). **Study Questions: 65, 68, 106, 107.**
c.  Understand that the molar mass of a compound (often called the molecular weight) is the mass in grams of Avogadro's number of molecules (or formula units) of a compound (Section 2.9). For ionic compounds, which do not consist of individual molecules, the sum of atomic masses is often called the formula mass (or formula weight).
d.  Calculate the molar mass of a compound from its formula and a table of atomic weights (Section 2.9). **Study Questions: 69, 71, 73.**
e.  Calculate the number of moles of a compound that is represented by a given mass, and vice versa (Section 2.9). **Study Questions: 73–75, 117.**

### Derive compoud formulas from experimental data

a.  Express the composition of a compound in terms of percent composition (Section 2.10). **Study Questions: 79, 81, 113.**
b.  Use percent composition or other experimental data to determine the empirical formula of a compound (Section 2.10). **Study Questions: 83, 85, 89, 91, 129.**
c.  Understand how mass spectrometry can be used to find a molar mass (Section 2.10). **Study Question: 159.**
d.  Use experimental data to find the number of water molecules in a hydrated compound (Section 2.11) **Study Questions: 153, 157.**

## Key Equations

**Equation 2.1 (page 54)** Percent abundance of an isotope.

$$\text{Percent abundance} = \frac{\text{number of atoms of a given isotope}}{\text{total number of atoms of all isotopes of that element}} \times 100\%$$

**Equation 2.2 (page 55)** Calculate the atomic weight from isotope abundances and the exact atomic mass of each isotope of an element.

$$\text{Atomic weight} = \left( \frac{\% \text{ abundance isotope 1}}{100} \right)(\text{mass of isotope 1})$$
$$+ \left( \frac{\% \text{ abundance isotope 2}}{100} \right)(\text{mass of isotope 2}) + \ldots$$

**Equation 2.3 (page 76)** **Coulomb's Law**, the force of attraction between oppositely charged ions.

charge on + and − ions                charge on electron

$$\text{Force} = -k\,\frac{(n^+e)\,(n^-e)}{d^2}$$

proportionality constant        distance between ions

## Study Questions

⭕WL Interactive versions of these questions are assignable in OWL.

▲ denotes challenging questions.

Blue-numbered questions have answers in Appendix R and fully worked solutions in the *Student Solutions Manual*.

## Practicing Skills

### Atoms: Their Composition and Structure

1. What are the three fundamental particles from which atoms are built? What are their electric charges? Which of these particles constitute the nucleus of an atom? Which is the least massive particle of the three?

2. Define mass number. What is the difference between mass number and atomic mass?

3. An atom has a very small nucleus surrounded by an electron "cloud." Figure 2.1 represents the nucleus with a diameter of about 2 mm and describes the electron cloud as extending over 200 m. If the diameter of an atom is $1 \times 10^{-8}$ cm, what is the approximate diameter of its nucleus?

4. A gold atom has a radius of 145 pm. If you could string gold atoms like beads on a thread, how many atoms would you need to have a necklace 36 cm long?

5. Give the complete symbol ($^A_Z X$), including atomic number and mass number, for each of the following atoms: (a) magnesium with 15 neutrons, (b) titanium with 26 neutrons, and (c) zinc with 32 neutrons.

6. Give the complete symbol ($^A_Z X$), including atomic number and mass number, of (a) a nickel atom with 31 neutrons, (b) a plutonium atom with 150 neutrons, and (c) a tungsten atom with 110 neutrons.

7. How many electrons, protons, and neutrons are there in each of the following atoms?
   (a) magnesium-24, $^{24}$Mg    (d) carbon-13, $^{13}$C
   (b) tin-119, $^{119}$Sn    (e) copper-63, $^{63}$Cu
   (c) thorium-232, $^{232}$Th    (f) bismuth-205, $^{205}$Bi

8. Atomic structure.
   (a) The synthetic radioactive element technetium is used in many medical studies. Give the number of electrons, protons, and neutrons in an atom of technetium-99.
   (b) Radioactive americium-241 is used in household smoke detectors and in bone mineral analysis. Give the number of electrons, protons, and neutrons in an atom of americium-241.

### Isotopes

9. The mass of an $^{16}$O atom is 15.995 u. What is its mass relative to the mass of an atom of $^{12}$C?

10. What is the mass of one $^{16}$O atom, in grams?

11. Cobalt has three radioactive isotopes used in medical studies. Atoms of these isotopes have 30, 31, and 33 neutrons, respectively. Give the symbol for each of these isotopes.

12. Naturally occurring silver exists as two isotopes having mass numbers 107 and 109. How many protons, neutrons, and electrons are there in each of these isotopes?

13. Name and describe the composition of the three hydrogen isotopes.

14. Which of the following are isotopes of element X, the atomic number for which is 9: $^{19}_9$X, $^{20}_9$X, $^9_{18}$X, and $^{21}_9$X?

### Isotope Abundance and Atomic Weight

*(See Examples 2.2 and 2.3.)*

15. Thallium has two stable isotopes, $^{203}$Tl and $^{205}$Tl. Knowing that the atomic weight of thallium is 204.4, which isotope is the more abundant of the two?

16. Strontium has four stable isotopes. Strontium-84 has a very low natural abundance, but $^{86}$Sr, $^{87}$Sr, and $^{88}$Sr are all reasonably abundant. Knowing that the atomic weight of strontium is 87.62, which of the more abundant isotopes predominates?

17. Verify that the atomic weight of lithium is 6.94, given the following information:
    $^6$Li, mass = 6.015121 u; percent abundance = 7.50%
    $^7$Li, mass = 7.016003 u; percent abundance = 92.50%

18. Verify that the atomic weight of magnesium is 24.31, given the following information:
    $^{24}$Mg, mass = 23.985042 u; percent abundance = 78.99%
    $^{25}$Mg, mass = 24.985837 u; percent abundance = 10.00%
    $^{26}$Mg, mass = 25.982593 u; percent abundance = 11.01%

19. Silver (Ag) has two stable isotopes, $^{107}$Ag and $^{109}$Ag. The isotopic mass of $^{107}$Ag is 106.9051, and the isotopic mass of $^{109}$Ag is 108.9047. The atomic weight of Ag, from the periodic table, is 107.868. Estimate the percent of $^{107}$Ag in a sample of the element.
    (a) 0%    (b) 25%    (c) 50%    (d) 75%

20. Copper exists as two isotopes: $^{63}$Cu (62.9298 u) and $^{65}$Cu (64.9278 u). What is the approximate percent of $^{63}$Cu in samples of this element?
    (a) 10%    (c) 50%    (e) 90%
    (b) 30%    (d) 70%

**21.** Gallium has two naturally occurring isotopes, $^{69}$Ga and $^{71}$Ga, with masses of 68.9257 u and 70.9249 u, respectively. Calculate the percent abundances of these isotopes of gallium.

**22.** Europium has two stable isotopes, $^{151}$Eu and $^{153}$Eu, with masses of 150.9197 u and 152.9212 u, respectively. Calculate the percent abundances of these isotopes of europium.

**The Periodic Table**

*(See Section 2.5.)*

**23.** Titanium and thallium have symbols that are easily confused with each other. Give the symbol, atomic number, atomic weight, and group and period number of each element. Are they metals, metalloids, or nonmetals?

**24.** In Groups 4A–6A, there are several elements whose symbols begin with S. Name these elements, and for each one give its symbol, atomic number, group number, and period. Describe each as a metal, metalloid, or nonmetal.

**25.** How many periods of the periodic table have 8 elements, how many have 18 elements, and how many have 32 elements?

**26.** How many elements occur in the seventh period? What is the name given to the majority of these elements, and what well-known property characterizes them?

**27.** Select answers to the questions listed below from the following list of elements whose symbols start with the letter C: C, Ca, Cr, Co, Cd, Cl, Cs, Ce, Cm, Cu, and Cf. (You should expect to use some symbols more than once.)
(a) Which are nonmetals?
(b) Which are main group elements?
(c) Which are lanthanides?
(d) Which are transition elements?
(e) Which are actinides?
(f) Which are gases?

**28.** Give the name and chemical symbol for the following.
(a) a nonmetal in the second period
(b) an alkali metal in the fifth period
(c) the third-period halogen
(d) an element that is a gas at 20°C and 1 atmosphere pressure

**29.** Classify the following elements as metals, metalloids, or nonmetals: N, Na, Ni, Ne, and Np.

**30.** Here are symbols for five of the seven elements whose names begin with the letter B: B, Ba, Bk, Bi, and Br. Match each symbol with one of the descriptions below.
(a) a radioactive element
(b) a liquid at room temperature
(c) a metalloid
(d) an alkaline earth element
(e) a group 5A element

**Molecular Formulas and Models**

**31.** A model of sulfuric acid is illustrated here. Write the molecular formula for sulfuric acid, and draw the structural formula. Describe the structure of the molecule. Is it flat? That is, are all the atoms in the plane of the paper? (Color code: sulfur atoms are yellow; oxygen atoms are red; and hydrogen atoms are white.)

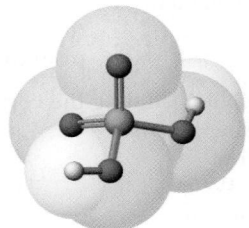

**32.** A model of nitric acid is illustrated here. Write the molecular formula for nitric acid, and draw the structural formula. Describe the structure of the molecule. Is it flat? That is, are all the atoms in the plane of the paper? (Color code: nitrogen atoms are blue; oxygen atoms are red; and hydrogen atoms are white.)

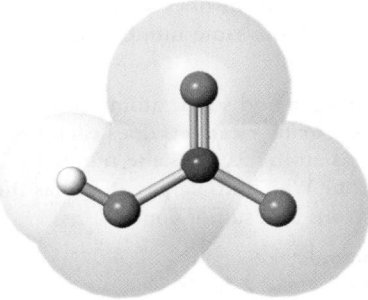

**33.** A model of the amino acid asparagine is illustrated here. Write the molecular formula for the compound, and draw its structural formula.

**Asparagine, an amino acid.**

**34.** A model of the platinum-based chemotherapy agent cisplatin is illustrated here. Write the molecular formula for the compound, and draw its structural formula.

## Ions and Ion Charges

*(See Figure 2.18 and Table 2.4.)*

**35.** What is the charge on the common monatomic ions of the following elements?
(a) magnesium        (c) nickel
(b) zinc             (d) gallium

**36.** What is the charge on the common monatomic ions of the following elements?
(a) selenium         (c) iron
(b) fluorine         (d) nitrogen

**37.** Give the symbol, including the correct charge, for each of the following ions:
(a) barium ion               (e) sulfide ion
(b) titanium(IV) ion         (f) perchlorate ion
(c) phosphate ion            (g) cobalt(II) ion
(d) hydrogen carbonate ion   (h) sulfate ion

**38.** Give the symbol, including the correct charge, for each of the following ions:
(a) permanganate ion         (d) ammonium ion
(b) nitrite ion              (e) phosphate ion
(c) dihydrogen phosphate ion (f) sulfite ion

**39.** When a potassium atom becomes a monatomic ion, how many electrons does it lose or gain? What noble gas atom has the same number of electrons as a potassium ion?

**40.** When oxygen and sulfur atoms become monatomic ions, how many electrons does each lose or gain? Which noble gas atom has the same number of electrons as an oxide ion? Which noble gas atom has the same number of electrons as a sulfide ion?

## Ionic Compounds

*(See Examples 2.4 and 2.5.)*

**41.** What are the charges on the ions in an ionic compound containing the elements barium and bromine? Write the formula for the compound.

**42.** What are the charges of the ions in an ionic compound containing cobalt(III) and fluoride ions? Write the formula for the compound.

**43.** Give the formula and the number of each ion that makes up each of the following compounds:
(a) $K_2S$              (d) $(NH_4)_3PO_4$
(b) $CoSO_4$           (e) $Ca(ClO)_2$
(c) $KMnO_4$           (f) $NaCH_3CO_2$

**44.** Give the formula and the number of each ion that makes up each of the following compounds:
(a) $Mg(CH_3CO_2)_2$   (d) $Ti(SO_4)_2$
(b) $Al(OH)_3$         (e) $KH_2PO_4$
(c) $CuCO_3$           (f) $CaHPO_4$

**45.** Cobalt forms $Co^{2+}$ and $Co^{3+}$ ions. Write the formulas for the two cobalt oxides formed by these transition metal ions.

**46.** Platinum is a transition element and forms $Pt^{2+}$ and $Pt^{4+}$ ions. Write the formulas for the compounds of each of these ions with (a) chloride ions and (b) sulfide ions.

**47.** Which of the following are correct formulas for ionic compounds? For those that are not, give the correct formula.
(a) $AlCl_2$           (c) $Ga_2O_3$
(b) $KF_2$             (d) $MgS$

**48.** Which of the following are correct formulas for ionic compounds? For those that are not, give the correct formula.
(a) $Ca_2O$            (c) $Fe_2O_5$
(b) $SrBr_2$           (d) $Li_2O$

## Naming Ionic Compounds

**49.** Name each of the following ionic compounds:
(a) $K_2S$             (c) $(NH_4)_3PO_4$
(b) $CoSO_4$           (d) $Ca(ClO)_2$

**50.** Name each of the following ionic compounds:
(a) $Ca(CH_3CO_2)_2$   (c) $Al(OH)_3$
(b) $Ni_3(PO_4)_2$     (d) $KH_2PO_4$

**51.** Give the formula for each of the following ionic compounds:
(a) ammonium carbonate   (d) aluminum phosphate
(b) calcium iodide       (e) silver(I) acetate
(c) copper(II) bromide

**52.** Give the formula for each of the following ionic compounds:
(a) calcium hydrogen carbonate
(b) potassium permanganate
(c) magnesium perchlorate
(d) potassium hydrogen phosphate
(e) sodium sulfite

**53.** Write the formulas for the four ionic compounds that can be made by combining each of the cations $Na^+$ and $Ba^{2+}$ with the anions $CO_3^{2-}$ and $I^-$. Name each of the compounds.

**54.** Write the formulas for the four ionic compounds that can be made by combining the cations $Mg^{2+}$ and $Fe^{3+}$ with the anions $PO_4^{3-}$ and $NO_3^-$. Name each compound formed.

## Coulomb's Law

*(See Equation 2.3 and Figure 2.21.)*

**55.** Sodium ions, $Na^+$, form ionic compounds with fluoride ions, $F^-$, and iodide ions, $I^-$. The radii of these ions are as follows: $Na^+ = 116$ pm; $F^- = 119$ pm; and $I^- = 206$ pm. In which ionic compound, NaF or NaI, are the forces of attraction between cation and anion stronger? Explain your answer.

**56.** Consider the two ionic compounds NaCl and CaO. In which compound are the cation–anion attractive forces stronger? Explain your answer.

## Naming Binary, Nonmetal Compounds

**57.** Name each of the following binary, nonionic compounds:
(a) $NF_3$    (b) HI    (c) $BI_3$    (d) $PF_5$

**58.** Name each of the following binary, nonionic compounds:
(a) $N_2O_5$    (b) $P_4S_3$    (c) $OF_2$    (d) $XeF_4$

59. Give the formula for each of the following compounds:
    (a) sulfur dichloride
    (b) dinitrogen pentaoxide
    (c) silicon tetrachloride
    (d) diboron trioxide (commonly called boric oxide)

60. Give the formula for each of the following compounds:
    (a) bromine trifluoride
    (b) xenon difluoride
    (c) hydrazine
    (d) diphosphorus tetrafluoride
    (e) butane

**Atoms and the Mole**
*(See Example 2.6.)*

61. Calculate the mass, in grams, of each the following:
    (a) 2.5 mol of aluminum
    (b) $1.25 \times 10^{-3}$ mol of iron
    (c) 0.015 mol of calcium
    (d) 653 mol of neon

62. Calculate the mass, in grams, of each the following:
    (a) 4.24 mol of gold
    (b) 15.6 mol of He
    (c) 0.063 mol of platinum
    (d) $3.63 \times 10^{-4}$ mol of Pu

63. Calculate the amount (moles) represented by each of the following:
    (a) 127.08 g of Cu
    (b) 0.012 g of lithium
    (c) 5.0 mg of americium
    (d) 6.75 g of Al

64. Calculate the amount (moles) represented by each of the following:
    (a) 16.0 g of Na
    (b) 0.876 g of tin
    (c) 0.0034 g of platinum
    (d) 0.983 g of Xe

65. You are given 1.0-g samples of He, Fe, Li, Si, and C. Which sample contains the largest number of atoms? Which contains the smallest?

66. You are given 0.10-g samples of K, Mo, Cr, and Al. List the samples in order of the amount (moles), from smallest to largest.

67. Analysis of a 10.0-g sample of apatite (a major component of tooth enamel) showed that it was made up of 3.99 g Ca, 1.85 g P, 4.14 g O, and 0.020 g H. List these elements based on relative amounts (moles), from smallest to largest.

68. A semiconducting material is composed of 52 g of Ga, 9.5 g of Al, and 112 g of As. Which element has the largest number of atoms in this material?

**Molecules, Compounds, and the Mole**
*(See Example 2.7.)*

69. Calculate the molar mass of each of the following compounds:
    (a) $Fe_2O_3$, iron(III) oxide
    (b) $BCl_3$, boron trichloride
    (c) $C_6H_8O_6$, ascorbic acid (vitamin C)

70. Calculate the molar mass of each of the following compounds:
    (a) $Fe(C_6H_{11}O_7)_2$, iron(II) gluconate, a dietary supplement
    (b) $CH_3CH_2CH_2CH_2SH$, butanethiol, has a skunk-like odor
    (c) $C_{20}H_{24}N_2O_2$, quinine, used as an antimalarial drug

71. Calculate the molar mass of each hydrated compound. Note that the water of hydration is included in the molar mass. (See Section 2.11.)
    (a) $Ni(NO_3)_2 \cdot 6\ H_2O$
    (b) $CuSO_4 \cdot 5\ H_2O$

72. Calculate the molar mass of each hydrated compound. Note that the water of hydration is included in the molar mass. (See Section 2.11.)
    (a) $H_2C_2O_4 \cdot 2\ H_2O$
    (b) $MgSO_4 \cdot 7\ H_2O$, Epsom salt

73. What mass is represented by 0.0255 mol of each of the following compounds?
    (a) $C_3H_7OH$, 2-propanol, rubbing alcohol
    (b) $C_{11}H_{16}O_2$, an antioxidant in foods, also known as BHA (butylated hydroxyanisole)
    (c) $C_9H_8O_4$, aspirin
    (d) $(CH_3)_2CO$, acetone, an important industrial solvent

74. Assume you have 0.123 mol of each of the following compounds. What mass of each is present?
    (a) $C_{14}H_{10}O_4$, benzoyl peroxide, used in acne medications
    (b) Dimethylglyoxime, used in the laboratory to test for nickel(II) ions

(c) The compound below, responsible for the "skunky" taste in poorly made beer.

(d) DEET, a mosquito repellent

75. Sulfur trioxide, $SO_3$, is made industrially in enormous quantities by combining oxygen and sulfur dioxide, $SO_2$. What amount (moles) of $SO_3$ is represented by 1.00 kg of sulfur trioxide? How many molecules? How many sulfur atoms? How many oxygen atoms?

76. How many ammonium ions and how many sulfate ions are present in an 0.20 mol sample of $(NH_4)_2SO_4$? How many atoms of N, H, S and O are contained in this sample?

77. Acetaminophen, whose structure is drawn below, is the active ingredient in some nonprescription pain killers. The recommended dose for an adult is two 500 mg caplets. How many molecules make up one dose of this drug?

78. An Alka-Seltzer tablet contains 324 mg of aspirin ($C_9H_8O_4$), 1904 mg of $NaHCO_3$, and 1000. mg of citric acid ($H_3C_6H_5O_7$). (The last two compounds react with each other to provide the "fizz," bubbles of $CO_2$, when the tablet is put into water.)
    (a) Calculate the amount (moles) of each substance in the tablet.
    (b) If you take one tablet, how many molecules of aspirin are you consuming?

### Percent Composition
*(See Example 2.8.)*

79. Calculate the mass percent of each element in the following compounds:
    (a) PbS, lead(II) sulfide, galena
    (b) $C_3H_8$, propane
    (c) $C_{10}H_{14}O$, carvone, found in caraway seed oil

80. Calculate the mass percent of each element in the following compounds:
    (a) $C_8H_{10}N_2O_2$, caffeine
    (b) $C_{10}H_{20}O$, menthol
    (c) $CoCl_2 \cdot 6\ H_2O$

81. Calculate the mass percent of copper in CuS, copper(II) sulfide. If you wish to obtain 10.0 g of copper metal from copper(II) sulfide, what mass of CuS (in grams) must you use?

82. Calculate the mass percent of titanium in the mineral ilmenite, $FeTiO_3$. What mass of ilmenite (in grams) is required if you wish to obtain 750 g of titanium?

### Empirical and Molecular Formulas
*(See Example 2.9.)*

83. Succinic acid occurs in fungi and lichens. Its empirical formula is $C_2H_3O_2$, and its molar mass is 118.1 g/mol. What is its molecular formula?

84. An organic compound has the empirical formula $C_2H_4NO$. If its molar mass is 116.1 g/mol, what is the molecular formula of the compound?

85. Complete the following table:

| Empirical Formula | Molar Mass (g/mol) | Molecular Formula |
|---|---|---|
| (a) CH | 26.0 | _____ |
| (b) CHO | 116.1 | _____ |
| (c) _____ | _____ | $C_8H_{16}$ |

86. Complete the following table:

| Empirical Formula | Molar Mass (g/mol) | Molecular Formula |
|---|---|---|
| (a) $C_2H_3O_3$ | 150.0 | _____ |
| (b) $C_3H_8$ | 44.1 | _____ |
| (c) _____ | _____ | $B_4H_{10}$ |

87. Acetylene is a colorless gas used as a fuel in welding torches, among other things. It is 92.26% C and 7.74% H. Its molar mass is 26.02 g/mol. What are the empirical and molecular formulas of acetylene?

88. A large family of boron-hydrogen compounds has the general formula $B_xH_y$. One member of this family contains 88.5% B; the remainder is hydrogen. What is its empirical formula?

89. Cumene, a hydrocarbon, is a compound composed only of C and H. It is 89.94% carbon, and its molar mass is 120.2 g/mol. What are the empirical and molecular formulas of cumene?

90. In 2006, a Russian team discovered an interesting molecule they called "sulflower" because of its shape and because it was based on sulfur. It is composed of 57.17% S and 42.83% C and has a molar mass of 448.70 g/mol. Determine the empirical and molecular formulas of "sulflower."

91. Mandelic acid is an organic acid composed of carbon (63.15%), hydrogen (5.30%), and oxygen (31.55%). Its molar mass is 152.14 g/mol. Determine the empirical and molecular formulas of the acid.

92. Nicotine, a poisonous compound found in tobacco leaves, is 74.0% C, 8.65% H, and 17.35% N. Its molar mass is 162 g/mol. What are the empirical and molecular formulas of nicotine?

### Determining Formulas from Mass Data
*(See Examples 2.10 and 2.11.)*

93. A compound containing xenon and fluorine was prepared by shining sunlight on a mixture of Xe (0.526 g) and excess $F_2$ gas. If you isolate 0.678 g of the new compound, what is its empirical formula?

94. Elemental sulfur (1.256 g) is combined with fluorine, $F_2$, to give a compound with the formula $SF_x$, a very stable, colorless gas. If you have isolated 5.722 g of $SF_x$, what is the value of $x$?

95. Zinc metal (2.50 g) combines with 9.70 g of iodine to produce zinc iodide, $Zn_xI_y$. What is the formula of this ionic compound?

96. You combine 1.25 g of germanium, Ge, with excess chlorine, $Cl_2$. The mass of product, $Ge_xCl_y$, is 3.69 g. What is the formula of the product, $Ge_xCl_y$?

## General Questions

*These questions are not designated as to type or location in the chapter. They may combine several concepts.*

97. Fill in the blanks in the table (one column per element).

| Symbol | $^{58}Ni$ | $^{33}S$ | | |
|---|---|---|---|---|
| Number of protons | _____ | _____ | 10 | _____ |
| Number of neutrons | _____ | _____ | 10 | 30 |
| Number of electrons in the neutral atom | _____ | _____ | _____ | 25 |
| Name of element | _____ | _____ | _____ | _____ |

98. Potassium has three naturally occurring isotopes ($^{39}K$, $^{40}K$, and $^{41}K$), but $^{40}K$ has a very low natural abundance. Which of the other two isotopes is more abundant? Briefly explain your answer.

99. Crossword Puzzle: In the $2 \times 2$ box shown here, each answer must be correct four ways: horizontally, vertically, diagonally, and by itself. Instead of words, use symbols of elements. When the puzzle is complete, the four spaces will contain the overlapping symbols of 10 elements. There is only one correct solution.

| 1 | 2 |
|---|---|
| 3 | 4 |

*Horizontal*
1–2: two-letter symbol for a metal used in ancient times
3–4: two-letter symbol for a metal that burns in air and is found in Group 5A

*Vertical*
1–3: two-letter symbol for a metalloid
2–4: two-letter symbol for a metal used in U.S. coins

**Single squares: All one-letter symbols**
1: a colorful nonmetal
2: colorless, gaseous nonmetal
3: an element that makes fireworks green
4: an element that has medicinal uses

*Diagonal*
1–4: two-letter symbol for an element used in electronics
2–3: two-letter symbol for a metal used with Zr to make wires for superconducting magnets

This puzzle first appeared in *Chemical & Engineering News*, p. 86, December 14, 1987 (submitted by S. J. Cyvin) and in *Chem Matters*, October 1988.

100. The chart below shows a general decline in abundance with increasing mass among the first 30 elements. The decline continues beyond zinc. (Notice that the scale on the vertical axis is logarithmic, that is, it progresses in powers of 10. The abundance of nitrogen, for example, is 1/10,000 ($1/10^4$) of the abundance of hydrogen. All abundances are plotted as the number of atoms per $10^{12}$ atoms of H. (The fact that the abundances of Li, Be, and B, as well as those of the elements near Fe, do not follow the general decline is a consequence of the way that elements are synthesized in stars.)

The abundance of the elements in the solar system from H to Zn.

(a) What is the most abundant main group metal?
(b) What is the most abundant nonmetal?
(c) What is the most abundant metalloid?
(d) Which of the transition elements is most abundant?
(e) Which halogens are included on this plot, and which is the most abundant?

101. Copper atoms.
(a) What is the average mass of one copper atom?
(b) Students in a college computer science class once sued the college because they were asked to calculate the cost of one atom and could not do it. But you are in a chemistry course, and you can do this. (See E. Felsenthal, *Wall Street Journal*, May 9, 1995.) If the cost of 2.0-mm diameter copper wire (99.999% pure) is currently $41.70 for 7.0 g, what is the cost of one copper atom?

102. Which of the following is impossible?
(a) silver foil that is $1.2 \times 10^{-4}$ m thick
(b) a sample of potassium that contains $1.784 \times 10^{24}$ atoms
(c) a gold coin of mass $1.23 \times 10^{-3}$ kg
(d) $3.43 \times 10^{-27}$ mol of $S_8$ molecules

103. Reviewing the periodic table.
(a) Name the element in Group 2A and the fifth period.
(b) Name the element in the fifth period and Group 4B.
(c) Which element is in the second period in Group 4A?
(d) Which element is in the fourth period in Group 5A?
(e) Which halogen is in the fifth period?
(f) Which alkaline earth element is in the third period?
(g) Which noble gas element is in the fourth period?
(h) Name the nonmetal in Group 6A and the third period.
(i) Name a metalloid in the fourth period.

104. Identify two nonmetallic elements that have allotropes and describe the allotropes of each.

105. In each case, decide which represents more mass:
(a) 0.5 mol of Na, 0.5 mol of Si, or 0.25 mol of U
(b) 9.0 g of Na, 0.50 mol of Na, or $1.2 \times 10^{22}$ atoms of Na
(c) 10 atoms of Fe or 10 atoms of K

**106.** The recommended daily allowance (RDA) of iron in your diet is 15 mg. How many moles is this? How many atoms?

**107.** Put the following elements in order from smallest to largest mass:
(a) $3.79 \times 10^{24}$ atoms Fe   (e) 9.221 mol Na
(b) 19.921 mol $H_2$   (f) $4.07 \times 10^{24}$ atoms Al
(c) 8.576 mol C   (g) 9.2 mol $Cl_2$
(d) 7.4 mol Si

**108.** ▲ When a sample of phosphorus burns in air, the compound $P_4O_{10}$ forms. One experiment showed that 0.744 g of phosphorus formed 1.704 g of $P_4O_{10}$. Use this information to determine the ratio of the atomic weights of phosphorus and oxygen (mass P/mass O). If the atomic weight of oxygen is assumed to be 16.000 u, calculate the atomic weight of phosphorus.

**109.** ▲ Although carbon-12 is now used as the standard for atomic weights, this has not always been the case. Early attempts at classification used hydrogen as the standard, with the weight of hydrogen being set equal to 1.0000 u. Later attempts defined atomic weights using oxygen (with a weight of 16.0000). In each instance, the atomic weights of the other elements were defined relative to these masses. (To answer this question, you need more precise data on current atomic weights: H, 1.00794 u; O, 15.9994 u.)
(a) If H = 1.0000 u was used as a standard for atomic weights, what would the atomic weight of oxygen be? What would be the value of Avogadro's number under these circumstances?
(b) Assuming the standard is O = 16.0000, determine the value for the atomic weight of hydrogen and the value of Avogadro's number.

**110.** A reagent occasionally used in chemical synthesis is sodium–potassium alloy. (Alloys are mixtures of metals, and Na-K has the interesting property that it is a liquid.) One formulation of the alloy (the one that melts at the lowest temperature) contains 68 atom percent K; that is, out of every 100 atoms, 68 are K and 32 are Na. What is the mass percent of potassium in sodium–potassium alloy?

**111.** Write formulas for all of the compounds that can be made by combining the cations $NH_4^+$ and $Ni^{2+}$ with the anions $CO_3^{2-}$ and $SO_4^{2-}$.

**112.** How many electrons are in a strontium atom (Sr)? Does an atom of Sr gain or lose electrons when forming an ion? How many electrons are gained or lost by the atom? When Sr forms an ion, the ion has the same number of electrons as which one of the noble gases?

**113.** Which of the following compounds has the highest mass percent of chlorine?
(a) $BCl_3$   (d) $AlCl_3$
(b) $AsCl_3$   (e) $PCl_3$
(c) $GaCl_3$

**114.** Which of the following samples has the largest number of ions?
(a) 1.0 g of $BeCl_2$   (d) 1.0 g of $SrCO_3$
(b) 1.0 g of $MgCl_2$   (e) 1.0 g of $BaSO_4$
(c) 1.0 g of CaS

**115.** The structure of one of the bases in DNA, adenine, is shown here. Which represents the greater mass: 40.0 g of adenine or $3.0 \times 10^{23}$ molecules of the compound?

**116.** Ionic and molecular compounds of the halogens.
(a) What are the names of $BaF_2$, $SiCl_4$, and $NiBr_2$?
(b) Which of the compounds in part (a) are ionic, and which are molecular?
(c) Which has the larger mass, 0.50 mol of $BaF_2$, 0.50 mol of $SiCl_4$, or 1.0 mol of $NiBr_2$?

**117.** A drop of water has a volume of about 0.050 mL. How many molecules of water are in a drop of water? (Assume water has a density of 1.00 $g/cm^3$.)

**118.** Capsaicin, the compound that gives the hot taste to chili peppers, has the formula $C_{18}H_{27}NO_3$.
(a) Calculate its molar mass.
(b) If you eat 55 mg of capsaicin, what amount (moles) have you consumed?
(c) Calculate the mass percent of each element in the compound.
(d) What mass of carbon (in milligrams) is there in 55 mg of capsaicin?

**119.** Calculate the molar mass and the mass percent of each element in the blue solid compound $Cu(NH_3)_4SO_4 \cdot H_2O$. What is the mass of copper and the mass of water in 10.5 g of the compound?

**120.** Write the molecular formula and calculate the molar mass for each of the molecules shown here. Which has the largest mass percent of carbon? Of oxygen?
(a) ethylene glycol (used in antifreeze)

(b) dihydroxyacetone (used in artificial tanning lotions)

(c) ascorbic acid, commonly known as vitamin C

121. Malic acid, an organic acid found in apples, contains C, H, and O in the following ratios: $C_1H_{1.50}O_{1.25}$. What is the empirical formula of malic acid?

122. Your doctor has diagnosed you as being anemic—that is, as having too little iron in your blood. At the drugstore, you find two iron-containing dietary supplements: one with iron(II) sulfate, $FeSO_4$, and the other with iron(II) gluconate, $Fe(C_6H_{11}O_7)_2$. If you take 100. mg of each compound, which will deliver more atoms of iron?

123. A compound composed of iron and carbon monoxide, $Fe_x(CO)_y$, is 30.70% iron. What is the empirical formula for the compound?

124. Ma huang, an extract from the ephedra species of plants, contains ephedrine. The Chinese have used this herb for more than 5000 years to treat asthma. More recently, ephedrine has been used in diet pills that can be purchased over the counter in herbal medicine shops. However, very serious concerns have been raised regarding these pills following reports that their use led to serious heart problems.
    (a) A molecular model of ephedrine is drawn below. From this determine the molecular formula for ephedrine and calculate its molar mass.
    (b) What is the weight percent of carbon in ephedrine?
    (c) Calculate the amount (moles) of ephedrine in a 0.125 g sample.
    (d) How many molecules of ephedrine are there in 0.125 g? How many C atoms?

125. Saccharin, a molecular model of which is shown below, is more than 300 times sweeter than sugar. It was first made in 1897, when it was common practice for chemists to record the taste of any new substances they synthesized.
    (a) Write the molecular formula for the compound, and draw its structural formula. (S atoms are yellow.)
    (b) If you ingest 125 mg of saccharin, what amount (moles) of saccharin have you ingested?
    (c) What mass of sulfur is contained in 125 mg of saccharin?

126. Name each of the following compounds and indicate which ones are best described as ionic:
    (a) $ClF_3$      (f) $OF_2$
    (b) $NCl_3$      (g) $KI$
    (c) $SrSO_4$     (h) $Al_2S_3$
    (d) $Ca(NO_3)_2$ (i) $PCl_3$
    (e) $XeF_4$      (j) $K_3PO_4$

127. Write the formula for each of the following compounds and indicate which ones are best described as ionic:
    (a) sodium hypochlorite
    (b) boron triiodide
    (c) aluminum perchlorate
    (d) calcium acetate
    (e) potassium permanganate
    (f) ammonium sulfite
    (g) potassium dihydrogen phosphate
    (h) disulfur dichloride
    (i) chlorine trifluoride
    (j) phosphorus trifluoride

128. Complete the table by placing symbols, formulas, and names in the blanks.

| Cation | Anion | Name | Formula |
|--------|-------|------|---------|
| _____ | _____ | ammonium bromide | _____ |
| $Ba^{2+}$ | _____ | _____ | BaS |
| _____ | $Cl^-$ | iron(II) chloride | _____ |
| _____ | $F^-$ | _____ | $PbF_2$ |
| $Al^{3+}$ | $CO_3^{2-}$ | _____ | _____ |
| _____ | _____ | iron(III) oxide | _____ |

129. Empirical and molecular formulas.
    (a) Fluorocarbonyl hypofluorite is composed of 14.6% C, 39.0% O, and 46.3% F. The molar mass of the compound is 82 g/mol. Determine the empirical and molecular formulas of the compound.
    (b) Azulene, a beautiful blue hydrocarbon, is 93.71% C and has a molar mass of 128.16 g/mol. What are the empirical and molecular formulas of azulene?

130. Cacodyl, a compound containing arsenic, was reported in 1842 by the German chemist Robert Wilhelm Bunsen. It has an almost intolerable garlic-like odor. Its molar mass is 210 g/mol, and it is 22.88% C, 5.76% H, and 71.36% As. Determine its empirical and molecular formulas.

131. The action of bacteria on meat and fish produces a compound called cadaverine. As its name and origin imply, it stinks! (It is also present in bad breath and adds to the odor of urine.) It is 58.77% C, 13.81% H, and 27.40% N. Its molar mass is 102.2 g/mol. Determine the molecular formula of cadaverine.

132. ▲ Transition metals can combine with carbon monoxide (CO) to form compounds such as $Fe_x(CO)_y$ (Study Question 123). Assume that you combine 0.125 g of nickel with CO and isolate 0.364 g of $Ni(CO)_x$. What is the value of $x$?

133. ▲ A compound called MMT was once used to boost the octane rating of gasoline. What is the empirical formula of MMT if it is 49.5% C, 3.2% H, 22.0% O, and 25.2% Mn?

134. ▲ Elemental phosphorus is made by heating calcium phosphate with carbon and sand in an electric furnace. What is the mass percent of phosphorus in calcium phosphate? Use this value to calculate the mass of calcium phosphate (in kilograms) that must be used to produce 15.0 kg of phosphorus.

135. ▲ Chromium is obtained by heating chromium(III) oxide with carbon. Calculate the mass percent of chromium in the oxide, and then use this value to calculate the quantity of $Cr_2O_3$ required to produce 850 kg of chromium metal.

136. ▲ Stibnite, $Sb_2S_3$, is a dark gray mineral from which antimony metal is obtained. What is the mass percent of antimony in the sulfide? If you have 1.00 kg of an ore that contains 10.6% antimony, what mass of $Sb_2S_3$ (in grams) is in the ore?

137. ▲ Direct reaction of iodine ($I_2$) and chlorine ($Cl_2$) produces an iodine chloride, $I_xCl_y$, a bright yellow solid. If you completely consume 0.678 g of $I_2$ in a reaction with excess $Cl_2$ and produce 1.246 g of $I_xCl_y$, what is the empirical formula of the compound? A later experiment showed that the molar mass of $I_xCl_y$ was 467 g/mol. What is the molecular formula of the compound?

138. ▲ In a reaction, 2.04 g of vanadium combined with 1.93 g of sulfur to give a pure compound. What is the empirical formula of the product?

139. ▲ Iron pyrite, often called "fool's gold," has the formula $FeS_2$. If you could convert 15.8 kg of iron pyrite to iron metal, what mass of the metal would you obtain?

140. Which of the following statements about 57.1 g of octane, $C_8H_{18}$, is (are) *not* true?
    (a) 57.1 g is 0.500 mol of octane.
    (b) The compound is 84.1% C by weight.
    (c) The empirical formula of the compound is $C_4H_9$.
    (d) 57.1 g of octane contains 28.0 g of hydrogen atoms.

141. The formula of barium molybdate is $BaMoO_4$. Which of the following is the formula of sodium molybdate?
    (a) $Na_4MoO$    (c) $Na_2MoO_3$    (e) $Na_4MoO_4$
    (b) $NaMoO$    (d) $Na_2MoO_4$

142. ▲ A metal M forms a compound with the formula $MCl_4$. If the compound is 74.75% chlorine, what is the identity of M?

143. Pepto-Bismol, which can help provide relief for an upset stomach, contains 300. mg of bismuth subsalicylate, $C_{21}H_{15}Bi_3O_{12}$, per tablet. If you take two tablets for your stomach distress, what amount (in moles) of the "active ingredient" are you taking? What mass of Bi are you consuming in two tablets?

144. ▲ The weight percent of oxygen in an oxide that has the formula $MO_2$ is 15.2%. What is the molar mass of this compound? What element or elements are possible for M?

145. The mass of 2.50 mol of a compound with the formula $ECl_4$, in which E is a nonmetallic element, is 385 g. What is the molar mass of $ECl_4$? What is the identity of E?

146. ▲ The elements A and Z combine to produce two different compounds: $A_2Z_3$ and $AZ_2$. If 0.15 mol of $A_2Z_3$ has a mass of 15.9 g and 0.15 mol of $AZ_2$ has a mass of 9.3 g, what are the atomic masses of A and Z?

147. ▲ Polystyrene can be prepared by heating styrene with tribromobenzoyl peroxide in the absence of air. A sample prepared by this method has the empirical formula $Br_3C_6H_3(C_8H_8)_n$, where the value of $n$ can vary from sample to sample. If one sample has 0.105% Br, what is the value of $n$?

148. A sample of hemoglobin is found to be 0.335% iron. What is the molar mass of hemoglobin if there are four iron atoms per molecule?

149. ▲ Consider an atom of $^{64}Zn$.
    (a) Calculate the density of the nucleus in grams per cubic centimeter, knowing that the nuclear radius is $4.8 \times 10^{-6}$ nm and the mass of the $^{64}Zn$ atom is $1.06 \times 10^{-22}$ g. (Recall that the volume of a sphere is $[4/3]\pi r^3$.)
    (b) Calculate the density of the space occupied by the electrons in the zinc atom, given that the atomic radius is 0.125 nm and the electron mass is $9.11 \times 10^{-28}$ g.
    (c) Having calculated these densities, what statement can you make about the relative densities of the parts of the atom?

150. ▲ Estimating the radius of a lead atom.
    (a) You are given a cube of lead that is 1.000 cm on each side. The density of lead is 11.35 g/cm³. How many atoms of lead are in the sample?
    (b) Atoms are spherical; therefore, the lead atoms in this sample cannot fill all the available space. As an approximation, assume that 60% of the space of the cube is filled with spherical lead atoms. Calculate the volume of one lead atom from this information. From the calculated volume (V) and the formula $(4/3)\pi r^3$ for the volume of a sphere, estimate the radius ($r$) of a lead atom.

151. A piece of nickel foil, 0.550 mm thick and 1.25 cm square, is allowed to react with fluorine, $F_2$, to give a nickel fluoride.
    (a) How many moles of nickel foil were used? (The density of nickel is 8.902 g/cm³.)
    (b) If you isolate 1.261 g of the nickel fluoride, what is its formula?
    (c) What is its complete name?

**152.** ▲ Uranium is used as a fuel, primarily in the form of uranium(IV) oxide, in nuclear power plants. This question considers some uranium chemistry.

    (a) A small sample of uranium metal (0.169 g) is heated to between 800 and 900 °C in air to give 0.199 g of a dark green oxide, $U_xO_y$. How many moles of uranium metal were used? What is the empirical formula of the oxide, $U_xO_y$? What is the name of the oxide? How many moles of $U_xO_y$ must have been obtained?

    (b) The naturally occurring isotopes of uranium are $^{234}U$, $^{235}U$, and $^{238}U$. Knowing that uranium's atomic weight is 238.02 g/mol, which isotope must be the most abundant?

    (c) If the hydrated compound $UO_2(NO_3)_2 \cdot z\ H_2O$ is heated gently, the water of hydration is lost. If you have 0.865 g of the hydrated compound and obtain 0.679 g of $UO_2(NO_3)_2$ on heating, how many waters of hydration are in each formula unit of the original compound? (The oxide $U_xO_y$ is obtained if the hydrate is heated to temperatures over 800°C in the air.)

## In the Laboratory

**153.** If Epsom salt, $MgSO_4 \cdot x\ H_2O$, is heated to 250 °C, all the water of hydration is lost. On heating a 1.687-g sample of the hydrate, 0.824 g of $MgSO_4$ remains. How many molecules of water occur per formula unit of $MgSO_4$?

**154.** The "alum" used in cooking is potassium aluminum sulfate hydrate, $KAl(SO_4)_2 \cdot x\ H_2O$. To find the value of $x$, you can heat a sample of the compound to drive off all of the water and leave only $KAl(SO_4)_2$. Assume you heat 4.74 g of the hydrated compound and that the sample loses 2.16 g of water. What is the value of $x$?

**155.** In an experiment, you need 0.125 mol of sodium metal. Sodium can be cut easily with a knife (Figure 2.6), so if you cut out a block of sodium, what should the volume of the block be in cubic centimeters? If you cut a perfect cube, what is the length of the edge of the cube? (The density of sodium is 0.97 g/cm³.)

**156.** ▲ When analyzed, an unknown compound gave these experimental results: C, 54.0%; H, 6.00%; and O, 40.0%. Four different students used these values to calculate the empirical formulas shown here. Which answer is correct? Why did some students not get the correct answer?

    (a) $C_4H_5O_2$         (c) $C_7H_{10}O_4$

    (b) $C_5H_7O_3$         (d) $C_9H_{12}O_5$

**157.** ▲ Two general chemistry students working together in the lab weigh out 0.832 g of $CaCl_2 \cdot 2\ H_2O$ into a crucible. After heating the sample for a short time and allowing the crucible to cool, the students determine that the sample has a mass of 0.739 g. They then do a quick calculation. On the basis of this calculation, what should they do next?

    (a) Congratulate themselves on a job well done.

    (b) Assume the bottle of $CaCl_2 \cdot 2\ H_2O$ was mislabeled; it actually contained something different.

    (c) Heat the crucible again, and then reweigh it.

**158.** Mass spectrometric analysis showed that there are four isotopes of an unknown element having the following masses and abundances:

| Isotope | Mass Number | Isotope Mass | Abundance (%) |
|---|---|---|---|
| 1 | 136 | 135.9090 | 0.193 |
| 2 | 138 | 137.9057 | 0.250 |
| 3 | 140 | 139.9053 | 88.48 |
| 4 | 142 | 141.9090 | 11.07 |

Three elements in the periodic table that have atomic weights near these values are lanthanum (La), atomic number 57, atomic weight 138.9055; cerium (Ce), atomic number 58, atomic weight 140.115; and praseodymium (Pr), atomic number 59, atomic weight 140.9076. Using the data above, calculate the atomic weight, and identify the element if possible.

**159.** The mass spectrum of $CH_3Cl$ is illustrated here. You know that carbon has two stable isotopes, $^{12}C$ and $^{13}C$ with relative abundances of 98.9% and 1.1%, respectively, and chlorine has two isotopes, $^{35}Cl$ and $^{37}Cl$ with abundances of 75.77% and 24.23%, respectively.

    (a) What molecular species gives rise to the lines at $m/Z$ of 50 and 52? Why is the line at 52 about 1/3 the height of the line at 50?

    (b) What species might be responsible for the line at $m/Z = 51$?

**160.** The highest mass peaks in the mass spectrum of $Br_2$ occur at $m/Z$ 158, 160, and 162. The ratio of intensities of these peaks is approximately 1:2:1. Bromine has two stable isotopes, $^{79}Br$ (50.7% abundance) and $^{81}Br$ (49.3% abundance).

    (a) What molecular species gives rise to each of these peaks?

    (b) Explain the relative intensities of these peaks. (*Hint:* Consider the probabilities of each atom combination.)

# Summary and Conceptual Questions

*The following questions may use concepts from this and the previous chapter.*

161. ▲ Identify, from the list below, the information needed to calculate the number of atoms in 1.00 cm³ of iron. Outline the procedure used in this calculation.
    (a) the structure of solid iron
    (b) the molar mass of iron
    (c) Avogadro's number
    (d) the density of iron
    (e) the temperature
    (f) iron's atomic number
    (g) the number of iron isotopes

162. Consider the plot of relative element abundances on page 103. Is there a relationship between abundance and atomic number? Is there any difference between the relative abundance of an element of even atomic number and the relative abundance of an element of odd atomic number?

163. The photo here depicts what happens when a coil of magnesium ribbon and a few calcium chips are placed in water.
    (a) Based on these observations, what might you expect to see when barium, another Group 2A element, is placed in water?
    (b) Give the period in which each element (Mg, Ca, and Ba) is found; what correlation do you think you might find between the reactivity of these elements and their positions in the periodic table?

**Magnesium (*left*) and calcium (*right*) in water.**

164. A jar contains some number of jelly beans. To find out precisely how many are in the jar, you could dump them out and count them. How could you estimate their number without counting each one? (Chemists need to do just this kind of "bean counting" when they work with atoms and molecules. Atoms and molecules are too small to count one by one, so chemists have worked out other methods to determine the number of atoms in a sample.)

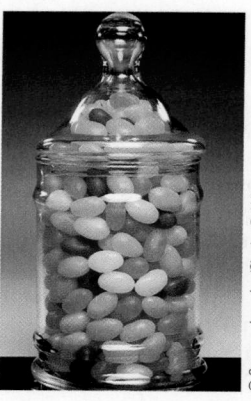

**How many jelly beans are in the jar?**

165. Cobalt(II) chloride hexahydrate, dissolves readily in water to give a red solution. If we use this solution as an "ink," we can write secret messages on paper. The writing is not visible when the water evaporates from the paper. When the paper is heated, however, the message can be read. Explain the chemistry behind this observation.

**A solution of CoCl₂ · 6 H₂O.**

**Using the secret ink to write on paper.**

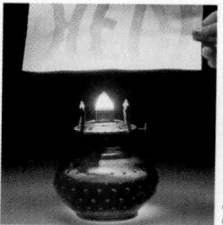

**Heating the paper reveals the writing.**

# Applying Chemical Principles

## Argon—An Amazing Discovery

The noble gas argon was discovered by Sir William Ramsay and John William Strutt (the third Lord Rayleigh) in England and reported in scientific journals in 1895. In making this discovery, Ramsay and Rayleigh made highly accurate measurements of gas densities. They found that gaseous nitrogen ($N_2$) formed by thermal decomposition of ammonia had a density that was slightly lower than the density of the gas that remained after $O_2$, $CO_2$, and $H_2O$ were removed from air. The reason for the difference is that the sample derived from air contained a very small amount of other gases. After removing $N_2$ from the sample by reacting it with red hot magnesium (to form $Mg_3N_2$), a small quantity of gas remained that was more dense than air. This was identified as argon.

Lord Rayleigh's experimentally determined densities for oxygen, nitrogen, and air are given below:

| Gas | Density (g/L) |
| --- | --- |
| Oxygen | 1.42952 |
| Nitrogen, derived from air | 1.25718 |
| Nitrogen, derived from ammonia | 1.25092 |
| Air, with water and $CO_2$ removed | 1.29327 |

**Sir William Ramsay (1852–1916).** Ramsay was a Scottish chemist who discovered the noble gases (for which he received the Nobel Prize in Chemistry in 1904. Lord Rayleigh received the Nobel Prize in Physics, also in 1904, for the discovery of argon.

AFP Photo/Toshifumi KITAMURA/Newscom

## Questions:

1. To determine the density of atmospheric nitrogen, Rayleigh removed the oxygen, water, and carbon dioxide from air, then filled an evacuated glass globe with the remaining gas. Rayleigh determined that a mass of 0.20389 g of nitrogen has a density of 1.25718 g/L under standard conditions of temperature and pressure. What is the volume of the globe (in $cm^3$)?

2. The density of a mixture of gases may be calculated by summing the products of the density of each gas and the fractional volume of space occupied by that gas. (Note the similarity to the calculation of the molar mass of an element from the isotopic masses and fractional abundances). Assume dry air with $CO_2$ removed is 20.96% (by volume) oxygen, 78.11% nitrogen, and 0.930% argon. Determine the density of argon.

3. Atmospheric argon is a mixture of three stable isotopes, $^{36}Ar$, $^{38}Ar$, and $^{40}Ar$. Use the information in the table below to determine the atomic mass and natural abundance of $^{40}Ar$.

| Isotope | Atomic Mass (u) | Abundance (%) |
| --- | --- | --- |
| $^{36}Ar$ | 35.967545 | 0.337 |
| $^{38}Ar$ | 37.96732 | 0.063 |
| $^{40}Ar$ | ? | ? |

4. Given that the density of argon is 1.78 g/L under standard conditions of temperature and pressure, how many argon atoms are present in a room with dimensions 4.0 m × 5.0 m × 2.4 m that is filled with pure argon under these conditions of temperature and pressure?

## References:

1. Proceedings of the Royal Society of London, Vol. 57, (1894–1895), pp. 265–287.
2. The Gases of the Atmosphere and Their History, 4th ed., William Ramsay, MacMillan and Co., Limited, London, 1915.

# 3  Chemical Reactions

© Ralph White/Corbis

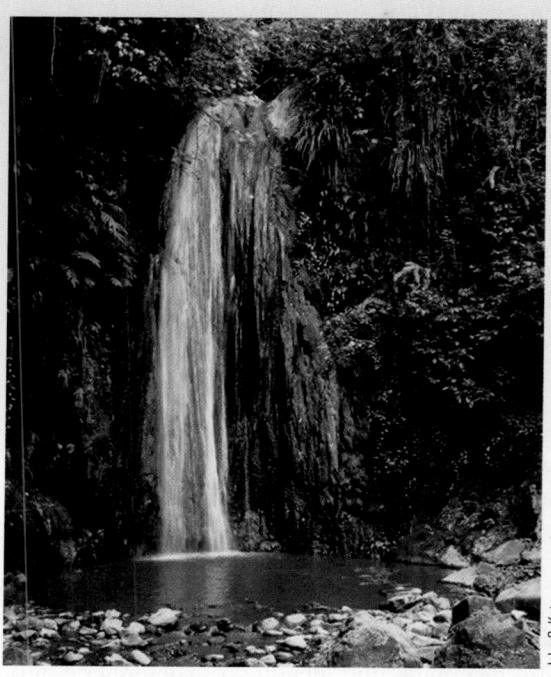

John C. Kotz

**Metal sulfides from a black smoker and a volcano.** *(above)* A "black smoker." This one was photographed deep in the Pacific Ocean along the East Pacific Rise. *(right)* The water in this waterfall (on the island of St. Lucia in the Caribbean) flows from a volcano. The sides of the rock wall are streaked with iron(III) hydroxide. The water in the pool and the rock wall are also blackened with insoluble sulfides of copper(II), iron(III), and manganese(II).

## Black Smokers and Volcanoes

In 1977, scientists were exploring the junction of two of the tectonic plates that form the floor of the Pacific Ocean. There they found thermal springs gushing a hot, black soup of minerals. Seawater seeps into cracks in the ocean floor and, as it sinks deeper into the earth's crust, the water is superheated to between 300 °C and 400 °C by the magma of the earth's core. This superhot water dissolves minerals in the crust and is pushed back to the surface. When this hot water, now laden with dissolved metal cations and rich in anions such as sulfide and sulfate, gushes through the surface, it cools, and metal sulfates such as calcium sulfate and sulfides—such as those of copper, manganese, iron, zinc, and nickel—precipitate. Many metal sulfides are black, and the plume of material coming from the sea bottom looks like black "smoke;" thus, the vents have been called "black smokers." The solid sulfides and other minerals settle around the edges of the vent on the sea floor and eventually form a "chimney" of precipitated minerals.

You can see the same deposits of metal sulfides around steam vents from volcanoes and in the water flowing away from a volcano or steam vent.

Scientists were amazed to discover that the vents were surrounded by peculiar animals living in the hot, sulfide-rich environment. Because black smokers are under hundreds of feet of water and sunlight does not penetrate to these depths, the animals have developed a way to live without the energy from sunlight. In a terrestrial environment, plants use the energy of the sun to create organic molecules by the process of photosynthesis. In the lightless ecosystem deep in the ocean, energy is derived from the oxidation of sulfides. With this source of energy, microbes are able to make the organic molecules that are the basis of life.

### Question:

Write balanced, net ionic equations for the reactions of $Fe^{2+}$ and $Bi^{3+}$ with $H_2S$ and for $Ca^{2+}$ with sulfate ions.

**The answer to this question is available in Appendix N.**

## CHAPTER GOALS

*See Chapter Goals Revisited (page 147) for Study Questions keyed to these goals.*

- Balance equations for simple chemical reactions.

- Understand the nature and characteristics of chemical equilibria.

- Understand the nature of ionic substances dissolved in water.

- Recognize common acids and bases and understand their behavior in aqueous solution.

- Recognize the common types of reactions in aqueous solution.

- Write chemical equations for the common types of reactions in aqueous solution.

- Recognize common oxidizing and reducing agents and identify oxidation–reduction reactions.

**☉WL**

Sign in to OWL at **www.cengage.com/owl** to view tutorials and simulations, develop problem-solving skills, and complete online homework assigned by your professor.

Chemical reactions are at the heart of chemistry. We begin a chemical reaction with one set of materials and end up with different materials. Just reading this sentence involves an untold number of chemical reactions in your body. Indeed, every activity of living things depends on carefully regulated chemical reactions. Our objective in this chapter is to introduce you to the symbolism used to represent chemical reactions and to describe several types of common chemical reactions.

## 3.1   Introduction to Chemical Equations

When a stream of chlorine gas, $Cl_2$, is directed onto solid phosphorus, $P_4$, the mixture bursts into flame, and a chemical reaction produces liquid phosphorus trichloride, $PCl_3$ (Figure 3.1). We can depict this reaction using a **balanced chemical equation**.

$$\underbrace{P_4(s) \ + \ 6 \ Cl_2(g)}_{\text{reactants}} \longrightarrow \underbrace{4 \ PCl_3(\ell)}_{\text{product}}$$

`go` `Chemistry`

Download mini lecture videos for key concept review and exam prep from OWL or purchase them from **www.cengagebrain.com**

In a chemical equation, the formulas for the **reactants** (the substances combined in the reaction) are written to the left of the arrow and the formulas of the **products** (the substances produced) are written to the right of the arrow. The physical states of reactants and products can also be indicated. The symbol (s) indicates a solid, (g) a gas, and ($\ell$) a liquid. A substance dissolved in water, that is, in an *aqueous* solution, is indicated by (aq).

In the 18th century, the French scientist Antoine Lavoisier (1743–1794) introduced the **law of conservation of matter**, which states that *matter can neither be created nor destroyed*. This means that if the total mass of reactants is 10 g, and if the reaction completely converts reactants to products, you must end up with 10 g of products. This also means that if 1000 atoms of a particular element are contained in the reactants, then those 1000 atoms must appear in the products in some fashion. *Atoms are conserved in chemical reactions.*

● **Information from Chemical Equations** The same number of atoms must exist after a reaction as before it takes place. However, these atoms are arranged differently. In the phosphorus/chlorine reaction, for example, the P atoms were in the form of $P_4$ molecules before reaction but appear in the $PCl_3$ molecules after reaction.

$$P_4(s) + 6\ Cl_2(g) \longrightarrow 4\ PCl_3(\ell)$$

$\underbrace{\phantom{P_4(s) + 6\ Cl_2(g)}}_{\text{REACTANTS}} \qquad \underbrace{\phantom{4\ PCl_3(\ell)}}_{\text{PRODUCT}}$

**FIGURE 3.1  Reaction of solid white phosphorus with chlorine gas.** The product is liquid phosphorus trichloride.

## A CLOSER LOOK

# Antoine Laurent Lavoisier, 1743–1794

On Monday, August 7, 1774, the Englishman Joseph Priestley (1733–1804) isolated oxygen. (The Swedish chemist Carl Scheele [1742–1786] also discovered the element, perhaps in 1773, but did not publish his results until later.) Priestley accomplished this by heating mercury(II) oxide, HgO, which caused the oxide to decompose to mercury and oxygen.

$$2\ HgO(s) \rightarrow 2\ Hg(\ell) + O_2(g)$$

Priestley did not immediately understand the significance of the discovery, but he mentioned it to the French chemist Antoine Lavoisier in October 1774. One of Lavoisier's contributions to science was his recognition of the importance of exact scientific measurements and of carefully planned experiments, and he applied these methods to the study of oxygen. From this

**The decomposition of red mercury(II) oxide.** The decomposition reaction gives mercury metal and oxygen gas. The mercury is seen as a film on the surface of the test tube.

work, Lavoisier proposed that oxygen was an element, that it was one of the constituents of the compound water, and that burning involved a reaction with oxygen. He also mistakenly came to believe Priestley's gas was present in all acids, so he named it "oxygen" from the Greek words meaning "to form an acid."

In other experiments, Lavoisier observed that the heat produced by a guinea pig when exhaling a given amount of carbon dioxide is similar to the quantity of heat produced by burning carbon to give the same amount of carbon dioxide. From these and other experiments he concluded that, "Respiration is a combustion, slow it is true, but otherwise perfectly similar to that of charcoal." Although he did not understand the details of the process, this was an important step in the development of biochemistry.

Lavoisier was a prodigious scientist, and the principles of naming chemical substances that he introduced are still in use today. Furthermore, he wrote a textbook in which he applied the principles of the conservation of matter to chemistry, and he used the idea to write early versions of chemical equations.

Because Lavoisier was an aristocrat, he came under suspicion during the Reign of Terror of the French Revolution. He was an investor in the Ferme Générale, the infamous tax-collecting organization in 18th-century France. Tobacco was a monopoly

product of the Ferme Générale, and it was common to cheat the purchaser by adding water to the tobacco, a practice that Lavoisier opposed. Nonetheless, because of his involvement with the Ferme, his career was cut short by the guillotine on May 8, 1794, on the charge of "adding water to the people's tobacco."

**Lavoisier and his wife, as painted in 1788 by Jacques-Louis David.** Lavoisier was then 45, and his wife, Marie Anne Pierrette Paulze, was 30. (The Metropolitan Museum of Art, Purchase, Mr. and Mrs. Charles Wrightsman gift, in honor of Everett Fahy, 1997. Photograph © 1989 The Metropolitan Museum of Art.)

When applied to the reaction of phosphorus and chlorine, the law of conservation of matter tells us that 1 molecule of phosphorus, $P_4$ (with 4 phosphorus atoms), and 6 diatomic molecules of $Cl_2$ (with 12 atoms of Cl) will produce four molecules of $PCl_3$. Because each $PCl_3$ molecule contains 1 P atom and 3 Cl atoms, the four $PCl_3$ molecules are needed to account for 4 P atoms and 12 Cl atoms in the product. The equation is balanced; the same number of P and Cl atoms appear on each side of the equation.

$$\underset{4 \text{ P atoms}}{P_4(s)} + \underset{\overset{6 \times 2 =}{12 \text{ Cl atoms}}}{6\ Cl_2(g)} \longrightarrow \underset{\overset{4 \times 3 =}{12 \text{ Cl atoms}}}{4\ PCl_3(\ell)}\quad 4 \text{ P atoms}$$

Next, consider the balanced equation for the reaction of iron and and chlorine (Figure 3.2). In this case, there are two iron atoms and six chlorine atoms on each side of the equation.

$$2\ Fe(s) + 3\ Cl_2(g) \longrightarrow 2\ FeCl_3(s)$$

stoichiometric coefficients

The numbers in front of the formulas in balanced chemical equations are required by the law of conservation of matter. They can be read as a number of atoms or molecules (2 atoms of Fe and 3 molecules of $Cl_2$), or as formula units (2 formula units of the ionic compound $FeCl_3$). They can refer equally well to amounts of reactants and products: 2 mol of solid iron combine with 3 mol of chlorine gas to produce 2 mol of solid $FeCl_3$. The relationship between the quantities of chemical reactants and products is called **stoichiometry** (pronounced "stoy-key-AHM-uh-tree") (▶ Chapter 4), and the coefficients in a balanced equation are the **stoichiometric coefficients**.

---

**REVIEW & CHECK FOR SECTION 3.1**

The reaction of aluminum with bromine is shown on page 67. The equation for the reaction is

$$2\ Al(s) + 3\ Br_2(\ell) \rightarrow Al_2Br_6(s)$$

1. What are the stoichiometric coefficients in this equation?

   (a) 1, 3, 4      (b) 2, 3, 1      (c) 1, 6, 8      (d) 1, 1, 1

2. If you were to use 8000 atoms of Al, how many molecules of $Br_2$ are required to consume the Al completely?

   (a) 5333      (b) 8000      (c) 12,000      (d) 20,000

---

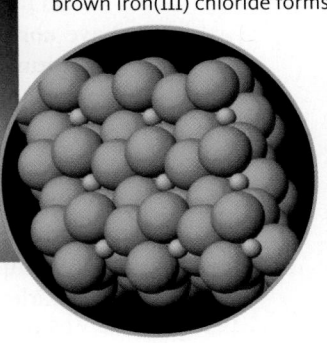

**FIGURE 3.2 The reaction of iron and chlorine.** Here, hot iron gauze is inserted into a flask containing chlorine gas. The heat from the reaction causes the iron gauze to glow, and brown iron(III) chloride forms.

$$2\ Fe(s) + 3\ Cl_2(g) \longrightarrow 2\ FeCl_3(s)$$

REACTANTS      PRODUCT

**FIGURE 3.3** Reactions of a metal and two nonmetals with oxygen.

**(a)** Reaction of iron and oxygen to give iron(III) oxide, $Fe_2O_3$.

**(b)** Reaction of sulfur (in the spoon) with oxygen.

**(c)** Reaction of phosphorus and oxygen to give tetraphosphorus decaoxide, $P_4O_{10}$.

● **The Importance of Balanced Chemical Equations** Balanced chemical equations are fundamentally important for understanding the quantitative basis of chemistry. *You must always begin with a balanced equation before carrying out a quantitative study of a chemical reaction.*

## 3.2 Balancing Chemical Equations

In a balanced chemical equation, the same number of atoms of each element appears on each side of the equation. Many chemical equations can be balanced by trial and error, and this is the method that will be used for now, but there are also more systematic methods to balance some chemical equations (▶ Section 20.1).

One general class of chemical reactions is the reaction of metals or nonmetals with oxygen to give oxides of the general formula $M_xO_y$. For example, iron reacts with oxygen to give iron(III) oxide (Figure 3.3a).

$$4\ Fe(s) + 3\ O_2(g) \rightarrow 2\ Fe_2O_3(s)$$

The nonmetals sulfur and oxygen react to form sulfur dioxide (Figure 3.3b),

$$S(s) + O_2(g) \rightarrow SO_2(g)$$

and phosphorus, $P_4$, reacts vigorously with oxygen to give tetraphosphorus decaoxide, $P_4O_{10}$ (Figure 3.3c).

$$P_4(s) + 5\ O_2(g) \rightarrow P_4O_{10}(s)$$

The equations written above are balanced. The same number of iron, sulfur, or phosphorus atoms and oxygen atoms occurs on each side of these equations.

The **combustion**, or burning, of a fuel in oxygen is accompanied by the evolution of energy as heat. You are familiar with combustion reactions such as the burning of octane, $C_8H_{18}$, a component of gasoline, in an automobile engine:

$$2\ C_8H_{18}(\ell) + 25\ O_2(g) \rightarrow 16\ CO_2(g) + 18\ H_2O(g)$$

In all combustion reactions, some or all of the elements in the reactants end up as oxides, compounds containing oxygen. When the reactant is a hydrocarbon (a compound that contains only C and H, such as octane), the products of complete combustion are always carbon dioxide and water.

So far, we have given you the balanced chemical equations for the reactions we have considered, but often this will not be the case; you will have to balance the equations. When balancing chemical equations, there are two important things to remember.

- Formulas for reactants and products must be correct or the equation is meaningless. Once the correct formulas for the reactants and products have been determined, the subscripts in their formulas cannot be changed to balance equations. Changing the subscripts changes the identity of the substance. For example, you cannot change $CO_2$ to $CO$ to balance an equation; carbon monoxide, $CO$, and carbon dioxide, $CO_2$, are different compounds.
- Chemical equations are balanced using stoichiometric coefficients. The entire chemical formula of a substance is multiplied by the stoichiometric coefficient.

As an example of equation balancing, let us write the balanced equation for the complete combustion of propane, $C_3H_8$.

**Step 1.** *Write correct formulas for the reactants and products.*

$$C_3H_8(g) + O_2(g) \xrightarrow{\text{unbalanced equation}} CO_2(g) + H_2O(g)$$

Here propane and oxygen are the reactants, and carbon dioxide and water are the products.

**Step 2.** *Balance the C atoms.* In combustion reactions such as this it is usually best to balance the carbon atoms first and leave the oxygen atoms until the end (because the oxygen atoms are often found in more than one product). In this case three carbon atoms are in the reactants, so three must occur in the products. Three $CO_2$ molecules are therefore required on the right side:

$$C_3H_8(g) + O_2(g) \xrightarrow{\text{unbalanced equation}} 3\ CO_2(g) + H_2O(g)$$

**Step 3.** *Balance the H atoms.* Propane, the reactant, contains 8 H atoms. Each molecule of water has two hydrogen atoms, so four molecules of water account for the required eight hydrogen atoms on the right side:

$$C_3H_8(g) + O_2(g) \xrightarrow{\text{unbalanced equation}} 3\ CO_2(g) + 4\ H_2O(g)$$

**Step 4.** *Balance the O atoms.* Ten oxygen atoms are on the right side ($3 \times 2 = 6$ in $CO_2$ plus $4 \times 1 = 4$ in $H_2O$). Therefore, five $O_2$ molecules are needed to supply the required ten oxygen atoms:

$$C_3H_8(g) + 5\ O_2(g) \rightarrow 3\ CO_2(g) + 4\ H_2O(g)$$

**Step 5.** *Verify that the number of atoms of each element is balanced.* The equation shows three carbon atoms, eight hydrogen atoms, and ten oxygen atoms on each side.

**A combustion reaction.** Here, propane, $C_3H_8$, burns to give $CO_2$ and $H_2O$. These simple oxides are always the products of the complete combustion of a hydrocarbon.

*© Cengage Learning/Charles D. Winters*

## ⓦWL   INTERACTIVE EXAMPLE 3.1   Balancing an Equation
### for a Combustion Reaction

**Problem** Write the balanced equation for the combustion of ammonia gas ($NH_3$) to give water vapor and nitrogen monoxide gas.

**What Do You Know?** You know the correct formulas and/or names for the reactants ($NH_3$ and oxygen, $O_2$) and the products ($H_2O$ and nitrogen monoxide, $NO$). Also, you know their states.

**Strategy** First write the unbalanced equation. Next balance the N atoms, then the H atoms, and finally the O atoms.

**Solution**

**Step 1.** *Write correct formulas for the reactants and products.* This is a combustion reaction, so the ammonia is reacting with $O_2$. The unbalanced equation for the combustion is

$$NH_3(g) + O_2(g) \xrightarrow{\text{unbalanced equation}} NO(g) + H_2O(g)$$

**Step 2.** *Balance the N atoms.* There is one N atom on each side of the equation. The N atoms are in balance, at least for the moment.

$$NH_3(g) + O_2(g) \xrightarrow{\text{unbalanced equation}} NO(g) + H_2O(g)$$

**Step 3.** *Balance the H atoms.* There are three H atoms on the left and two on the right. To have the same number on each side (6), let us use two molecules of $NH_3$ on the left and three molecules of $H_2O$ on the right (which gives us six H atoms on each side).

$$2\ NH_3(g) + O_2(g) \xrightarrow{\text{unbalanced equation}} NO(g) + 3\ H_2O(g)$$

**Strategy Map 3.1**

**PROBLEM**

**Balance the equation** for the reaction of **NH₃** and **O₂**

↓

**DATA/INFORMATION**

The **formulas** of the **reactants** and **products** are given

↓

STEP 1. Balance **N** atoms.

**N atoms balanced** but overall equation not balanced

↓

STEP 2. Balance **H** atoms.

**N and H atoms balanced** but overall equation not balanced

↓

STEP 3. Balance **O** atoms. Best left to final step.

↓

**N, H, and O atoms balanced.**
*Overall equation now balanced.*

Notice that when we balance the H atoms, the N atoms are no longer balanced. To bring them into balance, let us use 2 NO molecules on the right.

$$2\ NH_3(g) + O_2(g) \xrightarrow{\text{unbalanced equation}} 2\ NO(g) + 3\ H_2O(g)$$

**Step 4.** *Balance the O atoms.* After Step 3, there is an even number of O atoms (two) on the left and an odd number (five) on the right. Because there cannot be an odd number of O atoms on the left (O atoms are paired in $O_2$ molecules), multiply each coefficient on both sides of the equation by 2 so that an even number of oxygen atoms (10) now occurs on the right side:

$$4\ NH_3(g) + O_2(g) \xrightarrow{\text{unbalanced equation}} 4\ NO(g) + 6\ H_2O(g)$$

Now the oxygen atoms can be balanced by having five $O_2$ molecules on the left side of the equation:

$$4\ NH_3(g) + 5\ O_2(g) \xrightarrow{\text{balanced equation}} 4\ NO(g) + 6\ H_2O(g)$$

**Step 5.** *Verify the result.* Four N atoms, 12 H atoms, and 10 O atoms occur on each side of the equation.

**Think about Your Answer**  An alternative way to write this equation is

$$2\ NH_3(g) + {}^5\!/_2\ O_2(g) \rightarrow 2\ NO(g) + 3\ H_2O(g)$$

where a fractional coefficient has been used. This equation is correctly balanced and will be useful under some circumstances. In general, however, we balance equations with whole-number coefficients.

---

**Check Your Understanding**

(a)  Butane gas, $C_4H_{10}$, can burn completely in air [use $O_2(g)$ as the other reactant] to give carbon dioxide gas and water vapor. Write a balanced equation for this combustion reaction.

(b)  Write a balanced chemical equation for the complete combustion of liquid tetraethyl lead, $Pb(C_2H_5)_4$ (which was used until the 1970s as a gasoline additive). The products of combustion are $PbO(s)$, $H_2O(g)$, and $CO_2(g)$. (The PbO was a significant environmental pollutant!)

---

**REVIEW & CHECK FOR SECTION 3.2**

The (unbalanced) equation describing the oxidation of propanol is

$$2\ C_3H_7OH(\ell) + \underline{\quad} O_2(g) \rightarrow 6\ CO_2(g) + \underline{\quad} H_2O(g)$$

Determine the two missing stoichiometric coefficients.

(a)  $4.5\ O_2,\ 4\ H_2O$     (b)  $9\ O_2,\ 8\ H_2O$     (c)  $5\ O_2,\ 4\ H_2O$     (d)  $5\ O_2,\ 7\ H_2O$

---

## 3.3  Introduction to Chemical Equilibrium

To this point, we have treated chemical reactions as proceeding in one direction only, with reactants being converted *completely* to products. Nature, however, is more complex than this. Chemical reactions are reversible, and many reactions lead to incomplete conversion of reactants to products.

The formation of stalactites and stalagmites in a limestone cave is an example of a system that depends on the reversibility of a chemical reaction (Figure 3.4). Stalactites and stalagmites are made chiefly of calcium carbonate, a mineral found in underground deposits in the form of limestone, a leftover from ancient oceans. If water seeping through the limestone contains dissolved $CO_2$, a reaction occurs in which the mineral dissolves, giving an aqueous solution of $Ca(HCO_3)_2$.

$$CaCO_3(s) + CO_2(aq) + H_2O(\ell) \rightarrow Ca(HCO_3)_2(aq)$$

**FIGURE 3.4  Cave chemistry.**
Calcium carbonate stalactites cling to the roof of a cave, and stalagmites grow up from the cave floor. The chemistry producing these formations is a good example of the reversibility of chemical reactions.

Dr. Arthur N. Palmer

**a** Reactants: Solutions of $CaCl_2$ (left) and $NaHCO_3$ (right). $Na^+$ and $Cl^-$ are not shown.

**FORWARD** REACTION

**b** The solutions are mixed. Products: $H_2O$, a precipitate of $CaCO_3$, and $CO_2$ gas

$Ca^{2+}$(aq)  $HCO_3^-$(aq)  $CaCO_3$(s)  $CO_2$(g)

Equilibrium equation: $Ca^{2+}(aq) + 2\ HCO_3^-(aq) \rightleftharpoons CaCO_3(s) + CO_2(g) + H_2O(\ell)$

**c** The reaction can be reversed by bubbling $CO_2$ gas into the $CaCO_3$ suspension.

**REVERSE** REACTION

**d** The $CaCO_3$ dissolves when the solution has been saturated with $CO_2$.

$CaCO_3$(s) + $CO_2$(g) + $H_2O(\ell)$

Elapsing time...

$Ca^{2+}$(aq) + 2 $HCO_3^-$(aq)

Photos © Cengage Learning/Charles D. Winters

**FIGURE 3.5 The reversibility of chemical reactions.** The experiments here demonstrate the reversibility of chemical reactions. (top) Solutions of $CaCl_2$ (a source of $Ca^{2+}$ ions) and $NaHCO_3$ (a source of $HCO_3^-$ ions) are mixed **(a)** and produce a precipitate of $CaCO_3$ and $CO_2$ gas **(b)**. (bottom) If $CO_2$ gas is bubbled into a suspension of $CaCO_3$ **(c)**, the reverse of the reaction displayed in the top panel occurs. That is, solid $CaCO_3$ and gaseous $CO_2$ produce $Ca^{2+}$ and $HCO_3^-$ ions **(d)**.

When the mineral-laden water reaches a cave, the reverse reaction occurs, with $CO_2$ being evolved into the cave and solid $CaCO_3$ being deposited.

$$Ca(HCO_3)_2(aq) \rightarrow CaCO_3(s) + CO_2(g) + H_2O(\ell)$$

Cave chemistry can be done in a laboratory (Figure 3.5) using reactions that further demonstrate the reversibility of the reactions involved.

Another example of a reversible reaction is the reaction of nitrogen with hydrogen to form ammonia gas, a compound made industrially in enormous quantities and used directly as a fertilizer and in the production of other fertilizers.

$$N_2(g) + 3\ H_2(g) \rightarrow 2\ NH_3(g)$$

Nitrogen and hydrogen react to form ammonia, but, under the conditions of the reaction, the product ammonia also breaks down into nitrogen and hydrogen in the reverse reaction.

$$2\ NH_3(g) \rightarrow N_2(g) + 3\ H_2(g)$$

Let us consider what would happen if we mixed nitrogen and hydrogen in a closed container under the proper conditions for the reaction to occur. At first, $N_2$ and $H_2$ react to produce some ammonia. As the ammonia is produced, however,

**FIGURE 3.6 The reaction of N₂ and H₂ to produce NH₃.** N₂ and H₂ in a 1:3 mixture react to produce some NH₃. As the reaction proceeds, the rate or speed of NH₃ production slows, as does the rate of consumption of N₂ and H₂. Eventually, the amounts of N₂, H₂, and NH₃ no longer change. At this point, the reaction has reached equilibrium. Nonetheless, the forward reaction to produce NH₃ continues, as does the reverse reaction (the decomposition of NH₃).

$$N_2(g) + 3H_2(g) \rightleftharpoons 2\,NH_3(g)$$

Equilibrium achieved

H₂

NH₃

N₂

Amounts of products and reactants

Reactants proceeding toward equilibrium

some NH₃ molecules decompose to re-form nitrogen and hydrogen in the reverse reaction (Figure 3.6). At the beginning of the process, the forward reaction to give NH₃ predominates, but, as the reactants are consumed, the rate (or speed) of the forward reaction progressively slows. At the same time, the reverse reaction speeds up as the amount of ammonia increases. Eventually, the rate of the forward reaction will equal the rate of the reverse reaction. At this point, no further *macroscopic* change is observed; the amounts of nitrogen, hydrogen, and ammonia in the container stop changing but the forward and reverse reactions continue. We say the system has reached **chemical equilibrium**. The reaction vessel will contain all three substances: nitrogen, hydrogen, and ammonia. Because both the forward and reverse processes are still occurring (but at equal rates), we refer to this state as a **dynamic equilibrium**. We represent a system at dynamic equilibrium by writing a double arrow symbol ($\rightleftharpoons$) connecting the reactants and products.

$$N_2(g) + 3\,H_2(g) \rightleftharpoons 2\,NH_3(g)$$

*Chemical reactions always proceed spontaneously toward equilibrium.* A reaction will never proceed spontaneously in a direction that takes a system further from equilibrium. A key question that arises is "When a reaction reaches equilibrium, will the reactants be converted largely to products or will most of the reactants still be present?" The answer will depend on the nature of the substances involved, the temperature, and other factors, and that is the subject of later chapters (▶ Chapters 16–18). For the present, though, it is useful to define **product-favored reactions** as *reactions in which reactants are completely or largely converted to products when equilibrium is reached.* The combustion reactions we have been studying are examples of reactions that are product-favored at equilibrium. In fact, most of the reactions that we shall study in the rest of this chapter are product-favored reactions at equilibrium. We usually write the equations for reactions that are very product-favored using only the single arrows we have been using up to this point.

The opposite of a product-favored reaction is one that is **reactant-favored** at equilibrium. Such reactions lead to the conversion of only a small amount of the reactants to products. An example of such a reaction is the ionization of acetic acid in water where only a tiny fraction of the acid ionizes to produce ions.

● **Quantitative Description of Chemical Equilibrium** As you shall see in Chapters 16–18, the extent to which a reaction is product-favored can be described by a mathematical expression called the *equilibrium constant expression.* Each chemical reaction has a numerical value for the equilibrium constant, symbolized by $K$. Product-favored reactions have large values of $K$; small $K$ values indicate reactant-favored reactions. For the ionization of acetic acid in water, $K = 1.8 \times 10^{-5}$.

$$CH_3CO_2H(aq) + H_2O(\ell) \rightleftharpoons CH_3CO_2^-(aq) + H_3O^+(aq)$$

acetic acid        water        acetate ion        hydronium ion

As you shall see below, acetic acid is an example of a large number of acids called "weak acids" because the reaction is so reactant-favored at equilibrium that only a few percent of the molecules react with water to form ionic products.

---

**REVIEW & CHECK FOR SECTION 3.3**

Which of the following statements about chemical equilibrium is not true?

(a)  At equilibrium the rates of the forward and reverse reactions are equal.

(b)  There is no observable change in a chemical system at equilibrium.

(c)  Chemical reactions always proceed toward equilibrium.

(d)  All chemical equilibria are product-favored.

---

## 3.4  Aqueous Solutions

Many of the reactions you will study in your chemistry course and almost all of the reactions that occur in living things are carried out in solutions in which the reacting substances are dissolved in water. In Chapter 1, we defined a **solution** as a homogeneous mixture of two or more substances. One substance is generally considered the **solvent**, the medium in which another substance—the **solute**—is dissolved. The remainder of this chapter is an introduction to some of the types of reactions that occur in **aqueous solutions**, solutions in which *water* is the solvent. To understand these reactions, it is important first to understand something about the behavior of compounds dissolved in water.

### Ions and Molecules in Aqueous Solutions

Dissolving an ionic solid requires separating each ion from the oppositely charged ions that surround it in the solid state. Water is especially good at dissolving ionic compounds because each water molecule has a positively charged end and a negatively charged end (Figure 3.7). When an ionic compound dissolves in water, each negative ion becomes surrounded by water molecules with the positive ends of water molecules pointing toward it, and each positive ion becomes surrounded by the negative ends of several water molecules.

The water-encased ions produced by dissolving an ionic compound are free to move about in solution. Under normal conditions, the movement of ions is random, and the cations and anions from a dissolved ionic compound are dispersed uniformly throughout the solution. However, if two **electrodes** (conductors of electricity such as copper wire) are placed in the solution and connected to a battery, ion movement is no longer random. Positive cations move through the solution to the negative electrode and negative anions move to the positive electrode (Figure 3.8). If a light bulb is inserted into the circuit, the bulb lights, showing that ions are available to conduct charge in the solution just as electrons conduct charge in the wire part of the circuit. Compounds whose aqueous solutions conduct electricity are called **electrolytes**. *All ionic compounds that are soluble in water are electrolytes.*

For every mole of NaCl that dissolves, 1 mol of $Na^+$ and 1 mol of $Cl^-$ ions enter the solution.

$$NaCl(s) \rightarrow Na^+(aq) + Cl^-(aq)$$

100% Dissociation $\rightarrow$ strong electrolyte

Because the solute has dissociated (broken apart) completely into ions, the solution will be a good conductor of electricity. Substances whose solutions are good electrical conductors owing to the presence of ions are **strong electrolytes** (Figure 3.8). The ions into which an ionic compound will dissociate are given by the compound's name, and the relative amounts of these ions are given by its formula. For example,

**Module 5: Predicting the Water Solubility of Ionic Compounds** covers concepts in this section.

A water molecule is electrically positive on one side (the H atoms) and electrically negative on the other (the O atom). These charges enable water to interact with negative and positive ions in aqueous solution.

Copper(II) chloride is added to water. Interactions between water and the $Cu^{2+}$ and $Cl^-$ ions allow the solid to dissolve.

The ions are now sheathed in water molecules.

Water surrounding a cation

Water surrounding an anion

**(a)** Water molecules are attracted to both positive cations and negative anions in aqueous solution.

**(b)** When an ionic substance dissolves in water, each ion is surrounded by water molecules.

**FIGURE 3.7** Water as a solvent for ionic substances.

as we have seen, sodium chloride yields sodium ions ($Na^+$) and chloride ions ($Cl^-$) in solution in a 1:1 ratio. The ionic compound barium chloride, $BaCl_2$, is also a strong electrolyte. In this case there are two chloride ions for each barium ion in solution.

$$BaCl_2(s) \rightarrow Ba^{2+}(aq) + 2\ Cl^-(aq)$$

**Strong Electrolyte**

A **strong electrolyte** conducts electricity. $CuCl_2$ is completely dissociated into $Cu^{2+}$ and $Cl^-$ ions.

$CuCl_2$

$Cu^{2+}$   $2+$

$Cl^-$

**Weak Electrolyte**

A **weak electrolyte** conducts electricity poorly because only a few ions are present in solution.

Acetic acid

Acetate ion

$H^+$   $+$

**Nonelectrolyte**

A **nonelectrolyte** does not conduct electricity because no ions are present in solution.

Ethanol

**FIGURE 3.8** Classifying solutions by their ability to conduct electricity.

Notice that the two chloride ions per formula unit are present as two separate particles in solution; they are not present as diatomic particles, $Cl_2^{2-}$. In yet another example, the ionic compound barium nitrate yields barium ions and nitrate ions in solution. For each $Ba^{2+}$ ion in solution, there are two $NO_3^-$ ions.

$$Ba(NO_3)_2(s) \rightarrow Ba^{2+}(aq) + 2\ NO_3^-(aq)$$

Notice that the polyatomic ion stays together as one unit, $NO_3^-$, but that the two nitrate ions are separate ions in solution.

Compounds whose aqueous solutions do not conduct electricity are called **nonelectrolytes**. The solute particles present in these aqueous solutions are molecules, not ions. *Most molecular compounds that dissolve in water are nonelectrolytes.* For example, when the molecular compound ethanol ($C_2H_5OH$) dissolves in water, each molecule of ethanol stays together as a single unit. We do not get ions in the solution.

$$C_2H_5OH(\ell) \rightarrow C_2H_5OH(aq)$$

Other examples of nonelectrolytes are sucrose ($C_{12}H_{22}O_{11}$) and antifreeze (ethylene glycol, $HOCH_2CH_2OH$).

Some molecular compounds (strong acids, weak acids, and weak bases) (Section 3.6), however, react with water to form ions and thus are electrolytes. Gaseous hydrogen chloride, a molecular compound, reacts with water to form ions, and the solution is referred to as hydrochloric acid.

$$HCl(g) + H_2O(\ell) \rightarrow H_3O^+(aq) + Cl^-(aq)$$

This reaction is very product-favored. Each molecule of HCl produces ions in solution, so hydrochloric acid is a strong electrolyte.

Some molecular compounds are **weak electrolytes**. When these compounds dissolve in water only a small fraction of the molecules forms ions; the majority remains intact. These aqueous solutions are poor conductors of electricity (Figure 3.8). As described on page 118, the interaction of acetic acid with water is very reactant-favored. In vinegar, an aqueous solution of acetic acid, about 40 molecules in every 10,000 molecules of acetic acid are ionized to form acetate ($CH_3CO_2^-$) and hydronium ($H_3O^+$) ions. Thus, aqueous acetic acid is a weak electrolyte.

$$CH_3CO_2H(aq) + H_2O(\ell) \rightleftharpoons CH_3CO_2^-(aq) + H_3O^+(aq)$$

Figure 3.9 summarizes whether a given type of solute will be present in aqueous solution as ions, molecules, or a combination of ions and molecules.

● **Dissolving Halides** When an ionic compound with halide ions dissolves in water, the halide ions are released into aqueous solution. Thus, $BaCl_2$ produces two $Cl^-$ ions for each $Ba^{2+}$ ion (and not $Cl_2$ or $Cl_2^{2-}$ ions).

**FIGURE 3.9 Predicting the species present in aqueous solution.** When compounds dissolve in aqueous solution, ions may result from ionic or molecular compounds. Some molecular compounds may remain intact as molecules in solution. (Note that hydroxide-containing strong bases are ionic compounds.)

## SILVER COMPOUNDS

AgNO$_3$  AgCl  AgOH

**(a)** Nitrates are generally soluble, as are chlorides (except AgCl). Hydroxides are generally not soluble.

## SULFIDES

(NH$_4$)$_2$S  CdS  Sb$_2$S$_3$  PbS

**(b)** Sulfides are generally not soluble (exceptions include salts with NH$_4^+$ and Na$^+$).

## HYDROXIDES

NaOH  Ca(OH)$_2$  Fe(OH)$_3$  Ni(OH)$_2$

Photos © Cengage Learning/Charles D. Winters

**(c)** Hydroxides are generally not soluble, except when the cation is a Group 1A metal.

**FIGURE 3.10 Guidelines to predict the solubility of ionic compounds.** If a compound contains one of the ions in the column on the left in the top chart, it is predicted to be at least moderately soluble in water. There are exceptions, which are noted at the right. Most ionic compounds formed by the anions listed at the bottom of the chart are poorly soluble (with the exception of compounds with NH$_4^+$ and the alkali metal cations).

| SOLUBLE COMPOUNDS | EXCEPTIONS |
|---|---|
| Almost all salts of Na$^+$, K$^+$, NH$_4^+$ | |
| Salts of nitrate, NO$_3^-$<br>chlorate, ClO$_3^-$<br>perchlorate, ClO$_4^-$<br>acetate, CH$_3$CO$_2^-$ | |
| Almost all salts of Cl$^-$, Br$^-$, I$^-$ | Halides of Ag$^+$, Hg$_2^{2+}$, Pb$^{2+}$ |
| Salts containing F$^-$ | Fluorides of Mg$^{2+}$, Ca$^{2+}$, Sr$^{2+}$, Ba$^{2+}$, Pb$^{2+}$ |
| Salts of sulfate, SO$_4^{2-}$ | Sulfates of Ca$^{2+}$, Sr$^{2+}$, Ba$^{2+}$, Pb$^{2+}$, Ag$^+$ |

| INSOLUBLE COMPOUNDS | EXCEPTIONS |
|---|---|
| Most salts of carbonate, CO$_3^{2-}$<br>phosphate, PO$_4^{3-}$<br>oxalate, C$_2$O$_4^{2-}$<br>chromate, CrO$_4^{2-}$<br>sulfide, S$^{2-}$ | Salts of NH$_4^+$ and the alkali metal cations |
| Most metal hydroxides and oxides | Alkali metal hydroxides and Ba(OH)$_2$ and Sr(OH)$_2$ |

## Solubility of Ionic Compounds in Water

Many ionic compounds are soluble in water, but some dissolve only to a small extent; still others are essentially insoluble. Fortunately, we can make some general statements about which ionic compounds are water-soluble. In this chapter, we consider solubility as an "either-or" question, referring to those materials that are soluble beyond a certain extent as "soluble" and to those that do not dissolve to that extent as "insoluble." To get a better idea of the amounts that will actually dissolve in a given quantity of water, we could do an experiment or perform a calculation that uses the concept of equilibrium (▶ Chapter 18).

Figure 3.10 lists broad guidelines that can help you predict whether a particular ionic compound is soluble in water. For example, sodium nitrate, NaNO$_3$, contains an alkali metal cation, Na$^+$, and the nitrate anion, NO$_3^-$. The presence of either of these ions ensures that the compound is soluble in water. In contrast, calcium hydroxide is poorly soluble in water. If a spoonful of solid Ca(OH)$_2$ is added to 100 mL of water, only 0.17 g, or 0.0023 mol, will dissolve at 10 °C. Nearly all of the Ca(OH)$_2$ remains as a solid (Figure 3.10c).

● **Solubility Guidelines** Observations such as those shown in Figure 3.10 were used to create the solubility guidelines. Note, however, that these are general guidelines and not rules followed under all circumstances. There are exceptions, but the guidelines are a good place to begin. See B. Blake, *Journal of Chemical Education*, Vol. 80, pp. 1348–1350, 2003.

## EXAMPLE 3.2  Solubility Guidelines

**Problem**  Predict whether the following ionic compounds are likely to be water-soluble. For soluble compounds, list the ions present in solution.

(a)  KCl  (b)  MgCO$_3$  (c)  Fe$_2$O$_3$  (d)  Cu(NO$_3$)$_2$

**What Do You Know?**  You know the formulas of the compounds but need to be able to identify the ions that make up each of them in order to use the solubility guidelines in Figure 3.10.

**Strategy**  Decide the probable water solubility based on the solubility guidelines (Figure 3.10). Soluble compounds will dissociate into their respective ions in solution.

**Solution**

(a) KCl is composed of $K^+$ and $Cl^-$ ions. The presence of *either* of these ions means that the compound is likely to be soluble in water. The solution contains $K^+$ and $Cl^-$ ions dissolved in water.

$$KCl(s) \rightarrow K^+(aq) + Cl^-(aq)$$

(The solubility of KCl is about 35 g in 100 mL of water at 20 °C.)

(b) Magnesium carbonate is composed of $Mg^{2+}$ and $CO_3^{2-}$ ions. Salts containing the carbonate ion usually are insoluble, unless combined with an ion like $Na^+$ or $NH_4^+$. Therefore, $MgCO_3$ is predicted to be insoluble in water. (The solubility of $MgCO_3$ is less than 0.2 g/100 mL of water.)

(c) Iron(III) oxide is composed of $Fe^{3+}$ and $O^{2-}$ ions. Oxides are soluble only when $O^{2-}$ is combined with an alkali metal ion; $Fe^{3+}$ is a transition metal ion, so $Fe_2O_3$ is insoluble.

(d) Copper(II) nitrate is composed of $Cu^{2+}$ and $NO_3^-$ ions. Nitrate salts are soluble, so this compound dissolves in water, giving ions in solution as shown in the equation below.

$$Cu(NO_3)_2(s) \rightarrow Cu^{2+}(aq) + 2\ NO_3^-(aq)$$

**Think about Your Answer** For chemists, a set of simple guidelines like this is useful. However, it is possible to get accurate solubility information for many compounds in chemical resource books or databases.

**Check Your Understanding**

Predict whether each of the following ionic compounds is likely to be soluble in water. If it is soluble, write the formulas of the ions present in aqueous solution.

(a) $LiNO_3$      (b) $CaCl_2$      (c) $CuO$      (d) $NaCH_3CO_2$

---

**REVIEW & CHECK FOR SECTION 3.4**

1. Which of the compounds listed below is water-soluble?

   (a) $Ba(NO_3)_2$      (b) $CuS$      (c) $Fe_3(PO_4)_2$      (d) $Mg(OH)_2$

2. Calcium nitrate dihydrate is dissolved in water. What ions are present in solution?

   (a) $Ca^{2+}$ and $(NO_3)_2^{2-}$          (c) Ca and $2\ NO_3$

   (b) $Ca^{2+}$ and $2\ NO_3^-$          (d) $Ca^+$ and $NO_3^-$

3. A 1-g sample of each of the four compounds listed below was placed in a beaker with 100 mL of water. The mixture was then tested to see if it conducted an electric current. Which solution was a weak conductor of electricity?

   (a) ethanol      (b) acetic acid      (c) NaCl      (d) NaOH

---

# 3.5 Precipitation Reactions

Now that you can predict whether compounds will yield ions or molecules when they dissolve in water and whether ionic compounds are soluble or insoluble in water, we can begin to discuss the chemical reactions that occur in aqueous solutions. We will introduce you to four major categories of reactions in aqueous solution: precipitation, acid–base, gas-forming, and oxidation–reduction reactions. As you learn about these reactions, it will be useful to look for patterns that allow you to predict the reaction products. You will notice that precipitation, acid–base, and many gas-forming (but not oxidation–reduction) reactions are **exchange reactions** (sometimes called double dis-

**Module 6: Writing Net Ionic Equations** covers concepts in this section.

**FIGURE 3.11 Precipitation of silver chloride.** Mixing aqueous solutions of silver nitrate and potassium chloride produces white, insoluble silver chloride, AgCl.

**(b)** Initially, the $Ag^+$ ions (silver color) and $Cl^-$ ions (green) are widely separated.

**(c)** $Ag^+$ and $Cl^-$ ions approach and form ion pairs.

**(d)** As more and more $Ag^+$ and $Cl^-$ ions come together, a precipitate of solid AgCl forms.

**(a)** Mixing aqueous solutions of silver nitrate and potassium chloride produces white, insoluble silver chloride, AgCl.

placement, double replacement, or metathesis reactions) in which *the ions of the reactants change partners.*

$$A^+B^- \ + \ C^+D^- \ \longrightarrow \ A^+D^- \ + \ C^+B^-$$

For example, aqueous solutions of silver nitrate and potassium chloride react to produce solid silver chloride and aqueous potassium nitrate (Figure 3.11a).

$$AgNO_3(aq) + KCl(aq) \rightarrow AgCl(s) + KNO_3(aq)$$

This particular reaction is an example of the first type of reaction that we shall examine: a precipitation reaction. A **precipitation reaction** produces a water-insoluble solid product, known as a **precipitate**. The reactants in such reactions are generally water-soluble ionic compounds. When these substances dissolve in water, they dissociate to give the appropriate cations and anions. If the cation from one reactant can form an insoluble compound with the anion from the other reactant, precipitation occurs. In Figure 3.11, both silver nitrate and potassium chloride are water-soluble ionic compounds. When combined in water, they undergo an *exchange reaction* to produce insoluble silver chloride and soluble potassium nitrate.

$$AgNO_3(aq) + KCl(aq) \rightarrow AgCl(s) + KNO_3(aq)$$

| Reactants | Products |
|---|---|
| $Ag^+(aq) + NO_3^-(aq)$ | Insoluble AgCl(s) |
| $K^+(aq) + Cl^-(aq)$ | $K^+(aq) + NO_3^-(aq)$ |

## Predicting the Outcome of a Precipitation Reaction

Many combinations of positive and negative ions give insoluble substances (see Figure 3.10). For example, the solubility guidelines indicate that most compounds containing the chromate ion are not soluble (alkali metal chromates and ammonium chromate are exceptions). Thus, we can predict that yellow, solid lead(II) chromate will precipitate when a water-soluble lead(II) compound is combined with a water-soluble chromate compound (Figure 3.12a).

$$Pb(NO_3)_2(aq) + K_2CrO_4(aq) \rightarrow PbCrO_4(s) + 2\ KNO_3(aq)$$

| Reactants | Products |
|---|---|
| $Pb^{2+}(aq) + 2\ NO_3^-(aq)$ | Insoluble $PbCrO_4(s)$ |
| $2\ K^+(aq) + CrO_4^{2-}(aq)$ | $2\ K^+(aq) + 2\ NO_3^-(aq)$ |

Similarly, we know from the solubility guidelines that almost all metal sulfides are insoluble in water (Figure 3.12b). If a solution of a soluble metal compound comes in contact with a source of sulfide ions, the metal sulfide precipitates.

$$Pb(NO_3)_2(aq) + (NH_4)_2S(aq) \rightarrow PbS(s) + 2\ NH_4NO_3(aq)$$

| Reactants | Products |
|---|---|
| $Pb^{2+}(aq) + 2\ NO_3^-(aq)$ | Insoluble PbS(s) |
| $2\ NH_4^+(aq) + S^{2-}(aq)$ | $2\ NH_4^+(aq) + 2\ NO_3^-(aq)$ |

**(a)**

**(b)**

**(c)**

**(d)**

**FIGURE 3.12 Precipitation reactions.** Many ionic compounds are insoluble in water. Guidelines for predicting the solubilities of ionic compounds are given in Figure 3.10. **(a)** $Pb(NO_3)_2$ and $K_2CrO_4$ produce yellow, insoluble $PbCrO_4$ and soluble $KNO_3$. **(b)** $Pb(NO_3)_2$ and $(NH_4)_2S$ produce black, insoluble $PbS$ and soluble $NH_4NO_3$. **(c)** $FeCl_3$ and $NaOH$ produce orange, insoluble $Fe(OH)_3$ and soluble $NaCl$. **(d)** $AgNO_3$ and $K_2CrO_4$ produce orange, insoluble $Ag_2CrO_4$ and soluble $KNO_3$. (See Example 3.3.)

In yet another example, the solubility guidelines indicate that with the exception of the alkali metal cations (and $Sr^{2+}$ and $Ba^{2+}$), all metal cations form insoluble hydroxides. Thus, water-soluble iron(III) chloride and sodium hydroxide react to give insoluble iron(III) hydroxide (Figures 3.10c and 3.12c).

$$FeCl_3(aq) + 3\ NaOH(aq) \rightarrow Fe(OH)_3(s) + 3\ NaCl(aq)$$

| **Reactants** | **Products** |
|---|---|
| $Fe^{3+}(aq) + 3\ Cl^-(aq)$ | Insoluble $Fe(OH)_3(s)$ |
| $3\ Na^+(aq) + 3\ OH^-(aq)$ | $3\ Na^+(aq) + 3\ Cl^-(aq)$ |

## EXAMPLE 3.3    Writing the Equation for a Precipitation Reaction

**Problem** Is an insoluble product formed when aqueous solutions of potassium chromate and silver nitrate are mixed? If so, write the balanced equation.

**What Do You Know?** Names of the two reactants are given. You should recognize that this is an exchange reaction, and you will need the information on solubilities in Figure 3.10.

Strategy

- Determine the formulas from the names of the reactants.

- Determine the formulas for the cations and anions making up the reactants.

- Write formulas for the products in this reaction by exchanging cations and anions and determine whether either product is insoluble using information in Figure 3.10.

- Write and balance the equation.

**Solution** The reactants are silver nitrate and potassium chromate. The possible products of the exchange reaction are silver chromate ($Ag_2CrO_4$) and potassium nitrate ($KNO_3$). Based on the solubility guidelines, we know that silver chromate is an insoluble compound (chromates are insoluble except for those with Group 1A metals), whereas potassium nitrate is soluble in water. A precipitate of silver chromate will therefore form if these reactants are mixed.

$$2\ AgNO_3(aq) + K_2CrO_4(aq) \rightarrow Ag_2CrO_4(s) + 2\ KNO_3(aq)$$

**Think about Your Answer** This reaction is illustrated in Figure 3.12d.

### Check Your Understanding

In each of the following cases, does a precipitation reaction occur when solutions of the two water-soluble reactants are mixed? Give the formula of any precipitate that forms, and write a balanced chemical equation for the precipitation reactions that occur.

(a) sodium carbonate and copper(II) chloride

(b) potassium carbonate and sodium nitrate

(c) nickel(II) chloride and potassium hydroxide

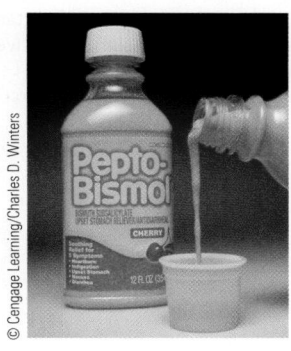

**Black tongue, a precipitate of $Bi_2S_3$.** Pepto-Bismol™ has anti-diarrheal, antibacterial, and antacid effects in the digestive tract, and has been used for over 100 years as an effective remedy. However, some people find their tongues blackened after taking this over-the-counter medicine. The active ingredient in Pepto-Bismol is bismuth subsalicylate. (It also contains pepsin, zinc salts, flavoring, and salol, a compound related to aspirin.) The tongue-blackening comes from the reaction of bismuth ions with traces of sulfide ions found in saliva to form black $Bi_2S_3$. The discoloration is harmless and lasts only a few days.

## Net Ionic Equations

We have seen that when aqueous solutions of silver nitrate and potassium chloride are mixed, insoluble silver chloride forms, leaving potassium nitrate in solution (Figure 3.11). The balanced chemical equation for this process is

$$AgNO_3(aq) + KCl(aq) \rightarrow AgCl(s) + KNO_3(aq)$$

We can represent this reaction in another way by writing an equation in which we show that the *soluble* ionic compounds are present in solution as dissociated ions. An aqueous solution of silver nitrate contains $Ag^+$ and $NO_3^-$ ions, and an aqueous solution of potassium chloride contains $K^+$ and $Cl^-$ ions. In the products, the potassium nitrate is present in solution as $K^+$ and $NO_3^-$ ions. The silver chloride, however, is insoluble and thus is not present in the solution as dissociated ions. It is shown in the equation by its entire formula, AgCl.

$$\underset{\text{before reaction}}{Ag^+(aq) + NO_3^-(aq) + K^+(aq) + Cl^-(aq)} \longrightarrow \underset{\text{after reaction}}{AgCl(s) + K^+(aq) + NO_3^-(aq)}$$

This type of equation is called a **complete ionic equation**.

The $K^+$ and $NO_3^-$ ions are present in solution both before and after reaction, so they appear on both the reactant and product sides of the complete ionic equation. Such ions are often called **spectator ions** because they do not participate in the net reaction; they only "look on" from the sidelines. Little chemical information is lost if the equation is written without them, so we can simplify the equation to

$$Ag^+(aq) + Cl^-(aq) \rightarrow AgCl(s)$$

● **Net Ionic Equations** All chemical equations, including net ionic equations, must be balanced. The same number of atoms of each kind must appear on both the product and reactant sides. In addition, the sum of positive and negative charges must be the same on both sides of the equation.

The balanced equation that results from leaving out the spectator ions is the **net ionic equation** for the reaction.

Leaving out the spectator ions does not mean that $K^+$ and $NO_3^-$ ions are unimportant in the $AgNO_3 + KCl$ reaction. Indeed, $Ag^+$ ions cannot exist alone in solution; a negative ion, in this case $NO_3^-$, must be present to balance the positive charge of $Ag^+$. Any anion will do, however, as long as it forms a water-soluble compound with $Ag^+$. Thus, we could have used $AgClO_4$ instead of $AgNO_3$. Similarly, there must be a positive ion present to balance the negative charge of $Cl^-$. In this case, the positive ion present is $K^+$ in KCl, but we could have used NaCl instead of KCl. The net ionic equation would have been the same.

Finally, notice that there must always be a *charge balance* as well as a mass balance in a balanced chemical equation. Thus, in the $Ag^+ + Cl^-$ net ionic equation, the cation and anion charges on the left add together to give a net charge of zero, the same as the zero charge on AgCl(s) on the right.

## Writing Net Ionic Equations

Net ionic equations are commonly written for chemical reactions in aqueous solution because they describe the actual chemical species involved in a reaction. To write net ionic equations we must know which compounds exist as ions in solution.

1. Strong acids, strong bases, and soluble salts exist as ions in solution. Examples include the acids HCl and $HNO_3$, a base such as NaOH, and salts such as NaCl and $CuCl_2$.
2. All other species should be represented by their complete formulas. Weak acids such as acetic acid ($CH_3CO_2H$) exist in aqueous solutions primarily as molecules.

(See Section 3.6.) Insoluble salts such as $CaCO_3(s)$ or insoluble bases such as $Mg(OH)_2(s)$ should not be written in ionic form, even though they are ionic compounds.

The best way to approach writing net ionic equations is to follow precisely a set of steps.

1. Write a complete, balanced equation. Indicate the state of each substance (aq, s, ℓ, g).
2. Next rewrite the whole equation, writing all strong acids, strong bases, and soluble salts as ions. (Consider only species labeled "(aq)" in this step.)
3. Some ions may remain unchanged in the reaction (the ions that appear in the equation both as reactants and products). These "spectator ions" are not part of the chemistry that is going on, and you can cancel them from each side of the equation.
4. Like full chemical equations, net ionic equations must be balanced. The same number of atoms appears on each side of the arrow, and the sum of the ion charges on the two sides must also be equal.

# ⦿WL    **INTERACTIVE EXAMPLE 3.4**    Writing and Balancing Net Ionic Equations

**Problem** Write a balanced, net ionic equation for the reaction of aqueous solutions of $BaCl_2$ and $Na_2SO_4$.

**What Do You Know?** The formulas for the reactants are given. You should recognize that this is an exchange reaction, and that you will need the information on solubilities in Figure 3.10.

**Strategy** Follow the strategy outlined in Problem Solving Tip 3.1.

**Solution**

**Step 1.** In this *exchange reaction*, the $Ba^{2+}$ and $Na^+$ cations exchange anions ($Cl^-$ and $SO_4^{2-}$) to give $BaSO_4$ and $NaCl$. Now that the reactants and products are known, we can write an equation for the reaction. To balance the equation, we place a 2 in front of the $NaCl$.

$$BaCl_2 + Na_2SO_4 \rightarrow BaSO_4 + 2\ NaCl$$

**Step 2.** Decide on the solubility of each compound (Figure 3.10). Compounds containing sodium ions are always water-soluble, and those containing chloride ions are almost always soluble. Sulfate salts are also usually soluble, one important exception being $BaSO_4$. We can therefore write

$$BaCl_2(aq) + Na_2SO_4(aq) \rightarrow BaSO_4(s) + 2\ NaCl(aq)$$

**Step 3.** Identify the ions in solution. All soluble ionic compounds dissociate to form ions in aqueous solution.

$$BaCl_2(s) \quad \rightarrow \quad Ba^{2+}(aq) \quad + \quad 2\ Cl^-(aq)$$

$$Na_2SO_4(s) \quad \rightarrow \quad 2\ Na^+(aq) \quad + \quad SO_4^{2-}(aq)$$

$$NaCl(s) \quad \rightarrow \quad Na^+(aq) \quad + \quad Cl^-(aq)$$

This results in the following complete ionic equation:

$$Ba^{2+}(aq) + 2\ Cl^-(aq) + 2\ Na^+(aq) + SO_4^{2-}(aq) \rightarrow BaSO_4(s) + 2\ Na^+(aq) + 2\ Cl^-(aq)$$

**Step 4.** Identify and eliminate the spectator ions ($Na^+$ and $Cl^-$) to give the net ionic equation.

$$Ba^{2+}(aq) + SO_4^{2-}(aq) \rightarrow BaSO_4(s)$$

**Think about Your Answer** Notice that the sum of ion charges is the same on both sides of the equation. On the left, 2+ and 2− give zero; on the right the charge on $BaSO_4$ is also zero.

---

**Check Your Understanding**

In each of the following cases, aqueous solutions containing the compounds indicated are mixed. Write balanced net ionic equations for the reactions that occur.

(a)  $CaCl_2 + Na_3PO_4$

(b)  iron(III) chloride and potassium hydroxide (a similar reaction is in Figure 3.12c)

(c)  lead(II) nitrate and potassium chloride

---

## REVIEW & CHECK FOR SECTION 3.5

1.  Which of the following compounds is not soluble in water?

    (a)  $Mg(NO_3)_2$        (b)  $Ag_2S$        (c)  $(NH_4)_2SO_4$        (d)  $Na_2CO_3$

2.  Aqueous solutions of the two reactants listed below are mixed. In which solutions will a precipitate form?

    (1)  $NaI(aq) + Pb(NO_3)_2(aq)$              (3)  $H_2SO_4(aq) + BaCl_2(aq)$

    (2)  $CaCl_2(aq) + Na_2CO_3(aq)$            (4)  $NaOH(aq) + AgNO_3(aq)$

    (a)  1, 2, and 3        (b)  2 and 3        (c)  1, 2, and 4        (d)  1, 2, 3, and 4

© Cengage Learning/Charles D. Winters

**Precipitation reaction.** The reaction of barium chloride and sodium sulfate produces insoluble barium sulfate and water-soluble sodium chloride.

**Strategy Map 3.4**

**PROBLEM**
Write **balanced net ionic equation** for the reaction of **$BaCl_2$ + $Na_2SO_4$.**

↓

**DATA/INFORMATION**
The **formulas** of the **reactants** are given

**STEP 1.** Decide on **products** and then write **complete balanced equation.**

**Complete balanced equation** with *reactants* and *products*

**STEP 2.** Decide if each reactant and product is **solid, liquid, gas,** or **dissolved in water.**

**Complete balanced equation** with **indication of state** of each reactant and product

**STEP 3.** Identify ions in solution.

↓

**Complete ionic equation** with reactants and products **dissociated into ions** if appropriate

**STEP 4.** Eliminate spectator ions.

↓

***Balanced net ionic equation***

3. What is the net ionic equation for the reaction of $AgNO_3(aq)$ and $Na_2CO_3(aq)$?

    (a) $Ag^+(aq) + CO_3{}^{2-}(aq) \rightarrow AgCO_3(s)$

    (b) $Na^+(aq) + NO_3{}^-(aq) \rightarrow NaNO_3(s)$

    (c) $2\,Ag^+(aq) + CO_3{}^{2-}(aq) \rightarrow Ag_2CO_3(s)$

    (d) $AgNO_3(aq) + Na_2CO_3(aq) \rightarrow 2\,NaNO_3(aq) + Ag_2CO_3(s)$

## 3.6 Acids and Bases

Acids and bases are two important classes of compounds. You may already be familiar with some common properties of acids. They produce bubbles of $CO_2$ gas when added to a metal carbonate such as $CaCO_3$ (Figure 3.13a), and they react with many metals to produce hydrogen gas ($H_2$) (Figure 3.13b). Although tasting substances is *never* done in a chemistry laboratory, you have probably experienced the sour taste of acids such as acetic acid in vinegar and citric acid (commonly found in fruits and added to candies and soft drinks). Acids and bases have some related properties. Solutions of acids or bases, for example, can change the colors of vegetable pigments (Figure 3.13c). You may have seen acids change the color of litmus, a dye derived from certain lichens, from blue to red. If an acid has made blue litmus paper turn red, adding a base reverses the effect, making the litmus blue again. Thus, acids and bases seem to be opposites. A base can neutralize the effect of an acid, and an acid can neutralize the effect of a base. Table 3.1 lists common acids and bases.

Over the years, chemists have examined the properties, chemical structures, and reactions of acids and bases and have proposed different definitions of the terms *acid* and *base*. In this section, we shall examine the two most commonly used definitions, one proposed by Svante Arrhenius (1859–1927) and another proposed by Johannes N. Brønsted (1879–1947) and Thomas M. Lowry (1874–1936).

### Acids and Bases: The Arrhenius Definition

The Swedish chemist Svante Arrhenius made a number of important contributions to chemistry, but he is perhaps best known for studying the properties of solutions of salts, acids, and bases. In the late 1800s, Arrhenius proposed that these compounds dissolve in water and ultimately form ions. This theory of electrolytes predated any

Photos © Cengage Learning/Charles D. Winters

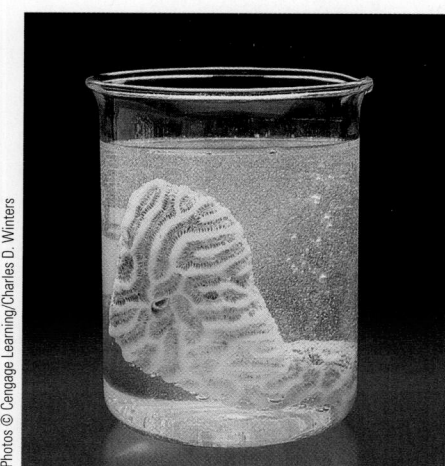

**(a)** A piece of coral (mostly $CaCO_3$) dissolves in acid to give $CO_2$ gas.

**(b)** Zinc reacts with hydrochloric acid to produce zinc chloride and hydrogen gas.

**(c)** The juice of a red cabbage is normally blue-purple. On adding acid, the juice becomes more red. Adding base produces a yellow color.

**FIGURE 3.13** Some properties of acids and bases.

**Table 3.1  Common Acids and Bases**

| Strong Acids (Strong Electrolytes)* | | Soluble Strong Bases | |
|---|---|---|---|
| HCl | Hydrochloric acid | LiOH | Lithium hydroxide |
| HBr | Hydrobromic acid | NaOH | Sodium hydroxide |
| HI | Hydroiodic acid | KOH | Potassium hydroxide |
| $HNO_3$ | Nitric acid | $Ba(OH)_2$ | Barium hydroxide |
| $HClO_4$ | Perchloric acid | $Sr(OH)_2$ | Strontium hydroxide |
| $H_2SO_4$ | Sulfuric acid | | |
| **Weak Acids (Weak Electrolytes)*** | | **Weak Base (Weak Electrolyte)*** | |
| HF | Hydrofluoric acid | $NH_3$ | Ammonia |
| $H_3PO_4$ | Phosphoric acid | | |
| $H_2CO_3$ | Carbonic acid | | |
| $CH_3CO_2H$ | Acetic acid | | |
| $H_2C_2O_4$ | Oxalic acid | | |
| $H_2C_4H_4O_6$ | Tartaric acid | | |
| $H_3C_6H_5O_7$ | Citric acid | | |
| $HC_9H_7O_4$ | Aspirin | | |

*The electrolytic behavior refers to aqueous solutions of these acids and bases.

Oxalic acid
$H_2C_2O_4$

Carboxyl group

Acetic acid
$CH_3CO_2H$

● **Weak Acids** Common acids and bases are listed in Table 3.1. There are numerous other weak acids and bases, and many of these are natural substances. Many of the natural acids contain $CO_2H$ groups. (The H of this group is lost as $H^+$.) The $CO_2H$ group is circled in the figures showing the structures of oxalic and acetic acids, two naturally occurring weak acids.

knowledge of the composition and structure of atoms and was not well accepted initially. With a knowledge of atomic structure, however, we now take it for granted.

The Arrhenius definitions for acids and bases derive from his theory of electrolytes and focuses on formation of $H^+$ and $OH^-$ ions in aqueous solutions.

- An acid is a substance that, when dissolved in water, increases the concentration of hydrogen ions, $H^+$, in solution.

$$HCl(g) \rightarrow H^+(aq) + Cl^-(aq)$$

- A base is a substance that, when dissolved in water, increases the concentration of hydroxide ions, $OH^-$, in the solution.

$$NaOH(s) \rightarrow Na^+(aq) + OH^-(aq)$$

- The reaction of an acid and a base produces a salt and water. Because the characteristic properties of an acid are lost when a base is added, and vice versa, acid–base reactions were logically described as resulting from the combination of $H^+$ and $OH^-$ to form water.

$$HCl(aq) + NaOH(aq) \rightarrow NaCl(aq) + H_2O(\ell)$$

Arrhenius further proposed that acid strength was related to the extent to which the acid ionized. Some acids such as hydrochloric acid (HCl) and nitric acid ($HNO_3$) ionize completely in water; they are strong electrolytes, and we now call them **strong acids**. Other acids such as acetic acid and hydrofluoric acid are incompletely ionized; they are weak electrolytes and are **weak acids**. Weak acids exist in solution primarily as acid molecules, and only a fraction of these molecules ionize to produce $H^+(aq)$ ions along with the appropriate anion.

Water-soluble compounds that contain hydroxide ions, such as sodium hydroxide (NaOH) and potassium hydroxide (KOH), are strong electrolytes and **strong bases**.

Aqueous ammonia, $NH_3(aq)$, is a weak electrolyte. Even though it does not have an $OH^-$ ion as part of its formula, it does produce ammonium ions and hydroxide ions from its reaction with water and so is a base (Figure 3.14). The fact that this is a weak electrolyte indicates that this reaction with water to form ions is reactant-favored at equilibrium. Most of the ammonia remains in solution in molecular form.

© Cengage Learning/Charles D. Winters

**FIGURE 3.14  Ammonia, a weak electrolyte.** Ammonia, $NH_3$, interacts with water to produce a very small number of $NH_4^+$ and $OH^-$ ions per mole of ammonia molecules. (The name on the bottle, ammonium hydroxide, is misleading. The solution consists almost entirely of $NH_3$ molecules dissolved in water. It is better referred to as "aqueous ammonia.")

Although the Arrhenius theory is still used to some extent and is interesting in an historical context, modern concepts of acid–base chemistry such as the Brønsted–Lowry theory have gained preference among chemists.

## Acids and Bases: The Brønsted–Lowry Definition

In 1923, Brønsted in Copenhagen (Denmark) and Lowry in Cambridge (England) independently suggested a new concept of acid and base behavior. They viewed acids and bases in terms of the transfer of a proton ($H^+$) from one species to another, and they described all acid–base reactions in terms of equilibria. The Brønsted–Lowry theory expanded the scope of the definition of acids and bases and helped chemists make predictions of product- or reactant-favorability based on acid and base strength. We will describe this theory here qualitatively; a more complete discussion will be given in Chapter 17.

The main concepts of the Brønsted–Lowry theory are the following:

- *An acid is a proton donor.* This is similar to the Arrhenius definition.
- *A base is a proton acceptor.* This definition includes the $OH^-$ ion but it also broadens the number and type of bases.
- *An acid–base reaction involves the transfer of a proton from an acid to a base to form a new base and a new acid. The reaction is written as an equilibrium reaction and the equilibrium favors the weaker acid and base.* This allows the prediction of product- or reactant-favored reactions based on acid and base strength.

From the point of view of the Brønsted–Lowry theory, the behavior of acids such as HCl or $CH_3CO_2H$ in water is written as an acid–base reaction. Both species (both Brønsted acids) donate a proton to water (a Brønsted base) forming $H_3O^+(aq)$, the hydronium ion. Hydrochloric acid, HCl(aq), is a strong electrolyte because it ionizes completely in aqueous solution; it is classified as a strong acid.

*Hydrochloric acid, a strong acid. 100% ionized. Equilibrium strongly favors products.*

$$HCl(aq) \quad + \quad H_2O(\ell) \quad \rightleftharpoons \quad H_3O^+(aq) \quad + \quad Cl^-(aq)$$

hydrochloric acid    water    hydronium ion    chloride ion
strong electrolyte
= 100% ionized

In contrast, $CH_3CO_2H$ is a weak electrolyte, evidence that it is only weakly ionized in water and is therefore a weak acid.

*Acetic acid, a weak acid, << 100% ionized. Equilibrium favors reactants.*

$$CH_3CO_2H(aq) \ + \ H_2O(\ell) \ \rightleftharpoons \ H_3O^+(aq) \ + \ CH_3CO_2^-(aq)$$
weak Brønsted acid

The different extent of ionization for these two acids relates to their acid strength. Hydrochloric acid is a strong acid, and the equilibrium strongly favors the products. In contrast, acetic acid is a weak acid and its reaction with water is reactant-favored.

Sulfuric acid, a *diprotic acid* (an acid capable of transferring two $H^+$ ions), reacts with water in two steps. The first step strongly favors products, whereas the second step is reactant-favored.

Strong acid: $H_2SO_4(aq) + H_2O(\ell) \rightleftharpoons H_3O^+(aq) + HSO_4^-(aq)$
sulfuric acid                   hydronium ion     hydrogen
100% ionized                                   sulfate ion

Weak acid: $HSO_4^-(aq) + H_2O(\ell) \rightleftharpoons H_3O^+(aq) + SO_4^{2-}(aq)$
hydrogen sulfate ion           hydronium ion     sulfate ion
<100% ionized

## A CLOSER LOOK

# The Hydronium Ion—The H⁺ Ion in Water

The H⁺ ion is a hydrogen atom that has lost its electron. Only the nucleus, a proton, remains. Because a proton is only about 1/100,000 as large as the average atom or ion, water molecules can approach closely, and the proton and water molecules are strongly attracted. In fact, the H⁺ ion in water is better represented as $H_3O^+$, called the **hydronium ion**. This ion is formed by combining H⁺ and $H_2O$. Experiments also show that other forms of the ion exist in water, one example being $[H_3O(H_2O)_3]^+$.

There will be instances when, for simplicity, we will use H⁺(aq). However, in this book we will usually use the $H_3O^+$(aq) symbol to represent the hydrogen ion in water. Thus, what we call hydrochloric acid is better represented as a solution of $H_3O^+$ and $Cl^-$.

hydronium ion
$H_3O^+$(aq)

chloride ion
$Cl^-$(aq)

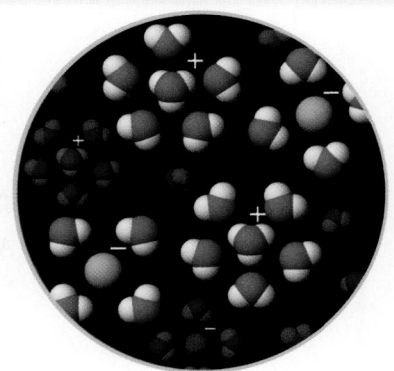

**Hydronium ions in solution.** When HCl ionizes in aqueous solution, it produces the hydronium ion, $H_3O^+$, and the chloride ion, $Cl^-$.

Ammonia, a weak base, reacts with water to produce $OH^-$(aq) ions. The reaction is reactant-favored at equilibrium.

*Ammonia, a weak base, << 100% ionized. Equilibrium favors reactants.*

$$NH_3(aq) + H_2O(\ell) \rightleftharpoons NH_4^+(aq) + OH^-(aq)$$

ammonia, base
weak electrolyte
< 100% ionized

water

ammonium
ion

hydroxide ion

Some species are described as **amphiprotic**, that is, they can function either as acids or as bases depending on the reaction. In the examples above, water functions as a base in reactions with acids (it accepts a proton) and as an acid in its reaction with ammonia (where it donates a proton to ammonia, forming the ammonium ion.)

## EXAMPLE 3.5    Brønsted Acids and Bases

**Problem** Write a balanced net ionic equation for the reaction that occurs when the cyanide ion, $CN^-$, accepts a proton (H⁺) from water to form HCN. Is $CN^-$ a Brønsted acid or base?

**What Do You Know?** You know the formulas of the ion ($CN^-$) and molecule ($H_2O$) involved as reactants and one of the products, (HCN). You also know a proton transfer occurs from water to $CN^-$.

**Strategy** As it is a proton transfer, you should move an H⁺ ion from $H_2O$ to $CN^-$ to give the products.

**Solution**

$$H_2O(\ell) + CN^-(aq) \rightleftharpoons OH^-(aq) + HCN(aq)$$

In this reaction the water is the Brønsted acid and the $CN^-$ ion is the Brønsted base.

**Think about Your Answer** The $CN^-$ ion is a proton acceptor and so is a Brønsted base.

**Check Your Understanding**

(a)   Write a balanced equation for the reaction that occurs when $H_3PO_4$, phosphoric acid, donates a proton to water to form the dihydrogen phosphate ion.

(b)   Write a net ionic equation showing the dihydrogen phosphate ion acting as a Brønsted acid in a reaction with water. Write another net ionic equation showing the dihydrogen phosphate ion acting as a Brønsted base in a reaction with water. What term is used to describe a species such as the dihydrogen phosphate ion that can act both as an acid or as a base?

## Reactions of Acids and Bases

Acids and bases in aqueous solution usually react to produce a salt and water. For example (Figure 3.15),

$$\underset{\text{hydrochloric acid}}{HCl(aq)} \;+\; \underset{\text{sodium hydroxide}}{NaOH(aq)} \longrightarrow \underset{\text{water}}{H_2O(\ell)} \;+\; \underset{\text{sodium chloride}}{NaCl(aq)}$$

The word "salt" has come into the language of chemistry to describe any ionic compound whose cation comes from a base (here $Na^+$ from NaOH) and whose anion comes from an acid (here $Cl^-$ from HCl). The reaction of any of the acids listed in Table 3.1 with any of the hydroxide-containing bases listed there produces a salt and water.

Hydrochloric acid and sodium hydroxide are strong electrolytes in water (Figure 3.15 and Table 3.1), so the complete ionic equation for the reaction of HCl(aq) and NaOH(aq) should be written as

$$\underset{\text{from HCl(aq)}}{\underbrace{H_3O^+(aq) + Cl^-(aq)}} + \underset{\text{from NaOH(aq)}}{\underbrace{Na^+(aq) + OH^-(aq)}} \longrightarrow \underset{\text{water}}{2\ H_2O(\ell)} + \underset{\text{from salt}}{\underbrace{Na^+(aq) + Cl^-(aq)}}$$

Because $Na^+$ and $Cl^-$ ions appear on both sides of the equation, the *net ionic equation* is just the combination of the ions $H_3O^+$ and $OH^-$ to give water.

$$H_3O^+(aq) + OH^-(aq) \rightarrow 2\ H_2O(\ell)$$

*This is always the net ionic equation when a strong acid reacts with a strong base.*

HCl (acid)     NaOH (base)

NaCl (salt) + $H_2O$

$H_3O^+(aq) + Cl^-(aq)$        $Na^+(aq) + OH^-(aq)$        $Na^+(aq) + Cl^-(aq)$

**FIGURE 3.15 An acid–base reaction, HCl and NaOH.** On mixing, the $H_3O^+$ and $OH^-$ ions combine to produce $H_2O$, whereas the ions $Na^+$ and $Cl^-$ remain in solution.

## Sulfuric Acid

For many years sulfuric acid has been the chemical produced in the largest quantity in the United States (as well as in many other industrialized countries). About 40–50 billion kilograms (40–50 million metric tons) is made annually in the United States. The acid is so important to the economy of industrialized nations that some economists have said sulfuric acid production is a measure of a nation's industrial strength.

Sulfuric acid is a colorless, syrupy liquid with a density of 1.84 g/mL and a boiling point of 337 °C. It has several desirable properties that have led to its widespread use: it is generally less expensive to produce than other acids, is a strong acid, and can be handled in steel containers. It reacts readily with many organic compounds to produce useful products and reacts readily with lime (CaO), the least expensive and most readily available base, to give calcium sulfate, a compound used to make wall board for the construction industry.

The first step in the industrial preparation of sulfuric acid is the production of sulfur dioxide. This comes from the combustion of sulfur in air,

$$S(s) + O_2(g) \rightarrow SO_2(g)$$

**Sulfur.** Much of the sulfur used in the U.S. used to be mined, but it is now largely a by-product from natural gas and oil-refining processes. It takes about 1 ton of sulfur to make 3 tons of the acid.

or from the $SO_2$ produced in smelting sulfur-containing copper, nickel, or other metal ores. The $SO_2$ is then combined with more oxygen, in the presence of a catalyst (a substance that speeds up the reaction), to give sulfur trioxide,

$$2\ SO_2(g) + O_2(g) \rightarrow 2\ SO_3(g)$$

which can give sulfuric acid when dissolved in water.

Some products that require sulfuric acid for their manufacture or use.

$$SO_3(g) + H_2O(\ell) \rightarrow H_2SO_4(aq)$$

Currently, over two thirds of the production is used in the fertilizer industry. The remainder is used to make pigments, explosives, pulp and paper, detergents, and as a component in storage batteries.

**"The Acid Touch,"** *Chemical and Engineering News,* April 14, 2008, p. 27.

---

Reactions between strong acids and strong bases are called **neutralization reactions** because, on completion of the reaction, the solution is neutral if exactly the same amounts (number of moles) of the acid and base are mixed; that is, it is neither acidic nor basic. The other ions (the cation of the base and the anion of the acid) remain unchanged. If the water is evaporated, however, the cation and anion form a solid salt. In the example above, NaCl can be obtained. If nitric acid, $HNO_3$, and NaOH were allowed to react, the salt sodium nitrate, $NaNO_3$, (and water) would be obtained.

$$HNO_3(aq) + NaOH(aq) \rightarrow H_2O(\ell) + NaNO_3(aq)$$

If acetic acid and sodium hydroxide are mixed, the following reaction will take place.

$$CH_3CO_2H(aq) + NaOH(aq) \rightarrow H_2O(\ell) + NaCH_3CO_2(aq)$$

Because acetic acid is a weak acid and ionizes to such a small extent (Figure 3.8), the molecular species is the predominant form in aqueous solutions. In ionic equations, therefore, acetic acid is shown as molecular $CH_3CO_2H(aq)$. The *complete ionic equation* for this reaction is

$$CH_3CO_2H(aq) + Na^+(aq) + OH^-(aq) \rightarrow H_2O(\ell) + Na^+(aq) + CH_3CO_2^-(aq)$$

The only spectator ions in this equation are the sodium ions, so the *net ionic equation* is

$$CH_3CO_2H(aq) + OH^-(aq) \rightarrow H_2O(\ell) + CH_3CO_2^-(aq)$$

© Cengage Learning/Charles D. Winters

**Reaction of gaseous HCl and NH$_3$.** Open dishes of aqueous ammonia and hydrochloric acid were placed side by side. When gas molecules of NH$_3$ and HCl escape from solution to the atmosphere and encounter one another, we observe a cloud of solid ammonium chloride, NH$_4$Cl.

**EXAMPLE 3.6**     **Net Ionic Equation for an Acid–Base Reaction**

**Problem** Ammonia, NH$_3$, is one of the most important chemicals in industrial economies. Not only is it used directly as a fertilizer but it is the raw material for the manufacture of nitric acid. As a base, it reacts with acids such as hydrochloric acid. Write a balanced, net ionic equation for this reaction.

**What Do You Know?** The reactants are NH$_3$(aq) and HCl(aq). A proton will transfer from the acid to the base.

**Strategy** Follow the general strategy for writing net ionic equations as outlined in Problem Solving Tip 3.1.

**Solution** A proton transfers from HCl to NH$_3$, a weak Brønsted base, to form the ammonium ion, NH$_4{}^+$. This positive ion must have a negative counterion from the acid, Cl$^-$, so the reaction product is NH$_4$Cl, and the complete balanced equation is

$$\underset{\text{ammonia}}{\text{NH}_3\text{(aq)}} \;+\; \underset{\text{hydrochloric acid}}{\text{HCl(aq)}} \;\longrightarrow\; \underset{\text{ammonium chloride}}{\text{NH}_4\text{Cl(aq)}}$$

To write the net ionic equation, start with the fact that hydrochloric acid is a strong acid and produces H$_3$O$^+$ and Cl$^-$ ions in water and that NH$_4$Cl is a soluble, ionic compound. On the other hand, ammonia is a weak base and so is predominantly present in the solution as the molecular species, NH$_3$.

$$\text{NH}_3\text{(aq)} + \text{H}_3\text{O}^+\text{(aq)} + \text{Cl}^-\text{(aq)} \;\longrightarrow\; \text{NH}_4{}^+\text{(aq)} + \text{Cl}^-\text{(aq)} + \text{H}_2\text{O}(\ell)$$

Eliminating the spectator ion, Cl$^-$, we have

$$\boxed{\text{NH}_3\text{(aq)} + \text{H}_3\text{O}^+\text{(aq)} \;\rightleftharpoons\; \text{NH}_4{}^+\text{(aq)} + \text{H}_2\text{O}(\ell)}$$

**Think about Your Answer** The net ionic equation shows that the important aspect of the reaction between the weak base ammonia and the strong acid HCl is the transfer of an H$^+$ ion from the acid to the NH$_3$. Any strong acid could be used here (HBr, HNO$_3$, HClO$_4$, H$_2$SO$_4$) and the net ionic equation would be the same. Also notice that, even though H$_2$O is not in the overall balanced equation, it is present in the net ionic equation because the H$^+$ from the acid is present in the initial solution as H$_3$O$^+$.

**Check Your Understanding**

Write the balanced, overall equation and the net ionic equation for the reaction of magnesium hydroxide with hydrochloric acid. (*Hint:* Think about the solubility guidelines.)

CO$_2$

SO$_2$

SO$_3$

NO$_2$

**Some common nonmetal oxides that form acids in water.**

## Oxides of Nonmetals and Metals

Each acid shown in Table 3.1 has one or more H atoms in the molecular formula that ionize in water to form H$_3$O$^+$ ions. There are, however, less obvious compounds that form acidic solutions. Oxides of nonmetals, such as carbon dioxide and sulfur trioxide, have no H atoms but react with water to produce H$_3$O$^+$ ions. Carbon dioxide, for example, dissolves in water to a small extent, and some of the dissolved molecules react with water to form the weak acid, carbonic acid. This acid then ionizes to a small extent to form the hydronium ion, H$_3$O$^+$, and the hydrogen carbonate (bicarbonate) ion, HCO$_3{}^-$.

$$\text{CO}_2\text{(g)} \;+\; \text{H}_2\text{O}(\ell) \;\rightleftharpoons\; \text{H}_2\text{CO}_3\text{(aq)}$$

$$\text{H}_2\text{CO}_3\text{(aq)} \;+\; \text{H}_2\text{O}(\ell) \;\rightleftharpoons\; \text{HCO}_3{}^-\text{(aq)} \;+\; \text{H}_3\text{O}^+\text{(aq)}$$

The $HCO_3^-$ ion can also function as an acid, ionizing to produce $H_3O^+$ and the carbonate ion, $CO_3^{2-}$.

$$HCO_3^-(aq) \ + \ H_2O(\ell) \ \rightleftharpoons \ CO_3^{2-}(aq) \ + \ H_3O^+(aq)$$

These reactions are important in our environment and in the human body. Carbon dioxide is normally found in small amounts in the atmosphere, so rainwater is always slightly acidic. In the human body, carbon dioxide is dissolved in body fluids where the $HCO_3^-$ and $CO_3^{2-}$ ions perform an important "buffering" action (▶ Chapter 18).

Oxides like $CO_2$ that can react with water to produce $H_3O^+$ ions are known as **acidic oxides**. Other acidic oxides include those of sulfur and nitrogen. For example, sulfur dioxide, $SO_2$, from human and natural sources, can react with oxygen to give sulfur trioxide, $SO_3$, which then reacts with water to form sulfuric acid.

$$2\ SO_2(g) + O_2(g) \longrightarrow 2\ SO_3(g)$$
$$SO_3(g) + H_2O(\ell) \longrightarrow H_2SO_4(aq)$$

Nitrogen dioxide, $NO_2$, reacts with water to give nitric and nitrous acids.

$$2\ NO_2(g) \ + \ H_2O(\ell) \rightarrow \ \underset{\text{nitric acid}}{HNO_3(aq)} \ + \ \underset{\text{nitrous acid}}{HNO_2(aq)}$$

Oxides of metals are called **basic oxides** because they give basic solutions if they dissolve appreciably in water. Perhaps the best example is calcium oxide, CaO, often called *lime*, or *quicklime*. Almost 20 billion kg of lime is produced annually in the United States for use in the metals and construction industries, in sewage and pollution control, in water treatment, and in agriculture. This metal oxide reacts with water to give calcium hydroxide, commonly called *slaked lime*. Although only slightly soluble in water (about 0.2 g/100 g $H_2O$ at 10 °C), $Ca(OH)_2$ is widely used in industry as a base because it is inexpensive.

$$\underset{\text{lime}}{CaO(s)} \ + \ H_2O(\ell) \ \rightarrow \ \underset{\text{slaked lime}}{Ca(OH)_2(s)}$$

● **Acid Rain** Oxides of sulfur and nitrogen are the major source of the acid in what is called *acid rain*. These acidic oxides arise from the burning of fossil fuels such as coal and gasoline. The gaseous oxides mix with water and other chemicals in the troposphere, and the rain that falls is more acidic than if it contained only dissolved $CO_2$. When the rain falls on areas that cannot easily tolerate this greater-than-normal acidity, serious environmental problems can occur.

---

**REVIEW & CHECK FOR SECTION 3.6**

1. Which of the following is a strong acid in aqueous solution?

   (a) HF     (b) $H_2CO_3$     (c) $CH_3CO_2H$     (d) $H_2SO_4$

2. The hydrogen phosphate ion is amphiprotic. Identify the product formed from this ion when it reacts with a base.

   (a) $H_3PO_4$     (b) $H_2PO_4^-$     (c) $HPO_4^{2-}$     (d) $PO_4^{3-}$

3. What is the net ionic equation for the reaction of acetic acid and sodium hydroxide?

   (a) $H_3O^+(aq) \ + \ OH^-(aq) \rightarrow 2\ H_2O(\ell)$

   (b) $Na^+(aq) \ + \ CH_3CO_2^-(aq) \ \rightarrow \ NaCH_3CO_2(aq)$

   (c) $CH_3CO_2H(aq) \ + \ OH^-(aq) \rightarrow \ H_2O(\ell) \ + \ CH_3CO_2^-(aq)$

   (d) $CH_3CO_2H(aq) \ + \ NaOH(aq) \rightarrow \ H_2O(\ell) \ + \ NaCH_3CO_2(aq)$

4. Identify the basic oxide from those listed below.

   (a) $SO_2$     (b) BaO     (c) $P_4O_{10}$     (d) $CO_2$

© Cengage Learning/Charles D. Winters

**FIGURE 3.16 Dissolving lime-stone (calcium carbonate, CaCO₃) in vinegar.** Notice the bubbles of $CO_2$ rising from the surface of the limestone. This reaction shows why vinegar can be used as a household cleaning agent. It can be used, for example, to clean the calcium carbonate deposited from hard water.

**Table 3.2  Gas-Forming Reactions**

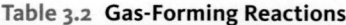

| Metal carbonate or hydrogen carbonate + acid → metal salt + $CO_2$(g) + $H_2O(\ell)$ |
|---|
| $Na_2CO_3(aq) + 2\ HCl(aq) \rightarrow 2\ NaCl(aq) + CO_2(g) + H_2O(\ell)$ |
| $NaHCO_3(aq) + HCl(aq) \rightarrow NaCl(aq) + CO_2(g) + H_2O(\ell)$ |
| **Metal sulfide + acid → metal salt + $H_2S$(g)** |
| $Na_2S(aq) + 2\ HCl(aq) \rightarrow 2\ NaCl(aq) + H_2S(g)$ |
| **Metal sulfite + acid → metal salt + $SO_2$(g) + $H_2O(\ell)$** |
| $Na_2SO_3(aq) + 2\ HCl(aq) \rightarrow 2\ NaCl(aq) + SO_2(g) + H_2O(\ell)$ |
| **Ammonium salt + strong base → metal salt + $NH_3$(g) + $H_2O(\ell)$** |
| $NH_4Cl(aq) + NaOH(aq) \rightarrow NaCl(aq) + NH_3(g) + H_2O(\ell)$ |

## 3.7  Gas-Forming Reactions

Several different chemical reactions lead to gas formation (Table 3.2), and the most common are those that produce $CO_2$. All metal carbonates (and bicarbonates) react with acids to produce carbonic acid, $H_2CO_3$, which in turn decomposes rapidly to carbon dioxide and water. For example, the reaction of calcium carbonate and hydrochloric acid is:

$$CaCO_3(s) + 2\ HCl(aq) \rightarrow CaCl_2(aq) + H_2CO_3(aq)$$

$$H_2CO_3(aq) \rightarrow H_2O(\ell) + CO_2(g)$$

Overall reaction:  $CaCO_3(s) + 2\ HCl(aq) \rightarrow CaCl_2(aq) + H_2O(\ell) + CO_2(g)$

If the reaction is done in an open beaker, most of the $CO_2$ gas bubbles out of the solution.

Calcium carbonate is a common residue from hard water in home heating systems and cooking utensils. Washing with vinegar is a good way to clean the system or utensils because the insoluble calcium carbonate is turned into water-soluble calcium acetate in the following gas-forming reaction (Figure 3.16).

$$2\ CH_3CO_2H(aq) + CaCO_3(s) \rightarrow Ca(CH_3CO_2)_2(aq) + H_2O(\ell) + CO_2(g)$$

What is the net ionic equation for this reaction? Acetic acid is a weak acid, and calcium carbonate is insoluble in water. Therefore, the reactants are simply $CH_3CO_2H(aq)$ and $CaCO_3(s)$. On the products side, calcium acetate is water-soluble and so is present in solution as aqueous calcium and acetate ions. Water and carbon dioxide are molecular compounds, so the complete and net ionic equation is

$$2\ CH_3CO_2H(aq) + CaCO_3(s) \rightarrow Ca^{2+}(aq) + 2\ CH_3CO_2^-(aq) + H_2O(\ell) + CO_2(g)$$

There are no spectator ions in this reaction.

Have you ever made biscuits or muffins? As you bake the dough, it rises in the oven (Figure 3.17) because a gas-forming reaction occurs between an acid and baking soda, sodium hydrogen carbonate (bicarbonate of soda, $NaHCO_3$). One acid used for this purpose is tartaric acid, a weak acid found in many foods. The net ionic equation for a typical reaction is

$$\underset{\text{tartaric acid}}{H_2C_4H_4O_6(aq)} + \underset{\text{hydrogen carbonate ion}}{HCO_3^-(aq)} \longrightarrow \underset{\text{hydrogen tartrate ion}}{HC_4H_4O_6^-(aq)} + H_2O(\ell) + CO_2(g)$$

In dry baking powder, the acid and $NaHCO_3$ are kept apart by using starch as a filler. When mixed into the moist batter, however, the acid and sodium hydrogen carbonate dissolve, come into contact, and react to produce $CO_2$, which causes the dough to rise.

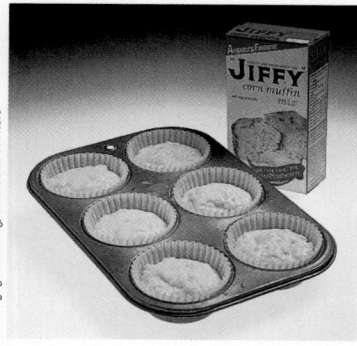

© Cengage Learning/Charles D. Winters

**FIGURE 3.17 Muffins rise because of a gas-forming reaction.** The acid and sodium bicarbonate in baking powder produce carbon dioxide gas. The acid used in many baking powders is $CaHPO_4$, but tartaric acid and $NaAl(SO_4)_2$ are also common. (Aqueous solutions containing the aluminum ion are acidic.)

## Recognizing Gas-Forming Reactions

How can you recognize that a particular reaction will lead to gas formation? After you predict the products of the exchange reaction, be alert for certain products:

(a) $H_2CO_3$: This will decompose into carbon dioxide gas and water.

(b) $H_2SO_3$: This will decompose into sulfur dioxide gas and water.

(c) $H_2S$: This is a gaseous product already.

(d) If $NH_4^+$ and $OH^-$ ions are produced, they will form ammonia gas and water.

## EXAMPLE 3.7    Gas-Forming Reactions

**Problem**  Write a balanced equation for the reaction that occurs when nickel(II) carbonate is treated with sulfuric acid.

**What Do You Know?**  You know the names of the reactants and therefore their formulas. You should recognize that the reaction of a metal carbonate with an acid is a gas-forming reaction ($CO_2$ is formed in these reactions).

**Strategy**

• Write the formulas for the reactants.

• Determine the products of the reaction and their formulas.

• Write and balance the equation.

**Solution**  The reactants are $NiCO_3$ and $H_2SO_4$, and the products of the reaction are $NiSO_4$, $CO_2$ and $H_2O$. The complete, balanced equation is

$$NiCO_3(s) + H_2SO_4(aq) \longrightarrow NiSO_4(aq) + H_2O(\ell) + CO_2(g)$$

**Think about Your Answer**  The products in this reaction were determined by first exchanging cations ($Ni^{2+}$ and 2 $H^+$) and anions ($CO_3^{2-}$ and $SO_4^{2-}$). This exchange reaction is then followed by a second reaction in which one product, $H_2CO_3$, decomposes to give $CO_2$ and $H_2O$.

**Check Your Understanding**

Barium carbonate, $BaCO_3$, is used in the brick, ceramic, glass, and chemical manufacturing industries. Write a balanced equation that shows what happens when barium carbonate is treated with nitric acid. Give the name of each of the reaction products.

---

**REVIEW & CHECK FOR SECTION 3.7**

Which of the following compounds, when treated with acid, results in gas evolution?

(a)  $NH_4Cl$        (b)  $Na_2CO_3$        (c)  $Na_2SO_4$        (d)  $Na_3PO_4$

## 3.8  Oxidation–Reduction Reactions

The terms *oxidation* and *reduction* come from reactions that have been known for centuries. Ancient civilizations learned how to change metal oxides and sulfides into the metal, that is, how to "reduce" ore to the metal. A modern example is the reduction of iron(III) oxide with carbon monoxide to give iron metal (Figure 3.18a).

$Fe_2O_3$ loses oxygen and is reduced.

$$Fe_2O_3(s) + 3\ CO(g) \longrightarrow 2\ Fe(s) + 3\ CO_2(g)$$

CO is the reducing agent. It gains oxygen and is oxidized.

Jan Halaska/Photo Researchers, Inc.

**(a)** Iron ore, which is largely $Fe_2O_3$, is reduced to metallic iron with carbon (C) or carbon monoxide (CO) in a blast furnace. Here iron(III) oxide is reduced to Fe by the reducing agent C or CO. The C or CO is oxidized to $CO_2$.

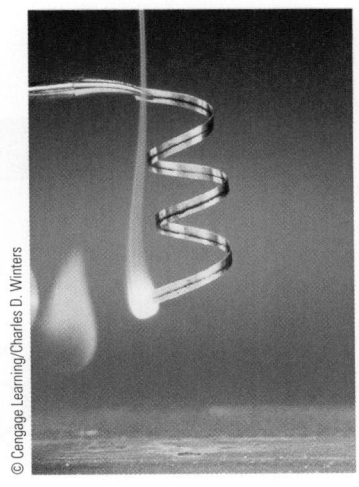

© Cengage Learning/Charles D. Winters

**(b)** Burning magnesium metal in air produces magnesium oxide. The magnesium is oxidized by the oxidizing agent $O_2$. Oxygen is reduced by the reducing agent Mg.

**FIGURE 3.18** Oxidation–reduction reactions.

In this reaction carbon monoxide is the agent that brings about the reduction of iron ore to iron metal, so carbon monoxide is called the **reducing agent**.

When $Fe_2O_3$ is reduced by carbon monoxide, oxygen is removed from the iron ore and added to the carbon monoxide. The carbon monoxide, therefore, is "oxidized" by the addition of oxygen to give carbon dioxide. *Any process in which oxygen is added to another substance is an oxidation.* In the reaction of oxygen with magnesium, for example (Figure 3.18b), oxygen is the **oxidizing agent** because it is the agent responsible for the oxidation of magnesium.

Mg combines with
oxygen and is oxidized.

$$2\ Mg(s) + O_2(g) \longrightarrow 2\ MgO(s)$$

$O_2$ is the oxidizing agent.

## Oxidation–Reduction Reactions and Electron Transfer

The concept of oxidation–reduction reactions has been extended from these and similar examples to a vast number of other reactions, many of which do not even involve oxygen. Rather than concentrate on whether oxygen is gained or lost, let us look at what is going on with electrons during the course of the reaction. All oxidation and reduction reactions can be accounted for by considering them to occur by means of a transfer of electrons between substances. When a substance accepts electrons, it is said to be reduced because there is a reduction in the numerical value of the charge on an atom of the substance. In the net ionic equation for the reaction of a silver salt with copper metal, positively charged $Ag^+$ ions accept electrons from copper metal and are reduced to uncharged silver atoms (Figure 3.19).

$Ag^+$ ions accept electrons from Cu and are
reduced to Ag. $Ag^+$ is the oxidizing agent.
$$Ag^+(aq) + e^- \rightarrow Ag(s)$$

$$2\ Ag^+(aq) + Cu(s) \longrightarrow 2\ Ag(s) + Cu^{2+}(aq)$$

Cu donates electrons to $Ag^+$ and is oxidized to $Cu^{2+}$.
Cu is the reducing agent.
$$Cu(s) \rightarrow Cu^{2+}(aq) + 2\ e^-$$

Pure copper
wire

Copper wire in dilute $AgNO_3$
solution after several hours

Blue color due to
$Cu^{2+}$ ions formed
in redox reaction

Silver crystals
formed after
several weeks

Photos © Cengage Learning/Charles D. Winters

**FIGURE 3.19** **The oxidation of copper metal by silver ions.** A clean piece of copper wire is placed in a solution of silver nitrate, $AgNO_3$. Over time, the copper reduces $Ag^+$ ions, forming silver crystals, and the copper metal is oxidized to copper ions, $Cu^{2+}$. The blue color of the solution is due to the presence of aqueous copper(II) ions.

Because copper metal supplies the electrons and causes $Ag^+$ ions to be reduced, Cu is the reducing agent.

When a substance *loses electrons*, the numerical value of the charge on an atom of the substance increases. The substance is said to have been **oxidized**. In our example, copper metal releases electrons on going to $Cu^{2+}$, so the metal is oxidized. For this to happen, something must be available to accept the electrons from copper. In this case, $Ag^+$ is the electron acceptor, and its charge is reduced to zero in silver metal. Therefore, $Ag^+$ is the "agent" that causes Cu metal to be oxidized; that is, $Ag^+$ is the *oxidizing agent*.

In every oxidation–reduction reaction, one reactant is reduced (and therefore is the oxidizing agent) and one reactant is oxidized (and therefore is the reducing agent). We can show this by dividing the general redox reaction $X + Y \rightarrow X^{n+} + Y^{n-}$ into two parts or *half-reactions*:

| Half Reaction | Electron Transfer | Result |
|---|---|---|
| $X \rightarrow X^{n+} + n\,e^-$ | X transfers electrons to Y | X is oxidized to $X^{n+}$. X is the reducing agent. |
| $Y + n\,e^- \rightarrow Y^{n-}$ | Y accepts electrons from X | Y is reduced to $Y^{n-}$. Y is the oxidizing agent. |

In the reaction of magnesium and oxygen, $O_2$ is reduced because it gains electrons (four electrons per molecule) on going to two oxide ions. Thus, because $O_2$ is involved in the oxidation of magnesium, it is the oxidizing agent.

Mg releases 2 $e^-$ per atom. Mg is oxidized to $Mg^{2+}$ and is the reducing agent.

$$2\,Mg(s) + O_2(g) \longrightarrow 2\,MgO(s)$$

$O_2$ gains 4 $e^-$ per molecule to form 2 $O^{2-}$. $O_2$ is reduced and is the oxidizing agent.

In the same reaction, magnesium is the reducing agent because it releases two electrons per atom on being oxidized to the $Mg^{2+}$ ion (and so two Mg atoms are required to supply the four electrons required by one $O_2$ molecule). All redox reactions can be analyzed in a similar manner.

The observations outlined so far lead to several important conclusions:

- If one substance is oxidized, another substance in the same reaction must be reduced. For this reason, such reactions are called *oxidation–reduction reactions,* or **redox reactions** for short.
- The reducing agent is itself oxidized, and the oxidizing agent is reduced.
- Oxidation is the opposite of reduction. For example, the removal of oxygen is reduction and the addition of oxygen is oxidation. The gain of electrons is reduction and the loss of electrons is oxidation.

## Oxidation Numbers

How can you tell an oxidation–reduction reaction when you see one? How can you tell which substance has gained or lost electrons and so decide which substance is the oxidizing (or reducing) agent? Sometimes it is obvious. For example, if an uncombined element becomes part of a compound (Mg becomes part of MgO, for example), the reaction is definitely a redox process. If it's not obvious, then the answer is to *look for a change in the oxidation number of an element in the course of the reaction*. The **oxidation number** of an atom in a molecule or ion is defined as the charge an atom has, *or appears to have,* as determined by the following guidelines for assigning oxidation numbers.

1.  **Each atom in a pure element has an oxidation number of zero.** The oxidation number of Cu in metallic copper is 0, and it is 0 for each atom in $I_2$ and $S_8$.
2.  **For monatomic ions, the oxidation number is equal to the charge on the ion.** You know that magnesium forms ions with a 2+ charge ($Mg^{2+}$); the oxidation number of magnesium in this ion is therefore +2.

● **Balancing Equations for Redox Reactions** The notion that a redox reaction can be divided into a reduction portion and an oxidation portion will lead us to a method of balancing more complex equations for redox reactions described in Chapter 20.

● **Writing Charges on Ions** Conventionally, charges on ions are written as (number, sign), whereas oxidation numbers are written as (sign, number). For example, the oxidation number of the $Cu^{2+}$ ion is +2 and its charge is 2+.

## Are Oxidation Numbers "Real"?

Do oxidation numbers reflect the actual electric charge on an atom in a molecule or ion? With the exception of monatomic ions such as Cl⁻ or Na⁺, the answer is no.

Oxidation numbers assume that the atoms in a molecule are positive or negative ions, which is not true. For example, in $H_2O$, the H atoms are not $H^+$ ions and the O atoms are not $O^{2-}$ ions. This is not to say, however, that atoms in molecules do not bear an electric charge of any kind. Calculations on water indicate the O atom

has a charge of about 0.4– (or 40% of the electron charge) and the H atoms are each about 0.2+.

So why use oxidation numbers? Oxidation numbers provide a way of dividing up the electrons among the atoms in a molecule or polyatomic ion. Because the distribution of electrons changes in a redox reaction, we use this method as a way to decide whether a redox reaction has

occurred and to distinguish the oxidizing and reducing agents.

Charge on O atom = 0.4–

Charge on each H atom = 0.2+

● **Peroxides** In peroxides, the oxidation number of oxygen is −1. For example, in hydrogen peroxide ($H_2O_2$), each hydrogen atom has an oxidation number of +1. To balance this, each oxygen must have an oxidation number of −1. A 3% aqueous solution of $H_2O_2$ is sometimes used as an antiseptic because it is a good oxidizing agent.

3. **When combined with another element, fluorine always has an oxidation number of −1**.

4. **The oxidation number of O is −2 in most compounds.** The exceptions to this rule occur
    (a) when oxygen is combined with fluorine (where oxygen takes on a positive oxidation number),
    (b) in compounds called *peroxides* (such as $Na_2O_2$) and *superoxides* (such as $KO_2$) in which oxygen has an oxidation number of −1 and −1/2, respectively.

5. **Cl, Br, and I have oxidation numbers of −1 in compounds, except when combined with oxygen and fluorine.** This means that Cl has an oxidation number of −1 in NaCl (in which Na's oxidation number is +1, as predicted by the fact that it is an element of Group 1A). In the ion $ClO^-$, however, the Cl atom has an oxidation number of +1 (and O has an oxidation number of −2; see Guideline 4).

6. **The oxidation number of H is +1 in most compounds.** The key exception to this guideline occurs when H forms a binary compound with a metal. In such cases, the metal forms a positive ion and H becomes a hydride ion, $H^-$. Thus, in $CaH_2$ the oxidation number of Ca is +2 (equal to the group number) and that of H is −1.

7. **The algebraic sum of the oxidation numbers for the atoms in a neutral compound must be zero; in a polyatomic ion, the sum must be equal to the ion charge.** For example, in $HClO_4$ the H atom is assigned +1 and each O atom is assigned −2. This means the Cl atom must be +7.

### EXAMPLE 3.8 Determining Oxidation Numbers

**Problem** Determine the oxidation number of the indicated element in each of the following compounds or ions:

(a) aluminum in aluminum oxide, $Al_2O_3$

(c) sulfur in the sulfate ion, $SO_4^{2-}$

(b) phosphorus in phosphoric acid, $H_3PO_4$

(d) each Cr atom in the dichromate ion, $Cr_2O_7^{2-}$

**What Do You Know?** Correct formulas for each species are given.

**Strategy** Follow the guidelines in the text, paying particular attention to Guidelines 4, 6, and 7, above.

**Solution**

(a) $Al_2O_3$ is a neutral compound. Assuming that oxygen has its usual oxidation number of −2, we can solve the following algebraic equation for the oxidation number of aluminum.

Net charge on $Al_2O_3$ = sum of oxidation numbers for two Al atoms + three O atoms

$$0 = 2(x) + 3(-2) \text{ and so } x = +3$$

The oxidation number of Al must be +3, in agreement with its position in the periodic table.

(b) $H_3PO_4$ has an overall charge of 0. If each of the oxygen atoms has an oxidation number of −2 and each of the H atoms is +1, then we can determine the oxidation number of phosphorus as follows:

Net charge on $H_3PO_4$ = sum of oxidation numbers for three H atoms + one P atom + four O atoms

$$0 = 3(+1) + (x) + 4(-2) \text{ and so } x = +5$$

The oxidation number of phosphorus in this compound is +5.

(c) The sulfate ion, $SO_4^{2-}$, has an overall charge of 2−. Oxygen is assigned its usual oxidation number of −2.

Net charge on $SO_4^{2-}$ = sum of oxidation number of one S atom + four O atoms

$$-2 = (x) + 4(-2) \text{ and so } x = +6$$

The sulfur in this ion has an oxidation number of +6.

(d) The net charge on the $Cr_2O_7^{2-}$ ion is 2−. Oxygen is assigned its usual oxidation number of −2.

Net charge on $Cr_2O_7^{2-}$ = sum of oxidation numbers for two Cr atoms + seven O atoms

$$-2 = 2(x) + 7(-2) \text{ and so } x = +6$$

The oxidation number of each chromium in this polyatomic ion is +6.

**Think about Your Answer** Notice that in each of these examples, the oxidation number matched the number of the group in which the element is found. This is often (but not always) the case.

**Check Your Understanding**

Assign an oxidation number to the underlined atom in each ion or molecule.

(a) $\underline{Fe}_2O_3$   (b) $H_2\underline{S}O_4$   (c) $\underline{C}O_3^{2-}$   (d) $\underline{N}O_2^+$

## Recognizing Oxidation–Reduction Reactions

You can always tell whether a reaction involves oxidation and reduction by assessing the oxidation number of each element and noting whether any of these numbers change in the course of the reaction. In many cases, however, this will not be necessary. For example, it will be obvious that a redox reaction has occurred if an uncombined element is converted to a compound or if a well-known oxidizing or reducing agent is involved (Table 3.3).

Like oxygen ($O_2$), the halogens ($F_2$, $Cl_2$, $Br_2$, and $I_2$) are oxidizing agents in their reactions with metals and nonmetals. An example is the reaction of chlorine with sodium metal (◀ Figure 1.2).

Na releases 1 e⁻ per atom.
Oxidation number increases.
Na is oxidized to Na⁺ and is the reducing agent.

$$2\,Na(s) + Cl_2(g) \longrightarrow 2\,NaCl(s)$$

$Cl_2$ gains 2 e⁻ per molecule.
Oxidation number decreases by 1 per Cl.
$Cl_2$ is reduced to Cl⁻ and is the oxidizing agent.

NO₂ gas

Copper metal oxidized to green Cu(NO₃)₂

**FIGURE 3.20 The reaction of copper with nitric acid.** Copper (a reducing agent) reacts vigorously with concentrated nitric acid (an oxidizing agent) to give the brown gas NO₂ and a deep blue-green solution of copper(II) nitrate.

**Table 3.3 Common Oxidizing and Reducing Agents**

| Oxidizing Agent | Reaction Product | Reducing Agent | Reaction Product |
|---|---|---|---|
| $O_2$, oxygen | $O^{2-}$, oxide ion or O combined in $H_2O$ or other molecule | $H_2$, hydrogen | $H^+(aq)$, hydrogen ion or H combined in $H_2O$ or other molecule |
| Halogen, $F_2$, $Cl_2$, $Br_2$, or $I_2$ | Halide ion, $F^-$, $Cl^-$, $Br^-$, or $I^-$ | M, metals such as Na, K, Fe, and Al | $M^{n+}$, metal ions such as $Na^+$, $K^+$, $Fe^{2+}$ or $Fe^{3+}$, and $Al^{3+}$ |
| $HNO_3$, nitric acid | Nitrogen oxides* such as NO and $NO_2$ | C, carbon (used to reduce metal oxides) | CO and $CO_2$ |
| $Cr_2O_7^{2-}$, dichromate ion | $Cr^{3+}$, chromium(III) ion (in acid solution) | | |
| $MnO_4^-$, permanganate ion | $Mn^{2+}$, manganese(II) ion (in acid solution) | | |

*NO is produced with dilute $HNO_3$, whereas $NO_2$ is a product of concentrated acid.

A chlorine molecule ends up as two $Cl^-$ ions, each atom having acquired an electron (from a Na atom). Thus, the oxidation number of each Cl atom has decreased from 0 to $-1$. This means $Cl_2$ has been reduced and therefore is the oxidizing agent.

Figure 3.20 illustrates the chemistry of another excellent oxidizing agent, nitric acid, $HNO_3$. Here, copper metal is oxidized to give copper(II) nitrate, and the nitrate ion is reduced to the brown gas $NO_2$. The net ionic equation for the reaction is

Oxidation number of Cu changes from 0 to +2. Cu is oxidized to $Cu^{2+}$ and is the reducing agent.

$$Cu(s) + 2\ NO_3^-(aq) + 4\ H_3O^+(aq) \longrightarrow Cu^{2+}(aq) + 2\ NO_2(g) + 6\ H_2O(\ell)$$

N in $NO_3^-$ changes from +5 to +4 in $NO_2$. $NO_3^-$ is reduced to $NO_2$ and is the oxidizing agent.

Nitrogen has been reduced from $+5$ (in the $NO_3^-$ ion) to $+4$ (in $NO_2$); therefore, the nitrate ion in acid solution is the oxidizing agent. Copper metal is the reducing agent; each metal atom has given up two electrons to produce the $Cu^{2+}$ ion.

In the reactions of sodium with chlorine and copper with nitric acid, the metals are oxidized. This is typical of metals, which characteristically lose electrons in chemical reactions. In yet another example of this, aluminum metal, a good reducing agent, is capable of reducing iron(III) oxide to iron metal in a reaction called the *thermite reaction* (Figure 3.21).

$$\underset{\substack{\text{oxidizing}\\\text{agent}}}{Fe_2O_3(s)} + \underset{\substack{\text{reducing}\\\text{agent}}}{2\ Al(s)} \rightarrow 2\ Fe(\ell) + Al_2O_3(s)$$

Such a large quantity of energy is evolved as heat in the reaction that the iron produced is in the molten state.

Tables 3.3 and 3.4 may help you organize your thinking as you look for oxidation–reduction reactions and use their terminology.

**FIGURE 3.21 Thermite reaction.** Here, $Fe_2O_3$ is reduced by aluminum metal to produce iron metal and aluminum oxide.

**Table 3.4  Recognizing Oxidation–Reduction Reactions**

|  | Oxidation | Reduction |
|---|---|---|
| In terms of oxidation number | Increase in oxidation number of an atom | Decrease in oxidation number of an atom |
| In terms of electrons | Loss of electrons by an atom | Gain of electrons by an atom |
| In terms of oxygen | Gain of one or more O atoms | Loss of one or more O atoms |

## EXAMPLE 3.9    Oxidation–Reduction Reaction

**Problem**  For the reaction of the iron(II) ion with permanganate ion in aqueous acid,

$$5\ Fe^{2+}(aq) + MnO_4^-(aq) + 8\ H_3O^+(aq) \rightarrow 5\ Fe^{3+}(aq) + Mn^{2+}(aq) + 12\ H_2O(\ell)$$

decide which atoms are undergoing a change in oxidation number and identify the oxidizing and reducing agents.

**What Do You Know?**  The equation given here is balanced (but, for practice, you might verify this). From the reactants and products ($MnO_4^-$ is a common oxidizing agent; iron changes from $Fe^{2+}$ to $Fe^{3+}$) you can quickly decide this is an oxidation–reduction reaction.

**Strategy**  Determine the oxidation number of the atoms in each molecule or ion in the equation and identify which atoms change oxidation number.

**Solution**  The Mn oxidation number in $MnO_4^-$ is +7, and it decreases to +2 in the product, the $Mn^{2+}$ ion. Thus, the $MnO_4^-$ ion has been reduced and is the oxidizing agent (Table 3.3).

$$5\ Fe^{2+}(aq) + MnO_4^-(aq) + 8\ H_3O^+(aq) \rightarrow 5\ Fe^{3+}(aq) + Mn^{2+}(aq) + 12\ H_2O(\ell)$$
$$\quad\ +2 \qquad\quad +7, -2 \qquad\quad +1, -2 \qquad\qquad +3 \qquad\quad +2 \qquad\quad +1, -2$$

The oxidation number of iron has increased from +2 to +3, so each $Fe^{2+}$ ion has lost one electron upon being oxidized to $Fe^{3+}$ (Table 3.4). This means the $Fe^{2+}$ ion is the reducing agent.

**Think about Your Answer**  If one of the reactants in a redox reaction is a simple substance (here $Fe^{2+}$), it usually is obvious whether its oxidation number has increased or decreased. Once a species has been established as having been reduced (or oxidized), you know another species has undergone the opposite process. It is also helpful to recognize common oxidizing and reducing agents (Table 3.3).

© Cengage Learning/Charles D. Winters

KMnO$_4$(aq) oxidizing agent

Fe$^{2+}$(aq) reducing agent

**The reaction of iron(II) ion and permanganate ion.**  The reaction of purple permanganate ion ($MnO_4^-$, the oxidizing agent) with the iron(II) ion ($Fe^{2+}$, the reducing agent) in acidified aqueous solution gives the nearly colorless manganese(II) ion ($Mn^{2+}$) and the iron(III) ion ($Fe^{3+}$).

---

**Check Your Understanding**

The following reaction occurs in a device for testing the breath of a person for the presence of ethanol. Identify the oxidizing and reducing agents, the substance oxidized, and the substance reduced.

$$3\ CH_3CH_2OH(aq) + 2\ Cr_2O_7^{2-}(aq) + 16\ H_3O^+(aq) \rightarrow 3\ CH_3CO_2H(aq) + 4\ Cr^{3+}(aq) + 27\ H_2O(\ell)$$

ethanol  dichromate ion; orange-red  acetic acid  chromium(III) ion; green

---

**REVIEW & CHECK FOR SECTION 3.8**

1.  What is the oxidation number of Cr in $(NH_4)_2Cr_2O_7$?

    (a)  0  (b)  +3  (c)  +6  (d)  +12

2.  Which of the following reactions are oxidation–reduction reactions?

    (1)  $NaOH(aq) + HNO_3(aq) \rightarrow NaNO_3(aq) + H_2O(\ell)$

    (2)  $Cu(s) + Cl_2(g) \rightarrow CuCl_2(s)$

    (3)  $Na_2CO_3(aq) + 2\ HClO_4(aq) \rightarrow CO_2(g) + H_2O(\ell) + 2\ NaClO_4(aq)$

    (4)  $2\ S_2O_3^{2-}(aq) + I_2(aq) \rightarrow S_4O_6^{2-}(aq) + 2\ I^-(aq)$

    (a)  all of them  (b)  2, 3, and 4  (c)  2 and 4  (d)  2 only

3.  In which of the manganese compounds below does Mn have the highest oxidation number?

    (a)  $MnO_2$        (b)  $Mn_2O_3$        (c)  $KMnO_4$        (d)  $MnCl_2$

## 3.9  Classifying Reactions in Aqueous Solution

One goal of this chapter has been to explore the most common types of reactions that can occur in aqueous solution. This helps you decide, for example, that a gas-forming reaction occurs when an Alka-Seltzer tablet (containing citric acid and $NaHCO_3$) is dropped into water (Figure 3.22).

$$\underset{\text{citric acid}}{H_3C_6H_5O_7(aq)} \quad + \quad \underset{\text{hydrogen carbonate ion}}{HCO_3^-(aq)} \quad \longrightarrow$$

$$\underset{\text{dihydrogen citrate ion}}{H_2C_6H_5O_7^-(aq)} + H_2O(\ell) + CO_2(g)$$

We have examined four types of reactions in aqueous solution: precipitation reactions, acid–base reactions, gas-forming reactions, and oxidation–reduction reactions. Three of these four (precipitation, acid–base, and gas-forming) fall into the category of exchange reactions.

**Precipitation Reactions** (Figure 3.12):  Ions combine in solution to form an insoluble reaction product.

*Overall Equation*

$$Pb(NO_3)_2(aq) + 2\ KI(aq) \rightarrow PbI_2(s) + 2\ KNO_3(aq)$$

*Net Ionic Equation*

$$Pb^{2+}(aq) + 2\ I^-(aq) \rightarrow PbI_2(s)$$

**FIGURE 3.22  A gas-forming reaction.** An Alka-Seltzer tablet contains an acid (citric acid) and sodium hydrogen carbonate ($NaHCO_3$), the reactants in a gas-forming reaction.

---

### CASE STUDY

## Killing Bacteria with Silver

There is a washing machine on the market that injects silver ions into the wash water, the purpose being to kill bacteria in the wash water. The advertisement for the machine tells us that 100 quadrillion silver ions are injected into a wash load. How does this machine work? Is 100 quadrillion silver ions a lot? Does the silver kill bacteria?

The washing machine works by using electrical energy to oxidize silver metal to give silver ions.

$$Ag(s) \rightarrow Ag^+(aq) + e^-$$

This is a simple electrolysis procedure. (More about that in Chapter 20.) And 100 quadrillion silver ions? This is $100 \times 10^{15}$ ions.

Do silver ions act as a bacteriocide? There is plenty of medical evidence for this property. In fact, when you were born, the physician or nurse may have put drops of a very dilute silver nitrate solution in your eyes to treat neonatal conjunctivitis. And severely burned patients are treated with silver sulfadiazine ($C_{10}H_9AgN_4O_2S$) to prevent bacterial or fungal infections.

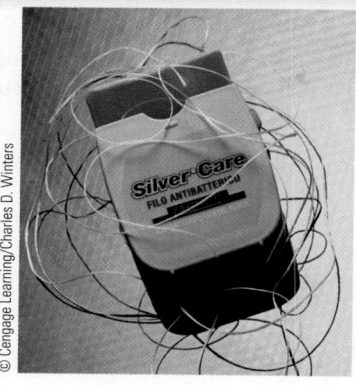

**Silver ions as a bacteriocide in dental floss.**

The use of silver to prevent infections has a long history. Phoenicians kept wine, water, and vinegar in silver vessels. Early settlers in America put silver coins into water barrels. And you might have been born with a "silver spoon in your mouth." Babies in wealthier homes, who were fed from silver spoons and used a silver pacifier, were found to be healthier.

The historical uses of silver carry over to modern society. One can buy many different kinds of silver-containing water purifiers for the home, and dental floss coated with silver nitrate is available.

Although silver does have health benefits, beware of fraudulent claims. For example, consuming large amounts of "colloidal silver" (nanosized particles of silver suspended in water) is claimed to have health-giving properties. One person who tried this, Stan Jones, ran for the U.S. Congress in 2002 and 2006. From consuming silver, he acquired argyria, a medically irreversible condition in which the skin turns a gray-blue color.

**Questions:**
1.  How many moles of silver are used in a wash cycle?
2.  What mass of silver is used?

**Answers to these questions are available in Appendix N.**

**Acid–Base Reactions** (Figures 3.13 and 3.15): Water is a product of many acid–base reactions, and the cation of the base and the anion of the acid form a salt.

*Overall Equation for the Reaction of a Strong Acid and a Strong Base*

$$HNO_3(aq) + KOH(aq) \rightarrow HOH(\ell) + KNO_3(aq)$$

*Net Ionic Equation for the Reaction of a Strong Acid and a Strong Base*

$$H_3O^+(aq) + OH^-(aq) \rightarrow 2\ H_2O(\ell)$$

*Overall Equation for the Reaction of a Weak Acid and a Strong Base*

$$CH_3CO_2H(aq) + NaOH(aq) \rightarrow NaCH_3CO_2(aq) + HOH(\ell)$$

*Net Ionic Equation for the Reaction of a Weak Acid and a Strong Base*

$$CH_3CO_2H(aq) + OH^-(aq) \rightarrow CH_3CO_2^-(aq) + H_2O(\ell)$$

**Gas-Forming Reactions** (Figures 3.16 and 3.22): The most common examples involve metal carbonates and acids but others exist (Table 3.2). One product with a metal carbonate is always carbonic acid, $H_2CO_3$, most of which decomposes to $H_2O$ and $CO_2$. Carbon dioxide is the gas in the bubbles you see during these reactions.

*Overall Equation:*

$$CuCO_3(s) + 2\ HNO_3(aq) \rightarrow Cu(NO_3)_2(aq) + CO_2(g) + H_2O(\ell)$$

*Net Ionic Equation*

$$CuCO_3(s) + 2\ H_3O^+(aq) \rightarrow Cu^{2+}(aq) + CO_2(g) + 3\ H_2O(\ell)$$

**Oxidation–Reduction Reactions** (Figure 3.19): These reactions are *not* ion exchange reactions. Rather, electrons are transferred from one material to another.

*Overall Equation*

$$Cu(s) + 2\ AgNO_3(aq) \rightarrow Cu(NO_3)_2(aq) + 2\ Ag(s)$$

*Net Ionic Equation*

$$Cu(s) + 2\ Ag^+(aq) \rightarrow Cu^{2+}(aq) + 2\ Ag(s)$$

These four types of reactions usually are easy to recognize, but keep in mind that a reaction may fall into more than one category. For example, barium hydroxide reacts readily with sulfuric acid to give barium sulfate and water, a reaction that is both a precipitation and an acid–base reaction.

$$Ba(OH)_2(aq) + H_2SO_4(aq) \rightarrow BaSO_4(s) + 2\ H_2O(\ell)$$

## ᴓWL  INTERACTIVE EXAMPLE 3.10   Types of Reactions

**Problem** Complete and balance each of the following equations and classify each as a precipitation, acid–base, or gas-forming reaction.

(a) $Na_2S(aq) + Cu(NO_3)_2(aq) \rightarrow$

(b) $Na_2SO_3(aq) + HCl(aq) \rightarrow$

(c) $HClO_4(aq) + NaOH(aq) \rightarrow$

**What Do You Know?** You know the formulas for the reactants and that these are all exchange reactions.

**Strategy Map 3.10a**

**PROBLEM**

Write equation for the reaction of **Na₂S** and **Cu(NO₃)₂** and decide on *reaction type*

**DATA/INFORMATION**

The **formulas** of the **reactants** are given

**STEP 1.** Decide on **products** and then write **complete balanced equation.**

**Complete balanced equation** with *reactants* and *products*

**STEP 2.** Decide if each reactant and product is **solid, liquid, gas,** or **dissolved in water.**

**Complete balanced equation** with **indication of state** of each reactant and product

**STEP 3.** Decide on **reaction type.**

One product is *insoluble in water,* so this is a **precipitation reaction.**

**Strategy**

- Recognize that these are exchange reactions. The products of each reaction can be found by exchanging cations and anions between the two reactants.

- Write and balance each equation.

- To determine the kind of reaction examine the reactants and products. Look specifically for common acids and bases, for a product that is insoluble, and for anions that react with acid to give a gas ($CO_3^{2-}$, $S^{2-}$, $SO_3^{2-}$).

**Solution**

(a) The products of the exchange reaction are predicted to be $NaNO_3$ and $CuS$. The first of these is water-soluble, but the second is an insoluble salt. Thus, this is a precipitation reaction. The balanced chemical equation is

$$Na_2S(aq) + Cu(NO_3)_2(aq) \rightarrow 2\ NaNO_3(aq) + CuS(s)$$

(b) The products of the exchange reaction are predicted to be $NaCl$ and $H_2SO_3$. The $H_2SO_3$ should immediately alert us to the fact that this is a gas-forming reaction because it will decompose into $SO_2(g)$ and $H_2O(\ell)$ (Table 3.2). The balanced equation is

$$Na_2SO_3(aq) + 2\ HCl\ (aq) \rightarrow 2\ NaCl(aq) + SO_2\ (g) + H_2O(\ell)$$

(c) The products of the exchange reaction are predicted to be $NaClO_4$ and $H_2O$, a salt and water; this is an acid–base reaction. The balanced equation is

$$HClO_4(aq) + NaOH(aq) \rightarrow NaClO_4(aq) + H_2O(\ell)$$

**Think about Your Answer** As practice, try writing the net ionic equations for each of the preceding reactions. The answers are:

(a) $S^{2-}(aq) + Cu^{2+}(aq) \rightarrow CuS(s)$

(b) $SO_3^{2-}(aq) + 2\ H_3O^+(aq) \rightarrow 3\ H_2O(\ell) + SO_2(g)$

(c) $H_3O^+(aq) + OH^-(aq) \rightarrow 2\ H_2O(\ell)$

**Check Your Understanding**

Classify each of the following reactions as a precipitation, acid–base, gas-forming, or oxidation–reduction reaction. Predict the products of the reaction, and then balance the completed equation. Write the net ionic equation for each.

(a) $CuCO_3(s) + H_2SO_4(aq) \rightarrow$

(b) $Ga(s) + O_2(g) \rightarrow$

(c) $Ba(OH)_2(s) + HNO_3(aq) \rightarrow$

(d) $CuCl_2(aq) + (NH_4)_2S(aq) \rightarrow$

**REVIEW & CHECK FOR SECTION 3.9**

Sometimes a reaction can fall in more than one category. Into what category (or categories) does the reaction of $Ba(OH)_2(aq) + H_3PO_4(aq)$ fit?

(a)  acid–base and oxidation–reduction

(b)  oxidation–reduction

(c)  acid–base and precipitation

(d)  precipitation

# CHAPTER GOALS REVISITED

*Now that you have studied this chapter, you should ask if you have met the chapter goals. In particular, you should be able to*

### Balance equations for simple chemical reactions

a. Understand the information conveyed by a balanced chemical equation (Section 3.1).
b. Balance simple chemical equations (Section 3.2). **Study Questions: 1, 3, 5, 51, 60.**

### Understand the nature and characteristics of chemical equilibria

a. Recognize that chemical reactions are reversible (Section 3.3).
b. Describe what is meant by the term *dynamic equilibrium*. **Study Question: 80.**
c. Recognize the difference between reactant-favored and product-favored reactions at equilibrium. **Study Questions: 7, 15.**

### Understand the nature of ionic substances dissolved in water

a. Explain the difference between electrolytes and nonelectrolytes and recognize examples of each (Section 3.4 and Figure 3.8). **Study Question: 9.**
b. Predict the solubility of ionic compounds in water (Sections 3.4 and Figure 3.10). **Study Questions: 11, 13, 15, 61, 63, 66, 72, and Go Chemistry Module 5.**
c. Recognize what ions are formed when an ionic compound or acid or base dissolves in water (Sections 3.4–3.6). **Study Questions: 13, 15, 66, 69, 77.**

### Recognize common acids and bases, and understand their behavior in aqueous solution

a. Know the names and formulas of common acids and bases (Section 3.6 and Table 3.1). **Study Questions: 21, 27, 30.**
b. Categorize acids and bases as strong or weak.
c. Define and use the Arrhenius concept of acids and bases.
d. Define and use the Brønsted–Lowry concept of acids and bases.
e. Recognize substances that are amphiprotic. **Study Question: 33.**
f. Identify the Brønsted acid and base in a reaction. **Study Questions: 21, 27, 28.**

### Recognize the common types of reactions in aqueous solution

a. Recognize the key characteristics of four types of reactions in aqueous solution.

| Reaction Type | Key Characteristic |
| --- | --- |
| Precipitation | Formation of an insoluble compound |
| Acid–base | Formation of a salt and water |
| Gas-forming | Evolution of a water-insoluble gas such as $CO_2$ |
| Oxidation–reduction | Transfer of electrons (with changes in oxidation numbers) |

**Study Questions: 51, 52, 55, 56, 82–84.**

b. Predict the products of precipitation reactions (Section 3.5), acid–base reactions (Section 3.6), and gas-forming reactions (Section 3.7). These are all examples of exchange reactions, which involve the exchange of anions between the cations involved in the reaction. **Study Questions: 17, 19, 27, 29, 41–43, 83.**

### Write chemical equations for the common types of reactions in aqueous solution

a. Write overall balanced equations for precipitation, acid–base, and gas-forming reactions. **Study Questions: 17, 19, 27, 29, 41, 43, 77.**
b. Write net ionic equations (Sections 3.5–3.7). **Study Questions: 17, 19, 35, 37, 39, 69, 73, 74, and Go Chemistry Module 6.**
c. Understand that the net ionic equation for the reaction of a strong acid with a strong base is $H_3O^+(aq) + OH^-(aq) \rightarrow 2\ H_2O(\ell)$ (Section 3.6).

 **and**

Sign in at **www.cengage.com/owl** to:
- View tutorials and simulations, develop problem-solving skills, and complete online homework assigned by your professor.
- For quick review and exam prep, download Go Chemistry mini lecture modules from OWL (or purchase them at **www.cengagebrain.com**)

❓ Access **How Do I Solve It?** tutorials on how to approach problem solving using concepts in this chapter.

Recognize common oxidizing and reducing agents and identify oxidation–reduction reactions

a. Determine oxidation numbers of elements in a compound and understand that these numbers represent the charge an atom has, or appears to have, when the electrons of the compound are counted according to a set of guidelines (Section 3.8). **Study Questions: 45, 46, 81.**

b. Identify oxidation–reduction reactions (often called *redox reactions*) and identify the oxidizing and reducing agents and substances oxidized and reduced in the reaction (Section 3.8 and Tables 3.3 and 3.4). **Study Questions: 47–50, 67, 85.**

# Study Questions

**OWL** Interactive versions of these questions are assignable in OWL.

▲ denotes challenging questions.

Blue-numbered questions have answers in Appendix R and fully worked solutions in the *Student Solutions Manual.*

## Practicing Skills

### Balancing Equations
*(See Example 3.1.)*

1. Write balanced chemical equations for the following reactions.
   (a) The reaction of aluminum and iron(III) oxide to form iron and aluminum oxide (known as the thermite reaction, page 142).
   (b) The reaction of carbon and water at high temperature to form a mixture of gaseous CO and $H_2$ (known as water gas and once used as a fuel).
   (c) The reaction of liquid silicon tetrachloride and magnesium forming silicon and magnesium chloride. This is one step in the preparation of ultrapure silicon used in the semiconductor industry.

2. Write balanced chemical equations for the following reactions:
   (a) production of ammonia, $NH_3(g)$, by combining $N_2(g)$ and $H_2(g)$
   (b) production of methanol, $CH_3OH(\ell)$ by combining $H_2(g)$ and $CO(g)$
   (c) production of sulfuric acid by combining sulfur, oxygen, and water

3. Balance the following equations:
   (a) $Cr(s) + O_2(g) \rightarrow Cr_2O_3(s)$
   (b) $Cu_2S(s) + O_2(g) \rightarrow Cu(s) + SO_2(g)$
   (c) $C_6H_5CH_3(\ell) + O_2(g) \rightarrow H_2O(\ell) + CO_2(g)$

4. Balance the following equations:
   (a) $Cr(s) + Cl_2(g) \rightarrow CrCl_3(s)$
   (b) $SiO_2(s) + C(s) \rightarrow Si(s) + CO(g)$
   (c) $Fe(s) + H_2O(g) \rightarrow Fe_3O_4(s) + H_2(g)$

5. Balance the following equations, and name each reactant and product:
   (a) $Fe_2O_3(s) + Mg(s) \rightarrow MgO(s) + Fe(s)$
   (b) $AlCl_3(s) + NaOH(aq) \rightarrow Al(OH)_3(s) + NaCl(aq)$
   (c) $NaNO_3(s) + H_2SO_4(aq) \rightarrow Na_2SO_4(s) + HNO_3(aq)$
   (d) $NiCO_3(s) + HNO_3(aq) \rightarrow$
   $$Ni(NO_3)_2(aq) + CO_2(g) + H_2O(\ell)$$

6. Balance the following equations, and name each reactant and product:
   (a) $SF_4(g) + H_2O(\ell) \rightarrow SO_2(g) + HF(\ell)$
   (b) $NH_3(aq) + O_2(aq) \rightarrow NO(g) + H_2O(\ell)$
   (c) $BF_3(g) + H_2O(\ell) \rightarrow HF(aq) + H_3BO_3(aq)$

### Chemical Equilibrium
*(See Section 3.3.)*

7. Equal amounts of two acids—HCl and $HCO_2H$ (formic acid)—are placed in solution. When equilibrium has been achieved, the HCl solution has a much greater electrical conductivity than the $HCO_2H$ solution. Which reaction is more product-favored at equilibrium?

$$HCl(aq) + H_2O(\ell) \rightleftharpoons H_3O^+(aq) + Cl^-(aq)$$

$$HCO_2H(aq) + H_2O(\ell) \rightleftharpoons H_3O^+(aq) + HCO_2^-(aq)$$

8. Two solutions were prepared, one containing 0.10 mol of boric acid ($H_3BO_3$) in 200 mL and the second containing 0.10 mol phosphoric acid ($H_3PO_4$) in 200 mL. Both were weak conductors of electricity, but the $H_3PO_4$ solution was a noticeably stronger conductor. Write equations to describe the equilibrium in each solution, and explain the observed difference in conductivity.

### Ions and Molecules in Aqueous Solution
*(See Section 3.4 and Example 3.2.)*

9. What is an electrolyte? How can you differentiate experimentally between a weak electrolyte and a strong electrolyte? Give an example of each.

10. Name and give the formulas of two acids that are strong electrolytes and one acid that is a weak electrolyte. Name and give formulas of two bases that are strong electrolytes and one base that is a weak electrolyte.

11. Which compound or compounds in each of the following groups is (are) expected to be soluble in water?
(a) $CuO$, $CuCl_2$, $FeCO_3$
(b) $AgI$, $Ag_3PO_4$, $AgNO_3$
(c) $K_2CO_3$, $KI$, $KMnO_4$

12. Which compound or compounds in each of the following groups is (are) expected to be soluble in water?
(a) $BaSO_4$, $Ba(NO_3)_2$, $BaCO_3$
(b) $Na_2SO_4$, $NaClO_4$, $NaCH_3CO_2$
(c) $AgBr$, $KBr$, $Al_2Br_6$

13. The following compounds are water-soluble. What ions are produced by each compound in aqueous solution?
(a) $KOH$   (c) $LiNO_3$
(b) $K_2SO_4$   (d) $(NH_4)_2SO_4$

14. The following compounds are water-soluble. What ions are produced by each compound in aqueous solution?
(a) $KI$   (c) $K_2HPO_4$
(b) $Mg(CH_3CO_2)_2$   (d) $NaCN$

15. Decide whether each of the following is water-soluble. If soluble, tell what ions are produced when the compound dissolves in water.
(a) $Na_2CO_3$   (c) $NiS$
(b) $CuSO_4$   (d) $BaBr_2$

16. Decide whether each of the following is water-soluble. If soluble, tell what ions are produced when the compound dissolves in water.
(a) $NiCl_2$   (c) $Pb(NO_3)_2$
(b) $Cr(NO_3)_3$   (d) $BaSO_4$

### Precipitation Reactions and Net Ionic Equations
*(See Section 3.5 and Examples 3.3 and 3.4.)*

17. Balance the equation for the following precipitation reaction, and then write the net ionic equation. Indicate the state of each species (s, ℓ, aq, or g).

$$CdCl_2 + NaOH \rightarrow Cd(OH)_2 + NaCl$$

18. Balance the equation for the following precipitation reaction, and then write the net ionic equation. Indicate the state of each species (s, ℓ, aq, or g).

$$Ni(NO_3)_2 + Na_2CO_3 \rightarrow NiCO_3 + NaNO_3$$

19. Predict the products of each precipitation reaction. Balance the completed equation, and then write the net ionic equation.
(a) $NiCl_2(aq) + (NH_4)_2S(aq) \rightarrow$
(b) $Mn(NO_3)_2(aq) + Na_3PO_4(aq) \rightarrow$

20. Predict the products of each precipitation reaction. Balance the completed equation, and then write the net ionic equation.
(a) $Pb(NO_3)_2(aq) + KBr(aq) \rightarrow$
(b) $Ca(NO_3)_2(aq) + KF(aq) \rightarrow$
(c) $Ca(NO_3)_2(aq) + Na_2C_2O_4(aq) \rightarrow$

### Acids and Bases and Their Reactions
*(See Section 3.6 and Example 3.5.)*

21. Write a balanced equation for the ionization of nitric acid in water.

22. Write a balanced equation for the ionization of perchloric acid in water.

23. Oxalic acid, $H_2C_2O_4$, which is found in certain plants, can provide two hydronium ions in water. Write balanced equations (like those for sulfuric acid on page 130) to show how oxalic acid can supply one and then a second $H_3O^+$ ion.

24. Phosphoric acid can supply one, two, or three $H_3O^+$ ions in aqueous solution. Write balanced equations (like those for sulfuric acid on page 130) to show this successive loss of hydrogen ions.

25. Write a balanced equation for reaction of the basic oxide, magnesium oxide, with water.

26. Write a balanced equation for the reaction of sulfur trioxide with water.

27. Complete and balance the equations for the following acid–base reactions. Name the reactants and products.
(a) $CH_3CO_2H(aq) + Mg(OH)_2(s) \rightarrow$
(b) $HClO_4(aq) + NH_3(aq) \rightarrow$

28. Complete and balance the equations for the following acid–base reactions. Name the reactants and products.
(a) $H_3PO_4(aq) + KOH(aq) \rightarrow$
(b) $H_2C_2O_4(aq) + Ca(OH)_2(s) \rightarrow$
($H_2C_2O_4$ is oxalic acid, an acid capable of donating two $H^+$ ions. See Study Question 23.)

29. Write a balanced equation for the reaction of barium hydroxide with nitric acid.

30. Write a balanced equation for the reaction of aluminum hydroxide with sulfuric acid.

31. Write an equation that describes the equilibrium that exists when nitric acid dissolves in water. Identify each of the four species in solution as either Brønsted acids or Brønsted bases. Does the equilibrium favor the products or the reactants?

32. Write an equation that describes the equilibrium that exists when the weak acid benzoic acid ($C_6H_5CO_2H$) dissolves in water. Identify each of the four species in solution as either Brønsted acids or Brønsted bases. Does the equilibrium favor the products or the reactants? (In acting as an acid, the $-CO_2H$ group supplies $H^+$ to form $H_3O^+$.)

33. Write two chemical equations, one that shows $H_2O$ reacting (with HBr) as a Brønsted base and a second that shows $H_2O$ reacting (with $NH_3$) as a Brønsted acid.

34. Write two chemical equations, one in which $H_2PO_4^-$ is a Brønsted acid (in reaction with the carbonate ion, $CO_3^{2-}$), and a second in which $HPO_4^{2-}$ is a Brønsted base (in reaction with acetic acid, $CH_3CO_2H$).

**Writing Net Ionic Equations**

*(See Examples 3.4 and 3.6.)*

35. Balance the following equations, and then write the net ionic equation.
    (a) $(NH_4)_2CO_3(aq) + Cu(NO_3)_2(aq) \rightarrow$
    $$CuCO_3(s) + NH_4NO_3(aq)$$
    (b) $Pb(OH)_2(s) + HCl(aq) \rightarrow PbCl_2(s) + H_2O(\ell)$
    (c) $BaCO_3(s) + HCl(aq) \rightarrow$
    $$BaCl_2(aq) + H_2O(\ell) + CO_2(g)$$
    (d) $CH_3CO_2H(aq) + Ni(OH)_2(s) \rightarrow$
    $$Ni(CH_3CO_2)_2(aq) + H_2O(\ell)$$

36. Balance the following equations, and then write the net ionic equation:
    (a) $Zn(s) + HCl(aq) \rightarrow H_2(g) + ZnCl_2(aq)$
    (b) $Mg(OH)_2(s) + HCl(aq) \rightarrow MgCl_2(aq) + H_2O(\ell)$
    (c) $HNO_3(aq) + CaCO_3(s) \rightarrow$
    $$Ca(NO_3)_2(aq) + H_2O(\ell) + CO_2(g)$$
    (d) $(NH_4)_2S(aq) + FeCl_2(aq) \rightarrow NH_4Cl(aq) + FeS(s)$

37. Balance the following equations, and then write the net ionic equation. Show states for all reactants and products (s, $\ell$, g, aq).
    (a) the reaction of silver nitrate and potassium iodide to give silver iodide and potassium nitrate
    (b) the reaction of barium hydroxide and nitric acid to give barium nitrate and water
    (c) the reaction of sodium phosphate and nickel(II) nitrate to give nickel(II) phosphate and sodium nitrate

38. Balance each of the following equations, and then write the net ionic equation. Show states for all reactants and products (s, $\ell$, g, aq).
    (a) the reaction of sodium hydroxide and iron(II) chloride to give iron(II) hydroxide and sodium chloride
    (b) the reaction of barium chloride with sodium carbonate to give barium carbonate and sodium chloride
    (c) the reaction of ammonia with phosphoric acid

39. Write balanced net ionic equations for the following reactions:
    (a) the reaction of nitrous acid (a weak acid) and sodium hydroxide in aqueous solution
    (b) the reaction of calcium hydroxide and hydrochloric acid

40. Write balanced net ionic equations for the following reactions:
    (a) the reaction of aqueous solutions of silver nitrate and sodium iodide
    (b) the reaction of aqueous solutions of barium chloride and potassium carbonate

**Gas-Forming Reactions**

*(See Section 3.7 and Example 3.7.)*

41. Siderite is a mineral consisting largely of iron(II) carbonate. Write an overall, balanced equation for its reaction with nitric acid, and name the products.

42. The beautiful red mineral rhodochrosite is manganese(II) carbonate. Write an overall, balanced equation for the reaction of the mineral with hydrochloric acid, and name the products.

**Rhodochrosite, a mineral consisting largely of $MnCO_3$.**

43. Write an overall, balanced equation for the reaction of $(NH_4)_2S$ with HBr, and name the reactants and products.

44. Write an overall, balanced equation for the reaction of $Na_2SO_3$ with $CH_3CO_2H$, and name the reactants and products.

**Oxidation Numbers**

*(See Section 3.8 and Example 3.8.)*

45. Determine the oxidation number of each element in the following ions or compounds.
    (a) $BrO_3^-$      (d) $CaH_2$
    (b) $C_2O_4^{2-}$      (e) $H_4SiO_4$
    (c) $F^-$      (f) $HSO_4^-$

46. Determine the oxidation number of each element in the following ions or compounds.
    (a) $PF_6^-$      (d) $N_2O_5$
    (b) $H_2AsO_4^-$      (e) $POCl_3$
    (c) $UO^{2+}$      (f) $XeO_4^{2-}$

**Oxidation–Reduction Reactions**

*(See Section 3.8 and Example 3.9.)*

47. Which two of the following reactions are oxidation–reduction reactions? Explain your answer in each case. Classify the remaining reaction.
    (a) $Zn(s) + 2 NO_3^-(aq) + 4 H_3O^+(aq) \rightarrow$
    $$Zn^{2+}(aq) + 2 NO_2(g) + 6 H_2O(\ell)$$
    (b) $Zn(OH)_2(s) + H_2SO_4(aq) \rightarrow$
    $$ZnSO_4(aq) + 2 H_2O(\ell)$$
    (c) $Ca(s) + 2 H_2O(\ell) \rightarrow Ca(OH)_2(s) + H_2(g)$

48. Which two of the following reactions are oxidation–reduction reactions? Explain your answer briefly. Classify the remaining reaction.
    (a) $CdCl_2(aq) + Na_2S(aq) \rightarrow CdS(s) + 2 NaCl(aq)$
    (b) $2 Ca(s) + O_2(g) \rightarrow 2 CaO(s)$
    (c) $4 Fe(OH)_2(s) + 2 H_2O(\ell) + O_2(g) \rightarrow$
    $$4 Fe(OH)_3(s)$$

49. In the following reactions, decide which reactant is oxidized and which is reduced. Designate the oxidizing agent and the reducing agent.
    (a) $C_2H_4(g) + 3 O_2(g) \rightarrow 2 CO_2(g) + 2 H_2O(\ell)$
    (b) $Si(s) + 2 Cl_2(g) \rightarrow SiCl_4(\ell)$

**50.** In the following reactions, decide which reactant is oxidized and which is reduced. Designate the oxidizing agent and the reducing agent.
(a) $Cr_2O_7^{2-}(aq) + 3\ Sn^{2+}(aq) + 14\ H_3O^+(aq) \rightarrow$
$2\ Cr^{3+}(aq) + 3\ Sn^{4+}(aq) + 21\ H_2O(\ell)$
(b) $FeS(s) + 3\ NO_3^-(aq) + 4\ H_3O^+(aq) \rightarrow$
$3\ NO(g) + SO_4^{2-}(aq) + Fe^{3+}(aq) + 6\ H_2O(\ell)$

**Types of Reactions in Aqueous Solution**
*(See Section 3.9 and Example 3.10.)*

**51.** Balance the following equations, and then classify each as a precipitation, acid–base, or gas-forming reaction.
(a) $Ba(OH)_2(aq) + HCl(aq) \rightarrow BaCl_2(aq) + H_2O(\ell)$
(b) $HNO_3(aq) + CoCO_3(s) \rightarrow$
$Co(NO_3)_2(aq) + H_2O(\ell) + CO_2(g)$
(c) $Na_3PO_4(aq) + Cu(NO_3)_2(aq) \rightarrow$
$Cu_3(PO_4)_2(s) + NaNO_3(aq)$

**52.** Balance the following equations, and then classify each as a precipitation, acid–base, or gas-forming reaction.
(a) $K_2CO_3(aq) + Cu(NO_3)_2(aq) \rightarrow$
$CuCO_3(s) + KNO_3(aq)$
(b) $Pb(NO_3)_2(aq) + HCl(aq) \rightarrow$
$PbCl_2(s) + HNO_3(aq)$
(c) $MgCO_3(s) + HCl(aq) \rightarrow$
$MgCl_2(aq) + H_2O(\ell) + CO_2(g)$

**53.** Balance the following equations, and then classify each as a precipitation, acid–base, or gas-forming reaction. Show states for the products (s, ℓ, g, aq), and then balance the completed equation. Write the net ionic equation.
(a) $MnCl_2(aq) + Na_2S(aq) \rightarrow MnS + NaCl$
(b) $K_2CO_3(aq) + ZnCl_2(aq) \rightarrow ZnCO_3 + KCl$

**54.** Balance the following equations, and then classify each as a precipitation, acid–base, or gas-forming reaction. Show states for the products (s, ℓ, g, aq), and then balance the completed equation. Write the net ionic equation.
(a) $Fe(OH)_3(s) + HNO_3(aq) \rightarrow Fe(NO_3)_3 + H_2O$
(b) $FeCO_3(s) + HNO_3(aq) \rightarrow Fe(NO_3)_2 + CO_2 + H_2O$

**55.** Balance each of the following equations, and classify them as precipitation, acid–base, gas-forming, or oxidation–reduction reactions. Show states for the products (s, ℓ, g, aq), and then balance the completed equation.
(a) $CuCl_2 + H_2S \rightarrow CuS + HCl$
(b) $H_3PO_4 + KOH \rightarrow H_2O + K_3PO_4$
(c) $Ca + HBr \rightarrow H_2 + CaBr_2$
(d) $MgCl_2 + NaOH \rightarrow Mg(OH)_2 + NaCl$

**56.** ▲ Complete and balance the equations below, and classify them as precipitation, acid–base, gas-forming, or oxidation–reduction reactions. Show states for the products (s, ℓ, g, aq), and then balance the completed equation.
(a) $NiCO_3 + H_2SO_4 \rightarrow$
(b) $Co(OH)_2 + HBr \rightarrow$
(c) $AgCH_3CO_2 + NaCl \rightarrow$
(d) $NiO + CO \rightarrow$

**57.** The products formed in several reactions are given below. Identify the reactants (labeled $x$ and $y$) and write the complete balanced equation for each reaction.
(a) $x + y \rightarrow H_2O(\ell) + CaBr_2(aq)$
(b) $x + y \rightarrow Mg(NO_3)_2(aq) + CO_2(g) + H_2O(\ell)$
(c) $x + y \rightarrow BaSO_4(s) + NaCl(aq)$
(d) $x + y \rightarrow NH_4^+(aq) + OH^-(aq)$

**58.** The products formed in several reactions are given below. Identify the reactants (labeled $x$ and $y$) and write the complete balanced equation for each reaction.
(a) $x + y \rightarrow (NH_4)_2SO_4(aq)$
(b) $x + y \rightarrow CaCl_2(aq) + CO_2(g) + H_2O(\ell)$
(c) $x + y \rightarrow Ba(NO_3)_2(aq) + AgCl(s)$
(d) $x + y \rightarrow H_3O^+(aq) + ClO_4^-(aq)$

## General Questions

*These questions are not designated as to type or location in the chapter. They may combine concepts.*

**59.** Balance the following equations:
(a) for the synthesis of urea, a common fertilizer
$$CO_2(g) + NH_3(g) \rightarrow NH_2CONH_2(s) + H_2O(\ell)$$
(b) for the reactions used to make uranium(VI) fluoride for the enrichment of natural uranium
$UO_2(s) + HF(aq) \rightarrow UF_4(s) + H_2O(\ell)$
$UF_4(s) + F_2(g) \rightarrow UF_6(s)$
(c) for the reaction to make titanium(IV) chloride, which is then converted to titanium metal
$TiO_2(s) + Cl_2(g) + C(s) \rightarrow TiCl_4(\ell) + CO(g)$
$TiCl_4(\ell) + Mg(s) \rightarrow Ti(s) + MgCl_2(s)$

**60.** Balance the following equations:
(a) for the reaction to produce "superphosphate" fertilizer
$$Ca_3(PO_4)_2(s) + H_2SO_4(aq) \rightarrow$$
$$Ca(H_2PO_4)_2(aq) + CaSO_4(s)$$
(b) for the reaction to produce diborane, $B_2H_6$
$$NaBH_4(s) + H_2SO_4(aq) \rightarrow$$
$$B_2H_6(g) + H_2(g) + Na_2SO_4(aq)$$
(c) for the reaction to produce tungsten metal from tungsten(VI) oxide
$$WO_3(s) + H_2(g) \rightarrow W(s) + H_2O(\ell)$$
(d) for the decomposition of ammonium dichromate
$$(NH_4)_2Cr_2O_7(s) \rightarrow N_2(g) + H_2O(\ell) + Cr_2O_3(s)$$

**61.** Give a formula for each of the following compounds:
(a) a soluble compound containing the bromide ion
(b) an insoluble hydroxide
(c) an insoluble carbonate
(d) a soluble nitrate-containing compound
(e) a weak Brønsted acid

**62.** Give the formula for each of the following compounds:
(a) a soluble compound containing the acetate ion
(b) an insoluble sulfide
(c) a soluble hydroxide
(d) an insoluble chloride
(e) a strong Brønsted base

63. Indicate which of the following copper(II) salts are soluble in water and which are insoluble: $Cu(NO_3)_2$, $CuCO_3$, $Cu_3(PO_4)_2$, $CuCl_2$.

64. Name two anions that combine with $Al^{3+}$ ion to produce water-soluble compounds.

65. Write the net ionic equation and identify the spectator ion or ions in the reaction of nitric acid and magnesium hydroxide. What type of reaction is this?

$$2\ H_3O^+(aq) + 2\ NO_3^-(aq) + Mg(OH)_2(s) \rightarrow$$
$$4\ H_2O(\ell) + Mg^{2+}(aq) + 2\ NO_3^-(aq)$$

66. Identify and name the water-insoluble product in each reaction and write the net ionic equation:
   (a) $CuCl_2(aq) + H_2S(aq) \rightarrow CuS + 2\ HCl$
   (b) $CaCl_2(aq) + K_2CO_3(aq) \rightarrow 2\ KCl + CaCO_3$
   (c) $AgNO_3(aq) + NaI(aq) \rightarrow AgI + NaNO_3$

67. Bromine is obtained from sea water by the following redox reaction:

$$Cl_2(g) + 2\ NaBr(aq) \rightarrow 2\ NaCl(aq) + Br_2(\ell)$$

   (a) What has been oxidized? What has been reduced?
   (b) Identify the oxidizing and reducing agents.

68. Identify each of the following substances as a likely oxidizing or reducing agent: $HNO_3$, $Na$, $Cl_2$, $O_2$, $KMnO_4$.

69. The mineral dolomite contains magnesium carbonate. This reacts with hydrochloric acid.

$$MgCO_3(s) + 2\ HCl(aq) \rightarrow$$
$$CO_2(g) + MgCl_2(aq) + H_2O(\ell)$$

   (a) Write the net ionic equation for this reaction and identify the spectator ions.
   (b) What type of reaction is this?

70. Aqueous solutions of ammonium sulfide, $(NH_4)_2S$, and $Hg(NO_3)_2$ react to produce $HgS$ and $NH_4NO_3$.
   (a) Write the overall balanced equation for the reaction. Indicate the state (s, aq) for each compound.
   (b) Name each compound.
   (c) What type of reaction is this?

71. Identify the primary species (atoms, molecules, or ions) present in an aqueous solution of each of the following compounds. Decide which species are Brønsted acids or bases and whether they are strong or weak.
   (a) $NH_3$   (b) $CH_3CO_2H$   (c) $NaOH$   (d) $HBr$

72. (a) Name and give formulas for two water-soluble compounds containing the $Cu^{2+}$ ion. Name two water-insoluble compounds containing the $Cu^{2+}$ ion.
   (b) Name and give formulas for two water-soluble compounds containing the $Ba^{2+}$ ion. Name two water-insoluble compounds containing the $Ba^{2+}$ ion.

73. Balance equations for these reactions that occur in aqueous solution, and then classify each as a precipitation, acid–base, or gas-forming reaction. Show states for the products (s, $\ell$, g, aq), give their names, and write the net ionic equation.
   (a) $K_2CO_3 + HClO_4 \rightarrow KClO_4 + CO_2 + H_2O$
   (b) $FeCl_2 + (NH_4)_2S \rightarrow FeS + NH_4Cl$
   (c) $Fe(NO_3)_2 + Na_2CO_3(aq) \rightarrow FeCO_3 + NaNO_3$
   (d) $NaOH + FeCl_3 \rightarrow NaCl + Fe(OH)_3$

74. For each reaction, write an overall, balanced equation and the net ionic equation.
   (a) the reaction of aqueous lead(II) nitrate and aqueous potassium hydroxide
   (b) the reaction of aqueous copper(II) nitrate and aqueous sodium carbonate

75. You are given mixtures containing the following compounds. Which compound in each pair could be separated by stirring the solid mixture with water?
   (a) $NaOH$ and $Ca(OH)_2$
   (b) $MgCl_2$ and $MgF_2$
   (c) $AgI$ and $KI$
   (d) $NH_4Cl$ and $PbCl_2$

76. Identify, from each list below, the compound or compounds that will dissolve in water to give a solution that strongly conducts electricity.
   (a) $CuCO_3$, $Cu(OH)_2$, $CuCl_2$, $CuO$
   (b) $HCl$, $H_2C_2O_4$, $H_3PO_4$, $H_2SO_4$

77. Identify, from each list below, the compound or compounds that will dissolve in water to give a solution that is only a very weak conductor of electricity.
   (a) $NH_3$, $NaOH$, $Ba(OH)_2$, $Fe(OH)_3$
   (b) $CH_3CO_2H$, $Na_3PO_4$, $HF$, $HNO_3$

78. Write net ionic equations for the following reactions:
   (a) The reaction of acetic acid, a weak acid, and $Sr(OH)_2(aq)$.
   (b) The reaction of zinc and hydrochloric acid to form zinc(II) chloride and hydrogen gas.

79. Gas evolution was observed when a solution of $Na_2S$ was treated with acid. The gas was bubbled into a solution containing $Pb(NO_3)_2$, and a black precipitate formed. Write net ionic equations for the two reactions.

80. Heating $HI(g)$ at 425 °C causes some of this compound to decompose, forming $H_2(g)$ and $I_2(g)$. Eventually, the amounts of the three species do not change further; the system has reached equilibrium. (At this point, approximately 22% of the HI has decomposed.) Describe what is happening in this system at the molecular level.

## In the Laboratory

81. The following reaction can be used to prepare iodine in the laboratory.

$$2\ NaI(s) + 2\ H_2SO_4(aq) + MnO_2(s) \rightarrow$$
$$Na_2SO_4(aq) + MnSO_4(aq) + I_2(g) + 2\ H_2O(\ell)$$

   (a) Determine the oxidation number of each atom in the equation.
   (b) What is the oxidizing agent, and what has been oxidized? What is the reducing agent, and what has been reduced?
   (c) Is the reaction observed product-favored or reactant-favored?
   (d) Name the reactants and products.

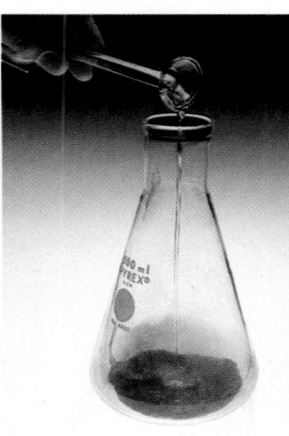

**Preparation of iodine.** A mixture of NaI and MnO$_2$ was placed in a flask *(left)*. On adding concentrated H$_2$SO$_4$ *(right)*, brown gaseous I$_2$ evolved.

**82.** ▲ If you have "silverware" in your home, you know it tarnishes easily. Tarnish is from the oxidation of silver in the presence of sulfur-containing compounds (in the atmosphere or in your food) to give black Ag$_2$S. To remove the tarnish, you can warm the tarnished object with some aluminum foil in water with a small amount of baking soda. The silver sulfide reacts with aluminum to produce silver as well as aluminum oxide and hydrogen sulfide.

$$3 \text{ Ag}_2\text{S(s)} + 2 \text{ Al(s)} + 3 \text{ H}_2\text{O}(\ell) \rightarrow$$
$$6 \text{ Ag(s)} + \text{Al}_2\text{O}_3\text{(s)} + 3 \text{ H}_2\text{S(aq)}$$

Hydrogen sulfide is foul smelling, but it is removed by reaction with the baking soda.

$$\text{NaHCO}_3\text{(aq)} + \text{H}_2\text{S(aq)} \rightarrow$$
$$\text{NaHS(aq)} + \text{H}_2\text{O}(\ell) + \text{CO}_2\text{(g)}$$

Classify the two reactions, and identify any acids, bases, oxidizing agents, or reducing agents.

**Removing silver tarnish. (a)** A badly tarnished piece of silver is placed in a dish with aluminum foil and aqueous sodium hydrogen carbonate. **(b)** The portion of the silver in contact with the solution is now free of tarnish.

**83.** ▲ Suppose you wish to prepare a sample of magnesium chloride. One way to do this is to use an acid–base reaction, the reaction of magnesium hydroxide with hydrochloric acid.

$$\text{Mg(OH)}_2\text{(s)} + 2 \text{ HCl(aq)} \rightarrow \text{MgCl}_2\text{(aq)} + 2 \text{ H}_2\text{O}(\ell)$$

When the reaction is complete, evaporating the water will give solid magnesium chloride. Suggest at least one other way to prepare MgCl$_2$.

**84.** ▲ Suggest a laboratory method for preparing barium phosphate. (See Study Question 89 for a way to approach this question.)

**85.** The Tollen's test for the presence of reducing sugars (say in a urine sample) involves treating the sample with silver ions in aqueous ammonia. The result is the formation of a silver mirror within the reaction vessel if a reducing sugar is present. Using glucose, C$_6$H$_{12}$O$_6$, to illustrate this test, the oxidation–reduction reaction occurring is

$$\text{C}_6\text{H}_{12}\text{O}_6 \text{ (aq)} + 2 \text{ Ag}^+\text{(aq)} + 2 \text{ OH}^-\text{(aq)} \rightarrow$$
$$\text{C}_6\text{H}_{12}\text{O}_7\text{(aq)} + 2 \text{ Ag(s)} + \text{H}_2\text{O}(\ell)$$

What has been oxidized, and what has been reduced? What is the oxidizing agent, and what is the reducing agent?

**(a)**          **(b)**

**Tollen's test.** The reaction of silver ions with a sugar such as glucose produces metallic silver. **(a)** The set-up for the reaction. **(b)** The silvered test tube.

## Summary and Conceptual Questions

*The following questions may use concepts from this and previous chapters.*

**86.** There are many ionic compounds that dissolve in water to a very small extent. One example is lead(II) chloride. When it dissolves an equilibrium is established between the solid salt and its component ions. Suppose you stir some solid PbCl$_2$ into water. Explain how you would prove that the compound dissolves but to a small extent? Is the dissolving process product-favored or reactant-favored?

$$\text{PbCl}_2\text{(s)} \rightleftharpoons \text{Pb}^{2+}\text{(aq)} + 2 \text{ Cl}^-\text{(aq)}$$

87. ▲ Most naturally occurring acids are weak acids. Lactic acid is one example.

$$CH_3CH(OH)CO_2H(s) + H_2O(\ell) \rightleftharpoons$$
$$H_3O^+(aq) + CH_3CH(OH)CO_2^-(aq)$$

If you place some lactic acid in water, it will ionize to a small extent, and an equilibrium will be established. Suggest some experiments to prove that this is a weak acid and that the establishment of equilibrium is a reversible process.

Lactic acid

88. ▲ You want to prepare barium chloride, $BaCl_2$, using an exchange reaction of some type. To do so, you have the following reagents from which to select the reactants: $BaSO_4$, $BaBr_2$, $BaCO_3$, $Ba(OH)_2$, $HCl$, $HgSO_4$, $AgNO_3$, and $HNO_3$. Write a complete, balanced equation for the reaction chosen. (*Note:* There are several possibilities.)

89. ▲ Describe how to prepare $BaSO_4$, barium sulfate, by (a) a precipitation reaction and (b) a gas-forming reaction. To do so, you have the following reagents from which to select the reactants: $BaCl_2$, $BaCO_3$, $Ba(OH)_2$, $H_2SO_4$, and $Na_2SO_4$. Write complete, balanced equations for the reactions chosen. (See page 127 for an illustration of the preparation of a compound.)

90. ▲ Describe how to prepare zinc chloride by (a) an acid–base reaction, (b) a gas-forming reaction, and (c) an oxidation–reduction reaction. The available starting materials are $ZnCO_3$, $HCl$, $Cl_2$, $HNO_3$, $Zn(OH)_2$, $NaCl$, $Zn(NO_3)_2$, and $Zn$. Write complete, balanced equations for the reactions chosen.

91. A common method for analyzing for the nickel content of a sample is to use a precipitation reaction. Adding the organic compound dimethylglyoxime to a solution containing $Ni^{2+}$ ions, precipitates a red solid.

Derive the empirical formula for the red solid based on the following composition: Ni, 20.315%; C, 33.258%; H, 4.884%; O, 22.151%; and N, 19.392%.

92. The lanthanide elements react with oxygen to give, generally, compounds of the type $Ln_2O_3$ (where Ln stands for a lanthanide element). However, there are interesting exceptions, such as a common oxide of terbium, $Tb_xO_y$. Given that the compound is 73.945% Tb, what is its formula? What is the oxidation number of terbium in this compound? Write a balanced equation for the reaction of terbium and oxygen to give this oxide.

93. The presence of arsenic in a sample that may also contain another Group 5A element, antimony, can be confirmed by first precipitating the $As^{3+}$ and $Sb^{3+}$ ions as yellow solid $As_2S_3$ and orange solid $Sb_2S_3$. If aqueous HCl is then added, only $Sb_2S_3$ dissolves, leaving behind solid $As_2S_3$. The $As_2S_3$ can then be dissolved using aqueous $HNO_3$.

$$3 As_2S_3(s) + 10 HNO_3(aq) + 4 H_2O(\ell) \rightarrow$$
$$6 H_3AsO_4(aq) + 10 NO(g) + 9 S(s)$$

Finally, the presence of arsenic is confirmed by adding $AgNO_3$ to the solution of $H_3AsO_4$ to precipitate a reddish brown solid $Ag_xAsO_y$. The composition of this solid is As, 16.199% and Ag, 69.964%.

(a) What are the oxidation numbers of As, S, and N in the reaction of $As_2S_3$ with nitric acid.

(b) What is the formula of the reddish brown solid $Ag_xAsO_y$?

# Applying Chemical Principles

## Superconductors

In 1987, the Nobel Prize in Physics was awarded to Georg Benorz and Karl Müller (IBM Labs, Zurich, Switzerland) for their pioneering work in superconductivity, including their discovery of a new class of superconductors based on a lanthanum, barium, copper, and oxygen compound. The superconductor was identified as $La_{2-x}Ba_xCuO_4$, where the value of $x$ varied from 0.10 to 0.20. In the same year, researchers at the University of Alabama at Huntsville synthesized $YBa_2Cu_3O_{7-x}$ (or YBCO), where $x$ varies from 0 to 0.50. YBCO was the first material discovered to superconduct at temperatures above the boiling point of liquefied nitrogen (77 K). Further research determined that the critical temperature for superconductivity of YBCO varies with changes to the ratios of its components. The highest superconducting temperature, 95 K, is found for $YBa_2Cu_3O_{6.93}$.

Superconductors are important because these materials have no resistance to the flow of electric current. Once a current (that is, a flow of electrons) is induced in a superconductor, it will continue indefinitely with no energy loss. A potential application for superconductors is electricity storage. Currently, electricity produced at power plants must be used as it is produced. If unused electricity could be fed into a superconducting storage ring, the current could be stored indefinitely. For a storage ring to be feasible, the superconductor must operate at a temperature where refrigeration is not cost prohibitive, and the superconductor must support high currents. YCBO meets the first criterion but not the second. To date, no superconductor has been discovered that can carry large currents at temperatures greater than 77 K.

Compound formulas containing subscripts that are not whole numbers are common for a variety of compounds, including high temperature superconductors. Answer the following questions concerning a couple of these superconductors.

**Superconductivity.** When a superconducting material is cooled to a low temperature, say in liquid nitrogen (boiling point 77 K), and is placed in a magnetic field, the field does not penetrate the superconductor but rather is rejected from the superconductor. The effect is seen here where a 1-pound magnet floats above cooled superconductors. In this photo, a 1-pound magnet is levitated in the field caused by the cooled superconductor.

*Courtesy of University of Kentucky Public Relations*

## Questions:

1. Use the following mass percentages to determine the value of $x$ in a sample of $La_{2-x}Ba_xCuO_4$: %La = 63.43, %Ba = 5.085, %Cu = 15.69, and %O = 15.80.
2. What is the percent by mass of each element in YBCO when $x = 0.07$?
3. Assuming the charges on the yttrium and barium ions are 3+ and 2+, respectively, what charges are present on the copper ions in $YBa_2Cu_3O_7$? (Note: Although most copper compounds are based on $Cu^{2+}$, charges of 1+ and 3+ are also possible. Assume at least one copper ion in this substance is $Cu^{2+}$.)
4. The reaction of $Y_2O_3$, $BaCO_3$, and $CuO$ produces $YBa_2Cu_3O_{7-x}$ with $CO_2(g)$ as the only byproduct. Write a balanced chemical equation of this reaction and determine the value of $x$.
5. The percentage of oxygen in YBCO is adjusted by heating it in the presence of elemental oxygen. What mass of oxygen is required to convert 1.00 g $YBa_2Cu_3O_{6.50}$ to $YBa_2Cu_3O_{6.93}$?

## References:

1. M. K. Wu, et al., *Phys. Rev. Lett.,* Vol. 58, page 908, 1987.
2. J. W. Cochrane and G. J. Russell, *Supercond. Sci. Technol.,* Vol. 11, page 1105, 1998.

# 4 Stoichiometry: Quantitative Information about Chemical Reactions

A sparkler.

## The Chemistry of Pyrotechnics

One of life's pleasures is to watch fireworks, but of course we usually don't think about this as being just an application of chemistry. The sparkler in the photograph, like many forms of fireworks, depends on some very straightforward chemistry. It consists of a mixture of finely powdered metals, such as Al or Fe, other substances such as $KClO_3$, and a binder that holds the mixture onto a wire handle. When ignited, the powdered metal reacts with oxygen in the air (or extracted from $KClO_3$) and the sparks fly!

$$4\ Fe(s) + 3\ O_2(g) \longrightarrow 2\ Fe_2O_3(s)$$

Thermite reaction.

Even more spectacular than the sparkler is the thermite reaction, the reduction of iron(III) oxide with metallic aluminum.

$$Fe_2O_3(s) + 2\ Al(s) \longrightarrow 2\ Fe(\ell) + Al_2O_3(s)$$

In the sparkler, the oxygen that combines with the iron comes from the air. In the thermite reaction, however, the oxygen of iron(III) oxide is transferred to the reducing agent, the aluminum metal.

These reactions generate an enormous amount of energy, sufficient to produce iron in the molten state. Although the thermite reaction in particular was originally developed as a way of producing metals from their oxides (copper, uranium, and others also work well), it was quickly realized that it can be used for welding. For some years it was used to weld the rails of train tracks.

### Questions:

1. If a sparkler contains 1.0 g of iron, what is the mass of the product of the reaction of iron with oxygen?
2. What mass of aluminum should be used to completely consume 10.0 g of iron(III) oxide in the thermite reaction?
3. What is the limiting reactant if you combine 20 g of aluminum metal with 10 g of iron(III) oxide?

Answers to these questions are available in Appendix N.

## CHAPTER GOALS

*See Chapter Goals Revisited (page 193) for Study Questions keyed to these goals.*

- Perform stoichiometry calculations using balanced chemical equations.
- Understand the meaning of a limiting reactant in a chemical reaction.
- Calculate the theoretical and percent yields of a chemical reaction.
- Use stoichiometry to analyze a mixture of compounds or to determine the formula of a compound.
- Define and use concentrations in solution stoichiometry.

The objective of this chapter is to introduce the quantitative study of chemical reactions. Quantitative studies are needed to determine, for example, how much oxygen is required for the complete combustion of a given quantity of gasoline and what masses of carbon dioxide and water can be obtained. This part of chemistry is fundamental to much of what chemists, chemical engineers, biochemists, molecular biologists, geochemists, and many others do.

## 4.1 Mass Relationships in Chemical Reactions: Stoichiometry

A balanced chemical equation shows the quantitative relationship between reactants and products in a chemical reaction. On the submicroscopic scale, the stoichiometric coefficients in the equation refer to atoms, molecules, or formula units. On the macroscopic level on which we work in the laboratory, the coefficients refer to the number of moles of each reactant and product. The coefficients in a balanced chemical equation thus allow us to relate the amount (moles) of one substance involved in a chemical reaction to the amount (moles) of another substance involved in that chemical reaction.

Let us apply this concept to the reaction of phosphorus and chlorine in Figure 3.1.

$$P_4(s) + 6 \ Cl_2(g) \rightarrow 4 \ PCl_3(\ell)$$

| | | |
|---|---|---|
| 1 mol | 6 mol | 4 mol |
| 124 g | 425 g | 549 g |

The chemical equation for this reaction means that 1 mol (124 g) of solid phosphorus ($P_4$) can react with 6 mol (425 g) of chlorine gas ($Cl_2$) to form 4 mol (549 g) of liquid phosphorus trichloride ($PCl_3$).

Now, suppose you want to use much less $P_4$ in the reaction, only 1.45 g. What amount of $Cl_2$ gas would be required and what amount of $PCl_3$ could be produced? This is an example of a situation common in chemistry and chemical engineering, so let us work carefully through the steps you should follow when solving a stoichiometry problem.

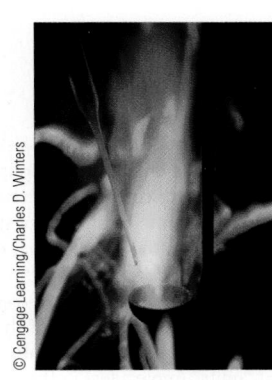

**Reaction of $P_4$ and $Cl_2$.** When white phosphorus, $P_4$, is placed in a flask of $Cl_2$, a reaction spontaneously occurs (see also Figure 3.1).

● **Stoichiometry and Reaction Completeness** *Stoichiometry calculations assume reactions are complete.* That is, *all* of at least one of the reactants has been converted to the product or products. Recall from the discussion of chemical equilibrium in Chapter 3 that some reactions do not reach completion, however.

**Modules 7: Simple Stoichiometry and 8: Limiting Reactants** cover concepts in this section.

● **Stoichiometry and Recipes** In one sense a balanced equation is a "recipe" for a chemical reaction: how much of one chemical is needed to consume another to produce a desired product. Food analogies have often been used in teaching stoichiometry. See, for example, "Learning Stoichiometry with Hamburger Sandwiches," by L. Haim, E. Cortón, S. Kocmur, and L. Galagovsky, *Journal of Chemical Education, Vol. 80,* pp. 1021-1022, 2003.

● **Mass Balance and Moles of Reactants and Products** Mass is always conserved in chemical reactions. Assuming complete conversion of reactants to products, the total mass of the reactants is always the same as that of the products. This does not mean, however, that the total *amount* (moles) of reactants is the same as that of the products. Atoms are rearranged into different "units" (molecules) in the course of a reaction. In the $P_4 + Cl_2$ reaction, 7 mol of reactants gives 4 mol of product.

**Part (a): Calculate the mass of $Cl_2$ required by 1.45 g of $P_4$**

**Step 1.** *Write the balanced equation* (using correct formulas for reactants and products). This is *always* the first step when dealing with chemical reactions.

$$P_4(s) + 6\ Cl_2(g) \longrightarrow 4\ PCl_3(\ell)$$

**Step 2.** *Calculate amount (moles) from mass (grams).* Recall that chemical equations reflect the relative amounts of reactants and products, not their masses. Therefore, first calculate the amount (moles) of $P_4$ available.

$$1.45\ g\ P_4 \times \frac{1\ mol\ P_4}{123.9\ g\ P_4} = 0.0117\ mol\ P_4$$

1/molar mass of $P_4$

**Step 3a.** *Use a stoichiometric factor.* The next step is to use the balanced equation to relate the amount of $P_4$ available to the amount of $Cl_2$ required to completely consume the $P_4$. This relationship is a **stoichiometric factor**, a mole ratio based on the stoichiometric coefficients for the chemicals in the balanced equation. Here the balanced equation specifies that 6 mol of $Cl_2$ is required for each mole of $P_4$, so the stoichiometric factor is (6 mol $Cl_2$/1 mol $P_4$).

$$0.0117\ mol\ P_4 \times \frac{6\ mol\ Cl_2\ required}{1\ mol\ P_4\ available} = 0.0702\ mol\ Cl_2\ required$$

↑

stoichiometric factor from balanced equation

This calculation shows that 0.0702 mol of $Cl_2$ is required to react with all the available phosphorus (1.45 g, 0.0117 mol).

**Step 4a.** *Calculate mass from amount.* Convert the amount (moles) of $Cl_2$ calculated in Step 3 to the mass of $Cl_2$ required.

$$0.0702\ mol\ Cl_2 \times \frac{70.91\ g\ Cl_2}{1\ mol\ Cl_2} = 4.98\ g\ Cl_2$$

**Part (b) Calculate mass of $PCl_3$ produced from 1.45 g of $P_4$ and 4.98 g of $Cl_2$**

What mass of $PCl_3$ can be produced from the reaction of 1.45 g of phosphorus with 4.98 g of $Cl_2$? From part (a), we know that these masses are the correct quantities needed for complete reaction. Because mass is conserved, the answer can be obtained by adding the masses of $P_4$ and $Cl_2$ used (giving 1.45 g + 4.98 g = 6.43 g of $PCl_3$ produced). Alternatively, Steps 3 and 4 can be repeated, but with the appropriate stoichiometric factor and molar mass.

**Step 3b.** *Use a stoichiometric factor.* Convert the amount of available $P_4$ to the amount of $PCl_3$ produced. Here the balanced equation specifies that 4 mol of $PCl_3$ is produced for each mole of $P_4$ used, so the stoichiometric factor is (4 mol $PCl_3$/1 mol $P_4$).

$$0.0117\ mol\ P_4 \times \frac{4\ mol\ PCl_3\ produced}{1\ mol\ P_4\ available} = 0.0468\ mol\ PCl_3\ produced$$

↑

stoichiometric factor from balanced equation

**Step 4b.** *Calculate the mass of product from its amount.* Convert the amount of $PCl_3$ produced to its mass in grams.

$$0.0468\ mol\ PCl_3 \times \frac{137.3\ g\ PCl_3}{1\ mol\ PCl_3} = 6.43\ g\ PCl_3$$

## Stoichiometry Calculations

You are asked to determine what mass of product can be formed from a given mass of reactant. It is not possible to calculate the mass of product in a single step. Instead, you must follow a route such as that illustrated in the strategy map here for the reaction of reactant A to give the product B according to an equation such as $x A \rightarrow y B$.

- The mass (g) of reactant A is converted to the amount (moles) of A using the molar mass of A.
- Next, using the stoichiometric factor, you find the amount (moles) of B.

- Finally, the mass (g) of B is obtained by multiplying amount of B by its molar mass.

When solving a stoichiometry problem, remember that you will always use a stoichiometric factor at some point.

$\times$ stoichiometric factor

The mole relationships of reactants and products in a reaction can be summarized in an **amounts table**, and you may find these tables helpful in organizing information in stoichiometry problems. The balanced chemical equation is written across the top. The next three lines indicate the following:

- *Initial* amount (moles) of each reactant and product present
- *Change* in amount that occurs during the reaction
- *Final* amount of each reactant and product present after the reaction.

The completed amounts table for the example just worked indicates that the reactants $P_4$ and $Cl_2$ were initially present in the correct stoichiometric ratio but no $PCl_3$ was present. During the course of the reaction, all of the reactants were consumed and formed the product.

| Equation | $P_4(s)$ | + | $6\ Cl_2(g)$ | $\rightarrow$ | $4\ PCl_3(\ell)$ |
|---|---|---|---|---|---|
| Initial amount (mol) | 0.0117 mol | | 0.0702 | | 0 mol |
| | (1.45 g) | | (4.98 g) | | (0 g) |
| Change in amount upon reaction (mol) | −0.0117 mol | | −0.0702 mol | | +0.0468 mol |
| Amount after complete reaction (mol) | 0 mol | | 0 mol | | 0.0468 mol |
| | (0 g) | | (0 g) | | (6.43 g) |

● **Amounts Tables** The mole (and mass) relationships of reactants and products in a reaction can be summarized in an *amounts table*. Such tables will be used extensively when studying chemical equilibria in Chapters 16–18.

## ♥WL INTERACTIVE EXAMPLE 4.1 Mass Relations in Chemical Reactions

**Problem** Glucose, $C_6H_{12}O_6$, reacts with oxygen to give $CO_2$ and $H_2O$. What mass of oxygen (in grams) is required for complete reaction of 25.0 g of glucose? What masses of carbon dioxide and water (in grams) are formed?

**What Do You Know?** This is a stoichiometry problem because you are given the mass of one of the reactants (glucose) and are asked to determine the mass of the other substances involved in the chemical reaction. In addition, you know formulas for the reactants and products and the mass of one of the reactants (glucose). You will need the molar masses of the reactants and products for the calculation.

**Strategy** Write the balanced chemical equation for this reaction. Then, follow the scheme outlined in Problem-Solving Tip 4.1.

- Find the amount (moles) of glucose available.
- Find the amount (moles) of $O_2$. Relate the amount of glucose to the amount of $O_2$ required using the stoichiometric factor based on the coefficients in the balanced equation.
- Find the mass (g) of $O_2$ required from the amount of $O_2$.
- Follow the same procedure to calculate the masses of carbon dioxide and water.

## Strategy Map 4.1

**PROBLEM**

Calculate mass of $O_2$ required for combustion of **25.0 g of glucose.**

↓

**DATA/INFORMATION**

**Formulas** for reactants and products and the **mass** of one reactant (glucose)

↓

STEP 1. Write the **balanced equation**.

↓

**Balanced equation** to give the required *stoichiometric factor*

↓

STEP 2. Amount glucose = mass × (1 molar mass).

↓

**Amount of reactant** (glucose)

↓

STEP 3. Use stoichiometric factor = [6 mol $O_2$/1 mol glucose].

↓

**Amount of $O_2$**

↓

STEP 4. Mass of $O_2$ = mol $O_2$ × mass/1 mol.

↓

**Mass of $O_2$**

## Solution

**Step 1.** *Write a balanced equation.*

$$C_6H_{12}O_6(s) + 6\ O_2(g) \rightarrow 6\ CO_2(g) + 6\ H_2O(\ell)$$

**Step 2.** *Convert the mass of glucose to amount of glucose.*

$$25.0\ \text{g glucose} \times \frac{1\ \text{mol}}{180.2\ \text{g}} = 0.139\ \text{mol glucose}$$

**Step 3.** *Use the stoichiometric factor.* Here we calculate the amount of $O_2$ required.

$$0.139\ \text{mol glucose} \times \frac{6\ \text{mol}\ O_2}{1\ \text{mol glucose}} = 0.832\ \text{mol}\ O_2$$

**Step 4.** *Calculate mass from amount.* Convert the required amount of $O_2$ to a mass in grams.

$$0.832\ \text{mol}\ O_2 \times \frac{32.00\ \text{g}}{1\ \text{mol}\ O_2} = 26.6\ \text{g}\ O_2$$

Repeat Steps 3 and 4 to find the mass of $CO_2$ produced in the combustion. First, relate the amount (moles) of glucose available to the amount of $CO_2$ produced using a stoichiometric factor. Then convert the amount of $CO_2$ to its mass in grams.

$$0.139\ \text{mol glucose} \times \frac{6\ \text{mol}\ CO_2}{1\ \text{mol glucose}} \times \frac{44.01\ \text{g}\ CO_2}{1\ \text{mol}\ CO_2} = \boxed{36.6\ \text{g}\ CO_2}$$

Now, how can you find the mass of $H_2O$ produced? You could go through Steps 3 and 4 again. However, recognize that the total mass of reactants

$$25.0\ \text{g}\ C_6H_{12}O_6 + 26.6\ \text{g}\ O_2 = 51.6\ \text{g reactants}$$

must be the same as the total mass of products. The mass of water that can be produced is therefore

$$\text{Total mass of products} = 51.6\ \text{g} = 36.6\ \text{g}\ CO_2\ \text{produced} + ?\ \text{g}\ H_2O$$

$$\text{Mass of}\ H_2O\ \text{produced} = \boxed{15.0\ \text{g}}$$

**Think about Your Answer** The results of this calculation can be summarized in an amounts table.

| Equation | $C_6H_{12}O_6(s)$ | + | $6\ O_2(g)$ | → | $6\ CO_2(g)$ | + | $6\ H_2O(\ell)$ |
|---|---|---|---|---|---|---|---|
| Initial amount (mol) | 0.139 mol | | 6(0.139 mol) = 0.832 mol | | 0 | | 0 |
| Change in amount upon reaction (mol) | −0.139 mol | | −0.832 mol | | +0.832 mol | | +0.832 mol |
| Amount after complete reaction (mol) | 0 | | 0 | | 0.832 mol | | 0.832 mol |

When you know the mass of all but one of the chemicals in a reaction, you can find the unknown mass using the principle of mass conservation (the total mass of reactants must equal the total mass of products; page 111).

## Check Your Understanding

What mass of oxygen, $O_2$, is required to completely combust 454 g of propane, $C_3H_8$? What masses of $CO_2$ and $H_2O$ are produced?

# 4.2   Reactions in Which One Reactant Is Present in Limited Supply

Reactions are often carried out with an excess of one reactant over that required by stoichiometry. This is usually done to make sure that one of the reactants is consumed completely, even though some of another reactant remains unused.

Suppose you burn a toy sparkler, a wire coated with a mixture of aluminum or iron powder and potassium nitrate or chlorate (Figure 4.1 and page 156). The aluminum or iron burns, consuming oxygen from the air or from the potassium salt and producing a metal oxide.

$$4\,Al(s) + 3\,O_2(g) \rightarrow 2\,Al_2O_3(s)$$

The sparkler burns until the metal powder is consumed completely. What about the oxygen? Four moles of aluminum require three moles of oxygen, but there is much, much more $O_2$ available in the air than is needed to consume the metal in a sparkler. How much metal oxide is produced? That depends on the quantity of metal powder in the sparkler, not on the quantity of $O_2$ in the atmosphere. The metal powder in this example is called the **limiting reactant** because its amount determines, or limits, the amount of product formed.

Now let us see how these same principles apply to another example, the reaction of oxygen and carbon monoxide to give carbon dioxide. The balanced equation for the reaction is

$$2\,CO(g) + O_2(g) \rightarrow 2\,CO_2(g)$$

Suppose you have a mixture of four CO molecules and three $O_2$ molecules. The four CO molecules require only two $O_2$ molecules (and produce four $CO_2$ molecules). This means that one $O_2$ molecule remains after reaction is complete.

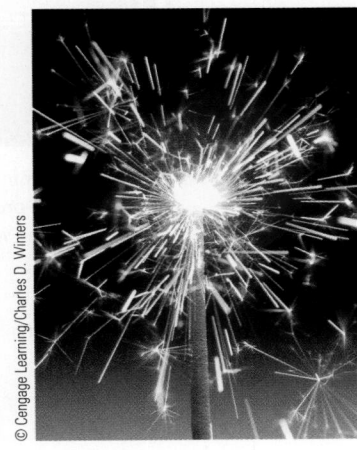

**FIGURE 4.1 Burning aluminum and iron powder.** A toy sparkler contains a metal powder such as Al or Fe and other chemicals such as $KNO_3$ or $KClO_3$. When ignited, the metal burns with a brilliant white light.

Reactants: 4 **CO** and 3 **O$_2$**          ⟶          Products: 4 **CO$_2$** and 1 **O$_2$**

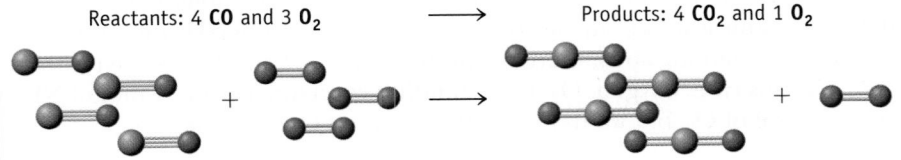

Because more $O_2$ molecules are available than are required, the number of $CO_2$ molecules produced is determined by the number of CO molecules available. Carbon monoxide, CO, is therefore the limiting reactant in this case.

## A Stoichiometry Calculation with a Limiting Reactant

The first step in the manufacture of nitric acid is the oxidation of ammonia to NO over a platinum-wire gauze (Figure 4.2).

$$4\,NH_3(g) + 5\,O_2(g) \rightarrow 4\,NO(g) + 6\,H_2O(\ell)$$

Suppose equal masses of $NH_3$ and $O_2$ are mixed (750. g of each). Are these reactants mixed in the correct stoichiometric ratio or is one of them in short supply? That is, will one of them limit the quantity of NO that can be produced? How much NO can be

● **Comparing Reactant Ratios** For the $CO/O_2$ reaction, the stoichiometric ratio of reactants should be (2 mol CO/1 mol $O_2$). However, the ratio of amounts of reactants available in the text example is (4 mol CO/3 mol $O_2$) or (1.33 mol CO/1 mol $O_2$). The fact that the $CO/O_2$ ratio is not large enough tells us that there is not enough CO to react with all of the available $O_2$. Carbon monoxide is the limiting reactant, and some $O_2$ will be left over when all of the CO is consumed.

**Module 8: Stoichiometry and Limiting Reactants** covers concepts in this section.

**FIGURE 4.2**
Oxidation of
ammonia.

**(a)** Burning ammonia on the surface of a platinum wire produces so much heat energy that the wire glows bright red.

**(b)** Billions of kilograms of $HNO_3$ are made annually starting with the oxidation of ammonia over a wire gauze containing platinum.

formed if the reaction using this reactant mixture goes to completion? And how much of the excess reactant is left over when the maximum amount of NO has been formed?

**Step 1.** *Find the amount of each reactant.*

$$750. \text{ g NH}_3 \times \frac{1 \text{ mol NH}_3}{17.03 \text{ g NH}_3} = 44.0 \text{ mol NH}_3 \text{ available}$$

$$750. \text{ g O}_2 \times \frac{1 \text{ mol O}_2}{32.00 \text{ g O}_2} = 23.4 \text{ mol O}_2 \text{ available}$$

**Step 2.** *What is the limiting reactant?* Examine the ratio of amounts of reactants. Are the reactants present in the correct stoichiometric ratio as given by the balanced equation?

$$\text{Stoichiometric ratio of reactants required by balanced equation} = \frac{5 \text{ mol O}_2}{4 \text{ mol NH}_3} = \frac{1.25 \text{ mol O}_2}{1 \text{ mol NH}_3}$$

$$\text{Ratio of reactants } \textit{actually available} = \frac{23.4 \text{ mol O}_2}{44.0 \text{ mol NH}_3} = \frac{0.532 \text{ mol O}_2}{1 \text{ mol NH}_3}$$

Dividing moles of $O_2$ available by moles of $NH_3$ available shows that the ratio of available reactants is much smaller than the 5 mol $O_2$/4 mol $NH_3$ ratio required by the balanced equation. Thus, there is not sufficient $O_2$ available to react with all of the $NH_3$. In this case, oxygen, $O_2$, is the limiting reactant. That is, 1 mol of $NH_3$ requires 1.25 mol of $O_2$, but we have only 0.532 mol of $O_2$ available.

**Step 3.** *Calculate the mass of product.* We can now calculate the expected mass of product, NO, based on the amount of the limiting reactant, $O_2$.

$$23.4 \text{ mol O}_2 \times \frac{4 \text{ mol NO}}{5 \text{ mol O}_2} \times \frac{30.01 \text{ g NO}}{1 \text{ mol NO}} = 562 \text{ g NO}$$

**Step 4.** *Calculate the mass of excess reactant.* Ammonia is the "excess reactant" in this $NH_3$/$O_2$ reaction because more than enough $NH_3$ is available to react with 23.4 mol of $O_2$. Let us calculate the quantity of $NH_3$ remaining after all the $O_2$ has been used. To do so, we first need to know the amount of $NH_3$ required to consume all the limiting reactant, $O_2$.

$$23.4 \text{ mol O}_2 \text{ available} \times \frac{4 \text{ mol NH}_3 \text{ required}}{5 \text{ mol O}_2} = 18.8 \text{ mol NH}_3 \text{ required}$$

Because 44.0 mol of $NH_3$ is available, the amount of excess $NH_3$ can be calculated,

$$\text{Excess } NH_3 = 44.0 \text{ mol } NH_3 \text{ available} - 18.8 \text{ mol } NH_3 \text{ required}$$

$$= 25.2 \text{ mol } NH_3 \text{ remaining}$$

and then converted to a mass.

$$25.2 \text{ mol } NH_3 \times \frac{17.03 \text{ g } NH_3}{1 \text{ mol } NH_3} = 429 \text{ g } NH_3 \text{ in excess of that required}$$

Finally, because 429 g of $NH_3$ is left over, this means that 321 g of $NH_3$ has been consumed (= 750. g − 429 g).

When solving limiting reactant problems you may find it helpful to organize your results in an amounts table.

| Equation | 4 NH₃(g) | + | 5 O₂(g) | → | 4 NO(g) | + | 6 H₂O(g) |
|---|---|---|---|---|---|---|---|
| Initial amount (mol) | 44.0 | | 23.4 | | 0 | | 0 |
| Change in amount upon reaction (mol) | −(4/5)(23.4) = −18.8 | | −23.4 | | +(4/5)(23.4) = +18.8 | | +(6/5)(23.4) = +28.1 |
| Amount after complete reaction (mol) | 25.2 | | 0 | | 18.8 | | 28.1 |

All of the limiting reactant, $O_2$, is consumed. Of the original 44.0 mol of $NH_3$, 18.8 mol is consumed and 25.2 mol remains. The balanced equation indicates that the amount of NO produced is equal to the amount of $NH_3$ consumed, so 18.8 mol of NO is produced from 18.8 mol of $NH_3$. In addition, 28.1 mol of $H_2O$ is produced.

## ⊙WL   INTERACTIVE EXAMPLE 4.2   A Reaction with a Limiting Reactant

**Problem** Methanol, $CH_3OH$, which is used as a fuel in racing cars and in fuel cells, can be made by the reaction of carbon monoxide and hydrogen.

$$CO(g) + 2\,H_2(g) \rightarrow \underset{\text{methanol}}{CH_3OH(\ell)}$$

Suppose 356 g of CO and 65.0 g of $H_2$ are mixed and allowed to react.

(a)  What mass of methanol can be produced?

(b)  What mass of the excess reactant remains after the limiting reactant has been consumed?

**What Do You Know?** You should suspect this problem might involve a limiting reactant because the masses of two reactants are given, and you are asked to determine the mass of the product. The equation for the reaction is given, and you know the masses of CO and $H_2$ that are available. You will need the molar masses of the two reactants and the product to solve the problem.

**Strategy**

- Calculate the amounts of each reactant. Compare the ratio of reactant amounts to the stoichiometric ratio defined by the equation, here (2 mol $H_2$/1 mol CO).

- If (mol $H_2$ available/mol CO available) is greater than 2/1, then CO is the limiting reactant. If (mol $H_2$ available/mol CO available) is less than 2/1, then $H_2$ is the limiting reactant.

- Use the amount of the limiting reactant to calculate the mass of product formed, following the scheme in Problem Solving Tip 4.1.

- The mass of the second reactant required in the reaction is determined from the limiting reactant in a similar calculation. The mass of excess reagent is the difference between its starting mass and what was used in the reaction.

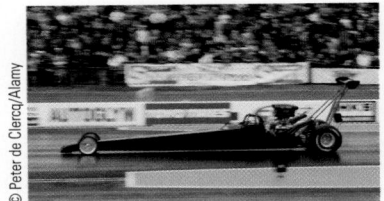

**Methanol as a Fuel.** Methanol can be used as an automotive fuel when blended with gasoline (in M85, which contains 85% methanol). It is also used as the pure liquid in Indianapolis race cars and in dragsters. Small fuel cells using methanol to produce electricity are also on the market.

## Strategy Map 4.2

**PROBLEM**

Calculate **mass** of **product** from a reaction.

↓

**DATA/INFORMATION**

- **Masses** of two reactants.
- Recognize as a **limiting reactant** problem.

**STEP 1.** Write the **balanced equation.**

**Balanced equation** gives **stoichiometric ratio.**

**STEP 2.** Calculate **amount** of each **reactant** = mass × (1 mol/molar mass).

**Amount** of each **reactant**

**STEP 3.** Decide which reactant is **limiting.** Is ratio of reactant amounts *greater than* or *less than* stoichiometric ratio?

**Limiting reactant** now known

**STEP 4.** Calculate **amount** of **product** based on amount of limiting reactant. Product amount = mol reactant × stoichiometric factor.

**Amount** of product expected based on amount of limiting reactant

**STEP 5.** Calculate **mass** of **product** = mol product × (molar mass/1 mol).

**Mass** of product

## Solution

(a) *What is the limiting reactant?* The amount of each reactant is

$$\text{Amount of CO} = 356 \text{ g CO} \times \frac{1 \text{ mol CO}}{28.01 \text{ g CO}} = 12.7 \text{ mol CO}$$

$$\text{Amount of H}_2 = 65.0 \text{ g H}_2 \times \frac{1 \text{ mol H}_2}{2.016 \text{ g H}_2} = 32.2 \text{ mol H}_2$$

Are these reactants present in a perfect stoichiometric ratio?

$$\frac{\text{Mol H}_2 \text{ available}}{\text{Mol CO available}} = \frac{32.2 \text{ mol H}_2}{12.7 \text{ mol CO}} = \frac{2.54 \text{ mol H}_2}{1.00 \text{ mol CO}}$$

The required mole ratio is 2 mol of $H_2$ to 1 mol of CO. Here you see that more hydrogen is available than is required to consume all the CO. It follows that not enough CO is present to use up all of the hydrogen. CO is the limiting reactant.

(b) *What is the maximum mass of $CH_3OH$ that can be formed?* This calculation must be based on the amount of the limiting reactant.

$$12.7 \text{ mol CO} \times \frac{1 \text{ mol CH}_3\text{OH formed}}{1 \text{ mol CO available}} \times \frac{32.04 \text{ g CH}_3\text{OH}}{1 \text{ mol CH}_3\text{OH}} = 407 \text{ g CH}_3\text{OH}$$

(c) *What mass of $H_2$ remains when all the CO has been converted to product?* First, you must find the mass of $H_2$ required to react with all the CO.

$$12.7 \text{ mol CO} \times \frac{2 \text{ mol H}_2}{1 \text{ mol CO}} \times \frac{2.016 \text{ g H}_2}{1 \text{ mol H}_2} = 51.2 \text{ g H}_2 \text{ required}$$

You began with 65.0 g of $H_2$, but only 51.2 g is required by the limiting reactant; thus, the mass that is present in excess is

$$65.0 \text{ g H}_2 \text{ present} - 51.2 \text{ g H}_2 \text{ required} = 13.8 \text{ g H}_2 \text{ left}$$

**Think about Your Answer** The amounts table for this reaction is as follows.

| Equation | CO(g) | + | 2 H₂(g) | → | CH₃OH(ℓ) |
|---|---|---|---|---|---|
| Initial amount (mol) | 12.7 | | 32.2 | | 0 |
| Change in amount upon reaction (mol) | −12.7 | | −2(12.7) | | +12.7 |
| Amount after complete reaction (mol) | 0 | | 6.8 | | 12.7 |

The mass of product formed plus the mass of $H_2$ remaining after reaction (407 g $CH_3OH$ produced + 14 g $H_2$ remaining = 421 g) is equal to the mass of reactants present before reaction (356 g CO + 65.0 g $H_2$ = 421 g).

### Check Your Understanding

The thermite reaction produces iron metal and aluminum oxide from a mixture of powdered aluminum metal and iron(III) oxide (page 156).

$$Fe_2O_3(s) + 2 \text{ Al}(s) \rightarrow 2 \text{ Fe}(\ell) + Al_2O_3(s)$$

A mixture of 50.0 g each of $Fe_2O_3$ and Al is used. Which is the limiting reactant? What mass of iron metal can be produced?

---

### REVIEW & CHECK FOR SECTION 4.2

The equation for the combustion of methanol is $2 \text{ CH}_3\text{OH}(\ell) + 3 \text{ O}_2(g) \rightarrow 2 \text{ CO}_2(g) + 4 \text{ H}_2\text{O}(\ell)$. If equal masses of the two reactants are allowed to react, which is the limiting reagent?

(a) $CH_3OH$

(b) $O_2$

(c) Neither, the reactants are present in the correct stoichiometric ratio.

## PROBLEM SOLVING TIP 4.2

# Moles of Reaction and Limiting Reactants

There is another method for solving stoichiometry problems that applies especially well to limiting reactant problems. This involves the useful concept of "moles of reaction."

One "mole of reaction" is said to have occurred when the reaction has taken place according to the number of moles given by the coefficients in the equation. For example, for the reaction of CO and $O_2$,

$$2\,CO(g) + O_2(g) \longrightarrow 2\,CO_2(g)$$

1 mole of reaction occurs when 2 mol of CO and 1 mol of $O_2$ produce 2 mol of $CO_2$. If the reaction mixture consists of only 1 mol of CO and 0.5 mol of $O_2$, then only 1 mol of $CO_2$ is produced and 0.5 mol of reaction has occurred according to this balanced equation.

To pursue this example further, suppose 9.5 g of CO and excess $O_2$ are combined. What amount of $CO_2$ (moles) can be produced?

$$9.5\text{ g CO} \times \frac{1\text{ mol CO}}{28.0\text{ g CO}} \times \frac{1\text{ mol-rxn}}{2\text{ mol CO}}$$
$$= 0.17\text{ mol-rxn}$$

$$0.17\text{ mol-rxn} \times \frac{2\text{ mol }CO_2}{1\text{ mol-rxn}} = 0.34\text{ mol }CO_2$$

The first equation above shows that the number of moles of reaction is calculated by multiplying the amount (moles) of the reactant CO by the factor, 1 mol-rxn/2 mol CO.

All reactants and products involved in a chemical reaction undergo the same number of moles of reaction because the reaction can only occur a certain number of times before the reactants are consumed and the reaction reaches completion.

If one of the reactants is in short supply the actual number of times a reaction can be carried out—the number of "moles of reaction"—will be determined by the limiting reactant. To use this approach you first calculate the amount of each reactant initially present and then calculate the moles of reaction that could occur with each

amount of reactant. [This is equivalent to dividing amount (moles) of each reactant by its stoichiometric coefficient.] The reactant producing the smaller number of moles of reaction is the limiting reactant. Once the limiting reactant is known, you proceed as before.

As an example, consider again the $NH_3/O_2$ reaction on page 162:

$$4\,NH_3(g) + 5\,O_2(g) \longrightarrow 4\,NO(g) + 6\,H_2O(\ell)$$

1. *Calculate the moles of reaction predicted for each reactant and decide on the limiting reactant.*

In the case of the $NH_3/O_2$ reaction, 1 "mole of reaction" uses 4 mol of $NH_3$ and 5 mol of $O_2$ and produces 4 mol of NO and 6 mol of $H_2O$. In the example on page 162, we started with 44.0 mol of $NH_3$, so 11.0 mol of reaction could result.

$$44.0\text{ mol }NH_3 \times \frac{1\text{ mol-rxn}}{4\text{ mol }NH_3} = 11.0\text{ mol-rxn}$$

Based on the amount of $O_2$ available, 4.68 mol of reaction could occur.

$$23.4\text{ mol }O_2 \times \frac{1\text{ mol-rxn}}{5\text{ mol }O_2} = 4.68\text{ mol-rxn}$$

Fewer moles of reaction can occur with the amount of $O_2$ available, so $O_2$ is the limiting reactant.

2. *Calculate the change in amount, and the amount upon completion of the reaction, for each reactant and product.* The number of moles of reaction predicted by the limiting reactant corresponds to the number of moles of reaction that can *actually* occur. Each reactant and product will undergo this number of moles of reaction, 4.68 mol-rxn in this case. To calculate the *change* in amount for a given reactant or product, multiply this number of moles of reaction by the stoichiometric coefficient of the reactant or product. To illustrate this step, for $NH_3$ this corresponds to the following calculation:

$$4.68\text{ mol-rxn} \times \left(\frac{4\text{ mole }NH_3}{1\text{ mol-rxn}}\right) =$$
$$18.8\text{ mol }NH_3$$

The amount of each reactant and product after reaction is calculated as usual.

Finally, from the amounts present after completion, you can calculate the masses of the products and of any reactant remaining.

*You may find this approach easier to use particularly when there are more than two reactants, each present initially in some designated quantity.*

Note: the concept of "moles of reaction" will be applied in this text in the discussion of thermochemistry in Chapters 5 and 19.

**Amounts Table**

| Equation | 4 NH₃(g) | + | 5 O₂(g) | → | 4 NO(g) | + | 6 H₂O(g) |
|---|---|---|---|---|---|---|---|
| Initial amount (mol) | 44.0 | | 23.4 | | 0 | | 0 |
| Moles of reaction based on limiting reactant (mol) | 4.68 | | 4.68 | | 4.68 | | 4.68 |
| Change in amount (mol)* | −4.68(4) = −18.8 | | −4.68(5) = −23.4 | | +4.68(4) = +18.8 | | +4.68(6) = +28.1 |
| Amount after complete reaction (mol) | 25.2 | | 0 | | 18.8 | | 28.1 |

*Moles of reaction are multiplied by the stoichiometric coefficient.

## 4.3 Percent Yield

The maximum mass of product that can be obtained from a chemical reaction is the **theoretical yield**. Frequently, however, the **actual yield** of the product—the mass of material that is actually obtained in the laboratory or a chemical plant—is less than the theoretical yield. Loss of product often occurs during the isolation and purification steps. In addition, some reactions do not go completely to products, and reactions are sometimes complicated by giving more than one set of products. For all these reasons, the actual yield is almost always less than the theoretical yield (Figure 4.3).

20 kernals

(a)

16 popped
4 unpopped
80% yield

(b)

**FIGURE 4.3 Percent yield.**
Although not a chemical reaction, popping corn is a good analogy to the difference between a theoretical yield and an actual yield. Here, we began with 20 popcorn kernels and found that only 16 of them popped. The percent yield from our "reaction" was (16/20) × 100%, or 80%.

**FIGURE 4.4 A modern analytical instrument.** This nuclear magnetic resonance (NMR) spectrometer is closely related to a magnetic resonance imaging (MRI) instrument found in a hospital. NMR is used to analyze compounds and to decipher their structure. (The instrument is controlled by a computer and console not seen in this photo.)

To provide information to other chemists who might want to carry out a reaction, it is customary to report a percent yield. **Percent yield**, which specifies how much of the theoretical yield was obtained, is defined as

$$\text{Percent yield} = \frac{\text{actual yield}}{\text{theoretical yield}} \times 100\% \qquad (4.1)$$

Suppose you made aspirin in the laboratory by the following reaction:

$$C_7H_6O_3(s) \quad + \quad C_4H_6O_3(\ell) \quad \longrightarrow \quad C_9H_8O_4(s) \quad + \quad CH_3CO_2H(\ell)$$

salicylic acid          acetic anhydride          aspirin          acetic acid

and that you began with 14.4 g of salicylic acid $(C_7H_6O_3)$ and an excess of acetic anhydride. That is, salicylic acid is the limiting reactant. If you obtain 6.26 g of aspirin, what is the percent yield of this product? The first step is to find the amount of the limiting reactant, salicylic acid.

$$14.4 \text{ g } C_7H_6O_3 \times \frac{1 \text{ mol } C_7H_6O_3}{138.1 \text{g } C_7H_6O_3} = 0.104 \text{ mol } C_7H_6O_3$$

Next, use the stoichiometric factor from the balanced equation to find the amount of aspirin expected based on the limiting reactant, $C_7H_6O_3$.

$$0.104 \text{ mol } C_7H_6O_3 \times \frac{1 \text{ mol aspirin}}{1 \text{ mol } C_7H_6O_3} = 0.104 \text{ mol aspirin}$$

The maximum amount of aspirin that can be produced—the theoretical yield—is 0.104 mol. Because the quantity you measure in the laboratory is the mass of the product, it is customary to express the theoretical yield as a mass in grams.

$$0.104 \text{ mol aspirin} \times \frac{180.2 \text{ g aspirin}}{1 \text{ mol aspirin}} = 18.8 \text{ g aspirin}$$

Finally, with the actual yield known to be only 6.26 g, the percent yield of aspirin can be calculated.

$$\text{Percent yield} = \frac{6.26 \text{ g aspirin obtained (actual yield)}}{18.8 \text{ g aspirin expected (theoretical yield)}} \times 100\% = 33.3\% \text{ yield}$$

---

**REVIEW & CHECK FOR SECTION 4.3**

Aluminum carbide, $Al_4C_3$, reacts with water to produce methane, $CH_4$.

$$Al_4C_3(s) + 12 \text{ H}_2O(\ell) \rightarrow 4 \text{ Al(OH)}_3(s) + 3 \text{ CH}_4(g)$$

1.  If 125 g of aluminum carbide is decomposed, what is the theoretical yield of methane?

    (a)  4.64 g          (b)  13.9 g          (c)  41.8 g          (d)  154 g

2.  If only 13.6 g of methane is obtained, what is the percent yield of this gas?

    (a)  34.1%          (b)  97.8%          (c)  32.5%          (d)  8.83%

## 4.4  Chemical Equations and Chemical Analysis

Analytical chemists use a variety of approaches to identify substances as well as to measure the quantities of components of mixtures. Analytical chemistry is often done now using instrumental methods (Figure 4.4), but classical chemical reactions and stoichiometry still play a central role.

## Quantitative Analysis of a Mixture

Quantitative chemical analysis generally depends on one of the following basic ideas:

- A substance, present in unknown amount, can be allowed to react with a known amount of another substance. If the stoichiometric ratio for their reaction is known, the unknown amount can be determined.
- A material of unknown composition can be converted to one or more substances of known composition. Those substances can be identified, their amounts determined, and these amounts related to the amount of the original, unknown substance.

An example of the first type of analysis is the analysis of a sample of vinegar containing an unknown amount of acetic acid, the ingredient that makes vinegar acidic. The acid reacts readily and completely with sodium hydroxide.

$$CH_3CO_2H(aq) + NaOH(aq) \rightarrow CH_3CO_2Na(aq) + H_2O(\ell)$$
$$\text{acetic acid}$$

If the exact amount of sodium hydroxide used in the reaction can be measured, the amount of acetic acid present can be calculated. This type of analysis is the subject of a later section in this chapter [▶ Section 4.7].

An example of the second type of analysis is the analysis of a sample of a mineral, thenardite, which is largely sodium sulfate, $Na_2SO_4$ (Figure 4.5). Sodium sulfate is soluble in water. Therefore, to find the quantity of $Na_2SO_4$ in an impure mineral sample, we would crush the rock and then wash the powdered sample thoroughly with water to dissolve the sodium sulfate. Next, we would treat this solution of sodium sulfate with barium chloride to precipitate the water-insoluble compound barium sulfate. The barium sulfate is collected on a filter and weighed (Figure 4.6).

$$Na_2SO_4(aq) + BaCl_2(aq) \rightarrow BaSO_4(s) + 2\ NaCl(aq)$$

We can then find the amount of sodium sulfate in the mineral sample because it is directly related to the amount of $BaSO_4$.

$$1\ mol\ Na_2SO_4(aq) \rightarrow 1\ mol\ BaSO_4(s)$$

Example 4.3 illustrates the analysis of another mineral, millerite, in this way.

**FIGURE 4.5 Thenardite.** The mineral thenardite is sodium sulfate, $Na_2SO_4$. It is named after the French chemist Louis Thenard (1777–1857). Sodium sulfate is used in making detergents, glass, and paper.

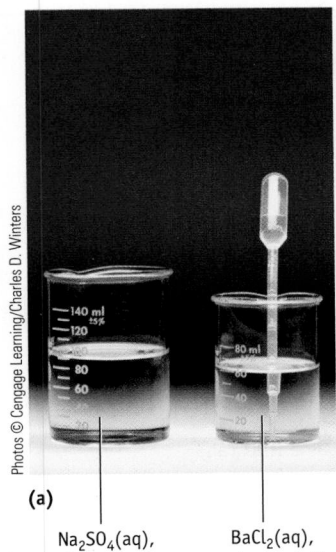

(a)

Na₂SO₄(aq), clear solution

BaCl₂(aq), clear solution

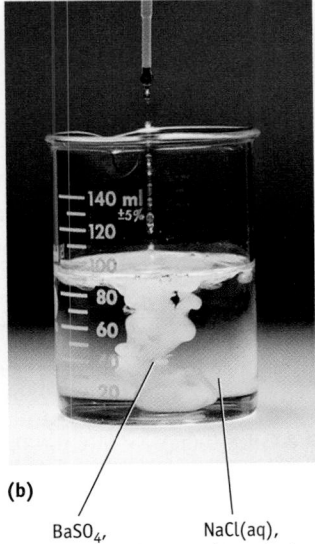

(b)

BaSO₄, white solid

NaCl(aq), clear solution

(c)

NaCl(aq), clear solution

BaSO₄, white solid caught in filter

(d)

Mass of dry BaSO₄ determined

**FIGURE 4.6 Analysis for the sulfate content of a sample.** The sulfate ions in a solution of $Na_2SO_4$ react with barium ions ($Ba^{2+}$) to form insoluble $BaSO_4$. The white precipitate is collected on a filter and weighed. The amount of $BaSO_4$ obtained can be related to the amount of $Na_2SO_4$ in the sample.

## CASE STUDY

# Green Chemistry and Atom Economy

Chemists and chemical industries are increasingly following the principles of "green chemistry." Among these principles are that it is better to prevent waste when producing chemicals than to clean it up later and to use and generate compounds that have little or no toxicity to human health and the environment.

Another principle of green chemistry is to try to convert all of the atoms of the reactants into the product; nothing should be wasted. To evaluate how well this occurs chemists usually report the percent yield of the product. As you will come to realize with your own laboratory experience, the percent yield can often be quite low.

Another way to evaluate the efficiency of a reaction is to calculate the "atom economy."

% atom economy =

$$\frac{\text{molar mass of atoms utilized}}{\text{molar mass of reactants}} \times 100\%$$

The principles of green chemistry helped in making "Green Works" cleaning products from a division of the Clorox Company. Most of the ingredients are naturally occurring substances.

A simple example of the concept is the reaction of methanol and carbon monoxide to produce acetic acid. The atom economy is 100% because all of the atoms of the reactants appear in the product.

$$CH_3OH(\ell) + CO(g) \rightarrow CH_3CO_2H(aq)$$

Ibuprofen is a widely used nonsteroidal anti-inflammatory drug, which is used in the United States in products under tradenames such as Motrin and Advil. A recently developed synthesis of ibuprofen involves the collection of compounds below (which combine in three reaction steps to give ibuprofen and, as a by-product, acetic acid).

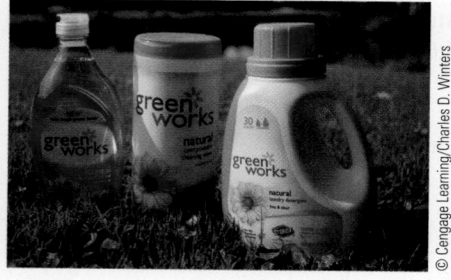

Ibruprofen

What is the atom economy for this reaction? The reactants, collectively, have 15 C atoms, 22 H atoms, and 4 O atoms. The "molar mass" of this collection is 266 g/mol. In contrast, ibuprofen has a molar mass of 206 g/mol. Therefore, the atom economy is 77%. This is

far superior to a competing commercial process for the synthesis of ibuprofen that has an atom economy of only 40%.

### Question:
Methyl methacrylate is the reactant used to prepare plastics you may know as Lucite or some other tradename. The substance was first introduced in 1933, but chemists have long sought better (and less costly) ways to make the compound. In a newly developed process, ethylene ($C_2H_4$), methanol ($CH_3OH$), CO, and formaldehyde ($CH_2O$) combine in two steps to give methyl methacrylate and water. What is the atom economy of this new process? (Not only does the new process have a much better atom economy than the previously used process, it also does not involve HCN, a toxic substance used in another method of making this compound.)

$$H_2C{=}CH_2 \quad CH_3OH \quad CO \quad H_2CO$$

Methyl methacrylate

**The answer to this question is available in Appendix N.**

### Reference:
M. C. Cann and M. E. Connelly, *Real-World Cases in Green Chemistry*, American Chemical Society, 2000.

---

## EXAMPLE 4.3   Mineral Analysis

**Problem** Nickel(II) sulfide, NiS, occurs naturally as the relatively rare mineral millerite. One of its occurrences is in meteorites. To analyze a mineral sample for the quantity of NiS, the sample is dissolved in nitric acid to form a solution of $Ni(NO_3)_2$.

$$NiS(s) + 4\ HNO_3(aq) \rightarrow Ni(NO_3)_2(aq) + S(s) + 2\ NO_2(g) + 2\ H_2O(\ell)$$

The aqueous solution of $Ni(NO_3)_2$ is then treated with the organic compound dimethylglyoxime ($C_4H_8N_2O_2$, DMG) to give the red solid $Ni(C_4H_7N_2O_2)_2$.

$$Ni(NO_3)_2(aq) + 2\ C_4H_8N_2O_2(aq) \rightarrow Ni(C_4H_7N_2O_2)_2(s) + 2\ HNO_3(aq)$$

Suppose a 0.468-g sample containing millerite produces 0.206 g of red, solid $Ni(C_4H_7N_2O_2)_2$. What is the mass percent of NiS in the sample?

**What Do You Know?** You know the mass of $Ni(C_4H_7N_2O_2)_2$ and the two balanced equations for the reactions leading to its formation. You will need molar masses of $Ni(C_4H_7N_2O_2)_2$ and NiS.

**A precipitate of nickel with dimethylglyoxime.** Red, insoluble $Ni(C_4H_7N_2O_2)_2$ precipitates when dimethylglyoxime ($C_4H_8N_2O_2$) is added to an aqueous solution of nickel(II) ions.

**Strategy** The balanced equations for the reactions show the following "road map":

$$1 \text{ mol NiS} \rightarrow 1 \text{ mol Ni(NO}_3)_2 \rightarrow 1 \text{ mol Ni(C}_4\text{H}_7\text{N}_2\text{O}_2)_2$$

From this you see that if you know the amount of $Ni(C_4H_7N_2O_2)_2$, you also know the amount of NiS. Therefore, first calculate the amount of $Ni(C_4H_7N_2O_2)_2$ from its mass. Because 1 mol of NiS was present in the sample for each mole of $Ni(C_4H_7N_2O_2)_2$ isolated, you therefore know the amount of NiS and can then calculate its mass and mass percent in the sample.

**Solution** The molar mass of $Ni(C_4H_7N_2O_2)_2$ is 288.9 g/mol. The amount of this red solid is

$$0.206 \text{ g Ni(C}_4\text{H}_7\text{N}_2\text{O}_2)_2 \times \frac{1 \text{ mol Ni(C}_4\text{H}_7\text{N}_2\text{O}_2)_2}{288.9 \text{ g Ni(C}_4\text{H}_7\text{N}_2\text{O}_2)_2} = 7.13 \times 10^{-4} \text{ mol Ni(C}_4\text{H}_7\text{N}_2\text{O}_2)_2$$

Because 1 mol of $Ni(C_4H_7N_2O_2)_2$ is ultimately produced from 1 mol of NiS, the amount of NiS in the sample must also have been $7.13 \times 10^{-4}$ mol.

With the amount of NiS known, we calculate the mass of NiS.

$$7.13 \times 10^{-4} \text{ mol NiS} \times \frac{90.76 \text{ g NiS}}{1 \text{ mol NiS}} = 0.0647 \text{ g NiS}$$

Finally, the mass percent of NiS in the 0.468-g sample is

$$\text{Mass percent NiS} = \frac{0.0647 \text{ g NiS}}{0.468 \text{ g sample}} \times 100\% = \boxed{13.8\% \text{ NiS}}$$

**Think about Your Answer** For an analytical procedure to be used, the reactants must be completely converted to products and the product being measured must be isolated without losses in handling. This calls for very careful experimental techniques.

**Check Your Understanding**

One method for determining the purity of a sample of titanium(IV) oxide, $TiO_2$, an important industrial chemical, is to react the sample with bromine trifluoride.

$$3 \text{ TiO}_2(s) + 4 \text{ BrF}_3(\ell) \rightarrow 3 \text{ TiF}_4(s) + 2 \text{ Br}_2(\ell) + 3 \text{ O}_2(g)$$

This reaction is known to occur completely and quantitatively. That is, all of the oxygen in $TiO_2$ is evolved as $O_2$. Suppose 2.367 g of a $TiO_2$-containing sample evolves 0.143 g of $O_2$. What is the mass percent of $TiO_2$ in the sample?

## Determining the Formula of a Compound by Combustion

The empirical formula of a compound can be determined if the percent composition of the compound is known [◀ Section 2.10]. But where do the percent composition data come from? One chemical method that works well for compounds that burn in oxygen is analysis by combustion. In this technique, each element in the compound combines with oxygen to produce the appropriate oxide.

Consider an analysis of the hydrocarbon methane, $CH_4$. A balanced equation for the combustion of methane shows that every carbon atom in the original compound appears as $CO_2$ and every hydrogen atom appears in the form of water. In other words, for every mole of $CO_2$ observed, there must have been one mole of carbon in the unknown compound. Similarly, for every mole of $H_2O$ observed from combustion, there must have been *two* moles of H atoms in the unknown compound.

$$CH_4(g) + 2 O_2(g) \longrightarrow CO_2(g) + 2 H_2O(\ell)$$

In the combustion experiment gaseous carbon dioxide and water are separated (as illustrated in Figure 4.7) and their masses determined. From these masses it is possible to calculate the amounts of C and H in $CO_2$ and $H_2O$, respectively and the

**FIGURE 4.7 Combustion analysis of a hydrocarbon.** If a compound containing C and H is burned in oxygen, $CO_2$ and $H_2O$ are formed, and the mass of each can be determined. The $H_2O$ is absorbed by magnesium perchlorate, and the $CO_2$ is absorbed by finely divided NaOH. The mass of each absorbent before and after combustion gives the masses of $CO_2$ and $H_2O$. Only a few milligrams of a combustible compound are needed for analysis.

ratio of amounts of C and H in a sample of the original compound can then be found. This ratio gives the empirical formula.

● **Finding an Empirical Formula by Chemical Analysis** Finding the empirical formula of a compound by chemical analysis always uses the following procedure:

1. The unknown but pure compound is converted in a chemical reaction into known products.
2. The reaction products are isolated, and the amount of each is determined.
3. The amount of each product is related to the amount of each element in the original compound.
4. The empirical formula is determined from the relative amounts of elements in the original compound.

◉WL    **INTERACTIVE EXAMPLE 4.4** Using Combustion Analysis
to Determine the Formula of a Hydrocarbon

**Problem** When 1.125 g of a liquid hydrocarbon, $C_xH_y$, was burned in an apparatus like that shown in Figure 4.7, 3.447 g of $CO_2$ and 1.647 g of $H_2O$ were produced. In a separate experiment the molar mass of the compound was found to be 86.2 g/mol. Determine the empirical and molecular formulas for the unknown hydrocarbon, $C_xH_y$.

**What Do You Know?** You know the mass of the hydrocarbon, the fact that it contains only C and H, and the molar mass of this compound. You are also provided with the masses of $H_2O$ and $CO_2$ formed when the hydrocarbon is burned. You will need the molar masses of the three compounds in this calculation.

**Strategy** The strategy to solve this problem is outlined in the diagram below and the Strategy Map for Example 4.4.

The steps in sequence are as follows:

•    Calculate the amount of $CO_2$ and $H_2O$ and from these values calculate the amounts of C and H.

•    Determine the lowest whole-number ratio of amounts of C and H. This gives you the subscripts for C and H in the empirical formula.

•    Compare the molar mass of the hydrocarbon with the empirical formula to determine the molecular formula.

**Solution** The amounts of $CO_2$ and $H_2O$ isolated from the combustion are

$$3.447 \text{ g } CO_2 \times \frac{1 \text{ mol } CO_2}{44.010 \text{ g } CO_2} = 0.07832 \text{ mol } CO_2$$

$$1.647 \text{ g } H_2O \times \frac{1 \text{ mol } H_2O}{18.015 \text{ g } H_2O} = 0.09142 \text{ mol } H_2O$$

For every mole of $CO_2$ isolated, 1 mol of C must have been present in the unknown compound.

$$0.07832 \text{ mol } CO_2 \times \frac{1 \text{ mol C in unknown}}{1 \text{ mol } CO_2} = 0.07832 \text{ mol C}$$

For every mole of $H_2O$ isolated, 2 mol of H must have been present in the unknown.

$$0.09142 \; \text{mol } H_2O \times \frac{2 \text{ mol H in unknown}}{1 \text{ mol } H_2O} = 0.1828 \text{ mol H}$$

The original 1.125-g sample of compound therefore contained 0.07832 mol of C and 0.1828 mol of H. To determine the empirical formula of the unknown, we find the ratio of moles of H to moles of C [◄ Section 2.10].

$$\frac{0.1828 \text{ mol H}}{0.07832 \text{ mol C}} = \frac{2.335 \text{ mol H}}{1.000 \text{ mol C}}$$

The empirical formula gives the simplest *whole-number* ratio. The translation of this ratio (2.335/1) to a whole-number ratio can usually be done quickly by trial and error. Multiplying the numerator and denominator by 3 gives 7/3. So, we know the ratio is 7 mol H to 3 mol C, which means the empirical formula of the hydrocarbon is $C_3H_7$.

Comparing the experimental molar mass with the molar mass calculated for the empirical formula,

$$\frac{\text{Experimental molar mass}}{\text{Molar mass of } C_3H_7} = \frac{86.2 \text{ g/mol}}{43.1 \text{ g/mol}} = \frac{2}{1}$$

we find that the molecular formula is twice the empirical formula. That is, the molecular formula is $(C_3H_7)_2$, or $C_6H_{14}$.

**Think about Your Answer** As noted in Problem-Solving Tip 2.3 (page 90), for problems of this type be sure to use data with enough significant figures to give accurate atom ratios. Finally, note that the determination of the molecular formula does not end the problem for a chemist. In this case, the formula $C_6H_{14}$ is appropriate for several distinctly different compounds. Two of the five compounds having this formula are shown here:

To determine the identity of the unknown compound, more laboratory experiments have to be done. One option is to use an NMR spectrometer, as pictured in Figure 4.4, or to compare the properties of the unknown with values listed in the chemical literature.

**Check Your Understanding**

A 0.523-g sample of the unknown compound $C_xH_y$ was burned in air to give 1.612 g of $CO_2$ and 0.7425 g of $H_2O$. A separate experiment gave a molar mass for $C_xH_y$ of 114 g/mol. Determine the empirical and molecular formulas for the hydrocarbon.

## EXAMPLE 4.5 Using Combustion Analysis to Determine an Empirical Formula of a Compound Containing C, H, and O

**Problem** Suppose you isolate an acid from clover leaves and know that it contains only the elements C, H, and O. Heating 0.513 g of the acid in oxygen produces 0.501 g of $CO_2$ and 0.103 g of $H_2O$. What is the empirical formula of the acid $C_xH_yO_z$?

---

**Strategy Map 4.4**

**PROBLEM**
Determine **empirical** and **molecular** **formulas** of a hydrocarbon.

↓

**DATA/INFORMATION**
- **Masses of $CO_2$ and $H_2O$** from combustion of given mass of $C_xH_y$
- **Molar mass** of **unknown**

STEP 1. Calculate **amounts** of $CO_2$ and $H_2O$.

**Amounts of $CO_2$ and $H_2O$**

STEP 2. Calculate **amount** of C and H from amounts of $CO_2$ and $H_2O$, respectively.

**Amounts of C and H** in unknown compound

STEP 3. Find **whole-number ratio** of amounts of C and H.

$C_xH_y$ = empirical formula

STEP 4. Determine ratio of **experimental molar mass** to **empirical formula mass**.

**Molecular formula $[C_xH_y]_n$**

**What Do You Know?** You know the mass of the compound and the fact that it contains only C, H, and O. You are also provided with the masses of $H_2O$ and $CO_2$ formed when the hydrocarbon is burned.

**Strategy** In order to determine the empirical formula, you need to determine the amounts (moles) of C, H, and O in the unknown compound. Follow the steps outlined below.

- Determine the amounts of C and H following the procedure in Example 4.4.

- Determine the masses of C and H from the amounts of C and H.

- The mass of O is the mass of the sample minus the masses of C and H.

- From the mass of O determine the amount of O.

- Finally, determine the smallest whole number ratio between the amounts of the three elements. This determines the subscripts for the elements in the empirical formula.

**Solution** The first step is to determine the amounts of C and H in the sample.

$$0.501 \text{ g CO}_2 \times \frac{1 \text{ mol CO}_2}{44.01 \text{ g CO}_2} \times \frac{1 \text{ mol C}}{1 \text{ mol CO}_2} = 0.0114 \text{ mol C}$$

$$0.103 \text{ g H}_2\text{O} \times \frac{1 \text{ mol H}_2\text{O}}{18.02 \text{ g H}_2\text{O}} \times \frac{2 \text{ mol H}}{1 \text{ mol H}_2\text{O}} = 0.0114 \text{ mol H}$$

From these amounts, you can determine the mass of C and the mass of H in the sample.

$$0.0114 \text{ mol C} \times \frac{12.01 \text{ g C}}{1 \text{ mol C}} = 0.137 \text{ g C}$$

$$0.0114 \text{ mol H} \times \frac{1.008 \text{ g H}}{1 \text{ mol H}} = 0.0115 \text{ g H}$$

Using the mass of the original sample and the masses of C and H in the sample, you can now determine the mass of O in the sample. From this, you can find the amount of O in the sample.

$$\text{Mass of sample} = 0.513 \text{ g} = 0.137 \text{ g C} + 0.0115 \text{ g H} + x \text{ g O}$$

$$\text{Mass of O} = 0.365 \text{ g O}$$

$$0.365 \text{ g O} \times \frac{1 \text{ mol O}}{16.00 \text{ g O}} = 0.0228 \text{ mol O}$$

To find the mole ratios of elements, divide the number of moles of each element by the smallest amount present. Because both C and H are present in the same amount in the sample, you know their ratio is 1 C : 1 H. What about O?

$$\frac{0.0228 \text{ mol O}}{0.0114 \text{ mol C}} = \frac{2 \text{ mol O}}{1 \text{ mol C}}$$

The mole ratios show that, for every C atom in the molecule, one H atom and two O atoms occur. The empirical formula of the acid is therefore $CHO_2$.

**Think about Your Answer** If the molar mass of the unknown compound were known, you would then be able to derive the molecular formula of the compound.

---

**Check Your Understanding**

A 0.1342-g sample of a compound composed of C, H, and O ($C_xH_yO_z$) was burned in oxygen and 0.240 g of $CO_2$ and 0.0982 g of $H_2O$ was isolated. What is the empirical formula of the compound? If the experimentally determined molar mass is 74.1 g/mol, what is the molecular formula of the compound?

---

**REVIEW & CHECK FOR SECTION 4.4**

A 0.509-g sample of an unknown organic compound containing C, H, and O was burned in air to give 1.316 g of $CO_2$ and 0.269 g of $H_2O$. What is the empirical formula for this compound?

(a)  CHO             (b)  $C_2H_2O$          (c)  $C_4H_4O$           (d)  $CHO_4$

## 4.5  Measuring Concentrations of Compounds in Solution

Most chemical studies require quantitative measurements, including experiments involving aqueous solutions. When doing such experiments, we continue to use balanced equations and moles, but we measure volumes of solutions rather than masses of solids, liquids, or gases. Solution concentration, expressed as molarity, relates the volume of solution in liters to the amount of substance in moles.

### Solution Concentration: Molarity

The concept of concentration is useful in many contexts. For example, about 5,628,000 people live in Wisconsin (as of July 2008), and the state has a land area of roughly 56,000 square miles; therefore, the average concentration of people is about $(5.6 \times 10^6$ people$/5.6 \times 10^4$ square miles) or $1.0 \times 10^2$ people per square mile. In chemistry the amount of solute dissolved in a given volume of solution, the concentration of the solution, can be found in the same way. A useful unit of solute concentration, $c$, is **molarity**, which is defined as amount of solute per liter of solution.

$$\text{Molarity of } x \ (c_x) = \frac{\text{amount of solute } x \text{ (mol)}}{\text{volume of solution (L)}} \qquad (4.2)$$

For example, if 58.4 g (1.00 mol) of NaCl is dissolved in enough water to give a total solution volume of 1.00 L, the molarity, $c$, is 1.00 mol/L. This is often abbreviated as 1.00 M, where the capital "M" stands for "moles per liter." Another common notation is to place the formula of the compound in square brackets (for example, [NaCl]); this implies that the concentration of the solute in moles per liter of solution is being specified.

$$c_{NaCl} = [\text{NaCl}] = 1.00 \text{ mol/L} = 1.00 \text{ M}$$

It is important to notice that molarity refers to the amount of solute *per liter of solution* and not per liter of solvent. If one liter of water is added to one mole of a solid compound, the final volume will not be exactly one liter, and the final concentration will not be exactly one mol/L (Figure 4.8). When making solutions of a given concentration, it is always the case that we dissolve the solute in a volume of

• **Molar and Molarity** Chemists use "molar" as an adjective to describe a solution. We use "molarity" as a noun. For example, we refer to a 0.1 molar solution or say the solution has a molarity of 0.1 mole per liter.

Volume of water remaining when 1.00 L of water was used to make 1.00 L of a solution

1.00 L of 0.100 M CuSO$_4$

25.0 g or 0.100 mol of CuSO$_4$ · 5 H$_2$O

© Cengage Learning/Charles D. Winters

**FIGURE 4.8  Volume of solution versus volume of solvent.** To make a 0.100 M solution of CuSO$_4$, 25.0 g or 0.100 mol of CuSO$_4$ · 5 H$_2$O (the blue crystalline solid) was placed in a 1.00-L volumetric flask. For this photo, we measured out exactly 1.00 L of water, which was slowly added to the volumetric flask containing 25.0 g of CuSO$_4$ · 5 H$_2$O. When enough water had been added so that the solution volume was exactly 1.00 L, approximately 8 mL (the quantity in the small graduated cylinder) was left over from the original 1.00 L of water. This emphasizes that molar concentrations are defined as moles of solute per liter of solution and not per liter of water or other solvent.

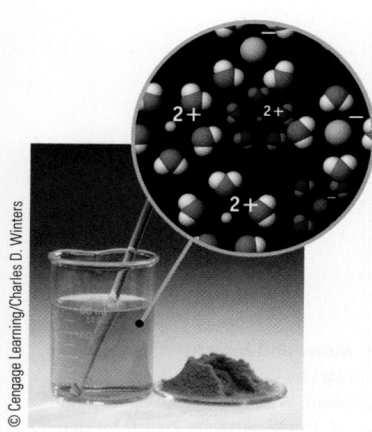

**Ion concentrations for a soluble ionic compound.** Here, 1 mol of $CuCl_2$ dissociates to 1 mol of $Cu^{2+}$ ions and 2 mol of $Cl^-$ ions. Therefore, the $Cl^-$ concentration is twice the concentration calculated for $CuCl_2$.

solvent smaller than the desired volume of solution, then add solvent until the final solution volume is reached.

Potassium permanganate, $KMnO_4$, which was used at one time as a germicide in the treatment of burns, is a shiny, purple-black solid that dissolves readily in water to give a deep purple solution. Suppose 0.435 g of $KMnO_4$ has been dissolved in enough water to give 250. mL of solution (Figure 4.9). What is the concentration of $KMnO_4$? The first step is to convert the mass of $KMnO_4$ to an amount (moles) of solute.

$$0.435 \text{ g } KMnO_4 \times \frac{1 \text{ mol } KMnO_4}{158.0 \text{ g } KMnO_4} = 0.00275 \text{ mol } KMnO_4$$

Now that the amount of $KMnO_4$ is known, this information can be combined with the volume of solution—which must be in liters—to give the concentration. Because 250. mL is equivalent to 0.250 L,

$$\text{Concentration of } KMnO_4 = c_{KMnO_4} = [KMnO_4] = \frac{0.00275 \text{ mol } KMnO_4}{0.250 \text{ L}} = 0.0110 \text{ M}$$

The $KMnO_4$ concentration is 0.0110 mol/L, or 0.0110 M. This is useful information, but it is often equally useful to know the concentration of each type of ion in a solution. Like all soluble ionic compounds, $KMnO_4$ dissociates completely into its ions, $K^+$ and $MnO_4^-$, when dissolved in water.

$$KMnO_4(aq) \longrightarrow K^+(aq) + MnO_4^-(aq)$$
100% dissociation

One mole of $KMnO_4$ provides 1 mol of $K^+$ ions and 1 mol of $MnO_4^-$ ions. Accordingly, 0.0110 M $KMnO_4$ gives a concentration of $K^+$ in the solution of 0.0110 M; similarly, the concentration of $MnO_4^-$ is also 0.0110 M.

Another example of ion concentrations is provided by the dissociation of $CuCl_2$.

$$CuCl_2(aq) \longrightarrow Cu^{2+}(aq) + 2 Cl^-(aq)$$
100% dissociation

If 0.10 mol of $CuCl_2$ is dissolved in enough water to make 1.0 L of solution, the concentration of the copper(II) ion is $[Cu^{2+}] = 0.10$ M. However, the concentration of chloride ions, $[Cl^-]$, is 0.20 M because the compound dissociates in water to provide 2 mol of $Cl^-$ ions for each mole of $CuCl_2$.

250-mL volumetric flask

0.435 g $KMnO_4$

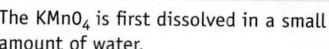

The $KMnO_4$ is first dissolved in a small amount of water.

Distilled water is added to fill the flask with solution just to the mark on the flask.

A mark on the neck of a volumetric flask indicates a volume of exactly 250. mL at 25 °C.

**FIGURE 4.9 Making a solution.** A 0.0110 M solution of $KMnO_4$ is made by adding enough water to 0.435 g of $KMnO_4$ to make 0.250 L of solution.

## EXAMPLE 4.6    Concentration

**Problem** If 25.3 g of sodium carbonate, $Na_2CO_3$, is dissolved in enough water to make 250. mL of solution, what is the concentration of $Na_2CO_3$? What are the concentrations of the $Na^+$ and $CO_3^{2-}$ ions?

**What Do You Know?** You know the mass of the solute, $Na_2CO_3$, and the volume of the solution. You will need the molar mass of $Na_2CO_3$ to calculate the amount of this compound.

**Strategy** The concentration (moles/L) of $Na_2CO_3$ is the amount of $Na_2CO_3$ (moles) divided by the volume (in liters). To determine the concentrations of the ions, recognize that one mole of this ionic compound contains two moles of $Na^+$ and one mole of $CO_3^{2-}$ ions.

$$Na_2CO_3(s) \rightarrow 2\ Na^+(aq) + CO_3^{2-}(aq)$$

**Solution** Let us first find the amount of $Na_2CO_3$.

$$25.3\ g\ Na_2CO_3 \times \frac{1\ mol\ Na_2CO_3}{106.0\ g\ Na_2CO_3} = 0.239\ mol\ Na_2CO_3$$

and then the concentration of $Na_2CO_3$,

$$\text{Concentration of } Na_2CO_3 = \frac{0.239\ mol\ Na_2CO_3}{0.250\ L} = 0.995\ mol/L$$

The ion concentrations follow from the knowledge that each mole of $Na_2CO_3$ produces 2 mol of $Na^+$ ions and 1 mol of $CO_3^{2-}$ ions.

$$0.955\ M\ Na_2CO_3(aq) \equiv 2 \times 0.955\ M\ Na^+(aq) + 0.955\ M\ CO_3^{2-}(aq)$$

That is, $[Na^+] = 1.91\ M$ and $[CO_3^{2-}] = 0.955\ M$.

**Think about Your Answer** Many chemical reactions are carried out in aqueous solution. The amount (moles) of a compound is readily calculated if you know the concentration and volume of solution.

### Check Your Understanding

Sodium bicarbonate, $NaHCO_3$, is used in baking powder formulations and in the manufacture of plastics and ceramics, among other things. If 26.3 g of the compound is dissolved in enough water to make 200. mL of solution, what is the concentration of $NaHCO_3$? What are the concentrations of the ions in solution?

## Preparing Solutions of Known Concentration

Chemists often have to prepare a given volume of solution of known concentration. There are two generally used ways to do this.

### Combining a Weighed Solute with the Solvent

Suppose you wish to prepare 2.00 L of a 1.50 M solution of $Na_2CO_3$. You have some solid $Na_2CO_3$ and distilled water. You also have a 2.00-L volumetric flask. To make the solution, you must weigh the required quantity of $Na_2CO_3$ as accurately as possible considering the number of significant figures desired for the concentration, carefully place all the solid in the volumetric flask, and then add some water to dissolve the solid. After the solid has dissolved completely, more water is added to bring the solution volume to 2.00 L. The solution then has the desired concentration and the volume specified.

But what mass of $Na_2CO_3$ is required to make 2.00 L of 1.50 M $Na_2CO_3$? First, calculate the amount of $Na_2CO_3$ required,

$$2.00\ L \times \frac{1.50\ mol\ Na_2CO_3}{1.00\ L\ solution} = 3.00\ mol\ Na_2CO_3\ required$$

● **Volumetric Flask** A volumetric flask is a special flask with a line marked on its neck (see page 36 and Figures 4.8 and 4.9). If the flask is filled with a solution to this line (at a given temperature), it contains precisely the volume of solution specified.

and then the mass in grams.

$$3.00 \text{ mol Na}_2\text{CO}_3 \times \frac{106.0 \text{ g Na}_2\text{CO}_3}{1 \text{ mol Na}_2\text{CO}_3} = 318 \text{ g Na}_2\text{CO}_3$$

Thus, to prepare the desired solution, you should dissolve 318 g of $Na_2CO_3$ in enough water to make 2.00 L of solution.

### Diluting a More Concentrated Solution

Another method of making a solution of a given concentration is to begin with a concentrated solution and add more solvent (usually water) until the desired, lower concentration is reached (Figure 4.10). Many of the solutions prepared for your laboratory course are probably made by this dilution method. It is more efficient to store a small volume of a concentrated solution and then, when needed, add water to make a much larger volume of a dilute solution.

Suppose you need 500. mL of 0.0010 M potassium dichromate, $K_2Cr_2O_7$, for use in chemical analysis. You have some 0.100 M $K_2Cr_2O_7$ solution available. To make the required 0.0010 M solution, place a measured volume of the more concentrated $K_2Cr_2O_7$ solution in a flask and then add water until the $K_2Cr_2O_7$ is contained in the appropriate, larger volume of water (Figure 4.10).

What volume of a 0.100 M $K_2Cr_2O_7$ solution must be diluted to make the 0.0010 M solution? If the volume and concentration of a solution are known, the amount of solute is also known. Therefore, the amount of $K_2Cr_2O_7$ that must be in the final dilute solution is

$$\text{Amount of } K_2Cr_2O_7 \text{ in dilute solution} = c_{K_2Cr_2O_7} \times V_{K_2Cr_2O_7} = \left(\frac{0.0010 \text{ mol}}{L}\right) \times (0.500 \text{ L})$$
$$= 0.00050 \text{ mol } K_2Cr_2O_7$$

The more concentrated solution containing this amount of $K_2Cr_2O_7$ must be placed in a 500.-mL flask and then diluted to the final volume. The volume of 0.100 M $K_2Cr_2O_7$ that must be transferred and diluted is 5.0 mL.

$$0.00050 \text{ mol } K_2Cr_2O_7 \times \frac{1.00 \text{ L}}{0.100 \text{ mol } K_2Cr_2O_7} = 0.0050 \text{ L or 5.0 mL}$$

Thus, to prepare 500. mL of 0.0010 M $K_2Cr_2O_7$, place 5.0 mL of 0.100 M $K_2Cr_2O_7$ in a 500.-mL flask and add water until a volume of 500. mL is reached (Figure 4.10).

5.00-mL pipet

500-mL volumetric flask

WATER

Photos © Cengage Learning/Charles D. Winters

0.100 M $K_2Cr_2O_7$

Use a 5.00-mL pipet to withdraw 5.00 mL of 0.100 M $K_2Cr_2O_7$ solution.

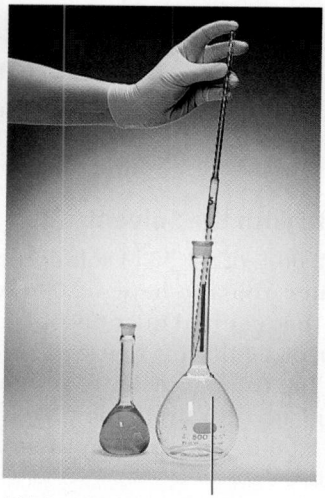

Add the 5.00-mL sample of 0.100 M $K_2Cr_2O_7$ solution to a 500-mL volumetric flask.

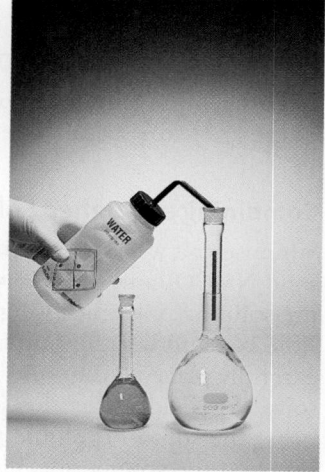

Fill the flask to the mark with distilled water to give 0.00100 M $K_2Cr_2O_7$ solution.

**FIGURE 4.10** **Making a solution by dilution.** Here, 5.00 mL of a $K_2Cr_2O_7$ solution is diluted to 500. mL. This means the solution is diluted by a factor of 100, from 0.100 M to 0.00100 M.

PROBLEM SOLVING TIP 4.3

There is a straightforward method to use for problems involving dilution. The central idea is that the amount of solute in the final, dilute solution has to be equal to the amount of solute taken from the more concentrated solution. If $c$ is the concentration (molarity) and $V$ is the volume (and the subscripts $d$ and $c$ identify the dilute and concentrated solutions, respectively), then the amount of solute in either solution (in the case of the $K_2Cr_2O_7$ example in the text) can be calculated as follows:

## Preparing a Solution by Dilution

(a) Amount of $K_2Cr_2O_7$ in the final dilute solution is

$$c_d \times V_d = 0.00050 \text{ mol}$$

(b) Amount of $K_2Cr_2O_7$ taken from the more concentrated solution is

$$c_c \times V_c = 0.00050 \text{ mol}$$

Because both $cV$ products are equal to the same amount of solute, we can use the following equation:

Amount in concentrated solution = Amount in dilute solution

$$c_c \times V_c = c_d \times V_d$$

This equation is valid for all cases in which a more concentrated solution is used to make a more dilute one.

## EXAMPLE 4.7    Preparing a Solution by Dilution

**Problem** What is the concentration of iron(III) ions in a solution prepared by diluting 1.00 mL of a 0.236 M solution of iron(III) nitrate to a volume of 100.0 mL?

**What Do I Know?** You know the initial concentration and volume and the final volume after dilution.

**Strategy** First calculate the amount of iron(III) ion in the 1.00-mL sample (amount = concentration × volume). The concentration of the ion in the final, dilute solution is equal to this amount of iron(III) divided by the new volume.

**Solution** The amount of iron(III) ion in the 1.00 mL sample is

$$\text{Amount of Fe}^{3+} = c_{Fe^{3+}}V_{Fe^{3+}} = \frac{0.236 \text{ mol Fe}^{3+}}{L} \times 1.00 \times 10^{-3} \text{ L} = 2.36 \times 10^{-4} \text{ mol Fe}^{3+}$$

This amount of iron(III) ion is distributed in the new volume of 100.0 mL, so the final concentration of the diluted solution is

$$c_{Fe^{3+}} = [\text{Fe}^{3+}] = \frac{2.36 \times 10^{-4} \text{ mol Fe}^{3+}}{0.1000 \text{ L}} = \boxed{2.36 \times 10^{-3} \text{ M}}$$

**Think about Your Answer** The sample has been diluted 100-fold, so we would expect the final concentration to be 1/100th of the initial value. See also Problem Solving Tip 4.3, which gives a quick and easy-to-use method for this calculation.

**Check Your Understanding**

An experiment calls for you to use 250. mL of 1.00 M NaOH, but you are given a large bottle of 2.00 M NaOH. Describe how to make the desired volume of 1.00 M NaOH.

---

**REVIEW & CHECK FOR SECTION 4.5**

1. A 1.71-g sample of $Ba(OH)_2(s)$ was dissolved in water to give 250 mL of solution. What is the $OH^-$ concentration in this solution?

    (a)  0.010 M          (b)  0.040 M          (c)  0.080 M          (d)  0.10 M

2. You have a 100.-mL volumetric flask containing 0.050 M HCl. A 2.0-mL sample of this solution was diluted to 10.0 mL. What is the concentration of HCl in the dilute solution?

    (a)  0.10 M          (b)  0.010 M          (c)  $1.0 \times 10^{-3}$ M          (d)  0.25 M

3. Which of the solutions below contains the greatest amount of $OH^-(aq)$?

    (a)  20 mL of 0.10 M NaOH                    (c)  10 mL of 0.25 M CsOH

    (b)  15 mL of 0.20 M KOH                    (d)  15 mL of 0.15 M LiOH

**A CLOSER LOOK**

## Serial Dilutions

We often find in the laboratory that a solution is too concentrated for the analytical technique we want to use. You might want to analyze a seawater sample for its chloride ion content, for instance. To obtain a solution with a chloride concentration of the proper magnitude for analysis by the Mohr method (Case Study, page 187), for example, you might want to dilute the sample, not once but several times.

Suppose you have 100.0 mL of a seawater sample that has an NaCl concentration of 0.550 mol/L. You transfer 10.00 mL of that sample to a 100.0-mL volumetric flask and fill to the mark with distilled water. You then transfer 5.00 mL of that diluted sample to another 100.0-mL flask and fill to the mark with distilled water. What is the NaCl concentration in the final 100.0-mL sample?

The original solution contains 0.550 mol/L of NaCl. If you remove 10.00 mL, you have removed

$$0.01000 \text{ L} \times 0.550 \text{ mol/L}$$
$$= 5.50 \times 10^{-3} \text{ mol NaCl}$$

and the concentration in 100.0 mL of the diluted solution is

$$c_{\text{NaCl}} = 5.50 \times 10^{-3} \text{ mol/0.1000 L}$$
$$= 5.50 \times 10^{-2} \text{ M}$$

or 1/10 of the concentration of the original solution (because we diluted the sample by a factor of 10).

Now we take 5.00 mL of the diluted solution and dilute that once again to 100.0 mL. The final concentration is

$$0.00500 \text{ L} \times 5.50 \times 10^{-2} \text{ mol/L}$$
$$= 2.75 \times 10^{-4} \text{ mol NaCl}$$

$$c_{\text{NaCl}} = 2.75 \times 10^{-4} \text{ mol/0.1000 L}$$
$$= 2.75 \times 10^{-3} \text{ M}$$

This is 1/200 of the concentration of the original solution.

A fair question at this point is why we did not just take 1 mL of the original solution and dilute to 200 mL. The answer is that there is

less error in using larger pipets such as 5.00- or 10.00-mL pipets rather than a 1.00-mL pipet. And then there is a limitation in available glassware. A 200.00-mL volumetric flask is not often available.

**Question:**
You have a 100.0-mL sample of a blue dye having a concentration of 0.36 M. You dilute a 10.0-mL sample of this to 100.0 mL and then a 2.00-mL sample of that solution to 100.0 mL. What is the final dye concentration?

**Answer: 7.2 × 10⁻⁴ M**

Transfer **10.0 mL**     Transfer **5.00 mL**

NaCl concentration 0.550 mol/L

Fill to mark with distilled water.

Fill to mark with distilled water.

1/10 original concentration

1/200 original concentration

**Original Solution**
100.0-mL seawater sample

10.0-mL sample diluted to 100.0 mL

5.00-mL sample diluted to 100.0 mL

---

**go Chemistry**

**Module 9: pH** covers concepts in this section.

## 4.6  pH, a Concentration Scale for Acids and Bases

A sample of vinegar, which contains the weak acid acetic acid, has a hydronium ion concentration of $1.6 \times 10^{-3}$ M and "pure" rainwater has $[H_3O^+] = 2.5 \times 10^{-6}$ M. These small values can be expressed using scientific notation, but a more convenient way to express such numbers is the logarithmic pH scale.

The pH of a solution is the negative of the base-10 logarithm of the hydronium ion concentration.

$$pH = -\log[H_3O^+] \tag{4.3}$$

● **Logarithms** Numbers less than 1 have negative logs. Defining pH as $-\log[H_3O^+]$ produces a positive number. See Appendix A for a discussion of logs.

Taking vinegar, pure water, blood, and ammonia as examples,

pH of vinegar $= -\log (1.6 \times 10^{-3} \text{ M}) = -(-2.80) = 2.80$

pH of pure water (at 25 °C) $= -\log (1.0 \times 10^{-7} \text{ M}) = -(-7.00) = 7.00$

pH of blood $= -\log (4.0 \times 10^{-8} \text{ M}) = -(-7.40) = 7.40$

pH of household ammonia $= -\log (4.3 \times 10^{-12} \text{ M}) = -(-11.37) = 11.37$

you see that something you recognize as acidic has a relatively low pH, whereas ammonia, a common base, has a very low hydronium ion concentration and a high pH.

**FIGURE 4.11** **pH values of some common substances.** Here, the "bar" is colored red at one end and blue at the other. These are the colors of litmus paper, commonly used in the laboratory to decide whether a solution is acidic (litmus is red) or basic (litmus is blue).

*For aqueous solutions at 25 °C, acids have pH values less than 7, bases have values greater than 7, and a pH of 7 represents a neutral solution* (Figure 4.11). Blood, which your common sense tells you is likely to be neither acidic nor basic, has a pH slightly greater than 7.

Suppose you know the pH of a solution. To find the hydronium ion concentration you take the antilog of the pH. That is,

$$[H_3O^+] = 10^{-pH} \tag{4.4}$$

For example, the pH of a diet soda is 3.12, and the hydronium ion concentration of the solution is

$$[H_3O^+] = 10^{-3.12} = 7.6 \times 10^{-4} \text{ M}$$

The approximate pH of a solution may be determined using any of a variety of dyes. Litmus paper contains a dye extracted from a type of lichen, but many other dyes are also available (Figure 4.12a). A more accurate measurement of pH is done with a pH meter such as that shown in Figure 4.12b. Here, a pH electrode is immersed in the solution to be tested, and the pH is read from the instrument.

● **Logs and Your Calculator** All scientific calculators have a key marked "log." To find an antilog, use the key marked "10$^x$" or the inverse log. In determining [H$_3$O$^+$] from a pH, when you enter the value of $x$ for 10$^x$, make sure it has a negative sign.

**FIGURE 4.12** **Determining pH.**

**(a)** Some household products. Each solution contains a few drops of a universal indicator, a mixture of several acid–base indicators. A color of yellow or red indicates a pH less than 7. A green to purple color indicates a pH greater than 7.

**(b)** The pH of a soda is measured with a modern pH meter. Soft drinks are often quite acidic, owing to dissolved $CO_2$ and other ingredients.

● **Weak and Strong Acids and Hydronium Ion Concentration**
Because a weak acid (e.g., acetic acid) does not ionize completely in water, the hydronium ion concentration in an aqueous solution of a weak acid does not equal the concentration of the acid (as is the case for strong acids) but must be calculated using the principles of chemical equilibrium (▶ Chapter 17).

## EXAMPLE 4.8   pH of Solutions

**Problem**

(a)   Lemon juice has $[H_3O^+] = 0.0032$ M. What is its pH?

(b)   Seawater has a pH of 8.30. What is the hydronium ion concentration of this solution?

(c)   A solution of nitric acid has a concentration of 0.0056 mol/L. What is the pH of this solution?

**What Do You Know?**  In part (a) you are given a concentration and asked to calculate the pH, whereas the opposite is true in (b). For part (c), however, you first must recognize that $HNO_3$ is a strong acid and is 100% ionized in water.

**Strategy**  Use Equation 4.3 to calculate pH from the $H_3O^+$ concentration and Equation 4.4 to find $[H_3O^+]$ from the pH.

**Solution**

(a)   Lemon juice: Because the hydronium ion concentration is known, the pH is found using Equation 4.3.

$$pH = -\log\,[H_3O^+] = -\log\,(3.2 \times 10^{-3}) = -(-2.49) = 2.49$$

(b)   Seawater: Here pH = 8.30. Therefore,

$$[H_3O^+] = 10^{-pH} = 10^{-8.30} = 5.0 \times 10^{-9}\ M$$

(c)   Nitric acid: Nitric acid, a strong acid (Table 3.1, page 129), is completely ionized in aqueous solution. Because the concentration of $HNO_3$ is 0.0056 mol/L, the ion concentrations are

$$[H_3O^+] = [NO_3^-] = 0.0056\ M$$

$$pH = -\log\,[H_3O^+] = -\log\,(0.0056\ M) = 2.25$$

**Think about Your Answer**  Our answers all agree with the fact that, at 25 °C, solutions with $[H_3O^+] > 10^{-7}$ M have pH < 7, and those with $[H_3O^+] < 10^{-7}$ have pH > 7. A comment on logarithms and significant figures (Appendix A) is useful. The number to the left of the decimal point in a logarithm is called the *characteristic*, and the number to the right is the *mantissa*. The mantissa has as many significant figures as the number whose log was found. For example, the logarithm of $3.2 \times 10^{-3}$ (two significant figures) is 2.49. (The significant figures are the two numbers to the right of the decimal point.)

**Check Your Understanding**

(a)   What is the pH of a solution of HCl in which $[HCl] = 2.6 \times 10^{-2}$ M?

(b)   What is the hydronium ion concentration in orange juice with a pH of 3.80?

---

**REVIEW & CHECK FOR SECTION 4.6**

1.   Which of the solutions listed below has the lowest pH?

(a)   0.10 M HCl                    (c)   $2.5 \times 10^{-5}$ M $HNO_3$

(b)   0.10 M NaOH                 (d)   pure $H_2O$

2.   A 0.365-g sample of HCl is dissolved in enough water to give $2.00 \times 10^2$ mL of solution. What is the pH?

(a)   2.000                         (c)   1.301

(b)   0.0500                        (d)   1.000

## 4.7 Stoichiometry of Reactions in Aqueous Solution

### Solution Stoichiometry

Suppose we want to know what mass of $CaCO_3$ is required to react completely with 25 mL of 0.750 M HCl. The first step in finding the answer is to write a balanced equation. In this case, we have a gas-forming exchange reaction involving a metal carbonate and an aqueous acid (Figure 4.13).

$$CaCO_3(s) + 2\ HCl(aq) \rightarrow CaCl_2(aq) + H_2O(\ell) + CO_2(g)$$
$$\text{metal carbonate} + \text{acid} \rightarrow \text{salt} + \text{water} + \text{carbon dioxide}$$

This problem differs from the previous stoichiometry problems in that the quantity of one reactant (HCl) is given as a volume of a solution of known concentration instead of as a mass in grams. Because our balanced equation is written in terms of amounts (moles), our first step will be to determine the number of moles of HCl present from the known information so that we can relate the amount of HCl available to the amount of $CaCO_3$

$$\text{Amount of HCl} = c_{HCl}V_{HCl} = \frac{0.750 \text{ mol HCl}}{1 \text{ L HCl}} \times 0.025 \text{ L HCl} = 0.019 \text{ mol HCl}$$

This is then related to the amount of $CaCO_3$ required using the stoichiometric factor from the balanced equation.

$$0.019 \text{ mol HCl} \times \frac{1 \text{ mol CaCO}_3}{2 \text{ mol HCl}} = 0.0094 \text{ mol CaCO}_3$$

Finally, the amount of $CaCO_3$ is converted to a mass in grams using the molar mass of $CaCO_3$ as the conversion factor.

$$0.0094 \text{ mol CaCO}_3 \times \frac{100. \text{ g CaCO}_3}{1 \text{ mol CaCO}_3} = 0.94 \text{ g CaCO}_3$$

If you follow the general scheme outlined in Problem-Solving Tip 4.4 and pay attention to the units on the numbers, you can successfully carry out any kind of stoichiometry calculations involving concentrations.

**FIGURE 4.13 A commercial remedy for excess stomach acid.** The tablet contains calcium carbonate, which reacts with hydrochloric acid, the acid present in the digestive system. The most obvious product is $CO_2$ gas, but $CaCl_2(aq)$ is also produced.

© Cengage Learning/Charles D. Winters

**PROBLEM SOLVING TIP 4.4**

In Problem-Solving Tip 4.1, you learned about a general approach to stoichiometry problems. We can now modify that scheme for a reaction involving solutions such as $x$ A(aq) + $y$ B(aq) → products.

## Stoichiometry Calculations Involving Solutions

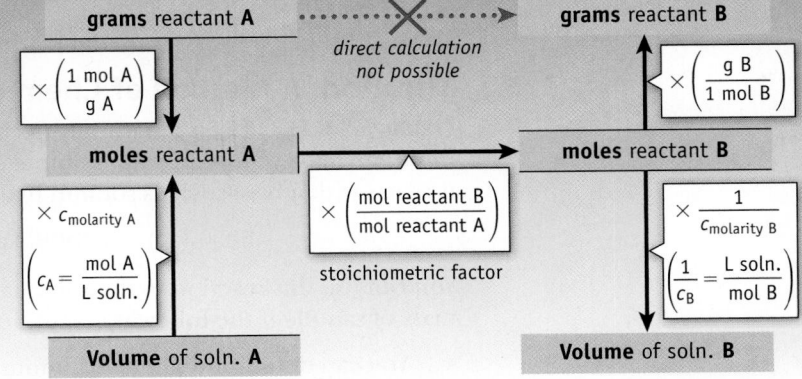

**Strategy Map** 4.9

**PROBLEM**

Calculate **volume of HCl solution** required to consume **given mass** of a **reactant (Zn)**

↓

**DATA/INFORMATION**

- **Mass** of **Zn**
- **Concentration** of **HCl**
- Balanced equation

↓

STEP 1. Write balanced equation.

↓

Balanced equation is **given**

↓

STEP 2. Amount reactant (mol) = mass × (1 mol/molar mass).

↓

**Amount** of **Zn**

↓

STEP 3. Use **stoichiometric factor** to relate moles Zn to amount (mol) acid required.

↓

**Amount** of acid required **(mol)**

↓

STEP 4. Volume of acid required = mol HCl required × (1 L/mol HCl).

↓

**Volume** of acid required **(L)**

 **INTERACTIVE EXAMPLE 4.9** Stoichiometry of a Reaction in Solution

**Problem** Metallic zinc reacts with aqueous HCl.

$$Zn(s) + 2\,HCl(aq) \rightarrow ZnCl_2(aq) + H_2(g)$$

What volume of 2.50 M HCl, in milliliters, is required to convert 11.8 g of Zn completely to products?

**What Do You Know?** The balanced equation for the reaction of Zn and HCl(aq) is provided. You know the mass of zinc and the concentration of HCl(aq).

**Strategy**

- Calculate the amount of zinc.

- Use a stoichiometric factor (= 2 mol HCl/1 mol Zn) to relate amount of HCl required to amount of Zn available.

- Calculate the volume of HCl solution from the amount of HCl and its concentration.

**Solution** Begin by calculating the amount of Zn.

$$11.8\ \text{g Zn} \times \frac{1\ \text{mol Zn}}{65.38\ \text{g Zn}} = 0.180\ \text{mol Zn}$$

Use the stoichiometric factor to calculate the amount of HCl required.

$$0.180\ \text{mol Zn} \times \frac{2\ \text{mol HCl}}{1\ \text{mol Zn}} = 0.360\ \text{mol HCl}$$

Use the amount of HCl and the solution concentration to calculate the volume.

$$0.360\ \text{mol HCl} \times \frac{1.00\ \text{L solution}}{2.50\ \text{mol HCl}} = 0.144\ \text{L HCl}$$

The answer is requested in units of milliliters, so we convert the volume to milliliters and find that 144 mL of 2.50 M HCl is required to convert 11.8 g of Zn completely to products.

**Think about Your Answer** You began with much less than 1 mol of zinc, and the concentration of the HCl solution is 2.50 M. Because the reaction requires 2 mol HCl/1 mol Zn, it makes sense that your answer should be significantly below 1 L of solution needed. Notice also that this is a redox reaction in which zinc is oxidized (oxidation number changes from 0 to +2) and hydrogen, in HCl(aq), is reduced (its oxidation number changes from +1 to 0).

**Check Your Understanding**

If you combine 75.0 mL of 0.350 M HCl and an excess of $Na_2CO_3$, what mass of $CO_2$, in grams, is produced?

$$Na_2CO_3(s) + 2\,HCl(aq) \rightarrow 2\,NaCl(aq) + H_2O(\ell) + CO_2(g)$$

## Titration: A Method of Chemical Analysis

Oxalic acid, $H_2C_2O_4$, is a naturally occurring acid. Suppose you are asked to determine the mass of this acid in an impure sample. Because the compound is an acid, it reacts with a base such as sodium hydroxide.

$$H_2C_2O_4(aq) + 2\,NaOH(aq) \rightarrow Na_2C_2O_4(aq) + 2\,H_2O(\ell)$$

You can use this reaction to determine the quantity of oxalic acid present in a given mass of sample if the following conditions are met:

- You can determine when the amount of sodium hydroxide added is just enough to react with all the oxalic acid present in solution.
- You know the concentration of the sodium hydroxide solution and volume that has been added at exactly the point of complete reaction.

**(a)**

Flask containing aqueous solution of sample being analyzed and an indicator

Buret containing aqueous NaOH of accurately known concentration.

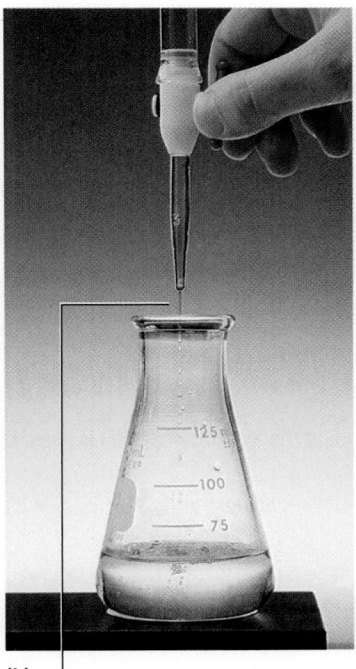

**(b)**

A solution of NaOH is added slowly to the sample being analyzed.

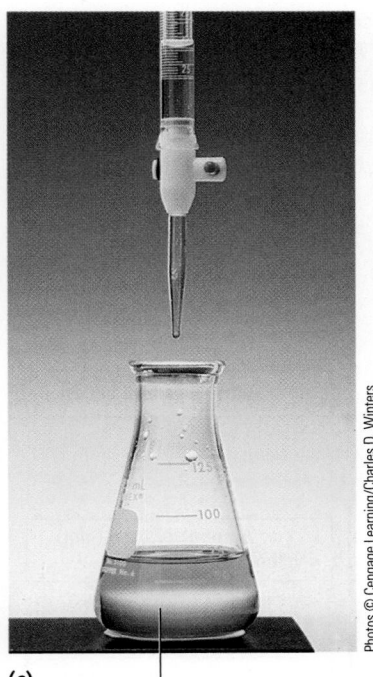

**(c)**

When the amount of NaOH added from the buret equals the amount of $H_3O^+$ supplied by the acid being analyzed, the dye (indicator) changes color.

Photos © Cengage Learning/Charles D. Winters

**FIGURE 4.14 Titration of an acid in aqueous solution with a base. (a)** A buret, a volumetric measuring device calibrated in divisions of 0.1 mL (and consequently read to the nearest 0.01 mL), is filled with an aqueous solution of a base of known concentration. **(b)** Base is added slowly from the buret to the solution containing the acid being analyzed and an indicator. **(c)** A change in the color of the indicator signals the equivalence point. (The indicator used here is phenolphthalein.)

These conditions are fulfilled in a titration, a procedure illustrated in Figure 4.14. The solution containing oxalic acid is placed in a flask along with an acid–base indicator, a dye that changes color when the pH of the reaction solution reaches a certain value. Aqueous sodium hydroxide of accurately known concentration is placed in a buret. The sodium hydroxide in the buret is added slowly to the acid solution in the flask. As long as some acid is present in solution, all the base supplied from the buret is consumed, the solution remains acidic, and the indicator color is unchanged. At some point, however, the amount of $OH^-$ added exactly equals the amount of $H_3O^+$ that can be supplied by the acid. This is called the **equivalence point**. As soon as the slightest excess of base has been added beyond the equivalence point, the solution becomes basic, and the indicator changes color (see Figure 4.14). Example 4.10 shows how to use the equivalence point and the other information to determine the percentage of oxalic acid in a mixture.

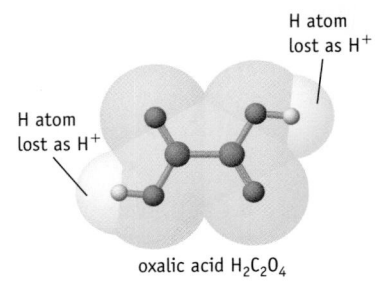

H atom lost as $H^+$

H atom lost as $H^+$

oxalic acid $H_2C_2O_4$

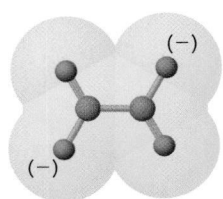

(−)

(−)

oxalate anion $C_2O_4{}^{2-}$

**Oxalic acid.** Oxalic acid has two groups that can supply an $H^+$ ion to solution. Hence, 1 mol of the acid requires 2 mol of NaOH for complete reaction.

## ⓦWL  INTERACTIVE EXAMPLE 4.10  Acid–Base Titration

**Problem** A 1.034-g sample of impure oxalic acid is dissolved in water and an acid–base indicator added. The sample requires 34.47 mL of 0.485 M NaOH to reach the equivalence point. What is the mass of oxalic acid, and what is its mass percent in the sample?

**What Do You Know?** You know the mass of oxalic acid (the formula is $H_2C_2O_4$) and the volume and concentration of NaOH solution used in the titration.

**Strategy Map 4.10**

**PROBLEM**

Calculate the **mass percent of acid** in an impure sample. Determine the **acid content** using an *acid-base titration*.

↓

**DATA/INFORMATION**

- **Mass** of impure sample containing *acid*.
- **Volume** and **concentration** of *base* used in titration.

STEP 1. Write balanced equation.

**Balanced equation** for reaction of **acid** (oxalic acid) with **base** (NaOH)

STEP 2. **Amount** of base (mol) = volume (L) × (mol/L).

**Amount of base** (mol)

STEP 3. Use a **stoichiometric factor** to relate amount of base (mol) to amount (mol) of acid.

**Amount of acid** (mol) in impure sample

STEP 4. **Mass** of acid in sample = mol acid × (g/mol).

**Mass of acid** in impure sample

STEP 5. **Mass %** of acid in sample = (g acid/g sample)100%.

**Mass % acid** in impure sample

**Strategy**

- Write a balanced chemical equation for this acid–base reaction.
- Calculate the amount of NaOH used in the titration from its volume and concentration.
- Use the stoichiometric factor defined by the equation to determine the amount of $H_2C_2O_4$.
- Calculate the mass of $H_2C_2O_4$ from the amount and its molar mass.
- Determine the percent by mass of $H_2C_2O_4$ in the sample.

**Solution** The balanced equation for the reaction of NaOH and $H_2C_2O_4$ is

$$H_2C_2O_4(aq) + 2\ NaOH(aq) \rightarrow Na_2C_2O_4(aq) + 2\ H_2O(\ell)$$

and the amount of NaOH is given by

$$\text{Amount of NaOH} = c_{NaOH} \times V_{NaOH} = \frac{0.485\ \text{mol NaOH}}{L} \times 0.03447\ L = 0.0167\ \text{mol NaOH}$$

The balanced equation for the reaction shows that 1 mol of oxalic acid requires 2 mol of sodium hydroxide. This is the required stoichiometric factor to obtain the amount of oxalic acid present.

$$0.0167\ \text{mol NaOH} \times \frac{1\ \text{mol}\ H_2C_2O_4}{2\ \text{mol NaOH}} = 0.00836\ \text{mol}\ H_2C_2O_4$$

The mass of oxalic acid is found from the amount of the acid and its molar mass.

$$0.00836\ \text{mol}\ H_2C_2O_4 \times \frac{90.04\ g\ H_2C_2O_4}{1\ \text{mol}\ H_2C_2O_4} = 0.753\ g\ H_2C_2O_4$$

This mass of oxalic acid represents 72.8% of the total sample mass.

$$\frac{0.753\ g\ H_2C_2O_4}{1.034\ g\ \text{sample}} \times 100\% = 72.8\%\ H_2C_2O_4$$

**Think about Your Answer** Problem Solving Tip 4.4 outlines the procedure used to solve this problem.

---

**Check Your Understanding**

A 25.0-mL sample of vinegar (which contains the weak acid acetic acid, $CH_3CO_2H$) requires 28.33 mL of a 0.953 M solution of NaOH for titration to the equivalence point. What is the mass of acetic acid, in grams, in the vinegar sample, and what is the concentration of acetic acid in the vinegar?

$$CH_3CO_2H(aq) + NaOH(aq) \rightarrow NaCH_3CO_2(aq) + H_2O(\ell)$$

## Standardizing an Acid or Base

In Example 4.10 the concentration of the base used in the titration was given. In actual practice this usually has to be found by a prior measurement. The procedure by which the concentration of an analytical reagent is determined accurately is called **standardization**, and there are two general approaches.

One approach is to weigh accurately a sample of a pure, solid acid or base (known as a *primary standard*) and then titrate this sample with a solution of the base or acid to be standardized (Example 4.11). An alternative approach to standardizing a solution is to titrate it with another solution that is already standardized (see "Check Your Understanding" in Example 4.11). This is often done using standard solutions purchased from chemical supply companies.

## EXAMPLE 4.11 Standardizing an Acid by Titration

**Problem** Sodium carbonate, $Na_2CO_3$, is a base, and an accurately weighed sample can be used to standardize an acid. A sample of sodium carbonate (0.263 g) requires 28.35 mL of aqueous HCl for titration to the equivalence point. What is the concentration of the HCl?

**What Do You Know?** The concentration of the HCl(aq) solution is the unknown in this problem. You know the mass of $Na_2CO_3$ and the volume of HCl(aq) solution needed to react completely with the $Na_2CO_3$. You need the molar mass of $Na_2CO_3$ and a balanced equation for the reaction.

**Strategy**

- Write a balanced equation for this acid–base reaction.

- Calculate the amount of $Na_2CO_3$ from the mass and molar mass.

- Use the stoichiometric factor (from the equation) to find the amount of HCl(aq).

- The amount of HCl divided by the volume of solution (in liters) gives its concentration (mol/L).

**Solution** The balanced equation for the reaction is written first.

$$Na_2CO_3(aq) + 2\ HCl(aq) \rightarrow 2\ NaCl(aq) + H_2O(\ell) + CO_2(g)$$

Calculate the amount of the base, $Na_2CO_3$, from its mass.

$$0.263\ g\ Na_2CO_3 \times \frac{1\ mol\ Na_2CO_3}{106.0\ g\ Na_2CO_3} = 0.00248\ mol\ Na_2CO_3$$

Next, use the stoichiometric factor to calculate the amount of HCl in 28.35 mL.

$$0.00248\ mol\ Na_2CO_3 \times \frac{2\ mol\ HCl\ required}{1\ mol\ Na_2CO_3\ available} = 0.00496\ mol\ HCl$$

Finally, the 28.35-mL (0.02835-L) sample of aqueous HCl contains 0.00496 mol of HCl, so the concentration of the HCl solution is 0.175 M.

$$[HCl] = \frac{0.00496\ mol\ HCl}{0.02835\ L} = 0.175\ M\ HCl$$

**Think about Your Answer** Sodium carbonate is commonly used as a primary standard. It can be obtained in pure form, can be weighed accurately, and it reacts completely with strong acids.

---

**Check Your Understanding**

Hydrochloric acid, HCl, can be purchased from chemical supply houses with a concentration of 0.100 M, and this solution can be used to standardize the solution of a base. If titrating 25.00 mL of a sodium hydroxide solution to the equivalence point requires 29.67 mL of 0.100 M HCl, what is the concentration of the base?

---

# Determining Molar Mass by Titration

In Chapter 2 and in this chapter we used analytical data to determine the empirical formula of a compound. The molecular formula could then be derived if the molar mass were known. If the unknown substance is an acid or a base, it is possible to determine the molar mass by titration.

## ⓦL INTERACTIVE EXAMPLE 4.12 Determining the Molar Mass of an Acid by Titration

**Problem** To determine the molar mass of an organic acid, HA, we titrate 1.056 g of HA with standardized NaOH. Calculate the molar mass of HA assuming the acid reacts with 33.78 mL of 0.256 M NaOH according to the equation

$$HA(aq) + NaOH(aq) \rightarrow NaA(aq) + H_2O(\ell)$$

**Strategy Map 4.12**

**PROBLEM**

Calculate the **molar mass** of an acid, **HA**, using an *acid-base titration*.

↓

**DATA/INFORMATION**

- **Mass** of *acid* sample.
- **Volume** and **concentration** of *base* used in titration

**STEP 1.** Write balanced equation.

**Balanced equation** for reaction of **acid** (HA) with **base** (NaOH)

**STEP 2. Amount** of base (mol) = volume (L) × (mol/L).

**Amount of base** (mol)

**STEP 3.** Use a **stoichiometric factor** to relate amount of base (mol) to amount (mol) of acid.

**Amount** of acid **HA** (mol)

**STEP 4. Molar mass** = mass of acid in sample/amount of acid in sample.

**Molar mass** of acid **HA**

**What Do You Know?** You know the mass of the sample of unknown acid, and the volume and concentration of NaOH(aq). From the equation given, you know that the acid and base react in a 1:1 fashion.

**Strategy** The key to this problem is to recognize that the molar mass of a substance is the ratio of the mass of the sample (g) to its amount (mol). You know the mass, but you need to determine the amount equivalent to that mass. The equation informs you that 1 mol of HA reacts with 1 mol of NaOH, so the amount of HA equals the amount of NaOH used in the titration. And, the amount of NaOH can be calculated from its concentration and volume.

**Solution** Let us first calculate the amount of NaOH used in the titration.

$$\text{Amount of NaOH} = c_{NaOH}V_{NaOH} = \frac{0.256 \text{ mol}}{L} \times 0.03378 \text{ } L = 8.65 \times 10^{-3} \text{ mol NaOH}$$

Next, recognize from the balanced equation that the amount of NaOH used in the titration is the same as the amount of acid titrated. That is,

$$8.65 \times 10^{-3} \text{ mol NaOH} \times \frac{1 \text{ mol HA}}{1 \text{ mol NaOH}} = 8.65 \times 10^{-3} \text{ mol HA}$$

Finally, calculate the molar mass of HA.

$$\text{Molar mass of acid} = \frac{1.056 \text{ g HA}}{8.65 \times 10^{-3} \text{ mol HA}} = 122 \text{ g/mol}$$

**Think about Your Answer** Note that we *assumed* the acid had the composition HA. That is, it could lose one $H^+$ ion per molecule. If the acid had the composition $H_2A$ (such as oxalic acid, page 183) or $H_3A$ (for example, citric acid, page 129), the calculated molar mass would not be correct.

**Check Your Understanding**

An acid reacts with NaOH according to the net ionic equation

$$HA(aq) + OH^-(aq) \rightarrow A^-(aq) + H_2O(\ell)$$

Calculate the molar mass of HA if 0.856 g of the acid requires 30.08 mL of 0.323 M NaOH.

## Titrations Using Oxidation–Reduction Reactions

Analysis by titration is not limited to acid–base chemistry. Many oxidation–reduction reactions go rapidly to completion in aqueous solution, and methods exist to determine their equivalence points.

### EXAMPLE 4.13    Using an Oxidation–Reduction Reaction in a Titration

**Problem** The iron in a sample of an iron ore can be converted quantitatively to the iron(II) ion, $Fe^{2+}$, in aqueous solution, and this solution can then be titrated with aqueous potassium permanganate, $KMnO_4$. The balanced, net ionic equation for the reaction occurring in the course of this titration is

$$MnO_4^-(aq) + 5 Fe^{2+}(aq) + 8 H_3O^+(aq) \rightarrow Mn^{2+}(aq) + 5 Fe^{3+}(aq) + 12 H_2O(\ell)$$

purple     colorless                    colorless   pale yellow

A 1.026-g sample of iron-containing ore requires 24.35 mL of 0.0195 M $KMnO_4$ to reach the equivalence point. What is the mass percent of iron in the ore?

**What Do You Know?** You know the concentration and volume of the $KMnO_4$ solution used to titrate $Fe^{2+}(aq)$ to the equivalence point. The stoichiometric factor relating amounts of $KMnO_4$ and $Fe^{2+}(aq)$ is derived from the balanced equation.

## CASE STUDY

# How Much Salt Is There in Seawater?

Saltiness is one of the basic taste sensations, and a taste of seawater quickly reveals it is salty. How did the oceans become salty?

A result of the interaction of atmospheric $CO_2$ and water is hydronium ions and bicarbonate ions.

$$CO_2(g) + H_2O(\ell) \rightarrow H_2CO_3(aq)$$

$$H_2CO_3(aq) + H_2O(\ell)$$
$$\rightleftharpoons H_3O^+(aq) + HCO_3^-(aq)$$

Indeed, this is the reason rain is normally acidic, and this slightly acidic rainwater can then cause substances such as limestone or corals to dissolve, producing calcium ions and more bicarbonate ions.

$$CaCO_3(s) + H_3O^+(aq) \rightarrow$$
$$Ca^{2+}(aq) + HCO_3^-(aq) + H_2O(\ell)$$

Sodium ions arrive in the oceans by a similar reaction with sodium-bearing minerals such as albite, $NaAlSi_3O_6$. Acidic rain falling on the land extracts sodium ions that are then carried by rivers to the ocean.

The average chloride content of rocks in the earth's crust is only 0.01%, so only a minute proportion of the chloride ion in the oceans can come from the weathering of rocks and minerals. What then is the origin of the chloride ions in seawater? The answer is volcanoes. Hydrogen chloride gas, HCl, is a constituent of volcanic gases. Early in Earth's history, the planet was much hotter, and volcanoes were much more widespread.

The HCl gas emitted from these volcanoes is very soluble in water and quickly dissolves to give a dilute solution of hydrochloric acid. The chloride ions from dissolved HCl gas and sodium ions from weathered rocks are the source of the salt in the sea.

Suppose you are an oceanographer, and you want to determine the concentration of chloride ions in a sample of seawater. How can you do this? And what results might you find?

There are several ways to analyze a solution for its chloride ion content; among them is the classic "Mohr method." Here, a solution containing chloride ions is titrated with standardized silver nitrate. You know that the following reaction should occur:

$$Ag^+(aq) + Cl^-(aq) \rightarrow AgCl(s)$$

and will continue until the chloride ions have been precipitated completely. To detect the equivalence point of the titration of $Cl^-$ with $Ag^+$, the Mohr method involves the addition of a few drops of a solution of potassium chromate. This "indicator" works because silver chromate is slightly more soluble than AgCl, so the red $Ag_2CrO_4$ precipitates only after all of the AgCl is precipitated.

$$2\ Ag^+(aq) + CrO_4^{2-}(aq) \rightarrow Ag_2CrO_4(s)$$

The appearance of the red color of $Ag_2CrO_4$ (◀ Figure 3.12d) signals the equivalence point.

John C. Kotz

**Question:**

Using the following information, calculate the chloride ion concentration in a sample of seawater.

a. Volume of original seawater sample = 100.0 mL.

b. A 10.00-mL sample of the seawater was diluted to 100.0 mL with distilled water.

c. 10.00 mL of the diluted sample was again diluted to 100.0 mL.

d. A Mohr titration was performed on 50.00 mL of the diluted sample (from step c) and required 26.25 mL of 0.100 M $AgNO_3$. What was the chloride ion concentration in the original seawater sample?

**The answer to this question is available in Appendix N.**

**Strategy**

- Use the volume and concentration of the $KMnO_4$ solution to calculate the amount of $KMnO_4$ used in the titration.

- Use the stoichiometric factor to determine the amount of $Fe^{2+}$ from the amount of $KMnO_4$.

- Convert the amount of $Fe^{2+}$ to mass of iron using the molar mass of iron.

- Calculate the mass percent of iron in the sample.

**Solution**  First, calculate the amount of $KMnO_4$.

$$\text{Amount of } KMnO_4 = c_{KMnO_4} \times V_{KMnO_4} = \frac{0.0195 \text{ mol } KMnO_4}{L} \times 0.02435\ L = 0.000475 \text{ mol}$$

Use the stoichiometric factor to calculate the amount of iron(II) ion.

$$0.000475 \text{ mol } KMnO_4 \times \frac{5 \text{ mol } Fe^{2+}}{1 \text{ mol } KMnO_4} = 0.00237 \text{ mol } Fe^{2+}$$

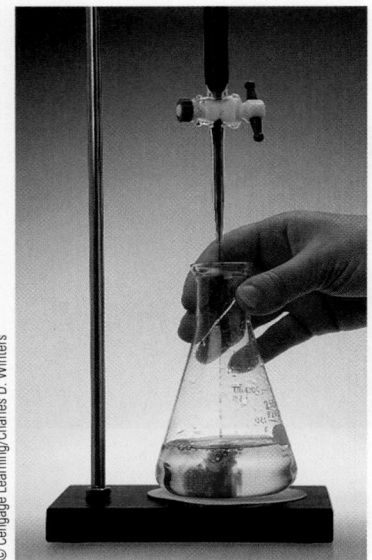

**Using an oxidation–reduction reaction for analysis by titration.** Purple, aqueous $KMnO_4$ is added to a solution containing $Fe^{2+}$. As $KMnO_4$ drops into the solution, colorless $Mn^{2+}$ and pale yellow $Fe^{3+}$ form. Here, an area of the solution containing unreacted $KMnO_4$ is seen. As the solution is mixed, this disappears until the equivalence point is reached.

Next, calculate the mass of iron.

$$0.00237 \ \text{mol Fe}^{2+} \times \frac{55.85 \ \text{g Fe}^{2+}}{1 \ \text{mol Fe}^{2+}} = 0.133 \ \text{g Fe}^{2+}$$

Finally, the mass percent can be determined.

$$\frac{0.133 \ \text{g Fe}^{2+}}{1.026 \ \text{g sample}} \times 100\% = \boxed{12.9\% \ \text{iron}}$$

**Think about Your Answer** The mass of the sample is 1.026 g, so the mass of iron in the sample must be less than this, as confirmed by the answer. The titration of iron(II) ions with $KMnO_4$ is a useful analytical reaction because it is easy to detect when all the iron(II) ion has reacted. The $MnO_4^-$ ion is a deep purple color, but when it reacts with $Fe^{2+}$ the color disappears because the reaction product, $Mn^{2+}$, is colorless. Therefore, $KMnO_4$ solution is added from a buret until the initially colorless, $Fe^{2+}$-containing solution just turns a faint purple color (due to unreacted $KMnO_4$), the signal that the equivalence point has been reached.

**Check Your Understanding**

Vitamin C, ascorbic acid ($C_6H_8O_6$), is a reducing agent. One way to determine the ascorbic acid content of a sample is to mix the acid with an excess of iodine,

$$C_6H_8O_6(aq) + I_2(aq) + 2 \ H_2O(\ell) \rightarrow C_6H_6O_6(aq) + 2 \ H_3O^+(aq) + 2 \ I^-(aq)$$

and then titrate the iodine that did not react with the ascorbic acid with sodium thiosulfate. The balanced, net ionic equation for the reaction occurring in this titration is

$$I_2(aq) + 2 \ S_2O_3^{2-}(aq) \rightarrow 2 \ I^-(aq) + S_4O_6^{2-}(aq)$$

Suppose 50.00 mL of 0.0520 M $I_2$ was added to the sample containing ascorbic acid. After the ascorbic acid/$I_2$ reaction was complete, the $I_2$ not used in this reaction required 20.30 mL of 0.196 M $Na_2S_2O_3$ for titration to the equivalence point. Calculate the mass of ascorbic acid in the unknown sample.

---

**REVIEW & CHECK FOR SECTION 4.7**

1.  A 25-mL sample of 0.40 M HCl is added to 32 mL of 0.30 M NaOH. Is the resulting solution acidic, basic, or neutral?

    (a)  acidic          (b)  basic          (c)  neutral

2.  What volume of 0.250 M NaOH is required to react completely with 0.0100 moles of $H_2SO_4$?

    (a)  80.0 mL        (b)  60.0 mL        (c)  40.0 mL        (d)  125 mL

---

# 4.8 Spectrophotometry

Solutions of many compounds are colored, a consequence of the absorption of light (Figure 4.15). It is possible to measure, quantitatively, the extent of light absorption and to relate this to the concentration of the dissolved solute. This kind of experiment, called **spectrophotometry**, is an important analytical method and you may have used it in your laboratory course.

Every substance absorbs or transmits certain wavelengths of radiant energy but not others (Figures 4.15 and 4.16). For example, nickel(II) ions (and chlorophyll) absorb red and blue/violet light while they transmit green light. Your eyes "see" the transmitted or reflected wavelengths, those not absorbed, as the color green. Furthermore, the specific wavelengths absorbed and transmitted are characteristic for a substance, so a spectrum serves as a "fingerprint" of the substance that can help identify an unknown.

# Forensic Chemistry: Titrations and Food Tampering

The U.S. Food and Drug Administration (FDA) has discovered cases of product tampering involving the addition of bleach to products such as soup, infant formula, and soft drinks. Household bleach is a dilute solution of sodium hypochlorite (NaClO), a compound that is an oxidizing agent and is dangerous if swallowed.

One method of detecting bleach uses starch-iodide paper. The bleach oxidizes the iodide ion to iodine in an acid solution,

$$2\ I^-(aq) + HClO(aq) + H_3O^+(aq) \rightarrow$$
$$I_2(aq) + 2\ H_2O(\ell) + Cl^-(aq)$$

and the presence of $I_2$ is detected by a deep blue color in the presence of starch.

This reaction is also used in the quantitative analysis of solutions containing bleach. Excess iodide ion (in the form of KI) is added to the sample. The bleach in the sample (which forms HClO in acid solution) oxidizes $I^-$ in a ratio of 1 mol HClO to 2 mol $I^-$. The iodine formed in the reaction is then titrated with sodium thiosulfate, $Na_2S_2O_3$ in another oxidation-reduction reaction (as in "Check Your Understanding" in Example 4.13).

$$I_2(aq) + 2\ S_2O_3^{2-}(aq) \rightarrow$$
$$2\ I^-(aq) + S_4O_6^{2-}(aq)$$

The amount of $Na_2S_2O_3$ used in the titration can then be used to determine the amount of NaClO in the original sample.

## Question:
Excess KI is added to a 100.0-mL sample of a soft drink that had been contaminated with bleach, NaClO. The iodine ($I_2$) generated in the solution is then titrated with 0.0425 M $Na_2S_2O_3$ and requires 25.3 mL to reach the equivalence point. What mass of NaClO was contained in the 100.0-mL sample of adulterated soft drink?

**The answer to this question is available in Appendix N.**

© Cengage Learning/Charles D. Winters

**A distinctive blue color is generated when iodine reacts with water-soluble starch.**

© Cengage Learning/Charles D. Winters

**FIGURE 4.15 Light absorption and color.** A beam of white light shines on a solution of nickel(II) ions in water, and the light that emerges is green. The color of a solution is due to the color of the light *not* absorbed by the solution. Here, red and blue/violet light was absorbed, and green light is transmitted.

Now suppose you look at two solutions containing copper(II) ions, one a deeper color than the other. Your common sense tells you that the intensely colored one is the more concentrated (Figure 4.17a). This is true: the intensity of the color is a measure of the concentration of the material in the solution.

In recent years, spectrophotometry has become one of the most frequently used methods of quantitative analysis. It is applicable to many industrial, clinical, and forensic problems involving the quantitative determination of compounds that are colored or that react to form a colored product.

## Transmittance, Absorbance, and the Beer–Lambert Law

To understand the exact relationship of light absorption and solution concentration, we need to define several terms. **Transmittance** ($T$) is the ratio of the amount

**FIGURE 4.16** **An absorption spectrophotometer.** A beam of white light passes through a prism or diffraction grating, which splits the light into its component wavelengths. After passing through the sample, the light reaches a detector. The spectrophotometer "scans" all wavelengths of light and determines the amount of light absorbed at each wavelength. The output is a *spectrum*, a plot of the amount of light absorbed as a function of the wavelength or frequency of the incoming or incident light. Here, the sample absorbs light in the green-blue part of the spectrum and transmits light in the remaining wavelengths. The sample would appear red to orange to your eye.

of light transmitted by or passing through the sample relative to the amount of light that initially fell on the sample (the incident light).

$$\text{Transmittance } (T) = \frac{P}{P_o} = \frac{\text{intensity of transmitted light}}{\text{intensity of incident light}}$$

The **absorbance** of a sample is defined as the negative logarithm of its transmittance. That is, absorbance and transmittance have an inverse relationship. As the absorbance of a solution increases, the transmittance decreases

$$\text{Absorbance} = -\log T = -\log P/P_o$$

Going back to our example of an aqueous solution of copper(II) ions in Figure 4.17a, if you have two solutions of copper(II) sulfate, you may deduce that the bluer solution appears more blue because it absorbs more of the light falling on it

**FIGURE 4.17** Light absorption, concentration, and path length.

**(a)** The test tube on the left has a solution of copper(II) sulfate with a concentration of 0.05 M. On the right, the concentration is 1.0 M in copper(II) sulfate. More light is absorbed by the more concentrated sample, and it appears more blue.

**(b)** The amount of light absorbed by a solution depends on the path length. Here, both solutions have the same concentration, but the distance the light travels is longer in one than the other.

and that this solution has a greater concentration of copper(II) sulfate. That is, the *absorbance, A, of a sample increases as the concentration increases.*

Next, suppose that there are two test tubes, both containing the same solution at the same concentration. The only difference is that one of the test tubes has a smaller diameter than the other (Figure 4.17b). We shine light of the same intensity ($P_0$) on both test tubes. In the first case, the light has to travel only a short distance through the sample before its strikes your eyes, whereas in the second case it has to pass through more of the sample. In the second case more of the light will be absorbed because the path length is longer. In other words, *absorbance increases as path length increases.*

The two observations described above constitute the **Beer–Lambert law:**

Absorbance ($A$) $\propto$ path length ($\ell$) $\times$ concentration ($c$)

$$A = \varepsilon \times \ell \times c$$

(4.5)

● **Beer–Lambert Law** The Beer–Lambert law applies strictly to relatively dilute solutions. At higher solute concentrations, the dependence of absorbance on concentration may not be linear.

where

- $A$, the absorbance of the sample, is a dimensionless number.
- $\varepsilon$, a proportionality constant, is called the *molar absorptivity*. It is a constant for a given substance, provided the temperature and wavelength are constant. It has units of L/mol · cm.
- $\ell$ and $c$ have the units of length (cm) and concentration (mol/L), respectively.

The important point is that the Beer–Lambert law shows *there is a linear relationship between a sample's absorbance and its concentration for a given path length.*

## Spectrophotometric Analysis

There are usually four steps in carrying out a spectrophotometric analysis.

- **Record the absorption spectrum of the substance to be analyzed.** In introductory chemistry laboratories, this is often done using instruments such as the ones shown in Figure 4.18. The result is a spectrum such as that for aqueous permanganate ions ($MnO_4^-$) in Figure 4.19. The spectrum is a plot of the absorbance of the sample versus the wavelength of incident light. Here, the maximum in absorbance is at about 525 nm.

- **Choose the wavelength for the measurement.** According to the Beer–Lambert law, the absorbance at each wavelength is proportional to concentration. Therefore, in theory we could choose any wavelength for quantitative estimations of concentration. However, the magnitude of the absorbance is important, especially when you are trying to detect very small amounts of material. In the

Photos © Cengage Learning/Charles D. Winters

Spectronic 20 from Spectronic Instruments.

Ocean Optics spectrometer (where the digital data are collected by a computer).

**FIGURE 4.18 Spectrophotometers.** The instruments illustrated here are often found in introductory chemistry laboratories.

**FIGURE 4.19 The absorption spectrum of solutions of potassium permanganate (KMnO₄) at different concentrations.** The solution for curve 1 has a higher concentration than that for curve 2.

spectra of permanganate ions in Figure 4.19, note that the difference in absorbance between curves 1 and 2 is largest at about 525 nm, and at this wavelength the change in absorbance is greatest for a given change in concentration. That is, the measurement of concentration as a function of concentration is most sensitive at this wavelength. For this reason, *we generally select the wavelength of maximum absorbance for our measurements.*

- **Prepare a calibration plot.** Once we have chosen the wavelength, the next step is to construct a **calibration curve** or **calibration plot** at this wavelength. This consists of a plot of absorbance versus concentration for a series of standard solutions whose concentrations are accurately known. Because of the linear relation between concentration and absorbance (at a given wavelength and path length), this plot is a straight line with a positive slope. (You will prepare a calibration plot in Example 4.14.)
- **Determine the concentration of the species of interest in other solutions.** Once the calibration plot has been made, and the equation for the line is known, you can find the concentration of an unknown sample from its absorbance.

Example 4.14 illustrates the preparation of a calibration curve and its use in determining the concentration of a species in solution.

### EXAMPLE 4.14   Using Spectrophotometry in Chemical Analysis

**Problem** A solution of KMnO₄ has an absorbance of 0.539 when measured at 540 nm in a 1.0-cm cell. What is the concentration of the KMnO₄? Prior to determining the absorbance for the unknown solution, the following calibration data were collected for the spectrophotometer.

| Concentration of KMnO₄ (M) | Absorbance |
|---|---|
| 0.0300 | 0.162 |
| 0.0600 | 0.330 |
| 0.0900 | 0.499 |
| 0.120 | 0.670 |
| 0.150 | 0.840 |

**What Do You Know?** The table relates concentration and absorbance for KMnO₄. The absorbance of the unknown sample is given.

**Strategy** Prepare a calibration plot from the data given above. You can then use this plot to estimate the concentration of the unknown from its absorbance. A more accurate value of the concentration can be obtained if you find the equation for the straight line in the calibration plot and calculate the unknown concentration using this equation.

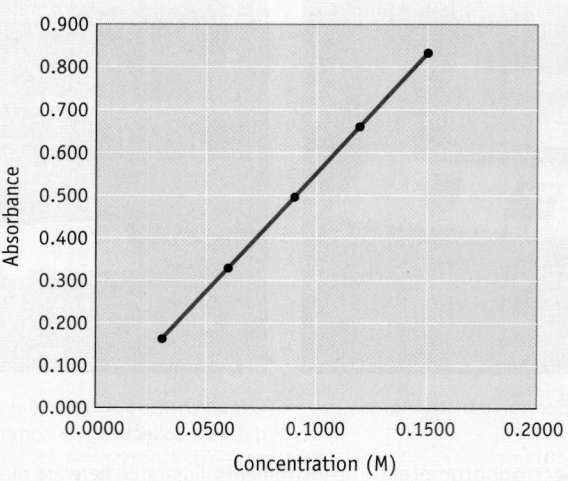

**Solution**  Using Microsoft Excel (or equivalent software) or a calculator, prepare a calibration plot from the experimental data. The equation for the straight line (as determined using Excel) is

$$y = 5.653x - 0.009$$

$$\text{Absorbance} = 5.653 \, (\text{Conc}) - 0.009$$

If we put in the absorbance for the unknown solution,

$$0.539 = 5.653 \, (\text{Conc}) - 0.009$$

$$\text{Unknown concentration} = 0.0969$$

**Think about Your Answer**  The absorbance of the unknown was 0.539. Looking back at our calibration data, we can see that this absorbance falls between the data points for absorbances of 0.499 and 0.670. Our answer determined for the concentration of $KMnO_4$ in the unknown (0.0969 M) falls between the concentrations for these two data points of 0.0900 M and 0.120 M, as it should (see pages 41 and 42 for information on graphing).

**Check Your Understanding**

Using the following data, calculate the concentration of copper(II) ions in the unknown solution. (The cell path length is 1.00 cm in all cases, and the wavelength used in the determination was 645 nm.)

**Calibration Data**

| Concentration of $Cu^{2+}$ (M) | Absorbance |
| --- | --- |
| 0.0562 | 0.720 |
| 0.0337 | 0.434 |
| 0.0281 | 0.332 |
| 0.0169 | 0.219 |

Absorbance of unknown solution containing $Cu^{2+}$ ions = 0.418

---

**REVIEW & CHECK FOR SECTION 4.8**

How is the absorbance (A) of a solution affected if a solution is diluted to twice the initial volume?

(a)  A is doubled.

(c)  A is not changed.

(b)  A is reduced to half the original value.

---

# CHAPTER GOALS REVISITED

*Now that you have completed this chapter, you should ask whether you have met the chapter goals. In particular, you should be able to*

### Perform stoichiometry calculations using balanced chemical equations

a.  Understand the principle of the conservation of matter, which forms the basis of chemical stoichiometry. **Study Question: 133.**

b.  Calculate the mass of one reactant or product from the mass of another reactant or product by using the balanced chemical equation (Section 4.1). **Study Questions: 2, 3, 5, 77, 81, 93, 95, 97, 100, and Go Chemistry Module 7.**

c.  Use amounts tables to organize stoichiometric information. **Study Questions: 7–10.**

  and

Sign in at **www.cengage.com/owl** to:
- View tutorials and simulations, develop problem-solving skills, and complete online homework assigned by your professor.
- For quick review and exam prep, download Go Chemistry mini lecture modules from OWL (or purchase them at **www.cengagebrain.com**)

Access **How Do I Solve It?** tutorials on how to approach problem solving using concepts in this chapter.

**Understand the meaning of a limiting reactant in a chemical reaction**
a.  Determine which of two reactants is the limiting reactant (Section 4.2). **Study Questions: 11–18, 96, 136, and Go Chemistry Module 8.**
b.  Determine the yield of a product based on the limiting reactant. **Study Questions: 11–18.**

**Calculate the theoretical and percent yields of a chemical reaction**
Explain the differences among actual yield, theoretical yield, and percent yield, and calculate percent yield (Section 4.3). **Study Question: 21.**

**Use stoichiometry to analyze a mixture of compounds or to determine the formula of a compound**
a.  Use stoichiometry principles to analyze a mixture (Section 4.4). **Study Questions: 23, 25, 27, 127, 129, 130.**
b.  Find the empirical formula of an unknown compound using chemical stoichiometry (Section 4.4). **Study Questions: 29, 31, 33–35.**

**Define and use concentrations in solution stoichiometry**
a.  Calculate the concentration of a solute in a solution in units of moles per liter (molarity), and use concentrations in calculations (Section 4.5). **Study Questions: 37, 39, 41.**
b.  Describe how to prepare a solution of a given concentration from the solute and a solvent or by dilution from a more concentrated solution (Section 4.5). **Study Questions: 45, 46, 47, 51.**
c.  Calculate the pH of a solution from the concentration of hydronium ion in the solution. Calculate the hydronium ion concentration of a solution from the pH (Section 4.6). **Study Questions: 53–58, and Go Chemistry Module 9.**
d.  Solve stoichiometry problems using solution concentrations (Section 4.7). **Study Questions: 59, 61, 62, 63, 65, 106, 107.**
e.  Explain how a titration is carried out, explain the procedure of standardization, and calculate concentrations or amounts of reactants from titration data (Section 4.7). **Study Questions: 67, 69, 71, 73.**
f.  Understand and use the principles of spectrophotometry to determine the concentration of a species in solution (Section 4.8). **Study Question: 75.**

# Key Equations

**Equation 4.1 (page 166)** Percent yield.

$$\text{Percent yield} = \frac{\text{actual yield}}{\text{theoretical yield}} \times 100\%$$

**Equation 4.2 (page 173)** Definition of molarity, a measure of the concentration of a solute in a solution.

$$\text{Molarity of } x \ (c_x) = \frac{\text{amount of solute } x \text{ (mol)}}{\text{volume of solution (L)}}$$

A useful form of this equation is

$$\text{Amount of solute } x \text{ (mol)} = c_x \text{ (mol/L)} \times \text{volume of solution (L)}$$

**Dilution Equation (page 177)** This is a shortcut to find, for example, the concentration of a solution ($c_d$) after diluting some volume ($V_c$) of a more concentrated solution ($c_c$) to a new volume ($V_d$).

$$c_c \times V_c = c_d \times V_d$$

**Equation 4.3 (page 178)** pH. The pH of a solution is the negative logarithm of the hydronium ion concentration.

$$pH = -\log[H_3O^+]$$

**Equation 4.4 (page 179)** Calculating $[H_3O^+]$ from pH. The equation for calculating the hydronium ion concentraton of a solution from the pH of the solution.

$$[H_3O^+] = 10^{-pH}$$

**Equation 4.5 (page 191)** Beer–Lambert law. The absorbance of light ($A$) by a substance in solution is equal to the product of the molar absorptivity of the substance ($\varepsilon$), the pathlength of the cell ($\ell$), and the concentration of the solute ($c$).

Absorbance ($A$) $\propto$ path length ($\ell$) $\times$ concentration ($c$)

$$A = \varepsilon \times \ell \times c$$

# Study Questions

**OWL** Interactive versions of these questions are assignable in OWL.

▲ denotes challenging questions.

Blue-numbered questions have answers in Appendix R and fully worked solutions in the *Student Solutions Manual*.

## Practicing Skills

**Mass Relationships in Chemical Reactions: Basic Stoichiometry**
*(See Example 4.1.)*

1. Aluminum reacts with oxygen to give aluminum oxide.

$$4\ Al(s)\ +\ 3\ O_2(g) \rightarrow 2\ Al_2O_3(s)$$

   What amount of $O_2$, in moles, is needed for complete reaction with 6.0 mol of Al? What mass of $Al_2O_3$, in grams, can be produced?

2. What mass of HCl, in grams, is required to react with 0.750 g of $Al(OH)_3$? What mass of water, in grams, is produced?

$$Al(OH)_3(s)\ +\ 3\ HCl(aq) \rightarrow AlCl_3(aq)\ +\ 3\ H_2O(\ell)$$

3. Like many metals, aluminum reacts with a halogen to give a metal halide (◀ Figure 2.12).

$$2\ Al(s)\ +\ 3\ Br_2(\ell) \rightarrow Al_2Br_6(s)$$

   What mass of $Br_2$, in grams, is required for complete reaction with 2.56 g of Al? What mass of white, solid $Al_2Br_6$ is expected?

4. The balanced equation for the reduction of iron ore to the metal using CO is

$$Fe_2O_3(s)\ +\ 3\ CO(g) \rightarrow 2\ Fe(s)\ +\ 3\ CO_2(g)$$

   (a) What is the maximum mass of iron, in grams, that can be obtained from 454 g (1.00 lb) of iron(III) oxide?
   (b) What mass of CO is required to react with 454 g of $Fe_2O_3$?

5. Methane, $CH_4$, burns in oxygen.
   (a) What are the products of the reaction?
   (b) Write the balanced equation for the reaction.
   (c) What mass of $O_2$, in grams, is required for complete combustion of 25.5 g of methane?
   (d) What is the total mass of products expected from the combustion of 25.5 g of methane?

6. The formation of water-insoluble silver chloride is useful in the analysis of chloride-containing substances. Consider the following *unbalanced* equation:

$$BaCl_2(aq)\ +\ AgNO_3(aq) \rightarrow AgCl(s)\ +\ Ba(NO_3)_2(aq)$$

   (a) Write the balanced equation.
   (b) What mass of $AgNO_3$, in grams, is required for complete reaction with 0.156 g of $BaCl_2$? What mass of AgCl is produced?

**Amounts Tables and Chemical Stoichiometry**
*For each question below, set up an amounts table that lists the initial amount or amounts of reactants, the changes in amounts of reactants and products, and the amounts of reactants and products after reaction (see page 159 and Example 4.1).*

7. The metals industry was a major source of air pollution years ago. One common process involved "roasting" metal sulfides in the air:

$$2\ PbS(s)\ +\ 3\ O_2(g) \rightarrow 2\ PbO(s)\ +\ 2\ SO_2(g)$$

   If 2.50 mol of PbS is heated in air, what amount of $O_2$ is required for complete reaction? What amounts of PbO and $SO_2$ are expected?

8. Iron ore is converted to iron metal in a reaction with carbon.

$$2\ Fe_2O_3(s)\ +\ 3\ C(s) \rightarrow 4\ Fe(s)\ +\ 3\ CO_2(g)$$

   If 6.2 mol of $Fe_2O_3(s)$ is used, what amount of C(s) is needed, and what amounts of Fe and $CO_2$ are produced?

9. Chromium metal reacts with oxygen to give chromium(III) oxide, $Cr_2O_3$.
   (a) Write a balanced equation for the reaction.
   (b) What mass (in grams) of $Cr_2O_3$ is produced if 0.175 g of chromium metal is converted completely to the oxide?
   (c) What mass of $O_2$ (in grams) is required for the reaction?

10. Ethane, $C_2H_6$, burns in oxygen.
    (a) What are the products of the reaction?
    (b) Write the balanced equation for the reaction.
    (c) What mass of $O_2$, in grams, is required for complete combustion of 13.6 of ethane?
    (d) What is the total mass of products expected from the combustion of 13.6 g of ethane?

## Limiting Reactants
*(See Example 4.2.)*

11. Sodium sulfide, $Na_2S$, is used in the leather industry to remove hair from hides. The $Na_2S$ is made by the reaction

$$Na_2SO_4(s) + 4\ C(s) \rightarrow Na_2S(s) + 4\ CO(g)$$

Suppose you mix 15 g of $Na_2SO_4$ and 7.5 g of C. Which is the limiting reactant? What mass of $Na_2S$ is produced?

12. Ammonia gas can be prepared by the reaction of a metal oxide such as calcium oxide with ammonium chloride.

$$CaO(s) + 2\ NH_4Cl(s) \rightarrow$$
$$2\ NH_3(g) + H_2O(g) + CaCl_2(s)$$

If 112 g of CaO and 224 g of $NH_4Cl$ are mixed, what is the limiting reactant, and what mass of $NH_3$ can be produced?

13. The compound $SF_6$ is made by burning sulfur in an atmosphere of fluorine. The balanced equation is

$$S_8(s) + 24\ F_2(g) \rightarrow 8\ SF_6(g)$$

If you begin with 1.6 mol of sulfur, $S_8$, and 35 mol of $F_2$, which is the limiting reagent?

14. Disulfur dichloride, $S_2Cl_2$, is used to vulcanize rubber. It can be made by treating molten sulfur with gaseous chlorine:

$$S_8(\ell) + 4\ Cl_2(g) \rightarrow 4\ S_2Cl_2(\ell)$$

Starting with a mixture of 32.0 g of sulfur and 71.0 g of $Cl_2$,
(a) Which is the limiting reactant?
(b) What is the theoretical yield of $S_2Cl_2$?
(c) What mass of the excess reactant remains when the reaction is completed?

15. The reaction of methane and water is one way to prepare hydrogen for use as a fuel:

$$CH_4(g) + H_2O(g) \rightarrow CO(g) + 3\ H_2(g)$$

If you begin with 995 g of $CH_4$ and 2510 g of water,
(a) Which reactant is the limiting reactant?
(b) What is the maximum mass of $H_2$ that can be prepared?
(c) What mass of the excess reactant remains when the reaction is completed?

16. Aluminum chloride, $AlCl_3$, is made by treating scrap aluminum with chlorine.

$$2\ Al(s) + 3\ Cl_2(g) \rightarrow 2\ AlCl_3(s)$$

If you begin with 2.70 g of Al and 4.05 g of $Cl_2$,
(a) Which reactant is limiting?
(b) What mass of $AlCl_3$ can be produced?
(c) What mass of the excess reactant remains when the reaction is completed?
(d) Set up an amounts table for this problem.

17. Hexane ($C_6H_{14}$) burns in air ($O_2$) to give $CO_2$ and $H_2O$.
(a) Write a balanced equation for the reaction.
(b) If 215 g of $C_6H_{14}$ is mixed with 215 g of $O_2$, what masses of $CO_2$ and $H_2O$ are produced in the reaction?
(c) What mass of the excess reactant remains after the hexane has been burned?
(d) Set up an amounts table for this problem.

18. Aspirin, $C_6H_4(OCOCH_3)CO_2H$, is produced by the reaction of salicylic acid, $C_6H_4(OH)CO_2H$, and acetic anhydride, $(CH_3CO)_2O$ (page 166).

$$C_6H_4(OH)CO_2H(s) + (CH_3CO)_2O(\ell) \rightarrow$$
$$C_6H_4(OCOCH_3)CO_2H(s) + CH_3CO_2H(\ell)$$

If you mix 100. g of each of the reactants, what is the maximum mass of aspirin that can be obtained?

## Percent Yield
*(See Section 4.3.)*

19. In Example 4.2, you found that a particular mixture of CO and $H_2$ could produce 407 g $CH_3OH$.

$$CO(g) + 2\ H_2(g) \rightarrow CH_3OH(\ell)$$

If only 332 g of $CH_3OH$ is actually produced, what is the percent yield of the compound?

20. Ammonia gas can be prepared by the following reaction:

$$CaO(s) + 2\ NH_4Cl(s) \rightarrow$$
$$2\ NH_3(g) + H_2O(g) + CaCl_2(s)$$

If 112 g of CaO and 224 g of $NH_4Cl$ are mixed, the theoretical yield of $NH_3$ is 68.0 g (Study Question 12). If only 16.3 g of $NH_3$ is actually obtained, what is its percent yield?

21. The deep blue compound $Cu(NH_3)_4SO_4$ is made by the reaction of copper(II) sulfate and ammonia.

$$CuSO_4(aq) + 4\ NH_3(aq) \rightarrow Cu(NH_3)_4SO_4(aq)$$

(a) If you use 10.0 g of $CuSO_4$ and excess $NH_3$, what is the theoretical yield of $Cu(NH_3)_4SO_4$?
(b) If you isolate 12.6 g of $Cu(NH_3)_4SO_4$, what is the percent yield of $Cu(NH_3)_4SO_4$?

22. Black smokers are found in the depths of the oceans (page 110). Thinking that the conditions in these smokers might be conducive to the formation of organic compounds, two chemists in Germany found the following reaction could occur in similar conditions.

$$2\ CH_3SH + CO \rightarrow CH_3COSCH_3 + H_2S$$

If you begin with 10.0 g of $CH_3SH$ and excess CO,
(a) What is the theoretical yield of $CH_3COSCH_3$?
(b) If 8.65 g of $CH_3COSCH_3$ is isolated, what is its percent yield?

## Analysis of Mixtures
*(See Example 4.3.)*

23. A mixture of $CuSO_4$ and $CuSO_4 \cdot 5\ H_2O$ has a mass of 1.245 g. After heating to drive off all the water, the mass is only 0.832 g. What is the mass percent of $CuSO_4 \cdot 5\ H_2O$ in the mixture? (See page 95.)

**24.** A 2.634-g sample containing impure $CuCl_2 \cdot 2H_2O$ was heated. The sample mass after heating to drive off the water was 2.125 g. What was the mass percent of $CuCl_2 \cdot 2H_2O$ in the original sample?

**25.** A sample of limestone and other soil materials was heated, and the limestone decomposed to give calcium oxide and carbon dioxide.

$$CaCO_3(s) \rightarrow CaO(s) + CO_2(g)$$

A 1.506-g sample of limestone-containing material gave 0.558 g of $CO_2$, in addition to CaO, after being heated at a high temperature. What was the mass percent of $CaCO_3$ in the original sample?

**26.** At higher temperatures, $NaHCO_3$ is converted quantitatively to $Na_2CO_3$.

$$2\,NaHCO_3(s) \rightarrow Na_2CO_3(s) + CO_2(g) + H_2O(g)$$

Heating a 1.7184-g sample of impure $NaHCO_3$ gives 0.196 g of $CO_2$. What was the mass percent of $NaHCO_3$ in the original 1.7184-g sample?

**27.** A pesticide contains thallium(I) sulfate, $Tl_2SO_4$. Dissolving a 10.20-g sample of impure pesticide in water and adding sodium iodide precipitates 0.1964 g of thallium(I) iodide, TlI.

$$Tl_2SO_4(aq) + 2\,NaI(aq) \rightarrow 2\,TlI(s) + Na_2SO_4(aq)$$

What is the mass percent of $Tl_2SO_4$ in the original 10.20-g sample?

**28.** ▲ The aluminum in a 0.764-g sample of an unknown material was precipitated as aluminum hydroxide, $Al(OH)_3$, which was then converted to $Al_2O_3$ by heating strongly. If 0.127 g of $Al_2O_3$ is obtained from the 0.764-g sample, what is the mass percent of aluminum in the sample?

## Using Stoichiometry to Determine Empirical and Molecular Formulas
*(See Examples 4.4 and 4.5.)*

**29.** Styrene, the building block of polystyrene, consists of only C and H. If 0.438 g of styrene is burned in oxygen and produces 1.481 g of $CO_2$ and 0.303 g of $H_2O$, what is the empirical formula of styrene?

**30.** Mesitylene is a liquid hydrocarbon. Burning 0.115 g of the compound in oxygen gives 0.379 g of $CO_2$ and 0.1035 g of $H_2O$. What is the empirical formula of mesitylene?

**31.** Cyclopentane is a simple hydrocarbon. If 0.0956 g of the compound is burned in oxygen, 0.300 g of $CO_2$ and 0.123 g of $H_2O$ are isolated.
   (a) What is the empirical formula of cyclopentane?
   (b) If a separate experiment gave 70.1 g/mol as the molar mass of the compound, what is its molecular formula?

**32.** Azulene is a beautiful blue hydrocarbon. If 0.106 g of the compound is burned in oxygen, 0.364 g of $CO_2$ and 0.0596 g of $H_2O$ are isolated.
   (a) What is the empirical formula of azulene?
   (b) If a separate experiment gave 128.2 g/mol as the molar mass of the compound, what is its molecular formula?

**33.** An unknown compound has the formula $C_xH_yO_z$. You burn 0.0956 g of the compound and isolate 0.1356 g of $CO_2$ and 0.0833 g of $H_2O$. What is the empirical formula of the compound? If the molar mass is 62.1 g/mol, what is the molecular formula?

**34.** An unknown compound has the formula $C_xH_yO_z$. You burn 0.1523 g of the compound and isolate 0.3718 g of $CO_2$ and 0.1522 g of $H_2O$. What is the empirical formula of the compound? If the molar mass is 72.1 g/mol, what is the molecular formula?

**35.** Nickel forms a compound with carbon monoxide, $Ni_x(CO)_y$. To determine its formula, you carefully heat a 0.0973-g sample in air to convert the nickel to 0.0426 g of NiO and the CO to 0.100 g of $CO_2$. What is the empirical formula of $Ni_x(CO)_y$?

**36.** To find the formula of a compound composed of iron and carbon monoxide, $Fe_x(CO)_y$, the compound is burned in pure oxygen to give $Fe_2O_3$ and $CO_2$. If you burn 1.959 g of $Fe_x(CO)_y$ and obtain 0.799 g of $Fe_2O_3$ and 2.200 g of $CO_2$, what is the empirical formula of $Fe_x(CO)_y$?

## Solution Concentration
*(See Examples 4.6 and 4.7.)*

**37.** If 6.73 g of $Na_2CO_3$ is dissolved in enough water to make 250. mL of solution, what is the molar concentration of the sodium carbonate? What are the molar concentrations of the $Na^+$ and $CO_3^{2-}$ ions?

**38.** Some potassium dichromate ($K_2Cr_2O_7$), 2.335 g, is dissolved in enough water to make exactly 500. mL of solution. What is the molar concentration of the potassium dichromate? What are the molar concentrations of the $K^+$ and $Cr_2O_7^{2-}$ ions?

**39.** What is the mass of solute, in grams, in 250. mL of a 0.0125 M solution of $KMnO_4$?

**40.** What is the mass of solute, in grams, in 125 mL of a $1.023 \times 10^{-3}$ M solution of $Na_3PO_4$? What is the molar concentration of the $Na^+$ and $PO_4^{3-}$ ion?

**41.** What volume of 0.123 M NaOH, in milliliters, contains 25.0 g of NaOH?

**42.** What volume of 2.06 M $KMnO_4$, in liters, contains 322 g of solute?

**43.** Identify the ions that exist in each aqueous solution, and specify the concentration of each ion.
   (a) 0.25 M $(NH_4)_2SO_4$
   (b) 0.123 M $Na_2CO_3$
   (c) 0.056 M $HNO_3$

**44.** Identify the ions that exist in each aqueous solution, and specify the concentration of each ion.
   (a) 0.12 M $BaCl_2$
   (b) 0.0125 M $CuSO_4$
   (c) 0.500 M $K_2Cr_2O_7$

## Preparing Solutions
*(See Examples 4.6 and 4.7.)*

**45.** An experiment in your laboratory requires 500. mL of a 0.0200 M solution of $Na_2CO_3$. You are given solid $Na_2CO_3$, distilled water, and a 500.-mL volumetric flask. Describe how to prepare the required solution.

46. What mass of oxalic acid, $H_2C_2O_4$, is required to prepare 250. mL of a solution that has a concentration of 0.15 M $H_2C_2O_4$?

47. If you dilute 25.0 mL of 1.50 M hydrochloric acid to 500. mL, what is the molar concentration of the dilute acid?

48. If 4.00 mL of 0.0250 M $CuSO_4$ is diluted to 10.0 mL with pure water, what is the molar concentration of copper(II) sulfate in the diluted solution?

49. Which of the following methods would you use to prepare 1.00 L of 0.125 M $H_2SO_4$?
    (a) Dilute 20.8 mL of 6.00 M $H_2SO_4$ to a volume of 1.00 L.
    (b) Add 950. mL of water to 50.0 mL of 3.00 M $H_2SO_4$.

50. Which of the following methods would you use to prepare 300. mL of 0.500 M $K_2Cr_2O_7$?
    (a) Add 30.0 mL of 1.50 M $K_2Cr_2O_7$ to 270. mL of water.
    (b) Dilute 250. mL of 0.600 M $K_2Cr_2O_7$ to a volume of 300. mL.

### Serial Dilutions
*(See A Closer Look: Serial Dilutions, page 178.)*

51. You have 250. mL of 0.136 M HCl. Using a volumetric pipet, you take 25.00 mL of that solution and dilute it to 100.00 mL in a volumetric flask. Now you take 10.00 mL of that solution, using a volumetric pipet, and dilute it to 100.00 mL in a volumetric flask. What is the concentration of hydrochloric acid in the final solution?

52. ▲ Suppose you have 100.00 mL of a solution of a dye and transfer 2.00 mL of the solution to a 100.00-mL volumetric flask. After adding water to the 100.00 mL mark, you take 5.00 mL of that solution and again dilute to 100.00 mL. If you find the dye concentration in the final diluted sample is 0.000158 M, what was the dye concentration in the original solution?

### Calculating and Using pH
*(See Example 4.8.)*

53. A table wine has a pH of 3.40. What is the hydronium ion concentration of the wine? Is it acidic or basic?

54. A saturated solution of milk of magnesia, $Mg(OH)_2$, has a pH of 10.5. What is the hydronium ion concentration of the solution? Is the solution acidic or basic?

55. What is the hydronium ion concentration of a 0.0013 M solution of $HNO_3$? What is its pH?

56. What is the hydronium ion concentration of a $1.2 \times 10^{-4}$ M solution of $HClO_4$? What is its pH?

57. Make the following conversions. In each case, tell whether the solution is acidic or basic.

| pH | [$H_3O^+$] |
|---|---|
| (a) 1.00 | ____ |
| (b) 10.50 | ____ |
| (c) ____ | $1.3 \times 10^{-5}$ M |
| (d) ____ | $2.3 \times 10^{-8}$ M |

58. Make the following conversions. In each case, tell whether the solution is acidic or basic.

| pH | [$H_3O^+$] |
|---|---|
| (a) ____ | $6.7 \times 10^{-10}$ M |
| (b) ____ | $2.2 \times 10^{-6}$ M |
| (c) 5.25 | |
| (d) ____ | $2.5 \times 10^{-2}$ M |

### Stoichiometry of Reactions in Solution
*(See Example 4.9.)*

59. What volume of 0.109 M $HNO_3$, in milliliters, is required to react completely with 2.50 g of $Ba(OH)_2$?

$$2\ HNO_3(aq) + Ba(OH)_2(s) \rightarrow$$
$$2\ H_2O(\ell) + Ba(NO_3)_2(aq)$$

60. What mass of $Na_2CO_3$, in grams, is required for complete reaction with 50.0 mL of 0.125 M $HNO_3$?

$$Na_2CO_3(aq) + 2\ HNO_3(aq) \rightarrow$$
$$2\ NaNO_3(aq) + CO_2(g) + H_2O(\ell)$$

61. When an electric current is passed through an aqueous solution of NaCl, the valuable industrial chemicals $H_2(g)$, $Cl_2(g)$, and NaOH are produced.

$$2\ NaCl(aq) + 2\ H_2O(\ell) \rightarrow$$
$$H_2(g) + Cl_2(g) + 2\ NaOH(aq)$$

What mass of NaOH can be formed from 15.0 L of 0.35 M NaCl? What mass of chlorine is obtained?

62. Hydrazine, $N_2H_4$, a base like ammonia, can react with sulfuric acid.

$$2\ N_2H_4(aq) + H_2SO_4(aq) \rightarrow 2\ N_2H_5^+(aq) + SO_4^{2-}(aq)$$

What mass of hydrazine reacts with 250. mL of 0.146 M $H_2SO_4$?

63. In the photographic developing process, silver bromide is dissolved by adding sodium thiosulfate.

$$AgBr(s) + 2\ Na_2S_2O_3(aq) \rightarrow$$
$$Na_3Ag(S_2O_3)_2(aq) + NaBr(aq)$$

If you want to dissolve 0.225 g of AgBr, what volume of 0.0138 M $Na_2S_2O_3$, in milliliters, should be used?

Photos © Cengage Learning/Charles D. Winters

**(a)**      **(b)**

**Silver chemistry.** **(a)** A precipitate of AgBr formed by adding $AgNO_3(aq)$ to KBr(aq). **(b)** On adding $Na_2S_2O_3(aq)$, sodium thiosulfate, the solid AgBr dissolves.

64. You can dissolve an aluminum soft drink can in an aqueous base such as potassium hydroxide.

$$2\ Al(s) + 2\ KOH(aq) + 6\ H_2O(\ell) \rightarrow$$
$$2\ KAl(OH)_4(aq) + 3\ H_2(g)$$

If you place 2.05 g of aluminum in a beaker with 185 mL of 1.35 M KOH, will any aluminum remain? What mass of $KAl(OH)_4$ is produced?

65. What volume of 0.750 M $Pb(NO_3)_2$, in milliliters, is required to react completely with 1.00 L of 2.25 M NaCl solution? The balanced equation is

$$Pb(NO_3)_2(aq) + 2\ NaCl(aq) \rightarrow$$
$$PbCl_2(s) + 2\ NaNO_3(aq)$$

66. What volume of 0.125 M oxalic acid, $H_2C_2O_4$, is required to react with 35.2 mL of 0.546 M NaOH?

$$H_2C_2O_4(aq) + 2\ NaOH(aq) \rightarrow$$
$$Na_2C_2O_4(aq) + 2\ H_2O(\ell)$$

## Titrations

*(See Examples 4.10–4.13.)*

67. What volume of 0.812 M HCl, in milliliters, is required to titrate 1.45 g of NaOH to the equivalence point?

$$NaOH(aq) + HCl(aq) \rightarrow H_2O(\ell) + NaCl(aq)$$

68. What volume of 0.955 M HCl, in milliliters, is required to titrate 2.152 g of $Na_2CO_3$ to the equivalence point?

$$Na_2CO_3(aq) + 2\ HCl(aq) \rightarrow$$
$$H_2O(\ell) + CO_2(g) + 2\ NaCl(aq)$$

69. If 38.55 mL of HCl is required to titrate 2.150 g of $Na_2CO_3$ according to the following equation, what is the concentration (mol/L) of the HCl solution?

$$Na_2CO_3(aq) + 2\ HCl(aq) \rightarrow$$
$$2\ NaCl(aq) + CO_2(g) + H_2O(\ell)$$

70. Potassium hydrogen phthalate, $KHC_8H_4O_4$, is used to standardize solutions of bases. The acidic anion reacts with strong bases according to the following net ionic equation:

$$HC_8H_4O_4{}^-(aq) + OH^-(aq) \rightarrow$$
$$C_8H_4O_4{}^{2-}(aq) + H_2O(\ell)$$

If a 0.902-g sample of potassium hydrogen phthalate is dissolved in water and titrated to the equivalence point with 26.45 mL of NaOH, what is the molar concentration of the NaOH?

71. You have 0.954 g of an unknown acid, $H_2A$, which reacts with NaOH according to the balanced equation

$$H_2A(aq) + 2\ NaOH(aq) \rightarrow Na_2A(aq) + 2\ H_2O(\ell)$$

If 36.04 mL of 0.509 M NaOH is required to titrate the acid to the second equivalence point, what is the molar mass of the acid?

72. An unknown solid acid is either citric acid or tartaric acid. To determine which acid you have, you titrate a sample of the solid with aqueous NaOH and from this determine the molar mass of the unknown acid. The appropriate equations are as follows:

*Citric acid:*

$$H_3C_6H_5O_7(aq) + 3\ NaOH(aq) \rightarrow$$
$$3\ H_2O(\ell) + Na_3C_6H_5O_7(aq)$$

*Tartaric acid:*

$$H_2C_4H_4O_6(aq) + 2\ NaOH(aq) \rightarrow$$
$$2\ H_2O(\ell) + Na_2C_4H_4O_6(aq)$$

A 0.956-g sample requires 29.1 mL of 0.513 M NaOH to consume the acid completely. What is the unknown acid?

73. To analyze an iron-containing compound, you convert all the iron to $Fe^{2+}$ in aqueous solution and then titrate the solution with standardized $KMnO_4$. The balanced, net ionic equation is

$$MnO_4{}^-(aq) + 5\ Fe^{2+}(aq) + 8\ H_3O^+(aq) \rightarrow$$
$$Mn^{2+}(aq) + 5\ Fe^{3+}(aq) + 12\ H_2O(\ell)$$

A 0.598-g sample of the iron-containing compound requires 22.25 mL of 0.0123 M $KMnO_4$ for titration to the equivalence point. What is the mass percent of iron in the sample?

74. Vitamin C has the formula $C_6H_8O_6$. Besides being an acid, it is a reducing agent. One method for determining the amount of vitamin C in a sample is to titrate it with a solution of bromine, $Br_2$, an oxidizing agent.

$$C_6H_8O_6(aq) + Br_2(aq) \rightarrow 2\ HBr(aq) + C_6H_6O_6(aq)$$

A 1.00-g "chewable" vitamin C tablet requires 27.85 mL of 0.102 M $Br_2$ for titration to the equivalence point. What is the mass of vitamin C in the tablet?

## Spectrophotometry

*(See Section 4.8 and Example 4.14. The problems below are adapted from Fundamentals of Analytical Chemistry, 8th ed., by D. A. Skoog, D. M. West, F. J. Holler, and S. R. Crouch, Thomson/Brooks-Cole, Belmont, CA 2004.)*

75. A solution of a dye was analyzed by spectrophotometry, and the following calibration data were collected.

| Dye Concentration | Absorbance (A) at 475 nm |
|---|---|
| $0.50 \times 10^{-6}$ M | 0.24 |
| $1.5 \times 10^{-6}$ M | 0.36 |
| $2.5 \times 10^{-6}$ M | 0.44 |
| $3.5 \times 10^{-6}$ M | 0.59 |
| $4.5 \times 10^{-6}$ M | 0.70 |

(a) Construct a calibration plot, and determine the slope and intercept.
(b) What is the dye concentration in a solution with $A = 0.52$?

76. The nitrite ion is involved in the biochemical nitrogen cycle. You can determine the nitrite ion content of a sample using spectrophotometry by first using several organic compounds to form a colored compound from the ion. The following data were collected.

| $NO_2^-$ Ion Concentration | Absorbance of Solution at 550 nm |
|---|---|
| $2.00 \times 10^{-6}$ M | 0.065 |
| $6.00 \times 10^{-6}$ M | 0.205 |
| $10.00 \times 10^{-6}$ M | 0.338 |
| $14.00 \times 10^{-6}$ M | 0.474 |
| $18.00 \times 10^{-6}$ M | 0.598 |
| Unknown solution | 0.402 |

   (a) Construct a calibration plot, and determine the slope and intercept.
   (b) What is the nitrite ion concentration in the unknown solution?

## General Questions

*These questions are not designated as to type or location in the chapter. They may combine several concepts.*

77. Suppose 16.04 g of benzene, $C_6H_6$, is burned in oxygen.
   (a) What are the products of the reaction?
   (b) Write a balanced equation for the reaction.
   (c) What mass of $O_2$, in grams, is required for complete combustion of benzene?
   (d) What is the total mass of products expected from the combustion of 16.04 g of benzene?

78. The metabolic disorder diabetes causes a buildup of acetone, $CH_3COCH_3$, in the blood. Acetone, a volatile compound, is exhaled, giving the breath of untreated diabetics a distinctive odor. The acetone is produced by a breakdown of fats in a series of reactions. The equation for the last step, the breakdown of acetoacetic acid to give acetone and $CO_2$, is

$$CH_3COCH_2CO_2H \rightarrow CH_3COCH_3 + CO_2$$

**Acetone, CH₃COCH₃.**

What mass of acetone can be produced from 125 mg of acetoacetic acid?

79. Your body deals with excess nitrogen by excreting it in the form of urea, $NH_2CONH_2$. The reaction producing it is the combination of arginine ($C_6H_{14}N_4O_2$) with water to give urea and ornithine ($C_5H_{12}N_2O_2$).

$$C_6H_{14}N_4O_2 + H_2O \rightarrow NH_2CONH_2 + C_5H_{12}N_2O_2$$
arginine        urea        ornithine

If you excrete 95 mg of urea, what mass of arginine must have been used? What mass of ornithine must have been produced?

80. The reaction of iron metal and chlorine gas to give iron(III) chloride is illustrated in Figure 3.2.
   (a) Write the balanced chemical equation for the reaction.
   (b) Beginning with 10.0 g of iron, what mass of $Cl_2$, in grams, is required for complete reaction? What mass of $FeCl_3$ can be produced?
   (c) If only 18.5 g of $FeCl_3$ is obtained from 10.0 g of iron and excess $Cl_2$, what is the percent yield?
   (d) If 10.0 g each of iron and chlorine are combined, what is the theoretical yield of iron(III) chloride?

81. Some metal halides react with water to produce the metal oxide and the appropriate hydrogen halide (see photo). For example,

$$TiCl_4(\ell) + 2 H_2O(\ell) \rightarrow TiO_2(s) + 4 HCl(g)$$

© Cengage Learning/Charles D. Winters

**The reaction of TiCl₄ with the water in moist air.**

   (a) Name the four compounds involved in this reaction.
   (b) If you begin with 14.0 mL of $TiCl_4$ ($d = 1.73$ g/mL), what mass of water, in grams, is required for complete reaction?
   (c) What mass of each product is expected?

82. The reaction of 750. g each of $NH_3$ and $O_2$ was found to produce 562 g of NO (see pages 161–162).

$$4 NH_3(g) + 5 O_2(g) \rightarrow 4 NO(g) + 6 H_2O(\ell)$$

   (a) What mass of water is produced by this reaction?
   (b) What mass of $O_2$ is required to consume 750. g of $NH_3$?

83. Sodium azide, an explosive chemical used in automobile airbags, is made by the following reaction:

$$NaNO_3 + 3 NaNH_2 \rightarrow NaN_3 + 3 NaOH + NH_3$$

If you combine 15.0 g of $NaNO_3$ with 15.0 g of $NaNH_2$, what mass of $NaN_3$ is produced?

84. Iodine is made by the following reaction

$$2 NaIO_3(aq) + 5 NaHSO_3(aq) \rightarrow$$
$$3 NaHSO_4(aq) + 2 Na_2SO_4(aq) + H_2O(\ell) + I_2(aq)$$

   (a) Name the two reactants.
   (b) If you wish to prepare 1.00 kg of $I_2$, what masses of $NaIO_3$ and $NaHSO_3$ are required?
   (c) What is the theoretical yield of $I_2$ if you mixed 15.0 g of $NaIO_3$ with 125 mL of 0.853 M $NaHSO_3$?

85. Saccharin, an artificial sweetener, has the formula $C_7H_5NO_3S$. Suppose you have a sample of a saccharin-containing sweetener with a mass of 0.2140 g. After decomposition to free the sulfur and convert it to the $SO_4^{2-}$ ion, the sulfate ion is trapped as water-insoluble $BaSO_4$ (Figure 4.6). The quantity of $BaSO_4$ obtained is 0.2070 g. What is the mass percent of saccharin in the sample of sweetener?

86. ▲ Boron forms a series of compounds with hydrogen, all with the general formula $B_xH_y$.

$$B_xH_y(s) + \text{excess } O_2(g) \rightarrow \frac{x}{2} B_2O_3(s) + \frac{y}{2} H_2O(g)$$

If 0.148 g of one of these compounds gives 0.422 g of $B_2O_3$ when burned in excess $O_2$, what is its empirical formula?

87. ▲ Silicon and hydrogen form a series of compounds with the general formula $Si_xH_y$. To find the formula of one of them, a 6.22-g sample of the compound is burned in oxygen. All of the Si is converted to 11.64 g of $SiO_2$, and all of the H is converted to 6.980 g of $H_2O$. What is the empirical formula of the silicon compound?

88. ▲ Menthol, from oil of mint, has a characteristic odor. The compound contains only C, H, and O. If 95.6 mg of menthol burns completely in $O_2$, and gives 269 mg of $CO_2$ and 111 mg of $H_2O$, what is the empirical formula of menthol?

89. ▲ Benzoquinone, a chemical used in the dye industry and in photography, is an organic compound containing only C, H, and O. What is the empirical formula of the compound if 0.105 g of the compound gives 0.257 g of $CO_2$ and 0.0350 g of $H_2O$ when burned completely in oxygen?

90. ▲ Aqueous solutions of iron(II) chloride and sodium sulfide react to form iron(II) sulfide and sodium chloride.
    (a) Write the balanced equation for the reaction.
    (b) If you combine 40. g each of $Na_2S$ and $FeCl_2$, what is the limiting reactant?
    (c) What mass of FeS is produced?
    (d) What mass of $Na_2S$ or $FeCl_2$ remains after the reaction?
    (e) What mass of $FeCl_2$ is required to react completely with 40. g of $Na_2S$?

91. Sulfuric acid can be prepared starting with the sulfide ore, cuprite ($Cu_2S$). If each S atom in $Cu_2S$ leads to one molecule of $H_2SO_4$, what is the theoretical yield of $H_2SO_4$ from 3.00 kg of $Cu_2S$?

92. ▲ In an experiment, 1.056 g of a metal carbonate, containing an unknown metal M, is heated to give the metal oxide and 0.376 g $CO_2$.

$$MCO_3(s) + \text{heat} \rightarrow MO(s) + CO_2(g)$$

What is the identity of the metal M?
(a) M = Ni          (c) M = Zn
(b) M = Cu          (d) M = Ba

93. ▲ An unknown metal reacts with oxygen to give the metal oxide, $MO_2$. Identify the metal if a 0.356-g sample of the metal produces 0.452 g of the metal oxide.

94. ▲ Titanium(IV) oxide, $TiO_2$, is heated in hydrogen gas to give water and a new titanium oxide, $Ti_xO_y$. If 1.598 g of $TiO_2$ produces 1.438 g of $Ti_xO_y$, what is the empirical formula of the new oxide?

95. ▲ Potassium perchlorate is prepared by the following sequence of reactions:

$$Cl_2(g) + 2 \, KOH(aq) \rightarrow$$
$$KCl(aq) + KClO(aq) + H_2O(\ell)$$

$$3 \, KClO(aq) \rightarrow 2 \, KCl(aq) + KClO_3(aq)$$

$$4 \, KClO_3(aq) \rightarrow 3 \, KClO_4(aq) + KCl(aq)$$

What mass of $Cl_2(g)$ is required to produce 234 kg of $KClO_4$?

96. ▲ Commercial sodium "hydrosulfite" is 90.1% $Na_2S_2O_4$. The sequence of reactions used to prepare the compound is

$$Zn(s) + 2 \, SO_2(g) \rightarrow ZnS_2O_4(s)$$

$$ZnS_2O_4(s) + Na_2CO_3(aq) \rightarrow ZnCO_3(s) + Na_2S_2O_4(aq)$$

(a) What mass of pure $Na_2S_2O_4$ can be prepared from 125 kg of Zn, 500. g of $SO_2$, and an excess of $Na_2CO_3$?
(b) What mass of the commercial product would contain the $Na_2S_2O_4$ produced using the amounts of reactants in part (a)?

97. What mass of lime, CaO, can be obtained by heating 125 kg of limestone that is 95.0% by mass $CaCO_3$?

$$CaCO_3(s) \rightarrow CaO(s) + CO_2(g)$$

98. ▲ The elements silver, molybdenum, and sulfur combine to form $Ag_2MoS_4$. What is the maximum mass of $Ag_2MoS_4$ that can be obtained if 8.63 g of silver, 3.36 g of molybdenum, and 4.81 g of sulfur are combined? (*Hint:* What is the limiting reactant?)

99. ▲ A mixture of butene, $C_4H_8$, and butane, $C_4H_{10}$, is burned in air to give $CO_2$ and water. Suppose you burn 2.86 g of the mixture and obtain 8.80 g of $CO_2$ and 4.14 g of $H_2O$. What are the mass percentages of butene and butane in the mixture?

100. ▲ Cloth can be waterproofed by coating it with a silicone layer. This is done by exposing the cloth to $(CH_3)_2SiCl_2$ vapor. The silicon compound reacts with OH groups on the cloth to form a waterproofing film (density = $1.0 \, \text{g/cm}^3$) of $[(CH_3)_2SiO]_n$, where $n$ is a large integer number.

$$n \, (CH_3)_2SiCl_2 + 2n \, OH^- \rightarrow$$
$$2n \, Cl^- + n \, H_2O + [(CH_3)_2SiO]_n$$

The coating is added layer by layer, with each layer of $[(CH_3)_2SiO]_n$ being 0.60 nm thick. Suppose you want to waterproof a piece of cloth that is 3.00 square meters, and you want 250 layers of waterproofing compound on the cloth. What mass of $(CH_3)_2SiCl_2$ do you need?

101. ▲ Copper metal can be prepared by roasting copper ore, which can contain cuprite ($Cu_2S$) and copper(II) sulfide.

$$Cu_2S(s) + O_2(g) \rightarrow 2\ Cu(s) + SO_2(g)$$

$$CuS(s) + O_2(g) \rightarrow Cu(s) + SO_2(g)$$

Suppose an ore sample contains 11.0% impurity in addition to a mixture of CuS and $Cu_2S$. Heating 100.0 g of the mixture produces 75.4 g of copper metal with a purity of 89.5%. What is the weight percent of CuS in the ore? The weight percent of $Cu_2S$?

102. Which has the larger concentration of hydronium ions, 0.015 M HCl or aqueous HCl with a pH of 1.20?

103. The mineral dolomite contains magnesium carbonate.

$$MgCO_3(s) + 2\ HCl(aq) \rightarrow$$
$$CO_2(g) + MgCl_2(aq) + H_2O(\ell)$$

(a) Write the net ionic equation for this reaction.
(b) What type of reaction is this?
(c) What mass of $MgCO_3$ will react with 125 mL of HCl(aq) with a pH of 1.56?

104. An Alka-Seltzer tablet contains exactly 100. mg of citric acid, $H_3C_6H_5O_7$, plus some sodium bicarbonate. What mass of sodium bicarbonate is required to consume 100. mg of citric acid by the following reaction?

$$H_3C_6H_5O_7(aq) + 3\ NaHCO_3(aq) \rightarrow$$
$$3\ H_2O(\ell) + 3\ CO_2(g) + Na_3C_6H_5O_7(aq)$$

105. ▲ Sodium bicarbonate and acetic acid react according to the equation

$$NaHCO_3(aq) + CH_3CO_2H(aq) \rightarrow$$
$$NaCH_3CO_2(aq) + CO_2(g) + H_2O(\ell)$$

What mass of sodium acetate can be obtained from mixing 15.0 g of $NaHCO_3$ with 125 mL of 0.15 M acetic acid?

106. A noncarbonated soft drink contains an unknown amount of citric acid, $H_3C_6H_5O_7$. If 100. mL of the soft drink requires 33.51 mL of 0.0102 M NaOH to neutralize the citric acid completely, what mass of citric acid does the soft drink contain per 100. mL? The reaction of citric acid and NaOH is

$$H_3C_6H_5O_7(aq) + 3\ NaOH(aq) \rightarrow$$
$$Na_3C_6H_5O_7(aq) + 3\ H_2O(\ell)$$

107. Sodium thiosulfate, $Na_2S_2O_3$, is used as a "fixer" in black-and-white photography. Suppose you have a bottle of sodium thiosulfate and want to determine its purity. The thiosulfate ion can be oxidized with $I_2$ according to the balanced, net ionic equation

$$I_2(aq) + 2\ S_2O_3^{2-}(aq) \rightarrow 2\ I^-(aq) + S_4O_6^{2-}(aq)$$

If you use 40.21 mL of 0.246 M $I_2$ in a titration, what is the weight percent of $Na_2S_2O_3$ in a 3.232-g sample of impure material?

108. You have a mixture of oxalic acid, $H_2C_2O_4$, and another solid that does not react with sodium hydroxide. If 29.58 mL of 0.550 M NaOH is required to titrate the oxalic acid in the 4.554-g sample to the second equivalence point, what is the mass percent of oxalic acid in the mixture? Oxalic acid and NaOH react according to the equation

$$H_2C_2O_4(aq) + 2\ NaOH(aq) \rightarrow$$
$$Na_2C_2O_4(aq) + 2\ H_2O(\ell)$$

109. (a) What is the pH of a 0.105 M HCl solution?
(b) What is the hydronium ion concentration in a solution with a pH of 2.56? Is the solution acidic or basic?
(c) A solution has a pH of 9.67. What is the hydronium ion concentration in the solution? Is the solution acidic or basic?
(d) A 10.0-mL sample of 2.56 M HCl is diluted with water to 250. mL. What is the pH of the dilute solution?

110. A solution of hydrochloric acid has a volume of 125 mL and a pH of 2.56. What mass of $NaHCO_3$ must be added to completely consume the HCl?

111. ▲ One half liter (500. mL) of 2.50 M HCl is mixed with 250. mL of 3.75 M HCl. Assuming the total solution volume after mixing is 750. mL, what is the concentration of hydrochloric acid in the resulting solution? What is its pH?

112. A solution of hydrochloric acid has a volume of 250. mL and a pH of 1.92. Exactly 250. mL of 0.0105 M NaOH is added. What is the pH of the resulting solution?

113. ▲ You place 2.56 g of $CaCO_3$ in a beaker containing 250. mL of 0.125 M HCl. When the reaction has ceased, does any calcium carbonate remain? What mass of $CaCl_2$ can be produced?

$$CaCO_3(s) + 2\ HCl(aq) \rightarrow$$
$$CaCl_2(aq) + CO_2(g) + H_2O(\ell)$$

114. The cancer drug cisplatin, $Pt(NH_3)_2Cl_2$, can be made by reacting $(NH_4)_2PtCl_4$ with ammonia in aqueous solution. Besides cisplatin, the other product is $NH_4Cl$.
(a) Write a balanced equation for this reaction.
(b) To obtain 12.50 g of cisplatin, what mass of $(NH_4)_2PtCl_4$ is required? What volume of 0.125 M $NH_3$ is required?
(c) ▲ Cisplatin can react with the organic compound pyridine, $C_5H_5N$, to form a new compound.

$$Pt(NH_3)_2Cl_2(aq) + x\ C_5H_5N(aq) \rightarrow$$
$$Pt(NH_3)_2Cl_2(C_5H_5N)_x(s)$$

Suppose you treat 0.150 g of cisplatin with what you believe is an excess of liquid pyridine (1.50 mL; $d = 0.979$ g/mL). When the reaction is complete, you can find out how much pyridine was not used by titrating the solution with standardized HCl. If 37.0 mL of 0.475 M HCl is required to titrate the excess pyridine,

$$C_5H_5N(aq) + HCl(aq) \rightarrow C_5H_5NH^+(aq) + Cl^-(aq)$$

what is the formula of the unknown compound $Pt(NH_3)_2Cl_2(C_5H_5N)_x$?

115. ▲ You need to know the volume of water in a small swimming pool, but, owing to the pool's irregular shape, it is not a simple matter to determine its dimensions and calculate the volume. To solve the problem, you stir in a solution of a dye (1.0 g of methylene blue, $C_{16}H_{18}ClN_3S$, in 50.0 mL of water). After the dye has mixed with the water in the pool, you take a sample of the water. Using a spectrophotometer, you determine that the concentration of the dye in the pool is $4.1 \times 10^{-8}$ M. What is the volume of water in the pool?

116. ▲ Calcium and magnesium carbonates occur together in the mineral dolomite. Suppose you heat a sample of the mineral to obtain the oxides, CaO and MgO, and then treat the oxide sample with hydrochloric acid. If 7.695 g of the oxide sample requires 125 mL of 2.55 M HCl,

$$CaO(s) + 2\ HCl(aq) \rightarrow CaCl_2(aq) + H_2O(\ell)$$

$$MgO(s) + 2\ HCl(aq) \rightarrow MgCl_2(aq) + H_2O(\ell)$$

what is the weight percent of each oxide (CaO and MgO) in the sample?

117. Gold can be dissolved from gold-bearing rock by treating the rock with sodium cyanide in the presence of oxygen.

$$4\ Au(s) + 8\ NaCN(aq) + O_2(g) + 2\ H_2O(\ell) \rightarrow$$
$$4\ NaAu(CN)_2(aq) + 4\ NaOH(aq)$$

   (a) Name the oxidizing and reducing agents in this reaction. What has been oxidized, and what has been reduced?
   (b) If you have exactly one metric ton (1 metric ton = 1000 kg) of gold-bearing rock, what volume of 0.075 M NaCN, in liters, do you need to extract the gold if the rock is 0.019% gold?

118. ▲ You mix 25.0 mL of 0.234 M $FeCl_3$ with 42.5 mL of 0.453 M NaOH.
   (a) What mass of $Fe(OH)_3$ (in grams) will precipitate from this reaction mixture?
   (b) One of the reactants ($FeCl_3$ or NaOH) is present in a stoichiometric excess. What is the molar concentration of the excess reactant remaining in solution after $Fe(OH)_3$ has been precipitated?

119. **ATOM ECONOMY:** One type of reaction used in the chemical industry is a substitution, where one atom or group is exchanged for another. In this reaction, an alcohol, 1-butanol, is transformed into 1-bromobutane by substituting Br for the –OH group in the presence of sulfuric acid.

$$CH_3CH_2CH_2CH_2OH + NaBr + H_2SO_4 \rightarrow$$
$$CH_3CH_2CH_2CH_2Br + NaHSO_4 + H_2O$$

Calculate the % atom economy for the desired product, $CH_3CH_2CH_2CH_2Br$.

120. **ATOM ECONOMY:** Ethylene oxide, $C_2H_4O$, is an important industrial chemical [as it is the starting place to make such important chemicals as ethylene glycol (antifreeze) and various polymers]. One way to make the compound is called the "chlorohydrin route."

$$C_2H_4 + Cl_2 + Ca(OH)_2 \rightarrow C_2H_4O + CaCl_2 + H_2O$$

Another route is the modern catalytic reaction.

$$C_2H_4 + 1/2\ O_2 \rightarrow C_2H_4O$$

   (a) Calculate the % atom economy for the production of $C_2H_4O$ in each of these reactions. Which is the more efficient method?
   (b) What is the percent yield of $C_2H_4O$ if 867 g of $C_2H_4$ is used to synthesize 762 g of the product by the catalytic reaction?

## In the Laboratory

121. Suppose you dilute 25.0 mL of a 0.110 M solution of $Na_2CO_3$ to exactly 100.0 mL. You then take exactly 10.0 mL of this diluted solution and add it to a 250-mL volumetric flask. After filling the volumetric flask to the mark with distilled water (indicating the volume of the new solution is 250. mL), what is the concentration of the diluted $Na_2CO_3$ solution?

122. ▲ In some laboratory analyses, the preferred technique is to dissolve a sample in an excess of acid or base and then "back-titrate" the excess with a standard base or acid. This technique is used to assess the purity of a sample of $(NH_4)_2SO_4$. Suppose you dissolve a 0.475-g sample of impure $(NH_4)_2SO_4$ in aqueous KOH.

$$(NH_4)_2SO_4(aq) + 2\ KOH(aq) \rightarrow$$
$$2\ NH_3(aq) + K_2SO_4(aq) + 2\ H_2O(\ell)$$

The $NH_3$ liberated in the reaction is distilled from the solution into a flask containing 50.0 mL of 0.100 M HCl. The ammonia reacts with the acid to produce $NH_4Cl$, but not all of the HCl is used in this reaction. The amount of excess acid is determined by titrating the solution with standardized NaOH. This titration consumes 11.1 mL of 0.121 M NaOH. What is the weight percent of $(NH_4)_2SO_4$ in the 0.475-g sample?

123. You wish to determine the weight percent of copper in a copper-containing alloy. After dissolving a 0.251-g sample of the alloy in acid, an excess of KI is added, and the $Cu^{2+}$ and $I^-$ ions undergo the reaction

$$2\ Cu^{2+}(aq) + 5\ I^-(aq) \rightarrow 2\ CuI(s) + I_3^-(aq)$$

The liberated $I_3^-$ is titrated with sodium thiosulfate according to the equation

$$I_3^-(aq) + 2\ S_2O_3^{2-}(aq) \rightarrow S_4O_6^{2-}(aq) + 3\ I^-(aq)$$

   (a) Designate the oxidizing and reducing agents in the two reactions above.
   (b) If 26.32 mL of 0.101 M $Na_2S_2O_3$ is required for titration to the equivalence point, what is the weight percent of Cu in the alloy?

**124.** ▲ A compound has been isolated that can have either of two possible formulas: (a) $K[Fe(C_2O_4)_2(H_2O)_2]$ or (b) $K_3[Fe(C_2O_4)_3]$. To find which is correct, you dissolve a weighed sample of the compound in acid, forming oxalic acid, $H_2C_2O_4$. You then titrate this acid with potassium permanganate, $KMnO_4$ (the source of the $MnO_4^-$ ion). The balanced, net ionic equation for the titration is

$$5\ H_2C_2O_4(aq) + 2\ MnO_4^-(aq) + 6\ H_3O^+(aq) \rightarrow$$
$$2\ Mn^{2+}(aq) + 10\ CO_2(g) + 14\ H_2O(\ell)$$

Titration of 1.356 g of the compound requires 34.50 mL of 0.108 M $KMnO_4$. Which is the correct formula of the iron-containing compound: (a) or (b)?

**125.** ▲ Chromium(III) chloride forms many compounds with ammonia. To find the formula of one of these compounds, you titrate the $NH_3$ in the compound with standardized acid.

$$Cr(NH_3)_xCl_3(aq) + x\ HCl(aq) \rightarrow$$
$$x\ NH_4^+(aq) + Cr^{3+}(aq) + (x + 3)\ Cl^-(aq)$$

Assume that 24.26 mL of 1.500 M HCl is used to titrate 1.580 g of $Cr(NH_3)_xCl_3$. What is the value of $x$?

**126.** ▲ Thioridazine, $C_{21}H_{26}N_2S_2$, is a pharmaceutical agent used to regulate dopamine. (Dopamine, a neurotransmitter, affects brain processes that control movement, emotional response, and ability to experience pleasure and pain.) A chemist can analyze a sample of the pharmaceutical for the thioridazine content by decomposing it to convert the sulfur in the compound to sulfate ion. This is then "trapped" as water-insoluble barium sulfate (see Figure 4.6).

$$SO_4^{2-}(aq, \text{from thioridazine}) + BaCl_2(aq) \rightarrow$$
$$BaSO_4(s) + 2\ Cl^-(aq)$$

Suppose a 12-tablet sample of the drug yielded 0.301 g of $BaSO_4$. What is the thioridazine content, in milligrams, of each tablet?

**127.** ▲ A herbicide contains 2,4-D (2,4-dichlorophenoxyacetic acid), $C_8H_6Cl_2O_3$. A 1.236-g sample of the herbicide was decomposed to liberate the chlorine as $Cl^-$ ion. This was precipitated as AgCl, with a mass of 0.1840 g. What is the mass percent of 2,4-D in the sample?

**2,4-D (2,4-dichlorophenoxyacetic acid).**

**128.** ▲ Sulfuric acid is listed in a catalog with a concentration of 95–98%. A bottle of the acid in the stockroom states that 1.00 L has a mass of 1.84 kg. To determine the concentration of sulfuric acid in the stockroom bottle, a student dilutes 5.00 mL to 500. mL. She then takes four 10.00-mL samples and titrates each with standardized sodium hydroxide ($c = 0.1760$ M).

| Sample | 1 | 2 | 3 | 4 |
|---|---|---|---|---|
| Volume NaOH (mL) | 20.15 | 21.30 | 20.40 | 20.35 |

(a) What is the average concentration of the diluted sulfuric acid sample?
(b) What is the mass percent of $H_2SO_4$ in the original bottle of the acid?

**129.** ▲ Anhydrous calcium chloride is a good drying agent because it will rapidly pick up water. Suppose you have stored some carefully dried $CaCl_2$ in a desiccator. Unfortunately, someone did not close the top of the desiccator tightly, and the $CaCl_2$ became partially hydrated. A 150-g sample of this partially hydrated material was dissolved in 80 g of hot water. When the solution was cooled to 20 °C, 74.9 g of $CaCl_2 \cdot 6\ H_2O$ precipitated. Knowing the solubility of calcium chloride in water at 20 °C is 74.5 g $CaCl_2$/100 g water, determine the water content of the 150-g sample of partially hydrated calcium chloride (in moles of water per mole of $CaCl_2$).

**130.** ▲ A 0.5510-g sample consisting of a mixture of iron and iron(III) oxide was dissolved completely in acid to give a solution containing iron(II) and iron(III) ions. A reducing agent was added to convert all of the iron to iron(II) ions, and the solution was then titrated with the standardized $KMnO_4$ (0.04240 M); 37.50 mL of the $KMnO_4$ solution was required. Calculate the mass percent of Fe and $Fe_2O_3$ in the 0.5510-g sample. (Example 4.13 gives the equation for the reaction of iron(II) ions and $KMnO_4$.)

**131.** ▲ Phosphate in urine can be determined by spectrophotometry. After removing protein from the sample, it is treated with a molybdenum compound to give, ultimately, a deep blue polymolybdate. The absorbance of the blue polymolybdate can be measured at 650 nm and is directly related to the urine phosphate concentration. A 24-hour urine sample was collected from a patient; the volume of urine was 1122 mL. The phosphate in a 1.00 mL portion of the urine sample was converted to the blue polymolybdate and diluted to 50.00 mL. A calibration curve was prepared using phosphate-containing solutions. (Concentrations are reported in grams of phosphorus (P) per liter of solution.)

| Solution (mass P/L) | Absorbance at 650 nm in a 1.0-cm cell |
|---|---|
| $1.00 \times 10^{-6}$ g | 0.230 |
| $2.00 \times 10^{-6}$ g | 0.436 |
| $3.00 \times 10^{-6}$ g | 0.638 |
| $4.00 \times 10^{-6}$ g | 0.848 |
| Urine sample | 0.518 |

(a) What are the slope and intercept of the calibration curve?
(b) What is the mass of phosphorus per liter of urine?
(c) What mass of phosphate did the patient excrete in the one-day period?

**132.** ▲ A 4.000-g sample containing KCl and KClO$_4$ was dissolved in sufficient water to give 250.00 mL of solution. A 50.00-mL portion of the solution required 41.00 mL of 0.0750 M AgNO$_3$ in a Mohr titration (page 187). Next, a 25.00-mL portion of the original solution was treated with V$_2$(SO$_4$)$_3$ to reduce the perchlorate ion to chloride,

$$8 \text{ V}^{3+}(aq) + \text{ClO}_4^-(aq) + 12 \text{ H}_2\text{O}(\ell) \rightarrow$$
$$\text{Cl}^-(aq) + 8 \text{ VO}^{2+}(aq) + 8 \text{ H}_3\text{O}^+(aq)$$

and the resulting solution was titrated with AgNO$_3$. This titration required 38.12 mL of 0.0750 M AgNO$_3$. What is the mass percent of KCl and KClO$_4$ in the mixture?

## Summary and Conceptual Questions

*The following questions may use concepts from this and previous chapters.*

**133.** Two beakers sit on a balance; the total mass is 167.170 g. One beaker contains a solution of KI; the other contains a solution of Pb(NO$_3$)$_2$. When the solution in one beaker is poured completely into the other, the following reaction occurs:

$$2 \text{ KI}(aq) + \text{Pb(NO}_3)_2(aq) \rightarrow 2 \text{ KNO}_3(aq) + \text{PbI}_2(s)$$

**Solutions of KI and Pb(NO$_3$)$_2$ before reaction.**

**Solutions after reaction.**

What is the total mass of the beakers and solutions after reaction? Explain completely.

**134.** ▲ A weighed sample of iron (Fe) is added to liquid bromine (Br$_2$) and allowed to react completely. The reaction produces a single product, which can be isolated and weighed. The experiment was repeated a number of times with different masses of iron but with the same mass of bromine (see graph below).

(a) What mass of Br$_2$ is used when the reaction consumes 2.0 g of Fe?
(b) What is the mole ratio of Br$_2$ to Fe in the reaction?
(c) What is the empirical formula of the product?
(d) Write the balanced chemical equation for the reaction of iron and bromine.
(e) What is the name of the reaction product?
(f) Which statement or statements best describe the experiments summarized by the graph?
   (i) When 1.00 g of Fe is added to the Br$_2$, Fe is the limiting reagent.
   (ii) When 3.50 g of Fe is added to the Br$_2$, there is an excess of Br$_2$.
   (iii) When 2.50 g of Fe is added to the Br$_2$, both reactants are used up completely.
   (iv) When 2.00 g of Fe is added to the Br$_2$, 10.8 g of product is formed. The percent yield must therefore be 20.0%.

**135.** Let us explore a reaction with a limiting reactant. Here, zinc metal is added to a flask containing aqueous HCl, and H$_2$ gas is a product.

$$\text{Zn}(s) + 2 \text{ HCl}(aq) \rightarrow \text{ZnCl}_2(aq) + \text{H}_2(g)$$

The three flasks each contain 0.100 mol of HCl. Zinc is added to each flask in the following quantities.

**Flask 1: 7.00 g Zn    Flask 2: 3.27 g Zn    Flask 3: 1.31 g Zn**

When the reactants are combined, the H$_2$ inflates the balloon attached to the flask. The results are as follows:

Flask 1: Balloon inflates completely, but some Zn remains when inflation ceases.
Flask 2: Balloon inflates completely. No Zn remains.
Flask 3: Balloon does not inflate completely. No Zn remains.

Explain these results. Perform calculations that support your explanation.

**136.** The reaction of aluminum and bromine is pictured below. The white solid on the lip of the beaker at the end of the reaction is $Al_2Br_6$. In the reaction pictured below, which was the limiting reactant, Al or $Br_2$?

**Before reaction.**

**After reaction.**

**137.** ▲ Two students titrate different samples of the same solution of HCl using 0.100 M NaOH solution and phenolphthalein indicator (Figure 4.14). The first student pipets 20.0 mL of the HCl solution into a flask, adds 20 mL of distilled water and a few drops of phenolphthalein solution, and titrates until a lasting pink color appears. The second student pipets 20.0 mL of the HCl solution into a flask, adds 60 mL of distilled water and a few drops of phenolphthalein solution, and titrates to the first lasting pink color. Each student correctly calculates the molarity of an HCl solution. What will the second student's result be?
(a) four times less than the first student's result
(b) four times greater than the first student's result
(c) two times less than the first student's result
(d) two times greater than the first student's result
(e) the same as the first student's result

**138.** In some states, a person will receive a "driving while intoxicated" (DWI) ticket if the blood alcohol level (BAL) is 100 mg per deciliter (dL) of blood or higher. Suppose a person is found to have a BAL of 0.033 mol of ethanol ($C_2H_5OH$) per liter of blood. Will the person receive a DWI ticket?

**139. ATOM ECONOMY:** Benzene, $C_6H_6$, is a common compound, and it can be oxidized to give maleic anhydride, $C_4H_2O_3$, which is used in turn to make other important compounds.

$$+ 9/2\ O_2 \longrightarrow \quad + 2\ CO_2 + 2\ H_2O$$

(a) What is the % atom economy for the synthesis of maleic anhydride from benzene by this reaction?

(b) If 972 g of maleic anhydride is produced from exactly 1.00 kg of benzene, what is the percent yield of the anhydride? What mass of the byproduct $CO_2$ is also produced?

## Applying Chemical Principles

### Antacids

Antacids are chemical compounds that relieve indigestion and heartburn. Antacids that advertise immediate relief from indigestion or heartburn contain carbonate or hydroxide salts that neutralize stomach acids. Some common active ingredients include $NaHCO_3$, $KHCO_3$, $CaCO_3$, $Mg(OH)_2$, and $Al(OH)_3$. Although these compounds give quick relief, they are not recommended for prolonged consumption. Calcium carbonate may contribute to the growth of kidney stones. In addition, calcium carbonate and aluminum hydroxide may cause constipation. Magnesium hydroxide, on the other hand, is a mild laxative that can cause diarrhea. Antacids containing magnesium, therefore, are often combined with aluminum hydroxide since the aluminum counteracts the laxative properties of the magnesium.

### Questions:

1. Which of the compounds listed above produce gas-forming reactions when combined with HCl?
2. One tablet of Tums Regular Strength Antacid™ contains 500. mg $CaCO_3$.
   a. Write a balanced chemical equation for the reaction of $CaCO_3$ and stomach acid (HCl).
   b. What volume (in mL) of 0.500 M HCl(aq) will react completely with one tablet of Tums?
3. The active ingredients in Rolaids™ are $CaCO_3$ and $Mg(OH)_2$.
   a. Write a balanced chemical equation for the reaction of $Mg(OH)_2$ and HCl.
   b. If 29.52 mL of 0.500 M HCl is required to titrate one tablet of Rolaids and the tablet contains 550 mg of $CaCO_3$, what mass of $Mg(OH)_2$ is present in one tablet?

**Antacids.** Antacids are chemical compounds such as $CaCO_3$, $MgCO_3$, $Mg(OH)_2$, and $Al(OH)_3$ that can relieve indigestion and heartburn.

4. Maalox may be purchased in either a liquid or solid form. One teaspoon of the liquid form of Maalox contains a mixture of 200. mg of $Al(OH)_3$ and 200. mg of $Mg(OH)_2$. What volume of 0.500 M HCl(aq) will react completely with one teaspoon of Maalox?
5. Which product neutralizes the greatest amount of acid when taken in the quantities presented above: one tablet of Tums or Rolaids or one teaspoon of Maalox?

John C. Kotz

# 5  Principles of Chemical Reactivity: Energy and Chemical Reactions

© Cengage Learning/Charles D. Winters

**Energy and Your Diet** Everywhere we turn today the topic of "energy" comes up. On the news we hear about the need for more petroleum, to conserve more, or to find alternative fuels. And then there are those who advocate wind turbines, nuclear power plants, or solar panels. You think about this, but you perhaps worry more about how much energy your automobile or home uses. But, if you are like the authors of this text, you also think about the energy in your food. How many Calories did I ingest today or how much energy did I "burn" in the gym?

Here is a quiz for you. The photo here shows a number of food products, including fruit, rice, chocolate, nuts, popcorn, and a donut. It also has a flask containing 100 g of

ethanol ($C_2H_5OH$), which has been promoted as a substitute fuel for automobiles.

**Questions:**

1.  Which food products in the photo do you believe have the highest energy content per 100 grams? Which have the least amount of energy? (Check your guess by going to the Nutrient Data Laboratory website www.ars.usda.gov/ba/bhnrc/ndl.)
2.  Calculate the energy evolved as heat if you burn 100. g of ethanol in air. How do you think this compares with the amount of energy that can be derived from 100. g of the foods in the photo? (Data for doing the calculation are available in Appendix L.)

**Answers to these questions are available in Appendix N.**

## CHAPTER GOALS

*See Chapter Goals Revisited (page 238) for Study Questions keyed to these goals.*

- Assess the transfer of energy as heat associated with changes in temperature and changes of state.
- Understand and apply the first law of thermodynamics.
- Define and understand state functions (enthalpy, internal energy).
- Describe how energy changes are measured.
- Calculate the energy evolved or required for physical changes and chemical reactions using tables of thermodynamic data.

The importance of energy is evident in our daily lives—in heating and cooling our homes, in powering our appliances, and in propelling our vehicles, among other things. Most of the energy we use for these purposes is obtained by carrying out chemical reactions, largely by burning fossil fuels. We use natural gas for heating, coal and natural gas to generate most of our electric power, and fuels derived from petroleum for automobiles and for heat. In addition, energy is required for living: Chemical reactions in our bodies provide the energy for body functions, for movement, and to maintain body temperature.

To scientists, however, energy has significance that goes well beyond these many practical uses. In this chapter, we will begin the discussion of **thermodynamics**, the science of heat and work. This subject will provide important insights on the following questions:

- How do we measure and calculate the energy changes that are associated with physical changes and chemical reactions?
- What is the relationship between energy changes, heat, and work?
- How can we determine whether a chemical reaction is product-favored or reactant-favored at equilibrium?
- How can we determine whether a chemical reaction or physical process will occur spontaneously, that is, without outside intervention?

We will concentrate attention on the first two questions in this chapter and address the other questions in Chapter 19.

## 5.1 Energy: Some Basic Principles

In Chapter 1, we defined energy as the capacity to do work and stated that energy could be divided into two basic categories: kinetic energy (the energy associated with motion) and potential energy (energy that results from an object's position). Furthermore, we learned that although energy can be converted from one type into another, the total amount of energy is conserved. This is formally stated in the **law of conservation of energy**: *Energy can neither be created nor destroyed.* Or, to state this law differently, *the total energy of the universe is constant.* In order to understand how important this law truly is, we shall need to introduce some new terminology and consider the implications of a number of experiments more carefully.

**OWL**

Sign in to OWL at **www.cengage.com/owl** to view tutorials and simulations, develop problem-solving skills, and complete online homework assigned by your professor.

**go Chemistry**

Download mini lecture videos for key concept review and exam prep from OWL or purchase them from **www.cengagebrain.com**

- **World Energy Consumption** Burning fossil fuels provides about 85% of the total energy used by people on our planet. Nuclear and hydroelectric power each contribute about 6%. The remaining 3% is provided from biomass, solar, wind, and geothermal sources.

- **Units of Energy** The SI unit used in chemistry for energy (the joule) is discussed on pages 29–30.

**FIGURE 5.1 Systems and their surroundings.** Earth can be considered a thermodynamic system, with the rest of the universe as its surroundings. A chemical reaction occurring in a laboratory is also a system, with the laboratory its surroundings.

● **Thermal Equilibrium** Although no change is evident at the macroscopic level once thermal equilibrium is reached, on the molecular level transfer of energy between individual molecules will continue. A general feature of systems at equilibrium is that there is no change on a macroscopic level but that processes still occur at the particulate level. (See Section 3.3, page 116.)

## Systems and Surroundings

In thermodynamics, the terms *system* and *surroundings* have precise and important scientific meanings. A **system** is defined as an object, or collection of objects, being studied (Figure 5.1). The **surroundings** include everything outside the system that can exchange energy and/or matter with the system. In the discussion that follows, we will need to define systems precisely. If we are studying the energy evolved in a chemical reaction carried out in solution, for example, the system might be defined as the reactants, products, and solvent. The surroundings would be the reaction vessel and the air in the room and anything else in contact with the vessel with which it might exchange energy or matter. At the atomic level, the system could be a single atom or molecule, and the surroundings would be the atoms or molecules in its vicinity. How the system and its surroundings for each situation are defined depends on the information we are trying to obtain or convey.

This concept of a system and its surroundings applies to nonchemical situations as well. If we want to study the energy balance on our planet, we might choose to define Earth as the system and outer space as the surroundings. On a cosmic level, the solar system might be defined as the system being studied, and the rest of the galaxy would be the surroundings.

## Directionality and Extent of Transfer of Heat: Thermal Equilibrium

Much of our initial study of thermodynamics will deal with the ways that energy can be transferred between a system and its surroundings or between different parts of the system. One way that energy can be transferred is as heat. Energy is transferred as heat if two objects at different temperatures are brought into contact. In Figure 5.2, for example, the beaker of water and the piece of metal being heated in a Bunsen burner flame have different temperatures. When the hot metal is plunged into the cold water, energy is transferred as heat from the metal to the water. The thermal energy (molecular motion) of the water molecules increases, and the thermal energy of the metal atoms decreases. Eventually, the two objects reach the same temperature, and the system has reached **thermal equilibrium**. The distinguishing feature of thermal equilibrium is that, on the macroscopic scale, no further temperature change occurs; both the metal and water are at the same temperature.

Putting a hot metal bar into a beaker of water and following the temperature change may seem like a rather simple experiment with an obvious outcome. However, the experiment illustrates three principles that are important in our further discussion:

• Energy transfer as heat will occur spontaneously from an object at a higher temperature to an object at a lower temperature.
• Transfer of energy as heat continues until both objects are at the same temperature and thermal equilibrium is achieved.
• After thermal equilibrium is attained, the object whose temperature increased has gained thermal energy, and the object whose temperature decreased has lost thermal energy.

**FIGURE 5.2 Energy transfer.** Energy transfer as heat occurs from the hotter metal cylinder to the cooler water. Eventually, the water and metal reach the same temperature and are said to be in thermal equilibrium.

## A CLOSER LOOK

## What Is Heat?

Two hundred years ago, scientists characterized heat as a real substance called the caloric fluid. The caloric hypothesis supposed that when a fuel burned and a pot of water was heated, for example, caloric fluid was transferred from the fuel to the water. Burning the fuel released caloric fluid, and the temperature of the water increased as the caloric fluid was absorbed.

Over the next 50 years, however, the caloric hypothesis lost favor, and we now know it is incorrect. Experiments by James Joule (1818–1889) and Benjamin Thompson (1753–1814) that showed the interrelationship between heat and other forms of energy such as mechanical energy provided the key to dispelling this idea. Even so, some of our everyday language retains the influence of this early theory. For example, we often speak of heat flowing as if it were a fluid.

From our discussion so far, we know one thing that "heat" is not—but what is it? Heat

**Work and heat.** A classic experiment that showed the relationship between work and heat was performed by Benjamin Thompson (also known as Count Rumford) (1753–1814) using an apparatus similar to that shown here. Thompson measured the rise in temperature of water (in the vessel mostly hidden at the back of the apparatus) that resulted from the energy expended to turn the crank.

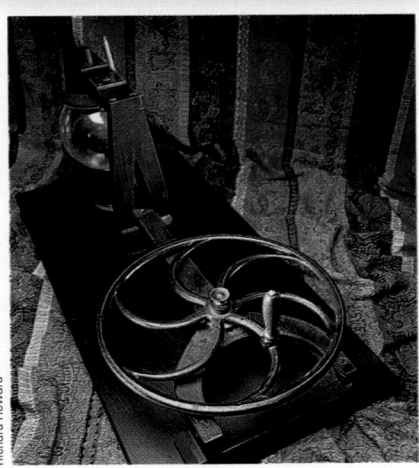

Richard Howard

is said to be a "process quantity." It is the *process* by which energy is transferred across the boundary of a system owing to a difference in temperature between the two sides of the boundary. In this process, the energy of the object at the lower temperature increases, and the energy of the object at the higher temperature decreases.

Heat is not the only process by which energy can be transferred. Specifically, work is another process that can transfer energy between objects.

The idea of energy transfer by the processes of heat and work is embodied in the definition of thermodynamics: the science of heat and work.

---

For the specific case where energy is transferred only as heat within an isolated system (that is, a system that cannot transfer either energy or matter with its surroundings), we can also say that the quantity of energy lost as heat by the hotter object and the quantity of energy gained as heat by the cooler object are numerically equal. (This is required by the law of conservation of energy.) When energy is transferred as heat between a system and its surroundings, we describe the directionality of this transfer as **exothermic** or **endothermic** (Figure 5.3).

- In an **exothermic process**, energy is transferred as heat from a system to its surroundings. The energy of the system decreases, and the energy of the surroundings increases.
- An **endothermic process** is the opposite of an exothermic process. Energy is transferred as heat from the surroundings to the system, increasing the energy of the system and decreasing the energy of the surroundings.

Exothermic
$q_{sys} < 0$
**SYSTEM**
**SURROUNDINGS**

Exothermic: energy transferred from system to surroundings

Endothermic
$q_{sys} > 0$
**SYSTEM**
**SURROUNDINGS**

Photos © Cengage Learning/Charles D. Winters

Endothermic: energy transferred from surroundings to system

**FIGURE 5.3 Exothermic and endothermic processes.** The symbol $q$ represents the energy transferred as heat, and the subscript sys refers to the system.

## 5.2   Specific Heat Capacity: Heating and Cooling

When an object is heated or cooled, the quantity of energy transferred depends on three things:

- the quantity of material
- the magnitude of the temperature change
- the identity of the material gaining or losing energy

**Specific heat capacity** *(C)* is defined as *the energy transferred as heat that is required to raise the temperature of 1 gram of a substance by one kelvin.* It has units of joules per gram per kelvin (J/g · K). A few specific heat capacities are listed in Figure 5.4, and a longer list of specific heat capacities is given in Appendix D (Table 11).

The energy gained or lost as heat when a given mass of a substance is warmed or cooled can be calculated using Equation 5.1.

$$q = C \times m \times \Delta T \tag{5.1}$$

Here, $q$ is the energy gained or lost as heat by a given mass of substance $(m)$, $C$ is the specific heat capacity, and $\Delta T$ is the change in temperature. The change in temperature, $\Delta T$, is calculated as the final temperature minus the initial temperature.

$$\Delta T = T_{final} - T_{initial} \tag{5.2}$$

Calculating a change in temperature using Equation 5.2 will give a result with an algebraic sign that indicates the direction of energy transfer. For example, we can use the specific heat capacity of copper, 0.385 J/g · K, to calculate the energy that

**Specific Heat Capacities of Some Elements, Compounds, and Substances**

| Substances | Specific Heat Capacity (J/g · K) | Molar Heat Capacity (J/mol · K) |
|---|---|---|
| Al, aluminum | 0.897 | 24.2 |
| Fe, iron | 0.449 | 25.1 |
| Cu, copper | 0.385 | 24.5 |
| Au, gold | 0.129 | 25.4 |
| Water (liquid) | 4.184 | 75.4 |
| Water (ice) | 2.06 | 37.1 |
| $HOCH_2CH_2OH(\ell)$, ethylene glycol (antifreeze) | 2.39 | 14.8 |
| Wood | 1.8 | — |
| Glass | 0.8 | — |

**FIGURE 5.4  Specific heat capacity.** Metals have different values of specific heat capacity on a per-gram basis. However, their molar heat capacities are all near 25 J/mol · K. Among common substances, liquid water has the highest specific heat capacity on a per-gram or per-mole basis, a fact that plays a significant role in Earth's weather and climate.

must be transferred from the surroundings to a 10.0-g sample of copper if the metal's temperature is raised from 298 K (25 °C) to 598 K (325 °C).

$$q = \left(0.385 \ \frac{J}{g \cdot K}\right)(10.0 \ g)(598 \ K - 298 \ K) = +1160 \ J$$

$T_{final}$  $T_{initial}$
Final temp.  Initial temp.

Notice that the answer has a positive sign. This indicates that the energy of the sample of copper has increased by 1160 J, which is in accord with energy being transferred as heat to the copper (the system) from the surroundings.

The relationship between energy, mass, and specific heat capacity has numerous implications. The high specific heat capacity of liquid water, $4.184 \ J/g \cdot K$, is a major reason why large bodies of water have a profound influence on weather. In spring, lakes warm up more slowly than the air. In autumn, the energy given off by a large lake as it cools moderates the drop in air temperature. The relevance of specific heat capacity is also illustrated when bread is wrapped in aluminum foil (specific heat capacity $0.897 \ J/g \cdot K$) and heated in an oven. You can remove the foil with your fingers after taking the bread from the oven. The bread and the aluminum foil are very hot, but the small mass of aluminum foil used and its low specific heat capacity result in only a small quantity of energy being transferred to your fingers (which have a larger mass and a higher specific heat capacity) when you touch the hot foil. This is also the reason why a chain of fast-food restaurants warns you that the filling of an apple pie can be much warmer than the paper wrapper or the pie crust. Although the wrapper, pie crust, and filling are at the same temperature, the quantity of energy transferred to your fingers (or your mouth!) from the filling is greater than that transferred from the wrapper and crust.

• **Molar Heat Capacity** Heat capacities can be expressed on a per-mole basis. The amount of energy that is transferred as heat in raising the temperature of one mole of a substance by one kelvin is the molar heat capacity. For water, the molar heat capacity is $75.4 \ J/mol \cdot K$. The molar heat capacity of metals at room temperature is always near $25 \ J/mol \cdot K$.

**A practical example of specific heat capacity.** The filling of the apple pie from a fast-food restaurant chain has a higher specific heat (and higher mass) than the pie crust and wrapper. Notice the warning on the wrapper.

⬤WL   **INTERACTIVE EXAMPLE 5.1**   Specific Heat Capacity

**Problem** How much energy must be transferred to raise the temperature of a cup of coffee (250 mL) from 20.5 °C (293.7 K) to 95.6 °C (368.8 K)? Assume that water and coffee have the same density (1.00 g/mL) and specific heat capacity (4.184 J/g · K).

**What Do You Know?** The energy required to warm a substance is related to its specific heat capacity ($C$), the mass of the substance, and the temperature change. A value for $C$ is given in the problem.

**Strategy** You can calculate the mass of coffee from the volume and density (mass = volume × density) and the temperature change from the initial and final temperatures ($\Delta T = T_{final} - T_{initial}$). Use Equation 5.1 to solve for $q$.

**Solution**       Mass of coffee = (250 mL)(1.00 g/mL) = 250 g

$$\Delta T = T_{final} - T_{initial} = 368.8 \ K - 293.7 \ K = 75.1 \ K$$

$$q = C \times m \times \Delta T$$

$$q = (4.184 \ J/g \cdot K)(250 \ g)(75.1 \ K)$$

$$q = 79,000 \ J \ (or \ 79 \ kJ)$$

**Think about Your Answer** The positive sign in the answer indicates that energy has been transferred to the coffee as heat. The thermal energy of the coffee is now higher.

**Strategy Map 5.1**

**PROBLEM**

Calculate the **energy** required to **raise temperature** of liquid.

↓

**DATA/INFORMATION**

• Specific heat capacity
• Volume
• Density of liquid
• $\Delta T$

**STEP 1.** Calculate the **sample mass** and $\Delta T$.

Mass of sample, $\Delta T$, and specific heat capacity

**STEP 2.** Use **Equation 5.1** to calculate $q$.

Energy required ($q$) to raise temperature of liquid by $\Delta T$

**Check Your Understanding**

In an experiment, it was determined that 59.8 J was required to raise the temperature of 25.0 g of ethylene glycol (a compound used as antifreeze in automobile engines) by 1.00 K. Calculate the specific heat capacity of ethylene glycol from these data.

## Quantitative Aspects of Energy Transferred as Heat

Like melting point, boiling point, and density, specific heat capacity is a characteristic intensive property of a pure substance. The specific heat capacity of a substance can be determined experimentally by accurately measuring temperature changes that occur when energy is transferred as heat from the substance to a known quantity of water (whose specific heat capacity is known).

Suppose a 55.0-g piece of metal is heated in boiling water to 99.8 °C and then dropped into cool water in an insulated beaker (Figure 5.5). Assume the beaker contains 225 g of water and its initial temperature (before the metal was dropped in) was 21.0 °C. The final temperature of the metal and water is 23.1 °C. What is the specific heat capacity of the metal? Here are the important aspects of this experiment.

- Let's define the metal and the water as the system and the beaker and environment as the surroundings and assume that energy is transferred only within the system. (This means that energy is not transferred between the system and the surroundings. This assumption is good, but not perfect; for a more accurate result, we would also want to account for any energy transfer to the surroundings.)
- The water and the metal bar end up at the same temperature. ($T_{final}$ is the same for both.)
- We will also assume energy is transferred *only as heat* within the system.
- The energy transferred as heat from the metal to the water, $q_{metal}$, has a negative value because the temperature of the metal drops. Conversely, $q_{water}$ has a positive value because its temperature increases.
- The values of $q_{water}$ and $q_{metal}$ are numerically equal but of opposite sign.

Because of the law of conservation of energy, *in an isolated system the sum of the energy changes within the system must be zero.* If energy is transferred only as heat, then

$$q_1 + q_2 + q_3 + \ldots = 0 \tag{5.3}$$

where the quantities $q_1$, $q_2$, and so on represent the energies transferred as heat for the individual parts of the system. For this specific problem, there are thermal energy changes associated with water and metal, $q_{water}$ and $q_{metal}$, the two components of the system; thus

$$q_{water} + q_{metal} = 0$$

Each of these quantities is related individually to specific heat capacities, masses, and changes of temperature, as defined by Equation 5.1. Thus

$$[C_{water} \times m_{water} \times (T_{final} - T_{initial, water})] + [C_{metal} \times m_{metal} \times (T_{final} - T_{initial, metal})] = 0$$

The specific heat capacity of the metal, $C_{metal}$, is the unknown in this problem. Using the specific heat capacity of water (4.184 J/g · K) and converting Celsius to kelvin temperatures gives

$$[(4.184 \text{ J/g} \cdot \text{K})(225 \text{ g})(296.3 \text{ K} - 294.2 \text{ K})] + [(C_{metal})(55.0 \text{ g})(296.3 \text{ K} - 373.0 \text{ K})] = 0$$

$$C_{metal} = 0.47 \text{ J/g} \cdot \text{K}$$

**FIGURE 5.5 Transfer of energy as heat.** When energy is transferred as heat from a hot metal to cool water, the thermal energy of the metal decreases and that of the water increases. The value of $q_{metal}$ is thus negative and that of $q_{water}$ is positive.

Hot metal (55.0 g iron)
99.8 °C

Immerse hot metal in water.

Metal cools in exothermic process.
$\Delta T$ of metal is negative.
$q_{metal}$ is negative.

Cool water (225 g)
21.0 °C

23.1 °C

Water is warmed in endothermic process.
$\Delta T$ of water is positive.
$q_{water}$ is positive.

## Calculating $\Delta T$

Virtually all calculations that involve temperature in chemistry are expressed in kelvins. In calculating $\Delta T$, however, we can use Celsius temperatures because a kelvin and a Celsius degree are the same size. That is, the difference between two temperatures is the same on both scales. For example, the difference between the boiling and freezing points of water is

$$\Delta T, \text{Celsius} = 100\ °C - 0\ °C = 100\ °C$$

$$\Delta T, \text{kelvin} = 373\ K - 273\ K = 100\ K$$

---

## ⓌWL  INTERACTIVE EXAMPLE 5.2  Using Specific Heat Capacity

**Problem** An 88.5-g piece of iron whose temperature is 78.8 °C (352.0 K) is placed in a beaker containing 244 g of water at 18.8 °C (292.0 K). When thermal equilibrium is reached, what is the final temperature? (Assume no energy is lost to warm the beaker and its surroundings.)

**What Do You Know?** Iron cools and the water warms until thermal equilibrium is reached. The energies associated with the cooling of iron and the heating of water are determined by the specific heat capacities, masses, and temperature changes for each species. If we define the system as the iron and water, the sum of these two energy quantities will be zero. The final temperature is the unknown in this problem. Masses and initial temperatures are given; the specific heat capacities of iron and water can be found in Appendix D or Figure 5.4.

**Strategy** The two energy quantities, $q_{Fe}$ and $q_{water}$, sum to zero ($q_{Fe} + q_{water} = 0$). Each energy quantity is defined using Equation 5.1; the value of $\Delta T$ in each is $T_{final} - T_{initial}$. We can use either kelvin or Celsius temperatures (Problem Solving Tip 5.1). Substituting gives the equation

$$C_{water} \times m_{water} \times (T_{final} - T_{initial,water}) + C_{Fe} \times m_{Fe} \times (T_{final} - T_{initial,Fe}) = 0.$$

Substitute in the given information and solve.

**Solution**

$$[C_{water} \times m_{water} \times (T_{final} - T_{initial, water})] + [C_{Fe} \times m_{Fe} \times (T_{final} - T_{initial, Fe})] = 0$$

$$[(4.184\ J/g \cdot K)(244\ g)(T_{final} - 292.0\ K)] + [(0.449\ J/g \cdot K)(88.5\ g)(T_{final} - 352.0\ K)] = 0$$

$$T_{final} = 294\ K\ (21\ °C)$$

**Think about Your Answer** Be sure to notice that $T_{initial}$ for the metal and $T_{initial}$ for the water in this problem have different values. Also, the low specific heat capacity and smaller quantity of iron result in the temperature of iron being reduced by about 60 degrees; in contrast, the temperature of the water has been raised by only a few degrees. Finally, as expected, $T_{final}$ (294 K) is between $T_{initial, Fe}$ and $T_{initial, water}$.

**Strategy Map 5.2**

**PROBLEM**

Calculate **final $T$** when piece of hot iron is added to **given mass** of cool water.

↓

**DATA/INFORMATION**

- **Specific heat capacities**
- **masses** of iron and water
- **initial $T$** for iron and water

↓

Use equation $q_{Fe} + q_{water} = 0$.
Solve for $T_{final}$.

↓

$T_{final}$ of water and iron

---

**Check Your Understanding**

A 15.5-g piece of chromium, heated to 100.0 °C, is dropped into 55.5 g of water at 16.5 °C. The final temperature of the metal and the water is 18.9 °C. What is the specific heat capacity of chromium? (Assume no energy is lost to the container or to the surrounding air.)

---

**REVIEW & CHECK FOR SECTION 5.2**

1. Which of the following processes requires the largest input of energy?

    (a)  warming 1.0 g of iron by 10 °C ($C_{Fe}$ = 0.449 J/g · K)

    (b)  warming 2.0 g of copper by 10 °C ($C_{Cu}$ = 0.385 J/g · K)

    (c)  warming 4.0 g of lead by 10 °C ($C_{Pb}$ = 0.127 J/g · K)

    (d)  warming 3.0 g of silver by 10 °C ($C_{Ag}$ = 0.236 J/g · K)

2. The samples of water listed below are mixed. After thermal equilibrium is reached, which mixture has the lowest temperature?

    (a) 10 g of water at 20 °C + 10 g of water at 30 °C

    (b) 10 g of water at 20 °C + 20 g of water at 30 °C

    (c) 20 g of water at 20 °C + 10 g of water at 30 °C

    (d) 20 g of water at 20 °C + 20 g of water at 30 °C

## 5.3 Energy and Changes of State

A *change of state* is a change, for example, between solid and liquid or between liquid and gas. When a solid melts, its atoms, molecules, or ions move about vigorously enough to break free of the attractive forces holding them in rigid positions in the solid lattice. When a liquid boils, the particles move much farther apart from one another, to distances at which attractive forces are minimal. In both cases, energy must be furnished to overcome attractive forces among the particles.

The energy transferred as heat that is required to convert a substance from a solid at its melting point to a liquid is called the **heat of fusion**. The energy transferred as heat to convert a liquid at its boiling point to a vapor is called the **heat of vaporization**. Heats of fusion and vaporization for many substances are provided along with other physical properties in reference books. Values for a few common substances are given in Appendix D (Table 12).

It is important to recognize that *temperature is constant throughout a change of state* (Figure 5.6). During a change of state, the added energy is used to overcome the forces holding one molecule to another, not to increase the temperature (Figures 5.6 and 5.7).

For water, the heat of fusion at 0 °C is 333 J/g, and the heat of vaporization at 100 °C is 2256 J/g. These values can be used to calculate the energy required for a given mass of water to melt or evaporate, respectively. For example, the energy required to convert 500. g of water from the liquid to gaseous state at 100 °C is

$$(2256 \text{ J/g})(500. \text{ g}) = 1.13 \times 10^6 \text{ J} (= 1130 \text{ kJ})$$

In contrast, to melt the same mass of ice to form liquid water at 0 °C requires only 167 kJ.

$$(333 \text{ J/g})(500. \text{ g}) = 1.67 \times 10^5 \text{ J} (= 167 \text{ kJ})$$

Figure 5.6 gives a profile of the energy changes occurring as 500. g of ice at −50 °C is converted to water vapor at 200 °C. This involves a series of steps: (1) warming ice to 0 °C, (2) conversion to liquid water at 0 °C, (3) warming liquid water to 100 °C, (4) evaporation at 100 °C, and (5) warming the water vapor to 200 °C. Each step requires the input of additional energy. The energy transferred as

**FIGURE 5.6 Energy transfer as heat and the temperature change for water.** This graph shows the energy transferred as heat to 500. g of water and the consequent temperature change as the water warms from −50 °C to 200 °C (at 1 atm).

State changes.
Temperature does **NOT** change.

Temperature changes.
State does **NOT** change.

Transferring 500 kJ of energy as heat to 2.0 kg of ice at 0 °C will cause 1.5 kg of ice to melt to water at 0 °C (and 0.5 kg of ice will remain). No temperature change occurs.

In contrast, transferring 500 kJ of energy as heat to 2.0 kg of iron at 0 °C will cause the temperature to increase to 557 °C (and the metal to expand slightly but not melt).

**FIGURE 5.7**  Changes of state.

heat to raise the temperature of solid, liquid, and vapor can be calculated with Equation 5.1, using the specific heat capacities of ice, liquid water, and water vapor (which are different), and the energies for the changes of state can be calculated using heats of fusion and vaporization. These calculations are done in Example 5.3.

## ⬤WL  INTERACTIVE EXAMPLE 5.3  Energy and Changes of State

**Problem**  Calculate the energy needed to convert 500. g of ice at −50.0 °C to steam at 200.0 °C. (The temperature change occurring in each step is illustrated in Figure 5.6.) The heat of fusion of water is 333 J/g, and the heat of vaporization is 2256 J/g. The specific heat capacities of ice, liquid water, and water vapor are given in Appendix D.

**What Do You Know?**  The overall process of converting ice at −50 °C to steam at 200 °C involves both temperature changes and changes of state; all require input of energy as heat. Given in the problem is the mass of water. Recall that melting occurs at 0 °C and boiling at 100 °C (at 1 atm pressure). You will need the specific heat capacities of ice, liquid water, and steam (available in Appendix D), the heat of fusion of water (333 J/g), and the heat of vaporization (2256 J/g).

**Strategy**  The problem is broken down into a series of steps:

**Step 1:**  Warm the ice from −50 °C to 0 °C.

**Step 2:**  Melt the ice at 0 °C.

**Step 3:**  Raise the temperature of the liquid water from 0 °C to 100 °C.

**Step 4:**  Boil the water at 100 °C.

**Step 5:**  Raise the temperature of the steam from 100 °C to 200 °C.

Use Equation 5.1 and the specific heat capacities of solid, liquid, and gaseous water to calculate the energy transferred as heat associated with the temperature changes. Use the heat of fusion and the heat of vaporization to calculate the energy transferred as heat associated with changes of state. The total energy transferred as heat is the sum of the energies of the individual steps.

**Solution**

**Step 1.**  (to warm ice from −50.0 °C to 0.0 °C)

$$q_1 = (2.06 \text{ J/g} \cdot \text{K})(500. \text{ g})(273.2 \text{ K} - 223.2 \text{ K}) = 5.15 \times 10^4 \text{ J}$$

**Step 2.**  (to melt ice at 0.0 °C)

$$q_2 = (500. \text{ g})(333 \text{ J/g}) = 1.67 \times 10^5 \text{ J}$$

**Strategy Map 5.3**

**PROBLEM**
Calculate **energy required** to heat a mass of water from **−50.0 °C** to steam at **200.0 °C**.

**DATA/INFORMATION**
- Mass of water
- $\Delta T$
- Heats of fusion and vaporization of water
- Specific heat capacities

Calculate **energy** involved in
STEP 1. warm ice to 0 °C ($q_1$)
STEP 2. melt ice at 0 °C ($q_2$)
STEP 3. warm water from 0 °C to 100 °C ($q_3$)
STEP 4. evaporate water at 100 °C ($q_4$)
STEP 5. heat steam to 200 °C ($q_5$)

Values of $q_1$, $q_2$, $q_3$, $q_4$, and $q_5$

STEP 6. Sum values of $q$.

$q_{total}$ for process

**Step 3.** (to raise temperature of liquid water from 0.0 °C to 100.0 °C)

$$q_3 = (4.184 \text{ J/g} \cdot \text{K})(500. \text{ g})(373.2 \text{ K} - 273.2 \text{ K}) = 2.09 \times 10^5 \text{ J}$$

**Step 4.** (to evaporate water at 100.0 °C)

$$q_4 = (2256 \text{ J/g})(500. \text{ g}) = 1.13 \times 10^6 \text{ J}$$

**Step 5.** (to raise temperature of water vapor from 100.0 °C to 200.0 °C)

$$q_5 = (1.86 \text{ J/g} \cdot \text{K})(500. \text{ g})(473.2 \text{ K} - 373.2 \text{ K}) = 9.30 \times 10^4 \text{ J}$$

The total energy transferred as heat is the sum of the energies of the individual steps.

$$q_{total} = q_1 + q_2 + q_3 + q_4 + q_5$$

$$q_{total} = 1.65 \times 10^6 \text{ J (or 1650 kJ)}$$

**Think about Your Answer** The conversion of liquid water to steam is the largest increment of energy by a considerable margin. (You may have noticed that it does not take much time to heat water to boiling on a stove, but to boil off the water takes a much longer time.)

**Check Your Understanding**

Calculate the amount of energy necessary to raise the temperature of 1.00 L of ethanol ($d = 0.7849 \text{ g/cm}^3$) from 25.0 °C to its boiling point (78.3 °C) and then to vaporize the liquid. ($C_{ethanol} = 2.44 \text{ J/g} \cdot \text{K}$; heat of vaporization at 78.3 °C = 38.56 kJ/mol.)

## Strategy Map 5.4

**PROBLEM**

Calculate **mass of ice** needed to cool mass of diet cola from $T_{initial}$ to **0 °C**.

**DATA/INFORMATION**
- Mass of diet cola
- $\Delta T$
- heat of fusion of water
- specific heat capacity

STEP 1. Calculate $q_{cola}$ from Equation 5.1.

$q_{cola}$ for cooling diet cola

STEP 2. Use $q_{cola} + q_{ice} = 0$ to calculate $q_{ice}$.

$q_{ice}$ for melting ice

STEP 3. Use heat of fusion and $q_{ice}$ to calculate $m_{ice}$.

**Mass** of ice required ($m_{ice}$)

##  INTERACTIVE EXAMPLE 5.4 Change of State

**Problem** What is the minimum mass of ice at 0 °C that must be added to the contents of a can of diet cola (340. mL) to cool the cola from 20.5 °C to 0.0 °C? Assume that the specific heat capacity and density of diet cola are the same as for water.

**What Do You Know?** The final temperature is 0 °C. Melting ice requires energy as heat, and cooling the cola evolves energy as heat. The sum of the energy changes for the two components in the system is zero; that is, the two energy changes (melting ice, cooling cola) will be the same magnitude but opposite in sign. (We also need to assume there is no transfer of energy between the surroundings and the system.) Use the data given in the question to calculate the energy changes for the two components of this system, $q_{cola}$ and $q_{ice}$. To solve the problem, we will also need the density and specific heat capacity of water (Appendix D).

**Strategy** Assuming only energy changes within the system, $q_{cola} + q_{ice} = 0$. The energy evolved by cooling the cola, $q_{cola}$, is calculated using Equation 5.1. The initial temperature is 20.5 °C and the final temperature is 0 °C. The mass of cola is calculated from the volume and density. The energy as heat required to melt the ice, $q_{ice}$, is determined from the heat of fusion (333 J/g, from text page 216). The mass of ice is the unknown.

**Solution** The mass of cola is 340. g [(340. mL)(1.00 g/mL) = 340. g], and its temperature changes from 293.7 K to 273.2 K. The heat of fusion of water is 333 J/g, and the mass of ice is the unknown.

$$q_{cola} + q_{ice} = 0$$

$$C_{cola} \times m_{cola} \times (T_{final} - T_{initial}) + (\text{heat of fusion of water}) (m_{ice}) = 0$$

$$[(4.184 \text{ J/g} \cdot \text{K})(340. \text{ g})(273.2 \text{ K} - 293.7 \text{ K})] + [(333 \text{ J/g}) (m_{ice})] = 0$$

$$m_{ice} = 87.6 \text{ g}$$

**Think about Your Answer** If more than 87.6 g of ice is added, the final temperature will still be 0 °C when thermal equilibrium is reached, but some ice will remain (see problem below). If less than 87.6 g of ice is added, the final temperature will be greater than 0 °C. In this case, all the ice will melt, and the liquid water formed by melting the ice will absorb additional energy to warm up to the final temperature (an example is given in Study Question 71, page 244).

**Check Your Understanding**

To make a glass of iced tea, you pour 250 mL of tea, whose temperature is 18.2 °C, into a glass containing five ice cubes. Each cube has a mass of 15 g. What quantity of ice will melt, and how much ice will remain floating in the tea? Assume iced tea has a density of 1.0 g/mL and a specific heat capacity of 4.2 J/g · K, that energy is transferred as heat only within the system, ice is at 0.0 °C, and no energy is transferred between system and surroundings.

---

**REVIEW & CHECK FOR SECTION 5.3**

1.  Which of the following processes requires the largest input of energy as heat?

    (a)  raising the temperature of 100 g of water by 1.0 °C

    (b)  vaporization of 0.10 g of water at 100 °C

    (c)  melting 1.0 g of ice at 0 °C

    (d)  warming 1.0 g of ice from $-50$ °C to 0 °C (specific heat of ice $= 2.06$ J/g · K)

2.  Ice (5.0 g) at 0 °C is added to 25 g of liquid water at 20 °C. Which statement best describes the system when thermal equilibrium is reached?

    (a)  Part of the ice has melted; the remaining ice and water are at 0 °C.

    (b)  All of the ice melts; liquid water is at a temperature between 0 °C and 10 °C.

    (c)  All of the ice melts; liquid water is at a temperature between 10 °C and 20 °C.

    (d)  Part of the ice melts; the ice-water mixture is at a temperature between 0 ° C and 10 °C.

---

# 5.4 The First Law of Thermodynamics

Recall that *thermodynamics is the science of heat and work.* To this point, we have only considered energy being transferred as heat, but now we need to broaden the discussion to include work.

Energy transferred as heat between a system and its surroundings changes the energy of the system, but work done by a system or on a system will also affect the energy in the system. If a system does work on its surroundings, energy must be expended by the system, and the system's energy will decrease. Conversely, if work is done by the surroundings on a system, the energy of the system will increase.

A system doing work on its surroundings is illustrated in Figure 5.8. A small quantity of dry ice, solid $CO_2$, is sealed inside a plastic bag, and a weight (a book) is placed on top of the bag. When energy is transferred as heat from the surroundings to the dry ice, the dry ice changes directly from solid to gas at $-78$ °C in a process called **sublimation**:

$$CO_2(s, -78 \text{ °C}) \rightarrow CO_2(g, -78 \text{ °C})$$

As sublimation proceeds, gaseous $CO_2$ expands within the plastic bag, lifting the book against the force of gravity. The system (the $CO_2$ inside the bag) is expending energy to do this work.

Even if the book had not been on top of the plastic bag, work would have been done by the expanding gas because the gas must push back the atmosphere when it expands. Instead of raising a book, the expanding gas moves a part of the atmosphere.

Now let us restate this example in terms of thermodynamics. First, we must identify the system and the surroundings. The system is the $CO_2$, initially a solid and later a gas. The surroundings consist of objects that exchange energy with the system. This includes the plastic bag, the book, the table-top, and the surrounding air. Sublimation requires energy, which is transferred as heat to the system (the $CO_2$)

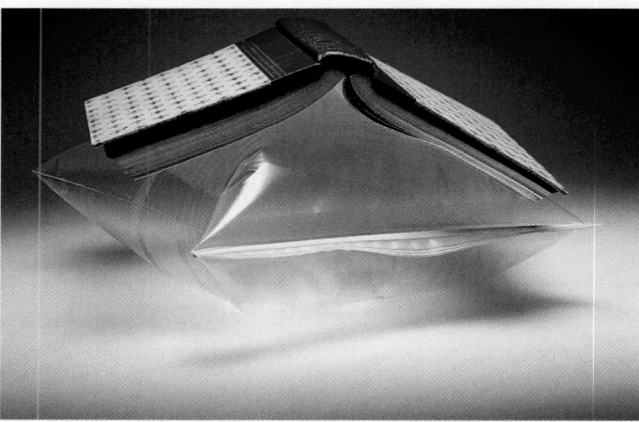

**(a)** Pieces of dry ice [$CO_2(s)$, $-78\ °C$] are placed in a plastic bag. The dry ice will sublime (change directly from a solid to a gas) upon the input of energy.

**(b)** Energy is absorbed by $CO_2(s)$ when it sublimes, and the system (the contents of the bag) does work on its surroundings by lifting the book against the force of gravity.

**FIGURE 5.8** Energy changes in a physical process.

from the surroundings. At the same time, the system does work on the surroundings by lifting the book. An energy balance for the system will include both quantities, energy transferred as heat and energy transferred as work.

This example can be generalized. For any system, we can identify energy transfers both as heat and as work between the system and surroundings. The change in energy for a system is given explicitly by Equation 5.4,

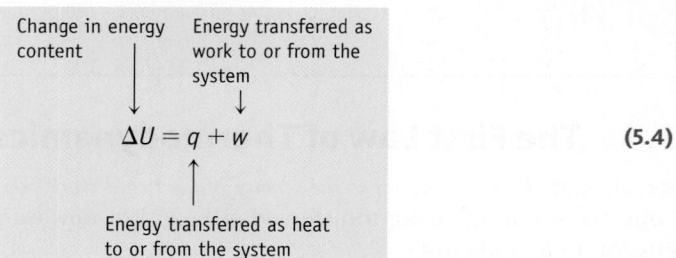

Change in energy content

Energy transferred as work to or from the system

$$\Delta U = q + w \qquad (5.4)$$

Energy transferred as heat to or from the system

which is a mathematical statement of the **first law of thermodynamics**: The energy change for a system ($\Delta U$) is the sum of the energy transferred as heat between the system and its surroundings ($q$) and the energy transferred as work between the system and its surroundings ($w$).

The equation defining the first law of thermodynamics can be thought of as a version of the general principle of conservation of energy. Because energy is conserved, we must be able to account for any change in the energy of the system. All energy transfers between a system and its surroundings occur by the processes of heat and work. Equation 5.4 thus states that the change in the energy of the system is exactly equal to the sum of all of the energy transfers (heat and/or work) between the system and its surroundings.

The quantity $U$ in Equation 5.4 has a formal name—**internal energy**—and a precise meaning in thermodynamics. The internal energy in a chemical system is the sum of the potential and kinetic energies inside the system, that is, the energies of the atoms, molecules, or ions in the system. The potential energy here is the energy associated with the attractive and repulsive forces between all the nuclei and electrons in the system. It includes the energy associated with bonds in molecules, forces between ions, and forces between molecules. The kinetic energy is the energy of motion of the atoms, ions, and molecules in the system. Actual values of internal energy are rarely determined or needed. Instead, in most instances, we are interested in the *change* in internal energy, a measurable quantity. In fact, Equation 5.4 tells us how to determine $\Delta U$: *Measure the energy transferred as heat and work to or from the system.*

The sign conventions for Equation 5.4 are important. The following table summarizes how the internal energy of a system is affected by energy transferred as heat and work.

**Sign Conventions for $q$ and $w$ of the System**

| Energy transferred as . . . | Sign Convention | Effect on $U_{system}$ |
|---|---|---|
| Heat to the system (endothermic) | $q > 0 \, (+)$ | $U$ increases |
| Heat from the system (exothermic) | $q < 0 \, (-)$ | $U$ decreases |
| Work done on system | $w > 0 \, (+)$ | $U$ increases |
| Work done by system | $w < 0 \, (-)$ | $U$ decreases |

The work in the example involving the sublimation of $CO_2$ (Figure 5.8) is of a specific type, called $P–V$ (pressure–volume) work. It is the work ($w$) associated with a change in volume ($\Delta V$) that occurs against a resisting external pressure ($P$). For a system in which the external pressure is constant, the value of $P–V$ work can be calculated using Equation 5.5:

● **Heat and Work** For an in-depth look at heat and work in thermodynamics, see E. A. Gislason and N. C. Craig, *Journal of Chemical Education*, Vol. 64, No. 8, pp. 660–668, 1987.

$$w = -P \times \Delta V \qquad (5.5)$$

Work (at constant pressure) · Pressure · Change in volume

Under conditions of constant volume, $\Delta V = 0$. If the only type of work possible is $P–V$ work, then the energy transferred as work will also be zero (because $\Delta V = 0$ and so $w = 0$). That is, the energy transferred as heat under conditions of constant volume ($q_v$) is equal to the change in the internal energy of the system

$$\Delta U = q_v + w_v$$

$$\Delta U = q_v + 0 \text{ when } w_v = 0 \text{ because } \Delta V = 0$$

$$\text{and so } \Delta U = q_v$$

## A CLOSER LOOK

## P–V Work

Work is done when an object of some mass is moved against an external resisting force.

To evaluate the work done when a gas is compressed, we can use, for example, a cylinder with a movable piston, as would occur in a bicycle pump (see figure). The drawing on the left shows the initial position of the piston, and the one on the right shows its final position. To depress the piston, we would have to expend some energy (the energy for this process comes from the energy obtained by food metabolism in our bodies). The work required to depress the piston is calculated from a law of physics, $w = F \times d$, or work equals the magnitude of the force ($F$) applied times the distance ($d$) over which the force is applied.

Pressure is defined as a force divided by the area over which the force is applied: $P = F/A$. In this example, the force is being applied to a piston with an area $A$. Substituting $P \times A$ for $F$ in the equation for

work gives $w = (P \times A) \times d$. The product of $A \times d$ is equivalent to the change in the volume of the gas in the pump, and, because $\Delta V = V_{final} - V_{initial}$, this change in volume is negative. Finally, because work done on a system is defined as positive, this means that $w = -P\Delta V$.

Pushing down on the piston means we have done work on the system, the gas contained within the cylinder. The gas is now compressed to a smaller volume and has attained a higher energy as a consequence. The additional energy is equal to $-P\Delta V$.

Notice how energy has been converted from one form to another—from chemical energy in food to mechanical energy used to depress the piston, to potential energy stored in a system of a gas at a higher pressure. In each step, energy was conserved, and the total energy of the universe remained constant.

## Enthalpy

Most experiments in a chemical laboratory are carried out in beakers or flasks open to the atmosphere, where the external pressure is constant. Similarly, chemical processes that occur in living systems are open to the atmosphere. Because many processes in chemistry and biology are carried out under conditions of constant pressure, it is useful to have a specific measure of the energy transferred as heat under this circumstance.

Under conditions of constant pressure,

$$\Delta U = q_p + w_p$$

where the subscript $p$ indicates conditions of constant pressure. If the only type of work that occurs is $P-V$ work, then

$$\Delta U = q_p - P\Delta V$$

Rearranging this gives

$$q_p = \Delta U + P\Delta V$$

We now introduce a new thermodynamic function called **enthalpy**, $H$, which is defined as

$$H = U + PV$$

The *change* in enthalpy for a system at constant pressure would be calculated from the following equation:

$$\Delta H = \Delta U + P\Delta V$$

Thus,

$$\Delta H = q_p$$

For a system where the only type of work possible is $P-V$ work, the change in enthalpy, $\Delta H$, is therefore equal to the energy transferred as heat at constant pressure, often symbolized by $q_p$. The directionality of energy transfer (under conditions of constant pressure) is signified by the sign of $\Delta H$.

- Negative values of $\Delta H$ specify that energy is transferred as heat from the system to the surroundings.
- Positive values of $\Delta H$ specify that energy is transferred as heat from the surroundings to the system.

Under conditions of constant pressure and where the only type of work possible is $P-V$ work, $\Delta U (= q_p - P\Delta V)$ and $\Delta H (= q_p)$ differ by $P\Delta V$ (the energy transferred to or from the system as work). We observe that in many processes—such as the melting of ice—the volume change, $\Delta V$, is small, and hence the amount of energy transferred as work is small. Under these circumstances, $\Delta U$ and $\Delta H$ have almost the same value. The amount of energy transferred as work will be significant, however, when the volume change is large, as when gases are formed or consumed. In the evaporation or condensation of water, the sublimation of $CO_2$, and chemical reactions in which the number of moles of gas changes, $\Delta U$ and $\Delta H$ have significantly different values.

## State Functions

Internal energy and enthalpy share a significant characteristic—namely, changes in these quantities depend only on the initial and final states. They do not depend on the path taken on going from the initial state to the final state. No matter how you go from reactants to products in a reaction, for example, the values of $\Delta H$ and $\Delta U$ for the reaction are always the same. A quantity that has this property is called a **state function**.

● **Energy Transferred as Heat** If the only type of work possible is P–V work, then, under conditions of constant volume, the energy transferred as heat is equal to $\Delta U$

$$\Delta U = q_v$$

Under conditions of constant pressure, the energy transferred as heat is equal to $\Delta H$.

$$\Delta H = q_p$$

● **Enthalpy and Internal Energy Differences** The difference between $\Delta H$ and $\Delta U$ will be quite small unless a large volume change occurs. For water at 1 atm pressure and 273 K, for example, the difference between $\Delta H$ and $\Delta U (= P\Delta V)$ is 0.142 J/mol for the conversion of ice to liquid water at 273 K, whereas it is 3100 J/mol for the conversion of liquid water to water vapor at 373 K.

Many commonly measured quantities, such as the pressure of a gas, the volume of a gas or liquid, and the temperature of a substance are state functions. For example, if the final temperature of a substance is 75 °C and its initial temperature is 25 °C, the change in temperature, $\Delta T$, is calculated as $T_{final} - T_{initial} = 75\ °C - 25\ °C = 50\ °C$. It does not matter if the substance was heated directly from 25 °C to 75 °C or if the substance was heated from 25 °C to 95 °C and then cooled to 75 °C; the overall change in temperature is still the same, 50 °C.

Not all quantities are state functions; some depend on the pathway taken to get from the initial condition to the final condition. For instance, distance traveled is not a state function (Figure 5.9). The travel distance from New York City to Denver depends on the route taken. Nor is the elapsed time of travel between these two locations a state function. In contrast, the altitude above sea level is a state function; in going from New York City (at sea level) to Denver (1600 m above sea level), there is an altitude change of 1600 m, regardless of the route followed.

Significantly, neither the energy transferred as heat nor the energy transferred as work individually is a state function but their sum, the change in internal energy, $\Delta U$, is. The value of $\Delta U$ is fixed by $U_{initial}$ and $U_{final}$. A transition between the initial and final states can be accomplished by different routes having different values of $q$ and $w$, but the sum of $q$ and $w$ for each path must always give the same $\Delta U$.

To get a better picture of how it might arise that the sum of two path-dependent functions can result in a state function, consider the size of your bank account. This is a state function. Let us assume that there are two path-dependent ways to transfer money into or out of your account: either as cash or as an electronic payment. You could have arrived at a current bank balance of $25 by having deposited $25 in cash or you could have deposited $100 in cash and then made a $75 electronic payment, or you could have deposited $100 in cash, made an electronic payment of $50 and withdrawn $25 in cash. In each of these cases, the change in your bank balance is determined by taking the final balance ($25) and subtracting the initial balance ($0), giving a value for $\Delta\$$ of +$25, but the pathway to get from $0 to $25 is different. In addition, the quantity of money transferred as cash and the quantity of money transferred by electronic payment are path-dependent with different values in each case, but by taking into account all of the transfers as cash and all of the transfers as electronic payments, we end up with a state function, the overall balance.

As previously stated, enthalpy is a state function. The enthalpy change occurring when 1.0 g of water is heated from 20 °C to 50 °C is independent of how the process is carried out.

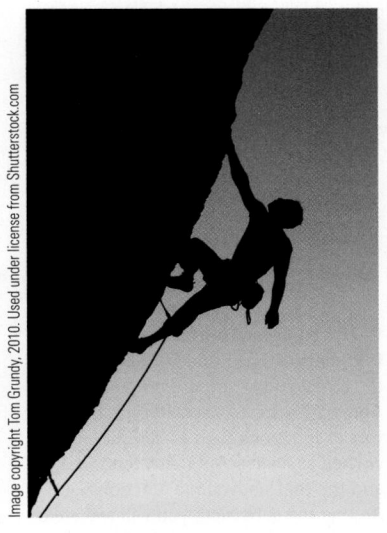

**FIGURE 5.9 State functions.** There are many ways to climb a mountain, but the change in altitude from the base of the mountain to its summit is the same. The change in altitude is a state function. The distance traveled to reach the summit is not.

---

**REVIEW & CHECK FOR SECTION 5.4**

1.  Which of the following processes will lead to a decrease in the internal energy of a system? (1) Energy is transferred as heat to the system; (2) energy is transferred as heat from the system; (3) energy is transferred as work done on the system; or (4) energy is transferred as work done by the system.

    (a)  1 and 3        (b)  2 and 4        (c)  1 and 4        (d)  2 and 3

2.  In chemical reactions, a significant amount of energy is transferred as work between systems and surroundings if there is a significant change in volume. This occurs if there is a change in the number of moles of gases. In which of the following reactions is there a significant transfer of energy as work from the system to the surroundings?

    (a)  $C(s) + O_2(g) \rightarrow CO_2(g)$

    (b)  $CH_4(g) + 2\ O_2(g) \rightarrow CO_2(g) + 2\ H_2O(g)$

    (c)  $2\ C(s) + O_2(g) \rightarrow 2\ CO(g)$

    (d)  $2\ Mg(s) + O_2(g) \rightarrow 2\ MgO(s)$

## 5.5 Enthalpy Changes for Chemical Reactions

Enthalpy changes accompany chemical reactions. For example, the **standard reaction enthalpy**, $\Delta_r H°$, for the decomposition of water vapor to hydrogen and oxygen at 25 °C is +241.8 kJ/mol-rxn.

$$H_2O(g) \rightarrow H_2(g) + \tfrac{1}{2} O_2(g) \qquad \Delta_r H° = +241.8 \text{ kJ/mol-rxn}$$

The positive sign of $\Delta_r H°$ in this case indicates that the decomposition is an endothermic process.

There are several important things to know about $\Delta_r H°$.

- The designation of $\Delta_r H°$ as a "standard enthalpy change" (where the superscript ° indicates standard conditions) means that the pure, unmixed reactants in their standard states have formed pure, unmixed products in their standard states. The **standard state** of an element or a compound is defined as the most stable form of the substance in the physical state that exists at a pressure of 1 bar and at a specified temperature. [Most sources report standard reaction enthalpies at 25 °C (298 K).]

- The "per mol-rxn" designation in the units for $\Delta_r H°$ means this is the enthalpy change for a "mole of reaction" (where *rxn* is an abbreviation for reaction). One mole of reaction is said to have occurred when a chemical reaction occurs exactly in the amounts specified by the coefficients of the balanced chemical equation. For example, for the reaction $H_2O(g) \rightarrow H_2(g) + 1/2\,O_2(g)$, a mole of reaction has occurred when 1 mol of water vapor has been converted completely to 1 mol of $H_2$ and 1/2 mol of $O_2$ gas.

Now consider the opposite reaction, the combination of hydrogen and oxygen to form 1 mol of water. The magnitude of the enthalpy change for this reaction is the same as that for the decomposition reaction, but the sign of $\Delta_r H°$ is reversed. The exothermic formation of 1 mol of water vapor from 1 mol of $H_2$ and 1/2 mol of $O_2$ transfers 241.8 kJ to the surroundings (Figure 5.10).

$$H_2(g) + \tfrac{1}{2} O_2(g) \rightarrow H_2O(g) \qquad \Delta_r H° = -241.8 \text{ kJ/mol-rxn}$$

The value of $\Delta_r H°$ depends on the chemical equation used. Let us write the equation for the formation of water again but without a fractional coefficient for $O_2$.

$$2\,H_2(g) + O_2(g) \rightarrow 2\,H_2O(g) \qquad \Delta_r H° = -483.6 \text{ kJ/mol-rxn}$$

● **Notation for Thermodynamic Parameters** NIST and IUPAC (International Union of Pure and Applied Chemistry) specify that descriptors of functions such as $\Delta H$ should be written as a subscript, between the $\Delta$ and the thermodynamic function. Among the subscripts you will see are a lower case r for "reaction," f for "formation," c for "combustion," fus for "fusion," and vap for "vaporization."

● **Moles of Reaction, Mol-rxn** This concept was also described in one of the methods shown for solving limiting reactant problems on page 165.

**(a)** A lighted candle is brought up to a balloon filled with hydrogen gas.

**(b)** When the balloon breaks, the candle flame ignites the hydrogen.

$\Delta_r H° = -241.8$ kJ/mol-rxn

Photos © Cengage Learning/Charles D. Winters

$\tfrac{1}{2}\,O_2(g) \qquad + \qquad H_2(g) \qquad \longrightarrow \qquad H_2O(g)$

**FIGURE 5.10 The exothermic combustion of hydrogen in air.** The reaction transfers energy to the surroundings in the form of heat, work, and light.

The value of $\Delta_r H°$ for 1 mol of this reaction, the formation of 2 mol of water, is twice the value for the formation of 1 mol of water.

It is important to identify the states of reactants and products in a reaction because the magnitude of $\Delta_r H°$ depends on whether they are solids, liquids, or gases. For the formation of 1 mol of *liquid water* from the elements, the enthalpy change is $-285.8$ kJ.

$$H_2(g) + \tfrac{1}{2} O_2(g) \rightarrow H_2O(\ell) \qquad \Delta_r H° = -285.8 \text{ kJ/mol-rxn}$$

Notice that this value is not the same as $\Delta_r H°$ for the formation of 1 mol of *water vapor* from hydrogen and oxygen. The difference between the two values is equal to the enthalpy change for the condensation of 1 mol of water vapor to 1 mol of liquid water.

These examples illustrate several general features of enthalpy changes for chemical reactions.

- Enthalpy changes are specific to the reaction being carried out. The identities of reactants and products and their states (s, $\ell$, g) are important, as are the amounts of reactants and products.
- The enthalpy change depends on the number of moles of reaction, that is, the number of times the reaction *as written* is carried out.
- $\Delta_r H°$ has a negative value for an exothermic reaction; it has a positive value for an endothermic reaction.
- Values of $\Delta_r H°$ are numerically the same, but opposite in sign, for chemical reactions that are the reverse of each other.

Standard reaction enthalpies can be used to calculate the energy transferred as heat under conditions of constant pressure for any given mass of a reactant or product. Suppose you want to know the energy transferred to the surroundings as heat if 454 g of propane, $C_3H_8$, is burned (at constant pressure), given the equation for the exothermic combustion and the enthalpy change for the reaction.

$$C_3H_8(g) + 5 O_2(g) \rightarrow 3 CO_2(g) + 4 H_2O(\ell) \qquad \Delta_r H° = -2220 \text{ kJ/mol-rxn}$$

Two steps are needed. First, find the amount of propane present in the sample:

$$454 \text{ g } C_3H_8 \left( \frac{1 \text{ mol } C_3H_8}{44.10 \text{ g } C_3H_8} \right) = 10.3 \text{ mol } C_3H_8$$

Second, use $\Delta_r H°$ to determine $\Delta H°$ for this amount of propane:

$$\Delta_r H° = 10.3 \text{ mol } C_3H_8 \left( \frac{1 \text{ mol-rxn}}{1 \text{ mol } C_3H_8} \right)\left( \frac{-2220 \text{ kJ}}{1 \text{ mol-rxn}} \right) = -22{,}900 \text{ kJ}$$

● **Fractional Stoichiometric Coefficients** When writing balanced equations to define thermodynamic quantities, chemists often use fractional stoichiometric coefficients. For example, to define $\Delta_r H$ for the decomposition or formation of 1 mol of $H_2O$, the coefficient for $O_2$ must be 1/2.

● **Standard Conditions** The superscript ° indicates standard conditions. It is applied to any type of thermodynamic data, such as enthalpy of fusion and vaporization ($\Delta_{fus}H°$ and $\Delta_{vap}H°$) and enthalpy of a reaction ($\Delta_r H°$). Standard conditions refers to reactants and products in their standard states at a pressure of 1 bar. One bar is approximately one atmosphere (1 atm = 1.013 bar; ► Appendix B).

**⊙WL   INTERACTIVE EXAMPLE 5.5**    Calculating the Enthalpy Change
for a Reaction

**Problem** Sucrose (table sugar, $C_{12}H_{22}O_{11}$) can be oxidized to $CO_2$ and $H_2O$, and the enthalpy change for the reaction can be measured.

$$C_{12}H_{22}O_{11}(s) + 12 O_2(g) \rightarrow 12 CO_2(g) + 11 H_2O(\ell) \qquad \Delta_r H° = -5645 \text{ kJ/mol-rxn}$$

What is the enthalpy change when 5.00 g of sugar is burned under conditions of constant pressure?

**What Do You Know?** The balanced equation for the combustion and the value of $\Delta_r H°$ are given. Also, the mass of sugar is given.

**Strategy** First determine the amount (mol) of sucrose in 5.00 g, and then use this with the value given for the enthalpy change for the oxidation of 1 mol of sucrose.

● **Burning Sugar and Gummi Bears** A person on a diet might note that a (level) teaspoonful of sugar (about 3.5 g) supplies about 15 Calories (dietary Calories; the conversion is 4.184 kJ = 1 Cal). As diets go, a single spoonful of sugar doesn't have a large caloric content. But will you use just one level teaspoonful? Or just one Gummi Bear? In the Cengage *YouBook*, **click on the bear** for a video of a Gummi bear consumed by an oxidizing agent.

© Cengage Learning/Charles D. Winters

## Strategy Map 5.5

**PROBLEM**

Calculate $\Delta_rH°$ for combustion of **given mass** of sucrose.

↓

**DATA/INFORMATION**

- **Mass** of sucrose
- $\Delta_rH°$ **per mol** for sucrose combustion

STEP 1. Calculate **amount** of sucrose.

**Amount** of sucrose

STEP 2. Multiply **amount of sucrose** by $\Delta_rH°$ **per mol** for sucrose combustion.

$\Delta H°$ for combustion of **given mass** of sucrose

### Solution

$$5.00 \ g \ sucrose \times \frac{1 \ mol \ sucrose}{342.3 \ g \ sucrose} = 1.46 \times 10^{-2} \ mol \ sucrose$$

$$\Delta H° = 1.46 \times 10^{-2} \ mol \ sucrose \left(\frac{1 \ mol\text{-}rxn}{1 \ mol \ sucrose}\right)\left(\frac{-5645 \ kJ}{1 \ mol\text{-}rxn}\right)$$

$$\Delta H° = -82.5 \ kJ$$

**Think about Your Answer** The calculated value is negative, as expected for a combustion reaction. The magnitude of $\Delta H°$ agrees with the fact that the mass of sucrose used, 5.00 g, is significantly less than that of one mole of sucrose (342.3 g).

### Check Your Understanding

The combustion of ethane, $C_2H_6$, has an enthalpy change of $-2857.3$ kJ for the reaction as written below. Calculate $\Delta H°$ for the combustion of 15.0 g of $C_2H_6$.

$$2 \ C_2H_6(g) + 7 \ O_2(g) \rightarrow 4 \ CO_2(g) + 6 \ H_2O(g) \qquad \Delta_rH° = -2857.3 \ kJ/mol\text{-}rxn$$

---

**REVIEW & CHECK FOR SECTION 5.5**

1.  For the reaction $2 \ Hg(\ell) + O_2(g) \rightarrow 2 \ HgO(s)$, $\Delta_rH° = -181.6$ kJ/mol-rxn. What is the enthalpy change to decompose 1.00 mol of HgO(s) to $O_2(g)$ and $Hg(\ell)$?

    (a)   181.6 kJ          (b)   $-90.8$ kJ          (c)   90.8 kJ          (d)   363.3 kJ

2.  For the reaction $2 \ CO(g) + O_2(g) \rightarrow 2 \ CO_2(g)$, $\Delta_rH° = -566$ kJ/mol-rxn. What is the enthalpy change for the oxidation of 42.0 g of CO(g)?

    (a)   $-283$ kJ          (b)   $-425$ kJ          (c)   $-566$ kJ          (d)   $-393.5$ kJ

---

# 5.6   Calorimetry

The energy evolved or absorbed as heat in a chemical or physical process can be measured by **calorimetry**. The apparatus used in this kind of experiment is a *calorimeter*.

## Constant Pressure Calorimetry, Measuring $\Delta H$

A constant pressure calorimeter can be used to measure the amount of energy transferred as heat under constant pressure conditions, that is, the enthalpy change for a chemical reaction.

The constant pressure calorimeter used in general chemistry laboratories is often a "coffee-cup calorimeter." This inexpensive device consists of two nested Styrofoam coffee cups with a loose-fitting lid and a temperature-measuring device such as a thermometer (Figure 5.11) or thermocouple. Styrofoam, a fairly good insulator, minimizes energy transfer as heat between the system and the surroundings. The reaction is carried out in solution in the cup. If the reaction is exothermic, it releases energy as heat to the solution, and the temperature of the solution rises. If the reaction is endothermic, energy is absorbed as heat from the solution, and a decrease in the temperature of the solution will be seen. The change in temperature of the solution is measured. Knowing the mass and specific heat capacity of the solution and the temperature change, the enthalpy change for the reaction can be calculated.

In this type of calorimetry experiment, it will be convenient to define the chemicals and the solution as the system. The surroundings are the cup and everything beyond the cup. As noted above, we assume there is no energy transfer to the cup

**FIGURE 5.11 A coffee-cup calorimeter.** A chemical reaction produces a change in temperature of the solution in the calorimeter. The Styrofoam container is fairly effective in preventing the transfer of energy as heat between the solution and its surroundings. Because the cup is open to the atmosphere, this is a constant pressure measurement.

Thermometer

Cardboard or Styrofoam lid

Nested Styrofoam cups

Reaction occurs in solution.

or beyond and that energy is transferred only as heat within the system. Two energy changes occur within the system. One is the change that takes place as the chemical reaction occurs, either releasing the potential energy stored in the reactants or absorbing energy and converting it to potential energy stored in the products. We label this energy as $q_r$. The other energy change is the energy gained or lost as heat by the solution ($q_{solution}$). Based on the law of conservation of energy,

$$q_r + q_{solution} = 0$$

The value of $q_{solution}$ can be calculated from the specific heat capacity, mass, and change in temperature of the solution. The quantity of energy evolved or absorbed as heat for the reaction ($q_r$) is the unknown in the equation.

The accuracy of a calorimetry experiment depends on the accuracy of the measured quantities (temperature, mass, specific heat capacity). In addition, it depends on how closely the assumption is followed that there is no energy transfer beyond the solution. A coffee-cup calorimeter is an unsophisticated apparatus, and the results obtained with it are not highly accurate, largely because this assumption is poorly met. In research laboratories, however, calorimeters are used that more effectively limit the energy transfer between system and surroundings. In addition, it is also possible to estimate and correct for the minimal energy transfer that occurs between the system and the surroundings.

## ⓦWL   INTERACTIVE EXAMPLE 5.6   Using a Coffee-Cup Calorimeter

**Problem** Suppose you place 0.0500 g of magnesium chips in a coffee-cup calorimeter and then add 100.0 mL of 1.00 M HCl. The reaction that occurs is

$$Mg(s) + 2\ HCl(aq) \rightarrow H_2(g) + MgCl_2(aq)$$

The temperature of the solution increases from 22.21 °C (295.36 K) to 24.46 °C (297.61 K). What is the enthalpy change for the reaction per mole of Mg? Assume that the specific heat capacity of the solution is 4.20 J/g · K and the density of the HCl solution is 1.00 g/mL.

**What Do You Know?** You know that energy is evolved as heat in this reaction because the temperature of the solution rises. Assuming no energy loss to the surroundings, the sum of the energy evolved as heat in the reaction, $q_r$, and the energy absorbed as heat by the solution, $q_{solution}$, will be zero, that is, $q_r + q_{solution} = 0$. The value of $q_{solution}$ can be calculated from data given; $q_r$ is the unknown.

**Strategy** Solving the problem has four steps.

**Step 1:** Calculate the amount of magnesium.

**Step 2:** Calculate $q_{solution}$ from the values of the mass, specific heat capacity, and $\Delta T$ using Equation 5.1.

**Step 3:** Calculate $q_r$, assuming no energy transfer as heat occurs beyond the solution, that is, $q_r + q_{solution} = 0$.

**Step 4:** Use the value of $q_r$ and the amount of Mg to calculate the enthalpy change per mole of Mg.

**Solution**

**Step 1.** Calculate the amount of Mg.

$$0.0500 \text{ g Mg} \times \frac{1 \text{ mol Mg}}{24.31 \text{ g Mg}} = 0.00206 \text{ mol Mg}$$

**Step 2.** Calculate $q_{solution}$. The mass of the solution is the mass of the 100.0 mL of HCl plus the mass of magnesium.

$$q_{solution} = (100.0 \text{ g HCl solution} + 0.0500 \text{ g Mg})(4.20 \text{ J/g} \cdot \text{K})(297.61 \text{ K} - 295.36 \text{ K})$$

$$= 945 \text{ J}$$

**Strategy Map 5.6**

**PROBLEM**

Calculate $\Delta H$ per mol for reaction of **Mg** with **HCl.**

↓

**DATA/INFORMATION**

- Mass of Mg and HCl solution
- $\Delta T$
- Specific heat capacity

**STEP 1.** Calculate amount of **Mg.**

↓

Amount of **Mg**

**STEP 2.** Use Equation 5.1 to calculate $q_{solution}$.

↓

$q_{solution}$

**STEP 3.** Use $q_r + q_{solution} = 0$ to calculate $q_r$.

↓

$q_r$, the energy evolved by given mass of Mg in HCl(aq)

**STEP 4.** Divide $q_r$ by amount of **Mg.**

↓

$\Delta_r H$ per mol of Mg

**Step 3.** Calculate $q_r$.

$$q_r + q_{solution} = 0$$

$$q_r + 945\ J = 0$$

$$q_r = -945\ J$$

**Step 4.** Calculate the value of $\Delta_r H$ per mole of Mg. The value of $q_r$ found in Step 2 resulted from the reaction of 0.00206 mol of Mg. The enthalpy change per mole of Mg is therefore

$$\Delta_r H = (-945\ J/0.00206\ mol\ Mg)$$

$$= -4.59 \times 10^5\ J/mol\ Mg\ (= -459\ kJ/mol\ Mg)$$

**Think about Your Answer** The calculation gives the correct sign of $q_r$ and $\Delta_r H$. The negative sign indicates that this is an exothermic reaction. The balanced equation states that one mole of magnesium is involved in one mole of reaction. The enthalpy change per mole of reaction, $\Delta_r H$, is therefore −459 kJ/mol-rxn.

---

**Check Your Understanding**

Assume 200. mL of 0.400 M HCl is mixed with 200. mL of 0.400 M NaOH in a coffee-cup calorimeter. The temperature of the solutions before mixing was 25.10 °C; after mixing and allowing the reaction to occur, the temperature is 27.78 °C. What is the enthalpy change when one mole of acid is neutralized? (Assume that the densities of all solutions are 1.00 g/mL and their specific heat capacities are 4.20 J/g · K.)

---

## Constant Volume Calorimetry, Measuring $\Delta U$

Constant volume calorimetry is often used to evaluate the energy released by the combustion of fuels and the caloric value of foods. A weighed sample of a combustible solid or liquid is placed inside a "bomb," often a cylinder about the size of a large fruit juice can with thick steel walls and ends (Figure 5.12). The bomb is placed in a water-filled container with well-insulated walls. After filling the bomb with pure oxygen, the sample is ignited, usually by an electric spark. The heat generated by the combustion reaction warms the bomb and the water around it. The bomb, its

**FIGURE 5.12 Constant volume calorimeter.** A combustible sample is burned in pure oxygen in a sealed metal container or "bomb." Energy released as heat warms the bomb and the water surrounding it. By measuring the increase in temperature, the energy evolved as heat in the reaction can be determined.

Thermometer    Water    Stirrer    Ignition wires

Insulated outside container    Steel container    Sample dish    Steel bomb

The sample burns in pure oxygen, warming the bomb.    The heat generated warms the water, and $\Delta T$ is measured by the thermometer.

contents, and the water are defined as the system. Assessment of energy transfers as heat within the system shows that

$$q_r + q_{bomb} + q_{water} = 0$$

where $q_r$ is the energy released as heat by the reaction, $q_{bomb}$ is the energy involved in heating the calorimeter bomb, and $q_{water}$ is the energy involved in heating the water in the calorimeter. Because the volume does not change in a constant volume calorimeter, energy transfer as work cannot occur (assuming only $P$–$V$ work is possible). Therefore, the energy transferred as heat at constant volume ($q_v$) is equal to the change in internal energy, $\Delta U$.

● **Calorimetry, $\Delta U$, and $\Delta H$** The two types of calorimetry (constant volume and constant pressure) highlight the differences between enthalpy and internal energy. The energy transferred as heat at constant pressure, $q_p$, is, by definition, $\Delta H$, whereas the energy transferred as heat at constant volume, $q_v$, is $\Delta U$.

## ⓌWL   INTERACTIVE EXAMPLE 5.7   Constant Volume Calorimetry

**Problem** Octane, $C_8H_{18}$, a primary constituent of gasoline, burns in air:

$$C_8H_{18}(\ell) + 25/2\ O_2(g) \rightarrow 8\ CO_2(g) + 9\ H_2O(\ell)$$

A 1.00-g sample of octane is burned in a constant volume calorimeter similar to that shown in Figure 5.12. The calorimeter is in an insulated container with 1.20 kg of water. The temperature of the water and the bomb rises from 25.00 °C (298.15 K) to 33.20 °C (306.35 K). The heat required to raise the bomb's temperature (its heat capacity), $C_{bomb}$, is 837 J/K. (a) What is the heat of combustion per gram of octane? (b) What is the heat of combustion per mole of octane?

**What Do You Know?** There are energy changes for the three components of this system: the energy evolved in the reaction, $q_r$; the energy absorbed by the water, $q_{water}$; and the energy absorbed by the calorimeter, $q_{bomb}$. You know the following: the molar mass of octane, masses of the sample and the calorimeter water, $T_{initial}$, $T_{final}$, $C_{bomb}$, and $C_{water}$. You can assume no energy loss to the surroundings.

**Strategy**

- The sum of all the energies transferred as heat in the system = $q_r + q_{bomb} + q_{water} = 0$. The first term, $q_r$, is the unknown. The second and third terms in the equation can be calculated from the data given: $q_{bomb}$ is calculated from the bomb's heat capacity and $\Delta T$, and $q_{water}$ is determined from the specific heat capacity, mass, and $\Delta T$ for water.

- The value of $q_r$ is the energy evolved in the combustion of 1.00 g of octane. Use this and the molar mass of octane (114.2 g/mol) to calculate the energy evolved as heat per mole of octane.

**Solution**

(a)  $q_{water} = C_{water} \times m_{water} \times \Delta T = (4.184\ J/g \cdot K)(1.20 \times 10^3\ g)(306.35\ K - 298.15\ K) = +41.2 \times 10^3\ J$

$q_{bomb} = (C_{bomb})(\Delta T) = (837\ J/K)(306.35\ K - 298.15\ K) = 6.86 \times 10^3\ J$

$q_r + q_{water} + q_{bomb} = 0$

$q_r + 41.2 \times 10^3\ J + 6.86 \times 10^3\ J = 0$

$q_r = -48.1 \times 10^3\ J\ (or\ -48.1\ kJ)$

Heat of combustion per gram = $-48.1$ kJ

(b)  Heat of combustion per mole of octane = $(-48.1\ kJ/g)(114.2\ g/mol) = -5.49 \times 10^3\ kJ/mol$

**Think about Your Answer** Because the volume does not change, no energy transfer in the form of work occurs. The change of internal energy, $\Delta_r U$, for the combustion of $C_8H_{18}(\ell)$ is $-5.49 \times 10^3$ kJ/mol. Also note that $C_{bomb}$ has no mass units. It is the heat required to warm the bomb by 1 kelvin.

**Strategy Map 5.7**

PROBLEM

Calculate $\Delta U$ per mol for combustion of octane.

DATA/INFORMATION

- Mass of octane
- Mass of water in calorimeter
- $C_{water}$
- $C_{bomb}$
- $\Delta T$

STEP 1. Use Equation 5.1 to calculate $q_{water}$.

$q_{water}$

STEP 2. Use $C_{bomb}$ and $\Delta T$ to calculate $q_{bomb}$.

$q_{bomb}$

STEP 3. Use $q_r + q_{water} + q_{bomb} = 0$ to calculate $q_r$.

$q_r$, the energy evolved as heat by given mass of octane (kJ)

STEP 4. Multiply $q_r$ by **molar mass** of octane.

$\Delta U$ per mol of octane

### Check Your Understanding

A 1.00-g sample of ordinary table sugar (sucrose, $C_{12}H_{22}O_{11}$) is burned in a bomb calorimeter. The temperature of $1.50 \times 10^3$ g of water in the calorimeter rises from 25.00 °C to 27.32 °C. The heat capacity of the bomb is 837 J/K, and the specific heat capacity of the water is 4.20 J/g · K. Calculate (a) the heat evolved per gram of sucrose and (b) the heat evolved per mole of sucrose.

---

**REVIEW & CHECK FOR SECTION 5.6**

1.  A student used a coffee-cup calorimeter to determine the enthalpy of solution for $NH_4NO_3$. When $NH_4NO_3$ is added to water, there is a decrease in temperature of the solution. Is the solution process exothermic or endothermic?

    (a)  exothermic                              (b)  endothermic

2.  What if, contrary to our assumption of no transfer of energy between system and surroundings in the calorimeter experiment, some energy as heat is transferred from the surroundings to the system. How will this affect the value of $\Delta_{solution}H°$?

    (a)  No effect will be seen.

    (b)  The calculated value of $\Delta_{solution}H°$ will be too small.

    (c)  The calculated value of $\Delta_{solution}H°$ will be too large.

---

**Module 10: Thermochemistry and Hess's Law** covers concepts in this section.

## 5.7   Enthalpy Calculations

Enthalpy changes for an enormous number of chemical and physical processes are available on the World Wide Web and in reference books. These data have been collected by scientists over a number of years from many experiments and are used to calculate enthalpy changes for chemical processes. Now we want to discuss how to use these data.

### Hess's Law

The enthalpy change can be measured by calorimetry for many, but not all, chemical processes. Consider, for example, the oxidation of carbon to form carbon monoxide.

$$C(s) + \tfrac{1}{2}\,O_2(g) \rightarrow CO(g)$$

The primary product of the reaction of carbon and oxygen is $CO_2$, even if a deficiency of oxygen is used. As soon as CO is formed, it reacts with $O_2$ to form $CO_2$. Because the reaction cannot be carried out in a way that allows CO to be the sole product, it is not possible to measure the change in enthalpy for this reaction by calorimetry.

The enthalpy change for the reaction forming $CO(g)$ from $C(s)$ and $O_2(g)$ can be determined indirectly, however, from enthalpy changes for other reactions for which values of $\Delta_r H°$ can be measured. The calculation is based on **Hess's law**, which states that if a reaction is the sum of two or more other reactions, $\Delta_r H°$ for the overall process is the sum of the $\Delta_r H°$ values of those reactions.

The oxidation of $C(s)$ to $CO_2(g)$ can be viewed as occurring in two steps: first the oxidation of $C(s)$ to $CO(g)$ (Equation 1) and second the oxidation of $CO(g)$ to $CO_2(g)$ (Equation 2). Adding these two equations gives the equation for the oxidation of $C(s)$ to $CO_2(g)$ (Equation 3).

| | | |
|---|---|---|
| Equation 1: | $C(s) + \tfrac{1}{2}\,O_2(g) \rightarrow CO(g)$ | $\Delta_r H_1° = ?$ |
| Equation 2: | $CO(g) + \tfrac{1}{2}\,O_2(g) \rightarrow CO_2(g)$ | $\Delta_r H_2° = -283.0$ kJ/mol-rxn |
| Equation 3: | $C(s) + O_2(g) \rightarrow CO_2(g)$ | $\Delta_r H_3° = -393.5$ kJ/mol-rxn |

Hess's law tells us that the enthalpy change for the overall reaction ($\Delta_r H_3°$) will equal the sum of the enthalpy changes for reactions 1 and 2 ($\Delta_r H_1° + \Delta_r H_2°$). Both $\Delta_r H_2°$ and $\Delta_r H_3°$ can be measured, and these values are then used to calculate the enthalpy change for reaction 1.

$$\Delta_r H_3° = \Delta_r H_1° + \Delta_r H_2°$$

$$-393.5 \text{ kJ/mol-rxn} = \Delta_r H_1° + (-283.0 \text{ kJ/mol-rxn})$$

$$\Delta_r H_1° = -110.5 \text{ kJ/mol-rxn}$$

Hess's law also applies to physical processes. The enthalpy change for the reaction of $H_2(g)$ and $O_2(g)$ to form 1 mol of $H_2O$ vapor is different from the enthalpy change to form 1 mol of liquid $H_2O$. The difference is the negative of the *enthalpy of vaporization* of water, $\Delta_r H_2^\circ$ ($= -\Delta_{vap}H^\circ$) as shown in the following analysis

| | | |
|---|---|---|
| Equation 1: | $H_2(g) + \frac{1}{2} O_2(g) \rightarrow H_2O(g)$ | $\Delta_r H_1^\circ = -241.8$ kJ/mol-rxn |
| Equation 2: | $H_2O(g) \rightarrow H_2O(\ell)$ | $\Delta_r H_2^\circ = -44.0$ kJ/mol-rxn |
| Equation 3: | $H_2(g) + \frac{1}{2} O_2(g) \rightarrow H_2O(\ell)$ | $\Delta_r H_3^\circ = -285.8$ kJ/mol-rxn |

## Energy Level Diagrams

When using Hess's law, it is often helpful to represent enthalpy data schematically in an energy level diagram. In such drawings, the various substances being studied—the reactants and products in a chemical reaction, for example—are placed on an arbitrary energy scale. The relative enthalpy of each substance is given by its position on the vertical axis, and numerical differences in enthalpy between them are shown by the vertical arrows. Such diagrams provide a visual perspective on the magnitude and direction of enthalpy changes and show how the enthalpies of the substances are related.

Energy level diagrams that summarize the two examples of Hess's law discussed earlier are shown in Figure 5.13. In Figure 5.13a, the elements $C(s)$ and $O_2(g)$ are at the highest enthalpy. The reaction of carbon and oxygen to form $CO_2(g)$ lowers the enthalpy by 393.5 kJ. This can occur either in a single step, shown on the left in Figure 5.13a, or in two steps via initial formation of $CO(g)$, as shown on the right. Similarly, in Figure 5.13b, the mixture of $H_2(g)$ and $O_2(g)$ is at the highest enthalpy. Both liquid and gaseous water have lower enthalpies, with the difference between the two being the enthalpy of vaporization.

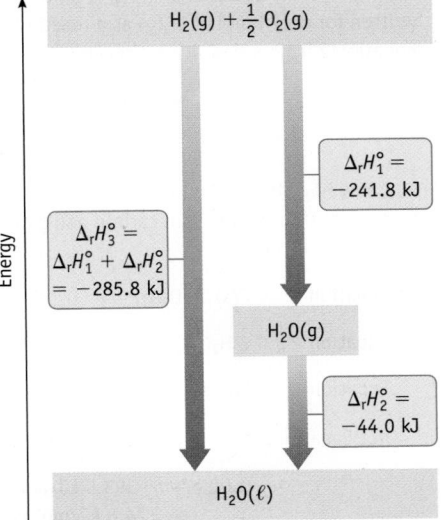

**(a)** The formation of $CO_2$ can occur in a single step or in a succession of steps. $\Delta_r H^\circ$ for the overall process is $-393.5$ kJ, no matter which path is followed.

**(b)** The formation of $H_2O(\ell)$ can occur in a single step or in a succession of steps. $\Delta_r H^\circ$ for the overall process is $-285.8$ kJ, no matter which path is followed.

**FIGURE 5.13 Energy level diagrams. (a)** Relating enthalpy changes in the formation of $CO_2(g)$. **(b)** Relating enthalpy changes in the formation of $H_2O(\ell)$. Enthalpy changes associated with changes between energy levels are given alongside the vertical arrows.

Strategy Map 5.8

**PROBLEM**

**Hess's Law:** Calculate $\Delta_r H°$ for **targeted reaction** from $\Delta_r H°$ values for other reactions.

**DATA/INFORMATION**

Three reactions with known $\Delta_r H°$ values

**STEP 1.** Combine equations with $\Delta_r H°$ values to give **targeted net equation**.

Targeted **net equation**

**STEP 2.** Add $\Delta_r H°$ **values** for equations that sum to targeted equation.

$\Delta_r H°$ for targeted reaction

# ⊙WL   INTERACTIVE EXAMPLE 5.8   Using Hess's Law

**Problem** Suppose you want to know the enthalpy change for the formation of methane, $CH_4$, from solid carbon (as graphite) and hydrogen gas:

$$C(s) + 2\ H_2(g) \rightarrow CH_4(g) \qquad \Delta_r H° = ?$$

The enthalpy change for this reaction cannot be measured in the laboratory because the reaction is very slow. We can, however, measure enthalpy changes for the combustion of carbon, hydrogen, and methane.

Equation 1:   $C(s) + O_2(g) \rightarrow CO_2(g)$        $\Delta_r H_1° = -393.5$ kJ/mol-rxn

Equation 2:   $H_2(g) + \frac{1}{2} O_2(g) \rightarrow H_2O(\ell)$        $\Delta_r H_2° = -285.8$ kJ/mol-rxn

Equation 3:   $CH_4(g) + 2\ O_2(g) \rightarrow CO_2(g) + 2\ H_2O(\ell)$   $\Delta_r H_3° = -890.3$ kJ/mol-rxn

Use this information to calculate $\Delta_r H°$ for the formation of methane from its elements.

**What Do You Know?** This is a Hess's law problem. You need to adjust the three equations so they can be added together to give the targeted equation, $C(s) + 2\ H_2(g) \rightarrow CH_4(g)$. When an adjustment in an equation is made, you need to also adjust the enthalpy change.

**Strategy** The three reactions (1, 2, and 3), as written, cannot be added together to obtain the equation for the formation of $CH_4$ from its elements. Methane, $CH_4$, is a product in the reaction for which we wish to calculate $\Delta_r H°$, but it is a reactant in Equation 3. Water appears in two of these equations although it is not a component of the reaction forming $CH_4$ from carbon and hydrogen. To use Hess's law to solve this problem, you first have to manipulate the equations and adjust $\Delta_r H°$ values accordingly before adding equations together. Recall, from Section 5.5, that writing an equation in the reverse direction changes the sign of $\Delta_r H°$ and that doubling the amount of reactants and products doubles the value of $\Delta_r H°$. Adjustments to Equations 2 and 3 will produce new equations that, along with Equation 1, can be combined to give the desired net reaction.

**Solution** To have $CH_4$ appear as a product in the overall reaction, reverse Equation 3, which changes the sign of its $\Delta_r H°$.

Equation 3′:   $CO_2(g) + 2\ H_2O(\ell) \rightarrow CH_4(g) + 2\ O_2(g)$

$\Delta_r H_3°{}' = -\Delta_r H_3° = +890.3$ kJ/mol-rxn

Next, you see that 2 mol of $H_2(g)$ is on the reactant side in our desired equation. Equation 2 is written for only 1 mol of $H_2(g)$ as a reactant. Therefore, multiply the stoichiometric coefficients in Equation 2 by 2 and multiply the value of its $\Delta_r H°$ by 2.

Equation 2′:   $2\ H_2(g) + O_2(g) \rightarrow 2\ H_2O(\ell)$

$\Delta_r H_2°{}' = 2\ \Delta_r H_2° = 2\ (-285.8\ \text{kJ/mol-rxn}) = -571.6$ kJ/mol-rxn

You now have three equations that, when added together, will give the targeted equation for the formation of methane from carbon and hydrogen. In this summation process, $O_2(g)$, $H_2O(\ell)$, and $CO_2(g)$ all cancel.

Equation 1:   $C(s) + O_2(g) \rightarrow CO_2(g)$                  $\Delta_r H_1° = -393.5$ kJ/mol-rxn

Equation 2′:   $2\ H_2(g) + O_2(g) \rightarrow 2\ H_2O(\ell)$              $\Delta_r H_2°{}' = 2\ \Delta_r H_2° = -571.6$ kJ/mol-rxn

Equation 3′:   $CO_2(g) + 2\ H_2O(\ell) \rightarrow CH_4(g) + 2\ O_2\ (g)$   $\Delta_r H_3°{}' = -\Delta_r H_3° = +890.3$ kJ/mol-rxn

Net Equation:   $C(s) + 2\ H_2(g) \rightarrow CH_4(g)$        $\Delta_r H°_{net} = \Delta_r H_1° + 2\ \Delta_r H_2°{}' + (-\Delta_r H_3°{}')$

$\Delta_r H°_{net} = (-393.5\ \text{kJ/mol-rxn}) + (-571.6\ \text{kJ/mol-rxn}) + (+890.3\ \text{kJ/mol-rxn})$
$= -74.8$ kJ/mol-rxn

Thus, for the formation of 1 mol of $CH_4(g)$ from the elements, $\Delta_r H° = -74.8$ kJ/mol-rxn.

**Think about Your Answer** Notice that the enthalpy change for the formation of the compound from its elements is exothermic, as it is for the great majority of compounds.

# Using Hess's Law

How did we know how the three equations should be adjusted in Example 5.8? Here is a general strategy for solving this type of problem.

**Step 1. Arrange the given equations to get the reactants and products in the equation whose $\Delta_r H°$ you wish to calculate on the correct sides of the equations.** You may need to reverse some of the given equations in order to do this. In Example 5.8, the reactants, C(s) and $H_2$(g), are reactants

in Equations 1 and 2, but the product, $CH_4$(g), is a reactant in Equation 3. Equation 3 was reversed to get $CH_4$ on the product side.

**Step 2. Get the correct amounts of the substances on each side.** In Example 5.8, only one adjustment was needed. There was 1 mol of $H_2$ on the left (reactant side) in Equation 2. We needed 2 mol of $H_2$ in the

overall equation; this required doubling the quantities in Equation 2.

**Step 3. Make sure other substances in the equations cancel when the equations are added.** In Example 5.8, equal amounts of $O_2$ and $H_2O$ appeared on the left and right sides in the three equations, and so they canceled when the equations were added together.

---

**Check Your Understanding**

Use Hess's law to calculate the enthalpy change for the formation of $CS_2(\ell)$ from C(s) and S(s) [C(s) + 2 S(s) $\rightarrow$ $CS_2(\ell)$] from the following enthalpy values.

$C(s) + O_2(g) \rightarrow CO_2(g)$ $\qquad\qquad$ $\Delta_r H_1° = -393.5$ kJ/mol-rxn

$S(s) + O_2(g) \rightarrow SO_2(g)$ $\qquad\qquad$ $\Delta_r H_2° = -296.8$ kJ/mol-rxn

$CS_2(\ell) + 3\ O_2(g) \rightarrow CO_2(g) + 2\ SO_2(g)$ $\quad$ $\Delta_r H_3° = -1103.9$ kJ/mol-rxn

---

## Standard Enthalpies of Formation

Calorimetry and the application of Hess's law have made available a great many $\Delta_r H°$ values for chemical reactions. The table in Appendix L, for example, lists **standard molar enthalpies of formation, $\Delta_f H°$**. *The standard molar enthalpy of formation is the enthalpy change for the formation of 1 mol of a compound directly from its component elements in their standard states.*

Several examples of standard molar enthalpies of formation will be helpful to illustrate this definition.

$\Delta_f H°$ **for NaCl(s):** At 25 °C and a pressure of 1 bar, Na is a solid, and $Cl_2$ is a gas. The standard enthalpy of formation of NaCl(s) is defined as the enthalpy change that occurs when 1 mol of NaCl(s) is formed from 1 mol of Na(s) and ½ mol of $Cl_2$(g).

$$Na(s) + ½\ Cl_2(g) \rightarrow NaCl(s) \qquad \Delta_f H° = -411.12 \text{ kJ/mol}$$

Notice that a fraction is required as the coefficient for the chlorine gas in this equation because the definition of $\Delta_f H°$ specifies the formation of *one* mole of NaCl(s).

$\Delta_f H°$ **for NaCl(aq):** The enthalpy of formation for an aqueous solution of a compound refers to the enthalpy change for the formation of a 1 mol/L solution of the compound starting with the elements making up the compound. It is thus the enthalpy of formation of the compound plus the enthalpy change that occurs when the substance dissolves in water.

$$Na(s) + ½\ Cl_2(g) \rightarrow NaCl(aq) \qquad \Delta_f H° = -407.27 \text{ kJ/mol}$$

$\Delta_f H°$ **for $C_2H_5OH(\ell)$:** At 25 °C and 1 bar, the standard states of the elements are C(s, graphite), $H_2$(g), and $O_2$(g). The standard enthalpy of formation of $C_2H_5OH(\ell)$ is defined as the enthalpy change that occurs when 1 mol of $C_2H_5OH(\ell)$ is formed from 2 mol of C(s), 3 mol of $H_2$(g), and 1/2 mol of $O_2$(g).

$$2\ C(s) + 3\ H_2(g) + ½\ O_2(g) \rightarrow C_2H_5OH(\ell) \qquad \Delta_f H° = -277.0 \text{ kJ/mol}$$

● $\Delta_f H°$ **Values** Consult the National Institute for Standards and Technology website (webbook.nist.gov/chemistry) for an extensive compilation of enthalpies of formation.

● **Units for Enthalpy of Formation** The units for values of $\Delta_f H°$ are usually given simply as kJ/mol where the denominator is really mol-rxn. However, because an enthalpy of formation is defined as the change in enthalpy for the formation of 1 mol of compound, it is understood that "per mol" also means "per mol of compound."

Notice that the reaction defining the enthalpy of formation for liquid ethanol is not a reaction a chemist can carry out in the laboratory. This illustrates an important point: *The enthalpy of formation of a compound does not necessarily correspond to a reaction that can be carried out.*

Appendix L lists values of $\Delta_f H°$ for some common substances, and a review of these values leads to some important observations.

- *The standard enthalpy of formation for an element in its standard state is zero.*
- Most $\Delta_f H°$ values are negative, indicating that formation of most compounds from the elements is exothermic. A very few values are positive, and these represent compounds that are unstable with respect to decomposition to the elements. (One example is $NO(g)$ with $\Delta_f H° = +90.29$ kJ/mol.)
- Values of $\Delta_f H°$ can often be used to compare the stabilities of related compounds. Consider the values of $\Delta_f H°$ for the hydrogen halides. Hydrogen fluoride is the most stable of these compounds with respect to decomposition to the elements, whereas HI is the least stable (as indicated by $\Delta_f H°$ of HF being the most negative value and that of HI being the most positive).

### ● $\Delta_f H°$ Values of Hydrogen Halides

| Compound | $\Delta_f H°$ (kJ/mol) |
|---|---|
| HF(g) | −273.3 |
| HCl(g) | −92.31 |
| HBr(g) | −35.29 |
| HI(g) | +25.36 |

● **Stoichiometric Coefficients** In Equation 5.6 a stoichiometric coefficient, *n*, is represented as the number of moles of the substance per mole of reaction.

● **Δ = Final − Initial** Equation 5.6 is another example of the convention that a change (Δ) is always calculated by subtracting the value for the initial state (the reactants) from the value for the final state (the products).

## Enthalpy Change for a Reaction

Using standard molar enthalpies of formation and Equation 5.6, it is possible to calculate the enthalpy change for a reaction under standard conditions.

$$\Delta_r H° = \Sigma n \Delta_f H°(\text{products}) - \Sigma n \Delta_f H°(\text{reactants}) \qquad (5.6)$$

In this equation, the symbol $\Sigma$ (the Greek capital letter sigma) means "take the sum." To find $\Delta_r H°$, add up the molar enthalpies of formation of the products, each multiplied by its stoichiometric coefficient *n*, and subtract from this the sum of the molar enthalpies of formation of the reactants, each multiplied by its stoichiometric coefficient. This equation is a logical consequence of the definition of $\Delta_f H°$ and Hess's law (see *A Closer Look: Hess's Law and Equation 5.6*, page 236).

Suppose you want to know how much energy is required to decompose 1 mol of calcium carbonate (limestone) to calcium oxide (lime) and carbon dioxide under standard conditions:

$$CaCO_3(s) \rightarrow CaO(s) + CO_2(g) \qquad \Delta_r H° = ?$$

You would use the following enthalpies of formation (from Appendix L):

| Compound | $\Delta_f H°$ (kJ/mol) |
|---|---|
| $CaCO_3(s)$ | −1207.6 |
| $CaO(s)$ | −635.1 |
| $CO_2(g)$ | −393.5 |

and then use Equation 5.6 to find the standard enthalpy change for the reaction, $\Delta_r H°$.

$$\Delta_r H° = \left[ \left( \frac{1 \text{ mol CaO}}{1 \text{ mol-rxn}} \right) \left( \frac{-635.1 \text{ kJ}}{\text{mol CaO}} \right) + \left( \frac{1 \text{ mol CO}_2}{1 \text{ mol-rxn}} \right) \left( \frac{-393.5 \text{ kJ}}{1 \text{ mol CO}_2} \right) \right]$$
$$- \left[ \left( \frac{1 \text{ mol CaCO}_3}{1 \text{ mol-rxn}} \right) \left( \frac{-1207.6 \text{ kJ}}{1 \text{ mol CaCO}_3} \right) \right]$$
$$= +179.0 \text{ kJ/mol-rxn}$$

The decomposition of limestone to lime and $CO_2$ is endothermic. That is, energy (179.0 kJ) must be supplied to decompose 1 mol of $CaCO_3(s)$ to $CaO(s)$ and $CO_2(g)$.

# ⓌWL   INTERACTIVE EXAMPLE 5.9   Using Enthalpies of Formation

**Problem** Nitroglycerin is a powerful explosive that forms four different gases when detonated:

$$2\ C_3H_5(NO_3)_3(\ell)\ \rightarrow\ 3\ N_2(g) + 1/2\ O_2(g) + 6\ CO_2(g) + 5\ H_2O(g)$$

Calculate the enthalpy change that occurs when 10.0 g of nitroglycerin is detonated. The standard enthalpy of formation of nitroglycerin, $\Delta_f H°$, is −364 kJ/mol. Use Appendix L to find other $\Delta_f H°$ values that are needed.

**What Do You Know?** From Appendix L, $\Delta_f H°[CO_2(g)] = -393.5$ kJ/mol, $\Delta_f H°[H_2O(g)] = -241.8$ kJ/mol, and $\Delta_f H° = 0$ for $N_2(g)$ and $O_2(g)$. The mass and $\Delta_f H°$ for nitroglycerin are also given.

**Strategy** Substitute the enthalpy of formation values for products and reactants into Equation 5.6 to determine the enthalpy change for 1 mol of reaction. This represents the enthalpy change for detonation of 2 mol of nitroglycerin. Determine the amount (mol) represented by 10.0 g of nitroglycerin, then use this value with $\Delta_r H°$ and the relationship between moles of nitroglycerin and moles of reaction to obtain the answer.

**Solution** Using Equation 5.6, we find the enthalpy change for the explosion of 2 mol of nitroglycerin is

$$\Delta_r H° = \left(\frac{6\ \text{mol}\ CO_2}{1\ \text{mol-rxn}}\right)\Delta_f H°[CO_2(g)] + \left(\frac{5\ \text{mol}\ H_2O}{1\ \text{mol-rxn}}\right)\Delta_f H°[H_2O(g)]$$

$$- \left(\frac{2\ \text{mol}\ C_3H_5(NO_3)_3}{1\ \text{mol-rxn}}\right)\Delta_f H°[C_3H_5(NO_3)_3(\ell)]$$

$$\Delta_r H° = \left(\frac{6\ \text{mol}\ CO_2}{1\ \text{mol-rxn}}\right)\left(\frac{-393.5\ \text{kJ}}{1\ \text{mol}\ CO_2}\right) + \left(\frac{5\ \text{mol}\ H_2O}{1\ \text{mol-rxn}}\right)\left(\frac{-241.8\ \text{kJ}}{1\ \text{mol}\ H_2O}\right)$$

$$- \left(\frac{2\ \text{mol}\ C_3H_5(NO_3)_3}{1\ \text{mol-rxn}}\right)\left(\frac{-364\ \text{kJ}}{1\ \text{mol}\ C_3H_5(NO_3)_3}\right) = -2842\ \text{kJ/mol-rxn}$$

The problem asks for the enthalpy change using 10.0 g of nitroglycerin. You next need to determine the amount of nitroglycerin in 10.0 g.

$$10.0\ \text{g nitroglycerin}\left(\frac{1\ \text{mol nitroglycerin}}{227.1\ \text{g nitroglycerin}}\right) = 0.0440\ \text{mol nitroglycerin}$$

The enthalpy change for the detonation of 0.0440 mol of nitroglycerin is

$$\Delta_r H° = 0.0440\ \text{mol nitroglycerin}\left(\frac{1\ \text{mol-rxn}}{2\ \text{mol nitroglycerin}}\right)\left(\frac{-2842\ \text{kJ}}{1\ \text{mol-rxn}}\right)$$

$$= -62.6\ \text{kJ}$$

**Think about Your Answer** The large negative value of $\Delta_r H°$ is in accord with the fact that this reaction is highly exothermic.

---

**Check Your Understanding**

Calculate the standard enthalpy of combustion for benzene, $C_6H_6$.

$$C_6H_6(\ell) + 15/2\ O_2(g)\ \rightarrow\ 6\ CO_2(g) + 3\ H_2O(\ell) \qquad \Delta_r H° = ?$$

The enthalpy of formation of benzene is known [$\Delta_f H°[C_6H_6(\ell)] = +49.0$ kJ/mol], and other values needed can be found in Appendix L.

---

## Strategy Map 5.9

**PROBLEM**

Calculate $\Delta_r H°$ for reaction of a **given mass** of compound.

↓

**DATA/INFORMATION**

- Mass and $\Delta_f H°$ of compound
- $\Delta_f H°$ values for products
- Balanced equation

**STEP 1.** Calculate $\Delta_r H°$ for reaction of compound using $\Delta_f H°$ **values** for reactants and products.

$\Delta_r H°$ for reaction of compound

**STEP 2.** Determine **amount** of compound.

**Amount** of compound

**STEP 3.** Convert from **mol** of compound to **mol-rxn** and then multiply by $\Delta_r H°$.

$\Delta_r H°$ for reaction of **given mass** of compound

---

## REVIEW & CHECK FOR SECTION 5.7

1.  The standard enthalpy of formation for $AlCl_3(s)$ is the enthalpy change for what reaction?

    (a)  $Al(s) + 3\ Cl_2(g) \rightarrow AlCl_3(s)$

    (b)  $Al(s) + 3\ Cl(g) \rightarrow AlCl_3(s)$

    (c)  $3\ HCl(aq) + Al(OH)_3(s) \rightarrow AlCl_3(s) + 3\ H_2O(\ell)$

    (d)  $Al(s) + 3/2\ Cl_2(g) \rightarrow AlCl_3(s)$

## A CLOSER LOOK

### Hess's Law and Equation 5.6

Equation 5.6 is an application of Hess's law. To illustrate this, let us look further at the decomposition of calcium carbonate.

$$CaCO_3(s) \rightarrow CaO(s) + CO_2(g) \qquad \Delta_rH° = ?$$

Because enthalpy is a state function, the change in enthalpy for this reaction is independent of the route from reactants to products. We can imagine an alternate route from reactant to products that involves first converting the reactant ($CaCO_3$) to elements in their standard states, then recombining these elements to give the reaction products. Notice that the enthalpy changes for these processes are the enthalpies of formation of the reactants and products in the equation above:

$$CaCO_3(s) \rightarrow Ca(s) + C(s) + 3/2\ O_2(g)$$
$$-\Delta_fH°[CaCO_3(s)] = \Delta_rH_1°$$

$$C(s) + O_2(g) \rightarrow CO_2(g)$$
$$\Delta_fH°[CO_2(g)] = \Delta_rH_2°$$

$$Ca(s) + \frac{1}{2}\ O_2(g) \rightarrow CaO(s)$$
$$\Delta_fH°[CaO(s)] = \Delta_rH_3°$$

$$CaCO_3(s) \rightarrow CaO(s) + CO_2(g) \qquad \Delta_rH°_{net}$$

$$\Delta_rH°_{net} = \Delta_rH_1° + \Delta_rH_2° + \Delta_rH_3°$$

$$\Delta_rH° = \Delta_fH°[CaO(s)] + \Delta_fH°[CO_2(g)]$$
$$- \Delta_fH°[CaCO_3(s)]$$

That is, the change in enthalpy for the reaction is equal to the enthalpies of formation of products ($CO_2$ and CaO) minus the enthalpy of formation of the reactant ($CaCO_3$), which is, of course, what one does when using Equation 5.6 for this calculation. The relationship among these enthalpy quantities is illustrated in the energy-level diagram.

Energy level diagram for the decomposition of $CaCO_3(s)$

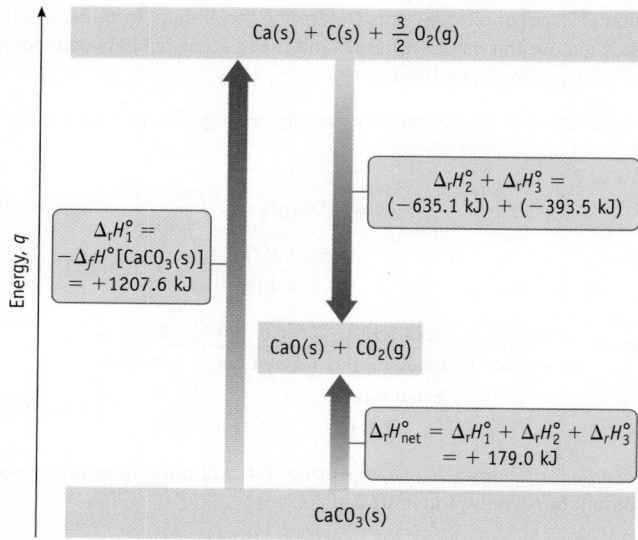

2. Acetic acid is made by the reaction $CH_3OH(\ell) + CO(g) \rightarrow CH_3CO_2H(\ell)$. Determine the enthalpy change for this reaction from the enthalpies of the three reactions below.

$$2\ CH_3OH(\ell) + 3\ O_2(g) \rightarrow 2\ CO_2(g) + 4\ H_2O(\ell) \qquad \Delta_rH_1°$$

$$CH_3CO_2H(\ell) + 2\ O_2(g) \rightarrow 2\ CO_2(g) + 2\ H_2O(\ell) \qquad \Delta_rH_2°$$

$$2\ CO(g) + O_2(g) \rightarrow 2\ CO_2(g) \qquad \Delta_rH_3°$$

(a) $\Delta_rH_1° + \Delta_rH_2° + \Delta_rH_3°$

(b) $\Delta_rH_1° - \Delta_rH_2° + \Delta_rH_3°$

(c) $1/2\ \Delta_rH_1° - \Delta_rH_2° + 1/2\ \Delta_rH_3°$

(d) $-1/2\ \Delta_rH_1° + \Delta_rH_2° - 1/2\ \Delta_rH_3°$

## 5.8 Product- or Reactant-Favored Reactions and Thermodynamics

At the beginning of this chapter, we noted that thermodynamics would provide answers to four questions:

- How do we measure and calculate the energy changes associated with physical changes and chemical reactions?
- What is the relationship between energy changes, heat, and work?
- How can we determine whether a chemical reaction is product-favored or reactant-favored at equilibrium?
- How can we determine whether a chemical reaction or physical process will occur spontaneously, that is, without outside intervention?

The first two questions were addressed in this chapter, but the other two important questions still remain (for Chapter 19).

In Chapter 3, we learned that chemical reactions proceed toward equilibrium, and spontaneous changes occur in a way that allows a system to approach equilibrium. Reactions in which reactants are largely converted to products when equilibrium is reached are said to be *product-favored at equilibrium*. Reactions in which only small amounts of products are present at equilibrium are called *reactant-favored at equilibrium* (◄ page 118).

---

## CASE STUDY

# The Fuel Controversy—Alcohol and Gasoline

It is clear that supplies of fossil fuels are declining and their prices are increasing, just as the nations of the earth have ever greater energy needs. We will have more to say about this in the Interchapter (Energy) that follows. Here, however, let's analyze the debate about replacing gasoline with ethanol ($C_2H_5OH$).

As Matthew Wald said in the article "Is Ethanol in for the Long Haul?" (*Scientific American*, January 2007), "The U.S. has gone on an ethanol binge." In 2005, the U.S. Congress passed an energy bill stating that ethanol production should be 7.5 billion gallons a year by 2012, up from about 5 billion gallons in 2005. The goal is to at least partially replace gasoline with ethanol.

Is a goal of replacing gasoline completely with ethanol reasonable? This is a lofty goal, given that present gasoline consumption in the U.S. is about 140 billion gallons annually. Again, according to Matthew Wald, "Even if 100 percent of the U.S. corn supply was distilled into ethanol, it would supply only a small fraction of the fuel consumed by the nation's vehicles." Wald's thesis in his article, which is supported by numerous scientific studies, is that if ethanol is to be pursued as an alternative to gasoline, more emphasis would have to be placed on deriving ethanol from sources other than corn, such as cellulose from cornstalks and various grasses.

Beyond this, there are other problems associated with ethanol. One is that it cannot be distributed through a pipeline system as gasoline can. Any water in the pipeline is miscible with ethanol, which causes the fuel value to decline.

Finally, even E85 fuel—a blend of 85% ethanol and 15% gasoline—cannot be used in most current vehicles because relatively few vehicles as yet have engines designed for fuels with a high ethanol content (so-called "flexible fuel" engines). The number of these vehicles would need to be increased in order for E85 to have a significant effect on our gasoline usage.

For more information, see the references in Wald's *Scientific American* article.

### Questions:

For the purposes of this analysis, let us use octane ($C_8H_{18}$) as a substitute for the complex mixture of hydrocarbons in gasoline. Data you will need for this question (in addition to Appendix L) are:

$$\Delta_f H^\circ \ [C_8H_{18}(\ell)] = -250.1 \text{ kJ/mol}$$

$$\text{Density of ethanol} = 0.785 \text{ g/mL}$$

$$\text{Density of octane} = 0.699 \text{ g/mL}$$

1. Calculate $\Delta_r H^\circ$ for the combustion of ethanol and octane, and compare the values per mole and per gram. Which provides more energy per mole? Which provides more energy per gram?

2. Compare the energy produced per liter of the two fuels. Which produces more energy for a given volume (something useful to know when filling your gas tank)?

3. What mass of $CO_2$, a greenhouse gas, is produced per liter of fuel (assuming complete combustion)?

4. Now compare the fuels on an energy-equivalent basis. What volume of ethanol would have to be burned to get the same energy as 1.00 L of octane? When you burn enough ethanol to have the same energy as a liter of octane, which fuel produces more $CO_2$?

5. On the basis of this analysis and assuming the same price per liter, which fuel will propel your car further? Which will produce less greenhouse gas?

**Answers to these questions are available in Appendix N.**

**Ethanol available at a service station.** E85 fuel is a blend of 85% ethanol and 15% gasoline. Be aware that you can only use E85 in vehicles designed for the fuel. In an ordinary vehicle, the ethanol leads to deterioration of seals in the engine and fuel system.

© GIPhotoStock Z/Alamy

**FIGURE 5.14 The product-favored oxidation of iron.** Iron powder, sprayed into a bunsen burner flame, is rapidly oxidized. The reaction is exothermic and is product-favored.

Let us look back at the many chemical reactions that we have seen. For example, all combustion reactions are exothermic, and the oxidation of iron (Figure 5.14) is clearly exothermic.

$$4 \text{ Fe}(s) + 3 \text{ O}_2(g) \rightarrow 2 \text{ Fe}_2\text{O}_3(s)$$

$$\Delta_r H^\circ = 2 \, \Delta_f H^\circ[\text{Fe}_2\text{O}_3(s)] = \left( \frac{2 \text{ mol Fe}_2\text{O}_3}{1 \text{ mol-rxn}} \right)\left( \frac{-825.5 \text{ kJ}}{1 \text{ mol Fe}_2\text{O}_3} \right) = -1651.0 \text{ kJ/mol-rxn}$$

The reaction has a negative value for $\Delta_r H^\circ$, and it is also product-favored at equilibrium.

Conversely, the decomposition of calcium carbonate is endothermic.

$$\text{CaCO}_3(s) \rightarrow \text{CaO}(s) + \text{CO}_2(g) \qquad \Delta_r H^\circ = +179.0 \text{ kJ/mol-rxn}$$

The decomposition of $CaCO_3$ proceeds to an equilibrium that favors the reactants; that is, it is reactant-favored at equilibrium.

Are all exothermic reactions product-favored at equilibrium and all endothermic reactions reactant-favored at equilibrium? From these examples, we might formulate that idea as a hypothesis that can be tested by experiment and by examination of other examples. You would find that *in most cases, product-favored reactions have negative values of* $\Delta_r H^\circ$, *and reactant-favored reactions have positive values of* $\Delta_r H^\circ$. But this is not *always* true; there are exceptions.

Clearly, a further discussion of thermodynamics must be tied to the concept of equilibrium. This relationship, and the complete discussion of the third and fourth questions, will be presented in Chapter 19.

---

 and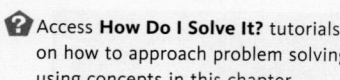

## CHAPTER GOALS REVISITED

*Now that you have completed this chapter, you should ask whether you have met the chapter goals. In particular, you should be able to:*

### Assess the transfer of energy as heat associated with changes in temperature and changes of state

a.   Describe the nature of energy transfers as heat (Section 5.1).
b.   Recognize and use the language of thermodynamics: the system and its surroundings; exothermic and endothermic reactions (Section 5.1). **Study Questions: 1, 3, 59.**
c.   Use specific heat capacity in calculations of energy transfer as heat and of temperature changes (Section 5.2). **Study Questions: 5, 7, 9, 11, 13, 15.**
d.   Understand the sign conventions in thermodynamics.
e.   Use enthalpy (heat) of fusion and enthalpy (heat) of vaporization to calculate the energy transferred as heat in changes of state (Section 5.3). **Study Questions: 17, 19, 21, 23, 83.**

### Understand and apply the first law of thermodynamics

a.   Understand the basis of the first law of thermodynamics (Section 5.4).
b.   Recognize how energy transferred as heat and work done on or by a system contribute to changes in the internal energy of a system (Section 5.4).

### Define and understand state functions (enthalpy, internal energy)

a.   Recognize state functions whose values are determined only by the state of the system and not by the pathway by which that state was achieved (Section 5.4).

### Describe how energy changes are measured

a.   Recognize that when a process is carried out under constant pressure conditions, the energy transferred as heat is the enthalpy change, $\Delta H$ (Section 5.5). **Study Questions: 25, 26, 27, 28, 48.**
b.   Describe how to measure the quantity of energy transferred as heat in a reaction by calorimetry (Section 5.6). **Study Questions: 29, 30, 31, 32, 34–40.**

**Calculate the energy evolved or required for physical changes and chemical reactions using tables of thermodynamic data.**

a.  Apply Hess's law to find the enthalpy change, $\Delta_r H°$, for a reaction (Section 5.7). **Study Questions: 41–44, 73, 79, and Go Chemistry Module 10.**

b.  Know how to draw and interpret energy level diagrams (Section 5.7). **Study Questions: 53, 54, 73, 74, 79, 101, 105.**

c.  Use standard molar enthalpies of formation, $\Delta_f H°$, to calculate the enthalpy change for a reaction, $\Delta_r H°$ (Section 5.7). **Study Questions: 47, 49, 51, 55, 56.**

## Key Equations

**Equation 5.1 (page 212)** The energy transferred as heat when the temperature of a substance changes. Calculated from the specific heat capacity ($C$), mass ($m$), and change in temperature ($\Delta T$).

$$q(J) = C(J/g \cdot K) \times m(g) \times \Delta T(K)$$

**Equation 5.2 (page 212)** Temperature changes are always calculated as final temperature minus initial temperature.

$$\Delta T = T_{final} - T_{initial}$$

**Equation 5.3 (page 214)** If no energy is transferred between a system and its surroundings and if energy is transferred within the system only as heat, the sum of the thermal energy changes within the system equals zero.

$$q_1 + q_2 + q_3 + \ldots = 0$$

**Equation 5.4 (page 220)** The first law of thermodynamics: The change in internal energy ($\Delta U$) in a system is the sum of the energy transferred as heat ($q$) and the energy transferred as work ($w$).

$$\Delta U = q + w$$

**Equation 5.5 (page 221)** $P–V$ work ($w$) at constant pressure is the product of pressure ($P$) and change in volume ($\Delta V$)

$$w = -P \times \Delta V$$

**Equation 5.6 (page 234)** This equation is used to calculate the standard enthalpy change of a reaction ($\Delta_r H°$) when the enthalpies of formation ($\Delta_f H°$) of all of the reactants and products are known. The parameter $n$ is the stoichiometric coefficient of each product or reactant in the balanced chemical equation.

$$\Delta_r H° = \Sigma n \Delta_f H°(\text{products}) - \Sigma n \Delta_f H°(\text{reactants})$$

## Study Questions

⏻WL Interactive versions of these questions are assignable in OWL

▲ denotes challenging questions.

Blue-numbered questions have answers in Appendix R and fully worked solutions in the *Student Solutions Manual*.

## Practicing Skills

**Energy: Some Basic Principles**
*(See Section 5.1.)*

1.  Define the terms *system* and *surroundings*. What does it mean to say that a system and its surroundings are in thermal equilibrium?

2.  What determines the directionality of energy transfer as heat ?

3.  Identify whether the following processes are exothermic or endothermic.
    (a) combustion of methane
    (b) melting of ice
    (c) raising the temperature of water from 25 °C to 100 °C
    (d) heating $CaCO_3(s)$ to form $CaO(s)$ and $CO_2(g)$

4.  Identify whether the following processes are exothermic or endothermic.
    (a) the reaction of $Na(s)$ and $Cl_2(g)$
    (b) cooling and condensing gaseous $N_2$ to form liquid $N_2$
    (c) cooling a soft drink from 25 °C to 0 °C
    (d) heating $HgO(s)$ to form $Hg(\ell)$ and $O_2(g)$

## Specific Heat Capacity
*(See Section 5.2 and Examples 5.1 and 5.2.)*

5. The molar heat capacity of mercury is 28.1 J/mol · K. What is the specific heat capacity of this metal in J/g · K?

6. The specific heat capacity of benzene ($C_6H_6$) is 1.74 J/g · K. What is its molar heat capacity (in J/mol · K)?

7. The specific heat capacity of copper metal is 0.385 J/g · K. How much energy is required to heat 168 g of copper from −12.2 °C to +25.6 °C?

8. How much energy as heat is required to raise the temperature of 50.00 mL of water from 25.52 °C to 28.75 °C? (Density of water at this temperature = 0.997 g/mL.)

9. The initial temperature of a 344-g sample of iron is 18.2 °C. If the sample absorbs 2.25 kJ of energy as heat, what is its final temperature?

10. After absorbing 1.850 kJ of energy as heat, the temperature of a 0.500-kg block of copper is 37 °C. What was its initial temperature?

11. A 45.5-g sample of copper at 99.8 °C was dropped into a beaker containing 152 g of water at 18.5 °C. What was the final temperature when thermal equilibrium was reached?

12. A 182-g sample of gold at some temperature was added to 22.1 g of water. The initial water temperature was 25.0 °C, and the final temperature was 27.5 °C. If the specific heat capacity of gold is 0.128 J/g · K, what was the initial temperature of the gold sample?

13. One beaker contains 156 g of water at 22 °C, and a second beaker contains 85.2 g of water at 95 °C. The water in the two beakers is mixed. What is the final water temperature?

14. When 108 g of water at a temperature of 22.5 °C is mixed with 65.1 g of water at an unknown temperature, the final temperature of the resulting mixture is 47.9 °C. What was the initial temperature of the second sample of water?

15. A 13.8-g piece of zinc was heated to 98.8 °C in boiling water and then dropped into a beaker containing 45.0 g of water at 25.0 °C. When the water and metal came to thermal equilibrium, the temperature was 27.1 °C. What is the specific heat capacity of zinc?

16. A 237-g piece of molybdenum, initially at 100.0 °C, was dropped into 244 g of water at 10.0 °C. When the system came to thermal equilibrium, the temperature was 15.3 °C. What is the specific heat capacity of molybdenum?

## Changes of State
*(See Section 5.3 and Examples 5.3 and 5.4.)*

17. How much energy is evolved as heat when 1.0 L of water at 0 °C solidifies to ice? (The heat of fusion of water is 333 J/g.)

18. The energy required to melt 1.00 g of ice at 0 °C is 333 J. If one ice cube has a mass of 62.0 g and a tray contains 16 ice cubes, what quantity of energy is required to melt a tray of ice cubes to form liquid water at 0 °C?

19. How much energy is required to vaporize 125 g of benzene, $C_6H_6$, at its boiling point, 80.1 °C? (The heat of vaporization of benzene is 30.8 kJ/mol.)

20. Chloromethane, $CH_3Cl$, arises from microbial fermentation and is found throughout the environment. It is also produced industrially, is used in the manufacture of various chemicals, and has been used as a topical anesthetic. How much energy is required to convert 92.5 g of liquid to a vapor at its boiling point, −24.09 °C? (The heat of vaporization of $CH_3Cl$ is 21.40 kJ/mol.)

21. The freezing point of mercury is −38.8 °C. What quantity of energy, in joules, is released to the surroundings if 1.00 mL of mercury is cooled from 23.0 °C to −38.8 °C and then frozen to a solid? (The density of liquid mercury is 13.6 g/cm³. Its specific heat capacity is 0.140 J/g · K and its heat of fusion is 11.4 J/g.)

22. What quantity of energy, in joules, is required to raise the temperature of 454 g of tin from room temperature, 25.0 °C, to its melting point, 231.9 °C, and then melt the tin at that temperature? (The specific heat capacity of tin is 0.227 J/g · K, and the heat of fusion of this metal is 59.2 J/g.)

23. Ethanol, $C_2H_5OH$, boils at 78.29 °C. How much energy, in joules, is required to raise the temperature of 1.00 kg of ethanol from 20.0 °C to the boiling point and then to change the liquid to vapor at that temperature? (The specific heat capacity of liquid ethanol is 2.44 J/g · K, and its enthalpy of vaporization is 855 J/g.)

24. A 25.0-mL sample of benzene at 19.9 °C was cooled to its melting point, 5.5 °C, and then frozen. How much energy was given off as heat in this process? (The density of benzene is 0.80 g/mL, its specific heat capacity is 1.74 J/g · K, and its heat of fusion is 127 J/g.)

## Enthalpy Changes
*(See Section 5.5 and Example 5.5.)*

25. Nitrogen monoxide, a gas recently found to be involved in a wide range of biological processes, reacts with oxygen to give brown $NO_2$ gas.

    $$2\ NO(g) + O_2(g) \rightarrow 2\ NO_2(g)$$
    $$\Delta_r H° = -114.1\ kJ/mol\text{-rxn}$$

    Is this reaction endothermic or exothermic? What is the enthalpy change if 1.25 g of NO is converted completely to $NO_2$?

26. Calcium carbide, $CaC_2$, is manufactured by the reaction of CaO with carbon at a high temperature. (Calcium carbide is then used to make acetylene.)

    $$CaO(s) + 3\ C(s) \rightarrow CaC_2(s) + CO(g)$$
    $$\Delta_r H° = +464.8\ kJ/mol\text{-rxn}$$

    Is this reaction endothermic or exothermic? What is the enthalpy change if 10.0 g of CaO is allowed to react with an excess of carbon?

27. Isooctane (2,2,4-trimethylpentane), one of the many hydrocarbons that make up gasoline, burns in air to give water and carbon dioxide.

    $$2\ C_8H_{18}(\ell) + 25\ O_2(g) \rightarrow 16\ CO_2(g) + 18\ H_2O(\ell)$$
    $$\Delta_r H° = -10{,}922\ kJ/mol\text{-rxn}$$

    What is the enthalpy change if you burn 1.00 L of isooctane ($d = 0.69$ g/mL)?

28. Acetic acid, $CH_3CO_2H$, is made industrially by the reaction of methanol and carbon monoxide.

    $$CH_3OH(\ell) + CO(g) \rightarrow CH_3CO_2H(\ell)$$
    $$\Delta_r H° = -134.6\ kJ/mol\text{-rxn}$$

    What is the enthalpy change for producing 1.00 L of acetic acid ($d = 1.044$ g/mL) by this reaction?

## Calorimetry
*(See Section 5.6 and Examples 5.6 and 5.7.)*

29. Assume you mix 100.0 mL of 0.200 M CsOH with 50.0 mL of 0.400 M HCl in a coffee-cup calorimeter. The following reaction occurs:

    $$CsOH(aq) + HCl(aq) \rightarrow CsCl(aq) + H_2O(\ell)$$

    The temperature of both solutions before mixing was 22.50 °C, and it rises to 24.28 °C after the acid–base reaction. What is the enthalpy change for the reaction per mole of CsOH? Assume the densities of the solutions are all 1.00 g/mL and the specific heat capacities of the solutions are 4.2 J/g · K.

30. You mix 125 mL of 0.250 M CsOH with 50.0 mL of 0.625 M HF in a coffee-cup calorimeter, and the temperature of both solutions rises from 21.50 °C before mixing to 24.40 °C after the reaction.

    $$CsOH(aq) + HF(aq) \rightarrow CsF(aq) + H_2O(\ell)$$

    What is the enthalpy of reaction per mole of CsOH? Assume the densities of the solutions are all 1.00 g/mL, and the specific heat capacities of the solutions are 4.2 J/g · K.

31. A piece of titanium metal with a mass of 20.8 g is heated in boiling water to 99.5 °C and then dropped into a coffee-cup calorimeter containing 75.0 g of water at 21.7 °C. When thermal equilibrium is reached, the final temperature is 24.3 °C. Calculate the specific heat capacity of titanium.

32. A piece of chromium metal with a mass of 24.26 g is heated in boiling water to 98.3 °C and then dropped into a coffee-cup calorimeter containing 82.3 g of water at 23.3 °C. When thermal equilibrium is reached, the final temperature is 25.6 °C. Calculate the specific heat capacity of chromium.

33. Adding 5.44 g of $NH_4NO_3(s)$ to 150.0 g of water in a coffee-cup calorimeter (with stirring to dissolve the salt) resulted in a decrease in temperature from 18.6 °C to 16.2 °C. Calculate the enthalpy change for dissolving $NH_4NO_3(s)$ in water, in kJ/mol. Assume the solution (whose mass is 155.4 g) has a specific heat capacity of 4.2 J/g · K. (Cold packs take advantage of the fact that dissolving ammonium nitrate in water is an endothermic process.)

A cold pack uses the endothermic enthalpy of a solution of ammonium nitrate.

34. You should use care when dissolving $H_2SO_4$ in water because the process is highly exothermic. To measure the enthalpy change, 5.2 g of concentrated $H_2SO_4(\ell)$ was added (with stirring) to 135 g of water in a coffee-cup calorimeter. This resulted in an increase in temperature from 20.2 °C to 28.8 °C. Calculate the enthalpy change for the process $H_2SO_4(\ell) \rightarrow H_2SO_4(aq)$, in kJ/mol.

35. Sulfur (2.56 g) was burned in a constant volume calorimeter with excess $O_2(g)$. The temperature increased from 21.25 °C to 26.72 °C. The bomb has a heat capacity of 923 J/K, and the calorimeter contained 815 g of water. Calculate $\Delta U$ per mole of $SO_2$ formed for the reaction

$$S_8(s) + 8\ O_2(g) \rightarrow 8\ SO_2(g)$$

**Sulfur burns in oxygen with a bright blue flame to give $SO_2(g)$.**

36. Suppose you burned 0.300 g of C(s) in an excess of $O_2(g)$ in a constant volume calorimeter to give $CO_2(g)$.

$$C(s) + O_2(g) \rightarrow CO_2(g)$$

The temperature of the calorimeter, which contained 775 g of water, increased from 25.00 °C to 27.38 °C. The heat capacity of the bomb is 893 J/K. Calculate $\Delta U$ per mole of carbon.

37. Suppose you burned 1.500 g of benzoic acid, $C_6H_5CO_2H$, in a constant volume calorimeter and found that the temperature increased from 22.50 °C to 31.69 °C. The calorimeter contained 775 g of water, and the bomb had a heat capacity of 893 J/K. Calculate $\Delta U$ per mole of benzoic acid.

**Benzoic acid, $C_6H_5CO_2H$, occurs naturally in many berries. Its heat of combustion is well known, so it is used as a standard to calibrate calorimeters.**

38. A 0.692-g sample of glucose, $C_6H_{12}O_6$, was burned in a constant volume calorimeter. The temperature rose from 21.70 °C to 25.22 °C. The calorimeter contained 575 g of water, and the bomb had a heat capacity of 650 J/K. What is $\Delta U$ per mole of glucose?

39. An "ice calorimeter" can be used to determine the specific heat capacity of a metal. A piece of hot metal is dropped onto a weighed quantity of ice. The energy transferred from the metal to the ice can be determined from the amount of ice melted. Suppose you heated a 50.0-g piece of silver to 99.8 °C and then dropped it onto ice. When the metal's temperature had dropped to 0.0 °C, it is found that 3.54 g of ice had melted. What is the specific heat capacity of silver?

40. A 9.36-g piece of platinum was heated to 98.6 °C in a boiling water bath and then dropped onto ice. (See Study Question 39.) When the metal's temperature had dropped to 0.0 °C, it was found that 0.37 g of ice had melted. What is the specific heat capacity of platinum?

## Hess's Law
*(See Section 5.7 and Example 5.8.)*

41. The enthalpy changes for the following reactions can be measured:

$$CH_4(g) + 2\ O_2(g) \rightarrow CO_2(g) + 2\ H_2O(g)$$
$$\Delta_r H° = -802.4\ \text{kJ/mol-rxn}$$

$$CH_3OH(g) + \tfrac{3}{2}\ O_2(g) \rightarrow CO_2(g) + 2\ H_2O(g)$$
$$\Delta_r H° = -676\ \text{kJ/mol-rxn}$$

   (a) Use these values and Hess's law to determine the enthalpy change for the reaction

$$CH_4(g) + \tfrac{1}{2}\ O_2(g) \rightarrow CH_3OH(g)$$

   (b) Draw an energy-level diagram that shows the relationship between the energy quantities involved in this problem.

42. The enthalpy changes of the following reactions can be measured:

$$C_2H_4(g) + 3\ O_2(g) \rightarrow 2\ CO_2(g) + 2\ H_2O(\ell)$$
$$\Delta_r H° = -1411.1\ \text{kJ/mol-rxn}$$

$$C_2H_5OH(\ell) + 3\ O_2(g) \rightarrow 2\ CO_2(g) + 3\ H_2O(\ell)$$
$$\Delta_r H° = -1367.5\ \text{kJ/mol-rxn}$$

   (a) Use these values and Hess's law to determine the enthalpy change for the reaction

$$C_2H_4(g) + H_2O(\ell) \rightarrow C_2H_5OH(\ell)$$

   (b) Draw an energy level diagram that shows the relationship between the energy quantities involved in this problem.

43. Enthalpy changes for the following reactions can be determined experimentally:

$$N_2(g) + 3 H_2(g) \rightarrow 2 NH_3(g)$$
$$\Delta_r H° = -91.8 \text{ kJ/mol-rxn}$$

$$4 NH_3(g) + 5 O_2(g) \rightarrow 4 NO(g) + 6 H_2O(g)$$
$$\Delta_r H° = -906.2 \text{ kJ/mol-rxn}$$

$$H_2(g) + \tfrac{1}{2} O_2(g) \rightarrow H_2O(g)$$
$$\Delta_r H° = -241.8 \text{ kJ/mol-rxn}$$

Use these values to determine the enthalpy change for the formation of NO(g) from the elements (an enthalpy change that cannot be measured directly because the reaction is reactant-favored).

$$\tfrac{1}{2} N_2(g) + \tfrac{1}{2} O_2(g) \rightarrow NO(g) \quad \Delta_r H° = ?$$

44. You wish to know the enthalpy change for the formation of liquid $PCl_3$ from the elements.

$$P_4(s) + 6 Cl_2(g) \rightarrow 4 PCl_3(\ell) \quad \Delta_r H° = ?$$

The enthalpy change for the formation of $PCl_5$ from the elements can be determined experimentally, as can the enthalpy change for the reaction of $PCl_3(\ell)$ with more chlorine to give $PCl_5(s)$:

$$P_4(s) + 10 Cl_2(g) \rightarrow 4 PCl_5(s)$$
$$\Delta_r H° = -1774.0 \text{ kJ/mol-rxn}$$

$$PCl_3(\ell) + Cl_2(g) \rightarrow PCl_5(s)$$
$$\Delta_r H° = -123.8 \text{ kJ/mol-rxn}$$

Use these data to calculate the enthalpy change for the formation of 1.00 mol of $PCl_3(\ell)$ from phosphorus and chlorine.

### Standard Enthalpies of Formation
*(See Section 5.7 and Example 5.9.)*

45. Write a balanced chemical equation for the formation of $CH_3OH(\ell)$ from the elements in their standard states. Find the value for $\Delta_f H°$ for $CH_3OH(\ell)$ in Appendix L.

46. Write a balanced chemical equation for the formation of $CaCO_3(s)$ from the elements in their standard states. Find the value for $\Delta_f H°$ for $CaCO_3(s)$ in Appendix L.

47. (a) Write a balanced chemical equation for the formation of 1 mol of $Cr_2O_3(s)$ from Cr and $O_2$ in their standard states. (Find the value for $\Delta_f H°$ for $Cr_2O_3(s)$ in Appendix L.)
    (b) What is the enthalpy change if 2.4 g of chromium is oxidized to $Cr_2O_3(s)$?

48. (a) Write a balanced chemical equation for the formation of 1 mol of MgO(s) from the elements in their standard states. (Find the value for $\Delta_f H°$ for MgO(s) in Appendix L.)
    (b) What is the standard enthalpy change for the reaction of 2.5 mol of Mg with oxygen?

49. Use standard enthalpies of formation in Appendix L to calculate enthalpy changes for the following:
    (a) 1.0 g of white phosphorus burns, forming $P_4O_{10}(s)$
    (b) 0.20 mol of NO(g) decomposes to $N_2(g)$ and $O_2(g)$
    (c) 2.40 g of NaCl(s) is formed from Na(s) and excess $Cl_2(g)$
    (d) 250 g of iron is oxidized with oxygen to $Fe_2O_3(s)$

50. Use standard enthalpies of formation in Appendix L to calculate enthalpy changes for the following:
    (a) 0.054 g of sulfur burns, forming $SO_2(g)$
    (b) 0.20 mol of HgO(s) decomposes to $Hg(\ell)$ and $O_2(g)$
    (c) 2.40 g of $NH_3(g)$ is formed from $N_2(g)$ and excess $H_2(g)$
    (d) $1.05 \times 10^{-2}$ mol of carbon is oxidized to $CO_2(g)$

51. The first step in the production of nitric acid from ammonia involves the oxidation of $NH_3$.

$$4 NH_3(g) + 5 O_2(g) \rightarrow 4 NO(g) + 6 H_2O(g)$$

    (a) Use standard enthalpies of formation to calculate the standard enthalpy change for this reaction.
    (b) How much energy is evolved or absorbed as heat in the oxidation of 10.0 g of $NH_3$?

52. The Romans used calcium oxide, CaO, to produce a strong mortar to build stone structures. Calcium oxide was mixed with water to give $Ca(OH)_2$, which reacted slowly with $CO_2$ in the air to give $CaCO_3$.

$$Ca(OH)_2(s) + CO_2(g) \rightarrow CaCO_3(s) + H_2O(g)$$

    (a) Calculate the standard enthalpy change for this reaction.
    (b) How much energy is evolved or absorbed as heat if 1.00 kg of $Ca(OH)_2$ reacts with a stoichiometric amount of $CO_2$?

53. The standard enthalpy of formation of solid barium oxide, BaO, is $-553.5$ kJ/mol, and the standard enthalpy of formation of barium peroxide, $BaO_2$, is $-634.3$ kJ/mol.
    (a) Calculate the standard enthalpy change for the following reaction. Is the reaction exothermic or endothermic?

$$2 BaO_2(s) \rightarrow 2 BaO(s) + O_2(g)$$

    (b) Draw an energy level diagram that shows the relationship between the enthalpy change of the decomposition of $BaO_2$ to BaO and $O_2$ and the enthalpies of formation of BaO(s) and $BaO_2(s)$.

54. An important step in the production of sulfuric acid is the oxidation of $SO_2$ to $SO_3$.

$$SO_2(g) + \tfrac{1}{2} O_2(g) \rightarrow SO_3(g)$$

    Formation of $SO_3$ from the air pollutant $SO_2$ is also a key step in the formation of acid rain.
    (a) Use standard enthalpies of formation to calculate the enthalpy change for the reaction. Is the reaction exothermic or endothermic?
    (b) Draw an energy level diagram that shows the relationship between the enthalpy change for the oxidation of $SO_2$ to $SO_3$ and the enthalpies of formation of $SO_2(g)$ and $SO_3(g)$.

55. The enthalpy change for the oxidation of naphthalene, $C_{10}H_8$, is measured by calorimetry.

$$C_{10}H_8(s) + 12\ O_2(g) \rightarrow 10\ CO_2(g) + 4\ H_2O(\ell)$$
$$\Delta_r H° = -5156.1\ kJ/mol\text{-rxn}$$

Use this value, along with the standard enthalpies of formation of $CO_2(g)$ and $H_2O(\ell)$, to calculate the enthalpy of formation of naphthalene, in kJ/mol.

56. The enthalpy change for the oxidation of styrene, $C_8H_8$, is measured by calorimetry.

$$C_8H_8(\ell) + 10\ O_2(g) \rightarrow 8\ CO_2(g) + 4\ H_2O(\ell)$$
$$\Delta_r H° = -4395.0\ kJ/mol\text{-rxn}$$

Use this value, along with the standard enthalpies of formation of $CO_2(g)$ and $H_2O(\ell)$, to calculate the enthalpy of formation of styrene, in kJ/mol.

## General Questions

*These questions are not designated as to type or location in the chapter. They may combine several concepts.*

57. The following terms are used extensively in thermodynamics. Define each and give an example.
    (a) exothermic and endothermic
    (b) system and surroundings
    (c) specific heat capacity
    (d) state function
    (e) standard state
    (f) enthalpy change, $\Delta H$
    (g) standard enthalpy of formation

58. For each of the following, tell whether the process is exothermic or endothermic. (No calculations are required.)
    (a) $H_2O(\ell) \rightarrow H_2O(s)$
    (b) $2\ H_2(g) + O_2(g) \rightarrow 2\ H_2O(g)$
    (c) $H_2O(\ell, 25\ °C) \rightarrow H_2O(\ell, 15\ °C)$
    (d) $H_2O(\ell) \rightarrow H_2O(g)$

59. For each of the following, define a system and its surroundings, and give the direction of energy transfer between system and surroundings.
    (a) Methane burns in a gas furnace in your home.
    (b) Water drops, sitting on your skin after a swim, evaporate.
    (c) Water, at 25 °C, is placed in the freezing compartment of a refrigerator, where it cools and eventually solidifies.
    (d) Aluminum and $Fe_2O_3(s)$ are mixed in a flask sitting on a laboratory bench. A reaction occurs, and a large quantity of energy is evolved as heat.

60. What does the term *standard state* mean? What are the standard states of the following substances at 298 K: $H_2O$, NaCl, Hg, $CH_4$?

61. Use Appendix L to find the standard enthalpies of formation of oxygen atoms, oxygen molecules ($O_2$), and ozone ($O_3$). What is the standard state of oxygen? Is the formation of oxygen atoms from $O_2$ exothermic? What is the enthalpy change for the formation of 1 mol of $O_3$ from $O_2$?

62. You have a large balloon containing 1.0 mol of gaseous water vapor at 80 °C. How will each step affect the internal energy of the system?
    (a) The temperature of the system is raised to 90 °C.
    (b) The vapor is condensed to a liquid, at 40 °C.

63. Determine whether energy as heat is evolved or required, and whether work was done on the system or whether the system does work on the surroundings, in the following processes at constant pressure:
    (a) Liquid water at 100 °C is converted to steam at 100 °C.
    (b) Dry ice, $CO_2(s)$, sublimes to give $CO_2(g)$.

64. Determine whether energy as heat is evolved or required, and whether work was done on the system or whether the system does work on the surroundings, in the following processes at constant pressure:
    (a) Ozone, $O_3$, decomposes to form $O_2$.
    (b) Methane burns:
    $$CH_4(g) + 2\ O_2(g) \rightarrow CO_2(g) + 2\ H_2O(\ell)$$

65. Use standard enthalpies of formation to calculate the enthalpy change that occurs when 1.00 g of $SnCl_4(\ell)$ reacts with excess $H_2O(\ell)$ to form $SnO_2(s)$ and HCl(aq).

66. Which evolves more energy on cooling from 50 °C to 10 °C: 50.0 g of water or 100. g of ethanol ($C_{ethanol} = 2.46\ J/g \cdot K$)?

67. You determine that 187 J of energy as heat is required to raise the temperature of 93.45 g of silver from 18.5 °C to 27.0 °C. What is the specific heat capacity of silver?

68. Calculate the quantity of energy required to convert 60.1 g of $H_2O(s)$ at 0.0 °C to $H_2O(g)$ at 100.0 °C. The enthalpy of fusion of ice at 0 °C is 333 J/g; the enthalpy of vaporization of liquid water at 100 °C is 2256 J/g.

69. You add 100.0 g of water at 60.0 °C to 100.0 g of ice at 0.00 °C. Some of the ice melts and cools the water to 0.00 °C. When the ice and water mixture reaches thermal equilibrium at 0 °C, how much ice has melted?

70. ▲ Three 45-g ice cubes at 0 °C are dropped into $5.00 \times 10^2$ mL of tea to make iced tea. The tea was initially at 20.0 °C; when thermal equilibrium was reached, the final temperature was 0 °C. How much of the ice melted, and how much remained floating in the beverage? Assume the specific heat capacity of tea is the same as that of pure water.

71. ▲ Suppose that only two 45-g ice cubes had been added to your glass containing $5.00 \times 10^2$ mL of tea (see Study Question 70). When thermal equilibrium is reached, all of the ice will have melted, and the temperature of the mixture will be somewhere between 20.0 °C and 0 °C. Calculate the final temperature of the beverage. (*Note:* The 90 g of water formed when the ice melts must be warmed from 0 °C to the final temperature.)

72. You take a diet cola from the refrigerator and pour 240 mL of it into a glass. The temperature of the beverage is 10.5 °C. You then add one ice cube (45 g). Which of the following describes the system when thermal equilibrium is reached?
    (a) The temperature is 0 °C, and some ice remains.
    (b) The temperature is 0 °C, and no ice remains.
    (c) The temperature is higher than 0 °C, and no ice remains.

    Determine the final temperature and the amount of ice remaining, if any.

73. ▲ The standard molar enthalpy of formation of diborane, $B_2H_6(g)$, cannot be determined directly because the compound cannot be prepared by the reaction of boron and hydrogen. It can be calculated from other enthalpy changes, however. The following enthalpy changes can be measured.

    $4\ B(s)\ +\ 3\ O_2(g)\ \rightarrow\ 2\ B_2O_3(s)$
    $$\Delta_rH° = -2543.8\ \text{kJ/mol-rxn}$$

    $H_2(g)\ +\ \tfrac{1}{2}\ O_2(g)\ \rightarrow\ H_2O(g)\ \ \Delta_rH° = -241.8\ \text{kJ/mol-rxn}$

    $B_2H_6(g)\ +\ 3\ O_2(g)\ \rightarrow\ B_2O_3(s)\ +\ 3\ H_2O(g)$
    $$\Delta_rH° = -2032.9\ \text{kJ/mol-rxn}$$

    (a) Show how these equations can be added together to give the equation for the formation of $B_2H_6(g)$ from $B(s)$ and $H_2(g)$ in their standard states. Assign enthalpy changes to each reaction.
    (b) Calculate $\Delta_fH°$ for $B_2H_6(g)$.
    (c) Draw an energy level diagram that shows how the various enthalpies in this problem are related.
    (d) Is the formation of $B_2H_6(g)$ from its elements exo- or endothermic?

74. Chloromethane, $CH_3Cl$, a compound found throughout the environment, is formed in the reaction of chlorine atoms with methane.

    $$CH_4(g)\ +\ 2\ Cl(g)\ \rightarrow\ CH_3Cl(g)\ +\ HCl(g)$$

    (a) Calculate the enthalpy change for the reaction of $CH_4(g)$ and Cl atoms to give $CH_3Cl(g)$ and $HCl(g)$. Is the reaction exo- or endothermic?
    (b) Draw an energy level diagram that shows how the various enthalpies in this problem are related.

75. When heated to a high temperature, coke (mainly carbon, obtained by heating coal in the absence of air) and steam produce a mixture called *water gas*, which can be used as a fuel or as a starting place for other reactions. The equation for the production of water gas is

    $$C(s)\ +\ H_2O(g)\ \rightarrow\ CO(g)\ +\ H_2(g)$$

    (a) Use standard enthalpies of formation to determine the enthalpy change for this reaction.
    (b) Is the reaction exo- or endothermic?
    (c) What is the enthalpy change if 1000.0 kg (1 metric ton) of carbon is converted to water gas?

76. Camping stoves are fueled by propane ($C_3H_8$), butane [$C_4H_{10}(g)$, $\Delta_fH° = -127.1$ kJ/mol], gasoline, or ethanol ($C_2H_5OH$). Calculate the enthalpy of combustion per gram of each of these fuels. [Assume that gasoline is represented by isooctane, $C_8H_{18}(\ell)$, with $\Delta_fH° = -259.3$ kJ/mol.] Do you notice any great differences among these fuels? How are these differences related to their composition?

A camping stove that uses butane as a fuel.

77. Methanol, $CH_3OH$, a compound that can be made relatively inexpensively from coal, is a promising substitute for gasoline. The alcohol has a smaller energy content than gasoline, but, with its higher octane rating, it burns more efficiently than gasoline in combustion engines. (It has the added advantage of contributing to a lesser degree to some air pollutants.) Compare the enthalpy of combustion per gram of $CH_3OH$ and $C_8H_{18}$ (isooctane), the latter being representative of the compounds in gasoline. ($\Delta_fH° = -259.2$ kJ/mol for isooctane.)

78. Hydrazine and 1,1-dimethylhydrazine both react spontaneously with $O_2$ and can be used as rocket fuels.

    $$N_2H_4(\ell)\ +\ O_2(g)\ \rightarrow\ N_2(g)\ +\ 2\ H_2O(g)$$
    hydrazine

    $N_2H_2(CH_3)_2(\ell)\ +\ 4\ O_2(g)\ \rightarrow$
    1,1-dimethylhydrazine    $2\ CO_2(g)\ +\ 4\ H_2O(g)\ +\ N_2(g)$

    The molar enthalpy of formation of $N_2H_4(\ell)$ is +50.6 kJ/mol, and that of $N_2H_2(CH_3)_2(\ell)$ is +48.9 kJ/mol. Use these values, with other $\Delta_fH°$ values, to decide whether the reaction of hydrazine or 1,1-dimethylhydrazine with oxygen provides more energy per gram.

A control rocket in the Space Shuttle uses hydrazine as fuel.

79. (a) Calculate the enthalpy change, $\Delta_r H°$, for the formation of 1.00 mol of strontium carbonate (the material that gives the red color in fireworks) from its elements.

$$Sr(s) + C(s) + \tfrac{3}{2} O_2(g) \rightarrow SrCO_3(s)$$

The experimental information available is

$$Sr(s) + \tfrac{1}{2} O_2(g) \rightarrow SrO(s) \quad \Delta_f H° = -592 \text{ kJ/mol-rxn}$$

$$SrO(s) + CO_2(g) \rightarrow SrCO_3(s) \quad \Delta_r H° = -234 \text{ kJ/mol-rxn}$$

$$C(graphite) + O_2(g) \rightarrow CO_2(g) \quad \Delta_f H° = -394 \text{ kJ/mol-rxn}$$

(b) Draw an energy level diagram relating the energy quantities in this problem.

80. You drink 350 mL of diet soda that is at a temperature of 5 °C.
(a) How much energy will your body expend to raise the temperature of this liquid to body temperature (37 °C)? Assume that the density and specific heat capacity of diet soda are the same as for water.
(b) Compare the value in part (a) with the caloric content of the beverage. (The label says that it has a caloric content of 1 Calorie.) What is the net energy change in your body resulting from drinking this beverage? (1 Calorie = 1000 kCal = 4184 J.)
(c) Carry out a comparison similar to that in part (b) for a nondiet beverage whose label indicates a caloric content of 240 Calories.

81. ▲ Chloroform, $CHCl_3$, is formed from methane and chlorine in the following reaction.

$$CH_4(g) + 3 Cl_2(g) \rightarrow 3 HCl(g) + CHCl_3(g)$$

Calculate $\Delta_r H°$, the enthalpy change for this reaction, using the enthalpies of formation of $CO_2(g)$, $H_2O(\ell)$, and $CHCl_3(g)$ ($\Delta_f H° = -103.1$ kJ/mol), and the enthalpy changes for the following reactions:

$$CH_4(g) + 2 O_2(g) \rightarrow 2 H_2O(\ell) + CO_2(g)$$
$$\Delta_r H° = -890.4 \text{ kJ/mol-rxn}$$

$$2 HCl(g) \rightarrow H_2(g) + Cl_2(g)$$
$$\Delta_r H° = +184.6 \text{ kJ/mol-rxn}$$

82. Water gas, a mixture of carbon monoxide and hydrogen, is produced by treating carbon (in the form of coke or coal) with steam at high temperatures. (See Study Question 75.)

$$C(s) + H_2O(g) \rightarrow CO(g) + H_2(g)$$

Not all of the carbon available is converted to water gas since some is burned to provide the heat for the endothermic reaction of carbon and water. What mass of carbon must be burned (to $CO_2$ gas) to provide the energy to convert 1.00 kg of carbon to water gas?

## In the Laboratory

83. A piece of lead with a mass of 27.3 g was heated to 98.90 °C and then dropped into 15.0 g of water at 22.50 °C. The final temperature was 26.32 °C. Calculate the specific heat capacity of lead from these data.

84. A 192-g piece of copper is heated to 100.0 °C in a boiling water bath and then dropped into a beaker containing 751 g of water (density = 1.00 g/cm³) at 4.0 °C. What was the final temperature of the copper and water after thermal equilibrium was reached? ($C_{Cu} = 0.385$ J/g · K.)

85. Insoluble $AgCl(s)$ precipitates when solutions of $AgNO_3(aq)$ and $NaCl(aq)$ are mixed.

$$AgNO_3(aq) + NaCl(aq) \rightarrow AgCl(s) + NaNO_3(aq)$$
$$\Delta_r H° = ?$$

To measure the energy evolved in this reaction, 250. mL of 0.16 M $AgNO_3(aq)$ and 125 mL of 0.32 M $NaCl(aq)$ are mixed in a coffee-cup calorimeter. The temperature of the mixture rises from 21.15 °C to 22.90 °C. Calculate the enthalpy change for the precipitation of $AgCl(s)$, in kJ/mol. (Assume the density of the solution is 1.0 g/mL and its specific heat capacity is 4.2 J/g · K.)

86. Insoluble $PbBr_2(s)$ precipitates when solutions of $Pb(NO_3)_2(aq)$ and $NaBr(aq)$ are mixed.

$$Pb(NO_3)_2(aq) + 2 NaBr(aq) \rightarrow PbBr_2(s) + 2 NaNO_3(aq)$$
$$\Delta_r H° = ?$$

To measure the enthalpy change, 200. mL of 0.75 M $Pb(NO_3)_2(aq)$ and 200. mL of 1.5 M $NaBr(aq)$ are mixed in a coffee-cup calorimeter. The temperature of the mixture rises by 2.44 °C. Calculate the enthalpy change for the precipitation of $PbBr_2(s)$, in kJ/mol. (Assume the density of the solution is 1.0 g/mL, and its specific heat capacity is 4.2 J/g · K.)

87. The value of $\Delta U$ for the decomposition of 7.647 g of ammonium nitrate can be measured in a bomb calorimeter. The reaction that occurs is

$$NH_4NO_3(s) \rightarrow N_2O(g) + 2 H_2O(g)$$

The temperature of the calorimeter, which contains 415 g of water, increases from 18.90 °C to 20.72 °C. The heat capacity of the bomb is 155 J/K. What is the value of $\Delta U$ for this reaction, in kJ/mol?

© Cengage Learning/Charles D. Winters

**The decomposition of ammonium nitrate is clearly exothermic.**

88. A bomb calorimetric experiment was run to determine the enthalpy of combustion of ethanol. The reaction is

$$C_2H_5OH(\ell) + 3\ O_2(g) \rightarrow 2\ CO_2(g) + 3\ H_2O(\ell)$$

The bomb had a heat capacity of 550 J/K, and the calorimeter contained 650 g of water. Burning 4.20 g of ethanol, $C_2H_5OH(\ell)$ resulted in a rise in temperature from 18.5 °C to 22.3 °C. Calculate the enthalpy of combustion of ethanol, in kJ/mol.

89. The meals-ready-to-eat (MREs) in the military can be heated on a flameless heater. You can purchase a similar product called "Heater Meals." Just pour water into the heater unit, wait a few minutes, and you have a hot meal. The source of energy in the heater is

$$Mg(s) + 2\ H_2O(\ell) \rightarrow Mg(OH)_2(s) + H_2(g)$$

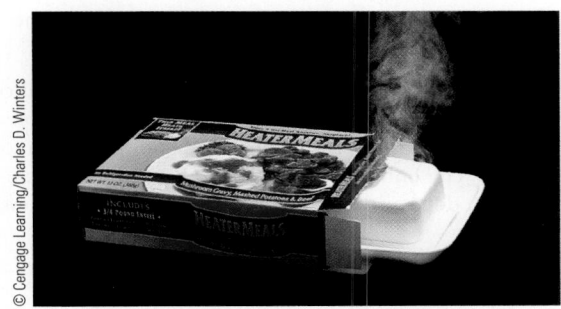

The "heater meal" uses the reaction of magnesium with water as a source of energy as heat.

Calculate the enthalpy change under standard conditions, in joules, for this reaction. What quantity of magnesium is needed to supply the energy required to warm 25 mL of water ($d = 1.00$ g/mL) from 25 °C to 85 °C? (See W. Jensen: *Journal of Chemical Education*, Vol. 77, pp. 713–717, 2000.)

90. On a cold day, you can warm your hands with a "heat pad," a device that uses the oxidation of iron to produce energy as heat.

$$4\ Fe(s) + 3\ O_2(g) \rightarrow 2\ Fe_2O_3(s)$$

A hand warmer uses the oxidation of iron as a source of thermal energy.

What mass of iron is needed to supply the energy required to warm 15 mL of water ($d = 1.00$ g/mL) from 23 °C to 37 °C?

## Summary and Conceptual Questions

*The following questions may use concepts from this and previous chapters.*

91. Without doing calculations, decide whether each of the following is exo- or endothermic.
    (a) the combustion of natural gas
    (b) the decomposition of glucose, $C_6H_{12}O_6$, to carbon and water

92. Which of the following are state functions?
    (a) the volume of a balloon
    (b) the time it takes to drive from your home to your college or university
    (c) the temperature of the water in a coffee cup
    (d) the potential energy of a ball held in your hand

93. ▲ You want to determine the value for the enthalpy of formation of $CaSO_4(s)$, but the reaction cannot be done directly.

    $$Ca(s) + S(s) + 2\ O_2(g) \rightarrow CaSO_4(s)$$

    You know, however, that (a) both calcium and sulfur react with oxygen to produce oxides in reactions that can be studied calorimetrically, and (b) the basic oxide CaO reacts with the acidic oxide $SO_3(g)$ to produce $CaSO_4(s)$ with $\Delta_rH° = -402.7$ kJ. Outline a method for determining $\Delta_fH°$ for $CaSO_4(s)$, and identify the information that must be collected by experiment. Using information in Appendix L, confirm that $\Delta_fH°$ for $CaSO_4(s) = -1433.5$ kJ/mol.

94. Prepare a graph of specific heat capacities for metals versus their atomic weights. Combine the data in Figure 5.4 and the values in the following table. What is the relationship between specific heat capacity and atomic weight? Use this relationship to predict the specific heat capacity of platinum. The specific heat capacity for platinum is given in the literature as 0.133 J/g · K. How good is the agreement between the predicted and actual values?

| Metal | Specific Heat Capacity (J/g · K) |
|---|---|
| Chromium | 0.450 |
| Lead | 0.127 |
| Silver | 0.236 |
| Tin | 0.227 |
| Titanium | 0.522 |

95. Observe the molar heat capacity values for the metals in Figure 5.4. What observation can you make about these values—specifically, are they widely different or very similar? Using this information, estimate the specific heat capacity for silver. Compare this estimate with the correct value for silver, 0.236 J/g · K.

96. ▲ You are attending summer school and living in a very old dormitory. The day is oppressively hot, there is no air-conditioner, and you can't open the windows of your room. There is a refrigerator in the room, however. In a stroke of genius, you open the door of the refrigerator, and cool air cascades out. The relief does not last long, though. Soon the refrigerator motor and condenser begin to run, and not long thereafter the room is hotter than it was before. Why did the room warm up?

97. You want to heat the air in your house with natural gas ($CH_4$). Assume your house has 275 m² (about 2800 ft²) of floor area and that the ceilings are 2.50 m from the floors. The air in the house has a molar heat capacity of 29.1 J/mol · K. (The number of moles of air in the house can be found by assuming that the average molar mass of air is 28.9 g/mol and that the density of air at these temperatures is 1.22 g/L.) What mass of methane do you have to burn to heat the air from 15.0 °C to 22.0 °C?

98. Water can be decomposed to its elements, $H_2$ and $O_2$, using electrical energy or in a series of chemical reactions. The following sequence of reactions is one possibility:

$$CaBr_2(s) + H_2O(g) \rightarrow CaO(s) + 2\ HBr(g)$$

$$Hg(\ell) + 2\ HBr(g) \rightarrow HgBr_2(s) + H_2(g)$$

$$HgBr_2(s) + CaO(s) \rightarrow HgO(s) + CaBr_2(s)$$

$$HgO(s) \rightarrow Hg(\ell) + \tfrac{1}{2}\ O_2(g)$$

(a) Show that the net result of this series of reactions is the decomposition of water to its elements.
(b) If you use 1000. kg of water, what mass of $H_2$ can be produced?
(c) Calculate the value of $\Delta_r H°$ for each step in the series. Are the reactions predicted to be exo- or endothermic?

$$\Delta_f H° \ [CaBr_2(s)] = -683.2\ kJ/mol$$

$$\Delta_f H° \ [HgBr_2(s)] = -169.5\ kJ/mol$$

(d) Comment on the commercial feasibility of using this series of reactions to produce $H_2(g)$ from water.

99. Suppose that an inch (2.54 cm) of rain falls over a square mile of ground (2.59 × 10⁶ m²). (Density of water is 1.0 g/cm³.) The enthalpy of vaporization of water at 25 °C is 44.0 kJ/mol. How much energy is transferred as heat to the surroundings from the condensation of water vapor in forming this quantity of liquid water? (The huge number tells you how much energy is "stored" in water vapor and why we think of storms as such great forces of energy in nature. It is interesting to compare this result with the energy given off, 4.2 × 10⁶ kJ, when a ton of dynamite explodes.)

100. ▲ Peanuts and peanut oil are organic materials and burn in air. How many burning peanuts does it take to provide the energy to boil a cup of water (250 mL of water)? To solve this problem, we assume each peanut, with an average mass of 0.73 g, is 49% peanut oil and 21% starch; the remainder is non-combustible. We further assume peanut oil is palmitic acid, $C_{16}H_{32}O_2$, with an enthalpy of formation of −848.4 kJ/mol. Starch is a long chain of $C_6H_{10}O_5$ units, each unit having an enthalpy of formation of −960 kJ.

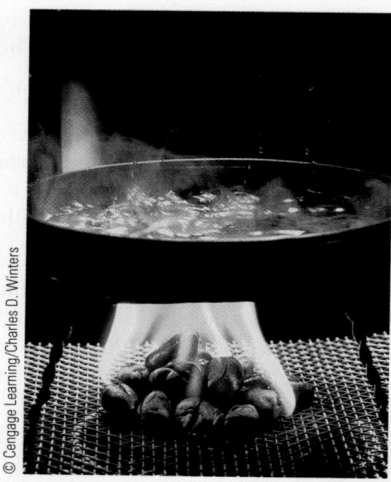

**How many burning peanuts are required to provide the energy to boil 250 mL of water?**

101. ▲ Isomers are molecules with the same elemental composition but a different atomic arrangement. Three isomers with the formula $C_4H_8$ are shown in the models below. The enthalpy of combustion ($\Delta_c H°$) of each isomer, determined using a calorimeter, is as follows:

| Compound | $\Delta_c H°$ (kJ/mol butene) |
|---|---|
| *cis*-2 butene | −2709.8 |
| *trans*-2-butene | −2706.6 |
| 1-butene | −2716.8 |

(a) Draw an energy level diagram relating the energy content of the three isomers to the energy content of the combustion products, $CO_2(g)$ and $H_2O(\ell)$.
(b) Use the $\Delta_c H°$ data in part (a), along with the enthalpies of formation of $CO_2(g)$ and $H_2O(\ell)$ from Appendix L, to calculate the enthalpy of formation for each of the isomers.
(c) Draw an energy level diagram that relates the enthalpies of formation of the three isomers to the energy of the elements in their standard states.
(d) What is the enthalpy change for the conversion of *cis*-2-butene to *trans*-2-butene?

*Cis*-2-butene.

*Trans*-2-butene.

**1-butene.**

**102.** Several standard enthalpies of formation (from Appendix L) are given below. Use these data to calculate
(a) the standard enthalpy of vaporization of bromine.
(b) the energy required for the reaction $Br_2(g) \rightarrow 2\ Br(g)$. (This is the Br—Br bond dissociation enthalpy.)

| Species | $\Delta_f H°$ (kJ/mol) |
|---------|------------------------|
| Br(g) | 111.9 |
| $Br_2(\ell)$ | 0 |
| $Br_2(g)$ | 30.9 |

**103.** When 0.850 g of Mg was burned in oxygen in a constant volume calorimeter, 25.4 kJ of energy as heat was evolved. The calorimeter was in an insulated container with 750. g of water at an initial temperature of 18.6 °C. The heat capacity of the bomb in the calorimeter is 820. J/K.
(a) Calculate $\Delta U$ for the oxidation of Mg (in kJ/mol Mg).
(b) What will be the final temperature of the water and the bomb calorimeter in this experiment?

**104.** ▲ A piece of gold (10.0 g, $C_{Au}$ = 0.129 J/g · K) is heated to 100.0 °C. A piece of copper (also 10.0 g, $C_{Cu}$ = 0.385 J/g · K) is chilled in an ice bath to 0 °C. Both pieces of metal are placed in a beaker containing 150. g $H_2O$ at 20 °C. Will the temperature of the water be greater than or less than 20 °C when thermal equilibrium is reached? Calculate the final temperature.

**105.** Methane, $CH_4$, can be converted to methanol, which, like ethanol, can be used as a fuel. The energy level diagram shown here presents relationships between energies of the fuels and their oxidation products. Use the information in the diagram to answer the following questions. (The energy terms are per mol-rxn.)

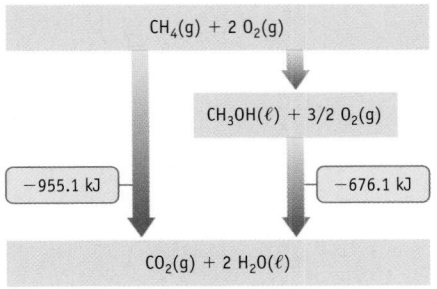

(a) Which fuel, methanol or methane, yields the most energy per mole when burned?
(b) Which fuel yields the most energy per gram when burned?
(c) What is the enthalpy change for the conversion of methane to methanol by reaction with $O_2(g)$?
(d) Each arrow on the diagram represents a chemical reaction. Write the equation for the reaction that converts methane to methanol.

**106.** Calculate $\Delta_r H°$ for the reaction
$$2\ C(s) + 3\ H_2(g) + \tfrac{1}{2}\ O_2(g) \rightarrow C_2H_5OH(\ell)$$
given the information below.

$C(s) + O_2(g) \rightarrow CO_2(g)$    $\Delta_r H° = -393.5$ kJ/mol-rxn

$2\ H_2(g) + O_2(g) \rightarrow 2\ H_2O(\ell)$
$$\Delta_r H° = -571.6 \text{ kJ/mol-rxn}$$

$C_2H_5OH(\ell) + 3\ O_2(g) \rightarrow 2\ CO_2(g) + 3\ H_2O(\ell)$
$$\Delta_r H° = -1367.5 \text{ kJ/mol-rxn}$$

**107.** ▲ You have the six pieces of metal listed below, plus a beaker of water containing $3.00 \times 10^2$ g of water. The water temperature is 21.00 °C.

| Metals | Specific Heat (J/g K) | Mass (g) |
|--------|----------------------|----------|
| 1. Al | 0.9002 | 100.0 |
| 2. Al | 0.9002 | 50.0 |
| 3. Au | 0.1289 | 100.0 |
| 4. Au | 0.1289 | 50.0 |
| 5. Zn | 0.3860 | 100.0 |
| 6. Zn | 0.3860 | 50.0 |

(a) In your first experiment you select one piece of metal and heat it to 100 °C, and then select a second piece of metal and cool it to −10 °C. Both pieces of metal are then placed in the beaker of water and the temperatures equilibrated. You want to select two pieces of metal to use, such that the final temperature of the water is as high as possible. What piece of metal will you heat? What piece of metal will you cool? What is the final temperature of the water?
(b) The second experiment is done in the same way as the first. However, your goal now is to cause the temperature to change the least, that is, the final temperature should be as near to 21.00 °C as possible. What piece of metal will you heat? What piece of metal will you cool? What is the final temperature of the water?

**108.** In lab, you plan to carry out a calorimetry experiment to determine $\Delta_r H$ for the exothermic reaction of $Ca(OH)_2(s)$ and HCl(aq). Predict how each of the following will affect the calculated value of $\Delta_r H$. (The value calculated for $\Delta_r H$ for this reaction is a negative value so choose your answer from the following: $\Delta_r H$ will be too low [that is, a larger negative value], $\Delta_r H$ will be unaffected, $\Delta_r H$ will be too high [that is, a smaller negative value.])
(a) You spill a little bit of the $Ca(OH)_2$ on the benchtop before adding it to the calorimeter.
(b) Because of a miscalculation, you add an excess of HCl to the measured amount of $Ca(OH)_2$ in the calorimeter.
(c) $Ca(OH)_2$ readily absorbs water from the air. The $Ca(OH)_2$ sample you weighed had been exposed to the air prior to weighing and had absorbed some water.
(d) After weighing out $Ca(OH)_2$, the sample sat in an open beaker and absorbed water.

(e) You delay too long in recording the final temperature.

(f) The insulation in your coffee-cup calorimeter was poor, so some energy as heat was lost to the surroundings during the experiment.

(g) You have ignored the fact that energy as heat also raised the temperature of the stirrer and the thermometer in your system.

109. Sublimation of 1.0 g of dry ice, $CO_2(s)$, forms 0.36 L of $CO_2(g)$ (at $-78$ °C and 1 atm pressure). The expanding gas can do work on the surroundings (Figure 5.8). Calculate the amount of work done on the surroundings using the equation $w = -P \times \Delta V$. (Note: L $\times$ atm is a unit of energy; 1 L atm = 101.3 J.)

110. In the reaction of two moles of gaseous hydrogen and one mole of gaseous oxygen to form two moles of gaseous water vapor, two moles of products are formed from 3 moles of reactants. If this reaction is done at 1.0 atm pressure (and at 0 °C), the volume is reduced by 22.4 L.

(a) In this reaction, how much work is done on the system ($H_2$, $O_2$, $H_2O$) by the surroundings?

(b) The enthalpy change for this reaction is $-483.6$ kJ. Use this value, along with the answer to (a), to calculate $\Delta_r U$, the change in internal energy in the system.

## Applying Chemical Principles

### Gunpowder

Gunpowder has been used in fireworks, explosives, and firearms for over one thousand years. Until the late 1800s, gunpowder was a mixture of saltpeter ($KNO_3$), charcoal (largely C), and sulfur. Today, this mixture is known as *black powder*. A simplified version of the reaction indicates that the components react to yield both solid and gaseous products.

$$2 \, KNO_3(s) + 3 \, C(s) + S(s) \rightarrow K_2S(s) + N_2(g) + 3 \, CO_2(g)$$

The actual reaction is more complicated because charcoal is not pure carbon. (It also contains some oxygen and hydrogen atoms.) Although black powder was used for hundreds of years, it has some disadvantages as a propellant: it produces a large quantity of white smoke, and the residues from the reaction are corrosive.

Modern firearms use smokeless powders. These powders are primarily composed of nitrocellulose (also known as guncotton) or a mixture of nitrocellulose and nitroglycerin. Nitrocellulose is the product of the reaction of cotton (cellulose, with an empirical formula of $C_6H_{10}O_5$) with nitric acid. The fully nitrated product has the empirical formula $C_6H_7(NO_3)_3O_2$, though guncotton is not usually fully nitrated. Decomposition of nitrocellulose and nitroglycerin releases more energy than the comparable mass of black powder. Just as important, this is a better propellant because all of the products are gaseous.

**Black gunpowder.** Black gunpowder has been known for over 1000 years and was used by both armies in the American Civil War in the 19th century. Here, a group reenacts a battle in that war. This photo shows one of the disadvantages of black powder: the great amount of smoke produced.

© Danita Delimont/Alamy

### Questions:

1. The standard enthalpies of formation of $KNO_3(s)$ and $K_2S(s)$ are $-494.6$ kJ/mol and $-376.6$ kJ/mol, respectively.
   a. Determine the standard enthalpy change for the reaction of black powder according to the balanced equation above.
   b. Determine the enthalpy change that occurs when 1.00 g of black powder decomposes according to the stoichiometry of the balanced equation above. (Even though black powder is a mixture, assume that we can designate 1 mol of black powder as consisting of exactly 2 mol of $KNO_3$, 3 mol of C, and 1 mol of S.)

2. The enthalpy of reaction of guncotton depends on the degree of nitration of the cellulose. For a particular sample, when 0.725 g of guncotton is decomposed in a bomb calorimeter, the temperature of the system increases by 1.32 K. Assuming the bomb has a heat capacity of 691 J/K and the calorimeter contains 1.200 kg of water, what is the energy of reaction per gram of guncotton?

3. The decomposition of nitroglycerin ($C_3H_5N_3O_9$) produces carbon dioxide, nitrogen, water, and oxygen gases.
   a. Write a balanced chemical equation for the decomposition of nitroglycerin.
   b. If the decomposition of 1.00 g nitroglycerin releases 6.23 kJ/g of energy in the form of heat, what is the standard molar enthalpy of formation of nitroglycerin?

### Reference:

J. Kelly, *Gunpowder, Alchemy, Bombards, and Pyrotechnics: The History of the Explosive that Changed the World*, Basic Books, New York, 2004.

# The Chemistry of Fuels and Energy Resources

Energy is necessary for everything we do. Look around you—energy is involved in anything that is moving or is emitting light, sound, or heat. Heating and lighting your home, propelling your automobile, powering your laptop computer—all are commonplace examples in which energy is used, and all are, at their origin, primarily based on chemical processes. In this interchapter, we want to examine how chemistry is fundamental to understanding and addressing current energy issues.

## Supply and Demand: The Balance Sheet on Energy

We take for granted that energy is available and that it will always be there to use. But will it? The late Richard Smalley, a chemist and Nobel Prize winner, stated that among the top 10 problems humanity will face over the next 50 years, the energy supply ranks as number one. What is the source of this prediction? Information such as the following is often quoted in the popular press:

- Global demand for energy has almost tripled in the past 40 years (Figure 1) and may triple again in the next 50 years. Most of the demand comes from industrialized nations, but most of the increase is coming from developing countries.
- Fossil fuels account for 85% of the total energy used by humans on our planet. (Of this total, petroleum accounts for 37%, coal 25%, and natural gas 23%.) Nuclear, biomass, and hydroelectric power contribute about 13% of the total energy budget. The remaining 2% derives from solar, wind, and geothermal energy generating facilities.

- With only about 5% of the world's population, the United States consumes 23% of all the energy used in the world. This usage is equivalent to the consumption of 7 gallons of oil or 70 pounds of coal per person per day.
- China and India, growing economic powerhouses, are increasing their energy usage by about 8% per year. In 2007, China passed the United States as the number one emitter of greenhouse gases in the world.

Two basic issues, *energy resources* and *energy usage*, instantly leap out from these statistics and form the basis for this discussion of energy.

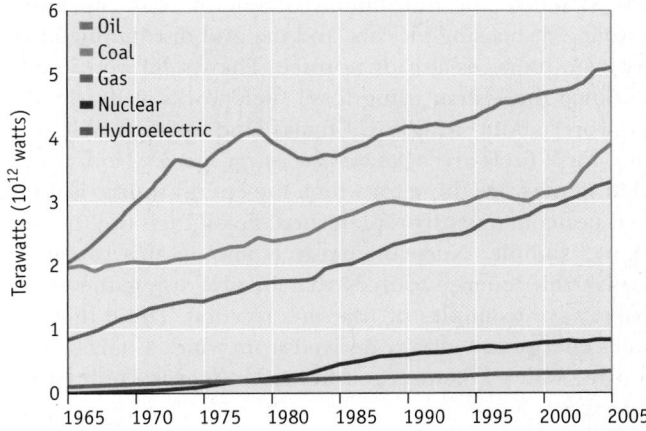

**FIGURE 1** Changes in world energy usage, 1965–2005. The vertical axis is in terawatts ($10^{12}$ watts) of power.

- **Photovoltaic panels.** The silicon-based panels can produce electricity to power a home or group of homes.

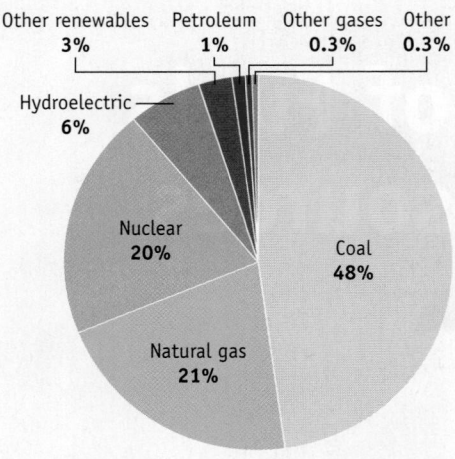

FIGURE 2 Fuel used in the electric power industry in the United States, 2008. Source: U.S. Energy Information Administration, *Electric Power Annual* (2010) (www.eia.doe.gov/).

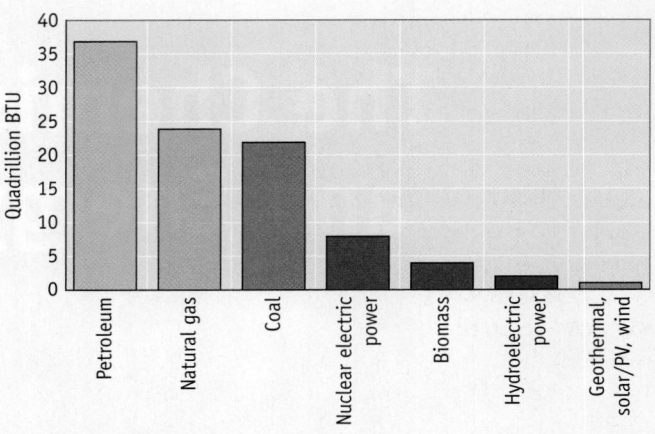

FIGURE 3 Primary sources of energy consumed for all purposes in the United States, 2008, by source. Source: U.S. Energy Information Administration (www.eia.doe.gov/). (The vertical axis units are quadrillion BTU, a measure of energy use in entire economies. One quadrillion is $10^{15}$ and a BTU is equivalent to 1.055 kJ.)

## Energy Resources

The world is hugely dependent on fossil fuels as a source of energy. Almost 70% of the electricity in the United States is generated using fossil fuels, mostly coal and natural gas (Figure 2), and over 80% of the energy consumed for all purposes is derived from fossil fuels (Figure 3).

Why is there such a dominance of fossil fuels on the resource side of the equation? An obvious reason is that fossil fuels are cheap raw materials compared to other energy sources. In addition, societies have made an immense investment in the infrastructure needed to distribute and use this energy. Power plants using coal or natural gas cannot be converted readily to accommodate another fuel. The infrastructure for distribution of energy—gas pipelines, gasoline dispensing for cars, and the grid distributing electricity to users—is already in place. The system works well.

Since the system using fossil fuels works well, why do we worry about using fossil fuels? One major problem is that fossil fuels are *nonrenewable energy sources*. Nonrenewable sources are those for which the energy source is used and not concurrently replenished. Fossil fuels are the obvious example. Nuclear energy is also in this category. Conversely, energy sources that involve using the sun's energy are examples of *renewable resources*. These include solar energy and energy derived from wind, biomass, and moving water. Likewise, geothermal energy is a renewable resource.

There is a limited supply of fossil fuels. No more sources are being created. As a consequence, we must ask how long our fossil fuels will last. Regrettably, there is not an exact answer to this question. One current estimate suggests that at current consumption rates the world's oil reserves will be depleted in 30–80 years. Natural gas and coal supplies are projected to last longer: 60–200 years for natural gas and from 150 to several hundred years for coal. These numbers are highly uncertain, however—in part because the estimates are based on guesses regarding fuel reserves not yet discovered, in part because assumptions must be made about the rate of consumption in future years. If the use of a commodity (such as oil) continues to rise by a fixed percentage every year, then we say that we are experiencing "exponential growth" for that usage. Even though the amount of oil consumed every year might rise by only 2%–4%, this still is a rapid growth in the total used if we look forward many years. A global growth rate of 4% per year for oil will reduce the estimate of petroleum resources lasting 80 years to only 36 years. A growth rate of 2% per year changes this estimate to 48 years. Estimates of how long these resources will last do not mean anything unless assumed growth rates are accurate.

We cannot ignore the fact that a change away from fossil fuels must occur someday. As supply diminishes and demand increases, expansion to other fuel types will inevitably occur. Increased cost of energy based on fossil fuels will encourage these changes. The technologies to facilitate change, and the answers regarding which alternative fuel types will be the most efficient and cost-effective, can be aided by research in chemistry.

One energy source that has been exploited extensively in some countries is nuclear power. For example, several countries in Europe generate more than 40% of their electricity using nuclear power plants (Figure 4). Certain regions on the planet (such as Iceland and New Zealand) are also able to exploit geothermal power as an energy source, and Germany and Spain plan on meeting 25% of their electrical energy needs with wind by the year 2020.

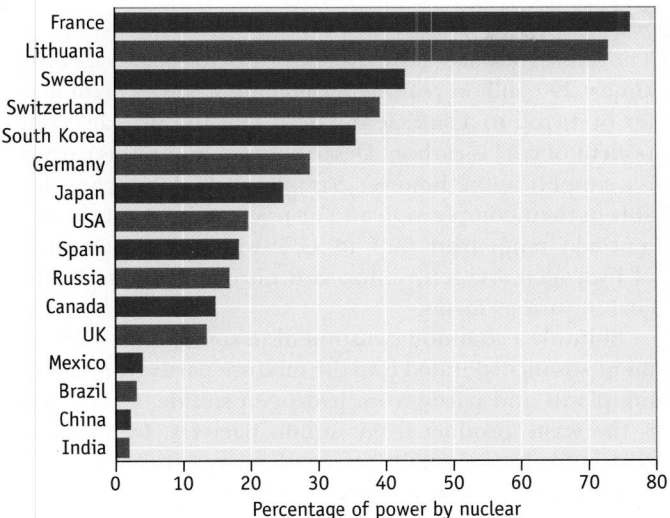

FIGURE 4 Use of nuclear power for electricity generation.

## Energy Usage

Many studies indicate that energy usage is related to the degree to which a country has industrialized. The more industrialized a country, the more energy is used by individuals on a per capita basis (Figure 5). As developing nations become more industrialized, personal energy usage worldwide will surely increase proportionally. There has been rapid growth in energy usage over the past two decades, and it is predicted that there will be continued rapid growth in the next half-century (Figure 1).

One way to alter energy consumption is through conservation. This can mean consciously using less energy (such as driving less, turning off lights when not in use, and turning the thermostat down [for heating] or up [for

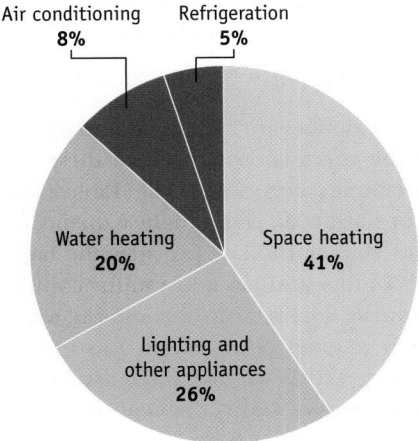

FIGURE 5 Energy use in homes in the United States, 2005. Source: U.S. Energy Information Administration, *Residential Energy Consumption Survey* (2005) (www.eia.doe.gov/).

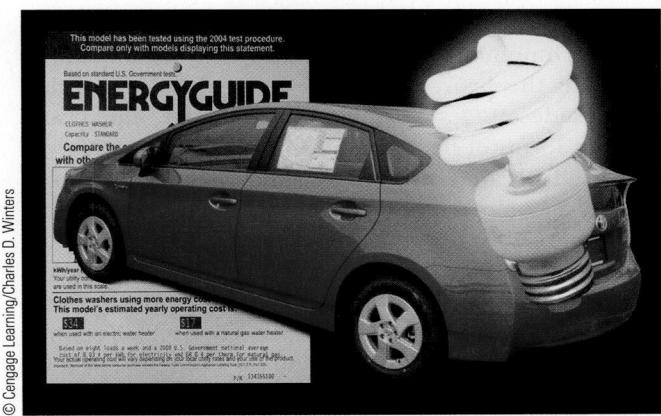

FIGURE 6 Energy-conserving devices. Energy-efficient home appliances, hybrid automobiles, and compact fluorescent bulbs all provide alternatives that consume less energy than their conventional counterparts to do the same task.

cooling]). It can also mean using energy more efficiently. Some examples (Figure 6) of this latter approach are:

- Aluminum is recycled because recovering aluminum requires only one third of the energy needed to produce the metal from its ore.
- Light-emitting diodes (LEDs) are now used in streetlights, and compact fluorescent lights are finding wider use in the home. Both use a fraction of the energy required by incandescent bulbs (in which only 5% of the energy used is delivered in the form of light; the remaining 95% is wasted as heat).
- Hybrid cars offer up to twice the gas mileage available with conventional cars.
- Many newer appliances (from refrigerators to air conditioners) are designed to use less energy per delivered output.

One of the exciting areas of current research in chemistry relating to energy conservation focuses on superconductivity. Superconductors are materials that, at temperatures of 30–150 K, offer virtually no resistance to electrical conductivity (◄ *Applying Chemical Principles,* page 155). When an electric current passes through a typical conductor such as a copper wire, some of the energy is lost as heat. As a result, there is substantial energy loss in power transmission lines. Substituting a superconducting wire for copper has the potential to greatly decrease this loss, so the search is on for materials that act as superconductors at moderate temperatures.

## Fossil Fuels

Fossil fuels originate from organic matter that was trapped under the earth's surface for many millennia. Due to the particular combination of temperature, pressure, and available oxygen, the decomposition process of the compounds that constitute organic matter resulted in the hydrocarbons we extract and use today: coal, crude oil, and natural gas—the solid, liquid, and gaseous forms of fossil fuels, respectively.

Fossil fuels are simple to use and relatively inexpensive to extract, compared with the current cost requirements of other sources for the equivalent amount of energy. To use the energy stored in fossil fuels, these materials are burned. The combustion process, when it goes to completion, converts fossil fuels to $CO_2$ and $H_2O$ (◄ Section 3.2). The thermal energy is converted to mechanical and then electrical energy (◄ Chapters 1 and 5).

The hydrocarbons of fossil fuels have varying ratios of carbon to hydrogen, and their energy output from burning (Table 1) is related to that ratio. You can analyze this relationship by considering data on enthalpies of formation and by looking at an example that is 100% carbon and another that is 100% hydrogen. The oxidation of 1.0 mol (12.01 g) of pure carbon produces 393.5 kJ of energy or 32.8 kJ/g.

$$C(s) + O_2(g) \rightarrow CO_2(g)$$

$$\Delta_r H° = -393.5 \text{ kJ/mol-rxn or } -32.8 \text{ kJ/g C}$$

Burning hydrogen to form water is much more exothermic on a per-gram basis, with about 120 kJ evolved per gram of hydrogen consumed.

$$H_2(g) + \tfrac{1}{2} O_2(g) \rightarrow H_2O(g)$$

$$\Delta_r H° = -241.8 \text{ kJ/mol-rxn or } -119.9 \text{ kJ/g } H_2$$

Coal is mostly carbon, so its heat output is similar to that of pure carbon. In contrast, methane is 25% hydrogen (by mass), and the higher–molecular-weight hydrocarbons in petroleum and products refined from petroleum average 16–17% hydrogen content. Therefore, their heat output on a per-gram basis is greater than that of pure carbon but less than that of hydrogen itself.

While the basic chemical principles for extracting energy from fossil fuels are simple, complications arise in practice. Let us look at each of these fuels in turn.

## Table 1 Energy Released by Combustion of Fossil Fuels

| Substance | Energy Released (kJ/g) |
|---|---|
| Coal | 29–37 |
| Crude petroleum | 43 |
| Gasoline (refined petroleum) | 47 |
| Natural gas (methane) | 50 |

## Coal

The solid rock-like substance we call *coal* began to form almost 290 million years ago. Decomposition of plant matter occurred to a sufficient extent that the primary component of coal is carbon. Describing coal simply as carbon is a simplification, however. Samples of coal vary considerably in their composition and characteristics. Carbon content may range from 60% to 95%, with variable amounts of hydrogen, oxygen, sulfur, and nitrogen present in the coal in various forms.

Sulfur is a common constituent in some coals. The element was incorporated into the mixture partly from decaying plants and partly from hydrogen sulfide, $H_2S$, which is the waste product from certain bacteria. In addition, coal is likely to contain traces of many other elements, including some that are toxic (such as arsenic, mercury, cadmium, and lead) along with some that are not (such as iron).

When coal is burned, some of the impurities are dispersed into the air, and some end up in the ash that is formed. In the United States, coal-fired power plants are responsible for 60% of the emissions of $SO_2$ and 33% of mercury emissions into the environment. (Power plants in the United States emit about 50 tons of mercury per year; worldwide, about 5500 tons are emitted.) Sulfur dioxide reacts with water and oxygen in the atmosphere to form sulfuric acid, which contributes (along with nitric acid) to the phenomenon known as *acid rain*.

$$2 SO_2(g) + O_2(g) \rightarrow 2 SO_3(g)$$

$$SO_3(g) + H_2O(\ell) \rightarrow H_2SO_4(aq)$$

Because these acids are harmful to the environment, legislation limits the extent of sulfur oxide emissions from coal-fired plants. These sulfur-based emissions can be removed in scrubbers in which the combustion gases are passed through a water spray with chemicals such as limestone (calcium carbonate) to form solids that can be removed:

$$2 SO_2(g) + 2 CaCO_3(s) + O_2(g) \rightarrow 2 CaSO_4(s) + 2 CO_2(g)$$

However, these devices are expensive, and they can increase the cost of the energy produced from these facilities.

There are three categories of coal (Table 2 and Figure 7). *Anthracite,* or hard coal, is the highest-quality coal. Among the forms of coal, anthracite provides the largest amount of energy per gram and has a low sulfur content. Unfortunately, anthracite coal is fairly uncommon, with only 2% of the U.S. coal reserves occurring in this form. *Bituminous coal,* also referred to as *soft coal,* accounts for about 45% of the U.S. coal reserves and is the coal most widely used in electric power generation. Soft coal typically has the highest sulfur content. *Lignite,* also called brown coal because of its paler color, is geologically the "youngest" form of coal. It releases a smaller amount of energy per gram than the

## Table 2 Types of Coal

| Type | Consistency | Sulfur Content | Energy Released (kJ/g) |
|------|-------------|----------------|------------------------|
| Lignite | Very soft | Very low | 28–30 |
| Bituminous coal | Soft | High | 29–37 |
| Anthracite | Hard | Low | 36–37 |

other forms of coal, often contains a significant amount of water, and is the least popular as a fuel.

Coal can be converted to coke by heating in the absence of air. Coke is almost pure carbon and is an excellent fuel. In the process of coke formation, a variety of organic compounds are driven off. These compounds are used as raw materials in the chemical industry for the production of polymers, pharmaceuticals, synthetic fabrics, waxes, tar, and numerous other products.

Technology to convert coal into gaseous fuels (coal gasification) or liquid fuels (liquefaction) is under well known but is hampered by cost. These processes provide fuels that burn more cleanly than coal, but 30–40% of the available energy is lost in the process. As petroleum and natural gas reserves dwindle and the costs of these fuels increase, liquid and gaseous fuels derived from coal are likely to become more important.

## Natural Gas

Natural gas is found deep under the earth's surface. There is some debate as to how natural gas formed, but one major theory is that it is formed by bacteria decomposing organic matter in an anaerobic environment (in which no $O_2$ is present). The major component of natural gas (70–95%) is methane ($CH_4$). Lesser quantities of gases such as ethane ($C_2H_6$), propane ($C_3H_8$), and butane ($C_4H_{10}$) may also be

FIGURE 7 Bituminous coal being extracted from a strip mine in Montana.

Courtesy of BLM Wyoming

present, along with other gases including $N_2$, He, $CO_2$, and $H_2S$. The impurities and higher–molecular-weight components of natural gas are separated out during the refining process, so the gas piped into our homes is primarily methane.

Natural gas is an increasingly popular choice as a fuel. It burns more cleanly than the other fossil fuels, emits fewer pollutants, and produces relatively more energy than the other fossil fuels. Natural gas can be transported by pipelines over land and piped into buildings such as your home, where it is used to heat ambient air, and to heat water for washing, bathing, or cooking. It is also a popular choice for new electrical power plants, which have high efficiencies due to new gas turbines and recovery of waste heat.

## Petroleum

Petroleum is often found in porous rock formations that are bounded by impermeable rock. Petroleum is a complicated mixture of hydrocarbons whose molar masses range from low to very high (▶ page 458). The hydrocarbons may have anywhere from one to twenty or more carbon atoms in their structures, and compounds containing sulfur, nitrogen, and oxygen may also be present, usually in small amounts.

Petroleum goes through extensive processing at refineries to separate the various components and convert less valuable compounds into more valuable ones. Nearly 85% of the crude petroleum pumped from the ground ends up being used as a fuel, either for transportation (gasoline and diesel fuel) or for heating (fuel oils).

## Other Fossil Fuel Sources

When natural gas pipelines were laid across the United States and Canada, pipeline operators soon found that, unless water was carefully kept out of the line, chunks of methane hydrate would form and clog the pipes. Methane hydrate (Figure 8) was a completely unexpected substance because it is composed of methane and water, two chemicals that would appear to have little affinity for each other. In methane hydrate, methane is trapped in cavities in the crystal structure of ice. Methane hydrate is stable only at temperatures below the freezing point of water or at high pressures. If a sample of methane hydrate is warmed above 0° C, it melts, and methane is released. The volume of gas released (at normal pressure and temperature) is about 165 times larger than the volume of the hydrate.

Methane hydrate is also found in nature. In 1970, oceanographers drilling into the seabed off the coast of South Carolina pulled up samples of a whitish solid that fizzed and oozed when it was removed from the drill casing. They quickly realized it was methane hydrate. Since this original discovery, methane hydrate has been found in many parts of the oceans as well as under permafrost in the Arctic. It is estimated that $1.5 \times 10^{13}$ tons of methane

FIGURE 8 **Methane hydrate.** This interesting substance is found in huge deposits hundreds of feet down on the floor of the ocean. When a sample is brought to the surface, the methane oozes out of the solid, and the gas readily burns. The structure of the solid hydrate consists of methane molecules trapped within a lattice of water molecules. Each red point of the lattice shown here is an oxygen atom of a water molecule (inset). The edges are O—H—O bonds. Such structures are often called *clathrates*. Methane hydrates also played a role in the massive oil spill in the Gulf of Mexico in 2010. There is speculation that it was methane released from hydrates that led to the initial explosion. Then, in the first attempt to contain the oil gushing from the well, a large dome was lowered over the well. However, this failed to contain the oil as methane hydrates accumulated in the dome, making it too buoyant and clogging the pipe to the surface.

hydrate are buried under the seafloor around the world. In fact, the energy available from this source may surpass that of all the other known fossil fuel reserves by as much as a factor of 2! Clearly, this is a potential source of an important fuel in the future.

There are other sources of methane in our environment. For example, methane is generated in swamps, where it is called *swamp gas* or *marsh gas*. Here, methane is formed by bacteria working on organic matter in an anaerobic environment—namely, in sedimentary layers of coastal waters and in marshes. The process of formation is thought to be similar to the processes occurring eons ago that generated the natural gas deposits that we currently use for fuel. In a marsh, the gas can escape if the sediment layer is thin. You see it as bubbles rising to the surface. Unfortunately, because of the relatively small amounts generated, it is impractical to collect and use this gas as a fuel.

FIGURE 9 **Athabasca oil sands in Canada.** Currently about 1 million barrels of oil are extracted per day from the tar sands in northern Alberta, Canada. Although the proven reserves are quite large (perhaps second in the world only to Saudi Arabia), there are significant environmental issues involved in obtaining oil from tar sands.

In a striking analogy to what occurs in nature, methane also forms in landfill sites as they contain a great deal of buried organic matter. It remains out of contact with oxygen in the air, and methane is formed as the organic matter is degraded by bacteria. Although landfill gases were once thought to be a nuisance, today it is possible to collect the methane and use it as a fuel.

Another source of fossil fuels is oil from tar sands. **Tar sands** (also called **oil sands**) contain a very viscous organic liquid called *bitumen*. This is chemically similar to the highest–molecular-weight fraction obtained by distillation of crude oil. What makes this source so enticing is the huge quantity of oil that could be obtained from such sites. The largest resource of tar sands in the world is found in Alberta, Canada (the *Athabasca Sands*, Figure 9). This is followed closely by those in Venezuela. Resources approaching 3.5 trillion barrels of oil are estimated in these two locations—twice the world's known reserves of petroleum. The United States imports more oil from Canada than any other country (about one million barrels per day), and most of this is from the Athabasca oil sands.

Extracting the oil from sands is quite costly. Essentially, the sands must be mined and then mixed with hot water or steam to extract the bitumen. In order to avoid an environmental catastrophe, the mined land must be restored (reclaimed). This adds to the cost of the process. Also, most of the Canadian oil sands are located in dry areas, so obtaining an adequate water supply for extraction is a constraint on increased production.

## Environmental Impacts of Fossil Fuel Use

We are a carbon-based society. As mentioned earlier, about 85% of the energy used in the world today comes from fossil fuels. As energy usage increases, the amount of gaseous emissions of carbon compounds into our environment continues to rise (Figure 10). These include mainly $CO_2$ but also $CH_4$ and CO.

The "greenhouse effect" is a name given to the trapping of energy in the earth's atmosphere by a process very similar to that occurring in glass-enclosed greenhouses in which plants are grown (Figure 11). The atmosphere, like window glass, is transparent to incoming solar radiation. This is absorbed by the earth and re-emitted as infrared radiation. Gases in the atmosphere, like window glass, trap some of these longer infrared rays, keeping the earth warmer than it would otherwise be. In the last century, there has been an increase in concentrations in the atmosphere of carbon dioxide and other so-called greenhouse gases (methane, nitrogen oxides) due to increases in fossil fuel burning. There has also been a corresponding increase in global average temperatures that most scientists attribute to increases in these greenhouse gas concentrations (Figure 12). The increase in global temperatures correlates well with increased concentrations of $CO_2$ in the atmosphere. For the next two decades, a warming of about 0.2 °C per decade is projected by some models. Such temperature changes will affect the earth's climate in many ways, such as more intense storms, precipitation changes, and sea level rise.

**Global warming**—the increase in average global temperatures—and accompanying **climate change** have become major social and political issues worldwide. Indeed, many of the steps made in the last decade to put increased emphasis on renewable energies is due to the concern for the earth's climate (see also *The Chemistry of the Environment*, page 947).

Another problem due to increased burning of fossil fuels is local and international air pollution. The high temperature and pressure used in the combustion process in automobile engines have the unfortunate consequence of also causing a reaction between atmospheric nitrogen and oxygen that results in some NO formation. The NO can then react further with oxygen to produce nitrogen dioxide. This poisonous brown gas is further oxidized to form nitric acid, $HNO_3$, in the presence of water.

$$N_2(g) + O_2(g) \rightarrow 2\ NO(g) \qquad \Delta_r H^\circ = 180.58 \text{ kJ/mol-rxn}$$

$$2\ NO(g) + O_2(g) \rightarrow 2\ NO_2(g) \qquad \Delta_r H^\circ = -114.4 \text{ kJ/mol-rxn}$$

$$3\ NO_2(g) + H_2O(\ell) \rightarrow$$
$$2\ HNO_3(aq) + NO(g) \qquad \Delta_r H^\circ = -71.4 \text{ kJ/mol-rxn}$$

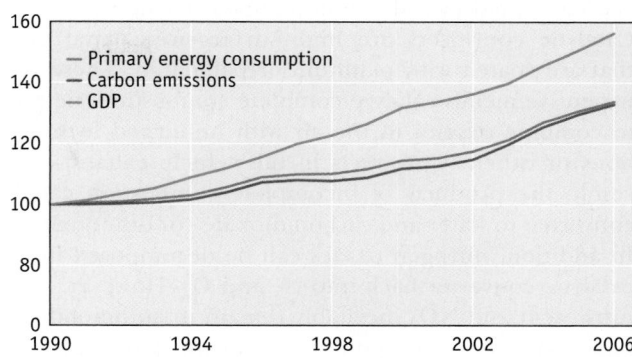

Index: 1990 = 100

FIGURE 10  World energy usage, carbon emissions, and GDP, 1990–2006. Notice that there is a strong correlation between carbon emissions and energy use. Also, gross domestic product (GDP) is rising faster than energy use, indicating increased energy efficiency.

Much of the incident energy associated with solar radiation is absorbed, warming the earth's surface.

The earth emits infrared radiation. Part of this radiation escapes into space, but a part is absorbed by greenhouse gases in the atmosphere. The absorbed energy warms the atmosphere.

Higher concentrations of greenhouse gases trap more of the energy reradiated by the earth, resulting in higher atmospheric temperatures.

FIGURE 11  The greenhouse effect.

FIGURE 12  Variation in global mean surface temperatures for 1850 to 2006. These are relative to the period 1961–1990.

To some extent, the amounts of pollutants released can be limited by use of automobile catalytic converters. Catalytic converters are high–surface-area metal grids that are coated with platinum or palladium. These very expensive metals catalyze complete combustion, helping to combine oxygen in the air with unburned hydrocarbons or other by-products in the vehicle exhaust. As a result, the products of incomplete combustion can be converted to water and carbon dioxide (or other oxides). In addition, nitrogen oxides can be decomposed in the catalytic converter back into $N_2$ and $O_2$. However, some nitric acid and $NO_2$ inevitably remain in automobile exhaust, and these compounds are major contributors to environmental pollution in the form of acid rain and smog. The brown acidic atmospheres in highly congested cities such as Beijing, Los Angeles, Mexico City, and Houston result largely from the automobile emissions. Such pollution problems have led to stricter emission standards for automobiles, and the development of low-emission or emission-free vehicles is a high priority in the automobile industry (motivated in part by emission standards of such states as California).

## Energy in the Future: Choices and Alternatives

### Fuel Cells

Most electricity in the United States is produced by burning fossil fuels. The heat of combustion is used to produce high-pressure steam, which spins a turbine in a generator. Unfortunately, not all of the energy from the combustion can be converted to usable work. Some of the energy stored in the chemical bonds of a fuel is transferred as heat to the surroundings, making this an inherently inefficient process. The efficiency is about 35–40% for a coal-fired steam turbine and 50–55% for the newer natural gas turbines.

A much more efficient process is possible if mobile electrons, the carriers of electricity, are generated directly from the chemical bonds themselves, rather than going through an energy conversion process from heat to mechanical work to electricity. Fuel cell technology makes this direct conversion to electricity possible. Fuel cells are similar to batteries, except that fuel is supplied from an external source (Figure 13 and Section 20.3). They are more efficient than combustion-based energy production, with up to 60% energy conversion.

Fuel cells are not a new discovery. In fact, the first fuel cell was demonstrated in 1839, and fuel cells have been used for some time in the Space Shuttle. Fuel cells are currently under development for use in homes, businesses, and automobiles.

The basic design of fuel cells is simple. Oxidation and reduction (◄ page 137) take place in two separate com-

partments. These compartments are connected in a way that allows electrons to flow from the oxidation compartment to the reduction compartment through a conductor such as a wire. In one compartment, a fuel is oxidized, producing electrons. The electrons move through the conductor to the other compartment, where they react with an oxidizing agent, typically $O_2$. The spontaneous flow of electrons in the electrical circuit constitutes the electric current. While electrons flow through the external circuit, ions move between the two compartments so that the charges in each compartment remain in balance.

The net reaction is the oxidation of the fuel and the consumption of the oxidizing agent. Because the fuel and the oxidant never come directly in contact with each other, there is no combustion and thus minimal loss of energy as heat. The energy evolved in the reaction is converted directly into electricity.

Hydrogen is the fuel used in the fuel cells on board the Space Shuttle and in some prototype automobiles and buses. The overall reaction in these fuel cells is the combination of hydrogen and oxygen to form water (Figure 13). Hydrocarbon-based fuels such as methane ($CH_4$) and methanol ($CH_3OH$) are also candidates for use as the fuel in fuel cells. When methanol is used in fuel cells, for example, the net reaction in the cell is

$$CH_3OH(\ell) + {}^3/_2\ O_2(g) \rightarrow CO_2(g) + 2\ H_2O(\ell)$$

$$\Delta_r H° = -727\ \text{kJ/mol-rxn or } -23\ \text{kJ/g } CH_3OH$$

Using enthalpies of formation data (◄ Section 5.7), you can confirm that the energy generated from this reac-

FIGURE 13 **Hydrogen-oxygen fuel cell.** The cell uses hydrogen gas, which is converted to hydrogen ions and electrons. The electrons flow through the external circuit and are consumed by the oxygen, which, along with $H^+$ ions, produces water. ($H_2$ is oxidized to $H^+$ and is the reducing agent. $O_2$ is reduced and is the oxidizing agent.)

tion is 727 kJ/mol-rxn (or 23 kJ/g) of liquid methanol. That is equivalent to 200 watt-hours (W-h) of energy per mol of methanol (1 W = 1 J/s), or 5.0 kW-h per liter of methanol.

Many automobile manufacturers have explored the use of fuel cells that use hydrogen or methanol. However, major problems need to be overcome (such as cost and difficulty in operating under freezing conditions). Efforts in this area seem to have slowed significantly in the past few years in favor of hybrid cars based on battery technology.

## A Hydrogen Economy

Predictions about the diminished supply of fossil fuels have led some to speculate about alternative fuels, and hydrogen, $H_2$, has been widely suggested as a possible choice. The term *hydrogen economy* has been coined to describe the combined processes of producing, storing, and using hydrogen as a fuel. As is the case with fuel cells, the hydrogen economy does not rely on a new energy resource; it merely provides a different scheme for the use of existing resources.

There are reasons to consider hydrogen an attractive option. Oxidation of hydrogen yields almost three times as much energy per gram as the oxidation of fossil fuels. Comparing the combustion of hydrogen with that of propane, a fuel used in some cars, we find that $H_2$ produces about 2.6 times more energy per gram than propane.

$$H_2(g) + \tfrac{1}{2} O_2(g) \rightarrow H_2O(g)$$

$$\Delta_r H^\circ = -241.83 \text{ kJ/mol-rxn or } -119.95 \text{ kJ/g } H_2$$

$$C_3H_8(g) + 5 O_2(g) \rightarrow 3 CO_2(g) + 4 H_2O(g)$$

$$\Delta_r H^\circ = -2043.15 \text{ kJ/mol-rxn or } -46.37 \text{ kJ/g } C_3H_8$$

Another advantage of using hydrogen instead of a hydrocarbon fuel is that the only product of $H_2$ oxidation is $H_2O$, which is environmentally benign.

Some have proposed that hydrogen might be able to replace gasoline in automobiles and natural gas in heating homes and even that it could be used as a fuel to generate electricity or to run industrial processes. Before this can occur, however, there are many practical problems to be solved, including the following as-yet-unmet needs:

- An inexpensive method of producing hydrogen
- A practical means of storing hydrogen
- A distribution system (hydrogen refueling stations)

Perhaps the most serious problem in the hydrogen economy is the task of producing hydrogen. Hydrogen is abundant on Earth, but not as the free element. Thus, elemental hydrogen has to be obtained from its compounds. Currently, most hydrogen is produced industrially from the reaction of natural gas and water by steam reforming at high temperature (Figure 14).

*Steam reforming*

$$CH_4(g) + H_2O(g) \rightarrow 3 H_2(g) + CO(g)$$

$$\Delta_r H^\circ = +206.2 \text{ kJ/mol-rxn}$$

Hydrogen can also be obtained from the reaction of coal and water at high temperature (the so-called *water–gas reaction*).

*Water–gas reaction*

$$C(s) + H_2O(g) \rightarrow H_2(g) + CO(g)$$

$$\Delta_r H^\circ = +131.3 \text{ kJ/mol-rxn}$$

Both steam reforming and the water–gas reaction are highly endothermic, and both rely on use of a fossil fuel as a raw material. This, of course, makes no sense if the overriding goal is to replace fossil fuels. If the hydrogen economy is ever to take hold, the logical source of hydrogen is water.

$$H_2O(\ell) \rightarrow H_2(g) + \tfrac{1}{2} O_2(g)$$

$$\Delta_r H^\circ = +285.83 \text{ kJ/mol-rxn}$$

The electrolysis of water provides hydrogen (◄ page 11) but also requires considerable energy. The first law of thermodynamics tells us that we can get no more energy from the oxidation of hydrogen than we expended to obtain $H_2$ from $H_2O$. In fact, we cannot even reach this break-even point because some of the energy produced will inevitably

**FIGURE 14 Steam reforming to produce hydrogen.** A fuel such as methanol ($CH_3OH$) or natural gas and water is heated and then passed into a steam reformer chamber. There, a catalyst promotes the decomposition to hydrogen and other compounds such as CO. The hydrogen gas passes out to a fuel cell, and the CO and unused carbon-based compounds are burned in a combustion chamber. A small unit may be suitable for a car or light truck. However, at this time the known technology to carry this out requires temperatures of 700–1000 °C to run the reformer, and the CO can be a poison in a fuel cell.

be dispersed (▶ Chapter 19). Hence, the only way to obtain hydrogen from water in the amounts that would be needed and in an economically favorable way is to use a cheap and abundant source of energy to drive this process. A logical candidate is solar energy. Unfortunately, the technology to use solar energy in this way has yet to become practical. This is another problem for chemists and engineers of the future to solve.

A way to store hydrogen gas easily and safely also has to be solved. A number of ways to accomplish this in a vehicle, in your home, or at a distribution point have been proposed. An experimental passenger car from Honda stores hydrogen for its fuel cell at high pressure (350 atm) in a 171-L tank. This is larger than the gasoline tanks found in most automobiles, so other storage methods that have smaller volumes and yet are safe are sought.

No matter how hydrogen is used, it has to be delivered to vehicles and homes in a safe and practical manner. Again, many problems remain to be solved. European researchers have found that a tanker truck that can deliver 2400 kg of compressed natural gas (mostly methane) can deliver only 288 kg of $H_2$ at the same pressure. Although hydrogen oxidation delivers about 2.4 times more energy per gram (119.95 kJ/g) than methane,

$$CH_4(g) + 2\ O_2(g) \rightarrow CO_2(g) + 2\ H_2O(g)$$

$$\Delta_r H° = -802.30\ kJ/mol\text{–}rxn\ or\ -50.14\ kJ/g\ CH_4$$

the tanker can carry about eight times more methane than $H_2$. That is, it will take more tanker trucks to deliver the hydrogen needed to power the same number of cars or homes running on hydrogen than those running on methane.

There is an interesting example in which the hydrogen economy has gained a toehold. About 10 years ago Iceland announced that the country will become a "carbon-free economy." Icelanders plan to rely on hydrogen-powered electric fuel cells to run vehicles and fishing boats. Iceland is fortunate in that two thirds of its energy and all of its electricity already come from renewable sources—hydroelectric and geothermal energy (Figure 15). The country has decided to use the electricity produced by geothermal heat or hydroelectric power to separate water into hydrogen and oxygen. The hydrogen will then be used in fuel cells or combined with $CO_2$ to make methanol, $CH_3OH$, a liquid fuel that can either be burned or be used in different types of fuel cells.

## Biosources of Energy

Biofuels now supply almost 2% of the fuel used worldwide for transportation, but some project that it may contribute 30% to U.S. transportation needs by 2030. Biofuels include substances ranging from solids such as wood to bioethanol and biodiesel.

**FIGURE 15** Iceland, a "carbon-free," hydrogen-based economy. A geothermal field in Iceland. The country plans to use such renewable resources to produce hydrogen from water and then to use the hydrogen to produce electricity in fuel cells.

Gasoline sold today often contains ethanol, $C_2H_5OH$. If the ethanol is derived from fermentation of materials derived from biological sources, then it is sometimes referred to as **bioethanol**. In addition to being a fuel, ethanol improves the burning characteristics of gasoline. Every state in the United States now has available a blend of ethanol and gasoline, the most common being 10% ethanol and 90% petroleum-based fuels. (See *Case Study: The Fuel Controversy: Alcohol and Gasoline,* page 237.)

Ethanol can be made readily by fermentation of sugars derived from renewable resources such as corn, sugar cane, sugar beets, or agricultural residues. Ethanol can also be derived from cellulosic materials such as trees and grasses, but the process is more difficult.

While the United States is stepping up its program to produce more ethanol from corn or other plant matter, Brazil has made the production of ethanol from sugar cane a top priority. About 40% of its motor fuel is ethanol. Most new cars sold in Brazil are "flex-fuel" cars that run on either gasoline or ethanol. The United States and Brazil produce 70% of the world's ethanol, with the United States having moved into the top position in 2006.

One significant problem with bioethanol is that the energy content of a liter of ethanol is only about two thirds that of a liter of gasoline. (We leave it to the reader to calculate this in Question 7 on page 265.) Unless the ethanol industry is subsidized, the cost of using ethanol for transportation may be greater than the cost of using gasoline at current prices.

There are several points to be made about the use of ethanol as a fuel. Green plants use the sun's energy to make biomass from $CO_2$ and $H_2O$ by photosynthesis. The sun is a renewable resource, as, in principle, is the ethanol derived from biomass. In addition, the process recycles

$CO_2$. Plants use $CO_2$ to create biomass, which is in turn used to make ethanol. In the final step in this cycle, oxidation of ethanol returns $CO_2$ to the atmosphere. One serious issue concerning the use of corn-derived ethanol is the net energy balance. One has to consider the energy expended in the fuel to run the tractors and trucks, harvest the corn, and make the fertilizer, among other things, versus the energy available in the ethanol produced as the end product. Recent analyses and improvements in corn-to-ethanol preparation seem to indicate more energy is available than is used in production, but not by much.

While ethanol is currently the predominant biofuel, **biodiesel** is becoming more widely used (Figure 16). It is made from feedstocks such as vegetable oils, animal fat, sunflower seeds, rapeseed, soybeans, or used cooking oil. Biodiesel currently makes up almost 80% of Europe's total biofuel production.

Chemically, biodiesel is a mixture of esters of long-chain fatty acids, one of which is shown in Figure 17. They are prepared by a reaction called *trans-esterification* (page 489) in which a fat or oil is reacted with an alcohol such as methanol, $CH_3OH$. After separating the byproducts (chiefly glycerol, $[HOCH_2CH(OH)CH_2OH]$), the mixture of esters can be used directly as a fuel in diesel engines, or it can be blended with petroleum products. In the latter case, the fuel mixture is identified by a designation such as B20 (B = biodiesel, 20 refers to 20% by volume). Biodiesel has the advantage of being clean burning with fewer environmental problems associated with exhaust gases. In particular, there are no $SO_2$ emissions, one of the common problems associated with petroleum-based diesel fuels.

## Solar Energy

Every year, the earth's surface receives about 10 times as much energy from sunlight as is contained in all the known reserves of coal, oil, natural gas, and uranium combined! The amount of solar energy incident on the earth's surface

**FIGURE 16** **A car that runs on biodiesel.** (U.S. Department of Energy: Energy Efficiency and Renewable Energy.)

**FIGURE 17** **Biodiesel.** This is an example of the molecules (this is an ester called methyl dodecanoate, $CH_3(CH_2)_{10}CO_2CH_3$) that make up biodiesel. The long carbon chains typically have 12 or more carbon atoms.

is equivalent to about 15,000 times the world's annual consumption of energy. Although solar energy is a renewable resource, today we are making very inefficient use of the sun's energy. Less than 3% of the electricity produced in the United States is generated using solar energy.

How might the sun's energy be better exploited? One strategy is the direct conversion of solar energy to electricity using photovoltaic (PV) cells (Figure 18) (▶ *The Chemistry of Modern Materials*, page 656). These devices are made from silicon and specific element combinations (often gallium and arsenic). They are now used in applications as diverse as spacecraft and pocket calculators. Many homes today use photovoltaic cells to provide a substantial percentage of their electricity, and what they don't use they can sell back to the utility. Commercial facilities are designed to produce electricity using photovoltaics. One of the largest photovoltaic farms in the world is located in southern Germany and has a maximum power output of 5 megawatts.

Before solar energy can be a viable alternative, a number of issues need to be addressed, including the collection, storage, and transmission of energy. Furthermore, electricity generated from solar power stations is intermittent. (The output fluctuation results from the normal cycles of daylight and changing weather conditions.) Our current power grid cannot handle intermittent energy, so solar energy would need to be stored in some way and then doled out at a steady rate.

Likewise, we need to find ways to make solar cells cost-effective. Research has produced photovoltaic cells that can convert 20–30% of the energy that falls on them

FIGURE 18 **Photovoltaic (PV) cells.** Manufacture of PV panels is growing rapidly. In 2006 the electricity generated by PV panels in the United States was over 300 megawatts.

FIGURE 19 **Solar thermal power.** Of the 11 such solar thermal power plants operating in the United States at the end of 2008, 9 are in California and 1 each in Arizona and Nevada.

(which is better than the efficiency of a green leaf). While the cost per watt output of solar cells has declined appreciably over the last few decades, currently, 1 kW-h of energy generated from solar cells costs about 35 cents, compared to about 4–5 cents per kW-h generated from fossil fuels.

Solar energy can also be collected using large reflectors that direct sunlight onto fluid-filled pipes (Figure 19). The fluid is heated to temperatures as high as 750 °C and is circulated to a "heat exchanger" in which the energy is transferred to water, producing steam. The steam is directed to turbines that produce electricity. A large solar thermal power plant in the Mojave Desert in California accounts for much of the power produced by the solar energy sector today.

## What Does the Future Hold for Energy?

Our society is at an energy cross-roads. The modern world is increasingly reliant on energy, but we have built an energy infrastructure that depends primarily on a type of fuel that is not renewable. Fossil fuels provide an inexpensive and simple approach for providing energy, but it is increasingly evident that their use also has serious drawbacks, among them climate change and atmospheric contamination. Alternative fuels, especially from renewable sources, and new ways of converting energy do exist. However, much more research and resources must be put into making them affordable and reliable. This is where the study of chemistry fits into the picture. Chemists will have a great deal of work to do in coming years to develop new means of generating, storing, and delivering energy. Meanwhile, numerous ways exist to conserve the resources we have. Ultimately, it will be necessary to bear in mind the various benefits and drawbacks of each technology so that they can be combined in the most rational ways, rather than remaining in a system that is dependent on a single type of nonrenewable energy resource.

## SUGGESTED READINGS

Much is changing in energy production and use worldwide. Some good websites (all accessed November 2010) are the following:

(a) United States Department of Energy:

(general) www.eia.doe.gov
(energy usage) www.eia.doe.gov/emeu/aer/pdf/pages/sec1.pdf
(energy efficiency and alternative energy) www.eere.energy.gov/

(b) Alternative energy:

www.alternative-energy-news.info

(c) The World Bank data:

www.data.worldbank.org/indicator/EG.USE.PCAP.KG.OE?cid=GPD_26

(d) BP Statistical review of world energy:

www.bp.com/statisticalreview

See also:

1. R. A. Hinrichs and M. Kleinbach: *Energy—Its Use and the Environment*, 3rd ed. Orlando: Harcourt, 2002.
2. M. L. Wald: "Questions About a Hydrogen Economy," *Scientific American*, pp. 67–73, May 2004.
3. F. Keppler and T. Rockmann: "Methane, Plants and Climate Change," *Scientific American*, pp. 52–57, February 2007.
4. S. Ashley: "Diesels Come Clean," *Scientific American*, pp. 66–71, March 2007.
5. Special Issue: "Energy's Future Beyond Carbon," *Scientific American*, September 2006.
6. Worldwatch Institute: Biofuels for Transport: *Global Potential and Implications for Sustainable Agriculture and Energy in the 21st Century*, New York, 2007.

## STUDY QUESTIONS

Blue-numbered questions have answers in Appendix Q and fully worked solutions in the *Student Solutions Manual*.

1. Hydrogen can be produced using the reaction of steam ($H_2O$) with various hydrocarbons. Compare the mass of $H_2$ expected from the reaction of steam with 100. g each of methane, petroleum, and coal. (Assume complete

reaction in each case. Use $CH_2$ and C as the representative formulas for petroleum and coal, respectively.)

2. Use the value for "energy released" in kilojoules per gram from gasoline listed in Table 1 to estimate the percentage of carbon, by mass, in gasoline. (*Hint:* Compare the value for gasoline to the $\Delta_r H°$ values for burning pure C and $H_2$.)

3. Per capita energy consumption in the United States has been equated to the energy obtained by burning 70. lb of coal per day. Use enthalpy of formation data to calculate the energy evolved, in kilojoules, when 70. lb of coal is burned. (Assume the enthalpy of combustion of coal is 33 kJ/g. 1.00 pound = 454 g)

4. The enthalpy of combustion of isooctane ($C_8H_{18}$), one of the many hydrocarbons in gasoline, is $5.45 \times 10^3$ kJ/mol. Calculate the enthalpy change per gram of isooctane and per liter of isooctane ($d = 0.688$ g/mL).

isooctane
$C_8H_{18}$

5. Energy consumption in the United States amounts to the equivalent of the energy obtained by burning 7.0 gal of oil or 70. lb of coal per day per person. Using data in Table 1, carry out calculations to show that the energy evolved from these quantities of oil and coal is approximately equivalent. The density of fuel oil is approximately 0.8 g/mL. (1.00 lb = 454 g; 1.00 gal = 3.785 L)

6. The energy required to recover aluminum is one third of the energy required to prepare aluminum from $Al_2O_3$ (bauxite). How much energy is saved by recycling 1.0 lb (= 454 g) of aluminum?

7. Comparing ethanol and gasoline. Here we use isooctane ($C_8H_{18}$) as a substitute for gasoline. (Isooctane is one of the many hydrocarbons in gasoline, and its enthalpy of combustion will approximate the energy obtained when gasoline burns.)
   (a) Calculate $\Delta_r H°$ for the combustion of 1.00 kg each of liquid ethanol and liquid isooctane. Which fuel releases more energy per kilogram? [$\Delta_f H° = -259.3$ kJ/mol for liquid isooctane at 298 K.] (Assume $H_2O(\ell)$ is one product of combustion.)
   (b) Compare the two fuels on the basis of the release of $CO_2$, a common greenhouse gas. Which fuel produces more $CO_2$ per kilogram?
   (c) On the basis of this simple comparison and neglecting the energy costs involved in producing 1.00 kg each of ethanol and isooctane, which is the better

fuel in terms of energy production and greenhouse gases?

8. Calculate the energy used, in kilojoules, to power a 100-watt light bulb continuously over a 24-hour period. How much coal would have to be burned to provide this quantity of energy, assuming that the enthalpy of combustion of coal is 33 kJ/g and the power plant has an efficiency of 35%? [Electrical energy for home use is measured in kilowatt hours (kW-h). One watt is defined as 1 J/s, and 1 kW-h is the quantity of energy involved when 1000 watt is dispensed over a 1.0-hour period.]

9. Major home appliances purchased in the United States are now labeled with bright yellow "Energy Guide" tags showing anticipated energy consumption. The tag on a recently purchased washing machine indicated the anticipated energy use would be 940 kW-h per year. Calculate the anticipated annual energy use in kilojoules. (See Question 8 for a definition of kilowatt-hour.) At 8 cents/kW-h, how much would it cost per month to operate this machine?

10. Define the terms *renewable* and *nonrenewable* as applied to energy resources. Which of the following energy resources are renewable: solar energy, coal, natural gas, geothermal energy, wind power?

11. Confirm the statement in the text that oxidation of 1.0 L of methanol to form $CO_2(g)$ and $H_2O(\ell)$ in a fuel cell will provide at least 5.0 kW-h of energy. (The density of methanol is 0.787 g/mL.)

12. List the following substances in order of energy released per gram: $C_8H_{18}$, $H_2$, C(s), $CH_4$. (See Question 4 for the enthalpy of combustion of isooctane, $C_8H_{18}$.)

13. A parking lot in Los Angeles receives an average of $2.6 \times 10^7$ J/m$^2$ of solar energy per day in the summer. If the parking lot is 325 m long and 50.0 m wide, what is the total quantity of energy striking the area per day?

14. Your home loses energy in the winter through doors, windows, and any poorly insulated walls. A sliding glass door (6 ft $\times$ 6.5 ft with 0.5 inch of insulating glass) allows $1.0 \times 10^6$ J/h to pass through the glass if the inside temperature is 22 °C (72 °F) and the outside temperature is 0 °C (32 °F). What quantity of energy, expressed in kilojoules, is lost per day? Assume that your house is heated by electricity. How many kilowatt-hours of energy are lost per day through the door? (See Question 8.)

15. Some fuel-efficient hybrid cars are rated at 55.0 miles per gallon of gasoline. Calculate the energy used to drive 1.00 mile if gasoline produces 48.0 kJ/g and the density of gasoline is 0.737 g/cm$^3$. (1.00 gal = 3.785 L)

16. Microwave ovens are highly efficient, compared to other means of cooking. A 1100-watt microwave oven, running at full power for 90 seconds will raise the temperature of 1 cup of water (225 mL) from 20 °C to 67 °C. As a rough measure of the efficiency of the microwave oven, compare its energy consumption with the energy required to raise the water temperature.

# 6 The Structure of Atoms

John C. Katz

**Fireworks** The colors of the beautiful displays of fireworks you see on holidays such as July 4 in the United States can light up the night sky. Colors can range from white to red, yellow, orange, and blue. As we shall see in this chapter, the colors arise from the emission of energy by excited atoms.

This photo shows fireworks with blue and yellow light. The next time you attend a fireworks display, watch for the blue fireworks. The color is particularly difficult to produce.

**Questions:**

This photo shows fireworks with blue and yellow light, but many other colors are possible.
1. Which has the longer wavelength, blue light or yellow light?
2. Which has the greater energy, blue or yellow light?
3. How do the colors of light emitted by excited atoms contribute to our understanding of electronic structure?

**Answers to these questions are available in Appendix N.**

## CHAPTER OUTLINE

## CHAPTER GOALS

*See Chapter Goals Revisited (page 290) for Study Questions keyed to these goals.*

- Describe the properties of electromagnetic radiation.
- Understand the origin of light emitted by excited atoms and its relationship to atomic structure.
- Describe the experimental evidence for particle–wave duality.
- Describe the basic ideas of quantum mechanics.
- Define the four quantum numbers ($n$, $\ell$, $m_\ell$, and $m_s$) and recognize their relationship to electronic structure.

The picture that most people have of the atom is that of a tiny nucleus, consisting of neutrons and protons, with nearly massless electrons orbiting the nucleus like planets around a star. Unfortunately, this simple picture is only partly correct. The tiny nucleus is indeed composed of neutrons and protons, and electrons are located in the space outside the nucleus, but, as you shall see, a more accurate picture describes the electrons as matter waves, and we can only define regions of space in which it is likely to find an electron.

This chapter lays out the experimental background to our current understanding of atomic structure and describes the modern view of the atom. With this model we can better predict the properties of atoms and better understand the underlying structure of the periodic table.

Much of our understanding of atomic structure comes from a knowledge of how atoms interact with electromagnetic radiation (visible light is one type of electromagnetic radiation) and how excited atoms emit electromagnetic radiation. The first three sections of this chapter describe electromagnetic radiation and its relation to our modern view of the atom.

### 6.1 Electromagnetic Radiation

In 1864, James Clerk Maxwell (1831–1879) developed a mathematical theory to describe light and other forms of radiation in terms of oscillating, or wave-like, electric and magnetic fields (Figure 6.1). Thus, light, microwaves, television and radio signals, x-rays, and other forms of radiation are now called **electromagnetic radiation**.

Electromagnetic radiation is characterized by its wavelength and frequency.

- **Wavelength**, symbolized by the Greek letter *lambda* ($\lambda$), is defined as the distance between successive crests or high points of a wave (or between successive troughs or low points). This distance can be given in meters, nanometers, or whatever unit of length is convenient.

- **Frequency**, symbolized by the Greek letter *nu* ($\nu$), refers to the number of waves that pass a given point in some unit of time, usually per second. The unit for frequency, written either as $s^{-1}$ or $1/s$ and standing for 1 per second, is now called a **hertz**.

Wavelength and frequency are related to the speed (*c*) at which the wave is propagated (Equation 6.1).

$$c \text{ (m/s)} = \lambda \text{ (m)} \times \nu \text{ (1/s)} \qquad (6.1)$$

Sign in to OWL at **www.cengage.com/owl** to view tutorials and simulations, develop problem-solving skills, and complete online homework assigned by your professor.

**go Chemistry**

Download mini lecture videos for key concept review and exam prep from OWL or purchase them from **www.cengagebrain.com**

- **Heinrich Hertz** Heinrich Hertz (1857–1894) was the first person to send and receive radio waves. He showed that they could be reflected and refracted the same as light, confirming that different forms of radiation such as radio and light waves are related. Scientists now use "hertz" as the unit of frequency.

**FIGURE 6.1 Electromagnetic radiation is characterized by its wavelength and frequency.** In the 1860s, James Clerk Maxwell developed the currently accepted theory that all forms of radiation are propagated through space as vibrating electric and magnetic fields at right angles to one another. Each field is described by a sine wave (the mathematical function describing the wave). Such oscillating fields emanate from vibrating charges in a source such as a light bulb or radio antenna.

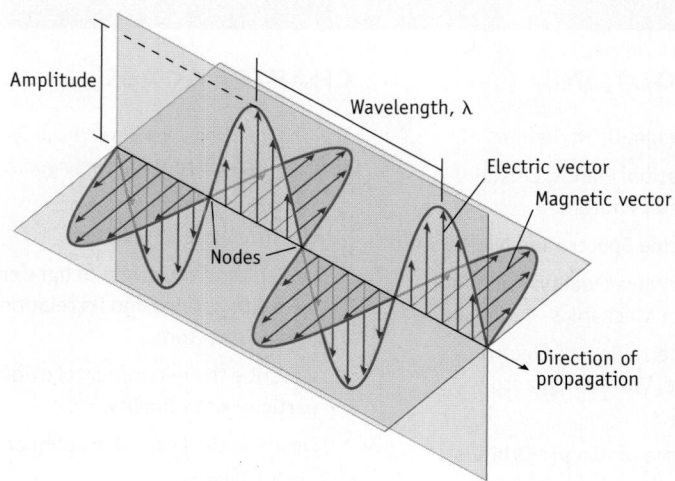

The speed of visible light and all other forms of electromagnetic radiation in a vacuum is a constant: $c = 2.99792458 \times 10^8$ m/s (approximately 186,000 miles/s or $1.079 \times 10^9$ km/h). For calculations, we will generally use the value of $c$ with four or fewer significant figures.

As the name suggests, electromagnetic radiation consists of oscillating electric and magnetic disturbances. This is important to recognize because the electric and magnetic fields can interact with charged particles such as electrons in atoms and molecules and with charged atoms in molecules. It is this that allows scientists to probe matter at the atomic and molecular levels using forms of radiation such as x-rays or radio waves (in an MRI or magnetic resonance imaging instrument), for example.

Visible light is only a tiny portion of the total spectrum of electromagnetic radiation (Figure 6.2). Ultraviolet (UV) radiation, the radiation that can lead to sunburn, has wavelengths shorter than those of visible light. X-rays and γ-rays, the latter emitted in the process of radioactive disintegration of some atoms, have even shorter wavelengths. At wavelengths longer than those of visible light, we first encounter infrared radiation (IR). The wavelengths of the radiation used in microwave ovens, in television and radio transmissions, in MRI instruments, and for cell phones are longer still.

## EXAMPLE 6.1    Wavelength-Frequency Conversions

**Problem** The frequency of the radiation used in cell phones covers a wide range from about 800 MHz to 2 GHz. (MHz stands for "megahertz," where 1 MHz = $10^6$ 1/s; GHz stands for "gigahertz," where 1 GHz = $10^9$ 1/s.) What is the wavelength (in meters) of a cell phone signal operating at 1.12 GHz?

**What Do You Know?** You are given a frequency of radiation, in GHz, and a factor to convert frequency from GHz to Hz (1/s). To calculate the wavelength of this radiation using Equation 6.1, you will need the value of the speed of light, $c = 2.998 \times 10^8$ m/s.

**Strategy** Rearrange Equation 6.1 to solve for λ. Substitute the values for the speed of light and the frequency (first convert $\nu$ to the units 1/s) into the equation and solve.

**Solution**

$$\lambda = \frac{c}{\nu} = \frac{2.998 \times 10^8 \text{ m/s}}{1.12 \times 10^9 \text{ 1/s}} = 0.268 \text{ m}$$

**Think about Your Answer** Pay attention to units when solving this problem. Note that by choosing frequency (in 1/s) and the speed of light (in m/s) the calculated wavelength will be in meters (m).

**Check Your Understanding**

(a)  Which color in the visible spectrum has the highest frequency? Which has the lowest frequency?

(b)  Is the frequency of the radiation used in a microwave oven (2.45 GHz) higher or lower than that from your favorite FM radio station (for example, 91.7 MHz)?

(c)  Are the wavelengths of x-rays longer or shorter than those of ultraviolet light?

**FIGURE 6.2 The electromagnetic spectrum.** Visible light (enlarged portion) is a very small part of the entire spectrum. The radiation's energy increases from the radio-wave end of the spectrum (low frequency, $\nu$, and long wavelength, $\lambda$) to the $\gamma$-ray end (high frequency and short wavelength).

---

**REVIEW & CHECK FOR SECTION 6.1**

Which of the following types of electromagnetic radiation has the longest wavelength?

(a)  ultraviolet light

(b)  x-rays

(c)  red light from a laser pointer

(d)  microwaves from a microwave oven

---

# 6.2  Quantization: Planck, Einstein, Energy, and Photons

## Planck's Equation

If a piece of metal is heated to a high temperature, electromagnetic radiation is emitted with wavelengths that depend on temperature. At lower temperatures, the color is a dull red (Figure 6.3). As the temperature increases, the red color brightens, and at even higher temperatures a brilliant white light is emitted.

Your eyes detect the emitted radiation in the visible region of the electromagnetic spectrum. Although not seen, both ultraviolet and infrared radiation are also given off by the hot metal (Figure 6.3). In addition, it is observed that the wavelength of the most intense radiation is related to temperature: As the temperature of the metal is raised, the maximum intensity shifts toward shorter wavelengths, that is, toward the ultraviolet. This corresponds to the change in color observed as the temperature is raised.

At the end of the 19th century, scientists were not able to explain the relationship between the intensity and the wavelength for radiation given off by a heated object (often called *blackbody radiation*). Theories available at the time predicted that the intensity should increase continuously with decreasing wavelength, instead of reaching a maximum and then declining as is actually observed. This perplexing situation became known as the *ultraviolet catastrophe* because predictions failed in the ultraviolet region.

**Blackbody radiation.** In physics a blackbody is a theoretical concept in which a body absorbs all radiation that falls on it. However, it will emit energy with a temperature-dependent wavelength. The light emanating from the spaces between the burning charcoal briquets in this photo is a close approximation to blackbody radiation. The color of the emitted light depends on the temperature of the briquets.

© Cengage Learning/Charles D. Winters

**FIGURE 6.3 The radiation given off by a heated body.** When an object is heated, it emits radiation covering a spectrum of wavelengths. For a given temperature, some of the radiation is emitted at long wavelengths and some at short wavelengths. Most, however, is emitted at some intermediate wavelength, the maximum in the curve. As the temperature of the object increases, the maximum moves from the red end of the spectrum to the violet end. At still higher temperatures, intense light is emitted at all wavelengths in the visible region, and the maximum in the curve is in the ultraviolet region. The object is described as "white hot." (Stars are often referred to as "red giants" or "white dwarfs," a reference to their temperatures and relative sizes.)

In 1900, a German physicist, Max Planck (1858–1947), offered an explanation for the ultraviolet catastrophe: The electromagnetic radiation emitted originated in vibrating atoms (called *oscillators*) in the heated object. He proposed that each oscillator had a fundamental frequency ($\nu$) of oscillation and that the atoms could only oscillate at either this frequency or whole-number multiples of it ($n\nu$). Because of this, the emitted radiation could have only certain energies, given by the equation

$$E = nh\nu$$

where $n$ must be a positive integer. That is, Planck proposed that the energy is *quantized*. **Quantization** means that only certain energies are allowed. The proportionality constant $h$ in the equation is now called **Planck's constant**, and its experimental value is $6.6260693 \times 10^{-34}$ J · s. The unit of frequency is $1/s$, so the energy calculated using this equation is in joules (J). If an oscillator changes from a higher energy to a lower one, energy is emitted as electromagnetic radiation, where the difference in energy between the higher and lower energy states is

$$\Delta E = E_{\text{higher } n} - E_{\text{lower } n} = \Delta n h \nu$$

If the value of $\Delta n$ is 1, which corresponds to changing from one energy level to the next lower one for that oscillator, then the energy change for the oscillator and the electromagnetic radiation emitted would have an energy equal to

$$E = h\nu \tag{6.2}$$

This equation is called **Planck's equation**.

Now, assume as Planck did that there must be a *distribution* of vibrations of atoms in an object—some atoms are vibrating at a high frequency, some are vibrating at a low frequency, but most have some intermediate frequency. The few atoms with high-frequency vibrations are responsible for some of the light, say in the ultraviolet region, and those few with low-frequency vibrations for energies in the infrared region. However, most of the light must come from the majority of the atoms that have intermediate vibrational frequencies. That is, a spectrum of light is emitted with a maximum intensity at some intermediate wavelength, in accord with experiment. The intensity should not become greater and greater on approaching the ultraviolet region. With this realization, the ultraviolet catastrophe was solved.

The key aspect of Planck's work for general chemistry is that Planck introduced the idea of quantized energies based on the equation $E = h\nu$, an equation that was

● **The relationship of energy, wavelength, and frequency**

As frequency ($\nu$) increases, energy ($E$) increases

↑

$$E = h\nu = \frac{hc}{\lambda}$$

↓

As wavelength ($\lambda$) decreases, energy ($E$) increases

to have a profound impact on the work of Albert Einstein in explaining another puzzling phenomenon.

## Einstein and the Photoelectric Effect

A few years after Planck's work, Albert Einstein (1879–1955) incorporated Planck's ideas into an explanation of the *photoelectric effect* and in doing so changed the description of electromagnetic radiation.

In the photoelectric effect, electrons are ejected when light strikes the surface of a metal (Figure 6.4), but only if the frequency of the light is high enough. If light with a lower frequency is used, no electrons are ejected, regardless of the light's intensity (its brightness). If the frequency is at or above a minimum, critical frequency, increasing the light intensity causes more electrons to be ejected.

Einstein decided the experimental observations could be explained by combining Planck's equation ($E = h\nu$) with a new idea, that light has particle-like properties. Einstein characterized these massless particles, now called **photons**, as packets of energy, and stated that the energy of each photon is proportional to the frequency of the radiation as defined by Planck's equation. In the photoelectric effect, photons striking atoms on a metal surface will cause electrons to be ejected only if the photons have high enough energy. The greater the number of photons that strike the surface at or above the threshold energy, the greater the number of electrons dislodged. The metal atoms will not lose electrons, however, if no individual photon has enough energy to dislodge an electron from an atom.

• **Einstein and Digital Cameras** When you take a photograph with a digital camera the detector in the camera (a CCD or "charged-coupled detector") works on a principle much like the photoelectric effect.

## Energy and Chemistry: Using Planck's Equation

Compact disc players use lasers that emit red light with a wavelength of 685 nm. What is the energy of one photon of this light? What is the energy of 1 mol of photons of red light? To answer these questions, first convert the wavelength to the frequency of the radiation,

For $\lambda = 685$ nm, $\nu = 4.38 \times 10^{14}$ 1/s (calculated using Equation 6.1)

**(a)** A photocell operates by the photoelectric effect. The main part of the cell is a light-sensitive cathode. This is a material, usually a metal, that ejects electrons if struck by photons of light of sufficient energy. No current is observed until the critical frequency is reached.

**(b)** When light of higher frequency than the minimum is used, the excess energy of the photon allows the electron to escape the atom with greater velocity. The ejected electrons move to the anode, and a current flows in the cell. Such a device can be used as a switch in electric circuits.

**(c)** If higher intensity light is used, the only effect is to cause more electrons to be released from the surface. The onset of current is observed at the same frequency as with lower intensity light, but more current flows with more intense light.

**FIGURE 6.4** A photoelectric cell.

**Strategy Map:** Planck's Equation

**PROBLEM**

Calculate energy of **red light photons.**

↓

**KNOWN DATA/INFORMATION**

- **Wavelength** of red light (685 nm)

↓

STEP 1. Convert **wavelength** to **frequency.** (Equation 6.1)

↓

**Frequency** in *cycles per second*

↓

STEP 2. Calculate **energy** using *Planck's equation.* (Equation 6.2)

↓

Obtain energy in **J/photon.**

↓

STEP 3. Use **Avogadro's number** to convert **J/atom** to **J/mol.**

↓

Obtain energy in **J/mol.**

and then use the frequency to calculate the energy per photon.

$$E \text{ per photon} = h\nu = (6.626 \times 10^{-34} \text{ J} \cdot \text{s/photon}) \times (4.38 \times 10^{14} \text{ 1/s})$$

$$= 2.90 \times 10^{-19} \text{ J/photon}$$

Finally, calculate the energy of a mole of photons by multiplying the energy per photon by Avogadro's number:

$$E \text{ per mole} = (2.90 \times 10^{-19} \text{ J/photon}) \times (6.022 \times 10^{23} \text{ photons/mol})$$

$$= 1.75 \times 10^5 \text{ J/mol (or 175 kJ/mol)}$$

The energy of red light photons with a wavelength of 685 nm is 175 kJ/mol, whereas the energy of blue light photons ($\lambda = 400$ nm) is about 300 kJ/mol. The energy of the blue light photons is in the range of the energies necessary to break some chemical bonds in proteins. Higher energy ultraviolet photons are even more likely to cause chemical bond breaking. This is what happens if you spend too much time unprotected in the sun. In contrast, light at the red end of the spectrum and infrared radiation has a lower energy, and, although it is generally not energetic enough to break chemical bonds, it can affect the vibrations of molecules. We sense infrared radiation as heat, such as the heat given off by a glowing burner on an electric stove or a burning log in a fire.

---

**REVIEW & CHECK FOR SECTION 6.2**

Various manufacturers have developed mixtures of compounds that protect skin from UVA (400-320 nm) and UVB (320-280 nm) radiation. These sunscreens are given "sun protection factor" (SPF) labels that indicate how long the user can stay in the sun without burning.

1. Calculate the energy of a mole of photons of UVB light with a wavelength of 310 nm.

   (a) $3.9 \times 10^5$ J/mol    (b) $1.2 \times 10^5$ J/mol    (c) 0.00039 J/mol

2. Which has the greater energy per photon, UVB light at 310 nm or microwave radiation having a frequency of 2.45 GHz (1 GHz = $10^9$ s$^{-1}$)?

   (a) UVB            (b) microwave

---

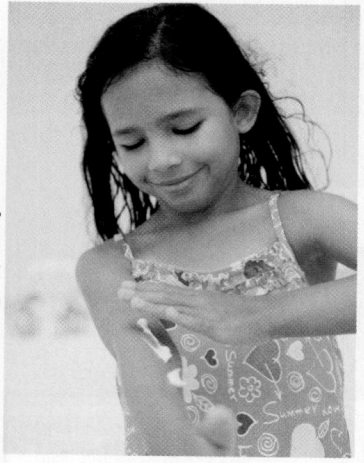

**Sunscreens and damage from radiation.** Higher-energy sunlight falling on the Earth is often classified as UVA and UVB radiation. UVB radiation has a higher energy than UVA radiation and is largely responsible for sunburns and tanning. Sunscreens containing organic compounds such as 2-ethylhexyl-p-methoxycinnamate and oxybenzone absorb UV radiation, preventing it from reaching your skin.

# 6.3 Atomic Line Spectra and Niels Bohr

If a high voltage is applied to atoms of an element in the gas phase at low pressure, the atoms absorb energy and are said to be "excited." The excited atoms can then emit light, and a familiar example is the colored light from neon advertising signs.

The light from excited atoms is composed of only a few different wavelengths of light. We can demonstrate this by passing a beam of light from excited neon or hydrogen through a prism (Figure 6.5); only a few colored lines are seen. The spectrum obtained in this manner, such as that for excited H atoms, is called a **line emission spectrum**. This is in contrast to the light falling on Earth from the Sun, or the light emitted by a very hot object, which consists of a continuous spectrum of wavelengths (Figures 6.2 and 6.3)

Every element has a unique emission spectrum, as exemplified by the spectra for hydrogen, mercury, and neon in Figure 6.6. Indeed, the characteristic lines in the emission spectrum of an element can be used in chemical analysis, both to identify the element and to determine how much of it is present.

A goal of scientists in the late 19th century was to explain why excited gaseous atoms emitted light of only certain frequencies. One approach was to look for a mathematical relationship among the observed wavelengths because a regular pattern of information implies a logical explanation. The first steps in this direction were taken by Johann Balmer (1825–1898) and later by Johannes Rydberg

*JGI/Jamie Grill/Blend Images/Jupiter Images*

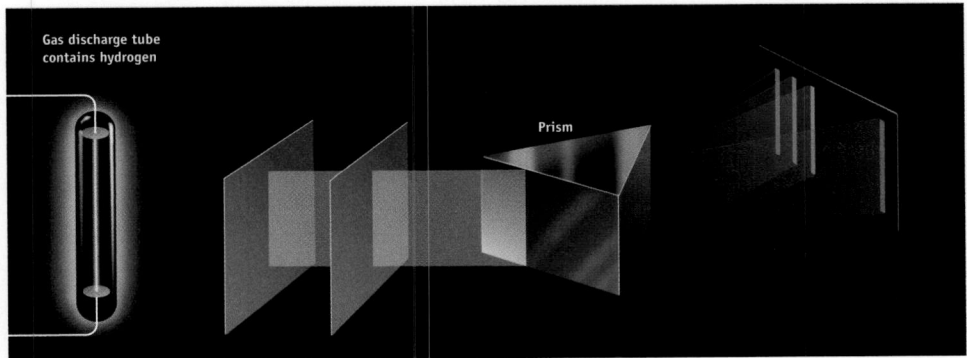

**FIGURE 6.5 The visible line emission spectrum of hydrogen.** The emitted light is passed through a series of slits to create a narrow beam of light, which is then separated into its component wavelengths by a prism. A photographic plate or photocell can be used to detect the separate wavelengths as individual lines. Hence, the name *line spectrum* for the light emitted by a glowing gas.

(1854–1919). From these studies, an equation—now called the **Balmer equation** (Equation 6.3)—was found that could be used to calculate the wavelength of the red, green, and blue lines in the visible emission spectrum of hydrogen (Figure 6.6).

$$\frac{1}{\lambda} = R\left(\frac{1}{2^2} - \frac{1}{n^2}\right) \quad \text{when } n > 2 \tag{6.3}$$

In this equation $n$ is an integer, and $R$, now called the **Rydberg constant**, has the value $1.0974 \times 10^7 \text{ m}^{-1}$. If $n = 3$, for example, the wavelength of the red line in the hydrogen spectrum is obtained ($6.563 \times 10^{-7}$ m, or 656.3 nm). If $n = 4$, the wavelength for the green line is calculated. Using $n = 5$ and $n = 6$ in the equation gives the wavelengths of the blue lines. The four visible lines in the spectrum of hydrogen atoms are now known as the **Balmer series**.

## The Bohr Model of the Hydrogen Atom

Early in the 20th century, the Danish physicist Niels Bohr (1885–1962) proposed a model for the electronic structure of atoms and with it an explanation for the emission spectra of excited atoms. Bohr proposed a planetary structure for the hydrogen atom in which the electron moved in a circular orbit around the nucleus, similar to a planet revolving about the sun. In proposing this model, however, he had to

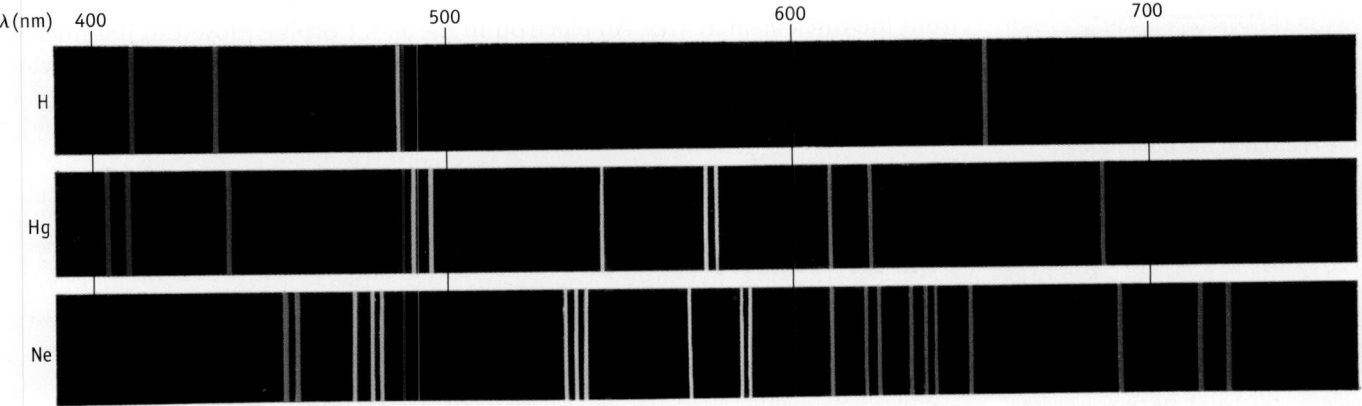

**FIGURE 6.6 Line emission spectra of hydrogen, mercury, and neon.** Excited gaseous elements produce characteristic spectra that can be used to identify the elements and to determine how much of each element is present in a sample.

contradict the laws of classical physics. According to classical theories, a charged electron moving in the positive electric field of the nucleus should lose energy; a consequence of the loss of energy is that the electron would eventually crash into the nucleus. This is clearly not the case; if it were, matter would eventually self-destruct. To solve this contradiction, Bohr postulated that there are certain orbits corresponding to particular energy levels where this would not occur. As long as an electron is in one of these energy levels, the system is stable. That is, Bohr introduced *quantization* into the description of electronic structure. By combining this quantization postulate with the laws of motion from classical physics, Bohr derived an equation for the total energy possessed by the single electron in the *n*th orbit (energy level) of the H atom.

$$\text{Total energy of electron in the } n\text{th level} = E_n = -\frac{Rhc}{n^2} \tag{6.4}$$

Here, $E_n$ is the energy of the electron (in J/atom); and $R$, $h$, and $c$ are constants [the Rydberg constant ($R = 1.097 \times 10^7$ m$^{-1}$), Planck's constant, and the speed of light, respectively]. The symbol $n$ is a positive, unitless integer called the **principal quantum number**. It can have integral values of 1, 2, 3, and so on.

Equation 6.4 has several important features (illustrated in Figure 6.7) such as the role of $n$ and the significance of the negative sign.

- The quantum number $n$ defines the energies of the allowed orbits in the H atom.
- The energy of an electron in an orbit has a negative value because the electron in the atom has a lower energy than when it is free. The zero of energy occurs when $n = \infty$, that is, when the electron is infinitely separated from the nucleus.
- An atom with its electrons in the lowest possible energy levels is said to be in its **ground state**; for the hydrogen atom, this is the level defined by the quantum number $n = 1$. The energy of this state is $-Rhc/1^2$, meaning that it has an amount of energy equal to $Rhc$ *below* the energy of the infinitely separated electron and nucleus.
- States for the H atom with higher energies (and $n > 1$) are called **excited states**, and, as the value of $n$ increases, these states have less negative energy values.
- Because the energy is dependent on $1/n^2$, the energy levels are progressively closer together as $n$ increases.

Bohr also showed that, as the value of $n$ increases, the distance of the electron from the nucleus increases. An electron in the $n = 1$ orbit is closest to the nucleus and has the lowest (most negative) energy. For higher integer values of $n$, the electron is further from the nucleus and has a higher (less negative) energy.

**FIGURE 6.7 Energy levels for the H atom in the Bohr model.** The energy of the electron in the hydrogen atom depends on the value of the principal quantum number $n$ ($E_n = -Rhc/n^2$). The larger the value of $n$, the larger the Bohr radius and the less negative the value of the energy. Energies are given in joules per atom (J/atom). Notice that the difference between successive energy levels becomes smaller as $n$ becomes larger.

The following values appear along the energy level diagram (left margin):

$0$ — $n = \infty$
$-\frac{1}{16}$ — $n = 6$, $n = 5$, $n = 4$
$-\frac{1}{9}$ — $n = 3$; $E_3 = -2.42 \times 10^{-19}$ J/atom
$-\frac{1}{4}$ — $n = 2$; $E_2 = -5.45 \times 10^{-19}$ J/atom

$-\frac{1}{n^2}\left(= \frac{E}{Rhc}\right)$

$-1$ — $n = 1$; $E_1 = -2.18 \times 10^{-18}$ J/atom

## EXAMPLE 6.2    Energies of the Ground and Excited States of the H Atom

**Problem** Calculate the energies of the $n = 1$ and $n = 2$ states of the hydrogen atom in joules per atom and in kilojoules per mole. What is the difference in energy of these two states in kJ/mol?

**What Do You Know?** The $n = 1$ and $n = 2$ states are the first and second states (lowest and next to lowest energy state) in the Bohr description of the hydrogen atom. Use Equation 6.4 to calculate the energy of each state. For the calculations you will need the following constants: $R$ (Rydberg constant) $= 1.097 \times 10^7$ m$^{-1}$; $h$ (Planck's constant) $= 6.626 \times 10^{-34}$ J $\cdot$ s; $c$ (speed of light) $= 2.998 \times 10^8$ m/s; and $N$ (Avogadro's number) $= 6.022 \times 10^{23}$ atoms/mol.

**Strategy** For each energy level, substituting the appropriate values into Equation 6.4 and solving gives the energy in J/atom. Multiply this value by $N$ to find the energy in J/mol. Subtract the energy for the $n = 1$ level from the energy of the $n = 2$ level to obtain the energy difference.

**Solution** When $n = 1$, the energy of an electron in a single H atom is

$$E_1 = -Rhc$$
$$E_1 = -(1.097 \times 10^7 \text{ m}^{-1})(6.626 \times 10^{-34} \text{ J} \cdot \text{s})(2.998 \times 10^8 \text{ m/s}) = -2.179 \times 10^{-18} \text{ J/atom}$$

In units of kJ/mol,

$$E_1 = \frac{-2.179 \times 10^{-18} \text{ J}}{\text{atom}} \times \frac{6.022 \times 10^{23} \text{ atoms}}{\text{mol}} \times \frac{1 \text{ kJ}}{1000 \text{ J}} = -1312 \text{ kJ/mol}$$

When $n = 2$, the energy is

$$E_2 = -\frac{Rhc}{2^2} = -\frac{E_1}{4} = -\frac{2.179 \times 10^{-18} \text{ J/atom}}{4} = -5.448 \times 10^{-19} \text{ J/atom}$$

In units of kJ/mol,

$$E_1 = \frac{-5.448 \times 10^{-19} \text{ J}}{\text{atom}} \times \frac{6.022 \times 10^{23} \text{ atoms}}{\text{mol}} \times \frac{1 \text{ kJ}}{1000 \text{ J}} = -328.1 \text{ kJ/mol}$$

The difference in energy, $\Delta E$, between the first two energy states of the H atom is

$$\Delta E = E_2 - E_1 = (-328.1 \text{ kJ/mol}) - (-1312 \text{ kJ/mol}) = 984 \text{ kJ/mol}$$

**Think about Your Answer** The calculated energies are negative, with $E_1$ more negative than $E_2$. The $n = 2$ state is higher in energy than the $n = 1$ state by 984 kJ/mol. Also, be sure to notice that 1312 kJ/mol is the value of $Rhc$ multiplied by Avogadro's number $N$ (i.e., $NRhc$). This will be useful in future calculations.

---

**Check Your Understanding**

Calculate the energy of the $n = 3$ state of the H atom in (a) joules per atom and (b) kilojoules per mole.

---

## The Bohr Theory and the Spectra of Excited Atoms

Bohr's theory describes electrons as having only specific orbits and energies. If an electron moves from one energy level to another, then energy must be absorbed or evolved. This idea allowed Bohr to relate energies of electrons and the emission spectra of hydrogen atoms.

To move an electron from the $n = 1$ state to an excited state, such as the $n = 2$ state, energy must be transferred to the atom. When $E_{final}$ has $n = 2$ and $E_{initial}$ has $n = 1$, then $1.63 \times 10^{-18}$ J/atom (or 984 kJ/mol) of energy must be transferred (Figure 6.8). This is the difference in energy between final and initial states:

$$\Delta E = E_{final\ state} - E_{initial\ state} = (-Rhc/2^2) - (-Rhc/1^2) = (0.75)Rhc = 1.63 \times 10^{-18} \text{ J/atom}$$

Moving an electron from the first to the second energy state requires *input* of $1.63 \times 10^{-18}$ J/atom, no more and no less. If $0.7Rhc$ or $0.8Rhc$ is provided, no transition between states is possible. Requiring a specific and precise amount of energy is a consequence of quantization.

Moving an electron from a state of low $n$ to one of higher $n$ always requires that energy be transferred to the atom from the surroundings. The opposite process, in which an electron "falls" from a level of higher $n$ to one of lower $n$, leads to emission of energy, a transfer of energy, usually as radiation, from the

**FIGURE 6.8 Absorption of energy by the atom as the electron moves to an excited state.** Energy is absorbed when an electron moves from the $n = 1$ state to the $n = 2$ state ($\Delta E > 0$). When the electron returns to the $n = 1$ state from $n = 2$, energy is evolved ($\Delta E < 0$). The energy emitted is 984 kJ/mol, as calculated in Example 6.2.

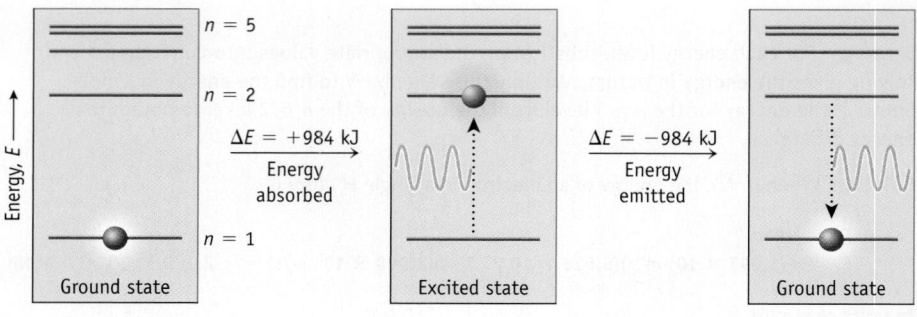

atom to its surroundings. For example, for a transition from the $n = 2$ level to $n = 1$ level,

$$\Delta E = E_{\text{final state}} - E_{\text{initial state}} = -1.63 \times 10^{-18} \text{ J/atom} \ (= -984 \text{ kJ/mol})$$

The negative sign indicates $1.63 \times 10^{-18}$ J/atom (or 984 kJ/mol) is *emitted*.

Now we can visualize the mechanism by which the characteristic line emission spectrum of hydrogen originates according to the Bohr model. Energy is provided to the atoms from an electric discharge or by heating. Depending on how much energy is added, some atoms have their electrons excited from the $n = 1$ state to the $n = 2, 3$, or even higher states. After absorbing energy, these electrons can return to any lower level (either directly or in a series of steps), releasing energy (Figure 6.9). We observe this released energy as photons of electromagnetic radiation, and, because only certain energy levels are possible, only photons with particular energies and wavelengths are emitted.

The energy of any emission line (in J/atom) for excited hydrogen atoms can be calculated using Equation 6.5.

$$\Delta E = E_{\text{final}} - E_{\text{initial}} = -Rhc \left( \frac{1}{n_{\text{final}}^2} - \frac{1}{n_{\text{initial}}^2} \right) \tag{6.5}$$

[The value of $\Delta E$ in J/atom may be related to the wavelength or frequency of radiation using Planck's equation ($\Delta E = h\nu$) or converted to units of kJ/mol if $\Delta E$ is multiplied by $(6.022 \times 10^{23} \text{ atoms/mol})(1 \text{ kJ/1000 J}).$]

For hydrogen, a series of emission lines having energies in the ultraviolet region (called the **Lyman series**; Figure 6.10) arises from electrons moving from states with $n > 1$ to the $n = 1$ state. The series of lines that have energies in the visible region— the **Balmer series**—arises from electrons moving from states with $n > 2$ to the $n = 2$ state. There are also series of lines in the infrared spectral region, arising from transitions from higher levels to the $n = 3, 4$ or 5 levels.

Bohr's model, introducing quantization into a description of the atom, tied the unseen (the structure of the atom) to the seen (the observable lines in the hydrogen

**FIGURE 6.9 Radiation emitted on changes in energy levels.** The greater the separation in the energy levels, the greater the energy, the higher the frequency, and the shorter the wavelength of the emitted radiation. Notice that an electron excited to $n = 3$ can return directly to $n = 1$, or it can drop to $n = 2$ and then to $n = 1$. These three possibilities are observed as three different wavelengths of emitted radiation. The energies and frequencies are in the order $E_3 - E_1 > E_2 - E_1 > E_3 - E_2$.

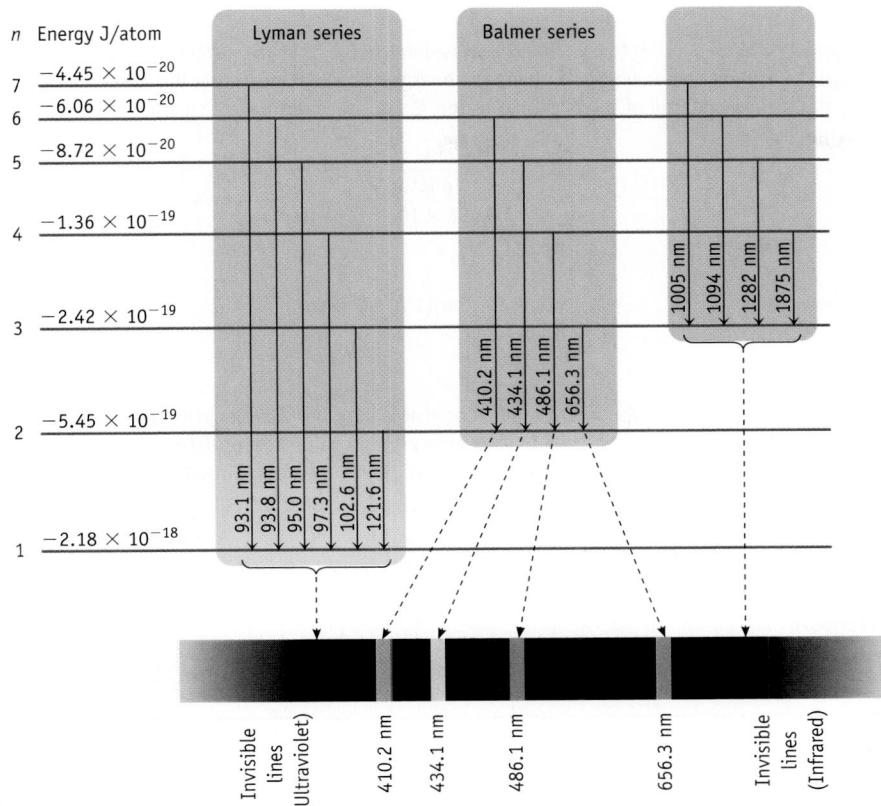

**FIGURE 6.10** **Some of the electronic transitions that can occur in an excited H atom.** The Lyman series of lines in the ultraviolet region results from transitions to the $n = 1$ level. The Balmer series (Figures 6.5 and 6.6) arises from transitions from levels with values of $n > 2$ to $n = 2$. Lines in the infrared region result from transitions from levels with $n > 3$ to the $n = 3$ level. (Transitions from $n = 8$ and higher levels to lower levels occur but are not shown in this figure.)

spectrum). Agreement between theory and experiment is taken as evidence that the theoretical model is valid. It became apparent, however, that Bohr's theory was inadequate. This model of the atom explained only the spectrum of hydrogen atoms and of other systems having one electron (such as He$^+$), but it failed for all other systems. A better model of electronic structure was needed.

⚫WL    **INTERACTIVE EXAMPLE 6.3**    **Energies of Emission Lines for Excited Atoms**

**Problem** Calculate the wavelength of the green line in the visible spectrum of excited H atoms.

**What Do You Know?** The green line in the spectrum of hydrogen arises from the electron transition from the $n = 4$ state ($n_{initial}$) to the $n = 2$ state ($n_{final}$) (Figure 6.10).

**Strategy**
- Calculate the difference in energy between the states using Equation 6.5. You can simplify this calculation by using the value of $Rhc$ from Example 6.2 ($= 2.179 \times 10^{-18}$ J/photon).

- Relate the difference in energy to the wavelength of light using the equation $E = hc/\lambda$. (This equation is derived by combining Equations 6.1 and 6.2.)

**Solution** Calculate $\Delta E$.

$$\Delta E = E_{final} - E_{initial} = \left(-\frac{Rhc}{2^2}\right) - \left(-\frac{Rhc}{4^2}\right)$$

$$\Delta E = -Rhc\left(\frac{1}{4} - \frac{1}{16}\right) = -Rhc(0.1875)$$

$$\Delta E = -(2.179 \times 10^{-18} \text{ J/photon})(0.1875) = -4.086 \times 10^{-19} \text{ J/photon}$$

**Strategy Map 6.3**

**PROBLEM**

Calculate energy of *green line* in **H spectrum.**

↓

**KNOWN DATA/INFORMATION**

- Green line involves transition from **$n = 4$** to **$n = 2$**

↓

**STEP 1.** Use $E = -Rhc/n^2$ to calculate $E$ for **$n = 4$** and **$n = 2$.**

Obtain $E_2$ ($= E_{final}$) and $E_4$ ($= E_{initial}$)

↓

**STEP 2.** Calculate $\Delta E = E_{final} - E_{initial}$

Obtain $\Delta E = E_{final} - E_{initial}$

↓

**STEP 3.** Use Planck's equation to convert $E_{photon}$ to wavelength.

↓

Obtain photon **wavelength**

Now apply Planck's equation to calculate the wavelength ($E_{photon} = h\nu = hc/\lambda$, and so $\lambda = hc/E_{photon}$). (Recognize that, while the change in energy has a sign indicating the "direction" of energy transfer, the energy of the photon emitted, $E_{photon}$, does not have a sign.)

$$\lambda = \frac{hc}{E_{photon}} = \frac{\left(6.626 \times 10^{-34} \, \dfrac{J \cdot s}{photon}\right)(2.998 \times 10^{8} \, m \cdot s^{-1})}{4.086 \times 10^{-19} \, J/photon}$$

$$= 4.862 \times 10^{-7} \, m$$

$$= (4.862 \times 10^{-7} \, m)(1 \times 10^{9} \, nm/m)$$

$$= 486.2 \, nm$$

**Think about Your Answer** You might recall that visible light has wavelengths of 400 to 700 nm. The calculated value is in this region, and your answer has a value appropriate for the green line. The experimentally determined value of 486.1 nm is in excellent agreement with this answer.

**Check Your Understanding**

The Lyman series of spectral lines for the H atom, in the ultraviolet region, arises from transitions from higher levels to $n = 1$. Calculate the frequency and wavelength of the least energetic line in this series.

---

**REVIEW & CHECK FOR SECTION 6.3**

1. Based on Bohr's theory, which of the following transitions for the hydrogen atom will evolve the most energy?

   (a) from $n = 3$ to $n = 2$        (c) from $n = 5$ to $n = 2$

   (b) from $n = 4$ to $n = 2$        (d) from $n = 6$ to $n = 2$

2. Based on Bohr's theory, which of the following transitions for the hydrogen atom will occur with emission of visible light?

   (a) from $n = 3$ to $n = 1$        (c) from $n = 5$ to $n = 3$

   (b) from $n = 4$ to $n = 2$        (d) from $n = 6$ to $n = 4$

---

## 6.4 Particle–Wave Duality: Prelude to Quantum Mechanics

The photoelectric effect demonstrated that light, usually considered to be a wave, can also have the properties of particles, albeit without mass. But what if matter, which is usually considered to be made of particles, could have wave properties? This was pondered by Louis Victor de Broglie (1892–1987), who, in 1925, proposed that a free electron of mass $m$ moving with a velocity $v$ should have an associated wavelength $\lambda$, calculated by the equation

$$\lambda = \frac{h}{mv} \tag{6.6}$$

De Broglie called the wave corresponding to the wavelength calculated from this equation a "matter wave."

This revolutionary idea linked the particle properties of the electron (mass and velocity) with a wave property (wavelength). Experimental proof was soon produced. In 1927, C. J. Davisson (1881–1958) and L. H. Germer (1896–1971) found that diffraction, a property of waves, was observed when a beam of electrons was

**The wave nature of electrons.** A beam of electrons was passed through a thin film of MgO. The atoms in the MgO lattice diffracted the electron beam, producing this pattern. Diffraction is best explained by assuming electrons have wave properties.

© R. K. Bohn, Department of Chemistry, University of Connecticut

# What Makes the Colors in Fireworks?

Typical fireworks have several important chemical components. For example, there must be an oxidizer. Today, this is usually potassium perchlorate ($KClO_4$), potassium chlorate ($KClO_3$), or potassium nitrate ($KNO_3$). Potassium salts are used instead of sodium salts because the latter have two important drawbacks. They are hygroscopic—they absorb water from the air—and so do not remain dry on storage. Also, when heated, sodium salts give off an intense, yellow light that is so bright it can mask other colors.

The parts of any fireworks display we remember best are the vivid colors and brilliant flashes. White light can be produced by oxidizing magnesium or aluminum metal at high temperatures. The flashes you see at rock concerts or similar events, for example, are typically $Mg/KClO_4$ mixtures.

Yellow light is easiest to produce because sodium salts give an intense light with a wavelength of 589 nm. Fireworks mixtures

FIGURE B **The design of an aerial rocket for a fireworks display.** When the fuse is ignited, it burns quickly to the delay fuses at the top of the red star mixture as well as to the black powder propellant at the bottom. The propellant ignites, sending the shell into the air. Meanwhile, the delay fuses burn. If the timing is correct, the shell bursts high in the sky into a red star. This is followed by a blue burst and then a flash and sound.

FIGURE A **Emission of light by excited atoms.** Flame tests are often used to identify elements in a chemical sample. Shown here are the colors produced in a flame (burning methanol) by NaCl (yellow), $SrCl_2$ (red), and boric acid (green).

usually contain sodium in the form of non-hygroscopic compounds such as cryolite, $Na_3AlF_6$. Strontium salts are most often used to produce a red light, and green is produced by barium salts such as $Ba(NO_3)_2$.

The next time you see a fireworks display, watch for the ones that are blue. Blue has always been the most difficult color to produce. Recently, however, fireworks designers have learned that the best way to get a really good "blue" is to decompose copper(I) chloride at low temperatures. To achieve this effect, CuCl is mixed with $KClO_4$, copper powder, and the organic chlorine-containing compound hexachloroethane, $C_2Cl_6$.

**Questions:**

1. The main lines in the emission spectrum of sodium are at wavelengths (nm) of 313.5, 589, 590, 818, and 819. Which one or ones are most responsible for the characteristic yellow color of excited sodium atoms?

2. Does the main emission line for $SrCl_2$ (in Figure A) have a longer or shorter wavelength than that of the yellow line from NaCl?

3. Mg is oxidized by $KClO_4$ to make white flashes. One product of the reaction is KCl. Write a balanced equation for the reaction.

Answers to these questions are available in Appendix N.

directed at a thin sheet of metal foil. Furthermore, assuming the electron beam to be a matter wave, de Broglie's relation was followed quantitatively. The experiment was taken as evidence that electrons can be described as having wave properties in certain situations.

De Broglie's equation suggests that, for the wavelength of a matter wave to be measurable, the product of $m$ and $v$ must be very small because $h$ is so small. A 114-g baseball, traveling at 110 mph, for example, has a large $mv$ product (5.6 kg · m/s) and therefore an incredibly small wavelength, $1.2 \times 10^{-34}$ m! Such a small value cannot be measured with any instrument now available, nor is such a value meaningful. As a consequence, wave properties are never assigned to a baseball or any other massive object. It is possible to observe wave-like properties only for particles of extremely small mass, such as protons, electrons, and neutrons.

Cathode ray tubes, such as were found in television sets before the advent of LCD and plasma TVs, generate a beam of electrons. When the electrons impact the screen, the beam gives rise to tiny flashes of colored light. In contrast to this effect, best explained by assuming electrons are particles, diffraction experiments suggest that electrons are waves. But, how can an electron be both a particle and a wave? In part, we are facing limitations in language; the words *particle* and *wave* accurately describe things encountered on a macroscopic scale. However, they apply less well on the submicroscopic scale associated with subatomic particles. In some experiments, electrons behave like particles. In other experiments, we find that they behave like waves. No single experiment can be done to show the electron behaving *simultaneously* as a wave and a particle. Scientists now accept this **wave–particle duality**—that is, the idea that the electron has the properties of both a wave and a particle. This concept is central to an understanding of the modern model of the atom that we take up in the remainder of the chapter.

## EXAMPLE 6.4    Using de Broglie's Equation

**Problem** Calculate the wavelength associated with an electron of mass $m = 9.109 \times 10^{-28}$ g that travels at 40.0% of the speed of light.

**What Do You Know?** The equation proposed by de Broglie, $\lambda = h/mv$, relates wavelength to the mass and velocity of a moving particle. Here you are given the mass of the electron and its velocity; you will need Planck's constant, $h = 6.626 \times 10^{-34}$ J · s. Note also that $1 \text{ J} = 1 \text{ kg} \cdot \text{m}^2/\text{s}^2$ (◀ page 29). Finally, you will need to manipulate units of $m$ and $h$ to be consistent in the solution.

**Strategy**

• Express the electron mass in kg and calculate the electron velocity in m · s⁻¹.

• Substitute values of $m$ (in kg), $v$ (in m/s), and $h$ in the de Broglie equation and solve for $\lambda$.

**Solution**
Electron mass $= 9.109 \times 10^{-31}$ kg

Electron speed (40.0% of light speed) $= (0.400)(2.998 \times 10^8 \text{ m} \cdot \text{s}^{-1}) = 1.20 \times 10^8 \text{ m} \cdot \text{s}^{-1}$

Substituting these values into de Broglie's equation, we have

$$\lambda = \frac{h}{mv} = \frac{6.626 \times 10^{-34} \ (\text{kg} \cdot \text{m}^2/\text{s}^2)(\text{s})}{(9.109 \times 10^{-31} \text{ kg})(1.20 \times 10^8 \text{ m/s})} = 6.07 \times 10^{-12} \text{ m}$$

In nanometers, the wavelength is

$$\lambda = (6.07 \times 10^{-12} \text{ m})(1.00 \times 10^9 \text{ nm/m}) = 6.07 \times 10^{-3} \text{ nm}$$

**Think about Your Answer** The calculated wavelength is about 1/12 of the diameter of the H atom. Also notice the care taken to monitor units in this problem.

**Check Your Understanding**

Calculate the wavelength associated with a neutron having a mass of $1.675 \times 10^{-24}$ g and a kinetic energy of $6.21 \times 10^{-21}$ J. (Recall that the kinetic energy of a moving particle is $E = \frac{1}{2}mv^2$.)

---

**REVIEW & CHECK FOR SECTION 6.4**

The wavelength associated with an electron moving at 40% of the speed of light is $6.07 \times 10^{-3}$ nm (see Example 6.4). How will the wavelength be changed if the velocity increased to 80% of the speed of light?

(a)   Wavelength will be longer.                    (c)   Wavelength will not change.

(b)   Wavelength will be shorter.

# 6.5 The Modern View of Electronic Structure: Wave or Quantum Mechanics

How does wave–particle duality affect our model of the arrangement of electrons in atoms? Following World War I, German scientists Erwin Schrödinger (1887–1961), Max Born (1882–1970), and Werner Heisenberg (1901–1976) provided the answer.

Erwin Schrödinger received the Nobel Prize in physics in 1933 for a comprehensive theory of the behavior of electrons in atoms. Starting with de Broglie's hypothesis that an electron could be described as a matter wave, Schrödinger developed a model for electrons in atoms that has come to be called **quantum mechanics** or **wave mechanics**. Unlike Bohr's model, Schrödinger's model can be difficult to visualize, and the mathematical approach is complex. Nonetheless, the consequences of the model are important, and understanding its implications is essential to understanding the modern view of the atom.

Let us start by thinking of the behavior of an electron in the atom as a **standing wave**. If you tie down a string at both ends, as you would the string of a guitar, and then pluck it, the string vibrates as a standing wave (Figure 6.11). There are only certain vibrations allowed for the standing wave formed by a plucked guitar string. That is, the vibrations are quantized. Similarly, as Schrödinger showed, only certain matter waves are possible for an electron in an atom.

Following the de Broglie concept, we can adopt the quantum-mechanical view that an electron in an atom behaves as a wave. To describe this wave, physicists introduced the concept of a **wavefunction**, which is designated by the Greek letter $\psi$ (psi). Schrödinger built on the idea that the electron in an atom has the characteristics of a standing wave and wrote an equation defining the energy of an electron in terms of wavefunctions. When this equation was solved for energy—a monumental task in itself—he found the following important outcomes:

- Only certain wavefunctions are found to be acceptable, and each is associated with an allowed energy value. That is, *the energy of the electron in the atom is quantized.*
- The solutions to Schrödinger's equation for an electron in three-dimensional space depend on three integers, $n$, $\ell$, and $m_\ell$, which are called **quantum numbers**. Only certain combinations of their values are possible, as we shall outline below.

The next step in understanding the quantum mechanical view is to explore the physical significance of the wavefunction, $\psi$ (psi). Here we owe much to Max Born's interpretation. He said that

(a) the value of the wavefunction $\psi$ at a given point in space is the amplitude (height) of the electron matter wave. This value has both a magnitude and a sign that can be either positive or negative. (Visualize a vibrating string

● **Wave Functions and Energy**
In Bohr's theory, the electron energy for the H atom is given by $E_n = -Rhc/n^2$. Schrödinger's electron wave model gives the same result.

**FIGURE 6.11 Standing waves.** A two-dimensional standing wave such as a vibrating string must have two or more points of zero amplitude (called **nodes**), and only certain vibrations are possible. These allowed vibrations have wavelengths of $n(\lambda/2)$, where $n$ is an integer ($n = 1, 2, 3, \ldots$). In the first vibration illustrated here, the distance between the ends of the string is half a wavelength, or $\lambda/2$. In the second, the string's length equals one complete wavelength, or $2(\lambda/2)$. In the third vibration, the string's length is $3(\lambda/2)$.

in a guitar or piano, for example (Figure 6.11). Points of positive amplitude are above the axis of the wave, and points of negative amplitude are below it.)

(b) the square of the value of the wavefunction ($\psi^2$) is related to the *probability* of finding an electron in a tiny region of space. Scientists refer to $\psi^2$ as a **probability density**. Just as we can calculate the mass of an object from the product of its density and volume, we can calculate the *probability* of finding an electron in a tiny volume from the product of $\psi^2$ and the volume. The Born interpretation of the wavefunction is that, for a given volume, whenever $\psi^2$ is large, the probability of finding the electron is larger than when $\psi^2$ is small.

There is one more important concept to touch on as we try to understand the modern quantum mechanical model. In Bohr's model of the atom, both the energy and location (the orbit) for the electron in the hydrogen atom can be described accurately. However, Werner Heisenberg postulated that, for a tiny object such as an electron in an atom, it is impossible to determine accurately *both* its position and its energy. That is, any attempt to determine accurately either the location or the energy will leave the other uncertain. This is now known as Heisenberg's **uncertainty principle**: *If we choose to know the energy of an electron in an atom with only a small uncertainty, then we must accept a correspondingly large uncertainty in its position.* The importance of this idea is that we can assess only the likelihood, or *probability*, of finding an electron with a given energy within a given region of space. Because electron energy is the key to understanding the chemistry of an atom, chemists accept the notion of knowing only the approximate location of the electron.

## Quantum Numbers and Orbitals

The wavefunction for an electron in an atom describes what we call an **atomic orbital**. Following the ideas of Born and Heisenberg, we know the energy of this electron, but we only know the region of space within which it is most probably located. Thus, when an electron has a particular wavefunction, it is said to "occupy" a particular orbital with a given energy, and each orbital is described by three quantum numbers: $n$, $\ell$, and $m_\ell$. Let us first describe the quantum numbers and the information they provide and then discuss the connection between quantum numbers and the energies and shapes of atomic orbitals.

### $n$, the Principal Quantum Number ($n = 1, 2, 3, \ldots$)

The principal quantum number $n$ can have any integer value from 1 to infinity. The value of $n$ is the primary factor in determining the *energy* of an orbital. It also defines the *size* of an orbital: for a given atom, the greater the value of $n$, the greater the size of the orbital.

In atoms having more than one electron, two or more electrons may have the same $n$ value. These electrons are then said to be in the same **electron shell**.

### $\ell$, the Orbital Angular Momentum Quantum Number ($\ell = 0, 1, 2, 3, \ldots, n - 1$)

Orbitals of a given shell can be grouped into **subshells**, where each subshell is characterized by a different value of the quantum number $\ell$. The quantum number $\ell$, referred to as the "orbital angular momentum" quantum number, can have any integer value from 0 to a maximum of $n - 1$. This quantum number defines the *characteristic shape of an orbital*; different $\ell$ values correspond to different orbital shapes.

Because $\ell$ can be no larger than $n - 1$, the value of $n$ limits the number of subshells possible for each shell. For the shell with $n = 1$, $\ell$ must equal 0; thus, only one subshell is possible. When $n = 2$, $\ell$ can be either 0 or 1. Because two values of $\ell$ are now possible, there are two subshells in the $n = 2$ electron shell.

● **Orbits and Orbitals** In Bohr's model of the H atom, the electron is confined to a prescribed path around the nucleus, its *orbit*, so we should be able to define its position and energy at a given moment in time. In the modern view, the term *orbital* is used to describe the fact that we have a less definite view of the electron's location. We know its energy but only the region of space within which it is probably located, that is, its orbital.

● **Electron Energy and Quantum Numbers** The electron energy in the H atom depends only on the value of $n$. In atoms with more electrons, the energy depends on both $n$ and $\ell$, as you shall see in Chapter 7.

Subshells are usually identified by letters. For example, an $\ell = 1$ subshell is called a "$p$ subshell," and an orbital in that subshell is called a "$p$ orbital."

| Value of $\ell$ | Subshell Label |
|:---:|:---:|
| 0 | $s$ |
| 1 | $p$ |
| 2 | $d$ |
| 3 | $f$ |

• **Orbital Symbols** Early studies of the emission spectra of elements classified lines into four groups on the basis of their appearance. These groups were labeled sharp, principal, diffuse, and fundamental. From these names came the labels we now apply to orbitals: *s, p, d,* and *f.*

### $m_\ell$, the Magnetic Quantum Number ($m_\ell = 0, \pm 1, \pm 2, \pm 3, \ldots, \pm \ell$)

The magnetic quantum number, $m_\ell$, is related to the *orientation in space of the orbitals within a subshell*. Orbitals in a given subshell differ in their orientation in space, not in their energy.

The value of $m_\ell$ can range from $+\ell$ to $-\ell$, with 0 included. For example, when $\ell = 2$, $m_\ell$ can have five values: $+2, +1, 0, -1$, and $-2$. The number of values of $m_\ell$ for a given subshell ($= 2\ell + 1$) specifies the number of orbitals in the subshell.

## Shells and Subshells

Allowed values of the three quantum numbers are summarized in Table 6.1. By analyzing the sets of quantum numbers in this table, you will discover the following:

- $n =$ the number of subshells in a shell
- $2\ell + 1 =$ the number of orbitals in a subshell = the number of values of $m_\ell$
- $n^2 =$ the number of orbitals in a shell

• **Shells, Subshells, and Orbitals— A Summary** Electrons in atoms are arranged in shells. Within each shell, there can be one or more electron subshells, each comprised of one or more orbitals.

| | Quantum Number |
|:---|:---:|
| Shell | $n$ |
| Subshell | $\ell$ |
| Orbital | $m_\ell$ |

### The First Electron Shell, $n = 1$

When $n = 1$, the value of $\ell$ can only be 0, so $m_\ell$ must also have a value of 0. This means that, in the shell closest to the nucleus, only one subshell exists, and that subshell consists of only a single orbital, the $1s$ orbital.

### The Second Electron Shell, $n = 2$

When $n = 2$, $\ell$ can have two values (0 and 1), so there are two subshells in the second shell. One of these is the $2s$ subshell ($n = 2$ and $\ell = 0$), and the other is the $2p$ subshell ($n = 2$ and $\ell = 1$). Because the values of $m_\ell$ can be $-1$, 0, and $+1$ when

**Table 6.1 Summary of the Quantum Numbers, Their Interrelationships, and the Orbital Information Conveyed**

| Principal Quantum Number<br><br>Symbol $= n$<br>Values $= 1, 2, 3, \ldots$ | Angular Momentum Quantum Number<br><br>Symbol $= \ell$<br>Values $= 0 \ldots n - 1$ | Magnetic Quantum Number<br><br>Symbol $= m_\ell$<br>Values $= +\ell \ldots 0 \ldots -\ell$ | Number and Type of Orbitals in the Subshell<br>$n =$ number of subshells<br>Number of orbitals in shell $= n^2$ and number of orbitals in subshell $= 2\ell + 1$ |
|:---:|:---:|:---:|:---|
| 1 | 0 | 0 | one $1s$ orbital<br>(one orbital of one type in the $n = 1$ shell) |
| 2 | 0<br>1 | 0<br>$+1, 0, -1$ | one $2s$ orbital<br>three $2p$ orbitals<br>(four orbitals of two types in the $n = 2$ shell) |
| 3 | 0<br>1<br>2 | 0<br>$+1, 0, -1$<br>$+2, +1, 0, -1, -2$ | one $3s$ orbital<br>three $3p$ orbitals<br>five $3d$ orbitals<br>(nine orbitals of three types in the $n = 3$ shell) |
| 4 | 0<br>1<br>2<br>3 | 0<br>$+1, 0, -1$<br>$+2, +1, 0, -1, -2$<br>$+3, +2, +1, 0, -1, -2, -3$ | one $4s$ orbital<br>three $4p$ orbitals<br>five $4d$ orbitals<br>seven $4f$ orbitals<br>(16 orbitals of four types in the $n = 4$ shell) |

$\ell = 1$, three $2p$ orbitals exist. All three orbitals have the same shape. However, because each has a different $m_\ell$ value, the three orbitals differ in their orientation in space.

### The Third Electron Shell, $n = 3$

When $n = 3$, three subshells are possible for an electron because $\ell$ can have the values 0, 1, and 2. The first two subshells within the $n = 3$ shell are the $3s$ ($\ell = 0$, one orbital) and $3p$ ($\ell = 1$, three orbitals) subshells. The third subshell is labeled $3d$ ($n = 3$, $\ell = 2$). Because $m_\ell$ can have five values ($-2$, $-1$, 0, $+1$, and $+2$) for $\ell = 2$, there are five $d$ orbitals in this $d$ subshell.

### The Fourth Electron Shell, $n = 4$

There are four subshells in the $n = 4$ shell. In addition to $4s$, $4p$, and $4d$ subshells, there is the $4f$ subshell for which $\ell = 3$. Seven such orbitals exist because there are seven values of $m_\ell$ when $\ell = 3$ ($-3$, $-2$, $-1$, 0, $+1$, $+2$, and $+3$).

---

**REVIEW & CHECK FOR SECTION 6.5**

1.  What label is given to an orbital with quantum numbers $n = 4$ and $\ell = 1$?

    (a)  $4s$  (b)  $4p$  (c)  $4d$  (d)  $4f$

2.  How many orbitals are in the $n = 4$ shell?

    (a)  1  (b)  4  (c)  9  (d)  16

3.  Which quantum number, or combination of quantum numbers, is needed to specify a given subshell in an atom?

    (a)  $n$  (b)  $\ell$  (c)  $n$ and $\ell$

---

## 6.6 The Shapes of Atomic Orbitals

We often say the electron is assigned to, or "occupies," an orbital. But what does this mean? What is an orbital? What does it look like? To answer these questions, we have to look at the wavefunctions for the orbitals. (To answer the question of *why* the quantum numbers—small, whole numbers—can be related to orbital shape and energy, see *A Closer Look: More About H Atomic Orbital Shapes and Wavefunctions* on page 287.)

### *s* Orbitals

A $1s$ orbital is associated with the quantum numbers $n = 1$ and $\ell = 0$. If we could photograph a $1s$ electron at one-second intervals for a few thousand seconds, the composite picture would look like the drawing in Figure 6.12a. This resembles a cloud of dots, and chemists often refer to such representations of electron orbitals as *electron cloud pictures*. In Figure 6.12a, the density of dots is greater close to the nucleus, that is, the electron cloud is denser close to the nucleus. This indicates that the $1s$ electron is most likely to be found near the nucleus. However, the density of dots declines on moving away from the nucleus and so, therefore, does the probability of finding the electron.

The thinning of the electron cloud at increasing distance is illustrated in a different way in Figure 6.12b. Here we have plotted the square of the wavefunction for the electron in a $1s$ orbital ($\psi^2$), times $4\pi$ and the distance squared ($r^2$), as a function of the distance of the electron from the nucleus. This plot represents the probability of finding the electron in a thin spherical shell at a distance $r$ from the nucleus. Chemists refer to the plot of $4\pi r^2\psi^2$ vs. $r$ as a **surface density plot** or **radial distribution plot**. For the $1s$ orbital, $4\pi r^2\psi^2$ is zero at the nucleus—there is no probability the electron will be exactly at the nucleus (where $r = 0$)—but the probability rises rapidly on moving away from the nucleus, reaches a maximum a short distance from the nucleus (at 52.9 pm), and then decreases rapidly as the distance from the nucleus increases. Notice that the probability of finding the electron approaches but never quite reaches zero, even at very large distances.

Figure 6.12a shows that, for the $1s$ orbital, the probability of finding an electron is the same at a given distance from the nucleus, no matter in which direction you proceed from the nucleus. Consequently, the *$1s$ orbital is spherical in shape.*

Because the probability of finding the electron approaches but never quite reaches zero, there is no sharp boundary beyond which the electron is never found (although the probability can be incalculably small at large distances). Nonetheless, the *s* orbital (and other types of orbitals as well) is often depicted as having a **boundary surface** (Figure 6.12c), largely because it is easier to draw such pictures. To create Figure 6.12c, we drew a sphere centered on the nucleus in such a way that the probability of finding the electron somewhere inside the sphere is 90%. The choice of 90% is arbitrary—we could have chosen a different value—and if we do, the shape would be the same, but the size of the sphere would be different.

All *s* orbitals ($1s$, $2s$, $3s$...) are spherical in shape. However, for any atom, the size of *s* orbitals increases as $n$ increases (Figure 6.13). For a given atom, the $1s$ orbital is more compact than the $2s$ orbital, which is in turn more compact than the $3s$ orbital.

It is important that you avoid some misconceptions about pictures of orbitals.

- First, there is not an impenetrable surface within which the electron is "contained."
- Second, the probability of finding the electron is not the same throughout the volume enclosed by the surface in Figure 6.12c. (An electron in the $1s$ orbital of a H atom has a greater probability of being 52.9 pm from the nucleus than of being closer or farther away.)
- Third, the terms "electron cloud" and "electron distribution" imply that the electron is a particle, but the basic premise in quantum mechanics is that the electron is treated as a wave, not a particle.

## *p* Orbitals

All atomic orbitals for which $\ell = 1$ ($p$ orbitals) have the same basic shape. If you enclose 90% of the electron density in a $p$ orbital within a surface, the electron cloud is often described as having a shape like a weight lifter's "dumbbell," and chemists

- **Surface Density Plot for 1s** The maximum value of the radial distribution plot for a $1s$ electron in a hydrogen atom occurs at 52.9 pm. It is interesting to note that this maximum is at exactly the same distance from the nucleus that Niels Bohr calculated for the radius of the orbit occupied by the $n = 1$ electron.

- **Nodal Surfaces** Nodal surfaces that cut through the nucleus occur for all $p$, $d$, and $f$ orbitals. These surfaces are usually flat, so they are often referred to as *nodal planes*. In some cases (for example, $d_{z^2}$), however, the "plane" is not flat and so is better referred to as a *nodal surface*.

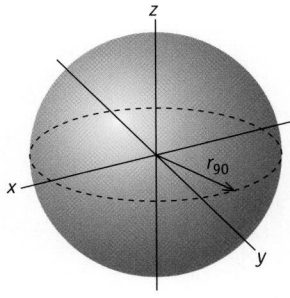

**(a)** Dot picture of an electron in a $1s$ orbital. Each dot represents the position of the electron at a different instant in time. Note that the dots cluster closest to the nucleus. $r_{90}$ is the radius of a sphere within which the electron is found 90% of the time.

**(b)** A plot of the surface density ($4\pi r^2 \psi^2$) as a function of distance for a hydrogen atom $1s$ orbital. This gives the probability of finding the electron at a given distance from the nucleus.

**(c)** The surface of the sphere within which the electron is found 90% of the time for a $1s$ orbital. This surface is often called a "boundary surface." (A 90% surface was chosen arbitrarily. If the choice was the surface within which the electron is found 50% of the time, the sphere would be considerably smaller.)

**FIGURE 6.12 Different views of a 1s ($n = 1$, $\ell = 0$) orbital.** In panel **(b)** the horizontal axis is marked in units called "Bohr radii," where 1 Bohr radius = 52.9 pm. This is common practice when plotting wave functions.

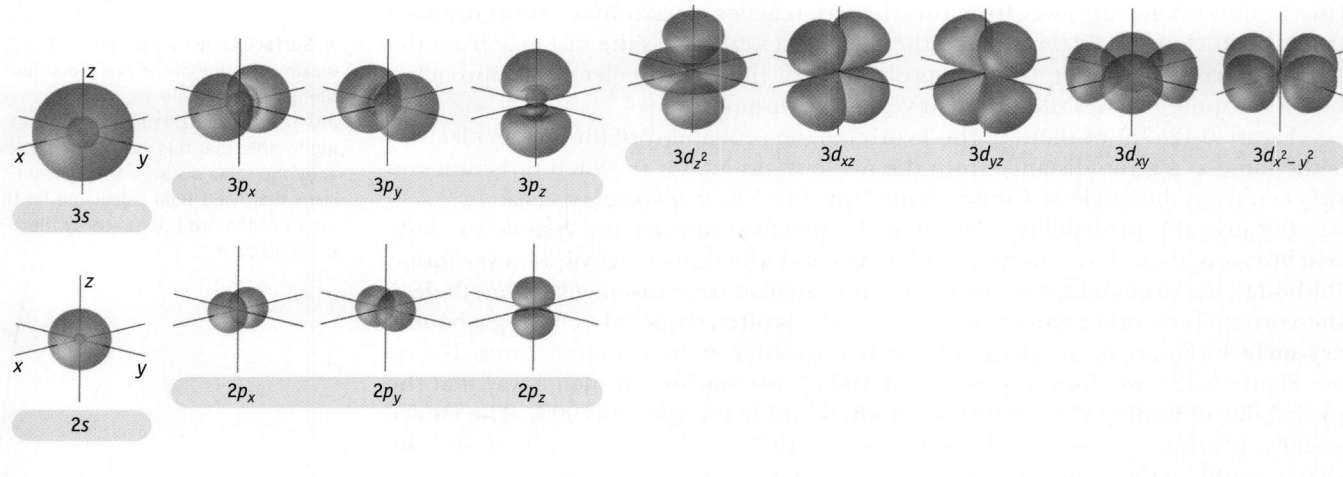

**FIGURE 6.13 Atomic orbitals.** Boundary surface diagrams for electron densities of 1s, 2s, 2p, 3s, 3p, and 3d orbitals for the hydrogen atom. For the p orbitals, the subscript letter indicates the cartesian axis along which the orbital lies. (For more about orbitals, see *A Closer Look: More About H Atom Orbital Shapes and Wavefunctions.*)

• **ℓ and Nodal Surfaces** The number of nodal surfaces passing through the nucleus for an orbital = ℓ.

| Orbital | ℓ | Number of Nodal Surfaces through the Nucleus |
|---------|---|---------------------------------------------|
| s | 0 | 0 |
| p | 1 | 1 |
| d | 2 | 2 |
| f | 3 | 3 |

describe p orbitals as having dumbbell shapes (Figures 6.13 and 6.14). A p orbital has a **nodal surface**—a surface on which the probability of finding the electron is zero—that passes through the nucleus. (The nodal surface is a consequence of the wavefunction for p orbitals, which has a value of zero at the nucleus but which rises rapidly in value on moving way from the nucleus. See *A Closer Look: More About H Atom Orbital Shapes and Wavefunctions.*)

There are three p orbitals in a subshell, and all have the same basic shape with one nodal plane through the nucleus. Usually, p orbitals are drawn along the x-, y-, and z-axes and labeled according to the axis along which they lie ($p_x$, $p_y$, or $p_z$).

## d Orbitals

Orbitals with $\ell = 0$, s orbitals, have no nodal surfaces through the nucleus, and p orbitals, for which $\ell = 1$, have one nodal surface through the nucleus. *The value of ℓ is equal to the number of nodal surfaces slicing through the nucleus.* It follows that the five d orbitals, for which $\ell = 2$, have two nodal surfaces through the nucleus, resulting in four regions of electron density. The $d_{xy}$ orbital, for example, lies in

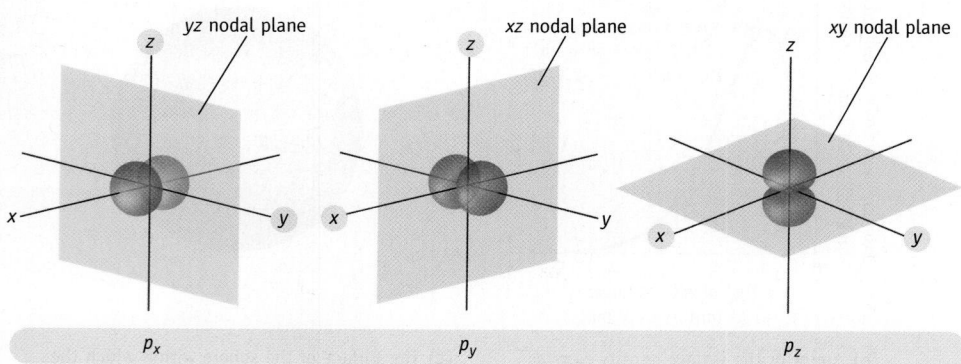

**(a)** The three p orbitals each have one nodal plane ($\ell = 1$) that is perpendicular to the axis along which the orbital lies.

**FIGURE 6.14 Nodal surfaces of p and d orbitals.** A nodal surface is a surface on which the probability of finding the electron is zero.

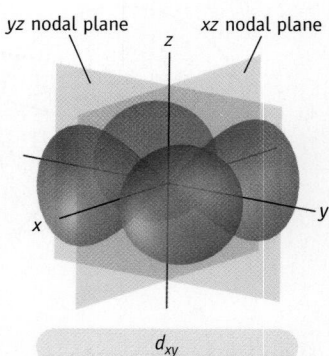

**(b)** The $d_{xy}$ orbital. All five d orbitals have two nodal surfaces ($\ell = 2$) passing through the nucleus. Here, the nodal surfaces are the xz- and yz-planes, so the regions of electron density lie between the x- and y-axes in the xy-plane.

## A CLOSER LOOK

# More about H Atom Orbital Shapes and Wavefunctions

There is an important question to answer: How do quantum numbers, which are small, integer numbers, tell us the shape of atomic orbitals? The answer lies in the orbital wavefunctions, which are reasonably simple mathematical equations.

The equations for wavefunctions ($\psi$) are the product of two functions: the *radial function* and the *angular function*. You need to look at each type to get a picture of an orbital.

Let's first consider the *radial function*, which depends on $n$ and $\ell$. This tells us how the value of $\psi$ depends on the distance from the nucleus. The radial functions for the hydrogen atom 1s ($n = 1$ and $\ell = 0$), 2s ($n = 2$ and $\ell = 0$) orbitals, and 2p orbitals ($n = 2$ and $\ell = 1$) are plotted in Figure A. (The horizontal axis has units of $a_o$, where $a_o$ is a constant equal to 52.9 pm.)

Waves have crests, troughs, and nodes, and plots of the wavefunctions show this. For the 1s orbital of the H atom, the radial wavefunction $\psi_{1s}$ approaches a maximum at the nucleus (Figure A), but the wave's amplitude declines rapidly at points farther removed from the nucleus. The sign of $\psi_{1s}$ is positive at all points in space.

For a 2s orbital, there is a different profile: the sign of $\psi_{2s}$ is positive near the nucleus, drops to zero (there is a node at $r = 2a_o = 2 \times 52.9$ pm), and then becomes

**FIGURE A  Plot of the wavefunctions for 1s, 2s, and 2p orbitals versus distance from the nucleus.** As in other plots of wavefunctions, the horizontal axis is marked in units called "Bohr radii," where 1 Bohr radius = 52.9 pm.

negative with increasing $r$ before approaching zero at greater distances.

Now to the *angular portion* of the wavefunction: this reflects changes that occur when you travel outward from the nucleus in different directions. It is a function of the quantum numbers $\ell$ and $m_\ell$.

As illustrated in Figure 6.12 the value of $\psi_{1s}$ is the same in every direction. This is a reflection of the fact that, while the radial portion of the wavefunction changes with $r$, the angular portion for all s orbitals is a constant. As a consequence, all s orbital are spherical.

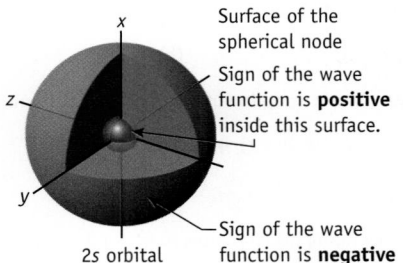

**FIGURE B  Wavefunction for a 2s orbital.** A 2s orbital for the H atom showing the spherical node (at $2a_0 = 105.8$ pm) around the nucleus.

For the 2s orbital, you see a node in Figure A at 105.8 pm ($= 2a_o$) when plotting the radial portion of the wavefunction. However, because the angular part of $\psi_{2s}$ has the same value in all directions, this means there is a node—a *spherical nodal surface*—at the same distance in every direction (as illustrated in Figure B). For any orbital, the number of spherical nodes is $n - \ell - 1$.

Now let's look at a p orbital, first the radial portion and then the angular portion. For a p orbital the radial portion of the wavefunction is 0 when $r = 0$. Thus, the value of $\psi_{2p}$ is zero at the nucleus and a nodal surface passes through the nucleus (Figures A and C). This is true for all p orbitals.

But what happens as you move away from the nucleus in one direction, say along the x-axis in the case of the $2p_x$ orbital. Now we see the value of $\psi_{2p}$ rise to a maximum at 105.9 pm ($= 2a_o$) before falling off at greater distances (Figures A and C).

But look at Figure C for the $2p_x$ orbital. Moving away along the $-x$ direction, the value of $\psi_{2p}$ is the same but opposite in sign

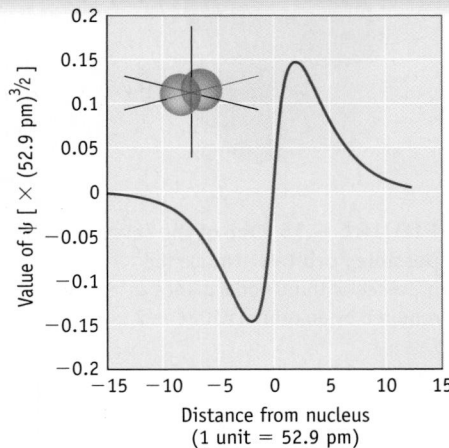

**FIGURE C  Wave functions for a 2p orbital.** The sign of $\psi$ for a 2p orbital is positive on one side of the nucleus and negative on the other (but it has a 0 value at the nucleus). A nodal plane separates the two lobes of this "dumbbell-shaped" orbital. (The vertical axis is the value of $\psi$, and the horizontal axis is the distance from the nucleus, where 1 unit = 52.9 pm.)

to the value in the +x direction. The 2p electron is a wave with a node at the nucleus. (In drawing orbitals, we indicate this with + or − signs or with two different colors as in Figure 6.13.)

Now, what about the *angular portion* of the wavefunction for $2p_x$? The angular portion for all three p orbitals has the same general form: $c(x/r)$ for the $p_x$ orbital, $c(y/r)$ for the $p_y$ orbital, and $c(z/r)$ for the $p_z$ orbital (where c is a constant). Consider a $2p_x$ orbital in Figure D. As long as x has a value, the wavefunction has a value. But when $x = 0$ (in the yz plane), then $\psi$ is zero. This is the nodal plane for the x orbital. Similarly, the angular portion of the wavefunction for the $2p_y$ orbital means its nodal plane is the xz plane.

**FIGURE D  The $2p_x$ orbital.** The wavefunction has no value when $x = 0$, that is, the yz plane is a nodal plane.

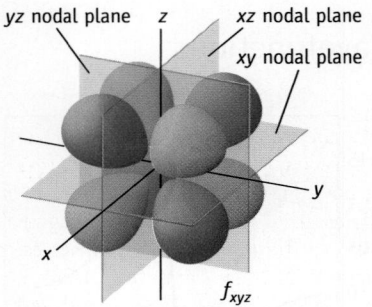

**FIGURE 6.15 One of the seven possible $f$ orbitals.** Notice the presence of three nodal planes as required by an orbital with $\ell = 3$.

the $xy$-plane, and the two nodal surfaces are the $xz$- and $yz$-planes (Figure 6.14). Two other orbitals, $d_{xz}$ and $d_{yz}$, lie in planes defined by the $xz$- and $yz$-axes, respectively; they also have two, mutually perpendicular nodal surfaces (Figure 6.13).

Of the two remaining $d$ orbitals, the $d_{x^2-y^2}$ orbital is easier to visualize. In the $d_{x^2-y^2}$ orbital, the nodal planes bisect the $x$- and $y$-axes, so the regions of electron density lie along the $x$- and $y$-axes. The $d_{z^2}$ orbital has two main regions of electron density along the $z$-axis, and a "doughnut" of electron density also occurs in the $xy$-plane. This orbital has two cone-shaped nodal surfaces.

## $f$ Orbitals

Seven $f$ orbitals arise with $\ell = 3$. Three nodal surfaces through the nucleus cause the electron density to lie in up to eight regions of space. One of the $f$ orbitals is illustrated in Figure 6.15.

---

**REVIEW & CHECK FOR SECTION 6.6**

1.  Which of the following is not a correct representation of an orbital?

    (a)  $3s$ (b)  $3p$ (c)  $3d$ (d)  $3f$

2.  Which of the following sets of quantum numbers correctly represents a $4p$ orbital?

    (a)  $n = 4, \ell = 0, m_\ell = -1$ (c)  $n = 4, \ell = 2, m_\ell = 1$

    (b)  $n = 4, \ell = 1, m_\ell = 0$ (d)  $n = 4, \ell = 1, m_\ell = 2$

3.  How many nodal planes exist for a $5d$ orbital?

    (a)  0 (b)  1 (c)  2 (d)  3

---

## 6.7  One More Electron Property: Electron Spin

There is one more property of the electron that plays an important role in the arrangement of electrons in atoms and gives rise to properties of elements you observe every day: electron spin.

### The Electron Spin Quantum Number, $m_s$

In 1921 Otto Stern and Walther Gerlach performed an experiment that probed the magnetic behavior of atoms by passing a beam of silver atoms in the gas phase through a magnetic field. Although the results were complex, they were best interpreted by *imagining* the electron has a spin and behaves as a tiny magnet that can be attracted or repelled by another magnet. If atoms with a single unpaired electron are placed in a magnetic field, the Stern-Gerlach experiment showed there are two orientations for the atoms: with the electron spin aligned with the field or opposed to the field. That is, *the electron spin is quantized,* which introduces a fourth quantum number, the **electron spin quantum number**, $m_s$. One orientation is associated with a value of $m_s$ of $+\frac{1}{2}$ and the other with $m_s$ of $-\frac{1}{2}$.

$m_s = +\frac{1}{2}$          $m_s = -\frac{1}{2}$

When it was recognized that electron spin is quantized, scientists realized that a complete description of an electron in any atom requires four quantum numbers, $n$, $\ell$, $m_\ell$, and $m_s$. The important consequences of this fact are explored in Chapter 7.

## Paramagnetism and Ferromagnetism

Magnetic materials are relatively common, and many are important in our economy. For example, a large magnet is at the heart of the magnetic resonance imaging (MRI) used in medicine, and tiny magnets are found in stereo speakers and in telephone handsets. Magnetic oxides are used in recording tapes and computer disks.

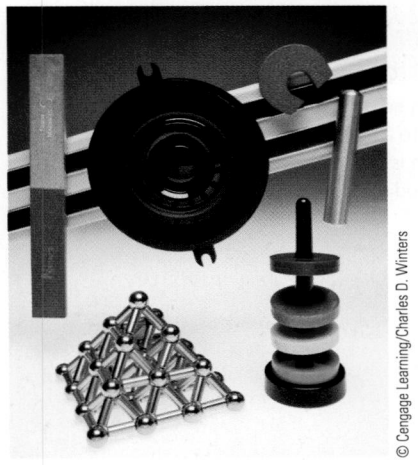

**Magnets.** Many common consumer products such as loudspeakers contain permanent magnets.

The magnetic materials we use are **ferromagnetic**. The magnetic effect of ferromagnetic materials is much larger than that of paramagnetic ones. Ferromagnetism occurs when the spins of unpaired electrons in a cluster of atoms (called a *domain*) in the solid align themselves in the same direction. Only the metals of the iron, cobalt, and nickel subgroups, as well as a few other metals such as neodymium, exhibit this property. They are also unique in that, once the domains are aligned in a magnetic field, the metal is permanently magnetized.

Many alloys exhibit greater ferromagnetism than do the pure metals themselves. One example of such a material is Alnico, which is composed of aluminum, nickel, and cobalt as well as copper and iron. The strongest permanent magnet is an alloy of neodymium, iron, and boron ($Nd_2Fe_{14}B$).

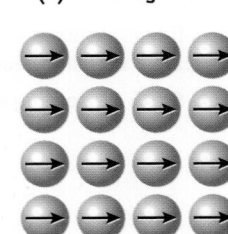

The spins of unpaired electrons align themselves in the same direction

**Magnetism.** **(a)** Paramagnetism: In the absence of an external magnetic field, the unpaired electrons in the atoms or ions of the substance are randomly oriented. If a magnetic field is imposed, however, these spins will tend to become aligned with the field. **(b)** Ferromagnetism: The spins of the unpaired electrons in a cluster of atoms or ions align themselves in the same direction even in the absence of a magnetic field.

## Diamagnetism and Paramagnetism

A hydrogen atom has a single electron. If a hydrogen atom is placed in a magnetic field, the magnetic field of the single electron will tend to align with the external field like the needle of a compass aligns with the magnetic lines of force on the Earth.

In contrast, helium atoms, each with two electrons, are not attracted to a magnet. In fact, they are slightly repelled by the magnet. To account for this observation, we assume the two electrons of helium have *opposite* spin orientations. We say their spins are *paired*, and the result is that the magnetic field of one electron can be canceled out by the magnetic field of the second electron with opposite spin. To account for this, the two electrons are assigned different values of $m_s$.

It is important to understand the relationship between electron spin and magnetism. *Elements and compounds that have unpaired electrons are attracted to a magnet.* Such species are said to be **paramagnetic**. The effect can be quite weak, but, by placing a sample of an element or compound in a magnetic field, it can be observed (Figure 6.16). For example, the oxygen you breathe is paramagnetic. You can observe this experimentally because liquid oxygen sticks to a magnet of the kind you may have in the speakers of a music player (Figure 6.16b).

Substances in which all electrons are paired (with the two electrons of each pair having opposite spins) experience a slight repulsion when subjected to a magnetic field; they are called **diamagnetic**. Therefore, by determining the magnetic behavior of a substance we can gain information about the electronic structure.

In summary, *substances in which the constituent ions or atoms contain unpaired electrons are paramagnetic and are attracted to a magnetic field.* Substances in which all electrons are paired with partners of opposite spin are diamagnetic. This explanation opens the way to understanding the arrangement of electrons in atoms with more than one electron as you shall learn in the next chapter.

(a) A magnetic balance is used to measure the magnetism of a sample. The sample is first weighed with the electromagnet turned off. The magnet is then turned on and the sample reweighed. If the substance is paramagnetic, the sample is drawn into the magnetic field, and the apparent weight increases.

(b) Liquid oxygen (boiling point 90.2 K) clings to a strong magnet. Elemental oxygen is paramagnetic because it has unpaired electrons. (See Chapter 9.)

**FIGURE 6.16** Observing and measuring paramagnetism.

 and

Sign in at **www.cengage.com/owl** to:
- View tutorials and simulations, develop problem-solving skills, and complete online homework assigned by your professor.
- For quick review and exam prep, download Go Chemistry mini lecture modules from OWL (or purchase them at **www.cengagebrain.com**)

❓ Access **How Do I Solve It?** tutorials on how to approach problem solving using concepts in this chapter.

## CHAPTER GOALS REVISITED

*Now that you have studied this chapter, you should ask whether you have met the chapter goals. In particular, you should be able to:*

**Describe the properties of electromagnetic radiation**

a. Use the terms wavelength, frequency, amplitude, and node (Section 6.1). **Study Question: 3.**

b. Use Equation 6.1 ($c = \lambda\nu$), relating wavelength ($\lambda$) and frequency ($\nu$) of electromagnetic radiation and the speed of light ($c$). **Study Question: 3.**

c. Recognize the relative wavelength (or frequency) of the various types of electromagnetic radiation (Figure 6.2). **Study Question: 1.**

d. Understand that the energy of a photon, a massless particle of radiation, is proportional to its frequency (Planck's equation, Equation 6.2) (Section 6.2). **Study Questions: 5, 7, 8, 9, 12, 14, 56, 57, 58, 63, 64, 66, 72, 73, 83.**

**Understand the origin of light emitted by excited atoms and its relationship to atomic structure**

a. Describe the Bohr model of the atom, its ability to account for the emission line spectra of excited hydrogen atoms, and the limitations of the model (Section 6.3). **Study Question: 74.**

b. Understand that, in the Bohr model of the H atom, the electron can occupy only certain energy states, each with an energy proportional to $1/n^2$ ($E_n = -Rhc/n^2$), where $n$ is the principal quantum number (Equation 6.4, Section 6.3). If an electron moves from one energy state to another, the amount of energy absorbed or emitted in the process is equal to the difference in energy between the two states (Equation 6.5, Section 6.3). **Study Questions: 16, 18, 19, 21, 22, 60.**

**Describe the experimental evidence for particle–wave duality**

a. Understand that in the modern view of the atom, electrons can be described either as particles or as waves (Section 6.4). The wavelength of an electron or any subatomic particle is given by de Broglie's equation (Equation 6.6). **Study Questions: 23–26, 82.**

# Quantized Spins and MRI

Just as electrons can be thought of as having a spin, so do atomic nuclei. In the hydrogen atom, the single proton can also be thought of having a spin. For most heavier atoms, the atomic nucleus includes both protons and neutrons, and the entire entity has a spin. This property is important, because nuclear spin allows scientists to detect these atoms in molecules and to learn something about their chemical environments.

The technique used to detect the spins of atomic nuclei is *nuclear magnetic resonance* (NMR). It is one of the most powerful methods currently available to determine molecular structures. About 20 years ago, it was adapted as a diagnostic technique in medicine, where it is known as *magnetic resonance imaging* (MRI).

Just as electron spin is quantized, so too is nuclear spin. The H atom nucleus (often referred to simply as a *proton*) can spin in either of two directions. If the H atom is placed in a strong, external magnetic field, however, the spinning nuclear magnet can align itself with or against the external field. If a sample of ethanol ($CH_3CH_2OH$), for example, is placed in a strong magnetic field, a slight excess of the H atom nuclei (and $^{13}C$ atom nuclei) is aligned with the lines of force of the field.

The nuclei aligned with the field have a slightly lower energy than when aligned against the field. The NMR and MRI technologies depend on the fact that energy in the radio-frequency region can be absorbed by the sample and can cause the nuclear spins to switch alignments—that is, to move to a higher energy state. This reemission of energy is detected by the instrument.

The most important aspect of the magnetic resonance technique is that the difference in energy between two different spin states depends on the electronic environment of atoms in the molecule. In the case of ethanol, the three $CH_3$ protons are different from the two $CH_2$ protons, and both sets are different from the OH proton. These three different sets of H atoms absorb radiation of slightly different energies. The instrument measures the frequencies absorbed, and a scientist familiar with the technique can quickly distinguish the three different environments in the molecule.

The MRI technique closely resembles the NMR method. Hydrogen is abundant in the human body as water and in numerous organic molecules. In the MRI device, the patient is placed in a strong magnetic field, and the tissues being examined are irradiated with pulses of radio-frequency radiation.

The MRI image is produced by detecting how fast the excited nuclei "relax"; that is, how fast they return to the lower energy state from the higher energy state. The "relaxation time" depends on the type of tissue. When the tissue is scanned, the H atoms in different regions of the body show different relaxation times, and an accurate "image" is built up.

MRI gives information on soft tissue—muscle, cartilage, and internal organs—which is unavailable from x-ray scans. This technology is also noninvasive, and the magnetic fields and radio-frequency radiation used are not harmful to the body.

**Magnetic resonance imaging. (a)** MRI instrument. The patient is placed inside a large magnet, and the tissues to be examined are irradiated with radio-frequency radiation. **(b)** An MRI image of the human brain.

**(a)** An NMR spectrometer (see Figure 4.4, page 166.)

**(b)** The NMR spectrum of ethanol

**Nuclear magnetic resonance. (a)** A schematic diagram of an NMR spectrometer. **(b)** The NMR spectrum of ethanol showing that the three different types of protons appear in distinctly different regions of the spectrum. The pattern observed for the $CH_2$ and $CH_3$ protons is characteristic of these groups of atoms and signals the chemist that they are present in the molecule.

**Describe the basic ideas of quantum mechanics**

a. Recognize the significance of quantum mechanics in describing atomic structure (Section 6.5).

b. Understand that an orbital for an electron in an atom corresponds to the allowed energy of that electron.

c. Understand that the position of the electron is not known with certainty; only the probability of the electron being at a given point of space can be calculated. This is a consequence of the Heisenberg uncertainty principle.

**Define the four quantum numbers ($n$, $\ell$, $m_\ell$, and $m_s$), and recognize their relationship to electronic structure**

a. Describe the allowed energy states of the orbitals in an atom using three quantum numbers $n$, $\ell$, and $m_\ell$ (Section 6.5). **Study Questions: 27–34, 36, 37, 38–41, 43, 44, 80, 83.**

b. Describe shapes of the orbitals (Section 6.6). **Study Questions: 46, 53, 67f, 68e.**

c. Recognize the spin quantum number, $m_s$, which has values of $\pm\frac{1}{2}$. Classify substances as paramagnetic (attracted to a magnetic field; characterized by unpaired electron spins) or diamagnetic (repelled by a magnetic field, all electrons paired) (Section 6.7). **Study Questions: 68j, 69.**

# Key Equations

**Equation 6.1 (page 267)** The product of the wavelength ($\lambda$) and frequency ($\nu$) of electromagnetic radiation is equal to the speed of light ($c$).

$$c = \lambda \times \nu$$

**Equation 6.2 (page 270)** Planck's equation: The energy of a photon, a massless particle of radiation, is proportional to its frequency ($\nu$). The proportionality constant, $h$, is called Planck's constant ($6.626 \times 10^{-34}$ J $\cdot$ s).

$$E = h\nu$$

**Equation 6.3 (page 273)** The Rydberg equation can be used to calculate the wavelengths of the lines in the Balmer series of the hydrogen spectrum. The Rydberg constant, $R$, is $1.0974 \times 10^7$ m$^{-1}$, and $n$ is 3 or larger.

$$\frac{1}{\lambda} = R\left(\frac{1}{2^2} - \frac{1}{n^2}\right) \text{ when } n > 2$$

**Equation 6.4 (page 274)** In Bohr's theory, the energy of the electron, $E_n$, in the $n$th quantum level of the H atom is proportional to $1/n^2$, where $n$ is a positive integer (the principal quantum number) and $Rhc = 2.179 = 10^{-18}$ J/atom or $NRhc = 1312$ kJ/mol.

$$E_n = -\frac{Rhc}{n^2}$$

**Equation 6.5 (page 276)** The energy change for an electron moving between two quantum levels ($n_{final}$ and $n_{initial}$) in the H atom.

$$\Delta E = E_{final} - E_{initial} = -Rhc\left(\frac{1}{n_{final}^2} - \frac{1}{n_{initial}^2}\right)$$

**Equation 6.6 (page 278)** De Broglie's equation: The wavelength of a particle ($\lambda$) is related to its mass ($m$) and speed ($v$) and to Planck's constant ($h$).

$$\lambda = \frac{h}{mv}$$

# Study Questions

**OWL** Interactive versions of these questions are assignable in OWL.

▲ denotes challenging questions.

Blue-numbered questions have answers in Appendix R and fully worked solutions in the *Student Solutions Manual*.

## Practicing Skills

### Electromagnetic Radiation
*(See Example 6.1 and Figure 6.2.)*

1. Answer the following questions based on Figure 6.2:
   (a) Which type of radiation involves less energy, x-rays or microwaves?
   (b) Which radiation has the higher frequency, radar or red light?
   (c) Which radiation has the longer wavelength, ultraviolet or infrared light?

2. Consider the colors of the visible spectrum.
   (a) Which colors of light involve less energy than green light?
   (b) Which color of light has photons of greater energy, yellow or blue?
   (c) Which color of light has the greater frequency, blue or green?

3. Traffic signals are often now made of LEDs (light-emitting diodes). Amber and green ones are pictured here.
   (a) The light from an amber signal has a wavelength of 595 nm, and that from a green signal has a wavelength of 500 nm. Which has the higher frequency?
   (b) Calculate the frequency of amber light.

(a)                           (b)

*Mike Condren/UW/MRSEC*

4. Suppose you are standing 225 m from a radio transmitter. What is your distance from the transmitter in terms of the number of wavelengths if
   (a) the station is broadcasting at 1150 kHz (on the AM radio band)? ($1$ kHz $= 1 \times 10^3$ Hz)
   (b) the station is broadcasting at 98.1 MHz (on the FM radio band)? ($1$ MHz $\times 10^6$ Hz)

### Electromagnetic Radiation and Planck's Equation
*(See Section 6.2.)*

5. Green light has a wavelength of $5.0 \times 10^2$ nm. What is the energy, in joules, of one photon of green light? What is the energy, in joules, of 1.0 mol of photons of green light?

6. Violet light has a wavelength of about 410 nm. What is its frequency? Calculate the energy of one photon of violet light. What is the energy of 1.0 mol of violet photons? Compare the energy of photons of violet light with those of red light. Which is more energetic?

7. The most prominent line in the emission spectrum of aluminum is at 396.15 nm. What is the frequency of this line? What is the energy of one photon with this wavelength? Of 1.00 mol of these photons?

8. The most prominent line in the emission spectrum of magnesium is 285.2 nm. Other lines are found at 383.8 and 518.4 nm. In what region of the electromagnetic spectrum are these lines found? Which is the most energetic line? What is the energy of 1.00 mol of photons with the wavelength of the most energetic line?

9. Place the following types of radiation in order of increasing energy per photon:
   (a) yellow light from a sodium lamp
   (b) x-rays from an instrument in a dentist's office
   (c) microwaves in a microwave oven
   (d) your favorite FM music station at 91.7 MHz

10. Place the following types of radiation in order of increasing energy per photon:
    (a) radiation within a microwave oven
    (b) your favorite radio station
    (c) gamma rays from a nuclear reaction
    (d) red light from a neon sign
    (e) ultraviolet radiation from a sun lamp

### Photoelectric Effect
*(See page 271 and Figure 6.4.)*

11. An energy of $3.3 \times 10^{-19}$ J/atom is required to cause a cesium atom on a metal surface to lose an electron. Calculate the longest possible wavelength of light that can ionize a cesium atom. In what region of the electromagnetic spectrum is this radiation found?

12. You are an engineer designing a switch that works by the photoelectric effect. The metal you wish to use in your device requires $6.7 \times 10^{-19}$ J/atom to remove an electron. Will the switch work if the light falling on the metal has a wavelength of 540 nm or greater? Why or why not?

### Atomic Spectra and the Bohr Atom
*(See Examples 6.2 and 6.3 and Figures 6.5–6.10.)*

13. The most prominent line in the spectrum of mercury is at 253.652 nm. Other lines are located at 365.015 nm, 404.656 nm, 435.833 nm, and 1013.975 nm.
    (a) Which of these lines represents the most energetic light?
    (b) What is the frequency of the most prominent line? What is the energy of one photon with this wavelength?
    (c) Are any of these lines found in the spectrum of mercury shown in Figure 6.6? What color or colors are these lines?

14. The most prominent line in the spectrum of neon is found at 865.438 nm. Other lines are located at 837.761 nm, 878.062 nm, 878.375 nm, and 885.387 nm.
    (a) In what region of the electromagnetic spectrum are these lines found?
    (b) Are any of these lines found in the spectrum of neon shown in Figure 6.6?
    (c) Which of these lines represents the most energetic radiation?
    (d) What is the frequency of the most prominent line? What is the energy of one photon with this wavelength?

15. A line in the Balmer series of emission lines of excited H atoms has a wavelength of 410.2 nm (Figure 6.10). What color is the light emitted in this transition? What quantum levels are involved in this emission line? That is, what are the values of $n_{initial}$ and $n_{final}$?

16. What are the wavelength and frequency of the radiation involved in the least energetic emission line in the Lyman series? What are the values of $n_{initial}$ and $n_{final}$?

17. Consider only transitions involving the $n = 1$ through $n = 5$ energy levels for the H atom (see Figures 6.7 and 6.10).
    (a) How many emission lines are possible, considering only the five quantum levels?
    (b) Photons of the highest frequency are emitted in a transition from the level with $n = $ ____ to a level with $n = $ ____.
    (c) The emission line having the longest wavelength corresponds to a transition from the level with $n = $ ____ to the level with $n = $ ____.

18. Consider only transitions involving the $n = 1$ through $n = 4$ energy levels for the hydrogen atom (see Figures 6.7 and 6.10).
    (a) How many emission lines are possible, considering only the four quantum levels?
    (b) Photons of the lowest energy are emitted in a transition from the level with $n = $ ____ to a level with $n = $ ____.
    (c) The emission line having the shortest wavelength corresponds to a transition from the level with $n = $ ____ to the level with $n = $ ____.

19. The energy emitted when an electron moves from a higher energy state to a lower energy state in any atom can be observed as electromagnetic radiation.
    (a) Which involves the emission of less energy in the H atom, an electron moving from $n = 4$ to $n = 2$ or an electron moving from $n = 3$ to $n = 2$?
    (b) Which involves the emission of more energy in the H atom, an electron moving from $n = 4$ to $n = 1$ or an electron moving from $n = 5$ to $n = 2$? Explain fully.

20. If energy is absorbed by a hydrogen atom in its ground state, the atom is excited to a higher energy state. For example, the excitation of an electron from $n = 1$ to $n = 3$ requires radiation with a wavelength of 102.6 nm. Which of the following transitions would require radiation of *longer wavelength* than this?
    (a) $n = 2$ to $n = 4$     (c) $n = 1$ to $n = 5$
    (b) $n = 1$ to $n = 4$     (d) $n = 3$ to $n = 5$

21. Calculate the wavelength and frequency of light emitted when an electron changes from $n = 3$ to $n = 1$ in the H atom. In what region of the spectrum is this radiation found?

22. Calculate the wavelength and frequency of light emitted when an electron changes from $n = 4$ to $n = 3$ in the H atom. In what region of the spectrum is this radiation found?

**De Broglie and Matter Waves**
*(See Example 6.4.)*

23. An electron moves with a velocity of $2.5 \times 10^8$ cm/s. What is its wavelength?

24. A beam of electrons ($m = 9.11 \times 10^{-31}$ kg/electron) has an average speed of $1.3 \times 10^8$ m/s. What is the wavelength of electrons having this average speed?

25. Calculate the wavelength, in nanometers, associated with a $1.0 \times 10^2$-g golf ball moving at 30. m/s (about 67 mph). At what speed must the ball travel to have a wavelength of $5.6 \times 10^{-3}$ nm?

26. A rifle bullet (mass = 1.50 g) has a velocity of $7.00 \times 10^2$ mph (miles per hour). What is the wavelength associated with this bullet?

**Quantum Mechanics**
*(See Sections 6.5–6.7.)*

27. (a) When $n = 4$, what are the possible values of $\ell$?
    (b) When $\ell$ is 2, what are the possible values of $m_\ell$?
    (c) For a 4s orbital, what are the possible values of $n$, $\ell$, and $m_\ell$?
    (d) For a 4f orbital, what are the possible values of $n$, $\ell$, and $m_\ell$?

28. (a) When $n = 4$, $\ell = 2$, and $m_\ell = -1$, to what orbital type does this refer? (Give the orbital label, such as 1s.)
    (b) How many orbitals occur in the $n = 5$ electron shell? How many subshells? What are the letter labels of the subshells?
    (c) How many orbitals occur in an $f$ subshell? What are the values of $m_\ell$?

29. A possible excited state of the H atom has the electron in a 4p orbital. List all possible sets of quantum numbers $n$, $\ell$, and $m_\ell$ for this electron.

30. A possible excited state for the H atom has an electron in a 5d orbital. List all possible sets of quantum numbers $n$, $\ell$, and $m_\ell$ for this electron.

31. How many subshells occur in the electron shell with the principal quantum number $n = 4$?

32. How many subshells occur in the electron shell with the principal quantum number $n = 5$?

33. Explain briefly why each of the following is *not* a possible set of quantum numbers for an electron in an atom.
    (a) $n = 2$, $\ell = 2$, $m_\ell = 0$
    (b) $n = 3$, $\ell = 0$, $m_\ell = -2$
    (c) $n = 6$, $\ell = 0$, $m_\ell = 1$

34. Which of the following represent valid sets of quantum numbers? For a set that is invalid, explain briefly why it is not correct.
    (a) $n = 3$, $\ell = 3$, $m_\ell = 0$   (c) $n = 6$, $\ell = 5$, $m_\ell = -1$
    (b) $n = 2$, $\ell = 1$, $m_\ell = 0$   (d) $n = 4$, $\ell = 3$, $m_\ell = -4$

35. What is the maximum number of orbitals that can be identified by each of the following sets of quantum numbers? When "none" is the correct answer, explain your reasoning.
    (a) $n = 3$, $\ell = 0$, $m_\ell = +1$   (c) $n = 7$, $\ell = 5$
    (b) $n = 5$, $\ell = 1$   (d) $n = 4$, $\ell = 2$, $m_\ell = -2$

36. What is the maximum number of orbitals that can be identified by each of the following sets of quantum numbers? When "none" is the correct answer, explain your reasoning.
    (a) $n = 4$, $\ell = 3$   (c) $n = 2$, $\ell = 2$
    (b) $n = 5$   (d) $n = 3$, $\ell = 1$, $m_\ell = -1$

37. Explain briefly why each of the following is not a possible set of quantum numbers for an electron in an atom. In each case, change the incorrect value (or values) to make the set valid.
    (a) $n = 4$, $\ell = 2$, $m_\ell = 0$, $m_s = 0$
    (b) $n = 3$, $\ell = 1$, $m_\ell = -3$, $m_s = -\frac{1}{2}$
    (c) $n = 3$, $\ell = 3$, $m_\ell = -1$, $m_s = +\frac{1}{2}$

38. Explain briefly why each of the following is not a possible set of quantum numbers for an electron in an atom. In each case, change the incorrect value (or values) to make the set valid.
    (a) $n = 2$, $\ell = 2$, $m_\ell = 0$, $m_s = +\frac{1}{2}$
    (b) $n = 2$, $\ell = 1$, $m_\ell = -1$, $m_s = 0$
    (c) $n = 3$, $\ell = 1$, $m_\ell = -2$, $m_s = +\frac{1}{2}$

39. State which of the following orbitals cannot exist according to the quantum theory: $2s$, $2d$, $3p$, $3f$, $4f$, and $5s$. Briefly explain your answers.

40. State which of the following are incorrect designations for orbitals according to the quantum theory: $3p$, $4s$, $2f$, and $1p$. Briefly explain your answers.

41. Write a complete set of quantum numbers ($n$, $\ell$, and $m_\ell$) that quantum theory allows for each of the following orbitals: (a) $2p$, (b) $3d$, and (c) $4f$.

42. Write a complete set of quantum numbers ($n$, $\ell$, and $m_\ell$) for each of the following orbitals: (a) $5f$, (b) $4d$, and (c) $2s$.

43. A particular orbital has $n = 4$ and $\ell = 2$. What must this orbital be: (a) $3p$, (b) $4p$, (c) $5d$, or (d) $4d$?

44. A given orbital has a magnetic quantum number of $m_\ell = -1$. This could *not* be a(n)
    (a) $f$ orbital   (c) $p$ orbital
    (b) $d$ orbital   (d) $s$ orbital

45. How many planar nodes are associated with each of the following orbitals?
    (a) $2s$   (b) $5d$   (c) $5f$

46. How many planar nodes are associated with each of the following atomic orbitals?
    (a) $4f$   (b) $2p$   (c) $6s$

## General Questions on Atomic Structure

*These questions are not designated as to type or location in the chapter. They may combine several concepts.*

47. Which of the following are applicable when explaining the photoelectric effect? Correct any statements that are wrong.
    (a) Light is electromagnetic radiation.
    (b) The intensity of a light beam is related to its frequency.
    (c) Light can be thought of as consisting of massless particles whose energy is given by Planck's equation, $E = h\nu$.

48. In what region of the electromagnetic spectrum for hydrogen is the Lyman series of lines found? The Balmer series?

49. Give the number of nodal surfaces through the nucleus (planar nodes) for each orbital type: $s$, $p$, $d$, and $f$.

50. What is the maximum number of $s$ orbitals found in a given electron shell? The maximum number of $p$ orbitals? Of $d$ orbitals? Of $f$ orbitals?

51. Match the values of $\ell$ shown in the table with orbital type ($s$, $p$, $d$, or $f$).

| $\ell$ Value | Orbital Type |
| --- | --- |
| 3 | _____ |
| 0 | _____ |
| 1 | _____ |
| 2 | _____ |

52. Sketch a picture of the 90% boundary surface of an $s$ orbital and the $p_x$ orbital. Be sure the latter drawing shows why the $p$ orbital is labeled $p_x$ and not $p_y$, for example.

53. Complete the following table.

| Orbital Type | Number of Orbitals in a Given Subshell | Number of Nodal Surfaces through the Nucleus |
| --- | --- | --- |
| s | _____ | _____ |
| p | _____ | _____ |
| d | _____ | _____ |
| f | _____ | _____ |

54. Excited H atoms have many emission lines. One series of lines, called the *Pfund series*, occurs in the infrared region. It results when an electron changes from higher energy levels to a level with $n = 5$. Calculate the wavelength and frequency of the lowest energy line of this series.

55. An advertising sign gives off red light and green light.
    (a) Which light has higher-energy photons?
    (b) One of the colors has a wavelength of 680 nm, and the other has a wavelength of 500 nm. Which color has which wavelength?
    (c) Which light has the higher frequency?

**56.** Radiation in the ultraviolet region of the electromagnetic spectrum is quite energetic. It is this radiation that causes dyes to fade and your skin to develop a sunburn. If you are bombarded with 1.00 mol of photons with a wavelength of 375 nm, what amount of energy, in kilojoules per mole of photons, are you being subjected to?

**57.** A cell phone sends signals at about 850 MHz (where 1 MHz = $1 \times 10^6$ Hz or cycles per second).
(a) What is the wavelength of this radiation?
(b) What is the energy of 1.0 mol of photons with a frequency of 850 MHz?
(c) Compare the energy in part (b) with the energy of a mole of photons of violet light (420 nm).
(d) Comment on the difference in energy between 850 MHz radiation and violet light.

**58.** Assume your eyes receive a signal consisting of blue light, $\lambda = 470$ nm. The energy of the signal is $2.50 \times 10^{-14}$ J. How many photons reach your eyes?

**59.** If sufficient energy is absorbed by an atom, an electron can be lost by the atom and a positive ion formed. The amount of energy required is called the ionization energy. In the H atom, the ionization energy is that required to change the electron from $n = 1$ to $n =$ infinity. Calculate the ionization energy for the $He^+$ ion. Is the ionization energy of the $He^+$ more or less than that of H? (Bohr's theory applies to $He^+$ because it, like the H atom, has a single electron. The electron energy, however, is now given by $E = -Z^2 Rhc/n^2$, where $Z$ is the atomic number of helium.)

**60.** Suppose hydrogen atoms absorb energy so that electrons are excited to the $n = 7$ energy level. Electrons then undergo these transitions, among others: (a) $n = 7 \rightarrow n = 1$; (b) $n = 7 \rightarrow n = 6$; and (c) $n = 2 \rightarrow n = 1$. Which of these transitions produces a photon with (i) the smallest energy, (ii) the highest frequency, and (iii) the shortest wavelength?

**61.** Rank the following orbitals in the H atom in order of increasing energy: $3s$, $2s$, $2p$, $4s$, $3p$, $1s$, and $3d$.

**62.** How many orbitals correspond to each of the following designations?
(a) $3p$      (d) $6d$      (g) $n = 5$
(b) $4p$      (e) $5d$      (h) $7s$
(c) $4p_x$      (f) $5f$

**63.** Cobalt-60 is a radioactive isotope used in medicine for the treatment of certain cancers. It produces $\beta$ particles and $\gamma$ rays, the latter having energies of 1.173 and 1.332 MeV. (1 MeV = $10^6$ electron-volts and 1 eV = $1.6022 \times 10^{-19}$ J.) What are the wavelength and frequency of a $\gamma$-ray photon with an energy of 1.173 MeV?

**64.** ▲ Exposure to high doses of microwaves can cause tissue damage. Estimate how many photons, with $\lambda = 12$ cm, must be absorbed to raise the temperature of your eye by 3.0 °C. Assume the mass of an eye is 11 g and its specific heat capacity is 4.0 J/g · K.

**65.** When the Sojourner spacecraft landed on Mars in 1997, the planet was approximately $7.8 \times 10^7$ km from Earth. How long did it take for the television picture signal to reach Earth from Mars?

**66.** The most prominent line in the emission spectrum of chromium is found at 425.4 nm. Other lines in the chromium spectrum are found at 357.9 nm, 359.3 nm, 360.5 nm, 427.5 nm, 429.0 nm, and 520.8 nm.
(a) Which of these lines represents the most energetic light?
(b) What color is light of wavelength 425.4 nm?

**67.** Answer the following questions as a summary quiz on the chapter.
(a) The quantum number $n$ describes the _____ of an atomic orbital.
(b) The shape of an atomic orbital is given by the quantum number _____.
(c) A photon of green light has _____ (less or more) energy than a photon of orange light.
(d) The maximum number of orbitals that may be associated with the set of quantum numbers $n = 4$ and $\ell = 3$ is _____.
(e) The maximum number of orbitals that may be associated with the quantum number set $n = 3$, $\ell = 2$, and $m_\ell = -2$ is _____.
(f) Label each of the following orbital pictures with the appropriate letter:

(g) When $n = 5$, the possible values of $\ell$ are _____.
(h) The number of orbitals in the $n = 4$ shell is _____.
(i) A $Co^{2+}$ ion has three unpaired electrons. Is a sample of $CoCl_2$ paramagnetic or diamagnetic?

**68.** Answer the following questions as a summary quiz on this chapter.
(a) The quantum number $n$ describes the _____ of an atomic orbital, and the quantum number $\ell$ describes its _____.
(b) When $n = 3$, the possible values of $\ell$ are _____.
(c) What type of orbital corresponds to $\ell = 3$? _____
(d) For a $4d$ orbital, the value of $n$ is _____, the value of $\ell$ is _____, and a possible value of $m_\ell$ is _____.
(e) Each of the following drawings represents a type of atomic orbital. Give the letter designation for the orbital, give its value of $\ell$, and specify the number of planar nodes.

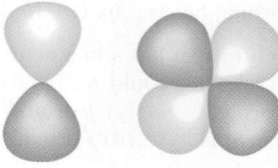

Letter =    _____      _____
$\ell$ value =    _____      _____
Planar nodes =    _____      _____

(f) An atomic orbital with three planar nodes through the nucleus is _____.
(g) Which of the following orbitals cannot exist according to modern quantum theory: $2s$, $3p$, $2d$, $3f$, $5p$, $6p$?

(h) Which of the following is not a valid set of quantum numbers?

| $n$ | $\ell$ | $m_\ell$ | $m_s$ |
|---|---|---|---|
| 3 | 2 | 1 | $-\frac{1}{2}$ |
| 2 | 1 | 2 | $+\frac{1}{2}$ |
| 4 | 3 | 0 | 0 |

(i) What is the maximum number of orbitals that can be associated with each of the following sets of quantum numbers? (One possible answer is "none.")
   (i)   $n = 2$ and $\ell = 1$
   (ii)  $n = 3$
   (iii) $n = 3$ and $\ell = 3$
   (iv)  $n = 2$, $\ell = 1$, and $m_\ell = 0$
(j) A $Cu^{2+}$ ion has one unpaired electron. Is a sample of $CuBr_2$ paramagnetic or diamagnetic?

**69.** The diagrams below represent a small section of a solid. Each circle represents an atom, and an arrow represents an electron.

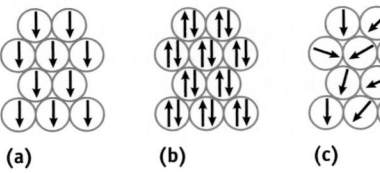

(a)            (b)            (c)

(a) Which represents a diamagnetic solid, which a paramagnetic solid, and which a ferromagnetic solid?
(b) Which is most strongly attracted to a magnetic field? Which is least strongly attracted?

## In the Laboratory

**70.** A solution of $KMnO_4$ absorbs light at 540 nm (page 192). What is the frequency of the light absorbed? What is the energy of one mole of photons with $\lambda = 540$ nm?

**71.** A large pickle is attached to two electrodes, which are then attached to a 110-V power supply. As the voltage is increased across the pickle, it begins to glow with a yellow color. Knowing that pickles are made by soaking the vegetable in a concentrated salt solution, describe why the pickle might emit light when electrical energy is added.

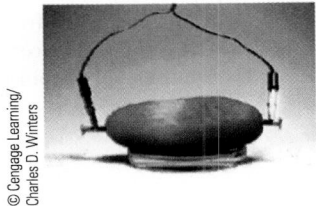

© Cengage Learning/ Charles D. Winters

**The "electric pickle."**

**72.** The spectrum shown here is for aspirin. The vertical axis is the amount of light absorbed, and the horizontal axis is the wavelength of incident light (in nm). (For more on spectroscopy, see pages 183–199.)

What is the frequency of light with a wavelength of 278 nm? What is the energy of one mole of photons with $\lambda = 278$ nm? What region of the electromagnetic spectrum is covered by the spectrum above? Knowing that aspirin only absorbs light in the region depicted by this spectrum, what is the color of aspirin?

**73.** The infrared spectrum for methanol, $CH_3OH$, is illustrated below. It shows the amount of light in the infrared region that methanol transmits as a function of wavelength. The vertical axis is the amount of light transmitted. At points near the top of the graph, most of the incident light is being transmitted by the sample (or, conversely, little light is absorbed.) Therefore, the "peaks" or "bands" that descend from the top indicate light absorbed; the longer the band, the more light is being absorbed. The horizontal scale is in units of "wavenumbers," abbreviated $cm^{-1}$. The energy of light is given by Planck's law as $E = hc/\lambda$; that is, $E$ is proportional to $1/\lambda$. Therefore, the horizontal scale is in units of $1/\lambda$ and reflects the energy of the light incident on the sample.

(a) One point on the horizontal axis is marked as 2000 $cm^{-1}$. What is the wavelength of light at this point?
(b) Which is the low energy end of this spectrum (left or right), and which is the high energy end?
(c) The broad absorption at about 3300–3400 $cm^{-1}$ indicates that infrared radiation is interacting with the OH group of the methanol molecule. The narrower absorptions around 2800–3000 $cm^{-1}$ are for interactions with C—H bonds. Which interaction requires more energy, with O—H or with C—H?

## Summary and Conceptual Questions

*The following questions may use concepts from this and previous chapters.*

**74.** Bohr pictured the electrons of the atom as being located in definite orbits about the nucleus, just as the planets orbit the sun. Criticize this model.

75. Light is given off by a sodium- or mercury-containing streetlight when the atoms are excited. The light you see arises for which of the following reasons?
    (a) Electrons are moving from a given energy level to one of higher energy.
    (b) Electrons are being removed from the atom, thereby creating a metal cation.
    (c) Electrons are moving from a given energy level to one of lower energy.

76. How do we interpret the physical meaning of the square of the wave function? What are the units of $4\pi r^2\psi^2$?

77. What does "wave–particle duality" mean? What are its implications in our modern view of atomic structure?

78. Which of these are observable?
    (a) position of an electron in an H atom
    (b) frequency of radiation emitted by H atoms
    (c) path of an electron in an H atom
    (d) wave motion of electrons
    (e) diffraction patterns produced by electrons
    (f) diffraction patterns produced by light
    (g) energy required to remove electrons from H atoms
    (h) an atom
    (i) a molecule
    (j) a water wave

79. In principle, which of the following can be determined?
    (a) the energy of an electron in the H atom with high precision and accuracy
    (b) the position of a high-speed electron with high precision and accuracy
    (c) at the same time, both the position and the energy of a high-speed electron with high precision and accuracy

80. ▲ Suppose you live in a different universe where a different set of quantum numbers is required to describe the atoms of that universe. These quantum numbers have the following rules:

    | | |
    |---|---|
    | $N$, principal | $1, 2, 3, \ldots, \infty$ |
    | $L$, orbital | $= N$ |
    | $M$, magnetic | $-1, 0, +1$ |

    How many orbitals are there altogether in the first three electron shells?

81. A photon with a wavelength of 93.8 nm strikes a hydrogen atom, and light is emitted by the atom. How many emission lines would be observed? At what wavelengths? Explain briefly (see Figure 6.10).

82. Explain why you could or could not measure the wavelength of a golf ball in flight.

83. The radioactive element technetium is not found naturally on earth; it must be synthesized in the laboratory. It is a valuable element, however, because it has medical uses. For example, the element in the form of sodium pertechnetate ($NaTcO_4$) is used in imaging studies of the brain, thyroid, and salivary glands and in renal blood flow studies, among other things.
    (a) In what group and period of the periodic table is the element found?

    (b) The valence electrons of technetium are found in the $5s$ and $4d$ subshells. What is a set of quantum numbers ($n$, $\ell$, and $m_\ell$) for one of the electrons of the $5s$ subshell?
    (c) Technetium emits a $\gamma$-ray with an energy of 0.141 MeV. (1 MeV = $10^6$ electron-volts, where 1 eV = $1.6022 \times 10^{-19}$ J.) What are the wavelength and frequency of a $\gamma$-ray photon with an energy of 0.141 MeV?
    (d) To make $NaTcO_4$, the metal is dissolved in nitric acid.

    $$7\ HNO_3(aq) + Tc(s) \rightarrow$$
    $$HTcO_4(aq) + 7\ NO_2(g) + 3\ H_2O(\ell)$$

    and the product, $HTcO_4$, is treated with NaOH to make $NaTcO_4$.
    (i) Write a balanced equation for the reaction of $HTcO_4$ with NaOH.
    (ii) If you begin with 4.5 mg of Tc metal, what mass of $NaTcO_4$ can be made? What mass of NaOH, in grams, is required to convert all of the $HTcO_4$ into $NaTcO_4$?
    (e) If you synthesize 1.5 micromoles of $NaTcO_4$, what mass of compound do you have? If the compound is dissolved in 10.0 mL of solution, what is the concentration?

84. ▲ Figure 6.12b shows the probability of finding a hydrogen 1$s$ electron at various distances from the nucleus. To create the graph in this figure, the electron cloud is first divided into a series of thin concentric shells about the nucleus and then the probability of finding the electron in each shell is evaluated. The volume of each shell is given by the equation $V = 4\pi r^2(d)$, where $d$ is the thickness of the shell and $r$ is the distance of the shell from the nucleus. The probability of finding the electron in each shell is

    $$\text{Probability} = 4\pi r^2\psi^2(d)$$

    where $\psi$ is the 1$s$ wave function for hydrogen ($a_o$ in this equation is 52.9 pm).

    $$\psi = \frac{1}{(\pi a_0^3)^{1/2}} e^{-r/a_0}$$

    (a) The most probable distance for a 1$s$ electron in the hydrogen atom is at 52.9 pm. Evaluate the probability of finding the electron in a concentric shell 1.0 pm thick at this distance from the nucleus.
    (b) Calculate the probability of finding the electron in a shell 1.0 pm thick at distances from the nucleus of 0.50 $a_o$ and 4 $a_o$. Compare the results with the probabilities at $a_o$. Are these probabilities in accord with the surface density plot shown in Figure 6.12b?

# Applying Chemical Principles

## Chemistry of the Sun

An optical spectrum of our sun reveals a continuous emission of radiation in the visible region with sharp, darkened lines at hundreds of different wavelengths. These lines are named Fraunhofer lines, after the German physicist Joseph von Fraunhofer who observed them in 1814. Fraunhofer was able to observe over 570 of these lines, but over one thousand dark lines may be observed with modern instrumentation. In 1859, Gustav Robert Kirchhoff and Robert Bunsen deduced that the dark lines are the result of absorption of sunlight by elements in the outer layers of the sun.

The fact that atoms of a particular element absorb or emit light of only a few wavelengths may be used to identify elements (page 272). Most stars are rich in hydrogen, so the Balmer series (page 273) is commonly observed in their spectra. The discovery and naming of helium is credited to Sir Joseph Norman Lockyer (1836–1920), who observed its yellow spectral line during a total solar eclipse in 1868. Helium is common in stars, but less common on Earth.

## Questions:

1. Helium absorbs light at 587.6 nm. What is the frequency of this light?
2. Iron atoms absorb light at a frequency of $5.688 \times 10^{14}\,s^{-1}$. What is the wavelength of this light (in nm)?
3. Sodium atoms are responsible for a closely spaced pair of lines in the yellow region of the Sun's visible spectrum at 589.00 nm and 589.59 nm. Determine the energy (in joules) of a photon at each of these wavelengths. Determine the difference in energy between the two photons.
4. Hydrogen has an absorption line at 434.1 nm. What is the energy (in kilojoules per mole) of photons with this wave length?
5. What are the final and initial electronic states ($n$) for the hydrogen line (in the Balmer series) labeled F in the figure?

**The spectrum of sunlight with Fraunhofer lines.** The German physicist Joseph von Fraunhofer (1787–1826) discovered the dark lines in the spectrum of sunlight and carefully mapped and measured them. He designated the principal lines with letters A through K and less prominent lines with lowercase letters. (He mapped over 570 lines (a few of which are shown here), but modern instruments can detect over one thousand such lines.) The phenomenon was later studied by Gustav Robert Kirchhoff (1824–1887) and Robert W. E. Bunsen (1811–1899), who deduced that the dark lines arise when elements in the outer layers of the sun absorb the light emitted by the Sun.

# 7 The Structure of Atoms and Periodic Trends

**Deep blue sapphire.** Deep blue sapphire is aluminum oxide with traces of iron(II) and titanium(IV) ions.

## Rubies and Sapphires—Pretty Stones

People have been fascinated by, and have coveted, precious stones such as sapphires and rubies for hundreds of years.

Sapphires and rubies are just aluminum oxide with traces of impurities. But it is the impurities that make simple aluminum oxide into a beautiful gemstone.

Rubies come in a variety of colors. Most are red, but they can have tints of brown, purple, and pink. The price of a ruby usually depends on its color, the most valuable being deep red, said to resemble "pigeon blood."

The most valuable rubies are clear, but others often have inclusions of tiny needles of titanium dioxide (rutile), which

**Synthetic rubies.** Rubies are aluminum oxide with a trace of chromium(III) in place of $Al^{3+}$ ions.

makes them a little cloudy. In fact, if a ruby is not slightly cloudy, it may be a synthetic stone with much less value.

Most rubies come from southeast and central Asia and east Africa, and there are a few deposits in the United States. Interestingly, as glaciers have receded in Greenland, large ruby deposits have been discovered.

Synthetic rubies were first made in the 19th century, the best known process being that developed by Auguste Verneuil in 1902. In this process, aluminum oxide and barium fluoride are fused with a chromium(III) compound. The synthetic materials produced in this way are now used in commercial lasers such as those in players of CDs and DVDs.

Sapphires are also based on aluminum oxide with other impurities that lead to their usual blue color. Like rubies, they can be synthesized, and synthetic sapphires are used in jewelry as well.

The red color of rubies comes from the substitution of a few of the $Al^{3+}$ ions in $Al_2O_3$ by $Cr^{3+}$ ions because their radii are similar. In contrast, the blue color of sapphires comes from a trace of elements such as iron and titanium. When iron and titanium are present as $Fe^{2+}$ and $Ti^{4+}$, the result is the deep blue color for which sapphires are famous.

### Questions:

1. What is the electron configuration for the Cr atom and for the $Cr^{3+}$ ion?
2. Is chromium in any of its ions ($Cr^{2+}$, $Cr^{3+}$, $CrO_4{}^{2-}$) paramagnetic?
3. The radius of the $Cr^{3+}$ ion is 64 pm. How does this compare with the radius of the $Al^{3+}$ ion?
4. What is the electron configuration for the $Fe^{2+}$ and $Ti^{4+}$ ions?

**Answers to these questions are available in Appendix N.**

## CHAPTER GOALS

*See Chapter Goals Revisited (page 326) for Study Questions keyed to these goals.*

- Recognize the relationship of the four quantum numbers ($n$, $\ell$, $m_\ell$, and $m_s$) to atomic structure.

- Write the electron configuration for atoms and monatomic ions.

- Rationalize trends in atom and ion sizes, ionization energy, and electron attachment enthalpy.

**OWL**

Sign in to OWL at **www.cengage.com/owl** to view tutorials and simulations, develop problem-solving skills, and complete online homework assigned by your professor.

The wave mechanical model of the atom developed in Chapter 6 describes electrons as matter waves. The electrons are assigned to orbitals, regions of space in which the probability of finding an electron is high. The orbitals are arranged in subshells that are in turn part of electron shells. One objective of this chapter is to apply this model to the electronic structure of all of the elements.

A second objective is to explore some of the properties of elements, among them the energy changes that occur when atoms lose or gain electrons to form ions and the sizes of atoms and ions. These properties are directly related to the arrangement of electrons in atoms and thus to the chemistry of the elements and their compounds.

## 7.1  The Pauli Exclusion Principle

To make the quantum theory consistent with experiment, the Austrian physicist Wolfgang Pauli (1900–1958) stated in 1925 his **exclusion principle**: *No more than two electrons can occupy the same orbital, and, if there are two electrons in the same orbital, they must have opposite spins.* This leads to the general statement that no two electrons in an atom can have the same set of four quantum numbers ($n$, $\ell$, $m_\ell$, and $m_s$).

An electron assigned to the $1s$ orbital of the H atom may have the set of quantum numbers $n = 1$, $\ell = 0$, $m_\ell = 0$, and $m_s = +\frac{1}{2}$. Let us represent an orbital by a box and the electron spin by an arrow ($\uparrow$ or $\downarrow$). A representation of the hydrogen atom is then:

Electrons in $1s$ orbital:  $\boxed{\uparrow}$  Quantum number set
$\qquad\qquad\qquad\qquad 1s \quad n = 1,\ \ell = 0,\ m_\ell = 0,\ m_s = +\frac{1}{2}$

The choice of $m_s$ (either $+\frac{1}{2}$ or $-\frac{1}{2}$) and the direction of the electron spin arrow are arbitrary; that is, we could choose either value, and the arrow may point in either direction. Diagrams such as these are called **orbital box diagrams**.

A helium atom has two electrons, both assigned to the $1s$ orbital. The Pauli exclusion principle requires that each electron must have a different set of quantum numbers, so the orbital box diagram now is:

$\qquad\qquad\qquad\qquad\qquad 1s$

Two electrons in $1s$ orbital:  $\boxed{\uparrow\downarrow}$ ◄——— This electron has $n = 1$, $\ell = 0$, $m_\ell = 0$, $m_s = -\frac{1}{2}$

$\qquad\qquad\qquad\qquad\qquad$ └——— This electron has $n = 1$, $\ell = 0$, $m_\ell = 0$, $m_s = +\frac{1}{2}$

**go Chemistry**

Download mini lecture videos for key concept review and exam prep from OWL or purchase them from **www.cengagebrain.com**

- **Orbitals Are Not Boxes** Orbitals are not boxes in which electrons are placed. Thus, it is not conceptually correct to talk about electrons being in orbitals or occupying orbitals, although this is commonly done for the sake of simplicity.

By having opposite or "paired" spins, the two electrons in the $1s$ orbital of a He atom have different sets of the four quantum numbers. Our understanding of orbitals and the knowledge that an orbital can accommodate no more than two electrons tell us the maximum number of electrons that can occupy each electron shell or subshell. For example, because two electrons can be assigned to each of the three orbitals in a $p$ subshell, $p$ subshells can hold a maximum of six electrons. By the same reasoning, the five orbitals of a $d$ subshell can accommodate a total of 10 electrons, and the seven $f$ orbitals can accommodate 14 electrons. Recall that there are $n$ subshells in the $n$th shell, and that there are $n^2$ orbitals in that shell (◄ Table 6.1, page 283). Thus, *the maximum number of electrons in any shell is* $2n^2$. The relationship among the quantum numbers and the numbers of electrons is shown in Table 7.1.

---

**REVIEW & CHECK FOR SECTION 7.1**

How many electrons can be accommodated in the $n = 7$ shell?

(a)  18          (b)  36          (c)  72          (d)  98

---

**Table 7.1 Number of Electrons Accommodated in Electron Shells and Subshells with $n = 1$ to 6**

| Electron Shell ($n$) | Subshells Available | Orbitals Available ($2\ell + 1$) | Number of Electrons Possible in Subshell $[2(2\ell + 1)]$ | Maximum Electrons Possible for $n$th Shell ($2n^2$) |
|---|---|---|---|---|
| 1 | $s$ | 1 | 2 | 2 |
| 2 | $s$ | 1 | 2 | 8 |
|   | $p$ | 3 | 6 |   |
| 3 | $s$ | 1 | 2 | 18 |
|   | $p$ | 3 | 6 |   |
|   | $d$ | 5 | 10 |   |
| 4 | $s$ | 1 | 2 | 32 |
|   | $p$ | 3 | 6 |   |
|   | $d$ | 5 | 10 |   |
|   | $f$ | 7 | 14 |   |
| 5 | $s$ | 1 | 2 | 50 |
|   | $p$ | 3 | 6 |   |
|   | $d$ | 5 | 10 |   |
|   | $f$ | 7 | 14 |   |
|   | $g^*$ | 9 | 18 |   |
| 6 | $s$ | 1 | 2 | 72 |
|   | $p$ | 3 | 6 |   |
|   | $d$ | 5 | 10 |   |
|   | $f^*$ | 7 | 14 |   |
|   | $g^*$ | 9 | 18 |   |
|   | $h^*$ | 11 | 22 |   |

*These orbitals are not occupied in the ground state of any known element.

## 7.2 Atomic Subshell Energies and Electron Assignments

Our goal in this section is to understand and predict the distribution of electrons in atoms with many electrons. The procedure by which electrons are assigned to orbitals is known as the *Aufbau principle* (the German word *Aufbau* means "building up"). Electrons in an atom are assigned to shells (defined by the quantum number $n$) and subshells (defined by the quantum numbers $n$ and $\ell$) in order of increasingly higher energy. In this way, the total energy of the atom is as low as possible.

### Order of Subshell Energies and Assignments

Quantum theory and the Bohr model state that the energy of the H atom, with a single electron, depends only on the value of $n$ (Equation 6.4, $E_n = -Rhc/n^2$). For atoms with more than one electron, however, the situation is more complex. The order of subshell energies for $n = 1, 2,$ and $3$ in Figure 7.1a shows that subshell energies in multielectron atoms depend on *both n and $\ell$*.

Based on theoretical and experimental studies of electron distributions in atoms, chemists have found there are two general rules that help predict these arrangements:

1. Electrons are assigned to subshells in order of increasing "$n + \ell$" value.
2. For two subshells with the same value of "$n + \ell$," electrons are assigned first to the subshell of lower $n$.

The following are examples of these rules:

- Electrons are assigned to the $2s$ subshell ($n + \ell = 2 + 0 = 2$) before the $2p$ subshell ($n + \ell = 2 + 1 = 3$).

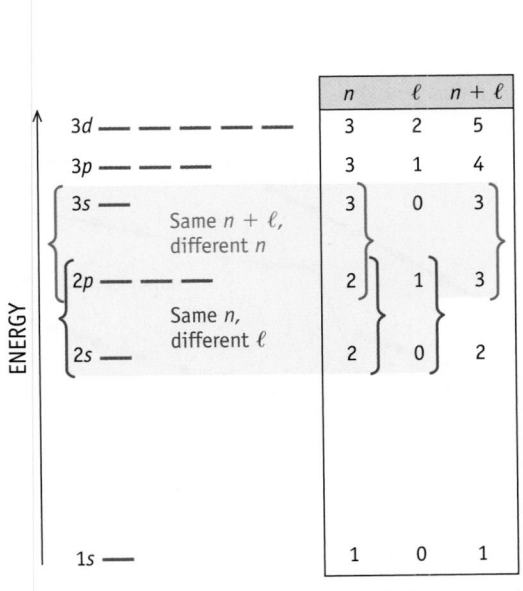

**(a) Order of subshell energies in a multielectron atom.** Energies of electron shells increase with increasing $n$, and, within a shell, subshell energies increase with increasing $\ell$. (The energy axis is not to scale.) The energy gaps between subshells of a given shell become smaller as $n$ increases.

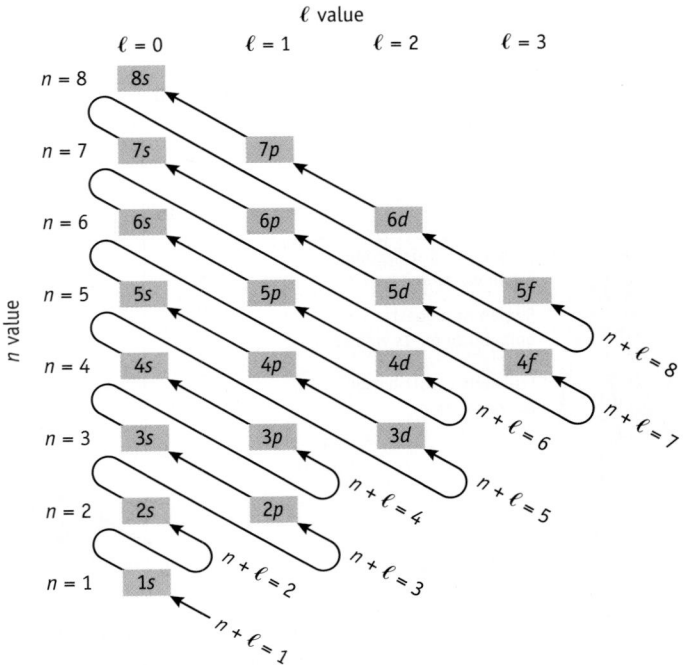

**(b) Subshell filling order.** Subshells in atoms are filled in order of increasing $n + \ell$. When two subshells have the same $n + \ell$ value, the subshell of lower $n$ is filled first. To use the diagram, begin at 1s and follow the arrows of increasing $n + \ell$. (Thus, the order of filling is $1s \Rightarrow 2s \Rightarrow 2p \Rightarrow 3s \Rightarrow 3p \Rightarrow 4s \Rightarrow 3d$ and so on.)

**FIGURE 7.1 Subshell energies and filling order in a multielectron atom.**

- Electrons are assigned to $2p$ orbitals ($n + \ell = 2 + 1 = 3$) before the $3s$ subshell ($n + \ell = 3 + 0 = 3$). ($n$ for the $2p$ electrons is less than $n$ for the $3s$ electrons.)
- Electrons are assigned to $4s$ orbitals ($n + \ell = 4 + 0 = 4$) before the $3d$ subshell ($n + \ell = 3 + 2 = 5$). ($n + \ell$ is less for $4s$ than for $3d$.)

Figure 7.1b summarizes the assignment of electrons according to increasing $n + \ell$ values. The discussion that follows explores the underlying causes and their consequences and connects atomic electron configurations to the periodic table.

### Effective Nuclear Charge, Z*

The order in which electrons are assigned to subshells in an atom, and many atomic properties, can be rationalized by introducing the concept of **effective nuclear charge (Z\*)**. This is the *net charge experienced by a particular electron in a multielectron atom resulting from a balance of the attractive force of the nucleus and the repulsive forces of other electrons.*

The surface density plot ($4\pi r^2 \psi^2$) for a $2s$ electron for lithium is plotted in Figure 7.2. (Lithium has three protons in the nucleus, two $1s$ electrons in the first shell, and a $2s$ electron in the second shell.) The probability of finding the $2s$ electron (recorded on the vertical axis) changes as one moves away from the nucleus (horizontal axis). The region in which the two $1s$ electrons have their highest probability is shaded in this figure. Observe that the $2s$ electron wave occurs partly within the region of space occupied by $1s$ electrons. Chemists say that the $2s$ orbital *penetrates* the region defining the $1s$ orbital.

At a large distance from the nucleus, the lithium $2s$ electron will experience a $+1$ charge, the net effect of the two $1s$ electrons (total charge $= -2$) and the nucleus ($+3$ charge.) The $1s$ electrons are said to *screen* the $2s$ electron from experiencing the full nuclear charge. However, this screening of the nuclear charge varies with the distance of the $2s$ electron from the nucleus. As the $2s$ electron wave penetrates the $1s$ electron region, it experiences an increasingly higher net positive

**FIGURE 7.2 Effective nuclear charge, Z\*.** *(left)* The two $1s$ electrons of lithium have their highest probability in the shaded region, but this region is penetrated by the $2s$ electron (whose approximate surface density plot is shown here). As the $2s$ electron penetrates the $1s$ region, however, the $2s$ electron experiences a larger and larger positive charge, to a maximum of $+3$. On average, the $2s$ electron experiences a charge, called the *effective nuclear charge (Z\*)*, which is smaller than $+3$ but greater than $+1$. *(above)* The value of Z\* *for the highest occupied orbital* is given by $(Z - S)$, where $Z$ is the atomic number and $S$ is the screening constant. ($S$ reflects how much the inner electrons shield or screen the outermost electron from the nucleus.) Notice that $S$ increases greatly on going from Ne in the second period to Na in the third period.

charge. Very near the nucleus, the $1s$ electrons do not effectively screen the electron from the nucleus, and the $2s$ electron experiences a charge close to $+3$. Figure 7.2 shows that a $2s$ electron has some probability of being inside and outside the region occupied by the $1s$ electrons. Thus, on average, a $2s$ electron experiences a positive charge greater than $+1$ but much smaller than $+3$. The *average* charge experienced by the electron is called the *effective nuclear charge* ($Z^*$). In the case of the $2s$ electron in Li, the value of $Z^*$ is 1.28 (Table 7.2).

In the hydrogen atom, with only one electron, the $2s$ and $2p$ subshells have the same energy. However, in atoms with two or more electrons, the energies of the $2s$ and $2p$ subshells are different. Why should this be true? It is observed that the relative extent to which an outer electron penetrates inner orbitals occurs in the order $s > p > d > f$. Thus, the effective nuclear charge experienced by electrons in a multielectron atom is in the order $ns > np > nd > nf$. The values of $Z^*$ for $s$ and $p$ electrons for the second- and third-period elements (Table 7.2) illustrate this. In each case, $Z^*$ is greater for $s$ electrons than for $p$ electrons. In a given shell, $s$ electrons always have a lower energy than $p$ electrons; $p$ electrons have a lower energy than $d$ electrons, and $d$ electrons have a lower energy than $f$ electrons. A consequence of this is that subshells within an electron shell are filled in the order $ns$ before $np$ before $nd$ before $nf$. (See *A Closer Look: Orbital Energies, Z\*, and Electron Configurations,* page 312.)

With this background on the order of shell and subshell energies and filling order, we turn to the periodic table as a guide to electron arrangements in atoms.

**Table 7.2 Effective Nuclear Charges, Z\*, for $n = 2$ Elements**

| Atom | Z*(2s) | Z*(2p) |
|------|--------|--------|
| Li | 1.28 | |
| B | 2.58 | 2.42 |
| C | 3.22 | 3.14 |
| N | 3.85 | 3.83 |
| O | 4.49 | 4.45 |
| F | 5.13 | 5.10 |

---

**REVIEW & CHECK FOR SECTION 7.2**

To which of the subshells should an electron be assigned first in each of the following pairs?

(a)  $4s$ or $4p$       (b)  $5d$ or $6s$       (c)  $4f$ or $5s$

---

## 7.3 Electron Configurations of Atoms

Arrangements of electrons in the elements up to 109—their **electron configurations**—are given in Table 7.3. Specifically, these are the ground state electron configurations, where electrons are found in the shells, subshells, and orbitals that result in the lowest energy for the atom. In general, electrons are assigned to orbitals in order of increasing $n + \ell$. The emphasis here, however, will be to connect the configurations of the elements with their positions in the periodic table (Figure 7.3).

**FIGURE 7.3 Electron configurations and the periodic table.** The periodic table can serve as a guide in determining the order of filling of atomic orbitals. As one moves from left to right in a period, electrons are assigned to the indicated orbitals. (See Table 7.3.)

## Table 7.3 Ground State Electron Configurations

| Z | Element | Configuration | Z | Element | Configuration | Z | Element | Configuration |
|---|---------|---------------|---|---------|---------------|---|---------|---------------|
| 1 | H | $1s^1$ | 37 | Rb | $[Kr]5s^1$ | 74 | W | $[Xe]4f^{14}5d^46s^2$ |
| 2 | He | $1s^2$ | 38 | Sr | $[Kr]5s^2$ | 75 | Re | $[Xe]4f^{14}5d^56s^2$ |
| 3 | Li | $[He]2s^1$ | 39 | Y | $[Kr]4d^15s^2$ | 76 | Os | $[Xe]4f^{14}5d^66s^2$ |
| 4 | Be | $[He]2s^2$ | 40 | Zr | $[Kr]4d^25s^2$ | 77 | Ir | $[Xe]4f^{14}5d^76s^2$ |
| 5 | B | $[He]2s^22p^1$ | 41 | Nb | $[Kr]4d^45s^1$ | 78 | Pt | $[Xe]4f^{14}5d^96s^1$ |
| 6 | C | $[He]2s^22p^2$ | 42 | Mo | $[Kr]4d^55s^1$ | 79 | Au | $[Xe]4f^{14}5d^{10}6s^1$ |
| 7 | N | $[He]2s^22p^3$ | 43 | Tc | $[Kr]4d^55s^2$ | 80 | Hg | $[Xe]4f^{14}5d^{10}6s^2$ |
| 8 | O | $[He]2s^22p^4$ | 44 | Ru | $[Kr]4d^75s^1$ | 81 | Tl | $[Xe]4f^{14}5d^{10}6s^26p^1$ |
| 9 | F | $[He]2s^22p^5$ | 45 | Rh | $[Kr]4d^85s^1$ | 82 | Pb | $[Xe]4f^{14}5d^{10}6s^26p^2$ |
| 10 | Ne | $[He]2s^22p^6$ | 46 | Pd | $[Kr]4d^{10}$ | 83 | Bi | $[Xe]4f^{14}5d^{10}6s^26p^3$ |
| 11 | Na | $[Ne]3s^1$ | 47 | Ag | $[Kr]4d^{10}5s^1$ | 84 | Po | $[Xe]4f^{14}5d^{10}6s^26p^4$ |
| 12 | Mg | $[Ne]3s^2$ | 48 | Cd | $[Kr]4d^{10}5s^2$ | 85 | At | $[Xe]4f^{14}5d^{10}6s^26p^5$ |
| 13 | Al | $[Ne]3s^23p^1$ | 49 | In | $[Kr]4d^{10}5s^25p^1$ | 86 | Rn | $[Xe]4f^{14}5d^{10}6s^26p^6$ |
| 14 | Si | $[Ne]3s^23p^2$ | 50 | Sn | $[Kr]4d^{10}5s^25p^2$ | 87 | Fr | $[Rn]7s^1$ |
| 15 | P | $[Ne]3s^23p^3$ | 51 | Sb | $[Kr]4d^{10}5s^25p^3$ | 88 | Ra | $[Rn]7s^2$ |
| 16 | S | $[Ne]3s^23p^4$ | 52 | Te | $[Kr]4d^{10}5s^25p^4$ | 89 | Ac | $[Rn]6d^17s^2$ |
| 17 | Cl | $[Ne]3s^23p^5$ | 53 | I | $[Kr]4d^{10}5s^25p^5$ | 90 | Th | $[Rn]6d^27s^2$ |
| 18 | Ar | $[Ne]3s^23p^6$ | 54 | Xe | $[Kr]4d^{10}5s^25p^6$ | 91 | Pa | $[Rn]5f^26d^17s^2$ |
| 19 | K | $[Ar]4s^1$ | 55 | Cs | $[Xe]6s^1$ | 92 | U | $[Rn]5f^36d^17s^2$ |
| 20 | Ca | $[Ar]4s^2$ | 56 | Ba | $[Xe]6s^2$ | 93 | Np | $[Rn]5f^46d^17s^2$ |
| 21 | Sc | $[Ar]3d^14s^2$ | 57 | La | $[Xe]5d^16s^2$ | 94 | Pu | $[Rn]5f^67s^2$ |
| 22 | Ti | $[Ar]3d^24s^2$ | 58 | Ce | $[Xe]4f^15d^16s^2$ | 95 | Am | $[Rn]5f^77s^2$ |
| 23 | V | $[Ar]3d^34s^2$ | 59 | Pr | $[Xe]4f^36s^2$ | 96 | Cm | $[Rn]5f^76d^17s^2$ |
| 24 | Cr | $[Ar]3d^54s^1$ | 60 | Nd | $[Xe]4f^46s^2$ | 97 | Bk | $[Rn]5f^97s^2$ |
| 25 | Mn | $[Ar]3d^54s^2$ | 61 | Pm | $[Xe]4f^56s^2$ | 98 | Cf | $[Rn]5f^{10}7s^2$ |
| 26 | Fe | $[Ar]3d^64s^2$ | 62 | Sm | $[Xe]4f^66s^2$ | 99 | Es | $[Rn]5f^{11}7s^2$ |
| 27 | Co | $[Ar]3d^74s^2$ | 63 | Eu | $[Xe]4f^76s^2$ | 100 | Fm | $[Rn]5f^{12}7s^2$ |
| 28 | Ni | $[Ar]3d^84s^2$ | 64 | Gd | $[Xe]4f^75d^16s^2$ | 101 | Md | $[Rn]5f^{13}7s^2$ |
| 29 | Cu | $[Ar]3d^{10}4s^1$ | 65 | Tb | $[Xe]4f^96s^2$ | 102 | No | $[Rn]5f^{14}7s^2$ |
| 30 | Zn | $[Ar]3d^{10}4s^2$ | 66 | Dy | $[Xe]4f^{10}6s^2$ | 103 | Lr | $[Rn]5f^{14}6d^17s^2$ |
| 31 | Ga | $[Ar]3d^{10}4s^24p^1$ | 67 | Ho | $[Xe]4f^{11}6s^2$ | 104 | Rf | $[Rn]5f^{14}6d^27s^2$ |
| 32 | Ge | $[Ar]3d^{10}4s^24p^2$ | 68 | Er | $[Xe]4f^{12}6s^2$ | 105 | Db | $[Rn]5f^{14}6d^37s^2$ |
| 33 | As | $[Ar]3d^{10}4s^24p^3$ | 69 | Tm | $[Xe]4f^{13}6s^2$ | 106 | Sg | $[Rn]5f^{14}6d^47s^2$ |
| 34 | Se | $[Ar]3d^{10}4s^24p^4$ | 70 | Yb | $[Xe]4f^{14}6s^2$ | 107 | Bh | $[Rn]5f^{14}6d^57s^2$ |
| 35 | Br | $[Ar]3d^{10}4s^24p^5$ | 71 | Lu | $[Xe]4f^{14}5d^16s^2$ | 108 | Hs | $[Rn]5f^{14}6d^67s^2$ |
| 36 | Kr | $[Ar]3d^{10}4s^24p^6$ | 72 | Hf | $[Xe]4f^{14}5d^26s^2$ | 109 | Mt | $[Rn]5f^{14}6d^77s^2$ |
| | | | 73 | Ta | $[Xe]4f^{14}5d^36s^2$ | | | |

*This table follows the general convention of writing the orbitals in order of increasing $n$ when writing electron configurations. For a given $n$, the subshells are listed in order of increasing $\ell$.

# Electron Configurations of the Main Group Elements

Hydrogen, the first element in the periodic table, has one electron in a $1s$ orbital. One way to depict its electron configuration is with the orbital box diagram used earlier, but an alternative and more frequently used method is the *spdf* notation. Using this method, the electron configuration of H is $1s^1$, read "one *s* one." This indicates that there is one electron (indicated by the superscript) in the $1s$ orbital.

Hydrogen electron configuration:  ↑    or    $1s^1$

               $1s$

- number of electrons assigned to designated orbital
- orbital type ($\ell$)
- electron shell ($n$)

Orbital Box Notation     *spdf* Notation

**Lithium.** Lithium-ion batteries are increasingly used in consumer products. All Group 1A elements such as lithium share an outer electron configuration of $ns^1$.

### Lithium (Li) and Other Elements of Group 1A

Lithium, with three electrons, is the first element in the second period of the periodic table. The first two electrons are in the $1s$ subshell, and the third electron must be in the $2s$ subshell of the $n = 2$ shell. The *spdf* notation, $1s^2 2s^1$, is read "one *s* two, two *s* one."

Lithium:    *spdf* notation     $1s^2 2s^1$

         Box notation     ↑↓   ↑   ☐☐☐

                          $1s$   $2s$   $2p$

Electron configurations are often written in abbreviated form by writing in brackets the symbol for the noble gas preceding the element (called the **noble gas notation**) and then indicating any electrons beyond those in the noble gas by using *spdf* or orbital box notation. In lithium, the arrangement preceding the $2s$ electron is the electron configuration of the noble gas helium. Instead of writing out $1s^2 2s^1$ for lithium's configuration, it can be written as $[\text{He}]2s^1$.

The electrons included in the noble gas notation are often referred to as the **core electrons** of the atom. The core electrons can generally be ignored when considering the chemistry of an element. The electrons beyond the core electrons—the $2s^1$ electron in the case of lithium—are called **valence electrons**; these are the electrons that determine the chemical properties of an element.

All the elements of Group 1A have one electron assigned to an *s* orbital of the $n$th shell, for which $n$ is the number of the period in which the element is found (Figure 7.3). For example, potassium is the first element in the $n = 4$ row (the fourth period), so potassium has the electron configuration of the element preceding it in the table (Ar) plus a final electron assigned to the $4s$ orbital: $[\text{Ar}]4s^1$.

### Beryllium (Be) and Other Elements of Group 2A

All elements of Group 2A have electron configurations of [electrons of preceding noble gas]$ns^2$, where $n$ is the period in which the element is found in the periodic table. Beryllium, for example, has two electrons in the $1s$ orbital plus two additional electrons.

Beryllium:    *spdf* notation     $1s^2 2s^2$    or    $[\text{He}]2s^2$

          Box notation     ↑↓   ↑↓   ☐☐☐

                           $1s$   $2s$   $2p$

**Beryllium.** Beryllium-copper alloy is used in the oil and gas industry and in electronics. All Group 2A elements like beryllium share an outer electron configuration of $ns^2$.

Because all the elements of Group 1A have the valence electron configuration $ns^1$ and those in Group 2A have $ns^2$, these elements are called ***s*-block elements**.

**Boron.** Boron carbide, $B_4C$, is used in body armor. All Group 3A elements share an outer electron configuration of $ns^2np^1$.

### Boron (B) and Other Elements of Group 3A

Boron (Group 3A) is the first element in the block of elements on the right side of the periodic table. Because the $1s$ and $2s$ orbitals are filled in a boron atom, the fifth electron must be assigned to a $2p$ orbital.

Boron:  *spdf* notation  $1s^22s^22p^1$  or  $[He]2s^22p^1$

Box notation

$$\boxed{\uparrow\downarrow}\quad\boxed{\uparrow\downarrow}\quad\boxed{\uparrow|\ |\ }$$
$\quad\quad 1s \quad\quad 2s \quad\quad 2p$

Elements from Group 3A through Group 8A are often called the *p*-block elements. All have the outer shell configuration $ns^2np^x$, where $x$ varies from 1 to 6. The elements in Group 3A, for example, have two *s* electrons and one *p* electron ($ns^2np^1$) in their outer shells.

### Carbon (C) and Other Elements of Group 4A

Carbon (Group 4A) is the second element in the *p* block, with two electrons assigned to the $2p$ orbitals. You can write the electron configuration of carbon by referring to the periodic table: Starting at H and moving from left to right across the successive periods, you write $1s^2$ to reach the end of period 1 and then $2s^2$ and finally $2p^2$ to bring the electron count to six. For carbon to be in its lowest energy (ground) state, these electrons must be assigned to different *p* orbitals, and both will have the same spin direction.

Carbon:  *spdf* notation  $1s^22s^22p^2$  or  $[He]2s^22p^2$

Box notation

$$\boxed{\uparrow\downarrow}\quad\boxed{\uparrow\downarrow}\quad\boxed{\uparrow|\uparrow|\ }$$
$\quad\quad 1s \quad\quad 2s \quad\quad 2p$

- **Hund's Rule and Exchange Energy**
The reason a configuration with the maximum number of unpaired electrons with parallel spins is more stable is due to the *exchange energy*, a concept that comes out of quantum mechanics. Due to the exchange interaction, each pair of unpaired electrons with parallel spins leads to a lowering of the overall energy of an atom. The first of the configurations below is more stable than the second by an amount of energy called the *exchange energy*.

$$\boxed{\uparrow|\uparrow|\uparrow}$$
$$\boxed{\uparrow|\uparrow|\downarrow}$$

When assigning electrons to *p*, *d*, or *f* orbitals, each successive electron is assigned to a different orbital of the subshell, and each electron has the same spin as the previous one, until the subshell is half full. Additional electrons must then be assigned to half-filled orbitals. This procedure follows **Hund's rule**, which states that *the most stable arrangement of electrons is that with the maximum number of unpaired electrons, all with the same spin direction.*

All elements in Group 4A have similar outer shell configurations, $ns^2np^2$, where *n* is the period in which the element is located in the periodic table.

### Nitrogen (N) and Oxygen (O) and Elements of Groups 5A and 6A

Nitrogen (Group 5A) has five valence electrons. Besides the two $2s$ electrons, it has three electrons, all with the same spin, in three different $2p$ orbitals.

Nitrogen:  *spdf* notation  $1s^22s^22p^3$  or  $[He]2s^22p^3$

Box notation

$$\boxed{\uparrow\downarrow}\quad\boxed{\uparrow\downarrow}\quad\boxed{\uparrow|\uparrow|\uparrow}$$
$\quad\quad 1s \quad\quad 2s \quad\quad 2p$

Oxygen (Group 6A) has six valence electrons. Two of these six electrons are assigned to the $2s$ orbital, and the other four electrons are assigned to $2p$ orbitals.

Oxygen:  *spdf* notation  $1s^22s^22p^4$  or  $[He]2s^22p^4$

Box notation

$$\boxed{\uparrow\downarrow}\quad\boxed{\uparrow\downarrow}\quad\boxed{\uparrow\downarrow|\uparrow|\uparrow}$$
$\quad\quad 1s \quad\quad 2s \quad\quad 2p$

The fourth $2p$ electron must pair up with one already present. It makes no difference to which orbital this electron is assigned (the $2p$ orbitals all have the same energy), but it must have a spin opposite to the other electron already assigned to that orbital so that each electron has a different set of quantum numbers.

All elements in Group 5A have an outer shell configuration of $ns^2np^3$, and all elements in Group 6A have an outer shell configuration of $ns^2np^4$, where $n$ is the period in which the element is located in the periodic table.

### Fluorine (F) and Neon (Ne) and Elements of Groups 7A and 8A

Fluorine (Group 7A) has seven electrons in the $n = 2$ shell. Two of these electrons occupy the $2s$ subshell, and the remaining five electrons occupy the $2p$ subshell.

Fluorine:  *spdf* notation    $1s^22s^22p^5$    or    $[He]2s^22p^5$

Box notation    $\boxed{\uparrow\downarrow}$  $\boxed{\uparrow\downarrow}$ $\boxed{\uparrow\downarrow}\boxed{\uparrow\downarrow}\boxed{\uparrow}$
　　　　　　　　　1s　  2s　　2p

**Fluorine.** Fluorine is found as the fluoride ion in the mineral fluorite ($CaF_2$), sometimes called *fluorspar*. The mineral, which is the state mineral of Illinois, comes in many colors. All Group 7A elements such as fluorine share an outer electron configuration of $ns^2np^5$.

All halogen atoms have similar outer shell configurations, $ns^2np^5$, where $n$ is the period in which the element is located.

Like all the elements in Group 8A, neon is a noble gas. The Group 8A elements (except helium) have eight electrons in the shell of highest $n$ value, so all have the outer shell configuration $ns^2np^6$, where $n$ is the period in which the element is found. That is, all the noble gases have filled $ns$ and $np$ subshells. The nearly complete chemical inertness of the noble gases is associated with this electron configuration.

Neon:    *spdf* notation    $1s^22s^22p^6$    or    $[He]2s^22p^6$

Box notation    $\boxed{\uparrow\downarrow}$  $\boxed{\uparrow\downarrow}$ $\boxed{\uparrow\downarrow}\boxed{\uparrow\downarrow}\boxed{\uparrow\downarrow}$
　　　　　　　　　1s　  2s　　2p

### Elements of Period 3

The elements of the third period have valence electron configurations similar to those of the second period, except that the preceding noble gas is neon and the valence shell is the third energy level. For example, silicon has four electrons and a neon core. Because it is the second element in the $p$ block, it has two electrons in $3p$ orbitals. Thus, its electron configuration is

Silicon:  *spdf* notation    $1s^22s^22p^63s^23p^2$    or    $[Ne]3s^23p^2$

Box notation    $\boxed{\uparrow\downarrow}$  $\boxed{\uparrow\downarrow}$ $\boxed{\uparrow\downarrow}\boxed{\uparrow\downarrow}\boxed{\uparrow\downarrow}$ $\boxed{\uparrow\downarrow}$ $\boxed{\uparrow}\boxed{\uparrow}\boxed{\ }$
　　　　　　　　　1s　  2s　　2p　　3s　 3p

**Silicon.** Si is the fourth element in the third period. The earth's crust is largely composed of silicon-containing minerals. This photo shows some elemental silicon and a thin wafer of silicon on which are etched electronic circuits.

### EXAMPLE 7.1    Electron Configurations

**Problem** Give the electron configuration of sulfur, using the *spdf*, noble gas, and orbital box notations.

**What Do You Know?** From the periodic table: sulfur, atomic number 16, is the sixth element in the third period ($n = 3$) and is in the $p$-block. You need to know the order of filling (Figure 7.1).

**Strategy**

- For the *spdf* and orbital box notations: Place the 16 electrons for sulfur into orbitals, based on the order of filling.

- For the noble gas notation: The first 10 electrons are identified by the symbol of the previous noble gas, Ne. The remaining 6 electrons are assigned to the $3s$ and $3p$ subshells. Make sure Hund's rule is followed in the box notation.

**Sulfur.** Sulfur is widely distributed on earth. Like all Group 6A elements, it has the outer electron configuration $ns^2np^4$.

**Solution** Sulfur, atomic number 16, is the sixth element in the third period ($n = 3$) and is in the $p$ block. The last six electrons assigned to the atom, therefore, have the configuration $3s^2 3p^4$. These are preceded by the completed shells $n = 1$ and $n = 2$, the electron arrangement for Ne.

Complete *spdf* notation:          $1s^2 2s^2 2p^6 3s^2 3p^4$

*spdf* with noble gas notation:          $[Ne]3s^2 3p^4$

Orbital box notation:          [Ne] ⇅   ⇅ ↑ ↑
                                        $3s$     $3p$

**Think about Your Answer** The noble gas and box notations convey slightly different information. The noble gas notation separates out the core electrons (which are not involved in chemical reactions). The box notation allows a quick identification of the number of unpaired electron.

---

**Check Your Understanding**

(a)   What element has the configuration $1s^2 2s^2 2p^6 3s^2 3p^5$?

(b)   Using *spdf* notation and a box diagram, show the electron configuration of phosphorus.

---

## EXAMPLE 7.2    Electron Configurations and Quantum Numbers

**Problem** Write the electron configuration for Al using the noble gas notation, and give a set of quantum numbers for each of the electrons with $n = 3$ (the valence electrons).

**What Do You Know?** The periodic table informs you that Al (atomic number 13) is the third element after the noble gas neon.

**Strategy** Aluminum is the third element in the third period. It therefore has three electrons with $n = 3$. Two of the electrons are assigned to $3s$, and the remaining electron is assigned to $3p$.

**Solution** The element is preceded by the noble gas neon, so the electron configuration is $[Ne]3s^2 3p^1$. Using the box notation, the configuration is

Aluminum configuration:          [Ne] ⇅   ↑
                                          $3s$     $3p$

The possible sets of quantum numbers for the two $3s$ electrons are

|  | $n$ | $\ell$ | $m_\ell$ | $m_s$ |
|---|---|---|---|---|
| For ↑ | 3 | 0 | 0 | $+\frac{1}{2}$ |
| For ↓ | 3 | 0 | 0 | $-\frac{1}{2}$ |

For the single $3p$ electron, one of six possible sets is $n = 3$, $\ell = 1$, $m_\ell = +1$, and $m_s = +\frac{1}{2}$.

**Think about Your Answer** It is only a convention that assigns $+\frac{1}{2}$ to an "up" arrow for electron spin. Two electrons in the same orbital have opposite electron spins. Which is $+\frac{1}{2}$ and which is $-\frac{1}{2}$ is not important.

---

**Check Your Understanding**

Write one possible set of quantum numbers for the valence electrons of calcium.

---

# Electron Configurations of the Transition Elements

The elements of the fourth through the seventh periods use $d$ and $f$ subshells, in addition to $s$ and $p$ subshells, to accommodate electrons (see Figure 7.3 and Tables 7.3 and 7.4). Elements whose atoms are filling $d$ subshells are called

**transition elements.** Those elements for which atoms are filling $f$ subshells are sometimes called the **inner transition elements** or, more usually, the **lanthanides** (filling $4f$ orbitals, Ce through Lu) and **actinides** (filling $5f$ orbitals, Th through Lr).

In a given period in the periodic table, the transition elements are always preceded by two $s$-block elements. After filling the $ns$ orbital in the period, we begin filling the $(n - 1)d$ orbitals. Scandium, the first transition element, has the configuration $[Ar]3d^1 4s^2$, and titanium follows with $[Ar]3d^2 4s^2$ (Table 7.4).

The general procedure for assigning electrons would suggest that the configuration of a chromium atom would be $[Ar]3d^4 4s^2$. The actual configuration, however, has one electron assigned to each of the six available $3d$ and $4s$ orbitals: $[Ar]3d^5 4s^1$. This configuration has a lower total energy (due to maximizing the number of unpaired electron spins) than the alternative configuration.

Following chromium, atoms of manganese, iron, and nickel have the configurations that would be expected from the order of orbital filling in Figure 7.1. Copper ($[Ar]3d^{10} 4s^1$) is the second "exception" in this series; it has a single electron in the $4s$ orbital, and the remaining 10 electrons beyond the argon core are assigned to the $3d$ orbitals. Zinc, with the configuration $[Ar]3d^{10} 4s^2$, ends the first transition series.

The fifth period transition elements follow the pattern of the fourth period but have more exceptions to the general rules of orbital filling.

## Lanthanides and Actinides

The sixth period includes the lanthanide series. As the first element in the $d$-block, lanthanum has the configuration $[Xe]5d^1 6s^2$. The next element, cerium (Ce), is set out in a separate row at the bottom of the periodic table, and it is with the elements in this row (Ce through Lu) that electrons are first assigned to $f$ orbitals. Thus, the configuration of cerium is $[Xe]4f^1 5d^1 6s^2$. Moving across the lanthanide series, the pattern continues (although with occasional variations in

**Lanthanides.** These elements have many uses. This is a sample of lanthanum metal.

### Table 7.4 Orbital Box Diagrams for the Elements Ca Through Zn

| | | 3d | 4s |
|---|---|---|---|
| Ca | $[Ar]4s^2$ | ☐☐☐☐☐ | ⇅ |
| Sc | $[Ar]3d^1 4s^2$ | ↑☐☐☐☐ | ⇅ |
| Ti | $[Ar]3d^2 4s^2$ | ↑↑☐☐☐ | ⇅ |
| V | $[Ar]3d^3 4s^2$ | ↑↑↑☐☐ | ⇅ |
| Cr* | $[Ar]3d^5 4s^1$ | ↑↑↑↑↑ | ↑ |
| Mn | $[Ar]3d^5 4s^2$ | ↑↑↑↑↑ | ⇅ |
| Fe | $[Ar]3d^6 4s^2$ | ⇅↑↑↑↑ | ⇅ |
| Co | $[Ar]3d^7 4s^2$ | ⇅⇅↑↑↑ | ⇅ |
| Ni | $[Ar]3d^8 4s^2$ | ⇅⇅⇅↑↑ | ⇅ |
| Cu* | $[Ar]3d^{10} 4s^1$ | ⇅⇅⇅⇅⇅ | ↑ |
| Zn | $[Ar]3d^{10} 4s^2$ | ⇅⇅⇅⇅⇅ | ⇅ |

● **Writing Configurations for Transition Metals** We follow the convention of writing configurations with shells listed in order of increasing $n$ and, within a given shell, writing subshells in order of increasing $\ell$. As an alternate representation, some chemists write them as, for example, $[Ar]4s^2 3d^2$ to reflect the order of orbital filling.

*See *A Closer Look: Questions About Transition Element Electron Configurations,* page 314.

# Orbital Energies, Z*, and Electron Configurations

The graph below shows how the energies of different atomic orbitals change as we go from one element to the next in the periodic table. Here are some significant observations drawn from the graph.

(1) Generally, as one moves from left to right in any period, the energies of the atomic orbitals decrease. This trend correlates with the changes in Z*, the effective charge experienced by an electron in a given orbital (Figure 7.2). As noted, Z* is a parameter related to the nuclear charge and the shielding of all the other electrons. When moving from one element to the next across each period, the attractive effect of an additional proton in the nucleus outweighs the repulsive effect of an additional electron.

(2) Electrons are classified as either valence electrons or core electrons. We can now

see from this graph the obvious distinction in these groups. Valence electrons are found in orbitals that have less negative energies. In contrast, the core electrons are in orbitals that have very low energy, because they experience a much higher Z*. Furthermore, as one moves from one period to the next period (for example, from Ar in period 3 to K in period 4) the energies of core orbitals plummet. The very low energy of electrons in these orbitals rules out the ability of these electrons to participate in chemical reactions.

(3) Notice also the orbital energies of the first transition series. Each step going across the transition series involves adding a proton to the nucleus and a 3d electron to an inner shell. The 4s energy

level decreases only slightly in this series of elements, reflecting the fact that the additional 3d electrons effectively shield a 4s electron from the higher charge resulting from addition of a proton. The additional nuclear charge has a greater effect on the 3d orbitals, and their energies decrease to a greater extent across the transition series. When the end of the transition series is reached, the 3d electrons become part of the core and their energies plummet.

(4) Finally, note the exceptional behavior of Cr and Cu in this sequence. These elements have unexpected electron configurations (page 314), arising because another factor, exchange energy (page 308), is a contributor to overall energy in the system.

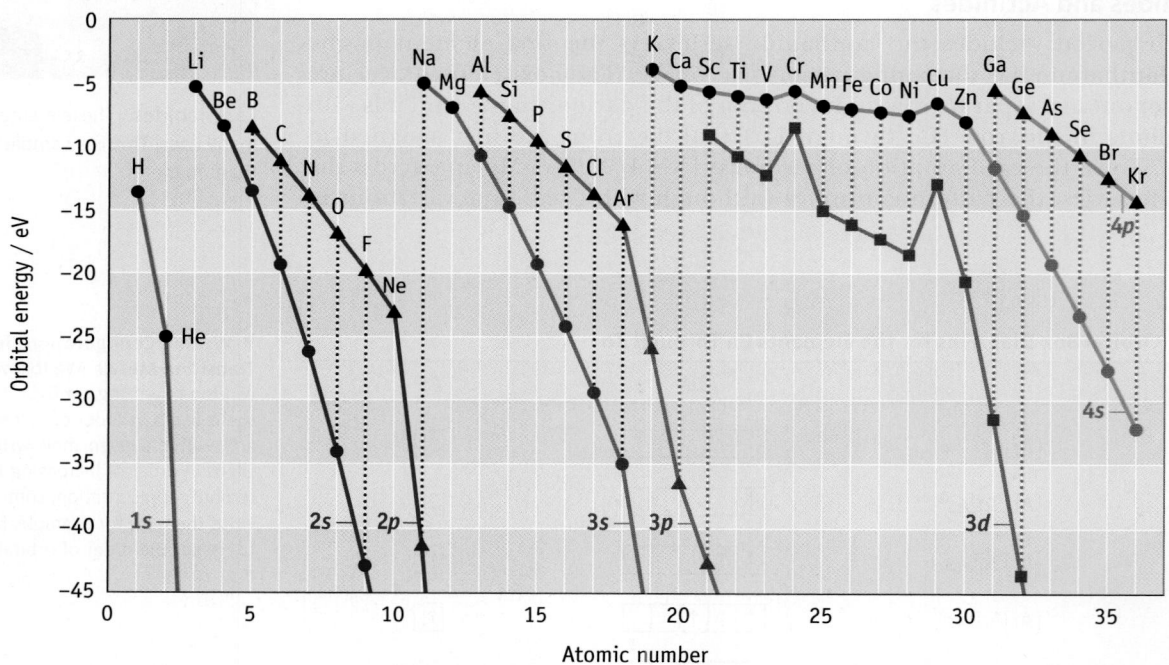

**Variation in orbital energies with atomic number.**  Note that the energies are in electron-volts (eV), where 1 eV = 1.602 × 10⁻¹⁹ J). (Figure redrawn from *Chemical Structure and Reactivity*, J. Keeler and P. Wothers, Oxford, 2008; used with permission.)

occupancy of the $5d$ and $4f$ orbitals). The lanthanide series ends with 14 electrons being assigned to the seven $4f$ orbitals in the last element, lutetium (Lu, [Xe]$4f^{14}5d^16s^2$) (see Table 7.3).

The seventh period also includes an extended series of elements utilizing $f$ orbitals, the actinides. Actinium has the configuration [Rn]$6d^17s^2$. The next element is thorium (Th), which is followed by protactinium (Pa) and uranium (U). The electron configuration of uranium is [Rn]$5f^36d^17s^2$.

## EXAMPLE 7.3    Electron Configurations of the Transition Elements

**Problem**  Using the *spdf* and noble gas notations, give electron configurations for (a) technetium, Tc, and (b) osmium, Os.

**What Do You Know?**  Base your answer on the positions of the elements in the periodic table. Technetium is the seventh element in period 5 and osmium is the 22nd element in the 6th period.

**Strategy**  For each element, find the preceding noble gas, and then note the number of *s, p, d*, and *f* electrons that lead from the noble gas to the element.

**Solution**

(a)  Technetium, Tc: The noble gas that precedes Tc is krypton, Kr, at the end of the $n = 4$ row. After 36 electrons are assigned to the core as [Kr], seven electrons remain. Two of these electrons are in the 5s orbital, and the remaining five are in 4d orbitals. Therefore, the technetium configuration is $[Kr]4d^5 5s^2$.

(b)  Osmium, Os: Osmium is a sixth-period element and the 22nd element following the noble gas xenon. Of the 22 electrons to be added after the Xe core, two are assigned to the 6s orbital and 14 to 4f orbitals. The remaining six are assigned to 5d orbitals. Thus, the osmium configuration is $[Xe]4f^{14}5d^6 6s^2$.

**Think about Your Answer**  In general, it is best to use the periodic table as a guide to determining electron configurations. Keep in mind, however, that some exceptions exist, particularly in the heavier transition elements and the lanthanides and actinides.

**Check Your Understanding**

Using the periodic table and without looking at Table 7.3, write electron configurations for the following elements:

(a)  P                  (c)  Zr                  (e)  Pb

(b)  Zn                 (d)  In                  (f)  U

Use the *spdf* and noble gas notations. When you have finished, check your answers with Table 7.3.

---

### REVIEW & CHECK FOR SECTION 7.3

1.  Find Se in the periodic table. What is the electron configuration beyond its noble gas core?

    (a)  $4p^4$              (b)  $4s^2 4p^4$          (c)  $3d^{10}4s^2 4p^4$          (d)  [Ar]

2.  Based on electron configurations, which of the following atoms has the smallest number of unpaired electrons?

    (a)  Cr                  (b)  Fe                  (c)  Ni                  (d)  Mn

## 7.4  Electron Configurations of Ions

The chemistry of the elements is often the chemistry of their anions and cations, so we want to determine their electron configurations. To form a cation from a neutral atom, one or more of the valence electrons is removed. Electrons are always removed first from the electron shell of highest $n$. If several subshells are present within the $n$th shell, the electron or electrons of maximum $\ell$ are removed. Thus, a sodium ion is formed by removing the $3s^1$ electron from the Na atom,

$$Na: [1s^2 2s^2 2p^6 3s^1] \rightarrow Na^+: [1s^2 2s^2 2p^6] + e^-$$

and $Ge^{2+}$ is formed by removing two $4p$ electrons from a germanium atom,

$$Ge: [Ar]3d^{10}4s^2 4p^2 \rightarrow Ge^{2+}: [Ar]3d^{10}4s^2 + 2\ e^-$$

# Questions about Transition Element Electron Configurations

Why don't all of the $n = 3$ subshells fill before beginning to fill the $n = 4$ subshells? Why is scandium's configuration [Ar]$3d^14s^2$ and not [Ar]$3d^3$? Why is chromium's configuration [Ar]$3d^54s^1$ and not [Ar]$3d^44s^2$? As we search for explanations keep in mind that the most stable configuration will be that with the lowest *total* energy.

From scandium to zinc the energies of the 3d orbitals are always lower than the energy of the 4s orbital (see *A Closer Look: Orbital Energies, Z\*, and Electron Configurations*, page 312), so for scandium the configuration [Ar]$3d^3$ would seem to be preferred. One way to understand why it is not is to consider the effect of electron–electron repulsion in 3d and 4s orbitals. The most stable configuration will be the one that most effectively minimizes electron–electron repulsions.

Plots of 3d and 4s orbitals (as was done for 1s and 2s in Figure 7.2) show the most probable distance of a 3d electron from the nucleus is less than that for a 4s electron. Being closer

to the nucleus, the 3d orbitals are more compact than the 4s orbital. This means the 3d electrons are closer together, so two 3d electrons would repel each other more strongly than two 4s electrons, for example. A consequence is that placing electrons in the slightly higher energy 4s orbital lessens the effect of electron–electron repulsions and lowers the overall energy of the atom.

For chromium the 4s and 3d orbital energies (see *A Closer Look: Orbital Energies, Z\*, and Electron Configurations*, page 312) are closer together than other 4th period transition elements. Again, thinking in terms of total energy, it is the effect of exchange energy (page 308) that tips the balance and causes the configuration [Ar]$3d^54s^1$, in which all electron spins are the same, to be most stable.

For more on these questions see the following papers in the *Journal of Chemical Education* and Chapter 9 of the book *The Periodic Table* by E. Scerri.

- E. Scerri, *The Periodic Table*, Oxford, 2007.
- F. L. Pilar, "4s is Always Above 3d," *Journal of Chemical Education*, Vol. 55, pp. 1–6, 1978.
- E. R. Scerri, "Transition Metal Configurations and Limitations of the Orbital Approximation," *Journal of Chemical Education*, Vol. 66, pp. 481–483, 1989.
- L. G. Vanquickenborne, K. Pierloot, and D. Devoghel, "Transition Metals and the Aufbau Principle," *Journal of Chemical Education*, Vol. 71, pp. 469–471, 1994.
- M. P. Melrose and E. R. Scerri, "Why the 4s Orbital is Occupied before the 3d," *Journal of Chemical Education*, Vol. 73, pp. 498–503, 1996.
- W. H. E. Schwarz, "The Full Story of the Electron Configurations of the Transition Elements," *Journal of Chemical Education*, Vol. 87, pp. 444–448, 2010.

The same general rule applies to transition metal atoms. This means, for example, that the titanium(II) cation has the configuration [Ar]$3d^2$:

$$\text{Ti: [Ar]}3d^24s^2 \rightarrow \text{Ti}^{2+}\text{: [Ar]}3d^2 + 2\text{ e}^-$$

Iron(II) and iron(III) cations have the configurations [Ar]$3d^6$ and [Ar]$3d^5$, respectively:

$$\text{Fe: [Ar]}3d^64s^2 \rightarrow \text{Fe}^{2+}\text{: [Ar]}3d^6 + 2\text{ e}^-$$

$$\text{Fe}^{2+}\text{: [Ar]}3d^6 \rightarrow \text{Fe}^{3+}\text{: [Ar]}3d^5 + \text{ e}^-$$

Note that in the ionization of transition metals the $ns$ electrons are always lost before $(n - 1)d$ electrons. All transition metals lose their $ns$ electrons first, and the cations formed all have electron configurations of the general type [noble gas core] $(n - 1)d^x$. This point is important to remember because the magnetic properties of transition metal cations are determined by the number of unpaired electrons in $d$ orbitals. For example, the Fe$^{3+}$ ion is paramagnetic to the extent of five unpaired electrons (See Figures 6.16, 7.4, and 7.5 and *A Closer Look: Paramagnetism and Ferromagnetism,* page 289). If three $3d$ electrons had been removed instead of two $4s$ electrons and one $3d$ electron, the Fe$^{3+}$ ion would still be paramagnetic but only to the extent of three unpaired electrons.

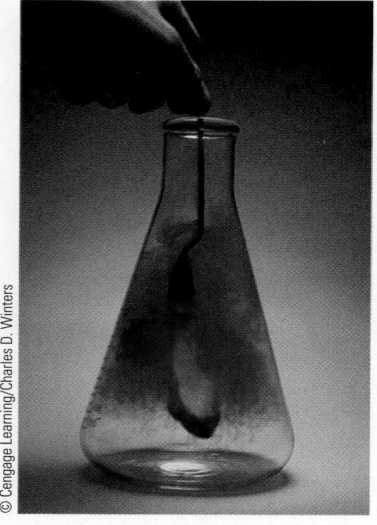

**FIGURE 7.4 Formation of iron(III) chloride.** Iron reacts with chlorine (Cl$_2$) to produce FeCl$_3$. The paramagnetic Fe$^{3+}$ ion has the configuration [Ar]$3d^5$.

## EXAMPLE 7.4 Configurations of Transition Metal Ions

**Problem** Give the electron configurations for Cu, Cu$^+$ and Cu$^{2+}$. Is either of the ions paramagnetic? How many unpaired electrons does each have?

**What Do You Know?** When forming a transition metal ion, the outermost $ns$ electrons are lost first, followed by the $(n - 1)d$ electrons.

**Strategy** Start with the electron configuration of copper (Table 7.4). It is always observed that the $ns$ electron or electrons are ionized first, followed by one or more $(n - 1)$ $d$ electrons.

**Solution** Copper has only one electron in the $4s$ orbital and 10 electrons in $3d$ orbitals:

Cu:    [Ar]$3d^{10}4s^1$

3d          4s

When copper is oxidized to $Cu^+$, the 4s electron is lost.

$Cu^+$:    [Ar]$3d^{10}$

3d          4s

The copper(II) ion is formed from copper(I) by removal of one of the $3d$ electrons.

$Cu^{2+}$:    [Ar]$3d^9$

3d          4s

A copper(II) ion ($Cu^{2+}$) has one unpaired electron, so it is paramagnetic. In contrast, $Cu^+$, with no unpaired electrons, is diamagnetic.

**Think about Your Answer** Note that the electron configuration for Cu is [Ar]$3d^{10}4s^1$ and not [Ar]$3d^9 4s^2$. Copper is one of two exceptions in the first transition series in the order of filling (Cr is the other) (See Table 7.4).

**Check Your Understanding**

Depict the electron configurations for $V^{2+}$, $V^{3+}$, and $Co^{3+}$. Use orbital box diagrams and the noble gas notation. Are any of the ions paramagnetic? If so, give the number of unpaired electrons.

---

**REVIEW & CHECK FOR SECTION 7.4**

1.  Three of the four ions shown below have the same electron configuration but the fourth does not. Identify the one that doesn't match.

    (a)  $Fe^{3+}$          (b)  $Cr^+$          (c)  $Mn^{2+}$          (d)  $Fe^{2+}$

2.  Which of the following ions has the largest number of unpaired electrons?

    (a)  $Cr^{3+}$          (b)  $Cu^{2+}$          (c)  $Co^{3+}$          (d)  $Ni^{2+}$

---

# 7.5  Atomic Properties and Periodic Trends

Once electron configurations were understood, chemists realized that *similarities in properties of the elements are the result of similar valence shell electron configurations.* An objective of this section is to describe how atomic electron configurations are related to some of the physical and chemical properties of the elements and why those properties, such as atomic size, change in a predictable manner when moving down groups and across periods.

## Atomic Size

The sizes of atoms (Figure 7.6) influence many aspects of their properties and reactivity. Size can determine the number of atoms that may surround and be bound to a central atom and can be a determining factor in the shape of a molecule. As you will see in the next chapter in particular, the shapes of molecules are important in how they function.

**(a)** A sample of iron(III) oxide is packed into a plastic tube and suspended from a thin nylon filament.

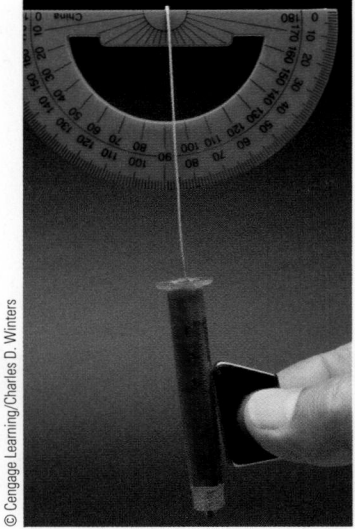

**(b)** When a powerful magnet is brought near, the paramagnetic iron(III) ions in $Fe_2O_3$ cause the sample to be attracted to the magnet.

**FIGURE 7.5 Paramagnetism of transition metals and their compounds.** The magnet is made of neodymium, iron, and boron [$Nd_2Fe_{14}B$]. These powerful magnets are used in acoustic speakers.

**Module 11: Periodic Trends** covers concepts in this section.

**FIGURE 7.6 Atomic radii in picometers for main group elements.** $1 \text{ pm} = 1 \times 10^{-12} \text{ m} = 1 \times 10^{-3}$ nm. *(Data taken from J. Emsley: The Elements, Clarendon Press, Oxford, 1998, 3rd ed.)*

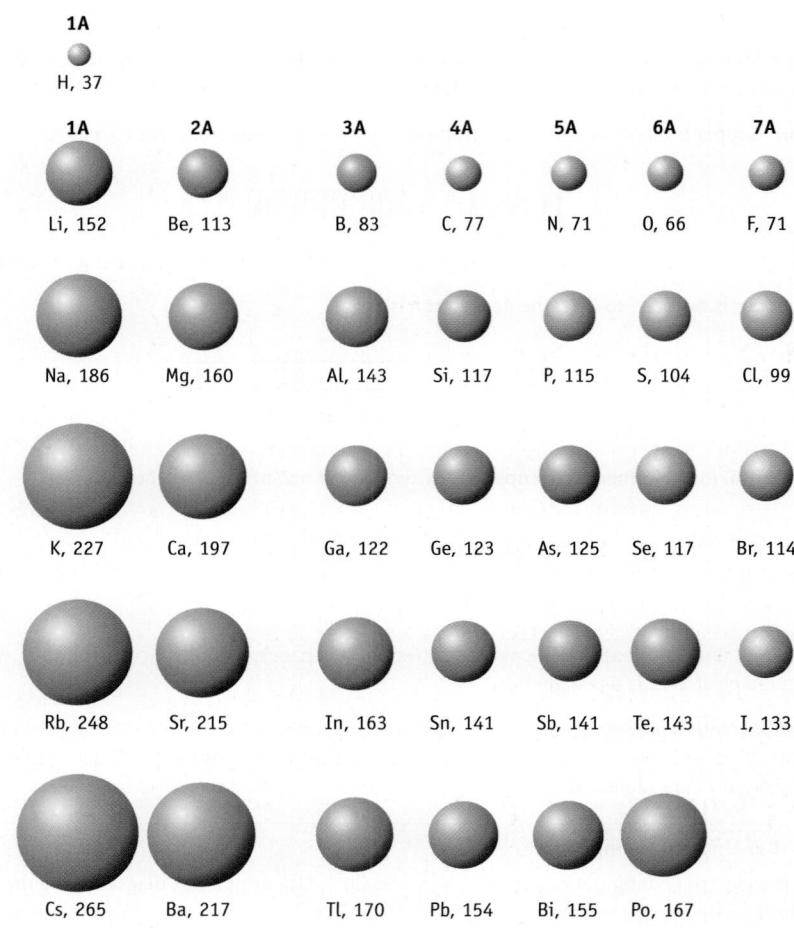

Main Group Metals
Transition Metals
Metalloids
Nonmetals

1A

H, 37

| 1A | 2A | 3A | 4A | 5A | 6A | 7A |
|---|---|---|---|---|---|---|
| Li, 152 | Be, 113 | B, 83 | C, 77 | N, 71 | O, 66 | F, 71 |
| Na, 186 | Mg, 160 | Al, 143 | Si, 117 | P, 115 | S, 104 | Cl, 99 |
| K, 227 | Ca, 197 | Ga, 122 | Ge, 123 | As, 125 | Se, 117 | Br, 114 |
| Rb, 248 | Sr, 215 | In, 163 | Sn, 141 | Sb, 141 | Te, 143 | I, 133 |
| Cs, 265 | Ba, 217 | Tl, 170 | Pb, 154 | Bi, 155 | Po, 167 | |

Atom size is also geochemically and technologically important. For example, one atom may take the place of a similarly sized atom in an alloy, a solid solution of various elements in a metallic matrix. Our technology-based industrial society depends on these materials. Substituting one element for another of similar size can often lead to alloys with different properties. But this is nothing new: humans made implements from iron meteorites (Figure 7.7) over 5000 years ago. Iron meteorites are an alloy composed of about 90% iron and 10% nickel, two elements of very similar size.

We know an orbital has no sharp boundary (◀ Figure 6.12a), so how can we define the size of an atom? There are actually several ways, and they can give slightly different results.

One of the simplest and most useful ways to define atomic size is to relate it to the distance between atoms in a sample of the element. Let us consider a diatomic molecule such as $Cl_2$ (Figure 7.8a). The radius of a Cl atom is assumed to be half the experimentally determined distance between the centers of

**FIGURE 7.7 The Willamette iron meteorite.** This 14150-kg meteorite is composed of 92.38% Fe and 7.62% Ni (with traces of Ga, Ge, and Ir). Iron and nickel atoms have nearly identical radii (124 pm and 125 pm, respectively), so one can substitute for the other in the solid. (The meteorite was discovered in Oregon in 1902, and it is now on display at the American Museum of Natural History in Washington, DC.)

© Ambient Images Inc./Alamy

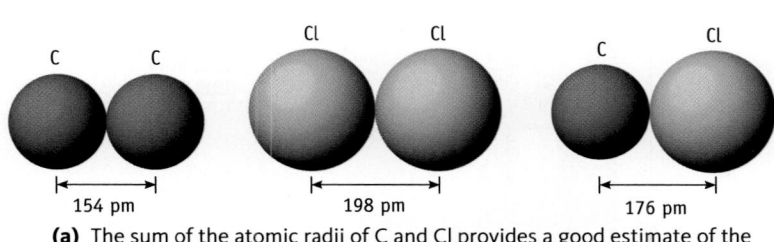

**FIGURE 7.8**
**Determining atomic radii.**
**(a)** The sum of the atomic radii of C and Cl provides a good estimate of the C–Cl distance in a molecule having such a bond.

A distance equivalent to 4 times the radius of an aluminum atom

**(b)** Pictured here is a tiny piece of an aluminum crystal. Each sphere represents an aluminum atom. Measuring the distance shown allows a scientist to estimate the radius of an aluminum atom.

the two atoms (198 pm), so the radius of one Cl atom is 99 pm. Similarly, the C—C distance in diamond is 154 pm, so a radius of 77 pm can be assigned to carbon. To test these estimates, we can add them together to estimate the C—Cl distance in $CCl_4$. The predicted distance of 176 pm agrees with the experimentally measured C—Cl distance of 176 pm. (Radii determined this way are often called *covalent radii*.)

This approach to determining atomic radii applies only if molecular compounds of the element exist (and so it is largely limited to nonmetals and metalloids). For metals, atomic radii are sometimes estimated from measurements of the atom-to-atom distance in a crystal of the element (Figure 7.8b).

Some interesting periodic trends are seen immediately on looking at the table of radii (Figure 7.6). *For the main group elements, atomic radii generally increase going down a group in the periodic table and decrease going across a period.* These trends reflect two important effects:

- The size of an atom is determined by the outermost electrons. In going from the top to the bottom of a group in the periodic table, the outermost electrons are assigned to orbitals with increasingly higher values of the principal quantum number, $n$. Because the underlying electrons require some space, these higher energy electrons are necessarily further from the nucleus.
- For main group elements of a given period, the principal quantum number, $n$, of the valence electron orbitals is the same. In going from one element to the next across a period, the effective nuclear charge ($Z^*$) increases (Figure 7.2). This results in an increased attraction between the nucleus and the valence electrons, and the atomic radius decreases.

The periodic trend in the atomic radii of transition metal atoms (Figure 7.9) across a period is somewhat different from that for main group elements. Going from left to right in a given period, the radii initially decrease. However, the sizes of the elements in the middle of a transition series change very little, and a small increase in size occurs at the end of the series. The size of transition metal atoms is determined largely by electrons in the outermost shell—that is, by the electrons of the $ns$ subshell—but electrons are being added to the $(n-1)d$ orbitals across the series. The increased nuclear charge on the atoms as one moves from left to right should cause the radius to decrease. This effect, however, is mostly canceled out by increased electron–electron repulsion. On reaching the Group 1B and 2B elements at the end of the series, the size increases slightly because the $d$ subshell is filled and electron–electron repulsions dominate.

## Ionization Energy

Ionization energy *(IE)* is the energy required to remove an electron from an atom in the gas phase (Table 7.5).

$$\text{Atom in ground state(g)} \rightarrow \text{Atom}^+(g) + e^-$$

$$\Delta U \equiv \text{ionization energy, } IE$$

To separate an electron from an atom, energy must be supplied to overcome the attraction of the nuclear charge. Because energy must be supplied, ionization energies always have positive values.

● **Atomic Radii—Caution** Numerous tabulations of atomic and covalent radii exist, and the values quoted in them often differ slightly. The variation comes about because several methods are used to determine the radii of atoms.

● **Valence and Core Electrons** Removal of core electrons requires much more energy than removal of a valence electron. Core electrons are not lost in chemical reactions. (See the plot of orbital energies on page 312.)

**FIGURE 7.9 Trends in atomic radii for the transition elements.** Atomic radii of the Group 1A and 2A metals and the transition metals of the fourth, fifth, and sixth periods.

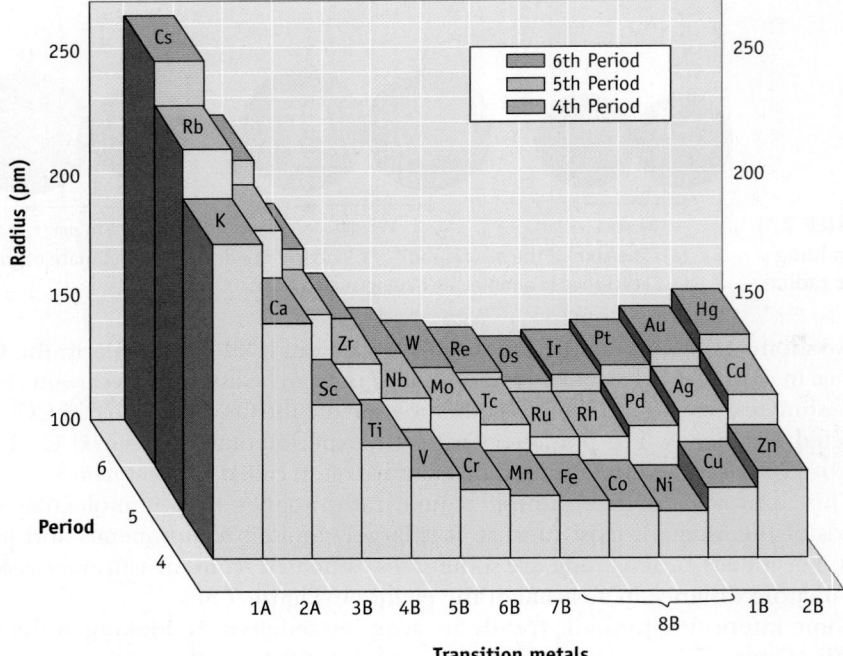

● **Measuring Ionization Energy** Ionization energy values can be measured accurately as compared with the estimations that must be made when measuring atomic radii.

Atoms other than hydrogen have a series of ionization energies as electrons are removed sequentially. For example, the first three ionization energies of magnesium are

First ionization energy, $IE_1$ = 738 kJ/mol

$$Mg(g) \longrightarrow Mg^+(g) + e^-$$
$$1s^22s^22p^63s^2 \qquad\qquad 1s^22s^22p^63s^1$$

Second ionization energy, $IE_2$ = 1451 kJ/mol

$$Mg^+(g) \longrightarrow Mg^{2+}(g) + e^-$$
$$1s^22s^22p^63s^1 \qquad\qquad 1s^22s^22p^6$$

Third ionization energy, $IE_3$ = 7732 kJ/mol

$$Mg^{2+}(g) \longrightarrow Mg^{3+}(g) + e^-$$
$$1s^22s^22p^6 \qquad\qquad 1s^22s^22p^5$$

**Table 7.5 First, Second, and Third Ionization Energies for the Main Group Elements in Periods 2–4 (kJ/mol)**

| 2nd Period | Li | Be | B | C | N | O | F | Ne |
|---|---|---|---|---|---|---|---|---|
| 1st | 513 | 899 | 801 | 1086 | 1402 | 1314 | 1681 | 2080 |
| 2nd | 7298 | 1757 | 2427 | 2352 | 2856 | 3388 | 3374 | 3952 |
| 3rd | 11815 | 14848 | 3660 | 4620 | 4578 | 5300 | 6050 | 6122 |
| **3rd Period** | **Na** | **Mg** | **Al** | **Si** | **P** | **S** | **Cl** | **Ar** |
| 1st | 496 | 738 | 577 | 787 | 1012 | 1000 | 1251 | 1520 |
| 2nd | 4562 | 1451 | 1817 | 1577 | 1903 | 2251 | 2297 | 2665 |
| 3rd | 6912 | 7732 | 2745 | 3231 | 2912 | 3361 | 3826 | 3928 |
| **4th Period** | **K** | **Ca** | **Ga** | **Ge** | **As** | **Se** | **Br** | **Kr** |
| 1st | 419 | 590 | 579 | 762 | 947 | 941 | 1140 | 1351 |
| 2nd | 3051 | 1145 | 1979 | 1537 | 1798 | 2044 | 2104 | 2350 |
| 3rd | 4411 | 4910 | 2963 | 3302 | 2735 | 2974 | 3500 | 3565 |

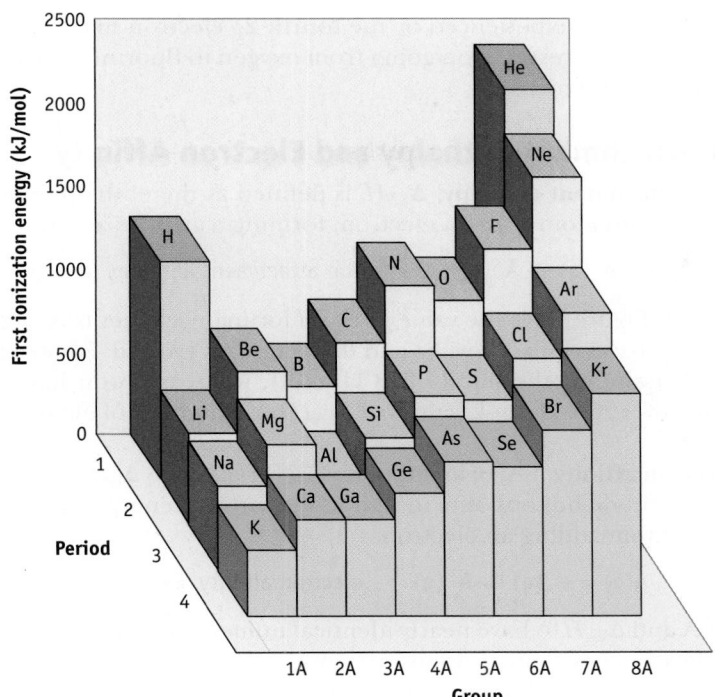

**FIGURE 7.10** **First ionization energies of the main group elements in the first four periods.** (For specific values of the ionization energies for these elements see Table 7.5 and Appendix F.)

Removing each subsequent electron requires more energy because the electron is being removed from an increasingly positive ion (Table 7.5), but there is a particularly large increase in ionization energy for removing the third electron to give $Mg^{3+}$. The first two ionization steps are for the removal of electrons from the outermost or valence shell of electrons. The third electron, however, must come from the $2p$ subshell, which has a much lower energy than the $3s$ subshell (Figure 7.1). *This large increase is experimental evidence for the electron shell structure of atoms.*

For main group ($s$- and $p$-block) elements, *first ionization energies generally increase across a period and decrease down a group* (Figure 7.10 and Table 7.5, and Appendix F). The trend across a period corresponds to the increase in effective nuclear charge, $Z^*$, with increasing atomic number (Figure 7.2). As $Z^*$ increases across a period, the energy required to remove an electron increases. Going down a group, the ionization energy decreases. The electron removed is increasingly farther from the nucleus and thus is held less strongly.

Notice that the trends in atomic radius and ionization energy for a given period are both linked to $Z^*$ although they are inversely related. *Owing to an increase in effective nuclear charge across a period, the atomic radius generally decreases and the ionization energy increases.*

A closer look at ionization energies reveals variations to the general trend in a period. One variation occurs on going from $s$-block to $p$-block elements—from beryllium to boron, for example. The $2p$ electrons are slightly higher in energy than the $2s$ electrons so the ionization energy for boron is slightly less than that for beryllium. Another dip to lower ionization energy occurs on going from nitrogen to oxygen. No change occurs in either $n$ or $\ell$, but electron–electron repulsions increase for the following reason. In Groups 3A through 5A, electrons are assigned to separate $p$ orbitals ($p_x$, $p_y$, and $p_z$). Beginning in Group 6A, however, two electrons must be assigned to the same $p$ orbital. The fourth $p$ electron shares an orbital with another electron and thus experiences greater repulsion than it would if it had been assigned to an orbital of its own.

$$O \text{ (oxygen atom)} \xrightarrow{+1314 \text{ kJ/mol}} O^+ \text{ (oxygen cation)} + e^-$$

[Ne] ↑↓   ↑↓ ↑ ↑          [Ne] ↑↓   ↑ ↑ ↑

 2s    2p                 2s    2p

The greater repulsion experienced by the fourth $2p$ electron makes it easier to remove. The usual trend resumes on going from oxygen to fluorine to neon, however, reflecting the increase in $Z^*$.

## Electron Attachment Enthalpy and Electron Affinity

● **Electron Affinity, Electron Attachment Enthalpy, and Sign Conventions** Changes in sign conventions for electron affinities over the years have caused confusion. For a useful discussion of electron affinity, see J. C. Wheeler: "Electron affinities of the alkaline earth metals and the sign convention for electron affinity," *Journal of Chemical Education*, Vol. 74, pp. 123–127, 1997. In this paper the electron affinity is taken as equivalent to the ionization energy of the anion (which is in fact the way electron affinities can be measured experimentally).

The **electron attachment enthalpy**, $\Delta_{EA}H$, is defined as the enthalpy change occurring when a gaseous atom adds an electron, forming a gaseous anion.

$$A(g) + e^-(g) \rightarrow A^-(g) \qquad \text{Electron attachment enthalpy} = \Delta_{EA}H$$

As illustrated in Figure 7.11, the value of $\Delta_{EA}H$ for many elements is negative, indicating that this process is exothermic and that energy is evolved. For example, $\Delta_{EA}H$ for fluorine is quite exothermic ($-328$ kJ/mol), whereas boron has a much less negative value of $-26.7$ kJ/mol. Values of $\Delta_{EA}H$ for a number of elements are given in Appendix F.

The **electron affinity**, EA, of an atom is closely related to $\Delta_{EA}H$. Electron affinity is equal in magnitude but opposite in sign to the internal energy change associated with a gaseous atom adding an electron.

$$A(g) + e^-(g) \rightarrow A^-(g) \qquad \text{electron affinity, } EA = -\Delta U$$

We expect EA and $\Delta_{EA}H$ to have nearly identical numerical values. However, current convention gives the two values opposite signs.

Because electron attachment enthalpy and ionization energy represent the energy involved in the gain or loss of an electron by an atom, respectively, it makes sense that periodic trends in these properties are also related. The increase in effective nuclear charge of atoms across a period (Figure 7.2) makes it more difficult to ionize the atom, and it also increases the attraction of the atom for an additional electron. Thus, an element with a high ionization energy generally has a more negative value for its electron attachment enthalpy.

As seen in Figure 7.11, the values of $\Delta_{EA}H$ generally become more negative on moving across a period, but the trend is not smooth. The elements in Group 2A and 5A appear as variations to the general trend, corresponding to cases where the added electron would start a $p$ subshell or would be paired with another electron in the $p$ subshell, respectively.

**FIGURE 7.11 Electron attachment enthalpy.** The larger the affinity of an atom for an electron, the more negative the value for $\Delta_{EA}H$. For numerical values, see Appendix F. (Data were taken from H. Hotop and W. C. Lineberger: "Binding energies of atomic negative ions," *Journal of Physical Chemistry*, Reference Data, Vol. 14, p. 731, 1985.)

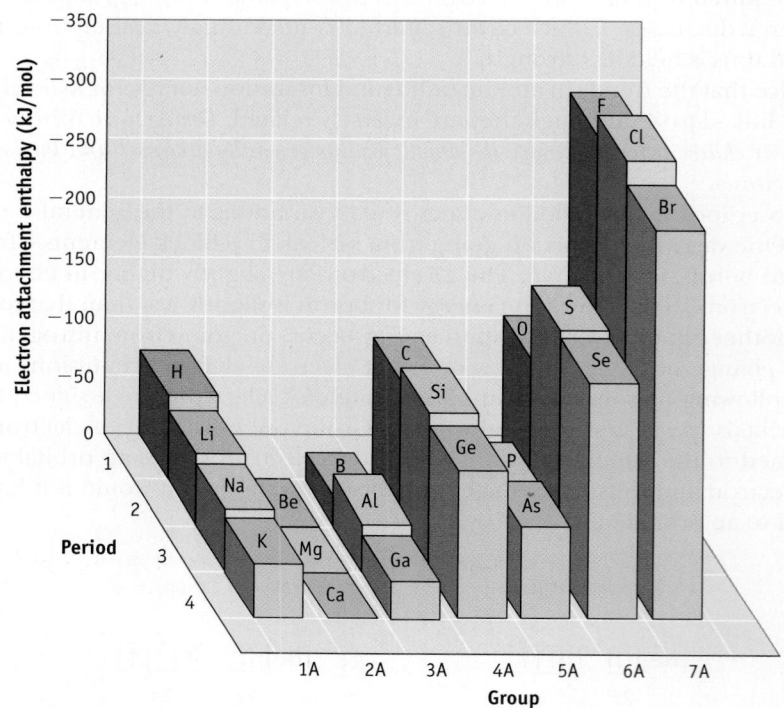

The value of electron attachment enthalpy usually becomes less negative on descending a group of the periodic table. Electrons are added increasingly farther from the nucleus, so the attractive force between the nucleus and electrons decreases. This general trend does not apply to second-period elements, however. For example, the value of the electron attachment enthalpy of fluorine is higher (less negative) than the value for chlorine. The same phenomenon is observed in Groups 3A through 6A. One explanation is that significant electron–electron repulsions occur in small anions such as $F^-$. That is, adding an electron to the seven electrons already present in the $n = 2$ shell of the small F atom leads to considerable repulsion between electrons. Chlorine has a larger atomic volume than fluorine, so adding an electron leads to a lesser degree of electron–electron repulsions.

A few elements, such as nitrogen and the Group 2A elements, have no affinity for electrons and are listed as having a $\Delta_{EA}H$ value of zero. The noble gases are generally not listed in tables of $\Delta_{EA}H$ values. They have no affinity for electrons, because any additional electron must be added to the next higher electron shell with a considerably higher energy.

No atom has a negative $\Delta_{EA}H$ value for a second electron. So what accounts for the existence of ions such as $O^{2-}$ that occur in many compounds? The answer is that doubly charged anions can be stabilized in crystalline environments by electrostatic attraction to neighboring positive ions (▶ Chapters 8 and 13).

● **Electron Attachment Enthalpy for the Halogens**

| Element | $\Delta_{EA}H$ (kJ/mol) | Atomic Radius (pm) |
|---------|-------------------------|--------------------|
| F | −328.0 | 77 |
| Cl | −349.0 | 99 |
| Br | −324.7 | 114 |
| I | −295.2 | 133 |

## EXAMPLE 7.5    Periodic Trends

**Problem**  Compare the three elements C, O, and Si.

(a)  Place them in order of increasing atomic radius.

(b)  Which has the largest ionization energy?

(c)  Which has the more negative electron attachment enthalpy, O or C?

**What Do You Know?**  Carbon and silicon are the first and second elements in Group 4A, and oxygen is the first element in Group 6A.

**Strategy**  Use the trends in atomic properties in Figures 7.6, 7.9–7.11, Table 7.5, and Appendix F.

**Solution**

(a)  *Atomic size:* Atomic radii decrease on moving across a period, so oxygen has a smaller radius than carbon. However, the radius increases on moving down a periodic group. Because C and Si are in the same group (Group 4A), silicon must be larger than carbon. The trend is O < C < Si.

(b)  *Ionization energy:* Ionization energies generally increase across a period and decrease down a group. Thus, the trend in ionization energies is Si (787 kJ/mol) < C (1086 kJ/mol) < O (1314 kJ/mol).

(c)  *Electron attachment enthalpy:* Values generally become less negative down a group (except for the second period elements) and more negative across a period. Therefore, O (−141.0 kJ/mol) has a more negative $\Delta_{EA}H$ than C (−121.9 kJ/mol).

**Think about Your Answer**  Notice that the trends in atom size and ionization energy are in the opposite order, as expected based on the values of Z*.

**Check Your Understanding**

Compare the three elements B, Al, and C.

(a)  Place the three elements in order of increasing atomic radius.

(b)  Rank the elements in order of increasing ionization energy. (Try to do this without looking at Table 7.5, then compare your prediction with the table.)

(c)  Which element, B or C, is expected to have the more negative electron attachment enthalpy value?

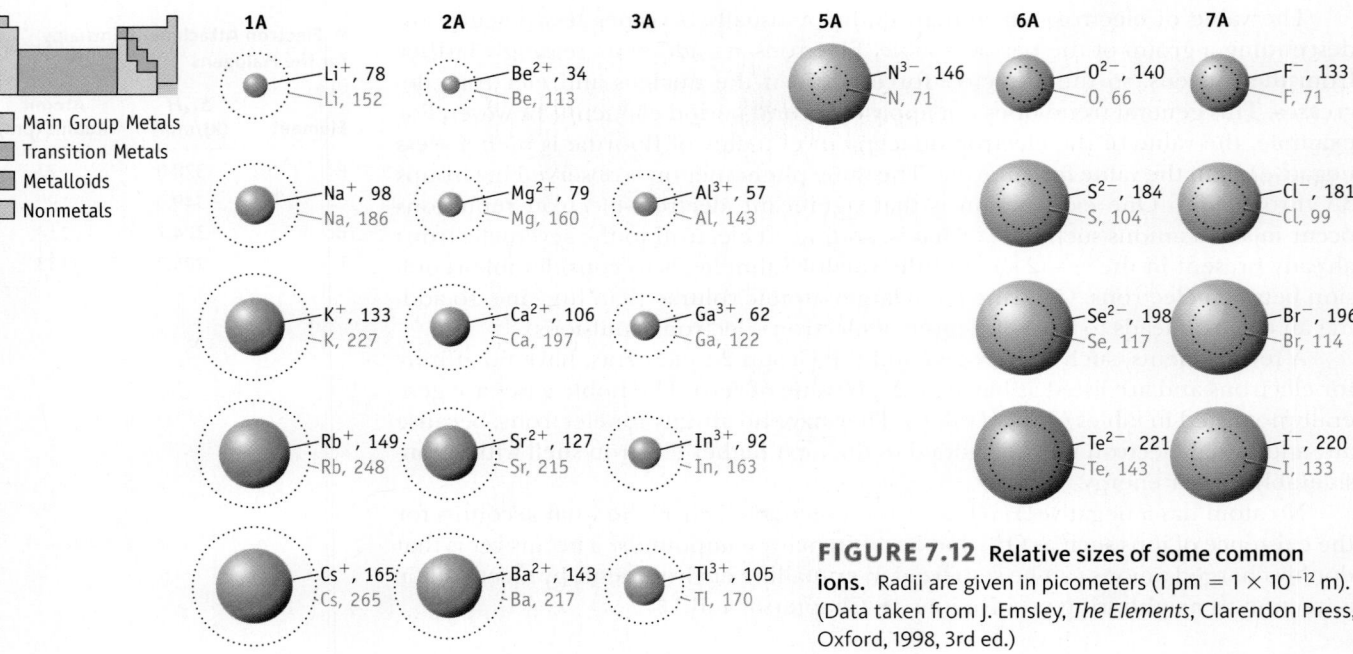

□ Main Group Metals
□ Transition Metals
□ Metalloids
□ Nonmetals

**FIGURE 7.12 Relative sizes of some common ions.** Radii are given in picometers (1 pm $= 1 \times 10^{-12}$ m). (Data taken from J. Emsley, *The Elements*, Clarendon Press, Oxford, 1998, 3rd ed.)

## Trends in Ion Sizes

The trend in the sizes of ions down a periodic group is the same as that for neutral atoms: Positive and negative ions increase in size when descending the group (Figure 7.12). Pause for a moment, however, and compare the ionic radii with the atomic radii, as also illustrated in Figure 7.12. When an electron is removed from an atom to form a cation, the size shrinks considerably. The radius of a cation is *always* smaller than that of the atom from which it is derived. For example, the radius of Li is 152 pm, whereas the radius of Li$^+$ is only 78 pm. When an electron is removed from a Li atom, the attractive force of three protons is now exerted on only two electrons, so the remaining electrons are drawn closer to the nucleus. The decrease in ion size is especially great when the last electron of a particular shell is removed, as is the case for Li. The loss of the 2$s$ electron from Li leaves Li$^+$ with no electrons in the $n = 2$ shell.

A large decrease in size is also expected if two or more electrons are removed from an atom. For example, an aluminum ion, Al$^{3+}$, has a radius of 57 pm, whereas the radius of an aluminum atom is 143 pm.

Al atom (radius = 143 pm)          Al$^{3+}$ cation (radius = 57 pm)

[Ne] ↑↓  ↑ □ □ □   $\xrightarrow{-3 \text{ electrons}}$   [Ne] □  □ □ □

  3$s$    3$p$                              3$s$    3$p$

You can also see in Figure 7.12 that anions are *always* larger than the atoms from which they are derived. Here, the argument is the opposite of that used to explain positive ion radii. The F atom, for example, has nine protons and nine electrons. On forming the anion, the nuclear charge is still +9, but the anion has 10 electrons. The $F^-$ ion is larger than the F atom because of increased electron–electron repulsions.

F atom (radius = 71 pm)          $F^-$ anion (radius = 133 pm)

71 pm                                    133 pm

Finally, it is useful to compare the sizes of isoelectronic ions across the periodic table. **Isoelectronic** ions have the same number of electrons (but a different number of protons). One such series of ions is $N^{3-}$, $O^{2-}$, $F^-$, $Na^+$, and $Mg^{2+}$:

| Ion | $N^{3-}$ | $O^{2-}$ | $F^-$ | $Na^+$ | $Mg^{2+}$ |
|---|---|---|---|---|---|
| Number of electrons | 10 | 10 | 10 | 10 | 10 |
| Number of protons | 7 | 8 | 9 | 11 | 12 |
| Ionic radius (pm) | 146 | 140 | 133 | 98 | 79 |

All these ions have 10 electrons, but they differ in the number of protons. As the number of protons increases in a series of isoelectronic ions, the balance between electron-proton attraction and electron–electron repulsion shifts in favor of attraction, and the radius decreases.

---

**REVIEW & CHECK FOR SECTION 7.5**

1. What is the trend in sizes of the ions $K^+$, $S^{2-}$, and $Cl^-$?

   (a)  $K^+ > S^{2-} > Cl^-$   (b)  $K^+ < S^{2-} < Cl^-$   (c)  $S^{2-} < Cl^- < K^+$   (d)  $S^{2-} > Cl^- > K^+$

2. Locate the elements C, N, Si, and P in the periodic table. Based on general trends, identify the elements in this group with the highest and lowest ionization energy.

   (a)  C highest, P lowest              (c)  N highest, Si lowest

   (b)  C highest, Si lowest             (d)  C lowest, N highest

---

## 7.6  Periodic Trends and Chemical Properties

Atomic and ionic radii, ionization energies, and electron attachment enthalpies are properties associated with atoms and their ions. It is reasonable to expect that knowledge of these properties will be useful as we explore the chemistry involving formation of ionic compounds.

The periodic table was created by grouping together elements having similar chemical properties (Figure 7.13). Alkali metals, for example, characteristically form compounds containing a 1+ ion, such as $Li^+$, $Na^+$, or $K^+$. Thus, the reaction between sodium and chlorine gives the ionic compound, NaCl (composed of $Na^+$ and $Cl^-$ ions) [Figure 1.2, page 3], and potassium and water react to form an aqueous solution of KOH, a solution containing the hydrated ions $K^+(aq)$ and $OH^-(aq)$.

$$2\ Na(s) + Cl_2(g) \rightarrow 2\ NaCl(s)$$

$$2\ K(s) + 2\ H_2O(\ell) \rightarrow 2\ K^+(aq) + 2\ OH^-(aq) + H_2(g)$$

The facile formation of Na⁺ and K⁺ ions in chemical reactions agrees with the fact that alkali metals have low ionization energies.

Ionization energies also account for the fact that these reactions of sodium and potassium do not produce compounds such as NaCl₂ or K(OH)₂. The formation of an Na²⁺ or K²⁺ ion would be a very unfavorable process. Removing a second electron from these metals requires a great deal of energy because a core electron would

**FIGURE 7.13 Examples of the periodicity of Group 1A and Group 7A elements.** Dmitri Mendeleev developed the first periodic table by listing elements in order of increasing atomic weight. Every so often, an element had properties similar to those of a lighter element, and these were placed in vertical columns or groups. We now recognize that the elements should be listed in order of increasing atomic number and that the periodic occurrence of similar properties is related to the electron configurations of the elements.

# Metals in Biochemistry and Medicine

Many main group and transition metals play an important role in biochemistry and in medicine. Your body has low levels of the following metals in the form of various compounds: Ca, 1.5%; Na, 0.1%; Mg, 0.05%, as well as iron, cobalt, zinc, and copper, all less than about 0.05%. (Levels are percentages by mass.)

Much of the 3–4 g of iron in your body is found in hemoglobin, the substance responsible for carrying oxygen to cells. Iron deficiency is marked by fatigue, infections, and mouth inflammations.

Iron in your diet can come from eggs and brewer's yeast, which has a very high iron content. In addition, foods such as some breakfast cereals are "fortified" with metallic iron. (In an interesting experiment you can do at home, you can remove the iron by stirring the cereal with a strong magnet.) Vitamin pills often contain iron(II) compounds with anions such as sulfate and succinate ($C_4H_4O_4^{2-}$).

The average person has about 75 mg of copper, about one third of which is found in the muscles. Copper is involved in many biological functions, and a deficiency shows up in many ways: anemia, degeneration of the nervous system, and impaired immunity. Wilson's disease, a genetic disorder, leads to the over-accumulation of copper in the body and results in hepatic and neurological damage.

Like silver ions (page 144), copper ions can also act as a bacteriocide. Scientists from Britain and India recently investigated a long-held belief among people in India that storing water in brass pitchers can ward off illness. (Brass is an alloy of copper and zinc.) They filled brass pitchers

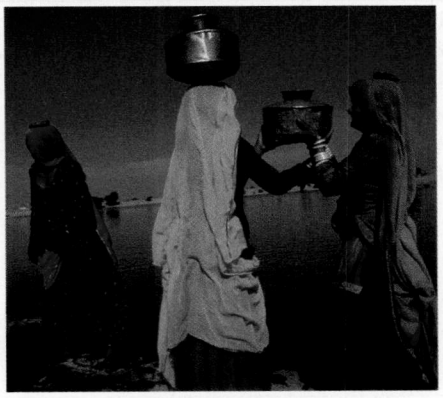

**Filling a brass water jug for drinking water in India.** Copper ions released in tiny amounts from the brass kill bacteria in contaminated water.

Jeremy Horner/Corbis

with previously sterile water to which they had added *E. coli* (a bacterium that lives in the lower intestine of many warm-blooded animals and consequently is found in their feces). Other brass pitchers were filled with contaminated river water from India. In both cases, they found fecal bacteria counts dropped from as high as 1,000,000 bacteria per milliliter to zero in two days. In contrast, bacteria levels stayed high in plastic or earthenware pots. Apparently, just enough copper ions are released by the brass to kill the bacteria but not enough to affect humans.

**Questions:**

1. Give the electron configurations for iron and the iron(II) and iron(III) ions.

2. In hemoglobin, iron can be in the iron(II) or iron(III) state. Is either of these iron ions paramagnetic?

3. Give the electron configurations for copper and the copper(I) and copper(II) ions. Is copper in any of these forms paramagnetic?

4. Why are copper atoms (radius = 128 pm) slightly larger than iron atoms (radius = 124 pm)?

5. In hemoglobin, the iron is enclosed by the porphyrin group (shown below), a flat grouping of carbon, hydrogen, and nitrogen atoms. (This is in turn encased in a protein.) When iron is in the form of the $Fe^{3+}$ ion, it just fits into the space within the four N atoms, and the arrangement is flat. Speculate on what occurs to the structure when iron is reduced to the $Fe^{2+}$ ion.

**Answers to these questions are available in Appendix N.**

have to be removed. The energetic barrier to this process is the underlying reason that *main group metals generally form cations with an electron configuration equivalent to that of the preceding noble gas.*

Why isn't $Na_2Cl$ another possible product from the sodium and chlorine reaction? This formula would imply that the compound contains $Na^+$ and $Cl^{2-}$ ions. Adding two electrons per atom to Cl means that the second electron must enter the next higher shell at much higher energy. Thus, anions such as $Cl^{2-}$ are not known. This example leads us to a general statement: *Nonmetals generally acquire enough electrons to form an anion with the electron configuration of the next noble gas.*

We can use similar logic to rationalize other observations. Ionization energies increase on going from left to right across a period. We have seen that elements from Groups 1A and 2A form ionic compounds, an observation directly related to the low ionization energies for these elements. Ionization energies for elements toward the middle and right side of a period, however, are sufficiently large that cation formation is unfavorable. On the right side of the second period, oxygen and fluorine much prefer taking on electrons to giving them up; these elements have high ionization energies and relatively large, negative electron attachment enthalpies. Thus, oxygen and fluorine form anions and not cations when they react.

Finally, let us think for a moment about carbon, the basis of thousands of chemical compounds. Its ionization energy is not favorable for cation formation, and it also does not generally form anions. Thus, we do not find many binary ionic compounds containing carbon; instead, we find carbon sharing electrons with other elements in compounds such as $CO_2$ and $CCl_4$, and we will take up those kinds of compounds in the next two chapters.

---

**REVIEW & CHECK FOR SECTION 7.6**

1. Which of the following is an incorrect formula?

   (a) $MgCl$          (b) $CaCl_2$          (c) $AlCl_3$          (d) $RbCl$

2. Which of the following is not the formula for a common ion?

   (a) $Cl^-$          (b) $K^+$          (c) $O^{2-}$          (d) $S^{3-}$

---

 and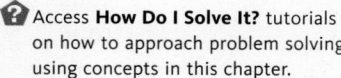

Sign in at **www.cengage.com/owl** to:
- View tutorials and simulations, develop problem-solving skills, and complete online homework assigned by your professor.
- For quick review and exam prep, download Go Chemistry mini lecture modules from OWL (or purchase them at **www.cengagebrain.com**)

 Access **How Do I Solve It?** tutorials on how to approach problem solving using concepts in this chapter.

## CHAPTER GOALS REVISITED

*Now that you have studied this chapter, you should ask whether you have met the chapter goals. In particular, you should be able to:*

**Recognize the relationship of the four quantum numbers ($n$, $\ell$, $m_\ell$, and $m_s$) to atomic structure**

a. Recognize that each electron in an atom has a different set of the four quantum numbers, $n$, $\ell$, $m_\ell$, and $m_s$ (Sections 6.5–6.7, 7.1–7.3). **Study Questions: 11, 13, 35, 37, 52.**

b. Understand that the Pauli exclusion principle leads to the conclusion that no atomic orbital can be assigned more than two electrons and that the two electrons in an orbital must have opposite spins (different values of $m_s$) (Section 7.1).

**Write the electron configuration for atoms and monatomic ions**

a. Recognize that electrons are assigned to the subshells of an atom in order of increasing energy (Aufbau principle, Section 7.2). In the H atom, the energies increase with increasing $n$, but, in a many-electron atom, the energies depend on both $n$ and $\ell$ (Figure 7.1).

b. Understand effective nuclear charge, $Z^*$, and its ability to explain why different subshells in the same shell of multielectron atoms have different energies. Also, understand the role of $Z^*$ in determining the properties of atoms (Sections 7.2 and 7.5).

c. Using the periodic table as a guide, depict electron configurations of neutral atoms (Section 7.3) and monatomic ions (Section 7.4) using the orbital box or *spdf* notation. In both cases, configurations can be abbreviated with the noble gas notation. **Study Questions: 1, 3, 5–10, 13, 15, 18, 20, 21, 33–36, 39, 71.**

d. When assigning electrons to atomic orbitals, apply the Pauli exclusion principle and Hund's rule (Sections 7.3 and 7.4). **Study Question: 59.**

e. Understand the role magnetism plays in revealing atomic structure (Section 7.4). **Study Questions: 19–21, 33, 39, 52.**

**Rationalize trends in atom and ion sizes, ionization energy, and electron attachment enthalpy**

a.  Predict how properties of atoms—size, ionization energy *(IE)*, and electron attachment enthalpy $(\Delta_{EA}H)$—change on moving down a group or across a period of the periodic table (Section 7.5). The general periodic trends for these properties are as follows: **Study Questions: 24, 26, 28, 30, 32, 40–43, 46–49, 57, 58, 64, and Go Chemisty Module 11.**

 (i)  Atomic size decreases across a period and increases down a group.

 (ii)  *IE* increases across a period and decreases down a group.

 (iii) The value of $\Delta_{EA}H$ becomes more negative across a period and becomes less negative down a group.

b.  Recognize the role that ionization energy and electron attachment enthalpy play in forming ionic compounds (Section 7.6). **Study Questions: 45, 72.**

# Study Questions

**⏻WL** Interactive versions of these questions are assignable in OWL.

▲ denotes challenging questions.

Blue-numbered questions have answers in Appendix R and fully worked solutions in the *Student Solutions Manual*.

## Practicing Skills

### Writing Electron Configurations of Atoms
*(See Section 7.3, Examples 7.1–7.3, and Tables 7.1, 7.3, and 7.4.)*

 1. Write the electron configurations for P and Cl using both *spdf* notation and orbital box diagrams. Describe the relationship between each atom's electron configuration and its position in the periodic table.

 2. Write the electron configurations for Mg and Ar using both *spdf* notation and orbital box diagrams. Describe the relationship of the atom's electron configuration to its position in the periodic table.

 3. Using *spdf* notation, write the electron configurations for atoms of chromium and iron, two of the major components of stainless steel.

 4. Using *spdf* notation, give the electron configuration of vanadium, V, an element found in some brown and red algae and some toadstools.

 5. Depict the electron configuration for each of the following atoms using *spdf* and noble gas notations.
 (a) Arsenic, As. A deficiency of As can impair growth in animals, but larger amounts are poisonous.
 (b) Krypton, Kr. It ranks seventh in abundance of the gases in Earth's atmosphere.

 6. Using *spdf* and noble gas notations, write electron configurations for atoms of the following elements. (Try to do this by looking at the periodic table but not at Table 7.3).
 (a) Strontium, Sr. This element is named for a town in Scotland.
 (b) Zirconium, Zr. The metal is exceptionally resistant to corrosion and so has important industrial applications. Moon rocks show a surprisingly high zirconium content compared with rocks on Earth.

 (c) Rhodium, Rh. This metal is used in jewelry and in catalysts in industry.
 (d) Tin, Sn. The metal was used in the ancient world. Alloys of tin (solder, bronze, and pewter) are important.

 7. Use noble gas and *spdf* notations to depict electron configurations for the following metals of the third transition series.
 (a) Tantalum, Ta. The metal and its alloys resist corrosion and are often used in surgical and dental tools.
 (b) Platinum, Pt. This metal was used by pre-Columbian Indians in jewelry. Now it is still used in jewelry but it is also the basis for anticancer drugs and catalysts (such as those in automobile exhaust systems).

 8. The lanthanides, once called the *rare earth elements*, are really only "medium rare." Using noble gas and *spdf* notations, depict reasonable electron configurations for the following elements.
 (a) Samarium, Sm. This lanthanide is used in magnetic materials.
 (b) Ytterbium, Yb. This element was named for the village of Ytterby in Sweden, where a mineral source of the element was found.

 9. The actinide americium, Am, is a radioactive element that has found use in home smoke detectors. Depict its electron configuration using noble gas and *spdf* notations.

 10. Predict electron configurations for the following elements of the actinide series of elements. Use noble gas and *spdf* notations.
 (a) Plutonium, Pu. The element is best known as a by-product of nuclear power plant operations.
 (b) Curium, Cm. This actinide was named for Marie Curie (page 338).

### Quantum Numbers and Electron Configurations
*(See Section 7.3 and Example 7.2.)*

 11. What is the maximum number of electrons that can be identified with each of the following sets of quantum numbers? In some cases, the answer is "none." Explain why this is true.
 (a) $n = 4, \ell = 3, m_\ell = 1$
 (b) $n = 6, \ell = 1, m_\ell = -1, m_s = -\frac{1}{2}$
 (c) $n = 3, \ell = 3, m_\ell = -3$

12. What is the maximum number of electrons that can be identified with each of the following sets of quantum numbers? In some cases, the answer may be "none." In such cases, explain why "none" is the correct answer.
    (a) $n = 3$
    (b) $n = 3$ and $\ell = 2$
    (c) $n = 4$, $\ell = 1$, $m_\ell = -1$, and $m_s = +\frac{1}{2}$
    (d) $n = 5$, $\ell = 0$, $m_\ell = -1$, $m_s = +\frac{1}{2}$

13. Depict the electron configuration for magnesium using an orbital box diagram and noble gas notation. Give a complete set of four quantum numbers for each of the electrons beyond those of the preceding noble gas.

14. Depict the electron configuration for phosphorus using an orbital box diagram and noble gas notation. Give one possible set of four quantum numbers for each of the electrons beyond those of the preceding noble gas.

15. Using an orbital box diagram and noble gas notation, show the electron configuration of gallium, Ga. Give a set of quantum numbers for the highest-energy electron.

16. Using an orbital box diagram and noble gas notation, show the electron configuration of titanium. Give one possible set of four quantum numbers for each of the electrons beyond those of the preceding noble gas.

### Electron Configurations of Atoms and Ions and Magnetic Behavior
*(See Section 7.4 and Example 7.4.)*

17. Using orbital box diagrams, depict an electron configuration for each of the following ions: (a) $Mg^{2+}$, (b) $K^+$, (c) $Cl^-$, and (d) $O^{2-}$.

18. Using orbital box diagrams, depict an electron configuration for each of the following ions: (a) $Na^+$, (b) $Al^{3+}$, (c) $Ge^{2+}$, and (d) $F^-$.

19. Using orbital box diagrams and noble gas notation, depict the electron configurations of (a) V, (b) $V^{2+}$, and (c) $V^{5+}$. Are any of the ions paramagnetic?

20. Using orbital box diagrams and noble gas notation, depict the electron configurations of (a) Ti, (b) $Ti^{2+}$, and (c) $Ti^{4+}$. Are any of these paramagnetic?

21. Manganese is found as $MnO_2$ in deep ocean deposits.
    (a) Depict the electron configuration of this element using the noble gas notation and an orbital box diagram.
    (b) Using an orbital box diagram, show the electrons beyond those of the preceding noble gas for the 4+ ion.
    (c) Is the 4+ ion paramagnetic?
    (d) How many unpaired electrons does the $Mn^{4+}$ ion have?

22. One compound found in alkaline batteries is NiOOH, a compound containing $Ni^{3+}$ ions. When the battery is discharged, the $Ni^{3+}$ is reduced to $Ni^{2+}$ ions [as in $Ni(OH)_2$]. Using orbital box diagrams and the noble gas notation, show electron configurations of these ions. Is either of these ions paramagnetic?

### Periodic Properties
*(See Section 7.5 and Example 7.5.)*

23. Arrange the following elements in order of increasing size: Al, B, C, K, and Na. (Try doing it without looking at Figure 7.6, then check yourself by looking up the necessary atomic radii.)

24. Arrange the following elements in order of increasing size: Ca, Rb, P, Ge, and Sr. (Try doing it without looking at Figure 7.6, then check yourself by looking up the necessary atomic radii.)

25. Select the atom or ion in each pair that has the larger radius.
    (a) Cl or $Cl^-$     (b) Al or O     (c) In or I

26. Select the atom or ion in each pair that has the larger radius.
    (a) Cs or Rb     (b) $O^{2-}$ or O     (c) Br or As

27. Which of the following groups of elements is arranged correctly in order of increasing ionization energy?
    (a) C < Si < Li < Ne     (c) Li < Si < C < Ne
    (b) Ne < Si < C < Li     (d) Ne < C < Si < Li

28. Arrange the following atoms in order of increasing ionization energy: Li, K, C, and N.

29. Compare the elements Na, Mg, O, and P.
    (a) Which has the largest atomic radius?
    (b) Which has the most negative electron attachment enthalpy?
    (c) Place the elements in order of increasing ionization energy.

30. Compare the elements B, Al, C, and Si.
    (a) Which has the most metallic character?
    (b) Which has the largest atomic radius?
    (c) Which has the most negative electron attachment enthalpy?
    (d) Place the three elements B, Al, and C in order of increasing first ionization energy.

31. Explain each answer briefly.
    (a) Place the following elements in order of increasing ionization energy: F, O, and S.
    (b) Which has the largest ionization energy: O, S, or Se?
    (c) Which has the most negative electron attachment enthalpy: Se, Cl, or Br?
    (d) Which has the largest radius: $O^{2-}$, $F^-$, or F?

32. Explain each answer briefly.
    (a) Rank the following in order of increasing atomic radius: O, S, and F.
    (b) Which has the largest ionization energy: P, Si, S, or Se?
    (c) Place the following in order of increasing radius: $O^{2-}$, $N^{3-}$, and $F^-$.
    (d) Place the following in order of increasing ionization energy: Cs, Sr, and Ba.

## General Questions

*These questions are not designated as to type or location in the chapter. They may combine several concepts.*

33. Using an orbital box diagram and noble gas notation, show the electron configurations of uranium and of the uranium(IV) ion. Is either of these paramagnetic?

**34.** The rare earth elements, or lanthanides, commonly exist as 3+ ions. Using an orbital box diagram and noble gas notation, show the electron configurations of the following elements and ions.
(a) Ce and $Ce^{3+}$ (cerium)
(b) Ho and $Ho^{3+}$ (holmium)

**35.** A neutral atom has two electrons with $n = 1$, eight electrons with $n = 2$, eight electrons with $n = 3$, and two electrons with $n = 4$. Assuming this element is in its ground state, supply the following information:
(a) atomic number
(b) total number of $s$ electrons
(c) total number of $p$ electrons
(d) total number of $d$ electrons
(e) Is the element a metal, metalloid, or nonmetal?

**36.** Element 109, now named meitnerium (in honor of the Austrian–Swedish physicist, Lise Meitner [1878–1968]), was produced in August 1982 by a team at Germany's Institute for Heavy Ion Research. Depict its electron configuration using *spdf* and noble gas notations. Name another element found in the same group as meitnerium.

**Lise Meitner (1878–1968) and Otto Hahn (1879–1968).**
Element 109 (Mt) was named after Meitner. She earned her Ph.D. in physics under Ludwig Boltzmann at the University of Vienna, and she was the first woman to earn a Ph.D. at that university.

**37.** Which of the following is *not* an allowable set of quantum numbers? Explain your answer briefly. For those sets that are valid, identify an element in which an outermost valence electron could have that set of quantum numbers.

|     | $n$ | $\ell$ | $m_\ell$ | $m_s$ |
|-----|-----|--------|----------|-------|
| (a) | 2   | 0      | 0        | $-\frac{1}{2}$ |
| (b) | 1   | 1      | 0        | $+\frac{1}{2}$ |
| (c) | 2   | 1      | $-1$     | $-\frac{1}{2}$ |
| (d) | 4   | 2      | $+2$     | $-\frac{1}{2}$ |

**38.** A possible excited state for the H atom has an electron in a $4p$ orbital. List all possible sets of quantum numbers $(n, \ell, m_\ell, m_s)$ for this electron.

**39.** The magnet in the photo is made from neodymium, iron, and boron.

**A magnet made of an alloy containing the elements Nd, Fe, and B.**
(a) Write the electron configuration of each of these elements using an orbital box diagram and noble gas notation.
(b) Are these elements paramagnetic or diamagnetic?
(c) Write the electron configurations of $Nd^{3+}$ and $Fe^{3+}$ using orbital box diagrams and noble gas notation. Are these ions paramagnetic or diamagnetic?

**40.** Name the element corresponding to each characteristic below.
(a) the element with the electron configuration $1s^2 2s^2 2p^6 3s^2 3p^3$
(b) the alkaline earth element with the smallest atomic radius
(c) the element with the largest ionization energy in Group 5A
(d) the element whose 2+ ion has the configuration $[Kr]4d^5$
(e) the element with the most negative electron attachment enthalpy in Group 7A
(f) the element whose electron configuration is $[Ar]3d^{10}4s^2$

**41.** Arrange the following atoms in order of increasing ionization energy: Si, K, P, and Ca.

**42.** Rank the following in order of increasing ionization energy: Cl, $Ca^{2+}$, and $Cl^-$. Briefly explain your answer.

**43.** Answer the questions below about the elements A and B, which have the electron configurations shown.
$$A = [Kr]5s^1 \quad B = [Ar]3d^{10}4s^2 4p^4$$
(a) Is element A a metal, nonmetal, or metalloid?
(b) Which element has the greater ionization energy?
(c) Which element has the less negative electron attachment enthalpy?
(d) Which element has the larger atomic radius?
(e) What is the formula for a compound formed between A and B?

**44.** Answer the following questions about the elements with the electron configurations shown here:
$$A = [Ar]4s^2 \quad B = [Ar]3d^{10}4s^2 4p^5$$
(a) Is element A a metal, metalloid, or nonmetal?
(b) Is element B a metal, metalloid, or nonmetal?
(c) Which element is expected to have the larger ionization energy?
(d) Which element has the smaller atomic radius?

45. Which of the following ions are unlikely to be found in a chemical compound: $Cs^+$, $In^{4+}$, $Fe^{6+}$, $Te^{2-}$, $Sn^{5+}$, and $I^-$? Explain briefly.

46. Place the following ions in order of decreasing size: $K^+$, $Cl^-$, $S^{2-}$, and $Ca^{2+}$.

47. Answer each of the following questions:
    (a) Of the elements S, Se, and Cl, which has the largest atomic radius?
    (b) Which has the larger radius, Br or $Br^-$?
    (c) Which should have the largest difference between the first and second ionization energy: Si, Na, P, or Mg?
    (d) Which has the largest ionization energy: N, P, or As?
    (e) Which of the following has the largest radius: $O^{2-}$, $N^{3-}$, or $F^-$?

48. ▲ The following are isoelectronic species: $Cl^-$, $K^+$, and $Ca^{2+}$. Rank them in order of increasing (a) size, (b) ionization energy, and (c) electron attachment enthalpy.

49. Compare the elements Na, B, Al, and C with regard to the following properties:
    (a) Which has the largest atomic radius?
    (b) Which has the most negative electron attachment enthalpy?
    (c) Place the elements in order of increasing ionization energy.

50. ▲ Two elements in the second transition series (Y through Cd) have four unpaired electrons in their 3+ ions. What elements fit this description?

51. The configuration for an element is given here.

    [Ar] ⊞ 3d    ⊞ 4s

    (a) What is the identity of the element with this configuration?
    (b) Is a sample of the element paramagnetic or diamagnetic?
    (c) How many unpaired electrons does a 3+ ion of this element have?

52. The configuration of an element is given here.

    [Ar] ⊞ 3d    ⊞ 4s

    (a) What is the identity of the element?
    (b) In what group and period is the element found?
    (c) Is the element a nonmetal, a main group metal, a transition metal, a lanthanide, or an actinide?
    (d) Is the element diamagnetic or paramagnetic? If paramagnetic, how many unpaired electrons are there?
    (e) Write a complete set of quantum numbers ($n$, $\ell$, $m_\ell$, $m_s$) for each of the valence electrons.
    (f) What is the configuration of the 2+ ion formed from this element? Is the ion diamagnetic or paramagnetic?

## In the Laboratory

53. Nickel(II) formate [$Ni(HCO_2)_2$] is widely used as a catalyst precursor and to make metallic nickel. It can be prepared in the general chemistry laboratory by treating nickel(II) acetate with formic acid ($HCO_2H$).

    $$Ni(CH_3CO_2)_2(aq) + 2\ HCO_2H(aq) \rightarrow$$
    $$Ni(HCO_2)_2(aq) + 2\ CH_3CO_2H(aq)$$

Green crystalline $Ni(HCO_2)_2$ is precipitated after adding ethanol to the solution.
    (a) What is the theoretical yield of nickel(II) formate from 0.500 g of nickel(II) acetate and excess formic acid?
    (b) Is nickel(II) formate paramagnetic or diamagnetic? If it is paramagnetic, how many unpaired electrons would you expect?
    (c) If nickel(II) formate is heated to 300 °C in the absence of air for 30 minutes, the salt decomposes to form pure nickel powder. What mass of nickel powder should be produced by heating 253 mg of nickel(II) formate? Are nickel atoms paramagnetic?

54. ▲ Spinels are solids with the general formula $M^{2+}(M'^{3+})_2O_4$ (where $M^{2+}$ and $M'^{3+}$ are metal cations of the same or different metals). The best-known example is common magnetite, $Fe_3O_4$ [which you can formulate as $(Fe^{2+})(Fe^{3+})_2O_4$].

**A crystal of a spinel.**

© Cengage Learning/Charles D. Winters

    (a) Given its name, it is evident that magnetite is ferromagnetic. How many unpaired electrons are there in iron(II) and in iron(III) ions?
    (b) Two other spinels are $CoAl_2O_4$ and $SnCo_2O_4$. What metal ions are involved in each? What are their electron configurations? Are the metal ions paramagnetic, and if so how many unpaired electrons are involved?

## Summary and Conceptual Questions

*The following questions may use concepts from this and previous chapters.*

55. Why is the radius of $Li^+$ so much smaller than the radius of Li? Why is the radius of $F^-$ so much larger than the radius of F?

56. Which ions in the following list are not likely to be found in chemical compounds: $K^{2+}$, $Cs^+$, $Al^{4+}$, $F^{2-}$, and $Se^{2-}$? Explain briefly.

57. ▲ Two elements have the following first through fourth ionization energies. Deduce the group in the periodic table to which they probably belong. Explain briefly.

| Ionization Energy (kJ/mol) | Element 1 | Element 2 |
|---|---|---|
| 1st $IE$ | 1086.2 | 577.4 |
| 2nd $IE$ | 2352 | 1816.6 |
| 3rd $IE$ | 4620 | 2744.6 |
| 4th $IE$ | 6222 | 11575 |

**58.** ▲ The ionization of the hydrogen atom can be calculated from Bohr's equation for the electron energy.

$$E = -(NRhc)(Z^2/n^2)$$

where $NRhc = 1312$ kJ/mol and $Z$ is the atomic number. Let us use this approach to calculate a possible ionization energy for helium. First, assume the electrons of the He experience the full 2+ nuclear charge. This gives us the upper limit for the ionization energy. Next, assume one electron of He completely screens the nuclear charge from the other electrons, so $Z = 1$. This gives us a lower limit to the ionization energy. Compare these calculated values for the upper and lower limits to the experimental value of 2372.3 kJ/mol. What does this tell us about the ability of one electron to screen the nuclear charge?

**59.** Compare the configurations below with two electrons located in $p$ orbitals. Which would be the most stable (have the lowest energy)? Which would be the least stable? Explain your answers.

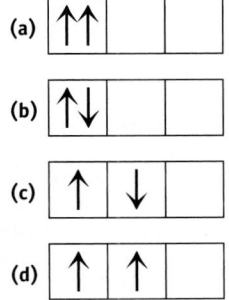

**60.** The bond lengths in $Cl_2$, $Br_2$, and $I_2$ are 200, 228, and 266 pm, respectively. Knowing that the tin radius is 141 pm, estimate the bond distances in Sn—Cl, Sn—Br, and Sn—I. Compare the estimated values with the experimental values of 233, 250, and 270 pm, respectively.

**61.** Write electron configurations to show the first two ionization processes for potassium. Explain why the second ionization energy is much greater than the first.

**62.** What is the trend in ionization energy when proceeding down a group in the periodic table. Rationalize this trend.

**63.** (a) Explain why the sizes of atoms change when proceeding across a period of the periodic table.
(b) Explain why the sizes of transition metal atoms change very little across a period.

**64.** Which of the following elements has the greatest difference between the first and second ionization energies: C, Li, N, Be? Explain your answer.

**65.** ▲ What arguments would you use to convince another student in general chemistry that MgO consists of the ions $Mg^{2+}$ and $O^{2-}$ and not the ions $Mg^+$ and $O^-$? What experiments could be done to provide some evidence that the correct formulation of magnesium oxide is $Mg^{2+}O^{2-}$?

**66.** Explain why the first ionization energy of Ca is greater than that of K, whereas the second ionization energy of Ca is lower than the second ionization energy of K.

**67.** The energies of the orbitals in many elements have been determined. For the first two periods they have the following values:

| Element | 1s (kJ/mol) | 2s (kJ/mol) | 2p (kJ/mol) |
|---|---|---|---|
| H | −1313 | | |
| He | −2373 | | |
| Li | | −520.0 | |
| Be | | −899.3 | |
| B | | −1356 | −800.8 |
| C | | −1875 | −1029 |
| N | | −2466 | −1272 |
| O | | −3124 | −1526 |
| F | | −3876 | −1799 |
| Ne | | −4677 | −2083 |

(a) ▲ Why do the orbital energies generally become more negative on proceeding across the second period?
(b) How are these values related to the ionization energy and electron attachment enthalpy of the elements?
(c) Use these energy values to explain the observation that the ionization energies of the first four second-period elements are in the order Li < Be > B < C.

(Data from J. B. Mann, T. L. Meek, and L. C. Allen: *Journal of the American Chemical Society*, Vol. 122, p. 2780, 2000.)

**68.** ▲ The ionization energies for the removal of the first electron in Si, P, S, and Cl are as listed in the table below. Briefly rationalize this trend.

| Element | First Ionization Energy (kJ/mol) |
|---|---|
| Si | 780 |
| P | 1060 |
| S | 1005 |
| Cl | 1255 |

**69.** Using your knowledge of the trends in element sizes on going across the periodic table, explain briefly why the density of the elements increases from K through V.

70. The densities (in g/cm³) of elements in Groups 6B, 8B, and 1B are given in the table below.

Period 4    Cr, 7.19    Co, 8.90    Cu, 8.96
Period 5    Mo, 10.22   Rh, 12.41   Ag, 10.50
Period 6    W, 19.30    Ir, 22.56   Au, 19.32

Transition metals in the sixth period all have much greater densities than the elements in the same groups in the fourth and fifth periods. Refer to Figure 7.9, and explain this observation.

71. The discovery of two new elements (atomic numbers 113 and 115) was announced in February 2004.

Some members of the team that discovered elements 113 and 115 at the Lawrence Livermore National Laboratory (left to right): Jerry Landrum, Dawn Shaughnessy, Joshua Patin, Philip Wilk, and Kenton Moody.

(a) Use *spdf* and noble gas notations to give the electron configurations of these two elements.
(b) For each of these elements, name another element in the same periodic group.
(c) Element 113 was made by firing the nucleus of a light atom at a heavy americium atom. The two nuclei combine to give a nucleus with 113 protons. What light atom was used as a projectile?

72. Explain why the reaction of calcium and fluorine does not form $CaF_3$.

73. ▲ Thionyl chloride, $SOCl_2$, is an important chlorinating and oxidizing agent in organic chemistry. It is prepared industrially by oxygen atom transfer from $SO_3$ to $SCl_2$.

$$SO_3(g) + SCl_2(g) \rightarrow SO_2(g) + SOCl_2(g)$$

(a) Give the electron configuration for an atom of sulfur using an orbital box diagram. Do not use the noble gas notation.
(b) Using the configuration given in part (a), write a set of quantum numbers for the highest-energy electron in a sulfur atom.
(c) What element involved in this reaction (O, S, Cl) should have the smallest ionization energy? The smallest radius?
(d) Which should be smaller: the sulfide ion, $S^{2-}$, or a sulfur atom, S?
(e) If you want to make 675 g of $SOCl_2$, what mass of $SCl_2$ is required?
(f) If you use 10.0 g of $SO_3$ and 10.0 g of $SCl_2$, what is the theoretical yield of $SOCl_2$?
(g) $\Delta_r H°$ for the reaction of $SO_3$ and $SCl_2$ is −96.0 kJ/mol $SOCl_2$ produced. Using data in Appendix L, calculate the standard molar enthalpy of formation of $SCl_2$.

74. Sodium metal reacts readily with chlorine gas to give sodium chloride.

$$Na(s) + ½ Cl_2(g) \rightarrow NaCl(s)$$

(a) What is the reducing agent in this reaction? What property of the element contributes to its ability to act as a reducing agent?
(b) What is the oxidizing agent in this reaction? What property of the element contributes to its ability to act as an oxidizing agent?
(c) Why does the reaction produce NaCl and not a compound such as $Na_2Cl$ or $NaCl_2$?

75. ▲ Slater's rules are a simple way to estimate the effective nuclear charge experienced by an electron. In this approach, the "shielding constant," S, is calculated. The effective nuclear charge is then the difference between S and the atomic number, Z. (Note that the results in Table 7.2 and Figure 7.2 were calculated in a slightly different way.)

$$Z^* = Z - S$$

The shielding constant, S, is calculated using the following rules:
1. The electrons of an atom are grouped as follows: (1s) (2s, 2p) (3s, 3p) (3d) (4s, 4p) (4d), and so on.
2. Electrons in higher groups (to the right) do not shield those in the lower groups.
3. For ns and np valence electrons
   (a) Electrons in the same ns, np group contribute 0.35 (for 1s 0.30 works better).
   (b) Electrons in the n − 1 group contribute 0.85.
   (c) Electrons in the n − 2 group (and lower) contribute 1.00.
4. For nd and nf electrons, electrons in the same nd or nf group contribute 0.35, and those in groups to the left contribute 1.00.

As an example, let us calculate $Z^*$ for the outermost electron of oxygen:

$$S = (2 \times 0.85) + (5 \times 0.35) = 3.45$$
$$Z^* = 8 - 3.45 = 4.55$$

Here is a calculation for a d electron in Ni:

$$Z^* = 28 - [18 \times 1.00] - [7 \times 0.35] = 7.55$$

and for an s electron in Ni:

$$Z^* = 28 - [10 \times 1.00] - [16 \times 0.85]$$
$$- [1 \times 0.35] = 4.05$$

(Here 3s, 3p, and 3d electrons are in the (n − 1) groups.)

(a) Calculate $Z^*$ for F and Ne. Relate the $Z^*$ values for O, F, and Ne to their relative atomic radii and ionization energies.
(b) Calculate $Z^*$ for one of the 3d electrons of Mn, and compare this with $Z^*$ for one of the 4s electrons of the element. Do the $Z^*$ values give us some insight into the ionization of Mn to give the cation?

# Applying Chemical Principles

## The Not-So-Rare Earths

Lanthanum and the block of fourteen elements stretching from cerium (element 58) through lutetium (element 71) are referred to as the lanthanides or, often, as the rare earth elements. The rare earth name is perhaps a misnomer because the elements are in fact not all that rare. With the exception of promethium, which is not found naturally, these elements are more abundant than gold. Cerium, for example, is the 26th most abundant element in the Earth's crust. Unfortunately, high concentrations of rare earth elements are rarely found in ore deposits. Furthermore, these elements are often mixed in the same deposits and their separation is difficult due to their similar chemical properties.

The rare earth elements possess electronic and optical properties that make them valuable in the production of electronics, lasers, magnets, superconductors, lighting devices, and even jewelry. Ferromagnetism is common among the rare earth elements, with neodymium and samarium used extensively in strong, permanent magnets (page 289). These magnets are commonly used in computer hard drives and electric motors. Neodymium is also used in high-powered scientific and industrial lasers, and yttrium is used in high-temperature superconductors. Europium and terbium are used to produce fluorescent phosphors for television displays and mercury-vapor lamps.

## Questions:

1.  The most common oxidation state of a rare earth element is +3.
    a) What is the ground state electron configuration of $Sm^{3+}$?
    b) Write a balanced chemical equation for the reaction of $Sm(s)$ and $O_2(g)$.

2.  This textbook places lanthanum directly below yttrium in the periodic table. However, there is a minor controversy about this in the scientific community, and other periodic tables locate lanthanum at the front of the lanthanide series and place lutetium directly below yttrium. Does the electronic configuration argue for the placement of La or Lu below Y? Explain.

3.  Gadolinium has eight unpaired electrons, the greatest number of any lanthanide element.
    a) Draw an orbital box diagram depicting the ground state electron configuration of Gd based upon its number of unpaired electrons.
    b) Predict the most common oxidation state for Gd. What is the ground state electron configuration of the most common oxidation state?

4.  Use the atomic radii of scandium, yttrium, lanthanum, and lutetium to answer the questions below.

| Element | Radii (pm) |
|---------|-----------|
| Sc      | 160       |
| Y       | 180       |
| La      | 195       |
| Lu      | 175       |

   a) Explain why lutetium has a smaller atomic radius than lanthanum, even though it has a greater number of electrons.
   b) Do the atomic radii argue for the placement of La or Lu below Y in the periodic table? Explain.

5.  Europium oxide ($Eu_2O_3$) is used in the production of red phosphors for television displays. If the europium compound emits light with a wavelength of 612 nm, what is the frequency ($s^{-1}$) and energy (J/photon) of the light?

6.  Neodymium is commonly used in magnets, usually as $Nd_2Fe_{14}B$. (Neodymium is combined with other elements to protect it from air oxidation.) Determine the mass percentage of neodymium in $Nd_2Fe_{14}B$.

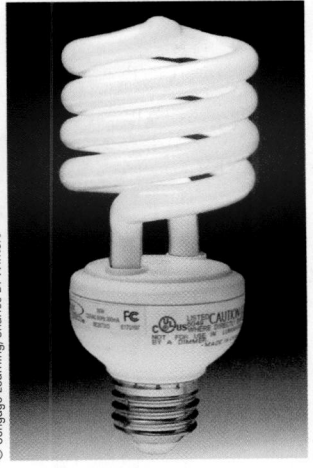

**Uses of lanthanides. (a)** Mixtures of lanthanides shoot showers of sparks when struck by iron. **(b)** Most compact fluorescent bulbs use europium phosphors to produce a pleasing spectrum of light.

Neodymium-iron-boron magnets.

# Milestones in the Development of Chemistry and the Modern View of Atoms and Molecules

**John Emsley**
**University of Cambridge**

The journey to our understanding of atoms and molecules began 2500 years ago in ancient Greece and continues today with developments in our understanding of chemical bonding and molecular structure. The journey may have started long ago, but it was only when chemistry developed in the 1700s that real progress was made. Today, we have instruments like the scanning tunneling microscope to help us visualize these tiny objects.

But let us start at the beginning and pay a short visit to the Greeks of 450 BC. Their civilization valued learning, and this led to various schools of philosophy. Their teachers did not engage in scientific research as we know it, so their theories were never more than thought experiments. Nevertheless, they correctly deduced that the world was made up of a few basic elements and that these existed as atoms, but they had no way of knowing which elements existed, or how small atoms were. Today, we know of 118 elements—at the last count—and that atoms are so tiny that the dot at the end of this sentence contains billions of them.

## Greek Philosophers and Medieval Alchemists

The early Greek philosophers thought that there would be just one element and debated what it might be. Some favored air, some fire, some water, and some said earth. Eventually, Empedocles (who lived from around 490 to 430 BC) argued that all four were elements. This theory was believed for 2000 years—and yet it was wrong.

What form did these elements take? The first person to give an answer was Leucippus, around 450 BC, who said they must exist as atoms. This idea was developed by his pupil Democritus (460–370 BC), who was the first to use the word *atom*, which means uncutable or indivisible. Epicurus (341–270 BC) said atoms were spherical, varied in size, and were constantly in motion. This theory also remained unchanged for 2000 years—but it was right.

Alchemy can trace its roots to ancient Egypt. The most famous Egyptian alchemist was Zosimos, who lived around 300 AD. He described such chemical processes as distillation and sublimation, crediting a female alchemist, Maria the Jewess, with their invention. She lived about 100 AD and experimented with mercury and sulfur, but her best-known invention was the bain-Marie, which is still used in cooking.

Early Muslim rulers encouraged learning, and alchemy flourished. The best-known alchemists were Geber (Jabir ibn Hayyan, 721–815 AD) and Rhazes (Abu Bakr Mohammad ibn Zakariyya al-Razi, 865–925 AD). Geber knew that when mercury and sulfur were combined, the product was a red compound, which we know as mercury(II) sulfide, but he believed that if the recipe were exactly right, then gold would be formed. Rhazes thought that all metals were made from mercury and sulfur, and his influential book, *Secret of Secrets*, contained a long list of chemicals, minerals, and apparatuses that a modern chemist would recognize.

In the early Middle Ages, alchemists were at work in Europe, but only a little progress was made. A Spaniard, who also called himself Geber, discovered how to make nitric acid and knew that a mixture of nitric and hydrochloric acids (*aqua regia*) would dissolve gold. The European center for alchemy was Prague, where many alchemists practiced their art while some of their number merely

● **The Alchymist in Search of the Philosopher's Stone, Discovers Phosphorus.** Painted by J. Wright of Derby (1734–1797).

practiced deception, often convincing onlookers that they could turn base metals into gold.

The 1600s saw the gradual emergence of chemistry from alchemy, and in this period we find several men who are now recognized as true scientists but who were also secret alchemists, such as Robert Boyle (1626–1691) and even the great Isaac Newton (1642–1727). Today, Boyle is considered one of the founding fathers of chemistry. His book, *The Sceptical Chymist*, is regarded as the seminal work that broke the link between chemistry and alchemy.

The Philosopher's Stone, a legendary substance that can supposedly turn ordinary substances into gold, was the ultimate prize sought by alchemists. So, when the alchemist Hennig Brandt of Hamburg discovered phosphorus in 1669, he believed it would lead him to the Philosopher's Stone because of the almost miraculous ability of phosphorus to shine in the dark and burst into flames. Some of this new wonder material was shown to Boyle, who eventually was able to make it himself. (It was formed by heating evaporated urine residues to red heat.) What Boyle did next distinguished him as a true chemist: He researched the properties of phosphorus and its reactions with other materials and published his findings, not in the secret language of the alchemists but in plain English, and in a manner that would allow even a modern chemist to repeat what he had done. Phosphorus was a new element, although it was not recognized as such for another century.

Boyle too thought about the nature of matter, and he came up with a definition of an element. He wrote:

> "I mean by Elements, as those Chymists that speak plainest do by the Principles, certain Primitive and Simple, or perfectly unmingled bodies; which not being made of any other bodies, or of one another, are the ingredients of which all those call'd perfectly mixt Bodies are immediately compounded, and into which they are ultimately resolved."

We can see that Boyle was struggling with the idea of elements and how these can be compounded together.

## Chemists of the 18th–19th Centuries

The theory of four elements was dealt its first body blow by a shy but extremely wealthy Englishman, Henry Cavendish (1731–1810), who had his own laboratory near London. There, he investigated gases. In 1784, he discovered hydrogen and observed that when it burned, water was formed. The French chemist Antoine Lavoisier (1743–1794) also studied gases, but he went one step further and noted that when a *mixture* of hydrogen and another newly discovered gas, oxygen, was sparked, it formed only water.

Henry Cavendish (1731–1810) *(left)* and John Dalton (1766–1844) *(right)*.

Obviously, water was not an element, but hydrogen and oxygen were.

In 1789, Lavoisier wrote his influential book *Elements of Chemistry*, in which he defined a chemical element as something that could not be further broken down, and he listed 33 of them. Most of these are still considered elements today, but some—such as light, heat, and the earths (later shown to be oxides)—are not. His list is given in Table 1. Lavoisier was the founder of modern chemistry, but, as described on page 112, he fell out of favor with the leaders of the French Revolution and was guillotined.

The next major advance in chemical understanding came from a modest school teacher, John Dalton (1766–1844), who lived in Manchester, England. He knew of the *Law of Fixed Proportions*, which said elements combined in definite ratios by weight, and said it could only be so if elements were composed of atoms. The idea of atoms had been revived by scientists like Newton in the 1600s, who said elements would cluster together, but nothing had come of such speculations because chemistry was still little more than mystical alchemy.

In 1803, Dalton gave a talk to the Manchester (England) Literary and Philosophical Society on the way gases dis-

### Table 1 The Elements According to Lavoisier (1789)

| Gases | Nonmetals | Metals | | Earths |
|-------|-----------|--------|--------|--------|
| Light | Sulfur | Antimony | Mercury | Lime |
| Heat | Phosphorus | Arsenic | Molybdenum | Magnesia |
| Oxygen | Carbon | Bismuth | Nickel | Barytes |
| Nitrogen | Chloride | Cobalt | Platinum | Alumina |
| Hydrogen | Fluoride | Copper | Silver | Silica |
| | Borate | Gold | Tin | |
| | | Iron | Tungsten | |
| | | Lead | Zinc | |
| | | Manganese | | |

solved in water, and when his talk was published in the Society's Proceedings he included a table of relative atomic weights, which were based on hydrogen having a value of 1. He listed 20 elements with their weights and said they combined to form "compound atoms," his name for what we now call *molecules*. At a stroke, Dalton not only revived the idea of atoms but gave them weight. In his book of 1808, *New System of Chemical Philosophy*, he went further, and he said an atom was a "solid, massy, hard, impenetrable, moveable particle." This description was eventually proved wrong on many counts, but he was right that atoms exist.

Chemists in the early 1800s were puzzled by the fact that most of the new atomic weights were whole numbers. An explanation was suggested in 1815 by William Prout (1785–1850), who went further than Dalton and reasoned that atoms were not indivisible but were composed of hydrogen. If the atomic weight of hydrogen was taken as 1, then it explained why all the other elements had weights that were whole numbers, or nearly so. In fact, most elements have atomic weights that fall within the limits of ± 0.1 of a whole number, with very few having fractional numbers. Nevertheless, it was the few exceptions that seemed to disprove Prout's theory, which could not explain the atomic weight of chlorine, which was 35.5, or copper, which was 63.5. (The explanation, of course, lies with their isotopic composition, a concept that lay 100 years in the future.)

Prout was almost right. Hydrogen, or at least 99.99% of it, consists of a single proton surrounded by a single electron. The proton is the nucleus, and that accounts for virtually all of the mass. We now classify elements based on how many protons their nuclei contain, with each element on the periodic table differing from the one immediately preceding it by one proton. In some ways, then, they differ according to the nucleus of hydrogen. When the proton was finally identified in 1919 and its importance realized, it was named from the Greek word *protos* meaning first, although Ernest Rutherford, who made the discovery, also said the name was chosen partly in honor of Prout.

Back in the early 1800s, chemists preferred atomic weights that were calculated relative to that of oxygen because oxygen forms compounds with almost all other elements. (Today, atomic weights are based on the carbon isotope carbon-12, which is taken as exactly 12.) Like Dalton, they believed water consisted of one oxygen and one hydrogen atom, so naturally their scale of atomic weights was of little use.

Inaccurate atomic weights, however, did not hinder the discovery of more and more elements. The 1860s was a particularly fruitful decade with the introduction of the atomic spectroscope, which revealed that each element had a characteristic "fingerprint" pattern of lines in its visible emission spectrum. As a result, the discoveries of rubidium, cesium, thallium, and indium were announced in the years 1860–1863. The total of known elements was now 65, and chemists were beginning to ask whether there was a limit to their number.

Meanwhile, the Italian chemist Stanislao Cannizzaro (1826–1910) had published a correct list of atomic weights, which he circulated at the First International Chemical Congress, held in Karlsruhe, Germany, in 1860. Dmitri Mendeleev attended the conference and took a copy of Cannizzaro's atomic weights back to St. Petersburg, Russia. What he did with it was to revolutionize chemistry, a story that is told in Chapter 2.

Dalton had suggested ways in which atoms might combine to form larger units. It was clear that the world was composed primarily not of single atoms but of molecules, and chemistry was the science of studying them. The word *molecule* was first given a chemical meaning in 1811; before then, it had simply been a French word for something extremely small. In 1873, its chemical meaning was spelled out by James Clerk Maxwell, who wrote a milestone paper in the journal *Nature* in which he defined a molecule as "the smallest possible portion of a particular substance" beyond which it would no longer have the properties associated with that substance. This is the meaning it still has.

In the 1800s, chemical analysis became quite sophisticated, and the elements in a chemical compound could be identified and expressed as numbers. For example, alcohol was $C_2H_6O$, but what was it really? And why did dimethyl ether, which was a different substance, have exactly the same formula? The concept of valency could explain how elements combined. Hydrogen had a valency of 1, oxygen of 2 as in $H_2O$, nitrogen of 3 as in $NH_3$, and carbon of 4 as in $CH_4$, but this in itself was not enough to explain what molecules really were. Turning valences into actual molecular arrangements was the next step, and two people were instrumental in doing this: 29-year-old August Kekulé (1829–1896) in 1858, and 22-year-old Jacobus van't Hoff (1852–1911) in 1878.

Kekulé was one of the great chemists of the second half of the 1800s. He is best known for his theory of molecule structures based on valence and especially of organic molecules in which carbon is four-valent and bonds in various ways to other atoms including carbon atoms. He published his

August Kekulé (1829–1896).

paper only weeks before one by Archibald Scott Couper (1831–1892), a young Scottish chemist, who was studying in Paris. In fact, Couper had written his paper before Kekulé, but his supervisor took rather a long time to read it, so he lost out. In some ways, Scott Couper's paper was even more advanced than Kekulé's because he drew lines between atoms to indicate actual chemical bonds. (Scott Couper's sad life was to end in an insane asylum.)

Kekulé also claimed some undeserved fame for having deduced that benzene, a molecule whose formula, $C_6H_6$, seemed to violate the laws of valency, consisted of a ring of six carbon atoms each with hydrogen attached. Late in life, he said it had come to him in a dream while he was working in London in the mid-1850s and fell asleep on the bus taking him home one evening. What he had conveniently forgotten was that Johann Loschmidt (1821–1895), a modest high school teacher from Vienna, had deduced the structure as many as 4 years earlier and published it in an essay that Kekulé had read.

Van't Hoff focused on the problem of how two compounds with exactly the same formula and physical properties could differ in two respects: Their crystal shapes could vary but were mirror images of each other and the way they rotated a beam of polarized light, one clockwise, the other counterclockwise. He put forward his theory, in 1874, that this could be explained if carbon formed four bonds arranged tetrahedrally. The idea was ridiculed by older chemists as "fantastic foolishness" and the "shallow speculations" of a youth, yet it could not be ignored because it explained why molecules could be left and right handed (▶ page 441). In any event, he had the laugh on them because he was awarded the first ever Nobel Prize in Chemistry in 1901.

## Atomic Structure: Remarkable Discoveries— 1890s and Beyond

Like the 1860s, the 1890s was another decade of remarkable chemical discovery, the most surprising being that atoms could spontaneously disintegrate. It began in 1896 when Henri Becquerel (1852–1908) started to investigate the mineral potassium uranyl sulfate [$K_2SO_4 \cdot UO_2(SO_4)_2 \cdot 2 H_2O$]. He found by chance that it was emitting invisible rays that caused a photographic plate to produce an image. Other uranium compounds also gave off these rays. What was equally intriguing was the observation that the common uranium ore pitchblende contained something that gave off more of this invisible radiation than could be explained by the uranium it contained. The husband and wife team of Pierre Curie (1859–1906) and Marie Curie (1867–1934) worked for weeks in an old shed in Paris to separate this impurity. Eventually they succeeded, and in 1898 they an-

**Marie Curie (1867–1934) and Pierre Curie (1859–1906).** Marie Curie is one of very few people and the only woman to have ever received two Nobel Prizes. She was born in Poland but studied and carried out her research in Paris. In 1903, she shared the Nobel Prize in Physics with H. Becquerel and her husband Pierre for their discovery of radioactivity. In 1911 she received the Nobel Prize in Chemistry for the discovery of two new chemical elements, radium and polonium (the latter named for her homeland, Poland). A unit of radioactivity (curie, Ci) and an element (curium, Cm) are named in her honor. Pierre, who died in an accident in 1906, was also well known for his research on magnetism. One of their daughters, Irène, married Frédèric Joliot, and they shared in the 1935 Nobel Prize in Chemistry for their discovery of artificial radioactivity.

nounced the discovery of two new, intensely radioactive elements: polonium and radium. Radioactivity was the word they invented to describe the new phenomenon of invisible rays (Figure 1), and they called one of the new elements radium because of its intense rays, and the other polonium after Marie's native country Poland.

In 1897, J. J. Thomson (1856–1940) reported his studies of another type of ray, cathode rays. Cathode ray tubes were glass vacuum tubes containing two metal electrodes. When a high voltage is applied to the electrodes, electricity flows from the negative electrode (cathode) to the positive electrode (anode) even though there is nothing there to conduct it. Thomson showed that there was, in fact, a stream of charged particles moving from the cathode to the anode and that these could be deflected by electric and magnetic fields, which showed they were negatively charged (Figure 2). He deduced they were two thousand times lighter than even the lightest element, hydrogen. They became known as *electrons*, a term already invented to describe the smallest particle of electricity.

**Sir Joseph John Thomson (1856–1940).** Cavendish Professor of Experimental Physics at the University of Cambridge in England. In 1896, he gave a series of lectures at Princeton University in the United States on the discharge of electricity in gases. It was this work on cathode rays that led to his discovery of the electron, which he announced at a lecture on Friday, April 30, 1897. He later published a number of books on the electron and was awarded the Nobel Prize in Physics in 1906.

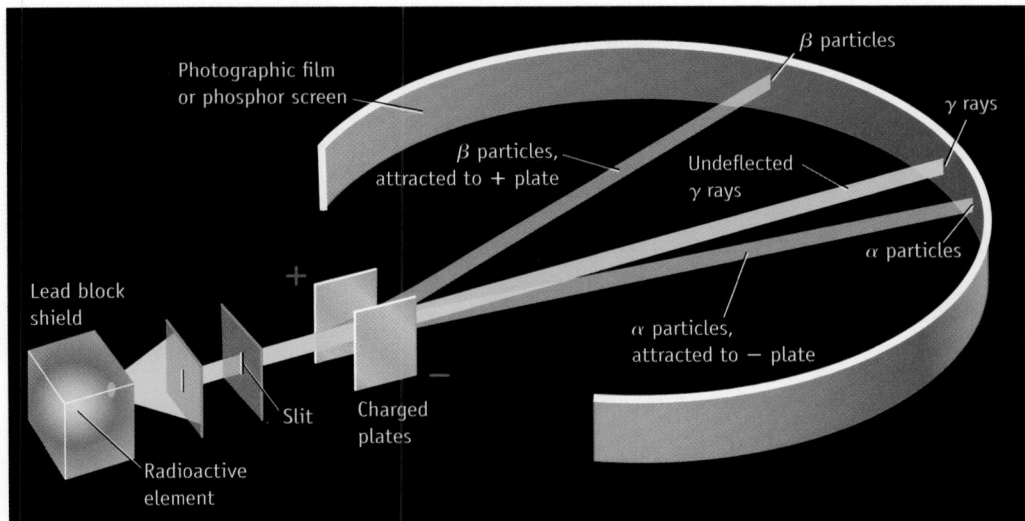

FIGURE 1 **Radioactivity.** Alpha ($\alpha$), beta ($\beta$), and gamma ($\gamma$) rays from a radioactive element are separated by passing them between electrically charged plates. Positively charged $\alpha$ particles are attracted to the negative plate, and negatively charged $\beta$ particles are attracted to the positive plate. (Note that the heavier $\alpha$ particles are deflected less than the lighter $\beta$ particles.) Gamma rays have no electric charge and pass undeflected between the charged plates.

1. A beam of electrons (cathode rays) is accelerated through two focusing slits.

2. When passing through an electric field, the beam of electrons is deflected.

3. The experiment is arranged so that the electric field causes the beam of electrons to be deflected in one direction. The magnetic field deflects the beam in the opposite direction.

4. By balancing the effects of the electrical and magnetic fields, the charge-to-mass ratio of the electron can be determined.

FIGURE 2 **Thomson's experiment to measure the electron's charge-to-mass ratio.** This experiment was done by J. J. Thomson in 1896–1897.

Thomson reasoned that electrons must originate from the atoms of the cathode, and he suggested that an atom was a uniform sphere of positively charged matter in which negative electrons were embedded. That view of an atom was not to persist for long.

In 1886, a few years before Thomson's report, Eugene Goldstein (1850–1930) had also explored cathode rays and had noticed something rather unexpected. Although negatively charged particles were streaming from the cathode to the anode, there were also positively charged particles moving in the opposite direction, and these could be observed if tiny holes were drilled into the cathode plate. These rays, which he called *Kanalstrahlen* from the German word meaning channel rays, became known as canal rays or anode rays (Figure 3). Goldstein thought he had discovered a basic type of atomic particle, the opposite of the

electron, but his positive particles were just formed from the residual gas in the cathode-ray tube.

The man most associated with discovering the true nature of the atom was Ernest Rutherford (1871–1937), better known as Lord Rutherford. He contributed to the story of atoms in three important ways: He identified the rays that radioactive atoms emitted; he proved that an atom has a tiny nucleus of positively charged protons; and he split the atom; in other words, he converted one element into another. Rutherford, who was born near Nelson on the South Island of New Zealand, went to the University of Cambridge in England, where he studied under Thomson. He concerned himself with radioactive phenomena and in the years 1898–1900 he identified the various types of radiation: alpha ($\alpha$), beta ($\beta$), and gamma ($\gamma$) rays. Alpha and beta rays were particles, the former with an electric charge (+2) twice as

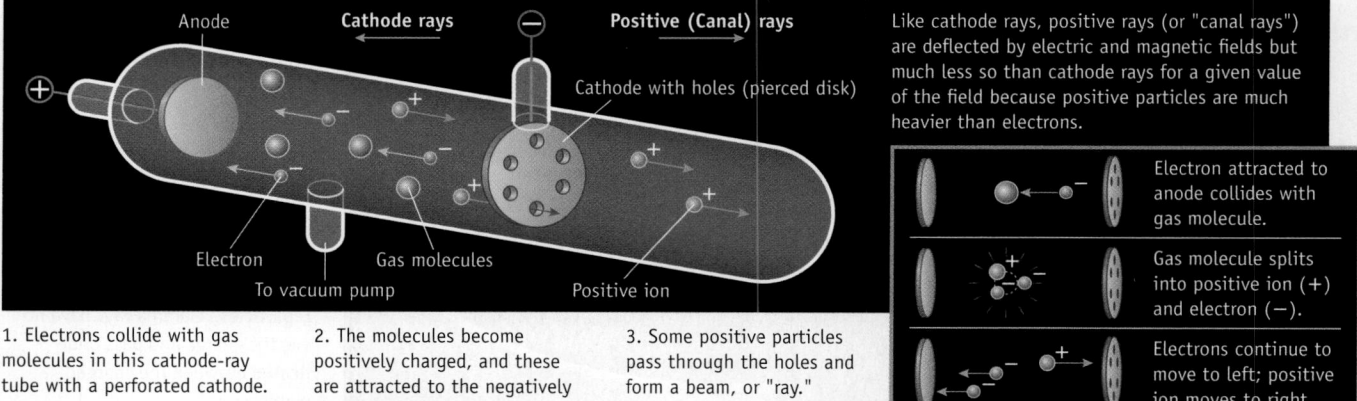

Like cathode rays, positive rays (or "canal rays") are deflected by electric and magnetic fields but much less so than cathode rays for a given value of the field because positive particles are much heavier than electrons.

Electron attracted to anode collides with gas molecule.

Gas molecule splits into positive ion (+) and electron (−).

Electrons continue to move to left; positive ion moves to right.

1. Electrons collide with gas molecules in this cathode-ray tube with a perforated cathode.

2. The molecules become positively charged, and these are attracted to the negatively charged, perforated cathode.

3. Some positive particles pass through the holes and form a beam, or "ray."

**FIGURE 3 Canal rays.** In 1886, Eugene Goldstein detected a stream of particles traveling in the direction opposite to that of the negatively charged cathode rays. We now know that these particles are positively charged ions formed by collisions of electrons with gaseous molecules in the cathode-ray tube.

large as that of the latter, which was negatively charged (−1). We now know that $\alpha$ particles are helium nuclei and that $\beta$ particles are electrons. Gamma rays are like light rays but with much shorter wavelengths.

Rutherford moved to McGill University in Montreal, Canada, where he collaborated with Frederick Soddy (1877–1956). Together they were able to show that another element, thorium, was radioactive and that it decayed via a series of elements, finally ending up as stable lead. They published their theory of radioactivity in 1908. That same year, Rutherford returned to England to become Professor of Physics at Manchester, where his research was to reveal even more spectacular discoveries about atoms.

Soddy had already returned to England in 1903 and was now working in University College London, where he was able to prove that as radium decayed it formed helium gas. He then moved to Glasgow, Scotland, and there his research showed that atoms of the same element could have more than one atomic mass, and the idea of isotopes was born. These made it possible to explain why an element could have an atomic weight that was not a whole number.

For example, chlorine's was 35.5 because it consisted of 76% of the isotope chlorine-35 plus 24% of chlorine-37.

Meanwhile at Manchester, two of Rutherford's students—Hans Geiger (1882–1945) and Ernest Marsden (1889–1970)—bombarded thin gold foil with $\alpha$ particles to test whether Thomson's model of a solid atom with embedded electrons was correct (Figure 4). Almost all the particles passed straight through the gold foil as if there was nothing there. However, they were surprised to find that a few were deflected sideways; some even bounced right back. This experiment proved that an atom of gold is mostly empty space with a tiny nucleus at its center. It was the electrons that accounted for most of its volume. Rutherford calculated that the central nucleus of an atom occupied only 1/10,000th of its volume. He also calculated that a gold nucleus had a positive charge of around 100 units and a radius of about $10^{-12}$ cm. (The currently accepted values are +79 for atomic charge and $10^{-13}$ cm for the radius.) Just as Dalton had done more than a century before, Rutherford announced his findings at a meeting of the Manchester Literary and Philosophical Society. The date was March 7, 1911.

In 1908, the American physicist Robert Millikan (1868–1953), based at the California Institute of Technology, measured the charge on the electron as $1.592 \times 10^{-19}$ coulombs (C), not far from today's accepted value of $1.602 \times 10^{-19}$ C (Figure 5). Millikan rightly assumed this was the fundamental unit of charge. Knowing this, and the charge-to-mass ratio determined by Thomson, enabled the mass of an electron to be calculated as $9.109 \times 10^{-28}$ g.

In 1913, Henry G. J. Moseley (1887–1915) realized it was not its atomic weight that defined an element but its atomic number, which he deduced from a study of the wavelengths of lines in x-ray spectra. Moseley was then able to put the periodic table of elements on a more secure footing. (Sadly, his life came to an end when a bullet from a sniper killed him in World War I.) Mendeleev had been

**Ernest Rutherford (1871–1937).** Rutherford was born in New Zealand in 1871 but went to the University of Cambridge in England to pursue his Ph.D. in physics in 1895. There, he worked with J. J. Thomson, and it was at Cambridge that he discovered $\alpha$ and $\beta$ radiation. At McGill University in Canada in 1899, Rutherford did further experiments to prove that $\alpha$ radiation is composed of helium nuclei and that $\beta$ radiation consists of electrons. He received the Nobel Prize in Chemistry for his work in 1908. His research on the structure of the atom was done after he moved to Manchester University in England. In 1919, he returned to the University of Cambridge, where he took up the position formerly held by Thomson. In his career, Rutherford guided the work of 10 future recipients of the Nobel Prize. Element 104 has been named *rutherfordium* in his honor.

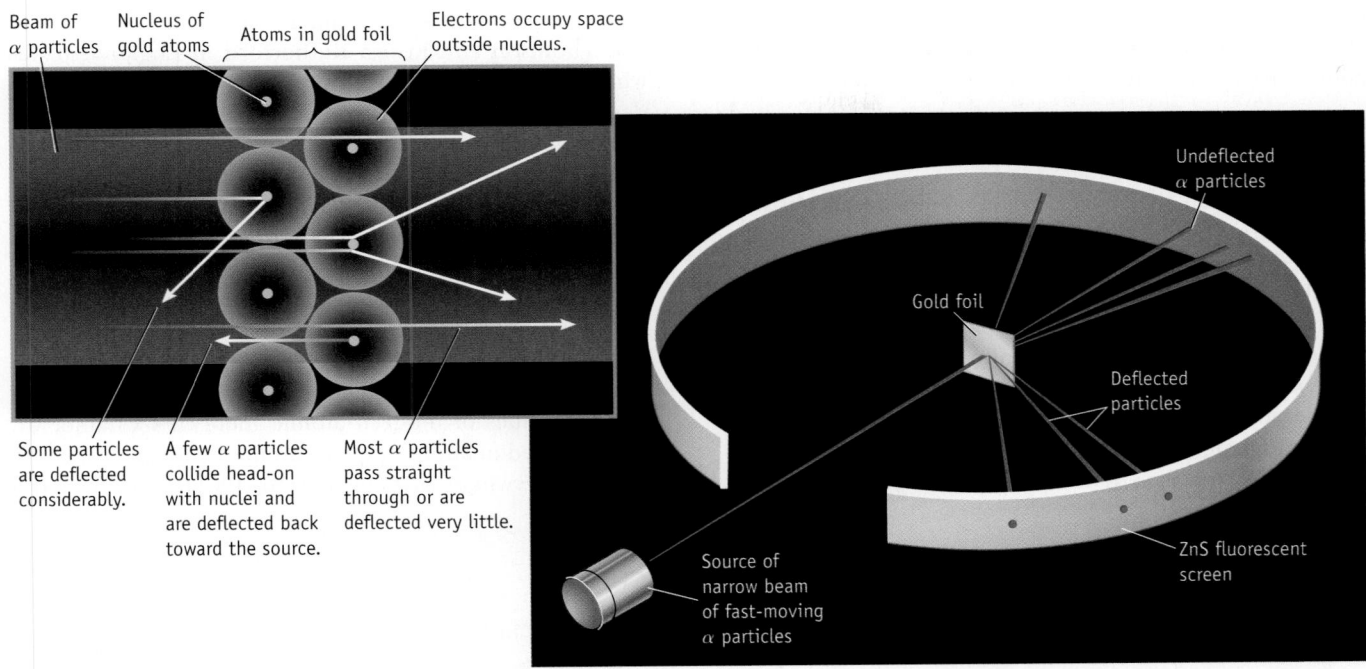

**FIGURE 4 Rutherford's experiment to determine the structure of the atom.** A beam of positively charged α particles was directed at a thin gold foil. A fluorescent screen coated with zinc sulfide (ZnS) was used to detect particles passing through or deflected by the foil. (A flash of light is seen when a particle strikes the screen.) Most of the particles passed through the foil, but some were deflected from their path. A few were even deflected backward.

perplexed by some elements when he arranged them in order of increasing atomic weight. For example, tellurium has an atomic weight of 127.6, and iodine has an atomic weight of 126.9. The problem was that their properties indicated that tellurium should be placed before iodine in the periodic table. Arranging the elements in order of increasing atomic number, however, removed this problem. Tellurium has an atomic number of 52, and iodine has an atomic number of 53, thus justifying placing tellurium before iodine in the table.

Although he was not to know it, Moseley's atomic number corresponded to the number of protons in the nucleus. In 1919, Rutherford proved there were such things as protons, and these were the positive charges located at the center of an atom. Atoms were at last correctly seen as consisting of positive protons balanced by the same number of negative electrons.

In 1919, Rutherford "split the atom" according to the newspapers of the day. What he had performed was the first-ever successful experiment deliberately designed to

1. A fine mist of oil drops is introduced into one chamber.

2. The droplets fall one by one into the lower chamber under the force of gravity.

3. Gas molecules in the bottom chamber are ionized (split into electrons and a positive fragment) by a beam of x-rays. The electrons adhere to the oil drops, some droplets having one electron, some two, and so on.

These negatively charged droplets continue to fall due to gravity.

4. By carefully adjusting the voltage on the plates, the force of gravity on the droplet is exactly counterbalanced

by the attraction of the negative droplet to the upper, positively charged plate.

Analysis of these forces led to a value for the charge on the electron.

**FIGURE 5 Millikan's experiment to determine the electron charge.** The experiment was done by R. A. Millikan in 1909.

convert one element into another. He bombarded nitrogen gas with $\alpha$ particles, and this led to its conversion to oxygen and hydrogen. We can express this as an equation:

$$^{14}\text{N (7 protons)} + \alpha \text{ particle (}^4\text{He, 2 protons)} \rightarrow$$
$$^{17}\text{O (8 protons)} + {}^1\text{H (1 proton)}$$

By about 1920, the image of an atom was that it consisted of a tight nucleus, where all the protons were located, surrounded by a fuzzy cloud of negatively charged electrons, and that these were circling the nucleus rather like planets orbiting the sun. And just as the planets don't move in a random way, so electrons were confined to particular orbits, some nearer the nucleus, some farther away.

The physical nature of atoms was known, but how could the arrangement of electrons be explained? Niels Bohr (1885–1962) was the scientist who helped solve that puzzle.

He lived in Copenhagen, Denmark, and had trained under J. J. Thomson and Ernest Rutherford in England. It was while studying atomic spectra in England that he began to develop his theory of electrons circulating in orbits around the nucleus and with specific quantized energies (◄ page 273). Bohr postulated that the electrons were confined to specific energy levels called *orbits*. He could then understand the atomic emission spectrum of hydrogen by postulating that the lines it displayed corresponded to discrete quantities of energy (quanta) that an electron emitted as it jumped from one orbit to another.

Bohr's idea of specific energy levels is still retained, but his idea of orbits at specific distances has been revised to be the orbitals of modern atomic theory (◄ Chapter 6). Also involved in applying quantum theory to electron energies were Erwin Schrödinger (1887–1961), who devised a

## A CLOSER LOOK

# 20th-Century Giants of Science

Many of the advances in science occurred during the early part of the 20th century, as the result of theoretical studies by some of the greatest minds in the history of science.

Max Karl Ernst Ludwig Planck (1858–1947) was raised in Germany, where his father was a professor at a university. While still in his teens, Planck decided to become a physicist, against the advice of the head of the physics department at Munich, who told him, "The important discoveries [in physics] have been made. It is hardly worth entering physics anymore." Fortunately, Planck did not take this advice and went on to study thermodynamics. This interest led him eventually to consider the ultraviolet catastrophe in explanations of blackbody radiation and to develop his revolutionary hypothesis of quantized energy, which was announced 2 weeks before Christmas in 1900. He was awarded the Nobel Prize in Physics in 1918 for this work. Einstein later said it was a longing to find harmony and order in nature, a "hunger in his soul," that spurred Planck on.

Erwin Schrödinger (1887–1961) was born in Vienna, Austria. Following his service as an artillery officer in World War I, he became a professor of physics. In 1928, he succeeded Planck as professor of physics at the University of Berlin. He shared the Nobel Prize in Physics in 1933.

**Max Planck**

*Edgar Fahs Smith Collection/University of Pennsylvania Library*

**Erwin Schrödinger**

*Edgar Fahs Smith Collection/University of Pennsylvania Library*

Niels Bohr (1885–1962) was born in Copenhagen, Denmark. He earned a Ph.D. in physics in Copenhagen in 1911 and then went to work first with J. J. Thomson and later with Ernest Rutherford in England. It was there that he began to develop his theory of atomic structure and his explanation of atomic spectra. (He received the Nobel Prize in Physics in 1922 for this work.) Bohr returned to Copenhagen, where he eventually became director of the Institute for Theoretical Physics. Many young physicists worked with him at the Institute, seven of whom eventually received Nobel Prizes in chemistry and physics. Among these scientists were Werner Heisenberg, Wolfgang Pauli, and Linus Pauling. Element 107 was recently named *bohrium* in Bohr's honor.

Werner Heisenberg (1901–1976) studied with Max Born and later with Bohr. He received the Nobel Prize in Physics in 1932. The recent play *Copenhagen*, which has been staged in London and New York, centers on the relationship between Bohr and Heisenberg and their involvement in the development of atomic weapons during World War II.

Gilbert Newton Lewis (1875–1946) introduced the theory of the shared electron-pair chemical bond in a paper published in the *Journal of the American Chemical Society* in

**Niels Bohr**

*Edgar Fahs Smith Collection/University of Pennsylvania Library*

**Werner Heisenberg**

*© AIP/Emilio Segre Visual Archives*

1916. Lewis also made major contributions in acid–base chemistry, thermodynamics, and the interaction of light with substances.

Lewis was born in Massachusetts but raised in Nebraska. After earning his B.A. and Ph.D. at Harvard, he began his career in 1912 at the University of California at Berkeley. He was not only a productive researcher but was also an influential teacher. Among his ideas was the use of problem sets in teaching, an idea still in use today.

Linus Pauling (1901–1994) was born in Portland, Oregon, earned a B.Sc. degree in chemical engineering from Oregon State College in 1922, and completed his Ph.D. in chemistry at the California Institute of Technology in 1925. In chemistry, he is best known for his book *The Nature of the Chemical Bond*. He also studied protein structure and, in the words of Francis Crick, was "one of the founders of molecular biology." It was this work and his study of chemical bonding that were cited in the award of the Nobel Prize in Chemistry in 1954. Although chemistry was the focus of his life, at the urging of his wife, Ava Helen, he was also involved in nuclear disarmament issues, and he received the Nobel Peace Prize in 1962 for the role he played in advocating for the nuclear test ban treaty.

**Gilbert Newton Lewis**

*Oesper Collection in the History of Chemistry/University of Cincinnati*

**Linus Pauling**

*© Tom Hollyman/Photo Researchers, Inc.*

mathematical equation that described orbitals, and Werner Heisenberg (1901–1976), whose *Uncertainty Principle* said that we cannot ever know exactly both the position and the energy of an electron.

The nucleus of an atom still presented a problem in 1930. How could a large number of positively charged protons co-exist in a nucleus without their repelling one another so much so that the atom falls apart? Lead, for example, had 82 protons. There had to be something else in the nucleus, and it had to be a heavy particle to account for the atomic weight of an element, which was more than double its atomic number and in the case of lead was 207. In 1932, the British physicist James Chadwick (1891–1974) found the missing particles. He directed the very powerful $\alpha$ rays that were released from radioactive polonium toward a beryllium target. The secondary emanations emitted by the latter metal were strange in that they carried no charge but were massive enough to knock protons out of the nuclei of other atoms. These new particles, now known as *neutrons*, had no electric charge and a mass of $1.674927 \times 10^{-24}$ g, slightly greater than the mass of a proton. (At the same time, Hans Falkenhagen in Germany also discovered neutrons, but he did not publish his results.) Chadwick had found the missing particle and completed the chemists' picture of an atom. It also made it possible to produce elements heavier than uranium—as well as to create atomic bombs.

## The Nature of the Chemical Bond

Molecules presented a more complex problem: How did atoms join together to form them? The first person to provide an answer based on the new view of the atom was the American chemist Gilbert Newton Lewis (1875–1946). In his chemistry lectures at the University of California–Berkeley in the early 1900s, he used dots to symbolize electrons, and he developed this idea so that it became more than just a teaching aid. Lewis said in 1916 that a single chemical bond was the sharing of a pair of electrons between two atoms; a double bond was the sharing of two pairs; and a triple bond the sharing of three pairs. This simple concept explained valency and structure and had enormous influence because it made so much of the chemistry of atoms and molecules understandable.

More sophisticated concepts of bonding were developed based on Max Planck's (1858–1947) theory that energy was quantized. Robert Mulliken (1896–1986) saw that this implied there were only certain energy levels within a molecule that its electrons could inhabit. Mulliken proposed a theory of chemical bonding based on combining atomic orbitals into molecular orbitals and showed how the energies of these related to the way the atomic orbitals overlapped. He also developed the theory of electronegativity, which is based on the relative abilities of atoms in molecules to attract electrons, again a concept useful in explaining chemical behavior.

For chemists, the man whose name is most famously linked to bonding is Linus Pauling (1901–1994). He wrote his first paper on the subject when he was only 27 years old, in 1928, and followed it with several more. He brought all his thoughts together in his seminal work *The Nature of the Chemical Bond* in 1939, a book that developed his approach to chemical bonding and the important concept of electronegativity.

Of course, there are still many things to be discovered about atoms and molecules, but as far as chemistry was concerned, the age-old questions of what elements, atoms, and molecules really were had been answered by the mid-20th century. The world of the nucleus and of subatomic particles could be left to the physicists to investigate.

## SUGGESTED READINGS

1. Eric Scerri, *The Periodic Table: Its Story and Its Significance,* Oxford University Press, New York, 2007.
2. John Emsley, *The 13th Element: The Sordid Tale of Murder, Fire, and Phosphorus,* John Wiley and Sons, New York, 2000.
3. John Emsley, *Nature's Building Blocks,* Oxford University Press, 2002.
4. Arthur Greenberg, *A Chemical History Tour: Picturing Chemistry from Alchemy to Modern Molecular Science,* Wiley-Interscience, New York, 2000.
5. Aaron Ihde, *The Development of Modern Chemistry,* Dover Publications, New York, 1984.
6. L. K. James, ed., *Nobel Laureates in Chemistry, 1901–1992,* American Chemical Society and Chemical Heritage Foundation, 1993.

## STUDY QUESTIONS

Blue-numbered questions have answers in Appendix Q and fully worked solutions in the *Student Solutions Manual.*

1. Dalton proposed that an atom was a "solid, massy, hard, impenetrable, moveable particle." Critique this description. How does this description misrepresent atomic structure?

2. Dalton's hypothesis on the structure of atoms was based in part on the observation of a "Law of definite proportions," which said that atoms combined in a definite ratio by weight. Using the formula for water and atomic weights from the current atomic mass scale, calculate the ratio of the mass of oxygen to the mass of hydrogen in water.

3. From cathode ray experiments, J. J. Thomson estimated that the mass of an electron was "about a thousandth" of the mass of a proton. How accurate is that estimate? Calculate the ratio of the mass of an electron to the mass of a proton.

4. Goldstein observed positively charged particles moving in the opposite direction to electrons in a cathode ray tube. From their mass, he concluded that these particles were formed from residual gas in the tube. For example, if the cathode ray tube contained helium, the canal rays consisted of $He^+$ ions. Describe the process that forms these ions.

# 8 Bonding and Molecular Structure

Thymine    Cytosine    Deoxyribose

## Chemical Bonding in DNA

The theme of this chapter and the next is molecular bonding and structure, and the subject is well illustrated by the structure of DNA. This molecule is a helical coil of two chains of tetrahedral phosphate groups and deoxyribose groups. Organic bases (such as thymine and cytosine) on one chain interact with complementary bases on the other chain.

## Questions:

Among the many questions you can answer from studying this chapter are the following:

1. Why are there four bonds to carbon and phosphorus?
2. Why are the C atoms and P atoms in the backbone and the C atoms in deoxyribose surrounded by other atoms at an angle of 109°?
3. What are the angles in the six-member rings of the bases thymine and cytosine? Why are the six-member rings flat?
4. Are thymine and cytosine polar molecules?

**Answers to these questions are available in Appendix N.**

## CHAPTER GOALS

*See Chapter Goals Revisited (page 389) for Study Questions keyed to these goals.*

- Understand the difference between ionic and covalent bonds.

- Draw Lewis electron dot structures for small molecules and ions.

- Use the valence shell electron-pair repulsion (VSEPR) theory to predict the shapes of simple molecules and ions and to understand the structures of more complex molecules.

- Use electronegativity and formal charge to predict the charge distribution in molecules and ions, to define the polarity of bonds, and to predict the polarity of molecules.

- Understand the properties of covalent bonds and their influence on molecular structure.

Scientists have long known that the key to interpreting the properties of a chemical substance is first to recognize and understand its structure and bonding. **Structure** refers to the way atoms are arranged in space, and **bonding** describes the forces that hold adjacent atoms together.

Our discussion of structure and bonding begins with small molecules and then progresses to larger molecules. From compound to compound, atoms of the same element participate in bonding and structure in a predictable way. This consistency allows us to develop principles that apply to many different chemical compounds, including such complex molecules as DNA.

## 8.1 Chemical Bond Formation

When a chemical reaction occurs between two atoms, their valence electrons are reorganized so that a net attractive force—a **chemical bond**—occurs between the atoms. There are two general types of bonds, ionic and covalent, and their formation can be depicted using Lewis symbols.

An **ionic bond** forms when *one or more valence electrons is transferred from one atom to another*, creating positive and negative ions. When sodium and chlorine react (Figure 8.1a), an electron is transferred from a sodium atom to a chlorine atom to form $Na^+$ and $Cl^-$.

$$Na\cdot \; + \; \cdot\ddot{\underset{\cdot\cdot}{Cl}}: \longrightarrow \left[ Na\cdot \;\; \overset{\frown}{\phantom{x}} \; \cdot\ddot{\underset{\cdot\cdot}{Cl}}: \right] \longrightarrow \left[ Na^+ \;\;\; :\ddot{\underset{\cdot\cdot}{Cl}}:^- \right]$$

metal atom   nonmetal atom

electron transfer from reducing agent to oxidizing agent

ionic compound. Ions have noble gas electron configurations.

The "bond" is the attractive force between the oppositely charged positive and negative ions.

**OWL**

Sign in to OWL at **www.cengage.com/owl** to view tutorials and simulations, develop problem-solving skills, and complete online homework assigned by your professor.

go Chemistry

Download mini lecture videos for key concept review and exam prep from OWL or purchase them from **www.cengagebrain.com**

- **Valence Electron Configurations and Ionic Compound Formation** For the formation of NaCl, Na $[1s^22s^22p^63s^1]$ gives up an electron to form $Na^+$ $[1s^22s^22p^6]$, which is equivalent to the Ne configuration. Cl $\{[Ne]3s^23p^5\}$ gains an electron to form $Cl^-$ $\{[Ne]3s^23p^6\}$, which is equivalent to the Ar configuration.

**FIGURE 8.1 Formation of ionic compounds.** Both reactions shown here are quite exothermic, as reflected by the very negative molar enthalpies of formation for the reaction products.

**(a)** The reaction of elemental sodium and chlorine to give sodium chloride.
$\Delta_f H°$ [NaCl(s)] = −411.12 kJ/mol

**(b)** The reaction of elemental calcium and oxygen to give calcium oxide.
$\Delta_f H°$ [CaO(s)] = −635.09 kJ/mol

**Covalent bonding**, in contrast, *involves sharing of valence electrons between atoms.* Two chlorine atoms, for example, share a pair of electrons, one electron from each atom, to form a covalent bond.

$$:\ddot{C}l\cdot + \cdot\ddot{C}l: \longrightarrow :\ddot{C}l:\ddot{C}l:$$

As bonding is described in greater detail, you will discover that the two types of bonding—complete electron transfer and the equal sharing of electrons—are extreme cases. In most chemical compounds, electrons are shared unequally, with the extent of sharing varying widely from very little sharing (largely ionic) to considerable sharing (largely covalent).

Ionic bonding will be described in more detail in Chapter 13, whereas the present chapter focuses on bonding in covalent compounds.

---

**REVIEW & CHECK FOR SECTION 8.1**

Which of the following compounds is not ionic?

(a)  NaBr      (b)  CaBr$_2$      (c)  SiBr$_4$      (d)  FeBr$_2$

---

**Module 12: Drawing Lewis Electron Dot Structures** covers concepts in this section.

## 8.2 Covalent Bonding and Lewis Structures

There are many examples of compounds having covalent bonds, including the gases in our atmosphere (O$_2$, N$_2$, H$_2$O, and CO$_2$), common fuels (CH$_4$), and most of the compounds in your body. Covalent bonding is also responsible for the atom-to-atom connections in polyatomic ions such as CO$_3^{2-}$, CN$^-$, NH$_4^+$, NO$_3^-$, and PO$_4^{3-}$. We will develop the basic principles of structure and bonding using these and other small molecules and ions, but the same principles apply to larger molecules from aspirin to proteins and DNA with thousands of atoms.

The molecules and ions just mentioned are composed entirely of *nonmetal* atoms. A point that needs special emphasis is that, in molecules or ions made up *only* of nonmetal atoms, the atoms are attached by covalent bonds. Conversely, the presence of a metal in a formula is often a signal that the compound is likely to be ionic.

### Valence Electrons and Lewis Symbols for Atoms

The electrons in an atom are of two types: **valence electrons** and **core electrons**. Chemical reactions result in the loss, gain, or rearrangement of valence electrons. The core electrons are not involved in bonding or in chemical reactions.

**Table 8.1  Core and Valence Electrons for Several Common Elements**

| Element | Periodic Group | Core Electrons | Valence Electrons | Total |
|---------|----------------|----------------|-------------------|-------|
| *Main Group Elements* | | | | |
| Na | 1A | $1s^2 2s^2 2p^6 = [\text{Ne}]$ | $3s^1$ | $[\text{Ne}]3s^1$ |
| Si | 4A | $1s^2 2s^2 2p^6 = [\text{Ne}]$ | $3s^2 3p^2$ | $[\text{Ne}]3s^2 3p^2$ |
| As | 5A | $1s^2 2s^2 2p^6 3s^2 3p^6 3d^{10} = [\text{Ar}]3d^{10}$ | $4s^2 4p^3$ | $[\text{Ar}]3d^{10}4s^2 4p^3$ |
| *Transition Elements* | | | | |
| Ti | 4B | $1s^2 2s^2 2p^6 3s^2 3p^6 = [\text{Ar}]$ | $3d^2 4s^2$ | $[\text{Ar}]3d^2 4s^2$ |
| Co | 8B | $[\text{Ar}]$ | $3d^7 4s^2$ | $[\text{Ar}]3d^7 4s^2$ |
| Mo | 6B | $[\text{Kr}]$ | $4d^5 5s^1$ | $[\text{Kr}]4d^5 5s^1$ |

For main group elements (elements of the A groups in the periodic table), the valence electrons are the *s* and *p* electrons in the outermost shell (Table 8.1). All electrons in inner shells are core electrons. A useful guideline for *main group elements* is that *the number of valence electrons is equal to the group number*. The fact that all elements in a periodic group have the same number of valence electrons accounts for the similarity of chemical properties among members of the group.

Valence electrons for transition elements include the electrons in the *ns* and $(n-1)d$ orbitals (Table 8.1). The remaining electrons are core electrons. As with main group elements, the valence electrons for transition metals determine the chemical properties of these elements.

The American chemist Gilbert Newton Lewis (1875–1946) introduced a useful way to represent electrons in the valence shell of an atom. The element's symbol represents the atomic nucleus together with the core electrons. Up to four valence electrons, represented by dots, are placed one at a time around the symbol; then, if any valence electrons remain, they are paired with ones already there. Chemists now refer to these pictures as **Lewis electron dot symbols**. Lewis dot symbols for main group elements of the second and third periods are shown in Table 8.2.

Arranging the valence electrons of a main group element around an atom in four groups suggests that the valence shell can accommodate four pairs of electrons. Because this represents eight electrons in all, this is referred to as an **octet** of electrons. An octet of electrons surrounding an atom is regarded as a stable configuration. The noble gases, with the exception of helium, have eight valence electrons and demonstrate a notable lack of reactivity. (Helium and neon do not undergo any chemical reactions, and the other noble gases have very limited chemical reactivity.) Because chemical reactions involve changes in the valence electron shell, the limited reactivity of the noble gases is taken as evidence of the stability of their noble gas ($ns^2 np^6$) electron configuration. Hydrogen, which in its compounds has two electrons in its valence shell, obeys the spirit of this rule by matching the electron configuration of He.

● **Gilbert Newton Lewis (1875–1946)** Lewis introduced the theory of shared electron-pair chemical bonds in a paper published in the *Journal of the American Chemical Society* in 1916. Lewis also made major contributions in acid–base chemistry, thermodynamics, and the interaction of light with substances.

**Gilbert Newton Lewis**

Lewis was born in Massachusetts but raised in Nebraska. After earning his B.A. and Ph.D. at Harvard, he began his career in 1912 at the University of California at Berkeley. He was not only a productive researcher but was also an influential teacher. Among his ideas was the use of problem sets in teaching, a practice still in use today.

**Table 8.2  Lewis Electron Dot Symbols for Main Group Atoms**

| 1A<br>$ns^1$ | 2A<br>$ns^2$ | 3A<br>$ns^2 np^1$ | 4A<br>$ns^2 np^2$ | 5A<br>$ns^2 np^3$ | 6A<br>$ns^2 np^4$ | 7A<br>$ns^2 np^5$ | 8A<br>$ns^2 np^6$ |
|----|----|----|----|----|----|----|----|
| Li· | ·Be· | ·B· | ·C· | ·N· | :O· | :F· | :Ne: |
| Na· | ·Mg· | ·Al· | ·Si· | ·P· | :S· | :Cl· | :Ar: |

## Lewis Electron Dot Structures and the Octet Rule

In a simple description of covalent bonding, a bond results when one or more electron pairs are shared between two atoms. The electron pair bond between the two atoms of an $H_2$ molecule is represented by a pair of dots or, alternatively, a line.

Electron pair bond

H : H      H — H

The representation of a molecule in this fashion is called a **Lewis electron dot structure** or just a **Lewis structure**.

Simple Lewis structures, such as that for $F_2$, can be drawn starting with Lewis dot symbols for atoms and arranging the valence electrons to form bonds. Fluorine, an element in Group 7A, has seven valence electrons. The Lewis symbol shows that an F atom has a single unpaired electron along with three electron pairs. In $F_2$, the single electrons, one on each F atom, pair up in the covalent bond.

Lone pair of electrons

:F· + ·F: ⟶ :F:F:   or   :F—F:

Shared or bonding electron pair

In the Lewis structure for $F_2$ the pair of electrons in the F—F bond is the bonding pair, or **bond pair**. The other six pairs reside on single atoms and are called **lone pairs**. Because they are not involved in bonding, they are also called **nonbonding electrons**.

Carbon dioxide, $CO_2$, and dinitrogen, $N_2$, are examples of molecules in which two atoms share more than one electron pair.

• **Importance of Lone Pairs** Lone pairs can be important in a structure. Since they are in the same valence electron shell as the bonding electrons, they can influence molecular shape. (See Section 8.6.)

:N≡N:
Octet of electrons around each N atom (six in triple bond and two in lone pair)

Octet of electrons around each O atom (four in double bond and four in lone pairs)

O=C=O
Octet of electrons around the C atom (four in each of two double bonds)

In carbon dioxide, the carbon atom shares two pairs of electrons with each oxygen and so is linked to each O atom by a double bond. The valence shell of each oxygen atom in $CO_2$ has two bonding pairs and two lone pairs. In dinitrogen, the two nitrogen atoms share three pairs of electrons, so they are linked by a triple bond. In addition, each N atom has a single lone pair.

An important observation can be made about the molecules you have seen so far: Each atom (except H) has a share in four pairs of electrons, so each has achieved a *noble gas configuration. Each atom is surrounded by an octet of eight electrons.* (Hydrogen typically forms a bond to only one other atom, resulting in two electrons in its valence shell.) *The tendency of molecules and polyatomic ions to have structures in which eight electrons surround each atom* is known as the **octet rule**. As an example, a triple bond is necessary in dinitrogen in order to have an octet around each nitrogen atom. The carbon atom and both oxygen atoms in $CO_2$ achieve the octet configuration by forming double bonds.

• **Exceptions to the Octet Rule** Although the octet rule is widely applicable, there are exceptions. Fortunately, many will be obvious, such as when there are more than four bonds to an element or when an odd number of electrons occurs. (See Section 8.5.)

The octet rule is extremely useful, but keep in mind that it is more a *guideline* than a rule. Particularly for the second period elements C, N, O, and F, a Lewis structure in which each atom achieves an octet is likely to be correct. Although there are a few exceptions, if an atom such as C, N, O, or F in a Lewis structure does not follow the octet rule, you should question the structure's validity. If a structure obeying the octet rule cannot be written, then it is possible an incorrect formula has been assigned to the compound or the atoms have been assembled in an incorrect way.

## Drawing Lewis Electron Dot Structures

There is a systematic approach to constructing Lewis structures of molecules and ions. Let us take formaldehyde, $CH_2O$, as an example.

1. *Determine the arrangement of atoms within a molecule.* The central atom is *usually* the one with the lowest affinity for electrons (least negative electron attachment enthalpy, page 320).

> In $CH_2O$, the central atom is C. You will come to recognize that certain elements often appear as the central atom, among them C, N, P, and S. Halogens are often terminal atoms forming a single bond to one other atom, but they can be the central atom when combined with O in oxoacids (such as in $HClO_4$). Oxygen is the central atom in water, but in conjunction with nitrogen, phosphorus, and the halogens it is usually a terminal atom. Hydrogen is a terminal atom because it typically bonds to only one other atom.

2. *Determine the total number of valence electrons in the molecule or ion.* In a neutral molecule, this number will be the sum of the valence electrons for each atom.

   - For an *anion, add* the number of electrons equal to the negative charge.
   - For a *cation, subtract* the number of electrons equal to the positive charge.

   The number of valence electron *pairs* will be half the total number of valence electrons. For $CH_2O$,

   $$\text{Valence electrons} = 12 \text{ electrons (or 6 electron pairs)}$$
   $$= 4 \text{ (for C)} + 2 \times 1 \text{ (for two H atoms)} + 6 \text{ (for O)}$$

3. *Place one pair of electrons between each pair of bonded atoms to form a single bond.*

   Here, three electron pairs are used to make three single bonds (which are represented by single lines). Three pairs of electrons remain to be used.

4. *Use any remaining pairs as lone pairs around each terminal atom (except H) so that each terminal atom is surrounded by eight electrons. If, after this is done, there are electrons left over, assign them to the central atom. (If the central atom is an element in the third or higher period, it can have more than eight electrons. See page 361.)*

   Here, all six pairs have been assigned, but notice that the C atom has a share in only three pairs.

5. *If the central atom has fewer than eight electrons at this point, change one or more of the lone pairs on the terminal atoms into a bonding pair between the central and terminal atom to form a multiple bond.*

   As a general rule, double or triple bonds are most often encountered when *both* atoms are from the following list: C, N, or O. That is, bonds such as C=C, C=N, and C=O will be encountered frequently.

● **Choosing the Central Atom**
1. The electronegativities of atoms can also be used to choose the central atom. Electronegativity is discussed in Section 8.7.
2. For simple compounds, the first atom in a formula is often the central atom (e.g., $SO_2$, $NH_4^+$, $NO_3^-$). This is not always a reliable predictor, however. Notable exceptions include water ($H_2O$) and most common acids ($HNO_3$, $H_2SO_4$), in which the acidic hydrogen is usually written first but where another atom (such as N or S) is the central atom.

## Strategy Map 8.1

Draw the **Lewis electron dot structure** for $ClO_3^-$.

↓

**DATA/INFORMATION**

• **Formula** of the ion

┌─ STEP 1. Decide on **central atom**

**Cl** is central atom, surrounded by three **O** atoms.

┌─ STEP 2. Calculate number of **valence electrons**

$ClO_3^-$ has **26** valence electrons or **13 pairs.**

┌─ STEP 3. Form **single bonds** between *central atom* and *terminal atoms*

Single bonds
$$\begin{matrix} & O \\ & \nearrow \\ & | \\ O & - Cl - O \end{matrix}$$

┌─ STEP 4. Place **electron pairs** on *terminal atoms* so each has an **octet** of electrons.

Electron pairs ⟶ $:\ddot{O}:$
$$: \ddot{O} - Cl - \ddot{O} :$$

┌─ STEP 5. Place **remaining electron pairs** on the *central atom* to achieve octet.

Complete
$$\left[ \begin{matrix} :\ddot{O}: \\ | \\ :\ddot{O} - Cl - \ddot{O}: \end{matrix} \right]^-$$

---

**◉WL    INTERACTIVE EXAMPLE 8.1    Drawing Lewis Electron Dot Structures**

**Problem**  Draw Lewis structures for the chlorate ion ($ClO_3^-$) and the nitronium ion ($NO_2^+$).

**What Do You Know?**  The formula of each ion is given, and you can expect that each atom will achieve an octet configuration.

**Strategy**  Follow the five steps outlined for $CH_2O$ in the preceding text.

**Solution for chlorate ion**

1.  Cl is the central atom, and the O atoms are terminal atoms.

2.  Valence electrons = 26 (13 pairs)
    = 7 (for Cl) + 18 (six for each O) + 1 (for the negative charge)

3.  Three electron pairs form single bonds from Cl to the O terminal atoms.

$$\begin{matrix} & O \\ & | \\ O & - Cl - O \end{matrix}$$

4.  Distribute three lone pairs on each of the terminal O atoms to complete the octet of electrons around each of these atoms.

$$\left[ \begin{matrix} :\ddot{O}: \\ | \\ :\ddot{O} - Cl - \ddot{O}: \end{matrix} \right]^-$$

5.  One pair of electrons remains, and it is placed on the central Cl atom to complete its octet.

$$\left[ \begin{matrix} :\ddot{O}: \\ | \\ :\ddot{O} - Cl - \ddot{O}: \end{matrix} \right]^-$$

Each atom now has a share in four pairs of electrons, and the Lewis structure is complete.

**Solution for nitronium ion**

1.  Nitrogen is the central atom. The electron affinity of nitrogen is lower than that of oxygen. (The electron attachment enthalpy of N is less negative than that of O.)

2.  Valence electrons = 16 (8 pairs)
    = 5 (for N) + 12 (six for each O) − 1 (for the positive charge)

3.  Two electron pairs form single bonds from the nitrogen to each oxygen:

$$O - N - O$$

4.  Distribute the remaining six pairs of electrons on the terminal O atoms:

$$\left[ :\ddot{O} - N - \ddot{O}: \right]^+$$

5.  The central nitrogen atom is two electron pairs short of an octet. Thus, a lone pair of electrons on each oxygen atom is converted to a bonding electron pair to give two N=O double bonds. Each atom in the ion now has four electron pairs. Nitrogen has four bonding pairs, and each oxygen atom has two lone pairs and shares two bond pairs.

$$\left[ :\ddot{O}\frown N \frown \ddot{O}: \right]^+ \xrightarrow{\begin{array}{c}\text{Move lone pairs to create}\\ \text{double bonds and satisfy}\\ \text{the octet for N.}\end{array}} \left[ \ddot{O}=N=\ddot{O} \right]^+$$

**Think about Your Answer**  Why don't we take two lone pairs from one side and none from the other (to give a NO triple bond and a NO single bond, respectively)? We shall discuss that after describing charge distribution in molecules and ions (page 373).

---

**Check Your Understanding**

Draw Lewis structures for $NH_4^+$, CO, $NO^+$, and $SO_4^{2-}$.

**A CLOSER LOOK**

## Useful Ideas to Consider When Drawing Lewis Electron Dot Structures

- The octet rule is a useful guideline when drawing Lewis structures.
- Carbon forms four bonds (four single bonds; two single bonds and one double bond; two double bonds; or one single bond and one triple bond). In uncharged species, nitrogen forms three bonds and oxygen forms two bonds. Hydrogen typically forms only one bond to another atom.

- When multiple bonds are formed, both atoms involved are usually one of the following: C, N, and O. Oxygen has the ability to form multiple bonds with a variety of elements. Carbon forms many compounds having multiple bonds to another carbon or to N or O.
- Nonmetals may form single, double, and triple bonds but never quadruple bonds.

- Always account for single bonds and lone pairs before determining whether multiple bonds are present.
- Be alert for the possibility the molecule or ion you are working on is isoelectronic (page 353) with a species you have seen before. If so, it may have a similar Lewis structure.

## Predicting Lewis Structures

Chemists find Lewis structures useful to gain a perspective on the structure and chemistry of a molecule or ion. The guidelines for drawing Lewis structures are helpful, but you will find you can also rely on patterns of bonding in related molecules.

### Hydrogen Compounds

Some common compounds and ions formed from second-period nonmetal elements and hydrogen are shown in Table 8.3. Their Lewis structures illustrate the fact that the Lewis symbol for an element is a useful guide in determining the number of bonds formed by the element. For example, if there is no charge, nitrogen has five valence electrons. Two electrons occur as a lone pair; the other three occur as unpaired electrons. To reach an octet, it is necessary to pair each of the unpaired electrons with an electron from another atom. Thus, N is predicted to form three bonds in uncharged molecules, and this is indeed the case. Similarly, carbon is expected to form four bonds, oxygen two, and fluorine one.

| Group 4A | Group 5A | Group 6A | Group 7A |
|----------|----------|----------|----------|
| $-\overset{\displaystyle |}{\underset{\displaystyle |}{C}}-$ | $-\overset{\displaystyle \cdot\cdot}{\underset{\displaystyle |}{N}}-$ | $-\overset{\displaystyle \cdot\cdot}{\underset{\displaystyle \cdot\cdot}{O}}-$ | $:\overset{\displaystyle \cdot\cdot}{\underset{\displaystyle \cdot\cdot}{F}}-$ |

**Table 8.3  Lewis Structures of Common Hydrogen-Containing Molecules and Ions of Second-Period Elements**

| Group 4A | | Group 5A | | Group 6A | | Group 7A | |
|----------|---|----------|---|----------|---|----------|---|
| CH$_4$ methane | H<br>H—C—H<br>H | NH$_3$ ammonia | H—N—H<br>H | H$_2$O water | H—O—H | HF hydrogen fluoride | H—F: |
| C$_2$H$_6$ ethane | H  H<br>H—C—C—H<br>H  H | N$_2$H$_4$ hydrazine | H—N—N—H<br>H  H | H$_2$O$_2$ hydrogen peroxide | H—O—O—H | | |
| C$_2$H$_4$ ethylene | H—C=C—H<br>H  H | NH$_4^+$ ammonium ion | $\left[\begin{array}{c}H\\H-N-H\\H\end{array}\right]^+$ | H$_3$O$^+$ hydronium ion | $\left[H-O-H\right]^+$ with H below | | |
| C$_2$H$_2$ acetylene | H—C≡C—H | NH$_2^-$ amide ion | $\left[H-N-H\right]^-$ | OH$^-$ hydroxide ion | $\left[:O-H\right]^-$ | | |

**EXAMPLE 8.2    Predicting Lewis Electron Dot Structures**

**Problem** Draw Lewis electron dot structures for $CCl_4$ and $NF_3$.

**What Do You Know?** Carbon tetrachloride ($CCl_4$) and $NF_3$ have stoichiometries similar to $CH_4$ and $NH_3$, so you might reasonably expect similar Lewis structures.

**Strategy** Recall that carbon is expected to form four bonds and nitrogen three bonds to achieve an octet of electrons. In addition, halogen atoms have seven valence electrons, so both Cl and F can attain an octet by forming one covalent bond, just as hydrogen does.

**Solution**

carbon tetrachloride          nitrogen trifluoride

**Think about Your Answer** As a check, count the number of valence electrons for each molecule, and verify that all are shown in the Lewis structure.

$CCl_4$: Valence electrons = 4 (for C) + 4 × 7 (for Cl) = 32 electrons (16 pairs)

The structure shows eight electrons in single bonds and 24 electrons as lone pair electrons, for a total of 32 electrons. The structure is correct.

$NF_3$: Valence electrons = 5 (for N) + 3 × 7 (for F) = 26 electrons (13 pairs)

The structure shows six electrons in single bonds and 20 electrons as lone pair electrons, for a total of 26 electrons. The structure is correct.

**Check Your Understanding**

Predict Lewis structures for methanol, $CH_3OH$, and hydroxylamine, $H_2NOH$. (In each molecule the central C or N atom is surrounded by H atoms and one OH group.)

## Oxoacids and Their Anions

Lewis structures of common acids and their anions are shown in Table 8.4. In the absence of water, these acids are covalently bonded molecular compounds, a conclusion that we should draw because all elements in the formula are nonmetals. (Nitric acid, for example, has properties that we associate with a covalent compound: It is a colorless liquid with a boiling point of 83 °C.) In aqueous solution, however, $HNO_3$, $H_2SO_4$, and $HClO_4$ ionize to give a hydronium ion and the appropriate anion. A Lewis structure for the nitrate ion, for example, can be created using the guidelines on page 349, and the result is a structure with two N—O single bonds and one N=O double bond. To form nitric acid from the nitrate ion, a hydrogen ion is attached utilizing a lone pair on one of the O atoms.

nitrate ion                    nitric acid

A characteristic property of acids in aqueous solution is their ability to donate a hydrogen ion ($H^+$) to water to give the hydronium ion. The $NO_3^-$ anion is formed when the acid, $HNO_3$, loses a hydrogen ion. The $H^+$ ion separates from the acid by breaking the H—O bond, the electrons of the bond staying with the O atom. As a result, $HNO_3$ and $NO_3^-$ have the same number of electrons, 24, and their structures are closely related.

**Table 8.4 Lewis Structures of Common Oxoacids and Their Anions**

| | | | | | |
|---|---|---|---|---|---|
| $HNO_3$ nitric acid | H—O—N=O: with :O: below N | $H_3PO_4$ phosphoric acid | :O—H above; :O—P—O:; H—O: H below | $H_2SO_4$ sulfuric acid | :O—H above; :O—S—O:; :O—H below |
| $NO_3^-$ nitrate ion | [:O—N=O:]⁻ with :O: below | $PO_4^{3-}$ phosphate ion | [:O—P—O:]³⁻ with :O: above and :O: below | $HSO_4^-$ hydrogen sulfate ion | [:O—H above; :O—S—O:; :O: below]⁻ |
| $HClO_4$ perchloric acid | :O—H above; :O—Cl—O:; :O: below | HOCl hypochlorous acid | H—O—Cl: | $SO_4^{2-}$ sulfate ion | [:O: above; :O—S—O:; :O: below]²⁻ |
| $ClO_4^-$ perchlorate ion | [:O: above; :O—Cl—O:; :O: below]⁻ | OCl⁻ hypochlorite ion | [:O—Cl:]⁻ | | |

## Isoelectronic Species

The species $NO^+$, $N_2$, CO, and $CN^-$ are similar in that they each have two atoms and the same total number of valence electrons, 10, which leads to a similar Lewis structure for each molecule or ion. The two atoms in each are linked with a triple bond. With three bonding pairs and one lone pair, each atom thus has an octet of electrons.

$$[:N\equiv O:]^+ \qquad :N\equiv N: \qquad :C\equiv O: \qquad [:C\equiv N:]^-$$

Molecules and ions having the *same number of valence electrons and similar Lewis structures* are said to be **isoelectronic** (Table 8.5). You will find it helpful to recognize isoelectronic molecules and ions because these species have similar electronic (Lewis) structures.

There are similarities and important differences in chemical properties of isoelectronic species. For example, both carbon monoxide, CO, and cyanide ion, $CN^-$, are very toxic, which results from the fact that they can bind to the iron of hemoglobin in blood and block the uptake of oxygen. They are different, though, in their

● **Isoelectronic and Isostructural** The term *isostructural* is often used in conjunction with isoelectronic species. Species that are isostructural have the same structure. For example, the $PO_4^{3-}$, $SO_4^{2-}$, and $ClO_4^-$ ions in Table 8.4 all have four oxygens bonded to the central atom. In addition, they are isoelectronic in that all have 32 valence electrons.

**Table 8.5 Some Common Isoelectronic Molecules and Ions**

| Formulas | Representative Lewis Structure | Formulas | Representative Lewis Structure |
|---|---|---|---|
| $BH_4^-$, $CH_4$, $NH_4^+$ | [H—N—H with H above and H below]⁺ | $CO_3^{2-}$, $NO_3^-$ | [:O—N=O: with :O: below]⁻ |
| $NH_3$, $H_3O^+$ | H—N—H with H below | $PO_4^{3-}$, $SO_4^{2-}$, $ClO_4^-$ | [:O: above; :O—P—O:; :O: below]³⁻ |
| $CO_2$, $OCN^-$, $SCN^-$, $N_2O$ $NO_2^+$, OCS, $CS_2$ | O=C=O | | |

acid–base chemistry. In aqueous solution, cyanide ion readily adds $H^+$ to form hydrogen cyanide, whereas CO is not protonated in water.

---

**REVIEW & CHECK FOR SECTION 8.2**

1.  Which of the following describes the sulfur atom in the Lewis structure of the sulfite ion, $SO_3^{2-}$?

    (a)  Sulfur has three single bonds to oxygen and a lone pair.

    (b)  Sulfur bonds to two oxygen atoms with single bonds and one oxygen atom with a double bond.

    (c)  Sulfur forms double bonds to three oxygen atoms.

    (d)  Sulfur forms three single bonds to oxygen and has no lone pairs.

2.  Which one of the species in the list below is NOT isoelectronic with $N_3^-$?

    (a)  $N_2O$    (b)  $NO_2^+$    (c)  $O_3$    (d)  $CO_2$

3.  Identify the species in the list below that is NOT isoelectronic with the others.

    (a)  $O_3$    (b)  $OCN^-$    (c)  $NO_2^-$    (d)  $SO_2$

---

## 8.3 Atom Formal Charges in Covalent Molecules and Ions

You have seen that Lewis structures show how electron pairs are placed in a covalently bonded species, whether it is a neutral molecule or a polyatomic ion. Now we turn to one of the consequences of the placement of electron pairs in this way: Individual atoms can be negatively or positively charged or have no electric charge. The location of a positive or negative charge in a molecule or ion will influence, among other things, the atom at which a reaction occurs. For example, does a positive $H^+$ ion attach itself to the Cl or the O of $ClO^-$? Is the product HClO or HOCl? It is reasonable to expect $H^+$ to attach to the more negatively charged atom, and we can predict this by evaluating atom formal charges in molecules and ions.

The **formal charge** is the charge that would reside on an atom in a molecule or polyatomic ion if we assume that all bonding electrons are shared equally. The formal charge for an atom in a molecule or ion is calculated based on the Lewis structure of the molecule or ion, using Equation 8.1,

$$\text{Formal charge of an atom in a molecule or ion} = NVE - [LPE + \tfrac{1}{2}(BE)] \quad (8.1)$$

where NVE = number of valence electrons in the uncombined atom (and equal to its group number in the periodic table), LPE = number of lone pair electrons on an atom, and BE = number of bonding electrons around an atom. The term in square brackets is the number of electrons assigned by the Lewis structure to an atom in a molecule or ion. *The difference between this term and the number of valence electrons on the uncombined atom is the formal charge.* An atom in a molecule or ion will be positive if it "contributes" more electrons to bonding than it "gets back." The atom's formal charge will be negative if the reverse is true.

There are two important assumptions in Equation 8.1. First, lone pairs are assumed to "belong" to the atom on which they reside in the Lewis structure. Second, bond pairs are assumed to be divided equally between the bonded atoms. (The factor of $\frac{1}{2}$ divides the bonding electrons equally between the atoms linked by the bond.)

*The sum of the formal charges on the atoms in a molecule or ion always equals the net charge on the molecule or ion.* Consider the hypochlorite ion, $ClO^-$. Oxygen is in Group 6A and so has six valence electrons. However, the oxygen atom in $OCl^-$ can lay claim to seven electrons (six lone pair electrons and one bonding electron), so the atom has a formal charge of $-1$. The O atom has formally gained an electron by bonding to chlorine.

Formal charge $= -1 = 6 - [6 + \frac{1}{2}(2)]$

$$\left[ :\overset{..}{\underset{..}{Cl}} - \overset{..}{\underset{..}{O}} : \right]^{-}$$

Formal charge $= 0 = 7 - [6 + \frac{1}{2}(2)]$   Assume a covalent bond, so bonding electrons are divided equally between Cl and O.

$\Big\}$ *Sum of formal charges* $= -1$

● **HClO$_x$ Acids and Formal Charge** Both ClO$^-$ and ClO$_3^-$ ions attract a proton to give the corresponding acid, HClO and HClO$_3$. In all of the HClO$_x$ acids, the H$^+$ ion is attached to an O atom, owing to the negative formal charge on that atom. (See Table 8.4.)

The formal charge on the Cl atom in ClO$^-$ is zero. So we have $-1$ for oxygen and 0 for chlorine, and the sum of these equals the net charge of $-1$ for the ion. An important conclusion we can draw from the formal charges in ClO$^-$ is that, if an H$^+$ ion approaches the ion, it should attach itself to the negatively charged O atom to give hypochlorous acid, HOCl.

## EXAMPLE 8.3    Calculating Formal Charges

**Problem**  Calculate formal charges for the atoms of the ClO$_3^-$ ion.

**What Do You Know?**  The Lewis structure of ClO$_3^-$ is required and was developed in Example 8.1.

**Strategy**  The first step is always to write the Lewis structure for the molecule or ion. Then Equation 8.1 can be used to calculate the formal charges.

**Solution**

Formal charge $= -1 = 6 - [6 + \frac{1}{2}(2)]$

$$\left[ \begin{array}{c} :\overset{..}{\underset{..}{O}}: \\ | \\ :\overset{..}{\underset{..}{O}} - Cl - \overset{..}{\underset{..}{O}}: \end{array} \right]^{-}$$

Formal charge $= +2 = 7 - [2 + \frac{1}{2}(6)]$

The formal charge on each O atom is $-1$, whereas for the Cl atom it is $+2$.

---

**A CLOSER LOOK**

## Comparing Oxidation Number and Formal Charge

In Chapter 3 you learned to calculate the oxidation number of an atom as a way to tell if a reaction involves oxidation and reduction. Are an atom's oxidation number and its formal charge related? To answer this question, let us look at the hydroxide ion. The formal charges are $-1$ on the O atom and 0 on the H atom. Recall that these formal charges are calculated assuming the O—H bond electrons are shared equally in an O—H covalent bond.

Formal charge $= -1 = 6 - [6 + \frac{1}{2}(2)]$

$$\left[ :\overset{..}{\underset{..}{O}} - H \right]^{-}$$    *Sum of formal charges* $= -1$

Formal charge $= 0 = 1 - [0 + \frac{1}{2}(2)]$

In contrast, in Chapter 3 (page 140), you learned that O has an oxidation number of $-2$ and H has a number of $+1$. *Oxidation numbers are determined by assuming that the bond between a pair of atoms is ionic, not covalent.* For OH$^-$ this means the pair of electrons between O and H is located *fully* on O. Thus, the O atom now has eight valence electrons instead of six and a charge of $-2$. The H atom now has no valence electrons and a charge of $+1$.

Oxidation number $= -2$

$$\left[ :\overset{..}{\underset{..}{O}} : \quad H \right]^{-}$$    *Sum of oxidation numbers* $= -1$

Assume an ionic bond       Oxidation number $= +1$

Formal charges and oxidation numbers are calculated using different assumptions. Both are useful, but for different purposes. Oxidation numbers allow us to follow changes in redox reactions. Formal charges provide insight into the distribution of charges in molecules and polyatomic ions.

**Think about Your Answer** Notice that the sum of the formal charges on all the atoms equals the charge on the ion.

**Check Your Understanding**

Calculate formal charges on each atom in **(a)** $CN^-$ and **(b)** $SO_3^{2-}$.

---

**REVIEW & CHECK FOR SECTION 8.3**

What is the formal charge of the P atom in the anion $H_2PO_4^-$? (The dihydrogen phosphate ion is the anion derived from $H_3PO_4$ by loss of $H^+$.)

(a)  +3    (b)  0    (c)  +1    (d)  +5

---

## 8.4 Resonance

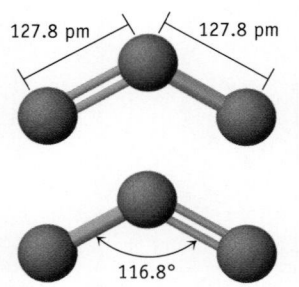

127.8 pm    127.8 pm

116.8°

Ozone, $O_3$, is a bent molecule with oxygen–oxygen bonds of the same length.

Ozone, $O_3$, an unstable, blue, diamagnetic gas with a characteristic pungent odor, protects the earth and its inhabitants from intense ultraviolet radiation from the sun. An important feature of its structure is that the two oxygen–oxygen bonds are the same length, which suggests that the two bonds are equivalent (as described more fully in Section 8.9). That is, equal O—O bond lengths imply an equal number of bond pairs in each O—O bond. Using the guidelines for drawing Lewis structures, however, you might come to a different conclusion. There are two possible ways of writing the Lewis structure for the molecule:

*Alternative Ways of Drawing the Ozone Structure*

Double bond on the left: $\ddot{O}=\ddot{O}-\ddot{\underset{..}{O}}:$

Double bond on the right: $:\ddot{\underset{..}{O}}-\ddot{O}=\ddot{O}$

These structures are equivalent in that each has a double bond on one side of the central oxygen atom and a single bond on the other side. If either were the actual structure of ozone, one bond (O=O) should be shorter than the other (O—O). The actual structure of ozone shows this is not the case. The inescapable conclusion is that these Lewis structures do not correctly represent the bonding in ozone.

Linus Pauling (1901–1994) proposed the theory of **resonance** to solve the problem. *Resonance structures are used to represent bonding in a molecule or ion when a single Lewis structure fails to describe accurately the actual electronic structure.* The alternative structures shown for ozone are called **resonance structures**. They have identical patterns of bonding and equal energy. The actual structure of this molecule is a *composite*, or **hybrid**, of the equivalent resonance structures. In this resonance hybrid, the bonds between the oxygens are between a single bond and a double bond in length, in this case corresponding to one and a half bonds. This is a reasonable conclusion because we see that the O—O bonds both have a length of 127.8 pm, intermediate between the average length of an O=O double bond (121 pm) and an O—O single bond (132 pm). Because we cannot accurately draw fractions of a bond, chemists draw the resonance structures and connect them with double-headed arrows (↔) to indicate that the true structure is a composite of these extreme structures.

$:\ddot{\underset{..}{O}}-\ddot{O}=\ddot{O}: \longleftrightarrow :\ddot{\underset{..}{O}}=\ddot{O}-\ddot{\underset{..}{O}}:$

● **Depicting Resonance Structures** The use of an arrow (↔) as a symbol to link resonance structures and the term *resonance* are somewhat unfortunate. An arrow might seem to imply that a change is occurring, and the term *resonance* has the connotation of vibrating or alternating back and forth between different forms. Neither view is correct. Electron pairs are not actually moving from one atom to another.

Benzene, $C_6H_6$, is the classic example of the use of resonance to represent a structure. The benzene molecule is a six-member ring of carbon atoms with six

## Resonance

- Resonance is a means of representing the bonding in a molecule or polyatomic ion when a single Lewis structure fails to give an accurate picture.
- The atoms must have the same arrangement in each resonance structure. Attaching the atoms in a different fashion creates a different compound.

- Resonance structures differ only in the assignment of electron-pair positions, never atom positions.
- Resonance structures differ in the number of bond pairs between a given pair of atoms.

- Resonance is not meant to indicate the motion of electrons.
- The actual structure of a molecule is a composite or hybrid of the resonance structures.
- There will always be at least one multiple bond (double or triple) in each resonance structure.

equivalent carbon–carbon bonds (and a hydrogen atom attached to each carbon atom). The carbon–carbon bonds are 139 pm long, intermediate between the average length of a C=C double bond (134 pm) and a C—C single bond (154 pm). Two resonance structures that differ only in double bond placement can be written for the molecule. A hybrid of these two structures, however, will lead to a molecule with six equivalent carbon–carbon bonds.

resonance structures of benzene, $C_6H_6$

abbreviated representation of resonance structures

Let us apply the concepts of resonance to describe bonding in the carbonate ion, $CO_3^{2-}$, an anion with 24 valence electrons (12 pairs).

Three equivalent structures can be drawn for this ion, differing only in the location of the C=O double bond, but no single structure correctly describes this ion. Instead, the actual structure is a composite of the three structures, in good agreement with experimental results. In the $CO_3^{2-}$ ion, all three carbon–oxygen bond distances are 129 pm, intermediate between C—O single bond (143 pm) and C=O double bond (122 pm) distances.

Formal charges can be calculated for each atom in the resonance structure for a molecule or ion. For example, using one of the resonance structures for the nitrate ion, we find that the central N atom has a formal charge of +1, and the singly bonded O atoms are both −1. The doubly bonded O atom has no charge. The net charge for the ion is thus −1.

Formal charge $= 0 \doteq 6 - [4 + \frac{1}{2}(4)]$

Sum of formal charges $= -1$

Formal charge $= +1 = 5 - [0 + \frac{1}{2}(8)]$

Formal charge $= -1 = 6 - [6 + \frac{1}{2}(2)]$

Is this a reasonable charge distribution for the nitrate ion? The answer is no. The actual structure of the nitrate ion is a resonance hybrid of three equivalent resonance structures. Because the three oxygen atoms in $NO_3^-$ are equivalent, the charge on one oxygen atom should not be different from the other two. This can be resolved, however, if the formal charges are averaged to give a formal charge of $-\frac{2}{3}$ on the oxygen atoms. Summing the charges on the three oxygen atoms and the $+1$ charge on the nitrogen atom then gives $-1$, the charge on the ion.

In the resonance structures for $O_3$, $CO_3^{2-}$, and $NO_3^-$ all the possible resonance structures are equally likely; they are "equivalent" structures. The molecule or ion therefore has a symmetrical distribution of electrons over all the atoms involved—that is, its electronic structure consists of an equal "mixture," or "hybrid," of the resonance structures.

## EXAMPLE 8.4    Drawing Resonance Structures

**Problem** Draw resonance structures for the nitrite ion, $NO_2^-$. Are the N—O bonds single, double, or intermediate in value? What are the formal charges on the N and O atoms?

**What Do You Know?** The N atom is the central atom in the Lewis structure, bonded to two terminal oxygen atoms. You need to determine whether two or more equivalent Lewis structures can be written for this ion.

**Strategy**

*   Using the guidelines for drawing Lewis structures, determine whether there is more than one way to achieve an octet of electrons around each atom.

*   Use one of the Lewis structures to determine the formal charges on the atoms.

*   If the formal charges on the two oxygen atoms are different, then the formal charge on oxygen will be an average of the two values.

**Solution** Nitrogen is the central atom in the nitrite ion, which has a total of 18 valence electrons.

Valence electrons = 5 (for the N atom) + 12 (6 for each O atom) + 1 (for negative charge)

After forming N—O single bonds and distributing lone pairs on the terminal O atoms, one electron pair remains, which is placed on the central N atom.

$$\left[ :\ddot{O}-\ddot{N}-\ddot{O}: \right]^-$$

To complete the octet of electrons about the N atom, form a N=O double bond. Because there are two ways to do this, two equivalent structures can be drawn, and the actual structure must be a composite or resonance hybrid of these two structures. The nitrogen–oxygen bonds are neither single nor double bonds but have an intermediate value.

$$\left[ :\ddot{O}=\ddot{N}-\ddot{O}: \right]^- \longleftrightarrow \left[ :\ddot{O}-\ddot{N}=\ddot{O}: \right]^-$$

Taking one of the resonance structures, you should find the formal charge for the N atom is 0. The charge on one O atom is 0 and $-1$ for the other O atom. Because the two resonance structures are of equal importance, however, the net formal charge on each O atom is $-\frac{1}{2}$.

Formal charge =
$0 = 6 - [4 + \frac{1}{2}(4)]$

Formal charge =
$-1 = 6 - [6 + \frac{1}{2}(2)]$

$$\left[ \ddot{O}=N-\ddot{O}: \right]^-$$

Formal charge = $0 = 5 - [2 + \frac{1}{2}(6)]$

# A Scientific Controversy—Are There Double Bonds in Sulfate and Phosphate Ions?

Now that you have learned about Lewis structures, resonance, and formal charge, we want to discuss a genuine scientific controversy: the disagreement among chemists about drawing Lewis structures for such simple species as sulfate ion and phosphate ion. For example, two different Lewis structures have been proposed for the sulfate ion:

When drawing Lewis structures, the most important step is first to satisfy the octet rule for each atom in a molecule or ion. If a single Lewis structure does not accurately represent a species, resonance can be introduced. [If two resonance structures are different (as with ions such as $OCN^-$ or a compound like $N_2O$), a decision can be made among the possible choices by giving preference to structures that minimize formal charges and place negative charges on the most electronegative atoms (page 373).] In the large majority of cases, Lewis structures created by this approach can then be used to determine molecular structure and provide a qualitative picture of bonding.

In this book, we choose to represent the sulfate ion with Lewis structure 1 in which all of the atoms achieve an octet of electrons. The S—O bond order is 1, the sulfur atom has a formal charge of +2, and each oxygen has a formal charge of −1.

The bonding in $SO_4^{2-}$ would involve single bonds between S and O. (As you shall see in Chapter 9, these bonds use the $3s$ and $3p$ orbitals for S and $sp^3$ hybridization.) Some chemists, however, choose to represent sulfate by a different Lewis structure (structure 2, one of six equivalent structures). Structure 2 is formally a resonance structure of 1. Here, the average sulfur–oxygen bond order is 1.5. This structure is attractive because it miminizes formal charges: sulfur has a formal charge of 0, two of the oxygen atoms have a formal charge of zero, and the other two have formal charges of −1. However, to describe the bonding here, six sulfur orbitals must be used in forming the six bonds. This means that $3d$ orbitals on sulfur must also be involved when describing bonding, in addition to the $3s$ and $3p$ orbitals.

A similar situation is encountered with the phosphate ion and a number of other related species. Several resonance structures can be drawn with or without double bonds.

The question: Which is the better representation of bonding in these species, 1 or 2? Here we find a controversy. A paper in the *Journal of Chemical Education*[1] presents arguments supporting the description of sulfate by structure 2. Among data offered to support multiple bonding between sulfur and oxygen is the observation that the sulfate ion has shorter SO bonds (149 pm) than the known S—O single bond length (about 170 pm) but longer than the double bond in sulfur monoxide (128 pm).

Support for structure 1 comes from a theoretical study also reported in the *Journal of Chemical Education*.[2] The authors of this paper conclude that structure 1 for sulfate is more reasonable and that structure 2 "should be given no weight at all." The basic argument is that the energy of the $3d$ orbitals is too high to allow any significant involvement of these orbitals in bonding. In keeping with this the authors determined that ". . . the calculated $d$-orbital occupancies . . . are quite small (less than 0.19 e in the entire shell) and inconsistent with any significant valence shell expansion." (In structure 2 the $d$ orbital occupancy would be 2.0 electrons.)

We give more credence to the theoretical study in reference 2 and believe that structure 1 better represents the sulfate ion (and related species) than 2. Others, however, believe structure 2 is the better structure. In any case, there is an important message here: *Lewis structures represent only an approximation when representing structure and bonding.*

**References:**
1. R. F. See, *J. Chem. Ed.*, **2009**, *86*, 1241–1247.
2. L. Suidan, J. K. Badenhoop, E. D. Glendening, and F. Weinhold, *J. Chem. Ed.*, **1995**, *72*, 583–586.

Additional comments on this matter are found in:

F. Weinhold and C. R. Landis, *Science*, **2007**, *316*, 61.

G. Frenking, R. Tanner, F. Weinhold, and C. R. Landis, *Science*, **2007**, *318*, 746a.

**Think about Your Answer** The NO bonds in $NO_2^-$ are equivalent, each being intermediate in length between a single N—O bond and a double N=O bond.

**Check Your Understanding**

Draw resonance structures for the bicarbonate ion, $HCO_3^-$.

(a) Does $HCO_3^-$ have the same number of resonance structures as the $CO_3^{2-}$ ion?

(b) What are the formal charges on the O and C atoms in $HCO_3^-$? What is the average formal charge on the O atoms? Compare this with the O atoms in $CO_3^{2-}$.

(c) Protonation of $HCO_3^-$ gives $H_2CO_3$. How do formal charges predict where the $H^+$ ion will be attached?

## 8.5 Exceptions to the Octet Rule

Although the vast majority of molecular compounds and ions obey the octet rule, there are exceptions. These include molecules and ions that have fewer than four pairs of electrons on a central atom, those that have more than four pairs, and those that have an odd number of electrons.

### Compounds in Which an Atom Has Fewer Than Eight Valence Electrons

Boron, a metalloid in Group 3A, has three valence electrons and so is expected to form three covalent bonds with other nonmetallic elements. This results in a valence shell for boron in its compounds with only six electrons, two short of an octet. Many boron compounds of this type are known, including such common compounds as boric acid ($B(OH)_3$), borax ($Na_2B_4O_5(OH)_4 \cdot 8\ H_2O$) (Figure 8.2), and the boron trihalides ($BF_3$, $BCl_3$, $BBr_3$, and $BI_3$).

boron trifluoride          boric acid

Boron compounds such as $BF_3$ that are two electrons short of an octet are quite reactive. The boron atom can accommodate a fourth electron pair when that pair is provided by another atom, and molecules or ions with lone pairs can fulfill this role. Ammonia, for example, reacts with $BF_3$ to form $H_3N{\rightarrow}BF_3$.

coordinate covalent bond

If a bonding pair of electrons originates on one of the bonded atoms, the bond is called a **coordinate covalent bond**. In Lewis structures, a coordinate covalent

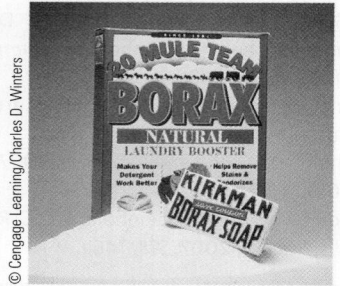

B atom surrounded by 4 electron pairs

B atom surrounded by 3 electron pairs

**FIGURE 8.2 The anion in Borax.** Borax is a common mineral that is used in soaps and contains an interesting anion, $B_4O_5(OH)_4^{2-}$. The anion has two B atoms surrounded by four electron pairs, and two B atoms surrounded by only three pairs.

bond is often designated by an arrow that points away from the atom donating the electron pair.

## Compounds in Which an Atom Has More Than Eight Valence Electrons

Elements in the third or higher periods form compounds and ions in which the central element can be surrounded by more than four valence electron pairs (Table 8.6). With most compounds and ions in this category, the central atom is bonded to fluorine, chlorine, or oxygen.

It is often obvious from the formula of a compound that an octet around an atom has been exceeded. As an example, consider sulfur hexafluoride, $SF_6$, a gas formed by the reaction of sulfur and excess fluorine. Sulfur is the central atom in this compound, and fluorine typically bonds to only one other atom with a single electron pair bond (as in HF and $CF_4$). Six S—F bonds are required in $SF_6$, meaning there will be six electron pairs in the valence shell of the sulfur atom.

If there are more than four groups bonded to a central atom, this is a reliable signal that there are more than eight electrons around a central atom. But be careful—the central atom octet can also be exceeded with four or fewer atoms bonded to the central atom. Consider three examples from Table 8.6: The central atom in $SF_4$, $ClF_3$, and $XeF_2$ has five electron pairs in its valence shell.

A useful observation is that *only elements of the third and higher periods in the periodic table form compounds and ions in which an octet is exceeded.* Second-period elements (B, C, N, O, F) are restricted to a maximum of eight electrons in their compounds. For example, nitrogen forms compounds and ions such as $NH_3$, $NH_4^+$, and $NF_3$, but $NF_5$ is unknown. Phosphorus, the third-period element just below nitrogen in the periodic table, forms many compounds similar to nitrogen ($PH_3$, $PH_4^+$, $PF_3$), but it also readily accommodates five or six valence electron pairs in compounds such as $PF_5$ or in ions such as $PF_6^-$. Arsenic, antimony, and bismuth, the elements below phosphorus in Group 5A, resemble phosphorus in their behavior.

The usual explanation for the contrasting behavior of second- and third-period elements centers on the number of orbitals in the valence shell of an atom. Second-period elements have four valence orbitals (one $2s$ and three $2p$ orbitals). Two electrons per orbital result in a total of eight electrons being accommodated around an atom. For elements in the third and higher periods, the $d$ orbitals in the outer shell are traditionally included among valence orbitals for the elements. Thus, for phosphorus, the $3d$ orbitals are included with the $3s$ and $3p$ orbitals as valence orbitals. The extra orbitals provide the element with an opportunity to accommodate up to 12 electrons.

• **Xenon Compounds** Compounds of xenon are among the more interesting entries in Table 8.6 because noble gas compounds were not discovered until the early 1960s. One of the more intriguing compounds is $XeF_2$, in part because of the simplicity of its synthesis. Xenon difluoride can be made by placing a flask containing xenon gas and fluorine gas in the sunlight. After several weeks, crystals of colorless $XeF_2$ are found in the flask (▶ page 400).

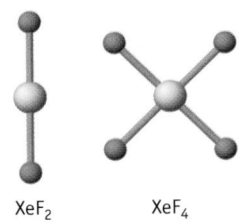

$XeF_2$          $XeF_4$

• **A Note on *d* Orbital Use** Chemists often invoke the use of *d* orbitals to explain bonding in molecules or ions if a central atom is surrounded by 5 or 6 single bonds or lone pairs. Some also assume *d* orbitals are involved in multiple bonds in ions such as $SO_4^{2-}$ and $PO_4^{3-}$. This is not necessary, however, because bonding in these and similar ions is adequately explained using *s* and *p* orbitals, and there is little theoretical evidence for multiple bonds. See page 359.

**Table 8.6 Lewis Structures in Which the Central Atom Exceeds an Octet**

| Group 4A | Group 5A | Group 6A | Group 7A | Group 8 |
|---|---|---|---|---|
| $SiF_5^-$ | $PF_5$ | $SF_4$ | $ClF_3$ | $XeF_2$ |
| $SiF_6^{2-}$ | $PF_6^-$ | $SF_6$ | $BrF_5$ | $XeF_4$ |

### EXAMPLE 8.5 Lewis Structures in Which the Central Atom Has More Than Eight Electrons

**Problem**  Sketch the Lewis structure of the $[ClF_4]^-$ ion.

**What Do You Know?**  Chlorine is the central atom, bonded to four fluorine atoms. The ion has 36 valence electrons (18 pairs) [7 (for Cl) + 4 × 7 (for F) + 1 (for ion charge) = 36].

**Strategy**  Use the guidelines on page 349 to complete the structure.

**Solution**  Draw the ion with four single covalent Cl-F bonds.

$$\begin{bmatrix} & \text{F} & \\ & | & \\ \text{F} - & \text{Cl} - & \text{F} \\ & | & \\ & \text{F} & \end{bmatrix}^-$$

Place lone pairs on the terminal atoms. Because two electron pairs remain after placing lone pairs on the four F atoms and because we know that Cl can accommodate more than four pairs, these two pairs are placed on the central Cl atom.

The last two electron pairs are added to the central Cl atom.

**Think about Your Answer**  The central atom, chlorine, has more than 8 electrons (4 bond pairs and 2 lone pairs.) Because chlorine is in the third period of the periodic table, this is reasonable.

**Check Your Understanding**

Sketch the Lewis structures for $[ClF_2]^+$ and $[ClF_2]^-$. How many lone pairs and bond pairs surround the Cl atom in each ion?

## Molecules with an Odd Number of Electrons

Two nitrogen oxides—NO, with 11 valence electrons, and $NO_2$, with 17 valence electrons—are among a very small group of stable molecules with an odd number of electrons. Because they have an odd number of electrons, it is impossible to draw a structure obeying the octet rule; at least one electron must be unpaired.

Even though $NO_2$ does not obey the octet rule, an electron dot structure can be written that approximates the bonding in the molecule. This Lewis structure places the unpaired electron on nitrogen. Two resonance structures show that the nitrogen-oxygen bonds are expected to be equivalent.

Experimental evidence for NO indicates that the bonding between N and O is intermediate between a double and a triple bond. It is not possible to write a Lewis structure for NO that is in accord with the properties of this substance, so a different theory is needed to understand bonding in this molecule. We shall return to compounds of this type when molecular orbital theory is introduced in Section 9.3.

The two nitrogen oxides, NO and $NO_2$, are members of a class of chemical substances called free radicals. A **free radical** is a chemical species with an unpaired electron. Free radicals are generally quite reactive. Atoms such as H and Cl, for example, are free radicals and readily combine with each other to give molecules such as $H_2$, $Cl_2$, and HCl.

## CASE STUDY

# Hydroxyl Radicals, Atmospheric Chemistry, and Hair Dyes

*Free radical* is a term chemists use for molecules containing an unpaired electron in their valence shell. Such molecules are often highly reactive and are crucially important in environmental chemistry and biochemistry. One example is the hydroxyl radical, ·OH. A paper in *Science* magazine recently called hydroxyl radicals "the 'detergent' of the atmosphere. . . . Hydroxyl radicals are the single most important oxidant in the atmosphere because they are the agent primarily responsible for removing the majority of gases emitted into the atmosphere by natural and anthropogenic activity."

The *Science* paper describes what happens when $NO_2$ molecules, free radicals and a common air pollutant, react with water in the presence of sunlight. One product is the hydroxyl radical, ·OH.

$$NO_2(g) + H_2O(g) \rightarrow$$
$$·OH(g) + HONO(g)$$

The other product, HONO, decomposes with sunlight, to also give a hydroxyl radical and another free radical, NO.

$$HONO(g) \rightarrow HO·(g) + ·NO(g)$$

© Cengage Learning/Charles D. Winters

The hydroxyl radicals then go on to react with trace gases (such as $SO_2$, $NH_3$, CO, and hydrocarbons) in the atmosphere.

Hydroxyl radicals also play a role in dyeing your hair. Most hair dyes are a mixture of a dye, ammonia, and hydrogen peroxide ($H_2O_2$). These species react to produce the perhydroxyl anion ($HOO^-$) and the ·OH radical. The $HOO^-$ ion is a base, and the basic solution causes the hair to swell. This helps in allowing the perhydroxyl anion to react with the melamine pigment in the hair and lighten it. The problem with this approach is that the ·OH radical damages hair, so chemists

came up with a new product. This is a mixture of ammonium carbonate, $(NH_4)_2CO_3$, and $H_2O_2$ in the presence of sodium glycinate, $Na[H_2NCH_2CO_2]$. The mixture is less basic and produces the peroxymonocarbonate ion ($HCO_4^-$) and a carbonate radical anion ($CO_3·^-$). The $HCO_4^-$ ion functions as the bleach, and the glycinate ion scavenges the carbonate radicals that could otherwise damage the hair.

**Questions:**
1. Draw a Lewis structure for HONO. Are there any resonance structures? What is the formal charge on each atom?
2. Draw a Lewis structure for the peroxymonocarbonate ion. (One feature of this ion is a C-O-O-H grouping.) Give the formal charge on each atom and draw any resonance structures.

**Answers to these questions are available in Appendix N.**

**References:**
1. S. Li, J. Matthews, and A. Sinha, *Science*, **2008**, *319*, 1657.
2. L. Jarvis, *Chemical & Engineering News*, February 11, 2008, 32.

---

Free radicals are involved in many reactions in the environment. For example, small amounts of NO are released from vehicle exhausts. The NO rapidly forms $NO_2$, which is even more harmful to human health and to plants. Exposure to $NO_2$ at concentrations of 50–100 parts per million can lead to significant inflammation of lung tissue. Nitrogen dioxide is also generated by natural processes. For example, when hay, which has a high level of nitrates, is stored in silos on farms, $NO_2$ can be generated as the hay ferments, and there have been reports of farm workers dying from exposure to this gas in the silo (because $NO_2$ reacts with water in the lungs to produce nitric acid).

The two nitrogen oxides, NO and $NO_2$, are unique in that they can be isolated, and neither has the extreme reactivity of most free radicals. When cooled, however, two $NO_2$ molecules join or "dimerize" to form colorless $N_2O_4$; the unpaired electrons combine to form an N—N bond in $N_2O_4$ (Figure 8.3).

---

**REVIEW & CHECK FOR SECTION 8.5**

1. In which of the following sulfur species, $SF_2$, $SF_3^+$, $SF_4$, $SF_5^+$, and $SF_6$, does S exceed the octet configuration?

   (a) $SF_5^+$ and $SF_6$    (c) $SF_6$ only

   (b) $SF_4$, $SF_5^+$, and $SF_6$    (d) all five species

2. How many lone pairs of electrons are on the central atom Xe in $XeF_2$?

   (a) 0    (b) 1    (c) 2    (d) 3

**FIGURE 8.3 Free radical chemistry.** When cooled, the concentration of the brown gas $NO_2$ drops dramatically. Nitrogen dioxide is a free radical, and two $NO_2$ molecules couple to form colorless $N_2O_4$, a molecule with an N—N single bond. ($N_2O_4$ has a boiling point of about 21 °C, so it is liquid at 0 °C. This photo shows some $NO_2$ remains at this temperature.)

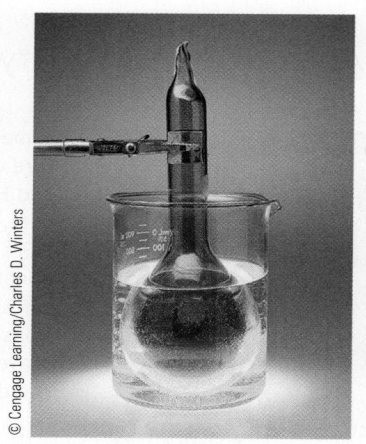

When cooled, $NO_2$ free radicals couple to form $N_2O_4$ molecules.

$N_2O_4$ gas is colorless.

A flask of brown $NO_2$ gas in warm water

A flask of $NO_2$ gas in ice water

## 8.6 Molecular Shapes

Lewis structures show the atom connectivity in molecules and polyatomic ions, but they do not show three-dimensional geometry. However, the three-dimensional geometry of molecules and ions is often crucial to their function, so we want to take the next step: Use the Lewis structures to predict the three-dimensional structure.

The **valence shell electron-pair repulsion (VSEPR)** model is a method for predicting the shapes of covalent molecules and polyatomic ions. This model is based on the idea that *bond and lone electron pairs in the valence shell of an element repel each other and seek to be as far apart as possible.* The positions assumed by the bond and lone electron pairs thus define the angles between bonds to surrounding atoms. VSEPR is remarkably successful in predicting structures of molecules and polyatomic ions of main group elements, although it is less effective (and seldom used) in predicting structures of compounds containing transition metals.

To have a sense of how valence shell electron pairs determine structure, blow up several balloons to a similar size. Imagine that each balloon represents an electron cloud. When two, three, four, five, or six balloons are tied together at a central point (representing the nucleus and core electrons of a central atom), the balloons naturally form the shapes shown in Figure 8.4. These geometric arrangements minimize interactions between the balloons.

### Central Atoms Surrounded Only by Single-Bond Pairs

The simplest application of VSEPR theory is with molecules and ions in which all the electron pairs around the central atom are involved in single covalent bonds. Figure 8.5 illustrates the geometries predicted for molecules or ions with the general formulas $AX_n$, where $A$ is the central atom and $n$ is the number of $X$ groups bonded to it.

Linear

Trigonal planar

Tetrahedral

Trigonal bipyramidal

Octahedral

**FIGURE 8.4 Balloon models of electron-pair geometries for two to six electron pairs.** If two to six balloons of similar size and shape are tied together, they will naturally assume the arrangements shown. These pictures illustrate the predictions of VSEPR.

**FIGURE 8.5 Various geometries predicted by VSEPR.** Geometries predicted by VSEPR for molecules that contain only single covalent bonds around the central atom.

The linear geometry for two single bond pairs and the trigonal-planar geometry for three single bond pairs involve a central atom that does not have an octet of electrons (see Section 8.5). In contrast, the central atom in a tetrahedral molecule obeys the octet rule with four bond pairs. The central atoms in trigonal-bipyramidal and octahedral molecules have five and six bonding pairs, respectively, and are expected only when the central atom is an element in Period 3 or higher in the periodic table (▶ page 368).

## EXAMPLE 8.6    Predicting Molecular Shapes

**Problem**  Predict the shape of silicon tetrachloride, $SiCl_4$.

**What Do You Know?**  You know the compound's formula and the number of valence electrons. In $SiCl_4$ you have 32 valence electrons or 16 pairs. You also know Si is the central atom. This information enables you to draw the electron dot structure.

**Strategy**  The first step is to draw the Lewis structure. However, you do not need to draw it in any particular way because its purpose is only to describe the number of bonds around an atom and to determine if there are any lone pairs. The shape of the molecule is dictated by the positions of the four electron pairs used in bonding to the four chlorine atoms.

**Solution**  The Lewis structure of $SiCl_4$ has four electron pairs, all of them bond pairs, around the central Si atom. Therefore, a tetrahedral structure is predicted for the $SiCl_4$ molecule, with Cl—Si—Cl bond angles of 109.5°. This agrees with the actual structure for $SiCl_4$.

Lewis structure          Molecular geometry

**Think about Your Answer**  Be sure to recognize that all four positions in a tetrahedral geometry are equivalent.

---

**Check Your Understanding**

What is the shape of the dichloromethane ($CH_2Cl_2$) molecule? Predict the Cl—C—Cl bond angle.

## Central Atoms with Single-Bond Pairs and Lone Pairs

To see how lone pairs affect the geometry of a molecule or polyatomic ion, return to the balloon models in Figure 8.4. If you assume the balloons represent *all* the electron pairs in the valence shell, the model predicts the "electron-pair geometry" rather than the "molecular geometry." The **electron-pair geometry** is the geometry assumed by *all* the valence electron pairs around a central atom (both bond and lone pairs), whereas the **molecular geometry** describes the arrangement in space of the central atom and the atoms directly attached to it. It is important to recognize that *lone pairs of electrons on the central atom occupy spatial positions, even though their location is not included in the verbal description of the shape of the molecule or ion.*

Let us use the VSEPR model to predict the molecular geometry and bond angles in the $NH_3$ molecule. On drawing the Lewis structure, we see there are four pairs of electrons in the nitrogen valence shell: three bond pairs and one lone pair. Thus, the predicted *electron-pair geometry* is tetrahedral. The *molecular geometry*, however, is said to be *trigonal pyramidal* because that describes the location of the atoms. The nitrogen atom is at the apex of the pyramid, and the three hydrogen atoms form the trigonal base.

Lewis structure — electron-pair geometry, tetrahedral — molecular geometry — Actual H–N–H angle = 107.5° / molecular geometry, trigonal pyramidal

## Effect of Lone Pairs on Bond Angles

Because the electron-pair geometry in $NH_3$ is tetrahedral, we would expect the H—N—H bond angle to be 109.5°. However, the experimentally determined bond angles in $NH_3$ are 107.5°, and the H—O—H angle in water is smaller still (104.5°) (Figure 8.6). These angles are close to the tetrahedral angle but not exactly that value. This highlights the fact that VSEPR theory does not give exact bond angles; it can only predict approximate geometry. Small variations in geometry (e.g., bond angles a few degrees different from predicted) are quite common and often arise

**FIGURE 8.6 The molecular geometries of methane, ammonia, and water.** All have four electron pairs around the central atom and have a tetrahedral electron-pair geometry. The decrease in bond angles in the series can be explained by the fact that the lone pairs have a larger spatial requirement than the bond pairs.

FOUR ELECTRON PAIRS
Electron-pair geometry = tetrahedral

**Tetrahedral** — **Trigonal pyramidal** — **Bent**

109.5° — 107.5° — 104.5°

Methane, $CH_4$ / 4 bond pairs / no lone pairs — Ammonia, $NH_3$ / 3 bond pairs / 1 lone pair — Water, $H_2O$ / 2 bond pairs / 2 lone pairs

**(a)** Methane has four bond pairs, so it has a tetrahedral molecular shape.

**(b)** Ammonia has three bond pairs and one lone pair, so it has a trigonal-pyramidal molecular shape.

**(c)** Water has two bond pairs and two lone pairs, so it has a bent, or angular, molecular shape.

because there is a difference between the spatial requirements of lone pairs and bond pairs. Lone pairs of electrons seem to occupy a larger volume than bonding pairs, and the increased volume of lone pairs causes bond pairs to squeeze closer together. In general, the relative strengths of repulsions are in the order

Lone pair–lone pair > lone pair–bond pair > bond pair–bond pair

The different spatial requirements of lone pairs and bond pairs can be used to predict variations in the bond angles in a series of molecules. For example, the bond angles decrease in the series $CH_4$, $NH_3$, and $H_2O$ as the number of lone pairs on the central atom increases (Figure 8.6).

## ⬤WL    INTERACTIVE EXAMPLE 8.7    Finding the Shapes of Molecules and Polyatomic Ions

**Problem** What are the shapes of the ions $H_3O^+$ and $ClF_2^+$?

**What Do You Know?** To determine electron-pair and molecular geometries you must first draw the Lewis structure.

**Strategy**

- Draw the Lewis structures for each ion.

- Count the number of lone and bond pairs around the central atom.

- Use Figure 8.5 to decide on the electron-pair geometry. The location of the atoms in the ion gives the geometry of the ion.

**Solution**

(a) The Lewis structure of the hydronium ion, $H_3O^+$, shows that the oxygen atom is surrounded by four electron pairs, so the electron-pair geometry is tetrahedral. Because three of the four pairs are used to bond terminal atoms, the central O atom and the three H atoms form a trigonal-pyramidal molecular shape like that of $NH_3$.

(b) Chlorine is the central atom in $ClF_2^+$. It is surrounded by four electron pairs, so the electron-pair geometry around chlorine is tetrahedral. Because only two of the four pairs are bonding pairs, the ion has a bent geometry.

**Think about Your Answer** In each of these ions the occurrence of lone pairs on the central atom influences the molecular geometry. In both ions the angle (H–O–H or F–Cl–F) is likely to be slightly less than 109.5°.

**Check Your Understanding**

Give the electron-pair geometry and molecular shape for $BF_3$ and $BF_4^-$. What is the effect on the molecular geometry of adding an $F^-$ ion to $BF_3$ to give $BF_4^-$?

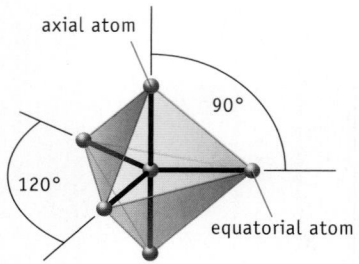

**FIGURE 8.7 The trigonal bipyramid showing the axial and equatorial atoms.** The angles between atoms in the equator are 120°. The angles between equatorial and axial atoms are 90°. If there are lone pairs they are generally found in the equatorial positions.

## Central Atoms with More Than Four Valence Electron Pairs

The situation becomes more complicated if the central atom has five or six electron pairs, some of which are lone pairs. A trigonal-bipyramidal structure (Figures 8.5 and 8.7) has two sets of positions that are not equivalent. The positions in the trigonal plane lie in the equator of an imaginary sphere around the central atom and are called *equatorial* positions. The north and south poles in this representation are called *axial* positions. Each equatorial atom has two neighboring groups (the axial atoms) at 90°, and each axial atom has three groups (the equatorial atoms) at 90°. If lone pairs are present in the valence shell, they require more space than bonding pairs and so prefer to occupy equatorial positions rather than axial positions.

The entries in the top row of Figure 8.8 show species having a total of five valence electron pairs, with zero, one, two, and three lone pairs. In $SF_4$, with one lone pair, the molecule assumes a *"seesaw"* shape with the lone pair in one of the equatorial positions. The $ClF_3$ molecule has three bond pairs and two lone pairs. The two lone pairs in $ClF_3$ are in equatorial positions; two bond pairs are axial, and the third is in the equatorial plane, so the molecular geometry is *T-shaped*. The third molecule shown is $XeF_2$. Here, all three equatorial positions are occupied by lone pairs, so the molecular geometry is *linear*.

The geometry assumed by six electron pairs is *octahedral* (Figure 8.8), and all the angles at adjacent positions are 90°. Unlike the trigonal bipyramid, the octahedron has no distinct axial and equatorial positions; all positions are the same. Therefore, if the molecule has one lone pair, as in $BrF_5$, it makes no difference which position it occupies. The lone pair is often drawn in the top or bottom position to make it easier to visualize the molecular geometry, which in this case is *square pyramidal*. If two pairs of electrons in an octahedral arrangement are lone pairs, they seek to be as far apart as possible. The result is a *square planar* molecule, as illustrated by $XeF_4$.

---

### EXAMPLE 8.8    Predicting Molecular Shape

**Problem** What is the shape of the $ICl_4^-$ ion?

**What Do You Know?** You know the number of valence electrons, so you can draw the Lewis electron dot structure.

**Strategy** Draw the Lewis structure, and then decide on the electron-pair geometry. The position of the atoms gives the molecular geometry of the ion. (See Example 8.7 and Figure 8.8.)

**Solution** A Lewis structure for the $ICl_4^-$ ion shows that the central iodine atom has six electron pairs in its valence shell. Two of these are lone pairs. Placing the lone pairs on opposite sides leaves the four chlorine atoms in a square-planar geometry.

electron-pair geometry,
octahedral

molecular geometry,
square planar

**Think about Your Answer** Square-planar geometry allows the two lone pairs on the central atom to be as far apart as possible.

---

**Check Your Understanding**

Draw the Lewis structure for $ICl_2^-$, and then decide on the geometry of the ion.

---

## Multiple Bonds and Molecular Geometry

Double and triple bonds involve more electron pairs than single bonds, but this has little effect on the overall molecular shape. All of the electron pairs in a multiple bond are shared between the same two nuclei and therefore occupy the

FIVE ELECTRON PAIRS
Electron-pair geometry = trigonal bipyramidal

Trigonal bipyramidal — PF₅ — 5 bond pairs, No lone pairs
Seesaw — SF₄ — 4 bond pairs, 1 lone pair
T-shaped — ClF₃ — 3 bond pairs, 2 lone pairs
Linear — XeF₂ — 2 bond pairs, 3 lone pairs

SIX ELECTRON PAIRS
Electron-pair geometry = octahedral

Octahedral — SF₆ — 6 bond pairs, No lone pairs
Square pyramidal — BrF₅ — 5 bond pairs, 1 lone pair
Square planar — XeF₄ — 4 bond pairs, 2 lone pairs

**FIGURE 8.8** Electron-pair and molecular geometries for molecules and ions with five or six electron pairs around the central atom.

same region of space. Therefore, all electron pairs in a multiple bond count as one bonding group and affect the molecular geometry the same as a single bond does. For example, the carbon atom in $CO_2$ has no lone pairs and participates in two double bonds. Each double bond is a region of electron density and effectively counts as one bond for the purpose of predicting geometry; the structure of $CO_2$ is linear.

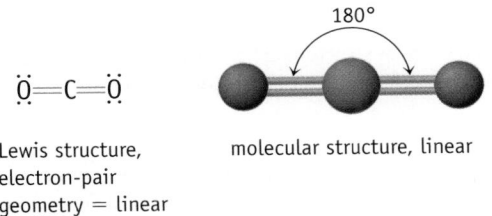

Lewis structure, electron-pair geometry = linear

180°

molecular structure, linear

When resonance structures are possible, the geometry can be predicted from any of the Lewis resonance structures or from the resonance hybrid structure. For example, the geometry of the $CO_3^{2-}$ ion is predicted to be trigonal planar because the carbon atom has three sets of bonds and no lone pairs.

Lewis structure, one resonance structure, electron-pair geometry = trigonal planar

120°

molecular structure, trigonal planar

The $NO_2^-$ ion also has a trigonal-planar electron-pair geometry. Because there is a lone pair on the central nitrogen atom, and bonds in the other two positions, the geometry of the ion is angular or bent.

$$\left[\ddot{\text{O}}\text{—}\ddot{\text{N}}\text{=}\underset{..}{\text{O}}\text{:}\right]^{-}$$

Lewis structure, one
resonance structure,
electron-pair geometry
= trigonal planar

115°

molecular structure,
angular or bent

The techniques just outlined can be used to find the geometries around the atoms in more complicated molecules. Consider, for example, cysteine, one of the natural amino acids.

Cysteine, $HSCH_2CH(NH_2)CO_2H$

Four pairs of electrons occur around the S, N, $C_2$, and $C_3$ atoms, and around the oxygen attached to the hydrogen, so the electron-pair geometry around each is tetrahedral. Thus, the H—S—C, S—C—H, H—N—H, and C—O—H angles are predicted to be approximately 109°. The angle made by O—$C_1$—O is 120° because the electron-pair geometry around $C_1$ is trigonal planar.

## EXAMPLE 8.9    Finding the Shapes of Molecules and Ions

**Problem**  What are the shapes of the nitrate ion, $NO_3^-$, and $XeOF_4$?

**What Do You Know?**  You know the number of valence electrons in each species. Also, note in the discussion above that multiple bonds are treated as one bonding group in determining geometry.

**Strategy**  Questions on molecular structure are answered using the following roadmap:
Formula → Lewis structure → electron-pair geometry → molecular geometry.

**Solution**

(a)  The $NO_3^-$ and $CO_3^{2-}$ ions are isoelectronic. Thus, like the carbonate ion described in the text above, the electron-pair geometry and molecular shape of $NO_3^-$ are trigonal planar.

(b)  The $XeOF_4$ molecule has a Lewis structure with a total of six electron pairs about the central Xe atom, one of which is a lone pair. It has a square-pyramidal molecular structure.

Lewis structure

electron-pair geometry,
octahedral

molecular geometry,
square pyramidal

**Think about Your Answer**  Two structures are possible for $XeOF_4$ based on the position occupied by the oxygen, but there is no way to predict which is correct. The actual structure is the one shown, with the oxygen in the apex of the square pyramid.

### Check Your Understanding

Use Lewis structures and the VSEPR model to determine the electron-pair and molecular geometries for (a) the phosphate ion, $PO_4^{3-}$; (b) the sulfite ion, $SO_3^{2-}$; and (c) $IF_5$.

**REVIEW & CHECK FOR SECTION 8.6**

1. Which of the following species has trigonal-pyramidal geometry?

    (a) $PCl_3$          (b) $BCl_3$          (c) $SO_3$          (d) $ClF_3$

2. What is the molecular geometry of $IF_5$?

    (a) octahedral                      (c) square pyramidal

    (b) trigonal bipyramidal            (d) tetrahedral

3. What is the approximate bond Cl—C—Cl bond angle in phosgene, $COCl_2$? (Carbon is the central atom in this compound.)

    (a) 90°          (b) 109.5°          (c) 120°          (d) 180°

4. What is the molecular geometry of $N_2O$ (where the atoms are connected in the order NNO)?

    (a) linear, 180° angle                (c) bent, 90° angle

    (b) bent, 109.5° angle                (d) bent, 120° angle

## 8.7 Bond Polarity and Electronegativity

The models used to represent covalent and ionic bonding are the extreme situations in bonding. Pure covalent bonding, in which atoms share an electron pair equally, occurs *only* when two identical atoms are bonded. When two dissimilar atoms form a covalent bond, the electron pair will be unequally shared. The result is a **polar covalent bond**, a bond in which the two atoms have partial charges (Figure 8.9).

Bonds are polar because not all atoms hold onto their valence electrons with the same force or take on additional electrons with equal ease. Recall from the discussion of atom properties that different elements have different values of ionization energy and electron affinity (electron attachment enthalpy) (Section 7.5). These differences in behavior for free atoms carry over to atoms in molecules.

If a bond pair is not equally shared between atoms, the bonding electrons are on average nearer to one of the atoms. The atom toward which the pair is displaced has a larger share of the electron pair and thus acquires a partial negative charge. At the same time, the atom at the other end of the bond is depleted in electrons and acquires a partial positive charge. The bond between the two atoms has a positive end and a negative end; that is, it has negative and positive poles. The bond is called a **polar bond**.

In ionic compounds, displacement of the bonding pair to one of the two atoms is essentially complete, and + and − symbols are written alongside the atom symbols in the Lewis drawings. For a polar covalent bond, the polarity is indicated by writing the symbols $\delta^+$ and $\delta^-$ alongside the atom symbols, where $\delta$ (the Greek lowercase letter "delta") stands for a *partial* charge. With so many atoms to use in covalent bond formation, it is not surprising that bonds between atoms can fall anywhere in a continuum from pure covalent to pure ionic (Figure 8.10). There is no sharp dividing line between an ionic bond and a covalent bond.

**FIGURE 8.9 A polar covalent bond.** Iodine has a larger share of the bonding electrons, and hydrogen has a smaller share. The result is that I has a partial negative charge ($\delta^-$), and H has a partial positive charge ($\delta^+$). Sometimes bond polarity is shown by an arrow pointing from + to − (as shown here).

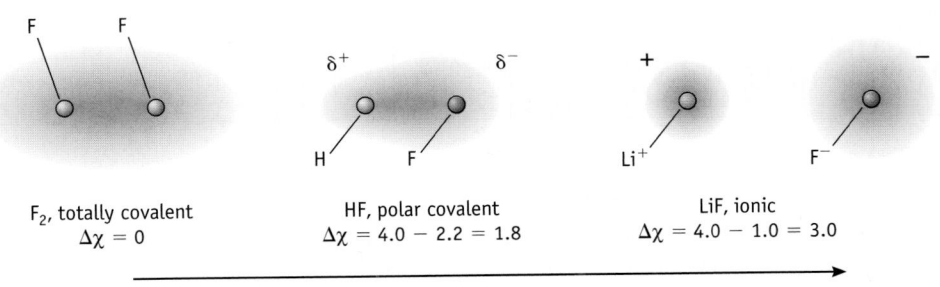

$F_2$, totally covalent
$\Delta\chi = 0$

HF, polar covalent
$\Delta\chi = 4.0 - 2.2 = 1.8$

LiF, ionic
$\Delta\chi = 4.0 - 1.0 = 3.0$

Increasing ionic character

**FIGURE 8.10 Covalent to ionic bonding.** As the electronegativity difference increases between the atoms of a bond, the bond becomes increasingly ionic.

**Linus Pauling (1901–1994).** Linus Pauling was born in Portland, Oregon, earned a B.Sc. degree in chemical engineering from Oregon State College in 1922, and completed his Ph.D. in chemistry at the California Institute of Technology in 1925. In chemistry, he is well known for his book *The Nature of the Chemical Bond*. He also studied protein structures and, in the words of Francis Crick, was "one of the founders of molecular biology." It was this work and his study of chemical bonding that were cited in the award of the Nobel Prize in Chemistry in 1954. Although chemistry was the focus of his life, at the urging of his wife, Ava Helen, he was also involved in nuclear disarmament issues, and he received the Nobel Peace Prize in 1962 for the role he played in advocating for the nuclear test ban treaty.

In the 1930s, Linus Pauling proposed a parameter called *atom electronegativity* that allows us to decide if a bond is polar, which atom of the bond is partially negative and which is partially positive, and if one bond is more polar than another. The **electronegativity**, $\chi$, of an atom is defined as a measure of *the ability of an atom in a molecule to attract electrons to itself.*

Looking at the values of electronegativity in Figure 8.11 you will notice several important features:

- The element with the largest electronegativity is fluorine; it is assigned a value of $\chi = 4.0$. The element with the smallest value is the alkali metal cesium.
- Electronegativities generally increase from left to right across a period and decrease down a group. This is the opposite of the trend observed for metallic character.
- Metals typically have low values of electronegativity, ranging from slightly less than 1 to about 2.
- Electronegativity values for the metalloids are around 2, whereas nonmetals have values greater than 2.

Notice that there is a large *difference* in electronegativity for atoms from the left- and right-hand sides of the periodic table. For cesium fluoride, for example, the difference in electronegativity values, $\Delta\chi$, is 3.2 [= 4.0 (for F) − 0.8 (for Cs)]. The bond is decidedly ionic in CsF, with Cs the cation (Cs⁺) and F the anion (F⁻). In contrast, the electronegativity difference between H and F in HF is only 1.8 [= 4.0 (for F) − 2.2 (for H)]. We conclude that bonding in HF must be more covalent, as expected for a compound formed from two nonmetals. Because the electronegativities of hydrogen and fluorine are different, the H—F bond is polar. In a polar bond, the more electronegative atom takes on the partial negative charge, and the less electronegative atom takes on the partial positive charge, thus the hydrogen is the positive end of this molecule and fluorine is the negative end ($H^{\delta+}$—$F^{\delta-}$).

$\delta^+$          $\delta^-$

HF

| 1A | 2A | | | | | | | | | | | 3A | 4A | 5A | 6A | 7A |
|---|---|---|---|---|---|---|---|---|---|---|---|---|---|---|---|---|
| | | | | | | | | | | | | | | H 2.2 | | |
| Li 1.0 | Be 1.6 | | | | | | | | | | | B 2.0 | C 2.5 | N 3.0 | O 3.5 | F 4.0 |
| Na 0.9 | Mg 1.3 | 3B | 4B | 5B | 6B | 7B | | 8B | | 1B | 2B | Al 1.6 | Si 1.9 | P 2.2 | S 2.6 | Cl 3.2 |
| K 0.8 | Ca 1.0 | Sc 1.4 | Ti 1.5 | V 1.6 | Cr 1.7 | Mn 1.5 | Fe 1.8 | Co 1.9 | Ni 1.9 | Cu 1.9 | Zn 1.6 | Ga 1.8 | Ge 2.0 | As 2.2 | Se 2.6 | Br 3.0 |
| Rb 0.8 | Sr 1.0 | Y 1.2 | Zr 1.3 | Nb 1.6 | Mo 2.2 | Tc 1.9 | Ru 2.2 | Rh 2.3 | Pd 2.2 | Ag 1.9 | Cd 1.7 | In 1.8 | Sn 2.0 | Sb 1.9 | Te 2.1 | I 2.7 |
| Cs 0.8 | Ba 0.9 | La 1.1 | Hf 1.3 | Ta 1.5 | W 2.4 | Re 1.9 | Os 2.2 | Ir 2.2 | Pt 2.3 | Au 2.5 | Hg 2.0 | Tl 1.6 | Pb 2.3 | Bi 2.0 | Po 2.0 | At 2.2 |

■ <1.0        □ 1.5–1.9        ▨ 2.5–2.9
▨ 1.0–1.4        ▨ 2.0–2.4        ■ 3.0–4.0

**FIGURE 8.11 Pauling electronegativity values for the elements.** Nonmetals have high values of electronegativity, the metalloids have intermediate values, and the metals have low values. (Values for these elements as well as for the noble gases and for the lanthanides and actinides are widely available; the values in this table are from J. Emsley, *The Elements*, 3rd ed., Clarendon Press, Oxford, 1998.)

## EXAMPLE 8.10    Estimating Bond Polarities

**Problem**  For each of the following bond pairs, decide which bond is more polar and indicate the negative and positive poles.

(a)   B—F and B—Cl

(b)   Si—O and P—P

**What Do You Know?**  The more polar bond is the one for which there is the larger difference in electronegativity of the two atoms.

**Strategy**  Locate the elements in the periodic table. Recall that electronegativity generally increases across a period and up a group.

**Solution**

(a)   B and F lie relatively far apart in the periodic table. B is a metalloid, and F is a nonmetal. Here, $\chi$ for B = 2.0, and $\chi$ for F = 4.0. Similarly, B and Cl are relatively far apart in the periodic table, but Cl is below F in the periodic table ($\chi$ for Cl = 3.2) and is therefore less electronegative than F. The difference in electronegativity for B—F is 2.0, and for B—Cl it is 1.2. Both bonds are expected to be polar, with B positive and the halide atom negative, but a B—F bond is more polar than a B—Cl bond.

(b)   Because the bond is between two atoms of the same kind, the P—P bond is nonpolar. Silicon is in Group 4A and the third period, whereas O is in Group 6A and the second period. Consequently, O has a greater electronegativity (3.5) than Si (1.9), and the bond is highly polar ($\Delta\chi$ = 1.6), with O the more negative atom.

**Think about Your Answer**  Polar bonds arise because one atom attracts the pair of electrons in a chemical bond more strongly than the atom to which it is bonded.

---

**Check Your Understanding**

For each of the following pairs of bonds, decide which is more polar. For each polar bond, indicate the positive and negative poles. First, make your prediction from the relative atom positions in the periodic table, then check your prediction by calculating $\Delta\chi$.

(a)   H—F and H—I      (b)   B—C and B—F      (c)   C—Si and C—S

## Charge Distribution: Combining Formal Charge and Electronegativity

The way electrons are distributed in a molecule or ion is called its **charge distribution**. Charge distribution can profoundly affect the properties of a molecule. Examples include physical properties such as melting and boiling points, and chemical properties such as susceptibility to attack by an anion or cation or whether the molecule is an acid or a base.

We saw earlier (◄ page 354) that formal charge calculations can often locate the site of a charge in a molecule or an ion. However, this can sometimes lead to results that are incorrect because formal charge calculations assume that there is equal sharing of electrons in all bonds. The ion $BF_4^-$ illustrates this point. Boron has a formal charge of $-1$ in this ion, and the formal charge calculated for the fluorine atoms is 0. Based on the electronegativity difference between fluorine and boron ($\Delta\chi$ = 2.0), the B—F bonds are expected to be polar and fluorine is the negative end of the bond ($B^{\delta+}$—$F^{\delta-}$). So, in this instance, predictions based on electronegativity and formal charge work in opposite directions. The formal charge calculation places the negative charge on boron, but the electronegativity difference leads us to say the negative charge is distributed onto the fluorine atoms, effectively spreading it out over the molecule.

Linus Pauling pointed out two basic guidelines to use when describing charge distributions in molecules and ions. The first is the **electroneutrality principle**: Electrons will be distributed in such a way that the charges on all atoms are as close to zero as possible. Second, he noted that if a negative charge is present, it should reside on the most electronegative atoms. Similarly, positive charges are expected on the least electronegative atoms. The effect of these principles is clearly seen in the

Formal charge =
$0 = 7 - [6 + \frac{1}{2}(2)]$

$$\left[ \begin{array}{c} :\!\ddot{F}\!: \\ | \\ :\!\ddot{F}\!-\!B\!-\!\ddot{F}\!: \\ | \\ :\!\ddot{F}\!: \end{array} \right]^{-}$$

Formal charge =
$-1 = 3 - [0 + \frac{1}{2}(8)]$

**Formal charges for the B and F atoms of the $BF_4^-$ anion.**

case of $BF_4^-$, where it turns out that the negative charge is indeed distributed over the four fluorine atoms, as predicted by the atoms' electronegativities, rather than residing on boron, as would be predicted by formal charge calculations.

Considering the concepts of electronegativity and formal charge together can help to decide which of several resonance structures is the more important. For example, Lewis structure A for $CO_2$ is the logical one to draw. But what is wrong with B, in which each atom also has an octet of electrons?

Formal charges          0   0   0        +1   0   −1

Resonance structures    $\overset{..}{O}=C=\overset{..}{O}$      $:O\equiv C-\overset{..}{O}:$

                              A                    B

For structure A, each atom has a formal charge of 0, a favorable situation. In B, however, one oxygen atom has a formal charge of +1, and the other has −1. This is contrary to the principle of electroneutrality. In addition, B places a positive charge on an O atom, even though oxygen has a greater electronegativity than carbon. Thus, we can conclude that structure B is a much less satisfactory structure than A.

Now use the same logic to decide which of the three possible resonance structures for the $OCN^-$ ion is the most reasonable. Formal charges for each atom are given above each element's symbol.

Formal charges          −1   0   0        0   0   −1        +1   0   −2

Resonance structures    $\left[:\overset{..}{\underset{..}{O}}-C\equiv N:\right]^-$ ⟷ $\left[:\overset{..}{\underset{..}{O}}=C=\overset{..}{N}\right]^-$ ⟷ $\left[:O\equiv C-\overset{..}{\underset{..}{N}}:\right]^-$

                        A                    B                    C

Structure C is not expected to contribute significantly to the overall electronic structure of the ion. It has a −2 formal charge on the N atom and a +1 formal charge on the O atom. Not only is the charge on the N atom high, but O is more electronegative than N and would be expected to take on a more negative charge than N. Structure A is more significant than structure B because the negative charge in A is placed on the most electronegative atom (O). We predict, therefore, that structure A is the best representation for this ion and that the carbon–nitrogen bond will most resemble a triple bond. The result for $OCN^-$ also allows us to predict that protonation of the ion will lead to HOCN and not HNCO. That is, an $H^+$ ion will add to the more negative oxygen atom.

## EXAMPLE 8.11    Calculating Formal Charges

**Problem** Boron-containing compounds often have a boron atom with only three bonds (and no lone pairs). Why not form a double bond with a terminal atom to complete the boron octet? To answer this, consider possible resonance structures of $BF_3$, and calculate the atoms' formal charges. Are the bonds polar in $BF_3$? If so, which is the more negative atom?

**What Do You Know?** Boron trifluoride is one of the examples of a compound that does not obey the octet rule. The most common Lewis structure given for $BF_3$ shows the boron atom with three pairs of electrons.

**Strategy**

• Draw the commonly used Lewis structure for $BF_3$. Then draw a resonance structure (one of three possible) in which boron achieves an octet structure, using one of the electron pairs for fluorine to create a double bond between boron and fluorine.

• Determine the formal charges on each atom in the two structures.

• Decide the importance of the different resonance structures based on the positions of charges in the molecule.

**Solution** The two possible structures for $BF_3$ are illustrated here with the calculated formal charges on the B and F atoms.

Formal charge = 0
= 7 − [6 + $\frac{1}{2}$(2)]

Formal charge = +1
= 7 − [4 + $\frac{1}{2}$(4)]

Formal charge = 0
= 3 − [0 + $\frac{1}{2}$(6)]

Formal charge = −1
= 3 − [0 + $\frac{1}{2}$(8)]

The structure on the left is strongly preferred because all atoms have a zero formal charge and the very electronegative F atom does not have a charge of +1.

F ($\chi$ = 4.0) is more electronegative than B ($\chi$ = 2.0), so the B—F bond is highly polar, the F atom being partially negative and the B atom partially positive.

**Think about Your Answer** When there are two resonance forms that are dissimilar, you need to decide which better represents the bonding in the compound. When discussing structures, you can say that one resonance form is more important than the other.

**Check Your Understanding**

Draw the resonance structures for $SCN^-$. What are the formal charges on each atom in each resonance structure? What are the bond polarities? Do they agree with the formal charges?

---

**REVIEW & CHECK FOR SECTION 8.7**

1.  Which bond among those listed below is the most polar?

    (a)  C—Cl          (b)  Si—Cl          (c)  B—Cl          (d)  Al—Cl

2.  The compound ICl is a red crystalline compound that melts to a red liquid at 27° C. Which of the following best describes the bonding in this compound?

    (a)  The I—Cl bond is not polar.

    (b)  The I—Cl bond is polar with I being the negative end.

    (c)  The I—Cl bond is polar with I being the positive end.

3.  Three resonance forms can be drawn for the molecule $N_2O$. Which resonance form is likely to more closely resemble the structure of this molecule?

    $:N{\equiv}N{-}\ddot{O}:$          $\ddot{N}{=}N{=}\ddot{O}$          $:\ddot{N}{-}N{\equiv}O:$

    (a)                    (b)                    (c)

---

# 8.8  Bond and Molecular Polarity

The term "polar" was used in Section 8.7 to describe a bond in which one atom has a partial positive charge and the other a partial negative charge. Because most molecules have polar bonds, molecules as a whole can also be polar. In a polar molecule, electron density accumulates toward one side of the molecule, giving that side a partial negative charge, $\delta^-$, and leaving the other side with a partial positive charge, $\delta^+$ (Figure 8.12a).

Before describing the factors that determine whether a molecule is polar, let us look at the experimental measurement of the polarity of a molecule. When placed in an electric field created by a pair of oppositely charged plates, polar molecules

**Module 13: Molecular Polarity** covers concepts in this section.

**FIGURE 8.12** Polar molecules in an electric field.

$\delta^+$ **H Cl** $\delta^-$

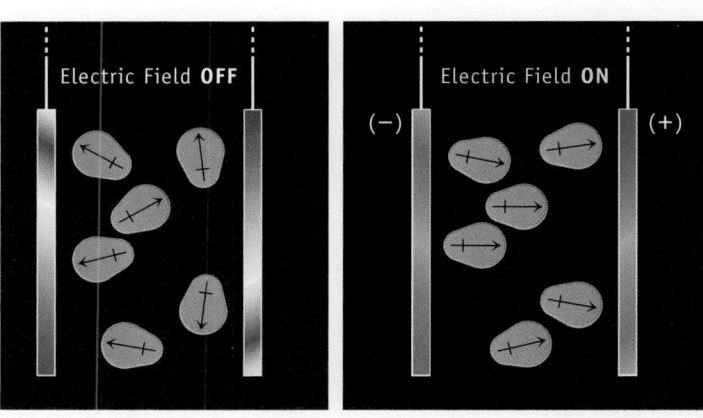

Electric Field **OFF**

Electric Field **ON**

(−) (+)

**(a)** A representation of a polar molecule. To indicate the direction of molecular polarity, an arrow is drawn with the head pointing to the negative side and a plus sign placed at the positive end.

**(b)** When placed in an electric field (between charged plates), polar molecules experience a force that tends to align them with the field. The negative end of the molecules is attracted to the positive plate, and vice versa. The orientation of the polar molecule affects the electrical capacitance of the plates (their ability to hold a charge), and this provides a way to measure experimentally the magnitude of the dipole moment.

AP Photo

● **Peter Debye and Dipoles** The commonly used unit of dipole moments is named in honor of Peter Debye (1884–1966). He was born in The Netherlands, but attended university in Germany and later studied for his Ph.D. in physics in Munich. He developed a theory on the diffraction of x-rays by solids, a new concept for magnetic cooling, and (with E. Hückel) a model for interionic attractions in aqueous solution. As his interests turned more to chemistry, he worked on methods of determining the shapes of polar molecules. Debye received the Nobel Prize in Chemistry in 1936 and was later a professor at Cornell University.

experience a force that tends to align them with the field (Figure 8.12). The positive end of each molecule is attracted to the negative plate, and the negative end is attracted to the positive plate (Figure 8.12b). The extent to which the molecules line up with the field depends on their **dipole moment**, $\mu$. In a molecule with partial charges equal to $+q$ and $-q$ and in which these charges are separated by a distance, $d$, in the molecule, the magnitude of the dipole moment is given by the equation $\mu = q \times d$. The SI unit of the dipole moment is the coulomb-meter, but dipole moments have traditionally been given using a derived unit called the *debye* (D; 1 D = 3.34 × $10^{-30}$ C · m). Experimental values of some dipole moments are listed in Table 8.7.

To predict if a molecule is polar, we need to consider if the molecule has polar bonds and how these bonds are positioned relative to one another. Diatomic molecules composed of two atoms with different electronegativities are always polar (Table 8.7); there is one bond, and the molecule has a positive and a negative end. But what happens with a molecule composed of three or more atoms, in which there are two or more polar bonds?

**Table 8.7  Dipole Moments of Selected Molecules**

| Molecule (*AX*) | Moment (μ, D) | Geometry | Molecule (*AX*₂) | Moment (μ, D) | Geometry |
|---|---|---|---|---|---|
| HF | 1.78 | Linear | $H_2O$ | 1.85 | Bent |
| HCl | 1.07 | Linear | $H_2S$ | 0.95 | Bent |
| HBr | 0.79 | Linear | $SO_2$ | 1.62 | Bent |
| HI | 0.38 | Linear | $CO_2$ | 0 | Linear |
| $H_2$ | 0 | Linear | | | |

| Molecule (*AX*₃) | Moment (μ, D) | Geometry | Molecule (*AX*₄) | Moment (μ, D) | Geometry |
|---|---|---|---|---|---|
| $NH_3$ | 1.47 | Trigonal pyramidal | $CH_4$ | 0 | Tetrahedral |
| $NF_3$ | 0.23 | Trigonal pyramidal | $CH_3Cl$ | 1.92 | Tetrahedral |
| $BF_3$ | 0 | Trigonal planar | $CH_2Cl_2$ | 1.60 | Tetrahedral |
| | | | $CHCl_3$ | 1.04 | Tetrahedral |
| | | | $CCl_4$ | 0 | Tetrahedral |

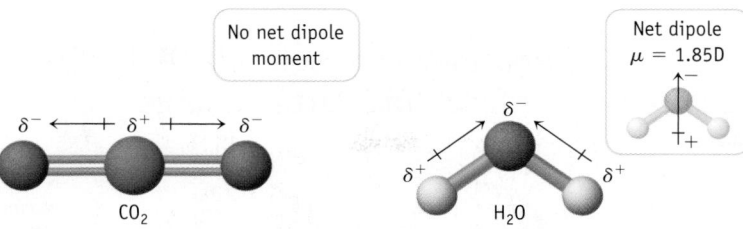

**FIGURE 8.13** Polarity of triatomic molecules, $AX_2$.

**(a)** For $CO_2$, the CO bonds are polar, but the electron density is distributed symmetrically over the molecule, and the charges of $\delta^-$ lie 180° apart. (Charges calculated using advanced molecular modeling software: O = −0.38 and C = +0.77.) The molecule has no net dipole.

**(b)** In a water molecule, the O atom is negative, and the H atoms are positive. (Calculated charges: H = +0.19 and O = −0.38.) However, the positively charged H atoms lie on one side of the molecule, and the negatively charged O atom is on the other side. The molecule is polar.

Consider first a linear triatomic molecule such as carbon dioxide, $CO_2$ (Figure 8.13). Here, each C=O bond is polar, with the oxygen atom the negative end of the bond dipole. The terminal atoms are at the same distance from the C atom; they both have the same $\delta^-$ charge, and they are symmetrically arranged around the central C atom. Therefore, $CO_2$ has no molecular dipole, even though each bond is polar. This is analogous to a tug-of-war in which the people at opposite ends of the rope are pulling with equal force.

In contrast, water is a bent triatomic molecule. Because O has a larger electronegativity ($\chi = 3.5$) than H ($\chi = 2.2$), each of the O—H bonds is polar, with the H atoms having the same $\delta^+$ charge and oxygen having a negative charge ($\delta^-$) (Figure 8.13). Electron density accumulates on the O side of the molecule, making the molecule electrically "lopsided" and therefore polar ($\mu = 1.85$ D).

In trigonal-planar $BF_3$, the B—F bonds are highly polar because F is much more electronegative than B ($\chi$ of B = 2.0 and $\chi$ of F = 4.0) (Figure 8.14). The molecule is nonpolar, however, because the three terminal F atoms have the same $\delta^-$ charge, are the same distance from the boron atom, and are arranged symmetrically around the central boron atom. In contrast, the trigonal-planar molecule phosgene is polar ($Cl_2CO$, $\mu = 1.17$ D) (Figure 8.14). Here, the angles are all about 120°, so the O and Cl atoms are symmetrically arranged around the C atom. The electronegativities of

● **Partial Charges, $\delta$**

The water molecule has a small positive charge on each H atom and a small negative charge on the O atom. When the atoms of molecular models are marked $\delta^{\pm}$, this is meant to indicate a small positive or negative charge but with no indication of the actual magnitude of the charge. (In the case of water, the actual charge on each hydrogen must be 1/2 the value of the charge on the oxygen to maintain electrical neutrality, but this is not indicated in the drawing shown below.)

$H_2O$

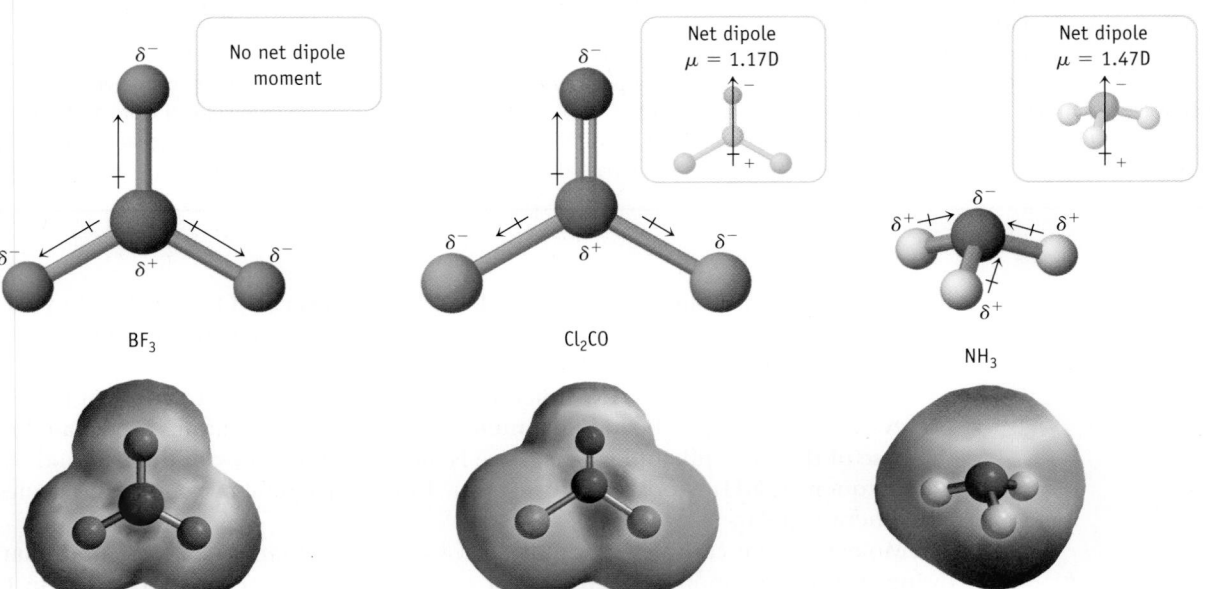

**FIGURE 8.14 Polar and nonpolar molecules of the type AX₃.** In $BF_3$, the negative charge on the F atoms is distributed symmetrically, so the molecular dipole is zero. In contrast, in $Cl_2CO$ and $NH_3$, the negative charge in the molecules is shifted to one side and the positive charge to the other side. These charge distributions are reflected in the electrostatic potential surfaces. (See *A Closer Look: Visualizing Charge Distributions and Molecular Polarity—Electrostatic Potential Surfaces and Partial Charge*, page 378.)

## A CLOSER LOOK

# Visualizing Charge Distributions and Molecular Polarity—Electrostatic Potential Surfaces and Partial Charge

In Chapter 6, you learned about atomic orbitals, regions of space within which an electron is most probably found. The boundary surface of these orbitals was created in such a way that the electron wave amplitude at all points of the surface was the same value. When we use advanced molecular modeling software, we can generate the same type of pictures for molecules, and in Figure A you see a surface defining the electron density in the HF molecule. The electron density surface, calculated using software from Wavefunction, is made up of all of the points in space around the HF molecule where the electron density is 0.002 e⁻/Å³ (where 1 Å = 0.1 nm). You can see that the surface bulges toward the F end of the molecule, an indication of the larger size of the F atom. The larger size of the F atom here is mainly related to the fact that it has more valence electrons than H, and to a lesser extent to the fact that H—F bond is polar and electron density in that bond is shifted toward the F atom.

We can add another layer of information to our picture. The electron density surface can be colored according to the *electrostatic potential*. (Hence, this figure is called an *electrostatic potential surface*.) The computer program calculates the electrostatic potential that would be observed by a proton ($H^+$) on the surface. This is the sum of the attractive and repulsive forces on that proton due to the nuclei and the electrons in the molecule. Regions of the molecule in which there is an attractive potential are colored red. That is, this is a region of negative charge on the molecule. Repulsive potentials occur in regions where the molecule is positively charged; these regions are colored blue. As

**FIGURE A** **Three views of the electrostatic potential surface for HF.**
(*left*) The electron density surface around HF. The F atom is at the left. The surface is made up of all of the points in space around the HF molecule where the electron density is 0.002 e⁻/Å³ (where 1 Å = 0.1 nm).
(*middle*) The surface is made more transparent, so you can see the HF atom nuclei inside the surface.
(*right*) The front of the electron density surface has been "peeled away" for a view of the HF molecule inside.
**Color scheme:** The colors on the electron density surface reflect the charge in the different regions of the molecule. Colors toward the blue end of the spectrum indicate a positive charge, whereas colors to the red end of the spectrum indicate a negative charge.

might be expected, the net electrostatic potential will change continuously as one moves from a negative portion of a molecule to a positive portion, and this is indicated by a progression of colors from red to blue (from negative to positive).

The electrostatic potential surface for HF shows the H atom is positive (the H atom end of the molecule is blue), and the F atom is negative (the F atom end is red). This is, of course, what we would predict based on electronegativity.

The program also calculated that the F atom has a charge of −0.3 and H has a charge of +0.3. Finally, the calculated dipole moment for the molecule is about 1.7 D, in good agreement with the experimental value in Table 8.7.

Other examples of electrostatic potential surfaces illustrate the polarity of water and methylamine, $CH_3NH_2$.

The surface for water shows the O atom of the molecule bears a partial negative

charge and the H atoms are positive. The surface for the amine shows the molecule is polar and that the region around the N atom is negative. Indeed, we know from experiment that an $H^+$ ion will attack the N atom to give the cation $CH_3NH_3^+$.

water          methylamine, $CH_3NH_2$

**FIGURE B** **Visualizing charge distribution**

You will see other examples of useful information chemists can learn from these surfaces in this book and as you move on to other courses in chemistry,

the three types of atoms in the molecule differ, however: $\chi(O) > \chi(Cl) > \chi(C)$. There is therefore a net displacement of electron density away from the center of the molecule, more toward the O atom than the Cl atoms.

Ammonia, like $BF_3$, has $AX_3$ stoichiometry and polar bonds. In contrast to $BF_3$, however, $NH_3$ is a trigonal-pyramidal molecule. The positive H atoms are located in the base of the pyramid, and the negative N atom is on the apex of the pyramid. As a consequence, $NH_3$ is polar (Figure 8.14). Indeed, trigonal-pyramidal molecules are generally polar.

Molecules like carbon tetrachloride, $CCl_4$, and methane, $CH_4$, are nonpolar, owing to their symmetrical, tetrahedral structures. The four atoms bonded to C have the same partial charge and are the same distance from the C atom. Tetrahedral molecules with both Cl and H atoms ($CHCl_3$, $CH_2Cl_2$, and $CH_3Cl$) are polar, however (Figure 8.15). The electronegativity for H atoms (2.2) is less than that of Cl atoms (3.2), and the carbon–hydrogen distance is different from the carbon–

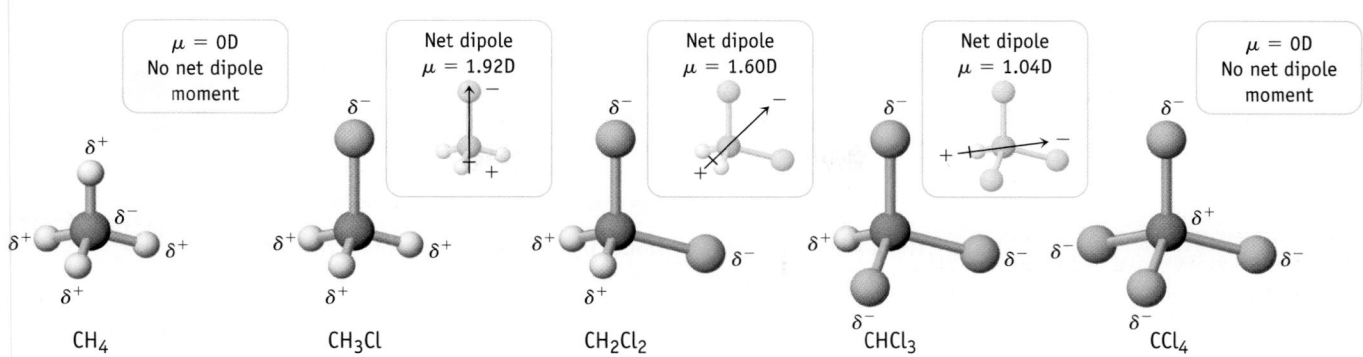

**FIGURE 8.15 Polarity of tetrahedral molecules.** The electronegativities of the atoms involved are in the order Cl (3.2) > C (2.5) > H (2.2). This means the C—H and C—Cl bonds are polar with a net displacement of electron density away from the H atoms and toward the Cl atoms [H $^{\delta+}$—C $^{\delta-}$ and C $^{\delta+}$—Cl $^{\delta-}$]. Although the electron-pair geometry around the C atom in each molecule is tetrahedral, only in $CH_4$ and $CCl_4$ are the polar bonds totally symmetrical in their arrangement. Therefore, $CH_3Cl$, $CH_2Cl_2$, and $CHCl_3$ are polar molecules, with the negative end toward the Cl atoms and the positive end toward the H atoms.

chlorine distances. Because Cl is more electronegative than H, the Cl atoms are on the more negative side of the molecule. This means the positive end of the molecular dipole is toward the H atom.

To summarize this discussion of molecular polarity, look again at Figure 8.5 (page 365). These are sketches of molecules of the type $AX_n$ where $A$ is the central atom and $X$ is a terminal atom. You can predict that a molecule $AX_n$ will not be polar, regardless of whether the $A$—$X$ bonds are polar, if

- all the terminal atoms (or groups), $X$, are identical, and
- all the $X$ atoms (or groups) are arranged symmetrically around the central atom, $A$.

On the other hand, if one of the $X$ atoms (or groups) is different in the structures in Figure 8.5 (as in Figures 8.14 and 8.15), or if one of the $X$ positions is occupied by a lone pair, the molecule will be polar.

## ⓌWL    INTERACTIVE EXAMPLE 8.12    Molecular Polarity

**Problem** Are sulfur tetrafluoride ($SF_4$) and nitrogen trifluoride ($NF_3$) polar or nonpolar? If polar, indicate the negative and positive sides of the molecule.

**What Do You Know?** Based on the discussion in this chapter, you know how to derive the molecular geometry of the molecules and you know how to decide which bonds are polar. These are the two features you use to decide if the molecule is polar.

**Strategy** Draw the Lewis structure, decide on the electron-pair geometry, and determine the molecular geometry. If the molecular geometry is one of the highly symmetrical geometries in Figure 8.5, the molecule is not polar. If it does not fit one of these categories, it will be polar if the bonds are polar.

**Solution**

(a)  The S—F bonds in sulfur tetrafluoride, $SF_4$, are polar, the bond dipole having F as the negative end ($\chi$ for S is 2.6 and $\chi$ for F is 4.0). The molecule has a trigonal bipyramidal electron-pair geometry (Figure 8.8). Because the lone pair occupies one of the positions, the S—F bonds are not arranged symmetrically. The axial S—F bond dipoles cancel each other because they point in opposite directions. The equatorial S—F bonds, however, both point to one side of the molecule, so $SF_4$ is polar.

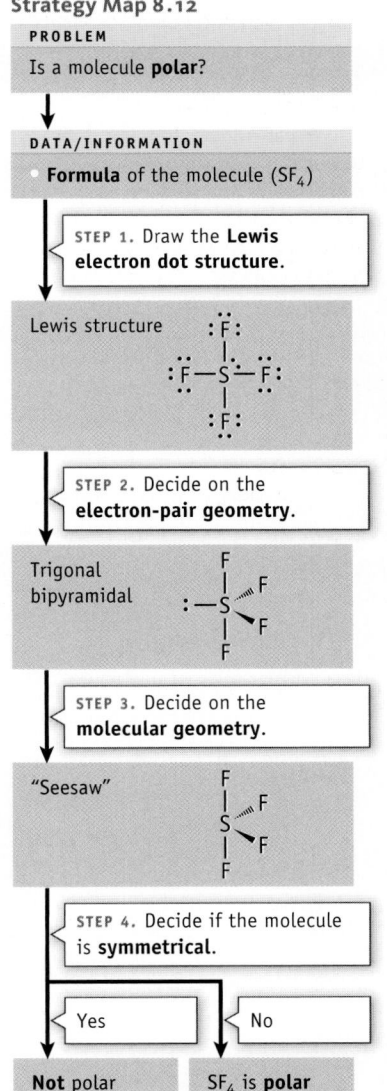

**Strategy Map 8.12**

**PROBLEM**

Is a molecule **polar?**

**DATA/INFORMATION**

- **Formula** of the molecule ($SF_4$)

**STEP 1.** Draw the **Lewis electron dot structure**.

Lewis structure

**STEP 2.** Decide on the **electron-pair geometry**.

Trigonal bipyramidal

**STEP 3.** Decide on the **molecular geometry**.

"Seesaw"

**STEP 4.** Decide if the molecule is **symmetrical**.

| Yes | No |

| **Not** polar | $SF_4$ is **polar** |

(b)    NF$_3$ has the same trigonal-pyramidal structure as NH$_3$. Because F is more electronegative than N, each bond is polar, the more negative end being the F atom. Because this molecule contains polar bonds and because the geometry is not symmetrical but instead has three positions of the tetrahedron occupied by bonding groups and one by a lone pair, the NF$_3$ molecule as a whole is expected to be polar.

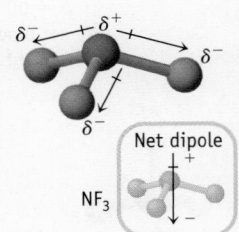

**Think about Your Answer**  Notice that the dipole moment for NF$_3$ is quite small (0.23 D, Table 8.7), much smaller than the dipole moment of NH$_3$. This illustrates the effect of lone pairs on molecular polarity. For NH$_3$, the bond polarity is N$^{\delta-}$—H$^{\delta+}$, and the dipole created by these bonds is reinforced by the negatively charged lone pair on the N atom. In contrast, the polarity of the bonds in NF$_3$ is N$^{\delta+}$—F$^{\delta-}$. This is counterbalanced by the lone pair, and the overall dipole is diminished. These effects are illustrated by the electrostatic potential surfaces for these two molecules.

NH$_3$                                     NF$_3$

Ammonia, $\mu$ = 1.47 D     Nitrogen trifluoride, $\mu$ = 0.23 D

**Check Your Understanding**

For each of the following molecules, decide whether the molecule is polar and which side is positive and which negative: BFCl$_2$, NH$_2$Cl, and SCl$_2$.

# EXAMPLE 8.13    Molecular Polarity

**Problem**  1,2-Dichloroethylene can exist in two forms. Is either of these planar molecules polar?

**What Do You Know?**  The structures for the two molecules are given. Note that these are planar molecules.

**Strategy**

•    Use electronegativity values to decide on the bond polarity.

•    Decide if the electron density in the bonds is distributed symmetrically or if it is shifted to one side of the molecule.

**Solution**  Here, the H and Cl atoms are arranged around the C=C double bonds with all bond angles 120° (and all the atoms lie in one plane). The electronegativities of the atoms involved are in the order Cl (3.2) > C (2.5) > H (2.2). This means the C—H and C—Cl bonds are polar with a net displacement of electron density away from the H atoms and toward the Cl atoms [H$^{\delta+}$—C$^{\delta-}$ and C$^{\delta+}$—Cl$^{\delta-}$]. In structure A, the Cl atoms are located on one side of the molecule, so electrons in the H—C and C—Cl bonds are displaced toward the side of the molecule with Cl atoms and away from the side with the H atoms. Molecule A is polar. In molecule B, the displacement of electron density toward the Cl atom on one end of the molecule is counterbalanced by an opposing displacement on the other end. Molecule B is not polar.

*Overall displacement of bonding electrons*

A, polar, displacement of bonding electrons to one side of the molecule

*Displacement of bonding electrons*

*Displacement of bonding electrons*

B, not polar, no net displacement of bonding electrons to one side of the molecule

**Think about Your Answer**  The electrostatic potential surfaces reflect the fact that molecule A is polar because the electron density is shifted to one side of the molecule. Molecule B is not polar because the electron density is distributed symmetrically.

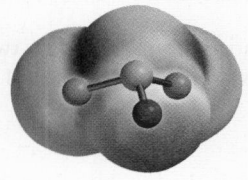

A = *cis*-1,2-dichloroethylene         B = *trans*-1,2-dichloroethylene

**Check Your Understanding**

The electrostatic potential surface for $OSCl_2$ is pictured here.

(a)   Draw a Lewis electron dot picture for the molecule, and give the formal charge of each atom.

(b)   What is the molecular geometry of $OSCl_2$? Is it polar?

---

**REVIEW & CHECK FOR SECTION 8.8**

1.   Which of the hydrogen halides is the most polar?

   (a)  HF                     (b)  HCl                     (c)  HBr                     (d)  HI

2.   Which of the molecules listed below is nonpolar?

   (a)  $BCl_3$               (b)  $PCl_3$               (c)  $POCl_3$               (d)  $SO_2Cl_2$

---

# 8.9   Bond Properties: Order, Length, and Energy

## Bond Order

The **order of a bond** is the number of bonding electron pairs shared by two atoms in a molecule (Figure 8.16). You will encounter bond orders of 1, 2, and 3, as well as fractional bond orders.

When the bond order is 1, there is only a single covalent bond between a pair of atoms. Examples are the bonds in molecules such as $H_2$, $NH_3$, and $CH_4$. The

**FIGURE 8.16 Bond order.** The four C—H bonds in methane each have a bond order of 1. The two C=O bonds of $CO_2$ each have a bond order of two, whereas the nitrogen–nitrogen bond in $N_2$ has an order of 3.

Bond order 1        Bond order 2        Bond order 3

bond order is 2 when two electron pairs are shared between atoms, such as the C=O bonds in $CO_2$ and the C=C bond in ethylene, $H_2C=CH_2$. The bond order is 3 when two atoms are connected by three bonds. Examples include the carbon–oxygen bond in carbon monoxide, CO, and the nitrogen–nitrogen bond in $N_2$.

Fractional bond orders occur in molecules and ions having resonance structures. For example, what is the bond order for each oxygen–oxygen bond in $O_3$? Each resonance structure of $O_3$ has one O—O single bond and one O=O double bond, for a total of three shared bonding pairs accounting for two oxygen–oxygen links.

Bond order = 1

Bond order = 2

Bond order for each oxygen–oxygen bond = $\frac{3}{2}$, or 1.5

One resonance structure

We can define the bond order between any bonded pair of atoms X and Y as

$$\text{Bond order} = \frac{\text{number of shared pairs in all X—Y bonds}}{\text{number of X—Y links in the molecule or ion}} \qquad (8.2)$$

For ozone, there are three bond pairs involved in two oxygen–oxygen links, so the bond order for each oxygen–oxygen bond is $\frac{3}{2}$, or 1.5.

## Bond Length

**Bond length**, the distance between the nuclei of two bonded atoms, is clearly related to the sizes of the atoms (Section 7.5). In addition, for a given pair of atoms, the order of the bond plays a role.

Table 8.8 lists average bond lengths for a number of common chemical bonds. It is important to recognize that these are *average* values. Neighboring parts of a molecule can affect the length of a particular bond, so there be a range of values for a particular bond type. For example, Table 8.8 gives the average C—H bond as 110 pm. However, in methane, $CH_4$, the measured bond length is 109.4 pm, whereas the C—H bond is only 105.9 pm long in acetylene, H—C≡C—H. Variations as great as 10% from the average values listed in Table 8.8 are possible.

Because atom sizes vary in a regular fashion with the position of the element in the periodic table (Figure 7.6), we can predict trends in bond lengths. For example, the H—X distance in the hydrogen halides increases in the order predicted by the relative sizes of the halogens: H—F < H—Cl < H—Br < H—I. Likewise, bonds between carbon and another element in a given period decrease going from left to right, in a predictable fashion; for example, C—C > C—N > C—O. Trends for multiple bonds are similar. A C=O bond is shorter than a C=S bond, and a C=N bond is shorter than a C=C bond.

The effect of bond order is evident when bonds between the same two atoms are compared. For example, the bonds become shorter as the bond order increases in the series C—O, C=O, and C≡O:

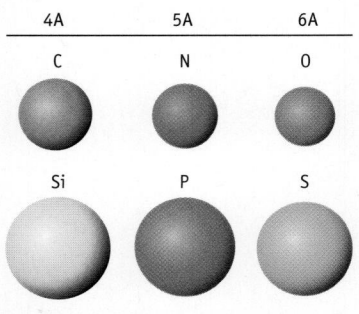

| 4A | 5A | 6A |
|----|----|----|
| C | N | O |
| Si | P | S |

**Relative sizes of some atoms of Groups 4A, 5A, and 6A.**

**Bond lengths are related to atom sizes.**

| C—H | N—H | O—H |
|-----|-----|-----|
| 110 | 98 | 94 pm |
| Si—H | P—H | S—H |
| 145 | 138 | 132 pm |

| Bond | C—O | C=O | C≡O |
|------|-----|-----|-----|
| Bond order | 1 | 2 | 3 |
| Average bond length (pm) | 143 | 122 | 113 |

**Table 8.8  Some Average Single- and Multiple-Bond Lengths in Picometers (pm)\***

| | Single Bond Lengths | | | | | | | | | | |
|---|---|---|---|---|---|---|---|---|---|---|---|
| | | | | **Group** | | | | | | | |
| | **1A** | **4A** | **5A** | **6A** | **7A** | **4A** | **5A** | **6A** | **7A** | **7A** | **7A** |
| | H | C | N | O | F | Si | P | S | Cl | Br | I |
| H | 74 | 110 | 98 | 94 | 92 | 145 | 138 | 132 | 127 | 142 | 161 |
| C | | 154 | 147 | 143 | 141 | 194 | 187 | 181 | 176 | 191 | 210 |
| N | | | 140 | 136 | 134 | 187 | 180 | 174 | 169 | 184 | 203 |
| O | | | | 132 | 130 | 183 | 176 | 170 | 165 | 180 | 199 |
| F | | | | | 128 | 181 | 174 | 168 | 163 | 178 | 197 |
| Si | | | | | | 234 | 227 | 221 | 216 | 231 | 250 |
| P | | | | | | | 220 | 214 | 209 | 224 | 243 |
| S | | | | | | | | 208 | 203 | 218 | 237 |
| Cl | | | | | | | | | 200 | 213 | 232 |
| Br | | | | | | | | | | 228 | 247 |
| I | | | | | | | | | | | 266 |

| Multiple Bond Lengths | | | |
|---|---|---|---|
| C=C | 134 | C≡C | 121 |
| C=N | 127 | C≡N | 115 |
| C=O | 122 | C≡O | 113 |
| N=O | 115 | N≡O | 108 |

\*1 pm = $10^{-12}$ m.

The carbonate ion, $CO_3^{2-}$, has three equivalent resonance structures. Each CO bond has a bond order of 1.33 (or ⁴⁄₃) because four electron pairs are used to form three carbon–oxygen links. The CO bond distance (129 pm) is intermediate between a C—O single bond (143 pm) and a C=O double bond (122 pm).

## Bond Dissociation Enthalpy

The **bond dissociation enthalpy** is the enthalpy change for breaking a bond in a molecule with the reactants and products *in the gas phase. The process of breaking bonds in a molecule is always endothermic,* so $\Delta_r H$ for bond breaking is always positive.

Molecule (g) ⇌ Molecular fragments (g)
Energy supplied = $\Delta H > 0$
Energy released = $\Delta H < 0$

Suppose you wish to break the carbon–carbon bonds in ethane ($H_3C$—$CH_3$), ethylene ($H_2C$=$CH_2$), and acetylene (HC≡CH). The carbon–carbon bond orders in these molecules are 1, 2, and 3, respectively, and these bond orders are reflected in the bond dissociation enthalpies. Breaking the single C—C bond in ethane requires the least energy in this group, whereas breaking the C—C triple bond in acetylene requires the most energy.

$$H_3C—CH_3(g) \rightarrow H_3C(g) + CH_3(g) \qquad \Delta_rH = +368 \text{ kJ/mol-rxn}$$

$$H_2C{=\!=}CH_2(g) \rightarrow H_2C(g) + CH_2(g) \qquad \Delta_rH = +682 \text{ kJ/mol-rxn}$$

$$HC{\equiv}CH(g) \rightarrow HC(g) + CH(g) \qquad \Delta_rH = +962 \text{ kJ/mol-rxn}$$

The energy supplied to break carbon–carbon bonds must be the same as the energy released when the same bonds form. *The formation of bonds from atoms or radicals in the gas phase is always exothermic.* This means, for example, that $\Delta_rH$ for the formation of $H_3C—CH_3$ from two $CH_3(g)$ radicals is $-368$ kJ/mol-rxn.

$$H_3C\cdot\,(g) + \cdot CH_3(g) \rightarrow H_3C—CH_3(g) \qquad \Delta_rH = -368 \text{ kJ/mol-rxn}$$

Generally, the bond energy for a given type of bond (a C—C bond, for example) varies somewhat, depending on the compound, just as bond lengths vary from one molecule to another. Thus, data provided in tables must be viewed as *average bond dissociation enthalpies* (Table 8.9). The values in such tables may be used to *estimate* the enthalpy change for a reaction, as described below.

In reactions between molecules, bonds in reactants are broken, and new bonds are formed as products form. If the total energy released when new bonds form exceeds the energy required to break the original bonds, the overall

● **Variability in Bond Dissociation Enthalpies** The values of $\Delta_rH$ for ethane, ethylene, and acetylene in the text are for those molecules in particular. The bond dissociation enthalpies in Table 8.9 are average values for a range of molecules containing the indicated bond.

**Table 8.9  Some Average Bond Dissociation Enthalpies (kJ/mol)\***

| | | | | | | | | | | | |
|---|---|---|---|---|---|---|---|---|---|---|---|
| | **Single Bonds** | | | | | | | | | | |
| | H | C | N | O | F | Si | P | S | Cl | Br | I |
| H | 436 | 413 | 391 | 463 | 565 | 328 | 322 | 347 | 432 | 366 | 299 |
| C | | 346 | 305 | 358 | 485 | — | — | 272 | 339 | 285 | 213 |
| N | | | 163 | 201 | 283 | — | — | — | 192 | — | — |
| O | | | | 146 | — | 452 | 335 | — | 218 | 201 | 201 |
| F | | | | | 155 | 565 | 490 | 284 | 253 | 249 | 278 |
| Si | | | | | | 222 | — | 293 | 381 | 310 | 234 |
| P | | | | | | | 201 | — | 326 | — | 184 |
| S | | | | | | | | 226 | 255 | — | — |
| Cl | | | | | | | | | 242 | 216 | 208 |
| Br | | | | | | | | | | 193 | 175 |
| I | | | | | | | | | | | 151 |

| **Multiple Bonds** | | | |
|---|---|---|---|
| N=N | 418 | C=C | 610 |
| N≡N | 945 | C≡C | 835 |
| C=N | 615 | C=O | 745 |
| C≡N | 887 | C≡O | 1046 |
| O=O (in O₂) | 498 | | |

\*Sources of dissociation enthalpies: I. Klotz and R. M. Rosenberg, *Chemical Thermodynamics,* 4th Ed., p. 55, New York, John Wiley, 1994; and J. E. Huheey, E. A. Keiter, and R. L. Keiter, *Inorganic Chemistry* 4th Ed., Table E. 1, New York, HarperCollins, 1993. See also Lange's *Handbook of Chemistry,* J. A. Dean (ed.), McGraw-Hill Inc., New York.

reaction is exothermic. If the opposite is true, then the overall reaction is endothermic.

Let us use bond dissociation enthalpies to estimate the enthalpy change for the hydrogenation of propene to propane:

The first step is to identify what bonds are broken and what bonds are formed. In this case, the C=C bond in propene and the H—H bond in hydrogen are broken. A C—C bond and two C—H bonds are formed.

*Bonds broken:*     1 mol of C=C bonds and 1 mol of H—H bonds

Energy required = 610 kJ for C=C bonds + 436 kJ for H—H bonds = 1046 kJ/mol-rxn

---

## CASE STUDY

# Ibuprofen, A Study in Green Chemistry

Ibuprofen, $C_{13}H_{18}O_2$, is now one of the world's most common, over-the-counter drugs. It is an effective anti-inflammatory drug and is used to treat arthritis and similar conditions. Unlike aspirin it does not decompose in solution, so ibuprofen can be applied to the skin as a topical gel, thus avoiding the gastrointestinal problems sometimes associated with aspirin.

**FIGURE A    Ibuprofen, $C_{13}H_{18}O_2$**

Ibuprofen was first synthesized in the 1960s by the Boots Company in England, and it soon became an important product. Millions of pounds are sold every year.

Chemists realized, however, that the method of making ibuprofen took six steps, wasted chemicals, and produced by-products that required disposal. Many of the atoms of the reagents used to make the drug did not end up in the drug itself, that is, the method had a very poor atom economy (page 168). Recognizing this, chemists looked for new approaches for the synthesis of ibuprofen. A method was soon found that uses only three steps, severely reduces waste, and uses reagents that can be recovered and reused. A plant in Texas now makes more than 7 million pounds of ibuprofen annually by the new method, enough to make over 6 billion tablets.

**Questions:**

1. The third and final step in the synthesis involves the transformation of an OH group with CO to a carboxylic acid group ($-CO_2H$) (Figure B). Using bond enthalpy data, is this an endothermic or exothermic step?
2. Do any of the atoms in an ibuprofen molecule have a formal charge of zero?
3. What is the most polar bond in the molecule?
4. Is the molecule polar?
5. What is the shortest bond in the molecule?

**FIGURE B  The final step in the synthesis of ibuprofen.**

6. What bond or bonds have the highest bond order?
7. Are there any 120° bond angles in ibuprofen? Any 180° angles?
8. If you were to titrate 200. mg of ibuprofen to the equivalence point with 0.0259 M NaOH, what volume of NaOH would be required?

**Answers to these questions are available in Appendix N.**

*Bonds formed:*    1 mol of C—C bonds and 2 mol of C—H bonds

$$
\begin{array}{c}
\text{H} \quad \text{H} \quad \text{H} \\
| \quad\quad | \quad\quad | \\
\text{H—C—C—C—H(g)} \\
| \quad\quad | \quad\quad | \\
\text{H} \quad \text{H} \quad \text{H}
\end{array}
$$

Energy evolved = 346 kJ for C—C bonds + 2 mol × 413 kJ/mol for C—H bonds =
1172 kJ/mol-rxn

By combining the enthalpy changes for breaking bonds and for making bonds, we can estimate $\Delta_r H$ for the hydrogenation of propene and predict that the reaction is exothermic.

$$\Delta_r H = 1046\ \text{kJ/mol-rxn} - 1172\ \text{kJ/mol-rxn} = -126\ \text{kJ/mol-rxn}$$

In general, the enthalpy change for any reaction can be estimated using the equation

$$\Delta_r H = \Sigma\Delta H(\text{bonds broken}) - \Sigma\Delta H(\text{bonds formed}) \qquad (8.3)$$

Such calculations can give acceptable results in many cases.

● **$\Delta_r H$ from Enthalpies of Formation** Using $\Delta_f H°$ values for propane and propene, we calculate $\Delta_r H° = -125.1$ kJ/mol-rxn. The bond dissociation enthalpy calculation is in excellent agreement with that from enthalpies of formation in this case.

### EXAMPLE 8.14   Using Bond Dissociation Enthalpies

**Problem** Acetone, a common industrial solvent, can be converted to 2-propanol, rubbing alcohol, by hydrogenation. Calculate the enthalpy change for this reaction using bond enthalpies.

$$
\text{H}_3\text{C}\overset{\displaystyle\overset{\text{O}}{\|}}{-}\text{C}-\text{CH}_3(\text{g}) + \text{H}-\text{H}(\text{g}) \longrightarrow \text{H}_3\text{C}\overset{\displaystyle\overset{\text{O}^{\nearrow\text{H}}}{|}}{-}\underset{\underset{\text{H}}{|}}{\text{C}}-\text{CH}_3(\text{g})
$$

acetone                                          2-propanol

**What Do You Know?** You know the molecular structures of the reactants and the products.

**Strategy** Determine which bonds are broken and which are formed. Add up the enthalpy changes for breaking bonds in the reactants and for forming bonds in the product. The difference in the sums of bond dissociation enthalpies can be used as an estimate of the enthalpy change of the reaction (Equation 8.3).

**Solution**

Bonds broken: 1 mol of C=O bonds and 1 mol of H—H bonds

$$
\text{H}_3\text{C}\overset{\displaystyle\overset{\text{O}}{\|}}{-}\text{C}-\text{CH}_3(\text{g}) + \text{H}-\text{H}(\text{g})
$$

$\Sigma\Delta H(\text{bonds broken})$ = 745 kJ for C=O bonds + 436 kJ for H—H bonds = 1181 kJ/mol-rxn

Bonds formed: 1 mol of C—H bonds, 1 mol of C—O bonds, and 1 mol of O—H bonds

$$
\text{H}_3\text{C}\overset{\displaystyle\overset{\overset{\text{H}}{|}}{\underset{}{\text{O}}}}{-}\underset{\underset{\text{H}}{|}}{\text{C}}-\text{CH}_3(\text{g})
$$

$\Sigma\Delta H$(bonds formed) = 413 kJ for C—H + 358 kJ for C—O + 463 kJ for O—H = 1234 kJ/mol-rxn

$\Delta_r H = \Sigma\Delta H$(bonds broken) $-\ \Sigma\Delta H$(bonds formed)

$\Delta_r H$ = 1181 kJ $-$ 1234 kJ = $-53$ kJ/mol-rxn

**Think about Your Answer** The overall reaction is predicted to be exothermic by 53 kJ per mol of product formed. This is in good agreement with the value calculated from $\Delta_f H°$ values ($-55.8$ kJ/mol-rxn).

**Check Your Understanding**

Using the bond dissociation enthalpies in Table 8.9, estimate the enthalpy of combustion of gaseous methane, $CH_4$ to give water vapor and carbon dioxide gas.

---

### REVIEW & CHECK FOR SECTION 8.9

1. Which of the following species has the largest N—O bond?

   (a) $NO_3^-$       (b) $NO^+$       (c) $NO_2^-$       (d) $H_2NOH$

2. Which of the following species has the largest C—N bond order?

   (a) $CN^-$       (b) $OCN^-$       (c) $CH_3NH_2$       (d) $N(CH_3)_3$

---

### A CLOSER LOOK

# DNA—Watson, Crick, and Franklin

DNA is the substance in every plant and animal that carries the exact blueprint of that plant or animal. The structure of this molecule, the cornerstone of life, was uncovered in 1953, and James D. Watson, Francis Crick, and Maurice Wilkins shared the 1962 Nobel Prize in Medicine and Physiology for the work. It was one of the most important scientific discoveries of the 20th century. The story of this discovery has been told by Watson in his book *The Double Helix*.

**James D. Watson and Francis Crick.** In a photo taken in 1953, Watson *(left)* and Crick *(right)* stand by their model of the DNA double helix (at The University of Cambridge, England). Together with Maurice Wilkins, Watson and Crick received the Nobel Prize in Medicine and Physiology in 1962.

When Watson was a graduate student at Indiana University, he had an interest in the gene and said he hoped that its biological role might be solved "without my learning any chemistry." Later, however, he and Crick found out just how useful chemistry can be when they began to unravel the structure of DNA.

Solving important problems requires teamwork among scientists of many kinds, so Watson went to Cambridge in 1951. There he met Crick, who, Watson said, talked louder and faster than anyone else. Crick shared Watson's belief in the fundamental importance of DNA, and the pair soon learned that Maurice Wilkins and Rosalind Franklin at King's College in London were using a technique called *x-ray crystallography* to learn more about DNA's structure. Watson and Crick believed that understanding this structure was crucial to understanding genetics. To solve the structural problem, however, they needed experimental data of the type that could come from the experiments at King's College.

The King's College group was initially reluctant to share their data, and, what is more, they did not seem to share Watson and Crick's sense of urgency. There was also an ethical dilemma: Could Watson and Crick work on a problem that others had claimed as theirs? "The English sense of fair play

**Rosalind Franklin of King's College, London.** She died in 1958 at the age of 37. Because Nobel Prizes are never awarded posthumously, she did not share in this honor with Watson, Crick, and Wilkins. For more on Rosalind Franklin, read *Rosalind Franklin: The Dark Lady of DNA*, by Brenda Maddox.

would not allow Francis to move in on Maurice's problem," said Watson.

Watson and Crick approached the problem through a technique chemists now use frequently—model building. They built models of the pieces of the DNA chain, and they tried various chemically reasonable ways of fitting them together. Finally, they discovered that one arrangement was "too pretty not to be true." Ultimately, the experimental evidence of Wilkins and Franklin confirmed the "pretty structure" to be the real DNA structure.

3.  Use bond dissociation enthalpies to estimate the enthalpy change for the decomposition of hydrogen peroxide.

$$2 H_2O_2(g) \rightarrow 2 H_2O(g) + O_2(g)$$

(a)  +352 kJ/mol-rxn

(c)  +1037 kJ/mol-rxn

(b)  −206 kJ/mol-rxn

(d)  −2204 kJ/mol-rxn

## 8.10 **DNA, Revisited**

This chapter opened with some questions about the structure of DNA, one of the key molecules in all biological organisms. Now that you have studied this chapter, we can say more about the structure of this important molecule and why it looks the way it does.

As shown in Figure 8.17, each strand of the double-stranded DNA molecule consists of three repeating parts: a phosphate, a deoxyribose molecule (a sugar molecule with a five-member ring), and a nitrogen-containing base. (The bases in DNA can be one of four molecules: adenine, guanine, cytosine, and thymine; in Figure 8.17, the base is adenine.) Two units of the backbone (without the adenine on the deoxyribose ring) are also illustrated in Figure 8.17a.

One important point here is that the repeating unit in the backbone of DNA consists of the atoms O—P—O—C—C—C. Each atom has a tetrahedral electron-pair geometry. Therefore, the chain cannot be linear. In fact, the chain twists as one moves along the backbone. This twisting gives DNA its helical shape.

Five-member deoxyribose ring is slightly puckered owing to tetrahedral geometry around each C and O atom.

Angles in this ring are all about 120°. In each major resonance structure for this ring, each C is surrounded by one double bond and two single bonds, and each N is surrounded by one double bond, one single bond, and one lone pair.

Repeating unit of DNA backbone:
1 P atom
2 O atoms
3 C atoms

Sugar (deoxyribose portion)

Adenine

**Phosphate group, PO₄³⁻** The electron pair and molecular geometry are both tetrahedral.

P—O—C geometry is bent. The O atom is surrounded by two bond pairs and two lone pairs resulting in a bent molecular geometry around this O.

Base

Base

**(a)** A repeating unit consists of a phosphate portion, a deoxyribose portion (a sugar molecule with a five-member ring), and a nitrogen-containing base (here adenine) attached to the deoxyribose ring.

**(b)** Two of the four bases in DNA, adenine and thymine. The electrostatic potential surfaces help to visualize where the partially charged atoms are in these molecules and how they can interact.

**FIGURE 8.17** Bonding in the DNA molecule.

In DNA this N atom is attached to a sugar.

**FIGURE 8.18 Adenine, one of the four bases in the DNA molecule.** Notice that all of the C and N atoms of the five- and six-member rings have trigonal-planar electron-pair geometry. The N atom in the five-member ring is attached to a sugar in DNA.

Why are there two strands in DNA with the O—P—O—C—C—C backbone on the outside and the nitrogen-containing bases on the inside? This structure arises from the polarity of the bonds in the base molecules attached to the backbone. For example, the N–H bonds in the adenine molecule are very polar, which leads to a special type of intermolecular force—hydrogen bonding—binding the adenine to thymine in the neighboring chain (Figure 8.17b). You will learn more about this in Chapter 12 when we explore intermolecular forces and also in *The Chemistry of Life: Biochemistry* (pages 491–507).

The rings in the nitrogen-containing bases are all flat with trigonal-planar electron-pair geometry around each atom in the rings. Let us examine the electron-pair geometries in one of the bases, adenine (Figure 8.18). There are two major resonance structures for this ring system. In these, each carbon atom is surrounded by one double bond and two single bonds, leading to a trigonal-planar electron-pair geometry. Each nitrogen atom in the rings, except the one attached to the sugar, is surrounded by a double bond, a single bond, and a lone pair, likewise leading to trigonal-planar electron-pair geometries around these atoms. The nitrogen attached to the sugar, however, is different from what we would normally predict. It is surrounded by three single bonds and one lone pair. We would normally expect it to have a tetrahedral electron-pair geometry (and trigonal-pyramidal molecular geometry), but it does not. Instead, the bonding groups assume a trigonal-planar geometry, and the lone pair is in a plane perpendicular to the bonds. After studying Chapter 9, you will understand how this allows the electrons in this lone pair to interact with the electrons in the rings' double bonds in a favorable way.

## CHAPTER GOALS REVISITED

*Now that you have studied this chapter, you should ask whether you have met the chapter goals. In particular, you should be able to:*

### Understand the difference between ionic and covalent bonds

a.  Describe the basic forms of chemical bonding—ionic and covalent—and the differences between them, and predict from the formula whether a compound has ionic or covalent bonding, based on whether a metal is part of the formula (Section 8.1).

b.  Write Lewis symbols for atoms (Section 8.2).

### Draw Lewis electron dot structures for small molecules and ions

a.  Draw Lewis structures for molecular compounds and ions (Section 8.2). **Study Questions: 5–12.**

b.  Understand and apply the octet rule; recognize exceptions to the octet rule (Sections 8.2–8.5). **Study Questions: 5–12, 60.**

  and

Sign in at **www.cengage.com/owl** to:
• View tutorials and simulations, develop problem-solving skills, and complete online homework assigned by your professor.
• For quick review and exam prep, download Go Chemistry mini lecture modules from OWL (or purchase them at **www.cengagebrain.com**)

Access **How Do I Solve It?** tutorials on how to approach problem solving using concepts in this chapter.

c.  Write resonance structures, understand what resonance means, and know how and when to use this means of representing bonding (Section 8.4). **Study Questions: 9, 10.**

**Use the valence shell electron-pair repulsion (VSEPR) theory to predict the shapes of simple molecules and ions and to understand the structures of more complex molecules.**

a.  Predict the shape or geometry of molecules and ions of main group elements using VSEPR theory (Section 8.6). Table 8.10 shows a summary of the relation between valence electron pairs, electron-pair and molecular geometry, and molecular polarity. **Study Questions: 17–24, and Go Chemistry Module 12.**

**Use electronegativity and formal charge to predict the charge distribution in molecules and ions, to define the polarity of bonds, and to predict the polarity of molecules.**

a.  Calculate formal charges for atoms in a molecule based on the Lewis structure (Section 8.3). **Study Questions: 13–16, 38.**

b.  Define electronegativity and understand how it is used to describe the unequal sharing of electrons between atoms in a bond (Section 8.7).

c.  Combine formal charge and electronegativity to gain a perspective on the charge distribution in covalent molecules and ions (Section 8.7). **Study Questions: 27–38, 79.**

d.  Understand why some molecules are polar whereas others are nonpolar (Section 8.8). (See Table 8.7.)

e.  Predict the polarity of a molecule (Section 8.8). **Study Questions: 41, 42, 82, 83, 85, 90, and Go Chemistry Module 13.**

**Understand the properties of covalent bonds and their influence on molecular structure**

a.  Define and predict trends in bond order, bond length, and bond dissociation enthalpy (Section 8.9). **Study Questions: 43–50, 62, 85.**

b.  Use bond dissociation enthalpies in calculations (Section 8.9 and Example 8.14). **Study Questions: 51–56, 73.**

**Table 8.10   Summary of Molecular Shapes and Molecular Polarity**

| Pairs of Valence Electrons | Electron-Pair Geometry | Number of Bond Pairs | Number of Lone Pairs | Molecular Geometry | Molecular Dipole?* | Examples |
|---|---|---|---|---|---|---|
| 2 | Linear | 2 | 0 | Linear | No | $BeCl_2$ |
| 3 | Trigonal planar | 3 | 0 | Trigonal planar | No | $BF_3$, $BCl_3$ |
|   |   | 2 | 1 | Bent | Yes | $SnCl_2(g)$ |
| 4 | Tetrahedral | 4 | 0 | Tetrahedral | No | $CH_4$, $BF_4^-$ |
|   |   | 3 | 1 | Trigonal pyramidal | Yes | $NH_3$, $PF_3$ |
|   |   | 2 | 2 | Bent | Yes | $H_2O$, $SCl_2$ |
| 5 | Trigonal bipyramidal | 5 | 0 | Trigonal bipyramidal | No | $PF_5$ |
|   |   | 4 | 1 | Seesaw | Yes | $SF_4$ |
|   |   | 3 | 2 | T-shaped | Yes | $ClF_3$ |
|   |   | 2 | 3 | Linear | No | $XeF_2$, $I_3^-$ |
| 6 | Octahedral | 6 | 0 | Octahedral | No | $SF_6$, $PF_6^-$ |
|   |   | 5 | 1 | Square pyramidal | Yes | $ClF_5$ |
|   |   | 4 | 2 | Square planar | No | $XeF_4$ |

*For molecules of $AX_n$, where the X atoms are identical.

# Key Equations

**Equation 8.1 (page 354)** Used to calculate the formal charge on an atom in a molecule.

Formal charge of an atom in a molecule or ion = NVE − [LPE + ½(BE)]

**Equation 8.2 (page 382)** Used to calculate bond order.

$$\text{Bond order} = \frac{\text{number of shared pairs in all X—Y bonds}}{\text{number of X—Y links in the molecule or ion}}$$

**Equation 8.3 (page 386)** Used to estimate the enthalpy change for a reaction using bond dissociation enthalpies.

$$\Delta_r H = \Sigma \Delta H(\text{bonds broken}) - \Sigma \Delta H(\text{bonds formed})$$

---

# Study Questions

⦿WL Interactive versions of these questions are assignable in OWL.

▲ denotes challenging questions.

Blue-numbered questions have answers in Appendix R and fully worked solutions in the *Student Solutions Manual*.

## Practicing Skills

### Valence Electrons and the Octet Rule
*(See Section 8.1.)*

1. Give the periodic group number and number of valence electrons for each of the following atoms.
   (a) O          (d) Mg
   (b) B          (e) F
   (c) Na         (f) S

2. Give the periodic group number and number of valence electrons for each of the following atoms.
   (a) C          (d) Si
   (b) Cl         (e) Se
   (c) Ne         (f) Al

3. For elements in Groups 4A–7A of the periodic table, give the number of bonds an element is expected to form if it obeys the octet rule.

4. Which of the following elements are capable of forming compounds in which the indicated atom has more than four valence electron pairs?
   (a) C          (d) F          (g) Se
   (b) P          (e) Cl         (h) Sn
   (c) O          (f) B

### Lewis Electron Dot Structures
*(See Sections 8.2, 8.4 and 8.5 and Examples 8.1, 8.2, 8.4, and 8.5.)*

5. Draw a Lewis structure for each of the following molecules or ions.
   (a) $NF_3$          (c) HOBr
   (b) $ClO_3^-$       (d) $SO_3^{2-}$

6. Draw a Lewis structure for each of the following molecules or ions:
   (a) $CS_2$
   (b) $BF_4^-$
   (c) $HNO_2$ (where the arrangement of atoms is HONO)
   (d) $OSCl_2$ (where S is the central atom)

7. Draw a Lewis structure for each of the following molecules:
   (a) chlorodifluoromethane, $CHClF_2$ (C is the central atom)
   (b) acetic acid, $CH_3CO_2H$ (basic structure pictured below)

   (c) acetonitrile, $CH_3CN$ (the framework is $H_3C$—C—N)
   (d) allene, $H_2CCCH_2$

8. Draw a Lewis structure for each of the following molecules:
   (a) methanol, $CH_3OH$
   (b) vinyl chloride, $H_2C{=}CHCl$, the molecule from which PVC plastics are made
   (c) acrylonitrile, $H_2C{=}CHCN$, the molecule from which materials such as Orlon are made

$$H—\overset{\overset{\displaystyle H}{|}}{C}—\overset{\overset{\displaystyle H}{|}}{C}—C—N$$

9. Show all possible resonance structures for each of the following molecules or ions:
   (a) sulfur dioxide, $SO_2$
   (b) nitrous acid, $HNO_2$
   (c) thiocyanate ion, $SCN^-$

10. Show all possible resonance structures for each of the following molecules or ions:
    (a) nitrate ion, $NO_3^-$
    (b) nitric acid, $HNO_3$
    (c) nitrous oxide (laughing gas), $N_2O$ (where the bonding is in the order N—N—O)

11. Draw a Lewis structure for each of the following molecules or ions:
    (a) $BrF_3$          (c) $XeO_2F_2$
    (b) $I_3^-$          (d) $XeF_3^+$

12. Draw a Lewis structure for each of the following molecules or ions:
    (a) $BrF_5$        (c) $IBr_2^-$
    (b) $IF_3$         (d) $BrF_2^+$

## Formal Charge
*(See Section 8.3 and Example 8.3.)*

13. Determine the formal charge on each atom in the following molecules or ions:
    (a) $N_2H_4$       (c) $BH_4^-$
    (b) $PO_4^{3-}$    (d) $NH_2OH$

14. Determine the formal charge on each atom in the following molecules or ions:
    (a) SCO
    (b) $HCO_2^-$ (formate ion)
    (c) $CO_3^{2-}$
    (d) $HCO_2H$ (formic acid)

15. Determine the formal charge on each atom in the following molecules and ions:
    (a) $NO_2^+$       (c) $NF_3$
    (b) $NO_2^-$       (d) $HNO_3$

16. Determine the formal charge on each atom in the following molecules and ions:
    (a) $SO_2$         (c) $O_2SCl_2$
    (b) $OSCl_2$       (d) $FSO_3^-$

## Molecular Geometry
*(See Section 8.6 and Examples 8.6–8.9.)*

17. Draw a Lewis structure for each of the following molecules or ions. Describe the electron-pair geometry and the molecular geometry around the central atom.
    (a) $NH_2Cl$
    (b) $Cl_2O$ (O is the central atom)
    (c) $SCN^-$
    (d) HOF

18. Draw a Lewis structure for each of the following molecules or ions. Describe the electron-pair geometry and the molecular geometry around the central atom.
    (a) $ClF_2^+$      (c) $PO_4^{3-}$
    (b) $SnCl_3^-$     (d) $CS_2$

19. The following molecules or ions all have two oxygen atoms attached to a central atom. Draw a Lewis structure for each one, and then describe the electron-pair geometry and the molecular geometry around the central atom. Comment on similarities and differences in the series.
    (a) $CO_2$         (c) $O_3$
    (b) $NO_2^-$       (d) $ClO_2^-$

20. The following molecules or ions all have three oxygen atoms attached to a central atom. Draw a Lewis structure for each one, and then describe the electron-pair geometry and the molecular geometry around the central atom. Comment on similarities and differences in the series.
    (a) $CO_3^{2-}$    (c) $SO_3^{2-}$
    (b) $NO_3^-$       (d) $ClO_3^-$

21. Draw a Lewis structure for each of the following molecules or ions. Describe the electron-pair geometry and the molecular geometry around the central atom.
    (a) $ClF_2^-$      (c) $ClF_4^-$
    (b) $ClF_3$        (d) $ClF_5$

22. Draw a Lewis structure for each of the following molecules or ions. Describe the electron-pair geometry and the molecular geometry around the central atom.
    (a) $SiF_6^{2-}$   (c) $SF_4$
    (b) $PF_5$         (d) $XeF_4$

23. Give approximate values for the indicated bond angles.
    (a) O—S—O in $SO_2$
    (b) F—B—F angle in $BF_3$
    (c) Cl—C—Cl angle in $Cl_2CO$
    (d) H—C—H (angle 1) and C—C≡N (angle 2) in acetonitrile

24. Give approximate values for the indicated bond angles:
    (a) Cl—S—Cl in $SCl_2$
    (b) N—N—O in $N_2O$
    (c) Bond angles 1, 2, and 3 in vinyl alcohol (a component of polymers and a molecule found in outer space)

25. Phenylalanine is one of the natural amino acids and is a "breakdown" product of aspartame. Estimate the values of the indicated angles in the amino acid. Explain why the —$CH_2$—$CH(NH_2)$—$CO_2H$ chain is not linear.

26. Acetylacetone has the structure shown here. Estimate the values of the indicated angles.

## Bond Polarity, Electronegativity, and Formal Charge
*(See Sections 8.7 and 8.8 and Examples 8.10 and 8.11.)*

27. For each pair of bonds, indicate the more polar bond, and use an arrow to show the direction of polarity in each bond.
    (a) C—O and C—N      (c) B—O and B—S
    (b) P—Br and P—Cl    (d) B—F and B—I

**28.** For each of the bonds listed below, tell which atom is the more negatively charged.
   (a) C—N          (c) C—Br
   (b) C—H          (d) S—O

**29.** Acrolein, $C_3H_4O$, is the starting material for certain plastics.

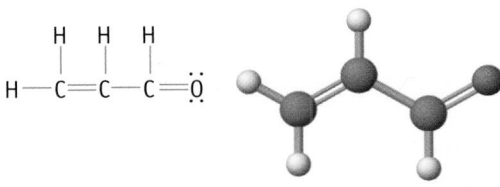

   (a) Which bonds in the molecule are polar, and which are nonpolar?
   (b) Which is the most polar bond in the molecule? Which is the more negative atom of this bond?

**30.** Urea, $(NH_2)_2CO$, is used in plastics and fertilizers. It is also the primary nitrogen-containing substance excreted by humans.
   (a) Which bonds in the molecule are polar, and which are nonpolar?
   (b) Which is the most polar bond in the molecule? Which atom is the negative end of the bond dipole?

**31.** Considering both formal charges and bond polarities, predict on which atom or atoms the negative charge resides in the following anions:
   (a) $OH^-$          (b) $BH_4^-$          (c) $CH_3CO_2^-$

**32.** Considering both formal charge and bond polarities, predict on which atom or atoms the positive charge resides in the following cations.
   (a) $H_3O^+$          (c) $NO_2^+$
   (b) $NH_4^+$          (d) $NF_4^+$

**33.** Three resonance structures are possible for dinitrogen monoxide, $N_2O$.
   (a) Draw the three resonance structures.
   (b) Calculate the formal charge on each atom in each resonance structure.
   (c) Based on formal charges and electronegativity, predict which resonance structure is the most reasonable.

**34.** Three resonance structures are possible for the thiocyanate ion.
   (a) Draw the three resonance structures.
   (b) Calculate the formal charge on each atom in each resonance structure.
   (c) Based on formal charges and electronegativity, predict which resonance structure most closely approximates the bonding in this ion?
   (d) What are the similarities and differences of bonding in $SCN^-$ compared to the bonding in $OCN^-$ (page 374).

**35.** Compare the electron dot structures of the hydrogen carbonate ion and nitric acid.
   (a) Are these species isoelectronic?
   (b) How many resonance structures does each species have?
   (c) What are the formal charges of each atom in these species?
   (d) Compare the two species with respect to their acid-base behavior.

**36.** Compare the electron dot structures of the carbonate ($CO_3^{2-}$) and borate ($BO_3^{3-}$) ions.
   (a) Are these ions isoelectronic?
   (b) How many resonance structures does each ion have?
   (c) What are the formal charges of each atom in these ions?
   (d) If an $H^+$ ion attaches to $CO_3^{2-}$ to form the bicarbonate ion, $HCO_3^-$, does it attach to an O atom or to the C atom?

**37.** The chemistry of the nitrite ion and $HNO_2$:
   (a) Two resonance structures are possible for $NO_2^-$. Draw these structures, and then find the formal charge on each atom in each resonance structure.
   (b) If an $H^+$ ion is attached to $NO_2^-$ (to form the acid $HNO_2$), it attaches to the O atom and not the N atom. Explain why you would predict this structure.
   (c) Two resonance structures are possible for $HNO_2$. Draw these structures, and then find the formal charge on each atom in each resonance structure. Is either of these structures strongly preferred over the other?

**38.** Draw the resonance structures for the formate ion, $HCO_2^-$, and find the formal charge on each atom. If an $H^+$ ion is attached to $HCO_2^-$ (to form formic acid), does it attach to C or O?

**Molecular Polarity**
*(See Section 8.8 and Examples 8.12 and 8.13.)*

**39.** Consider the following molecules:
   (a) $H_2O$          (c) $CO_2$          (e) $CCl_4$
   (b) $NH_3$          (d) $ClF$
   (i)   In which compound are the bonds most polar?
   (ii)  Which compounds in the list are *not* polar?
   (iii) Which atom in $ClF$ is more negatively charged?

**40.** Consider the following molecules:
   (a) $CH_4$          (c) $BF_3$
   (b) $NH_2Cl$          (d) $CS_2$
   (i)   In which compound are the bonds most polar?
   (ii)  Which compounds are *not* polar?
   (iii) Are the H atoms in $NH_2Cl$ negative or positive?

**41.** Which of the following molecules is (are) polar? For each polar molecule, indicate the direction of polarity—that is, which is the negative end, and which is the positive end of the molecule.
   (a) $BeCl_2$          (c) $CH_3Cl$
   (b) $HBF_2$          (d) $SO_3$

**42.** Which of the following molecules is (are) not polar? For each polar molecule, indicate the direction of polarity—that is, which is the negative end and which is the positive end.
   (a) $CO$          (d) $PCl_3$
   (b) $BCl_3$          (e) $GeH_4$
   (c) $CF_4$

## Bond Order and Bond Length
*(See Section 8.9.)*

43. Give the bond order for each bond in the following molecules or ions:
    (a) $CH_2O$
    (b) $SO_3^{2-}$
    (c) $NO_2^+$
    (d) NOCl

44. Give the bond order for each bond in the following molecules or ions:
    (a) $CN^-$
    (b) $CH_3CN$
    (c) $SO_3$
    (d) $CH_3CH{=}CH_2$

45. In each pair of bonds, predict which is shorter.
    (a) B—Cl or Ga—Cl
    (b) Sn—O or C—O
    (c) P—S or P—O
    (d) C=O or C≡N

46. In each pair of bonds, predict which is shorter.
    (a) Si—N or Si—O
    (b) Si—O or C—O
    (c) C—F or C—Br
    (d) The C—N bond or the C≡N bond in $H_2NCH_2C{\equiv}N$

47. Consider the nitrogen–oxygen bond lengths in $NO_2^+$, $NO_2^-$, and $NO_3^-$. In which ion is the bond predicted to be longest? In which is it predicted to be the shortest? Explain briefly.

48. Compare the carbon–oxygen bond lengths in the formate ion ($HCO_2^-$), in methanol ($CH_3OH$), and in the carbonate ion ($CO_3^{2-}$). In which species is the carbon–oxygen bond predicted to be longest? In which is it predicted to be shortest? Explain briefly.

## Bond Strength and Bond Dissociation Enthalpy
*(See Section 8.9, Table 8.9, and Example 8.14.)*

49. Consider the carbon–oxygen bond in formaldehyde ($CH_2O$) and carbon monoxide (CO). In which molecule is the CO bond shorter? In which molecule is the CO bond stronger?

50. Compare the nitrogen–nitrogen bond in hydrazine, $H_2NNH_2$, with that in "laughing gas," $N_2O$. In which molecule is the nitrogen–nitrogen bond shorter? In which is the bond stronger?

51. Ethanol can be made by the reaction of ethylene and water:

$$H_2C{=}CH_2(g) + H_2O(g) \rightarrow CH_3CH_2OH(g)$$

Use bond dissociation enthalpies to estimate the enthalpy change in this reaction. Compare the value obtained to the value calculated from enthalpies of formation.

52. Methanol can be made by partial oxidation of methane using $O_2$ in the presence of a catalyst:

$$2\ CH_4(g) + O_2(g) \rightarrow 2\ CH_3OH(\ell)$$

Use bond dissociation enthalpies to estimate the enthalpy change for this reaction. Compare the value obtained to the value calculated using standard enthalpies of formation.

53. Hydrogenation reactions, which involve the addition of $H_2$ to a molecule, are widely used in industry to transform one compound into another. For example, 1-butene ($C_4H_8$) is converted to butane ($C_4H_{10}$) by addition of $H_2$.

Use the bond dissociation enthalpies in Table 8.9 to estimate the enthalpy change for this hydrogenation reaction.

54. Phosgene, $Cl_2CO$, is a highly toxic gas that was used as a weapon in World War I. Using the bond dissociation enthalpies in Table 8.9, estimate the enthalpy change for the reaction of carbon monoxide and chlorine to produce phosgene.

$$CO(g) + Cl_2(g) \rightarrow Cl_2CO(g)$$

55. The compound oxygen difluoride is quite reactive, giving oxygen and HF when treated with water:

$$OF_2(g) + H_2O(g) \rightarrow O_2(g) + 2\ HF(g)$$

$$\Delta_r H^{\circ} = -318\ \text{kJ/mol-rxn}$$

Using bond dissociation enthalpies, calculate the bond dissociation enthalpy of the O—F bond in $OF_2$.

56. Oxygen atoms can combine with ozone to form oxygen:

$$O_3(g) + O(g) \rightarrow 2\ O_2(g)$$

$$\Delta_r H^{\circ} = -392\ \text{kJ/mol-rxn}$$

Using $\Delta_r H^{\circ}$ and the bond dissociation enthalpy data in Table 8.9, estimate the bond dissociation enthalpy for the oxygen–oxygen bond in ozone, $O_3$. How does your estimate compare with the energies of an O—O single bond and an O=O double bond? Does the oxygen–oxygen bond dissociation enthalpy in ozone correlate with its bond order?

## General Questions

*These questions are not designated as to type or location in the chapter. They may combine several concepts.*

57. Specify the number of valence electrons for Li, Ti, Zn, Si, and Cl.

58. In boron compounds, the B atom often is not surrounded by four valence electron pairs. Illustrate this with $BCl_3$. Show how the molecule can achieve an octet configuration by forming a coordinate covalent bond with ammonia ($NH_3$).

59. Which of the following compounds or ions do not have an octet of electrons surrounding the central atom: $BF_4^-$, $SiF_4$, $SeF_4$, $BrF_4^-$, $XeF_4$?

60. In which of the following does the central atom obey the octet rule: $NO_2$, $SF_4$, $NH_3$, $SO_3$, $ClO_2$, and $ClO_2^-$? Are any of these species odd-electron molecules or ions?

**61.** Draw resonance structures for the formate ion, $HCO_2^-$ and then determine the C—O bond order in the ion.

**62.** Consider a series of molecules in which carbon is attached by single covalent bonds to atoms of second-period elements: C—O, C—F, C—N, C—C, and C—B. Place these bonds in order of increasing bond length.

**63.** To estimate the enthalpy change for the reaction

$$O_2(g) + 2 H_2(g) \rightarrow 2 H_2O(g)$$

what bond dissociation enthalpies do you need? Outline the calculation, being careful to show correct algebraic signs.

**64.** What is the principle of electroneutrality? Use this rule to exclude a possible resonance structure of $CO_2$.

**65.** Draw Lewis structures (and resonance structures where appropriate) for the following molecules and ions. What similarities and differences are there in this series?
(a) $CO_2$          (b) $N_3^-$          (c) $OCN^-$

**66.** Draw resonance structures for the $SO_2$ molecule, and determine the formal charges on the S and O atoms. Are the S—O bonds polar, and is the molecule as a whole polar? If so, what is the direction of the net dipole in $SO_2$? Is your prediction confirmed by the electrostatic potential surface? Explain briefly.

**Electrostatic potential surface for sulfur dioxide.**

**67.** What are the orders of the N—O bonds in $NO_2^-$ and $NO_2^+$? The nitrogen–oxygen bond length in one of these ions is 110 pm and 124 pm in the other. Which bond length corresponds to which ion? Explain briefly.

**68.** Which has the greater O—N—O bond angle, $NO_2^-$ or $NO_2^+$? Explain briefly.

**69.** Compare the F—Cl—F angles in $ClF_2^+$ and $ClF_2^-$. Using Lewis structures, determine the approximate bond angle in each ion. Decide which ion has the greater bond angle, and explain your reasoning.

**70.** Draw an electron dot structure for the cyanide ion, $CN^-$. In aqueous solution, this ion interacts with $H^+$ to form the acid. Should the acid formula be written as HCN or CNH?

**71.** Draw the electron dot structure for the sulfite ion, $SO_3^{2-}$. In aqueous solution, the ion interacts with $H^+$. Predict whether a $H^+$ ion will attach to the S atom or the O atom of $SO_3^{2-}$.

**72.** Dinitrogen monoxide, $N_2O$, can decompose to nitrogen and oxygen gas:

$$2 N_2O(g) \rightarrow 2 N_2(g) + O_2(g)$$

Use bond dissociation enthalpies to estimate the enthalpy change for this reaction.

**73.** ▲ The equation for the combustion of gaseous methanol is

$$2 CH_3OH(g) + 3 O_2(g) \rightarrow 2 CO_2(g) + 4 H_2O(g)$$

(a) Using the bond dissociation enthalpies in Table 8.9, estimate the enthalpy change for this reaction. What is the enthalpy of combustion of one mole of gaseous methanol?
(b) Compare your answer in part (a) with the value of $\Delta_r H°$ calculated using enthalpies of formation data.

**74.** ▲ Acrylonitrile, $C_3H_3N$, is the building block of the synthetic fiber Orlon.

**Electrostatic potential surface for acrylonitrile.**

(a) Give the approximate values of angles 1, 2, and 3.
(b) Which is the shorter carbon–carbon bond?
(c) Which is the stronger carbon–carbon bond?
(d) Based on the electrostatic potential surface, where are the positive and negative charges located in the molecule?
(e) Which is the most polar bond?
(f) Is the molecule polar?

**75.** ▲ The cyanate ion, $OCN^-$, has the least electronegative atom, C, in the center. The very unstable fulminate ion, $CNO^-$, has the same molecular formula, but the N atom is in the center.
(a) Draw the three possible resonance structures of $CNO^-$.
(b) On the basis of formal charges, decide on the resonance structure with the most reasonable distribution of charge.
(c) Mercury fulminate is so unstable it is used in blasting caps for dynamite. Can you offer an explanation for this instability? (*Hint:* Are the formal charges in any resonance structure reasonable in view of the relative electronegativities of the atoms?)

**76.** Vanillin is the flavoring agent in vanilla extract and in vanilla ice cream. Its structure is shown here:

(a) Give values for the three bond angles indicated.
(b) Indicate the shortest carbon–oxygen bond in the molecule.
(c) Indicate the most polar bond in the molecule.

**77.** ▲ Given that the spatial requirement of a lone pair is greater than that of a bond pair, explain why
(a) $XeF_2$ has a linear molecular structure and not a bent one.
(b) $ClF_3$ has a T-shaped structure and not a trigonal-planar one.

**78.** The formula for nitryl chloride is $ClNO_2$.
   (a) Draw the Lewis structure for the molecule, including all resonance structures.
   (b) What is the N—O bond order?
   (c) Describe the electron-pair and molecular geometries, and give values for all bond angles.
   (d) What is the most polar bond in the molecule? Is the molecule polar?
   (e) ▲ The computer program used to calculate electrostatic potential surfaces gave the following charges on atoms in the molecule: A = −0.03, B = −0.26, and C = +0.56. Identify the atoms A, B, and C. Are these calculated charges in accord with your predictions?

Electrostatic potential surface for $ClNO_2$.

**79.** Hydroxyproline is a less-common amino acid.

(a) Give approximate values for the indicated bond angles.
(b) Which are the most polar bonds in the molecule?

**80.** Amides are an important class of organic molecules. They are usually drawn as sketched here, but another resonance structure is possible.

(a) Draw a second resonance structure of the structure above. Do you think that this should be a significant contributor to the bonding? Explain your answer.
(b) The H—N—H angle is close to 120° in this molecule. Does this fact influence your thoughts on the importance of this structure?

**81.** Use the bond dissociation enthalpies in Table 8.9 to estimate the enthalpy change for the decomposition of urea (See Study Question 30) to hydrazine, $H_2N—NH_2$, and carbon monoxide. (Assume all compounds are in the gas phase.)

**82.** The molecule shown here, 2-furylmethanethiol, is responsible for the aroma of coffee:

(a) What are the formal charges on the S and O atoms?
(b) Give approximate values of angles 1, 2, and 3.
(c) Which are the shorter carbon–carbon bonds in the molecule?
(d) Which bond in this molecule is the most polar?
(e) Is the molecule polar or nonpolar?
(f) The molecular model makes it clear that the four C atoms of the ring are all in a plane. Is the O atom in that same plane (making the five-member ring planar), or is the O atom bent above or below the plane?

**83.** ▲ Dihydroxyacetone is a component of quick-tanning lotions. (It reacts with the amino acids in the upper layer of skin and colors them brown in a reaction similar to that occurring when food is browned as it cooks.)
   (a) Use bond dissociation enthalpies to estimate the enthalpy change for the following reaction. Is the reaction exothermic or endothermic?

**Acetone.**          **Dihydroxyacetone.**

(b) Are dihydroxyacetone and acetone polar molecules?
(c) A proton ($H^+$) can be removed from a molecule of dihydroxyacetone with strong bases (which is in part what happens in the tanning reaction). Which H atoms are the most positive in dihydroxyacetone?

**84.** Nitric acid, $HNO_3$, has three resonance structures. One of them, however, contributes much less to the resonance hybrid than the other two. Sketch the three resonance structures, and assign a formal charge to each atom. Which one of your structures is the least important?

**85.** ▲ Acrolein is used to make plastics. Suppose this compound can be prepared by inserting a carbon monoxide molecule into the C—H bond of ethylene.

**Ethylene.**          **Acrolein.**

(a) Which is the stronger carbon–carbon bond in acrolein?
(b) Which is the longer carbon–carbon bond in acrolein?
(c) Is ethylene or acrolein polar?
(d) Use bond dissociation enthalpies to predict whether the reaction of CO with $C_2H_4$ to give acrolein is endothermic or exothermic?

86. Molecules in space:
    (a) In addition to molecules such as CO, HCl, $H_2O$, and $NH_3$, glycolaldehyde has been detected in outer space. Is the molecule polar?

    **HOCH₂CHO, glycolaldehyde**

    (b) Where do the positive and negative charges lie in the molecule?
    (c) One molecule found in the 1995 Hale-Bopp comet is $HC_3N$. Suggest a structure for this molecule.

87. 1,2-Dichloroethylene can be synthesized by adding $Cl_2$ to the carbon–carbon triple bond of acetylene.

$$H-C\equiv C-H + Cl_2 \longrightarrow \begin{array}{c} H \\ C=C \\ Cl \end{array} \begin{array}{c} Cl \\ \\ H \end{array}$$

    Using bond dissociation enthalpies, estimate the enthalpy change for this reaction in the gas phase.

88. The molecule pictured below is epinephrine, a compound used as a bronchodilator and antiglaucoma agent.

    (a) Give a value for each of the indicated bond angles.
    (b) What are the most polar bonds in the molecule?

## In the Laboratory

89. You are doing an experiment in the laboratory and want to prepare a solution in a polar solvent. Which solvent would you choose, methanol ($CH_3OH$) or toluene ($C_6H_5CH_3$)? Explain your choice.

**Methanol.**

**Toluene.**

90. Methylacetamide, $CH_3CONHCH_3$, is a small molecule with an amide link (CO—NH), the group that binds one amino acid to another in proteins.
    (a) Is this molecule polar?
    (b) Where do you expect the positive and negative charges to lie in this molecule? Does the electrostatic potential surface confirm your predictions?

**Methylacetamide
Ball-and-stick model.**

**Electrostatic potential surface.**

91. ▲ A paper published in the research journal *Science* in 2007 (S. Vallina and R. Simo, *Science*, Vol. 315, p. 506, January 26, 2007) reported studies of dimethylsulfide (DMS), an important greenhouse gas that is released by marine phytoplankton. This gas "represents the largest natural source of atmospheric sulfur and a major precursor of hygroscopic (i.e., cloud-forming) particles in clean air over the remote oceans, thereby acting to reduce the amount of solar radiation that crosses the atmosphere and is absorbed by the ocean."
    (a) Sketch the Lewis structure of dimethylsulfide, $CH_3SCH_3$, and list the bond angles in the molecule.
    (b) Use electronegativities to decide where the positive and negative charges lie in the molecule. Is the molecule polar?
    (c) The mean seawater concentration of DMS in the ocean in the region between 15° north latitude and 15° south latitude is 2.7 nM (nanomolar). How many molecules of DMS are present in 1.0 $m^3$ of seawater?

**92.** Uracil is one of the bases in DNA.

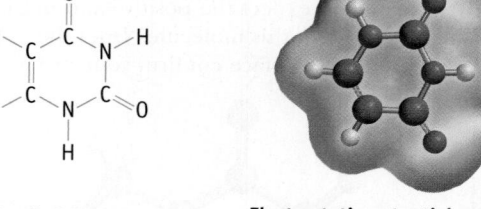

**Uracil, $C_4H_4N_2O_2$.**      **Electrostatic potential surface for uracil.**

(a) What are the values of the O—C—N and C—N—H angles?

(b) There are two carbon–carbon bonds in the molecule. Which is predicted to be shorter?

(c) If a proton attacks the molecule, decide on the basis of the electrostatic potential surface to which atom or atoms it could be attached.

## Summary and Conceptual Questions

*The following questions may use concepts from this and previous chapters.*

**93.** White phosphorus exists as $P_4$ molecules with phosphorus atoms at the corners of a tetrahedron.

**White phosphorus, $P_4$.**

(a) Elemental phosphorus reacts with $Cl_2$ to form $PCl_3$. Write a balanced chemical equation for this reaction.

(b) The standard enthalpy of formation ($\Delta_f H$) of $P_4(g)$ is +58.9 kJ/mol; for $PCl_3(g)$ it is −287.0 kJ/mol. Use these numbers to calculate the enthalpy of the reaction of $P_4(g)$ and $Cl_2(g)$ to give $PCl_3(g)$.

(c) Based on the equation in (a), determine what bonds are broken and what bonds are formed. Then, use this information along with the value of $\Delta_r H$ calculated in (b) and the bond dissociation enthalpies for the P—P and Cl—Cl bonds from Table 8.9 to estimate the bond dissociation enthalpy for the P—Cl bonds. How does your estimate compare with the value in Table 8.9?

**94.** The answer in Study Question 93 does not exactly match the value for the bond dissociation enthalpy of P—Cl in Table 8.9. The reason is that the numbers in the table are averages, derived from data on a number of different compounds. Values calculated from different compounds do vary, sometimes widely. To illustrate this, let's do another calculation. Next look at the following reaction:

$$PCl_3(g) + Cl_2(g) \rightarrow PCl_5(g)$$

The enthalpy of formation of $PCl_5(g)$ is −374.9 kJ/mol. Use this and $\Delta_f H$ of $PCl_3(g)$ to determine the enthalpy change for this reaction. Then, use that value of $\Delta_r H$, along with the bond dissociation enthalpy of $Cl_2$, to calculate the enthalpy change for the formation of a P—Cl bond in this reaction.

**95.** Bromine-containing species play a role in environmental chemistry. For example, they are evolved in volcanic eruptions.

(a) The following molecules are important in bromine environmental chemistry: HBr, BrO, and HOBr. Which are odd-electron molecules?

(b) Use bond dissociation enthalpies to estimate $\Delta_r H$ for three reactions of bromine:

$$Br_2(g) \rightarrow 2\ Br(g)$$

$$2\ Br(g) + O_2(g) \rightarrow 2\ BrO(g)$$

$$BrO(g) + H_2O(g) \rightarrow HOBr(g) + OH(g)$$

(c) Using bond dissociation enthalpies, estimate the standard enthalpy of formation of HOBr(g) from $H_2(g)$, $O_2(g)$, and $Br_2(g)$.

(d) Are the reactions in parts (b) and (c) exothermic or endothermic?

**96.** Acrylamide, $H_2C=CHC(=O)NH_2$, is a known neurotoxin and possible carcinogen. It was a shock to all consumers of potato chips and french fries a few years ago when it was found to occur in those products.

(a) Sketch the molecular structure of acrylamide and identify all bond angles.

(b) Indicate which carbon–carbon bond is the stronger of the two.

(c) Is the molecule polar or nonpolar?

(d) The amount of acrylamide found in potato chips is 1.7 mg/kg. If a serving of potato chips is 28 g, how many moles of acrylamide are you consuming?

## Applying Chemical Principles

### Linus Pauling and Electronegativity

Linus Pauling noticed that, when he compared the bond dissociation enthalpies ($\Delta_{diss}H$) between identical atoms, say A—A or B—B, with the bond dissociation enthalpies of different atoms, A—B, the energy for the A—B bond was always larger than the average of the A—A and B—B energies.

$$\Delta_{diss}H(A\text{—}B) > 1/2\,[\Delta_{diss}H(A\text{—}A) + \Delta_{diss}H(B\text{—}B)]$$

Why should this be true, and what useful information can be derived from it?

When a bond forms between two identical atoms, the bonding electrons are shared equally between the two atoms. In a bond between dissimilar atoms, the atoms do not share the electrons equally. When this is the case, one atom incurs a slightly positive charge and the other a slightly negative one. A coulombic attraction between the oppositely charged atoms increases the strength of the bond. Pauling said that this difference in energy is related to the electronegativities of the atoms involved and defined electronegativity ($\chi$) as "the ability of an atom in a molecule to attract electrons to itself." More specifically, he said the difference he observed is mathematically related to the difference in electronegativities by

$$\chi_A - \chi_B = 0.102\sqrt{\Delta_{diss}H(AB) - \frac{\Delta_{diss}H(AA) + \Delta_{diss}H(BB)}{2}}$$

Using bond dissociation enthalpies, Pauling created absolute electronegativity values by assigning fluorine a value of 4.0. Because they are so useful, Pauling's values have been continually refined since Pauling's 1932 publication, but Pauling's calculated electronegativity values are close to those computed today.

A variety of methods for quantifying electronegativity values have been developed since Pauling's initial work. One notable method, developed by Robert Mulliken (1896–1986) in 1934, calculates electronegativity values for individual elements using ionization energy (IE) and the electron attachment enthalpy ($\Delta_{EA}H$). The electronegativity of an element may be calculated from the following equation,

$$\chi_A = 1.97 \times 10^{-3}\,(IE - \Delta_{EA}H) + 0.19$$

where the ionization energy and $\Delta_{EA}H$ have units of kJ/mol.

### Questions:

1. Calculate the difference in electronegativity between hydrogen and chlorine ($\chi_{Cl} - \chi_H$) in hydrogen

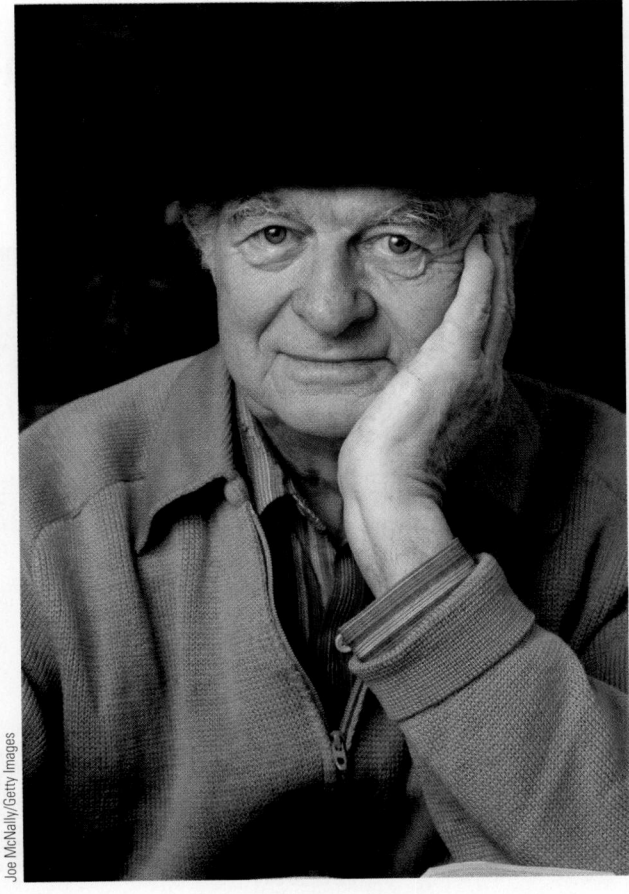

Joe McNally/Getty Images

Linus Pauling (1901–1994)

chloride using average bond dissociation enthalpy values (Table 8.9). Compare your results with those calculated using electronegativity values from Figure 8.11.

2. Predict the bond dissociation enthalpy for a nitrogen–iodine bond in $NI_3$ using bond dissociation enthalpy values (Table 8.9) and electronegativity values (Figure 8.11).

3. Calculate the electronegativity of sulfur atoms using ionization energy and electron attachment enthalpy values (Appendix F). Compare the value with the one in Figure 8.11.

### References:

Pauling, L., *Journal of the American Chemical Society,* Vol. 54, p. 3570, 1932.

Mulliken, R. S., *Journal of Chemical Physics,* Vol. 2, p. 782, 1934.

# 9 Bonding and Molecular Structure: Orbital Hybridization and Molecular Orbitals

© Gary J. Schrobilgen

## The Noble Gases: Not So Inert

Generations of chemistry professors once taught that the noble gases were chemically inert. However, in 1962 chemists learned this was not so. Xenon at the very least was found to form compounds! The first was an ionic compound, now known to be $XeF^+Pt_2F_{11}^-$. However, this was followed shortly thereafter with the discovery of a large number of covalently bonded compounds, including $XeF_4$, $XeF_6$, $XeOF_4$, and $XeO_3$.

Since 1962, the field of noble gas chemistry has expanded with the discovery of such interesting molecules as FXeOXeF and, at low temperatures, species such as HArF, HXeH, HXeCl, and HKrF.

Initially, xenon compounds were thought to form only under the most severe conditions. Therefore, it was again a surprise when it was learned that irradiating a mixture of xenon and fluorine gases at room temperature with sunlight gave crystals of $XeF_2$ (as seen in the photo).

### Questions:

1. What is the most reasonable structure of $XeF_2$? Does knowing that the molecule has no dipole moment confirm your structural choice? Why or why not?
2. Describe the bonding in $XeF_2$ using valence bond theory.
3. Predict a structure for FXeOXeF.

**Answers to these questions are available in Appendix N.**

## CHAPTER GOALS

*See Chapter Goals Revisited (page 428) for Study Questions keyed to these goals.*

- Understand the differences between valence bond theory and molecular orbital theory.

- Identify the hybridization of an atom in a molecule or ion.

- Understand the differences between bonding and antibonding molecular orbitals and be able to write the molecular orbital configurations for simple diatomic molecules.

Just how are molecules held together? Millions of organic compounds are based on carbon atoms surrounded tetrahedrally by other atoms. How can a carbon atom be bonded to atoms at the corners of a tetrahedron when its atomic orbitals don't point in those directions? How can a dye molecule absorb light? Why is oxygen paramagnetic, and how is this property connected with bonding in the molecule? These are just a few of the fundamental and interesting questions that are raised in this chapter and that require us to take a more advanced look at bonding.

# 9.1 Orbitals and Theories of Chemical Bonding

From Chapter 6, you know that the location of the valence electrons in an atom is described by an orbital model. It seems reasonable that an orbital model can also be used to describe electrons in molecules.

Two common approaches to rationalizing chemical bonding based on orbitals are **valence bond (VB) theory** and **molecular orbital (MO) theory**. The former was developed largely by Linus Pauling (page 342) and the latter by another American scientist, Robert S. Mulliken (1896–1986). The valence bond approach is closely tied to Lewis's idea of bonding electron pairs between atoms and lone pairs of electrons localized on a particular atom. In contrast, Mulliken's approach was to derive molecular orbitals that are "spread out," or *delocalized*, over the molecule. One way to do this is to combine atomic orbitals to form a set of orbitals that are the property of the molecule and then to distribute the electrons of the molecule within those orbitals.

Why are two theories used? Is one more correct than the other? Actually, both give good descriptions of the bonding in molecules and polyatomic ions, but they are most useful in different situations. Valence bond theory is generally the method of choice to provide a qualitative, visual picture of molecular structure and bonding. This theory is particularly useful for molecules made up of many atoms. In contrast, molecular orbital theory is used when a more quantitative picture of bonding is needed. Valence bond theory provides a good description of bonding for molecules in their ground or lowest energy state. Molecular orbital theory is essential if we want to describe molecules in higher-energy, excited states. Among other things, this is important in explaining the colors of compounds. Finally, for a few molecules such as NO and $O_2$, MO theory is the only one of the two theories that can describe their bonding accurately.

- **Bonds Are a "Figment of Our Own Imagination"** C. A. Coulson, a prominent theoretical chemist at the University of Oxford, England, has said that "Sometimes it seems to me that a bond between atoms has become so real, so tangible, so friendly, that I can almost see it. Then I awake with a little shock, for a chemical bond is not a real thing. It does not exist. No one has ever seen one. No one ever can. It is a figment of our own imagination" (*Chemical and Engineering News*, January 29, 2007, page 37). Nonetheless, bonds are a useful figment, and this chapter presents some of these useful ideas.

**Module 14: Hybrid Atomic Orbitals** covers concepts in this section.

## 9.2 Valence Bond Theory

### The Orbital Overlap Model of Bonding

What happens if two atoms at an infinite distance apart are brought together to form a bond? This process is often illustrated with $H_2$ because, with two electrons and two nuclei, this is the simplest neutral molecule known (Figure 9.1). Initially, when two hydrogen atoms are widely separated, they do not interact. If the atoms move closer together, however, the electron on one atom begins to experience an attraction to the positive charge of the nucleus of the other atom. Because of the attractive forces, the electron clouds on the atoms distort as the electron of one atom is drawn toward the nucleus of the second atom, and the potential energy of the system is lowered.

Calculations show that when the distance between the H atoms is 74 pm, the potential energy reaches a minimum and the $H_2$ molecule is most stable. Significantly, 74 pm corresponds to the experimentally measured bond distance in the $H_2$ molecule.

When the distance between the H atoms is less than 74 pm, the potential energy rises rapidly, and the $H_2$ molecule is less stable. At separations less than 74 pm there is a significant repulsive force between the nuclei of the two atoms and between the electrons of the atoms. In Figure 9.1 for the $H_2$ molecule, you see that 74 pm is the distance at which there is a minimum in the potential energy diagram.

In the $H_2$ molecule two electrons, one from each atom, pair up to form the bond. There is a net stabilization, representing the extent to which the energies of the two electrons are lowered from their value in the free atoms. The net stabilization (the extent to which the potential energy is lowered) can be calculated, and the calculated value closely matches the experimentally determined bond energy. Agreement between theory and experiment on both bond distance and energy is evidence that this theoretical approach has merit.

Bond formation is depicted in Figures 9.1 and 9.2 as occurring when the electron clouds on the two atoms interpenetrate or overlap. This **orbital overlap** increases the probability of finding the bonding electrons in the region of space between the two nuclei. *The idea that bonds are formed by overlap of atomic orbitals is the basis for valence bond theory.*

When the single covalent bond is formed in $H_2$, the 1s electron cloud of each atom is distorted in a way that gives the electrons a higher probability of being in the region between the two hydrogen atoms (Figure 9.2a). This makes sense because this distortion results in the electrons being situated so that they are attracted

**FIGURE 9.1 Potential energy change during H—H bond formation from isolated hydrogen atoms.** There is little or no overlap of 1s orbitals when the atoms are 400 pm apart. When the separation is about 200 pm there is some overlap, but the attractive forces are weak. The lowest potential energy is reached at an H—H separation of 74 pm. Here there is a balance of the attractive and repulsive forces. At H—H distances less than 74 pm, repulsions between the nuclei and between the electrons of the two atoms increase rapidly, and the curve rises steeply. (The red color reflects the increase in electron density between the H atoms as the distance decreases.)

equally to the two positively charged nuclei. Placing the electrons between the nuclei also matches the Lewis electron dot model.

The covalent bond that arises from the overlap of two *s* orbitals, one from each of two atoms as in $H_2$, is called a **sigma ($\sigma$) bond**. *A sigma bond is a bond in which electron density is greatest along the axis of the bond.*

In summary, the main points of the valence bond approach to bonding are as follows:

- Orbitals overlap to form a bond between two atoms.
- Two electrons, *of opposite spin*, can be accommodated in the overlapping orbitals. Usually, one electron is supplied by each of the two bonded atoms.
- Because of orbital overlap, the bonding electrons have a higher probability of being found within a region of space influenced by both nuclei. Both electrons are thus simultaneously attracted to both nuclei.

What happens for elements beyond hydrogen? In the Lewis structure of HF, for example, a bonding electron pair is placed between H and F, and three lone pairs of electrons are depicted as localized on the F atom (Figure 9.2b). To use an orbital approach, look at the valence shell electrons and orbitals for each atom that can overlap. The hydrogen atom will use its $1s$ orbital in bond formation. The electron configuration of fluorine is $1s^2 2s^2 2p^5$, and the unpaired electron for this atom is assigned to one of the $2p$ orbitals. A sigma bond results from overlap of the hydrogen $1s$ and this fluorine $2p$ orbital.

Formation of the H—F bond is similar to formation of an H—H bond. A hydrogen atom approaches a fluorine atom along the axis containing the $2p$ orbital with a single electron. The orbitals ($1s$ on H and $2p$ on F) distort as each atomic nucleus influences the electron and orbital of the other atom. Still closer together, the $1s$ and $2p$ orbitals overlap, and the two electrons, with opposite spins, pair up to give a $\sigma$ bond (Figure 9.2b). There is an optimum distance (92 pm) at which the energy is lowest, and this corresponds to the bond distance in HF. The net stabilization achieved in this process is the energy for the H—F bond.

The remaining electrons on the fluorine atom (a pair of electrons in the $2s$ orbital and two pairs of electrons in the other two $2p$ orbitals) are not involved in bonding. They are nonbonding electrons, the lone pairs associated with this element in the Lewis structure.

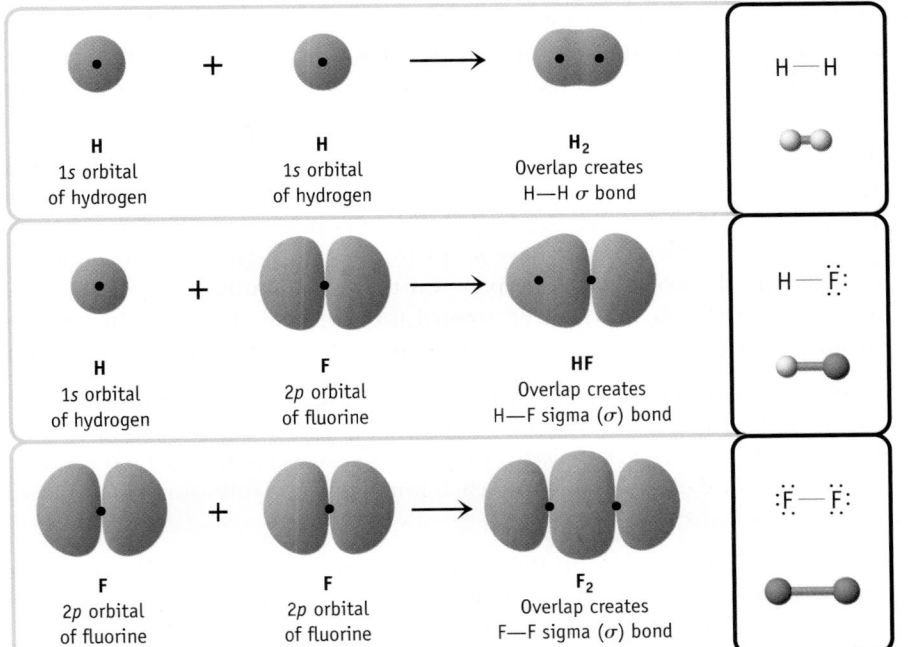

**(a)** Overlap of hydrogen $1s$ orbitals to form the H—H sigma ($\sigma$) bond.

**(b)** Overlap of hydrogen $1s$ and fluorine $2p$ orbitals to form the sigma ($\sigma$) bond in HF.

**(c)** Overlap of $2p$ orbitals on two fluorine atoms forming the sigma ($\sigma$) bond in $F_2$.

**FIGURE 9.2** Covalent bond formation in $H_2$, HF, and $F_2$.

Extension of this model gives a description of bonding in $F_2$. The $2p$ orbitals on the two atoms overlap, and the single electron from each atom is paired in the resulting $\sigma$ bond (Figure 9.2c). The $2s$ and the $2p$ electrons not involved in the bond are the lone pairs on each atom.

## Hybridization of Atomic Orbitals

The simple picture using orbital overlap to describe bonding in $H_2$, HF, and $F_2$ works well, but we run into difficulty when molecules with more atoms are considered. For example, a Lewis dot structure of methane, $CH_4$, shows four C—H covalent bonds. VSEPR theory predicts, and experiments confirm, that the electron-pair geometry of the C atom in $CH_4$ is tetrahedral, with an angle of 109.5° between the bond pairs. The hydrogens are identical in this structure. This means that four equivalent bonding electron pairs occur around the C atom. An orbital picture of the bonds should convey both the geometry and the fact that all C—H bonds are the same.

Lewis structure          molecular model          electron-pair geometry

If we apply the orbital overlap model used for $H_2$ and $F_2$ without modification to describe the bonding in $CH_4$, a problem arises. The three $p$-orbitals for the valence electrons of carbon ($2p_x$, $2p_y$, $2p_z$) are at right angles, 90°, and do not match the tetrahedral angle of 109.5°.

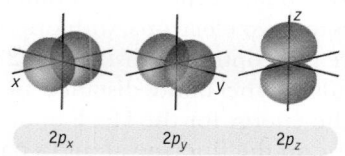

The spherical $2s$ orbital could bond in any direction. Furthermore, a carbon atom in its ground state ($1s^2 2s^2 2p^2$) has only two unpaired electrons (in the $2p$ orbitals), not the four that are needed to allow formation of four bonds.

To describe the bonding in methane and other molecules, Linus Pauling proposed the theory of **orbital hybridization**. He suggested that a new set of orbitals, called **hybrid orbitals**, could be created by mixing the $s$, $p$, and (when required) $d$ atomic orbitals on an atom (Figure 9.3). There are three important principles that govern the outcome.

- The number of hybrid orbitals is always equal to the number of atomic orbitals that are mixed to create the hybrid orbital set.
- Hybrid orbital sets are always built by combining an $s$ orbital with as many $p$ orbitals (and $d$ orbitals if necessary) to have enough hybrid orbitals to accommodate the bond and lone pairs on the central atom.
- The hybrid orbitals are directed toward the terminal atoms, leading to better orbital overlap and a stronger bond between the central and terminal atoms.

The sets of hybrid orbitals that arise from mixing $s$, $p$, and $d$ atomic orbitals are illustrated in Figure 9.3. *The hybrid orbitals required by an atom in a molecule or ion are chosen to match the electron-pair geometry of the atom* because a hybrid orbital is required for each sigma bond electron pair and each lone pair. The following types of hybridization are important:

- **$sp$**: If the valence shell $s$ orbital on the central atom in a molecule or ion is mixed with a valence shell $p$ orbital on that same atom, two $sp$ hybrid orbitals are created. They are separated by 180°.
- **$sp^2$**: If an $s$ orbital is combined with two $p$ orbitals, all in the same valence shell, three $sp^2$ hybrid orbitals are created. They are in the same plane and are separated by 120°.

• **Hybridization and Geometry** Hybridization reconciles the electron-pair geometry with the orbital overlap criterion of bonding. A statement such as "the atom is tetrahedral because it is $sp^3$ hybridized" is backward. That the electron-pair geometry around the atom is tetrahedral is a fact. Hybridization is one way to rationalize that strong bonds can occur in this geometry.

- **$sp^3$**: When the *s* orbital in a valence shell is combined with three *p* orbitals, the result is four hybrid orbitals, each labeled $sp^3$. The hybrid orbitals are separated by 109.5°, the tetrahedral angle.
- **$sp^3d$** and **$sp^3d^2$**: If one or two *d* orbitals are combined with *s* and *p* orbitals in the same valence shell, two other hybrid orbital sets are created. These are utilized by the central atom of a molecule or ion with a trigonal-bipyramidal or octahedral electron-pair geometry, respectively.

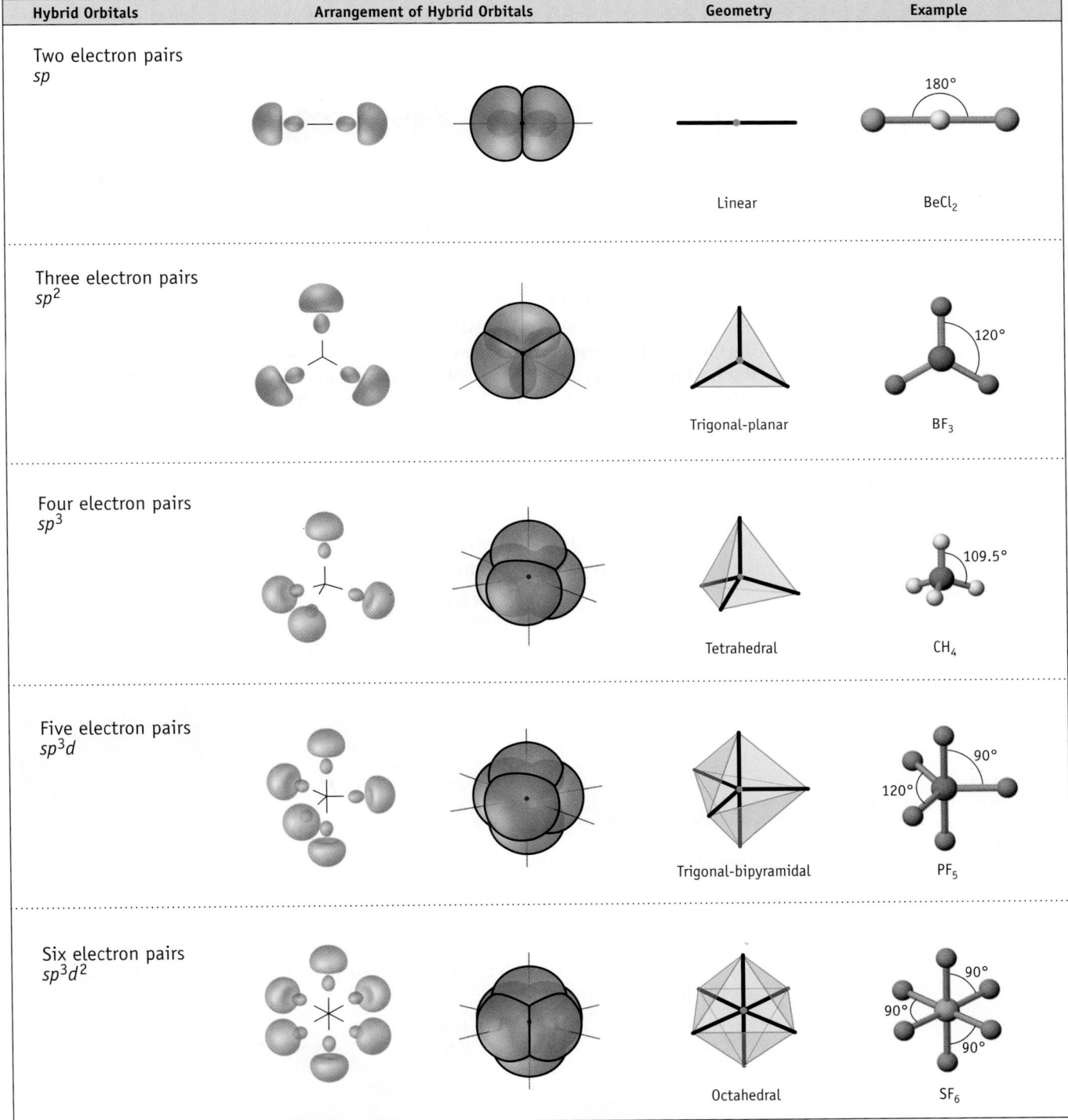

| Hybrid Orbitals | Arrangement of Hybrid Orbitals | Geometry | Example |
|---|---|---|---|
| Two electron pairs<br>*sp* | | Linear | BeCl$_2$ |
| Three electron pairs<br>$sp^2$ | | Trigonal-planar | BF$_3$ |
| Four electron pairs<br>$sp^3$ | | Tetrahedral | CH$_4$ |
| Five electron pairs<br>$sp^3d$ | | Trigonal-bipyramidal | PF$_5$ |
| Six electron pairs<br>$sp^3d^2$ | | Octahedral | SF$_6$ |

**FIGURE 9.3 Hybrid orbitals for two to six electron pairs.** The geometry of the hybrid orbital sets for two to six valence shell electron pairs is given in the right column. In forming a hybrid orbital set, the *s* orbital is always used, plus as many *p* orbitals (and *d* orbitals) as are required to give the necessary number of $\sigma$-bonding and lone-pair orbitals.

**FIGURE 9.4** **Bonding in the methane (CH₄) molecule.**

Hybridization produces four $sp^3$ hybrid orbitals all having the same energy.

## Valence Bond Theory for Methane, CH₄

In methane, four orbitals directed to the corners of a tetrahedron are needed to match the electron-pair geometry on the central carbon atom. By combining the four valence shell orbitals, the $2s$ and all three of the $2p$ orbitals on carbon, a new set of four hybrid orbitals is created that has tetrahedral geometry (Figures 9.3 and 9.4). Each of the four hybrid orbitals is labeled $sp^3$ to indicate the atomic orbital combination (an $s$ orbital and three $p$ orbitals) from which it is derived. All four $sp^3$ orbitals have an identical shape, and the angle between them is 109.5°, the tetrahedral angle. Because the orbitals have the same energy, one electron can be assigned to each according to Hund's rule (◄ Section 7.3, page 308). Then, each C—H bond is formed by overlap of one of the carbon $sp^3$ hybrid orbitals with the $1s$ orbital from a hydrogen atom; one electron from the C atom is paired with an electron from an H atom.

Lewis structure    electron-pair geometry    molecular model    electrostatic potential surface

## Valence Bond Theory for Ammonia, NH₃

The Lewis structure for ammonia shows there are four electron pairs in the valence shell of nitrogen: three bond pairs and a lone pair. VSEPR theory predicts a tetrahedral electron-pair geometry and a trigonal-pyramidal molecular geometry. The actual structure is a close match to the predicted structure; the H—N—H bond angles are 107.5° in this molecule.

Lewis structure    electron-pair geometry    molecular model    electrostatic potential surface

Based on the electron-pair geometry of $NH_3$, we predict $sp^3$ hybridization to accommodate the four electron pairs on the N atom. The lone pair is assigned to one of the hybrid orbitals, and each of the other three hybrid orbitals is occupied by a single electron. Overlap of each of the singly occupied, $sp^3$ hybrid orbitals with a $1s$ orbital from a hydrogen atom, and pairing of the electrons in these orbitals, create the N—H bonds.

## Valence Bond Theory for Water, $H_2O$

The oxygen atom of water has two bonding pairs and two lone pairs in its valence shell, and the H—O—H angle is 104.5°. Four $sp^3$ hybrid orbitals are created from the $2s$ and $2p$ atomic orbitals of oxygen. Two of these $sp^3$ orbitals are occupied by unpaired electrons and are used to form O—H bonds. Lone pairs occupy the other two hybrid orbitals.

O atom lone pairs use $sp^3$ hybrid orbitals.

O—H bond is formed from overlap of O atom $sp^3$ hybrid orbital and H atom $1s$ orbital.

This shows the partial negative charge for the lone electron pairs on the O atom.

The electron density and partial positive charge on the two H atoms are the same.

104.5°

| Lewis structure | electron-pair geometry | molecular model | electrostatic potential surface |

---

**⬛WL INTERACTIVE EXAMPLE 9.1** Valence Bond Description of Bonding in Ethane

**Problem** Describe the bonding in ethane, $C_2H_6$, using valence bond theory.

**What Do You Know?** The formula is known, so the number of valence electrons can be calculated. From this you can derive the electron-pair geometry and the bonding model.

**Strategy**

- Draw the Lewis structure and determine the electron-pair geometry at both carbon atoms.

- Assign hybridization to the carbon atoms based upon the electron-pair geometry.

- Describe covalent bonds based on orbital overlap, and place electron pairs in their proper locations.

**Solution** Each carbon atom has an octet configuration, sharing electron pairs with three hydrogen atoms and with the other carbon atom. The electron pairs around carbon have tetrahedral geometry, so carbon is assigned $sp^3$ hybridization. The C—C bond is formed by overlap of $sp^3$ orbitals on each C atom, and each of the C—H bonds is formed by overlap of an $sp^3$ orbital on carbon with a hydrogen $1s$ orbital.

C—H bond is formed from overlap of C atom $sp^3$ hybrid orbital and H $1s$ orbital.

C—C bond is formed from overlap of C atom $sp^3$ hybrid orbitals.

$sp^3$ hybridized carbon atom

109.5°

| Lewis structure | molecular model | orbital representation |

**Think about Your Answer** For carbon, the four $sp^3$ hybrid orbitals are created from the four valence orbitals (one $2s$ and three $2p$ atomic orbitals). All the valence orbitals on carbon and hydrogen are utilized in forming bonds.

**Strategy Map 9.1**

**PROBLEM**

Describe the bonding in $C_2H_6$.

**DATA/INFORMATION**

- The **formula** of the molecule and thus the **number of valence electrons**

STEP 1. Draw the **Lewis electron dot structure.**

Lewis structure

STEP 2. Decide on **electron-pair geometry** at each atom.

Each C atom has **tetrahedral** geometry.

STEP 3. Decide on **atom hybridization**

$sp^3$ hybrid orbitals for the **C** atom

STEP 4. Describe the bonding in **VB** terms.

**C—C** bond formed by the overlap of C atom $sp^3$ orbitals. **C—H** bonds formed by overlap of C atom $sp^3$ orbital with H atom **1s** orbital.

**Check Your Understanding**

Use valence bond theory to describe the bonding in $CHCl_3$.

### EXAMPLE 9.2    Valence Bond Description of Bonding in Methanol

**Problem** Describe the bonding in the methanol molecule, $CH_3OH$, using valence bond theory.

**What Do You Know?** The formula, $CH_3OH$, helps to define how atoms are linked together. Three hydrogen atoms are linked to carbon. The fourth bond from carbon is to oxygen, and oxygen is attached to the remaining hydrogen.

**Strategy** First, construct the Lewis structure for the molecule. The electron-pair geometry around each atom determines the hybrid orbital set used by that atom.

**Solution** The electron-pair geometry around both the C and O atoms in $CH_3OH$ is tetrahedral. Thus, we may assign $sp^3$ hybridization to each atom, and the C—O bond is formed by overlap of $sp^3$ orbitals on these atoms. Each C—H bond is formed by overlap of a carbon $sp^3$ orbital with a hydrogen 1s orbital, and the O—H bond is formed by overlap of an oxygen $sp^3$ orbital with the hydrogen 1s orbital. Two lone pairs on oxygen occupy the remaining $sp^3$ orbitals on the atom.

O—H bond formed from O atom $sp^3$ hybrid orbital and H 1s orbital

Lone pairs use $sp^3$ hybrid orbitals on O atom.

C—O bond formed from O and C $sp^3$ hybrid orbitals

C—H bond formed from C atom $sp^3$ hybrid orbital and H 1s orbital

Lewis structure     molecular model     orbital representation

**Think about Your Answer** Notice that one end of the $CH_3OH$ molecule (the $CH_3$ or methyl group) is just like the $CH_3$ group in the methane molecule, and the OH group resembles the OH group in water. This example also shows how to predict the structure and bonding in a complicated molecule by looking at each part separately. This is an important idea when dealing with molecules made up of many atoms.

**Check Your Understanding**

Use valence bond theory to describe the bonding in methylamine, $CH_3NH_2$.

methylamine, $CH_3NH_2$

## Hybrid Orbitals for Molecules and Ions with Trigonal-Planar Electron-Pair Geometries

The central atoms in species such as $BF_3$, $O_3$, $NO_3^-$, and $CO_3^{2-}$ all have a trigonal-planar electron-pair geometry, which requires a central atom with three hybrid orbitals in a plane, 120° apart. Three hybrid orbitals mean three atomic orbitals must be combined, and the combination of an s orbital with two p orbitals is appropriate (Figure 9.5). If $p_x$ and $p_y$ orbitals are used in hybrid orbital formation, the three hybrid $sp^2$ orbitals will lie in the xy-plane. The $p_z$ orbital not used to form these hybrid orbitals is perpendicular to the plane containing the three $sp^2$ orbitals.

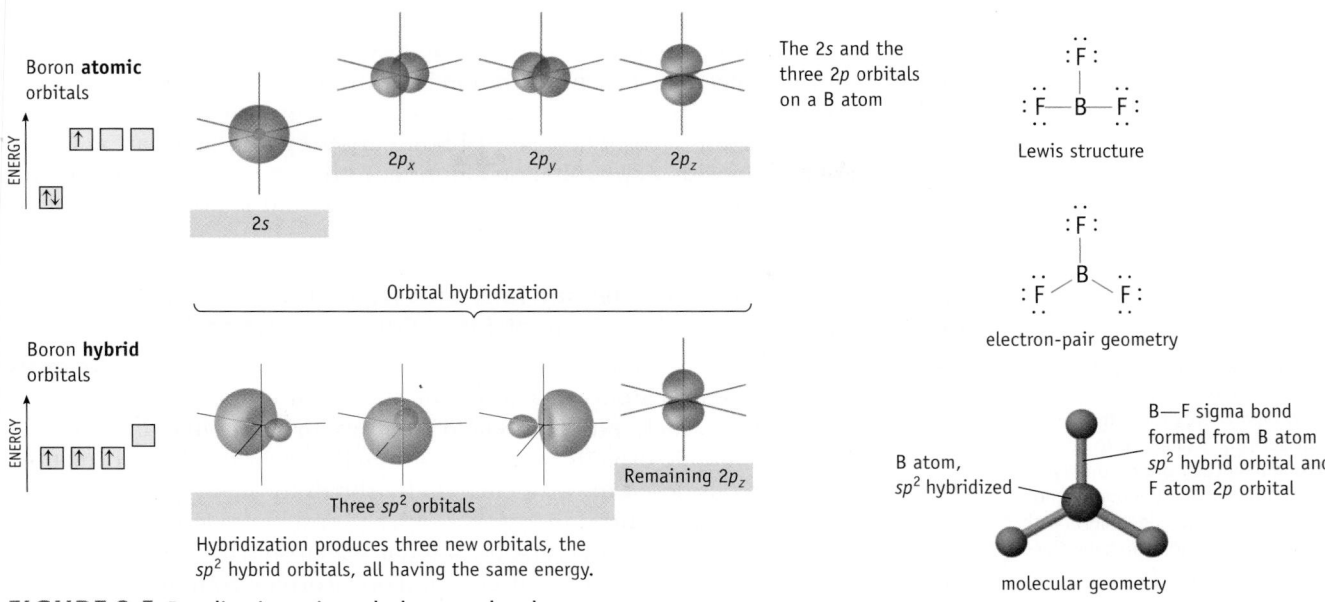

**FIGURE 9.5** Bonding in a trigonal-planar molecule.

Boron trifluoride has a trigonal-planar electron-pair and molecular geometry. Each boron–fluorine bond in this compound results from overlap of an $sp^2$ orbital on boron with a $p$ orbital on fluorine. Notice that the $p_z$ orbital on boron, which is not used to form the $sp^2$ hybrid orbitals, is not occupied by electrons.

### Hybrid Orbitals for Molecules and Ions with Linear Electron-Pair Geometries

For molecules in which the central atom has a linear electron-pair geometry, two hybrid orbitals, 180° apart, are required. One $s$ and one $p$ orbital can be hybridized to form two $sp$ hybrid orbitals (Figure 9.6). If the $p_z$ orbital is used, then the $sp$ orbitals are oriented along the $z$-axis. The $p_x$ and $p_y$ orbitals are perpendicular to this axis.

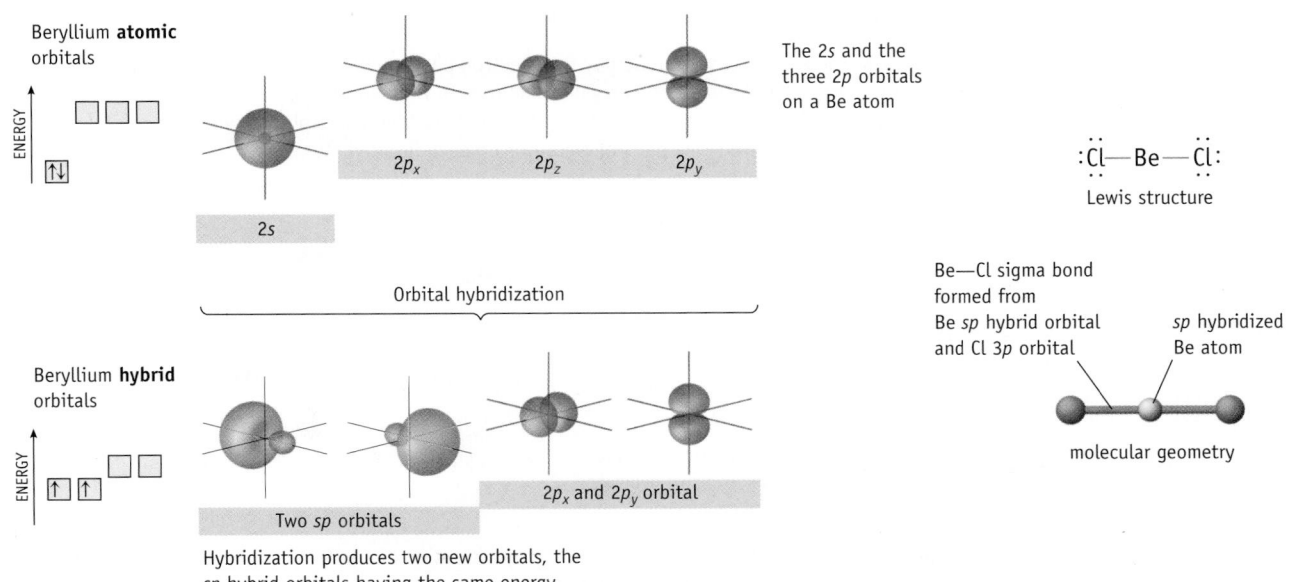

**FIGURE 9.6** Bonding in a linear molecule. Because only one $p$ orbital is incorporated in the hybrid orbital, two $p$ orbitals remain unhybridized. These orbitals are perpendicular to each other and to the axis along which the two $sp$ hybrid orbitals lie.

Beryllium dichloride, $BeCl_2$, is a solid under ordinary conditions. When it is heated to over 520 °C, however, it vaporizes to give $BeCl_2$ vapor. In the gas phase, $BeCl_2$ is a linear molecule, so $sp$ hybridization is appropriate for the beryllium atom in this species. Combining beryllium's $2s$ and $2p_z$ orbitals gives the two $sp$ hybrid orbitals that lie along the $z$-axis. Each Be—Cl bond arises by overlap of an $sp$ hybrid orbital on beryllium with a $3p$ orbital on chlorine. In this molecule, there are only two electron pairs around the beryllium atom, so the $p_x$ and $p_y$ orbitals are not occupied (Figure 9.6).

### Hybrid Orbitals for Molecules and Ions with Trigonal-Bipyramidal or Octahedral Electron-Pair Geometries: *d*-Orbital Participation

• **Do *nd* orbitals participate in bonding?** Because the *nd* orbitals are at a relatively high energy their involvement in bonding is believed to be minimal. Using molecular orbital theory, it is possible to describe the bonding in compounds with expanded octets without using *d* orbitals to form hybrid orbital sets. (See page 427.)

Using valence bond theory to explain the bonding in compounds having five or six electron pairs on a central atom (such as $PF_5$ or $SF_6$) requires the atom to have five or six hybrid orbitals, which must be created from five or six atomic orbitals. This requires the use of atomic orbitals from the *d* subshell in hybrid orbital formation. The *d* orbitals are considered to be valence shell orbitals for main group elements of the third period and beyond.

Five coordination and trigonal-bipyramidal electron-pair geometries are matched to $sp^3d$ hybridization. One *s*, three *p*, and one *d* orbital combine to produce five $sp^3d$ hybrid orbitals. To accommodate six electron pairs in the valence shell of an atom, six $sp^3d^2$ hybrid orbitals can be created from one *s*, three *p*, and two *d* orbitals. The six $sp^3d^2$ hybrid orbitals are directed to the corners of an octahedron (Figure 9.3) and can accommodate the valence electron pairs for a compound that has an octahedral electron-pair geometry.

### EXAMPLE 9.3 Hybridization Involving *d* Orbitals

**Problem** Describe the bonding in $PF_5$ using valence bond theory.

**What Do You Know?** Phosphorus is the central atom in this compound, and it is bonded to five fluorine atoms.

**Strategy** The first step in this problem is to identify the hybridization of the central atom. A roadmap to follow is Formula → Lewis structure → electron-pair geometry → hybridization. Bonding can then be described as the overlap of the P atom hybrid orbitals with appropriate orbitals on the fluorine atoms (the half-filled $2p$ orbital on each fluorine).

**Solution** The P atom is surrounded by five electron pairs, so $PF_5$ has a trigonal-bipyramidal electron-pair and molecular geometry (see Figure 9.3). The hybridization scheme is therefore $sp^3d$. Each P—F bond is formed by overlap of an $sp^3d$ orbital on phosphorus with a $2p$ orbital on fluorine. There are three lone pairs of electrons on each fluorine atom.

Lewis structure and
electron-pair geometry

Sigma bonds formed from
P $sp^3d$ hybrid orbital and
F $2p$ orbital

$sp^3d$ hybridized P atom

molecular model

**Think about Your Answer** To decide on the hybridization of an atom in a molecule you need to know the electron-pair geometry around that atom.

**Check Your Understanding**

Describe the bonding in $XeF_2$ (page 400) using valence bond theory.

## EXAMPLE 9.4    Recognizing Hybridization

**Problem** Identify the hybridization of the central atom in the following compounds and ions:

(a)  $SF_3^+$                 (b)  $SO_4^{2-}$           (c)  $SF_4$            (d)  $I_3^-$

**What Do You Know?** To determine hybridization, you need to know the electron-pair geometry.

**Strategy** The roadmap here is the same as in Example 9.3: Formula → Lewis structure → electron-pair geometry → hybridization.

**Solution** The structures for $SF_3^+$, and $SO_4^{2-}$ are written as follows:

Four electron pairs surround the central atom in each of these ions, and the electron-pair geometry for these atoms is tetrahedral. Thus, $sp^3$ hybridization for the central atom is used to describe the bonding.

For $SF_4$ and $I_3^-$, five pairs of electrons are in the valence shell of the central atom and both have trigonal-bipyramidal electron-pair geometry. For both species $sp^3d$ hybridization is appropriate for the central atom.

**Think about Your Answer** Notice that in both $SF_4$ and $I_3^-$ the central atom lone pairs are in equatorial positions, a feature that leads to minimum repulsion of the valence electron pairs.

**Check Your Understanding**

Identify the hybridization of the underlined central atom in the following compounds and ions:

(a)  $\underline{B}H_4^-$              (c)  $O\underline{S}F_4$          (e)  $\underline{B}Cl_3$

(b)  $\underline{S}F_5^-$              (d)  $\underline{Cl}F_3$           (f)  $\underline{Xe}O_6^{4-}$

# Multiple Bonds

According to valence bond theory, bond formation requires that two orbitals on adjacent atoms overlap. Many molecules have double or triple bonds, that is, there are two or three bonds, respectively, between pairs of atoms. Therefore, according to valence bond theory, a double bond requires *two* sets of overlapping orbitals and *two* electron pairs. For a triple bond, *three* sets of atomic orbitals are required, each set accommodating a pair of electrons.

## Double Bonds

Consider ethylene, $H_2C{=}CH_2$, a common molecule with a double bond. The molecular structure of ethylene places all six atoms in a plane, with H—C—H and H—C—C angles of approximately 120°. Each carbon atom has trigonal-planar geometry, so $sp^2$ hybridization is assumed for these atoms.

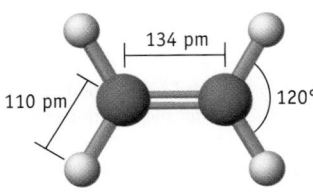

ethylene, $C_2H_4$

A description of bonding in ethylene starts with each carbon atom having three $sp^2$ hybrid orbitals in the molecular plane and an unhybridized $p$ orbital perpendicular to that plane. Because each carbon atom is involved in four bonds, a single unpaired electron is placed in each of these orbitals.

[↑]  Unhybridized $p$ orbital. Used for $\pi$ bonding in $C_2H_4$.

[↑|↑|↑]  Three $sp^2$ hybrid orbitals. Used for C—H and C—C $\sigma$ bonding in $C_2H_4$.

The C—H bonds of $C_2H_4$ arise from overlap of $sp^2$ orbitals on carbon with hydrogen $1s$ orbitals. After accounting for these bonds, one $sp^2$ orbital on each carbon atom remains. These hybrid orbitals point toward each other and overlap to form one of the bonds linking the carbon atoms (Figure 9.7). This leaves only one other orbital unaccounted for on each carbon, an unhybridized $p$ orbital, and it is these orbitals that can be used to create the second bond between carbon atoms in $C_2H_4$. If they are aligned correctly, the unhybridized $p$ orbitals on the two carbons can overlap, allowing the electrons in these orbitals to be paired. The overlap does not occur directly along the C—C axis, however. Instead, the arrangement compels these orbitals to overlap sideways, and the electron pair occupies an orbital with electron density above and below the plane containing the six atoms.

This description results in two types of bonds in $C_2H_4$. One type is the C—H and C—C bonds that arise from the overlap of atomic orbitals so that the bonding electrons that lie along the bond axes form sigma ($\sigma$) bonds. The other is the bond formed by sideways overlap of $p$ atomic orbitals, called a **pi ($\pi$) bond**. In a $\pi$ bond, the overlap region is above and below the internuclear axis, and the electron density of the $\pi$ bond is above and below the bond axis.

Be sure to notice that a $\pi$ bond can form *only* if (a) there are unhybridized $p$ orbitals on adjacent atoms and (b) the $p$ orbitals are perpendicular to the plane of the molecule and parallel to one another. This happens only if the $sp^2$ orbitals of both carbon atoms are in the same plane. A consequence of this is that both atoms involved in the $\pi$ bond have trigonal-planar geometry, and the six atoms in and around the $\pi$ bond (the two atoms involved in the $\pi$ bond and the four atoms attached to the $\pi$-bonded atoms) lie in one plane.

Double bonds between carbon and oxygen, sulfur, or nitrogen are quite common. Consider formaldehyde, $CH_2O$, in which a carbon–oxygen $\pi$ bond occurs (Figure 9.8). A trigonal-planar electron-pair geometry indicates $sp^2$ hybridization for the C atom. The $\sigma$ bonds from carbon to the O atom and the two H atoms form by overlap of $sp^2$ hybrid orbitals with half-filled orbitals from the oxygen and two hydrogen atoms. An unhybridized $p$ orbital on carbon is oriented perpendicular to

Computer-generated representation
of the $\pi$ bond in ethylene, $C_2H_4$

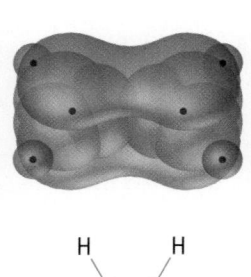

**(a)** Lewis structure and bonding of ethylene, $C_2H_4$.

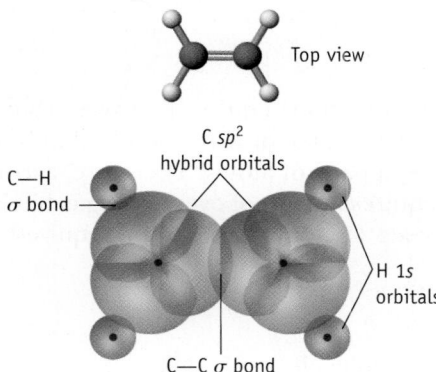

Top view

C $sp^2$
hybrid orbitals

C—H
$\sigma$ bond

H $1s$
orbitals

C—C $\sigma$ bond

**(b)** The C—H $\sigma$ bonds are formed by overlap of C atom $sp^2$ hybrid orbitals with H atom $1s$ orbitals. The $\sigma$ bond between C atoms arises from overlap of $sp^2$ orbitals.

Almost
side view

Overlapping unhybridized
$2p$ orbitals

C—C $\pi$ bond

**(c)** The carbon–carbon $\pi$ bond is formed by overlap of an unhybridized $2p$ orbital on each atom. Note the lack of electron density along the C—C bond axis from this bond.

**FIGURE 9.7** The valence bond model of bonding in ethylene, $C_2H_4$. Each C atom is assumed to be $sp^2$ hybridized.

H
|
C=Ö
|
H

**(a)** Lewis structure and bonding of formaldehyde, $CH_2O$.

Top view

$sp^2$ hybridized C atom

$sp^2$ hybridized O atom

C—H σ bonds

Lone pairs on the O atom

C—O σ bond

**(b)** The C—H σ bonds are formed by overlap of C atom $sp^2$ hybrid orbitals with H atom $1s$ orbitals. The σ bond between C and O atoms arises from overlap of $sp^2$ orbitals.

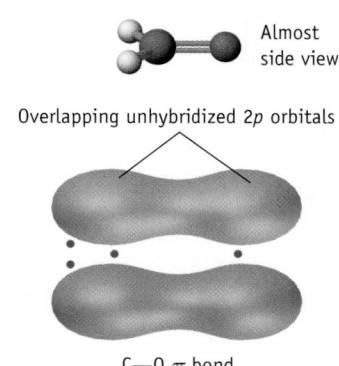

Almost side view

Overlapping unhybridized $2p$ orbitals

C—O π bond

**(c)** The C—O π bond comes from the side-by-side overlap of unhybridized $p$ orbitals on the two atoms.

**FIGURE 9.8** Valence bond description of bonding in formaldehyde, $CH_2O$.

the molecular plane (just as for the carbon atoms of $C_2H_4$). This $p$ orbital is available for π bonding, this time with an oxygen orbital.

What orbitals on oxygen are used in this model? The approach in Figure 9.8 assumes $sp^2$ hybridization for oxygen. This uses one O atom $sp^2$ orbital in σ bond formation, leaving two $sp^2$ orbitals to accommodate lone pairs. The remaining $p$ orbital on the O atom participates in the π bond.

## EXAMPLE 9.5    Bonding in Acetic Acid

**Problem** Using valence bond theory, describe the bonding in acetic acid, $CH_3CO_2H$, the important ingredient in vinegar.

**What Do You Know?** You know the formula for the compound of interest. You may recognize from the earlier discussion of acids that this compound contains the $CO_2H$ group in which both oxygen atoms are attached to the carbon.

**Strategy** Write a Lewis electron dot structure, and determine the geometry around each atom using VSEPR theory. Use this geometry to decide on the hybrid orbitals used in σ bonding. If unhybridized $p$ orbitals are available on adjacent C and O atoms, then C—O π bonding can occur.

**Solution** The carbon atom of the $CH_3$ group has tetrahedral electron-pair geometry, which means it is $sp^3$ hybridized. Three $sp^3$ orbitals are used to form the C—H bonds. The fourth $sp^3$ orbital is used to bond to the adjacent carbon atom. This carbon atom has a trigonal-planar electron-pair geometry; it must be $sp^2$ hybridized. The C—C bond is formed using one of these hybrid orbitals, and the other two $sp^2$ orbitals are used to form the σ bonds to the two oxygens. The oxygen of the O—H group has four electron pairs; it must be tetrahedral and $sp^3$ hybridized. Thus, this O atom uses two $sp^3$ orbitals to bond to the adjacent carbon and the hydrogen, and two $sp^3$ orbitals accommodate the two lone pairs.

Finally, the carbon–oxygen double bond can be described by assuming the C and O atoms are both $sp^2$ hybridized (like the C—O π bond in formaldehyde, Figure 9.8). The unhybridized $p$ orbital remaining on each atom is used to form the carbon–oxygen π bond, and the lone pairs on the O atom are accommodated in $sp^2$ hybrid orbitals.

Lewis dot structure

molecular model

acetone

**Think about Your Answer** Notice that the hybridization around each central atom in a complex structure is determined by considering its electron-pair geometry.

**Check Your Understanding**

Use valence bond theory to describe the bonding in acetone, $CH_3COCH_3$.

## Triple Bonds

Acetylene, H—C≡C—H, is an example of a molecule with a triple bond. VSEPR theory predicts that the four atoms lie in a straight line with H—C—C angles of 180°. This implies that the carbon atom is *sp* hybridized (Figure 9.9). For each carbon atom, there are two *sp* orbitals, one directed toward hydrogen and used to create the C—H σ bond, and the second directed toward the other carbon and used to create a σ bond between the two carbon atoms. Two unhybridized *p* orbitals remain on each carbon, and they are oriented so that it is possible to form *two* π bonds in HC≡CH.

⟨↑│↑⟩ Two unhybridized *p* orbitals. Used for π bonding in $C_2H_2$.

⟨↑│↑⟩ Two *sp* hybrid orbitals. Used for C—H and C—C σ bonding in $C_2H_2$.

These π bonds are perpendicular to the molecular axis and perpendicular to each other. Three electrons on each carbon atom are paired to form the triple bond consisting of a σ bond and two π bonds (Figure 9.9).

Now that we have examined several cases involving double and triple bonds, let us summarize several important points:

- In valence bond theory a double bond *always* consists of a σ bond and a π bond. Similarly, a triple bond *always* consists of a σ bond and *two* π bonds.
- A π bond may form only if unhybridized *p* orbitals remain on the bonded atoms.
- If a Lewis structure shows multiple bonds, the atoms involved must be either $sp^2$ or *sp* hybridized. Only in this manner will unhybridized *p* orbitals be available to form a π bond.

## *Cis-Trans* Isomerism: A Consequence of π Bonding

Ethylene, $C_2H_4$, is a planar molecule, a geometry that allows the unhybridized *p* orbitals on the two carbon atoms to line up and form a π bond (Figure 9.7). Let us speculate on what would happen if one end of the ethylene molecule were twisted relative to the other end (Figure 9.10). This action would distort the molecule away from planarity, and the *p* orbitals would rotate out of alignment. Rotation would diminish the extent of overlap of these orbitals, and, if a twist of 90° were achieved, the two *p* orbitals would no longer overlap at all; the π bond would be broken. However, so much energy is required to break this bond (about 260 kJ/mol) that rotation around a C=C bond is not expected to occur at room temperature.

H—C≡C—H

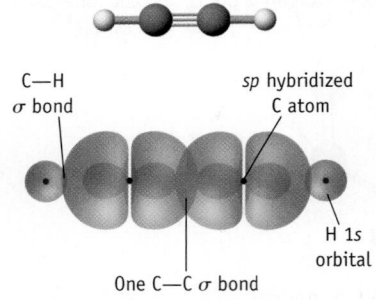

C—H σ bond

*sp* hybridized C atom

One C—C σ bond

H 1s orbital

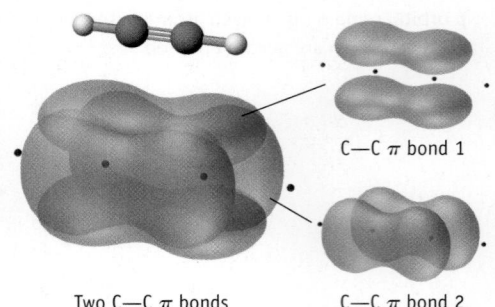

Two C—C π bonds

C—C π bond 1

C—C π bond 2

**FIGURE 9.9** Bonding in acetylene.

**FIGURE 9.10** Rotation around bonds.

**(a)** In ethane nearly free rotation can occur around the single ($\sigma$) bond.

**(b)** Rotation around the C$=$C bond in ethylene is severely restricted because doing so would mean breaking the $\pi$ bond, a process requiring considerable energy.

A consequence of restricted rotation is that isomers occur for many compounds containing a C$=$C bond. **Isomers** are compounds that have the same formula but different structures. In this case, the two isomeric compounds differ with respect to the orientation of the groups attached to the carbons of the double bond. Two isomers of $C_2H_2Cl_2$ are *cis-* and *trans-*1,2-dichloroethylene. Their structures resemble ethylene, except that two hydrogen atoms have been replaced by chlorine atoms. Because a large amount of energy is required to break the $\pi$ bond, the *cis* compound cannot rearrange to the *trans* compound under ordinary conditions. Each compound can be obtained separately, and each has its own identity. *Cis*-1,2-dichloroethylene boils at 60.3 °C, whereas *trans-*1,2-dichloroethylene boils at 47.5 °C.

*cis*-1,2-dichloroethylene    *trans*-1,2-dichloroethylene

Although *cis* and *trans* isomers do not interconvert at ordinary temperatures, they will do so at higher temperatures. If the temperature is sufficiently high, the molecular motions can become sufficiently energetic that rotation around the C$=$C bond can occur. This may also occur under other special conditions, such as when the molecule absorbs light energy.

## Benzene: A Special Case of $\pi$ Bonding

Benzene, $C_6H_6$, is the simplest member of a large group of substances known as *aromatic* compounds, a historical reference to their odor. It occupies a pivotal place in the history and practice of chemistry.

To 19th-century chemists, benzene was a perplexing substance with an unknown structure. Based on its chemical reactions, however, August Kekulé (1829–1896) suggested that the molecule has a planar, symmetrical ring structure. We know now he was correct. The ring is flat, and all the carbon–carbon bonds are the same length, 139 pm, a distance intermediate between the average single bond (154 pm) and double bond (134 pm) lengths. Assuming the molecule has two resonance structures with alternating double bonds, the observed structure is rationalized. The C—C bond order in $C_6H_6$(1.5) is the average of a single and a double bond.

  or

resonance structures          resonance hybrid

benzene, $C_6H_6$

**FIGURE 9.11 Bonding in benzene, $C_6H_6$.** *(left)* The C atoms of the ring are bonded to each other through $\sigma$ bonds using C atom $sp^2$ hybrid orbitals. The C—H bonds also use C atom $sp^2$ hybrid orbitals. The $\pi$ framework of the molecule arises from overlap of C atom $p$ orbitals not used in hybrid orbital formation. Because these orbitals are perpendicular to the ring, $\pi$ electron density is above and below the plane of the ring. *(right)* A composite of $\sigma$ and $\pi$ bonding in benzene.

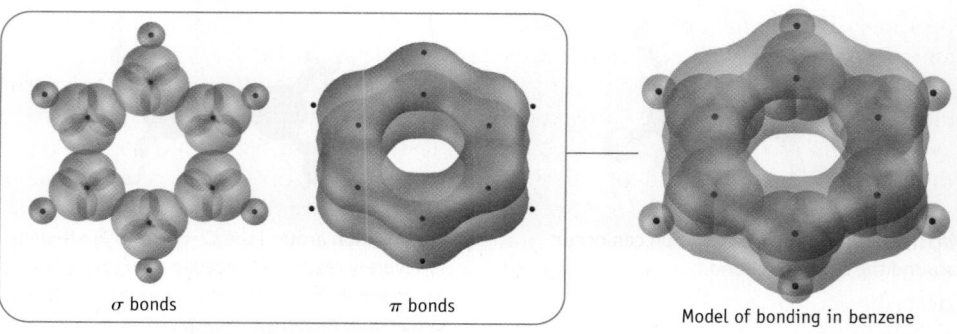

$\sigma$ bonds   $\pi$ bonds

$\sigma$ and $\pi$ bonding in benzene

Model of bonding in benzene

Understanding the bonding in benzene (Figure 9.11) is important because the benzene ring structure occurs in an enormous number of chemical compounds. We assume that the trigonal-planar carbon atoms have $sp^2$ hybridization. Each C—H bond is formed by overlap of an $sp^2$ orbital of a carbon atom with a $1s$ orbital of hydrogen, and the C—C $\sigma$ bonds arise by overlap of $sp^2$ orbitals on adjacent carbon atoms. After accounting for the $\sigma$ bonding, an unhybridized $p$ orbital remains on each C atom, and each is occupied by a single electron. These six orbitals and six electrons form $\pi$ bonds. Because all carbon–carbon bond lengths are the same, each $p$ orbital overlaps equally well with the $p$ orbitals of both adjacent carbons, and the $\pi$ interaction is unbroken around the six-member ring.

---

**REVIEW & CHECK FOR SECTION 9.2**

1. What is the hybridization of S in $SF_4$?

   (a) $sp^3$      (b) $sp^3d$      (c) $sp^3d^2$      (d) $sp^2$

2. What orbitals overlap to form the B—F $\sigma$ bonds in $BF_4^-$?

   (a) Boron $sp^3$ + fluorine $2p$      (c) Boron $sp^3$ + fluorine $2s$

   (b) Boron $sp^2$ + fluorine $2p$      (d) Boron $sp^2$ + fluorine $2s$

3. Which of the following is incorrect?

   (a) The hybridization of N in $NH_4^+$ is $sp^3$.      (c) The hybridization of I in $ICl_4^-$ is $sp^3$.

   (b) The hybridization of S in $SO_4^{2-}$ is $sp^3$.      (d) The hybridization of O in $H_3O^+$ is $sp^3$.

4. $\pi$ bonds between two atoms are formed by overlap of what orbitals?

   (a) $sp^3$ on atom A with $sp^3$ on atom B      (c) $sp$ on atom A with $sp$ on atom B

   (b) $sp^2$ on atom A with $sp^2$ on atom B      (d) $p$ on atom A with $p$ on atom B

5. Which description of the bond between nitrogen atoms in $N_2$ is correct?

   (a) The nitrogens are attached by a single $\sigma$ bond.

   (b) The nitrogens are attached by one $\sigma$ and two $\pi$ bonds.

   (c) The nitrogen atoms are $sp^3$ hybridized.

   (d) The bonds in $N_2$ are formed by overlap of $sp$ orbitals.

---

## 9.3 Molecular Orbital Theory

Molecular orbital (MO) theory is an alternative way to view orbitals in molecules. In contrast to the localized bond and lone pair electrons of valence bond theory, MO theory assumes that pure atomic orbitals of the atoms in the molecule combine to produce orbitals that are spread out, or delocalized, over several atoms or even over an entire molecule. These orbitals are called **molecular orbitals**.

One reason for learning about the MO concept is that it correctly predicts the electronic structures of molecules such as $O_2$ that do not follow the electron-pairing assumptions of the Lewis approach. The rules of Section 8.2 would guide you to draw the electron dot structure of $O_2$ with all the electrons paired, which fails to explain its paramagnetism (Figure 9.12). The molecular orbital approach can account for this property, but valence bond theory cannot. To see how MO theory can be used to describe the bonding in $O_2$ and other diatomic molecules, let us first describe four principles of the theory.

## Principles of Molecular Orbital Theory

In MO theory, we begin with a given arrangement of atoms in the molecule at the known bond distances and then determine the *sets* of molecular orbitals. One way to do this is to combine available valence orbitals on all the constituent atoms. These molecular orbitals more or less encompass all the atoms of the molecule, and the valence electrons for all the atoms in the molecule occupy the molecular orbitals. Just as with orbitals in atoms, electrons are assigned in order of increasing orbital energy and according to the Pauli principle and Hund's rule (Sections 7.1 and 7.3).

The **first principle of molecular orbital theory** is that *the total number of molecular orbitals is always equal to the total number of atomic orbitals contributed by the atoms that have combined.* To illustrate this orbital conservation principle, let us consider the $H_2$ molecule.

### Molecular Orbitals for $H_2$

Molecular orbital theory specifies that when the $1s$ orbitals of two hydrogen atoms overlap, *two* molecular orbitals result. One molecular orbital results from the *addition* of the $1s$ atomic orbital wave functions, leading to an increased probability

• **Orbitals and Electron Waves**
Orbitals are characterized as electron waves; therefore, a way to view molecular orbital formation is to assume that two electron waves, one from each atom, interfere with each other. The interference can be constructive, giving a bonding MO, or destructive, giving an antibonding MO. (See Figure 9.13.)

**(a)** Oxygen gas can be liquified by passing it through a coil immersed in liquid nitrogen (at −196 °C). Here you see the liquid dripping into an insulated flask.

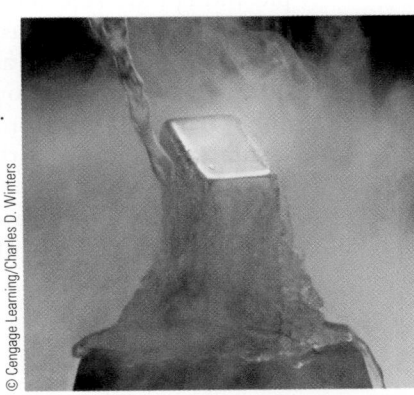

**(c)** Because $O_2$ molecules have two unpaired electrons, oxygen in the liquid state is paramagnetic and clings to a relatively strong neodymium magnet.

**(b)** Liquid oxygen (boiling point, −183 °C) is a pale blue liquid.

**(d)** In contrast, liquid $N_2$ is diamagnetic and does not stick to the magnet. It just splashes on the surface when poured onto the magnet.

**FIGURE 9.12** The paramagnetism of liquid oxygen.

**FIGURE 9.13 Bonding molecular orbital in H₂.**
The matter waves for the 1s electrons overlap along the bond axis. There is an enhancement of the wave amplitude between the nuclei, the result of which is that there is an increased probability of finding the electrons between the nuclei.

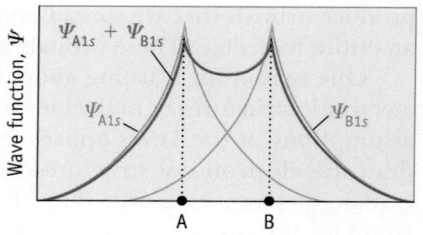

that electrons will reside in the bond region between the two nuclei (Figures 9.13 and 9.14). This is called a **bonding molecular orbital**. It is also a $\sigma$ orbital because the region of electron probability lies directly along the bond axis. This molecular orbital is labeled $\sigma_{1s}$, the subscript 1s indicating that 1s atomic orbitals were used to create the molecular orbital.

The other molecular orbital is constructed by *subtracting* one atomic orbital wave function from the other (Figure 9.14). When this happens, the probability of finding an electron between the nuclei in the molecular orbital is reduced, and the probability of finding the electron in other regions is higher. Without significant electron density between them, the nuclei repel one another. This type of orbital is called an **antibonding molecular orbital**. Because it is also a $\sigma$ orbital, derived from 1s atomic orbitals, it is labeled $\sigma^*_{1s}$. The asterisk signifies that it is antibonding. *Antibonding orbitals have no counterpart in valence bond theory.*

A **second principle of molecular orbital theory** is that *the bonding molecular orbital is lower in energy than the parent orbitals, and the antibonding orbital is higher in energy* (Figure 9.14). This means that the energy of a group of atoms is lower than the energy of the separated atoms when electrons occupy bonding molecular orbitals. Chemists say the system is "stabilized" by chemical bond formation. Conversely, the system is "destabilized" when electrons occupy antibonding orbitals because the energy of the system is higher than that of the atoms themselves.

A **third principle of molecular orbital theory** is that the *electrons of the molecule are assigned to orbitals of successively higher energy* according to the Pauli exclusion principle and Hund's rule. This is analogous to the procedure for building up electronic structures of atoms. Thus, electrons occupy the lowest energy orbitals available, and when two electrons are assigned to an orbital, their spins must be paired. Because the energy of the electrons in the bonding orbital of H₂ is lower than the energy of either parent 1s electron (Figure 9.14b), the H₂ molecule is more stable than two separate H atoms. We write the electron configuration of H₂ as $(\sigma_{1s})^2$.

What would happen if we tried to combine two helium atoms to form dihelium, He₂? Both He atoms have a 1s valence orbital that can produce the same kind of molecular orbitals as in H₂. Unlike H₂, however, four electrons need to be assigned

**FIGURE 9.14 Molecular orbitals for H₂.**

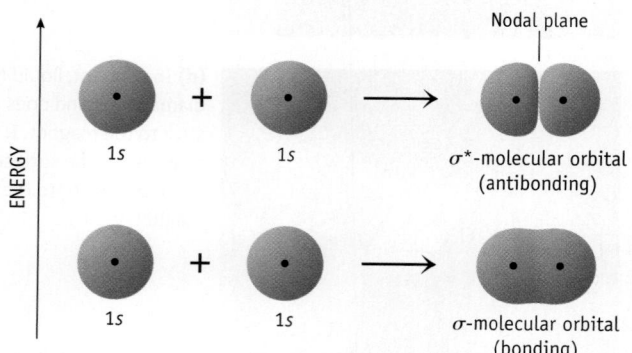

**(a)** Bonding and antibonding $\sigma$-molecular orbitals are formed from two 1s atomic orbitals on adjacent atoms. Notice the presence of a node between the nuclei in the antibonding orbital. (The node is a plane on which there is zero probability of finding an electron.)

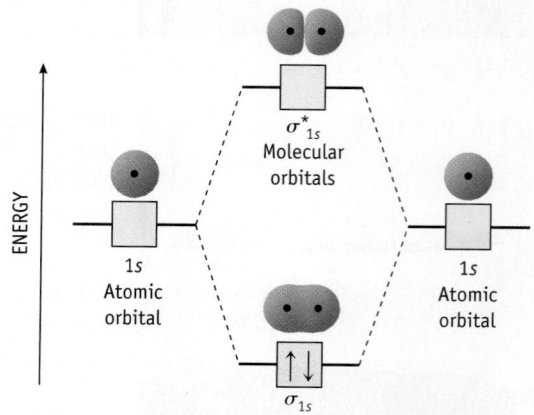

**(b)** A molecular orbital diagram for H₂. The two electrons are placed in the $\sigma_{1s}$ orbital. This molecular orbital is lower in energy.

**(a) Dihelium molecule, He$_2$.**
This diagram provides a rationalization for the nonexistence of the molecule. In He$_2$, both the bonding ($\sigma_{1s}$) and antibonding orbitals ($\sigma^*_{1s}$) would be fully occupied.

**(b) Dilithium molecule, Li$_2$.**
Notice that the molecular orbitals are created by combining orbitals of similar energies. Dilithium will utilize 1s and 2s atomic orbitals.

**FIGURE 9.15** Molecular orbital diagrams for atoms with 1s and 2s orbitals.

to these orbitals (Figure 9.15a). The pair of electrons in the $\sigma_{1s}$ orbital stabilizes He$_2$. The two electrons in $\sigma^*_{1s}$, however, destabilize the He$_2$ molecule. The energy decrease from the electrons in the $\sigma_{1s}$-bonding molecular orbital is fully offset by the energy increase due to the electrons in the $\sigma^*_{1s}$-antibonding molecular orbital. Thus, molecular orbital theory predicts that He$_2$ has no net stability; that is, two He atoms should have no tendency to combine. This confirms what we already know, that elemental helium exists in the form of single atoms and not as a diatomic molecule.

## Bond Order

Bond order was defined in Section 8.9 as the net number of bonding electron pairs linking a pair of atoms. This same concept can be applied directly to molecular orbital theory, but now bond order is defined as

$$\text{Bond order} = 1/2 \text{ (number of electrons in bonding MOs} - \text{number of electrons in antibonding MOs)} \qquad (9.1)$$

In the H$_2$ molecule, there are two electrons in a bonding orbital and none in an antibonding orbital, so H$_2$ has a bond order of 1. In contrast, in the hypothetical molecule He$_2$ the stabilizing effect of the $\sigma_{1s}$ pair would be canceled by the destabilizing effect of the $\sigma^*_{1s}$ pair, and so the bond order would be 0.

Fractional bond orders are possible. Consider the ion He$_2{}^+$. Its molecular orbital electron configuration is $(\sigma_{1s})^2(\sigma^*_{1s})^1$. In this ion, there are two electrons in a bonding molecular orbital, but only one in an antibonding orbital. MO theory predicts that He$_2{}^+$ should have a bond order of 0.5; that is, a weak bond should exist between helium atoms in such a species. Interestingly, this ion has been identified in the gas phase using special experimental techniques.

## EXAMPLE 9.6    Molecular Orbitals and Bond Order

**Problem** Write the electron configuration of the H$_2{}^-$ ion in molecular orbital terms. What is the bond order of the ion?

**What Do You Know?** Combining the 1s orbitals on the two hydrogen atoms will give two molecular orbitals (Figure 9.14). One is a bonding orbital ($\sigma_{1s}$) and the second is an antibonding orbital ($\sigma^*_{1s}$).

**Strategy** Count the number of valence electrons in the ion, and then place those electrons in the MO diagram for the H$_2$ molecule. Find the bond order from Equation 9.1.

**Solution** This ion has three electrons (one each from the H atoms plus one for the negative charge). Therefore, its electronic configuration is $(\sigma_{1s})^2(\sigma^*_{1s})^1$, identical with the configuration for He$_2{}^+$. This means H$_2{}^-$ has a net bond order of 0.5.

**Think about Your Answer** There is a weak bond in this ion, so it is predicted to exist only under special circumstances.

**Check Your Understanding**

What is the electron configuration of the $H_2^+$ ion? Compare the bond order of this ion with $He_2^+$ and $H_2^-$. Do you expect $H_2^+$ to exist?

## Molecular Orbitals of Li₂ and Be₂

A **fourth principle of molecular orbital theory** is that *atomic orbitals combine to form molecular orbitals most effectively when the atomic orbitals are of similar energy.* This principle becomes important when we move past $He_2$ to $Li_2$, dilithium, and heavier molecules such as $O_2$ and $N_2$.

A lithium atom has electrons in two orbitals of the *s* type ($1s$ and $2s$), so a $1s \pm 2s$ combination is theoretically possible. Because the $1s$ and $2s$ orbitals are quite different in energy, however, this interaction can be disregarded. Thus, the molecular orbitals come only from $1s \pm 1s$ and $2s \pm 2s$ combinations (Figure 9.15b). This means the molecular orbital electron configuration of dilithium, $Li_2$, is

$$Li_2 \text{ MO Configuration:} \quad (\sigma_{1s})^2(\sigma^*_{1s})^2(\sigma_{2s})^2$$

The bonding effect of the $\sigma_{1s}$ electrons is canceled by the antibonding effect of the $\sigma^*_{1s}$ electrons, so these pairs make no net contribution to bonding in $Li_2$. Bonding in $Li_2$ is due to the electron pair assigned to the $\sigma_{2s}$ orbital, and the bond order is 1.

The fact that the $\sigma_{1s}$ and $\sigma^*_{1s}$ electron pairs of $Li_2$ make no net contribution to bonding is exactly what you observed in drawing electron dot structures in Section 8.2: *Core electrons are ignored.* In molecular orbital terms, core electrons are assigned to bonding and antibonding molecular orbitals that offset one another.

A diberyllium molecule, $Be_2$, is not expected to exist. Its electron configuration would be

$$Be_2 \text{ MO Configuration:} \quad [\text{core electrons}](\sigma_{2s})^2(\sigma^*_{2s})^2$$

The effects of $\sigma_{2s}$ and $\sigma^*_{2s}$ electrons cancel, and there is no net bonding. The bond order is 0, so the molecule does not exist.

- **Diatomic Molecules** Molecules such as $H_2$, $Li_2$, and $N_2$, in which two identical atoms are bonded, are examples of *homonuclear* diatomic molecules.

## EXAMPLE 9.7    Molecular Orbitals in Homonuclear Diatomic Molecules

**Problem** Should the $Be_2^+$ ion exist? Describe its electron configuration in molecular orbital terms, and give the net bond order.

**What Do You Know?** The MO diagram in Figure 9.15b applies to this question because we are dealing only with $1s$ and $2s$ orbitals in the original atoms.

**Strategy** Count the number of electrons in the ion, and place them in the MO diagram in Figure 9.15b. Write the electron configuration, and calculate the bond order from Equation 9.1.

**Solution** The $Be_2^+$ ion has only seven electrons (in contrast to eight for $Be_2$), of which four are core electrons. (The four core electrons are assigned to $\sigma_{1s}$ and $\sigma^*_{1s}$ molecular orbitals.) The remaining three electrons are assigned to the $\sigma_{2s}$ and $\sigma^*_{2s}$ molecular orbitals, so the MO electron configuration is [core electrons]$(\sigma_{2s})^2(\sigma^*_{2s})^1$. This means the net bond order is 0.5.

**Think about Your Answer** $Be_2^+$ is predicted to exist under special circumstances. Scientists might search for such species in gas discharge experiments (gaseous atoms subjected to a strong electrical potential) and use spectroscopy to confirm their existence.

**Check Your Understanding**

Could the anion $Li_2^-$ exist? What is the ion's bond order?

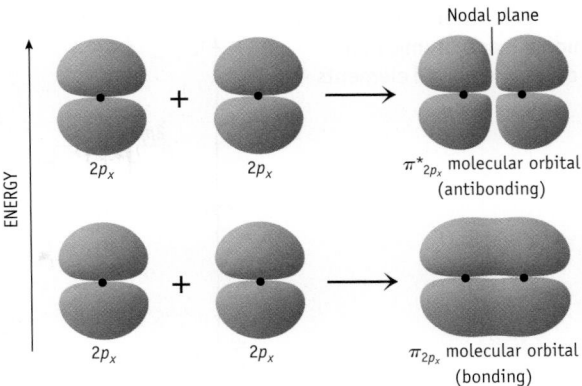

**(a) Sigma ($\sigma$) molecular orbitals from $p$ atomic orbitals.**
Sigma-bonding ($\sigma_{2p}$) and antibonding ($\sigma^{*}_{2p}$) molecular orbitals arise from overlap of $2p$ orbitals. Each orbital can accommodate two electrons. The $p$ orbitals in electron shells of higher $n$ give molecular orbitals of the same basic shape.

**(b) Pi ($\pi$) molecular orbitals.** Sideways overlap of atomic $2p$ orbitals that lie in the same direction in space gives rise to pi-bonding ($\pi_{2p}$) and pi-antibonding ($\pi^{*}_{2p}$) molecular orbitals. The $p$ orbitals in shells of higher $n$ give molecular orbitals of the same basic shape.

**FIGURE 9.16** Combinations of $p$ atomic orbitals to yield $\sigma$ and $\pi$ molecular orbitals.

## Molecular Orbitals from Atomic $p$ Orbitals

With the principles of molecular orbital theory in place, we are ready to account for bonding in such important homonuclear diatomic molecules as $N_2$, $O_2$, and $F_2$. To describe the bonding in these molecules, we will have to use both $s$ and $p$ valence orbitals in forming molecular orbitals.

For $p$-block elements, sigma-bonding and antibonding molecular orbitals are formed by their $s$ orbitals interacting as in Figure 9.14. Similarly, it is possible for a $p$ orbital on one atom to interact with a $p$ orbital on the other atom to produce a pair of $\sigma$-bonding and $\sigma^{*}$-antibonding molecular orbitals (Figure 9.16a).

In addition, each $p$-block atom has *two* $p$ orbitals in planes perpendicular to the $\sigma$ bond connecting the two atoms. These $p$ orbitals can interact in a side-by-side fashion to give *two* $\pi$-bonding molecular orbitals ($\pi_p$) and *two* $\pi$-antibonding molecular orbitals ($\pi^{*}_p$) (Figure 9.16b).

## Electron Configurations for Homonuclear Molecules for Boron Through Fluorine

Orbital interactions in a second-period, homonuclear, diatomic molecule lead to the energy level diagram in Figure 9.17. Electron assignments can be made using this diagram, and the results for the diatomic molecules $B_2$ through $F_2$ are assembled in Table 9.1, which has two noteworthy features.

First, notice the correlation between the electron configurations and the bond orders, bond lengths, and bond energies at the bottom of Table 9.1. As the bond order between a pair of atoms increases, the energy required to break the bond increases, and the bond distance decreases. Dinitrogen, $N_2$, with a bond order of 3, has the largest bond energy and shortest bond distance.

Second, notice the configuration for dioxygen, $O_2$. Dioxygen has 12 valence electrons (six from each atom), so it has the molecular orbital configuration

$$O_2 \text{ MO Configuration:} \quad [\text{core electrons}](\sigma_{2s})^2(\sigma^{*}_{2s})^2(\sigma_{2p})^2(\pi_{2p})^4(\pi^{*}_{2p})^2$$

This configuration leads to a bond order of 2 in agreement with experiment, and it specifies two unpaired electrons (in $\pi^{*}_{2p}$ molecular orbitals). Thus, molecular orbital theory succeeds where valence bond theory fails. MO theory explains both the observed bond order and, as illustrated in Figure 9.12, the paramagnetic behavior of $O_2$.

• **Phases of Atomic Orbitals and Molecular Orbitals** Recall from page 287 in Chapter 6 that electron orbitals describe electron waves and as such have positive and negative phases. For this reason, the atomic orbitals in Figure 9.16 are drawn with two different colors. Looking at the $p$ orbitals in Figure 9.16, you see that a bonding MO is formed when $p$ orbitals with the same wave function sign overlap ($+$ with $+$). An antibonding orbital arises if they overlap out of phase ($+$ with $-$). (Wave function phases are signified by different colors.)

• **HOMO and LUMO** Chemists often refer to the highest energy MO that contains electrons as the HOMO (for "highest occupied molecular orbital"). For $O_2$, this is the $\pi^{*}_{2p}$ orbital. Chemists also use the term LUMO for the "lowest unoccupied molecular orbital." For $O_2$, this would be $\sigma^{*}_{2p}$.

**FIGURE 9.17** Molecular orbitals for homonuclear diatomic molecules of second period elements

(a) Energy level diagram for $B_2$, $C_2$, and $N_2$. Although the diagram leads to the correct conclusions regarding bond order and magnetic behavior for $O_2$ and $F_2$, the energy ordering of the MOs in this figure is correct only for $B_2$, $C_2$, and $N_2$. For $O_2$ and $F_2$, the $\sigma_{2p}$ MO is lower in energy than the $\pi_{2p}$ MOs. See *A Closer Look,* page 423.

(b) Calculated molecular orbitals for $N_2$. (Color scheme: occupied MOs are blue/green. Unoccupied MOs are red/yellow. The different colors in a given orbital reflect the different phases [positive or negative signs] of the wave functions.)

## EXAMPLE 9.8    Electron Configuration for a Homonuclear Diatomic Ion

**Problem**  Potassium superoxide, $KO_2$, is one of the products from the reaction of K and $O_2$. This is an ionic compound, and the anion is the superoxide ion, $O_2^-$. Write the molecular orbital electron configuration for the ion. Predict its bond order and magnetic behavior.

**What Do You Know?**  The 2s and 2p orbitals on the two oxygen atoms can be combined to give the series of molecular orbitals shown in Table 9.1. The $O_2^-$ ion has 13 valence electrons.

**Strategy**  Use the energy level diagram for $O_2$ in Table 9.1 to generate the electron configuration of this ion, and use Equation 9.1 to determine the bond order. The magnetism is determined by whether there are unpaired electrons.

**Solution**  The MO electron configuration for $O_2^-$ is

$O_2^-$ MO Configuration:    [core electrons]$(\sigma_{2s})^2(\sigma^*_{2s})^2(\sigma_{2p})^2(\pi_{2p})^4(\pi^*_{2p})^3$

The ion is predicted to be paramagnetic to the extent of one unpaired electron, a prediction confirmed by experiment. The bond order is 1.5, because there are eight bonding electrons and five antibonding electrons. The bond order for $O_2^-$ is lower than $O_2$ so we predict the O—O bond in $O_2^-$ should be longer than the oxygen–oxygen bond in $O_2$. The superoxide ion in fact has an O—O bond length of 134 pm, whereas the bond length in $O_2$ is 121 pm.

**Think about Your Answer**  The superoxide ion ($O_2^-$), contains an odd number of electrons. This is another diatomic species (in addition to NO and $O_2$) for which it is not possible to write a Lewis structure that accurately represents the bonding.

**Check Your Understanding**

The cations $O_2^+$ and $N_2^+$ are important components of Earth's upper atmosphere. Write the electron configuration for $O_2^+$. Predict its bond order and magnetic behavior.

**A CLOSER LOOK**

# Molecular Orbitals for Molecules Formed from *p*-Block Elements

Several features of the molecular orbital energy level diagram in Figure 9.17 should be described in more detail.

(a) The bonding and antibonding $\sigma$ orbitals from 2s interactions are lower in energy than the $\sigma$ and $\pi$ MOs from 2p interactions. The reason is that 2s orbitals have a lower energy than 2p orbitals in the separated atoms.

(b) The energy separation of the bonding and antibonding orbitals is greater for $\sigma_{2p}$ than for $\pi_{2p}$. This happens because p orbitals overlap to a greater extent when they are oriented head to head (to give $\sigma_{2p}$ MOs) than when they are side by side (to give $\pi_{2p}$ MOs). The greater the orbital overlap, the greater the stabilization of the bonding MO and the greater the destabilization of the antibonding MO.

You may have been surprised that Figure 9.17 shows the $\pi_{2p}$ orbitals lower in energy than the $\sigma_{2p}$ orbital. Why would these orbitals be lower? A more sophisticated approach takes into account the "mixing" of s and p atomic orbitals, which have similar energies. This causes the $\sigma_{2s}$ and $\sigma^*_{2s}$ molecular orbitals to be lower in energy than otherwise expected, and the $\sigma_{2p}$ and $\sigma^*_{2p}$ orbitals to be higher in energy.

The mixing of s and p orbitals is important for $B_2$, $C_2$, and $N_2$, so Figure 9.17 applies strictly only to these molecules. For $O_2$ and $F_2$, $\sigma_{2p}$ is lower in energy than $\pi_{2p}$, and Table 9.1 takes this into account.

**Table 9.1  Molecular Orbital Occupations and Physical Data for Homonuclear Diatomic Molecules of Second-Period Elements**

| | $B_2$ | $C_2$ | $N_2$ | | $O_2$ | $F_2$ |
|---|---|---|---|---|---|---|
| $\sigma^*_{2p}$ | ☐ | ☐ | ☐ | $\sigma^*_{2p}$ | ☐ | ☐ |
| $\pi^*_{2p}$ | ☐☐ | ☐☐ | ☐☐ | $\pi^*_{2p}$ | ↑ ↑ | ↑↓ ↑↓ |
| $\sigma_{2p}$ | ☐ | ☐ | ↑↓ | $\pi_{2p}$ | ↑↓ ↑↓ | ↑↓ ↑↓ |
| $\pi_{2p}$ | ↑ ↑ | ↑↓ ↑↓ | ↑↓ ↑↓ | $\sigma_{2p}$ | ↑↓ | ↑↓ |
| $\sigma^*_{2s}$ | ↑↓ | ↑↓ | ↑↓ | $\sigma^*_{2s}$ | ↑↓ | ↑↓ |
| $\sigma_{2s}$ | ↑↓ | ↑↓ | ↑↓ | $\sigma_{2s}$ | ↑↓ | ↑↓ |
| | | | | | | |
| Bond order | One | Two | Three | | Two | One |
| Bond-dissociation energy (kJ/mol) | 290 | 620 | 945 | | 498 | 155 |
| Bond distance (pm) | 159 | 131 | 110 | | 121 | 143 |
| Observed magnetic behavior (paramagnetic or diamagnetic) | Para | Dia | Dia | | Para | Dia |

*The $\pi_{2p}$ and $\sigma_{2p}$ orbitals are inverted in energy on going to elements later in the second period. See *A Closer Look* at the top of this page.

## Electron Configurations for Heteronuclear Diatomic Molecules

The molecules CO, NO, and ClF, containing two different elements, are examples of *heteronuclear* diatomic molecules. Molecular orbital descriptions for heteronuclear diatomic molecules resemble those for homonuclear diatomic molecules, but there are significant differences.

Carbon monoxide is an important molecule, so it is worth looking at its bonding. First, in its MO diagram (Figure 9.18) notice that similar atomic orbitals for the individual atoms have different energies. The 2s and 2p orbitals of O are at a lower relative energy than the 2s and 2p orbitals of C (◄ page 312). Second, these can nonetheless be combined in the same way as in homonuclear diatomic molecules to give an ordering of molecular orbitals that is similar to homonuclear diatomics.

The 10 valence electrons of CO are added to the available molecular orbitals from lowest to highest energy as we have done before, and the molecular electron configuration for CO is

*CO MO Configuration:*    [core electrons]$(\sigma_{2s})^2(\sigma^*_{2s})^2(\pi_{2p})^4(\sigma_{2p})^2$

This clearly shows that CO has a bond order of 3, as expected from an electron dot structure.

**FIGURE 9.18 The molecular orbitals of carbon monoxide and the HOMO of the molecule.** The highest occupied molecular orbital (the HOMO) for CO, a sigma orbital, contains an electron pair that chemists identify as the lone pair on the C atom. The CO dipole is small (0.12 D) because the lone pair on the carbon atom slightly balances the greater electronegativity of O relative to C. (Compare with $NF_3$ on page 380.)

## Resonance and MO Theory

Ozone, $O_3$, is a simple triatomic molecule with equal oxygen–oxygen bond lengths. Equal X—O bond lengths are also observed in other molecules and ions, such as $SO_2$, $NO_2^-$, and $HCO_2^-$. Valence bond theory introduced resonance to rationalize the equivalent bonding to the oxygen atoms in these structures, but MO theory provides a useful view of this problem.

To understand the bonding in ozone, let's begin by looking at the valence bond picture. First, assume that all three O atoms are $sp^2$ hybridized. The central atom uses its $sp^2$ hybrid orbitals to form two $\sigma$ bonds and to accommodate a lone pair. The terminal atoms use their $sp^2$ hybrid orbitals to form one $\sigma$ bond and to accommodate two lone pairs. Seven of the nine valence electron pairs in $O_3$ are either lone pairs or bonding pairs in the $\sigma$ framework of $O_3$ (Figure 9.19a). The $\pi$ bond in ozone arises from the two remaining pairs (Figure 9.19b). Because we have assumed that each oxygen atom in $O_3$ is $sp^2$ hybridized, an unhybridized $p$ orbital perpendicular to the $O_3$ plane remains on each of the three oxygen atoms. These orbitals are in the correct orientation to form $\pi$ bonds.

To simplify matters, let's now apply MO theory only to these three $p$ orbitals that can be involved in $\pi$ bonding in ozone (rather than on all of the orbitals in the molecule). A principle of MO theory is that the number of molecular orbitals must equal the number of atomic orbitals. Thus, the three $2p$ atomic orbitals must be combined in a way that forms three molecular orbitals.

One $\pi_p$ MO for ozone is a bonding orbital because the three $p$ orbitals are "in phase" across the molecule (Figure 9.19b). Another $\pi_p$ MO is an antibonding orbital because the atomic orbital on the central atom is "out of phase" with the terminal atom $p$ orbitals. The third $\pi_p$ MO is a *nonbonding* orbital because the middle $p$ orbital does not participate in the MO. (As the name implies, electrons in this molecular orbital neither help nor hinder the bonding in the molecule.)

One of the two pairs of $\pi_p$ electrons of $O_3$ occupies the lowest energy or $\pi_p$-bonding MO, which is delocalized, or "spread over," the molecule (just as the resonance hybrid of valence bond theory implies). The $\pi_p$-nonbonding orbital is also occupied, but the electrons in this orbital are concentrated near the two

Lewis structure of $O_3$.
All O atoms are $sp^2$
hybridized.

molecular model

Representation of the $\sigma$ bonding
framework of $O_3$ using $sp^2$ hybrid orbitals

$\sigma$ bond        $\sigma$ bond

**(a)** Ozone, $O_3$, has equal-length oxygen–oxygen bonds, which, in valence bond theory, would be ratio-nalized by resonance structures. The $\sigma$ bonding framework of $O_3$ is formed by utilizing $sp^2$ hybrid orbitals on each O atom. These accommodate two $\sigma$ bonds and five lone pairs.

**FIGURE 9.19.** A bonding model for ozone, $O_3$.

Node  Node

$\pi$ antibonding MO
= LUMO

Node

$\pi$ nonbonding MO
= HOMO

$\pi$ bonding MO

ENERGY

**(b)** The $\pi$ molecular orbital diagram for ozone. Notice that, as in the other MO diagrams illustrated (especially Figure 9.20), the energy of the molecular orbitals increases as the number of nodes increases.

terminal oxygens. Thus, there is a net of only one pair of $\pi_p$-bonding electrons for two O—O bonds, giving a $\pi$ bond order for $O_3$ of 0.5. Because the $\sigma$ bond order is 1.0 and the $\pi$ bond order is 0.5, the net oxygen–oxygen bond order is 1.5—the same value given by valence bond theory.

The observation that two of the $\pi$ molecular orbitals for ozone extend over three atoms illustrates an important point regarding molecular orbital theory: *Orbitals can extend beyond two atoms.* In valence bond theory, in contrast, all representations for bonding are based on being able to localize pairs of electrons in bonds between two atoms. To further illustrate the MO approach, look again at benzene (Figure 9.20). On page 416, we noted that the $\pi$ electrons in this molecule were spread out over all six carbon atoms. We can now see how the same case can be made with MO theory. Six $p$ orbitals contribute to the $\pi$ system. Based on the

ENERGY

$\pi$ antibonding MOs

$\pi$ bonding MOs

**FIGURE 9.20 Molecular orbital energy level diagram for benzene.** Because there are six unhybridized $p$ orbitals (one on each C atom), six $\pi$ molecular orbitals can be formed—three bonding and three antibonding. The three bonding molecular orbitals accommodate the six $\pi$ electrons.

premise that the number of molecular orbitals must equal the number of atomic orbitals, there must be six $\pi$ molecular orbitals in benzene. An energy level diagram for benzene shows that the six $\pi$ electrons reside in the three lowest-energy (bonding) molecular orbitals.

---

**CASE STUDY**

# Green Chemistry, Safe Dyes, and Molecular Orbitals

An important obligation of chemists is not only to search for useful materials but also to ensure they are safe to use and to produce them in the safest manner possible. This is the essence of "green chemistry," and one recent success has been in the dye industry.

Dyes and pigments have been used for centuries because humans want colorful clothing and objects that have color. Dyes were extracted from plants such as onion skins, carrots, turmeric, butternuts, walnuts, tea, red cabbage, and fruits and berries. Some came from animals, and one, Tyrian purple (Figure A), was especially prized. This dye, which was known to the ancient Greeks, is extracted from a marine gastropod, the *Murex brandaris*. The problem is that it takes over 12,000 of these organisms to produce 1.4 g of the dye, which is only enough to dye a portion of one garment. This is the reason the dye is also called *royal purple* because only royalty could afford to acquire it.

The first synthetic dye was produced quite by accident in 1856. William Perkin, then 18, was searching for an antimalarial drug, but the route he chose to make it led

instead to the dye mauveine. Because dyes were so highly prized, his discovery led to the synthesis of many more dyes. Indeed, some say Perkin's discovery led to the modern chemical industry.

Chemists have developed large numbers of dyes, among them azo dyes, so named because they contain a N=N double bond (an azo group). One example is "butter yellow" (Figure B). It was given this name because it was originally used to give butter a more appealing yellow color. The problem is that the molecule is carcinogenic.

The fact that some dyes were unsafe led chemists to look for ways to achieve the desired color and to ensure they were not toxic. In the case of butter yellow, the solution was to add an –$NO_2$ group to the molecule to give a new yellow dye that is easy to synthesize and safe to use.

The structure of Tyrian purple is typical of many dyes. Notice that it has alternating double bonds (C=C and C=O) extending across the molecule. Azo dyes similarly have extended frameworks of alternating double bonds. Indeed, all organic dye molecules have extended $\pi$ bonding networks, and it is this that leads to their color. The extended $\pi$

bonds give rise to low-energy $\pi$ antibonding molecular orbitals. When visible light strikes such a molecule, an electron can be excited from a bonding or nonbonding molecular orbital to an antibonding molecular orbital, and light is absorbed (Figure C). Your eye sees the wavelengths of light not absorbed by the molecule, so it has the color of the remaining wavelengths of light. For example, on page 190 you see a case where a substance absorbs wavelengths of light in the blue region of the spectrum, so you see red light.

## Questions:

1. What is the empirical formula of Tyrian purple?

2. Butter yellow absorbs light with a wavelength of 408 nm, whereas the nitrated form absorbs at 478 nm. Which absorbs the higher energy light?

3. How many alternating double bonds are there in Tyrian purple? In nitrated butter yellow?

**Answers to these questions are available in Appendix N.**

Public Domain image courtesy Brochis

**FIGURE A  The structure of Tyrian purple or 6,6′-dibromoindigo.** Its formula is $C_{16}H_8N_2O_2Br_2$.

butter yellow

nitrated butter yellow

**FIGURE B  The structure of "butter yellow" and "nitrated butter yellow."** The first is a synthetic dye originally used to color butter. It is in the class of azo dyes, all characterized by an N=N double bond. The nitrated version is safe for human consumption.

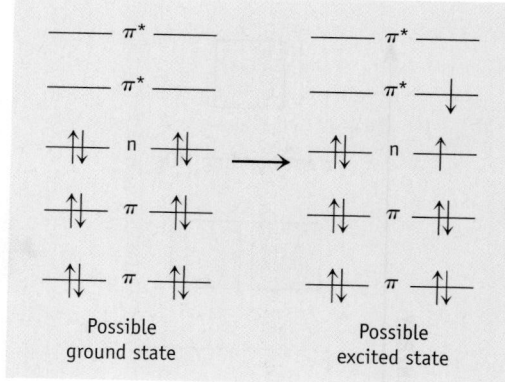

Possible ground state          Possible excited state

**FIGURE C** Light is absorbed by an azo dye by the promotion of an electron from a nonbonding molecular orbital to an antibonding $\pi$ molecular orbital. (Light absorption by all molecules occurs by promotion of an electron from a low-lying to a higher-lying molecular orbital.)

**A CLOSER LOOK**

# Three-Center Bonds and Hybrid Orbitals with *d* Orbitals

Although a large majority of known compounds can be described by Lewis electron dot pictures, nature (and chemistry) has a surprise now and then. You have already seen several examples (most notably $O_2$ and NO) where it is not possible to draw simple dot structures. In these instances we turned to MO theory to understand the bonding.

An interesting chemical species is the ion $HF_2^-$, formed in a product-favored reaction between $F^-$ and HF. This ion has a linear structure (F—H—F) with the hydrogen midway between the two fluorine atoms. Of the 16 valence electrons in the ion, there are 4 that can be utilized in bonding (the other 12 are lone pairs on F).

But how can we account for bonding in the ion? The best way is to use MO theory. We begin with three atomic orbitals, the $2p_z$ orbitals on each fluorine atom and the 1s orbital on hydrogen.

valence orbitals available in F—H—F$^-$

**The bonding MO of the FHF$^-$ ion extends across the ion. The three-center bond has a bond order of $\frac{1}{2}$.**

As in the model to account for π bonding in ozone (Figure 9.19), the 1s and $2p_z$ orbitals combine to form three molecular orbitals, one bonding, one nonbonding, and one antibonding. One pair of valence electrons is placed in the bonding MO and one in the nonbonding MO, to give a net of one bond. This result, which nicely accounts for the bonding, is often referred to as a *three-center/four-electron bond* model.

Another example for which an acceptable Lewis dot structure cannot be drawn is for diborane, $B_2H_6$, the simplest member of a large group of compounds. As the structure below shows, each boron atom has distorted tetrahedral geometry.

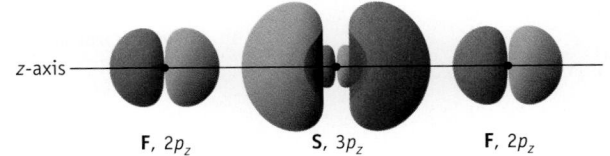

(a)    (b)

The molecule has two terminal hydrogen atoms bonded to each boron atom, and two hydrogen atoms bridge the two boron atoms. Chemists refer to diborane as "electron deficient" because two B atoms and six H atoms do not contribute enough electrons for eight, two-electron bonds.

We can again account for the bonding in this molecule using MO theory with a three-center bond involving an H atom. Let's begin by assuming that each B atom is $sp^3$ hybridized. The four terminal H atoms bond to the B atoms with two-electron bonds using 8 of the 12 electrons and two of the $sp^3$ hybrid orbitals on each B atom. The 4 remaining electrons account for the B—H—B bridges. Three molecular orbitals encompassing the B—H—B atoms in each bridge can be constructed from the remaining two $sp^3$ hybrid orbitals on each B atom and a H atom 1s orbital. Again, one MO is bonding, one is nonbonding, and one is antibonding. Two electrons are assigned to the bonding orbital, giving us a *three-center/two-electron* bond. Not surprisingly, this kind of bond is weaker than a typical two-electron/two-center bond, and diborane dissociates to two $BH_3$ molecules at fairly low temperatures.

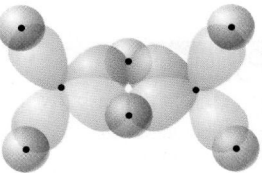

**An overlap of $sp^3$ orbitals, one from each B atom, and an H 1s creates two, three-center/two-electron bonds.**

And finally we return to an issue introduced earlier: *whether* d *orbitals are involved in bonding in some main group element compounds.* Theory suggests that *d* orbitals are not significantly involved in bonding in ions such as $SO_4^{2-}$ and $PO_4^{3-}$ (page 359). If we accept the premise that *d* orbitals are too high in energy to be used in bonding in main group element compounds, do we need to describe $PF_5$ and $SF_6$ bonding, for example, using $sp^3d$ and $sp^3d^2$ hybrid orbitals? Another bonding model is needed and molecular orbital theory provides the alternative without the use of *d* orbitals.

Consider $SF_6$, for instance. The molecule has a total of 48 valence electrons. Of these, 36 are involved as lone pairs on the F atoms, so 12 electrons remain to account for 6 S-F bonds. Let's look specifically at the bonding between sulfur and two fluorine atoms across from each other along each of the three axes.

Along the z-axis, for example, bonding, nonbonding, and antibonding orbitals can be constructed from combinations of the $3p_z$ orbital on sulfur and the two $2p_z$ orbitals on fluorine. Four electrons are placed in the bonding and nonbonding orbitals. This description is repeated on the x- and y-axis, which means that two electron pairs are involved in the F—S—F group along each axis. That is, each of the three F—S—F "groups" is bonded with a three-center/four-electron bond, thus accounting nicely for the bonding in $SF_6$ without using *d* orbitals.

**REVIEW & CHECK FOR SECTION 9.3**

1. What is the N—O bond order in nitrogen monoxide, NO?

   (a) 2          (b) 2.5          (c) 3.0          (d) 1

2. What is the HOMO in the peroxide ion, $O_2^{2-}$?

   (a) $\pi_{2p}$      (b) $\pi^*_{2p}$      (c) $\sigma^*_{2p}$      (d) $\sigma^*_{2s}$

3. Which of the following species is diamagnetic?

   (a) $O_2$          (b) $B_2$          (c) $C_2$          (d) $N_2^+$

4. Among the known dioxygen species ($O_2^+$, $O_2$, $O_2^-$, and $O_2^{2-}$), which is expected to have the shortest bond length?

   (a) $O_2^+$          (b) $O_2$          (c) $O_2^-$          (d) $O_2^{2-}$

## CHAPTER GOALS REVISITED

*Now that you have studied this chapter, you should ask whether you have met the chapter goals. In particular, you should be able to:*

**Understand the differences between valence bond theory and molecular orbital theory**

a. Describe the main features of valence bond theory and molecular orbital theory, the two commonly used theories for covalent bonding (Section 9.1).

b. Recognize that the premise for valence bond theory is that bonding results from the overlap of atomic orbitals. By virtue of the overlap of orbitals, electrons are concentrated (or localized) between two atoms (Section 9.2).

c. Distinguish how sigma ($\sigma$) and pi ($\pi$) bonds arise. For $\sigma$ bonding, orbitals overlap in a head-to-head fashion, concentrating electrons along the bond axis. Sideways overlap of $p$ atomic orbitals results in $\pi$ bond formation, with electron density above and below the molecular plane (Section 9.2).

d. Understand how molecules having double bonds can have isomeric forms. **Study Questions: 19, 20.**

**Identify the hybridization of an atom in a molecule or ion**

a. Use the concept of hybridization to rationalize molecular structure (Section 9.2). **Study Questions: 1–18, 31–33, 37, 42, 45, 46, 48, 54, 55, 57–62, and Go Chemistry Module 14.**

| Hybrid Orbitals | Atomic Orbitals Used | Number of Hybrid Orbitals | Electron-Pair Geometry |
|---|---|---|---|
| $sp$ | $s + p$ | 2 | Linear |
| $sp^2$ | $s + p + p$ | 3 | Trigonal-planar |
| $sp^3$ | $s + p + p + p$ | 4 | Tetrahedral |
| $sp^3d$ | $s + p + p + p + d$ | 5 | Trigonal-bipyramidal |
| $sp^3d^2$ | $s + p + p + p + d + d$ | 6 | Octahedral |

**Understand the differences between bonding and antibonding molecular orbitals and be able to write the molecular orbital configurations for simple diatomic molecules.**

a. Understand molecular orbital theory (Section 9.3), in which atomic orbitals are combined to form bonding orbitals, nonbonding orbitals, or antibonding orbitals that are delocalized over several atoms. In this description, the electrons of the molecule or ion are assigned to the orbitals beginning with the one at lowest energy, according to the Pauli exclusion principle and Hund's rule.

b. Use molecular orbital theory to explain the properties of $O_2$ and other diatomic molecules. **Study Questions: 21–30, 49–53.**

# Key Equation

**Equation 9.1 (page 419)** Used to calculate the order of a bond from the molecular orbital electron configuration.

Bond order = 1/2 (number of electrons in bonding MOs
— number of electrons in antibonding MOs)

## Study Questions

 WL Interactive versions of these questions are assignable in OWL.

▲ denotes challenging questions.

Blue-numbered questions have answers in Appendix R and fully worked solutions in the *Student Solutions Manual*.

## Practicing Skills

### Valence Bond Theory
*(See Examples 9.1–9.5.)*

1. Draw the Lewis structure for chloroform, $CHCl_3$. What are its electron-pair and molecular geometries? What orbitals on C, H, and Cl overlap to form bonds involving these elements?

2. Draw the Lewis structure for $NF_3$. What are its electron-pair and molecular geometries? What is the hybridization of the nitrogen atom? What orbitals on N and F overlap to form bonds between these elements?

3. Draw the Lewis structure for hydroxylamine, $H_2NOH$. What is the hybridization for nitrogen and oxygen in this molecule? What orbitals overlap to form the bond between nitrogen and oxygen?

4. Draw the Lewis structure for 1,1-dimethylhydrazine $[(CH_3)_2NNH_2$, a compound used as a rocket fuel]. What is the hybridization for the two nitrogen atoms in this molecule? What orbitals overlap to form the bond between the nitrogen atoms?

5. Draw the Lewis structure for carbonyl fluoride, $COF_2$. What are its electron-pair geometry and molecular geometry? What is the hybridization of the carbon atom? What orbitals overlap to form the $\sigma$ and $\pi$ bonds between carbon and oxygen?

6. Draw the Lewis structure for acetamide, $CH_3CONH_2$. What are its electron-pair geometry and molecular geometry? What is the hybridization of the central C atom? What orbitals overlap to form the $\sigma$ and $\pi$ bonds between carbon and oxygen?

7. Specify the electron-pair and molecular geometry for each underlined atom in the following list. Describe the hybrid orbital set used by this atom in each molecule or ion.
   (a) $\underline{B}Br_3$   (b) $\underline{C}O_2$   (c) $\underline{C}H_2Cl_2$   (d) $\underline{C}O_3{}^{2-}$

8. Specify the electron-pair and molecular geometry for each underlined atom in the following list. Describe the hybrid orbital set used by this atom in each molecule or ion.
   (a) $\underline{C}Se_2$   (b) $\underline{S}O_2$   (c) $\underline{C}H_2O$   (d) $\underline{N}H_4{}^+$

9. What hybrid orbital set is used by each of the indicated atoms in the molecules below?
   (a) the carbon atoms and the oxygen atom in dimethyl ether, $CH_3OCH_3$
   (b) each carbon atom in propene

$$H_3C-\underset{\underset{H}{|}}{C}=CH_2$$

   (c) the two carbon atoms and the nitrogen atom in the amino acid glycine

$$H-\underset{\underset{\cdot\cdot}{|}}{N}-\underset{\underset{H}{|}}{\overset{\overset{H}{|}}{C}}-\overset{\overset{:O:}{\|}}{C}-\overset{\cdot\cdot}{\underset{\cdot\cdot}{O}}-H$$

10. What is the hybrid orbital set used by each of the underlined atoms in the following molecules?
   (a) $H-\underset{\underset{H}{|}}{\overset{\overset{H}{|}}{N}}-\overset{\overset{:O:}{\|}}{C}-\underset{\underset{H}{|}}{N}-H$
   (c) $H-\underset{\underset{H}{|}}{\overset{\overset{H}{|}}{C}}=\underline{C}-\underline{C}\equiv N:$
   (b) $H_3\underline{C}-\underset{\underset{H}{|}}{C}=\underset{\underset{H}{|}}{\overset{\overset{H}{|}}{C}}-\underline{C}=\overset{\cdot\cdot}{\underset{\cdot\cdot}{O}}$

11. Draw the Lewis structure, and then specify the electron-pair and molecular geometries for each of the following molecules or ions. Identify the hybridization of the central atom.
   (a) $SiF_6{}^{2-}$   (b) $SeF_4$   (c) $ICl_2{}^-$   (d) $XeF_4$

12. Draw the Lewis structure, and then specify the electron-pair and molecular geometries for each of the following molecules or ions. Identify the hybridization of the central atom.
   (a) $XeOF_4$          (c) central S in $SOF_4$
   (b) $BrF_5$           (d) central Br in $Br_3{}^-$

13. Draw the Lewis structures of the acid $HPO_2F_2$ and its anion $PO_2F_2{}^-$. What is the molecular geometry and hybridization for the phosphorus atom in each species? (H is bonded to an O atom in the acid.)

14. Draw the Lewis structures of $HSO_3F$ and $SO_3F^-$. What is the molecular geometry and hybridization for the sulfur atom in each species? (H is bonded to an O atom in the acid.)

15. What is the hybridization of the carbon atom in phosgene, $Cl_2CO$? Give a complete description of the $\sigma$ and $\pi$ bonding in this molecule.

16. What is the hybridization of the carbon atoms in benzene, $C_6H_6$? Describe the $\sigma$ and $\pi$ bonding in this compound.

17. What is the electron-pair and molecular geometry around the central S atom in thionyl chloride, $SOCl_2$? What is the hybridization of sulfur in this compound?

18. What is the electron-pair and molecular geometry around the central S atom in sulfuryl chloride, $SO_2Cl_2$? What is the hybridization of sulfur in this compound?

19. The arrangement of groups attached to the C atoms involved in a C=C double bond leads to *cis* and *trans* isomers. For each compound below, draw the other isomer.

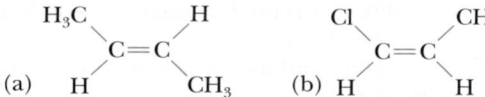

(a)     (b)

20. For each compound below, decide whether *cis* and *trans* isomers are possible. If isomerism is possible, draw the other isomer.

(a)

(b)     (c)

## Molecular Orbital Theory
*(See Examples 9.6–9.8.)*

21. The hydrogen molecular ion, $H_2^+$, can be detected spectroscopically. Write the electron configuration of the ion in molecular orbital terms. What is the bond order of the ion? Is the hydrogen–hydrogen bond stronger or weaker in $H_2^+$ than in $H_2$?

22. Give the electron configurations for the ions $Li_2^+$ and $Li_2^-$ in molecular orbital terms. Compare the Li—Li bond order in these ions with the bond order in $Li_2$.

23. Calcium carbide, $CaC_2$, contains the acetylide ion, $C_2^{2-}$. Sketch the molecular orbital energy level diagram for the ion. How many net $\sigma$ and $\pi$ bonds does the ion have? What is the carbon–carbon bond order? How has the bond order changed on adding electrons to $C_2$ to obtain $C_2^{2-}$? Is the $C_2^{2-}$ ion paramagnetic?

24. Platinum hexafluoride is an extremely strong oxidizing agent. It can even oxidize oxygen, its reaction with $O_2$ giving $O_2^+PtF_6^-$. Sketch the molecular orbital energy level diagram for the $O_2^+$ ion. How many net $\sigma$ and $\pi$ bonds does the ion have? What is the oxygen–oxygen bond order? How has the bond order changed on taking away electrons from $O_2$ to obtain $O_2^+$? Is the $O_2^+$ ion paramagnetic?

25. When sodium and oxygen react, one of the products obtained is sodium peroxide, $Na_2O_2$. The anion in this compound is the peroxide ion, $O_2^{2-}$. Write the electron configuration for this ion in molecular orbital terms, and then compare it with the electron configuration of the $O_2$ molecule with respect to the following criteria:
    (a) magnetic character
    (b) net number of $\sigma$ and $\pi$ bonds
    (c) bond order
    (d) oxygen–oxygen bond length

26. When potassium and oxygen react, one of the products obtained is potassium superoxide, $KO_2$. The anion in this compound is the superoxide ion, $O_2^-$. Write the electron configuration for this ion in molecular orbital terms, and then compare it with the electron configuration of the $O_2$ molecule with respect to the following criteria:
    (a) magnetic character
    (b) net number of $\sigma$ and $\pi$ bonds
    (c) bond order
    (d) oxygen–oxygen bond length

*Courtesy of the Mine Safety Appliances Company*

**A closed-circuit breathing apparatus that generates its own oxygen.** One source of oxygen is potassium superoxide ($KO_2$). Both carbon dioxide and moisture exhaled by the wearer into the breathing tube react with the $KO_2$ to generate oxygen.

27. Among the following, which has the shortest bond and which has the longest: $Li_2$, $B_2$, $C_2$, $N_2$, $O_2$?

28. Consider the following list of small molecules and ions: $C_2$, $O_2^-$, $CN^-$, $O_2$, $CO$, $NO$, $NO^+$, $C_2^{2-}$, $OF^-$. Identify
    (a) all species that have a bond order of 3
    (b) all species that are paramagnetic
    (c) species that have a fractional bond order

29. Assume the energy level diagram shown in Figure 9.18 can be applied to the heteronuclear molecule ClO.
    (a) Write the electron configuration for chlorine monoxide, ClO.
    (b) What is the highest-energy, occupied molecular orbital?
    (c) Is the molecule diamagnetic or paramagnetic?
    (d) What is the net number of $\sigma$ and $\pi$ bonds? What is the ClO bond order?

30. The nitrosyl ion, $NO^+$, has an interesting chemistry.
    (a) Is $NO^+$ diamagnetic or paramagnetic? If paramagnetic, how many unpaired electrons does it have?
    (b) Assume the molecular orbital diagram shown in Figure 9.18 applies to $NO^+$. What is the highest-energy molecular orbital occupied by electrons?
    (c) What is the nitrogen–oxygen bond order?
    (d) Is the N—O bond in $NO^+$ stronger or weaker than the bond in NO?

# General Questions

*These questions are not designated as to type or location in the chapter. They may combine several concepts.*

31. Draw the Lewis structure for $AlF_4^-$. What are its electron-pair and molecular geometries? What orbitals on Al and F overlap to form bonds between these elements? What are the formal charges on the atoms? Is this a reasonable charge distribution?

32. Draw the Lewis structure for $ClF_3$. What are its electron-pair and molecular geometries? What is the hybridization of the chlorine atom? What orbitals on Cl and F overlap to form bonds between these elements?

33. What is the O—S—O angle and the hybrid orbital set used by sulfur in each of the following molecules or ions?
    (a) $SO_2$  (b) $SO_3$  (c) $SO_3^{2-}$  (d) $SO_4^{2-}$

    Do all have the same value for the O—S—O angle? Does the S atom in all these species use the same hybrid orbitals?

34. Sketch the Lewis structures of $ClF_2^+$ and $ClF_2^-$. What are the electron-pair and molecular geometries of each ion? Do both have the same F—Cl—F angle? What hybrid orbital set is used by Cl in each ion?

35. Sketch the resonance structures for the nitrite ion, $NO_2^-$. Describe the electron-pair and molecular geometries of the ion. From these geometries, decide on the O—N—O bond angle, the average NO bond order, and the N atom hybridization.

36. Sketch the resonance structures for the nitrate ion, $NO_3^-$. Is the hybridization of the N atom the same or different in each structure? Describe the orbitals involved in bond formation by the central N atom.

37. Sketch the resonance structures for the $N_2O$ molecule. Is the hybridization of the N atoms the same or different in each structure? Describe the orbitals involved in bond formation by the central N atom.

38. Compare the structure and bonding in $CO_2$ and $CO_3^{2-}$ with regard to the O—C—O bond angles, the CO bond order, and the C atom hybridization.

39. Numerous molecules are detected in deep space. Three of them are illustrated here.

Ethylene oxide

Acetaldehyde

Vinyl alcohol

(a) Are these compounds isomers?
(b) Indicate the hybridization of each C atom in each molecule.
(c) What is the value of the H—C—H angle in each of the three molecules?
(d) Are any of these molecules polar?
(e) Which molecule should have the strongest carbon–carbon bond? The strongest carbon–oxygen bond?

40. Acrolein, a component of photochemical smog, has a pungent odor and irritates eyes and mucous membranes.

(a) What are the hybridizations of carbon atoms 1 and 2?
(b) What are the approximate values of angles *A*, *B*, and *C*?
(c) Is *cis-trans* isomerism possible here?

41. The organic compound below is a member of a class known as oximes.

$$H-\underset{\underset{H}{|}}{\overset{\overset{H}{|}}{C}}-C=N:$$

with $:\ddot{O}-H$

(a) What are the hybridizations of the two C atoms and of the N atom?
(b) What is the approximate C—N—O angle?

42. The compound sketched below is acetylsalicylic acid, commonly known as aspirin.

(a) What are the approximate values of the angles marked *A*, *B*, *C*, and *D*?
(b) What hybrid orbitals are used by carbon atoms 1, 2, and 3?

43. Phosphoserine is a less-common amino acid.

(a) Describe the hybridizations of atoms 1 through 5.
(b) What are the approximate values of the bond angles *A*, *B*, *C*, and *D*?
(c) What are the most polar bonds in the molecule?

**44.** Lactic acid is a natural compound found in sour milk.

(a) How many $\pi$ bonds occur in lactic acid? How many $\sigma$ bonds?

(b) What is the hybridization of atoms 1, 2, and 3?

(c) Which CO bond is the shortest in the molecule? Which CO bond is the strongest?

(d) What are the approximate values of the bond angles *A*, *B*, and *C*?

**45.** Cinnamaldehyde occurs naturally in cinnamon oil.

**Cinnamaldehyde.**

(a) What is the most polar bond in the molecule?

(b) How many $\sigma$ bonds and how many $\pi$ bonds are there?

(c) Is *cis-trans* isomerism possible? If so, draw the isomers of the molecule.

(d) Give the hybridization of the C atoms in the molecule.

(e) What are the values of the bond angles *1*, *2*, and *3*?

**46.** Iodine and oxygen form a series of ions, among them $IO_4^-$ and $IO_5^{3-}$. Draw the Lewis structures for these ions, and specify their electron-pair geometries and the shapes of the ions. What is the hybridization of the I atom in these ions?

**47.** Antimony pentafluoride reacts with HF according to the equation

$$2\ HF + SbF_5 \rightarrow [H_2F]^+[SbF_6]^-$$

(a) What is the hybridization of the Sb atom in the reactant and product?

(b) Draw a Lewis structure for $H_2F^+$. What is the geometry of $H_2F^+$? What is the hybridization of F in $H_2F^+$?

**48.** Xenon forms well-characterized compounds (◀ page 400). Two xenon–oxygen compounds are $XeO_3$ and $XeO_4$. Draw the Lewis structures of these compounds, and give their electron-pair and molecular geometries. What are the hybrid orbital sets used by xenon in these two oxides?

**49.** The simple valence bond picture of $O_2$ does not agree with the molecular orbital view. Compare these two theories with regard to the peroxide ion, $O_2^{2-}$.

(a) Draw an electron dot structure for $O_2^{2-}$. What is the bond order of the ion?

(b) Write the molecular orbital electron configuration for $O_2^{2-}$. What is the bond order based on this approach?

(c) Do the two theories of bonding lead to the same magnetic character and bond order for $O_2^{2-}$?

**50.** Nitrogen, $N_2$, can ionize to form $N_2^+$ or add an electron to give $N_2^-$. Using molecular orbital theory, compare these species with regard to (a) their magnetic character, (b) net number of $\pi$ bonds, (c) bond order, (d) bond length, and (e) bond strength.

**51.** Which of the homonuclear, diatomic molecules of the second-period elements (from $Li_2$ to $Ne_2$) are paramagnetic? Which have a bond order of 1? Which have a bond order of 2? Which diatomic molecule has the highest bond order?

**52.** Which of the following molecules or ions are paramagnetic? What is the highest occupied molecular orbital (HOMO) in each one? Assume the molecular orbital diagram in Figure 9.18 applies to all of them.

(a) NO          (c) $O_2^{2-}$          (e) CN

(b) $OF^-$      (d) $Ne_2^+$

**53.** The CN molecule has been found in interstellar space. Assuming the electronic structure of the molecule can be described using the molecular orbital energy level diagram in Figure 9.18, answer the following questions.

(a) What is the highest energy occupied molecular orbital (HOMO) to which an electron (or electrons) is (are) assigned?

(b) What is the bond order of the molecule?

(c) How many net $\sigma$ bonds are there? How many net $\pi$ bonds?

(d) Is the molecule paramagnetic or diamagnetic?

**54.** The structure of amphetamine, a stimulant, is shown below. (Replacing one H atom on the $NH_2$, or amino, group with $CH_3$ gives methamphetamine, a particularly dangerous drug commonly known as "speed.")

**Amphetamine.**

(a) What are the hybrid orbitals used by the C atoms of the $C_6$ ring, by the C atoms of the side chain, and by the N atom?
(b) Give approximate values for the bond angles *A*, *B*, and *C*.
(c) How many $\sigma$ bonds and $\pi$ bonds are in the molecule?
(d) Is the molecule polar or nonpolar?
(e) Amphetamine reacts readily with a proton ($H^+$) in aqueous solution. Where does this proton attach to the molecule? Does the electrostatic potential map shown above confirm this possibility?

55. Menthol is used in soaps, perfumes, and foods. It is present in the common herb mint, and it can be prepared from turpentine.
(a) What are the hybridizations used by the C atoms in the molecule?
(b) What is the approximate C—O—H bond angle?
(c) Is the molecule polar or nonpolar?
(d) Is the six-member carbon ring planar or nonplanar? Explain why or why not.

**Menthol.**

56. The elements of the second period from boron to oxygen form compounds of the type $X_nE$—$EX_n$, where X can be H or a halogen. Sketch possible Lewis structures for $B_2F_4$, $C_2H_4$, $N_2H_4$, and $O_2H_2$. Give the hybridizations of E in each molecule and specify approximate X—E—E bond angles.

## In the Laboratory

57. Suppose you carry out the following reaction of ammonia and boron trifluoride in the laboratory.

$$H-\underset{H}{\overset{H}{N}}: + B-\underset{F}{\overset{F}{F}} \longrightarrow H-\underset{H}{\overset{H}{N}}\rightarrow B-\underset{F}{\overset{F}{F}}$$

(a) What is the geometry of the boron atom in $BF_3$? In $H_3N\rightarrow BF_3$?
(b) What is the hybridization of the boron atom in the two compounds?
(c) Does the boron atom's hybridization change on formation of the coordinate covalent bond?

(d) Considering the structures and bonding of $NH_3$ and $BF_3$, why do you expect the nitrogen on $NH_3$ to donate an electron pair to the B atom of $BF_3$?
(e) $BF_3$ also reacts readily with water. Based on the ammonia reaction above, speculate on how water can interact with $BF_3$.

58. ▲ Ethylene oxide is an intermediate in the manufacture of ethylene glycol (antifreeze) and polyester polymers. More than 4 million tons is produced annually in the United States. The molecule has a three-member ring of two C atoms and an O atom.

**Ethylene oxide.**

(a) What are the bond angles in the ring?
(b) What is the hybridization of each atom in the ring?
(c) Comment on the relation between the bond angles expected based on hybridization and the bond angles expected for a three-member ring.
(d) Is the molecule polar? Based on the electrostatic potential map shown below, where do the negative and positive charges lie in the molecule?

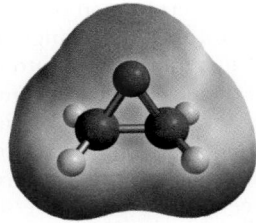

**Electrostatic potential map for ethylene oxide.**

59. The sulfamate ion, $H_2NSO_3^-$, can be thought of as having been formed from the amide ion, $NH_2^-$, and sulfur trioxide, $SO_3$.
(a) What are the geometries of the amide ion and of $SO_3$? What are the hybridizations of the N and S atoms, respectively?
(b) Sketch a structure for the sulfamate ion, and estimate the bond angles.
(c) What changes in hybridization do you expect for N and S in the course of the reaction

$$NH_2^- + SO_3 \rightarrow H_2N-SO_3^-?$$

(d) Is $SO_3$ the donor of an electron pair or the acceptor of an electron pair in the reaction with amide ion? Does the electrostatic potential map shown below confirm your prediction?

**Electrostatic potential map for sulfur trioxide.**

**60.** ▲ The compound whose structure is shown here is acetylacetone. It exists in two forms: the *enol* form and the *keto* form.

*enol* form                                    *keto* form

The molecule reacts with OH⁻ to form an anion, [CH₃COCHCOCH₃]⁻ (often abbreviated acac⁻ for acetylacetonate ion). One of the most interesting aspects of this anion is that one or more of them can react with transition metal cations to give stable, highly colored compounds.

© Cengage Learning/ Charles D. Winters

**Acetylacetonate complexes of (left to right) cobalt, chromium, and iron.**

(a) Are the *keto* and *enol* forms of acetylacetone resonance forms? Explain your answer.

(b) What is the hybridization of each atom (except H) in the *enol* form? What changes in hybridization occur when it is transformed into the *keto* form?

(c) What are the electron-pair geometry and molecular geometry around each C atom in the *keto* and *enol* forms? What changes in geometry occur when the *keto* form changes to the *enol* form?

(d) Draw three possible resonance structures for the acac⁻ ion.

(e) Is *cis-trans* isomerism possible in either the *enol* or the *keto* form of acetylacetone?

(f) Is the *enol* form of acetylacetone polar? Where do the positive and negative charges lie in the molecule?

**61.** Draw the two resonance structures that describe the bonding in the acetate ion. What is the hybridization of the carbon atom of the —CO₂⁻ group? Select one of the two resonance structures and identify the orbitals that overlap to form the bonds between carbon and the three elements attached to it.

**62.** Carbon dioxide ($CO_2$), dinitrogen monoxide ($N_2O$), the azide ion ($N_3^-$), and the cyanate ion ($OCN^-$) have the same arrangement of atoms and the same number of valence shell electrons. However, there are significant differences in their electronic structures.

(a) What hybridization is assigned to the central atom in each species? Which orbitals overlap to form the bonds between atoms in each structure.

(b) Evaluate the resonance structures of these four species. Which most closely describe the bonding in these species? Comment on the differences in bond lengths and bond orders that you expect to see based on the resonance structures.

**63.** Draw the two resonance structures that describe the bonding in $SO_2$. Then describe the bonding in this compound using MO theory. How does MO theory rationalize the bond order of 1.5 for the two S—O bonds in this compound?

**64.** Draw a Lewis structure for diimide, H—N=N—H. Then, using valence bond theory, describe the bonding in this compound. What orbitals overlap to form the bond between nitrogen atoms in this compound?

## Summary and Conceptual Questions

*The following questions may use concepts from this and previous chapters.*

**65.** What is the maximum number of hybrid orbitals that a carbon atom may form? What is the minimum number? Explain briefly.

**66.** Consider the three fluorides $BF_4^-$, $SiF_4$, and $SF_4$.
(a) Identify a molecule that is isoelectronic with $BF_4^-$.
(b) Are $SiF_4$ and $SF_4$ isoelectronic?
(c) What is the hybridization of the central atom in each of these species?

**67.** ▲ When two amino acids react with each other, they form a linkage called an *amide group*, or a peptide link. (If more linkages are added, a protein or polypeptide is formed.)
(a) What are the hybridizations of the C and N atoms in the peptide linkage?
(b) Is the structure illustrated the only resonance structure possible for the peptide linkage? If another resonance structure is possible, compare it with the one shown. Decide which is the more important structure.
(c) The computer-generated structure shown here, which contains a peptide linkage, shows that this linkage is flat. This is an important feature of proteins. Speculate on reasons that the CO—NH linkage is planar. What are the sites of positive and negative charge in this dipeptide?

peptide linkage

**68.** What is the connection between bond order, bond length, and bond energy? Use ethane ($C_2H_6$), ethylene ($C_2H_4$), and acetylene ($C_2H_2$) as examples.

**69.** When is it desirable to use MO theory rather than valence bond theory?

**70.** How do valence bond theory and molecular orbital theory differ in their explanation of the bond order of 1.5 for ozone?

**71.** Three of the four $\pi$ molecular orbitals for cyclobutadiene are pictured here. Place them in order of increasing energy. (As shown in Figures 9.17, 9.19, and 9.20 orbitals increase in energy in order of an increasing number of nodes. If a pair of orbitals have the same number of nodes, they have the same energy.)

Orbital A

Orbital B                    Orbital C

**72.** Let's look more closely at the process of hybridization.
  (a) What is the relationship between the number of hybrid orbitals produced and the number of atomic orbitals used to create them?
  (b) Do hybrid atomic orbitals form between different *p* orbitals without involving *s* orbitals?
  (c) What is the relationship between the energy of hybrid atomic orbitals and the atomic orbitals from which they are formed?

**73.** Borax has the molecular formula $Na_2B_4O_5(OH)_2$. The structure of the anion in this compound is shown below. What is the electron pair geometry and molecular geometry surrounding each of the boron atoms in this anion? What hybridization can be assigned to each of the boron atoms? What is the formal charge of each boron atom?

B atom surrounded by 4 electron pairs

B atom surrounded by 3 electron pairs

**The stucture of the borax anion.**

**74.** A model of the organic compound allene is shown below.

**Allene, CH₂CCH₂.**

  (a) Explain why the allene molecule is not flat. That is, explain why the $CH_2$ groups at opposite ends do not lie in the same plane.
  (b) What is the hybridization of each of the carbon atoms in allene?
  (c) What orbitals overlap to form the bonds between carbon atoms in allene?

**75.** Should the energy required to break one of the H—F bonds in $HF_2^-$ ($HF_2^- \rightarrow HF + F^-$) be greater than, less than, or the same as the energy required to break the bond in HF (HF → H + F). Explain your answer, considering the 3-center-4-electron bond model for $HF_2^-$ described in the *Closer Look* box on page 427.

**76.** Describe the bonding in $XeF_2$ with the two bonding models described in this chapter.
  (a) Valence bond theory: What is the hybridization of the xenon atom in this model? What orbitals overlap to form the Xe—F bonds in this ion? What orbitals contain the lone pairs on xenon?
  (b) MO theory: Use the 3-center-4-electron model described in the *Closer Look* box on page 427 to describe the bonding in $XeF_2$.

**77.** Bromine and fluorine react at temperatures higher than 150 °C to give a compound that is 45.69% Br and 54.31% F.
  (a) What is the empirical formula of the compound?
  (b) Assuming the molecular formula of the compound is the same as its empirical formula, suggest a structure for the molecule. What is the Br atom hybridization in the molecule?
  (c) The molecule has a small dipole moment. Does this agree with your structural proposal in (b) above? Why or why not? If it does not agree, can you propose an alternative structure?

78. Melamine is an important industrial chemical, used to make fertilizers and plastics.

(a) The carbon-nitrogen bond lengths in the ring are all the same length (about 140 pm). Explain.

(b) Melamine is made by the decomposition of urea, $(H_2N)_2CO$.

$$6 \ (H_2N)_2CO(s) \rightarrow C_3H_6N_6(s) + 6 \ NH_3(g) + 3 \ CO_2(g)$$

Calculate the enthalpy change for this reaction. Is it endo- or exothermic? $[\Delta_f H°$ for melamine(s) $= -66.1$ kJ/mol and for urea(s) $= -333.1$ kJ/mol]

79. Bromine forms a number of oxides of varying stability.

(a) One oxide has 90.90% Br and 9.10% O. Assuming its empirical and molecular formulas are the same, draw a Lewis structure of the molecule and specify the hybridization of the central atom (O).

(b) Another oxide is unstable BrO. Assuming the molecular orbital diagram in Figure 9.18 applies to BrO, write its electron configuration (where Br uses $4s$ and $4p$ orbitals). What is the HOMO for the molecule?

# Applying Chemical Principles

## Probing Molecules with Photoelectron Spectroscopy

Photoelectron spectroscopy is an instrumental technique that enables the measurement of orbital energies in atoms and molecules. In this technique gas phase atoms or molecules are ionized by high energy radiation. For a molecule (M), the process is as follows:

$$M + h\nu \rightarrow M^+ + e^-$$

A photon with sufficient energy ($h\nu$) can cause an electron to be ejected from the atom or molecule. If the photon has energy that is above the threshold required for ionization, the excess energy is imparted as kinetic energy to the ejected electron. The ionization energy, the energy of the absorbed photon, and the kinetic energy of the ejected electron are related by the equation.

$$IE = h\nu - KE(electron)$$

Photoelectron spectroscopy may be used to study orbital energies of either core or valence electrons. Ionization of a core electron requires x-ray radiation, whereas ionization of valence electrons (which are responsible for bonding in molecules) requires lower energy ultraviolet (UV) radiation.

Helium gas is the most common UV radiation source used for the photoelectron spectroscopy of molecules. When electronically excited, He atoms emit nearly monochromatic (single wavelength) radiation at a wavelength of 58.4 nm. The energy of these photons is above the threshold required to eject electrons from many valence shell molecular orbitals.

The figure shows the valence shell photoelectron spectrum for $N_2$ molecules. The molecular orbital diagram (Figure 9.17 and Table 9.1 ) indicates that $N_2$ has four types of filled orbitals: $\sigma_{2s}$, $\sigma^*_{2s}$, $\pi_{2p}$, and $\sigma_{2p}$. The photoelectron spectrum detects three groupings of ejected electrons with average ionization energies of 15.6 eV, 16.7 eV, and 18.6 eV (where 1 electron volt = $1.60218 \times 10^{-19}$ J). These electrons are ejected from the $\sigma_{2s}^*$, $\pi_{2p}$, and $\sigma_{2p}$ orbitals, respectively. A fourth peak is not seen because the energy required to remove an electron from the $\sigma_{2s}$ orbital is higher than that of the photons emitted by the excited helium atoms.

The extra peaks, most obvious around 16.7 eV, are associated with ionization from the $\pi$ orbital. They result from coupling of the ionization energy and the energy resulting from molecular vibrations.

## Questions:

1. Photoelectron spectroscopy is similar to the photoelectric effect (Section 6.2). However, in the photoelectric effect, electrons are ejected when light strikes the surface of a(n) _____.

2. What is the energy of a photon with a wavelength of 58.4 nm in kilojoules/mole?

3. Using the accompanying figure, state which molecular orbital ($\sigma^*_{2s}$, $\pi_{2p}$, or $\sigma_{2p}$) has an ionization energy of 15.6 eV.

4. The kinetic energy of an electron ejected from the $\sigma_{2s}^*$ molecular orbital of $N_2$ using 58.4 nm radiation is $4.23 \times 10^{-19}$ J. What is the ionization energy, in both kJ/mol and eV, of an electron from this orbital?

5. The $N_2^+$ ions that are formed when electrons with ionization energies of 15.6 eV and 16.7 eV are ejected have longer bond lengths than the ion when an electron with an ionization energy of 18.6 eV is created. Why?

**The photoelectron spectrum of $N_2$ gas.** (Adapted from G. L. Miessler and D. A. Tarr, Inorganic Chemistry, Pearson, 3rd edition, 2004, page 131.)

# 10 Carbon: Not Just Another Element

Cacao pods on a tree in an island in the Caribbean and the ultimate product.

**Theobromine,** $C_7H_8N_4O_2$, one of many molecules in chocolate. It is a smooth muscle stimulator.

**Caffeine,** $C_8H_{10}N_4O_2$, like theobromine is a member of a class of compounds called *xanthines*.

## The Food of the Gods

There is a tree that grows in the tropics called *Theobroma cacao,* a name given to it in 1735 by the great biologist Linneas. The root of the name comes from the Greek, meaning "food of the gods."

What could be the "food of the gods"? Chocolate, of course.

The history of chocolate can be traced back to Central America. When the Spanish came to the New World, they discovered cocoa beans were highly prized by the natives—100 beans would purchase a slave in 1500 AD—and that a drink made from the beans was quite delicious. The Spanish explorers first took cocoa to Spain in the late 1500s, and by the 17th century chocolate was popular with the Spanish court.

The appeal of chocolate soon spread to the rest of Europe, and, in the late 1800s two Swiss, Henry Nestlé and Daniel Peter, added dried milk to produce the first milk chocolate.

This chapter is all about organic chemistry, the branch of chemistry that studies molecules based on carbon. Carbon compounds are the basis of all living species on this planet. Chocolate certainly fits that definition, as there are almost 400 organic compounds in chocolate.

The main ingredient that gives chocolate its character is the organic compound theobromine. In spite of the name, there is no bromine in the molecule; it is named for the tree where it is found. In medicine, it can be used as a vasodilator, a diuretic, and a heart stimulator. It has even been reputed to be an aphrodisiac! But it can also cause restlessness, tremors, sleeplessness, and anxiety.

Chocolate products usually contain only a few milligrams of theobromine per gram and are quite safe to consume. However, chocolate can be toxic to dogs, and they should not be given chocolate even if they have a sweet tooth.

Theobromine is one of a class of molecules called *xanthines*, a class that includes caffeine. In fact, caffeine is metabolized in the body to theobromine, among other xanthine derivatives.

### Questions:

1. How do theobromine and caffeine differ structurally?
2. A 5.00-g sample of Hershey's cocoa contains 2.16% theobromine. What is the mass of the compound in the sample?

**Answers to these questions are available in Appendix N.**

### Reference:

G. Tannenbaum, *Journal of Chemical Education,* Vol. 81, p. 1131, 2004.

## CHAPTER GOALS

*See Chapter Goals Revisited (page 482) for Study Questions keyed to these goals.*

- Classify organic compounds based on formula and structure.

- Recognize and draw structures of structural isomers and stereoisomers for carbon compounds.

- Name and draw structures of common organic compounds.

- Know the common reactions of organic functional groups.

- Relate properties to molecular structure.

- Identify common polymers.

The vast majority of the millions of chemical compounds currently known are organic; that is, they are compounds built on a carbon framework. Organic compounds vary greatly in size and complexity, from the simplest hydrocarbon, methane, to molecules made up of many thousands of atoms. As you read this chapter, you will see why the range of possible materials is huge and why they are so interesting and very often useful.

## 10.1 Why Carbon?

We begin this discussion of organic chemistry with a question: What features of carbon lead to both the abundance and the complexity of organic compounds? The answers to this question revolve around two main issues: structural diversity and stability.

### Structural Diversity

With four electrons in its outer shell, carbon will form four bonds to reach an octet configuration. In contrast, the elements boron and nitrogen generally form three bonds in molecular compounds; oxygen forms two bonds; and hydrogen and the halogens form one bond. With a larger number of bonds comes the opportunity to create more complex structures. This will become increasingly evident in this brief tour of organic chemistry.

A carbon atom can reach an octet of electrons in various ways (Figure 10.1):

- *By forming four single bonds.* A carbon atom can bond to four other atoms, which can be either atoms of other elements (often H, N, or O) or other carbon atoms.
- *By forming a double bond and two single bonds.* The carbon atoms in ethylene, $H_2C=CH_2$, are linked in this way.
- *By forming two double bonds,* as in carbon dioxide ($O=C=O$).
- *By forming a triple bond and a single bond,* an arrangement seen in acetylene, $HC\equiv CH$.

Recognize, with each of these arrangements, the various possible geometries around carbon: tetrahedral, trigonal-planar, and linear. Carbon's tetrahedral

ethylene, $H_2C=CH_2$

acetylene, $HC\equiv CH$

**Ethylene and acetylene.** These two-carbon hydrocarbons can be the building blocks of more complex molecules. These are their common names; their systematic names are ethene and ethyne, respectively.

(a) Acetic acid. One carbon atom in this compound is attached to four other atoms by single bonds and has tetrahedral geometry. The second carbon atom, connected by a double bond to one oxygen and by single bonds to the other oxygen and to the first carbon, has trigonal-planar geometry.

(b) Benzonitrile. Six trigonal-planar carbon atoms make up the benzene ring. The seventh C atom, bonded by a single bond to carbon and a triple bond to nitrogen, has a linear geometry.

(c) Carbon is linked by double bonds to two other carbon atoms in $C_3H_4$, a linear molecule commonly called allene.

**FIGURE 10.1 Ways that carbon atoms bond.**

geometry is of special significance because it leads to three-dimensional chains and rings of carbon atoms, as in propane and cyclopentane.

propane, $C_3H_8$       cyclopentane, $C_5H_{10}$

The ability to form multiple bonds leads to families of compounds with double and triple bonds.

## Isomers

A hallmark of carbon chemistry is the remarkable array of isomers that can exist. **Isomers** are compounds that have identical composition but different structures. Two broad categories exist: structural isomers and stereoisomers.

**Structural isomers** are compounds having the same elemental composition but in which the atoms are linked together in different ways. Ethanol and dimethyl ether are structural isomers, as are 1-butene and 2-methylpropene.

ethanol        dimethyl ether        1-butene        2-methylpropene

$C_2H_6O$        $C_2H_6O$        $C_4H_8$        $C_4H_8$

$CH_3CH_2OH$        $CH_3OCH_3$        $CH_3CH_2CH{=}CH_2$        $CH_2$
                                                                      $\|$
                                                                      $CH_3CCH_3$

**Stereoisomers** are compounds with the same formula and the same attachment of atoms. However, the atoms have different orientations in space. Two types of stereoisomers exist: *geometric isomers* and *optical isomers*.

## A CLOSER LOOK

## Writing Formulas and Drawing Structures

In Chapter 2, you learned that there are various ways of presenting structures (page 67). It is appropriate to return to this topic as we look at organic compounds. Consider methane and ethane, for example. We can represent these molecules in several ways:

1. *Molecular formula:* $CH_4$ or $C_2H_6$. This type of formula gives information on composition only.

2. *Condensed formula:* For ethane, this would typically be written $CH_3CH_3$. This method of writing the formula gives some information on the way atoms are connected.

3. *Structural formula:* You will recognize this formula as the Lewis structure. An elaboration on the condensed formula in (2), this representation defines more clearly how the atoms are connected,

but it fails to describe the shapes of molecules.

methane, $CH_4$        ethane, $C_2H_6$

4. *Perspective drawings:* These drawings are used to convey the three-dimensional nature of molecules. Bonds extending out of the plane of the paper are drawn with wedges, and bonds behind the plane of the paper are represented as dashed wedges (page 68). Using these guidelines, the structures of methane and ethane could be drawn as follows:

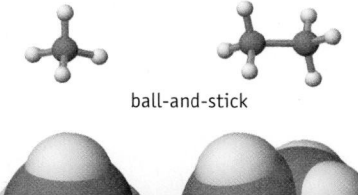

5. *Computer-drawn ball-and-stick and space-filling models.*

ball-and-stick

space-filling

*Cis-* and *trans*-2-butene are **geometric isomers**. Geometric isomerism in these compounds occurs as a result of the $C{=}C$ double bond. *Recall that the carbon atom and the attached groups cannot rotate around a double bond* (page 415). Thus, the geometry around the $C{=}C$ double bond is fixed in space. *Cis-trans* isomerism occurs if each carbon atom involved in the double bond has two different groups attached. If, on the adjacent carbons, it turns out that identical groups are on the same side of the double bond, then it is a *cis* isomer. If those groups appear on opposite sides, a *trans* isomer is produced.

cis-2-butene, $C_4H_8$        trans-2-butene, $C_4H_8$

**Optical isomerism** is a second type of stereoisomerism. Optical isomers are molecules that have nonsuperimposable mirror images (Figure 10.2). Molecules (and other objects) that have nonsuperimposable mirror images are termed **chiral**. Pairs of nonsuperimposable, mirror-image molecules are called **enantiomers**.

Pure samples of enantiomers have the same physical properties, such as melting point, boiling point, density, and solubility in common solvents. They differ in one significant way, however: When a beam of plane-polarized light passes through a solution of a pure enantiomer, the plane of polarization rotates. The two enantiomers rotate polarized light to an equal extent, but in opposite directions (Figure 10.3). The term *optical isomerism* is used because this effect involves light.

The most common examples of chiral compounds are those in which four different atoms (or groups of atoms) are attached to a tetrahedral carbon atom. Lactic acid, found in milk and a product of normal human metabolism, is an example of a chiral compound (Figure 10.2). Optical isomerism is particularly important in the amino acids and other biologically important molecules. Among the many

**FIGURE 10.2 Optical isomers.**
Lactic acid, CH₃CH(OH)CO₂H, is produced when milk is fermented to make cheese. It is also found in other sour foods such as sauerkraut and is a preservative in pickled foods such as onions and olives. In our bodies, it is produced by muscle activity and normal metabolism.

**(a)** Optical isomerism occurs if a molecule and its mirror image cannot be superimposed. The situation is seen if four different groups are attached to carbon.

**(b)** Lactic acid is a chiral molecule because four different groups (H, OH, CH₃, and CO₂H) are attached to the central carbon atom.

interesting examples is a compound, frontalin, produced naturally by male elephants (see *A Closer Look*: *Chirality and Elephants* on the next page).

## Stability of Carbon Compounds

Carbon compounds are notable for their resistance to chemical change. This resistance is a result of two things: strong bonds and slow reactions.

Strong bonds are needed for molecules to survive in their environment. Energetic collisions between molecules in gases, liquids, and solutions can provide enough energy to break some bonds, and bonds can be broken if the energy associated with photons of visible and ultraviolet light exceeds the bond energy. Carbon–carbon bonds are relatively strong, however, as are the bonds between carbon and most other atoms. The average C—C bond energy is 346 kJ/mol; the C—H bond energy is 413 kJ/mol; and carbon–carbon double and triple bond energies are even higher (◀ Section 8.9). Contrast these values with bond energies for the Si—H bond (328 kJ/mol) and the Si—Si bond (222 kJ/mol). The consequence of high bond energies for bonds to carbon is that, for the most part, organic compounds do not decompose thermally under normal conditions.

Oxidation of most organic compounds is strongly product-favored, but most organic compounds survive continual and prolonged contact with O₂. The reason is that reactions of most organic compounds with oxygen are very slow. Typically, organic compounds burn only if their combustion is initiated by heat or by a spark. As

**FIGURE 10.3 Rotation of plane-polarized light by an optical isomer.**
Monochromatic light (light of only one wavelength) is produced by a sodium lamp. After it passes through a polarizing filter, the light vibrates in only one direction—it is polarized. A solution of an optical isomer placed between the first and second polarizing filters causes rotation of the plane of polarized light. The second filter is rotated to a point where a maximum of light is transmitted and the angle of rotation is calculated. The magnitude and direction of rotation are unique physical properties of the optical isomer being tested.

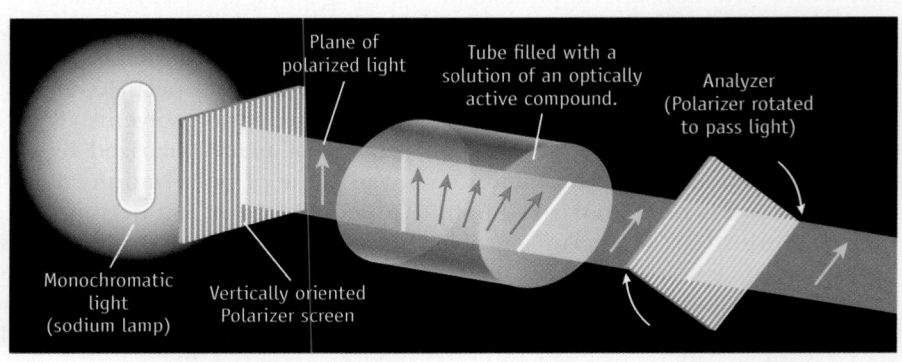

## Chirality and Elephants

During a period known as musth, male elephants undergo a time of heightened sexual activity. They can become more aggressive and can work themselves into a frenzy. At the same time, the males also produce a chemical signal. A secretion containing the enantiomers of frontalin ($C_8H_{14}O_2$) is emitted from a gland between the eye and the ear. Young males produce mixtures containing more of one enantiomer than the other, whereas older elephants produce a more balanced and more concentrated mixture. When that occurs in older elephants, other males are repelled, but ovulating female elephants are more highly attracted.

frontalin

**One enantiomer of frontalin.**

John C. Kotz

**An African elephant in musth.** Fluid containing the enantiomers of frontalin flows from a gland between the elephant's eye and ear.

a consequence, oxidative degradation is not a barrier to the existence of organic compounds.

---

**REVIEW & CHECK FOR SECTION 10.1**

|  |  |  |
|---|---|---|
| H⟍   ⟋CH₃  C=C  H⟋   ⟍Cl  **(a)** | H⟍   ⟋CH₃  C=C  Cl⟋   ⟍H  **(b)** | Cl⟍   ⟋CH₃  C=C  H⟋   ⟍H  **(c)** |

1. Which pair of the three compounds pictured above are stereoisomers?

   (a) a and b          (b) a and c          (c) b and c

2. Which pair of compounds are structural isomers?

   (a) a and b          (b) b and c

3. How many chiral carbon atoms are there in frontalin? (See *A Closer Look: Chirality and Elephants*, above)

   (a) 0          (b) 1          (c) 2          (d) 3

---

## 10.2 Hydrocarbons

**Hydrocarbons**, compounds made only of carbon and hydrogen, are divided into several subgroups: alkanes, cycloalkanes, alkenes, alkynes, and aromatic compounds (Table 10.1). We begin our discussion by considering alkanes and cycloalkanes, compounds in which each carbon atom is linked with four single bonds to other carbon atoms or to hydrogen.

### Alkanes

**Alkanes** have the general formula $C_nH_{2n+2}$, with $n$ having integer values (Table 10.2). Formulas of specific compounds can be generated from this general formula, the first four of which are $CH_4$ (methane), $C_2H_6$ (ethane), $C_3H_8$ (propane), and $C_4H_{10}$ (butane) (Figure 10.4). Methane has four hydrogen atoms arranged tetrahedrally around a single carbon atom. Replacing a hydrogen atom in methane by a —$CH_3$ group gives ethane. If an H atom of ethane is replaced by yet another —$CH_3$ group, propane results. Butane is derived from propane by replacing an H atom of

**Table 10.1  Some Types of Hydrocarbons**

| Type of Hydrocarbon | Characteristic Features | General Formula | Example |
|---|---|---|---|
| Alkanes | C—C single bonds and all C atoms have four single bonds | $C_nH_{2n+2}$ | $CH_4$, methane $C_2H_6$, ethane |
| Cycloalkanes | C—C single bonds, C atoms arranged in a ring | $C_nH_{2n}$ | $C_6H_{12}$, cyclohexane |
| Alkenes | C=C double bond | $C_nH_{2n}$ | $H_2C=CH_2$, ethylene |
| Alkynes | C≡C triple bond | $C_nH_{2n-2}$ | $HC≡CH$, acetylene |
| Aromatics | Rings with $\pi$ bonding extending over several C atoms | — | Benzene, $C_6H_6$ |

one of the chain-ending carbon atoms with a —CH₃ group. In all of these compounds, each C atom is attached to four other atoms, either C or H, so alkanes are often called **saturated compounds**.

## Structural Isomers

Structural isomers are possible for all alkanes larger than propane. For example, there are two structural isomers for $C_4H_{10}$ and three for $C_5H_{12}$. As the number of carbon atoms in an alkane increases, the number of possible structural isomers greatly increases; there are five isomers possible for $C_6H_{14}$, nine isomers for $C_7H_{16}$, 18 for $C_8H_{18}$, 75 for $C_{10}H_{22}$, and 1858 for $C_{14}H_{30}$.

To recognize the isomers corresponding to a given formula, keep in mind the following points:

- Each alkane has a framework of tetrahedral carbon atoms, and each carbon has four single bonds.
- An effective approach to deriving isomer structures is to create a framework of carbon atoms and then fill the remaining positions around carbon with H atoms so that each C atom has four bonds.

$$CH_3CH_2CH_2CH_3 \qquad CH_3\overset{\displaystyle CH_3}{\underset{|}{C}}HCH_3$$

butane                    2-methylpropane

structural isomers of butane, $C_4H_{10}$

$$CH_3CH_2CH_2CH_2CH_3$$
pentane

$$CH_3\overset{\displaystyle CH_3}{\underset{|}{C}}HCH_2CH_3$$
2-methylbutane

$$H_3C\overset{\displaystyle CH_3}{\underset{\displaystyle \underset{|}{CH_3}}{\overset{|}{C}}}CH_3$$
2,2-dimethylpropane

structural isomers of pentane, $C_5H_{12}$

**Table 10.2  Selected Hydrocarbons of the Alkane Family, $C_nH_{2n+2}$***

| Name | Molecular Formula | State at Room Temperature |
|---|---|---|
| Methane | $CH_4$ | |
| Ethane | $C_2H_6$ | |
| Propane | $C_3H_8$ | Gas |
| Butane | $C_4H_{10}$ | |
| Pentane | $C_5H_{12}$ (pent- = 5) | |
| Hexane | $C_6H_{14}$ (hex- = 6) | |
| Heptane | $C_7H_{16}$ (hept- = 7) | |
| Octane | $C_8H_{18}$ (oct- = 8) | Liquid |
| Nonane | $C_9H_{20}$ (non- = 9) | |
| Decane | $C_{10}H_{22}$ (dec- = 10) | |
| Octadecane | $C_{18}H_{38}$ (octadec- = 18) | Solid |
| Eicosane | $C_{20}H_{42}$ (eicos- = 20) | |

*This table lists only selected alkanes. At 25 °C straight-chain alkanes with 11–17 C atoms are liquid. Those with more than 17 C atoms are solid.

**FIGURE 10.4** **Alkanes.** The lowest–molar-mass alkanes, all gases under normal conditions, are methane, ethane, propane, and butane.

- Nearly free rotation occurs around carbon–carbon single bonds. Therefore, when atoms are assembled to form the skeleton of an alkane, the emphasis is on how carbon atoms are attached to one another and not on how they might lie relative to one another in the plane of the paper.

⚙WL    **INTERACTIVE EXAMPLE 10.1**    Drawing Structural Isomers of Alkanes

**Problem** Draw structures of the five isomers of $C_6H_{14}$. Are any of these isomers chiral?

**What Do You Know?** Each structure must have six carbon and 14 hydrogen atoms. There must be four single bonds to each carbon atom, and each hydrogen will form one bond.

**Strategy** Focus first on the different frameworks that can be built from six carbon atoms. Having created a carbon framework, fill hydrogen atoms into the structure so that each carbon has four bonds.

**Solution**

**Step 1.** Placing six carbon atoms in a chain gives the framework for the first isomer. Now fill in hydrogen atoms: three on the carbons on the ends of the chain and two on each of the carbons in the middle. You have created the first isomer, hexane.

C—C—C—C—C—C ⟶ (hexane structure with all H atoms)

carbon framework of hexane          hexane

**Step 2.** Draw a chain of five carbon atoms, then add the sixth carbon atom to one of the carbons in the middle of this chain. (Adding it to a carbon at the end of the chain gives a six-carbon chain, the same framework drawn in Step 1.) Two different carbon frameworks can be built from the five-carbon chain, depending on whether the sixth carbon is linked to the 2 or 3 position. For each of these frameworks, fill in the hydrogens.

carbon framework of methylpentane isomers          2-methylpentane

3-methylpentane

**Strategy Map 10.1**

**PROBLEM**
Draw *structural isomers* of an *alkane*.

↓

**DATA/INFORMATION**
- The **formula** is known, so the *longest possible* **C atom chain** is known.

> **STEP 1.** Draw the *longest* **C atom chain** possible.

Simplest **straight-chain alkane**

> **STEP 2.** Draw C atom chain *one atom shorter* and place a C atom at other places on the chain. Fill in **H** atoms.

Alkane with **one less C atom** but with *substituent group* with **one C atom**

> **STEP 3.** Draw *shorter chains,* and place remaining C atoms at various positions on the chain.

Remaining isomers

● **Chirality in Alkanes** To be chiral, *a compound must have at least one C atom attached to four different groups.* Thus, the $C_7H_{16}$ isomer here is chiral.

$$CH_3$$
$$|$$
$$H-\overset{*}{C}-CH_2CH_3$$
$$|$$
$$CH_2CH_2CH_3$$

The center of chirality is often indicated with an asterisk.

● **Naming Guidelines** For more details on naming organic compounds, see Appendix E.

one possible isomer of an alkane with the formula $C_7H_{16}$

**Module 15: Naming Organic Compounds** covers concepts in this section.

**Step 3.** Draw a chain of four carbon atoms. Add in the two remaining carbons, again being careful not to extend the chain length. Two different structures are possible: one with the remaining carbon atoms in the 2 and 3 positions, and another with both extra carbon atoms attached at the 2 position. Fill in the 14 hydrogens. You have now drawn the fourth and fifth isomers.

carbon atom frameworks for dimethylbutane isomers

2,3-dimethylbutane

2,2-dimethylbutane

None of the isomers of $C_6H_{14}$ is chiral. *To be chiral, a compound must have at least one C atom with four different groups attached.* This condition is not met in any of these isomers.

**Think about Your Answer** Should we look for structures in which the longest chain is three carbon atoms? Try it, but you will see that it is not possible to add the three remaining carbons to a three-carbon chain without creating one of the carbon chains already drawn in a previous step. Thus, we have completed the analysis, with five isomers of this compound being identified.

Names have been given to each of these compounds. See the text that follows this Example, and see Appendix E for guidelines on nomenclature.

**Check Your Understanding**

(a)  Draw the nine isomers having the formula $C_7H_{16}$. (*Hint:* There is one structure with a seven-carbon chain, two structures with six-carbon chains, five structures with a five-carbon chain [one is illustrated in the margin], and one structure with a four-carbon chain.)

(b)  Identify the isomers of $C_7H_{16}$ that are chiral.

## Naming Alkanes

With so many possible isomers for a given alkane, chemists need a systematic way of naming them. The guidelines for naming alkanes and their derivatives follow:

*   The names of alkanes end in "-ane."
*   The names of alkanes with chains of one to 10 carbon atoms are given in Table 10.2. After the first four compounds, the names are derived from Greek and Latin numbers—pentane, hexane, heptane, octane, nonane, decane—and this regular naming continues for higher alkanes.
*   When naming a specific alkane, the root of the name corresponds to the longest carbon chain in the compound. One isomer of $C_5H_{12}$ has a three-carbon chain

**PROBLEM SOLVING TIP 10.1**

An error students sometimes make is to suggest that the three carbon skeletons drawn here are different. They are, in fact, the same. All are five-carbon chains with another C atom in the 2 position.

## Drawing Structural Formulas

$$\begin{matrix} & C & & & & C & & & & & & C \\ & | & & & & | & & & & & & | \\ C-C-C-C-C & & C-C-C-C & & C-C-C-C-C \\ 1\ 2\ 3\ 4\ 5 & & |2\ 3\ 4\ 5 & & 5\ 4\ 3\ 2\ 1 \\ & & C \\ & & 1 \end{matrix}$$

Remember that Lewis structures do not indicate the geometry of molecules.

with two —$CH_3$ groups on the second C atom of the chain. Thus, its name is based on propane.

$$\begin{matrix} & & CH_3 \\ & & | \\ H_3C & - & C & - & CH_3 \\ & & | \\ & & CH_3 \end{matrix}$$

2,2-dimethylpropane

- Substituent groups on a hydrocarbon chain are identified by a name and the position of substitution in the carbon chain; this information precedes the root of the name. The position is indicated by a number that refers to the carbon atom to which the substituent is attached. Numbering of the carbon atoms in a chain should begin at the end of the carbon chain that allows the first substituent encountered to have the lowest possible number. (If there is no distinction at this point, then number so to give the second substituent encountered the lowest number.) Both —$CH_3$ groups in 2,2-dimethylpropane are located at the 2 position.
- Names of hydrocarbon substituents, called **alkyl groups**, are derived from the name of the hydrocarbon. The group —$CH_3$, derived by taking a hydrogen from methane, is called the methyl group; the —$C_2H_5$ group is the ethyl group.
- If two or more of the same substituent groups are present in the molecule, the prefixes di-, tri-, and tetra- are added. When different substituent groups are present, they are generally listed in alphabetical order.

● **Systematic and Common Names** The IUPAC (International Union of Pure and Applied Chemistry) has formulated rules for systematic names, which are generally used in this book. (See Appendix E.) However, many organic compounds are known by common names. For example, 2,2-dimethylpropane is also called neopentane.

## EXAMPLE 10.2    Naming Alkanes

**Problem**  Give the systematic name for

$$\begin{matrix} CH_3 & & CH_2CH_3 \\ | & & | \\ CH_3CHCH_2CH_2CHCH_2CH_3 \end{matrix}$$

**What Do You Know?**  You know the condensed formula and can recognize that the compound is an alkane. You also know the rules for naming alkanes.

**Strategy**  Identify the longest carbon chain and base the name of the compound on that alkane. Identify the substituent groups on the chain and their locations. When there are two or more substituents (the groups attached to the chain), number the parent chain from the end that gives the lower number to the substituent encountered first. If the substituents are different, list them in alphabetical order. (For more on naming compounds, see Appendix E.)

**Solution**  Here, the longest chain has seven C atoms, so the root of the name is *heptane*. There is a methyl group (—$CH_3$) on C-2 and an ethyl group (—$C_2H_5$) on C-5. Giving the substituents in alphabetical order and numbering the chain from the end having the methyl group, the systematic name is 5-ethyl-2-methylheptane.

**FIGURE 10.5 Paraffin wax and mineral oil.** These common consumer products are mixtures of alkanes.

**Think about Your Answer** Notice that the carbon atoms in the longest chain are numbered so that the lower number is given to the substituent encountered first.

**Check Your Understanding**

Name the nine isomers of $C_7H_{16}$ in "Check Your Understanding" in Example 10.1.

## Properties of Alkanes

Methane, ethane, propane, and butane are gases at room temperature and pressure, whereas the higher-molar-mass compounds are liquids or solids (Table 10.2). An increase in melting point and boiling point with molar mass in a series of similar compounds is a general phenomenon (▶ Sections 12.3 and 12.4).

You already know about alkanes in a nonscientific context because several are common fuels. Natural gas, gasoline, kerosene, fuel oils, and lubricating oils are all mixtures of various alkanes. White mineral oil is also a mixture of alkanes, as is paraffin wax (Figure 10.5).

Pure alkanes are colorless. The gases and liquids have noticeable but not unpleasant odors. All of these substances are insoluble in water, a property typical of compounds that are nonpolar or nearly so. Low polarity is expected for alkanes because the electronegativities of carbon ($\chi = 2.5$) and hydrogen ($\chi = 2.2$) are not greatly different (◀ Section 8.8).

All alkanes burn readily in air to give $CO_2$ and $H_2O$ in very exothermic reactions. This is, of course, the reason they are widely used as fuels.

$$CH_4(g) + 2\ O_2(g) \rightarrow CO_2(g) + 2\ H_2O(\ell) \qquad \Delta_rH° = -890.3\ \text{kJ/mol-rxn}$$

Other than in combustion reactions, alkanes exhibit relatively low chemical reactivity. One reaction that does occur, however, is the replacement of the hydrogen atoms of an alkane by chlorine atoms on reaction with $Cl_2$. It is formally an oxidation because $Cl_2$, like $O_2$, is a strong oxidizing agent. These reactions, which can be initiated by ultraviolet radiation, are free radical reactions. Highly reactive Cl atoms are formed from $Cl_2$ under ultraviolet (UV) radiation. Reaction of methane with $Cl_2$ under these conditions proceeds in a series of steps, eventually yielding $CCl_4$, commonly known as carbon tetrachloride. (HCl is the other product of these reactions.)

| | | | |
|---|---|---|---|
| Systematic name: | chloromethane | dichloromethane | trichloromethane | tetrachloromethane |
| Common name: | methyl chloride | methylene chloride | chloroform | carbon tetrachloride |

The last three compounds are used as solvents, albeit less frequently today because of their toxicity.

## Cycloalkanes, $C_nH_{2n}$

cyclopropane, $C_3H_6$      cyclobutane, $C_4H_8$

**Cyclopropane and cyclobutane.** Cyclopropane was at one time used as a general anesthetic in surgery. However, its explosive nature when mixed with oxygen soon eliminated this application.

**Cycloalkanes** are constructed with tetrahedral carbon atoms joined together to form a ring. Cyclopropane and cyclobutane are the simplest cycloalkanes, although the bond angles in these species are much less than 109.5°. As a result, chemists say they are **strained hydrocarbons**, so named because an unfavorable geometry is imposed around carbon. One of the features of strained hydrocarbons is that the C—C bonds are weaker and the molecules readily undergo ring-opening reactions that relieve the bond angle strain.

The most common cycloalkane is cyclohexane, $C_6H_{12}$, which has a nonplanar ring with six —$CH_2$ groups. If the carbon atoms were in the form of a regular hexagon with all carbon atoms in one plane, the C—C—C bond angles would be 120°. To have tetrahedral bond angles of 109.5° around each C atom, the ring has to pucker. The $C_6$ ring is flexible and exists in two interconverting forms (see below for *A Closer Look: Flexible Molecules*).

## Alkenes and Alkynes

The diversity seen for alkanes is repeated with **alkenes**, hydrocarbons with one or more C=C double bonds. The presence of a double bond adds two features missing in alkanes: the possibility of geometric isomerism and increased reactivity.

The general formula for alkenes with a single double bond is $C_nH_{2n}$. The first two members of the series of alkenes are ethene, $C_2H_4$ (common name, ethylene), and propene, $C_3H_6$ (common name, propylene). Only a single structure can be drawn for these compounds. As with alkanes, the occurrence of isomers begins with species containing four carbon atoms. Four alkene isomers have the formula $C_4H_8$, and each has distinct chemical and physical properties (Table 10.3). There are three structural isomers, one of which ($CH_3CH=CHCH_3$) exists as two stereoisomers.

$C_2H_4$
Systematic name: ethene
Common name: ethylene

$C_3H_6$
Systematic name: propene
Common name: propylene

1-butene    2-methylpropene    cis-2-butene    trans-2-butene

Alkene names end in "-ene." As with alkanes, the root for the name of an alkene is determined by the longest carbon chain that contains the double bond. The position of the double bond is indicated with a number, and, when appropriate, the prefix *cis* or *trans* is added.

Three of the $C_4H_8$ isomers have four-carbon chains and so are butenes. One has a three-carbon chain and is a propene. Notice that the carbon chain is numbered from the end that gives the double bond the lowest number. In the first isomer at the left, the double bond is between C atoms 1 and 2, so the name is 1-butene and not 3-butene.

## A CLOSER LOOK

# Flexible Molecules

Most organic molecules are flexible; that is, they can twist and bend in various ways. Few molecules better illustrate this behavior than cyclohexane. Two structures are possible: "chair" and "boat" forms. These forms can interconvert by partial rotation of several bonds.

The more stable structure is the chair form, which allows the hydrogen atoms to remain as far apart as possible. A side view of this form of cyclohexane reveals two sets of hydrogen atoms in this molecule. Six hydrogen atoms, called the *equatorial hydrogens*, lie in a plane

around the carbon ring. The other six hydrogens are positioned above and below the plane and are called *axial hydrogens*. Flexing the ring (a rotation around the C—C single bonds) moves the hydrogen atoms between axial and equatorial environments.

axial H atom

equatorial H atom

chair form          boat form          chair form

Table 10.3 **Properties of Butene Isomers**

| Name | Boiling Point | Melting Point | Dipole Moment (D) | $\Delta_f H°$ (gas) (kJ/mol) |
|---|---|---|---|---|
| 1-Butene | −6.26 °C | −185.4 °C | — | −0.63 |
| 2-Methylpropene | −6.95 °C | −140.4 °C | 0.503 | −17.9 |
| *Cis*-2-butene | 3.71 °C | −138.9 °C | 0.253 | −7.7 |
| *Trans*-2-butene | 0.88 °C | −105.5 °C | 0 | −10.8 |

## EXAMPLE 10.3    Determining Isomers of Alkenes from a Formula

**Problem** Draw structures for the six possible alkene isomers with the formula $C_5H_{10}$. Give the systematic name of each.

**What Do You Know?** When linking the five carbon atoms together, two will be joined with a double bond. Each carbon must have four bonds, and hydrogen atoms will fill into the remaining positions.

**Strategy** A procedure that involved drawing the carbon skeleton and then adding hydrogen atoms served well when drawing structures of alkanes (Example 10.1), and a similar approach can be used here. It will be necessary to put one double bond into the framework and to be alert for *cis-trans* isomerism.

**Solution**

**Step 1.** A five-carbon chain with one double bond can be constructed in two ways. *Cis-trans* isomers are possible for 2-pentene.

1-pentene

*cis*-2-pentene

*trans*-2-pentene

**Step 2.** Draw the possible four-carbon chains containing a double bond. Add the fifth carbon atom to either the 2 or 3 position. When all the possible combinations are found, fill in the hydrogen atoms. This results in three more structures:

2-methyl-1-butene

3-methyl-1-butene

cyclohexene, $C_6H_{10}$

$H_2C=CHCH=CH_2$

1,3-butadiene, $C_4H_6$

**Cycloalkenes and dienes.**
Cyclohexene, $C_6H_{10}$ (*top*), and
1,3-butadiene ($C_4H_6$) (*bottom*).

C—C=C—C  ⟶  2-methyl-2-butene

**Think about Your Answer** With questions like this, it is important to be very organized in your approach. When you complete your answer, you should look carefully to see that each structure is unique, that is, that no two are the same.

**Check Your Understanding**

There are 17 possible alkene isomers with the formula $C_6H_{12}$. Draw structures of the five isomers in which the longest chain has six carbon atoms, and give the name of each. Which of these isomers is chiral? (There are also eight isomers in which the longest chain has five carbon atoms, and four isomers in which the longest chain has four carbon atoms. How many can you find?)

Hydrocarbons exist that have two or more double bonds. Butadiene, for example, has two double bonds and is known as a *diene*. Many natural products have numerous double bonds (Figure 10.6). There are also cyclic hydrocarbons, such as cyclohexene, with double bonds.

**Alkynes**, compounds with a carbon–carbon triple bond, have the general formula ($C_nH_{2n-2}$). Table 10.4 lists alkynes that have four or fewer carbon atoms. The first member of this family is ethyne (common name, acetylene), a gas used as a fuel in metal cutting torches.

## Properties of Alkenes and Alkynes

Like alkanes, alkenes and alkynes are colorless. Low–molar-mass compounds are gases, whereas compounds with higher molar masses are liquids or solids. Alkenes and alkynes are also oxidized by $O_2$ to give $CO_2$ and $H_2O$.

Alkenes and alkynes have an elaborate chemistry. We get some insight into their chemical behavior by recognizing that they are called **unsaturated compounds**. Carbon atoms are capable of bonding to a maximum of four other atoms, and they do so in alkanes and cycloalkanes. In alkenes, however, each carbon atom linked by a double bond is bonded to a total of only three atoms. In alkynes, each carbon atom linked by a triple bond is bonded to a total of only two atoms. It is possible to

**FIGURE 10.6 Carotene, a naturally occurring compound with 11 C=C bonds.** The $\pi$ electrons can be excited by visible light in the blue-violet region of the spectrum. As a result, carotene appears orange-yellow to the observer. Carotene or carotene-like molecules are partnered with chlorophyll in nature in the role of assisting in the harvesting of sunlight. Green leaves have a high concentration of carotene. In autumn, green chlorophyll molecules are destroyed, and the yellows and reds of carotene and related molecules are seen. The red color of tomatoes, for example, comes from a molecule very closely related to carotene. As a tomato ripens, its chlorophyll disintegrates, and the green color is replaced by the red of the carotene-like molecule.

© Cengage Learning/Charles D. Winters

Table 10.4 **Some Simple Alkynes** $C_nH_{2n-2}$

| Structure | Systematic Name | Common Name | BP (°C) |
|---|---|---|---|
| HC≡CH | ethyne | acetylene | −85 |
| $CH_3C≡CH$ | propyne | methylacetylene | −23 |
| $CH_3CH_2C≡CH$ | 1-butyne | ethylacetylene | 9 |
| $CH_3C≡CCH_3$ | 2-butyne | dimethylacetylene | 27 |

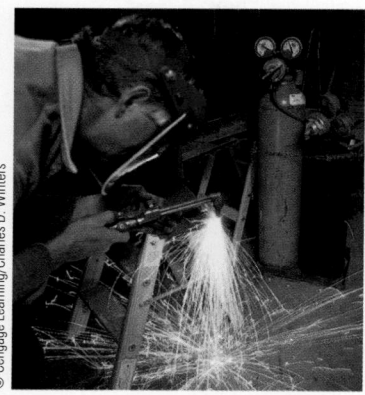

**An oxy-acetylene torch.** The reaction of ethyne (acetylene) with oxygen produces a very high temperature. Oxy-acetylene torches, used in welding, take advantage of this fact.

increase the number of groups attached to a carbon atom in an alkene or alkyne by **addition reactions**, in which molecules with the general formula X—Y (such as hydrogen, halogens, hydrogen halides, and water) add across the carbon–carbon double or triple bond (Figure 10.7). For an alkene the result is a compound with four groups bonded to each carbon.

$$X—Y = H_2, Cl_2, Br_2; H—Cl, H—Br, H—OH, HO—Cl$$

The products of some addition reactions are substituted alkanes. For example, the addition of bromine to ethene (ethylene) forms 1,2-dibromoethane.

1,2-dibromoethane

The addition of 2 mol of chlorine to ethyne (acetylene) gives 1,1,2,2-tetrachloro-ethane.

● **Nomenclature of Substituted Alkanes** The substituent groups in substituted alkanes are identified by the name and position of the substituent on the alkane chain.

$$HC≡CH + 2\ Cl_2 \longrightarrow$$

1,1,2,2-tetrachloroethane

During the 1860s, the Russian chemist Vladimir Markovnikov examined a large number of alkene addition reactions. In cases in which two isomeric products were possible, he found that one was more likely to predominate. Based on these results, Markovnikov formulated a rule (now called *Markovnikov's rule*) stating that, when a

**FIGURE 10.7** **Bacon fat and addition reactions.** The fat in bacon is partially unsaturated. Like other unsaturated compounds, bacon fat reacts with $Br_2$ in an addition reaction. Here, you see the color of $Br_2$ vapor fade when a strip of bacon is introduced.

a few minutes
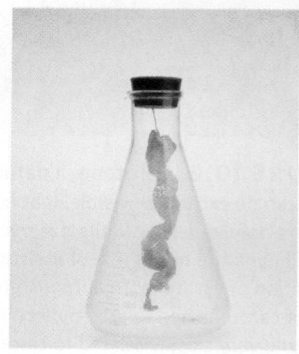

reagent HX adds to an unsymmetrical alkene, the hydrogen atom in the reagent becomes attached to the carbon that already has the largest number of hydrogens. An example of Markovnikov's rule is the reaction of 2-methylpropene with HCl that results in formation of 2-chloro-2-methylpropane rather than 1-chloro-2-methylpropane.

$$H_3C \diagdown \atop H_3C \diagup C{=}CH_2 + HCl \longrightarrow H_3C{-}\underset{\underset{CH_3}{|}}{\overset{\overset{Cl}{|}}{C}}{-}CH_3 \quad + \quad H_3C{-}\underset{\underset{CH_3}{|}}{\overset{\overset{H}{|}}{C}}{-}CH_2Cl$$

2-methylpropene          2-chloro-2-methylpropane     1-chloro-2-methylpropane
                              sole product                 *not* formed

If the reagent added to a double bond is hydrogen (X—Y = $H_2$), the reaction is called **hydrogenation**. Hydrogenation is usually a very slow reaction, but it can be speeded up by adding a catalyst, often a specially prepared form of a metal, such as platinum, palladium, and rhodium. You may have heard the term *hydrogenation* because certain foods contain "hydrogenated" or "partially hydrogenated" ingredients. One brand of crackers has a label that says, "Made with 100% pure vegetable shortening . . . (partially hydrogenated soybean oil with hydrogenated cottonseed oil)." One reason for hydrogenating an oil is to make it less susceptible to spoilage; another is to convert it from a liquid to a solid.

● **Catalysts** A catalyst is a substance that causes a reaction to occur at a faster rate without itself being permanently changed in the reaction. We will describe catalysts in more detail in Chapter 15.

## EXAMPLE 10.4    Reaction of an Alkene

**Problem** Draw the structure of the compound obtained from the reaction of $Br_2$ with propene, and name the compound.

**What Do You Know?** Propene is the three-carbon alkene. Addition reactions are among the most common reactions of alkenes, and it is known that bromine is one of several common reagents that adds to double bonds.

**Strategy** Bromine adds across the C=C double bond. The name of the product is based on the name of the carbon chain and indicates the positions of the Br atoms.

**Solution**

$$\underset{H}{\overset{H}{\diagdown}}C{=}C\underset{CH_3}{\overset{H}{\diagup}} \quad + Br_2 \longrightarrow H{-}\underset{\underset{H}{|}}{\overset{\overset{Br}{|}}{C}}{-}\underset{\underset{H}{|}}{\overset{\overset{Br}{|}}{C}}{-}CH_3$$

propene                    1,2-dibromopropane

**Think about Your Answer** This reaction converts an unsaturated hydrocarbon to a substituted alkane. It is named as an alkane (propane) with substituents (Br atoms) identified by name and position on the three-carbon chain.

**Check Your Understanding**

(a) Draw the structure of the compound obtained from the reaction of HBr with ethylene, and name the compound.

(b) Draw the structure of the product of the reaction of $Br_2$ with *cis*-2-butene, and name this compound.

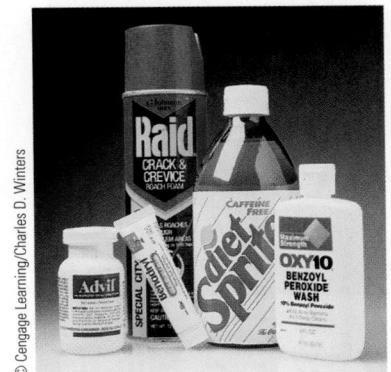

© Cengage Learning/Charles D. Winters

**Some products containing compounds based on benzene.**
Examples include sodium benzoate in soft drinks, ibuprofen in Advil, and benzoyl peroxide in Oxy-10.

## Aromatic Compounds

Benzene, $C_6H_6$, is a key molecule in chemistry. It is the simplest **aromatic compound**, a class of compounds so named because they have significant, and usually not unpleasant, odors. Other members of this class, which are all based on benzene, include toluene and naphthalene. A source of many aromatic compounds is coal.

These compounds, along with other volatile substances, are released when coal is heated to a high temperature in the absence of air (Table 10.5).

benzene          toluene          naphthalene

**Saccharin ($C_7H_5NO_3S$).** This compound, an artificial sweetener, contains an aromatic ring.

Benzene occupies a pivotal place in the history and practice of chemistry. Michael Faraday discovered this compound in 1825 as a by-product of illuminating gas, a fuel produced by heating coal. Today, benzene is an important industrial chemical, usually ranking among the top 25 chemicals in production annually in the United States. It is used as a solvent and is also the starting point for making thousands of different compounds by replacing the H atoms of the ring.

Toluene was originally obtained from tolu balsam, the pleasant-smelling gum of a South American tree, *Toluifera balsamum*. This balsam has been used in cough syrups and perfumes. Naphthalene is an ingredient in "moth balls," although 1,4-dichlorobenzene is now more commonly used. Aspartame and another artificial sweetener, saccharin, are also benzene derivatives.

### The Structure of Benzene

The formula of benzene suggested to 19th-century chemists that this compound should be unsaturated, but, if viewed this way, its chemistry was perplexing. Whereas alkenes readily undergo addition reactions, benzene does not do so under similar conditions. We now recognize that benzene's different reactivity relates to its structure and bonding, both of which are quite different from the structure and bonding in alkenes. Benzene has equivalent carbon–carbon bonds, 139 pm in length, intermediate between a C—C single bond (154 pm) and a C=C double bond (134 pm). The $\pi$ bonds are formed by the continuous overlap of the $p$ orbitals on the six carbon atoms (page 416). Using valence bond terminology, the structure is represented by two resonance structures.

● **August Kekulé and the Structure of Benzene** The structural question was solved by August Kekulé (1829–1896). Kekulé, one of the most prominent organic chemists in Europe in the late 19th century, argued for the ring structure with alternating double bonds based on the number of isomers possible for the structure. The legend in chemistry is that Kekulé proposed the ring structure after dreaming of a snake biting its tail.

or simply

representations of benzene, $C_6H_6$

**Table 10.5  Some Aromatic Compounds from Coal Tar**

| Common Name | Formula | Boiling Point (°C) | Melting Point (°C) |
|---|---|---|---|
| Benzene | $C_6H_6$ | 80 | +6 |
| Toluene | $C_6H_5CH_3$ | 111 | −95 |
| *o*-Xylene | 1,2-$C_6H_4(CH_3)_2$ | 144 | −25 |
| *m*-Xylene | 1,3-$C_6H_4(CH_3)_2$ | 139 | −48 |
| *p*-Xylene | 1,4-$C_6H_4(CH_3)_2$ | 138 | +13 |
| Naphthalene | $C_{10}H_8$ | 218 | +80 |

## Benzene Derivatives

Toluene, chlorobenzene, benzoic acid, aniline, styrene, and phenol are common examples of benzene derivatives.

chlorobenzene    benzoic acid    aniline    styrene    phenol

The systematic nomenclature for benzene derivatives with two or more substituent groups involves naming these groups and identifying their positions on the ring by numbering the six carbon atoms (▶ Appendix E). Some common names, which are based on an older naming scheme, are also used. This scheme identified isomers of disubstituted benzenes with the prefixes *ortho* (*o*-, substituent groups on adjacent carbons in the benzene ring), *meta* (*m*-, substituents separated by one carbon atom), and *para* (*p*-, substituent groups on carbons on opposite sides of the ring).

● **Drawing Aromatic Rings** When drawing benzene rings chemists often allow the vertices of the hexagon to represent the carbon atoms and do not show the H atoms attached to those carbon atoms.

| | | | |
|---|---|---|---|
| Systematic name: | 1,2-dichlorobenzene | 1,3-dimethylbenzene | 1,4-dinitrobenzene |
| Common name: | *o*-dichlorobenzene | *m*-xylene | *p*-dinitrobenzene |

## EXAMPLE 10.5    Isomers of Substituted Benzenes

**Problem** Draw and name the isomers of $C_6H_3Cl_3$.

**What Do You Know?** From the formula you can infer that $C_6H_3Cl_3$ is a substituted benzene with three hydrogen atoms replaced by chlorine atoms.

**Strategy** Begin by drawing the carbon framework of benzene, and attach a chlorine atom to one of the carbon atoms. Place a second Cl atom on the ring in the *ortho*, *meta*, and *para* positions. Add the third Cl in one of the remaining positions, being careful not to repeat a structure already drawn.

**Solution** The three isomers of $C_6H_3Cl_3$ are shown here. They are named as derivatives of benzene by specifying the number of substituent groups with the prefix "tri-," the name of the substituent, and the positions of the three groups around the six-member ring.

1,2,3-trichlorobenzene    1,2,4-trichlorobenzene    1,3,5-trichlorobenzene

**Think about Your Answer** Are there other possibilities? Try moving the chlorine atoms around in each isomer. In every case, you will find that moving one Cl atom to a different position generates one of these three isomers. For example, in the first structure, moving the Cl atom at position 1 to either position 5 or 6 leads to structures identical to the second structure.

**Check Your Understanding**

Aniline, $C_6H_5NH_2$, is the common name for aminobenzene. Draw a structure for *p*-diaminobenzene, a compound used in dye manufacture. What is the systematic name for *p*-diaminobenzene?

## Properties of Aromatic Compounds

Benzene is a colorless liquid, and simple substituted benzenes are liquids or solids under normal conditions. The properties of aromatic hydrocarbons are typical of hydrocarbons in general: They are insoluble in water, soluble in nonpolar solvents, and oxidized by $O_2$ to form $CO_2$ and $H_2O$.

One of the most important properties of benzene and other aromatic compounds is an unusual stability that is associated with the unique $\pi$ bonding in this molecule. Because the $\pi$ bonding in benzene is typically described using resonance structures, the extra stability is termed **resonance stabilization**. The extent of resonance stabilization in benzene is evaluated by comparing the energy evolved in the hydrogenation of benzene to form cyclohexane

$$C_6H_6(\ell) + 3\ H_2(g) \xrightarrow{catalyst} C_6H_{12}(\ell) \qquad \Delta_rH° = -206.7 \text{ kJ/mol-rxn}$$

with the energy evolved in hydrogenation of three isolated double bonds.

$$3\ H_2C{=}CH_2(g) + 3\ H_2(g) \rightarrow 3\ C_2H_6(g) \qquad \Delta_rH° = -410.8 \text{ kJ/mol-rxn}$$

The hydrogenation of benzene is about 200 kJ/mol less exothermic than the hydrogenation of three moles of ethene. The difference is attributable to the added stability associated with $\pi$ bonding in benzene.

Although aromatic compounds are unsaturated hydrocarbons, they do not undergo the addition reactions typical of alkenes and alkynes. Instead, *substitution reactions* occur, in which one or more hydrogen atoms are replaced by other groups. Such reactions require higher temperatures and a strong Brønsted acid such as $H_2SO_4$ or a Lewis acid such as $AlCl_3$ or $FeBr_3$.

● **Lewis Acids and Bases** G. N. Lewis (page 342) defined an acid as an electron-pair acceptor (such as $AlCl_3$) and a base as an electron-pair donor (such as $NH_3$). (See Chapter 17, Section 11.)

*Nitration:* $\quad C_6H_6(\ell) + HNO_3(\ell) \xrightarrow{H_2SO_4} C_6H_5NO_2(\ell) + H_2O(\ell)$

*Alkylation:* $\quad C_6H_6(\ell) + CH_3Cl(\ell) \xrightarrow{AlCl_3} C_6H_5CH_3(\ell) + HCl(g)$

*Halogenation:* $C_6H_6(\ell) + Br_2(\ell) \xrightarrow{FeBr_3} C_6H_5Br(\ell) + HBr(g)$

---

**REVIEW & CHECK FOR SECTION 10.2**

1. What is the systematic name for this alkane?

(a) nonane

(b) 2-ethyl-5-methylhexane

(c) 2, 5-dimethylheptane

(d) dimethyloctane

2.  Which statement below correctly describes the following compound?

$$H_3C-\underset{\underset{H}{|}}{\overset{\overset{H}{|}}{C}}-\underset{\underset{CH_3}{|}}{\overset{\overset{CH_3}{|}}{C}}-CH_3$$

(a)  The compound is an isomer of pentane, is chiral, and is named 2,3-dimethylbutane.

(b)  The compound is an isomer of octane, is not chiral, and is named 2,2-dimethylbutane.

(c)  The compound is an isomer of hexane, is not chiral, and is named 2,2-dimethylbutane.

(d)  The compound is an isomer of hexane, is not chiral, and is named 3,3-dimethylbutane.

3.  Consider the following list of compounds:

   1.  $C_2H_4$          2.  $C_5H_{10}$          3.  $C_{14}H_{30}$          4.  $C_7H_8$

(i)  Which compound or compounds in the list can be an alkane?

   (a)  only 1          (b)  2 and 3          (c)  only 3          (d)  3 and 4

(ii)  Which compound or compounds in the list can be an alkene?

   (a)  only 1          (b)  only 2          (c)  1 and 2          (d)  3 and 4

4.  What is the product of the following reaction?

$$\underset{H_3C}{\overset{H_3C}{>}}C=C\underset{H}{\overset{CH_2CH_3}{<}} \quad + \; HBr \longrightarrow$$

$$Br-\underset{\underset{CH_3}{|}}{\overset{\overset{CH_3}{|}}{C}}-\underset{\underset{H}{|}}{\overset{\overset{CH_2CH_3}{|}}{C}}-H \qquad H-\underset{\underset{CH_3}{|}}{\overset{\overset{CH_3}{|}}{C}}-\underset{\underset{H}{|}}{\overset{\overset{CH_2CH_3}{|}}{C}}-Br$$

   **(a)**                                 **(b)**

5.  How many isomers are possible for $C_6H_4(CH_3)Cl$, a benzene derivative?

   (a)  1          (b)  2          (c)  3

# 10.3  Alcohols, Ethers, and Amines

Organic compounds often contain other elements in addition to carbon and hydrogen. Two elements in particular, oxygen and nitrogen, add a rich dimension to carbon chemistry.

Organic chemistry organizes compounds containing elements other than carbon and hydrogen as derivatives of hydrocarbons. Formulas (and structures) are represented by substituting one or more hydrogens in a hydrocarbon molecule by a **functional group**. A functional group is an atom or group of atoms attached to a carbon atom in the hydrocarbon. Formulas of hydrocarbon derivatives are then written as R—X, in which R is a hydrocarbon lacking a hydrogen atom, and X is the functional group (such as $-OH$, $-NH_2$, a halogen atom, or $-CO_2H$) that has replaced the hydrogen. The chemical and physical properties of the hydrocarbon derivatives are a blend of the properties associated with hydrocarbons and the group that has been substituted for hydrogen.

Table 10.6 identifies some common functional groups and the families of organic compounds resulting from their attachment to a hydrocarbon.

**A CLOSER LOOK**

# Petroleum Chemistry

Much of the world's current technology relies on petroleum. Burning fuels derived from petroleum provides by far the largest amount of energy in the industrial world (◄ *The Chemistry of Fuels and Energy Sources*, pages 252–265). Petroleum and natural gas are also the chemical raw materials used in the manufacture of many plastics, pharmaceuticals, and a vast array of other compounds.

The petroleum that is pumped out of the ground is a complex mixture whose composition varies greatly, depending on its source. The primary components of petroleum are always alkanes, but, to varying degrees, nitrogen- and sulfur-containing compounds are also present. Aromatic compounds are present as well, but alkenes and alkynes are not.

An early step in the petroleum refining process is distillation, in which the crude

**A modern petrochemical plant.**

mixture is separated into a series of fractions based on boiling point: first a gaseous fraction (mostly alkanes with one to four carbon atoms; this fraction is often burned off), and then gasoline, kerosene, and fuel oils. After distillation, considerable material, in the form of a semi-solid, tar-like residue, remains.

The petrochemical industry seeks to maximize the amounts of the higher-valued fractions of petroleum produced and to make specific compounds for which a particular need exists. This means carrying out chemical reactions involving the raw materials on a huge scale. One process to which petroleum is subjected is known as *cracking*. At very high temperatures, bond breaking or "cracking" can occur, and longer-chain hydrocarbons will fragment into smaller molecular units. These reactions are carried out in the presence of a wide array of catalysts, materials that speed up reactions and direct them toward specific products. Among the important products of cracking is ethylene, which serves as the raw material for the formation of materials such as polyethylene. Cracking also produces other alkenes and gaseous hydrogen, both widely used raw materials in the chemical industry.

Other important reactions involving petroleum are run at elevated temperatures and in the presence of specific catalysts. Such reactions include *isomerization* reac-

tions, in which the carbon skeleton of an alkane rearranges to form a new isomeric species, and *reformation* processes, in which alkanes become cycloalkanes or aromatic hydrocarbons. Each process is directed toward achieving a specific goal, such as increasing the proportion of branched-chain hydrocarbons in gasoline to obtain higher octane ratings. A great amount of chemical research has gone into developing and understanding these highly specialized processes.

**Producing gasoline.** Branched hydrocarbons have a higher octane rating in gasoline. Therefore, an important process in producing gasoline is the isomerization of octane to a branched hydrocarbon such as isooctane, 2,2,4-trimethylpentane.

## Alcohols and Ethers

**Methanol, $CH_3OH$, the simplest alcohol.** Methanol is often called *wood alcohol* because it was originally produced by heating wood in the absence of air.

If one of the hydrogen atoms of an alkane is replaced by a hydroxyl (—OH) group, the result is an **alcohol**, ROH. Methanol, $CH_3OH$, and ethanol, $CH_3CH_2OH$, are the most important alcohols, but others are also commercially important (Table 10.7). Notice that several have more than one OH functional group.

More than $5 \times 10^8$ kg of methanol is produced in the United States annually. Most of this production is used to make formaldehyde ($CH_2O$) and acetic acid ($CH_3CO_2H$), both important chemicals in their own right. Methanol is also used as a solvent, as a de-icer in gasoline, and as a fuel in high-powered racing cars. It is found in low concentration in new wine, where it contributes to the odor, or "bouquet." Like ethanol, methanol causes intoxication, but methanol differs in being more poisonous, largely because the human body converts it to formic acid ($HCO_2H$) and formaldehyde ($CH_2O$). These compounds attack the cells of the retina in the eye, leading to permanent blindness.

Ethanol is the "alcohol" of alcoholic beverages, in which it is formed by the anaerobic (without air) fermentation of sugar. On a much larger scale, ethanol for use

**Table 10.6  Common Functional Groups and Derivatives of Alkanes**

| Functional Group* | General Formula* | Class of Compound | Examples |
|---|---|---|---|
| F, Cl, Br, I | RF, RCl, RBr, RI | Haloalkane | $CH_3CH_2Cl$, chloroethane |
| OH | ROH | Alcohol | $CH_3CH_2OH$, ethanol |
| OR′ | ROR′ | Ether | $(CH_3CH_2)_2O$, diethyl ether |
| $NH_2$† | $RNH_2$ | (Primary) Amine | $CH_3CH_2NH_2$, ethylamine |
| —CHO (—CH with =O) | RCHO | Aldehyde | $CH_3CHO$, ethanal (acetaldehyde) |
| —C(=O)—R′ | RCOR′ | Ketone | $CH_3COCH_3$, propanone (acetone) |
| —C(=O)—OH | $RCO_2H$ | Carboxylic acid | $CH_3CO_2H$, ethanoic acid (acetic acid) |
| —C(=O)—OR′ | $RCO_2R′$ | Ester | $CH_3CO_2CH_3$, methyl acetate |
| —C(=O)—$NH_2$ | $RCONH_2$ | Amide | $CH_3CONH_2$, acetamide |

* R and R′ can be the same or different hydrocarbon groups.
† Secondary amines ($R_2NH$) and tertiary amines ($R_3N$) are also possible, see discussion in the text.

as a fuel is made by fermentation of corn and other plant materials. Some ethanol (about 5%) is made from petroleum, by the reaction of ethylene and water.

$$CH_2{=}CH_2 (g) + H_2O(g) \xrightarrow{catalyst} CH_3CH_2OH(\ell)$$

ethylene → ethanol

Beginning with three-carbon alcohols, structural isomers are possible. For example, 1-propanol and 2-propanol (common names, propyl alcohol and isopropyl alcohol) are different compounds (Table 10.7).

Ethylene glycol and glycerol are common alcohols having two and three —OH groups, respectively. Ethylene glycol is used as antifreeze in automobiles. Glycerol's

**Table 10.7  Some Important Alcohols**

| Condensed Formula | BP (°C) | Systematic Name | Common Name | Use |
|---|---|---|---|---|
| $CH_3OH$ | 65.0 | Methanol | Methyl alcohol | Fuel, gasoline additive, making formaldehyde |
| $CH_3CH_2OH$ | 78.5 | Ethanol | Ethyl alcohol | Beverages, gasoline additive, solvent |
| $CH_3CH_2CH_2OH$ | 97.4 | 1-Propanol | Propyl alcohol | Industrial solvent |
| $CH_3CH(OH)CH_3$ | 82.4 | 2-Propanol | Isopropyl alcohol | Rubbing alcohol |
| $HOCH_2CH_2OH$ | 198 | 1,2-Ethanediol | Ethylene glycol | Antifreeze |
| $HOCH_2CH(OH)CH_2OH$ | 290 | 1,2,3-Propanetriol | Glycerol (glycerin) | Moisturizer in consumer products |

**Rubbing alcohol.** Common rubbing alcohol is 2-propanol, also called *isopropyl alcohol*.

**FIGURE 10.8**  Nitroglycerin.
**(a)** Concentrated nitric acid and glycerin react to form an oily, highly unstable compound called *nitroglycerin*, $C_3H_5(ONO_2)_3$. **(b)** Nitroglycerin is more stable if absorbed onto an inert solid, a combination called *dynamite*. **(c)** The fortune of Alfred Nobel (1833–1896), built on the manufacture of dynamite, now funds the Nobel Prizes.

(a)          (b)          (c)

most common use is as a softener in soaps and lotions. It is also a raw material for the preparation of nitroglycerin (Figure 10.8).

|                  | H   H                    | H   H   H                    |
|------------------|--------------------------|------------------------------|
|                  | H—C—C—H                  | H—C—C—C—H                    |
|                  | OH  OH                   | OH  OH  OH                   |
| Systematic name: | 1,2-ethanediol           | 1,2,3-propanetriol           |
| Common name:     | ethylene glycol          | glycerol or glycerin         |

**Ethers** have the general formula ROR′. The best-known ether is diethyl ether, $CH_3CH_2OCH_2CH_3$. Lacking an —OH group, the properties of ethers are in sharp contrast to those of alcohols. Diethyl ether, for example, has a lower boiling point (34.5 °C) than ethanol, $CH_3CH_2OH$ (78.3 °C), and is only slightly soluble in water.

## EXAMPLE 10.6    Structural Isomers of Alcohols

**Problem**  How many different alcohols are derivatives of pentane? Draw their structures, and name each alcohol.

**What Do You Know?**  The formula for pentane is $C_5H_{12}$. In an alcohol an —OH group will replace one H atom.

**Strategy**  Pentane, $C_5H_{12}$, has a five-carbon chain. An —OH group can replace a hydrogen atom on one of the carbon atoms. Alcohols are named as derivatives of the alkane (pentane) by replacing the "-e" at the end with "-ol" and indicating the position of the —OH group by a numerical prefix (Appendix E).

**Solution**  Three different alcohols are possible, depending on whether the —OH group is placed on the first, second, or third carbon atom in the chain. (The fourth and fifth positions are identical to the second and first positions in the chain, respectively.)

$$
\begin{array}{cccccc}
 & H & H & H & H & H \\
 & | & | & | & | & | \\
HO— & C & —C & —C & —C & —C—H \\
 & | & | & | & | & | \\
 & H & H & H & H & H
\end{array}
$$

1-pentanol

2-pentanol

3-pentanol

**Think about Your Answer** Additional structural isomers with the formula $C_5H_{11}OH$ are possible in which the longest carbon chain has three C atoms (one isomer) or four C atoms (four isomers).

**Check Your Understanding**

Draw the structure of 1-butanol and alcohols that are structural isomers of the compound.

## Properties of Alcohols

Methane, $CH_4$, is a gas (boiling point, $-161$ °C) with low solubility in water. Methanol, $CH_3OH$, by contrast, is a liquid that is *miscible* with water in all proportions. The boiling point of methanol, 65 °C, is 226 °C higher than the boiling point of methane. What a difference the addition of a single atom into the structure can make in the properties of simple molecules!

Alcohols are related to water, with one of the H atoms of $H_2O$ being replaced by an organic group. If a methyl group is substituted for one of the hydrogens of water, methanol results. Ethanol has a $—C_2H_5$ (ethyl) group, and propanol has a $—C_3H_7$ (propyl) group in place of one of the hydrogens of water. Viewing alcohols as related to water also helps in understanding their properties.

The two parts of methanol, the $—CH_3$ group and the $—OH$ group, contribute to its properties. For example, methanol will burn, a property associated with hydrocarbons. On the other hand, its boiling point is more like that of water. The temperature at which a substance boils is related to the forces of attraction between molecules, called *intermolecular forces:* The stronger the attractive, intermolecular forces in a sample, the higher the boiling point (▶ Section 12.4). These forces are particularly strong in water, a result of the polarity of the $—OH$ group in this molecule (◀ Section 8.8). Methanol is also a polar molecule, and it is the polar $—OH$ group that leads to a high boiling point. In contrast, methane is nonpolar and its low boiling point is the result of weak intermolecular forces.

It is also possible to explain the differences in the solubility of methane, methanol, and other alcohols in water (Figure 10.9). The solubility of methanol and ethylene glycol is conferred by the polar $—OH$ portion of the molecule. Methane, which is nonpolar, has low water-solubility.

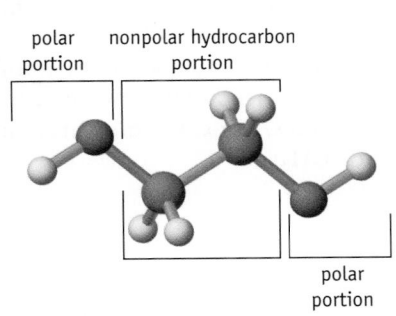

polar portion    nonpolar hydrocarbon portion

polar portion

Methanol is often added to automobile gasoline tanks in the winter to prevent water in the fuel lines from freezing. It is soluble in water and lowers the water's freezing point.

Ethylene glycol is used in automobile radiators. It is soluble in water, and lowers the freezing point and raises the boiling point of the water in the cooling system. (▶ Section 14.4.)

Ethylene glycol, a major component of automobile antifreeze, is completely miscible with water.

**FIGURE 10.9** Properties and uses of two alcohols, methanol and ethylene glycol.

As the size of the alkyl group in an alcohol increases, the alcohol boiling point rises, a general trend seen in families of similar compounds and related to molar mass (see Table 10.7). The solubility in water in this series decreases. Methanol and ethanol are completely miscible in water, whereas 1-propanol is moderately water-soluble; 1-butanol is less soluble than 1-propanol. With an increase in the size of the hydrocarbon group, the organic group (the nonpolar part of the molecule) has become a larger fraction of the molecule, and properties associated with nonpolarity begin to dominate. Space-filling models show that in methanol, the polar and nonpolar parts of the molecule are approximately similar in size, but in 1-butanol the —OH group is less than 20% of the molecule. The molecule is less like water and more "organic." Electrostatic potential surfaces amplify this point.

methanol          1-butanol

## Amines

It is often convenient to think about water and ammonia as being similar molecules: They are the simplest hydrogen compounds of adjacent second-period elements. Both are polar and exhibit some similar chemistry, such as protonation (to give $H_3O^+$ and $NH_4^+$) and deprotonation (to give $OH^-$ and $NH_2^-$).

This comparison of water and ammonia can be extended to alcohols and amines. Alcohols have formulas related to water in which one hydrogen in $H_2O$ is replaced with an organic group (R—OH). In organic **amines**, one or more hydrogen atoms of $NH_3$ are replaced with an organic group. Amine structures are similar to ammonia's structure; that is, the geometry about the N atom is trigonal pyramidal.

Amines are categorized based on the number of organic substituents as primary (one organic group), secondary (two organic groups), or tertiary (three organic groups). As examples, consider the three amines with methyl groups: $CH_3NH_2$, $(CH_3)_2NH$, and $(CH_3)_3N$.

$CH_3NH_2$                $(CH_3)_2NH$              $(CH_3)_3N$
primary amine          secondary amine          tertiary amine
methylamine            dimethylamine            trimethylamine

## Properties of Amines

Amines usually have offensive odors. You know what the odor is if you have ever smelled decaying fish. Two appropriately named amines, putrescine and cadaverine, add to the odor of urine, rotten meat, and bad breath.

$H_2NCH_2CH_2CH_2CH_2NH_2$
putrescine
1,4-butanediamine

$H_2NCH_2CH_2CH_2CH_2CH_2NH_2$
cadaverine
1,5-pentanediamine

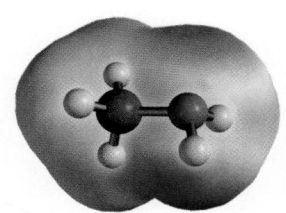

**Electrostatic potential surface for methylamine.** The surface for methylamine shows that this water-soluble amine is polar with the partial negative charge on the N atom.

The smallest amines are water-soluble, but most amines are not. All amines are bases, however, and they react with acids to give salts, many of which are water-soluble. As with ammonia, the reactions involve adding $H^+$ to the lone pair of electrons on the N atom. This is illustrated by the reaction of aniline (aminobenzene) with $H_2SO_4$ to give anilinium hydrogen sulfate.

$$C_6H_5NH_2(aq) + H_2SO_4(aq) \longrightarrow C_6H_5NH_3^+(aq) + HSO_4^-(aq)$$

aniline                    anilinium ion

The facts that an amine can be protonated and that the proton can be removed again by treating the compound with a base have practical and physiological importance. Nicotine in cigarettes is normally found in the protonated form. (This water-soluble form is often also used in insecticides.) Adding a base such as ammonia removes the $H^+$ ion to leave nicotine in its "free-base" form.

$$NicH_2^{2+}(aq) + 2\ NH_3(aq) \rightarrow Nic(aq) + 2\ NH_4^+(aq)$$

In this form, nicotine is much more readily absorbed by the skin and mucous membranes, so the compound is a much more potent poison.

nicotine

**Nicotine, an amine.** Two nitrogen atoms in the nicotine molecule can be protonated, which is the form in which nicotine is normally found. The protons can be removed, by treating it with a base. This "free-base" form is much more poisonous and addictive.

---

**REVIEW & CHECK FOR SECTION 10.3**

1. How many different compounds (alcohols and ethers) exist with the molecular formula $C_4H_{10}O$?

   (a) 2    (b) 3    (c) 4    (d) more than 4

2. Which of the following compounds is not chiral, that is, which does not possess a carbon atom attached to four different groups?

   (a) 2-propanol    (c) 2-methyl-3-pentanol
   (b) 2-butanol    (d) 1,2-propanediol

3. What is the hybridization of nitrogen in dimethylamine?

   (a) $sp^3$    (c) $sp$
   (b) $sp^2$    (d) nitrogen is not hybridized

4. What chemical reagent will react with the ethylammonium ion $[CH_3CH_2NH_3]^+$ to form ethylamine?

   (a) $O_2$    (b) $N_2$    (c) $H_2SO_4$    (d) NaOH

## 10.4 Compounds with a Carbonyl Group

Formaldehyde, acetic acid, and acetone are among the organic compounds referred to in previous examples. These compounds have a common structural feature: Each contains a trigonal-planar carbon atom doubly bonded to an oxygen. The C=O group is called the **carbonyl group**, and these compounds are members of a large class of compounds called **carbonyl compounds**.

## An Awakening with L-DOPA

From about 1917 to 1928, millions of people worldwide were affected by a condition known as *encephalitis lethargica*, or a form of sleeping sickness. Those who suffered from the condition were in a state of semi-consciousness that lasted for decades. In his book, *Awakenings*, Oliver Sacks wrote about treating a patient with the compound L-DOPA, which "was started in early March 1969 and raised by degrees to 5.0 g a day. Little effect was seen for two weeks, and then a sudden 'conversion' took place. . . . Mr. L enjoyed a mobility, a health, and a happiness which he had not known in thirty years. Everything about him filled with delight: he was like a man who had awoken from a nightmare or a serious illness . . . ."

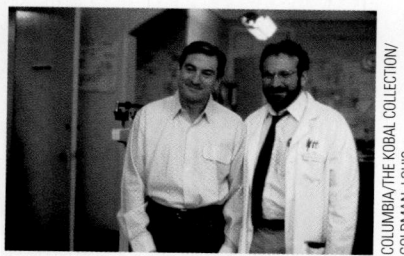

**Robert DeNiro as Leonard Lowe and Robin Williams as Malcolm Sayer, a fictionalized portrayal of Oliver Sacks, in the movie version of *Awakenings*.**

If you have read the book or have seen the movie of the same name, you know that Mr. L eventually could not tolerate the treatment, but that Sacks treated many others who benefitted from it. L-DOPA is now widely used in the treatment of another condition, Parkinson's disease, a degenerative disorder of the central nervous system.

L-DOPA or L-dopamine (L-3,4-dihydroxy–phenylalanine) is chiral. The symbol L stands for "levo," which means a solution of the compound rotates polarized light to the left.

The compound is also a derivative of phenylalanine, one of many naturally occurring alpha-amino acids that play such an important role in protein formation and other natural processes.

L-DOPA also illustrates why chiral molecules are so interesting to chemists: Only the "levo" enantiomer is physiologically active. The enantiomer that rotates polarized light in the opposite direction has no biological function.

L-DOPA, $C_9H_{11}NO_4$,
a treatment for Parkinson's disease

When L-DOPA is ingested, it is metabolized to dopamine in a process that removes the carboxylic acid group, $—CO_2H$, and it is dopamine that is physiologically active. Dopamine is a neurotransmitter that occurs in a wide variety of animals.

dopamine, $C_8H_{11}NO_2$, a neurotransmitter

Interestingly, both L-DOPA and dopamine are closely related to another amine, epinephrine. This is sometimes referred to as adrenaline, the hormone that is released from the adrenal glands when there is an emergency or danger threatens.

epinephrine or adrenaline, $C_9H_{13}NO_3$

**Questions:**
1. L-DOPA is chiral. What is the center of chirality in the molecule?
2. Is either dopamine or epinephrine chiral? If so, what is the center of chirality?
3. If you are treated with 5.0 g of L-DOPA, what amount (in moles) is this?

**Answers to these questions are available in Appendix N.**

**References:**
1. Oliver Sacks, *Awakenings*, Vintage Books, New York, 1999.
2. N. Angier, "A Molecule of Motivation, Dopamine Excels at its Task," *New York Times*, October 27, 2009.

| carbonyl group | formaldehyde $CH_2O$ *aldehyde* | acetic acid $CH_3CO_2H$ *carboxylic acid* | acetone $CH_3COCH_3$ *ketone* |
|---|---|---|---|

Primary alcohol: ethanol

Secondary alcohol: 2-propanol

Tertiary alcohol: 2-methyl-2-propanol

In this section, we will examine five groups of carbonyl compounds (Table 10.6, page 459):

- *Aldehydes* (RCHO) have an organic group (—R) and an H atom attached to a carbonyl group.
- *Ketones* (RCOR′) have two —R groups attached to the carbonyl carbon; they may be the same groups, as in acetone, or different groups.
- *Carboxylic acids* ($RCO_2H$) have an —R group and an —OH group attached to the carbonyl carbon.
- *Esters* ($RCO_2R′$) have —R and —OR′ groups attached to the carbonyl carbon.
- *Amides* ($RCONR_2′$, RCONHR′, and $RCONH_2$) have an —R group and an amino group (—$NH_2$, —NHR, —$NR_2$) bonded to the carbonyl carbon.

Aldehydes, ketones, and carboxylic acids are oxidation products of alcohols and, indeed, are commonly made by this route. The product obtained through oxidation of an alcohol depends on the alcohol's structure, which is classified according to the number of carbon atoms bonded to the C atom bearing the —OH group. *Primary alcohols* have one carbon and two hydrogen atoms attached, whereas *secondary alcohols* have two carbon atoms and one hydrogen atom attached. *Tertiary alcohols* have three carbon atoms attached to the C atom bearing the —OH group.

A *primary alcohol* is oxidized in two steps, first to an aldehyde and then to a carboxylic acid:

$$R—CH_2—OH \xrightarrow[\text{agent}]{\text{oxidizing}} R—\overset{\overset{\textstyle O}{\|}}{C}—H \xrightarrow[\text{agent}]{\text{oxidizing}} R—\overset{\overset{\textstyle O}{\|}}{C}—OH$$

primary alcohol          aldehyde          carboxylic acid

For example, the air oxidation of ethanol in wine produces wine vinegar, the most important ingredient of which is acetic acid.

$$\text{ethanol} \xrightarrow{\text{oxidizing agent}} \text{acetic acid}$$

ethanol          acetic acid

Acids have a sour taste. The word "vinegar" (from the French *vin aigre*) means sour wine. A device to test one's breath for alcohol relies on the oxidation of ethanol (Figure 10.10).

Oxidation of a *secondary alcohol* produces a ketone:

$$R—\overset{\overset{\textstyle OH}{|}}{\underset{\underset{\textstyle H}{|}}{C}}—R′ \xrightarrow[\text{agent}]{\text{oxidizing}} R—\overset{\overset{\textstyle O}{\|}}{C}—R′$$

secondary alcohol          ketone

(—R and —R′ are organic groups. They may be the same or different.)

Common oxidizing agents used for these reactions are reagents such as $KMnO_4$ and $K_2Cr_2O_7$ (◄ Table 3.3).

**FIGURE 10.10  Alcohol tester.** This device for testing a person's breath for the presence of ethanol relies on the oxidation of the alcohol. If present, ethanol is oxidized by potassium dichromate, $K_2Cr_2O_7$, to acetaldehyde, and then to acetic acid. The yellow-orange dichromate ion is reduced to green $Cr^{3+}$(aq), the color change indicating that ethanol was present.

© Cengage Learning/Charles D. Winters

Finally, tertiary alcohols do *not* react with the usual oxidizing agents.

$$(CH_3)_3COH \xrightarrow{\text{oxidizing agent}} \text{no reaction}$$

## Aldehydes and Ketones

**Aldehydes** and **ketones** can have pleasant odors and are often used in fragrances. Benzaldehyde is responsible for the odor of almonds and cherries; cinnamaldehyde is found in the bark of the cinnamon tree; and the ketone 4-(*p*-hydroxyphenyl)-2-butanone is responsible for the odor of ripe raspberries (a favorite of the authors of this book). Table 10.8 lists several simple aldehydes and ketones.

benzaldehyde, $C_6H_5CHO$     *trans*-cinnamaldehyde, $C_6H_5CH=CHCHO$

Aldehydes and ketones are the oxidation products of primary and secondary alcohols, respectively. The reverse reactions—reduction of aldehydes to primary alcohols and reduction of ketones to secondary alcohols—are also known. Commonly used reagents for such reductions are $NaBH_4$ and $LiAlH_4$, although $H_2$ is used on an industrial scale.

$$\underset{\text{aldehyde}}{R-\overset{\overset{\displaystyle O}{\|}}{C}-H} \xrightarrow{NaBH_4 \text{ or } LiAlH_4} \underset{\text{primary alcohol}}{R-\overset{\overset{\displaystyle OH}{|}}{\underset{\underset{\displaystyle H}{|}}{C}}-H}$$

$$\underset{\text{ketone}}{R-\overset{\overset{\displaystyle O}{\|}}{C}-R} \xrightarrow{NaBH_4 \text{ or } LiAlH_4} \underset{\text{secondary alcohol}}{R-\overset{\overset{\displaystyle OH}{|}}{\underset{\underset{\displaystyle H}{|}}{C}}-R}$$

**Table 10.8 Simple Aldehydes and Ketones**

| Structure | Common Name | Systematic Name | BP (°C) |
|---|---|---|---|
| $\overset{\overset{\displaystyle O}{\|}}{HCH}$ | Formaldehyde | Methanal | −19 |
| $\overset{\overset{\displaystyle O}{\|}}{CH_3CH}$ | Acetaldehyde | Ethanal | 20 |
| $\overset{\overset{\displaystyle O}{\|}}{CH_3CCH_3}$ | Acetone | Propanone | 56 |
| $\overset{\overset{\displaystyle O}{\|}}{CH_3CCH_2CH_3}$ | Methyl ethyl ketone | Butanone | 80 |
| $\overset{\overset{\displaystyle O}{\|}}{CH_3CH_2CCH_2CH_3}$ | Diethyl ketone | 3-Pentanone | 102 |

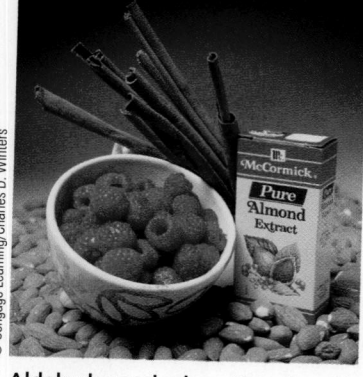

**Aldehydes and odors.** The odors of almonds and cinnamon are due to aldehydes, whereas the odor of fresh raspberries comes from a ketone.

## Carboxylic Acids

Acetic acid is the most common and most important **carboxylic acid**. For many years, acetic acid was made by oxidizing ethanol produced by fermentation. Now, however, acetic acid is generally made by combining carbon monoxide and methanol in the presence of a catalyst:

$$CH_3OH(\ell) + CO(g) \xrightarrow{\text{catalyst}} CH_3CO_2H(\ell)$$
$$\text{methanol} \qquad\qquad\qquad \text{acetic acid}$$

About 1 billion kilograms of acetic acid are produced annually in the United States for use in plastics, synthetic fibers, and fungicides.

Many organic acids are found naturally (Table 10.9). Acids are recognizable by their sour taste (Figure 10.11) and are found in common foods: Citric acid in fruits, acetic acid in vinegar, and tartaric acid in grapes are just three examples.

Some carboxylic acids have common names derived from the source of the acid (Table 10.9). Because formic acid is found in ants, its name comes from the Latin word for ant (*formica*). Butyric acid gives rancid butter its unpleasant odor, and the name is related to the Latin word for butter (*butyrum*). The systematic names of acids (Table 10.10) are formed by dropping the "-e" on the name of the corresponding alkane and adding "-oic" (and the word "acid").

---

**A CLOSER LOOK**

## Glucose and Other Sugars

Glucose, the most common, naturally occurring carbohydrate, has the alcohol and carbonyl functional groups.

As their name implies, formulas of most carbohydrates can be written as though they are a combination of carbon and water, $C_x(H_2O)_y$. Thus, the formula of glucose, $C_6H_{12}O_6$, is equivalent to $C_6(H_2O)_6$. This compound is a sugar, or, more accurately, a **monosaccharide**.

Carbohydrates are polyhydroxy aldehydes or ketones. Glucose is an interesting molecule that exists in three different isomeric forms. Two of the isomers contain six-member rings; the third isomer features a chain structure. In solution, the three forms rapidly interconvert.

Notice that glucose is a chiral molecule. In the chain structure, four of the carbon atoms are bonded to four different groups. In nature, glucose occurs in just one of its enantiomeric forms; thus, a solution of glucose rotates polarized light.

**Home test for glucose.**

Knowing glucose's structure allows one to predict some of its properties. With five polar —OH groups in the molecule, glucose is, not surprisingly, soluble in water.

The aldehyde group is susceptible to chemical oxidation to form a carboxylic acid, and detection of glucose (in urine or blood) takes advantage of this fact. Diagnostic tests for glucose involve oxidation with subsequent detection of the products.

Glucose is in a class of sugar molecules called hexoses, monosaccharides having six carbon atoms. 2-Deoxyribose, the sugar in the backbone of the DNA molecule, is a pentose, a molecule with five carbon atoms.

Glucose and other monosaccharides serve as the building blocks for larger carbohydrates. Sucrose, or "table sugar," is a disaccharide and is formed from a molecule of glucose and a molecule of fructose, another monosaccharide. Starch is a polymer composed of many monosaccharide units.

α-D-glucose   open-chain form   β-D-glucose

deoxyribose, a pentose, part of the DNA backbone

α-D-glucose

fructose

**The structure of sucrose.** Sucrose is formed from α-D-glucose and fructose. An ether linkage is formed by loss of $H_2O$ from two —OH groups.

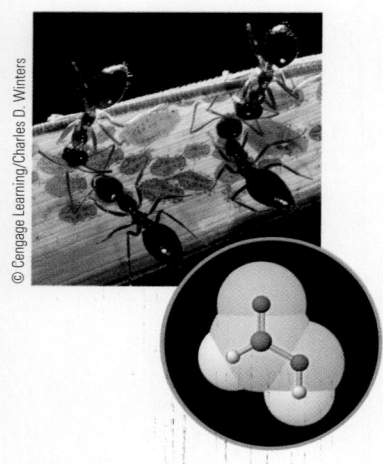

Formic acid, HCO₂H. This acid puts the sting in ant bites.

**Table 10.9 Some Naturally Occurring Carboxylic Acids**

| Name | Structure | Natural Source |
|------|-----------|----------------|
| Benzoic acid | ⬡—CO₂H | Berries |
| Citric acid | HO₂C—CH₂—C(OH)(CO₂H)—CH₂—CO₂H | Citrus fruits |
| Lactic acid | H₃C—CH(OH)—CO₂H | Sour milk |
| Malic acid | HO₂C—CH₂—CH(OH)—CO₂H | Apples |
| Oleic acid | CH₃(CH₂)₇—CH=CH—(CH₂)₇—CO₂H | Vegetable oils |
| Oxalic acid | HO₂C—CO₂H | Rhubarb, spinach, cabbage, tomatoes |
| Stearic acid | CH₃(CH₂)₁₆—CO₂H | Animal fats |
| Tartaric acid | HO₂C—CH(OH)—CH(OH)—CO₂H | Grape juice, wine |

Because of the substantial electronegativity of oxygen, the two O atoms of the carboxylic acid group are slightly negatively charged, and the H atom of the —OH group is positively charged. This charge distribution has several important implications:

- The polar acetic acid molecule dissolves readily in water, which you already know because vinegar is an aqueous solution of acetic acid. (Acids with larger organic groups are less soluble, however.)
- The hydrogen of the —OH group is the acidic hydrogen. As noted in Chapter 3, acetic acid is a weak acid in water, as are most other organic acids.

Carboxylic acids undergo a number of reactions. Among these is the reduction of the acid (with reagents such as $LiAlH_4$ or $NaBH_4$) first to an aldehyde and then

**FIGURE 10.11 Acetic acid in bread.** Acetic acid is produced in bread leavened with the yeast *Saccharomyces exigus*. Another group of bacteria, *Lactobacillus sanfrancisco*, contributes to the flavor of sourdough bread. These bacteria metabolize the sugar maltose, excreting acetic acid and lactic acid, CH₃CH(OH)CO₂H, thereby giving the bread its unique sour taste.

**Table 10.10 Some Simple Carboxylic Acids**

| Structure | Common Name | Systematic Name | BP (°C) |
|-----------|-------------|-----------------|---------|
| HCOH (O) | Formic acid | Methanoic acid | 101 |
| CH₃COH (O) | Acetic acid | Ethanoic acid | 118 |
| CH₃CH₂COH (O) | Propionic acid | Propanoic acid | 141 |
| CH₃(CH₂)₂COH (O) | Butyric acid | Butanoic acid | 163 |
| CH₃(CH₂)₃COH (O) | Valeric acid | Pentanoic acid | 187 |

to an alcohol. For example, acetic acid is reduced first to acetaldehyde and then to ethanol.

$$CH_3CO_2H \xrightarrow{LiAlH_4} CH_3CHO \xrightarrow{LiAlH_4} CH_3CH_2OH$$

acetic acid       acetaldehyde       ethanol

Yet another important aspect of carboxylic acid chemistry is the reaction with bases to give carboxylate anions. For example, acetic acid reacts with hydroxide ions to give acetate ions and water.

$$CH_3CO_2H(aq) + OH^-(aq) \rightarrow CH_3CO_2^-(aq) + H_2O(\ell)$$

## Esters

Carboxylic acids ($RCO_2H$) react with alcohols ($R'OH$) to form esters ($RCO_2R'$) in an **esterification** reaction. (These reactions are generally carried out in the presence of strong acids because acids speed up the reaction.)

Acetic acid. The H atom of the carboxylic acid group ($-CO_2H$) is the acidic proton of this and other carboxylic acids.

carboxylic acid       alcohol       ester

$$CH_3COH + CH_3CH_2OH \xrightarrow{H_3O^+} CH_3COCH_2CH_3 + H_2O$$

acetic acid   ethanol       ethyl acetate

When a carboxylic acid and an alcohol react to form an ester, the OR' group of the alcohol ends up as part of the ester (as shown above). This fact is known because of isotope labeling experiments. If the reaction is run using an alcohol in which the alcohol oxygen is $^{18}O$, all of the $^{18}O$ ends up in the ester molecule.

Table 10.11 lists a few common esters and the acid and alcohol from which they are formed. The two-part name of an ester is given by (1) the name of the hydrocarbon group from the alcohol and (2) the name of the carboxylate group derived from the acid name by replacing "-ic" with "-ate." For example, ethanol (commonly called *ethyl alcohol*) and acetic acid combine to give the ester ethyl acetate.

An important reaction of esters is their **hydrolysis** (literally, reaction with water), a reaction that is the reverse of the formation of the ester. The reaction, generally done in the presence of a base such as NaOH, produces the alcohol and a sodium salt of the carboxylic acid:

portion from acetic acid       portion from ethanol

ethyl acetate, an ester
$CH_3CO_2CH_2CH_3$

$$RCOR' + NaOH \xrightarrow[\text{in water}]{\text{heat}} RCO^-Na^+ + R'OH$$

ester                   carboxylate salt  alcohol

$$CH_3COCH_2CH_3 + NaOH \xrightarrow[\text{in water}]{\text{heat}} CH_3CO^-Na^+ + CH_3CH_2OH$$

ethyl acetate                       sodium acetate       ethanol

The carboxylic acid can be recovered if the sodium salt is treated with a strong acid such as HCl:

$$CH_3CO^-Na^+(aq) + HCl(aq) \longrightarrow CH_3COH(aq) + NaCl(aq)$$

sodium acetate                       acetic acid

Esters. Many fruits such as bananas and strawberries as well as consumer products (here, perfume and oil of wintergreen) contain esters.

**Table 10.11 Some Acids, Alcohols, and Their Esters**

| Acid | Alcohol | Ester | Odor of Ester |
|------|---------|-------|---------------|
| $CH_3CO_2H$<br>acetic acid | $CH_3CHCH_2CH_2OH$ (with $CH_3$ branch)<br>3-methyl-1-butanol | $CH_3COCH_2CH_2CHCH_3$ (with O double bond and $CH_3$ branch)<br>3-methylbutyl acetate | Banana |
| $CH_3CH_2CH_2CO_2H$<br>butanoic acid | $CH_3CH_2CH_2CH_2OH$<br>1-butanol | $CH_3CH_2CH_2COCH_2CH_2CH_2CH_3$ (with O double bond)<br>butyl butanoate | Pineapple |
| $CH_3CH_2CH_2CO_2H$<br>butanoic acid | ⬡—$CH_2OH$<br>benzyl alcohol | $CH_3CH_2CH_2COCH_2$—⬡ (with O double bond)<br>benzyl butanoate | Rose |

Unlike the acids from which they are derived, esters often have pleasant odors (Table 10.11). Typical examples are methyl salicylate, or "oil of wintergreen," and benzyl acetate. Methyl salicylate is derived from salicylic acid, the parent compound of aspirin.

Aspirin, a commonly used analgesic. It is based on benzoic acid with an acetate group, —$O_2CCH_3$, in the *ortho* position. Aspirin has both carboxylic acid and ester functional groups.

$$\text{⬡(COH)(OH)} + CH_3OH \longrightarrow \text{⬡(COCH}_3\text{)(OH)} + H_2O$$

salicylic acid     methanol     methyl salicylate, oil of wintergreen

Benzyl acetate, the active component of "oil of jasmine," is formed from benzyl alcohol ($C_6H_5CH_2OH$) and acetic acid. The chemicals are inexpensive, so synthetic jasmine is a common fragrance in less expensive perfumes and toiletries.

$$CH_3COH + \text{⬡—}CH_2OH \longrightarrow CH_3COCH_2\text{—⬡} + H_2O$$

acetic acid     benzyl alcohol     benzyl acetate oil of jasmine

## Amides

An acid and an alcohol react by loss of water to form an ester. In a similar manner, another class of organic compounds—amides—form when an acid reacts with an amine, again with loss of water.

$$R-C-\text{(OH)} + \text{(H)}-N-R' \longrightarrow R-C-N-R' + H_2O$$

carboxylic acid     amine     amide

Amides have an organic group and an amino group (—$NH_2$, —$NHR'$, or —$NR'R$) attached to the carbonyl group.

The C atom involved in the amide bond has three bonded groups and no lone pairs around it. We would predict it should be $sp^2$ hybridized with trigonal-planar geometry and bond angles of approximately 120°—and this is what is found. However, the structure of the amide group offers a surprise. The N atom is also observed to have trigonal-planar geometry with bonds to three attached atoms at 120°. Because the amide nitrogen is surrounded by four pairs of electrons, we would have predicted the N atom would have $sp^3$ hybridization and bond angles of about 109°.

Based on the observed geometry of the amide N atom, the atom is assigned $sp^2$ hybridization. To rationalize the observed angle and to rationalize $sp^2$ hybridization, we can introduce a second resonance form of the amide.

Form B contains a C=N double bond, and the O and N atoms have negative and positive charges, respectively. The N atom can be assigned $sp^2$ hybridization, and the π bond in B arises from overlap of p orbitals on C and N.

The second resonance structure for an amide link also explains why the carbon–nitrogen bond is relatively short, about 132 pm, a value between that of a C—N single bond (149 pm) and a C=N double bond (127 pm). In addition, restricted rotation occurs around the C=N bond, making it possible for isomeric species to exist if the two groups bonded to N are different.

The amide grouping is particularly important in some synthetic polymers (Section 10.5) and in proteins, where it is referred to as a *peptide* link. The compound *N*-acetyl-*p*-aminophenol, an analgesic known by the generic name acetaminophen, is another amide. Use of this compound as an analgesic was apparently discovered by accident when a common organic compound called acetanilide (like acetaminophen but without the —OH group) was mistakenly put into a prescription for a patient. Acetanilide acts as an analgesic, but it can be toxic. An —OH group *para* to the amide group makes the compound nontoxic, an interesting example of how a seemingly small structural difference affects chemical function.

An amide, *N*-methylacetamide. The *N*-methyl portion of the name derives from the amine portion of the molecule, where the *N* indicates that the methyl group is attached to the nitrogen atom. The "-acet" portion of the name indicates the acid on which the amide is based. The electrostatic potential surface shows the polarity and planarity of the amide linkage.

Acetaminophen, *N*-acetyl-*p*-aminophenol. This analgesic is an amide. It is used in over-the-counter painkillers such as Tylenol.

## EXAMPLE 10.7    Functional Group Chemistry

**Problem**

(a)  Draw the structure of the product of the reaction between propanoic acid and 1-propanol. What is the systematic name of the reaction product, and what functional group does it contain?

(b)  What is the result of reacting 2-butanol with an oxidizing agent? Give the name, and draw the structure of the reaction product.

**What Do You Know?** From the material covered in this chapter, you should know the names, structures, and common chemical reactions of organic compounds mentioned in this question.

**Strategy** Determine the products of these reactions, based on the discussion in the text. Propanoic acid is a carboxylic acid (page 468), and 1-propanol and 2-butanol are both alcohols. Consult the discussion regarding their chemistry.

**Solution**

(a)  Carboxylic acids such as propanoic acid react with alcohols to give esters.

$$
\underset{\text{propanoic acid}}{CH_3CH_2\overset{\overset{\displaystyle O}{\|}}{C}OH} + \underset{\text{1-propanol}}{CH_3CH_2CH_2OH} \longrightarrow \underset{\text{propyl propanoate, an ester}}{CH_3CH_2\overset{\overset{\displaystyle O}{\|}}{C}OCH_2CH_2CH_3} + H_2O
$$

(b)  2-Butanol is a secondary alcohol. Such alcohols are oxidized to ketones.

$$
\underset{\text{2-butanol}}{CH_3\overset{\overset{\displaystyle OH}{|}}{C}HCH_2CH_3} \xrightarrow{\text{oxidizing agent}} \underset{\text{butanone, a ketone}}{CH_3\overset{\overset{\displaystyle O}{\|}}{C}CH_2CH_3}
$$

**Think about Your Answer**  Students sometimes find themselves overwhelmed by the large amount of information presented in organic chemistry. Your study of this material will be more successful if you carefully organize information based on the type of compound.

**Check Your Understanding**

(a)  Name each of the following compounds and its functional group.

$$
\text{(1)  } CH_3CH_2CH_2OH \qquad \text{(2)  } CH_3\overset{\overset{\displaystyle O}{\|}}{C}OH \qquad \text{(3)  } CH_3CH_2NH_2
$$

(b)  Name the product from the reaction of compounds 1 and 2 above.

(c)  What is the name and structure of the product from the oxidation of 1 with an excess of oxidizing agent?

(d)  Give the name and structure of the compound that results from combining 2 and 3.

(e)  What is the result of adding an acid (say HCl) to compound 3?

---

**REVIEW & CHECK FOR SECTION 10.4**

1.  How many aldehydes and ketones are possible that have the formula $C_5H_{10}O$ and that have a five-carbon chain?

   (a)  2 aldehydes and 1 ketone           (c)  1 aldehyde and 1 ketone

   (b)  1 aldehyde and 3 ketones           (d)  1 aldehyde and 2 ketones

2.  Addition of water to 2-butene gives a single product. Oxidation of this product with $K_2Cr_2O_7$ gives a single compound. What is its name?

   (a)  butanal                            (c)  2-butanol

   (b)  2-butanone                         (d)  butane

3.  What is the bond angle of the O—C—O group of atoms in benzoic acid and what is the hybridization of the carbonyl carbon atom?

   (a)  90°, not hybridized                (c)  180°, *sp* hybridized

   (b)  109.5°, *sp*$^3$ hybridized        (d)  120°, *sp*$^2$ hybridized

4.  A sample of ethanol is divided into two portions. One portion is oxidized with excess oxidizing agent to give an acid. The acid and the remaining alcohol react to give an ester. What is the name of the ester?

   (a)  ethyl propanoate                   (c)  ethyl ethanoate

   (b)  ethanoic acid                      (d)  methyl propanoate

# 10.5 Polymers

We turn now to the very large molecules known as *polymers*. These can be either synthetic materials or naturally occurring substances such as proteins or nucleic acids. Although many different types of polymers are known and they have widely different compositions and structures, their properties are understandable, based on the principles developed for small molecules.

## Classifying Polymers

The word *polymer* means "many parts" (from the Greek, *poly* and *meros*). **Polymers** are giant molecules made by chemically joining together many small molecules called **monomers**. Polymer molar masses range from thousands to millions.

Extensive use of synthetic polymers is a fairly recent development. A few synthetic polymers (Bakelite, rayon, and celluloid) were made early in the 20th century, but most of the products with which you are likely to be familiar originated in the last 75 years. By 1976, synthetic polymers outstripped steel as the most widely used materials in the United States. The average production of synthetic polymers in the United States is now 150 kg or more per person annually.

The polymer industry classifies polymers in several different ways. One is their response to heating. **Thermoplastics** (such as polyethylene) soften and flow when they are heated and harden when they are cooled. **Thermosetting plastics** (such as Formica) are initially soft but set to a solid when heated and cannot be resoftened. Another classification scheme depends on the end use of the polymer—for example, plastics, fibers, elastomers, coatings, and adhesives.

A more chemically oriented approach to polymer classification is based on the method of synthesis. **Addition polymers** are made by directly adding monomer units together. **Condensation polymers** are made by combining monomer units and splitting out a small molecule, often water.

## Addition Polymers

Polyethylene, polystyrene, and polyvinyl chloride (PVC) are common addition polymers (Figure 10.12). They are built by "adding together" simple alkenes such as ethylene ($CH_2{=}CH_2$), styrene ($C_6H_5CH{=}CH_2$), and vinyl chloride ($CH_2{=}CHCl$). These and other addition polymers (Table 10.12), all derived from alkenes, have widely varying properties and uses.

### Polyethylene and Other Polyolefins

Polyethylene is by far the leader in amount of polymer produced. Ethylene ($C_2H_4$), the monomer from which polyethylene is made, is a product of petroleum refining and one of the top five chemicals produced in the United States. When ethylene is

**(a)** High-density polyethylene.

**(b)** Polystyrene.

**(c)** Polyvinyl chloride.

**FIGURE 10.12  Common polymer-based consumer products.** Recycling information is provided on most plastics (often molded into the bottom of bottles). High-density polyethylene is designated with a "2" inside a triangular symbol and the letters "HDPE." Polystyrene is designated by "6" with the symbol PS, and polyvinyl chloride, PVC, is designated with a "3" inside a triangular symbol with the symbol "V" or "PVC" below.

**(a)** The linear form, high-density polyethylene (HDPE).   **(b)** Branched chains occur in low-density polyethylene (LDPE).   **(c)** Cross-linked polyethylene (CLPE).

**FIGURE 10.13** **Polyethylene.**

heated to between 100 and 250 °C at a pressure of 1000 to 3000 atm in the presence of a catalyst, polymers with molar masses up to several million are formed. The reaction can be expressed as the chemical equation:

$$n \; H_2C{=}CH_2 \longrightarrow \left( \begin{array}{cc} \text{H} & \text{H} \\ | & | \\ \text{C} & \text{C} \\ | & | \\ \text{H} & \text{H} \end{array} \right)_n$$

ethylene            polyethylene

The abbreviated formula of the reaction product, $({-}CH_2CH_2{-})_n$, shows that polyethylene is a chain of carbon atoms, each bearing two hydrogens. The chain length for polyethylene can be very long. A polymer with a molar mass of 1 million would contain almost 36,000 ethylene molecules linked together.

Samples of polyethylene formed under various pressures and catalytic conditions have different properties, as a result of different molecular structures. For example, when chromium(III) oxide is used as a catalyst, the product is almost exclusively a linear chain (Figure 10.13a). If ethylene is heated to 230 °C at high pressure, however, irregular branching occurs. Still other conditions lead to cross-linked polyethylene, in which different chains are linked together (Figures 10.13b and c).

The high–molar-mass chains of linear polyethylene pack closely together and result in a material with a density of 0.97 g/cm³. This material, referred to as high-density polyethylene (HDPE), is hard and tough, which makes it suitable for items such as milk bottles. If the polyethylene chain contains branches, however, the chains cannot pack as closely together, and a lower-density material (0.92 g/cm³) known as low-density polyethylene (LDPE) results. This material is softer and more flexible than HDPE. It is used in plastic wrap and sandwich bags, among other things. Linking up the polymer chains in cross-linked polyethylene (CLPE) causes the material to be even more rigid and inflexible. Plastic bottle caps are often made of CLPE.

Polymers formed from substituted ethylenes ($CH_2{=}CHX$) have a range of properties and uses (Table 10.12). Sometimes, the properties are predictable based on the molecule's structure. Polymers without polar substituent groups, such as polystyrene, often dissolve in organic solvents, a property useful for some types of fabrication (Figure 10.14).

**Polyethylene film.** The polymer film is produced by extruding the molten plastic through a ring-like gap and inflating the film like a balloon.

polymers based on substituted ethylenes, $H_2C{=}CHX$

$$\left( \begin{array}{c} CH_2CH \\ | \\ OH \end{array} \right)_n \qquad \left( \begin{array}{c} CH_2CH \\ | \\ OCCH_3 \\ \| \\ O \end{array} \right)_n \qquad \left( \begin{array}{c} CH_2CH \\ | \end{array} \right)_n$$

polyvinyl alcohol     polyvinyl acetate      polystyrene

**Table 10.12  Ethylene Derivatives That Undergo Addition Polymerization**

| Formula | Monomer Common Name | Polymer Name (Trade Names) | Uses |
|---|---|---|---|
| $H_2C=CH_2$ | Ethylene | Polyethylene (polythene) | Squeeze bottles, bags, films, toys and molded objects, electric insulation |
| $H_2C=CHCH_3$ | Propylene | Polypropylene (Vectra, Herculon) | Bottles, films, indoor-outdoor carpets |
| $H_2C=CHCl$ | Vinyl chloride | Polyvinyl chloride (PVC) | Floor tile, raincoats, pipe |
| $H_2C=CHCN$ | Acrylonitrile | Polyacrylonitrile (Orlan, Acrilan) | Rugs, fabrics |
| $H_2C=CH(C_6H_5)$ | Styrene | Polystyrene (Styrofoam, Styron) | Food and drink coolers, building material insulation |
| $H_2C=CH-O-C(=O)CH_3$ | Vinyl acetate | Polyvinyl acetate (PVA) | Latex paint, adhesives, textile coatings |
| $H_2C=C(CH_3)-C(=O)-O-CH_3$ | Methyl methacrylate | Polymethyl methacrylate (Plexiglas, Lucite) | High-quality transparent objects, latex paints, contact lenses |
| $F_2C=CF_2$ | Tetrafluoroethylene | Polytetrafluoroethylene (Teflon) | Gaskets, insulation, bearings, pan coatings |

Polyvinyl alcohol is a polymer with little affinity for nonpolar solvents but an affinity for water, which is not surprising, based on the large number of polar OH groups (Figure 10.15). Vinyl alcohol itself is not a stable compound (it isomerizes to acetaldehyde $CH_3CHO$), so polyvinyl alcohol cannot be made from this compound. Instead, it is made by hydrolyzing the ester groups in polyvinyl acetate.

$$\left(\begin{matrix} H & H \\ | & | \\ -C-C- \\ | & | \\ H & OCCH_3 \\ & \| \\ & O \end{matrix}\right)_n + n\,H_2O \longrightarrow \left(\begin{matrix} H & H \\ | & | \\ -C-C- \\ | & | \\ H & OH \end{matrix}\right)_n + n\,CH_3CO_2H$$

Solubility in water or organic solvents can be a liability for polymers. The many uses of polytetrafluoroethylene [Teflon, $(-CF_2CF_2-)_n$] stem from the fact that it does not interact with water or organic solvents.

Polystyrene, with $n = 5700$, is a clear, hard, colorless solid that can be molded easily at 250 °C. You are probably more familiar with the very light, foam-like material known as Styrofoam that is used widely for food and beverage containers and for home insulation (Figure 10.14). Styrofoam is produced by a process called "expansion molding." Polystyrene beads containing 4% to 7% of a low-boiling liquid like pentane are placed in a mold and heated with steam or hot air. Heat causes the

**FIGURE 10.14 Polystyrene.**
(a) The polymer is a clear, hard, color-less solid, but it may be more familiar as a light, foam-like material called *Styrofoam*. (b) Styrofoam has no polar groups and thus dissolves in organic solvents such as acetone. (See also Figure 10.12b.)

(a)                    (b)

**FIGURE 10.15 Slime.** When boric acid, $B(OH)_3$, is added to an aqueous suspension of polyvinyl alcohol, $(CH_2CHOH)_n$, the mixture becomes very viscous because boric acid reacts with the —OH groups on the polymer chain, causing cross-linking to occur. (The model shows an idealized structure of a portion of the polymer.)

isoprene, 2-methyl-1,3-butadiene

solvent to vaporize, creating a foam in the molten polymer that expands to fill the shape of the mold.

### Natural and Synthetic Rubber

Natural rubber was first introduced in Europe in 1740, but it remained a curiosity until 1823, when Charles Macintosh invented a way of using it to waterproof cotton cloth. The mackintosh, as rain coats are still sometimes called, became popular despite major problems: Natural rubber is notably weak and is soft and tacky when warm but brittle at low temperatures. In 1839, after 5 years of research on natural rubber, the American inventor Charles Goodyear (1800–1860) discovered that heating gum rubber with sulfur produces a material that is elastic, water-repellent, resilient, and no longer sticky.

Rubber is a naturally occurring polymer, the monomers of which are molecules of 2-methyl-1,3-butadiene, commonly called *isoprene*. In natural rubber, isoprene monomers are linked together through carbon atoms 1 and 4—that is, through the end carbon atoms of the $C_4$ chain (Figure 10.16). This leaves a double bond between carbon atoms 2 and 3. In natural rubber, these double bonds have a *cis* configuration.

In vulcanized rubber, the material that Goodyear discovered, the polymer chains of natural rubber are cross-linked by short chains of sulfur atoms. Cross-linking helps to align the polymer chains, so the material does not undergo a permanent change when stretched and it springs back when the stress is removed. Substances that behave this way are called **elastomers**.

With a knowledge of the composition and structure of natural rubber, chemists began searching for ways to make synthetic rubber. When they first tried to make the polymer by linking isoprene monomers together, however, what they made was sticky and useless. The problem was that synthesis procedures gave a mixture of *cis-* and *trans*-polyisoprene. In 1955, however, chemists at the Goodyear and Firestone companies discovered special catalysts to prepare the all-*cis* polymer. This synthetic material, which was structurally identical to natural rubber, is now manufactured cheaply. In fact, more than $8.0 \times 10^8$ kg of synthetic polyisoprene is produced annually in the United States. Other kinds of polymers have further expanded the repertoire of elastomeric materials now available. Polybutadiene, for example, is currently used in the production of tires, hoses, and belts.

Some elastomers, called **copolymers**, are formed by polymerization of two (or more) different monomers. A copolymer of butadiene and styrene, made with a 3 : 1 ratio of these raw materials, is the most important synthetic rubber now made; more than about 1 billion kilograms of styrene-butadiene rubber (SBR) is produced each year in the United States for making tires. And a little is left over each year to make bubble gum. The stretchiness of bubble gum once came from natural rubber, but SBR is now used to help you blow bubbles.

3*n*  HC—CH    +    *n* H₂C=C

1,3-butadiene            styrene

styrene-butadiene rubber (SBR)

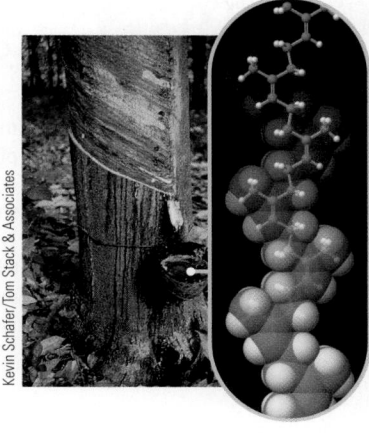

**FIGURE 10.16  Natural rubber.** The sap that comes from the rubber tree is a natural polymer of isoprene. All the linkages in the carbon chain are *cis*. When natural rubber is heated strongly in the absence of air, it smells of isoprene. This observation provided a clue that rubber is composed of this building block.

## Condensation Polymers

A chemical reaction in which two molecules react by splitting out, or eliminating, a small molecule is called a **condensation reaction**. The reaction of an alcohol with a carboxylic acid to give an ester is an example of a condensation reaction. One way to form a condensation polymer uses *two* different reactant molecules, each containing *two* functional groups. Another route uses a single molecule with two different functional groups. Commercial polyesters are made using both types of reactions.

### A CLOSER LOOK

## Copolymers and the Book Cover

The front cover of this book is a photograph of polymers. The green bead is polystyrene, 2 micrometers in diameter. (The green color is false, done for photographic purposes.) The "tentacles" around the bead are threads of epoxy resin. The precursor to the resin is a copolymer of epichlorohydrin and bisphenol-A. (See the back cover for more information.)

epichlorohydrin

bisphenol-A

**A copolymer of epichlorohydrin and bisphenol-A.**

## A CLOSER LOOK

# Copolymers and Engineering Plastics for Lego Bricks and Tattoos

Many commonly used products are not made of a single monomer but are copolymers or a combination of polymers. One example is ABS plastic. This is a copolymer of acrylonitrile (A) and styrene (S), which is made in the presence of polybutadiene (B).

The result is a thermoplastic that holds color well and has a shiny, impervious surface. It is used to make many consumer items: toys (such as Lego bricks), automobile body parts, and pressure tubing for water and other fluids. There is evidence that some tattoo inks with vivid colors also contain ABS plastic.

When acrylonitrile and styrene are polymerized in the presence of polybutadiene, short chains of the acrylonitrile-styrene polymer are mingled with longer polybutadiene chains. The polar –CN groups from neighboring ABS chains interact with each other and bind the chains together. The result is a stronger plastic than polystyrene.

acrylonitrile          styrene

© Cengage Learning/Charles D. Winters

## Polyesters

Terephthalic acid contains two carboxylic acid groups, and ethylene glycol contains two alcohol groups. When mixed, the acid and alcohol functional groups at both ends of these molecules can react to form ester linkages, splitting out water. The result is a condensation polymer called polyethylene terephthalate (PET). The multiple ester linkages make this substance a **polyester**.

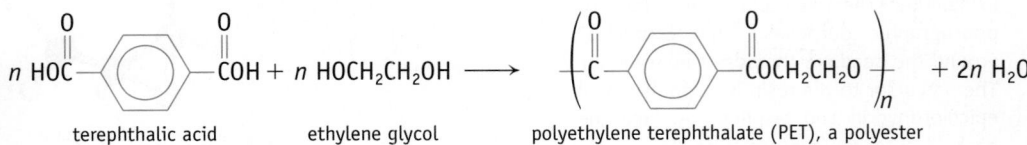

terephthalic acid          ethylene glycol          polyethylene terephthalate (PET), a polyester

Polyester textile fibers made from PET are marketed as Dacron and Terylene. The inert, nontoxic, nonflammable, and non-blood-clotting properties of Dacron polymers make Dacron tubing an excellent substitute for human blood vessels in heart bypass operations, and Dacron sheets are sometimes used as temporary skin for burn victims. A polyester film, Mylar, has unusual strength and can be rolled into sheets one-thirtieth the thickness of a human hair. Magnetically coated Mylar films are used to make audio and video tapes (Figure 10.17).

There is considerable interest in another polyester, polylactic acid (PLA). Lactic acid contains both carboxylic acid and alcohol functional groups, so condensation between molecules of this monomer gives a polymer.

$$n \ HO-\underset{\underset{CH_3}{|}}{\overset{\overset{H}{|}}{C}}-\overset{\overset{O}{||}}{C}-OH \longrightarrow \left(\underset{\underset{CH_3}{|}}{\overset{\overset{H}{|}}{C}}-\overset{\overset{O}{||}}{C}-O\right)_n + n \ H_2O$$

© Cengage Learning/Charles D. Winters

**FIGURE 10.17 Polyesters.**
Polyethylene terephthalate is used to make clothing, soda bottles, car parts, and many other consumer products. Mylar film, another polyester, is used to make recording tape as well as balloons. Because the film has smaller pores than other materials used for making balloons, such as latex, Mylar is a better material for helium-filled balloons; the atoms of gaseous helium move through the tiny pores in the film very slowly.

The interest in polylactic acid arises because it is "green." First, the monomer used to make this polymer is obtained by biological fermentation of plant materials. (Most of the chemicals used in the manufacture of other types of polymers are derived from petroleum, and there is increased concern about the availability and cost of raw materials in the future.) Second, its formation is carbon-neutral. All of the carbon in this polymer came from $CO_2$ in the atmosphere, and degradation at some future time will return the same quantity of $CO_2$ into the environment. Third, this polymer, which is currently being used in packaging material, is biodegradable, which has the potential to alleviate land-fill disposal problems.

## Polyamides

In 1928, the DuPont Company embarked on a basic research program headed by Wallace Carothers (1896–1937). Carothers was interested in high molar mass compounds, such as rubbers, proteins, and resins. In 1935, his research yielded nylon-6,6 (Figure 10.18), a **polyamide** prepared from adipoyl chloride, a derivative of adipic acid (a diacid) and hexamethylenediamine (a diamine):

$$n\ \text{ClC(CH}_2)_4\text{CCl} + n\ \text{H}_2\text{N(CH}_2)_6\text{NH}_2 \longrightarrow \left(\!\!\begin{array}{c}\text{O}\quad\text{O}\\ \|\quad\ \|\\ \text{C(CH}_2)_4\text{C}-\text{N(CH}_2)_6\text{N}\\ \ \ \ \ \ \ \ \ \ \ \ \ |\qquad\ |\\ \ \ \ \ \ \ \ \ \ \ \ \ \text{H}\quad\ \text{H}\end{array}\!\!\right)_n + 2n\ \text{HCl}$$

adipoyl chloride    hexamethylenediamine    amide link in nylon-6,6, a polyamide

Nylon can be extruded easily into fibers that are stronger than natural fibers and chemically more inert. The discovery of nylon jolted the American textile industry at a critical time. Natural fibers were not meeting 20th-century needs. Silk was expensive and not durable, wool was scratchy, linen crushed easily, and cotton did not have a high-fashion image. Perhaps the most identifiable use for the new fiber was in nylon stockings. The first public sale of nylon hosiery took place on October 24, 1939, in Wilmington, Delaware (the site of DuPont's main office). This use of nylon in commercial products ended shortly thereafter, however, with the start of World

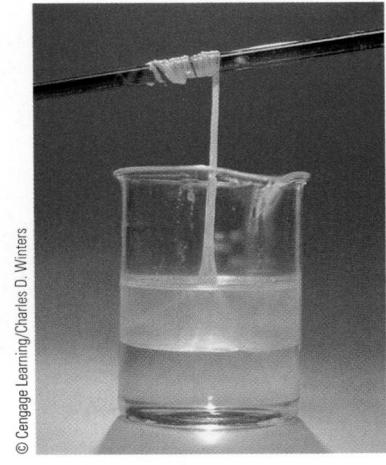

**FIGURE 10.18** Nylon-6,6. Hexamethylenediamine is dissolved in water *(bottom layer)*, and adipoyl chloride (a derivative of adipic acid) is dissolved in hexane *(top layer)*. The two compounds react at the interface between the layers to form nylon, which is being wound onto a stirring rod.

---

## A CLOSER LOOK

## Green Chemistry: Recycling PET

In 1997 the United States and Canada produced more than 2 billion kilograms of polyethylene terephthalate (PET). Over half of the PET is used to produce bottles and food containers, and the remainder is used for automobile parts, luggage, filters, and much more. Fortunately, some of the bottles can be recycled, and the PET recovered for use in surfboards, carpet fibers, and fiberfill for winter clothing. But up to half of the PET cannot be recycled, so it is disposed of in landfills. It is also unfortunate that the recycled PET cannot be used in bottles for foods again because harmful impuri-

ties that may be present are not removed in the process.

Recently, however, a new process developed by DuPont may change this. This new process uses scrap PET and recycles it to produce first-quality PET. The scrap PET is dissolved at over 220 °C in dimethylphthalate (DMT) and then treated with methanol at 260–300 °C and 340–650 kPa. In this process, the methanol reacts with the polymer to break the chains down into more dimethylphthalate

and ethylene glycol. DMT and ethylene glycol are separated, purified, and used to make more PET. In the process of making more PET from these two species the methanol is recovered so it can be reused for further reactions.

The recovery of DMT and ethylene glycol means that increasingly scarce petroleum is not needed to make the starting materials for the manufacture of billions of kilograms of new PET!

$$\left[\!\!\begin{array}{c}\text{O}\qquad\qquad\text{O}\\ \|\qquad\qquad\ \|\\ \text{O}-\text{C}-\!\!\!\bigcirc\!\!\!-\text{C}-\text{O}-\text{CH}_2\text{CH}_2\end{array}\!\!\right]$$

DMT and $CH_3OH$ at high temperature and pressure

$$\text{H}_3\text{CO}-\overset{\overset{\text{O}}{\|}}{\text{C}}-\!\!\!\bigcirc\!\!\!-\overset{\overset{\text{O}}{\|}}{\text{C}}-\text{OCH}_3 + \text{HOCH}_2\text{CH}_2\text{OH}$$

These two students are wearing jackets made from recycled PET soda bottles.

War II. All nylon was diverted to making parachutes and other military gear. It was not until about 1952 that nylon reappeared in the consumer marketplace.

Figure 10.19 illustrates why nylon makes such a good fiber. To have good tensile strength (the ability to resist tearing), the polymer chains should be able to attract one another, albeit not so strongly that the plastic cannot be drawn into fibers. Ordinary covalent bonds between the chains (cross-linking) would be too strong. Instead, cross-linking occurs by a somewhat weaker intermolecular force called *hydrogen bonding* (▶ Section 12.3) between the hydrogens of N—H groups on one chain and the carbonyl oxygens on another chain. The polarities of the $N^{\delta-}$—$H^{\delta+}$ group and the $C^{\delta+}$=$O^{\delta-}$ group lead to attractive forces between the polymer chains of the desired magnitude.

### EXAMPLE 10.8   Condensation Polymers

**Problem** What is the repeating unit of the condensation polymer obtained by combining $HO_2CCH_2CH_2CO_2H$ (succinic acid) and $H_2NCH_2CH_2NH_2$ (1,2-ethylenediamine)?

**What Do You Know?** Carboxylic acids and amines react to form amides, splitting out water. Here we have a diacid and diamine that will react. The repeating unit will be the shortest sequence that when repeated gives a long polymer chain.

**Strategy** Recognize that the polymer will link the two monomer units through the amide linkage. The smallest repeating unit of the chain will contain two parts, one from the diacid and the other from the diamine.

**Solution** The repeating unit of this polyamide is

amide linkage

$$\left(\!-\!\!\underset{O}{\overset{O}{\underset{\|}{\overset{\|}{C}}}}CH_2CH_2\overset{O}{\overset{\|}{C}}-NCH_2CH_2N\!-\!\right)_n$$

**Think about Your Answer** Alternating fragments of the diacid and diamine appear in the polymer chain. The fragments are linked by amide bonds making this a polyamide.

**Check Your Understanding**

Kevlar is a polymer that is now well known because it is used to make sports equipment and bulletproof vests. This polymer has the formula shown below. Is this a condensation polymer or an addition polymer? What chemicals could be used to make this polymer? Write a balanced equation for the formation of Kevlar.

**FIGURE 10.19 Hydrogen bonding between polyamide chains.** Carbonyl oxygen atoms with a partial negative charge on one chain interact with an amine hydrogen with a partial positive charge on a neighboring chain. (This form of bonding is described in more detail in Section 12.3.)

# Green Adhesives

Chemist Kaichang Li was trained in the chemistry of wood and is now doing research at Oregon State University. Oregon has a beautiful and rugged coast, and Li went there in search of mussels to make a special dish. As the waves pounded onshore, he was struck by the fact that the mussels could cling stubbornly to the rocks in spite of the force of the waves and tides. What glue enabled them to do this?

Back in his lab Li found that the strands of glue were largely protein-based. Proteins are simply polymers of amino acids with an

**FIGURE A** A portion of a protein chain made of repeating glycine molecules ($H_2NCH_2CO_2H$).

amide link between units (page 471 and Figure A). Li realized that such polymers could have enormous application in the wood industry.

Adhesives, or glues in common terminology, have been known and used for thousands of years. Early glues were based on animal or plant products. Now, however, adhesives are largely synthetic, among them condensation polymers based on the combination of phenol or urea with formaldehyde. These have been used for well over a half-century in the manufacture of plywood and particle board, and your home or dormitory likely contains a significant amount of these building materials. Unfortunately, they have a disadvantage. In their manufacture and use, formaldehyde, a suspected carcinogen, can be released into the air.

Li's work with the mussels eventually led to a new, safer adhesive that could be used in these same wood products. His first problem was how to make a protein-based adhesive in the laboratory. The idea came to him one day at lunch when he was eating tofu, a soy-based food very high in protein. Why not modify soy protein to make a new adhesive? Using mussels as his model, Li did exactly that, and, as he said, "We turned soy proteins into mussel adhesive proteins."

Scientists at Hercules Chemical Company provided expertise to cure (or

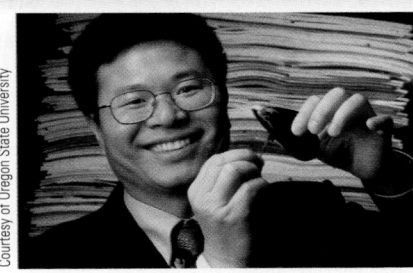

Courtesy of Oregon State University

**Professor K. Li, a discoverer of "green" adhesives.**

harden) the new "green" adhesive, and the Columbia Forest Products Company adopted the environmentally friendly adhesive for use in plywood and particle board.

In 2007 Li and his coworkers, as well as Columbia Forest Products and Hercules, shared a Presidential Green Chemistry Award.

**Questions:**
1. Draw structures of phenol, urea, and formaldehyde.
2. Describe the bonding in formaldehyde.
3. It has been said that nylon is similar to a protein. Compare and contrast the structures of nylon 6,6 and a protein (for more information on the structure of proteins, see p. 491).

**Answers to these questions are available in Appendix N.**

---

**REVIEW & CHECK FOR SECTION 10.5**

Polyacrylic acid, shown below, is made from which of the following monomers? (The sodium salt of this polymer, sodium polyacrylate, and cellulose are the important ingredients in disposable baby diapers.)

$$\left[ CH_2-\underset{\underset{\underset{OH}{|}}{\overset{O=C}{|}}{\overset{H}{\underset{|}{C}}}-CH_2-\underset{\underset{\underset{OH}{|}}{\overset{O=C}{|}}{\overset{H}{\underset{|}{C}}}-CH_2-\underset{\underset{\underset{OH}{|}}{\overset{O=C}{|}}{\overset{H}{\underset{|}{C}}} \right]_n$$

(a) $CH_2{=}CH_2$  (b) $CH_2{=}\underset{\underset{CN}{|}}{CH}$  (c) $CH_2{=}\underset{\underset{CO_2H}{|}}{CH}$  (d) $CH_2{=}\underset{\underset{OH}{|}}{CH}$

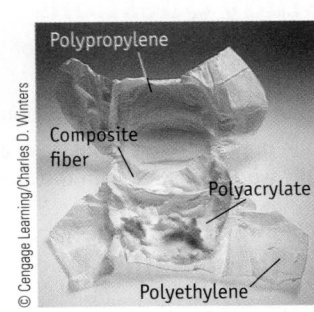

© Cengage Learning/Charles D. Winters

**Polymers in a disposable baby diaper.** At least three polymeric materials are used: sodium polyacrylate, polypropylene, and polyethylene.

and

## CHAPTER GOALS REVISITED

*Now that you have studied this chapter, you should ask whether you have met the chapter goals. In particular, you should be able to:*

### Classify organic compounds based on formula and structure

a. Understand the factors that contribute to the large numbers of organic compounds and the wide array of structures (Section 10.1). **Study Question: 103.**

### Recognize and draw structures of structural isomers and stereoisomers for carbon compounds

a. Recognize and draw structures of geometric isomers and optical isomers (Section 10.1). **Study Questions: 11, 12, 15, 19, 69.**

### Name and draw structures of common organic compounds

a. Draw structural formulas, and name simple hydrocarbons, including alkanes, alkenes, alkynes, and aromatic compounds (Section 10.2). **Study Questions: 1–16, 69, 70, 77, and Go Chemistry Module 15.**

b. Identify possible isomers for a given formula (Section 10.2). **Study Questions: 6, 8, 11, 15, 16, 19–22, 28.**

c. Name and draw structures of alcohols and amines (Section 10.3). **Study Questions: 37–42.**

d. Name and draw structures of carbonyl compounds—aldehydes, ketones, acids, esters, and amides (Section 10.4). **Study Questions: 47–50.**

### Know the common reactions of organic functional groups

a. Predict the products of the reactions of alkenes, aromatic compounds, alcohols, amines, aldehydes and ketones, and carboxylic acids. **Study Questions: 23–26, 29, 30, 33–36, 43–46, 51–56, 59, 62, 71–74, 89, 91, 93, 94.**

### Relate properties to molecular structure

a. Describe the physical and chemical properties of the various classes of hydrocarbon compounds (Section 10.2). **Study Question: 17.**

b. Recognize the connection between the structures and the properties of alcohols (Section 10.3). **Study Questions: 45, 46, 72.**

c. Know the structures and properties of some natural products, including carbohydrates (Section 10.4). **Study Questions: 57, 58, 83, 84, 87.**

### Identify common polymers

a. Write equations for the formation of addition polymers and condensation polymers, and describe their structures (Section 10.5). **Study Questions: 63–66.**

b. Relate properties of polymers to their structures (Section 10.5). **Study Question: 105.**

## Study Questions

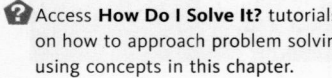 Interactive versions of these questions are assignable in OWL.

▲ denotes challenging questions.

Blue-numbered questions have answers in Appendix R and fully worked solutions in the *Student Solutions Manual.*

## Practicing Skills

### Alkanes and Cycloalkanes
*(See Section 10.2 and Examples 10.1 and 10.2.)*

1. What is the name of the straight (unbranched) chain alkane with the formula $C_7H_{16}$?

2. What is the molecular formula for an alkane with 12 carbon atoms?

3. Which of the following compounds can be an alkane?
   (a) $C_2H_4$         (c) $C_{14}H_{30}$
   (b) $C_5H_{12}$        (d) $C_7H_8$

4. Which of the following compounds can be a cycloalkane?
   (a) $C_3H_5$         (c) $C_{14}H_{30}$
   (b) $C_5H_{10}$        (d) $C_8H_8$

5. One of the structural isomers with the formula $C_9H_{20}$ has the name 3-ethyl-2-methylhexane. Draw its structure. Draw and name another structural isomer of $C_9H_{20}$ in which there is a five-carbon chain.

**6.** Isooctane, 2,2,4-trimethylpentane, is one of the possible structural isomers with the formula $C_8H_{18}$. Draw the structure of this isomer, and draw and name structures of two other isomers of $C_8H_{18}$ in which the longest carbon chain is five atoms.

**7.** Give the systematic name for the following alkane:

$$CH_3$$
$$|$$
$$CH_3CHCHCH_3$$
$$|$$
$$CH_3$$

**8.** Give the systematic name for the following alkane. Draw a structural isomer of the compound, and give its name.

$$CH_3$$
$$|$$
$$CH_3CHCH_2CH_2CHCH_3$$
$$|$$
$$CH_2CH_3$$

**9.** Draw the structure of each of the following compounds:
   (a) 2,3-dimethylhexane
   (b) 2,3-dimethyloctane
   (c) 3-ethylheptane
   (d) 3-ethyl-2-methylhexane

**10.** Draw structures for the following compounds.
   (a) 3-ethylpentane
   (b) 2,3-dimethylpentane
   (c) 2,4-dimethylpentane
   (d) 2,2-dimethylpentane

**11.** Draw Lewis structures and name all possible alkanes that have a seven-carbon chain with one methyl substituent group. Which of these isomers has a chiral carbon center?

**12.** Four (of six possible) dimethylhexanes are named below. Draw the structures of each, and determine which of these isomers has a chiral carbon center.
   (a) 2,2-dimethylhexane
   (b) 2,3-dimethylhexane
   (c) 2,4-dimethylhexane
   (d) 2,5-dimethylhexane

**13.** Draw the structure of the chair form of cyclohexane. Identify the axial and equatorial hydrogen atoms in this drawing.

**14.** Draw a structure for cycloheptane. Is the seven-member ring planar? Explain your answer.

**15.** There are two ethylheptanes (compounds with a seven-carbon chain and one ethyl substituent). Draw the structures, and name these compounds. Is either isomer chiral?

**16.** Among the 18 structural isomers with the formula $C_8H_{18}$ are two with a five-carbon chain having one ethyl and one methyl substituent group. Draw their structures, and name these two isomers.

**17.** List several typical physical properties of $C_4H_{10}$. Predict the following physical properties of dodecane, $C_{12}H_{26}$: color, state (s, ℓ, g), solubility in water, solubility in a nonpolar solvent.

**18.** Write balanced equations for the following reactions of alkanes.
   (a) The reaction of methane with excess chlorine.
   (b) Complete combustion of cyclohexane, $C_6H_{12}$, with excess oxygen.

**Alkenes and Alkynes**
*(See Section 10.2 and Examples 10.3 and 10.4.)*

**19.** Draw structures for the *cis* and *trans* isomers of 4-methyl-2-hexene.

**20.** What structural requirement is necessary for an alkene to have *cis* and *trans* isomers? Can *cis* and *trans* isomers exist for an alkane? For an alkyne?

**21.** A hydrocarbon with the formula $C_5H_{10}$ can be either an alkene or a cycloalkane.
   (a) Draw a structure for each of the six isomers possible for $C_5H_{10}$, assuming it is an alkene. Give the systematic name of each isomer.
   (b) Draw a structure for a cycloalkane having the formula $C_5H_{10}$.

**22.** Five alkenes have the formula $C_7H_{14}$ and a seven-carbon chain. Draw their structures and name them.

**23.** Draw the structure and give the systematic name for the products of the following reactions:
   (a) $CH_3CH{=}CH_2 + Br_2 \rightarrow$
   (b) $CH_3CH_2CH{=}CHCH_3 + H_2 \rightarrow$

**24.** Draw the structure and give the systematic name for the products of the following reactions:

$$\begin{array}{ccc} H_3C & & CH_2CH_3 \\ & C{=}C & \\ H_3C & & H \end{array} + H_2 \longrightarrow$$

   (a) 
   (b) $CH_3C{\equiv}CCH_2CH_3 + 2\ Br_2 \longrightarrow$

**25.** The compound 2-bromobutane is a product of addition of HBr to three different alkenes. Identify the alkenes and write an equation for the reaction of HBr with one of the alkenes.

**26.** The compound 2,3-dibromo-2-methylhexane is formed by addition of $Br_2$ to an alkene. Identify the alkene, and write an equation for this reaction.

**27.** Draw structures for alkenes that have the formula $C_3H_5Cl$, and name each compound. (These are derivatives of propene in which a chlorine atom replaces one hydrogen atom.)

**28.** There are six possible dichloropropene isomers (molecular formula $C_3H_4Cl_2$). Draw their structures and name each isomer. (Hint: don't overlook *cis-trans* isomers.)

**29.** Hydrogenation is an important chemical reaction of compounds that contain double bonds. Write a chemical equation for the hydrogenation of 1-hexene. This reaction is used extensively in the food industry. Describe this reaction and explain its use and importance.

**30.** Elemental analysis of a colorless liquid has given its formula as $C_5H_{10}$. You recognize that this could be either a cycloalkane or an alkene. A chemical test to determine the class to which this compound belongs involves adding bromine. Explain how this would allow you to distinguish between the two classes.

## Aromatic Compounds
*(See Section 10.2 and Example 10.5.)*

**31.** Draw structural formulas for the following compounds:
(a) 1,3-dichlorobenzene (alternatively called *m*-dichlorobenzene)
(b) 1-bromo-4-methylbenzene (alternatively called *p*-bromotoluene)

**32.** Give the systematic name for each of the following compounds:

**33.** Write the equation for the reaction of 1,4-dimethylbenzene with $CH_3Cl$ and $AlCl_3$. What is the structure and name of the single organic compound produced?

**34.** Write an equation for the preparation of hexylbenzene from benzene and other appropriate reagents.

**35.** A single compound is formed by alkylation of 1,4-dimethylbenzene. Write the equation for the reaction of this compound with $CH_3Cl$ and $AlCl_3$. What is the structure and name of the product?

**36.** Nitration of toluene gives a mixture of two products, one with the nitro group ($-NO_2$) in the *ortho* position and one with the nitro group in the *para* position. Draw structures of the two products.

## Alcohols, Ethers, and Amines
*(See Section 10.3 and Example 10.6.)*

**37.** Give the systematic name for each of the following alcohols, and tell if each is a primary, secondary, or tertiary alcohol:
(a) $CH_3CH_2CH_2OH$
(b) $CH_3CH_2CH_2CH_2OH$
(c)
$$H_3C-\overset{\overset{\displaystyle CH_3}{|}}{\underset{\underset{\displaystyle CH_3}{|}}{C}}-OH$$
(d)
$$H_3C-\overset{\overset{\displaystyle CH_3}{|}}{\underset{\underset{\displaystyle OH}{|}}{C}}-CH_2CH_3$$

**38.** Draw structural formulas for the following alcohols, and tell if each is primary, secondary, or tertiary:
(a) 1-butanol
(b) 2-butanol
(c) 3,3-dimethyl-2-butanol
(d) 3,3-dimethyl-1-butanol

**39.** Write the formula, and draw the structure for each of the following amines:
(a) ethylamine
(b) dipropylamine
(c) butyldimethylamine
(d) triethylamine

**40.** Name the following amines:
(a) $CH_3CH_2CH_2NH_2$
(b) $(CH_3)_3N$
(c) $(CH_3)(C_2H_5)NH$
(d) $C_6H_{13}NH_2$

**41.** Draw structural formulas for all the alcohols with the formula $C_4H_{10}O$. Give the systematic name of each.

**42.** Draw structural formulas for all primary amines with the formula $C_4H_9NH_2$.

**43.** Complete and balance the following equations:
(a) $C_6H_5NH_2(\ell) + HCl(aq) \rightarrow$
(b) $(CH_3)_3N(aq) + H_2SO_4(aq) \rightarrow$

**44.** The structure of dopamine, a neurotransmitter, is given on page 464. Predict its reaction with aqueous hydrochloric acid.

**45.** Draw structures of the product formed by oxidation of the following alcohols. Assume an excess of oxidizing agent is used in each case.
(a) 2-methyl-1-pentanol
(b) 3-methyl-2-pentanol
(c) $HOCH_2CH_2CH_2CH_2OH$
(d) $H_2NCH_2CH_2CH_2OH$

**46.** Aldehydes and carboxylic acids are formed by oxidation of primary alcohols, and ketones are formed when secondary alcohols are oxidized. Give the name and formula for the alcohol that, when oxidized, gives the following products:
(a) $CH_3CH_2CH_2CHO$
(b) 2-hexanone

## Compounds with a Carbonyl Group
*(See Section 10.4 and Example 10.7.)*

**47.** Draw structural formulas for (a) 2-pentanone, (b) hexanal, and (c) pentanoic acid.

**48.** Draw structural formulas for the following acids and esters:
(a) 2-methylhexanoic acid
(b) pentyl butanoate (which has the odor of apricots)
(c) octyl acetate (which has the odor of oranges)

**49.** Identify the class of each of the following compounds, and give the systematic name for each:
(a)
$$CH_3CH_2\overset{\overset{\displaystyle CH_3}{|}}{C}HCH_2CO_2H$$
(b)
$$CH_3CH_2\overset{\overset{\displaystyle O}{\|}}{C}OCH_3$$
(c)
$$CH_3\overset{\overset{\displaystyle O}{\|}}{C}OCH_2CH_2CH_2CH_3$$
(d)
$$Br-\underset{}{\bigcirc}-\overset{\overset{\displaystyle O}{\|}}{C}OH$$

**50.** Identify the class of each of the following compounds, and give the systematic name for each:

(a)
$$CH_3\overset{\displaystyle O}{\overset{\displaystyle \|}{C}}CH_3$$

(b)
$$CH_3CH_2CH_2\overset{\displaystyle O}{\overset{\displaystyle \|}{C}}H$$

(c)
$$CH_3\overset{\displaystyle O}{\overset{\displaystyle \|}{C}}CH_2CH_2CH_3$$

**51.** Give the structural formula and systematic name for the organic product, if any, from each of the following reactions:
(a) pentanal and $KMnO_4$
(b) 2-octanone and $LiAlH_4$

**52.** Give the structural formula and name for the organic product from the following reactions.
(a) $CH_3CH_2CH_2CH_2CHO + LiAlH_4$
(b) $CH_3CH_2CH_2CH_2OH + KMnO_4$

**53.** Describe how to prepare propyl propanoate beginning with 1-propanol as the only carbon-containing reagent.

**54.** Give the name and structure of the product of the reaction of benzoic acid and 2-propanol.

**55.** Draw structural formulas and give the names for the products of the following reaction:

$$CH_3\overset{\displaystyle O}{\overset{\displaystyle \|}{C}}OCH_2CH_2CH_2CH_3 + NaOH$$

**56.** Draw structural formulas, and give the names for the products of the following reaction:

**57.** The structure of phenylalanine, one of the 20 amino acids that make up proteins, is drawn below (without lone pairs of electrons). The carbon atoms are numbered for the purpose of this question.
(a) What is the geometry of $C_3$?
(b) What is the O—C—O bond angle?
(c) Is this molecule chiral? If so, which carbon atom is chiral?
(d) Which hydrogen atom in this compound is acidic?

**58.** The structure of vitamin C, whose chemical name is ascorbic acid, is drawn below (without lone pairs of electrons).

(a) What is the approximate value for the O—C—O bond angle?
(b) There are four OH groups in this structure. Estimate the C—O—H bond angles for these groups. Will they be the same value (more or less), or should there be significant differences in these bond angles?
(c) Is the molecule chiral? How many chiral carbon atoms can be identified in this structure?
(d) Identify the shortest bond in this molecule.
(e) What are the functional groups of the molecule?

**59.** What is the structure of the product from the reaction of butanoic acid and methylamine? To what class of compounds does this belong? Write a balanced chemical equation for the reaction.

**60.** The structure of acetaminophen is shown on page 471. Using structural formulas, write an equation for the reaction of an acid and an amine to form this compound.

**Functional Groups**
*(See Section 10.4 and Example 10.7.)*

**61.** Identify the functional groups in the following molecules.
(a) $CH_3CH_2CH_2OH$
(b)
$$H_3C\overset{\displaystyle O}{\overset{\displaystyle \|}{C}}NHCH_3$$
(c)
$$CH_3CH_2\overset{\displaystyle O}{\overset{\displaystyle \|}{C}}OH$$
(d)
$$CH_3CH_2\overset{\displaystyle O}{\overset{\displaystyle \|}{C}}OCH_3$$

**62.** Consider the following molecules:
(1)
$$CH_3CH_2\overset{\displaystyle O}{\overset{\displaystyle \|}{C}}CH_3$$
(2)
$$CH_3CH_2\overset{\displaystyle O}{\overset{\displaystyle \|}{C}}OH$$
(3) $H_2C{=}CHCH_2OH$
(4)
$$CH_3CH_2\overset{\displaystyle OH}{\overset{\displaystyle |}{C}H}CH_3$$

(a) What is the result of treating compound 1 with $NaBH_4$? What is the functional group in the product? Name the product.
(b) Draw the structure of the reaction product from compounds 2 and 4. What is the functional group in the product?
(c) What compound results from adding $H_2$ to compound 3? Name the reaction product.
(d) What compound results from adding NaOH to compound 2?

**Polymers**
*(See Section 10.5 and Example 10.8.)*

63. Polyvinyl acetate is the binder in water-based paints.
    (a) Write an equation for its formation from vinyl acetate.
    (b) Show a portion of this polymer with three monomer units.
    (c) Describe how to make polyvinyl alcohol from polyvinyl acetate.

64. Neoprene (polychloroprene, a kind of rubber) is a polymer formed from the chlorinated butadiene $H_2C=CHCCl=CH_2$.
    (a) Write an equation showing the formation of polychloroprene from the monomer.
    (b) Show a portion of this polymer with three monomer units.

65. Saran is a copolymer of 1,1-dichloroethene and chloroethene (vinyl chloride). Draw a possible structure for this polymer.

66. The structure of methyl methacrylate is given in Table 10.12. Draw the structure of a polymethyl methacrylate (PMMA) polymer that has four monomer units. (PMMA has excellent optical properties and is used to make hard contact lenses.)

# General Questions

*These questions are not designated as to type or location in the chapter. They may combine several concepts.*

67. Three different compounds with the formula $C_2H_2Cl_2$ are known.
    (a) Two of these compounds are geometric isomers. Draw their structures.
    (b) The third compound is a structural isomer of the other two. Draw its structure.

68. Draw the structure of 2-butanol. Identify the chiral carbon atom in this compound. Draw the mirror image of the structure you first drew. Are the two molecules superimposable?

69. Draw Lewis structures and name three structural isomers with the formula $C_6H_{12}$. Are any of these isomers chiral?

70. Draw structures and name the four alkenes that have the formula $C_4H_8$.

71. Write equations for the reactions of *cis*-2-butene with the following reagents, representing the reactants and products using structural formulas.
    (a) $H_2O$
    (b) HBr
    (c) $Cl_2$

72. Draw the structure and name the product formed if the following alcohols are oxidized. Assume an excess of the oxidizing agent is used. If the alcohol is not expected to react with a chemical oxidizing agent, write NR (no reaction).
    (a) $CH_3CH_2CH_2CH_2OH$
    (b) 2-butanol
    (c) 2-methyl-2-propanol
    (d) 2-methyl-1-propanol

73. Write equations for the following reactions, representing the reactants and products using structural formulas.
    (a) The reaction of acetic acid and sodium hydroxide
    (b) The reaction of methylamine with HCl

74. Write equations for the following reactions, representing the reactants and products using structural formulas.
    (a) The formation of ethyl acetate from acetic acid and ethanol
    (b) The hydrolysis of glyceryl tristearate (the triester of glycerol with stearic acid, a fatty acid; Table 10.9)

75. Write an equation for the formation of the following polymers.
    (a) Polystyrene, from styrene ($C_6H_5CH=CH_2$)
    (b) PET (polyethylene terephthalate), from ethylene glycol and terephthalic acid

76. Write equations for the following reactions, representing the reactants and products using structural formulas.
    (a) The hydrolysis of the amide $C_6H_5CONHCH_3$ to form benzoic acid and methylamine
    (b) The hydrolysis of $(-CO(CH_2)_4CONH(CH_2)_6NH-)_n$, (nylon-6,6, a polyamide) to give a carboxylic acid and an amine

77. Draw the structure of each of the following compounds:
    (a) 2,2-dimethylpentane
    (b) 3,3-diethylpentane
    (c) 3-ethyl-2-methylpentane
    (d) 3-ethylhexane

78. ▲ Structural isomers.
    (a) Draw all of the isomers possible for $C_3H_8O$. Give the systematic name of each, and tell into which class of compound it fits.
    (b) Draw the structural formulas for an aldehyde and a ketone with the molecular formula $C_4H_8O$. Give the systematic name of each.

79. ▲ Draw structural formulas for possible isomers of the dichlorinated propane, $C_3H_6Cl_2$. Name each compound.

80. Draw structural formulas for possible isomers with the formula $C_3H_6ClBr$, and name each isomer.

81. Give structural formulas and systematic names for the three structural isomers of trimethylbenzene, $C_6H_3(CH_3)_3$.

82. Give structural formulas and systematic names for possible isomers of dichlorobenzene, $C_6H_4Cl_2$.

83. Voodoo lilies depend on carrion beetles for pollination. Carrion beetles are attracted to dead animals, and because dead and putrefying animals give off the horrible-smelling amine cadaverine, the lily likewise releases cadaverine (and the closely related compound putrescine, page 463). A biological catalyst, an enzyme, converts the naturally occurring amino acid lysine to cadaverine.

$$H_2NCH_2CH_2CH_2CH_2-\overset{\displaystyle H}{\underset{\displaystyle \underset{\parallel}{\overset{|}{C}}-OH}{\underset{|}{C}}}-NH_2$$

**Lysine.**

What group of atoms must be replaced in lysine to make cadaverine? (Lysine is essential to human nutrition but is not synthesized in the human body.)

84. Benzoic acid occurs in many berries. When humans eat berries, benzoic acid is converted to hippuric acid in the body by reaction with the amino acid glycine $H_2NCH_2CO_2H$. Draw the structure of hippuric acid, knowing it is an amide formed by reaction of the carboxylic acid group of benzoic acid and the amino group of glycine. Why is hippuric acid referred to as an acid?

85. Consider the reaction of *cis*-2-butene with $H_2$ (in the presence of a catalyst).
    (a) Draw the structure, and give the name of the reaction product. Is this reaction product chiral?
    (b) Draw an isomer of the reaction product.

86. Give the name of each compound below, and name the functional group involved.

    (a) 
    $$H_3C-\overset{\overset{\displaystyle OH}{|}}{\underset{\underset{\displaystyle H}{|}}{C}}-CH_2CH_2CH_3$$

    (b) 
    $$H_3C-\overset{\overset{\displaystyle O}{\|}}{C}CH_2CH_2CH_3$$

    (c) 
    $$H_3C-\overset{\overset{\displaystyle H}{|}}{\underset{\underset{\displaystyle CH_3}{|}}{C}}-\overset{\overset{\displaystyle O}{\|}}{C}-H$$

    (d) 
    $$H_3CCH_2CH_2-\overset{\overset{\displaystyle O}{\|}}{C}-OH$$

87. Draw the structure of glyceryl trilaurate, a fat. Lauric acid (page 489) has the formula $C_{11}H_{23}CO_2H$.
    (a) Write an equation for the saponification of glyceryl trilaurate.
    (b) Write an equation for the reaction that could be used to prepare biodiesel fuel from this fat.

88. A well-known company selling outdoor clothing has recently introduced jackets made of recycled polyethylene terephthalate (PET), the principal material in many soft drink bottles. Another company makes PET fibers by treating recycled bottles with methanol to give the diester dimethyl terephthalate and ethylene glycol and then repolymerizes these compounds to give new PET. Write a chemical equation to show how the reaction of PET with methanol can give dimethyl terephthalate and ethylene glycol.

89. Identify the reaction products, and write an equation for the following reactions of $CH_2=CHCH_2OH$.
    (a) $H_2$ (hydrogenation, in the presence of a catalyst)
    (b) Oxidation (excess oxidizing agent)
    (c) Addition polymerization
    (d) Ester formation, using acetic acid

90. Write a chemical equation describing the reaction between glycerol and stearic acid (Table 10.9) to give glyceryl tristearate.

91. The product of an addition reaction of an alkene is often predicted by Markovnikov's rule.
    (a) Draw the structure of the product of adding HBr to propene, and give the name of the product.
    (b) Draw the structure and give the name of the compound that results from adding $H_2O$ to 2-methyl-1-butene.
    (c) If you add $H_2O$ to 2-methyl-2-butene, is the product the same or different than the product from the reaction in part (b)?

92. An unknown colorless liquid has the formula $C_4H_{10}O$. Draw the structures for the four alcohol compounds that have this formula.

## In the Laboratory

93. Which of the following compounds produces acetic acid when treated with an oxidizing agent such as $KMnO_4$?

    (a) $H_3C-CH_3$

    (c) 
    $$H_3C-\overset{\overset{\displaystyle OH}{|}}{\underset{\underset{\displaystyle H}{|}}{C}}-H$$

    (b) 
    $$H_3C-\overset{\overset{\displaystyle O}{\|}}{C}-H$$

    (d) 
    $$H_3C-\overset{\overset{\displaystyle O}{\|}}{C}-CH_3$$

94. Consider the reactions of $C_3H_7OH$.

    $$H_3CCH_2-\overset{\overset{\displaystyle H}{|}}{\underset{\underset{\displaystyle H}{|}}{C}}-O-H \xrightarrow[H_2SO_4]{Rxn\ A} H_3C-\overset{\overset{\displaystyle H}{|}}{C}=\overset{\overset{\displaystyle H}{|}}{\underset{\underset{\displaystyle H}{|}}{C}} + H_2O$$

    $$\downarrow Rxn\ B \quad + CH_3CO_2H$$

    $$H_3CCH_2-\overset{\overset{\displaystyle H}{|}}{\underset{\underset{\displaystyle H}{|}}{C}}-O-\overset{\overset{\displaystyle O}{\|}}{C}CH_3$$

    (a) Name the reactant $C_3H_7OH$.
    (b) Draw a structural isomer of the reactant, and give its name.
    (c) Name the product of reaction A.
    (d) Name the product of reaction B.

95. You have a liquid that is either cyclohexene or benzene. When the liquid is exposed to dark-red bromine vapor, the vapor is immediately decolorized. What is the identity of the liquid? Write an equation for the chemical reaction that has occurred.

96. ▲ Hydrolysis of an unknown ester of butanoic acid, $CH_3CH_2CH_2CO_2R$, produces an alcohol A and butanoic acid. Oxidation of this alcohol forms an acid B that is a structural isomer of butanoic acid. Give the names and structures for alcohol A and acid B.

97. ▲ You are asked to identify an unknown colorless, liquid carbonyl compound. Analysis has determined that the formula for this unknown is $C_3H_6O$. Only two compounds match this formula.
    (a) Draw structures for the two possible compounds.
    (b) To decide which of the two structures is correct, you react the compound with an oxidizing agent and isolate from that reaction a compound that is found to give an acidic solution in water. Use this result to identify the structure of the unknown.
    (c) Name the acid formed by oxidation of the unknown.

98. Describe a simple chemical test to tell the difference between $CH_3CH_2CH_2CH{=}CH_2$ and its isomer cyclopentane.

99. Describe a simple chemical test to tell the difference between 2-propanol and its isomer methyl ethyl ether.

100. ▲ An unknown ester has the formula $C_4H_8O_2$. Hydrolysis gives methanol as one product. Identify the ester, and write an equation for the hydrolysis reaction.

101. ▲ Addition of water to alkene X gives an alcohol Y. Oxidation of Y produces 3,3-dimethyl-2-pentanone. Identify X and Y, and write equations for the two reactions.

102. 2-Iodobenzoic acid, a tan, crystalline solid, can be prepared from 2-aminobenzoic acid. Other required reagents are $NaNO_2$ and KI (as well as HCl).

2-aminobenzoic acid.          2-iodobenzoic acid.

   (a) If you use 4.0 g of 2-aminobenzoic acid, 2.2 g of $NaNO_2$, and 5.3 g of KI, what is the theoretical yield of 2-iodobenzoic acid?
   (b) Are other isomers of 2-iodobenzoic acid possible?
   (c) You titrate the product in a mixture of water and ethanol. If you use 15.62 mL of 0.101 M NaOH to titrate 0.399 g of the product, what is its molar mass? Is it in reasonable agreement with the theoretical molar mass?

## Summary and Conceptual Questions

*The following questions may use concepts from this and previous chapters.*

103. Carbon atoms appear in organic compounds in several different ways with single, double, and triple bonds combining to give an octet configuration. Describe the various ways that carbon can bond to reach an octet, and give the name and draw the structure of a compound that illustrates that mode of bonding.

104. There is a high barrier to rotation around a carbon–carbon double bond, whereas the barrier to rotation around a carbon–carbon single bond is considerably smaller. Use the orbital overlap model of bonding (Chapter 9) to explain why there is restricted rotation around a double bond.

105. What important properties do the following characteristics impart to a polymer?
   (a) Cross-linking in polyethylene
   (b) The OH groups in polyvinyl alcohol
   (c) Hydrogen bonding in a polyamide like nylon

106. One of the resonance structures for pyridine is illustrated here. Draw another resonance structure for the molecule. Comment on the similarity between this compound and benzene.

Pyridine.

107. Write balanced equations for the combustion of ethane gas and liquid ethanol (to give gaseous products).
   (a) Calculate the enthalpy of combustion of each compound. Which has the more negative enthalpy change for combustion per gram?
   (b) If ethanol is assumed to be partially oxidized ethane, what effect does this have on the enthalpy of combustion?

108. Plastics make up about 20% of the volume of landfills. There is, therefore, considerable interest in reusing or recycling these materials. To identify common plastics, a set of universal symbols is now used, five of which are illustrated here. They symbolize low- and high-density polyethylene, polyvinyl chloride, polypropylene, and polyethylene terephthalate.

```
 ⟁      ⟁      ⟁
  1       2       3
PETE    HDPE     V

     ⟁      ⟁
      4       5
    LDPE     PP
```

   (a) Tell which symbol belongs to which type of plastic.
   (b) Find an item in the grocery or drug store made from each of these plastics.
   (c) Properties of several plastics are listed in the table. Based on this information, describe how to separate samples of these plastics from one another.

| Plastic | Density (g/cm³) | Melting Point (°C) |
| --- | --- | --- |
| Polypropylene | 0.92 | 170 |
| High-density polyethylene | 0.97 | 135 |
| Polyethylene terephthalate | 1.34–1.39 | 245 |

109. ▲ Maleic acid is prepared by the catalytic oxidation of benzene. It is a dicarboxylic acid; that is, it has two carboxylic acid groups.
   (a) Combustion of 0.125 g of the acid gives 0.190 g of $CO_2$ and 0.0388 g of $H_2O$. Calculate the empirical formula of the acid.
   (b) A 0.261-g sample of the acid requires 34.60 mL of 0.130 M NaOH for complete titration (so that the H ions from both carboxylic acid groups are used). What is the molecular formula of the acid?
   (c) Draw a Lewis structure for the acid.
   (d) Describe the hybridization used by the C atoms.
   (e) What are the bond angles around each C atom?

## Applying Chemical Principles

### Biodiesel—An Attractive Fuel for the Future?

Biodiesel, promoted as an alternative to petroleum-based fuels used in diesel engines, is made from plant and animal oils. Chemically, biodiesel is a mixture of esters of long-chain fatty acids prepared from plant and animal fats and oils by *trans-esterification*. This is a reaction between an ester and an alcohol in which the −OR″ on the alcohol exchanges with the OR′ group of the ester (where R′ and R″ are organic groups):

$$
\underset{\text{O}}{R-\overset{\overset{\text{O}}{\|}}{C}-\boxed{O-R' + H}-O-R'' \longrightarrow R-\overset{\overset{\text{O}}{\|}}{C}-O-R'' + R'OH}
$$

Fats and oils are esters, derivatives of glycerol [$HOCH_2CH(OH)CH_2OH$] and high–molar-mass organic acids with at least twelve carbon atoms in the chain. Common fatty acids found in fats and oils are

| | |
|---|---|
| lauric acid | $CH_3(CH_2)_{10}CO_2H$ |
| myristic acid | $CH_3(CH_2)_{12}CO_2H$ |
| palmitic acid | $CH_3(CH_2)_{14}CO_2H$ |
| stearic acid | $CH_3(CH_2)_{16}CO_2H$ |
| oleic acid | $CH_3(CH_2)_7CH{=}CH(CH_2)_7CO_2H$ |

The reaction of fats and oils with methanol (in the presence of a catalyst to speed up the reaction) produces a mixture of the methyl esters of the fatty acids and glycerol.

$$
\begin{array}{l}
H_2C-O-\overset{\overset{\text{O}}{\|}}{C}-R \\
HC-O-\overset{\overset{\text{O}}{\|}}{C}-R' + 3\,CH_3OH \longrightarrow \\
H_2C-O-\overset{\underset{\text{O}}{\|}}{C}-R''
\end{array}
\quad
\begin{array}{l}
H_2C-O-H \\
HC-O-H \\
H_2C-O-H
\end{array}
+
\left\{
\begin{array}{l}
H_3C-O-\overset{\overset{\text{O}}{\|}}{C}-R \\
H_3C-O-\overset{\overset{\text{O}}{\|}}{C}-R' \\
H_3C-O-\overset{\overset{\text{O}}{\|}}{C}-R''
\end{array}
\right.
$$

Glycerol, a by-product of the reaction, is a valuable commodity for the health care industry, so it is separated and sold. The mixture of esters that remains can be used directly as a fuel in existing diesel engines, or it can

Biodiesel, a mixture of esters of long-chain fatty acids.

be blended with petroleum products. In the latter case, the fuel mixture is identified by a designation such as B20 (B = biodiesel, 20 refers to 20% by volume). Biodiesel has the advantage of being clean burning with fewer environmental problems associated with exhaust gases. In particular, there are no $SO_2$ emissions, one of the common problems associated with petroleum-based diesel fuels.

### Questions:

1. Write a balanced chemical equation for the reaction that occurs when 1 mol of methyl myristate, $C_{13}H_{27}CO_2CH_3(\ell)$, is burned, forming $CO_2(g)$ and $H_2O(g)$.

2. Using enthalpy of formation data, calculate the standard enthalpy change for the oxidation of 1.00 mol of methyl myristate ($\Delta_f H° = -771.0$ kJ/mol) to form $CO_2(g)$ and $H_2O(g)$.

3. Which compound, methyl myristate [$C_{13}H_{27}CO_2CH_3$ ($\ell$)] or hexadecane ($C_{16}H_{34}$, one of many hydrocarbons in petroleum based diesel fuel), is predicted to provide the greater energy per mole of fuel? Per liter? ($\Delta_f H°$ for $C_{16}H_{34} = -456.1$ kJ/mol) [$d$(methyl myristate) = 0.86 g/mL, and $d(C_{16}H_{34})$ = 0.77 g/mL].

# The Chemistry of Life: Biochemistry

You are a marvelously complex biological organism. So is every other living thing on Earth. What molecules are present in you, and what are their properties? How is genetic information passed from generation to generation? How does your body carry out the numerous reactions that are needed for life?

These questions and many others fall into the realm of biochemistry, a rapidly expanding area of science. As the name implies, biochemistry exists at the interface of two scientific disciplines: biology and chemistry.

What separates a biochemist's perspective of biological phenomena from a biologist's perspective? The difference is becoming less distinct, but biochemists tend to concentrate on the specific molecules involved in biological processes and on how chemical reactions occur in an organism. They use the strategies of chemists to understand processes in living things.

The goal of this interchapter is to consider how chemistry is involved in answering important biological questions. To do so, we will examine three major classes of biological compounds: proteins, nucleic acids, and lipids. We will also discuss some chemical reactions that occur in living things, including some reactions involved in obtaining energy from food.

The human body with areas of interest to biologists, biochemists, and chemists.

## Proteins

Your body contains thousands of different proteins, and about 50% of the dry weight of your body consists of proteins. Proteins provide structural support (muscle, collagen), help organisms move (muscle), store and transport chemicals from one area to another (hemoglobin), regulate when certain chemical reactions will occur (hormones), and catalyze a host of chemical reactions (enzymes). All of these different functions and others are accomplished using this one class of compounds.

• **Different representations of double helical DNA.** (*bottom to top*) Structural formula, ball-and-stick model, and space-filling model. (The hydrogen atoms are omitted.)

## Amino Acids Are the Building Blocks of Proteins

Proteins are condensation polymers (◀ Section 10.5) formed from amino acids. **Amino acids** are organic compounds that contain an amino group (—NH$_2$) and a carboxylic acid group (—CO$_2$H) (Figure 1). Each of these functional groups can exist in two different states: an ionized form (—NH$_3^+$ and —CO$_2^-$) and an unionized form (—NH$_2$ and —CO$_2$H). If both groups are in their ionized forms, the resulting species contains both a positive and a negative charge and is called a **zwitterion**. In an aqueous environment at physiological pH (about 7.4), amino acids are predominantly in the zwitterionic form.

Almost all amino acids that make up proteins are α-amino acids. In an α-amino acid, the amino group is at one end of the molecule, and the acid group is at the other end. In between these two groups, a single carbon atom (the α-carbon) has attached to it a hydrogen atom and either another hydrogen atom or an organic group, denoted R (Figure 1). Naturally occurring proteins are predominantly built using 20 amino acids, which differ only in terms of the identity of the organic group, R. These organic groups can be nonpolar (groups derived from alkanes or aromatic hydrocarbons) or polar (with alcohol, acidic, basic,

**(a)** generic α-amino acid

**(b)** zwitterionic form of an α-amino acid

**(c)** alanine

**FIGURE 1** α-**Amino acids. (a)** α-Amino acids have a C atom to which are attached an amino group (—NH$_2$), a carboxylic acid group (—CO$_2$H), an organic group (R), and an H atom. **(b)** The zwitterionic form of an α-amino acid. **(c)** Alanine, one of the naturally occurring amino acids.

**FIGURE 2** The 20 most common amino acids. All (except proline and glycine) share the characteristic of having an NH$_3^+$ group, a CO$_2^-$ group, an H atom, and an organic group attached to a chiral C atom, called the alpha (α) carbon. The organic groups may be polar, nonpolar, or electrically charged. (Histidine is shown in the electrically charged column because the unprotonated N in the organic group can easily be protonated.)

**FIGURE 3** Formation of a peptide. Two α-amino acids condense to form an amide linkage, which is often called a *peptide bond*. Proteins are polypeptides, polymers consisting of many amino acid units linked through peptide bonds.

or other polar functional groups) (Figure 2). Depending on which amino acids are present, a region in a protein may be nonpolar, very polar, or anything in between.

All α-amino acids, except glycine, have four different groups attached to the α-carbon. The α-carbon is thus a chiral center (◀ page 442), and two enantiomers exist. Interestingly, all of these amino acids occur in nature in a single enantiomeric form.

Condensation reactions between two amino acids result in the elimination of water and the formation of an amide linkage (Figure 3). The amide linkage in proteins is often referred to as a **peptide bond**, and the polymer (the protein) that results from a series of these reactions is called a **polypeptide**. The amide linkage is planar (◀ page 471), and both the carbon and the nitrogen atoms are $sp^2$ hybridized. There is partial double-bond character in the C—O and C—N bonds, leading to restricted rotation about the carbon–nitrogen bond. As a consequence, each peptide bond in a protein possesses a rigid, planar section, which plays a role in determining its structure.

Proteins consist of one or more polypeptide chains that are often hundreds of amino acids long. Their molar masses are thus often thousands of grams per mole.

## Protein Structure and Hemoglobin

With this basic understanding of amino acids and peptide bonds, let us examine some larger issues related to protein structure. One of the central tenets of biochemistry is that "structure determines function." In other words, what a molecule can do is determined by which atoms or groups of atoms are present and how they are arranged in space. It is not surprising, therefore, that much effort has been devoted to determining the structures of proteins.

To simplify their discussions, biochemists describe proteins as having different structural levels. Each level of structure can be illustrated using hemoglobin.

Hemoglobin is the molecule in red blood cells that carries oxygen from the lungs to all of the body's other cells. It is a large iron-containing protein, made up of more than 10,000 atoms and having a molar mass of 64,500 g/mol. Hemoglobin consists of four polypeptide segments: two identical segments called the α subunits containing 141 amino acids each and two other segments called the β subunits containing 146 amino acids each. The β subunits are identical to each other but different from the α subunits. Each subunit contains an iron(II) ion locked inside an organic ion called a **heme** unit (Figure 4). The oxygen molecules transported by hemoglobin bind to these iron(II) ions.

**heme**
(Fe-protoporphyrin IX)

**FIGURE 4** Heme. The heme unit in hemoglobin (and in myoglobin, a related protein) consists of an iron ion in the center of a porphyrin ring system. (For more information about the heme group, see *A Closer Look* on page 1032.)

Let us focus on the polypeptide part of hemoglobin (Figure 5). The first step in describing a structure is to identify how the atoms are linked together. This is called the **primary structure** of a protein, which is simply the sequence of amino acids linked together by peptide bonds. For example, a glycine unit can be followed by an alanine, followed by a valine, and so on.

The remaining levels of structure all deal with noncovalent (nonbonding) interactions between amino acids in the protein. The **secondary structure** of a protein refers to how amino acids near one another in the sequence arrange themselves in space. Some regular patterns often emerge, such as helices, sheets, and turns. In hemoglobin, the amino acids in large portions of the polypeptide chains arrange themselves into many helical regions, a commonly observed polypeptide secondary structure.

The **tertiary structure** of a protein refers to how the chain is folded, including how amino acids far apart in the sequence interact with each other. In other words, this structure deals with how the regions of the polypeptide chain fold into the overall three-dimensional structure.

**FIGURE 5** The primary, secondary, tertiary, and quaternary structures of hemoglobin.

For proteins consisting of only one chain, the tertiary structure is the highest level of structure present. In proteins consisting of more than one polypeptide chain, such as hemoglobin, there is a fourth level of structure, called the **quaternary structure**. It is concerned with how the different chains interact. The quaternary structure of hemoglobin shows how the four subunits are related to one another in the overall protein.

## Sickle Cell Anemia

The subtleties of sequence, structure, and function are dramatically illustrated in the case of hemoglobin. Seemingly small changes in the amino acid sequence of hemoglobin and other molecules can be important in determining function, as is clearly illustrated by the disease called *sickle cell anemia*. This disease, which is sometimes fatal, affects some individuals of African descent. Persons affected by this disease are anemic; that is, they have low red blood cell counts. In addition, many of their red blood cells are elongated and curved like a sickle instead of being round disks (Figure 6a). These elongated red blood cells are more fragile than normal blood cells, leading to the anemia that is observed. They also restrict the flow of blood within the capillaries,

thereby decreasing the amount of oxygen that the individual's cells receive.

The cause of sickle cell anemia has been traced to a small structural difference in hemoglobin. In the $\beta$ subunits of the hemoglobin in individuals carrying the sickle cell trait, a valine has been substituted for a glutamic acid at position 6. An amino acid in this position ends up on the surface of the protein, where it is exposed to the aqueous environment of the cell. Glutamic acid and valine are quite different from each other. The side chain in glutamic acid is ionic, whereas that in valine is nonpolar. The nonpolar side chain on valine causes a nonpolar region to stick out from the molecule where one should not occur. When hemoglobin (normal or sickle cell) is in the deoxygenated state, it has a nonpolar cavity in another region. The nonpolar region around the valine on one sickle cell hemoglobin molecule fits nicely into this nonpolar cavity on another hemoglobin. The sickle cell hemoglobins thus link together, forming long chainlike structures that lead to the symptoms described (Figure 6b).

Just one amino acid substitution in each $\beta$ subunit causes sickle cell anemia! While other amino acid substitutions may not lead to such severe consequences, sequence, structure, and function are intimately linked and of crucial importance throughout biochemistry.

**FIGURE 6 Normal and sickled red blood cells. (a)** Red blood cells are normally rounded in shape, but people afflicted with sickle cell anemia have cells with a characteristic "sickle" shape. **(b)** Sickle cell hemoglobin has a nonpolar region that can fit into a nonpolar cavity on another hemoglobin. Sickle cell hemoglobins can link together to form long chainlike structures.

## Enzymes, Active Sites, and Lysozyme

Many reactions necessary for life occur too slowly on their own, so organisms speed them up to the appropriate level using biological catalysts called **enzymes**. Almost every metabolic reaction in a living organism requires an enzyme, and most of these enzymes are proteins. Enzymes are often able to speed up reaction rates tremendously, typically $10^7$ to $10^{14}$ times faster than uncatalyzed rates.

For an enzyme to catalyze a reaction, several key steps must occur:

1. A reactant (often called the **substrate**) must bind to the enzyme.
2. The chemical reaction must take place.
3. The product(s) of the reaction must leave the enzyme so that more substrate can bind and the process can be repeated.

Typically, enzymes are very specific; that is, only a limited number of compounds (often only one) serve as substrates for a given enzyme, and the enzyme catalyzes only one type of reaction. The place in the enzyme where the substrate binds and the reaction occurs is called the **active site**. The active site often consists of a cavity or cleft in the enzyme into which the substrate or part of the substrate can fit. The R groups of amino acids or the presence of metal ions in an active site, for example, are often important factors in binding a substrate and catalyzing a reaction.

Lysozyme is an enzyme that can be obtained from human mucus and tears and from other sources, such as egg whites. Alexander Fleming (1881–1955) (who later discovered penicillin) is said to have discovered its presence in mucus when he had a cold. He purposely allowed some of the mucus from his nose to drip onto a dish containing a bacteria culture and found that some of the bacteria died. The chemical in the mucus responsible for this effect was a protein. Fleming called it *lysozyme* because it is an enzyme that causes some bacteria to undergo lysis (rupture).

Lysozyme's antibiotic activity results from its catalysis of a reaction that breaks down the cell walls of some bacteria.

These cell walls contain a polysaccharide, a polymer of sugar molecules. This polysaccharide is composed of two alternating sugars: *N*-acetylmuramic acid (NAM) and *N*-acetylglucosamine (NAG). Lysozyme speeds up the reaction that breaks the bond between carbon-1 of NAM and carbon-4 of NAG (Figure 7). Lysozyme also catalyzes the breakdown of polysaccharides containing only NAG.

**FIGURE 7 Cleavage of a bond between *N*-acetylmuramic acid (NAM) and *N*-acetylglucosamine (NAG).** This reaction is accelerated by the enzyme lysozyme.

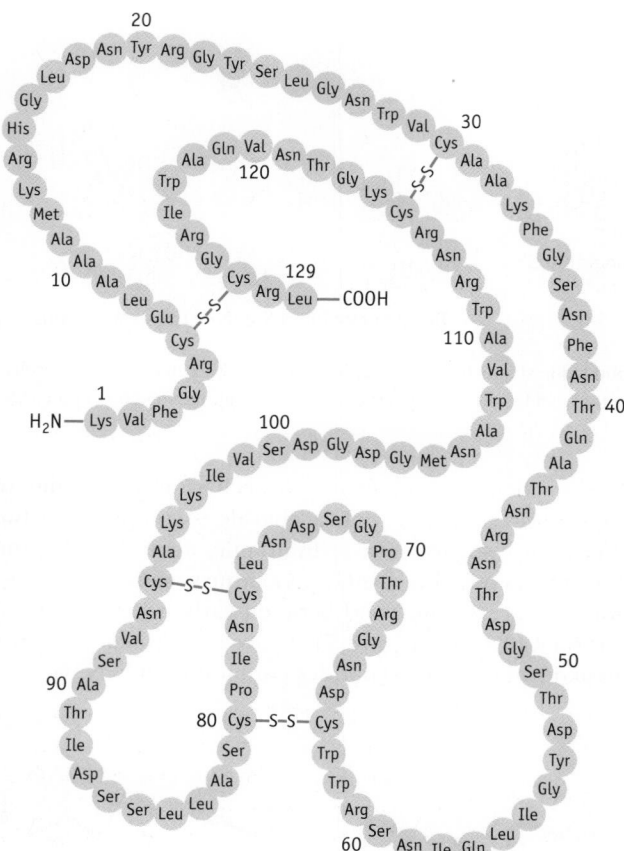

**FIGURE 8 The primary structure of lysozyme.** The cross-chain disulfide links (—S—S—) are links between cysteine amino acid residues.

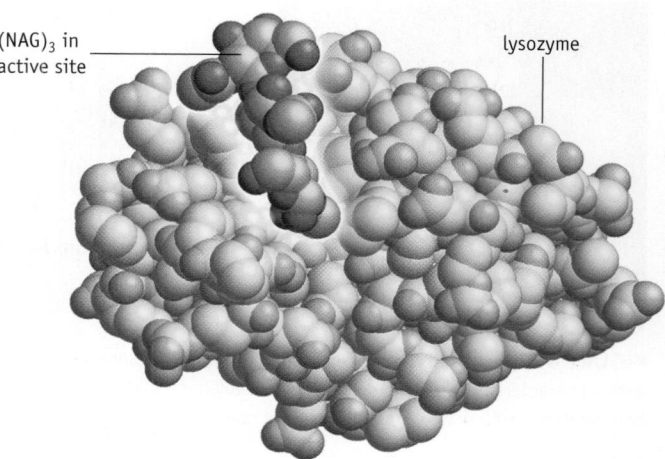

**FIGURE 9** Lysozyme with (NAG)₃.

Lysozyme (Figure 8) is a protein containing 129 amino acids linked together in a single polypeptide chain. Its molar mass is 14,000 g/mol. As was true in the determination of the double-helical structure of DNA (◄ pages 387 and 490), x-ray crystallography and model building were key techniques used in determining lysozyme's three-dimensional structure and method of action.

What is the location of the active site in the enzyme? The enzyme–substrate complex lasts too short a time to be observed by a technique such as x-ray crystallography. Another method had to be used to identify the active site.

Lysozyme is not very effective in cleaving molecules consisting of only two or three NAG units [(NAG)₃]. In fact, these molecules act as inhibitors of the enzyme. Researchers surmised that the inhibition resulted from these small molecules binding to the active site in the enzyme. Therefore, x-ray crystallography was performed on crystals of lysozyme that had been treated with (NAG)₃. It revealed that (NAG)₃ binds to a cleft in lysozyme (Figure 9).

The cleft in lysozyme where (NAG)₃ binds has room for a total of six NAG units. Molecular models of the enzyme and (NAG)₆ showed that five of the six sugars fit nicely into the cleft but that the fourth sugar in the sequence did not fit well. To get this sugar into the active site, its

structure has to be distorted in the direction that the sugar must move during the cleavage reaction (assuming the bond cleaved is the one connecting it and the next sugar). Amino acids immediately around this location could also assist in the cleavage reaction. In addition, models showed that if an alternating sequence of NAM and NAG binds to the enzyme in this cleft, NAM must bind to this location in the active site: NAM cannot fit into the sugar-binding site immediately before this one, whereas NAG can. Cleavage must therefore occur only between carbon-1 of NAM and carbon-4 of the following NAG, not the other way around—and this is exactly what occurs.

## Nucleic Acids

In the first half of the 20th century, researchers identified **deoxyribonucleic acid (DNA)** as the genetic material in cells. Also found in cells was a close relative of DNA called **ribonucleic acid (RNA)**.

### Nucleic Acid Structure

RNA and DNA are polymers (Figure 10). They consist of sugars having five carbon atoms (β-D-ribose in RNA and β-D-2-deoxyribose in DNA) that are connected by phosphodiester groups. A phosphodiester group links the 3′ (pronounced "three prime") position of one sugar to the 5′ position of the next sugar. Attached at the 1′ position of each sugar is an aromatic, nitrogen-containing (nitrogenous) base. The bases in DNA are adenine (A), cytosine (C), guanine (G), and thymine (T); in RNA, the nitrogenous bases are the same as in DNA, except that uracil (U) is used rather than thymine. A single sugar with a nitrogenous base attached is called a **nucleoside**. If a phosphate group is also attached, then the combination is called a **nucleotide** (Figure 11).

The principal chemical difference between RNA and DNA is the identity of the sugar (Figure 12). Ribose has a

DNA

sugar    phosphodiester group

nitrogenous bases (A, C, G, T)

adenine (A)    cytosine (C)    guanine (G)    thymine (T)

RNA

sugar    phosphodiester group

nitrogenous bases (A, C, G, U)

adenine (A)    cytosine (C)    guanine (G)    uracil (U)

**FIGURE 10  DNA and RNA.**

**FIGURE 12  Ribose and deoxyribose.** The sugars found in RNA and DNA, respectively.

ribose    deoxyribose

hydroxyl group (—OH) at the 2 position, whereas 2-deoxyribose has only a hydrogen atom at this position. This seemingly small difference turns out to have profound effects. The polymer chain of RNA is cleaved many times faster than a corresponding chain of DNA under similar conditions due

to the involvement of this hydroxyl group in the cleavage reaction. The greater stability of DNA contributes to it being a better repository for genetic information.

How does DNA store genetic information? DNA consists of a double helix; one strand of DNA is paired with another strand running in the opposite direction. The key parts of the structure of DNA for this function are the nitrogenous bases. James Watson and Francis Crick (page 387) noticed that A can form two hydrogen bonds (▶ Section 12.3) with T and that C can form three hydrogen bonds with G. The spacing in the double helix is just right for either an A–T pair or for a C–G pair to fit, but other combinations (such as A–G) do not fit properly (Figure 13). Thus, if we know the identity of a nucleotide on one strand of the double helix, then we can figure out which nucleotide must be bound to it on the other strand. The two strands are referred to as **complementary strands**.

If the two strands are separated from each other, as they are before the cell division process called *mitosis*, the cell can construct a new complementary strand for each of the original strands by placing a G wherever there is a C, a T wherever there is an A, and so forth. Through this process, called **replication**, the cell ends up with two

adenine (A)    cytosine (C)    guanine (G)

thymine (T)    uracil (U)

**(a)**

nucleoside    5′-nucleotide    3′-nucleotide

**(b)**

**FIGURE 11  Bases, nucleosides, and nucleotides. (a)** The five bases present in DNA and RNA. **(b)** A nucleoside, a 5′-nucleotide, and a 3′-nucleotide. (R = H or OH)

**FIGURE 13** **Base pairs and complementary strands in DNA.** With the four bases in DNA, the usual pairings are adenine with thymine and cytosine with guanine. The pairing is promoted by hydrogen bonding, the interaction of an H atom bound to an O or N atom with an O or N atom in a neighboring molecule.

identical double-stranded DNA molecules for each molecule of DNA initially present. When the cell divides, each of the two resulting cells gets one copy of each DNA molecule (Figure 14). In this way, genetic information is passed along from one generation to the next.

The power of DNA was demonstrated further in 2010 in an experiment conducted by researchers at the J. Craig Venter Institute. They designed a sequence of DNA with a little over one million base pairs that was similar to that of a species of bacteria, *Mycoplasma mycoides.* Beginning with chemically synthesized strands of DNA that were only about one thousand base pairs long, they constructed the overall desired DNA sequence. They then replaced the DNA in cells of another species of bacteria, *M. capricolum,* with this synthesized DNA. The

resulting organisms could perform cell division and grew into colonies of bacteria. These bacteria had characteristics not of *M. capricolum* but of the modified *M. mycoides.* The synthetic DNA, designed and constructed by humans, was not only capable of carrying out the normal functions of DNA but had transformed one species into another!

## Protein Synthesis

The sequence of nucleotides in a cell's DNA contains the instructions to make the proteins the cell needs. DNA is the information storage molecule. To use this information, the cell first makes a complementary copy of the required portion of the DNA using RNA. This step is called **transcription**. The molecule of RNA that results is called **messenger RNA (mRNA)** because it takes this message to where protein synthesis occurs in the cell. The cell uses the less stable (more rapidly cleaved) RNA rather than DNA to carry out this function.

It makes sense to use DNA, the more stable molecule, to store the genetic information because the cell wants this information to be passed from generation to generation intact. Conversely, it makes sense to use RNA to send the message to make a particular protein. By using the less-stable RNA, the message will not be permanent but rather will be destroyed after a certain time, thus allowing the cell to turn off the synthesis of the protein.

Protein synthesis occurs in **ribosomes**, complex bodies in a cell consisting of a mixture of proteins and RNA. The new protein is made as the ribosome moves along the strand of mRNA. The sequence of nucleotides in mRNA contains information about the order of amino acids in the desired

Two strands of DNA. Each base is paired with its partner: adenine (A) with thymine (T), guanine (G) with cytosine (C).

The two DNA strands are separated from each other.

Two new complementary strands are built using the original strands.

Replication results in two identical double-stranded DNA molecules.

At this stage during cell division, the chromosomes containing the DNA have been duplicated, and the two sets have been separated.

**FIGURE 14** **The main steps in DNA replication.** The products of this replication are two identical double-helical DNA molecules. When a cell divides, each resulting cell gets one set.

protein. Following the signal in mRNA to start protein synthesis, every sequence of three nucleotides provides the code for an amino acid until the ribosome reaches the signal to stop (Table 1). These three-nucleotide sequences in mRNA are referred to as **codons**, and the correspondence between each codon and its message (start, add a particular amino acid, or stop) is referred to as the **genetic code**.

How is the genetic code used to make a protein? In the ribosome–mRNA complex, there are two neighboring binding sites, the P site and the A site. (The ribosomes of eukaryotic cells, cells that contain nuclei, also have a third binding site, called the E site.) Each cycle that adds an amino acid to a growing protein begins with that part of the protein already constructed being located in the P site. The A site is where the next amino acid is brought in. Yet another type of RNA becomes involved at this point. This **transfer RNA (tRNA)** consists of a strand of RNA to which an amino acid can be attached (Figure 15). A strand of tRNA has a particular region that contains a sequence of three nucleotides that can attempt to form base pairs to a codon in the mRNA at the ribosome's A site. This three-nucleotide sequence in the tRNA is called the **anticodon**. Only if the base pairing between the codon and anticodon is complementary (for example, A with U) will the tRNA be able to bind to the mRNA–ribosome complex. Not only does the anticodon determine to which codon a particular strand of tRNA can bind, but it also determines which amino acid will be attached to the end of the tRNA molecule. Thus, a codon in the mRNA selects for a particular tRNA anticodon, which in turn selects for the correct amino acid.

The growing protein chain in the P site reacts with the amino acid in the A site, resulting in the protein chain being elongated by one amino acid and moving the chain into the A site. The ribosome then moves down the mRNA chain, moving the tRNA along with the protein strand from the A site into the P site and exposing a new codon in the A site. The tRNA that had been in the P site and

**FIGURE 15** tRNA structure.

### Table 1 Examples of the 64 Codons in the Genetic Code

| Codon Base Sequence* | Amino Acid to Be Added |
|---|---|
| AAA | Lysine |
| AAC | Asparagine |
| AUG | Start |
| CAA | Glutamine |
| CAU | Histidine |
| GAA | Glutamic acid |
| GCA | Alanine |
| UAA | Stop |
| UAC | Tyrosine |

\* A = Adenine, C = cytosine, G = guanine, U = uracil.

that no longer has an amino acid attached either leaves the ribosome directly or, if there is an E site present, moves into the E site before exiting from the ribosome. The process is then repeated (Figure 16).

Converting the information from a nucleotide sequence in mRNA into an amino acid sequence in a protein is called **translation**. Protein synthesis thus consists of two main processes: transcription of the DNA's information into RNA, followed by translation of the RNA's message into the amino acid sequence of the protein. There is more involved. but the processes of transcription and translation as discussed here provide a basic introduction to this important topic.

## The RNA World and the Origin of Life

One of the most fascinating and persistent questions scientists pursue is how life arose on earth. Plaguing those trying to answer this question is a molecular chicken-and-egg problem: Which came first, DNA or proteins? DNA is good at storing genetic information, but it is not good at catalyzing reactions. Proteins are good at catalyzing reactions, but they are not good at storing genetic information. In trying to picture an early self-replicating molecule,

**FIGURE 16** **Protein synthesis.** The tRNA with an anticodon complementary to the mRNA codon exposed in the A site of the ribosome brings the next amino acid to be added to the growing protein chain. After the new peptide bond is formed, the ribosome moves down the mRNA, exposing a new codon in the A site and transferring the previous tRNA and the protein chain to the P site.

deciding whether it should be based on DNA or proteins seemed hopeless. Ultimately, both functions are important. These problems have caused some scientists to turn away from considering either DNA or proteins as candidates for the first molecule of life. One hypothesis that has gained support in recent years suggests that the first life on earth may have been based on RNA instead.

Like DNA, RNA is a nucleic acid and can serve as a genetic storage molecule. We have already seen how it serves as an information molecule in the process of protein synthesis. In addition, scientists have discovered that retroviruses, like the human immunodeficiency virus (HIV) that causes AIDS, use RNA as the repository of genetic information instead of DNA. Perhaps the first organisms on Earth also used RNA to store genetic information.

In the 1980s, researchers discovered that particular strands of RNA catalyze some reactions involving cutting and joining together strands of RNA. Thomas Cech and Sidney Altman shared the 1989 Nobel Prize in chemistry for their independent discoveries of systems that utilize "catalytic RNA." One might imagine that an organism could use RNA both as the genetic material and as a catalyst. Information and action are thus combined in this one molecule.

According to proponents of the "RNA World" hypothesis, the first organism used RNA for both information and catalysis. At some later date, DNA evolved and had better information storage capabilities, so it took over the genetic information storage functions from RNA. Likewise, pro-

teins eventually evolved and proved better at catalysis than RNA, so they took over this role for most reactions in a cell. RNA still plays a central role in the flow of genetic information, however. Genetic information does not go directly from DNA to proteins; it must pass through RNA along the way. Those favoring the RNA World hypothesis also point out that many enzyme cofactors, molecules that must be present for an enzyme to work, are RNA nucleotides or are based on RNA nucleotides. As we shall see, one of the most important molecules in metabolism is an RNA nucleotide, adenosine 5'-triphosphate (ATP). The importance of these nucleotides might date back to an earlier time when organisms were based on RNA alone.

The RNA World hypothesis is interesting and can answer some of the questions that arise in research on the origins of life, but it is not the only current hypothesis dealing with the origin of a self-replicating system. Much research remains to be done before we truly understand how life could have arisen on Earth.

## Lipids and Cell Membranes

**Lipids** are another important type of compound found in organisms. Among other things, they are the principal components of cell membranes and a repository of chemical energy in the form of fat. In addition, some of the chemical messengers called **hormones** are lipids.

Lipids include a wide range of compounds because classification of a compound as a lipid is based on its solubility rather than on a particular chemical functional group. A lipid is a compound that is at best slightly soluble in water but is soluble in organic solvents.

Polar compounds tend to be soluble in a polar solvent such as water. Nonpolar compounds tend not to be soluble in polar solvents but in nonpolar solvents instead. This tendency is sometimes referred to as "like dissolves like" (▶ Section 14.2). Compounds in biological organisms that are nonpolar, or at least substantially nonpolar, have limited solubility in water and are therefore lipids.

A major category of lipids consists of molecules that have one end that is polar and another end that is nonpolar. The polar end provides the slight water solubility necessary for it to be compatible with being in the aqueous environment of the cell, but the nonpolar end greatly limits the solubility. Many of these compounds are fats, oils, or fatty acids or are related to these compounds.

**Fats** and **oils** serve many functions in the body, a primary one being the storage of energy. Fats (solids) and oils (liquids) are triesters formed from glycerol (1,2,3-propanetriol)

and three carboxylic acids that can be the same or different. Because they are triesters of glycerol, they are sometimes referred to as **triglycerides**.

$$
\begin{array}{c}
H_2C-O-\overset{\overset{\displaystyle O}{\|}}{C}R \\
HC-O-\overset{\overset{\displaystyle O}{\|}}{C}R \\
H_2C-O-\overset{\overset{\displaystyle O}{\|}}{C}R
\end{array}
$$

The carboxylic acids in fats and oils are known as **fatty acids** and have a lengthy carbon chain, usually containing between 12 and 18 carbon atoms (Table 2). Fatty acids and triglycerides are lipids of the type where one end of the molecule is polar and the other end is nonpolar. The polar end in fatty acids is a carboxylic acid group, and the nonpolar end is a long hydrocarbon chain.

The hydrocarbon chains can be saturated (pages 444 and 451) or may include one or more double bonds. Saturated

## A CLOSER LOOK

# HIV and Reverse Transcriptase

One of the major health crises in modern times is the epidemic associated with the disease called acquired immune deficiency syndrome (AIDS). A person develops AIDS in the final stages of infection with the human immunodeficiency virus (HIV). At the time of this writing, an estimated 33 million people worldwide are infected with HIV. HIV is a retrovirus. Unlike all organisms and most viruses, a retrovirus does not use DNA as its genetic material but rather uses single-stranded RNA.

During the course of infection, the viral RNA is transcribed into DNA by means of an enzyme called *reverse transcriptase*. It is so named because the direction of information flow is in the opposite direction (RNA → DNA) than that usually found in cells. The resulting DNA is inserted into the cell's DNA. The infected cell then produces the proteins and RNA to make new virus particles.

Reverse transcriptase consists of two subunits (see Figure). One subunit has a molar mass of approximately $6.6 \times 10^4$ g/mol, and the other has a molar mass of roughly $5.1 \times 10^4$ g/mol. Reverse transcriptase is not a very accurate enzyme, however. It makes an error in transcription for every 2000 to 4000 nucleotides copied. This is a much larger error rate than that for most

**Reverse transcriptase.** The reverse transcriptase enzyme consists of two subunits (shown in red and purple). Reverse transcriptase catalyzes the transcription of viral RNA into DNA. The cell then constructs a complementary strand of DNA. The resulting double-stranded DNA is inserted into the cell's DNA.

cellular enzymes that copy DNA, which typically make one error for every $10^9$ to $10^{10}$ nucleotides copied. The high error rate for reverse transcriptase contributes to the challenge scientists face in trying to combat HIV because these reverse transcription errors in the resulting DNA lead to frequent mutations in the virus. That is, the virus

keeps changing, which means that developing a treatment that works and will continue to work is very difficult. Some treatments have been successful in significantly delaying the onset of AIDS, but none has yet proven to be a cure. More research is needed to combat this deadly disease.

**Table 2 Common Fatty Acids**

| Name | Number of C Atoms | Formula |
|---|---|---|
| *Saturated Acids* | | |
| Lauric | $C_{12}$ | $CH_3(CH_2)_{10}CO_2H$ |
| Myristic | $C_{14}$ | $CH_3(CH_2)_{12}CO_2H$ |
| Palmitic | $C_{16}$ | $CH_3(CH_2)_{14}CO_2H$ |
| Stearic | $C_{18}$ | $CH_3(CH_2)_{16}CO_2H$ |
| *Unsaturated Acid* | | |
| Oleic | $C_{18}$ | $CH_3(CH_2)_7CH{=}CH(CH_2)_7CO_2H$ |

compounds are more common in animal products while unsaturated fats and oils are more common in plants. In general, triglycerides containing saturated fatty acids are solids, and those containing unsaturated fatty acids are liquids at room temperature. The difference in melting point relates to the molecular structure. With only single bonds linking carbon atoms in saturated fatty acids, the hydrocarbon group is flexible, allowing the molecules to pack more closely together. The double bonds in unsaturated triglycerides introduce kinks that make the hydrocarbon group less flexible; consequently, the molecules pack less tightly together.

**Steroids** are another category of lipids. Steroid molecules consist of four hydrocarbon rings joined together (Figure 17a). Three of the rings contain six carbon atoms, and one contains five carbon atoms. Examples of steroids are the sex hormones testosterone, estradiol, and progesterone. Cholesterol (Figure 17b) is also an important steroid. You may have heard of cholesterol because of its correlation with heart disease. While some cholesterol is necessary for humans, excess cholesterol can deposit in blood vessels, thus partially blocking them and causing the heart to work harder than it should.

The most prevalent molecules in most cell membranes are **phospholipids** (Figure 18a). These are similar to triglycerides in that they are based on glycerol. Two of the alcohol groups in glycerol are esterified to long-chain fatty acids. The third alcohol group, however, is bonded to a phosphate that has another hydrocarbon chain attached to it. Phosphate groups are very polar. In phospholipid molecules, the phosphate end is sometimes called the "head," and the nonpolar hydrocarbon chains comprise the "tail."

When phospholipids are placed in water, they typically arrange themselves in a **bilayer structure** (Figure 18b). This is exactly the arrangement that phospholipids have in a cell membrane. Water is present on both the inside and the outside of the bilayer, corresponding to the inside and outside of the cell. In the outside layer of the membrane, the phospholipids line up alongside each other such that their polar heads face the aqueous environment outside the cell. Moving inward, next come the tails of these lipids. The phospholipids in the second layer align themselves so that their nonpolar tails are in contact with the outer layer's nonpolar tails. Finally, the polar heads of the

**FIGURE 17** Steroids. **(a)** The ring structure present in all steroids. There are three six-member rings (A, B, and C) and one five-member ring (D). **(b)** Cholesterol.

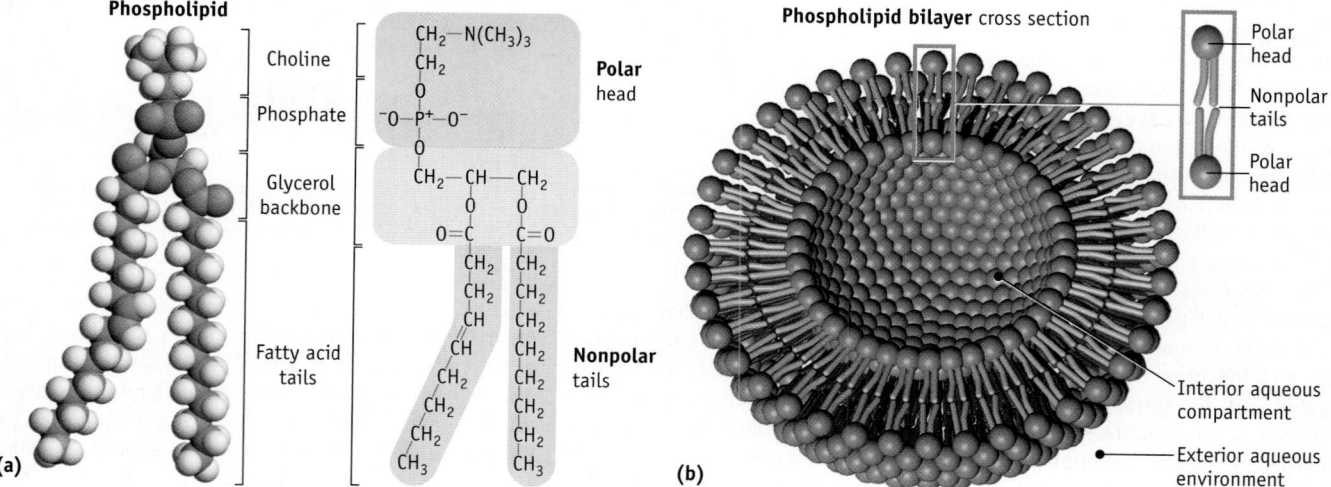

**FIGURE 18** Phospholipids. **(a)** The structure of a phospholipid. **(b)** A cross-section of a phospholipid bilayer. The polar heads of the phospholipids are exposed to water, whereas the nonpolar tails are located in the interior of the bilayer.

FIGURE 19 **The fluid-mosaic model of cell membranes.** A cell membrane is made up primarily of a phospholipid bilayer in which are embedded cholesterol, other lipids, and proteins. Movement within a layer occurs, but movement from one side of the bilayer to the other is rare.

second layer face the aqueous environment inside the cell. The phospholipid bilayer nicely encloses the cell and provides a good barrier between the inside and the outside of the cell, due to the different solubility characteristics of the nonpolar region in the middle of the bilayer.

There are other molecules present in cell membranes. Cholesterol is an important part of animal cell membranes, helping to give the membranes greater rigidity. Some proteins in the cell membrane allow select materials to cross from one side of the membrane to the other (*transport proteins*). Others accept chemical signals from other cells or respond to materials in the cell's environment (*receptor proteins*). Finally, some enzymes are also associated with the membrane.

The overall model for a cell membrane is called the **fluid-mosaic model** (Figure 19). In this model, the membrane's structure is largely that of a phospholipid bilayer described earlier. Embedded in this bilayer are molecules such as cholesterol and proteins. Movement of all of these components within each layer of the bilayer occurs readily; the membrane is thus fluid to a certain extent. On the other hand, there is little movement of components between layers. The "like dissolves like" observation provides the reason for this lack of exchange between layers. The head of a phospholipid in the outer layer, for example, would not be compatible with the very nonpolar region within the bilayer that it would need to pass through in order to traverse from one side of the bilayer to the other.

A cell membrane serves as the boundary between the cell and the rest of the universe, but an exchange of some materials between the cell and the outside world needs to occur. There are different mechanisms by which this happens (Figure 20). The simplest is *passive diffu-*

*sion.* In this process, a molecule moves through the phospholipid bilayer from a region of higher concentration to a region of lower concentration, the natural direction of flow. Because the bilayer provides such a good barrier, only a few very small uncharged molecules (such as $N_2$, $O_2$, $CO_2$, and $H_2O$) can pass through the membrane this way. Many more species enter or leave the cell through a process called *facilitated diffusion.* In this process, ions or molecules still travel from a region of higher concentration to a region of lower concentration, but they do not pass directly through the bilayer. Instead, they pass through channels formed by proteins embedded in the cell membrane.

Sometimes, it is necessary for the cell to move species from a region of lower concentration to a region of higher concentration, the opposite direction that would normally occur on its own. The cell accomplishes this by means of *active transport.* This is again mediated by transport proteins in the cell membrane. Because the species of interest must move in the opposite direction than it would normally go, the cell must expend energy in order to make this occur.

Finally, cells sometimes transport materials into themselves by means of *endocytosis.* This process is usually mediated by a receptor protein. The species of interest (called

FIGURE 20 **Transport of materials across a cell membrane. (a)** Passive diffusion. **(b)** Facilitated diffusion. **(c)** Active transport. **(d)** Endocytosis.

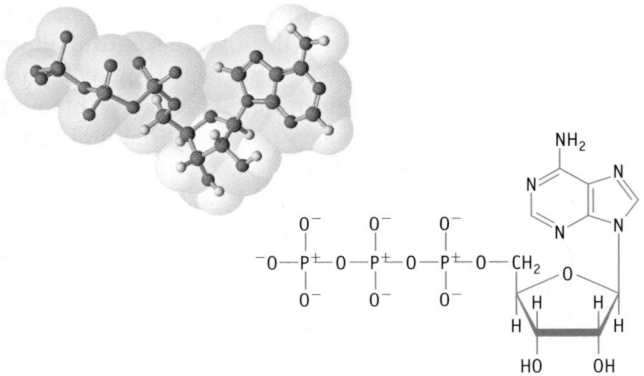

**FIGURE 21** Adenosine-5′-triphosphate (ATP).

**FIGURE 22** The exothermic conversion of adenosine-5′-triphosphate (ATP) to adenosine-5′-diphosphate (ADP).

the *substrate*) binds to the receptor protein. A portion of the cell membrane surrounds the receptor–substrate complex. This portion of the cell membrane is then broken off, bringing the complex into the cell.

In this section, we have seen that the simple "like dissolves like" rule explains much about the formation and function of a cell membrane, which defines the boundary between a cell and the rest of the universe.

## Metabolism

Why do we eat? Some components of our food, such as water, are used directly in our bodies. We break down other chemicals to obtain the molecular building blocks we need to make the many chemicals in our bodies. Oxidation of foods also provides the energy we need to perform the activities of life. The many different chemical reactions that foods undergo in the body to provide energy and chemical building blocks fall into the area of biochemistry called **metabolism**. We have already studied some aspects of energy changes in chemical reactions in Chapter 5 and some aspects of oxidation-reduction reactions in Chapter 3. We shall now examine some of these same processes in biochemical reactions.

### Energy and ATP

Substances in food, such as carbohydrates and fats, are oxidized in part of the metabolic process. These oxidations are energetically favorable reactions, releasing large quantities of energy. For example, the thermochemical equation for the oxidation of the sugar glucose ($C_6H_{12}O_6$) to form carbon dioxide and water is

$$C_6H_{12}O_6(s) + 6\ O_2(g) \rightarrow 6\ CO_2(g) + 6\ H_2O(\ell)$$

$$\Delta_rH° = -2803 \text{ kJ/mol-rxn}$$

Rather than carry out this reaction in one rapid and exothermic step, a cell carries out a more controlled oxidation in a series of steps so that it can obtain the energy in small increments. In addition, it would be inefficient if every part of a cell needed to have all the mechanisms necessary to carry out the oxidation of every type of molecule used for energy. Instead, it carries out the oxidation of compounds such as glucose in one location and stores the energy in a small set of compounds that can be used almost anywhere in the cell.

The principal compound used to perform this function is adenosine 5′-triphosphate (ATP). This ribonucleotide consists of a ribose molecule to which the nitrogenous base adenine is connected at the 1′ position and a triphosphate group is connected at the 5′ position (Figure 21). In aerobic respiration, the equivalent of 30–32 mol of ATP is typically produced per mole of glucose oxidized. Based on the $\Delta H$ values for the processes, a greater production of ATP might be expected, but the process is not completely efficient.

The hydrolysis of ATP to adenosine 5′-diphosphate (ADP) and inorganic phosphate ($P_i$) is an exothermic process (Figure 22).

$$\text{ATP} + H_2O \rightarrow \text{ADP} + P_i \qquad \Delta_rH \approx -24 \text{ kJ/mol-rxn}$$

Why is this reaction exothermic? In this reaction, we must break two bonds, a P—O bond in ATP and an H—O bond in water. But we also form two new bonds: a P—O bond connecting the phosphate group being cleaved off the ATP with the OH of the original water and an H—O bond connecting the hydrogen from the water with the portion of the ATP that forms ADP. In this overall process, more energy is released in forming these new bonds in the products than is required to break the necessary bonds in the reactants.

In cells, many chemical processes that would be endothermic on their own are linked with the hydrolysis of ATP.

**FIGURE 23** The structures of NADH and NAD$^+$.

The combination of an energetically unfavorable process with the energetically favorable hydrolysis of ATP can yield a process that is energetically favorable. For example, most cells have a greater concentration of potassium ions and a smaller concentration of sodium ions inside them than are present outside them. The natural tendency, therefore, is for sodium ions to flow into the cell and for potassium ions to flow out. To maintain the correct concentrations, the cell must counteract this movement and use active transport to pump sodium ions out of the cell and potassium ions into the cell. This requires energy. To accomplish this feat, the cell links this pumping process to the hydrolysis of ATP to ADP. The energy released from the hydrolysis reaction provides the energy to run a molecular pump (a transport protein) that moves the ions in the direction the cell needs.

## Oxidation–Reduction and NADH

Cells also need compounds that can be used to carry out oxidation–reduction reactions. Just as ATP is a compound used in many biochemical reactions when energy is needed, so nature uses another small set of compounds to run many redox reactions. An important example is **nicotinamide adenine dinucleotide (NADH)**. This compound consists of two ribonucleotides joined at their 5′ positions via a diphosphate linkage. One of the nucleotides has adenine as its nitrogenous base, whereas the other has a nicotinamide ring (Figure 23). When NADH is oxidized, changes occur in the nicotinamide ring, such that the equivalent of a hydride ion (H$^-$) is lost. Because this hydride ion has two electrons associated with it, the nicotinamide ring loses two electrons in the process. The resulting species, referred to as NAD$^+$, is shown on the right in Figure 23.

In many biochemical reactions, when a particular species needs to be reduced, it reacts with NADH. The NADH is

oxidized to NAD$^+$, losing two electrons in the process, and the species of interest is reduced by gaining these electrons. If a species must be oxidized, the opposite process often occurs; that is, it reacts with NAD$^+$. The NAD$^+$ is reduced to NADH, and the species of interest is oxidized.

## Respiration and Photosynthesis

In the process of **respiration**, a cell breaks down molecules such as glucose, oxidizing them to $CO_2$ and $H_2O$.

$$C_6H_{12}O_6(s) + 6\ O_2(g) \rightarrow 6\ CO_2(g) + 6\ H_2O(\ell)$$

The energy released in these reactions is used to generate the ATP needed by the cell. The sugars used in this process can be traced back to green plants, where sugars are made via the process of **photosynthesis**. In photosynthesis, plants carry out the reverse of glucose oxidation—that is, the synthesis of glucose from $CO_2$ and $H_2O$.

$$6\ CO_2(g) + 6\ H_2O(\ell) \rightarrow C_6H_{12}O_6(s) + 6\ O_2(g)$$

Green plants have found a way to use light to provide the energy needed to run this endothermic reaction.

The key molecule involved in trapping the energy from light in photosynthesis is chlorophyll. Green plants contain two types of chlorophyll: chlorophyll *a* and chlorophyll *b* (Figure 24). The absorbance spectra of chlorophyll *a* and chlorophyll *b* are also shown in Figure 24. Notice that these molecules absorb best in the blue-violet and red-orange regions of the visible spectrum. Not much light is absorbed in the green region. When white light shines on chlorophyll, red-orange and blue-violet light are absorbed by the chlorophyll; green light is not absorbed but rather is reflected. We see the reflected light, so plants appear green to us. The light energy absorbed by the chlorophyll is used to drive the process of photosynthesis.

**FIGURE 24** The structure of chlorophyll and the visible absorbance spectra of chlorophylls *a* and *b*.

## Concluding Remarks

In this brief overview of biochemistry, we have examined proteins and their structures, nucleic acids, protein synthesis, lipids, and metabolism. As you have seen, the principles of chemistry you have been learning in general chemistry can be applied to understanding biological processes. We hope you have begun to recognize the marvelous complexity of life as well as some of the underlying patterns that exist within this complexity. This discussion has, however, merely scratched the surface of this fascinating and important field of study. Vast areas of biochemistry remain to be studied, and many questions persist for which the answers are currently unknown.

## SUGGESTED READINGS

1. M. K. Campbell and S. O. Farrell: *Biochemistry*, 7th ed., Belmont, California: Cengage Learning: Brooks/Cole, 2012.
2. W. C. Galley: "Exothermic Bond Breaking: A Persistent Misconception." *Journal of Chemical Education*, Vol. 81, pp. 523–525, 2004.
3. D. G. Gibson, J. I. Glass, C. Lartigue, V. N. Noskov, R. Chuang, M. A. Algire, G. A. Benders, M. G. Montague, L. Ma, M. M. Moodie, C. Merryman, S. Vashee, R. Krishnakumar, N. Assad-Garcia, C. Andrews-Pfannkoch, E. A. Denisova, L. Young, Z. Qi, T. H. Segall-Shapiro, C. H. Calvey, P. P. Parmar, C. A. Hutchison III, H. O. Smith, J. C. Venter: "Creation of a Bacterial Cell Controlled by a Chemically Synthesized Genome." *Science*, Vol. 215, Issue 5987, pp. 52–56, 2010.
4. D. C. Phillips: "The Three-dimensional Structure of an Enzyme Molecule." *Scientific American*, Vol. 215, No. 5, pp. 78–90, 1966.
5. J. D. Watson: *The Double Helix: A Personal Account of the Discovery of the Structure of DNA*, New York: Mentor, 1968.

## STUDY QUESTIONS

Blue-numbered questions have answers in Appendix Q and fully worked solutions in the *Student Solutions Manual*.

1. (a) Draw the Lewis structure for the amino acid valine, showing the amino group and the carboxylic acid group in their unionized forms.
   (b) Draw the Lewis structure for the zwitterionic form of valine.
   (c) Which of these structures will be the predominant form at physiological pH?

2. Consider the amino acids alanine, leucine, serine, phenylalanine, lysine, and aspartic acid. Which have polar R groups, and which have nonpolar R groups?

3. Draw Lewis structures for the two dipeptides that contain both alanine and glycine.

4. When listing the sequence of amino acids in a polypeptide or protein, the sequence always begins with the amino acid that has the free amino group and ends with the amino acid that has the free carboxylic acid group. Draw the Lewis structure for the tripeptide serine-leucine-valine.

5. Draw two Lewis structures for the dipeptide alanine-isoleucine that show the resonance structures of the amide linkage.

6. Identify the type of structure (primary, secondary, tertiary, or quaternary) that corresponds to the following statements.
   (a) This type of structure is the amino acid sequence in the protein.
   (b) This type of structure indicates how different peptide chains in the overall protein are arranged with respect to one another.
   (c) This type of structure refers to how the polypeptide chain is folded, including how amino acids that are far apart in the sequence end up in the overall molecule.
   (d) This type of structure deals with how amino acids near one another in the sequence arrange themselves.

7. (a) Draw the Lewis structure for the sugar ribose.
   (b) Draw the Lewis structure for the nucleoside adenosine (it consists of ribose and adenine).
   (c) Draw the Lewis structure for the nucleotide adenosine 5'-monophosphate.

8. A DNA or RNA sequence is usually written from the end with a free 5'-OH to the end with a free 3'-OH. Draw the Lewis structure for the tetranucleotide AUGC.

9. Do the DNA sequences ATGC and CGTA represent the same molecule?

10. (a) What type of interaction holds DNA's double-helical strands together?
    (b) Why would it not be good for DNA's double-helical strands to be held together by covalent bonds?

11. Complementary strands of nucleic acids run in opposite directions. That is, the 5' end of one strand will be lined up with the 3' end of the other. Given the following nucleotide sequence in DNA: 5'—ACGCGATTC—3':
    (a) Determine the sequence of the complementary strand of DNA. Report this sequence by writing it from its 5' end to its 3' end (the usual way of reporting nucleic acid sequences).
    (b) Write the sequence (5'–3') for the strand of mRNA that would be complementary to the original strand of DNA.
    (c) Assuming that this sequence is part of the coding sequence for a protein and that it is properly lined up so that the first codon of this sequence begins with the 5' nucleotide of the mRNA, write the sequences for the three anticodons that would be complementary to this strand of mRNA in this region.
    (d) What sequence of amino acids is coded for by this mRNA? (The complete genetic code is listed in several sites on the Internet.)

12. (a) According to the genetic code in Table 1, which amino acid is coded for by the mRNA codon GAA?
    (b) What is the sequence in the original DNA that led to this codon being present in the mRNA?
    (c) If a mutation occurs in the DNA in which a G is substituted for the nucleotide at the second position of this coding region in the DNA, which amino acid will now be selected?

13. (a) Describe what occurs in the process of transcription.
    (b) Describe what occurs in the process of translation.

14. Sketch a section of a phospholipid bilayer in which you let a circle represent the polar head group and curvy lines represent the hydrocarbon tails. Label the regions of the bilayer as being polar or nonpolar.

15. What structure do all steroids have in common?

16. The section about metabolism provided a value for $\Delta_r H°$ for the oxidation of one mole of glucose. Using $\Delta_f H°$ values at 25 °C, verify that this is the correct value for the equation

$$C_6H_{12}O_6(s) + 6\ O_2(g) \rightarrow 6\ CO_2(g) + 6\ H_2O(\ell)$$

$$\Delta_f H°[C_6H_{12}O_6(s)] = -1273.3\ \text{kJ/mol}$$

17. Which of the following statements are true?
    (a) Breaking the P—O bond in ATP is an exothermic process.
    (b) Making a new bond between the phosphorus atom in the phosphate group being cleaved off ATP and the OH group of water is an exothermic process.
    (c) Breaking bonds is an endothermic process.
    (d) The energy released in the hydrolysis of ATP may be used to run endothermic reactions in a cell.

18. Consider the following reaction:
    NADH + H$^+$ + ½ O$_2$ → NAD$^+$ + H$_2$O
    (a) Which species is being oxidized (NADH, H$^+$, or O$_2$)?
    (b) Which species is being reduced?
    (c) Which species is the oxidizing agent?
    (d) Which species is the reducing agent?

19. (a) Calculate the enthalpy change for the production of one mole of glucose by the process of photosynthesis at 25 °C. $\Delta_f H°$ [glucose(s)] = −1273.3 kJ/mol

$$6\ CO_2(g) + 6\ H_2O(\ell) \rightarrow C_6H_{12}O_6(s) + 6\ O_2(g)$$

    (b) What is the enthalpy change involved in producing one molecule of glucose by this process?
    (c) Chlorophyll molecules absorb light of various wavelengths. One wavelength absorbed is 650 nm. Calculate the energy of a photon of light having this wavelength.
    (d) Assuming that all of this energy goes toward providing the energy required for the photosynthetic reaction, can the absorption of one photon at 650 nm lead to the production of one molecule of glucose, or must multiple photons be absorbed?

# 11 Gases and Their Properties

©Davis Barber/PhotoEdit

## The Atmosphere and Altitude Sickness
Some of you may have dreamed of climbing to the summits of the world's tallest mountains, or you may be an avid skier and visit high-mountain ski areas. In either case, "acute mountain sickness" (AMS) is a possibility. AMS is common at higher altitudes and is characterized by a headache, nausea, insomnia, dizziness, lassitude, and fatigue. It can be prevented by a slow ascent, and its symptoms can be relieved by a mild pain reliever.

AMS and more serious forms of high-altitude sickness are generally due to oxygen deprivation, also called *hypoxia*. The oxygen concentration in Earth's atmosphere is 21%. As you go higher into the atmosphere, the concentration remains 21%, but the atmospheric pressure drops. When you reach 3000 m (the altitude of some ski resorts), the barometric pressure is about 70% of that at sea level. At 5000 m, barometric pressure is only 50% of sea level, and on the summit of Mt. Everest, it is only 29% of the sea level pressure. At sea level, your blood is nearly saturated with oxygen,

but as the partial pressure of oxygen [$P(O_2)$] drops, the percent saturation drops as well. At $P(O_2)$ of 50 mm Hg, hemoglobin in the red blood cells is about 80% saturated. Other saturation levels are given in the table (for a pH of 7.4).

| $P(O_2)$(mm Hg) | Approximate Percent Saturation |
|---|---|
| 90 | 95% |
| 80 | 92% |
| 70 | 90% |
| 60 | 85% |
| 50 | 80% |
| 40 | 72% |

For more information on the atmosphere, see page 528.

### Questions:

1. Assume a sea level pressure of 1 atm (760 mm Hg). What are the $O_2$ partial pressures at a 3000-m ski resort and on top of Mt. Everest?
2. What are the approximate blood saturation levels under these conditions?

**Answers to these questions are available in Appendix N.**

## CHAPTER GOALS

*See Chapter Goals Revisited (page 537) for Study Questions keyed to these goals.*

- Understand the basis of the gas laws and know how to use those laws (Boyle's law, Charles's law, Avogadro's hypothesis, Dalton's law).

- Use the ideal gas law.

- Apply the gas laws to stoichiometric calculations.

- Understand kinetic-molecular theory as it is applied to gases, especially the distribution of molecular speeds (energies).

- Recognize why gases do not behave like ideal gases under some conditions.

Hot air balloons, SCUBA diving tanks, and automobile air bags (Figure 11.1) depend on the properties of gases. Aside from understanding how these work, there are other reasons for studying gases. First, some common elements and compounds (such as oxygen, nitrogen, and methane) exist in the gaseous state under normal conditions of pressure and temperature. Second, atmospheric gases provide one means of transferring energy and material throughout the globe, and they are a source of life-sustaining chemicals. In addition, the question of "global warming" is one of the major debates of our time, and gases such as carbon dioxide and methane play a role in this apparent problem.

But there is yet another reason for studying gases. Of the three states of matter, the behavior of gases is reasonably simple when viewed at the molecular level, and, as a result, it is well understood. It is possible to describe the properties of gases *qualitatively* in terms of the behavior of the molecules that make up the gas. Even more impressive, it is possible to describe the properties of gases *quantitatively* using simple mathematical models. One objective of scientists is to develop precise mathematical and conceptual models of natural phenomena, and a study of gas behavior

**◑WL**

Sign in to OWL at **www.cengage.com/owl** to view tutorials and simulations, develop problem-solving skills, and complete online homework assigned by your professor.

**go Chemistry**

Download mini lecture videos for key concept review and exam prep from OWL or purchase them from **www.cengagebrain.com**

Don Johnston/Getty Images

**FIGURE 11.1 Automobile air bags.** Most automobiles are now equipped with air bags to protect the driver and passengers in the event of a head-on or side crash. Such bags are inflated with nitrogen gas, which is generated by the explosive decomposition of sodium azide (in the presence of $KNO_3$ and silica):

$$2 \, NaN_3(s) \rightarrow 2 \, Na(s) + 3 \, N_2(g)$$

The air bag is fully inflated in about 0.050 s. This is important because the typical automobile collision lasts about 0.125 s.

**FIGURE 11.2 A barometer.** The pressure of the atmosphere on the surface of the mercury in the dish is balanced by the downward pressure exerted by the column of mercury. The barometer was invented in 1643 by Evangelista Torricelli (1608–1647). A unit of pressure called the *torr* in his honor is equivalent to 1 mm Hg.

will introduce you to this approach. A remarkably accurate description of most gases requires knowing only four quantities: the pressure ($P$), volume ($V$), and temperature ($T$, kelvins) of the gas, and its amount ($n$, mol).

## 11.1 Gas Pressure

**Pressure** is the force exerted on an object divided by the area over which it is exerted, and a barometer is a device used to measure atmospheric pressure. A barometer can be made by filling a tube with a liquid, often mercury, and inverting the tube in a dish containing the same liquid (Figure 11.2). If the air has been removed completely from the vertical tube, the liquid in the tube assumes a level such that the pressure exerted by the mass of the column of liquid in the tube is balanced by the pressure of the atmosphere pressing down on the surface of the liquid in the dish.

Pressure is often reported in units of **millimeters of mercury (mm Hg)**, the height (in mm) of the mercury column in a mercury barometer above the surface of the mercury in the dish. At sea level, this height is about 760 mm. Pressures are also reported as **standard atmospheres (atm)**, a unit defined as follows:

$$1 \text{ standard atmosphere (1 atm)} = 760 \text{ mm Hg (exactly)}$$

The SI unit of pressure is the **pascal (Pa)**.

$$1 \text{ pascal (Pa)} = 1 \text{ newton/meter}^2$$

(The newton is the SI unit of force.) Because the pascal is a very small unit compared with ordinary pressures, the unit kilopascal (kPa) is more often used. Another unit used for gas pressures is the **bar**, where 1 bar = 100,000 Pa. To summarize, the units used in science for pressure are

$$1 \text{ atm} = 760 \text{ mm Hg (exactly)} = 101.325 \text{ kilopascals (kPa)} = 1.01325 \text{ bar}$$

or

$$1 \text{ bar} = 1 \times 10^5 \text{ Pa (exactly)} = 1 \times 10^2 \text{ kPa} = 0.9872 \text{ atm}$$

---

### EXAMPLE 11.1   Pressure Unit Conversions

**Problem** Convert a pressure of 635 mm Hg into its corresponding value in units of atmospheres (atm), bars, and kilopascals (kPa).

**What Do You Know?** You will need the following conversion factors:

$$1 \text{ atm} = 760 \text{ mm Hg} = 1.013 \text{ bar} \qquad 760 \text{ mm Hg} = 101.3 \text{ kPa}$$

**Strategy** Use the relationships between millimeters of Hg, atmospheres, bars, and pascals described in the text. (The use of dimensional analysis, page 39, is highly recommended.)

**Solution**

(a)  Convert pressure in units of mm Hg to units of atm.

$$635 \text{ mm Hg} \times \frac{1 \text{ atm}}{760 \text{ mm Hg}} = 0.836 \text{ atm}$$

(b)  Convert pressure in units of atm to units of bar.

$$0.836 \text{ atm} \times \frac{1.013 \text{ bar}}{1 \text{ atm}} = 0.846 \text{ bar}$$

(c)  Convert pressure in units of mm Hg to units of kilopascals.

$$635 \text{ mm Hg} \times \frac{101.3 \text{ kPa}}{760 \text{ mm Hg}} = 84.6 \text{ kPa}$$

## A CLOSER LOOK

### Measuring Gas Pressure

Pressure is the force exerted on an object divided by the area over which the force is exerted:

*Pressure = force/area*

This book, for example, weighs more than 4 lb and has an area of 85 in², so it exerts a pressure of about 0.05 lb/in² when it lies flat on a surface. (In metric units, the pressure is about 320 Pa.)

Now consider the pressure that the column of mercury exerts on the mercury in the dish in the barometer shown in Figure 11.2. This pressure exactly balances the pressure of the atmosphere. Thus, the pressure of the atmosphere (or of any other gas) can be measured by relating it to the height of the column of mercury (or any other liquid) the gas can support.

Mercury is the liquid of choice for barometers because of its high density. A barometer filled with water would be over 10 m in height. [The water column is about 13.6 times as high as a column of mercury because mercury's density (13.53 g/cm³) is

13.6 times that of water (density = 0.997 g/cm³, at 25 °C).]

In the laboratory, we often use a U-tube manometer, which is a mercury-filled, U-shaped glass tube. The closed side of the tube has been evacuated so that no gas remains to exert pressure on the mercury on that side. The other side is open to the gas whose pressure we want to measure. When the gas presses on the mercury in the open side, the gas pressure is read directly (in mm Hg) as the difference in mercury levels on the closed and open sides.

You may have used a tire gauge to check the pressure in your car or bike tires. In the United States, such gauges usually indicate the pressure in pounds per square inch (psi) where 1 atm = 14.7 psi. Some newer gauges give the pressure in kilopascals as well. Be sure to recognize that the reading on the scale refers to the pressure *in excess of atmospheric pressure*. (A flat tire is not a vacuum; it contains air at atmospheric pressure.) For example, if the gauge reads 35 psi (2.4 atm), the pressure in the tire is actually about 50 psi or 3.4 atm.

**Think about Your Answer** The original pressure, 635 mm Hg, is less than 1 atm, so the pressure is also less than 1 bar and less than 100 kPa.

---

**Check Your Understanding**

Rank the following pressures in decreasing order of magnitude (from largest to smallest): 75 kPa 250 mm Hg, 0.83 bar, and 0.63 atm.

---

### REVIEW & CHECK FOR SECTION 11.1

1.  In a lab experiment you measure a gas pressure of 120 mm Hg. This pressure in units of kPa is approximately

    (a)  12 kPa          (b)  16 kPa          (c)  900 kPa

2.  Suppose you construct a barometer filled with an oil (*d* = 1.25 g/cm³) instead of mercury (*d* = 13.5 g/cm³) in the vertical tube. If the atmosphere has a pressure of 0.95 atm, what is the approximate height of the oil in the tube?

    (a)  7.2 m          (b)  7.8 m          (c)  8.3 m

## 11.2 Gas Laws: The Experimental Basis

### Boyle's Law: The Compressibility of Gases

When you pump up the tires of your bicycle, the pump squeezes the air into a smaller volume. This shows that a gas is compressed into a smaller volume when the pressure is increased. While studying the compressibility of gases, the Englishman Robert Boyle (1627–1691) (see page 518) observed that the volume of a fixed amount of gas at a given temperature is inversely proportional to the pressure exerted by the gas. All gases behave in this manner, and we now refer to this relationship as **Boyle's law**.

A syringe filled with air was sealed. Pressure was applied by adding lead shot to the beaker on top of the syringe. As the mass of lead increased, the pressure on the air in the sealed syringe increased, and the gas was compressed.

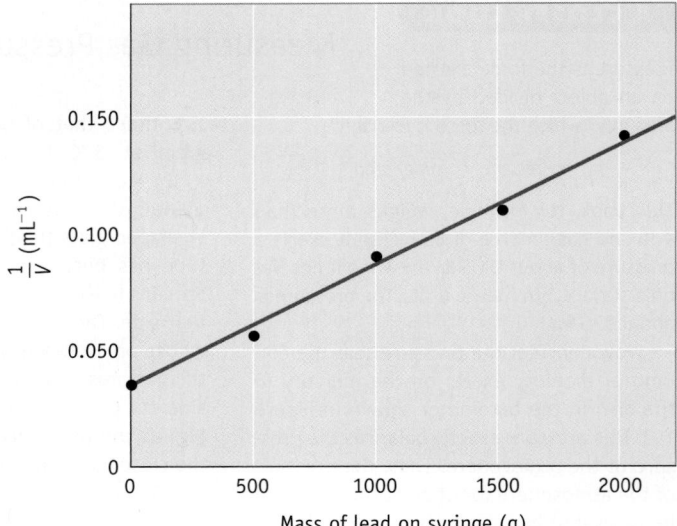

A plot of 1/$V$ (volume of air in the syringe) versus $P$ (as measured by the mass of lead) is a straight line.

**FIGURE 11.3 An experiment to demonstrate Boyle's law.**

Boyle's law can be demonstrated in many ways. In Figure 11.3, a hypodermic syringe is filled with air ($n$ moles) and sealed. When pressure is applied to the movable plunger of the syringe, the air inside is compressed. As the pressure ($P$) increases on the syringe, the gas volume in the syringe ($V$) decreases. When 1/$V$ of the gas in the syringe is plotted as a function of $P$ (as measured by mass of lead), a straight line results. This type of plot demonstrates that the pressure and volume of the gas are inversely proportional; that is, they change in opposite directions.

Mathematically, we can write Boyle's law as:

$$P \propto \frac{1}{V} \quad \text{when } n \text{ (= amount of gas) and } T \text{ are constant}$$

where the symbol $\propto$ means "proportional to."

When two quantities are proportional to each other, they can be equated if a *proportionality constant*, here called $C_B$, is introduced.

$$P = C_B \times \frac{1}{V} \quad \text{or} \quad PV = C_B \text{ at constant } n \text{ and } T$$

This form of Boyle's law expresses the fact that *the product of the pressure and volume of a gas sample is a constant at a given temperature*, where the constant $C_B$ is determined by the amount of gas (in moles) and its temperature (in kelvins). Because the $PV$ product is always equal to $C_B$ [assuming no change in the number of moles of gas ($n$) and the temperature ($T$)], it follows that, if $PV$ is known for a gas sample under one set of conditions ($P_1$ and $V_1$), then it is known for another set of conditions ($P_2$ and $V_2$).

$$P_1V_1 = P_2V_2 \text{ at constant } n \text{ and } T \qquad \qquad \text{(11.1)}$$

This form of **Boyle's law** is useful when we want to know, for example, what happens to the volume of a given amount of gas when the pressure changes at a constant temperature.

# ⊙WL  INTERACTIVE EXAMPLE 11.2  Boyle's Law

**Problem**  A bicycle pump has a volume of 1400 cm³. If a sample of air in the pump has a pressure of 730 mm Hg, what is the pressure when the volume is reduced to 170 cm³?

**What Do You Know?**  This is a Boyle's law problem because you are dealing with changes in pressure and/or volume of a given amount of gas at constant temperature. Here the original pressure and volume of gas ($P_1$ and $V_1$) and the new volume ($V_2$) are known, but the final pressure ($P_2$) is not known. Both volumes are in the same unit so no unit changes are necessary.

| Initial Conditions | Final Conditions |
|---|---|
| $P_1$ = 730 mm Hg | $P_2$ = ? |
| $V_1$ = 1400 cm³ | $V_2$ = 170 cm³ |

**Strategy**  Use Boyle's law, Equation 11.1.

**Solution**  You can solve this problem by substituting data into a rearranged version of Boyle's law.

$$P_2 = P_1 (V_1/V_2)$$

$$P_2 = (730 \text{ mm Hg}) \times \frac{1400 \text{ cm}^3}{170 \text{ cm}^3} = 6.0 \times 10^3 \text{ mm Hg}$$

**Think about Your Answer**  You know $P$ and $V$ change in opposite directions. In this case, the volume has decreased, so the new pressure ($P_2$) must be greater than the original pressure ($P_1$). The answer of about 6000 mm Hg is reasonable because the volume decreased by a factor of more than 8.

---

**Check Your Understanding**

A large balloon contains 65.0 L of helium gas at 25 °C and a pressure of 745 mm Hg. The balloon ascends to 3000 m, at which the external pressure has decreased by 30.%. What would be the volume of the balloon, assuming it expands so that the internal and external pressures are equal. (Assume the temperature is still 25 °C.)

---

**Strategy Map 11.2**

**PROBLEM**
Calculate the **pressure** when the *volume of a gas* is **reduced**.

↓

**DATA/INFORMATION**
- *Initial* pressure
- *Initial* volume
- *Final* volume

Rearrange **Boyle's law** (Equation 11.1) to calculate **final pressure** ($P_2$).

↓

**Pressure** ($P_2$) after reducing the volume

## The Effect of Temperature on Gas Volume: Charles's Law

In 1787, the French scientist Jacques Charles (1746–1823) discovered that the volume of a fixed quantity of gas at constant pressure decreases with decreasing temperature. The demonstration in Figure 11.4 shows a dramatic decrease in volume with temperature, but Figure 11.5 illustrates more quantitatively how the volumes of two different gas samples change with temperature (at a constant pressure). When

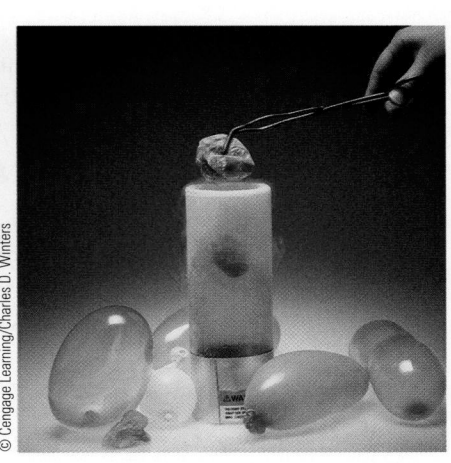

**(a)** Air-filled balloons are placed in liquid nitrogen (77 K). The volume of the gas in the balloons is dramatically reduced at this temperature.

**(b)** Here all of the balloons have been placed in the flask of liquid nitrogen.

**(c)** When the balloons are removed they warm to room temperature and reinflate to their original volume.

**FIGURE 11.4**  A dramatic illustration of Charles's law.

| T (°C) | T (K) | Vol. H₂ (mL) | Vol. O₂ (mL) |
|--------|-------|--------------|--------------|
| 300 | 573 | 47.0 | 21.1 |
| 200 | 473 | 38.8 | 17.5 |
| 100 | 373 | 30.6 | 13.8 |
| 0 | 273 | 22.4 | 10.1 |
| −100 | 173 | 14.2 | 6.39 |
| −200 | 73 | 6.00 | — |

**FIGURE 11.5 Charles's law.** The solid lines represent the volumes of samples of hydrogen (0.00100 mol) and oxygen (0.000450 mol) at a pressure of 1.00 atm but at different temperatures. The volumes decrease as the temperature is lowered (at constant pressure). These lines, if extended, intersect the temperature axis at approximately −273 °C.

the plots of volume versus temperature are extrapolated to lower temperatures, they all reach zero volume at the same temperature, −273.15 °C. (Of course, gases will not actually reach zero volume; they liquefy above that temperature.) This temperature is significant, however. William Thomson (1824–1907), also known as Lord Kelvin, proposed a temperature scale—now known as the Kelvin scale—for which the zero point is −273.15 °C (◀ page 26).

When Kelvin temperatures are used with volume measurements, the volume–temperature relationship is

$$V = C_c \times T$$

where $C_c$ is a proportionality constant (which depends on the amount of gas and its pressure). This is **Charles's law**, which states that if a given amount of gas is held at a constant pressure, its volume is directly proportional to the Kelvin temperature.

Writing Charles's law another way, we have $V/T = C_c$; that is, the volume of a gas divided by the temperature of the gas (in kelvins) is constant for a given sample of gas at a specified pressure. Therefore, if we know the volume and temperature of a given quantity of gas ($V_1$ and $T_1$), we can find the volume, $V_2$, at some other temperature, $T_2$, using the equation

$$\frac{V_1}{T_1} = \frac{V_2}{T_2} \quad \text{at constant } n \text{ and } P \tag{11.2}$$

A calculation using Charles's law is illustrated by the following example. Be sure to notice that the temperature $T$ *must always be expressed in kelvins.*

## EXAMPLE 11.3 Charles's Law

**Problem** A sample of $CO_2$ in a gas-tight syringe (as in Figure 11.3) has a volume of 25.0 mL at room temperature (20.0 °C). What is the final volume of the gas if you hold the syringe in your hand to raise its temperature to 37 °C?

**What Do You Know?** This is a Charles's law problem: There is a change in volume of a gas sample with temperature at constant pressure. You know the original volume and temperature, and you want to know the volume at a new temperature. Be sure to recall that, to use Charles's law, the temperature must be expressed in kelvins.

| Initial Conditions | Final Conditions |
|---|---|
| $V_1 = 25.0$ mL | $V_2 = ?$ |
| $T_1 = 20.0 + 273.2 = 293.2$ K | $T_2 = 37 + 273 = 310.$ K |

**Strategy** Use Charles's Law, Equation 11.2.

**Solution** Rearrange Equation 11.2 to solve for $V_2$:

$$V_2 = V_1 \times \frac{T_2}{T_1} = 25.0 \text{ mL} \times \frac{310. \text{ K}}{293.2 \text{ K}} = 26.4 \text{ mL}$$

**Think about Your Answer** While the temperature increase in degrees Celsius seemed large, the change in volume is small. Mathematically, this is because the change depends on the *ratio* of Kelvin temperatures, which is only slightly greater than 1.

**Check Your Understanding**

A balloon is inflated with helium to a volume of 45 L at room temperature (25 °C). If the balloon is cooled to −10 °C, what is the new volume of the balloon? Assume that the pressure does not change.

## Combining Boyle's and Charles's Laws: The General Gas Law

You now know that the volume of a given amount of gas is inversely proportional to its pressure at constant temperature (Boyle's law) and directly proportional to the Kelvin temperature at constant pressure (Charles's law). But what if you need to know what happens to the gas when two of the three parameters (*P*, *V*, and *T*) change? For example, what would happen to the pressure of a sample of nitrogen in an automobile air bag if the same amount of gas were placed in a smaller bag and heated to a higher temperature? You can deal with this situation by combining the two equations that express Boyle's and Charles's laws.

$$\frac{P_1V_1}{T_1} = \frac{P_2V_2}{T_2} \quad \text{for a given amount of gas, } n \qquad (11.3)$$

This equation is sometimes called the **general gas law** or **combined gas law**. It applies specifically to situations in which the *amount of gas does not change.*

### ⓦWL  INTERACTIVE EXAMPLE 11.4  General Gas Law

**Problem** Helium-filled balloons are used to carry scientific instruments high into the atmosphere. Suppose a balloon is launched when the temperature is 22.5 °C and the barometric pressure is 754 mm Hg. If the balloon's volume is $4.19 \times 10^3$ L (and no helium escapes from the balloon), what will the volume be at a height of 20 miles, where the pressure is 76.0 mm Hg and the temperature is −33.0 °C?

**What Do You Know?** Here you know the initial volume, temperature, and pressure of the gas. You want to know the volume of the same amount of gas at a new pressure and temperature.

| Initial Conditions | Final Conditions |
|---|---|
| $V_1 = 4.19 \times 10^3$ L | $V_2 = ?$ L |
| $P_1 = 754$ mm Hg | $P_2 = 76.0$ mm Hg |
| $T_1 = 22.5$ °C (295.7 K) | $T_2 = -33.0$ °C (240.2 K) |

**Strategy** It is most convenient to use Equation 11.3, the general gas law.

**Solution** You can rearrange the general gas law to calculate the new volume $V_2$:

$$V_2 = \left(\frac{T_2}{P_2}\right) \times \left(\frac{P_1V_1}{T_1}\right) = V_1 \times \frac{P_1}{P_2} \times \frac{T_2}{T_1}$$

$$= 4.19 \times 10^3 \text{ L} \times \left(\frac{754 \text{ mm Hg}}{76.0 \text{ mm Hg}}\right) \times \left(\frac{240.2 \text{ K}}{295.7 \text{ K}}\right) = 3.38 \times 10^4 \text{ L}$$

**Strategy Map 11.4**

**PROBLEM**

Calculate the **volume** of a gas sample after it undergoes a change in *T* and *P*.

**DATA/INFORMATION**

- *Initial* pressure, volume, and temperature
- *Final* pressure and temperature

Rearrange the **general gas law** (Equation 11.3) to calculate **final volume** ($V_2$).

**Volume** ($V_2$) after change in *T* and *P*

**A weather balloon is filled with helium.** As it ascends into the tropo-sphere, does the volume increase or decrease?

**Think about Your Answer** The pressure decreased by almost a factor of 10, which should lead to about a ten-fold volume increase. This increase is partly offset by a drop in temperature that leads to a volume decrease. On balance, the volume increases because the pressure has dropped so substantially.

**Check Your Understanding**

You have a 22-L cylinder of helium at a pressure of 150 atm (above atmospheric pressure) and at 31 °C. How many balloons can you fill, each with a volume of 5.0 L, on a day when the atmospheric pressure is 755 mm Hg and the temperature is 22 °C?

The general gas law leads to other, useful predictions of gas behavior. For example, if a given amount of gas is held in a closed container, the pressure of the gas will increase with increasing temperature.

$$\frac{P_1}{T_1} = \frac{P_2}{T_2} \text{ when } V_1 = V_2, \text{ so } P_2 = P_1 \times \frac{T_2}{T_1}$$

That is, when $T_2$ is greater than $T_1$, $P_2$ will be greater than $P_1$. In fact, this is the reason tire manufacturers recommend checking tire pressures when the tires are cold. After driving for some distance, friction warms a tire and increases the internal pressure. Filling a warm tire to the recommended pressure may lead to an underinflated tire.

## Avogadro's Hypothesis

Front and side air bags are now common in automobiles. In the event of an accident, a bag is rapidly inflated with nitrogen gas generated by a chemical reaction. The air bag unit has a sensor that is sensitive to sudden deceleration of the vehicle and will send an electrical signal that will trigger the reaction (Figures 11.1 and 11.6). In many types of air bags, the explosion of sodium azide generates nitrogen gas.

$$2 \text{ NaN}_3(s) \rightarrow 2 \text{ Na}(s) + 3 \text{ N}_2(g)$$

(The sodium produced in the reaction is converted to harmless salts by adding $KNO_3$ and silica to the mixture.) Driver-side air bags inflate to a volume of about 35–70 L, and passenger air bags inflate to about 60–160 L. The final volume of the bag will depend on the amount of nitrogen gas generated.

The relationship between volume and amount of gas was first noted by Amedeo Avogadro. In 1811, he used work on gases by the chemist (and early experimenter with hot air balloons) Joseph Gay-Lussac (1778–1850) to propose that *equal volumes of gases under the same conditions of temperature and pressure have equal numbers of particles* (either molecules or atoms, depending on the composition of

When a car decelerates in a collision, an electrical contact is made in the sensor unit. The propellant (green solid) detonates, releasing nitrogen gas, and the folded nylon bag explodes out of the plastic housing.

Driver-side air bags inflate with 35–70 L of $N_2$ gas, whereas passenger air bags hold about 60–160 L.

The bag deflates within 0.2 second, the gas escaping through holes in the bottom of the bag.

**FIGURE 11.6** Automobile air bags.

the gas). This idea is now called **Avogadro's hypothesis**. Stated another way, the volume of a gas at a given temperature and pressure is directly proportional to the amount of gas in moles:

$$V \propto n \quad \text{at constant } T \text{ and } P$$

## EXAMPLE 11.5    Avogadro's Hypothesis

**Problem**  Ammonia can be made directly from the elements:

$$N_2(g) + 3\,H_2(g) \rightarrow 2\,NH_3(g)$$

If you begin with 15.0 L of $H_2(g)$, what volume of $N_2(g)$ is required for complete reaction (both gases being at the same $T$ and $P$)? What is the theoretical yield of $NH_3$, in liters, under the same conditions?

**What Do You Know?**  From Avogadro's hypothesis, you know that gas volume is proportional to the amount of gas. You know the volume of hydrogen, and, from the balanced equation, you know the stoichiometric factors that relate the known amount of $H_2$ to the unknown amounts of $N_2$ and $NH_3$.

**Strategy**  This is a stoichiometry problem where you can substitute gas volumes for moles. That is, you can calculate the volumes of $N_2$ required and $NH_3$ produced (here in liters) by multiplying the volume of $H_2$ available by a stoichiometric factor obtained from the chemical equation.

**Solution**

$$V\,(N_2 \text{ required}) = (15.0 \text{ L } H_2 \text{ available})\left(\frac{1 \text{ L } N_2 \text{ required}}{3 \text{ L } H_2 \text{ available}}\right) = 5.00 \text{ L } N_2 \text{ required}$$

$$V\,(NH_3 \text{ produced}) = (15.0 \text{ L } H_2 \text{ available})\left(\frac{2 \text{ L } NH_3 \text{ produced}}{3 \text{ L } H_2 \text{ available}}\right) = 10.0 \text{ L } NH_3 \text{ produced}$$

**Think about Your Answer**  The balanced equation informs you that the amount of $N_2$ required is only 1/3 of the amount of $H_2$ present, and the amount of $NH_3$ produced is 2/3 of the amount of $H_2$.

**Check Your Understanding**

Methane burns in oxygen to give $CO_2$ and $H_2O$, according to the balanced equation

$$CH_4(g) + 2\,O_2(g) \rightarrow CO_2(g) + 2\,H_2O(g)$$

If 22.4 L of gaseous $CH_4$ is burned, what volume of $O_2$ is required for complete combustion? What volumes of $CO_2$ and $H_2O$ are produced? Assume all gases have the same temperature and pressure.

## REVIEW & CHECK FOR SECTION 11.2

1.  A sample of a gas has a volume of 222 mL at 695 mm Hg and 0 °C. What is the volume of this same sample of gas if it is measured at 333 mm Hg and 0 °C?

    (a)  894 mL          (b)  463 mL          (c)  657 mL          (d)  359 mL

2.  The volume of a gas sample is 235 mL at a temperature of 25 °C. At what temperature would that same gas sample have a volume of 310. mL, if the pressure of the gas sample is held constant?

    (a)  −47.0 °C          (b)  69.4 °C          (c)  33.1 °C          (d)  120. °C

3.  A gas at 25 °C in a 10.0-L tank has a pressure of 1.00 atm. The gas is transferred to a 20.0-L tank at 0 °C. Which statement is true?

    (a)  The pressure of the gas is halved.          (c)  The gas pressure is 1.00 atm

    (b)  The pressure in the tank is doubled.          (d)  None of the above

## Studies on Gases—Robert Boyle and Jacques Charles

Robert Boyle (1627–1691) was born in Ireland as the 14th and last child of the first Earl of Cork. In his book *Uncle Tungsten*, Oliver Sacks tells us that "Chemistry as a true science made its first emergence with the work of Robert Boyle in the middle of the seventeenth century. Twenty years [Isaac] Newton's senior, Boyle was born at a time when the practice of alchemy still held sway, and he maintained a variety of alchemical beliefs and practices, side by side with his scientific ones. He believed gold could be created, and that he had succeeded in creating it (Newton, also an alchemist, advised him to keep silent about this)."

Boyle examined crystals, explored color, devised an acid–base indicator from the syrup of violets, and provided the first modern definition of an element. He was also a physiologist and was the first to show that the healthy human body has a constant temperature. Today, Boyle is best known for his studies of gases, which were described in his book *The Sceptical Chymist*, published in 1680.

The French chemist and inventor Jacques Alexandre César Charles began his career as a clerk in the finance ministry, but his real interest was science. He developed several inventions and was best known in his lifetime for inventing the hydrogen balloon. In August 1783, Charles exploited his recent studies on hydrogen gas by inflating a balloon with this gas. Because hydrogen would escape easily from a paper bag, he made a silk bag coated with rubber. Inflating the bag took several days and required nearly 225 kg of sulfuric acid and 450 kg of iron to produce the $H_2$ gas. The balloon stayed aloft for almost 45 minutes and traveled about 15 miles. When it landed in a village, however, the people were so terrified they tore it to shreds. Several months later, Charles and a passenger flew a new hydrogen-filled balloon some distance across the French countryside and ascended to the then-incredible altitude of 2 miles.

See K. R. Williams, "Robert Boyle: Founder of Modern Chemistry," *Journal of Chemical Education*, Vol. 86, page 148, 2009.

**Robert Boyle (1627–1691).**

Oesper Collection in the History of Chemistry, University of Cincinnati

**Jacques Alexandre César Charles (1746–1823).**

Image Courtesy of the Library of Congress

Smithsonian National Air & Space Museum

**Jacques Charles and Aivé Roberts ascended over Paris on December 1, 1783, in a hydrogen-filled balloon.**

## 11.3 The Ideal Gas Law

Four interrelated quantities can be used to describe a gas: pressure, volume, temperature, and amount (moles). We know from experiments that the following gas laws can be used to describe the relationship of these properties (Section 11.2).

| Boyle's Law | Charles's Law | Avogadro's Hypothesis |
|---|---|---|
| $V \propto (1/P)$ | $V \propto T$ | $V \propto n$ |
| (constant $T$, $n$) | (constant $P$, $n$) | (constant $T$, $P$) |

If all three laws are combined, the result is

$$V \propto \frac{nT}{P}$$

This can be made into a mathematical equation by introducing a proportionality constant, now labeled **R**. This constant, called the **gas constant**, is a *universal constant*, a number you can use to interrelate the properties of any gas:

$$V = R\left(\frac{nT}{P}\right)$$

or

$$PV = nRT \qquad\qquad (11.4)$$

The equation $PV = nRT$ is called the **ideal gas law**. It describes the behavior of a so-called ideal gas. As you will learn in Section 11.8, however, there is no such thing as an "ideal" gas. Nonetheless, real gases at pressures around one atmosphere or less and temperatures around room temperature usually behave close enough to the ideal that $PV = nRT$ adequately describes their behavior.

To use the equation $PV = nRT$, we need a value for $R$. This is readily determined experimentally. By carefully measuring $P$, $V$, $n$, and $T$ for a sample of gas, we can calculate the value of $R$ from these values using the ideal gas law equation. For example, under conditions of **standard temperature and pressure (STP)** (a gas temperature of 0 °C or 273.15 K and a pressure of 1 atm), 1 mol of an ideal gas occupies 22.414 L, a quantity called the **standard molar volume**. Substituting these values into the ideal gas law gives a value for $R$:

$$R = \frac{PV}{nT} = \frac{(1.0000 \text{ atm})(22.414 \text{ L})}{(1.0000 \text{ mol})(273.15 \text{ K})} = 0.082057 \frac{\text{L} \cdot \text{atm}}{\text{K} \cdot \text{mol}}$$

With a value for $R$, we can now use the ideal gas law in calculations.

- **Properties of an Ideal Gas** For ideal gases, it is assumed that there are no forces of attraction between molecules and that the molecules themselves occupy no volume.

- **STP—What Is It?** A gas is at STP, or standard temperature and pressure, when its temperature is 0 °C or 273.15 K and its pressure is 1 atm. Under these conditions, exactly 1 mol of an ideal gas occupies 22.414 L.

## OWL   INTERACTIVE EXAMPLE 11.6       Ideal Gas Law

**Problem** The nitrogen gas in an automobile air bag, with a volume of 65 L, exerts a pressure of 829 mm Hg at 25 °C. What amount of $N_2$ gas (in moles) is in the air bag?

**What Do You Know?** You are given $P$, $V$, and $T$ for a gas sample and want to calculate the amount of gas ($n$). $P = 829$ mm Hg, $V = 65$ L, $T = 25$ °C, $n = ?$ You also know $R = 0.082057$ L · atm/K · mol.

**Strategy** Use the ideal gas law, Equation 11.4.

**Solution** To use the ideal gas law with $R$ having units of L · atm/K · mol, the pressure must be expressed in atmospheres and the temperature in kelvins. Therefore, you should first convert the pressure and temperature to values with these units.

$$P = 829 \text{ mm Hg} \left( \frac{1 \text{ atm}}{760 \text{ mm Hg}} \right) = 1.09 \text{ atm}$$

$$T = 25 + 273 = 298 \text{ K}$$

Now substitute the values of $P$, $V$, $T$, and $R$ into the ideal gas law, and solve for the amount of gas, $n$:

$$n = \frac{PV}{RT} = \frac{(1.09 \text{ atm})(65 \text{ L})}{(0.082057 \text{ L} \cdot \text{atm/K} \cdot \text{mol})(298 \text{ K})} = 2.9 \text{ mol}$$

Notice that units of atmospheres, liters, and kelvins cancel to leave the answer in units of moles.

**Think about Your Answer** You know that 1 mol of an ideal gas at STP occupies about 22.4 L, so it is reasonable to guess that 65 L of gas (under only slightly different conditions) would be about 3 mol.

**Strategy Map 11.6**

**PROBLEM**

Calculate the amount of a gas using the **ideal gas law**.

↓

**DATA/INFORMATION**

- **Pressure** of the gas
- **Volume** of the gas
- **Temperature** of the gas

Rearrange the **ideal gas law** (Equation 11.4) to calculate the **amount** ($n$).

**Amount** of gas, $n$

---

**Check Your Understanding**

The balloon used by Jacques Charles in his historic balloon flight in 1783 (see page 518) was filled with about 1300 mol of $H_2$. If the temperature of the gas was 23 °C and the gas pressure was 750 mm Hg, what was the volume of the balloon?

---

## The Density of Gases

The density of a gas at a given temperature and pressure is a useful quantity (Figure 11.7). Because the amount ($n$, mol) of any compound is given by its mass ($m$) divided by its molar mass ($M$), we can substitute $m/M$ for $n$ in the ideal gas equation.

$$PV = \left( \frac{m}{M} \right) RT$$

**FIGURE 11.7 Gas density.**
**(a)** The balloons are filled with nearly equal amounts of gas at the same temperature and pressure. One yellow balloon contains helium, a low-density gas ($d$ = 0.179 g/L at STP). The other balloons contain air, a higher density gas ($d$ = 1.29 g/L). **(b)** A hot-air balloon rises because the heated air in the balloon has a lower density than the surrounding air.

(a)

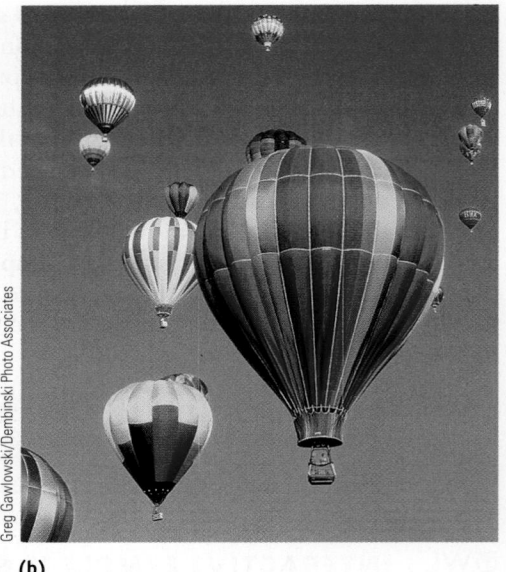

(b)

Density *(d)* is defined as mass divided by volume *(m/V)*. We can rearrange the form of the gas law above to give the following equation, which has the term *(m/V)* on the left. This is the density of the gas.

$$d = \frac{m}{V} = \frac{PM}{RT}$$ (11.5)

Gas density is directly proportional to the pressure and molar mass and inversely proportional to the temperature. Equation 11.5 is useful because gas density can be calculated from the molar mass, or the molar mass can be found from a measurement of gas density at a given pressure and temperature.

### EXAMPLE 11.7 Density and Molar Mass

**Problem** Calculate the density of $CO_2$ at STP. Is $CO_2$ more or less dense than air (whose density is 1.29 g/L at STP)?

**What Do You Know?** The known quantities are molar mass of $CO_2$ ($M$ = 44.0 g/mol), gas pressure *(P)* = 1.00 atm, temperature *(T)* = 273.15 K, and the gas constant *(R)*. The density of $CO_2$ gas *(d)* is unknown.

**Strategy** Use Equation 11.5, the equation relating gas density and molar mass.

**Solution** The known values are substituted into Equation 11.5, which is then solved for density *(d)*:

$$d = \frac{PM}{RT} = \frac{(1.00 \text{ atm})(44.0 \text{ g/mol})}{(0.082057 \text{ L} \cdot \text{atm/K} \cdot \text{mol})(273 \text{ K})} = \boxed{1.96 \text{ g/L}}$$

**Think about Your Answer** The density of $CO_2$ is considerably greater than that of dry air at STP (1.29 g/L). (See Figure 11.8.)

**Check Your Understanding**

The density of an unknown gas is 5.02 g/L at 15.0 °C and 745 mm Hg. Calculate its molar mass.

**FIGURE 11.8 Gas density.** Because carbon dioxide from fire extinguishers is denser than air, it settles on top of a fire and smothers it. (When $CO_2$ gas is released from the tank, it expands and cools significantly. The white cloud is condensed moisture from the air.)

Gas density has practical implications. From the equation $d = PM/RT$, we recognize that the density of a gas is directly proportional to its molar mass. Dry air, which has an average molar mass of about 29 g/mol, has a density of about 1.29 g/L at 1 atm and 25 °C. Gases or vapors with molar masses greater than 29 g/mol have densities larger than 1.3 g/L under these same conditions (1 atm and 25 °C). There-fore, gases such as $CO_2$, $SO_2$, and gasoline vapor settle along the ground if released into the atmosphere (Figure 11.8). Conversely, gases such as $H_2$, He, CO, $CH_4$ (methane), and $NH_3$ rise if released into the atmosphere.

## Calculating the Molar Mass of a Gas from *P*, *V*, and *T* Data

When a new compound is isolated in the laboratory, one of the first things to be done is to determine its molar mass. If the compound is easily volatilized, a classical method of determining the molar mass is to measure the pressure and volume ex-erted by a given mass of the gas at a given temperature.

---

**⚙WL   INTERACTIVE EXAMPLE 11.8**   Calculating the Molar Mass of a Gas from *P*, *V*, and *T* Data

**Problem**  You are trying to determine, by experiment, the formula of a gaseous compound you made to replace chlorofluorocarbons in air conditioners. You have determined the empirical for-mula is $CHF_2$, but now you want to know the molecular formula. You therefore do an experiment to determine its molar mass and find that a 0.100-g sample of the compound exerts a pressure of 70.5 mm Hg in a 256-mL container at 22.3 °C. What is the molar mass of the compound? What is its molecular formula?

**What Do You Know?**  You know the mass of a gas in a given volume at a known pressure and temperature. The molar mass of the gas, *M*, is unknown.

$m$ = mass of gas = 0.100 g      $P$ = 70.5 mm Hg, or 0.0928 atm

$V$ = 256 mL, or 0.256 L      $T$ = 22.3 °C, or 295.5 K

**Strategy**  The quotient of the mass of the gas and its volume gives its density, and this is related to the molar mass through Equation 11.5. Alternatively, the *P*, *V*, and *T* data can be used to calcu-late the amount of gas (moles). The molar mass is then the quotient of the mass of gas and its amount.

**Solution**  The density of the gas is the mass of the gas divided by the volume.

$$d = \frac{0.100 \text{ g}}{0.256 \text{ L}} = 0.391 \text{ g/L}$$

Use this value of density along with the values of pressure and temperature in Equation 11.5 ($d = PM/RT$), and solve for the molar mass (*M*).

$$M = \frac{dRT}{P} = \frac{(0.391 \text{ g/L})(0.082057 \text{ L} \cdot \text{atm/K} \cdot \text{mol})(295.5 \text{ K})}{0.0928 \text{ atm}} = 102 \text{ g/mol}$$

With this result, you can compare the experimentally determined molar mass with the mass of a mole of gas having the empirical formula $CHF_2$.

$$\frac{\text{Experimental molar mass}}{\text{Mass of 1 mol CHF}_2} = \frac{102 \text{ g/mol}}{51.0 \text{ g/formula unit}} = 2 \text{ formula units of CHF}_2 \text{ per mole}$$

Therefore, the formula of the compound is $C_2H_2F_4$.

In the alternative approach, you use the ideal gas law to calculate the amount of gas, *n*.

$$n = \frac{PV}{RT} = \frac{(0.0928 \text{ atm})(0.256 \text{ L})}{(0.082057 \text{ L} \cdot \text{atm/K} \cdot \text{mol})(295.5 \text{ K})} = 9.80 \times 10^{-4} \text{ mol}$$

You now know that 0.100 g of gas is equivalent to $9.80 \times 10^{-4}$ mol. Therefore,

$$\text{Molar mass} = \frac{0.100 \text{ g}}{9.80 \times 10^{-4} \text{ mol}} = 102 \text{ g/mol}$$

**Think about Your Answer**  If the calculated molar mass is not the same as that for the empirical formula or a simple multiple of that value, then you can assume that there is an error somewhere.

---

**Strategy Map 11.8**

**PROBLEM**

Calculate the molar mass of a gas using the **ideal gas law**.

↓

**DATA/INFORMATION**

- **Pressure** of the gas
- **Volume** of the gas
- **Temperature** of the gas

**STEP 1.** Rearrange the **ideal gas law** (Equation 11.4) to calculate the **amount** (*n*).

**Amount** of gas, *n*

**STEP 2.** Divide the **mass** of gas by its **amount** (*n*).

**Molar mass** of gas

**Check Your Understanding**

A 0.105-g sample of a gaseous compound has a pressure of 561 mm Hg in a volume of 125 mL at 23.0 °C. What is its molar mass?

---

**REVIEW & CHECK FOR SECTION 11.3**

1.  Which gas has the greatest density at 25 °C and 1.00 atm pressure?

    (a)  $O_2$          (b)  $N_2$          (c)  $H_2$          (d)  $CO_2$          (e)  Xe

2.  Gas A is in a 2-L flask with a pressure of 1 atm at 298 K. Gas B is in a 4-L flask with a pressure of 0.5 atm at 273 K. Which gas is present in greater amount, A or B?

    (a)  A          (b)  B

3.  Measured at a pressure of 1.0 atm and 298 K, gas C has a density of 2.0 g/L. The density of gas D, measured at a pressure of 0.5 atm and 298 K, is 1.3 g/L. Which gas, C or D, has the larger molar mass?

    (a)  C          (b)  D

---

## 11.4  Gas Laws and Chemical Reactions

Many industrially important reactions involve gases. Two examples are the combination of nitrogen and hydrogen to produce ammonia,

$$N_2(g) + 3\ H_2(g) \rightarrow 2\ NH_3(g)$$

and the electrolysis of aqueous NaCl to produce hydrogen and chlorine,

$$2\ NaCl(aq) + 2\ H_2O(\ell) \rightarrow 2\ NaOH(aq) + H_2(g) + Cl_2(g)$$

If we want to understand the quantitative aspects of such reactions, we need to carry out stoichiometry calculations. The scheme in Figure 11.9 connects these calculations for gas reactions with the stoichiometry calculations in Chapter 4.

**Strategy Map 11.9**

PROBLEM

Calculate the **mass of reactant** needed to produce a gas at a known *P*, *V*, and *T*.

↓

DATA/INFORMATION

- **Pressure** of the gas
- **Volume** of the gas
- **Temperature** of the gas
- Balanced equation

STEP 1. Calculate the *amount of gas* (*n*) using the **ideal gas law**.

↓

**Amount** of gas, *n*

STEP 2. Use **stoichiometric factor** to relate *amount of gas* (*n*) to *amount of reactant* required.

↓

**Amount** of reactant

STEP 3. Calculate **mass of reactant** from its amount.

↓

**Mass** of reactant

⊘WL  **INTERACTIVE EXAMPLE 11.9**    Gas Laws and Stoichiometry

**Problem**  You are asked to design an air bag for a car. You know that the bag should be filled with gas with a pressure higher than atmospheric pressure, say 829 mm Hg, at a temperature of 22.0 °C. The bag has a volume of 45.5 L. What quantity of sodium azide, $NaN_3$, should be used to generate the required quantity of gas? The gas-producing reaction is

$$2\ NaN_3(s) \rightarrow 2\ Na(s) + 3\ N_2(g)$$

**What Do You Know?**  You know the pressure, volume, and temperature of the $N_2$ gas to be produced, and you know the balanced equation that connects the reactant, $NaN_3$, to the product, $N_2$.

$$P = 829 \text{ mm Hg (1 atm/760 mm Hg)} = 1.09 \text{ atm}$$

$$V = 45.5 \text{ L}$$

$$T = 22.0 \text{ °C, or } 295.2 \text{ K}$$

You want to know the mass of $NaN_3$ required to produce a given amount of $N_2$. This will require the molar mass of $NaN_3$.

**Strategy**  The general logic to be used here follows a pathway in Figure 11.9 and in the Strategy Map in the margin. First, use $PV = nRT$ with gas data to calculate the amount of $N_2$ required. Then use that amount with a stoichiometric factor to calculate the amount of $NaN_3$ required. Finally, use the molar mass of $NaN_3$ to calculate the mass of $NaN_3$ required.

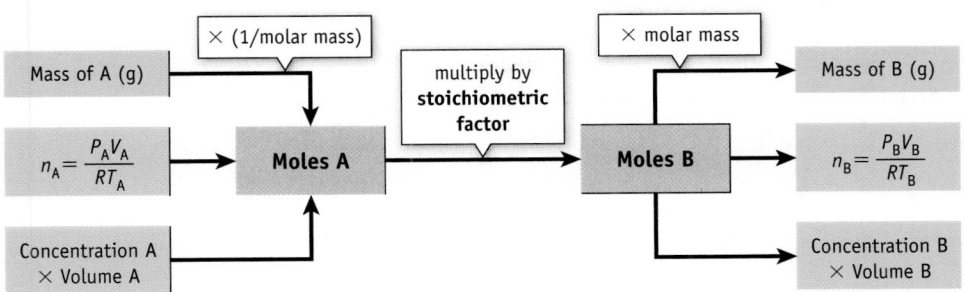

**FIGURE 11.9 A scheme for stoichiometry calculations.** Here, A and B may be either reactants or products. The amount of A (mol) can be calculated from its mass in grams and its molar mass, from the concentration and volume of a solution, or from $P$, $V$, and $T$ data by using the ideal gas law. Once the amount of B is determined, this value can be converted to a mass or solution concentration or volume, or to a property of a gas using the ideal gas law.

**Solution**

**Step 1:** Find the amount (mol) of gas required.

$$n = N_2 \text{ required (mol)} = \frac{PV}{RT}$$

$$n = \frac{(1.09 \text{ atm})(45.5 \text{ L})}{(0.082057 \text{ L} \cdot \text{atm/K} \cdot \text{mol})(295.2 \text{ K})} = 2.05 \text{ mol N}_2$$

**Step 2:** Calculate the quantity of sodium azide that will produce 2.05 mol of $N_2$ gas.

$$\text{Mass of NaN}_3 = 2.05 \text{ mol N}_2 \left(\frac{2 \text{ mol NaN}_3}{3 \text{ mol N}_2}\right)\left(\frac{65.01 \text{ g}}{1 \text{ mol NaN}_3}\right) = 88.8 \text{ g NaN}_3$$

**Think about Your Answer** You know that at STP, 1 mol of an ideal gas has a volume of 22.4 L. While not at STP exactly, the conditions are close to it, so a volume of 45.5 L should correspond to about 2 mol of $N_2$. Based on the stoichiometry of the reaction, you will need 2/3 of this amount of $NaN_3$, or about 1.4 mol. Based on the molar mass of $NaN_3$ (65 g/mol) this will be about 90 g. The amount of $N_2$ produced is substantial, so it is reasonable that around 90 g of sodium azide is required.

**Check Your Understanding**

If you need 25.0 L of $N_2$ gas, at $P = 1.10$ atm and 25.0 °C, what mass of Na will be produced?

## EXAMPLE 11.10  Gas Laws and Stoichiometry

**Problem** You wish to prepare some deuterium gas, $D_2$, for use in an experiment. One way to do this is to react heavy water, $D_2O$, with an active metal such as lithium.

$$2 \text{ Li(s)} + 2 \text{ D}_2\text{O}(\ell) \rightarrow 2 \text{ LiOD(aq)} + \text{D}_2\text{(g)}$$

What amount of $D_2$ (in moles) can be prepared from 0.125 g of Li metal combined with 15.0 mL of $D_2O$ ($d = 1.11$ g/mL). If dry $D_2$ gas is captured in a 1450-mL flask at 22.0 °C, what is the pressure of the gas in mm Hg? (Deuterium, D, has an atomic weight of 2.0147 g/mol.)

**What Do You Know?** You know the quantities of each of the two reactants, which you can use to calculate the amount of $D_2$ gas that can be produced. Based on the amount (moles) of $D_2$ gas, its temperature, and the volume of the flask, you can calculate the pressure.

**Strategy** You are combining two reactants with no guarantee they are in the correct stoichiometric ratio. Therefore, you should approach this as a limiting reactant problem. Once the limiting reactant is known, the amount of $D_2$ produced can be calculated. From this value, and the values of $V$ and $T$, the pressure is calculated using the ideal gas law, $PV = nRT$.

Lithium metal (in the spoon) reacts with drops of water, $H_2O$, to produce LiOH and hydrogen gas, $H_2$. If heavy water, $D_2O$, is used, deuterium gas, $D_2$, can be produced.

**Solution**

**Step 1.** Calculate the amounts (mol) of Li and of $D_2O$:

$$0.125 \text{ g Li} \left( \frac{1 \text{ mol Li}}{6.941 \text{ g Li}} \right) = 0.0180 \text{ mol Li}$$

$$15.0 \text{ mL } D_2O \left( \frac{1.11 \text{ g } D_2O}{1 \text{ mL } D_2O} \right) \left( \frac{1 \text{ mol } D_2O}{20.03 \text{ g } D_2O} \right) = 0.831 \text{ mol } D_2O$$

**Step 2.** Decide which reactant is the limiting reactant:

$$\text{Ratio of moles of reactants available} = \frac{0.831 \text{ mol } D_2O}{0.0180 \text{ mol Li}} = \frac{46.2 \text{ mol } D_2O}{1 \text{ mol Li}}$$

The balanced equation shows that the ratio should be 1 mol of $D_2O$ to 1 mol of Li. From the calculated values, we see that $D_2O$ is in large excess, and so Li is the limiting reactant. Therefore, further calculations are based on the amount of Li available.

**Step 3.** Use the limiting reactant to calculate the amount of $D_2$ produced:

$$0.0180 \text{ mol Li} \left( \frac{1 \text{ mol } D_2 \text{ produced}}{2 \text{ mol Li}} \right) = 0.00900 \text{ mol } D_2 \text{ produced}$$

**Step 4.** Calculate the pressure of $D_2$:

$P = ?$          $T = 22.0 \text{ °C, or } 295.2 \text{ K}$

$V = 1450 \text{ mL, or } 1.45 \text{ L}$      $n = 0.00900 \text{ mol } D_2$

$$P = \frac{nRT}{V} = \frac{(0.00900 \text{ mol})(0.082057 \text{ L} \cdot \text{atm/K} \cdot \text{mol})(295.2 \text{ K})}{1.45 \text{ L}} = \boxed{0.150 \text{ atm}}$$

**Think about Your Answer** Be sure to recognize that this is a limiting reactant problem. The two reactants were not present in the correct stoichiometric ratio.

**Check Your Understanding**

Gaseous ammonia is synthesized by the reaction

$$N_2(g) + 3 H_2(g) \rightarrow 2 NH_3(g)$$

Assume that 355 L of $H_2$ gas at 25.0 °C and 542 mm Hg is combined with excess $N_2$ gas. What amount of $NH_3$ gas, in moles, can be produced? If this amount of $NH_3$ gas is stored in a 125-L tank at 25.0 °C, what is the pressure of the gas?

---

**REVIEW & CHECK FOR SECTION 11.4**

Diborane reacts with $O_2$ to give boric oxide and water vapor.

$$B_2H_6(g) + 3 O_2(g) \rightarrow B_2O_3(s) + 3 H_2O(g)$$

1.  What mass of $O_2$ gas is required to react completely with 1.5 L of $B_2H_6$ at 25 °C and 0.15 atm?

    (a)  0.29 g      (b)  0.59 g      (c)  0.44 g      (d)  0.88 g

2.  If you mix 1.5 L of $B_2H_6$ with 4.0 L of $O_2$, each at 0 °C and a pressure of 1.0 atm, what amount of water is produced?

    (a)  0.18 mol      (b)  0.067 ml      (c)  0.060 mol      (d)  0.25 mol

## 11.5 Gas Mixtures and Partial Pressures

The air you breathe is a mixture of nitrogen, oxygen, argon, carbon dioxide, water vapor, and small amounts of other gases (Table 11.1). Each of these gases exerts its own pressure, and atmospheric pressure is the sum of the pressures

**Table 11.1 Major Components of Atmospheric Dry Air**

| Constituent | Molar Mass* | Mole Percent | Partial Pressure at STP (atm) |
|---|---|---|---|
| $N_2$ | 28.01 | 78.08 | 0.7808 |
| $O_2$ | 32.00 | 20.95 | 0.2095 |
| Ar | 39.95 | 0.934 | 0.00934 |
| $CO_2$ | 44.01 | 0.0385 | 0.00039 |

*The average molar mass of dry air = 28.960 g/mol.

exerted by each gas. The pressure of each gas in the mixture is called its **partial pressure**.

John Dalton (1766–1844) was the first to observe that the pressure of a mixture of ideal gases is the sum of the partial pressures of the different gases in the mixture. This observation is now known as **Dalton's law of partial pressures** (Figure 11.10). Mathematically, we can write Dalton's law of partial pressures as

$$P_{total} = P_1 + P_2 + P_3 \ldots \tag{11.6}$$

where $P_1$, $P_2$, and $P_3$ are the pressures of the different gases in a mixture, and $P_{total}$ is the total pressure.

In a mixture of gases, each gas behaves independently of all others in the mixture. Therefore, we can consider the behavior of each gas in a mixture separately. As an example, take a mixture of three ideal gases, labeled A, B, and C. There are $n_A$ moles of A, $n_B$ moles of B, and $n_C$ moles of C. Assume that the mixture ($n_{total} = n_A + n_B + n_C$) is contained in a given volume $(V)$ at a given temperature $(T)$. We can calculate the pressure exerted by each gas from the ideal gas law equation:

$$P_A V = n_A RT \qquad P_B V = n_B RT \qquad P_C V = n_C RT$$

where each gas (A, B, and C) is in the same volume $V$ and is at the same temperature $T$. According to Dalton's law, the total pressure exerted by the mixture is the sum of the pressures exerted by each component:

$$P_{total} = P_A + P_B + P_C = n_A\left(\frac{RT}{V}\right) + n_B\left(\frac{RT}{V}\right) + n_C\left(\frac{RT}{V}\right)$$

$$P_{total} = (n_A + n_B + n_C)\left(\frac{RT}{V}\right)$$

$$P_{total} = (n_{total})\left(\frac{RT}{V}\right) \tag{11.7}$$

**FIGURE 11.10** Dalton's law.

In a 1.0-L flask at 25 °C, 0.010 mol of $N_2$ exerts a pressure of 186 mm Hg, and 0.0050 mol of $O_2$ in a 1.0-L flask at 25 °C exerts a pressure of 93 mm Hg.

The $N_2$ and $O_2$ samples are both placed in a 1.0-L flask at 25 °C. The total pressure, 279 mm Hg, is the sum of the pressures that each gas alone exerts in the flask.

For mixtures of gases, it is convenient to introduce a quantity called the **mole fraction**, *X*, which is defined as the number of moles of a particular substance in a mixture divided by the total number of moles of all substances present. Mathematically, the mole fraction of a substance A in a mixture with B and C is expressed as

$$X_A = \frac{n_A}{n_A + n_B + n_C} = \frac{n_A}{n_{total}}$$

Now we can combine this equation (written as $n_{total} = n_A/X_A$) with the equations for $P_A$ and $P_{total}$, and derive the equation

$$P_A = X_A P_{total} \qquad (11.8)$$

This equation tells us that *the pressure of a gas in a mixture of gases is the product of its mole fraction and the total pressure of the mixture.* In other words, the partial pressure of a gas is directly related to the fraction of particles of that gas in the mixture. For example, the mole fraction of $N_2$ in air is 0.78, so, at STP, its partial pressure is 0.78 atm or 590 mm Hg.

## Strategy Map 11.11

**PROBLEM**

Calculate the **partial pressure** of two gases in a mixture.

↓

**DATA/INFORMATION**

- **Mass** of each gas
- **Total pressure**

> STEP 1. Calculate *amount* (*n*) of each gas from its **mass**.

**Amount** of each gas, *n*

> STEP 2. Calculate **mole fraction** of each gas, *X*.

**Mole fraction** of each gas, *X*

> STEP 3. Calculate **partial pressure** of gases using Equation 11.8.

**Partial pressure** of each gas

## ⓌWL    INTERACTIVE EXAMPLE 11.11    Partial Pressures of Gases

**Problem**  Halothane, $C_2HBrClF_3$, is a nonflammable, nonexplosive, and nonirritating gas that is commonly used as an inhalation anesthetic. The total pressure of a mixture of 15.0 g of halothane vapor and 23.5 g of oxygen gas is 855 mm Hg. What is the partial pressure of each gas?

**What Do You Know?**  You know the identity and mass of each gas, so you can calculate the amount of each. You also know the total pressure of the gas mixture.

**Strategy**  The partial pressure of a gas is given by the total pressure of the mixture multiplied by the mole fraction of the gas (Equation 11.8). Because you can calculate the amount of each gas, you can determine the total amount (moles) of gas and thus the mole fraction of each.

**Solution**

**Step 1.**  Calculate mole fractions.

$$\text{Amount of } C_2HBrClF_3 = 15.0 \text{ g}\left(\frac{1 \text{ mol}}{197.4 \text{ g}}\right) = 0.0760 \text{ mol}$$

$$\text{Amount of } O_2 = 23.5 \text{ g}\left(\frac{1 \text{ mol}}{32.00 \text{ g}}\right) = 0.734 \text{ mol}$$

$$\text{Total amount of gas} = 0.0760 \text{ mol } C_2HBrClF_3 + 0.734 \text{ mol } O_2 = 0.810 \text{ mol}$$

$$\text{Mole fraction of } C_2HBrClF_3 = \frac{0.0760 \text{ mol } C_2HBrClF_3}{0.810 \text{ total moles}} = 0.0938$$

Because the sum of the mole fraction of halothane and of $O_2$ must equal 1.0000, this means that the mole fraction of oxygen is 0.906.

$$X_{halothane} + X_{oxygen} = 1.0000$$

$$0.0938 + X_{oxygen} = 1.0000$$

$$X_{oxygen} = 0.906$$

**Step 2.**  Calculate partial pressures.

$$\text{Partial pressure of halothane} = P_{halothane} = X_{halothane} \cdot P_{total}$$

$$P_{halothane} = 0.0938 \cdot P_{total} = 0.0938 \, (855 \text{ mm Hg})$$

$$P_{halothane} = 80.2 \text{ mm Hg}$$

The total pressure of the mixture is the sum of the partial pressures of the gases in the mixture.

$$P_{halothane} + P_{oxygen} = 855 \text{ mm Hg}$$

1,1,1-trifluorobromochloroethane, halothane

and so

$$P_{oxygen} = 855 \text{ mm Hg} - P_{halothane}$$

$$P_{oxygen} = 855 \text{ mm Hg} - 80.2 \text{ mm Hg} = \boxed{775 \text{ mm Hg}}$$

**Think about Your Answer** The amount of halothane is about 1/10th of the amount of oxygen so we would expect the ratio of partial pressures of the two gases to be in a similar ratio.

**Check Your Understanding**

The halothane–oxygen mixture described in this Example is placed in a 5.00-L tank at 25.0 °C. What is the total pressure (in mm Hg) of the gas mixture in the tank? What are the partial pressures (in mm Hg) of the gases?

© Cengage Learning/Charles D. Winters

---

**REVIEW & CHECK FOR SECTION 11.5**

Acetylene reacts with $O_2$ to give carbon dioxide and water vapor.

$$2 C_2H_2(g) + 5 O_2(g) \rightarrow 4 CO_2(g) + 2 H_2O(g)$$

If you mix $C_2H_2$ and $O_2$ in the correct stoichiometric ratio, and if the total pressure of the mixture is 140. mm Hg, what are the partial pressures of the gases before the reaction occurs?

(a)  100. mm Hg $C_2H_2$ and 40. mm Hg $O_2$

(b)  140. mm Hg $C_2H_2$ and 700. mm Hg $O_2$

(c)  40. mm Hg $C_2H_2$ and 100. mm Hg $O_2$

(d)  140. mm Hg $C_2H_2$ and 56.0 mm Hg $O_2$

**FIGURE 11.11 A molecular view of gases and liquids.** The fact that a large volume of $N_2$ gas can be condensed to a small volume of liquid indicates that the distance between molecules in the gas phase is very large as compared with the distances between molecules in liquids.

# 11.6  The Kinetic-Molecular Theory of Gases

So far, we have discussed the macroscopic properties of gases, properties such as pressure and volume that result from the behavior of a system with a large number of particles. Now we turn to the kinetic-molecular theory (◄ page 7) for a description of the behavior of matter at the molecular or atomic level. Hundreds of experimental observations have led to the following postulates regarding the behavior of gases.

**go Chemistry**

**Module 16: Gas Laws and the Kinetic Molecular Theory** covers concepts in this section.

- Gases consist of particles (molecules or atoms) whose separation is much greater than the size of the particles themselves (Figure 11.11).
- The particles of a gas are in continual, random, and rapid motion. As they move, they collide with one another and with the walls of their container, but they do so in a way in which the total energy is unchanged.
- The average kinetic energy of gas particles is proportional to the gas temperature. *All gases, regardless of their molecular mass, have the same average kinetic energy at the same temperature.*

Let us discuss the behavior of gases from this point of view.

## Molecular Speed and Kinetic Energy

If your friend walks into your room carrying a pizza, how do you know it? In scientific terms, we know that the odor-causing molecules of food enter the gas phase and drift through space until they reach the cells of your body that react to odors. The same thing happens in the laboratory when bottles of aqueous ammonia ($NH_3$) and hydrochloric acid (HCl) sit side by side (Figure 11.12). Molecules of the two compounds enter the gas phase and drift along until they encounter one another, at which time they react and form a cloud of tiny particles of solid ammonium chloride ($NH_4Cl$).

If you change the temperature of the environment of the containers in Figure 11.12 and measure the time needed for the cloud of ammonium chloride to form, you would find the time would be longer at lower temperatures. The rea-

© Cengage Learning/Charles D. Winters

**FIGURE 11.12 The movement of gas molecules.** Open dishes of aqueous ammonia and hydrochloric acid are placed side by side. When molecules of $NH_3$ and HCl escape from solution to the atmosphere and encounter one another, a cloud of solid ammonium chloride, $NH_4Cl$, is observed.

# The Earth's Atmosphere

Earth's atmosphere is a fascinating mixture of gases in more or less distinct layers with widely differing temperatures.

Up through the troposphere, there is a gradual decline in temperature (and pressure) with altitude. The temperature climbs again in the stratosphere due to the absorption of energy from the sun by stratospheric ozone, $O_3$.

Above the stratosphere, the pressure declines because there are fewer molecules present. At still higher altitudes, we observe a dramatic increase in temperature in the thermosphere. This is an illustration of the difference between *temperature* and *thermal energy*. The temperature of a gas reflects the average kinetic energy of the molecules of the gas, whereas the thermal energy present in an object is the *total* kinetic energy of the molecules. In the thermosphere, the few molecules present have a very high temperature, but the thermal energy is exceedingly small because there are so few molecules.

Gases within the troposphere are well mixed by convection. Pollutants that are evolved on Earth's surface can rise up to the stratosphere, but it is said that the stratosphere acts as a "thermal lid" on the troposphere and prevents significant mixing of polluting gases into the stratosphere and beyond.

The pressure of the atmosphere declines with altitude, and so the partial pressure of $O_2$ declines. The figure shows why climbers have a hard time breathing on Mt. Everest, where the altitude is 29,028 ft (8848 m) and the $O_2$ partial pressure is only 29% of the sea level partial pressure. With proper training, a climber could reach the summit without supplemental oxygen. However, this same feat would not be possible if Everest were farther north. Earth's atmosphere thins toward the poles, and so the $O_2$ partial pressure would be even less if Everest's summit were in the northern part of North America, for example.

See G. N. Eby, *Environmental Geochemistry,* Cengage Learning/Brooks/Cole, 2004.

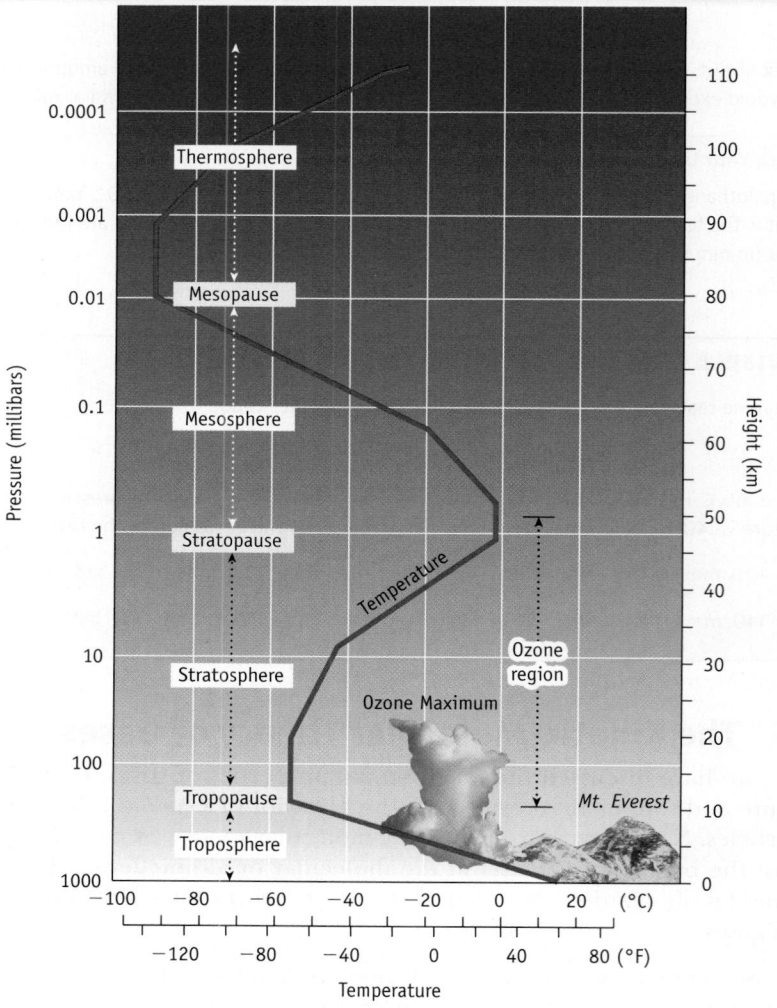

**Average Composition of Earth's Atmosphere to a Height of 25 km**

| Gas | Volume % | Source | Gas | Volume % | Source |
|---|---|---|---|---|---|
| $N_2$ | 78.08 | Biologic | He | 0.0005 | Radioactivity |
| $O_2$ | 20.95 | Biologic | $H_2O$ | 0 to 4 | Evaporation |
| Ar | 0.93 | Radioactivity | $CH_4$ | 0.00017 | Biologic |
| $CO_2$ | 0.0385 | Biologic, industrial | $N_2O$ | 0.00003 | Biologic, industrial |
| Ne | 0.0018 | Earth's interior | $O_3$ | 0.000004 | Photochemical |

son for this is that the speed at which molecules move depends on the temperature. Let us expand on this idea.

The molecules in a gas sample do not all move at the same speed. Rather, as illustrated in Figure 11.13 for $O_2$ molecules, there is a distribution of speeds. Figure 11.13 shows the number of particles in a gas sample that are moving at certain speeds at a given temperature, and there are two important observations we can make. First, at a given temperature some molecules in a sample have high speeds,

At 25 °C more molecules are moving at about 400 m/s than at any other speed.

Very few molecules have very low speeds.

$O_2$ at 25 °C

Many more molecules are moving at 1600 m/s when the sample is at 1000 °C than when it is at 25 °C.

$O_2$ at 1000 °C

Number of molecules →

Molecular speed (m/s)

**FIGURE 11.13 The distribution of molecular speeds.** A graph of the number of molecules with a given speed versus that speed shows the distribution of molecular speeds. The red curve shows the effect of increased temperature. Even though the curve for the higher temperature is "flatter" and broader than the one at a lower temperature, the areas under the curves are the same because the number of molecules in the sample is fixed.

• **Maxwell-Boltzmann Curves**
Plots such as those in Figures 11.13 and 11.14 are often referred to as Maxwell-Boltzmann curves. They are named for two scientists who studied the physical properties of gases: James Clerk Maxwell (1831–1879) and Ludwig Boltzmann (1844–1906).

and others have low speeds. Most of the molecules, however, have some intermediate speed, and their most probable speed corresponds to the maximum in the curve. For oxygen gas at 25 °C, for example, most molecules have speeds in the range from 200 m/s to 700 m/s, and their most probable speed is about 400 m/s. (These are very high speeds, indeed. A speed of 400 m/s corresponds to about 900 miles per hour!)

A second observation regarding the distribution of speeds is that as the temperature increases the most probable speed increases, and the number of molecules traveling at very high speeds increases greatly.

The kinetic energy of a single molecule of mass $m$ in a gas sample is given by the equation

$$KE = \frac{1}{2}(mass)(speed)^2 = \frac{1}{2}mu^2$$

where $u$ is the speed of that molecule. We can calculate the kinetic energy of a single gas molecule from this equation but not of a collection of molecules because not all of the molecules in a gas sample are moving at the same speed. However, we can calculate the average kinetic energy of a collection of molecules by relating it to other averaged quantities of the system. In particular, the average kinetic energy of a mole of molecules in a gas sample is related to the average speed:

$$\overline{KE} = \frac{1}{2}Nm\overline{u^2}$$

where $N$ is Avogadro's number. (The horizontal bar over the symbols $\overline{KE}$ and $\overline{u}$ indicate an average value.) The product of the mass per molecule and Avogadro's constant is the molar mass, so we can write

$$\overline{KE} = \frac{1}{2}M\overline{u^2}$$

where the molar mass $(M)$ has units of kg/mol (and $KE$ is in joules). This equation states that the average kinetic energy of the molecules in a gas sample, $\overline{KE}$, is related to $\overline{u^2}$, the average of the squares of their speeds (called the "mean square speed").

Experiments also show that the average kinetic energy, $\overline{KE}$, of a mole of gas molecules is directly proportional to temperature with a proportionality constant of $\frac{3}{2}R$,

$$\overline{KE} = \frac{3}{2}RT$$

where $R$ is the gas constant expressed in SI units (8.314472 J/K · mol).

**FIGURE 11.14 The effect of molecular mass on the distribution of speeds.** At a given temperature, molecules with higher masses have lower speeds.

The two kinetic energy equations can be combined to yield an equation that relates mass, average speed, and temperature (Equation 11.9).

$$\sqrt{\overline{u^2}} = \sqrt{\frac{3RT}{M}}$$

(11.9)

Here, the square root of the mean square speed ($\sqrt{\overline{u^2}}$, called the **root-mean-square speed**, or **rms speed**), the temperature ($T$, in kelvins), and the molar mass $(M)$ are related. This equation shows that the speeds of gas molecules are indeed related to the temperature (Figure 11.13). The rms speed is a useful quantity because of its relationship to the average kinetic energy and because it is very close to the true average speed for a sample. (The average speed is 92% of the rms speed.)

*All gases have the same average kinetic energy at the same temperature.* However, if you compare a sample of one gas with another, say compare $O_2$ and $N_2$, this does not mean the molecules have the same rms speed (Figure 11.14). Instead, Equation 11.9 shows that the smaller the molar mass of the gas the greater the rms speed.

## EXAMPLE 11.12 Molecular Speed

**Problem** Calculate the rms speed of oxygen molecules at 25 °C.

**What Do You Know?** You know the molar mass of $O_2$ and the temperature, the main determinants of speed.

**Strategy** Use Equation 11.9 with $M$ in units of kg/mol. The reason for this is that $R$ is in units of J/K · mol, and 1 J = 1 kg · m²/s².

**Solution** The molar mass of $O_2$ is $32.0 \times 10^{-3}$ kg/mol.

$$\sqrt{\overline{u^2}} = \sqrt{\frac{3(8.3145 \text{ J/K} \cdot \text{mol})(298 \text{ K})}{32.0 \times 10^{-3} \text{ kg/mol}}} = \sqrt{2.32 \times 10^5 \text{ J/kg}}$$

To obtain the answer in meters per second, use the relation 1 J = 1 kg · m²/s². This means you have

$$\sqrt{\overline{u^2}} = \sqrt{2.32 \times 10^5 \text{ kg} \cdot \text{m}^2/(\text{kg} \cdot \text{s}^2)} = \sqrt{2.32 \times 10^5 \text{ m}^2/\text{s}^2} = 482 \text{ m/s}$$

**Think about Your Answer** The calculated speed is equivalent to about 1100 miles per hour! This is somewhat greater than the speed of sound in air, 343 m/s.

**Check Your Understanding**

Calculate the rms speeds of helium atoms and $N_2$ molecules at 25 °C.

## Kinetic-Molecular Theory and the Gas Laws

The gas laws, which come from experiment, can be explained by the kinetic-molecular theory. The starting place is to describe how pressure arises from collisions of gas molecules with the walls of the container holding the gas (Figure 11.15). Remember that pressure is related to the force of the collisions (Section 11.1).

$$\text{Gas pressure} = \frac{\text{force of collisions}}{\text{area}}$$

The force exerted by the collisions depends on the number of collisions and the average force per collision. When the temperature of a gas is increased, we know the average kinetic energy of the molecules increases. This causes the average force of the collisions with the walls to increase as well. (This is much like the difference in the force exerted by a car traveling at high speed versus one moving at only a few kilometers per hour.) Also, because the speed of gas molecules increases with temperature, more collisions occur per second. Thus, the collective force per square centimeter is greater, and the pressure increases. Mathematically, this is related to the direct proportionality between $P$ and $T$ when $n$ and $V$ are fixed, that is, $P = (nR/V)T$.

Increasing the number of molecules of a gas at a fixed temperature and volume does not change the average collision force, but it does increase the number of collisions occurring per second. Thus, the pressure increases, and we can say that $P$ is proportional to $n$ when $V$ and $T$ are constant, that is, $P = n(RT/V)$.

If the pressure is to remain constant when either the number of molecules of gas or the temperature is increased, then the volume of the container (and the area over which the collisions can take place) must increase. This is expressed by stating that $V$ is proportional to $nT$ when $P$ is constant $[V = nT(R/P)]$, a statement that is a *combination of Avogadro's hypothesis and Charles's law.*

Finally, if the temperature is constant, the average impact force of molecules of a given mass with the container walls must be constant. If $n$ is kept constant while the volume of the container is made smaller, the number of collisions with the container walls per second must increase. This means the pressure increases, and so $P$ is proportional to $1/V$ when $n$ and $T$ are constant, as stated by *Boyle's law*, that is, $P = (1/V)(nRT)$.

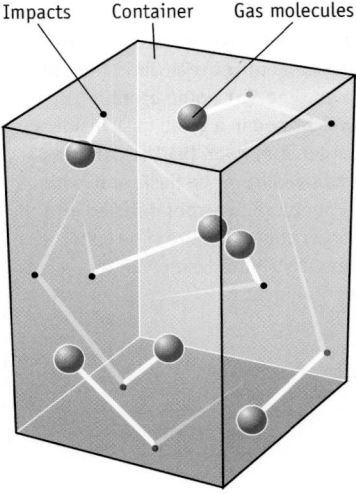

**FIGURE 11.15 Gas pressure.** According to the kinetic-molecular theory, gas pressure is caused by gas molecules bombarding the container walls.

---

**REVIEW & CHECK FOR SECTION 11.6**

The species identified with each curve in the Maxwell-Boltzmann plot below are: (Assume all gases are at the same temperature.)

(a)   A = Xe, B = $O_2$, C = Ne, and D = He

(b)   A = Xe, B = He, C = Ne, and D = $O_2$

(c)   A = He, B = Ne, C = $O_2$, and D = Xe

(d)   A = He, B = $O_2$, C = Ne, and D = Xe

**FIGURE 11.16 Gaseous diffusion.** Here bromine diffuses out of a flask and mixes with air in the bottle over time. **(a)** Liquid bromine, $Br_2$, was placed in a small flask inside a larger container. **(b)** The cork was removed from the flask, and, with time, bromine vapor diffused into the larger container. Bromine vapor is now distributed evenly in the containers.

(a)                    (b)

## 11.7 Diffusion and Effusion

When a warm pizza is brought into a room, the volatile aroma-causing molecules vaporize into the atmosphere, where they mix with the oxygen, nitrogen, carbon dioxide, water vapor, and other gases present. Even if there were no movement of the air in the room caused by fans or people moving about, the odor would eventually reach everywhere in the room. This mixing of molecules of two or more gases due to their random molecular motions is the result of **diffusion**. Given time, the molecules of one component in a gas mixture will thoroughly and completely mix with all other components of the mixture (Figure 11.16).

Diffusion is also illustrated by the experiment in Figure 11.17. Here, we have placed cotton moistened with hydrochloric acid at one end of a U-tube and cotton moistened with aqueous ammonia at the other end. Molecules of HCl and $NH_3$ diffuse into the tube, and, when they meet, they produce white, solid $NH_4Cl$ (just as in Figure 11.12).

$$HCl(g) + NH_3(g) \rightarrow NH_4Cl(s)$$

We find that the gases do not meet in the middle. Rather, because the heavier HCl molecules diffuse less rapidly than the lighter $NH_3$ molecules, the molecules meet closer to the HCl end of the U-tube.

Closely related to diffusion is **effusion**, which is the movement of gas through a tiny opening in a container into another container where the pressure is very low (Figure 11.17). Thomas Graham (1805–1869), a Scottish chemist, studied the

**Gaseous diffusion.** Here, HCl gas (from hydrochloric acid) and ammonia gas (from aqueous ammonia) diffuse from opposite ends of a glass U-tube. When they meet, they produce white, solid $NH_4Cl$. It is clear that the $NH_4Cl$ is formed closer to the end from which the HCl gas begins because HCl molecules move slower, on average, than $NH_3$ molecules.

**Gaseous effusion.** $H_2$ and $N_2$ gas molecules effuse through the pores of a porous barrier. Lighter molecules ($H_2$) with higher average speeds strike the barrier more often and pass more often through it than heavier, slower molecules ($N_2$) at the same temperature. According to Graham's law, $H_2$ molecules effuse 3.72 times faster than $N_2$ molecules.

**FIGURE 11.17 Gaseous diffusion and effusion.**

effusion of gases and found that the rate of effusion of a gas—the amount of gas moving from one place to another in a given amount of time—is inversely proportional to the square root of its molar mass. Based on these experimental results, the rates of effusion of two gases can be compared:

$$\frac{\text{Rate of effusion of gas 1}}{\text{Rate of effusion of gas 2}} = \sqrt{\frac{\text{molar mass of gas 2}}{\text{molar mass of gas 1}}} \qquad \text{(11.10)}$$

The relationship in Equation 11.10—now known as **Graham's law**—is readily derived from Equation 11.9 by recognizing that the rate of effusion depends on the speed of the molecules. The ratio of the rms speeds is the same as the ratio of the effusion rates:

$$\frac{\text{Rate of effusion of gas 1}}{\text{Rate of effusion of gas 2}} = \frac{\sqrt{\overline{u^2} \text{ of gas 1}}}{\sqrt{\overline{u^2} \text{ of gas 2}}} = \frac{\sqrt{3RT/(M \text{ of gas 1})}}{\sqrt{3RT/(M \text{ of gas 2})}}$$

Canceling out like terms gives the expression in Equation 11.10.

## EXAMPLE 11.13   Using Graham's Law of Effusion to Calculate a Molar Mass

**Problem** Tetrafluoroethylene, $C_2F_4$, effuses through a barrier at a rate of $4.6 \times 10^{-6}$ mol/h. An unknown gas, consisting only of boron and hydrogen, effuses at the rate of $5.8 \times 10^{-6}$ mol/h under the same conditions. What is the molar mass of the unknown gas?

**What Do You Know?** You have two gases, one with a known molar mass ($C_2F_4$, 100.0 g/mol) and the other unknown. The rate of effusion for both gases is known.

**Strategy** Substitute the experimental data into Graham's law equation (Equation 11.10).

**Solution**

$$\frac{5.8 \times 10^{-6} \text{ mol/h}}{4.6 \times 10^{-6} \text{ mol/h}} = 1.3 = \sqrt{\frac{100.0 \text{ g/mol}}{M \text{ of unknown}}}$$

To solve for the unknown molar mass, square both sides of the equation and rearrange to find $M$ for the unknown.

$$1.6 = \frac{100.0 \text{ g/mol}}{M \text{ of unknown}}$$

$$M = 63 \text{ g/mol}$$

**Think about Your Answer** From Graham's law, we know that a light molecule will effuse more rapidly than a heavier one. Because the unknown gas effuses more rapidly than $C_2F_4$ ($M = 100.0$ g/mol), the unknown must have a molar mass less than 100 g/mol. A boron–hydrogen compound corresponding to this molar mass is $B_5H_9$, called *pentaborane*.

**Check Your Understanding**

A sample of pure methane, $CH_4$, is found to effuse through a porous barrier in 1.50 minutes. Under the same conditions, an equal number of molecules of an unknown gas effuses through the barrier in 4.73 minutes. What is the molar mass of the unknown gas?

---

### REVIEW & CHECK FOR SECTION 11.7

In Figure 11.17, ammonia gas and hydrogen chloride are introduced from opposite ends of a glass U-tube. The gases react to produce white, solid $NH_4Cl$. What are the relative root mean square speeds of HCl and $NH_3$?

(a)  rms for HCl/rms for $NH_3$ = 2.2

(b)  rms for HCl/rms for $NH_3$ = 1.5

(c)  rms for HCl/rms for $NH_3$ = 0.68

(d)  rms for HCl/rms for $NH_3$ = 0.46

## SCUBA Diving—An Applicaton of the Gas Laws

Diving with a self-contained underwater breathing apparatus (SCUBA) is exciting. If you want to dive much beyond about 60 ft (18 m), however, you need to take special precautions.

When you breathe air from a SCUBA tank, the pressure of the gas in your lungs is equal to the pressure exerted on your body. When you are at the surface, atmospheric pressure is about 1 atm, and, because air has an oxygen concentration of 21%, the partial pressure of $O_2$ is about 0.21 atm. If you are at a depth of about 33 ft, the water pressure is 2 atm. This means the oxygen partial pressure is double the surface partial pressure, or about 0.4 atm. Similarly, the partial pressure of $N_2$, which is about 0.8 atm at the surface, doubles to about 1.6 atm at a depth of 33 ft. The solubility of gases in water (and in blood) is directly proportional to pressure. Therefore, more oxygen and nitrogen dissolve in blood under these conditions, and this can lead to several problems.

Nitrogen narcosis, also called *rapture of the deep* or the *martini effect*, results from the toxic effect on nerve conduction of $N_2$ dissolved in blood. Its effect is comparable to drinking a martini on an empty stomach or taking laughing gas (nitrous oxide, $N_2O$) at the dentist; it makes you slightly giddy. In severe cases, it can impair a diver's judgment and even cause a diver to take

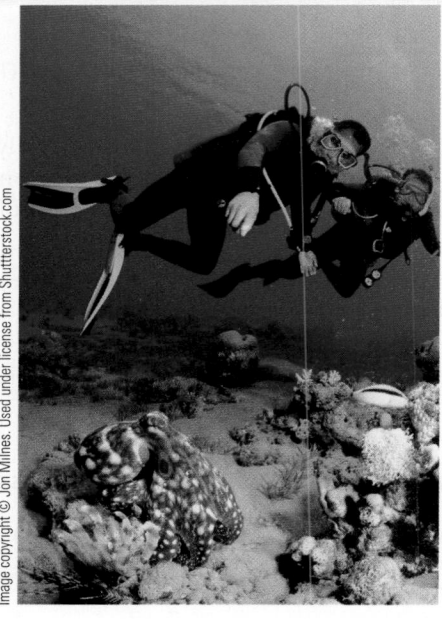

Image copyright © Jon Milnes. Used under license from Shutterstock.com

the regulator out of his or her mouth and hand it to a fish! Some people can go as deep as 130 ft with no problem, but others experience nitrogen narcosis at 80 ft.

Another problem with breathing air at depths beyond 100 ft or so is oxygen toxicity. Our bodies are regulated for a partial pressure of $O_2$ of 0.21 atm. At a depth of 130 ft, the

**SCUBA diving.** Ordinary recreational dives can be made with compressed air to depths of about 60 feet. With a gas mixture called *Nitrox* (which has up to 36% $O_2$), one can stay at such depths for a longer period. To go even deeper, however, divers must breathe special gas mixtures such as Trimix. This is a breathing mixture consisting of oxygen, helium, and nitrogen.

partial pressure of $O_2$ is comparable to breathing 100% oxygen at sea level. These higher partial pressures can harm the lungs and cause central nervous system damage. Oxygen toxicity is the reason deep dives are done not with compressed air but with gas mixtures with a much lower percentage of $O_2$, say about 10%.

Because of the risk of nitrogen narcosis, divers going beyond about 130 ft, such as those who work for offshore oil drilling companies, use a mixture of oxygen and helium. This solves the nitrogen narcosis problem, but it introduces another. If the diver has a voice link to the surface, the diver's speech sounds like Donald Duck! Speech is altered because the velocity of sound in helium is different from that in air.

## 11.8  **Nonideal Behavior of Gases**

If you are working with a gas at approximately room temperature and a pressure of 1 atm or less, the ideal gas law is remarkably successful in relating the amount of gas and its pressure, volume, and temperature. At higher pressures or lower temperatures, however, deviations from the ideal gas law occur. The origin of these deviations is explained by the breakdown of the assumptions used when describing ideal gases, specifically the assumptions that the particles have no size and that there are no forces between them.

At standard temperature and pressure (STP), the volume occupied by a single molecule is *very* small relative to its share of the total gas volume. Relatively speaking, a helium atom with a radius of 31 pm has about the same space to move about as a pea has inside a basketball. Now suppose the pressure is increased significantly, to 1000 atm. The volume available to each molecule is a sphere with a radius of only about 200 pm, which means the situation is now like that of a pea inside a sphere a bit larger than a Ping-Pong ball.

The kinetic-molecular theory and the ideal gas law are concerned with the volume available to the molecules to move about, not the total volume of the container. For example, suppose you have a flask marked with a volume of 500 mL. This does not mean the space available to molecules is 500 mL. Rather, the available volume is less than 500 mL because the molecules themselves occupy some of the volume. At low pressures, the volume occupied by the gas molecules in the container is so small in comparison to the space available that neglecting to subtract it

● **How Much Space Does a Molecule Take Up?** The volume of a methane ($CH_4$) molecule is $3.31 \times 10^{-23}$ cm$^3$. Suppose you have 1.00 mol of $CH_4$ gas in a 22.4-L flask at 273 K. The pressure would be high, 22.4 atm, and 19.9 cm$^3$ of the space in the flask would be occupied by $CH_4$ molecules or about 0.09% of the flask volume.

from the total volume does not introduce significant error. The problem is that the volume occupied by gas molecules is not negligible at higher pressures.

Another assumption of the kinetic-molecular theory is that the atoms or molecules of the gas never stick to one another by some type of intermolecular force. This is clearly not true as well. All gases can be liquefied—although some gases require a very low temperature (Figure 11.11)—and the only way this can happen is if there are forces between the molecules. When a molecule is about to strike the wall of its container, other molecules in its vicinity exert a slight pull on the molecule and pull it away from the wall. The effect of the intermolecular forces is that molecules strike the wall with less force than in the absence of intermolecular attractive forces. Thus, because collisions between molecules in a real gas and the wall are softer, the observed gas pressure is less than that predicted by the ideal gas law. This effect can be particularly pronounced when the temperature is low (near the condensation temperature).

The Dutch physicist Johannes van der Waals (1837–1923) studied the breakdown of the ideal gas law equation and developed an equation to correct for the errors arising from nonideality. This equation is known as the **van der Waals equation**:

**Table 11.2  van der Waals Constants**

| Gas | *a* Values (atm · L²/mol²) | *b* Values (L/mol) |
|---|---|---|
| He | 0.034 | 0.0237 |
| Ar | 1.34 | 0.0322 |
| $H_2$ | 0.244 | 0.0266 |
| $N_2$ | 1.39 | 0.0391 |
| $O_2$ | 1.36 | 0.0318 |
| $CO_2$ | 3.59 | 0.0427 |
| $Cl_2$ | 6.49 | 0.0562 |
| $H_2O$ | 5.46 | 0.0305 |

observed pressure     container *V*

$$\left(P + a\left[\frac{n}{V}\right]^2\right)(V - bn) = nRT \qquad (11.11)$$

correction for intermolecular forces     correction for molecular volume

where $a$ and $b$ are experimentally determined constants (Table 11.2). Although Equation 11.11 might seem complicated at first glance, the terms in parentheses are those of the ideal gas law, each corrected for the effects discussed previously. The pressure correction term, $a(n/V)^2$, accounts for intermolecular forces. Owing to intermolecular forces, the observed gas pressure is lower than the ideal pressure ($P_{observed} < P_{ideal}$ where $P_{ideal}$ is calculated using the equation $PV = nRT$). Therefore, the term $a(n/V)^2$ is *added* to the observed pressure. The constant $a$ typically has values in the range 0.01 to 10 atm · L²/mol².

The actual volume available to the molecules is smaller than the volume of the container because the molecules themselves take up space. Therefore, an amount is *subtracted* from the container volume (= $bn$) to take this into account. Here, $n$ is the number of moles of gas, and $b$ is an experimental quantity that corrects for the molecular volume. Typical values of $b$ range from 0.01 to 0.1 L/mol, roughly increasing with increasing molecular size.

As an example of the importance of these corrections, consider a sample of 4.00 mol of chlorine gas, $Cl_2$, in a 4.00-L tank at 100.0 °C. The ideal gas law would lead you to expect a pressure of 30.6 atm. A better estimate of the pressure, obtained from the van der Waals equation, is 26.0 atm, about 4.6 atm less than the ideal pressure!

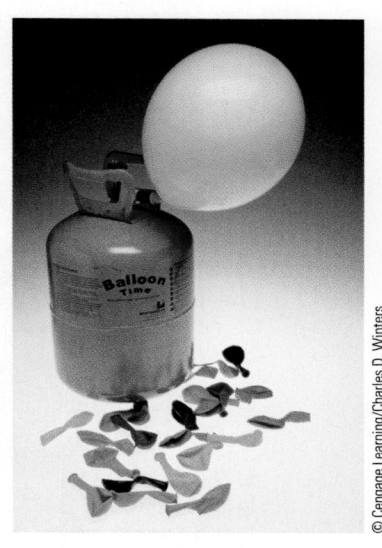

**A flask of helium gas for filling party balloons.** The tank holds about 15 cubic feet (about 425 L) of helium. (*Note:* These tanks are not designed to be reused! Dispose of them properly. Also, use helium sparingly. The supply of the gas on the planet is not limitless.)

---

**REVIEW & CHECK FOR SECTION 11.8**

You can purchase tanks of helium at a party store to fill balloons. Such a tank may hold 343 mol of He in a volume of 473 L. Use van der Waals's equation to calculate the pressure in the tank at 25 °C.

(a)  18.0 atm        (b)  17.7 atm        (c)  17.3 atm

# What to Do with All of That $CO_2$? More on Green Chemistry

Most scientists, including the authors of this book, believe that global warming is occurring and that it is a problem. They also believe this increase is related to the increase in the percentage of greenhouse gases, especially $CO_2$, in the atmosphere. The percentage of $CO_2$ in the atmosphere has been on the rise since the beginning of the Industrial Revolution and is projected to continue to rise in the future. Are there ways to stabilize the concentration of $CO_2$ at the current level, or at least limit its future increase? This in turn focuses attention on the obvious source of $CO_2$ in the atmosphere, the combustion of fossil fuels.

What is wrong with $CO_2$ in the atmosphere? After all, it is used by plants as their carbon source, and the oceans can absorb the gas, much of which ends up incorporated in corals. But there is a danger these "sinks" could be overwhelmed.

The United States obtains over half its electricity from coal-fired power plants. So, one question is why not capture and dispose of the $CO_2$ from power plants. In fact, this is being considered. One way of removing $CO_2$ generated by burning fossil fuels involves geological sequestration, a process in which $CO_2$ is pumped into rock formations thousands of feet underground. There, it would presumably remain trapped for thousands of years.

An experiment is underway at the Mountaineer Power Plant in New Haven, West Virginia, to do just that. For this process to succeed, however, the $CO_2$ to be sequestered needs to be pure, free of impurities. This is accomplished in two steps. The flue gas from the coal-based electricity generating plant is first routed through a scrubber, to remove most of the $SO_2$, a typical contaminant produced in coal combustion. The gas stream is then cooled to about 35 °F and introduced under pressure into a cooled slurry of ammonium carbonate, $(NH_4)_2CO_3$. As set up in this pilot program, a portion of the $CO_2$ reacts with the slurry to form ammonium hydrogen carbonate, $NH_4(HCO_3)$:

$$(NH_4)_2CO_3 + CO_2 + H_2O \rightleftharpoons 2\ NH_4(HCO_3)$$

The remaining flue gases, mainly $N_2$ and unreacted $CO_2$, exit the system. The slurry is then separated and heated, reversing the chemical process, giving back pure $CO_2$ and regenerating $(NH_4)_2CO_3$ which is recycled back into the system. The pure $CO_2$ is then pumped underground.

The pilot project is currently set up to remove about 100,000 tons of $CO_2$ annually. This is only about 1.5% of $CO_2$ from the exhaust gases, but it is believed that the process could be scaled up to remove as much as 90% of the $CO_2$ in the future if the method proves economically feasible.

## Questions:

1. A large coal-fired plant can burn 10,000 tons of coal a day. We will make the assumption for this problem that the coal is pure carbon, so this is about $9.1 \times 10^9$ g of carbon. What mass of $CO_2$ will be generated?

2. What mass of ammonium carbonate is needed to remove 1.0 million grams of $CO_2$ per day?

**Answers to these questions are available in Appendix N.**

## Reference:

*New York Times*, p. A1, September 22, 2009.

### Captured, Then Buried

A coal-fired electricity plant in West Virginia plans to capture some of the carbon dioxide it emits and inject it underground. Some environmentalists are wary.

**1** A scrubber removes sulfur from the plant's exhaust. The remaining exhaust is cooled to reduce its volume in preparation for removal of carbon dioxide.

**2** The exhaust enters a chemical reactor where it is mixed with an ammonia-based chemical, also chilled, that binds with the carbon dioxide. Then the exhaust is washed and sent to a smokestack.

**3** The ammonia solution is reheated and gives off its carbon dioxide. The ammonia is rechilled and sent for reuse; the carbon dioxide is squeezed down to a fluid.

**4** The carbon dioxide is pumped into porous rock layers deep underground, beneath impermeable layers that should prevent its escape. Underground, it spreads horizontally.

*Schematic diagram*

Source: American Electric Power; Alstom; Battelle

MIKA GRÖNDAHL/THE NEW YORK TIMES

## CHAPTER GOALS REVISITED

*Now that you have studied this chapter, you should ask whether you have met the chapter goals. In particular, you should be able to:*

**Understand the basis of the gas laws and how to use those laws (Boyle's law, Charles's law, Avogadro's hypothesis, Dalton's law)**

a.   Describe how pressure measurements are made and the units of pressure, especially atmospheres (atm) and millimeters of mercury (mm Hg) (Section 11.1). **Study Questions: 1, 3.**

b.   Understand the basis of the gas laws and how to apply them (Section 11.2). **Study Questions: 6, 8, 10, 12, 14–16.**

**Use the ideal gas law**

a.   Understand the origin of the ideal gas law and how to use the equation (Section 11.3). **Study Questions: 17–24, 59, 63, 77, 85, 102.**

b.   Calculate the molar mass of a compound from a knowledge of the pressure of a known quantity of a gas in a given volume at a known temperature (Section 11.3). **Study Questions: 25–30, 66, 89, 90.**

**Apply the gas laws to stoichiometric calculations**

a.   Apply the gas laws to a study of the stoichiometry of reactions (Section 11.4). **Study Questions: 31–36, 65, 79, 82.**

b.   Use Dalton's law of partial pressures (Section 11.5). **Study Questions: 39, 40, 70, 80, 87.**

**Understand kinetic-molecular theory as it is applied to gases, especially the distribution of molecular speeds (energies)**

a.   Apply the kinetic-molecular theory of gas behavior at the molecular level (Section 11.6). **Study Questions: 41–46, 107, and Go Chemistry Module 16.**

b.   Understand the phenomena of diffusion and effusion and how to use Graham's law (Section 11.7). **Study Questions: 47–50, 75, 76.**

**Recognize why gases do not behave like ideal gases under some conditions**

a.   Appreciate the fact that gases usually do not behave as ideal gases. Deviations from ideal behavior are largest at high pressure and low temperature (Section 11.8). **Study Questions: 51, 52.**

 **and**

Sign in at **www.cengage.com/owl** to:
•   View tutorials and simulations, develop problem-solving skills, and complete online homework assigned by your professor.
•   For quick review and exam prep, download Go Chemistry mini lecture modules from OWL (or purchase them at **www.cengagebrain.com**)

**?** Access **How Do I Solve It?** tutorials on how to approach problem solving using concepts in this chapter.

# Key Equations

**Equation 11.1 (page 512)** Boyle's law (where $P$ is the pressure and $V$ is the volume).

$$P_1V_1 = P_2V_2 \text{ at constant } n \text{ and } T$$

**Equation 11.2 (page 514)** Charles's law (where $T$ is the Kelvin temperature).

$$\frac{V_1}{T_1} = \frac{V_2}{T_2} \text{ at constant } n \text{ and } P$$

**Equation 11.3 (page 515)** General gas law (combined gas law).

$$\frac{P_1V_1}{T_1} = \frac{P_2V_2}{T_2} \text{ for a given amount of gas, } n$$

**Equation 11.4 (page 518)** Ideal gas law (where $n$ is the amount of gas in moles and $R$ is the universal gas constant, 0.082057 L · atm/K · mol).

$$PV = nRT$$

**Equation 11.5 (page 520)**  Density of gases (where *d* is the gas density in g/L and *M* is the molar mass of the gas).

$$d = \frac{m}{V} = \frac{PM}{RT}$$

**Equation 11.6 (page 525)**  Dalton's law of partial pressures. The total pressure of a gas mixture is the sum of the partial pressures of the component gases ($P_n$).

$$P_{total} = P_1 + P_2 + P_3 + \ldots$$

**Equation 11.7 (page 525)**  The total pressure of a gas mixture is equal to the total number of moles of gases multiplied by $(RT/V)$.

$$P_{total} = (n_{total})\left(\frac{RT}{V}\right)$$

**Equation 11.8 (page 526)**  The pressure of a gas (A) in a mixture is the product of its mole fraction ($X_A$) and the total pressure of the mixture.

$$P_A = X_A P_{total}$$

**Equation 11.9 (page 530)**  The rms speed ($\sqrt{u^2}$) depends on the molar mass of a gas *(M)* and its temperature *(T)*.

$$\sqrt{u^2} = \sqrt{\frac{3RT}{M}}$$

**Equation 11.10 (page 533)**  Graham's law. The rate of effusion of a gas is inversely proportional to the square root of its molar mass.

$$\frac{\text{Rate of effusion of gas 1}}{\text{Rate of effusion of gas 2}} = \sqrt{\frac{\text{molar mass of gas 2}}{\text{molar mass of gas 1}}}$$

**Equation 11.11 (page 535)**  The van der Waals equation, which relates pressure, volume, temperature, and amount of gas for a nonideal gas.

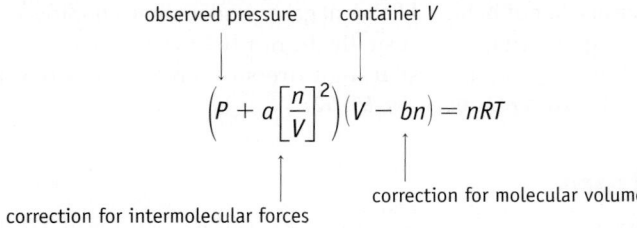

$$\left(P + a\left[\frac{n}{V}\right]^2\right)(V - bn) = nRT$$

correction for intermolecular forces        correction for molecular volume

# Study Questions

OWL Interactive versions of these questions are assignable in OWL.

▲ denotes challenging questions.

Blue-numbered questions have answers in Appendix R and fully worked solutions in the *Student Solutions Manual*.

## Practicing Skills

### Pressure

*(See Section 11.1 and Example 11.1.)*

1. The pressure of a gas is 440 mm Hg. Express this pressure in units of (a) atmospheres, (b) bars, and (c) kilopascals.

2. The average barometric pressure at an altitude of 10 km is 210 mm Hg. Express this pressure in atmospheres, bars, and kilopascals.

3. Indicate which represents the higher pressure in each of the following pairs:
   (a) 534 mm Hg or 0.754 bar
   (b) 534 mm Hg or 650 kPa
   (c) 1.34 bar or 934 kPa

4. Put the following in order of increasing pressure: 363 mm Hg, 363 kPa, 0.256 atm, and 0.523 bar.

### Boyle's Law and Charles's Law

*(See Section 11.2 and Examples 11.2 and 11.3.)*

5. A sample of nitrogen gas has a pressure of 67.5 mm Hg in a 500.-mL flask. What is the pressure of this gas sample when it is transferred to a 125-mL flask at the same temperature?

**6.** A sample of $CO_2$ gas has a pressure of 56.5 mm Hg in a 125-mL flask. The sample is transferred to a new flask, where it has a pressure of 62.3 mm Hg at the same temperature. What is the volume of the new flask?

**7.** You have 3.5 L of NO at a temperature of 22.0 °C. What volume would the NO occupy at 37 °C? (Assume the pressure is constant.)

**8.** A 5.0-mL sample of $CO_2$ gas is enclosed in a gas-tight syringe (Figure 11.3) at 22 °C. If the syringe is immersed in an ice bath (0 °C), what is the new gas volume, assuming that the pressure is held constant?

**The General Gas Law**
*(See Section 11.2 and Example 11.4.)*

**9.** You have 3.6 L of $H_2$ gas at 380 mm Hg and 25 °C. What is the pressure of this gas if it is transferred to a 5.0-L flask at 0.0 °C?

**10.** You have a sample of $CO_2$ in flask A with a volume of 25.0 mL. At 20.5 °C, the pressure of the gas is 436.5 mm Hg. To find the volume of another flask, B, you move the $CO_2$ to that flask and find that its pressure is now 94.3 mm Hg at 24.5 °C. What is the volume of flask B?

**11.** You have a sample of gas in a flask with a volume of 250 mL. At 25.5 °C, the pressure of the gas is 360 mm Hg. If you decrease the temperature to −5.0 °C, what is the gas pressure at the lower temperature?

**12.** A sample of gas occupies 135 mL at 22.5 °C; the pressure is 165 mm Hg. What is the pressure of the gas sample when it is placed in a 252-mL flask at a temperature of 0.0 °C?

**13.** One of the cylinders of an automobile engine has a volume of 400. $cm^3$. The engine takes in air at a pressure of 1.00 atm and a temperature of 15 °C and compresses the air to a volume of 50.0 $cm^3$ at 77 °C. What is the final pressure of the gas in the cylinder? (The ratio of before and after volumes—in this case, 400:50 or 8:1—is called the *compression ratio*.)

**14.** A helium-filled balloon of the type used in long-distance flying contains 420,000 $ft^3$ ($1.2 \times 10^7$ L) of helium. Suppose you fill the balloon with helium on the ground, where the pressure is 737 mm Hg and the temperature is 16.0 °C. When the balloon ascends to a height of 2 miles, where the pressure is only 600. mm Hg and the temperature is −33 °C, what volume is occupied by the helium gas? Assume the pressure inside the balloon matches the external pressure. Comment on the result.

**Avogadro's Hypothesis**
*(See Section 11.2 and Example 11.5.)*

**15.** Nitrogen monoxide reacts with oxygen to give nitrogen dioxide.
$$2\,NO(g) + O_2(g) \rightarrow 2\,NO_2(g)$$
(a) You wish to react NO and $O_2$ in the correct stoichiometric ratio. The sample of NO has a volume of 150 mL. What volume of $O_2$ is required (at the same pressure and temperature)?
(b) What volume of $NO_2$ (at the same pressure and temperature) is formed in this reaction?

**16.** Ethane burns in air to give $H_2O$ and $CO_2$.
$$2\,C_2H_6(g) + 7\,O_2(g) \rightarrow 4\,CO_2(g) + 6\,H_2O(g)$$
What volume of $O_2$ (L) is required for complete reaction with 5.2 L of $C_2H_6$? What volume of $H_2O$ vapor (L) is produced? Assume all gases are measured at the same temperature and pressure.

**Ideal Gaw Law**
*(See Section 11.3 and Example 11.6.)*

**17.** A 1.25-g sample of $CO_2$ is contained in a 750.-mL flask at 22.5 °C. What is the pressure of the gas?

**18.** A balloon holds 30.0 kg of helium. What is the volume of the balloon if its pressure is 1.20 atm and the temperature is 22 °C?

**19.** A flask is first evacuated so that it contains no gas at all. Then, 2.2 g of $CO_2$ is introduced into the flask. On warming to 22 °C, the gas exerts a pressure of 318 mm Hg. What is the volume of the flask?

**20.** A steel cylinder holds 1.50 g of ethanol, $C_2H_5OH$. What is the pressure of the ethanol vapor if the cylinder has a volume of 251 $cm^3$ and the temperature is 250 °C? (Assume all of the ethanol is in the vapor phase at this temperature.)

**21.** A balloon for long-distance flying contains $1.2 \times 10^7$ L of helium. If the helium pressure is 737 mm Hg at 25 °C, what mass of helium (in grams) does the balloon contain? (See Study Question 14.)

**22.** What mass of helium, in grams, is required to fill a 5.0-L balloon to a pressure of 1.1 atm at 25 °C?

**Gas Density and Molar Mass**
*(See Section 11.3 and Examples and 11.7 and 11.8.)*

**23.** Forty miles above Earth's surface, the temperature is 250 K, and the pressure is only 0.20 mm Hg. What is the density of air (in grams per liter) at this altitude? (Assume the molar mass of air is 28.96 g/mol.)

**24.** Diethyl ether, $(C_2H_5)_2O$, vaporizes easily at room temperature. If the vapor exerts a pressure of 233 mm Hg in a flask at 25 °C, what is the density of the vapor?

**25.** A gaseous organofluorine compound has a density of 0.355 g/L at 17 °C and 189 mm Hg. What is the molar mass of the compound?

**26.** Chloroform is a common liquid used in the laboratory. It vaporizes readily. If the pressure of chloroform vapor in a flask is 195 mm Hg at 25.0 °C and the density of the vapor is 1.25 g/L, what is the molar mass of chloroform?

**27.** A 1.007-g sample of an unknown gas exerts a pressure of 715 mm Hg in a 452-mL container at 23 °C. What is the molar mass of the gas?

**28.** A 0.0125-g sample of a gas with an empirical formula of $CHF_2$ is placed in a 165-mL flask. It has a pressure of 13.7 mm Hg at 22.5 °C. What is the molecular formula of the compound?

29. A new boron hydride, $B_xH_y$, has been isolated. To find its molar mass, you measure the pressure of the gas in a known volume at a known temperature. The following experimental data are collected:

    Mass of gas = 12.5 mg    Pressure of gas = 24.8 mm Hg

    Temperature = 25 °C    Volume of flask = 125 mL

    Which formula corresponds to the calculated molar mass?
    (a) $B_2H_6$                    (d) $B_6H_{10}$
    (b) $B_4H_{10}$                   (e) $B_{10}H_{14}$
    (c) $B_5H_9$

30. Acetaldehyde is a common liquid compound that vaporizes readily. Determine the molar mass of acetaldehyde from the following data:

    Sample mass = 0.107 g    Volume of gas = 125 mL

    Temperature = 0.0 °C    Pressure = 331 mm Hg

**Gas Laws and Chemical Reactions**
*(See Section 11.4 and Examples 11.9 and 11.10.)*

31. Iron reacts with hydrochloric acid to produce iron(II) chloride and hydrogen gas:

    $$Fe(s) + 2 HCl(aq) \rightarrow FeCl_2(aq) + H_2(g)$$

    The $H_2$ gas from the reaction of 2.2 g of iron with excess acid is collected in a 10.0-L flask at 25 °C. What is the pressure of the $H_2$ gas in this flask?

32. Silane, $SiH_4$, reacts with $O_2$ to give silicon dioxide and water:

    $$SiH_4(g) + 2 O_2(g) \rightarrow SiO_2(s) + 2 H_2O(\ell)$$

    A 5.20-L sample of $SiH_4$ gas at 356 mm Hg pressure and 25 °C is allowed to react with $O_2$ gas. What volume of $O_2$ gas, in liters, is required for complete reaction if the oxygen has a pressure of 425 mm Hg at 25 °C?

33. Sodium azide, the explosive compound in automobile air bags, decomposes according to the following equation:

    $$2 NaN_3(s) \rightarrow 2 Na(s) + 3 N_2(g)$$

    What mass of sodium azide is required to provide the nitrogen needed to inflate a 75.0-L bag to a pressure of 1.3 atm at 25 °C?

34. The hydrocarbon octane ($C_8H_{18}$) burns to give $CO_2$ and water vapor:

    $$2 C_8H_{18}(g) + 25 O_2(g) \rightarrow 16 CO_2(g) + 18 H_2O(g)$$

    If a 0.048-g sample of octane burns completely in $O_2$, what will be the pressure of water vapor in a 4.75-L flask at 30.0 °C? If the $O_2$ gas needed for complete combustion was contained in a 4.75-L flask at 22 °C, what would its pressure be?

35. Hydrazine reacts with $O_2$ according to the following equation:

    $$N_2H_4(g) + O_2(g) \rightarrow N_2(g) + 2 H_2O(\ell)$$

    Assume the $O_2$ needed for the reaction is in a 450-L tank at 23 °C. What must the oxygen pressure be in the tank to have enough oxygen to consume 1.00 kg of hydrazine completely?

36. A self-contained underwater breathing apparatus uses canisters containing potassium superoxide. The superoxide consumes the $CO_2$ exhaled by a person and replaces it with oxygen.

    $$4 KO_2(s) + 2 CO_2(g) \rightarrow 2 K_2CO_3(s) + 3 O_2(g)$$

    What mass of $KO_2$, in grams, is required to react with 8.90 L of $CO_2$ at 22.0 °C and 767 mm Hg?

**Gas Mixtures and Dalton's Law**
*(See Section 11.5 and Example 11.11.)*

37. What is the total pressure in atmospheres of a gas mixture that contains 1.0 g of $H_2$ and 8.0 g of Ar in a 3.0-L container at 27 °C? What are the partial pressures of the two gases?

38. A cylinder of compressed gas is labeled "Composition (mole %): 4.5% $H_2S$, 3.0% $CO_2$, balance $N_2$." The pressure gauge attached to the cylinder reads 46 atm. Calculate the partial pressure of each gas, in atmospheres, in the cylinder.

39. A halothane–oxygen mixture ($C_2HBrClF_3 + O_2$) can be used as an anesthetic. A tank containing such a mixture has the following partial pressures: $P$ (halothane) = 170 mm Hg and $P$ ($O_2$) = 570 mm Hg.
    (a) What is the ratio of the number of moles of halothane to the number of moles of $O_2$?
    (b) If the tank contains 160 g of $O_2$, what mass of $C_2HBrClF_3$ is present?

40. A collapsed balloon is filled with He to a volume of 12.5 L at a pressure of 1.00 atm. Oxygen, $O_2$, is then added so that the final volume of the balloon is 26 L with a total pressure of 1.00 atm. The temperature, which remains constant throughout, is 21.5 °C.
    (a) What mass of He does the balloon contain?
    (b) What is the final partial pressure of He in the balloon?
    (c) What is the partial pressure of $O_2$ in the balloon?
    (d) What is the mole fraction of each gas?

**Kinetic-Molecular Theory**
*(See Section 11.6 and Example 11.12.)*

41. You have two flasks of equal volume. Flask A contains $H_2$ at 0 °C and 1 atm pressure. Flask B contains $CO_2$ gas at 25 °C and 2 atm pressure. Compare these two gases with respect to each of the following:
    (a) average kinetic energy per molecule
    (b) root mean square speed
    (c) number of molecules
    (d) mass of gas

42. Equal masses of gaseous $N_2$ and Ar are placed in separate flasks of equal volume at the same temperature. Tell whether each of the following statements is true or false. Briefly explain your answer in each case.
    (a) There are more molecules of $N_2$ present than atoms of Ar.
    (b) The pressure is greater in the Ar flask.
    (c) The Ar atoms have a greater rms speed than the $N_2$ molecules.
    (d) The $N_2$ molecules collide more frequently with the walls of the flask than do the Ar atoms.

43. If the rms speed of an oxygen molecule is $4.28 \times 10^4$ cm/s at 25 °C, what is the rms speed of a $CO_2$ molecule at the same temperature?

**44.** Calculate the rms speed for CO molecules at 25 °C. What is the ratio of this speed to that of Ar atoms at the same temperature?

**45.** Place the following gases in order of increasing rms speed at 25 °C: Ar, $CH_4$, $N_2$, $CH_2F_2$.

**46.** The reaction of $SO_2$ with $Cl_2$ gives dichlorine oxide, which is used to bleach wood pulp and to treat wastewater:

$$SO_2(g) + 2\ Cl_2(g) \rightarrow OSCl_2(g) + Cl_2O(g)$$

All of the compounds involved in the reaction are gases. List them in order of increasing rms speed.

### Diffusion and Effusion
*(See Section 11.7 and Example 11.13.)*

**47.** In each pair of gases below, tell which will effuse faster:
(a) $CO_2$ or $F_2$
(b) $O_2$ or $N_2$
(c) $C_2H_4$ or $C_2H_6$
(d) two chlorofluorocarbons: $CFCl_3$ or $C_2Cl_2F_4$

**48.** Argon gas is 10 times denser than helium gas at the same temperature and pressure. Which gas is predicted to effuse faster? How much faster?

**49.** A gas whose molar mass you wish to know effuses through an opening at a rate one third as fast as that of helium gas. What is the molar mass of the unknown gas?

**50.** ▲ A sample of uranium fluoride is found to effuse at the rate of 17.7 mg/h. Under comparable conditions, gaseous $I_2$ effuses at the rate of 15.0 mg/h. What is the molar mass of the uranium fluoride? (*Hint:* Rates must be converted to units of moles per time.)

### Nonideal Gases
*(See Section 11.8)*

**51.** In the text, it is stated that the pressure of 4.00 mol of $Cl_2$ in a 4.00-L tank at 100.0 °C should be 26.0 atm if calculated using the van der Waals equation. Verify this result, and compare it with the pressure predicted by the ideal gas law.

**52.** You want to store 165 g of $CO_2$ gas in a 12.5-L tank at room temperature (25 °C). Calculate the pressure the gas would have using (a) the ideal gas law and (b) the van der Waals equation. (For $CO_2$, $a = 3.59$ atm $\cdot$ $L^2$/$mol^2$ and $b = 0.0427$ L/mol.)

## General Questions

*These questions are not designated as to type or location in the chapter. They may combine several concepts.*

**53.** Complete the following table:

|  | atm | mm Hg | kPa | bar |
|---|---|---|---|---|
| Standard atmosphere | ____ | ____ | ____ | ____ |
| Partial pressure of $N_2$ in the atmosphere | ____ | 593 | ____ | ____ |
| Tank of compressed $H_2$ | ____ | ____ | ____ | 133 |
| Atmospheric pressure at the top of Mount Everest | ____ | ____ | 33.7 | ____ |

**54.** On combustion, 1.0 L of a gaseous compound of hydrogen, carbon, and nitrogen gives 2.0 L of $CO_2$, 3.5 L of $H_2O$ vapor, and 0.50 L of $N_2$ at STP. What is the empirical formula of the compound?

**55.** ▲ You have a sample of helium gas at −33 °C, and you want to increase the rms speed of helium atoms by 10.0%. To what temperature should the gas be heated to accomplish this?

**56.** If 12.0 g of $O_2$ is required to inflate a balloon to a certain size at 27 °C, what mass of $O_2$ is required to inflate it to the same size (and pressure) at 5.0 °C?

**57.** Butyl mercaptan, $C_4H_9SH$, has a very bad odor and is among the compounds added to natural gas to help detect a leak of otherwise odorless natural gas. In an experiment, you burn 95.0 mg of $C_4H_9SH$ and collect the product gases ($SO_2$, $CO_2$, and $H_2O$) in a 5.25-L flask at 25 °C. What is the total gas pressure in the flask, and what is the partial pressure of each of the product gases?

**58.** A bicycle tire has an internal volume of 1.52 L and contains 0.406 mol of air. The tire will burst if its internal pressure reaches 7.25 atm. To what temperature, in degrees Celsius, does the air in the tire need to be heated to cause a blowout?

**59.** The temperature of the atmosphere on Mars can be as high as 27 °C at the equator at noon, and the atmospheric pressure is about 8 mm Hg. If a spacecraft could collect 10. $m^3$ of this atmosphere, compress it to a small volume, and send it back to Earth, how many moles would the sample contain?

**60.** If you place 2.25 g of solid silicon in a 6.56-L flask that contains $CH_3Cl$ with a pressure of 585 mm Hg at 25 °C, what mass of dimethyldichlorosilane, $(CH_3)_2SiCl_2(g)$, can be formed?

$$Si(s) + 2\ CH_3Cl(g) \rightarrow (CH_3)_2SiCl_2(g)$$

What pressure of $(CH_3)_2SiCl_2(g)$ would you expect in this same flask at 95 °C on completion of the reaction? (Dimethyldichlorosilane is one starting material used to make silicones, polymeric substances used as lubricants, antistick agents, and water-proofing caulk.)

**61.** $Ni(CO)_4$ can be made by reacting finely divided nickel with gaseous CO. If you have CO in a 1.50-L flask at a pressure of 418 mm Hg at 25.0 °C, along with 0.450 g of Ni powder, what is the theoretical yield of $Ni(CO)_4$?

**62.** Ethane burns in air to give $H_2O$ and $CO_2$.

$$2\ C_2H_6(g) + 7\ O_2(g) \rightarrow 4\ CO_2(g) + 6\ H_2O(g)$$

(a) Four gases are involved in this reaction. Place them in order of increasing rms speed. (Assume all are at the same temperature.)
(b) A 3.26-L flask contains $C_2H_6$ at a pressure of 256 mm Hg and a temperature of 25 °C. Suppose $O_2$ gas is added to the flask until $C_2H_6$ and $O_2$ are in the correct stoichiometric ratio for the combustion reaction. At this point, what is the partial pressure of $O_2$ and what is the total pressure in the flask?

63. You have four gas samples:
    1. 1.0 L of $H_2$ at STP
    2. 1.0 L of Ar at STP
    3. 1.0 L of $H_2$ at 27 °C and 760 mm Hg
    4. 1.0 L of He at 0 °C and 900 mm Hg
    (a) Which sample has the largest number of gas particles (atoms or molecules)?
    (b) Which sample contains the smallest number of particles?
    (c) Which sample represents the largest mass?

64. Propane reacts with oxygen to give carbon dioxide and water vapor.

    $$C_3H_8(g) + 5\ O_2(g) \rightarrow 3\ CO_2(g) + 4\ H_2O(g)$$

    If you mix $C_3H_8$ and $O_2$ in the correct stoichiometric ratio, and if the total pressure of the mixture is 288 mm Hg, what are the partial pressures of $C_3H_8$ and $O_2$? If the temperature and volume do not change, what is the pressure of the water vapor?

65. Iron carbonyl can be made by the direct reaction of iron metal and carbon monoxide.

    $$Fe(s) + 5\ CO(g) \rightarrow Fe(CO)_5(\ell)$$

    What is the theoretical yield of $Fe(CO)_5$ if 3.52 g of iron is treated with CO gas having a pressure of 732 mm Hg in a 5.50-L flask at 23 °C?

66. Analysis of a gaseous chlorofluorocarbon, $CCl_xF_y$, shows that it contains 11.79% C and 69.57% Cl. In another experiment, you find that 0.107 g of the compound fills a 458-mL flask at 25 °C with a pressure of 21.3 mm Hg. What is the molecular formula of the compound?

67. There are five compounds in the family of sulfur–fluorine compounds with the general formula $S_xF_y$. One of these compounds is 25.23% S. If you place 0.0955 g of the compound in a 89-mL flask at 45 °C, the pressure of the gas is 83.8 mm Hg. What is the molecular formula of $S_xF_y$?

68. A miniature volcano can be made in the laboratory with ammonium dichromate. When ignited, it decomposes in a fiery display.

    $$(NH_4)_2Cr_2O_7(s) \rightarrow N_2(g) + 4\ H_2O(g) + Cr_2O_3(s)$$

    If 0.95 g of ammonium dichromate is used and the gases from this reaction are trapped in a 15.0-L flask at 23 °C, what is the total pressure of the gas in the flask? What are the partial pressures of $N_2$ and $H_2O$?

**Thermal decomposition of $(NH_4)_2Cr_2O_7$.**

69. The density of air 20 km above Earth's surface is 92 g/m³. The pressure of the atmosphere is 42 mm Hg, and the temperature is −63 °C.
    (a) What is the average molar mass of the atmosphere at this altitude?
    (b) If the atmosphere at this altitude consists of only $O_2$ and $N_2$, what is the mole fraction of each gas?

70. A 3.0-L bulb containing He at 145 mm Hg is connected by a valve to a 2.0-L bulb containing Ar at 355 mm Hg (see figure below). Calculate the partial pressure of each gas and the total pressure after the valve between the flasks is opened.

71. Chlorine dioxide, $ClO_2$, reacts with fluorine to give a new gas that contains Cl, O, and F. In an experiment, you find that 0.150 g of this new gas has a pressure of 17.2 mm Hg in a 1850-mL flask at 21 °C. What is the identity of the unknown gas?

72. A xenon fluoride can be prepared by heating a mixture of Xe and $F_2$ gases to a high temperature in a pressure-proof container. Assume that xenon gas was added to a 0.25-L container until its pressure reached 0.12 atm at 0.0 °C. Fluorine gas was then added until the total pressure reached 0.72 atm at 0.0 °C. After the reaction was complete, the xenon was consumed completely, and the pressure of the $F_2$ remaining in the container was 0.36 atm at 0.0 °C. What is the empirical formula of the xenon fluoride?

73. Which of the following is *not* correct?
    (a) Diffusion of gases occurs more rapidly at higher temperatures.
    (b) Effusion of $H_2$ is faster than effusion of He (assume similar conditions and a rate expressed in units of mol/h).
    (c) Diffusion will occur faster at low pressure than at high pressure.
    (d) The rate of effusion of a gas (mol/h) is directly proportional to molar mass.

74. The ideal gas law is least accurate under conditions of high pressure and low temperature. In those situations, using the van der Waals equation is advisable.
    (a) Calculate the pressure exerted by 12.0 g of $CO_2$ in a 500-mL vessel at 298 K, using the ideal gas equation. Then, recalculate the pressure using the van der Waals equation. Assuming the pressure calculated from van der Waal's equation is correct, what is the percent error in the answer when using the ideal gas equation?

(b) Next, cool this sample to −70 °C. Then perform the same calculation for the pressure exerted by $CO_2$ at this new temperature, using both the ideal gas law and the van der Waals equation. Again, what is the percent error when using the ideal gas equation?

75. Carbon dioxide, $CO_2$, was shown to effuse through a porous plate at the rate of 0.033 mol/min. The same quantity of an unknown gas, 0.033 moles, is found to effuse through the same porous barrier in 104 seconds. Calculate the molar mass of the unknown gas.

76. In an experiment, you have determined that 0.66 moles of $CF_4$ effuse through a porous barrier over a 4.8 minute period. How long will it take for 0.66 moles of $CH_4$ to effuse through the same barrier?

77. A balloon is filled with helium gas to a gauge pressure of 22 mm Hg at 25 °C. The volume of the gas is 305 mL, and the barometric pressure is 755 mm Hg. What amount of helium is in the balloon? (Remember that gauge pressure = total pressure − barometric pressure. See page 511.)

78. If you have a sample of water in a closed container, some of the water will evaporate until the pressure of the water vapor, at 25 °C, is 23.8 mm Hg. How many molecules of water per cubic centimeter exist in the vapor phase?

79. You are given 1.56 g of a mixture of $KClO_3$ and KCl. When heated, the $KClO_3$ decomposes to KCl and $O_2$,

$$2 \, KClO_3(s) \rightarrow 2 \, KCl(s) + 3 \, O_2(g)$$

and 327 mL of $O_2$ with a pressure of 735 mm Hg is collected at 19 °C. What is the weight percentage of $KClO_3$ in the sample?

80. ▲ A study of climbers who reached the summit of Mount Everest without supplemental oxygen showed that the partial pressures of $O_2$ and $CO_2$ in their lungs were 35 mm Hg and 7.5 mm Hg, respectively. The barometric pressure at the summit was 253 mm Hg. Assume the lung gases are saturated with moisture at a body temperature of 37 °C [which means the partial pressure of water vapor in the lungs is $P(H_2O) = 47.1$ mm Hg]. If you assume the lung gases consist of only $O_2$, $N_2$, $CO_2$, and $H_2O$, what is the partial pressure of $N_2$?

81. Nitrogen monoxide reacts with oxygen to give nitrogen dioxide:

$$2 \, NO(g) + O_2(g) \rightarrow 2 \, NO_2(g)$$

(a) Place the three gases in order of increasing rms speed at 298 K.
(b) If you mix NO and $O_2$ in the correct stoichiometric ratio and NO has a partial pressure of 150 mm Hg, what is the partial pressure of $O_2$?
(c) After reaction between NO and $O_2$ is complete, what is the pressure of $NO_2$ if the NO originally had a pressure of 150 mm Hg and $O_2$ was added in the correct stoichiometric amount?

82. ▲ Ammonia gas is synthesized by combining hydrogen and nitrogen:

$$3 \, H_2(g) + N_2(g) \rightarrow 2 \, NH_3(g)$$

(a) If you want to produce 562 g of $NH_3$, what volume of $H_2$ gas, at 56 °C and 745 mm Hg, is required?
(b) Nitrogen for this reaction will be obtained from air. What volume of air, measured at 29 °C and 745 mm Hg pressure, will be required to provide the nitrogen needed to produce 562 g of $NH_3$? Assume the sample of air contains 78.1 mole % $N_2$.

83. Nitrogen trifluoride is prepared by the reaction of ammonia and fluorine.

$$4 \, NH_3(g) + 3 \, F_2(g) \rightarrow 3 \, NH_4F(s) + NF_3(g)$$

If you mix $NH_3$ with $F_2$ in the correct stoichiometric ratio, and if the total pressure of the mixture is 120 mm Hg, what are the partial pressures of $NH_3$ and $F_2$? When the reactants have been completely consumed, what is the total pressure in the flask? (Assume $T$ is constant.)

84. Chlorine trifluoride, $ClF_3$, is a valuable reagent because it can be used to convert metal oxides to metal fluorides:

$$6 \, NiO(s) + 4 \, ClF_3(g) \rightarrow 6 \, NiF_2(s) + 2 \, Cl_2(g) + 3 \, O_2(g)$$

(a) What mass of NiO will react with $ClF_3$ gas if the gas has a pressure of 250 mm Hg at 20 °C in a 2.5-L flask?
(b) If the $ClF_3$ described in part (a) is completely consumed, what are the partial pressures of $Cl_2$ and of $O_2$ in the 2.5-L flask at 20 °C (in mm Hg)? What is the total pressure in the flask?

85. ▲ Relative humidity is the ratio of the partial pressure of water in air at a given temperature to the vapor pressure of water at that temperature. Calculate the mass of water per liter of air under the following conditions:
(a) at 20 °C and 45% relative humidity
(b) at 0 °C and 95% relative humidity

Under which circumstances is the mass of $H_2O$ per liter greater? (See Appendix G for the vapor pressure of water.)

86. How much water vapor is present in a dormitory room when the relative humidity is 55% and the temperature is 23 °C? The dimensions of the room are 4.5 $m^2$ floor area and 3.5 m ceiling height. (See Study Question 85 for a definition of relative humidity and Appendix G for the vapor pressure of water.)

## In the Laboratory

87. ▲ You have a 550.-mL tank of gas with a pressure of 1.56 atm at 24 °C. You thought the gas was pure carbon monoxide gas, CO, but you later found it was contaminated by small quantities of gaseous $CO_2$ and $O_2$. Analysis shows that the tank pressure is 1.34 atm (at 24 °C) if the $CO_2$ is removed. Another experiment shows that 0.0870 g of $O_2$ can be removed chemically. What are the masses of CO and $CO_2$ in the tank, and what is the partial pressure of each of the three gases at 25 °C?

88. ▲ Methane is burned in a laboratory Bunsen burner to give $CO_2$ and water vapor. Methane gas is supplied to the burner at the rate of 5.0 L/min (at a temperature of 28 °C and a pressure of 773 mm Hg). At what rate must oxygen be supplied to the burner (at a pressure of 742 mm Hg and a temperature of 26 °C)?

89. ▲ Iron forms a series of compounds of the type $Fe_x(CO)_y$. In air, these compounds are oxidized to $Fe_2O_3$ and $CO_2$ gas. After heating a 0.142-g sample of $Fe_x(CO)_y$ in air, you isolate the $CO_2$ in a 1.50-L flask at 25 °C. The pressure of the gas is 44.9 mm Hg. What is the empirical formula of $Fe_x(CO)_y$?

90. ▲ Group 2A metal carbonates are decomposed to the metal oxide and $CO_2$ on heating:

$$MCO_3(s) \rightarrow MO(s) + CO_2(g)$$

You heat 0.158 g of a white, solid carbonate of a Group 2A metal (M) and find that the evolved $CO_2$ has a pressure of 69.8 mm Hg in a 285-mL flask at 25 °C. Identify M.

91. One way to synthesize diborane, $B_2H_6$, is the reaction

$$2\ NaBH_4(s) + 2\ H_3PO_4(\ell) \rightarrow$$
$$B_2H_6(g) + 2\ NaH_2PO_4(s) + 2\ H_2(g)$$

   (a) If you have 0.136 g of $NaBH_4$ and excess $H_3PO_4$, and you collect the $B_2H_6$ in a 2.75-L flask at 25 °C, what is the pressure of the $B_2H_6$ in the flask?
   (b) A by-product of the reaction is $H_2$ gas. If both $B_2H_6$ and $H_2$ gas come from this reaction, what is the *total* pressure in the 2.75-L flask (after reaction of 0.136 g of $NaBH_4$ with excess $H_3PO_4$) at 25 °C?

92. You are given a solid mixture of $NaNO_2$ and $NaCl$ and are asked to analyze it for the amount of $NaNO_2$ present. To do so, you allow the mixture to react with sulfamic acid, $HSO_3NH_2$, in water according to the equation

$$NaNO_2(aq) + HSO_3NH_2(aq) \rightarrow$$
$$NaHSO_4(aq) + H_2O(\ell) + N_2(g)$$

What is the weight percentage of $NaNO_2$ in 1.232 g of the solid mixture if reaction with sulfamic acid produces 295 mL of dry $N_2$ gas with a pressure of 713 mm Hg at 21.0 °C?

93. ▲ You have 1.249 g of a mixture of $NaHCO_3$ and $Na_2CO_3$. You find that 12.0 mL of 1.50 M HCl is required to convert the sample completely to NaCl, $H_2O$, and $CO_2$.

$$NaHCO_3(aq) + HCl(aq) \rightarrow$$
$$NaCl(aq) + H_2O(\ell) + CO_2(g)$$

$$Na_2CO_3(aq) + 2\ HCl(aq) \rightarrow$$
$$2\ NaCl(aq) + H_2O(\ell) + CO_2(g)$$

What volume of $CO_2$ is evolved at 745 mm Hg and 25 °C?

94. ▲ A mixture of $NaHCO_3$ and $Na_2CO_3$ has a mass of 2.50 g. When treated with HCl(aq), 665 mL of $CO_2$ gas is liberated with a pressure of 735 mm Hg at 25 °C. What is the weight percent of $NaHCO_3$ and $Na_2CO_3$ in the mixture? (See Study Question 93 for the reactions that occur.)

95. ▲ Many nitrate salts can be decomposed by heating. For example, blue, anhydrous copper(II) nitrate produces the gases nitrogen dioxide and oxygen when heated. In the laboratory, you find that a sample of this salt produced a 0.195-g mixture of gaseous $NO_2$ and $O_2$ with a total pressure of 725 mm Hg at 35 °C in a 125-mL flask (and black, solid CuO was left as a residue). What is the average molar mass of the gas mixture? What are the mole fractions of $NO_2$ and $O_2$ in the mixture? What amount of each gas is in the mixture? Do these amounts reflect the relative amounts of $NO_2$ and $O_2$ expected based on the balanced equation? Is it possible that the fact that some $NO_2$ molecules combine to give $N_2O_4$ plays a role?

**Heating copper(II) nitrate produces nitrogen dioxide and oxygen gas and leaves a residue of copper(II) oxide.**

96. ▲ A compound containing C, H, N, and O is burned in excess oxygen. The gases produced by burning 0.1152 g are first treated to convert the nitrogen-containing product gases into $N_2$, and then the resulting mixture of $CO_2$, $H_2O$, $N_2$, and excess $O_2$ is passed through a bed of $CaCl_2$ to absorb the water. The $CaCl_2$ increases in mass by 0.09912 g. The remaining gases are bubbled into water to form $H_2CO_3$, and this solution is titrated with 0.3283 M NaOH; 28.81 mL is required to achieve the second equivalence point. The excess $O_2$ gas is removed by reaction with copper metal (to give CuO). Finally, the $N_2$ gas is collected in a 225.0-mL flask, where it has a pressure of 65.12 mm Hg at 25 °C. In a separate experiment, the unknown compound is found to have a molar mass of 150 g/mol. What are the empirical and molecular formulas of the unknown compound?

97. You have a gas, one of the three known phosphorus–fluorine compounds ($PF_3$, $PF_5$, and $P_2F_4$). To find out which, you have decided to measure its molar mass.
    (a) First, you determine that the density of the gas is 5.60 g/L at a pressure of 0.971 atm and a temperature of 18.2 °C. Calculate the molar mass and identify the compound.
    (b) To check the results from part (a), you decide to measure the molar mass based on the relative rates of effusion of the unknown gas and $CO_2$. You find that $CO_2$ effuses at a rate of 0.050 mol/min, whereas the unknown phosphorus fluoride effuses at a rate of 0.028 mol/min. Calculate the molar mass of the unknown gas based on these results.

98. A 1.50 L constant volume calorimeter (Figure 5.12) contains $C_3H_8(g)$ and $O_2(g)$. The partial pressure of $C_3H_8$ is 0.10 atm and the partial pressure of $O_2$ is 5.0 atm. The temperature is 20.0 °C. A reaction occurs between the two compounds, forming $CO_2(g)$ and $H_2O(\ell)$. The heat from the reaction causes the temperature to rise to 23.2 °C.
    (a) Write a balanced chemical equation for the reaction.
    (b) How many moles of $C_3H_8(g)$ are present in the flask initially?
    (c) What is the mole fraction of $C_3H_8(g)$ in the flask before reaction?
    (d) After the reaction, the flask contains excess oxygen and the products of the reaction, $CO_2(g)$ and $H_2O(\ell)$. What amount of unreacted $O_2(g)$ remains?
    (e) After the reaction, what is the partial pressure exerted by the $CO_2(g)$ in this system?
    (f) What is the partial pressure exerted by the excess oxygen remaining after the reaction?

## Summary and Conceptual Questions

*The following questions may use concepts from this and previous chapters.*

99. A 1.0-L flask contains 10.0 g each of $O_2$ and $CO_2$ at 25 °C.
    (a) Which gas has the greater partial pressure, $O_2$ or $CO_2$, or are they the same?
    (b) Which molecules have the greater rms speed, or are they the same?
    (c) Which molecules have the greater average kinetic energy, or are they the same?

100. If equal masses of $O_2$ and $N_2$ are placed in separate containers of equal volume at the same temperature, which of the following statements is true? If false, explain why it is false.
    (a) The pressure in the flask containing $N_2$ is greater than that in the flask containing $O_2$.
    (b) There are more molecules in the flask containing $O_2$ than in the flask containing $N_2$.

101. You have two pressure-proof steel cylinders of equal volume, one containing 1.0 kg of CO and the other containing 1.0 kg of acetylene, $C_2H_2$.
    (a) In which cylinder is the pressure greater at 25 °C?
    (b) Which cylinder contains the greater number of molecules?

102. Two flasks, each with a volume of 1.00 L, contain $O_2$ gas with a pressure of 380 mm Hg. Flask A is at 25 °C, and flask B is at 0 °C. Which flask contains the greater number of $O_2$ molecules?

103. ▲ State whether each of the following samples of matter is a gas. If there is not enough information for you to decide, write "insufficient information."
    (a) A material is in a steel tank at 100 atm pressure. When the tank is opened to the atmosphere, the material suddenly expands, increasing its volume by 1%.
    (b) A 1.0-mL sample of material weighs 8.2 g.
    (c) The material is transparent and pale green in color.
    (d) One cubic meter of material contains as many molecules as 1.0 m³ of air at the same temperature and pressure.

104. Each of four flasks is filled with a different gas. Each flask has the same volume, and each is filled to the same pressure, 3.0 atm, at 25 °C. Flask A contains 116 g of air, flask B has 80.7 g of neon, flask C has 16.0 g of helium, and flask C has 160. g of an unknown gas.
    (a) Do all four flasks contain the same number of gas molecules? If not, which one has the greatest number of molecules?
    (b) How many times heavier is a molecule of the unknown gas than an atom of helium?
    (c) In which flask do the molecules have the largest kinetic energy? The highest rms speed?

105. You have two gas-filled balloons, one containing He and the other containing $H_2$. The $H_2$ balloon is twice the size of the He balloon. The pressure of gas in the $H_2$ balloon is 1 atm, and that in the He balloon is 2 atm. The $H_2$ balloon is outside in the snow (−5 °C), and the He balloon is inside a warm building (23 °C).
    (a) Which balloon contains the greater number of molecules?
    (b) Which balloon contains the greater mass of gas?

106. The sodium azide required for automobile air bags is made by the reaction of sodium metal with dinitrogen monoxide in liquid ammonia:

    $$3\ N_2O(g) + 4\ Na(s) + NH_3(\ell) \rightarrow$$
    $$NaN_3(s) + 3\ NaOH(s) + 2\ N_2(g)$$

    (a) You have 65.0 g of sodium, a 35.0-L flask containing $N_2O$ gas with a pressure of 2.12 atm at 23 °C, and excess ammonia. What is the theoretical yield (in grams) of $NaN_3$?
    (b) Draw a Lewis structure for the azide ion. Include all possible resonance structures. Which resonance structure is most likely?
    (c) What is the shape of the azide ion?

107. If the absolute temperature of a gas doubles, by how much does the rms speed of the gaseous molecules increase?

108. ▲ Chlorine gas ($Cl_2$) is used as a disinfectant in municipal water supplies, although chlorine dioxide ($ClO_2$) and ozone are becoming more widely used. $ClO_2$ is a better choice than $Cl_2$ in this application because it leads to fewer chlorinated by-products, which are themselves pollutants.
    (a) How many valence electrons are in $ClO_2$?
    (b) The chlorite ion, $ClO_2^-$, is obtained by reducing $ClO_2$. Draw a possible electron dot structure for $ClO_2^-$. (Cl is the central atom.)
    (c) What is the hybridization of the central Cl atom in $ClO_2^-$? What is the shape of the ion?
    (d) Which species has the larger bond angle, $O_3$ or $ClO_2^-$? Explain briefly.
    (e) Chlorine dioxide, $ClO_2$, a yellow-green gas, can be made by the reaction of chlorine with sodium chlorite:

    $$2\ NaClO_2(s) + Cl_2(g) \rightarrow 2\ NaCl(s) + 2\ ClO_2(g)$$

    Assume you react 15.6 g of $NaClO_2$ with chlorine gas, which has a pressure of 1050 mm Hg in a 1.45-L flask at 22 °C. What mass of $ClO_2$ can be produced?

## Applying Chemical Principles

### The Goodyear Blimp

Goodyear blimps are a familiar sight at sporting events. They hover at altitudes between 1000–3000 feet, providing a stable platform for television cameras. The outer surface, or envelope, of a Goodyear blimp is constructed of polyester fabric impregnated with neoprene rubber. The envelope contains the lighter-than-air gas helium. Within the fore and aft sections of the envelope are two air-filled structures called ballonets, which serve two purposes. As the blimp changes altitude, the ballonets are inflated or deflated with air to maintain a helium pressure within the envelope that is similar to the external air pressure. The ballonets also are used to keep the craft level. The pilot and passengers ride in the gondola, which is attached to the bottom of the envelope.

One of the Goodyear blimps has a gross weight of 12,840 lbs (5820 kg), and the volume of the inner envelope is 202,700 ft³ (5740 m³). The ballonets, when both fully inflated with air, occupy a total of 18,000 ft³ (510 m³) of the envelope. Helium is neither added nor removed from the envelope during operation. Loss of helium through the rubber impregnated polyester fabric is slow, at approximately 10,000 ft³ (280 m³) per month.

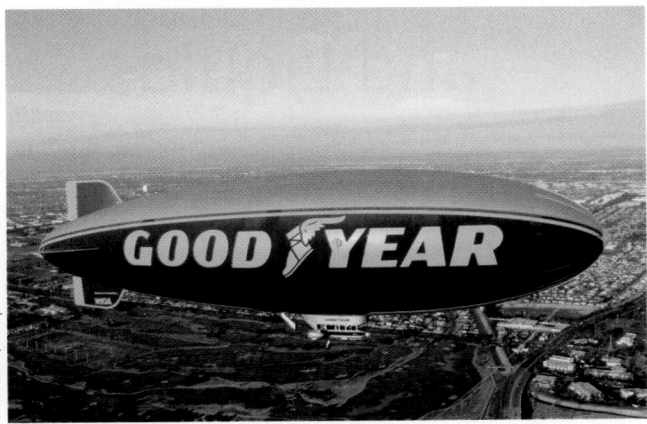

**Goodyear blimp.** Here the blimp flies over a packed stadium at Ohio State University.

### Questions:

1. At sea level, atmospheric pressure is 1.00 atm. Calculate the density (in g/L) of helium at this pressure and 25 °C.

2. Use the data provided in Table 11.1 to calculate the density of dry air at 1.00 atm and 25 °C.

3. To stay aloft, a blimp must achieve neutral buoyancy; that is, its density must equal that of the surrounding air. The density of the blimp is its total weight (blimp, helium and air, passengers, and ballast) divided by its volume. Assume that the gross weight of the blimp includes the blimp's structure and the helium, but does not include the air in the ballonets or the weights of the passengers and ballast. If the ballonets are filled with 12,000 ft³ (340 m³) of air at 1.00 atm and 25 °C, what additional weight (of passengers and ballast) is required for neutral buoyancy?

# 12 Intermolecular Forces and Liquids

## Geckos Can Climb Up der Waals

Just like the comic-book hero Spiderman, a little lizard, the gecko, can climb walls and hang from the ceiling.

This fact intrigued Kellar Autumn, a professor of biology at Lewis and Clark College in Portland, Oregon. An interdisciplinary team of Autumn and his students, along with scientists and engineers from Stanford University, and the Universities of California at Berkeley and Santa Barbara, realized that gecko toes are covered with an array of stiff hairlike setae. Each of these is about as long as the thickness of a human hair or about 0.1 mm long. But each seta is further divided into about 1000 even more minute pads called *spatulae*. And these are only about 200 nm wide, a distance smaller than the wavelength of visible light!

The design of gecko feet is the secret to their wall-crawling abilities. Autumn said, "We discovered that the seta is 10 times more adhesive than predicted from prior measurements on whole animals. In fact, the adhesive is so strong that a single seta can lift the weight of an ant. A million setae, which could easily fit onto the area of a dime, could lift a 45-pound child. Our discovery explains why the gecko can support its entire body weight with only a single finger."

"When the gecko attaches itself to a surface, it uncurls its toes like a party favor that uncurls when you blow into it," Autumn says. "But," he adds, "getting yourself to stick isn't really that difficult. It's getting off the surface that is the major problem. When a gecko runs, it has to attach and detach its feet 15 times a second."

But what is the "adhesive effect" that allows a gecko to climb a wall? It is an intermolecular force, called a *van der Waals force*. This is ordinarily a weak force that operates only over a very short distance. However, each spatula of the millions in each toe experiences an attractive van der Waals force with the surface. It has been calculated that the force between each spatula and the surface is about 0.4 μN (micronewtons). But given that there are millions of spatula in each toe, the total force can easily be 10 N or more.

One of the topics in this chapter is the importance of van der Waals forces. As you learn about this, think about the possibilities of using the design of gecko feet to make even more useful adhesives.

### References:

1. www.kellarautumn.com/photography/Welcome.html
2. geckolab.lclark.edu/dept/AutumnLab/ Welcome.html

**A Tokay gecko.** This is a nocturnal arboreal gecko found from northeast India to southeast Asia.

**A close-up of a gecko foot.** Notice the adhesive lamellae at the end of each toe. The lamellae consist of arrays of setae.

**Rows of setae.** Each is about 75 μm long. Each seta is composed of millions of spatulae, the basis of the gecko's stickiness.

## CHAPTER GOALS

*See Chapter Goals Revisited (page 574) for Study Questions keyed to these goals.*

- Describe intermolecular forces and their effects.

- Understand the importance of hydrogen bonding.

- Understand the properties of liquids.

OWL

Sign in to OWL at **www.cengage.com/owl** to view tutorials and simulations, develop problem-solving skills, and complete online homework assigned by your professor.

go Chemistry

Download mini lecture videos for key concept review and exam prep from OWL or purchase them from **www.cengagebrain.com**

In the last chapter, we studied gases, one of the states of matter. Most of the time we were able to assume that the attractions between the molecules, intermolecular forces, were negligible and so we could ignore them. At the end of that chapter, however, we saw that at high pressures and/or low temperatures this assumption did not work as well; we had to consider intermolecular forces when dealing with the nonideal behavior of gases. In the other two states of matter, the liquid and solid states, intermolecular forces play a major role. In order to describe these states of matter, we will first need to explore the different types and relative strengths of intermolecular forces.

The primary objectives of this chapter are to examine the intermolecular forces that allow molecules to interact and then to look at liquids, a state of matter that results from such interactions. You will find this a useful chapter because it explains, among other things, why your body is cooled when you sweat and why ice can float on liquid water, a property shared by very few other substances.

## 12.1   States of Matter and Intermolecular Forces

The kinetic-molecular theory of gases (◄ Section 11.6) assumes that gas molecules or atoms are widely separated and that these particles can be considered to be independent of one another. Consequently, we can relate the properties of gases under most conditions by the ideal gas law equation, $PV = nRT$ (◄ Equation 11.4). In real gases, however, there are intermolecular forces between molecules. If these forces are strong enough, the gas can condense to a liquid and eventually to a solid. The existence of intermolecular forces in liquids makes the picture more complex, and it is not possible to create a simple "ideal liquid equation."

How different are the states of matter at the particulate level? We can get a sense of this by comparing the volumes occupied by equal numbers of molecules of a material in different states. Figure 12.1a shows a flask containing about 300 mL of liquid nitrogen. If all of the liquid were allowed to evaporate, the gaseous nitrogen, at 1 atm and room temperature, would fill a large balloon (more than 200 L). A great amount of space exists between molecules in a gas, whereas in liquids the molecules are much closer together.

The increase in volume when converting liquids to gases is strikingly large. In contrast, no dramatic change in volume occurs when a solid is converted to a liquid. Figure 12.1b shows the same amount of liquid and solid benzene, $C_6H_6$, side by side.

Nitrogen gas

Liquid nitrogen

**(a)** When a 300-mL sample of liquid nitrogen evaporates, it will produce more than 200 L of gas at 25 °C and 1.0 atm. In the liquid phase, the molecules of $N_2$ are close together; in the gas phase, they are far apart.

Liquid benzene    Solid benzene

**(b)** The same volume of liquid benzene, $C_6H_6$, is placed in two test tubes, and one tube *(right)* is cooled, freezing the liquid. The solid and liquid states have almost the same volume, showing that the molecules are packed together almost as tightly in the liquid state as they are in the solid state.

**FIGURE 12.1** Contrasting gases, liquids, and solids.

They are not appreciably different in volume. This means the molecules in the liquid are packed together about as tightly as the molecules in the solid phase.

Intermolecular forces influence chemistry in many ways:

- They are directly related to properties such as melting point, boiling point, and the energy needed to convert a solid to a liquid or a liquid to a vapor.
- They are important in determining the solubility of gases, liquids, and solids in various solvents.
- They are crucial in determining the structures of biologically important molecules such as DNA and proteins.

Bonding in ionic compounds depends on the electrostatic forces of attraction between oppositely charged ions (▶ Section 13.4). Similarly, the intermolecular forces attracting one molecule to another are electrostatic. The energy associated with the attractive forces between the ions in ionic compounds are usually in the range of 700 to 1100 kJ/mol, and most covalent bond energies are in the range of 100 to 400 kJ/mol (◀ Table 8.9). As a rough guideline, intermolecular forces are generally less than about 15% of the values of covalent bond energies. Nonetheless, these interactions can have a profound effect on molecular properties.

Collectively, forces between molecules are called **van der Waals forces**, and these include the attractive and repulsive forces between

- molecules with permanent dipoles (dipole-dipole forces, Section 12.3)
- polar molecules and nonpolar ones (dipole-induced dipole forces, Section 12.4)
- nonpolar molecules (induced dipole-induced dipole forces, also known as *London forces*, Section 12.4)

## 12.2 Interactions between Ions and Molecules with a Permanent Dipole

**Module 17: Intermolecular Forces** covers concepts in this section.

Many molecules are polar, a result of the polarity of individual bonds and a nonsymmetrical geometry (Section 8.7). Conceptually, we can view polar molecules as having positive and negative ends. What happens when a polar molecule encounters an ionic compound? The negative end of the dipole is attracted to a positive cation (Figure 12.2). Similarly, the positive end of the dipole is attracted to a negative anion. Forces of attraction between a positive or negative ion and polar molecules—ion–dipole forces—are less than those for ion–ion attractions, but they are greater than other types of forces between molecules, whether polar or nonpolar.

Ion–dipole attractions can be evaluated using Coulomb's law (◀ Equation 2.3), which informs us that the force of attraction between two charged objects depends

**Table 12.1** **Radii and Enthalpies of Hydration of Alkali Metal Ions**

| Cation | Ion Radius (pm) | Enthalpy of Hydration (kJ/mol) |
|--------|-----------------|--------------------------------|
| $Li^+$ | 78 | −515 |
| $Na^+$ | 98 | −405 |
| $K^+$ | 133 | −321 |
| $Rb^+$ | 149 | −296 |
| $Cs^+$ | 165 | −263 |

water surrounding
a cation

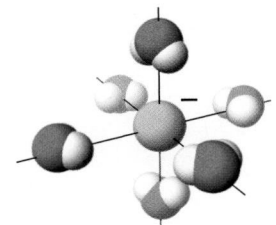

water surrounding
an anion

**FIGURE 12.2 Ion–dipole interactions.** When an ionic compound such as NaCl is placed in water, the polar water molecules surround the cations and anions.

on the product of their charges divided by the square of the distance between them (Section 2.7). Therefore, when a polar molecule encounters an ion, the attractive forces depend on three factors:

- The distance between the ion and the dipole. The closer they are, the stronger the attraction.
- The charge on the ion. The higher the ion charge, the stronger the attraction.
- The magnitude of the dipole. The greater the magnitude of the dipole, the stronger the attraction.

The formation of hydrated ions in aqueous solution is one of the most important examples of the interaction between an ion and a polar molecule (Figure 12.2). The enthalpy change associated with the hydration of ions—which is generally called the *enthalpy of solvation* or, for ions in water, the *enthalpy of hydration*—is substantial. The solvation enthalpy for an individual ion cannot be measured directly, but values can be estimated. For example, the hydration of sodium ions is described by the following reaction:

$$Na^+(g) + water \rightarrow Na^+(aq) \qquad \Delta_{hydration}H° = -405 \text{ kJ/mol}$$

The enthalpy of hydration depends on the charge of the ion and on $1/d$, where $d$ is the distance between the center of the ion and the oppositely charged "pole" of the dipole.

The effect of ion radius is illustrated by the enthalpies of hydration of the alkali metal cations in Table 12.1, and the effects of radius *and* charge by $\Delta_{hydration}H°$ for $Mg^{2+}$, $Li^+$, and $K^+$ (Figure 12.3). It is interesting to compare these values with the enthalpy of hydration of the $H^+$ ion, estimated to be −1090 kJ/mol. This extraordinarily large value is due to the tiny size of the $H^+$ ion.

## EXAMPLE 12.1    Hydration Energy

**Problem** Explain why the enthalpy of hydration of $Na^+$ (−405 kJ/mol) is more exothermic than that of $Cs^+$ (−263 kJ/mol), whereas that of $Mg^{2+}$ is much more exothermic (−1922 kJ/mol) than that of either $Na^+$ or $Cs^+$.

**What Do You Know?** You know the ion charges and their sizes (◄ Figure 7.12): $Na^+ = 98$ pm, $Cs^+ = 165$ pm, and $Mg^{2+} = 79$ pm.

**Strategy** The energy associated with ion–dipole attractions depends directly on the size of the ion charge and the magnitude of the dipole, and inversely on the distance between them. Here the water dipole is a constant factor, so the answer depends on ion size and charge.

**Solution** From the ion sizes, we can predict that the distances between the center of the positive charge of the ion and the water dipole will vary in this order: $Mg^{2+} < Na^+ < Cs^+$. The hydration energy varies in the reverse order (with the hydration energy of $Mg^{2+}$ being the most negative value). Notice also that $Mg^{2+}$ has a 2+ charge, whereas the other ions are 1+. The greater charge on $Mg^{2+}$ leads to a much greater force of ion–dipole attraction than for the other two ions, which have only a 1+ charge. As a result, the hydration energy for $Mg^{2+}$ is much more negative than for the other two ions.

● **Coulomb's Law** The force of attraction between oppositely charged particles depends directly on the product of their charges and inversely on the square of the distance ($d$) between the ions ($1/d^2$) (◄ Equation 2.3, page 76). The energy of the attraction is also proportional to the charge product, but it is inversely proportional to the distance between them ($1/d$).

**FIGURE 12.3 Enthalpy of hydration.** The energy evolved when an ion is hydrated depends on the dipole moment of water, the ion charge, and the distance $d$ between centers of the ion and the polar water molecule. The distance $d$ increases as ion size increases.

K$^+$, $r$ = 133 pm
$\Delta H$ = −321 kJ/mol

Li$^+$, $r$ = 78 pm
$\Delta H$ = −515 kJ/mol

Mg$^{2+}$, $r$ = 79 pm
$\Delta H$ = −1922 kJ/mol

Increasing force of attraction; more exothermic enthalpy of hydration

**Thinking about Your Answer** The charge difference between Mg$^{2+}$ and the other ions has a much greater effect than the size difference. The values for hydration energies for the three ions are Mg$^{2+}$(aq) = −1922 kJ/mol (from Table 12.1), Na$^+$(aq) = −405 kJ/mol, and Cs$^+$(aq) = −263 kJ/mol.

**Check Your Understanding**

Which should have the more negative hydration energy, F$^-$ or Cl$^-$? Explain briefly.

**REVIEW & CHECK FOR SECTION 12.2**

Which should have the more negative enthalpy of hydration?

(a)  MgCl$_2$                (b)  AlCl$_3$

## 12.3 Interactions between Molecules with a Dipole

### Dipole–Dipole Forces

When a polar molecule encounters another polar molecule, of the same or a different kind, the positive end of one molecule is attracted to the negative end of the other polar molecule. This is called a **dipole-dipole interaction**.

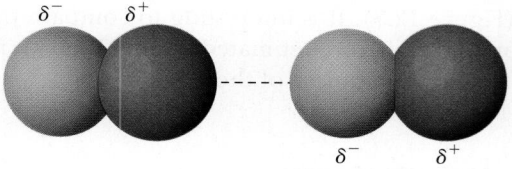

For polar molecules, dipole–dipole attractions influence, among other things, the evaporation of a liquid and the condensation of a gas (Figure 12.4). An energy change occurs in both processes. Evaporation requires the input of energy, specifically the enthalpy of vaporization ($\Delta_{vap}H°$) [see Sections 5.3 and 12.6]. The value for the enthalpy of vaporization has a positive sign, indicating that evaporation is an endothermic process. The enthalpy change for the condensation process—the reverse of evaporation—has a negative value.

The greater the forces of attraction between molecules in a liquid, the greater the energy that must be supplied to separate them. Thus, we expect polar compounds to have a higher value for their enthalpy of vaporization than nonpolar compounds with similar molar masses. For example, notice in Table 12.2 that $\Delta_{vap}H°$ for polar molecules is greater than for nonpolar molecules of approximately the same size and mass.

The boiling point of a liquid also depends on intermolecular forces of attraction. As the temperature of a substance is raised, its molecules gain kinetic energy. Eventually, when the boiling point is reached, the molecules have sufficient kinetic

## Hydrated Salts

Solid salts with waters of hydration are common. The formulas of these compounds are given by appending a specific number of water molecules to the end of the formula, as in $BaCl_2 \cdot 2\ H_2O$. Sometimes, the water molecules simply fill in empty spaces in a crystalline lattice, but often the cation in these salts is directly bound to water molecules. For example, the compound $CrCl_3 \cdot 6\ H_2O$ is better written as $[Cr(H_2O)_4Cl_2]Cl \cdot 2\ H_2O$. Four of the six water molecules are bound to the $Cr^{3+}$ ion by ion–dipole attractive forces; the remaining two water molecules are in the lattice. Common examples of hydrated salts are listed in the table.

| Compound | Common Name | Uses |
|---|---|---|
| $Na_2CO_3 \cdot 10\ H_2O$ | Washing soda | Water softener |
| $Na_2S_2O_3 \cdot 5\ H_2O$ | Hypo | Photography |
| $MgSO_4 \cdot 7\ H_2O$ | Epsom salt | Cathartic, dyeing and tanning |
| $CaSO_4 \cdot 2\ H_2O$ | Gypsum | Wallboard |
| $CuSO_4 \cdot 5\ H_2O$ | Blue vitriol | Biocide |

**Hydrated cobalt(II) chloride, $CoCl_2 \cdot 6\ H_2O$.** In the solid state, the compound is best described by the formula $[Co(H_2O)_4Cl_2] \cdot 2\ H_2O$. The cobalt(II) ion is surrounded by four water molecules and two chloride ions in an octahedral arrangement. In water, the ion is completely hydrated, now being surrounded by six water molecules. Cobalt(II) ions and water molecules interact by ion–dipole forces. This is an example of a coordination compound, a class of compounds discussed in detail in Chapter 22.

**FIGURE 12.4 Evaporation at the molecular level.** Energy must be supplied to separate molecules in the liquid state against intermolecular forces of attraction.

energy to escape the forces of attraction of their neighbors. For molecules of similar molar mass, the greater the polarity, the higher the temperature required for the liquid to boil. In Table 12.2, you see that the boiling point for polar ICl is greater than that for nonpolar $Br_2$, for example.

Intermolecular forces also influence solubility. A qualitative observation on solubility is that "like dissolves like." In other words, polar molecules are likely to dissolve in a polar solvent, and nonpolar molecules are likely to dissolve in a nonpolar solvent (Figure 12.5) (◄ Chapter 8). The converse is also true; that is, it is unlikely that polar molecules will dissolve in nonpolar solvents or that nonpolar molecules will dissolve in polar solvents.

For example, water and ethanol ($C_2H_5OH$) can be mixed in any ratio to give a homogeneous mixture. In contrast, water does not dissolve in gasoline to an appreciable extent. The difference in these two situations is that ethanol and water are

**Table 12.2 Molar Masses, Boiling Points, and $\Delta_{vap}H°$ of Nonpolar and Polar Substances**

| | Nonpolar | | | | Polar | | |
|---|---|---|---|---|---|---|---|
| | $M$ (g/mol) | BP (°C) | $\Delta_{vap}H°$ (kJ/mol) | | $M$ (g/mol) | BP (°C) | $\Delta_{vap}H°$ (kJ/mol) |
| $N_2$ | 28 | −196 | 5.57 | CO | 28 | −192 | 6.04 |
| $SiH_4$ | 32 | −112 | 12.10 | $PH_3$ | 34 | −88 | 14.06 |
| $GeH_4$ | 77 | −90 | 14.06 | $AsH_3$ | 78 | −62 | 16.69 |
| $Br_2$ | 160 | 59 | 29.96 | ICl | 162 | 97 | — |

polar molecules, whereas the hydrocarbon molecules in gasoline (e.g., octane, $C_8H_{18}$) are nonpolar. The water–ethanol interactions are strong enough that the energy expended in pushing water molecules apart to make room for ethanol molecules is compensated for by the energy of attraction between the two kinds of polar molecules. In contrast, water–hydrocarbon attractions are weak. The hydrocarbon molecules cannot disrupt the stronger water–water attractions.

## Hydrogen Bonding

Hydrogen fluoride, water, ammonia, and many other compounds with O—H and N—H bonds have exceptional properties, and we can see that by looking at the boiling points for hydrogen compounds of elements in Groups 4A through 7A in Figure 12.6. Generally, the boiling points of related compounds increase with molar mass, and this trend is seen in the boiling points of the hydrogen compounds of Group 4A elements, for example ($CH_4 < SiH_4 < GeH_4 < SnH_4$). The same effect is also operating for the heavier molecules of the hydrogen-containing compounds of Group 5A, 6A, and 7A elements. The boiling points of $NH_3$, $H_2O$, and HF, however, deviate significantly from what might be expected based on molar mass alone. If we extrapolate the curve for the boiling points of $H_2Te$, $H_2Se$, and $H_2S$, the boiling point of water is predicted to be around −90 °C. However, the boiling point of water is almost 200 °C higher than this value! Similarly, the boiling points of $NH_3$ and HF

(a) Ethylene glycol ($HOCH_2CH_2OH$), a polar compound used as antifreeze in automobiles, dissolves in water.

(b) Nonpolar motor oil (a hydrocarbon) dissolves in nonpolar solvents such as gasoline or $CCl_4$. It will not dissolve in a polar solvent such as water, however. Commercial spot removers use nonpolar solvents to dissolve oil and grease from fabrics.

**FIGURE 12.5** "Like dissolves like."

**FIGURE 12.6 The boiling points of some simple hydrogen compounds.** The effect of hydrogen bonding is apparent in the unusually high boiling points of $H_2O$, HF, and $NH_3$. (Also, notice that the boiling point of HCl is somewhat higher than expected based on the data for HBr and HI. It is apparent that some degree of hydrogen bonding also occurs in liquid HCl.)

are much higher than would be expected based on molar mass. Because the temperature at which a substance boils depends on the attractive forces between molecules, the extraordinarily high boiling points of $H_2O$, HF, and $NH_3$ indicate strong intermolecular attractions.

Why should $H_2O$, $NH_3$, and HF have such strong intermolecular forces? The answer starts with the electronegativities of N (3.0), O (3.5), and F (4.0), which are among the highest of all the elements, whereas the electronegativity of hydrogen is much lower (2.2). This large difference in electronegativity means that N—H, O—H, and F—H bonds are very polar. In bonds between H and N, O, or F, the more electronegative element takes on a significant negative charge (◀ Figure 8.11), and the hydrogen atom acquires a significant positive charge.

There is an unusually strong attraction between an electronegative atom with a lone pair of electrons (most often, an N, O, or F atom in another molecule or even in the same molecule) and the hydrogen atom of the N—H, O—H, or F—H bond. This type of interaction is known as a **hydrogen bond**. Hydrogen bonds are an extreme form of dipole–dipole interaction where one atom involved is always H and the other atom is highly electronegative, most often O, N, or F. A hydrogen bond can be represented as

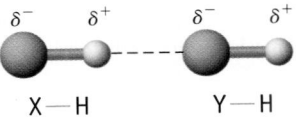

$$\delta^- \quad \delta^+ \qquad \delta^- \quad \delta^+$$
$$X—H \qquad\quad Y—H$$

The hydrogen atom becomes a bridge between the two electronegative atoms X and Y, and the dashed line represents the hydrogen bond. The most pronounced effects of hydrogen bonding occur where both X and Y are N, O, or F. Energies associated with most hydrogen bonds involving these elements are in the range of 5 to 30 kJ/mol.

### Types of Hydrogen Bonds [X—H - - - :Y]

| | | |
|---|---|---|
| N—H - - - :N— | O—H - - - :N— | F—H - - - :N— |
| N—H - - - :O— | O—H - - - :O— | F—H - - - :O— |
| N—H - - - :F— | O—H - - - :F— | F—H - - - :F— |

Hydrogen bonding has important implications for any property of a compound that is influenced by intermolecular forces of attraction. For example,

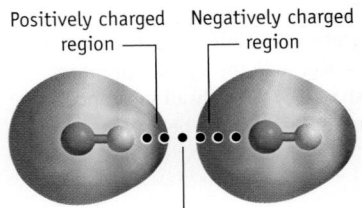

Positively charged region — Negatively charged region

Hydrogen bond

**Hydrogen bonding between HF molecules.** The partially negative F atom of one HF molecule interacts through hydrogen bonding with a neighboring HF molecule. (Red regions of the molecule are negatively charged, whereas blue regions are positively charged. For more on electrostatic potential surfaces, ◀ page 378.)

● **The Importance of H Atom Charge Density in Hydrogen Bonding** Not only are the bonds between H and O, N, and F significantly polar, but the H atom has an extraordinarily small radius. This means that the partial charge on the H atom is concentrated in a small volume; that is, it has a high charge density. The result is that it is strongly attractive to the negative charge on a neighboring molecule.

**FIGURE 12.7 Hydrogen bonding.** Two acetic acid molecules can interact through hydrogen bonds. This photo shows partly solid glacial acetic acid. Notice that the solid is denser than the liquid, a property shared by virtually all substances, the notable exception being water.

hydrogen bonding affects the structures of molecular solids. In solid acetic acid, $CH_3CO_2H$, for example, two molecules are joined to one another by hydrogen bonding (Figure 12.7).

### EXAMPLE 12.2    The Effect of Hydrogen Bonding

**Problem** Ethanol, $CH_3CH_2OH$, and dimethyl ether, $CH_3OCH_3$, have the same molecular formula but a different arrangement of atoms. Predict which of these compounds has the higher boiling point.

ethanol, $CH_3CH_2OH$      dimethyl ether, $CH_3OCH_3$

**What Do You Know?** You know the molecular structures for the two compounds and that the compound with the stronger intermolecular forces will have the higher boiling point.

**Strategy** Inspect the structure of each molecule to decide whether each is polar and, if polar, whether hydrogen bonding is possible.

**Solution** Although these two compounds have identical masses, they have different structures. Ethanol possesses a polar O—H group and so can participate in hydrogen bonding. Dimethyl ether is a polar molecule, and the O atom has a partial negative charge. However, no H atom is attached to the O atom. Thus, there is no opportunity for hydrogen bonding in dimethyl ether. We can predict, therefore, that intermolecular forces will be larger in ethanol than in dimethyl ether and that ethanol will have the higher boiling point.

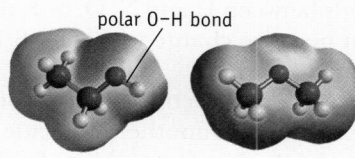

polar O—H bond

$$CH_3CH_2-\overset{..}{\underset{|}{O}}:\cdots H-\overset{..}{\underset{|}{O}}:$$
$$\phantom{CH_3CH_2-O:\cdots}H\phantom{-O:}CH_2CH_3$$

hydrogen bonding in ethanol, $CH_3CH_2OH$

**Think about Your Answer** According to the literature, ethanol boils at 78.3 °C, whereas dimethyl ether has a boiling point of −24.8 °C, more than 100 °C lower. Under similar conditions (room temperature and 1 atm pressure), dimethyl ether is a gas, whereas ethanol is a liquid.

**Check Your Understanding**

Using structural formulas, describe the hydrogen bonding between methanol ($CH_3OH$) molecules. What physical properties of methanol are likely to be affected by hydrogen bonding?

## Hydrogen Bonding and the Unusual Properties of Water

One of the most striking differences between our planet and others in our solar system is the presence of large amounts of water on Earth. Three fourths of the planet is covered by oceans; the polar regions are vast ice fields; and even soil and rocks hold large amounts of water. Although we tend to take water for granted, almost no other substance behaves in a similar manner. Water's unique features are a consequence of the ability of $H_2O$ molecules to cling tenaciously to one another by hydrogen bonding.

The unusually high intermolecular forces of attraction between water molecules are a result of the fact that each water molecule can participate in *four* hydrogen bonds. An individual water molecule has two polar O—H bonds and two lone pairs. Both hydrogen atoms are available to hydrogen bond to oxygen atoms in adjacent water molecules. In addition, the oxygen lone pairs can participate in hydrogen bonding to the hydrogen atoms in two other water molecules (Figure 12.8a).

**Earth from space.** Three quarters of the earth is covered by water, and vast amounts of water are locked in the polar ice caps. Many of the unique properties of water depend on the presence of hydrogen bonding in water.

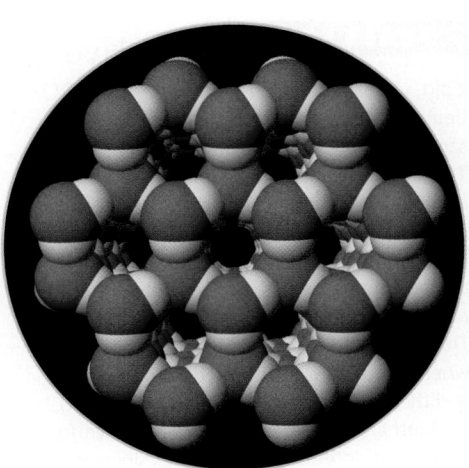

**(a)** Electrostatic potential surfaces for two water molecules shows the hydrogen bond involving the negatively charged O atom of one molecule and the positively charged H atom of a neighboring molecule.

**(b)** The oxygen atom of a water molecule attaches itself to two other water molecules by hydrogen bonds. Notice that the four groups that surround an oxygen atom are arranged as a distorted tetrahedron. Each oxygen atom is covalently bonded to two hydrogen atoms and hydrogen bonded to hydrogen atoms from two other molecules. The hydrogen bonds are longer than the covalent bonds.

**(c)** In ice, the structural unit shown in part (b) is repeated in the crystalline lattice. This computer-generated structure shows a small portion of the extensive lattice. Notice the six-member, hexagonal rings. The vertices of each hexagon are O atoms, and each side is composed of two oxygen atoms with a hydrogen atom in between. One of the oxygen atoms is covalently bonded to the hydrogen atom, and the other is attracted to it by a hydrogen bond.

**FIGURE 12.8 Hydrogen bonding in water and the structure of ice.**

The result, seen particularly in ice, is a tetrahedral arrangement for the hydrogen atoms around each oxygen, involving two covalently bonded hydrogen atoms and two hydrogen-bonded hydrogen atoms.

As a consequence of the regular arrangement of water molecules linked by hydrogen bonding, ice has an open-cage structure with lots of empty space (Figure 12.8c). The result is that ice has a density about 10% less than that of liquid water, which explains why ice floats. (In contrast, virtually all other solids sink in their liquid phase.) We can also see in this structure that the oxygen atoms are arranged at the corners of puckered, hexagonal rings. Snowflakes are always based on six-sided figures (◀ page 68), a reflection of this internal molecular structure of ice.

When ice melts at 0 °C, the regular structure imposed on the solid state by hydrogen bonding breaks down, and a relatively large increase in density occurs (Figure 12.9). Another surprising thing occurs when the temperature of liquid water is raised from 0 °C to 4 °C: The density of water increases. For almost every other substance known, density decreases as the temperature is raised. Once again, hydrogen bonding is the reason for water's seemingly odd behavior. At a temperature just above the melting point, some of the water molecules continue to cluster in ice-like arrangements, which require extra space. As the temperature is raised from 0 °C to 4 °C, the final vestiges of the ice structure disappear, and the volume contracts further, giving rise to the increase in density. Water's density reaches a maximum at about 4 °C. From this point, the density declines with increasing temperature in the normal fashion.

Because of the way that water's density changes as the temperature approaches the freezing point, lakes do not freeze from the bottom up in the winter. When lake water cools with the approach of winter, its density increases, the cooler water sinks, and the warmer water rises. This "turn over" process continues until all the water reaches 4 °C, the maximum density. (This is the way oxygen-rich water moves to the lake bottom to restore the oxygen used during the summer and nutrients are brought to the top layers of the lake.) As the temperature decreases further, the

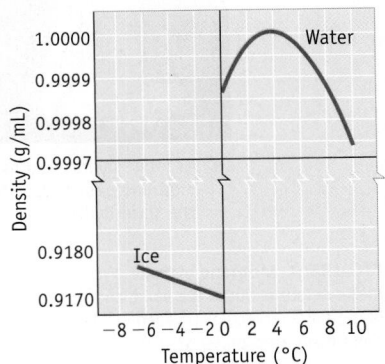

**FIGURE 12.9 The temperature dependence of the densities of ice and water.**

# Hydrogen Bonding & Methane Hydrates: Opportunities and Problems

Cold water under pressure begins to form complex solid structures at temperatures above 273 K. These are unstable networks of hydrogen-bonded water molecules with large, open cavities. If a small "guest" molecule of the right size is present, however, it can be trapped in the cavities, and the network does not collapse to form the usual ice structure. This phenomenon is most often observed when cold water is saturated with methane, and the result is methane hydrate (Figure A).

Methane hydrates have been known for years, but interest in them has increased because vast deposits of hydrate were recently discovered deep within sediments on the floor of the oceans. It is estimated that global methane hydrate deposits contain approximately $10^{13}$ tons of carbon, or about twice the combined amount in all known reserves of coal, oil, and natural gas. Methane hydrate is also an efficient energy storehouse; a cubic meter of methane hydrate releases about 160 cubic meters of methane gas.

If methane is to be captured from hydrates and used as a fuel, there are problems to be solved. One significant problem is how to bring commercially useful quantities to the surface from deep in the ocean. Yet another is the possibility of a large, uncontrolled release of methane. Methane is a very effective greenhouse gas, so the release of a significant quantity into the atmosphere could damage the earth's climate. (Indeed, some believe a massive release of methane from hydrates about 55 million years ago led to significant global warming.)

In May 2010 methane hydrates may have led to an environmental catastrophe. The Deepwater Horizon rig used for drilling for oil in very deep water in the Gulf of Mexico was destroyed by a fire triggered by a methane explosion. There is a strong suggestion that the ultimate cause may have been the explosive release of the gas from methane hydrates under the sea bed. The methane shot to the surface through the drilling pipe and was ignited. This then led to an uncontrolled leak of oil from the well, followed by attempts to shut it down. The first attempt to cap the well was to lower a 100-ton steel and concrete dome over the well, which would contain the oil and allow it to be pumped to the surface (Figure B). This was a failure because methane coming from the rupture formed a slush of methane hydrate. The "crystals" of hydrate were trapped in the dome, increased its buoyancy, and prevented it from being anchored to the sea floor.

© Chris Graythen/Getty Images

**FIGURE B A containment dome used to control the oil leak in the Gulf of Mexico, May, 2010.** The first containment dome that was tried did not work because methane hydrate prevented it from being anchored to the sea floor.

The realization that methane hydrates may be the cause of a significant accident will surely lead to reassessment of oil exploration in very deep water. But it may also renew interest in using more accessible methane hydrates as an energy source. For example, in Alaska's North Slope there are recoverable deposits of 2400 billion cubic meters of methane, roughly the equivalent of four years of U.S. natural gas production And there are extensive deposits in other places in the world. Indeed, the deepest oceans may be a better source of methane than of oil.

## Questions:

1. In a methane hydrate the methane molecule is trapped in a cage of water molecules. Describe the structure: (a) how many water molecules make up the cage, (b) how many hydrogen bonds are involved, and (c) how many faces does the cage have?

2. One cubic meter of methane hydrate has 164 m³ of $CH_4$ (at STP). If you burn the methane in 1.00 m³ of hydrate [to give $CO_2(g)$ and $H_2O(g)$], how much energy can be obtained?

**Answers to these questions are available in Appendix N**

## Reference:

A good article on methane hydrates is: E. Suess, G. Bohrmann, J. Greinert, and E. Lausch, *Scientific American*, November 1999, pp. 76–83.

Jim Pinkston and Laura Stern/U.S. Geological Survey/*Science News*/ 11/9/96

**(a)** Methane hydrate burns as methane gas escapes from the solid hydrate.

**(b)** Methane hydrate consists of a lattice of water molecules with methane molecules trapped in the cavity.

**FIGURE A Methane hydrate.** When a sample is brought to the surface from the depths of the ocean, the methane oozes out of the solid, and the gas readily burns. The structure of the solid methane hydrate consists of methane molecules trapped in a lattice of water molecules. The lattice shown here is a common structural unit of a more complex structure. Each point of the lattice shown here is an O atom of an $H_2O$ molecule. The edges consist of an O—H—O series of atoms connected by a hydrogen bond and covalent bond. (Other, more complex structural units are known.) Such structures are often called "clathrates."

colder water stays on the top of the lake, because water cooler than 4 °C is less dense than water at 4 °C. With further heat loss, ice can then begin to form on the surface, floating there and protecting the underlying water and aquatic life from further heat loss.

Extensive hydrogen bonding is also the origin of the extraordinarily high heat capacity of water. Although liquid water does not have the regular structure of ice, hydrogen bonding still occurs. When the temperature is raised, there must be a significant input of energy to disrupt the intermolecular forces and to raise the temperature even a small amount.

The high specific heat capacity of water is, in large part, why oceans and lakes have such an enormous effect on weather. In autumn, when the temperature of the air is lower than the temperature of the ocean or lake, water transfers energy as heat to the atmosphere, moderating the drop in air temperature. Furthermore, so much energy is available to be transferred for each degree drop in temperature that the decline in water temperature is gradual. For this reason, the temperature of the ocean or of a large lake is generally higher than the average air temperature until late in the autumn.

---

**REVIEW & CHECK FOR SECTION 12.3**

1.  In which of the following substances would hydrogen bonding be expected?

    (a)  $CH_4$        (b)  $CH_3OH$        (c)  $H_3COCH_3$        (d)  $H_2C{=}CH_2$

2.  Which compound has the strongest intermolecular forces?

    (a)  $H_2O$        (b)  $H_2S$        (c)  $H_2Se$        (d)  $H_2Te$

---

## 12.4 Intermolecular Forces Involving Nonpolar Molecules

Many important molecules such as $O_2$, $N_2$, and the halogens are not polar. Why, then, does $O_2$ dissolve in polar water? Why can the $N_2$ of the atmosphere be liquefied? Some intermolecular forces must be acting between $O_2$ and water and between $N_2$ molecules, but what is their nature?

### Dipole-Induced Dipole Forces

Polar molecules such as water can induce, or create, a dipole in molecules that do not have a permanent dipole. To see how this can happen, picture a polar water molecule approaching a nonpolar molecule such as $O_2$ (Figure 12.10). The electron cloud of an isolated (gaseous) $O_2$ molecule is symmetrically distributed between the two oxygen atoms. As the negative end of the polar $H_2O$ molecule approaches, however, the $O_2$ electron cloud becomes distorted. In this process, the $O_2$ molecule itself becomes polar; that is, a dipole is *induced* in the otherwise nonpolar $O_2$ molecule. The result is that $H_2O$ and $O_2$ molecules are now attracted to one another, albeit only weakly. Oxygen can dissolve in water because a force of attraction exists between water's permanent dipole and the induced dipole in $O_2$. Chemists refer to such interactions as **dipole-induced dipole interactions**.

The process of inducing a dipole is called **polarization**, and the degree to which the electron cloud of an atom or a molecule can be distorted depends on the **polarizability** of that atom or molecule. The electron cloud of an atom or molecule with a large, extended electron cloud such as $I_2$ can be polarized more readily than the electron cloud in a much smaller atom or molecule, such as He or $H_2$, in which the valence electrons are close to the nucleus and more tightly held. In general, for an analogous series of substances, say the halogens or alkanes (such as $CH_4$, $C_2H_6$, $C_3H_8$, and so on), the higher the molar mass, the greater the polarizability of the molecule.

**(a)** A polar molecule such as water can induce a dipole in nonpolar $O_2$ by distorting the molecule's electron cloud.

The dipole of water induces a dipole in $O_2$ by distorting the $O_2$ electron cloud.

**(b)** Nonpolar $I_2$ dissolves in polar ethanol ($C_2H_5OH$). The intermolecular force involved is a dipole-induced dipole force.

Polar ethanol ($C_2H_5OH$) induces a dipole in nonpolar $I_2$.

© Cengage Learning/Charles D. Winters

© Cengage Learning/Charles D. Winters

**FIGURE 12.10 Dipole-induced dipole interaction.**

The solubilities of common gases in water illustrate the effect of interactions between a dipole and an induced dipole. In Table 12.3, you see a trend to higher solubility with increasing mass of the nonpolar gas. As the molar mass of the gas increases, the polarizability of the electron cloud increases and the strength of the dipole-induced dipole interaction increases.

## London Dispersion Forces: Induced Dipole-Induced Dipole Forces

Iodine, $I_2$, is a solid and not a gas around room temperature and pressure, illustrating that nonpolar molecules must also experience intermolecular forces. An indication of the magnitude of these forces is provided by the enthalpy of vaporization of the substance at its boiling point. The data in Table 12.4 suggest that these forces can range from very weak ($N_2$, $O_2$, and $CH_4$ with low enthalpies of vaporization and very low boiling points) to more substantial ($I_2$ and benzene).

To understand how two nonpolar molecules can attract each other, recall that the electrons in atoms or molecules are in a state of constant motion. When two atoms or nonpolar molecules approach each other, attractions or repulsions between their electrons and nuclei can lead to distortions in their electron clouds (Figure 12.11).

**Table 12.3 The Solubility of Some Gases in Water\***

|  | Molar Mass (g/mol) | Solubility at 20 °C (g gas/100 g water)† |
|---|---|---|
| $H_2$ | 2.01 | 0.000160 |
| $N_2$ | 28.0 | 0.00190 |
| $O_2$ | 32.0 | 0.00434 |

\*Data taken from J. Dean: *Lange's Handbook of Chemistry*. 14th Ed., pp. 5.3–5.8, New York, McGraw-Hill, 1992.

†Measured under conditions where pressure of gas + pressure of water vapor = 760 mm Hg.

**Table 12.4 Enthalpies of Vaporization and Boiling Points of Some Nonpolar Substances**

|  | $\Delta_{vap}H°$ (kJ/mol) | Element/Compound BP (°C) |
|---|---|---|
| $N_2$ | 5.57 | −196 |
| $O_2$ | 6.82 | −183 |
| $CH_4$ (methane) | 8.2 | −161.5 |
| $Br_2$ | 29.96 | +58.8 |
| $C_6H_6$ (benzene) | 30.7 | +80.1 |
| $I_2$ | 41.95 | +185 |

# Hydrogen Bonding in Biochemistry

It is arguable that our world is what it is because of hydrogen bonding in water and in biochemical systems. Perhaps the most important occurrence is in DNA and RNA where the organic bases adenine, cytosine, guanine, and thymine (in DNA) or uracil (in RNA) are attached to sugar-phosphate chains (**Figure A**). The chains in DNA are joined by the pairing of bases, adenine with thymine and guanine with cytosine.

**Figure B** illustrates the hydrogen bonding between adenine and thymine. These models show that the molecules naturally fit together to form a six-sided ring, where two of the six sides involve hydrogen bonds. One side consists of a N $\cdots$ H—N grouping, and the other side is N—H $\cdots$ O. Here, the electrostatic potential surfaces show that the N atoms of adenine and the O atoms of thymine bear partial negative charges, and the H atoms of the N—H groups bear a positive charge. These charges and the geometry of the bases lead to these very specific interactions.

The fact that base pairing through hydrogen bonding leads to the joining of the sugar-phosphate chains of DNA, and to the double helical form of DNA, was first recognized by James Watson and Francis Crick on the basis of experimental work by Rosalind Franklin and Maurice Wilkins in the 1950s. Determination of the DNA structure was a key development in the molecular biology revolution in the last part of the 20th century. (See page 387 for more on these scientists.)

**FIGURE A** **Hydrogen bonding in DNA.** With the four bases in DNA, the usual pairings are adenine with thymine and guanine with cytosine. This pairing is promoted by hydrogen bonding.

**FIGURE B** **Hydrogen bonding between adenine and thymine.** Electrostatic potential surfaces depict the hydrogen bonding interactions between adenine and thymine. The polar N—H bond on one molecule can hydrogen bond to an electronegative N or O atom in a neighboring molecule.

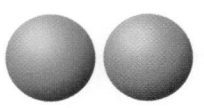

Two nonpolar atoms or molecules (depicted as having an electron cloud that has a time-averaged spherical shape).

Momentary attractions and repulsions between nuclei and electrons in neighboring molecules lead to induced dipoles.

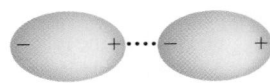

Correlation of the electron motions between the two atoms or molecules (which are now polar) leads to a lower energy and stabilizes the system.

Br₂        I₂

**FIGURE 12.11** **Induced dipole-induced dipole interactions or London dispersion forces.** Momentary attractions and repulsions between nuclei and electrons create induced dipoles and lead to a net stabilization due to attractive forces. Nonpolar $Br_2$ and $I_2$ both exemplify such forces. They are a liquid and a solid, respectively, indicating that there are forces between the molecules sufficient to cause them to be in a condensed phase.

That is, dipoles can be induced momentarily in neighboring atoms or molecules, and these *induced* dipoles lead to intermolecular attractions. The intermolecular force of attraction in liquids and solids composed of nonpolar molecules is an **induced dipole-induced dipole force**. Chemists often call them **London dispersion forces**. *Dispersion forces actually arise between all molecules, both nonpolar and polar, but dispersion forces are the only intermolecular forces between nonpolar molecules.*

## EXAMPLE 12.3    Intermolecular Forces

**Problem**  Suppose you have a mixture of solid iodine, $I_2$, and the liquids water and carbon tetrachloride ($CCl_4$). What intermolecular forces exist between each possible pair of compounds?

**What Do You Know?**  Iodine, $I_2$, is a nonpolar molecule composed of large iodine atoms. It has an extensive electron cloud and is polarizable. $CCl_4$ is a symmetrical tetrahedral molecule and is not polar. Polar $H_2O$ could be involved in hydrogen bonding with other water molecules or with other molecules with highly polar groups.

**Strategy**  You know whether each substance is polar or nonpolar so you need only to determine the types of intermolecular forces that can exist between the different pairs.

**Solution**  Nonpolar iodine, $I_2$, is easily polarized, and iodine can interact with polar water molecules by dipole-induced dipole forces. Nonpolar carbon tetrachloride can interact with nonpolar iodine only by dispersion forces. Water and $CCl_4$ could interact by dipole-induced dipole forces.

**Think about Your Answer**  The photos here show the result of mixing these three compounds. Iodine does dissolve to a small extent in water to give a brown solution. When this brown solution is added to a test tube containing $CCl_4$, the liquid layers do not mix. (Polar water does not dissolve in nonpolar $CCl_4$.) (Notice the more dense $CCl_4$ layer [$d = 1.58$ g/mL] is underneath the less dense water layer.) When the test tube is shaken, nonpolar $I_2$ is extracted into nonpolar $CCl_4$, as evidenced by the disappearance of the color of $I_2$ in the water layer (top) and the appearance of the purple $I_2$ color in the $CCl_4$ layer (bottom).

Nonpolar $I_2$
Polar $H_2O$

Nonpolar $CCl_4$

Shake the test tube

Polar $H_2O$

Nonpolar $CCl_4$ and $I_2$

© Cengage Learning/Charles D. Winters

© Cengage Learning/Charles D. Winters

### Check Your Understanding

You mix water, $CCl_4$, and hexane ($CH_3CH_2CH_2CH_2CH_2CH_3$). What type of intermolecular forces can exist between each pair of these compounds?

---

### REVIEW & CHECK FOR SECTION 12.4

1.  In which of the following solids are the component particles attracted to each other only by induced dipole-induced dipole forces?

    (a)  ice

    (b)  solid $NH_3$ at low temperature

    (c)  NaCl

    (d)  $I_2$

2.  Which of the following compounds has the largest intermolecular forces?

    (a)  pentane, $C_5H_{12}$

    (b)  hexane, $C_6H_{14}$

    (c)  heptane, $C_7H_{16}$

    (d)  octane, $C_8H_{18}$

**Table 12.5  Summary of Intermolecular Forces (in descending order of strength)**

| Type of Interaction | Factors Responsible for Interaction | Example |
|---|---|---|
| Ion–dipole | Ion charge, magnitude of dipole | $Na^+ \ldots H_2O$ |
| Hydrogen bonding, X—H . . . :Y | Very polar X—H bond and atom Y with lone pair of electrons (where X and Y = F, N, O). Typical energy = 20 kJ/mol. | $H_2O \ldots H_2O$ |
| Dipole–dipole . . . $(CH_3)_2O$ | Dipole moment (depends on electronegativities and molecular structure). Typical energy = 5–20 kJ/mol. | $(CH_3)_2O \ldots (CH_3)_2O$ |
| Dipole-induced dipole | Dipole moment of polar molecule and polarizability of nonpolar molecule. Typical energy <2 kJ/mol. | $H_2O \ldots I_2$ |
| Induced dipole-induced dipole (London dispersion forces) | Polarizability | $I_2 \ldots I_2$ |

## 12.5  A Summary of van der Waals Intermolecular Forces

Van der Waals intermolecular forces involve molecules that are polar or those in which polarity can be induced (Table 12.5). It is important to recognize that

- several types of intermolecular forces contribute to the overall ability of a molecule (Figure 12.12) to interact with another of the same or different kind.
- induced dipole-induced dipole forces can be quite substantial, even in polar molecules (Figure 12.12).

### EXAMPLE 12.4   Intermolecular Forces

**Problem** Decide which are the most important intermolecular forces between each of the following and compare the strength of the interactions: (a) between molecules in liquid methane, $CH_4$; (b) between molecules of water and methanol ($CH_3OH$) in a mixture of these species; and (c) between molecules of bromine and water in a mixture of these compounds.

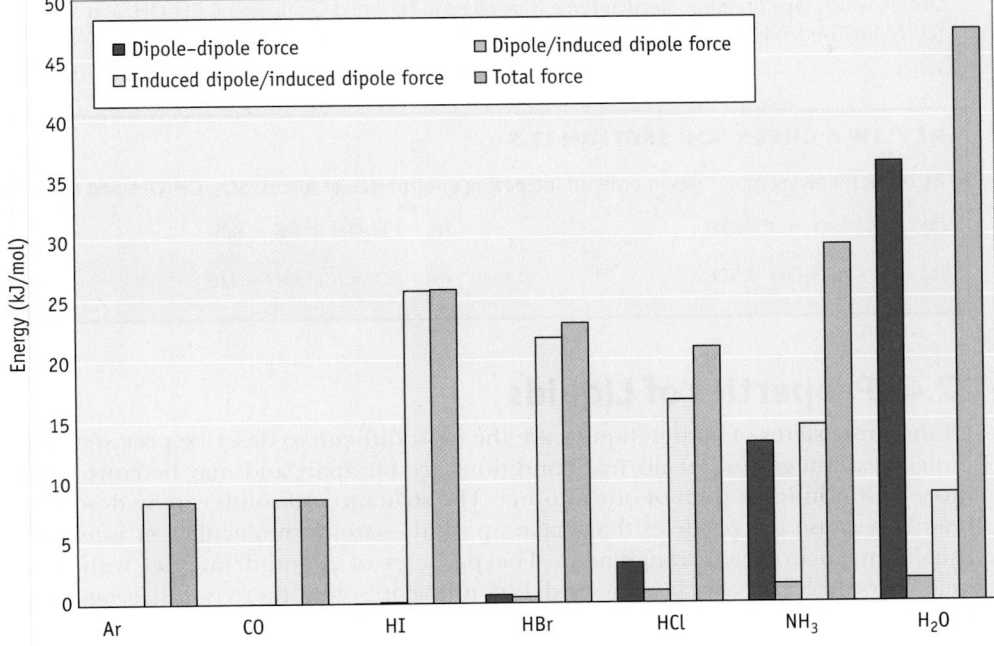

**FIGURE 12.12** Energies associated with intermolecular forces.

Hydrogen bonding involving methanol ($CH_3OH$) and water.

**What Do You Know?** Methane, $CH_4$, is a symmetrical, tetrahedral molecule and so is not polar. Both water and methanol are polar, and both have —OH groups that can be involved in hydrogen bonding. Bromine, $Br_2$, is nonpolar, but it is a large molecule and has an extensive, polarizable electron cloud.

**Strategy** Determine the type of interaction possible between pairs of molecules based on the structure and characteristics of each species. To evaluate their relative importance, consult Table 12.5 on relative strengths of interactions.

**Solution**

(a)  Methane is not polar. Therefore, the only way methane molecules can interact with one another is through induced dipole-induced dipole forces (dispersion forces).

(b)  Both water and methanol are polar, and both have an O—H bond. They therefore interact through the special dipole–dipole force called hydrogen bonding as well as dispersion forces.

$$\delta^+H \quad \overset{\delta^-}{O}\cdots\overset{\delta^+}{H}-\overset{\delta^-}{O} \quad \text{and} \quad \delta^+H \quad \overset{\delta^-}{O}\cdots\overset{\delta^+}{H}-\overset{\delta^-}{O}$$
$$\underset{\delta^+H}{\big|} \qquad \underset{CH_3}{\big|} \qquad\qquad \underset{H_3C}{\big|} \qquad \underset{H^{\delta^+}}{\big|}$$

(c)  Nonpolar molecules of bromine, $Br_2$, and polar water molecules interact through dipole-induced dipole forces (and dispersion forces). (This is similar to the $I_2$–ethanol interaction in Figure 12.10.)

In order of increasing strength, the likely order of interactions is

liquid $CH_4 < H_2O$ and $Br_2 < H_2O$ and $CH_3OH$

**Think about Your Answer** The fact that $CH_4$ is a liquid only at very low temperatures suggests it has the weakest attractive forces. We would expect the highest forces of attraction to be those involving hydrogen bonding. Thus, the strongest interaction is expected to be between $H_2O$ and $CH_3OH$, whereas the weakest interaction occurs between two nonpolar molecules of $CH_4$.

**Check Your Understanding**

Decide which type of intermolecular force is involved in (a) liquid $O_2$; (b) liquid $CH_3OH$; and (c) $N_2$ dissolved in $H_2O$. Place the interactions in order of increasing strength.

---

**REVIEW & CHECK FOR SECTION 12.5**

Rank the following molecules in order of increasing intermolecular forces: $SO_2$, $CH_3OH$, and He.

(a)  He $< SO_2 < CH_3OH$

(b)  He $< CH_3OH < SO_2$

(c)  $CH_3OH <$ He $< SO_2$

(d)  $SO_2 < CH_3OH <$ He

---

# 12.6  Properties of Liquids

Of the three states of matter, liquids are the most difficult to describe precisely. The molecules in a gas under normal conditions are far apart and may be considered more or less independent of one another. The structures of solids can be described readily because the particles that make up solids—atoms, molecules, or ions—are usually in an orderly arrangement. The particles of a liquid interact with their neighbors, like the particles in a solid, but, unlike in solids, there is little long-range order.

In spite of the difficulty in describing liquids, we can still consider the behavior of liquids at the molecular level. Here we want to look further at the process of va-

## CASE STUDY

# A Pet Food Catastrophe

In early 2007 pet owners all over the United States reported pets becoming seriously ill or dying from eating apparently adulterated food. Dogs and cats developed symptoms of kidney failure, which included loss of appetite, vomiting, extreme thirst, and lethargy. Many ultimately died. Round, greenish-brown kidney stones were also found to be clogging the kidneys of stricken pets. This was mysterious at first, but, within two months, chemists and toxicologists traced the ailments to two compounds in the pet food: melamine and cyanuric acid.

Melamine          Cyanuric acid

Melamine is used to make plastics and fertilizers. It is not approved for food use. Cyanuric acid is used to stabilize chlorine in swimming pools and to sanitize food processing equipment. The acid is sometimes formed as a by-product in the manufacture of melamine, so melamine samples can be contaminated with cyanuric acid.

But why was melamine in pet food in the first place? A U.S. manufacturer of pet food, which also supplied other companies that in turn distributed the food under their brand names, had purchased wheat gluten from a supplier in China. Wheat gluten is a concentrated vegetable protein used as a thickener and binder in pet food. The speculation is that the Chinese supplier had added melamine to the wheat gluten to raise the apparent nitrogen content. When products are tested for protein content, any nitrogen found is assumed to come from protein. Adding melamine is an inexpensive way to deceive

the buyer into thinking that the product contains a higher percentage of protein.

Melamine and cyanuric acid by themselves are not toxic, but when they are present together they are. The reason is hydrogen bonding! Mixing melamine and cyanuric acid in water produces insoluble crystals of melamine cyanurate.

The structure above shows only the hydrogen bonding between two molecules. How-

ever, additional hydrogen bonding to other molecules is possible, and the result is further aggregation of cyanuric acid and melamine to form an insoluble material.

The behavior of the hydrogen-bonded complex depends on pH. In the stomach, a very acidic medium with a low pH, hydrogen bonding does not occur between these compounds, and the compounds are soluble. The body seeks to get rid of these chemicals through the kidneys, however, and there the compounds encounter a near neutral pH. Hydrogen bonding can then occur, and the molecules aggregate to form solid melamine cyanurate.

The adulteration of food with melamine was not limited to the pet food industry. In 2008, a year after the pet food adulteration scandal, melamine was found in milk products including infant formula. Several thousand babies in China became ill, having suffered acute kidney failure, and several fatalities resulted. These babies had been fed formula milk contaminated with melamine.

**Questions:**
1. Calculate the weight percent of nitrogen in melamine and cyanuric acid and compare this value to the average percent of nitrogen in protein (14%).
2. An infant formula was found to have 0.14 ppm melamine. (ppm stands for parts per million. This means, for example, there is 1 g of a substance per million grams of the product.) What mass of melamine is there in a package of infant formula with a mass of 454 g (one pound)?

**Answers to these questions are available in Appendix N.**

---

porization, at the vapor pressure of liquids, at their boiling points and critical properties, and at surface tension, capillary action, and viscosity.

## Vaporization and Condensation

**Vaporization** or evaporation is the process in which a substance in the liquid state becomes a gas. In this process, molecules escape from the liquid surface and enter the gaseous state.

To understand evaporation, we have to look at molecular energies. Molecules in a liquid have a range of energies (Figure 12.13) that resembles the distribution of energies for molecules of a gas (◄ Figure 11.14). As with gases, the average energy for molecules in a liquid depends only on temperature: The higher the

**FIGURE 12.13** **The distribution of energy among molecules in a liquid sample.** $T_2$ is a higher temperature than $T_1$, and at the higher temperature, there are more molecules with an energy greater than E.

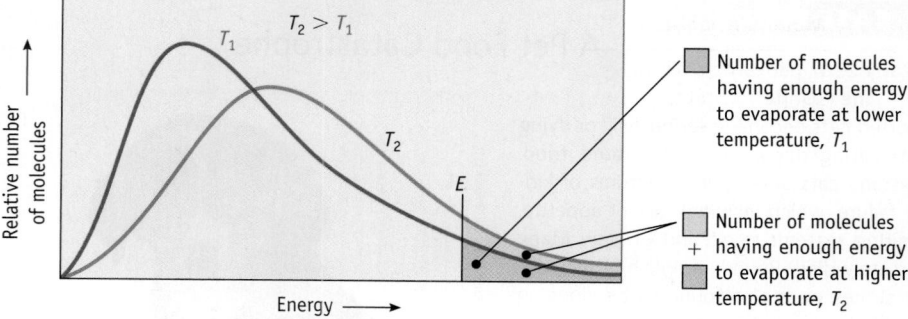

temperature, the higher the average energy and the greater the relative number of molecules with high kinetic energy. In a sample of a liquid, at least a few molecules have more kinetic energy than the potential energy of the intermolecular attractive forces holding the liquid molecules to one another. If these high-energy molecules are at the surface of the liquid and if they are moving in the right direction, they can break free of their neighbors and enter the gas phase (Figure 12.14).

Vaporization is an endothermic process because energy is required to overcome the intermolecular forces of attraction holding the molecules together. The energy required to vaporize a sample is often given as the standard **molar enthalpy of vaporization, $\Delta_{vap}H°$** (in units of kilojoules per mole; see Tables 12.4 and 12.6 and Figure 12.4).

$$liquid \xrightarrow[\substack{\text{energy absorbed} \\ \text{by liquid}}]{\text{vaporization}} vapor \qquad \Delta_{vap}H° = \text{molar enthalpy of vaporization}$$

A molecule in the gas phase can transfer some of its kinetic energy by colliding with slower gaseous molecules and solid objects. If this molecule loses sufficient energy and comes in contact with the surface of the liquid, it can reenter the liquid phase in the process called **condensation**.

$$vapor \xrightarrow[\substack{\text{energy released} \\ \text{by vapor}}]{\text{condensation}} liquid \qquad -\Delta_{vap}H° = \text{molar enthalpy of condensation}$$

Condensation is the reverse of vaporization and so is an exothermic process. Energy is transferred to the surroundings. *The enthalpy change for condensation is equal but opposite in sign to the enthalpy of vaporization.* For example, the enthalpy change for the vaporization of 1.00 mol of water at 100 °C is +40.7 kJ. On condensing 1.00 mol of water vapor to liquid water at 100 °C, the enthalpy change is −40.7 kJ.

In the discussion of intermolecular forces, we pointed out the relationship between the $\Delta_{vap}H°$ values for various substances and the temperatures at which they

**FIGURE 12.14** **Evaporation.** Some molecules at the surface of a liquid have enough energy to escape the attractions of their neighbors and enter the gaseous state. At the same time, some molecules in the gaseous state can reenter the liquid.

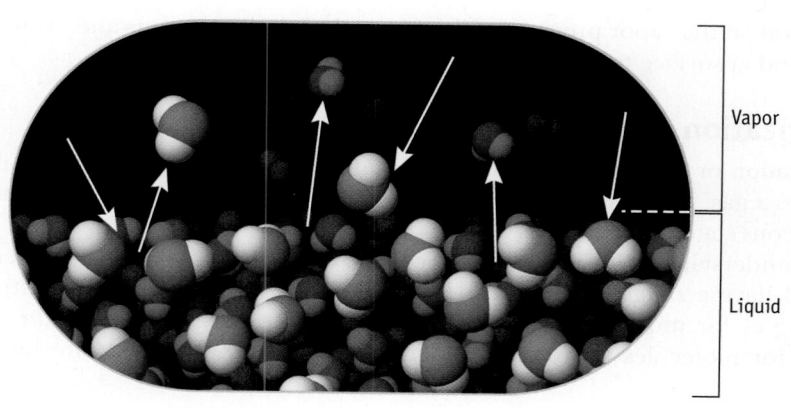

**Table 12.6  Molar Enthalpies of Vaporization and Boiling Points for Common Substances***

| Compound | Molar Mass (g/mol) | $\Delta_{vap}H°$ (kJ/mol)† | Boiling Point (°C) (Vapor Pressure = 760 mm Hg) |
|---|---|---|---|
| *Polar Compounds* | | | |
| HF | 20.0 | 25.2 | 19.7 |
| HCl | 36.5 | 16.2 | −84.8 |
| HBr | 80.9 | 19.3 | −66.4 |
| HI | 127.9 | 19.8 | −35.6 |
| $NH_3$ | 17.0 | 23.3 | −33.3 |
| $H_2O$ | 18.0 | 40.7 | 100.0 |
| $SO_2$ | 64.1 | 24.9 | −10.0 |
| *Nonpolar Compounds* | | | |
| $CH_4$ (methane) | 16.0 | 8.2 | −161.5 |
| $C_2H_6$ (ethane) | 30.1 | 14.7 | −88.6 |
| $C_3H_8$ (propane) | 44.1 | 19.0 | −42.1 |
| $C_4H_{10}$ (butane) | 58.1 | 22.4 | −0.5 |
| *Monatomic Elements* | | | |
| He | 4.0 | 0.08 | −268.9 |
| Ne | 20.2 | 1.7 | −246.1 |
| Ar | 39.9 | 6.4 | −185.9 |
| Xe | 131.3 | 12.6 | −108.0 |
| *Diatomic Elements* | | | |
| $H_2$ | 2.0 | 0.90 | −252.9 |
| $N_2$ | 28.0 | 5.6 | −195.8 |
| $O_2$ | 32.0 | 6.8 | −183.0 |
| $F_2$ | 38.0 | 6.6 | −188.1 |
| $Cl_2$ | 70.9 | 20.4 | −34.0 |
| $Br_2$ | 159.8 | 30.0 | 58.8 |

*Data taken from D. R. Lide: *Basic Laboratory and Industrial Chemicals,* Boca Raton, FL, CRC Press, 1993.
†$\Delta_{vap}H°$ is measured at the normal boiling point of the liquid.

boil (Table 12.6). Both properties reflect the attractive forces between particles in the liquid. The boiling points of nonpolar liquids (e.g., the hydrocarbons, atmospheric gases, and the halogens) increase with increasing atomic or molecular mass, a reflection of increased intermolecular dispersion forces. The alkanes (such as methane) listed in Table 12.6 show this trend clearly. Similarly, the boiling points and enthalpies of vaporization of the heavier hydrogen halides (HX, where X = Cl, Br, and I) increase with increasing molecular mass. For these molecules, dispersion forces and ordinary dipole–dipole forces account for their intermolecular attractions (Figure 12.12). Because dispersion forces become increasingly important with increasing mass, the enthalpies of vaporization and the boiling points are in the order HCl < HBr < HI. Among the hydrogen halides HF is the exception; the high enthalpy of vaporization and boiling point are a direct result of extensive hydrogen bonding.

**⌁WL  INTERACTIVE EXAMPLE 12.5**  Enthalpy of Vaporization

**Problem**  You put 925 mL of water (about 4 cupsful) in a pan at 100 °C, and the water slowly evaporates. How much energy is transferred as heat to vaporize all the water?

**What Do You Know?**  You know the volume of water and wish to know the energy required for evaporation. Three pieces of information are needed to solve this problem:

1.  $\Delta_{vap}H°$ for water = +40.7 kJ/mol at 100 °C.

2.  Density of water at 100 °C = 0.958 g/cm³.

3.  Molar mass of water = 18.02 g/mol.

**Strategy Map 12.5**

**PROBLEM**
Calculate the **energy** required to **evaporate** water sample.

↓

**DATA/INFORMATION**
• Enthalpy of vaporization at boiling point
• Volume of water

**STEP 1.** Use **density** and **molar mass** to convert **volume** of water to **amount** (mol).

**Amount** of sample

**STEP 2.** Multiply **amount** of sample by **molar enthalpy.**

**Energy** required (kJ) to evaporate sample at boiling point

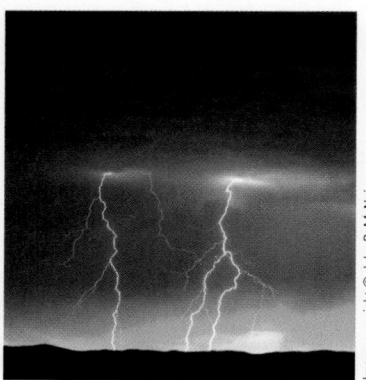

**FIGURE 12.15 Rainstorms release an enormous quantity of energy.** When water vapor condenses, energy is transferred to the surroundings. The enthalpy of condensation of water is large, so a large quantity of energy is released in a rainstorm.

**Strategy** $\Delta_{vap}H°$ has units of kilojoules per mole, so you first must find the mass of water and then the amount. Finally, use the enthalpy of vaporization (in kJ/mol) to calculate the energy required as heat.

**Solution** Using the density of water at this temperature, we find that 925 mL of water is equivalent to 886 g, and this mass is in turn equivalent to 49.2 mol of water.

$$925 \text{ mL} \left( \frac{0.958 \text{ g}}{1 \text{ mL}} \right) \left( \frac{1 \text{ mol}}{18.02 \text{ g}} \right) = 49.2 \text{ mol H}_2\text{O}$$

Therefore, the amount of energy required is

$$49.2 \text{ mol H}_2\text{O} \left( \frac{40.7 \text{ kJ}}{\text{mol}} \right) = 2.00 \times 10^3 \text{ kJ}$$

**Think about Your Answer** 2000 kJ is equivalent to the energy obtained by burning about 60 g of carbon.

**Check Your Understanding**

The molar enthalpy of vaporization of methanol, $CH_3OH$, is 35.2 kJ/mol at 64.6 °C. How much energy is required to evaporate 1.00 kg of methanol at 64.6 °C?

Liquid water is an exceptional substance; an enormous amount of energy as heat is required to convert liquid water to water vapor. This fact is important to your own physical well-being. When you exercise vigorously, your body responds by sweating. Energy from your body is transferred to sweat in the process of evaporation, and your body is cooled.

Enthalpies of vaporization and condensation of water also play a role in weather (Figure 12.15). For example, if enough water condenses from the air to fall as an inch of rain on an acre of ground, the energy released exceeds $2.0 \times 10^8$ kJ! This is equivalent to about 50 tons of exploded dynamite, the energy released by a small bomb.

## Vapor Pressure

If you put some water in an open beaker, it will eventually evaporate completely. Air movement and gas diffusion remove the water vapor from the vicinity of the liquid surface, so many water molecules are not able to return to the liquid.

If you put water in a sealed flask (Figure 12.16), however, the water vapor cannot escape, and some will recondense to form liquid water. Eventually, the masses of liquid and vapor in the flask remain constant. This is another example of a **dynamic equilibrium** (◀ page 116).

$$\text{liquid} \rightleftharpoons \text{vapor}$$

**FIGURE 12.16 Vapor pressure.** A volatile liquid is placed in an evacuated flask *(left)*. At the beginning, no molecules of the liquid are in the vapor phase. After a short time, however, some of the liquid evaporates, and the molecules now in the vapor phase exert a pressure. The pressure of the vapor measured when the liquid and the vapor are in equilibrium is called the *equilibrium vapor pressure (right)*.

**FIGURE 12.17** Vapor pressure curves for diethyl ether [$(C_2H_5)_2O$], ethanol ($C_2H_5OH$), and water. Each curve represents conditions of $T$ and $P$ at which the two phases, liquid and vapor, are in equilibrium. These compounds exist as liquids for temperatures and pressures to the left of the curve and as gases under conditions to the right of the curve.

Molecules still move continuously from the liquid phase to the vapor phase and from the vapor phase back to the liquid phase. At equilibrium, the rate at which molecules move from liquid to vapor is the same as the rate at which they move from vapor to liquid; thus, there is no net change in the masses of the two phases.

When a liquid–vapor equilibrium has been established, the equilibrium vapor pressure (often just called the vapor pressure) can be measured. The **equilibrium vapor pressure** of a substance is the pressure exerted by the vapor in equilibrium with the liquid phase. Conceptually, the vapor pressure of a liquid is a measure of the tendency of its molecules to escape from the liquid phase and enter the vapor phase at a given temperature. This tendency is referred to qualitatively as the **volatility** of the compound. The higher the equilibrium vapor pressure at a given temperature, the more volatile the substance.

As described previously (Figure 12.13), the distribution of molecular energies in the liquid phase is a function of temperature. At a higher temperature, more molecules have sufficient energy to escape the surface of the liquid. The equilibrium vapor pressure must, therefore, increase with temperature.

It is useful to represent vapor pressure as a function of temperature. Figure 12.17 shows the vapor pressure curves for several liquids as a function of temperature. *All points along the vapor pressure versus temperature curves represent conditions of pressure and temperature at which liquid and vapor are in equilibrium.* For example, at 60 °C the vapor pressure of water is 149 mm Hg. (Vapor pressures of water at various temperatures are given in Appendix G.) If water is placed in an evacuated flask that is maintained at 60 °C, liquid water will evaporate until the pressure exerted by the water vapor is 149 mm Hg (assuming enough water is in the flask so that some liquid remains when equilibrium is reached).

## ⊘WL   INTERACTIVE EXAMPLE 12.6   Using Vapor Pressure

**Problem**  You place 2.00 L of water in an open container in your dormitory room; the room has a amount of $4.25 \times 10^4$ L. You seal the room and wait for the water to evaporate. Will all of the water evaporate at 25 °C? (At 25 °C the density of water is 0.997 g/mL, and its vapor pressure is 23.8 mm Hg.)

**What Do You Know?**  You know the volume of water, the density of the water, the volume of the room, and the vapor pressure of the water at 25 °C.

**Strategy**  One approach to solving this problem is to use the ideal gas law to calculate the amount of liquid water that must evaporate for the vapor produced to exert a pressure of 23.8 mm Hg in a volume of $4.25 \times 10^4$ L at 25 °C. Next, determine the volume of liquid water from the amount and compare the answer to the 2.00 L of water available.

**Strategy Map 12.6**

**PROBLEM**

Will a sample of water **evaporate completely** in a given volume at known *T*?

↓

**DATA/INFORMATION**

- Volume of water
- Density of water
- Vapor pressure at *T*

**STEP 1.** Use **ideal gas law** to calculate *amount of water vapor* needed to have a *P* equal to vapor pressure in *given* volume.

↓

**Amount of water** (mol) in the vapor phase to achieve *P* equal to the vapor pressure at given *T*.

**STEP 2.** Convert **amount of water** to a **volume of liquid water** using **molar mass** and **density**.

↓

**Volume of water** that evaporated to achieve the **vapor pressure** at given *T*.

**STEP 3. Compare** *volume of water evaporated* to volume *available before evaporation.*

↓

Volume of water that evaporated is *less* than that available. **Some liquid water remains.**

**Solution**

$$P = 23.8 \text{ mm Hg}\left(\frac{1 \text{ atm}}{760 \text{ mm Hg}}\right) = 0.0313 \text{ atm}$$

$$n = \frac{PV}{RT} = \frac{(0.0313 \text{ atm})(4.25 \times 10^4 \text{ L})}{\left(0.082057 \dfrac{\text{L} \cdot \text{atm}}{\text{K} \cdot \text{mol}}\right)(298 \text{ K})} = 54.4 \text{ mol}$$

$$54.4 \text{ mol H}_2\text{O}\left(\frac{18.02 \text{ g}}{1 \text{ mol H}_2\text{O}}\right) = 980. \text{ g H}_2\text{O}$$

$$980. \text{ g H}_2\text{O}\left(\frac{1 \text{ mL}}{0.997 \text{ g H}_2\text{O}}\right) = 983 \text{ mL}$$

Only about half of the available water needs to evaporate to achieve the equilibrium water vapor pressure of 23.8 mm Hg at 25 °C.

**Think about Your Answer** Another approach to the problem is to calculate the pressure exerted if all of the water had evaporated. The answer would be 48.4 mm Hg. This is about twice the equilibrium vapor pressure at 25 °C, so only about half of the water needs to evaporate, as you found in the other approach.

**Check Your Understanding**

Examine the vapor pressure curve for ethanol in Figure 12.17.

(a) What is the approximate vapor pressure of ethanol at 40 °C?

(b) Are liquid and vapor in equilibrium when the temperature is 60 °C and the pressure is 600 mm Hg? If not, does liquid evaporate to form more vapor, or does vapor condense to form more liquid?

# Vapor Pressure, Enthalpy of Vaporization, and the Clausius–Clapeyron Equation

Plotting the vapor pressure for a liquid at a series of temperatures results in a curved line (Figure 12.17). However, the German physicist R. Clausius (1822–1888) and the Frenchman B. P. E. Clapeyron (1799–1864) showed that, for a pure liquid, a linear relationship exists between the reciprocal of the Kelvin temperature $(1/T)$ and the logarithm of the vapor pressure $(\ln P)$ (Figure 12.18).

$$\ln P = -(\Delta_{\text{vap}}H^\circ/RT) + C \tag{12.1}$$

Here, $\Delta_{\text{vap}}H^\circ$ is the enthalpy of vaporization of the liquid, $R$ is the ideal gas constant $(8.314472 \text{ J/K} \cdot \text{mol})$, and $C$ is a constant characteristic of the liquid in question. This equation, now called the **Clausius–Clapeyron equation**, provides a method of obtaining values for $\Delta_{\text{vap}}H^\circ$. The equilibrium vapor pressure of a liquid can be measured at several different temperatures, and the logarithm of these pressures is plotted versus $1/T$. The result is a straight line with a slope of $-\Delta_{\text{vap}}H^\circ/R$. For example, plotting data for water (Figure 12.18), we find the slope of the line is $-4.90 \times 10^3$ $\text{K}^{-1}$, which gives $\Delta_{\text{vap}}H^\circ = 40.7 \text{ kJ/mol}$.

As an alternative to plotting $\ln P$ versus $1/T$, we can write the following equation that allows us to calculate $\Delta_{\text{vap}}H^\circ$ if we know the vapor pressure of a liquid at two different temperatures.

$$\ln P_2 - \ln P_1 = \left[\frac{-\Delta_{\text{vap}}H^\circ}{RT_2} + C\right] - \left[\frac{-\Delta_{\text{vap}}H^\circ}{RT_1} + C\right]$$

This can be simplified to

$$\ln \frac{P_2}{P_1} = -\frac{\Delta_{\text{vap}}H^\circ}{R}\left[\frac{1}{T_2} - \frac{1}{T_1}\right] \tag{12.2}$$

Ethylene glycol has a vapor pressure of 14.9 mm Hg ($P_1$) at 373 K ($T_1$), and a vapor pressure of 49.1 mm Hg ($P_2$) at 398 K ($T_2$). Using Equation 12.2, we can calculate the enthalpy of vaporization, 59.0 kJ/mol.

$$\ln\left(\frac{49.1 \text{ mm Hg}}{14.9 \text{ mm Hg}}\right) = -\frac{\Delta_{vap}H^\circ}{0.0083145 \text{ kJ/K} \cdot \text{mol}}\left[\frac{1}{398 \text{ K}} - \frac{1}{373 \text{ K}}\right]$$

$$1.192 = -\frac{\Delta_{vap}H^\circ}{0.0083145 \text{ kJ/K} \cdot \text{mol}}\left(-\frac{0.000168}{K}\right)$$

$$\Delta_{vap}H^\circ = 59.0 \text{ kJ/mol}$$

## Boiling Point

If you have a beaker of water open to the atmosphere, the atmosphere presses down on the surface. If enough energy is added, a temperature is eventually reached when the vapor pressure of the liquid equals the atmospheric pressure. At this temperature, bubbles of the liquid's vapor will not be crushed by the atmospheric pressure. Instead, bubbles can rise to the surface, and the liquid boils (Figure 12.19).

The boiling point of a liquid is the temperature at which its vapor pressure is equal to the external pressure. If the external pressure is 760 mm Hg, this temperature is called the **normal boiling point**. This point is highlighted on the vapor pressure curves for the substances in Figure 12.17.

The normal boiling point of water is 100 °C, and in a great many places in the United States, water boils at or near this temperature. If you live at higher altitudes, however, such as in Salt Lake City, Utah, where the barometric pressure is about 650 mm Hg, water will boil at a noticeably lower temperature. The curve in Figure 12.17 shows that a pressure of 650 mm Hg corresponds to a boiling temperature of about 95 °C. Food, therefore, has to be cooked a little longer in Salt Lake City to achieve the same result as in New York City at sea level.

## Critical Temperature and Pressure

On first thought, it might seem that vapor pressure–temperature curves (such as shown in Figure 12.17) should continue upward without limit, but this is not so. Instead, when a high enough temperature and pressure are reached, the interface between the liquid and the vapor disappears at the **critical point**. The temperature at which this occurs is the **critical temperature, $T_c$**, and the corresponding pressure is the **critical pressure, $P_c$** (Figure 12.20). The substance that exists under these conditions is called a **supercritical fluid**. It is like a gas under such a high pressure that its density resembles that of a liquid, while its viscosity (resistance to flow) remains close to that of a gas.

Consider what the substance looks like at the molecular level under these conditions. The molecules have been forced almost as close together as they are in the liquid state, but, unlike the situation in liquids, each molecule in the supercritical fluid has enough kinetic energy to exceed the forces holding molecules together.

For most substances, the critical point is at a very high temperature and pressure (Table 12.7). Water, for instance, has a critical temperature of 374 °C and a critical pressure of 217.7 atm.

Supercritical fluids can have beneficial uses, such as the ability to extract caffeine from coffee beans. As described in *A Closer Look: Supercritical CO₂ and Green Chemistry* (page 574), this property can also be useful in our movement to "green chemistry."

## Surface Tension, Capillary Action, and Viscosity

Molecules in the interior of a liquid interact with molecules all around them (Figure 12.21). In contrast, molecules on the surface of a liquid are affected only by those molecules located at or below the surface layer. This leads to a net inward force of attraction on the surface molecules, contracting the surface area and making the liquid behave as though it had a skin. The toughness of this skin is measured

**FIGURE 12.18 Clausius–Clapeyron equation.** When the natural logarithm of the vapor pressure (ln P) of water at various temperatures (T) is plotted against 1/T, a straight line is obtained. The slope of the line equals $-\Delta_{vap}H^\circ/R$. Values of T and P for water are from Appendix G.

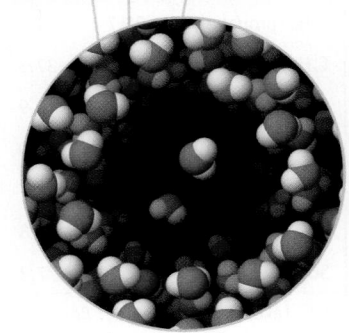

**FIGURE 12.19 Vapor pressure and boiling.** When the vapor pressure of the liquid equals the atmospheric pressure, bubbles of vapor begin to form within the body of liquid, and the liquid boils.

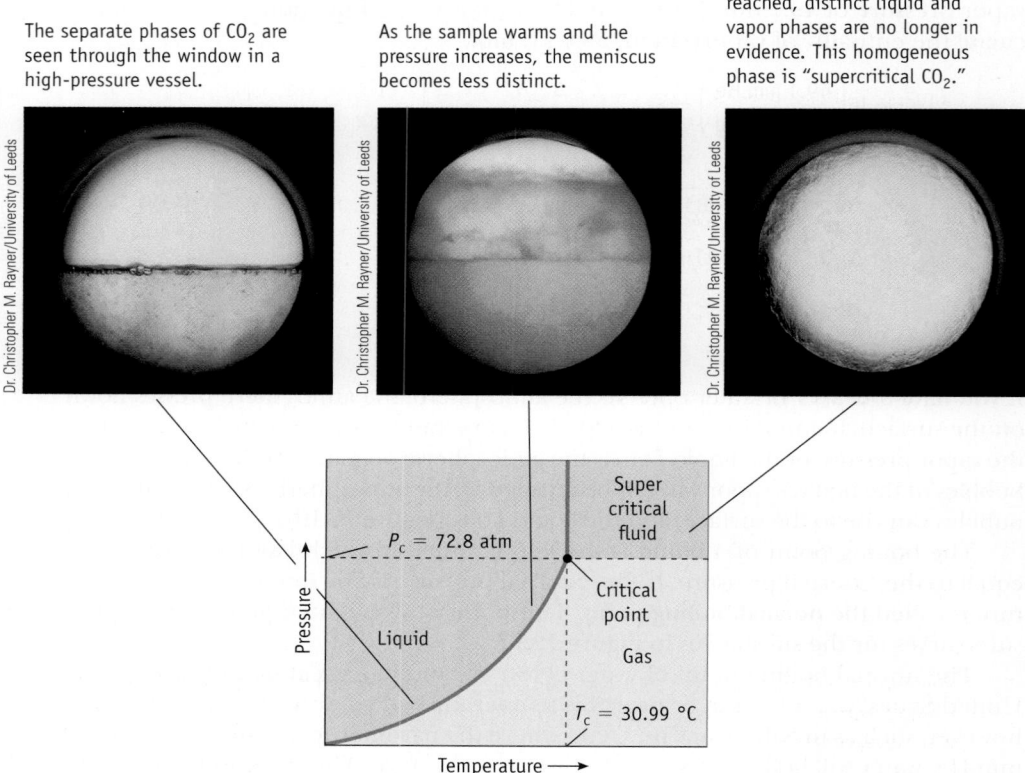

The separate phases of $CO_2$ are seen through the window in a high-pressure vessel.

As the sample warms and the pressure increases, the meniscus becomes less distinct.

Once the critical $T$ and $P$ are reached, distinct liquid and vapor phases are no longer in evidence. This homogeneous phase is "supercritical $CO_2$."

**FIGURE 12.20** **Critical temperature and pressure for $CO_2$.** The pressure versus temperature curve representing equilibrium conditions for liquid and gaseous carbon dioxide ends at the critical point; above that temperature and pressure, water becomes a supercritical fluid.

**TABLE 12.7 Critical Temperatures and Pressures for Common Compounds***

| Compound | $T_c$ (°C) | $P_c$ (atm) |
|---|---|---|
| $CH_4$ (methane) | −82.6 | 45.4 |
| $C_2H_6$ (ethane) | 32.3 | 49.1 |
| $C_3H_8$ (propane) | 96.7 | 41.9 |
| $C_4H_{10}$ (butane) | 152.0 | 37.3 |
| $CCl_2F_2$ (CFC-12) | 111.8 | 40.9 |
| $NH_3$ | 132.4 | 112.0 |
| $H_2O$ | 374.0 | 217.7 |
| $CO_2$ | 30.99 | 72.8 |
| $SO_2$ | 157.7 | 77.8 |

*Data taken from D. R. Lide: *Basic Laboratory and Industrial Chemicals*, Boca Raton, FL, CRC Press, 1993.

by its **surface tension**—the energy required to break through the surface or to disrupt a liquid drop and spread the material out as a film. Surface tension causes water drops to be spheres and not little cubes, for example (Figure 12.22a), because a sphere has a smaller surface area than any other shape of the same volume.

**Capillary action** is closely related to surface tension. When a small-diameter glass tube is placed in water, the water rises in the tube, just as water rises in a piece of paper in water (Figures 12.22b and 12.22c). Because polar Si—O bonds are present on the surface of glass, polar water molecules are attracted to the surface by **adhesive forces**. These forces are strong enough that they can compete with the **cohesive forces** between the water molecules themselves. Thus, some water molecules can adhere to the walls; other water molecules are attracted to them by cohesive forces and build a "bridge" back into the liquid. The adhesive forces between the water and the glass are great enough that the water level rises in the tube. The rise will continue until the attractive forces—adhesion between water and glass, cohesion between water molecules—are balanced by the force of gravity pulling down on the water column. These forces lead to the characteristic concave, or downward-curving, meniscus seen with water in a test tube (Figure 12.22c).

In some liquids, cohesive forces (high surface tension) are much greater than adhesive forces with glass. Mercury is one example. Mercury does not climb the walls of a glass capillary. In fact, when it is in a glass tube, mercury will form a convex, or upward-curving, meniscus (Figure 12.22c).

One other important property of liquids in which intermolecular forces play a role is **viscosity**, the resistance of liquids to flow. When you turn over a glassful of water, it empties quickly. In contrast, it takes much more time to empty a glassful of olive oil or honey. Olive oil consists of molecules with long chains of carbon atoms,

Water molecules on the surface are not completely surrounded by other water molecules.

Water molecules under the surface are completely surrounded by other water molecules.

**FIGURE 12.21 Intermolecular forces in a liquid.** Forces acting on a molecule at the surface of a liquid are different than those acting on a molecule in the interior of a liquid.

and it is about 70 times more viscous than ethanol, a small molecule with only two carbons and one oxygen. Longer chains have greater intermolecular forces because there are more atoms to attract one another, with each atom contributing to the total force. Honey (a concentrated aqueous solution of sugar molecules), however, is also a viscous liquid, even though the size of the molecules is fairly small. In this case, the sugar molecules have numerous —OH groups. These lead to greater forces of attraction due to hydrogen bonding.

---

**REVIEW & CHECK FOR SECTION 12.6**

1.  *Vapor pressure:* Suppose 0.50 g of pure water is sealed in an evacuated 5.0-L flask and the whole assembly is heated to 60 °C. Will any liquid water be left in the flask or does all of the water evaporate?

    (a)  liquid is left        (b)  all the water evaporates

2.  *Using the Clausius-Clapeyron equation:* Calculate the enthalpy of vaporization of diethyl ether, $(C_2H_5)_2O$ (Figure 12.17). This compound has vapor pressures of 57.0 mm Hg and 534 mm Hg at −22.8 °C and 25.0 °C, respectively.

    (a)  29.0 kJ/mol        (b)  122 kJ/mol        (c)  2.44 kJ/mol

---

**FIGURE 12.22 Adhesive and cohesive forces.**

**(a)** A series of photographs showing the different stages when a water drop falls. The drop was illuminated by a strobe light of 5-ms duration. (The total time for this sequence was 0.05 second.) Water droplets take a spherical shape because of surface tension.

**(b)** Capillary action. Polar water molecules are attracted to the — OH bonds in paper fibers, and water rises in the paper. If a line of ink is placed in the path of the rising water, the different components of the ink are attracted differently to the water and paper and are separated in a process called paper chromatography.

**(c)** Water (top layer) forms a concave meniscus, while mercury (bottom layer) forms a convex meniscus. The different shapes are determined by the adhesive forces of the molecules of the liquid with the walls of the tube and the cohesive forces between molecules of the liquid.

## A CLOSER LOOK

# Supercritical CO₂ and Green Chemistry

Much has been written recently about CO₂, particularly its role as a greenhouse gas. But there are useful sides to this molecule: one is as a solvent when its physical state is a supercritical fluid.

Carbon dioxide is widely available, essentially nontoxic, nonflammable, and inexpensive. Importantly, it is relatively easy to reach its critical temperature of 30.99 °C and critical pressure of 72.8 atm. In the supercritical state, the molecules are in close proximity, so the substance behaves as a liquid. However, because the kinetic energy of CO₂ molecules is greater than the energy associated with the forces of attraction between molecules, supercritical CO₂ has some properties of a gas. As a result, the supercritical fluid has the density of a liquid but the low viscosity of a gas.

One use of supercritical CO₂ is to extract caffeine from coffee. Coffee beans are treated with steam to bring the caffeine to the surface. The beans are then immersed in supercritical CO₂, which selectively dissolves the caffeine but leaves intact the compounds that give flavor to coffee. (Decaffeinated coffee contains less than 3% of the original caffeine.) The solution of caffeine in supercritical CO₂ is poured off, and the CO₂ is evaporated, trapped, and reused.

Supercritical CO₂ is also being used more and more as a replacement for organic solvents used to clean parts during the manufacture of electronic devices and for

Liquid CO₂ inside high-pressure chamber

dry cleaning clothing. This is an important advance because the organic solvents used for these purposes are often atmospheric pollutants.

Solvents such as alcohols and toluene (C₆H₅CH₃) are classified as VOCs (volatile organic compounds). To give you an idea of the scale of their use, it has been estimated that, between the United States and Canada, 26 million tons of VOCs are released into the atmosphere each year.

In addition to VOCs, there are halogenated compounds such as perchloroethylene (PERC) used in dry cleaning. Replacing VOCs and halogen-bearing solvents with supercritical CO₂ would help our environment greatly. Simply replacing VOCs, PERC, and related compounds with liquid or supercritical CO₂ won't work, however, because grease and dirt do not dis-

solve in CO₂. Fortunately, the problem was solved by Professor J. DeSimone of the University of North Carolina. His solution was to add a surfactant, just as you find in detergents in the kitchen. A surfactant is generally a long chain organic molecule with one end that can bind to an organic particle such as grease and another end that is soluble in the bulk solvent, in this case CO₂.

"CO₂-phobic" hydrocarbon head

$$\left[ H_2C - CH \right]_n$$
$$C = O$$
$$O$$
$$CH_2CF_2CF_2CF_2CF_2CF_2CF_2CF_3$$

"CO₂-philic" fluorocarbon tail

The "CO₂-phobic" ends of these molecules surround the grease or dirt to be removed while the "CO₂-philic" ends extend into the supercritical fluid. The dirt is taken into the solvent and washed away, leaving no toxic chemicals behind. The CO₂ is evaporated and recovered, and the dirt is collected.

**Reference:**
*Real World Cases in Green Chemistry*, M. C. Cann and M. E. Connelly, American Chemical Society, Washington, DC, 2000.

---

 and **go Chemistry**

Sign in at **www.cengage.com/owl** to:
• View tutorials and simulations, develop problem-solving skills, and complete online homework assigned by your professor.
• For quick review and exam prep, download Go Chemistry mini lecture modules from OWL (or purchase them at **www.cengagebrain.com**)

❓ Access **How Do I Solve It?** tutorials on how to approach problem solving using concepts in this chapter.

## CHAPTER GOALS REVISITED

*Now that you have studied this chapter, you should ask whether you have met the chapter goals. In particular, you should be able to:*

### Describe intermolecular forces and their effects
a. Describe the various intermolecular forces found in liquids and solids (Sections 12.3 and 12.4). **Study Questions: 1–10, 29–32, 34, 36, 43, and Go Chemistry Module 17.**
b. Tell when two molecules can interact through a dipole–dipole attraction and when hydrogen bonding may occur. The latter occurs most strongly when H is attached to O, N, or F (Section 12.3). **Study Questions: 1–8.**
c. Identify instances in which molecules interact by induced dipoles (dispersion forces) (Section 12.4). **Study Questions: 1–8.**

### Understand the importance of hydrogen bonding
a. Explain how hydrogen bonding affects the properties of water (Section 12.3). **Study Questions: 1–8.**

### Understand the properties of liquids
a. Explain the processes of evaporation and condensation, and use the enthalpy of vaporization in calculations (Section 12.6). **Study Questions: 11, 12, 18, 35, 57.**

b.   Define the equilibrium vapor pressure of a liquid, and explain the relationship between the vapor pressure and boiling point of a liquid (Section 12.6). **Study Questions: 14, 15, 17, 19, 20, 33, 42, 54.**

c.   Describe the phenomena of the critical temperature, $T_c$, and critical pressure, $P_c$, of a substance (Section 12.6). **Study Questions: 23, 24, 53.**

d.   Describe how intermolecular interactions affect the cohesive forces between identical liquid molecules, the energy necessary to break through the surface of a liquid (surface tension), capillary action, and the resistance to flow, or viscosity, of liquids (Section 12.6). **Study Questions: 25, 26, 27, 28, 45, 46.**

e.   Use the Clausius–Clapeyron equation, which connects temperature, vapor pressure, and enthalpy of vaporization for liquids (Section 12.6). **Study Questions: 21, 22, 38, 39.**

# Key Equations

**Equation 12.1 (page 570)** The Clausius–Clapeyron equation relates the equilibrium vapor pressure, $P$, of a volatile liquid to the molar enthalpy of vaporization ($\Delta_{vap}H°$) at a given temperature, $T$. ($R$ is the universal constant, 8.314472 J/K · mol.)

$$\ln P = -(\Delta_{vap}H°/RT) + C$$

**Equation 12.2 (page 570)** This modification of the Clausius–Clapeyron equation allows you to calculate $\Delta_{vap}H°$ if you know the vapor pressures at two different temperatures.

$$\ln\frac{P_2}{P_1} = -\frac{\Delta_{vap}H°}{R}\left[\frac{1}{T_2} - \frac{1}{T_1}\right]$$

# Study Questions

**⊙WL** Interactive versions of these questions are assignable in OWL.

▲ denotes challenging questions.

Blue-numbered questions have answers in Appendix R and fully worked solutions in the *Student Solutions Manual*.

## Practicing Skills

**Intermolecular Forces**
*(See Sections 12.1–12.5 and Examples 12.1–12.4.)*

1.   What intermolecular force(s) must be overcome to perform the following?
   (a) melt ice
   (b) sublime solid $I_2$
   (c) convert liquid $NH_3$ to $NH_3$ vapor

2.   What type of forces must be overcome when solid $I_2$ dissolves in methanol, $CH_3OH$? What type of forces must be disrupted between $CH_3OH$ molecules when $I_2$ dissolves? What type of forces exist between $I_2$ and $CH_3OH$ molecules in solution?

3.   What type of intermolecular forces must be overcome in converting each of the following from a liquid to a gas?
   (a) liquid $O_2$          (c) $CH_3I$ (methyl iodide)
   (b) mercury          (d) $CH_3CH_2OH$ (ethanol)

4.   What type of intermolecular forces must be overcome in converting each of the following from a liquid to a gas?
   (a) $CO_2$          (c) $CHCl_3$
   (b) $NH_3$          (d) $CCl_4$

5.   Rank the following atoms or molecules in order of increasing strength of intermolecular forces in the pure substance. Which of these substances exists as a gas at 25 °C and 1 atm?
   (a) Ne          (c) CO
   (b) $CH_4$          (d) $CCl_4$

6.   Rank the following in order of increasing strength of intermolecular forces in the pure substances. Which substance exists as a gas at 25 °C and 1 atm?
   (a) $CH_3CH_2CH_2CH_3$ (butane)
   (b) $CH_3OH$ (methanol)
   (c) He

7.   Which of the following compounds would be expected to form intermolecular hydrogen bonds in the liquid state?
   (a) $CH_3OCH_3$ (dimethyl ether)
   (b) $CH_4$
   (c) HF
   (d) $CH_3CO_2H$ (acetic acid)
   (e) $Br_2$
   (f) $CH_3OH$ (methanol)

8.   Which of the following compounds would be expected to form intermolecular hydrogen bonds in the liquid state?
   (a) $H_2Se$
   (b) $HCO_2H$ (formic acid)
   (c) HI
   (d) acetone (see structure below)

$$H_3C-\overset{\overset{\displaystyle O}{\|}}{C}-CH_3$$

9. In each pair of ionic compounds, which is more likely to have the more negative enthalpy of hydration? Briefly explain your reasoning in each case.
   (a) LiCl or CsCl
   (b) $NaNO_3$ or $Mg(NO_3)_2$
   (c) RbCl or $NiCl_2$

10. When salts of $Mg^{2+}$, $Na^+$, and $Cs^+$ are placed in water, the ions are hydrated. Which of these three cations is most strongly hydrated? Which one is least strongly hydrated?

### Liquids

*(See Section 12.6 and Examples 12.5 and 12.6.)*

11. Ethanol, $CH_3CH_2OH$, has a vapor pressure of 59 mm Hg at 25 °C. What quantity of energy as heat is required to evaporate 125 mL of the alcohol at 25 °C? The enthalpy of vaporization of the alcohol at 25 °C is 42.32 kJ/mol. The density of the liquid is 0.7849 g/mL.

12. The enthalpy of vaporization of liquid mercury is 59.11 kJ/mol. What quantity of energy as heat is required to vaporize 0.500 mL of mercury at 357 °C, its normal boiling point? The density of mercury is 13.6 g/mL.

13. Answer the following questions using Figure 12.17:
   (a) What is the approximate equilibrium vapor pressure of water at 60 °C? Compare your answer with the data in Appendix G.
   (b) At what temperature does water have an equilibrium vapor pressure of 600 mm Hg?
   (c) Compare the equilibrium vapor pressures of water and ethanol at 70 °C. Which is higher?

14. Answer the following questions using Figure 12.17:
   (a) What is the equilibrium vapor pressure of diethyl ether at room temperature (approximately 20 °C)?
   (b) Place the three compounds in Figure 12.17 in order of increasing intermolecular forces.
   (c) If the pressure in a flask is 400 mm Hg and if the temperature is 40 °C, which of the three compounds (diethyl ether, ethanol, and water) are liquids, and which are gases?

15. Assume you seal 1.0 g of diethyl ether (Figure 12.17) in an evacuated 100.-mL flask. If the flask is held at 30 °C, what is the approximate gas pressure in the flask? If the flask is placed in an ice bath, does additional liquid ether evaporate, or does some ether condense to a liquid?

16. Refer to Figure 12.17 to answer these questions:
   (a) You put some water at 60 °C in a plastic milk bottle and seal the top very tightly so gas cannot enter or leave the carton. What happens when the water cools?
   (b) If you put a few drops of liquid diethyl ether on your hand, does it evaporate completely or remain a liquid?

17. Which member of each of the following pairs of compounds has the higher boiling point?
   (a) $O_2$ or $N_2$
   (b) $SO_2$ or $CO_2$
   (c) HF or HI
   (d) $SiH_4$ or $GeH_4$

18. Place the following four compounds in order of increasing boiling point:
   (a) $SCl_2$
   (b) $NH_3$
   (c) $C_2H_6$
   (d) Ne

19. Vapor pressure curves for $CS_2$ (carbon disulfide) and $CH_3NO_2$ (nitromethane) are drawn here.
   (a) What are the approximate vapor pressures of $CS_2$ and $CH_3NO_2$ at 40 °C?
   (b) What type(s) of intermolecular forces exist in the liquid phase of each compound?
   (c) What is the normal boiling point of $CS_2$? Of $CH_3NO_2$?
   (d) At what temperature does $CS_2$ have a vapor pressure of 600 mm Hg?
   (e) At what temperature does $CH_3NO_2$ have a vapor pressure of 60 mm Hg?

20. You are comparing three different substances, A, B, and C, all liquids. The vapor pressure at 25 °C for substance A is less than the vapor pressure for B at this temperature. Substance C has the highest boiling point of the three substances. List the three substances A, B, or C in order of the strength of intermolecular forces, from least to greatest.

21. Equilibrium vapor pressures of benzene, $C_6H_6$, at various temperatures are given in the table.

| Temperature (°C) | Vapor Pressure (mm Hg) |
|---|---|
| 7.6 | 40. |
| 26.1 | 100. |
| 60.6 | 400. |
| 80.1 | 760. |

   (a) What is the normal boiling point of benzene?
   (b) Plot these data so that you have a graph resembling the one in Figure 12.17. At what temperature does the liquid have an equilibrium vapor pressure of 250 mm Hg? At what temperature is the vapor pressure 650 mm Hg?
   (c) Calculate the molar enthalpy of vaporization for benzene using the the Clausius–Clapeyron equation.

22. Vapor pressure data are given here for octane, $C_8H_{18}$.

| Temperature (°C) | Vapor Pressure (mm Hg) |
|---|---|
| 25 | 13.6 |
| 50. | 45.3 |
| 75 | 127.2 |
| 100. | 310.8 |

Use the Clausius–Clapeyron equation to calculate the molar enthalpy of vaporization of octane and its normal boiling point.

23. Can carbon monoxide ($T_c$ = 132.9 K; $P_c$ = 34.5 atm) be liquefied at or above room temperature? Explain briefly.

24. Methane ($CH_4$) cannot be liquefied at room temperature, no matter how high the pressure. Propane ($C_3H_8$), another simple hydrocarbon, has a critical pressure of 42 atm and a critical temperature of 96.7 °C. Can this compound be liquefied at room temperature?

25. What is surface tension? Give an example illustrating the phenomenon of surface tension. Explain why surface tension is the consequence of intermolecular forces.

26. What factors affect the viscosity of a substance? Which of the following substances, water ($H_2O$), ethanol ($CH_3CH_2OH$), ethylene glycol ($HOCH_2CH_2OH$), and glycerol ($HOCH_2CH(OH)CH_2OH$), is expected to have the highest viscosity? Should viscosity of a substance be affected by temperature? Explain your answers.

27. If a piece of filter paper (an absorbent paper used in laboratories) is suspended above a beaker of water and just touching the surface, water will slowly climb up the paper. What is the name given to this phenomenon, and how is this behavior explained?

28. When water is placed in a buret it forms a concave meniscus at the surface. In contrast, mercury (in a manometer for example) forms a convex meniscus (Figure 12.22). Explain why this phenomenon occurs, and why the two liquids give different results. Predict the meniscus shape if the buret is filled with ethylene glycol ($HOCH_2CH_2OH$).

## General Questions

*These questions are not designated as to type or location in the chapter. They may combine several concepts.*

29. Rank the following substances in order of increasing strength of intermolecular forces: (a) Ar, (b) $CH_3OH$, and (c) $CO_2$.

30. What types of intermolecular forces are important in the liquid phase of (a) $C_2H_6$ and (b) $(CH_3)_2CHOH$.

31. Which of the following salts, $Li_2SO_4$ or $Cs_2SO_4$, is expected to have the more exothermic enthalpy of hydration?

32. Select the substance in each of the following pairs that should have the higher boiling point:
    (a) $Br_2$ or ICl
    (b) neon or krypton
    (c) $CH_3CH_2OH$ (ethanol) or $C_2H_4O$ (ethylene oxide, structure below)

$$H_2C \overset{\displaystyle}{-} CH_2$$
$$\diagdown \diagup$$
$$O$$

33. Use the vapor pressure curves illustrated here to answer the questions that follow.

   (a) What is the vapor pressure of ethanol, $C_2H_5OH$, at 60 °C?
   (b) Considering only carbon disulfide ($CS_2$) and ethanol, which has the stronger intermolecular forces in the liquid state?
   (c) At what temperature does heptane ($C_7H_{16}$) have a vapor pressure of 500 mm Hg?
   (d) What are the approximate normal boiling points of each of the three substances?
   (e) At a pressure of 400 mm Hg and a temperature of 70 °C, is each substance a liquid, a gas, or a mixture of liquid and gas?

34. Which of the following ionic compounds will have the most negative enthalpy of hydration?
    (a) $Fe(NO_3)_2$     (c) NaCl
    (b) $CoCl_2$          (d) $Al(NO_3)_3$

35. Rank the following compounds in order of increasing molar enthalpy of vaporization: $CH_3OH$, $C_2H_6$, HCl.

36. Rank the following molecules in order of increasing intermolecular forces: $CH_3Cl$, $HCO_2H$ (formic acid), and $CO_2$.

37. Mercury and many of its compounds are dangerous poisons if breathed, swallowed, or even absorbed through the skin. The liquid metal has a vapor pressure of 0.00169 mm Hg at 24 °C. If the air in a small room is saturated with mercury vapor, how many atoms of mercury vapor occur per cubic meter?

38. ▲ The following data are the equilibrium vapor pressure of limonene, $C_{10}H_{16}$, at various temperatures. (Limonene is used as a scent in commercial products.)

| Temperature (°C) | Vapor Pressure (mm Hg) |
|---|---|
| 14.0 | 1.0 |
| 53.8 | 10. |
| 84.3 | 40. |
| 108.3 | 100. |
| 151.4 | 400. |

   (a) Plot these data as ln P versus 1/T so that you have a graph resembling the one in Figure 12.18.
   (b) At what temperature does the liquid have an equilibrium vapor pressure of 250 mm Hg? At what temperature is it 650 mm Hg?
   (c) What is the normal boiling point of limonene?
   (d) Calculate the molar enthalpy of vaporization for limonene using the the Clausius–Clapeyron equation.

# In the Laboratory

**39.** You are going to prepare a silicone polymer, and one of the starting materials is dichlorodimethylsilane, $SiCl_2(CH_3)_2$. You need its normal boiling point and to measure equilibrium vapor pressures at various temperatures.

| Temperature (°C) | Vapor Pressure (mm Hg) |
|---|---|
| −0.4 | 40. |
| +17.5 | 100. |
| 51.9 | 400. |
| 70.3 | 760. |

(a) What is the normal boiling point of dichlorodimethylsilane?

(b) Plot these data as ln $P$ versus $1/T$ so that you have a plot resembling the one in Figure 12.18. At what temperature does the liquid have an equilibrium vapor pressure of 250 mm Hg? At what temperature is it 650 mm Hg?

(c) Calculate the molar enthalpy of vaporization for dichlorodimethylsilane using the Clausius–Clapeyron equation.

**40.** A "hand boiler" can be purchased in toy stores or at science supply companies. If you cup your hand around the bottom bulb, the volatile liquid in the boiler boils, and the liquid moves to the upper chamber. Using your knowledge of kinetic molecular theory and intermolecular forces, explain how the hand boiler works.

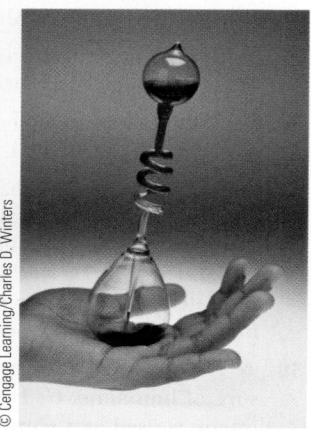

**41.** ▲ The photos below illustrate an experiment you can do yourself. Place 10 mL of water in an empty soda can, and heat the water to boiling. Using tongs or pliers, turn the can over in a pan of cold water, making sure the opening in the can is below the water level in the pan.

(a)                (b)

(a) Describe what happens, and explain it in terms of the subject of this chapter.

(b) Prepare a molecular level sketch of the situation inside the can before heating and after heating (but prior to inverting the can).

**42.** If you place 1.0 L of ethanol ($C_2H_5OH$) in a small laboratory that is 3.0 m long, 2.5 m wide, and 2.5 m high, will all the alcohol evaporate? If some liquid remains, how much will there be? The vapor pressure of ethyl alcohol at 25 °C is 59 mm Hg, and the density of the liquid at this temperature is 0.785 g/cm$^3$.

# Summary and Conceptual Questions

*The following questions may use concepts from this and previous chapters.*

**43.** Acetone, $CH_3COCH_3$, is a common laboratory solvent. It is usually contaminated with water, however. Why does acetone absorb water so readily? Draw molecular structures showing how water and acetone can interact. What intermolecular force(s) is(are) involved in the interaction?

$$\begin{matrix} & O & \\ & \parallel & \\ H_3C & - C - & CH_3 \end{matrix}$$

**44.** Cooking oil floats on top of water. From this observation, what conclusions can you draw regarding the polarity or hydrogen-bonding ability of molecules found in cooking oil?

**45.** Liquid ethylene glycol, $HOCH_2CH_2OH$, is one of the main ingredients in commercial antifreeze. Do you predict its viscosity to be greater or less than that of ethanol, $CH_3CH_2OH$?

**46.** Liquid methanol, $CH_3OH$, is placed in a glass tube. Is the meniscus of the liquid concave or convex? Explain briefly.

**47.** Account for these facts:

(a) Although ethanol ($C_2H_5OH$) (bp, 80 °C) has a higher molar mass than water (bp, 100 °C), the alcohol has a lower boiling point.

(b) Mixing 50 mL of ethanol with 50 mL of water produces a solution with a volume slightly less than 100 mL.

**48.** Rationalize the observation that $CH_3CH_2CH_2OH$, 1-propanol, has a boiling point of 97.2 °C, whereas a compound with the same empirical formula, methyl ethyl ether ($CH_3CH_2OCH_3$), boils at 7.4 °C.

**49.** Cite two pieces of evidence to support the statement that water molecules in the liquid state exert considerable attractive force on one another.

**50.** During thunderstorms in the Midwest, very large hailstones can fall from the sky. (Some are the size of golf balls!) To preserve some of these stones, we put them in the freezer compartment of a frost-free refrigerator. Our friend, who is a chemistry student, tells us to use an older model that is not frost-free. Why?

51. Refer to Figure 12.12 to answer the following questions:
    (a) Of the three hydrogen halides (HX), which has the largest total intermolecular force?
    (b) Why are the dispersion forces greater for HI than for HCl?
    (c) Why are the dipole–dipole forces greater for HCl than for HI?
    (d) Of the seven molecules in Figure 12.12, which involves the largest dispersion forces? Explain why this is reasonable.

52. ▲ What quantity of energy is evolved (in joules) when 1.00 mol of liquid ammonia cools from −33.3 °C (its boiling point) to −43.3 °C? (The specific heat capacity of liquid $NH_3$ is 4.70 J/g · K.) Compare this with the quantity of heat evolved by 1.00 mol of liquid water cooling by exactly 10 °C. Which evolves more heat per mole on cooling 10 °C, liquid water or liquid ammonia? *(The underlying reason for the difference in energy evolved is scientifically illuminating and interesting. You can learn more by searching the Internet for specific heat capacity and its dependence on molecular properties.)*

53. A fluorocarbon, $CF_4$, has a critical temperature of −45.7 °C and a critical pressure of 37 atm. Are there any conditions under which this compound can be a liquid at room temperature? Explain briefly.

54. ▲ The figure below is a plot of vapor pressure versus temperature for dichlorodifluoromethane, $CCl_2F_2$. The enthalpy of vaporization of the liquid is 165 kJ/g, and the specific heat capacity of the liquid is about 1.0 J/g · K.

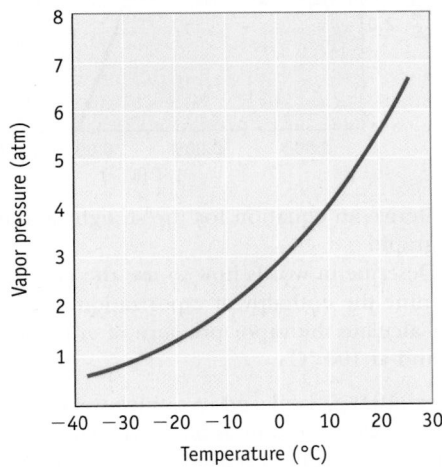

(a) What is the approximate normal boiling point of $CCl_2F_2$?
(b) A steel cylinder containing 25 kg of $CCl_2F_2$ in the form of liquid and vapor is set outdoors on a warm day (25 °C). What is the approximate pressure of the vapor in the cylinder?
(c) The cylinder valve is opened, and $CCl_2F_2$ vapor gushes out of the cylinder in a rapid flow. Soon, however, the flow becomes much slower, and the outside of the cylinder is coated with ice frost. When the valve is closed and the cylinder is reweighed, it is found that 20 kg of $CCl_2F_2$ is still in the cylinder. Why is the flow fast at first? Why does it slow down long before the cylinder is empty? Why does the outside become icy?

(d) Which of the following procedures would be effective in emptying the cylinder rapidly (and safely)? (1) Turn the cylinder upside down, and open the valve. (2) Cool the cylinder to −78 °C in dry ice, and open the valve. (3) Knock off the top of the cylinder, valve and all, with a sledgehammer.

55. Acetaminophen is used in analgesics. A model of the molecule is shown here with its electrostatic potential surface. Where are the most likely sites for hydrogen bonding?

56. Shown here are models of two bases in DNA with the electrostatic potential surfaces: cytosine and guanine. What sites in these molecules are involved in hydrogen bonding with each other? Draw molecular structures showing how cytosine can hydrogen bond with guanine.

cytosine

guanine

57. List four properties of liquids that are directly determined by intermolecular forces.

58. List the following ions in order of hydration energies: $Na^+$, $K^+$, $Mg^{2+}$, $Ca^{2+}$. Explain how you determined this order.

59. Compare the boiling points of the various isomeric hydrocarbons shown in the table below. Notice the relationship between boiling point and structure; branched-chain hydrocarbons have lower boiling points than the unbranched isomer. Speculate on possible reasons for this trend. Why might the intermolecular forces be slightly different in these compounds?

| Compound | Boiling point (°C) |
|---|---|
| Hexane | 68.9 |
| 3-Methylpentane | 63.2 |
| 2-Methylpentane | 60.3 |
| 2,3-Dimethylbutane | 58.0 |
| 2,2-Dimethylbutane | 49.7 |

60. An 8.82 g sample of $Br_2$ is placed in an evacuated 1.00 L flask and heated to 58.8 °C, the normal boiling point of bromine. Describe the contents of the flask under these conditions.

61. Polarizability is defined as the extent to which the electron cloud surrounding an atom or molecule can be distorted by an external charge. Rank the halogens ($F_2$, $Cl_2$, $Br_2$, $I_2$) and the noble gases (He, Ne, Ar, Kr, Xe) in order of polarizability (from least polarizable to most polarizable). What characteristics of these substances could be used to determine this ranked order?

62. In which of the following organic molecules might we expect hydrogen bonding to occur?
    (a) methyl acetate, $CH_3CO_2CH_3$
    (b) acetaldehyde (ethanal), $CH_3CHO$
    (c) acetone (2-propanone) (see Question 8)
    (d) benzoic acid ($C_6H_5CO_2H$)
    (e) acetamide ($CH_3CONH_2$ an amide formed from acetic acid and ammonia)
    (f) N,N-dimethylacetamide [$CH_3CON(CH_3)_2$, an amide formed from acetic acid and dimethylamine]

63. A pressure cooker (a kitchen appliance) is a pot on which the top seals tightly, allowing pressure to build up inside. You put water in the pot and heat it to boiling. At the higher pressure, water boils at a higher temperature and this allows food to cook at a faster rate. Most pressure cookers have a setting of 15 psi, which means that the pressure in the pot is 15 psi above atmospheric pressure (1 atm = 14.70 psi). Use the Clausius–Clapeyron equation to calculate the temperature at which water boils in the pressure cooker.

64. Vapor pressures of $NH_3(\ell)$ at several temperatures are given in the table below. Use this information to calculate the enthalpy of vaporization of ammonia.

| Temperature (°C) | Vapor Pressure (atm) |
|---|---|
| −68.4 | 0.132 |
| −45.4 | 0.526 |
| −33.6 | 1.000 |
| −18.7 | 2.00 |
| 4.7 | 5.00 |
| 25.7 | 10.00 |
| 50.1 | 20.00 |

65. Chemists sometimes carry out reactions in liquid ammonia as a solvent. With adequate safety protection these reactions can be done at temperatures above ammonia's boiling point in a sealed, thick-walled glass tube. If the reaction is being carried out at 20 °C, what is the pressure of ammonia inside the tube? (Use data from the previous question to answer this question.)

66. The data in the following table were used to create the graph shown below (vp = vapor pressure of ethanol ($CH_3CH_2OH$) expressed in mm Hg, $T$ = kelvin temperature)

| ln(vp) | $1/T$ ($K^{-1}$) |
|---|---|
| 2.30 | 0.00369 |
| 3.69 | 0.00342 |
| 4.61 | 0.00325 |
| 5.99 | 0.00297 |
| 6.63 | 0.00285 |

(a) Derive an equation for the straight line in this graph.
(b) Describe in words how to use the graph to determine the enthalpy of vaporization of ethanol.
(c) Calculate the vapor pressure of ethanol at 0.00 °C and at 100 °C.

67. Water (10.0 g) is placed in a thick walled glass tube whose internal volume is 50.0 $cm^3$. Then all the air is removed, the tube is sealed, and then the tube and contents are heated to 100 °C.
    (a) Describe the appearance of the system at 100 °C.
    (b) What is the pressure inside the tube?
    (c) At this temperature, liquid water has a density of 0.958 g/$cm^3$. Calculate the volume of liquid water in the tube.
    (d) Some of the water is in the vapor state. Determine the mass of water in the gaseous state.

## Applying Chemical Principles

### Chromatography

Separation of mixtures into pure components is important in both the synthesis and the analysis of chemical compounds. A variety of methods are used for separations, including distillation, precipitation, and filtration. However, the most common means of separation of mixtures is chromatography, and the photo on page 4 shows a forensic chemist using an instrument called a high performance liquid chromatograph.

Chromatography is a general term for a collection of related separation methods. It entails using a mobile phase (commonly a liquid or gas) to move a sample (that is, the components in a mixture) through an immiscible stationary phase (usually a liquid or solid). The mobile and stationary phases are chosen so that the components in the mixture distribute themselves to varying degrees between the two phases. The rate at which components in a mixture move through the stationary phase is dependent on their intermolecular interactions with the mobile and stationary phases. Components that interact weakly with the stationary phase move more quickly through the stationary phase than the components that interact more strongly with that phase.

In one common form of chromatography, called partition chromatography, both the mobile and stationary phases are liquids. For example, a polar mobile phase (such as a mixture of methanol and water) is passed through a very thin column containing a nonpolar stationary phase. A common stationary phase is nonpolar octadecane. The linear, eighteen-carbon chain (referred to as C-18) is usually covalently bonded to a solid support, such as small silica particles, to immobilize it inside the column. As the mixture passes through the C-18 column, the components continuously move back and forth between the two liquid phases, with the less polar components spending more time in the nonpolar phase than the more polar components. In an ideal separation, the components that emerge from the column (that is, the eluents) are completed separated.

### Questions:

1.  Assume that a mixture of the three molecules below are separated on a C-18 column using a methanol/water mixture as the mobile phase.
    (a) Which of the three molecules is most attracted to the mobile phase? What are the forces that attract the molecule to the water/methanol phase?

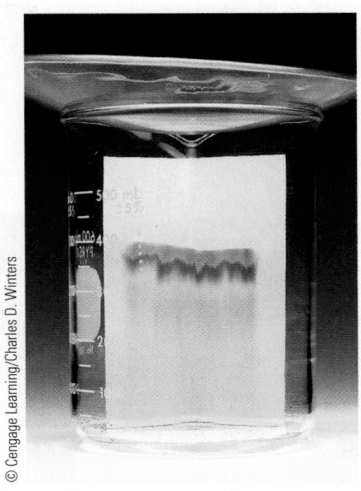

© Cengage Learning/Charles D. Winters

**The separation of black ink by paper chromatography.** Typically, the stationary phase (the paper) is suspended vertically. A spot or line of ink is placed near the bottom of the paper. The liquid phase rises up the paper by capillary action, and carries the various components upward at different rates.

(b) Which molecule is most attracted to the stationary phase? What are the forces that attract the molecule to the nonpolar phase?
(c) In what order will the three molecules exit (or "elute from") the column?

$$H_3C \diagdown CH_2 \diagdown CH_2 \diagdown CH_2 \diagdown CH_2 \diagdown OH$$
1-pentanol

$$H_3C \diagdown CH_2 \diagdown O \diagdown CH_2 \diagdown CH_3$$
propyl ethyl ether

$$HO \diagdown CH_2 \diagdown CH_2 \diagdown CH_2 \diagdown CH_2 \diagdown OH$$
1,5-pentanediol

2.  In gas chromatography the mobile phase is an inert gas such as $N_2$ or He. A mixture's components must be volatile if they are to move in the mobile phase. As with liquid chromatography, the separation is based upon forces of attraction of the various sample components with the mobile and the stationary phases; greater attractive forces between a compound and the column will result in a longer elution time. Assume that you want to separate a group of hydrocarbons, such as pentane ($C_5H_{12}$), hexane ($C_6H_{14}$), heptane ($C_7H_{16}$), and octane ($C_8H_{18}$) using a column with a nonpolar stationary phase. Predict the order of elution of these species from the column and explain your answer.

# 13   The Chemistry of Solids

**Lithium and "Green Cars"** The focus of much of this chapter is on metals and metal-containing compounds, the vast majority of which are solids.

You are well aware of the use of metals in our world: copper in electric wiring; aluminum in airplanes and soft drink cans; lead and zinc in batteries; and iron in cars, buses, and bridges. You may be less aware of metals such as the platinum group metals (platinum, palladium, rhodium, iridium, and ruthenium) in the catalytic converter in your car or in the chemicals industry. Approximately 2700 metric tons of these metals is used in cars and another 1000 metric tons in industry annually. Fortunately, many of the platinum group metals are recycled, but scientists are concerned about the depletion of metals such as copper, zinc, gallium, indium, and hafnium. They won't become "extinct" because their atoms are immutable, but they may be increasingly difficult to recover.

One metal that seems, fortunately, to be quite abundant on the earth is lithium. We say "fortunately" because lithium compounds are used in ceramics and glass, in reagents for the production of pharmaceuticals, and in lubricating greases. But their most important and largest use may be in batteries for appliances and most recently in cars. Your laptop computer may have a "lithium ion" battery, and several brands of hybrid cars now use lithium-based batteries.

Much of the world's lithium comes from northern Chile and southern Bolivia. There, groundwater with high concentrations of Group 1A salts is pumped into ponds. The solution slowly evaporates in the intense sun of the high Andes plateau,

**Lithium and lithium salts.** The high plateau in Bolivia where ground water contains high concentrations of Group 1A salts, among them lithium carbonate. The water is left in the sun to deposit the salts by evaporation.

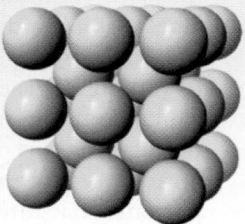

A sample of lithium metal and a view of the solid state structure of lithium.

and, after about a year, the highly concentrated solution is finally taken to a chemical plant where it is evaporated to give white, powdered lithium carbonate. It is estimated that Bolivia alone has a reserve of about 73 million metric tons of $Li_2CO_3$. To produce lithium metal, the carbonate is converted to LiCl, which is then electrolyzed to produce the metal.

In 2008 *Forbes* magazine said that "the green-car revolution could make lithium one of the planet's most strategic commodities." This remains to be seen, however. Some automobile companies are planning to continue using nickel-metal hydride batteries well into the future.

## Questions:

1. What mass of lithium can be obtained from 73 million metric tons of lithium carbonate? (1 metric ton = 1000 kg.)
2. Describe the unit cell of lithium (see Figure).
3. The lithium unit cell is a cube with sides of 351 pm. Use this information, and a knowledge of unit cells, to calculate the density of lithium metal.
4. In the process of making lithium metal, $Li_2CO_3$ is converted to LiCl. Suggest a way to do this.

**Answers to these questions are available in Appendix N.**

## CHAPTER GOALS

*See Chapter Goals Revisited (page 605) for Study Questions keyed to these goals.*

- Understand cubic unit cells.
- Relate unit cells for ionic compounds to formulas.
- Describe bonding in ionic and metallic solids and the nature of semiconductors.
- Describe the properties of solids.
- Interpret phase diagrams.

**OWL**

Sign in to OWL at **www.cengage.com/ owl** to view tutorials and simulations, develop problem-solving skills, and complete online homework assigned by your professor.

Many kinds of solids exist in the world around us (Figure 13.1 and Table 13.1). As the description of lithium and lithium-based batteries shows, solid-state chemistry is one of the booming areas of science, especially because it relates to the development of interesting new materials. As we describe various kinds of solids, we hope to provide a glimpse of the reasons this area is exciting.

## 13.1  Crystal Lattices and Unit Cells

In both gases and liquids, molecules move continually and randomly, and they rotate and vibrate as well. Because of this movement, an orderly arrangement of molecules in the gaseous or liquid state is not possible. In solids, however, the molecules, atoms, or ions cannot change their relative positions (although they vibrate and

Download mini lecture videos for key concept review and exam prep from OWL or purchase them from **www.cengagebrain.com**

**Table 13.1  Structures and Properties of Various Types of Solid Substances**

| Type | Examples | Structural Units | Forces Holding Units Together | Typical Properties |
|------|----------|------------------|-------------------------------|--------------------|
| Ionic | NaCl, K$_2$SO$_4$, CaCl$_2$, (NH$_4$)$_3$PO$_4$ | Positive and negative ions; no discrete molecules | Ionic; attractions among charges on positive and negative ions | Hard; brittle; high melting point; poor electric conductivity as solid, good as liquid; often water-soluble |
| Metallic | Iron, silver, copper, other metals and alloys | Metal atoms (positive metal ions with delocalized electrons) | Metallic; electrostatic attraction among metal ions and electrons | Malleable; ductile; good electric conductivity in solid and liquid; good heat conductivity; wide range of hardness and melting points |
| Molecular | H$_2$, O$_2$, I$_2$, H$_2$O, CO$_2$, CH$_4$, CH$_3$OH, CH$_3$CO$_2$H | Molecules | Dispersion forces, dipole–dipole forces, hydrogen bonds | Low to moderate melting points and boiling points; soft; poor electric conductivity in solid and liquid |
| Network | Graphite, diamond, quartz, feldspars, mica | Atoms held in an infinite two- or three-dimensional network | Covalent; directional electron-pair bonds | Wide range of hardness and melting points (three-dimensional bonding > two-dimensional bonding); poor electric conductivity, with some exceptions |
| Amorphous | Glass, polyethylene, nylon | Covalently bonded networks with no long-range regularity | Covalent; directional electron-pair bonds | Noncrystalline; wide temperature range for melting; poor electric conductivity, with some exceptions |

**FIGURE 13.1**
Some common
solids.

occasionally rotate). Thus, a regular, repeating pattern of atoms or molecules within the structure—a long-range order—is a characteristic of most solids. The beautiful, external (macroscopic) regularity of many crystalline compounds (such as those of salt, Figure 13.1) is a consequence of this internal order.

Structures of solids can be described as three-dimensional lattices of atoms, ions, or molecules. For a crystalline solid, we can identify the **unit cell**, the smallest repeating unit that has all of the symmetry characteristic of the way the atoms, ions, or molecules are arranged in the solid.

To understand unit cells, consider first a two-dimensional lattice model, the repeating pattern of circles shown in Figure 13.2. The yellow square at the left is a unit cell because the overall pattern can be created from a group of these cells by joining them edge to edge. It is also a requirement that unit cells reflect the stoichiometry of the solid. Here, the square unit cell at the left contains one smaller sphere and one fourth of each of the four larger circles, giving a total of one small and one large circle per two-dimensional unit cell.

You may recognize that it is possible to draw other unit cells for this two-dimensional lattice. One option is the square in the middle of Figure 13.2 that fully encloses a single large circle and parts of small circles that add up to one net small circle. Yet another possible unit cell is the parallelogram at the right. Other unit cells can be drawn, but it is conventional to draw unit cells in which atoms or ions are placed at the **lattice points**; that is, at the corners of the cube or other geometric object that constitutes the unit cell.

**FIGURE 13.2** Unit cells for a flat, two-dimensional solid made from circular "atoms."
A lattice can be represented as being built from repeating unit cells. This two-dimensional lattice can be built by translating the unit cells throughout the plane of the figure. Each unit cell must move by the length of one side of the cell. In this figure, all unit cells contain a net of one large circle and one small circle. Be sure to notice that several unit cells are possible, with two of the most obvious being squares.

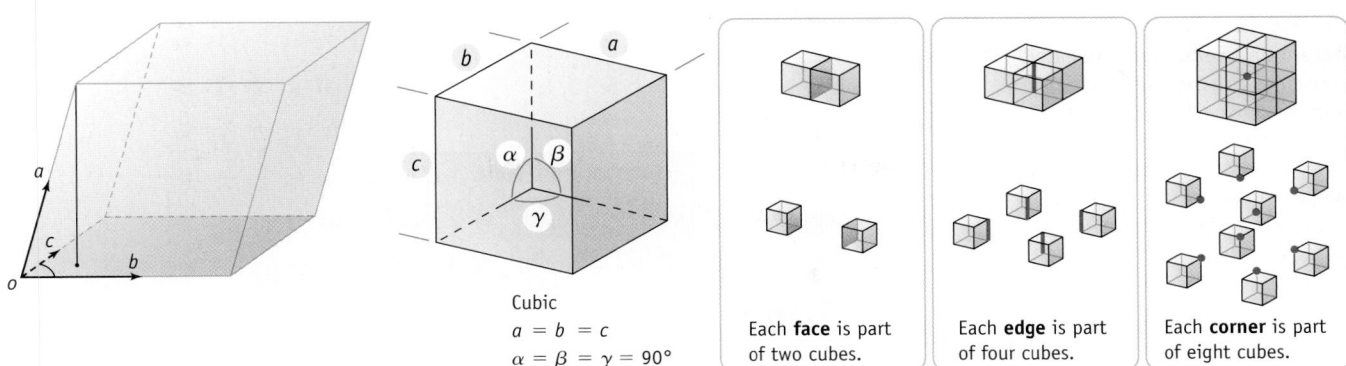

**(a) Types of cells.** Of the possible unit cells, all are parallelepipeds (except for the hexagonal cell), figures in which opposite sides are parallel. In a cube, all angles ($a$-$o$-$c$, $a$-$o$-$b$, and $c$-$o$-$b$; where $o$ is the origin) are 90°, and all sides are equal. In other cells, the angles and sides may be the same or different. For example, in a tetragonal cell, the angles are 90°, but $a = b \neq c$. In a triclinic cell, the sides have different lengths, the angles are different, and none equals 90°.

**(b) Cubic cell.** The cube is one of the seven basic unit cells that describe crystal systems. In a cube, all sides are of equal length, and all angles are 90°.

**(c) Building a lattice.** Stacking cubes to build a crystal lattice. Each crystal face is part of two cubes; each edge is part of four cubes; and each corner is part of eight cubes.

**FIGURE 13.3  Unit cells.**

The three-dimensional lattices of solids can be built by assembling three-dimensional unit cells much like building blocks (Figure 13.3). The assemblage of these three-dimensional unit cells defines the **crystal lattice**.

To construct crystal lattices, nature can use any of seven three-dimensional unit cells. They differ from one another in that their sides have different relative lengths and their edges meet at different angles. The simplest of the seven crystal lattices is the **cubic unit cell**, a cell with edges of equal length that meet at 90° angles (Figure 13.3). We shall look in detail at only this structure because cubic unit cells are commonly encountered.

Within the cubic class, three cell symmetries occur: **primitive cubic (pc)**, **body-centered cubic (bcc)**, and **face-centered cubic (fcc)** (Figure 13.4). All three have identical atoms, molecules, or ions at the corners of the cubic unit cell. The bcc and

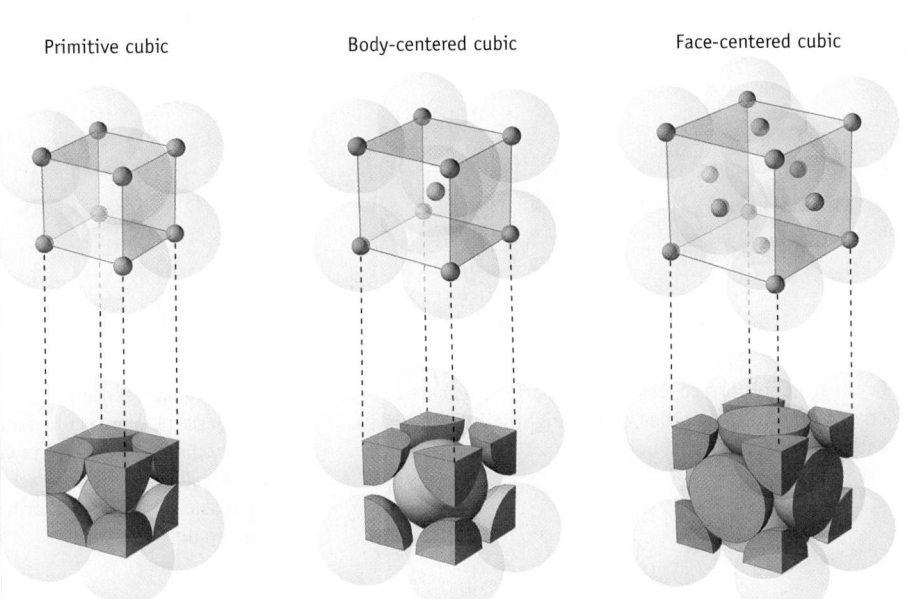

Primitive cubic    Body-centered cubic    Face-centered cubic

**FIGURE 13.4  The three cubic unit cells.** The top row shows the lattice points of the three cells, and the bottom row shows the same cells using space-filling spheres. The spheres in each figure represent identical atoms (or ions) centered on the lattice points. Because eight unit cells share a corner atom, only ⅛ of each corner atom lies within a given unit cell; the remaining ⅞ lies in seven other unit cells. Because each face of an fcc unit cell is shared with another unit cell, one half of each atom in the face of a face-centered cube lies in a given unit cell, and the other half lies in the adjoining cell.

**FIGURE 13.5 Metals use four different unit cells.** Three are based on the cube, and the fourth is the hexagonal unit cell (see the next page). (Many metals can crystallize in more than one structure. Mn, for example, can be bcc or fcc, and La exists in all but the primitive unit cell.)

fcc arrangements, however, differ from the primitive cube in that they have additional particles at other locations. The bcc structure is called *body-centered* because it has an additional particle, of the same type as those at the corners, at the center of the cube. The fcc arrangement is called *face-centered* because it has a particle, of the same type as the corner atoms, in the center of each of the six faces of the cube. Examples of each structure are found among the crystal lattices of the metals (Figure 13.5). The alkali metals, for example, are body-centered cubic, whereas nickel, copper, and aluminum are face-centered cubic. Notice that only one metal, polonium, has a primitive cubic lattice.

When the cubes pack together to make a three-dimensional crystal of a metal, the atom at each corner is shared among eight cubes (Figures 13.3, 13.4, and 13.6a). Because of this, only one eighth of each corner atom is actually within a given unit cell. Furthermore, because a cube has eight corners, and because one eighth of the atom at each corner "belongs to" a particular unit cell, the corner atoms contribute a net of one atom to a given unit cell. Thus, *the primitive cubic arrangement has one net atom within the unit cell.*

(8 corners of a cube)($\frac{1}{8}$ of each corner atom within a unit cell) =

1 net atom per unit cell for the primitive cubic unit cell

In contrast to the primitive cubic lattice, a body-centered cube has an additional atom wholly within the unit cell at the cube's center. The center particle is present

**FIGURE 13.6 Atom sharing at cube corners and faces.**

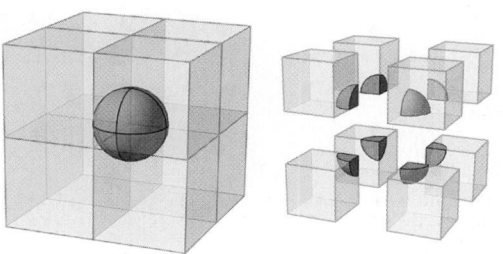

**(a)** In any cubic lattice, each corner particle is shared equally among eight cubes, so one eighth of the particle is within a particular cubic unit cell.

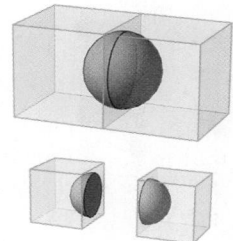

**(b)** In a face-centered lattice, each particle on a cube face is shared equally between two unit cells. One half of each particle of this type is within a given unit cell.

## Packing Oranges and Marbles

It is a "rule" that nature does things as efficiently as possible. You know this if you have ever tried to stack some oranges into a pile that doesn't fall over and that takes up as little space as possible. How did you do it? Clearly, the pyramid arrangement below on the right works, whereas the cubic one on the left does not.

Open space between balls

If you could look inside the pile, you would find that less open space is left in the pyramid stacking than in the cube stacking. Only 52% of the space is filled in the cubic packing arrangement. (If you could stack oranges as a body-centered cube, that would be slightly better; 68% of the space is used.) However, the best method is the pyramid stack, which is really a face-centered cubic arrangement. Oranges, atoms, or ions packed this way occupy 74% of the available space.

To fill three-dimensional space, the most efficient way to pack oranges or atoms is to begin with a hexagonal arrangement of spheres, as in this arrangement of marbles.

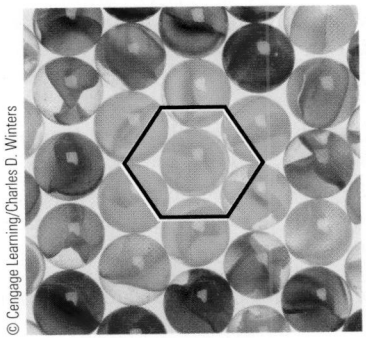

Succeeding layers of atoms or ions are then stacked one on top of the other in two different ways. Depending on the stacking pattern (Figure A), you will get either a **cubic close-packed (ccp)** or **hexagonal close-packed (hcp)** arrangement.

In the hcp arrangement, additional layers of particles are placed above and below a given layer, fitting into the same depressions on either side of the middle layer. In a three-dimensional crystal, the layers repeat their pattern in the manner ABABAB. . . . Atoms in each A layer are directly above the ones in another A layer; the same holds true for the B layers.

In the ccp arrangement, the atoms of the "top" layer (A) rest in depressions in the middle layer (B), and those of the "bottom" layer (C) are oriented opposite to those in the top layer. In a crystal, the pattern is repeated ABCABCABC. . . . By turning the whole crystal, you can see that the ccp arrangement is the face-centered cubic structure (Figure B).

**(a)** Hexagonal close-packing (hcp)

**(b)** Cubic close-packing = face-centered cubic (fcc)

Top layer — A

Middle layer — B

Bottom layer — A

A

B

C

**FIGURE A  Efficient packing.** The most efficient ways to pack atoms or ions in crystalline materials are hexagonal close-packing (hcp) and cubic close packing (ccp).

**(a)**　　　　　**(b)**

**FIGURE B  Models of close packing. (a)** A model of hexagonal close-packing, where the layers repeat in the order ABABAB. . . . **(b)** A face-centered unit cell (cubic close-packing), where the layers repeat in the order ABCABC. . . . (A kit from which these models can be built is available from the Institute for Chemical Education at the University of Wisconsin at Madison.)

**FIGURE 13.7** **X-ray crystallography.** In the x-ray diffraction experiment, a beam of x-rays is directed at a crystalline solid. The photons of the x-ray beam are scattered by the atoms of the solid. The scattered x-rays are detected by a photographic film or an electronic detector, and the pattern of scattered x-rays is related to the locations of the atoms or ions in the crystal.

in addition to those at the cube corners, so *the body-centered cubic arrangement has a net of two atoms within the unit cell.*

In a face-centered cubic arrangement, there is an atom on each of the six faces of the cube in addition to those at the cube corners. One half of each atom on a face belongs to a given unit cell (Figure 13.6b). Three net particles are therefore contributed by the particles on the faces of the cube:

(6 faces of a cube)($^1/_2$ of an atom within a unit cell) =

3 net face-centered atoms within a face-centered cubic unit cell

Thus, *the face-centered cubic arrangement has a net of four atoms within the unit cell,* one contributed by the corner atoms and another three contributed by the atoms centered in the six faces.

An experimental technique, x-ray crystallography, can be used to determine the structure of a crystalline substance (Figure 13.7). Once the structure is known, the information can be combined with other experimental information to calculate such useful parameters as the radius of an atom (Example 13.1).

**⍟WL   INTERACTIVE EXAMPLE 13.1** **Determining an Atom Radius from Lattice Dimensions**

**Problem** Aluminum has a density of 2.699 g/cm³, and the atoms are packed in a face-centered cubic crystal lattice. What is the radius of an aluminum atom?

**What Do You Know?** You are trying to find the radius of an aluminum atom and begin with a knowledge of its unit cell geometry. It is important to recognize the atoms in a face-centered cube do not touch along the cell edges but do so in the faces (as illustrated just below).

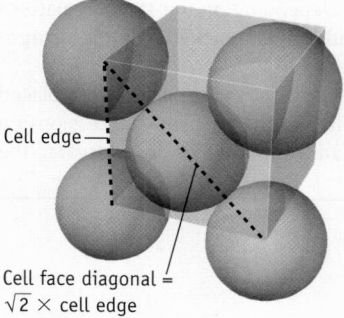

Cell edge

Cell face diagonal = $\sqrt{2}$ × cell edge

**One face of a face-centered cubic unit cell.** This shows the cell face diagonal, $\sqrt{2}$ × edge, is equal to four times the radius of the atoms in the lattice.

**Aluminum metal.** The metal has a face-centered cubic unit cell with a net of four Al atoms in each unit cell.

**Strategy** If you know the cell edge length, you can calculate the diagonal distance across a face, and the illustration above shows the atom radius is one fourth of this distance. So, the problem comes down to finding the length of the cell edge. This dimension is the cube root of the cell volume. But where do you find the cell volume? From the density and mass of the unit cell. The density is given, and the mass of the cell is 4 times the mass of an atom. As described in Chapter 2, the mass of an Al atom can be found from its atomic mass and Avogadro's number. Therefore, you should proceed as follows:

1. Find the mass of a unit cell from the knowledge that it is face-centered cubic.

2. Combine the density of aluminum with the mass of the unit cell to find the cell volume.

3. Find the length of a side of the unit cell from its volume.

4. Calculate the atom radius from the edge dimension.

**Solution**

*1. Calculate the mass of the unit cell.*

$$\text{Mass of 1 Al atom} = \left(\frac{26.98 \text{ g}}{1 \text{ mol}}\right)\left(\frac{1 \text{ mol}}{6.022 \times 10^{23} \text{ atoms}}\right) = 4.480 \times 10^{-23} \text{ g/atom}$$

$$\text{Mass of unit cell} = \left(\frac{4.480 \times 10^{-23} \text{ g}}{1 \text{ Al atom}}\right)\left(\frac{4 \text{ Al atoms}}{1 \text{ unit cell}}\right) = 1.792 \times 10^{-22} \text{ g/unit cell}$$

*2. Calculate the volume of the unit cell from the unit cell mass and density.*

$$\text{Volume of unit cell} = \left(\frac{1.792 \times 10^{-22} \text{ g}}{\text{unit cell}}\right)\left(\frac{1 \text{ cm}^3}{2.699 \text{ g}}\right) = 6.640 \times 10^{-23} \text{ cm}^3/\text{unit cell}$$

*3. Calculate the length of a unit cell edge.* The length of the unit cell edge is the cube root of the cell volume.

$$\text{Length of unit cell edge} = \sqrt[3]{6.640 \times 10^{-23} \text{ cm}^3} = 4.049 \times 10^{-8} \text{ cm}$$

*4. Calculate the atom radius.* As illustrated in the model above, the diagonal distance across the face of the cell is equal to four times the Al atom radius.

$$\text{Cell face diagonal} = 4 \times (\text{Al atom radius})$$

The cell diagonal is the hypotenuse of a right isosceles triangle, so, using the Pythagorean theorem,

$$(\text{Diagonal distance})^2 = 2 \times (\text{edge})^2$$

Taking the square root of both sides, we have

$$\text{Diagonal distance} = \sqrt{2} \times (\text{cell edge})$$
$$= \sqrt{2} \times (4.049 \times 10^{-8} \text{ cm}) = 5.727 \times 10^{-8} \text{ cm}$$

We divide the diagonal distance by 4 to obtain the Al atom radius in cm.

$$\text{Al atom radius} = \frac{5.727 \times 10^{-8} \text{ cm}}{4} = 1.432 \times 10^{-8} \text{ cm}$$

Atomic dimensions are often expressed in picometers, so we convert the radius to that unit.

$$1.432 \times 10^{-8} \text{ cm}\left(\frac{1 \text{ m}}{100 \text{ cm}}\right)\left(\frac{1 \text{ pm}}{1 \times 10^{-12} \text{ m}}\right) = 143.2 \text{ pm}$$

**Think about Your Answer** The radius in Figure 7.8 was calculated from experimental data as in this Example.

**Check Your Understanding**

(a) *Determining an Atom Radius from Lattice Dimensions:* Gold has a face-centered unit cell, and its density is 19.32 g/cm³. Calculate the radius of a gold atom.

(b) *The Structure of Solid Iron:* Iron has a density of 7.8740 g/cm³, and the radius of an iron atom is 126 pm. Verify that solid iron has a body-centered cubic unit cell. (Be sure to note that the atoms in a body-centered cubic unit cell touch along the diagonal across the cell. They do not touch along the edges of the cell.) (*Hint:* The diagonal distance across the unit cell = edge × $\sqrt{3}$.)

---

**Strategy Map 13.1**

**PROBLEM**

What is the **radius** of **Al** in solid Al?

**DATA/INFORMATION**
- Al unit cell is **FCC** with $d = 2.699$ g/cm³
- Need Al **atomic weight**
- Need **Avogadro's number**

STEP 1. Calculate **mass** of unit cell (= 4 Al atoms).

**Mass** of Al atom, **mass** of unit cell

STEP 2. Calculate **volume** of unit cell from mass and density.

**Volume** of unit cell

STEP 3. Calculate **length** of unit cell **edge** from cell volume.

**Length** of unit cell edge

STEP 4. Relate **atom radius** to **unit cell edge length**.

**Radius** of atom

A portion of the solid state structure of potassium.

**Module 18: The Solid State** covers concepts in this section.

## 13.2 Structures and Formulas of Ionic Solids

The lattices of many ionic compounds are built by taking a primitive cubic or face-centered cubic lattice of ions of one type and placing ions of opposite charge in the holes within the lattice. This produces a three-dimensional lattice of regularly placed ions. The smallest repeating unit in these structures is, by definition, the unit cell for the ionic compound.

The choice of the lattice and the number and location of the holes in the lattice that are filled are the keys to understanding the relationship between the lattice structure and the formula of a salt. Consider, for example, the ionic compound cesium chloride, CsCl (Figure 13.8). The structure of CsCl has a primitive cubic unit cell of chloride ions. The cesium ion fits into a hole in the center of the cube. (An equivalent unit cell has a primitive cubic unit cell of $Cs^+$ ions with a $Cl^-$ ion in the center of the cube.)

Next, consider the structure for NaCl. An extended view of the lattice and one unit cell are illustrated in Figures 13.9a and 13.9b, respectively. The $Cl^-$ ions are arranged in a face-centered cubic unit cell, and the $Na^+$ ions are arranged in a regular manner between these ions. Notice that each $Na^+$ ion is surrounded by six $Cl^-$ ions in an octahedral geometry. Thus, the $Na^+$ ions are said to be in **octahedral holes** (Figure 13.9c).

The formula of an ionic compound must always be reflected in the composition of its unit cell; therefore, the formula can always be derived from the unit cell structure. The formula for NaCl can be related to this structure by counting the number of cations and anions contained in one unit cell. A face-centered cubic lattice of $Cl^-$ ions has a net of four $Cl^-$ ions within the unit cell. There is one $Na^+$ ion in the center of the unit cell, contained totally within the unit cell. In addition, there are 12 $Na^+$ ions along the edges of the unit cell. Each of these $Na^+$ ions is shared among four unit cells, so each contributes one fourth of an $Na^+$ ion to the unit cell, giving three additional $Na^+$ ions within the unit cell.

(1 $Na^+$ ion in the center of the unit cell) + (¼ of a $Na^+$ ion in each edge × 12 edges)

= net of 4 $Na^+$ ions in NaCl unit cell

This accounts for all of the ions contained in the unit cell: four $Cl^-$ and four $Na^+$ ions. Thus, a unit cell of NaCl has a 1:1 ratio of $Na^+$ and $Cl^-$ ions, as the formula requires.

**FIGURE 13.8 Cesium chloride (CsCl) unit cell.** The unit cell of CsCl may be viewed in two ways. The only requirement is that the unit cell must have a net of one $Cs^+$ ion and one $Cl^-$ ion. Either way, it is a primitive cubic unit cell of ions of one type ($Cl^-$ on the left or $Cs^+$ on the right). Generally, ionic lattices are assembled by placing the larger ions (here $Cl^-$) at the lattice points and placing the smaller ions (here $Cs^+$) in the lattice holes.

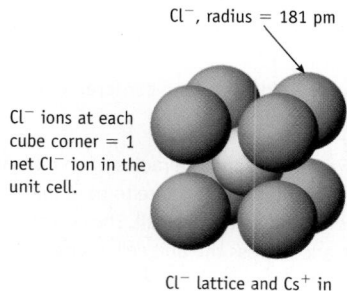

$Cl^-$, radius = 181 pm

$Cl^-$ ions at each cube corner = 1 net $Cl^-$ ion in the unit cell.

$Cl^-$ lattice and $Cs^+$ in lattice hole

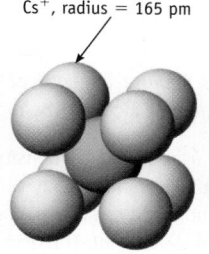

$Cs^+$, radius = 165 pm

One $Cs^+$ ion at each cube corner = 1 net $Cs^+$ ion in the unit cell.

$Cs^+$ lattice and $Cl^-$ in lattice hole

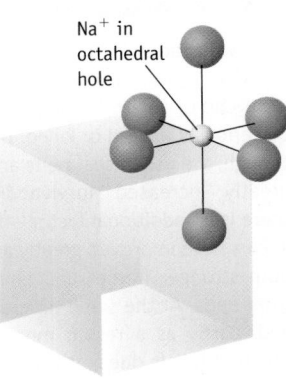

NaCl unit cell (expanded)

1 hole of this kind in the center of the unit cell

12 holes of this kind in the 12 edges of the unit cell (a net of 3 holes)

**(a) Cubic NaCl.** The solid is based on a face-centered cubic unit cell of $Na^+$ and $Cl^-$ ions.

**(b) Expanded view of the NaCl lattice.** (The lines are not bonds; they are there to help visualize the lattice.) The smaller $Na^+$ ions (silver) are packed into a face-centered cubic lattice of larger $Cl^-$ ions (yellow).

**(c) Octahedral holes.** A view showing the octahedral holes in the lattice.

**FIGURE 13.9  Sodium chloride.**

Another common unit cell has a different placement of ions. Again, there are ions of one type in a face-centered cubic unit cell. Ions of the other type are located in **tetrahedral holes**, wherein each ion is surrounded by four oppositely charged ions. As illustrated in Figure 13.10, there are eight tetrahedral holes in a face-centered cubic unit cell. In ZnS (zinc blende), the sulfide ions ($S^{2-}$) form a face-centered cubic unit cell. The zinc ions ($Zn^{2+}$) then occupy one half of the tetrahedral holes, and each $Zn^{2+}$ ion is surrounded by four $S^{2-}$ ions. The unit cell has four $S^{2-}$ ions (making up the fcc lattice) and four $Zn^{2+}$ ions contained wholly within the unit cell (in tetrahedral holes). This 1 : 1 ratio of ions matches the ratio in the formula.

In summary, compounds with the formula MX commonly form one of three possible crystal structures:

1. $M^{n+}$ ions occupying the cubic hole in a primitive cubic $X^{n-}$ lattice. Example: CsCl.
2. $M^{n+}$ ions in all the octahedral holes in a face-centered cubic $X^{n-}$ lattice. Example: NaCl.
3. $M^{n+}$ ions occupying half of the tetrahedral holes in a face-centered cube lattice of $X^{n-}$ ions. Example: ZnS.

Single tetrahedron with a tetrahedral hole shown as a white sphere.

Tetrahedral hole

**(a)**

**(b)**

Fcc lattice of $S^{2-}$ ions

$Zn^{2+}$ ions in half of the tetrahedral holes

**FIGURE 13.10  Tetrahedral holes and two views of the ZnS (zinc blende) unit cell. (a)** The tetrahedral holes in a face-centered cubic lattice. **(b)** This unit cell is an example of a face-centered cubic lattice of ions of one type with ions of the opposite type in one half of the tetrahedral holes.

© Cengage Learning/Charles D. Winters

## CASE STUDY

# High-Strength Steel and Unit Cells

A few decades ago if you rolled a car over or suffered a front end or side collision, you were likely to be seriously injured or killed. In recent years, though, the use of seat belts and air bags has greatly increased survivability. However, there is an additional factor—the steels used in cars have improved greatly and have led to both stronger frames and energy-absorbing front ends. At the same time cars are lighter and, partly as a result, more fuel-efficient. Much of this is due to the "design" of better steel.

Iron and steel are still made the same way they have always been: First, iron ore is reduced with carbon to produce raw iron. This is then heated in a "basic oxygen furnace" to remove impurities (▶ Chapter 22). Stronger steels were traditionally produced by adding very small amounts of other metals at this point to produce alloys that have very specific properties, but this can be expensive. So, the steel industry has developed new methods for producing steels that are less expensive.

When steel is produced, it is not a single, large crystal of iron atoms neatly arranged in a lattice. Rather, it consists of grains or crystallites of iron in various forms as well as carbon. The characteristics of this material can be changed by rolling a slab at room temperature, by annealing, or by quenching. Quenching refers to a process in which the steel slab is rolled at room temperature, heated to a high temperature, and then rapidly cooled or "quenched" in cold water.

**FIGURE A** Modern high-strength steels can save the lives of passengers in serious accidents such as rollovers.

Ferrite has a unit cell consisting only of iron atoms (Figure C); carbon atoms are not part of in the lattice. However, when the steel is heated, the lattice can rearrange, and carbon atoms become part of the unit cell. This new form with an embedded carbon atom is called the *austinite form*. When the steel is then quenched, another rearrangement occurs, this time to the martensite form, still with an embedded carbon atom.

Steel that has gone through this process will consist of crystallites of ferrite, austenite, and martensite. Depending on the precise conditions used, the proportion of these can vary, and so can the strength of the steel. For example, steel with a high proportion of martensite is very strong and is used in car bumpers.

Some steels may have added boron, which gives an ultra-high-strength steel that can be used in door pillars and beams. The lives of passengers can be saved in the event of a rollover.

### Questions:

1. What is the unit cell of ferrite?
2. Describe the unit cell of austenite.
3. What change has occurred on going from the austenite form to the martensite form?

**Answers to these questions are available in Appendix N.**

### Reference:

*New York Times*, September 25, 2009, page D1.

■ Ultra-High-Strength Steel
■ High-Strength Steel
■ Boron Steel

**FIGURE B** Steels used in a recent automobile.

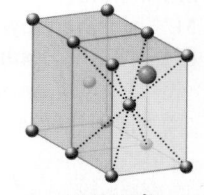

**FIGURE C** The transformation that occurs on treating ferrite in steel.

Chemists and geologists in particular have observed that the sodium chloride or "rock salt" structure is adopted by many ionic compounds, most especially by all the alkali metal halides (except CsCl, CsBr, and CsI), all the oxides and sulfides of the alkaline earth metals, and all the oxides of formula MO of the transition metals of the fourth period.

## EXAMPLE 13.2 Ionic Structure and Formula

**Problem** One unit cell of the common mineral perovskite is illustrated in the margin. This compound is composed of calcium and titanium cations and oxide anions. Based on the unit cell, what is the formula of perovskite?

**What Do You Know?** The cell is composed of the ions $Ca^{2+}$, $Ti^{4+}$, and $O^{2-}$. The $Ca^{2+}$ ion is wholly within the cell, the $Ti^{4+}$ ions are at the corners of the cell, and the $O^{2-}$ ions are in the cell edges. From this you can decide how many net ions are within the unit cell and thus know the formula.

**Strategy** Based on the locations of the ions, decide on the net number of ions of each kind in the cell.

**Solution**

Number of $Ti^{4+}$ ions:

(8 $Ti^{4+}$ ions at cube corners) × (⅛ of each ion inside unit cell) = 1 net $Ti^{4+}$ ion

Number of $Ca^{2+}$ ions:

One ion is in the cube center = 1 net $Ca^{2+}$ ion

Number of $O^{2-}$ ions:

(12 $O^{2-}$ ions in cube edges) × (¼ of each ion inside unit cell) = 3 net $O^{2-}$ ions

Thus, the formula of perovskite is $CaTiO_3$.

**Think about Your Answer** $CaTiO_3$ is a reasonable formula. One $Ca^{2+}$ ion and three $O^{2-}$ ions would require a titanium ion with a 4+ charge, a reasonable value because titanium is in Group 4B of the periodic table.

**Check Your Understanding**

If an ionic solid has an fcc lattice of anions (X) and all of the tetrahedral holes are occupied by metal cations (M), is the formula of the compound MX, $MX_2$, or $M_2X$?

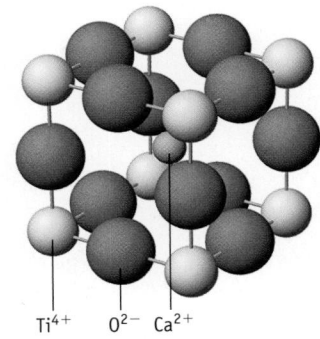

$Ti^{4+}$ $O^{2-}$ $Ca^{2+}$

**The unit cell of the mineral perovskite.** See Example 13.2.

## EXAMPLE 13.3 The Relation of the Density of an Ionic Compound and Its Unit Cell Dimensions

**Problem** Magnesium oxide has a face-centered cubic unit cell of oxide ions with magnesium ions in octahedral holes. If the radius of $Mg^{2+}$ is 79 pm and the density of MgO is 3.56 g/cm³, what is the radius of an oxide ion?

**What Do You Know?** This is similar to Example 13.1 in that you wish to know the size of one ion or atom in the cell. You are given the density of the compound and the fact that the unit cell is face-centered cubic. In addition, you know the radius of a $Mg^{2+}$ ion.

**Strategy** You can use the atomic masses of Mg and O and Avogadro's number to calculate the mass of one formula unit of MgO. You know that the unit cell is face-centered cubic. Because the lattice points are $O^{2-}$ ions, this tells you that there are 4 $O^{2-}$ ions within the cell. There are $Mg^{2+}$ ions in the octahedral holes, so you know there are also 4 $Mg^{2+}$ ions within the cell. The unit cell thus contains 4 MgO units. This, along with the mass per formula unit, can be used to calculate the mass per unit cell. The density of the cell relates the mass of the cell and the cell volume, so you can now calculate the volume of the unit cell and from this the length of one edge (Length = volume^{1/3}). As illustrated in the margin, the edge of the unit cell is twice the radius of a $Mg^{2+}$ ion (2 × 79 pm) plus twice the radius of an $O^{2-}$ ion (the unknown).

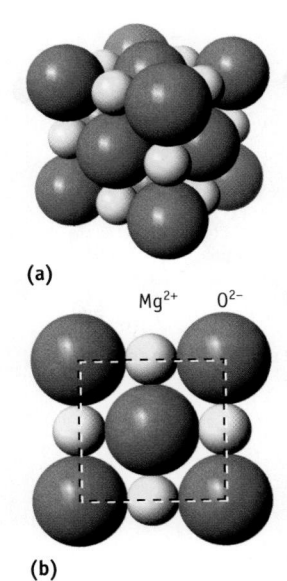

**(a)**

$Mg^{2+}$ $O^{2-}$

**(b)**

**Magnesium oxide. (a)** A unit cell showing oxide ions in a face-centered cubic lattice with magnesium ions in the octahedral holes. **(b)** One face of the cell.

**Solution**

1.  *Calculate the mass of the unit cell.* An ionic compound of formula MX (here MgO) and based on a face-centered cubic lattice of $X^-$ ions with $M^+$ ions in the octahedral holes has 4 MX units per unit cell.

$$\text{Unit cell mass} = \left(\frac{40.304 \text{ g}}{1 \text{ mol MgO}}\right)\left(\frac{1 \text{ mol MgO}}{6.022 \times 10^{23} \text{ units of MgO}}\right)\left(\frac{4 \text{ MgO units}}{1 \text{ unit cell}}\right)$$

$$= 2.677 \times 10^{-22} \text{ g/unit cell}$$

2.  *Calculate the volume of the unit cell from the unit cell mass and density.*

$$\text{Unit cell volume} = \left(\frac{2.667 \times 10^{-22} \text{ g}}{\text{unit cell}}\right)\left(\frac{1 \text{ cm}^3}{3.56 \text{ g}}\right) = 7.52 \times 10^{-23} \text{ cm}^3/\text{unit cell}$$

3.  *Calculate the edge dimension of the unit cell in pm.*

$$\text{Unit cell edge} = (7.52 \times 10^{-23} \text{ cm}^3)^{1/3} = 4.22 \times 10^{-8} \text{ cm}$$

$$\text{Unit cell edge} = 4.22 \times 10^{-8} \text{ cm}\left(\frac{1 \text{ m}}{100 \text{ cm}}\right)\left(\frac{1 \times 10^{12} \text{ pm}}{1 \text{ m}}\right) = 422 \text{ pm}$$

4.  *Calculate the oxide ion radius.*

One face of the MgO unit cell is shown on the previous page. The $O^{2-}$ ions define the lattice, and the $Mg^{2+}$ and $O^{2-}$ ions along the cell edge just touch one another. This means that one edge of the cell is equal to one $O^{2-}$ radius ($x$) plus twice the $Mg^{2+}$ radius plus one more $O^{2-}$ radius.

$$\text{MgO unit cell edge} = x \text{ pm} + 2(79 \text{ pm}) + x \text{ pm} = 422 \text{ pm}$$

$$x = \boxed{\text{oxide ion radius} = 132 \text{ pm}}$$

**Think about Your Answer** Chemists often check the chemical literature to judge the reasonableness of an answer. The calculated result here is very close to the value in Table 7.12 (140 pm).

---

**Check Your Understanding**

Potassium chloride has the same unit cell as NaCl. Using the ion sizes in Figure 7.12, calculate the density of KCl.

---

**Unit cell of silicon carbide, SiC.**

**REVIEW & CHECK FOR SECTION 13.2**

1.  The unit cell of silicon carbide, SiC, is illustrated in the margin. In what type of unit cell are the (dark gray) C atoms arranged?

    (a)  primitive cubic                        (c)  face-centered cubic

    (b)  body-centered cubic

2.  If one edge of the silicon carbide unit cell is 436.0 pm, what is the calculated density of this compound?

    (a)  0.803 g/cm³       (b)  0.311 g/cm³       (c)  3.21 g/cm³

## 13.3 Bonding in Metals and Semiconductors

Molecular orbital (MO) theory was introduced in Chapter 9 to rationalize covalent bonding in molecules, but it can also be used to describe metallic bonding. A metal is a kind of "supermolecule," and to describe the bonding in a metal we have to look at all the atoms in a given sample.

Even a tiny piece of metal contains a very large number of atoms and an even larger number of valence orbitals. In 1 mol of lithium atoms, for example, there are $6 \times 10^{23}$ atoms. Considering only the $2s$ valence orbitals of lithium, there are $6 \times 10^{23}$ atomic orbitals, from which $6 \times 10^{23}$ molecular orbitals can be created

**FIGURE 13.11 Bands of molecular orbitals in a metal crystal.** Here, the 2s valence orbitals of Li atoms are combined to form molecular orbitals. As more and more atoms with the same valence orbitals are added, the number of molecular orbitals grows until the orbitals are so close in energy that they merge into a band of molecular orbitals. If 1 mol of Li atoms, each with its 2s valence orbital, is combined, $6 \times 10^{23}$ molecular orbitals are formed. However, only 1 mol of electrons, or $3 \times 10^{23}$ electron pairs, is available, so only half of these molecular orbitals are filled. (See Section 9.3 for the discussion of molecular orbital theory.)

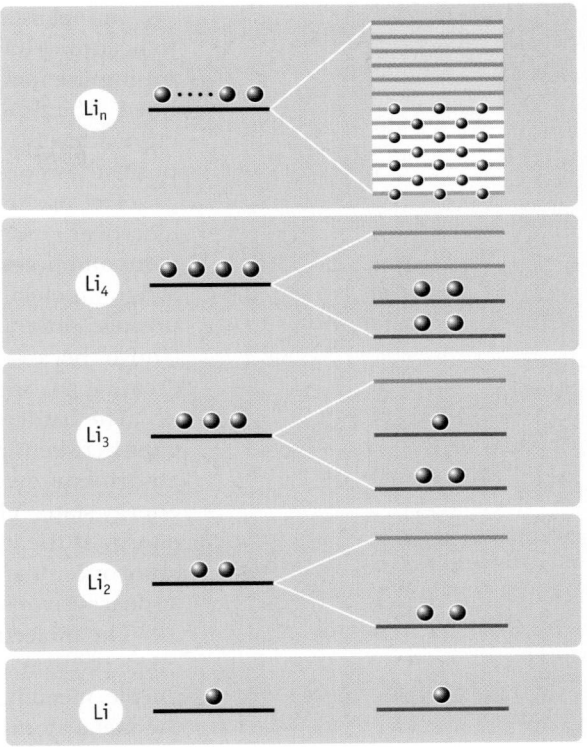

(◄ Section 9.3). The molecular orbitals that we envision in lithium will span all the atoms in the crystalline solid. A mole of lithium has 1 mol of valence electrons, and these electrons occupy the lower-energy bonding orbitals. The bonding is described as *delocalized* because the electrons are associated with all the atoms in the crystal and not with a specific bond between two atoms.

This theory of metallic bonding is called **band theory.** An energy-level diagram would show the bonding and antibonding molecular orbitals blending together into a band of molecular orbitals (Figure 13.11), with the individual MOs being so close together in energy that they are not distinguishable. The band is composed of as many molecular orbitals as there are contributing atomic orbitals, and each molecular orbital can accommodate two electrons of opposite spin.

In metals, there are not enough electrons to fill all of the molecular orbitals. In 1 mol of Li atoms, for example, $6 \times 10^{23}$ electrons, or $3 \times 10^{23}$ electron pairs, are sufficient to fill only half of the $6 \times 10^{23}$ molecular orbitals. The lowest energy for a system occurs with all electrons in orbitals with the lowest possible energy, but this is reached only at 0 K. The highest filled level at 0 K is called the **Fermi level** (Figure 13.12).

**Metals.** The highest filled level at 0 K is referred to as the *Fermi level.*

**Semiconductors.** In contrast to metals, the band of filled levels (the valence band) is separated from the band of empty levels (the conduction band) by a band gap. In insulators, the energy of the band gap is large.

**FIGURE 13.12 Band theory applied to metals, semiconductors, and insulators.** The bonding in metals and semiconductors can be described using molecular orbital theory. Molecular orbitals are constructed from the valence orbitals on each atom and are delocalized over all the atoms.

In metals at temperatures above 0 K, thermal energy will cause some electrons to occupy orbitals above the Fermi level. Even a small input of energy (for example, raising the temperature a few degrees above 0 K) will cause electrons to move from filled orbitals to higher-energy orbitals. For each electron promoted, two singly occupied levels result: a negative electron in an orbital above the Fermi level and a positive "hole"—from the absence of an electron—below the Fermi level.

The positive holes and negative electrons in a piece of metal account for its electrical conductivity. Electrical conductivity arises from the movement of electrons and holes in singly occupied states in the presence of an applied electric field. When an electric field is applied to the metal, negative electrons move toward the positive side, and the positive "holes" move to the negative side. (Positive holes "move" because an electron from an adjacent atom can move into the hole, thereby creating a fresh "hole.")

The band of energy levels in a metal is essentially continuous, that is, the energy gaps between levels are extremely small. A consequence of this is that a metal can absorb energy of nearly any wavelength, causing an electron to move to a higher energy state. The now-excited system can immediately emit a photon of the same energy as the electron returns to the original energy level. This rapid and efficient absorption *and* reemission of light make polished metal surfaces be reflective and appear lustrous (shiny).

The molecular orbital picture for metallic bonding provides an interpretation for other physical characteristics of metals. For example, most metals are malleable and ductile, meaning they can be rolled into sheets and drawn into wires. In these processes, the metal atoms must be able to move fairly freely with respect to their nearest neighbors. This is possible because metallic bonding is delocalized—that is, nondirectional. The layers of atoms can slip past one another relatively easily (as if the delocalized electrons were ball bearings that facilitate this motion), while at the same time the layers are bonded through coulombic attractions between the nuclei and the electrons.

In contrast to metals, rigid network solids such as diamond, silicon, and silica ($SiO_2$) have localized bonding, which anchors the component atoms or ions in fixed positions. Movement of atoms in these structures relative to their neighbors requires breaking covalent bonds. As a result, such substances are typically hard and brittle. They will not deform under stress as metals do, but instead tend to cleave along crystal planes.

## Semiconductors

Semiconducting materials are at the heart of all solid-state electronic devices, including such well-known devices as computer chips and diode lasers. Semiconductors do not conduct electricity easily but can be encouraged to do so by the input of energy. This property allows devices made from semiconductors to essentially have "on" and "off" states, which form the basis of the binary logic used in computers. We can understand how semiconductors function by looking at their electronic structure, following the band theory approach used for metals.

### Bonding in Semiconductors: The Band Gap

The Group 4A elements carbon (in the diamond form), silicon, and germanium have similar structures. Each atom is surrounded by four other atoms at the corners of a tetrahedron (Figure 13.13). Using the band model of bonding, the orbitals of each atom are combined to form molecular orbitals that are delocalized over the solid. Unlike metals, however, the result for carbon, silicon, and germanium is two bands, a lower-energy valence band and a higher-energy conduction band. In metals, there is only a small energy barrier for an electron to go from the filled molecular orbitals to empty molecular orbitals, and electricity can flow easily. However, in electrical insulators, such as diamond, and in semiconductors, such as silicon and germanium, the valence and conduction bands are separated from each other resulting in a **band gap**, a barrier to the promotion of electrons to higher energy levels (Figure 13.12). In the Group 4A elements, the orbitals of the valence band are completely filled, but the conduction band is empty.

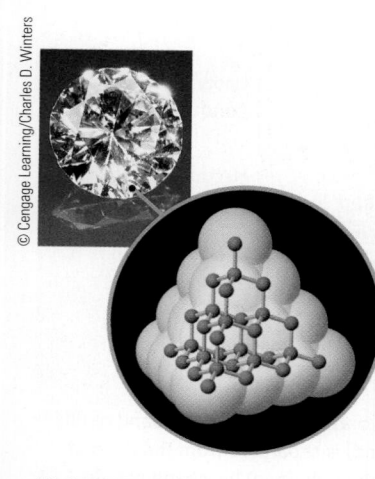

**FIGURE 13.13 The structure of diamond, an insulator.** The structures of silicon and germanium, semiconductors, are similar in that each atom is bound tetrahedrally to four others.

Semiconductors can conduct a current because thermal energy is sufficient to promote a few electrons from the valence band, across the band gap, to the conduction band (Figure 13.14). Conduction then occurs when the electrons in the conduction band migrate in one direction and the positive holes in the valence band migrate in the opposite direction.

The band gap in diamond is 580 kJ/mol—so large that electrons are trapped in the filled valence band and cannot make the transition to the conduction band, even at elevated temperatures. Thus, it is not possible to create positive "holes," and so diamond is an insulator, a nonconductor. Semiconductors, in contrast, have a smaller band gap. For common semiconducting materials, this band gap is usually in the range of 10 to 240 kJ/mol. (The band gap is 106 kJ/mol in silicon, whereas it is 68 kJ/mol in germanium.) The magnitude of the band gap in semiconductors is such that these substances are able to conduct small quantities of current under ambient conditions, but, as their name implies, they are much poorer conductors than metals.

Pure silicon and germanium are called **intrinsic semiconductors**, with the name referring to the fact that this is an intrinsic or naturally occurring property of the pure material. In intrinsic semiconductors, the number of electrons in the conduction band is determined by the temperature and the magnitude of the band gap. The smaller the band gap, the smaller the energy required to promote a significant number of electrons. As the temperature increases, more electrons are promoted into the conduction band, and a higher conductivity results.

There are also **extrinsic semiconductors**. The conductivity of these materials is controlled by adding small numbers of different atoms (typically 1 in $10^6$ to 1 in $10^8$) called *dopants*. That is, the characteristics of semiconductors can be changed by altering their chemical makeup.

Suppose a few silicon atoms in the silicon lattice are replaced by aluminum atoms (or atoms of some other Group 3A element). Aluminum has only three valence electrons, whereas silicon has four. Four Si-Al bonds are created per aluminum atom in the lattice, but these bonds must be deficient in electrons. According to band theory, the Si-Al bonds form a discrete but empty band at an energy level higher than the valence band but lower than the conduction band. This level is referred to as an *acceptor level* because it can accept electrons from the valence band. The gap between the valence band and the acceptor level is usually quite small, so electrons can be promoted readily to the acceptor level. The positive holes created in the valence band are able to move under the influence of an electric potential, so current results from the hole mobility. Because *positive* holes are created in an aluminum-doped semiconductor, this is called a **p-type semiconductor** (Figure 13.14b, left).

● **Intrinsic and Extrinsic** The term *intrinsic* means something is "essential" or "belongs naturally." The converse, *extrinsic*, means that a property is not part of the essential nature of an object.

**FIGURE 13.14** Intrinsic (a) and extrinsic (b) semiconductors.

**Gallium arsenide, GaAs.** The unit cell of GaAs has Ga atoms in an fcc lattice with As atoms in tetrahedral holes. It is an important semiconductor used in infrared emitting diodes, laser diodes, and solar cells.

Now suppose phosphorus atoms (or atoms of some other Group 5A element such as arsenic) are incorporated into the silicon lattice instead of aluminum atoms. This material is also a semiconductor, but it now has extra electrons because each phosphorus atom has one more valence electron than the silicon atom it replaces in the lattice. Semiconductors doped in this manner have a discrete, partially filled donor level that resides just below the conduction band. Electrons can be promoted to the conduction band from this donor band, and electrons in the conduction band carry the charge. Such a material, consisting of *negative* charge carriers, is called an **n-type semiconductor** (Figure 13.14b, right).

One group of materials that have desirable semiconducting properties is the III-V semiconductors, so called because they are formed by combining elements from Group 3A (such as Ga and In) with elements from Group 5A (such as As or Sb).

GaAs is a common semiconducting material that has electrical conductivity properties that are sometimes preferable to those of pure silicon or germanium. The crystal structure of GaAs is similar to that of diamond and silicon; each Ga atom is tetrahedrally coordinated to four As atoms, and vice versa.

It is also possible for Group 2B and 6A elements to form semiconducting compounds, such as CdS. The farther apart the elements are found in the periodic table, however, the more ionic the bonding becomes. As the ionic character of the bonding increases, the band gap will increase, and the material will become an insulator rather than a semiconductor. For example, the band gap in GaAs is 140 kJ/mol, whereas it is 232 kJ/mol in CdS.

These materials can also be modified by substituting other atoms into the structure. For example, in one widely used semiconductor, aluminum atoms are substituted for gallium atoms in GaAs, giving materials with a range of compositions ($Ga_{1-x}Al_xAs$). The importance of this modification is that the band gap depends on the relative proportions of the elements, so it is possible to control the size of the band gap by adjusting the stoichiometry. As Al atoms are substituted for Ga atoms, for example, the band gap energy increases. This consideration is important for the specific uses of these materials in devices such as LEDs (light-emitting diodes).

---

**REVIEW & CHECK FOR SECTION 13.3**

Germanium was one of the first materials used as a semiconductor. Given that it has a band gap of 68 kJ/mol, what is the maximum wavelength of light that can excite an electron transition across the band gap of Ge? To what region of the electromagnetic spectrum does this correspond?

(a)   1800 nm, infrared

(b)   29 nm, ultraviolet

(c)   $15 \times 10^6$ nm, microwave

---

## 13.4  Bonding in Ionic Compounds: Lattice Energy

Ionic compounds typically have high melting points, an indication of the strength of the bonding in the ionic crystal lattice. A measure of that is the lattice energy, the main topic of this section.

### Lattice Energy

Ionic compounds have positive and negative ions arranged in a three-dimensional lattice in which there are extensive attractions between ions of opposite charge and repulsions between ions of like charge. Each of these interactions is governed by an equation related to Coulomb's law (◄ page 76). For example, $U_{\text{ion pair}}$, the energy of attractive interactions between a pair of ions, is given by

$$U_{\text{ion pair}} = C \times \frac{(n^+ e)(n^- e)}{d}$$

The symbol $C$ represents a constant, $d$ is the distance between the ion centers, and $e$ is the charge on an electron. The term $n^+e$ represents the charge on the cation in the ion pair, and the term $n^-e$ is the charge on the negative ion. Because $n^-e$ is negative, the energy will have a negative value. Be sure to notice that *the energy depends directly on the charges on the ions and inversely on the distance between them.*

In an extended ionic lattice, there are multiple cation–anion interactions. Taking NaCl as an example (Figure 13.9), focus on an $Na^+$ ion in the center of the unit cell. We see it is surrounded by, and attracted to, six $Cl^-$ ions. Just a bit farther away from this $Na^+$ ion, however, there are 12 $Na^+$ ions along the edges of the cubes, and there is a force of repulsion between the center $Na^+$ and these ions. And if we still focus on the $Na^+$ ion in the "center" of the unit cell, we see there are eight more $Cl^-$ ions at the corners of the cube, and these are attracted to the center $Na^+$ ion. Taking into account *all* of the interactions between the ions in a lattice, we can calculate the **lattice energy,** $\Delta_{lattice}U$, the energy of formation of one mole of a solid crystalline ionic compound when ions in the gas phase combine (Table 13.2). For sodium chloride, this reaction is

$$Na^+(g) + Cl^-(g) \rightarrow NaCl(s)$$

When dealing with ionic compounds chemists often use **lattice enthalpy,** $\Delta_{lattice}H$. The same trends are seen in both lattice energy and enthalpy, and, because we are dealing with a condensed phase, the numerical values are nearly identical.

We shall focus here on the dependence of lattice enthalpy on ion charges and sizes. As given by Coulomb's law, the higher the ion charges, the greater the attraction between oppositely charged ions, so $\Delta_{lattice}H$ has a larger negative value for more highly charged ions. This is illustrated by the lattice enthalpies of MgO and NaF. The value of $\Delta_{lattice}H$ for MgO ($-4050$ kJ/mol) is about four times more negative than the value for NaF ($-926$ kJ/mol) because the charges on the $Mg^{2+}$ and $O^{2-}$ ions [$(2+) \times (2-)$] are twice as large as those on $Na^+$ and $F^-$ ions.

Because the attraction between ions is inversely proportional to the distance between them, the effect of ion size on lattice enthalpy is also predictable: A lattice built from smaller ions generally leads to a more negative value for the lattice enthalpy (Table 13.2 and Figure 13.15). For alkali metal halides, for example, the lattice enthalpy for lithium compounds is generally more negative than that for potassium compounds because the $Li^+$ ion is much smaller than the $K^+$ cation. Similarly, lattice enthalpies of fluorides are more negative than those for iodides with the same cation.

## Calculating a Lattice Enthalpy from Thermodynamic Data

Lattice enthalpies can be calculated using a thermodynamic approach known as a **Born–Haber cycle,** an application of Hess's law (◄ page 230). The relationship of various enthalpy changes is illustrated in Figure 13.16 for solid sodium chloride.

**Table 13.2 Lattice Energies of Some Ionic Compounds**

| Compound | $\Delta_{lattice}U$ (kJ/mol) |
|---|---|
| LiF | −1037 |
| LiCl | −852 |
| LiBr | −815 |
| LiI | −761 |
| NaF | −926 |
| NaCl | −786 |
| NaBr | −752 |
| NaI | −702 |
| KF | −821 |
| KCl | −717 |
| KBr | −689 |
| KI | −649 |

Source: D. Cubicciotti: Lattice energies of the alkali halides and electron affinities of the halogens. *Journal of Chemical Physics*, Vol. 31, p. 1646, 1959.

**FIGURE 13.15 Lattice energy.** $\Delta_{lattice}U$ is illustrated for the formation of the alkali metal halides, MX(s), from the ions $M^+(g) + X^-(g)$.

Steps 1 and 2 in Figure 13.16 involve formation of $Na^+(g)$ and $Cl^-(g)$ ions from the elements; the enthalpy change for each of these steps is known (Appendices F and L). Step 3 in Figure 13.16 gives the lattice enthalpy, $\Delta_{lattice}H$. $\Delta_fH°$ is the standard molar enthalpy of formation of $NaCl(s)$ (Appendix L). The enthalpy values for each step are related by the following equation:

$$\Delta_fH° \, [NaCl(s)] = \Delta H_{Step\ 1a} + \Delta H_{Step\ 1b} + \Delta H_{Step\ 2a} + \Delta H_{Step\ 2b} + \Delta H_{Step\ 3}$$

Because the values for all of these quantities are known except for $\Delta H_{Step\ 3}$ ($\Delta_{lattice}H$), the value for this step can be calculated.

Step 1a. Enthalpy of formation of $Cl(g)$     = +121.3 kJ/mol (Appendix L)
Step 1b. $\Delta H°$ for $Cl(g) + e^- \rightarrow Cl^-(g)$   = −349 kJ/mol (Appendix F)
Step 2a. Enthalpy of formation of $Na(g)$   = +107.3 kJ/mol (Appendix L)
Step 2b. $\Delta H°$ for $Na(g) \rightarrow Na^+(g) + e^-$   = +496 kJ/mol (Appendix F)

The standard enthalpy of formation of $NaCl(s)$, $\Delta_fH°$, is −411.12 kJ/mol. Combining this with the known values of Steps 1 and 2, we can calculate $\Delta H_{step\ 3}$, which is the lattice enthalpy, $\Delta_{lattice}H$.

Step 3. Formation of $NaCl(s)$ from the ions in the gas phase $= \Delta H_{step\ 3}$

$$\begin{aligned}\Delta H_{step\ 3} &= \Delta_fH° \, [NaCl(s)] - \Delta H_{Step\ 1a} - \Delta H_{Step\ 1b} - \Delta H_{Step\ 2a} - \Delta H_{Step\ 2b}\\ &= -411.12 \text{ kJ/mol} - 121.3 \text{ kJ/mol} - (-349 \text{ kJ/mol})\\ &\quad - 107.3 \text{ kJ/mol} - 496 \text{ kJ/mol}\\ &= -787 \text{ kJ/mol}\end{aligned}$$

---

**REVIEW & CHECK FOR SECTION 13.4**

1. Which sodium halide has the most negative lattice enthalpy?

   (a) NaI      (b) NaBr      (c) NaCl      (d) NaF

2. The lattice enthalpy for NaCl is defined as the enthalpy change for which of the following reactions?

   (a) $Na(s) + Cl_2(g) \rightarrow NaCl(s)$      (c) $Na^+(g) + Cl^-(g) \rightarrow NaCl(s)$

   (b) $Na(g) + Cl(g) \rightarrow NaCl(s)$      (d) $NaOH(s) + HCl(g) \rightarrow NaCl(s) + H_2O(\ell)$

3. Calculate the molar enthalpy of formation, $\Delta_fH°$, of solid sodium iodide using the approach outlined in Figure 13.16. The required data can be found in Appendices F and L and in Table 13.2.

   (a) +1710 kJ/mol      (c) −287 kJ/mol

   (b) −702 kJ/mol      (d) +1120 kJ/mol

---

**FIGURE 13.16 Born–Haber cycle for the formation of NaCl(s) from the elements.** The calculation in the text uses enthalpy values, and the value obtained is the lattice enthalpy, $\Delta_{lattice}H$. The difference between $\Delta_{lattice}U$ and $\Delta_{lattice}H$ is generally small and can be corrected for, if desired. (Note that the energy diagram is not to scale.)

Calculation of lattice energies by this procedure (a Born–Haber cycle) is named for Max Born (1882–1970) and Fritz Haber (1868–1934), German scientists who played prominent roles in thermodynamic research.

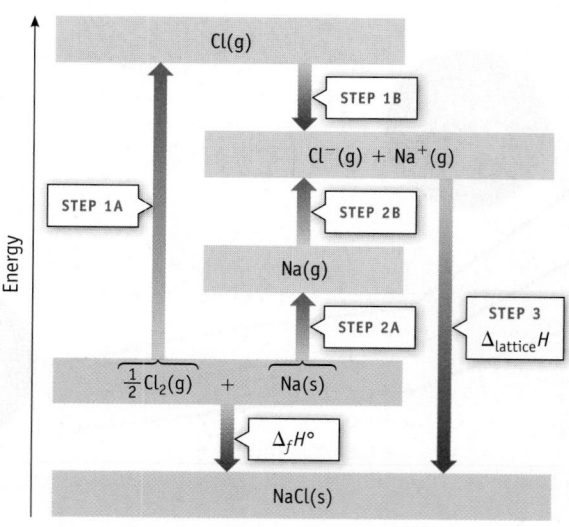

# 13.5 The Solid State: Other Types of Solid Materials

So far, we have described the structures of metals and simple ionic solids. Now we turn briefly to the other categories of solids: molecular solids, network solids, and amorphous solids (Table 13.1).

## Molecular Solids

Compounds such as $H_2O$ and $CO_2$ exist as solids under appropriate conditions. In these cases, it is molecules, rather than atoms or ions, that pack in a regular fashion in a three-dimensional lattice. You have already seen an example of a molecular solid: ice (◄ Figure 12.8).

The way molecules are arranged in a crystalline lattice depends on the shape of the molecules and the types of intermolecular forces. Molecules tend to pack in the most efficient manner and to align in ways that maximize intermolecular forces of attraction. Thus, the water structure was established to gain the maximum intermolecular attraction through hydrogen bonding.

It is from structural studies on molecular solids that most of the information on molecular geometries, bond lengths, and bond angles discussed in Chapter 8 was assembled.

**Graphite, a network solid.**

## Network Solids

**Network solids** are composed entirely of a three-dimensional array of covalently bonded atoms. Common examples include two allotropes of carbon: graphite and diamond. Elemental silicon is also a network solid with a diamond-like structure.

Graphite consists of carbon atoms bonded together in flat sheets that cling only weakly to one another. Within the layers, each carbon atom is surrounded by three other carbon atoms in a trigonal-planar arrangement. The layers can slip easily over another, which explains why graphite is soft, a good lubricant, and used in pencil lead. (Pencil "lead" is not the element lead but rather a composite of clay and graphite.)

Diamonds, which have a relatively low density ($d = 3.51$ g/cm$^3$), are the hardest material and the best conductor of heat known. They are transparent to visible light, as well as to infrared and ultraviolet radiation. In addition to their use in jewelry, diamonds are used as abrasives and in diamond-coated cutting tools. In the structure of diamond (Figure 13.13), each carbon atom is bonded to four other carbon atoms at the corners of a tetrahedron, and this pattern extends throughout the solid.

Silicates, compounds composed of silicon and oxygen, are also network solids and represent an enormous class of chemical compounds. You know them in the form of sand, quartz, talc, and mica, or as a major constituent of rocks such as granite. The structure of quartz is illustrated in Figure 13.17. It consists of tetrahedral silicon atoms covalently bonded to oxygen atoms in a giant three-dimensional lattice.

Most network solids are hard and rigid and are characterized by high melting and boiling points. These characteristics reflect the fact that a great deal of energy must be provided to break the covalent bonds in the lattice. For example, silicon dioxide melts at temperatures higher than 1600 °C.

## Amorphous Solids

A characteristic property of pure crystalline solids—whether metals, ionic solids, or molecular solids—is that they melt at a specific temperature. For example, water in the form of ice melts at 0 °C, aspirin at 135 °C, lead at 327.5 °C, and NaCl at 801 °C. Because they are specific and reproducible values, melting points are often used as a means of identifying chemical compounds.

Another property of crystalline solids is that they form well-defined crystals, with smooth, flat faces. When a sharp force is applied to a crystal, it will most often cleave to give smooth, flat faces. The resulting solid particles are smaller versions of the original crystal (Figure 13.18a).

**FIGURE 13.17 Silicon dioxide, a network solid.** Common quartz, $SiO_2$, is a network solid consisting of silicon and oxygen atoms.

**FIGURE 13.18 Crystalline and amorphous solids.**

(a) A salt crystal, a crystalline solid, can be cleaved cleanly into smaller and smaller crystals that are duplicates of the larger crystal.

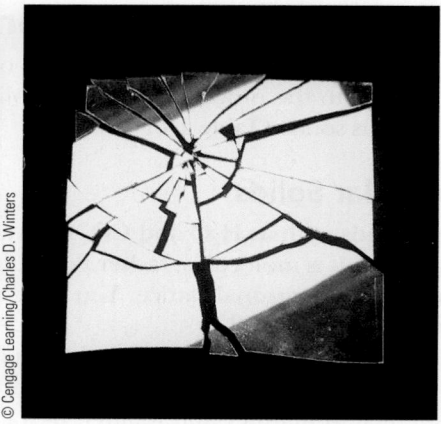

(b) Glass is an amorphous solid composed of silicon and oxygen atoms. It has, however, no long-range order as in crystalline quartz.

Many common solids, including ones that we encounter every day, do not have these properties, however. These are *amorphous solids*, solids that do not have a regular structure. Glass is a good example. When glass is heated, it softens over a wide temperature range, a property useful for artisans and craftsmen who can create beautiful and functional products for our enjoyment and use. Glass also possesses a property that we would rather it not have: When glass breaks, it leaves randomly shaped pieces. Other amorphous solids that behave similarly include common polymers such as polyethylene, nylon, and other plastics.

---

**REVIEW & CHECK FOR SECTION 13.5**

1.  Which of the following allotropes of carbon is not a network solid?

    (a) graphite          (b) diamond          (c) Buckyballs ($C_{60}$)

2.  A soft, white waxy solid melts over a temperature range from 120 °C to 130 °C. It doesn't dissolve in water and it doesn't conduct electricity. These properties are consistent with its identity as

    (a) a network solid                    (c) an ionic solid

    (b) an amorphous solid                 (d) a metallic solid

---

## 13.6 Phase Changes Involving Solids

The shape of a crystalline solid is a reflection of its internal structure. But what about physical properties of solids, such as the temperatures at which they melt? This and many other physical properties of solids are of interest to chemists, geologists, and engineers, among others.

### Melting: Conversion of Solid into Liquid

The melting point of a solid is the temperature at which the lattice collapses and the solid is converted into a liquid. Like any phase change, melting requires energy, called the *enthalpy of fusion* (given in kilojoules per mole) (◄ Chapter 5).

Energy absorbed as heat on melting = enthalpy of fusion = $\Delta_{fusion}H$ (kJ/mol)

Energy evolved as heat on freezing = enthalpy of crystallization = $-\Delta_{fusion}H$ (kJ/mol)

Enthalpies of fusion can range from just a few thousand joules per mole to many thousands of joules per mole (Table 13.3). A low melting temperature will certainly mean a low value for the enthalpy of fusion, whereas high melting points

# Graphene—The Hottest New Network Solid

One of the most interesting developments in chemistry in the last 20 years has been the discovery of new forms of carbon. First, there were buckyballs and then single-wall and multiwall carbon nanotubes.

Common graphite, from which your pencil lead is made, consists of six-member rings of carbon atoms connected in sheets, and the sheets stack one on top of another like cards in a deck. But if carbon compounds are heated under the right conditions, the carbon atoms assemble into sheets, and the sheets close on themselves to form tubes. These are called **nanotubes** because the tubes are only a nanometer or so in diameter. Sometimes they are single tubes, and other times there are tubes within tubes. Carbon nanotubes are at least 100 times stronger than steel but only one sixth as dense, and they conduct heat and electricity far better than copper. Thus, there has been enormous interest in their commercial applications, but it has also been difficult to make them with consistent properties.

Now there is **graphene**, a single sheet of six-member carbon atoms. Researchers in England, Andre Geim and Kostya Novoselov, discovered graphene in a simple way: Put a flake of graphite on Scotch tape, fold the tape over, and then pull it apart. The graphite layers come apart, and, if you do it enough times, only one layer—one C atom thick!—is left on the tape. Now graphene can be made in much

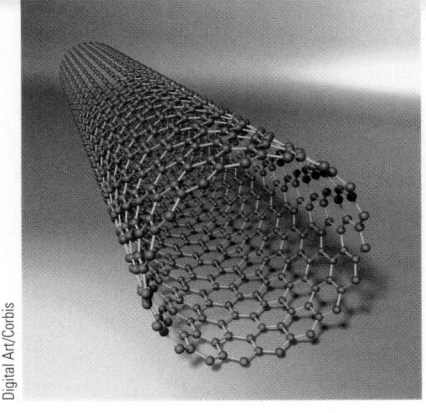

Digital Art/Corbis

**Carbon nanotube.** These tubes are assembled from six-member rings of carbon atoms and are typically about 1 nm in diameter.

Image courtesy: Dmitriy Dikin (Northwestern University)

**Graphene "paper."** Researchers at Northwestern University have reassembled graphene sheets to create a tough, flexible, paper-like material.

larger quantities by other methods, and more than 1000 scientific papers have been published on this substance. Chemists and physicists have found that the material is extremely strong and stiff and that it is a better conductor of electrons than any other material at room temperature. It was no surprise when Geim and Novoselov received the 2010 Nobel Prize in physics for their discovery.

*Chemical and Engineering News* (March 2009) said that although it was "considered a hypothetical curiosity just a few years ago, one-atom-thick graphene has stormed the world of scientific research." Research is

proceeding worldwide on its use in electronics and the dream is of making flexible displays. Watch for graphene-based devices to make a difference in your life in the next few years!

**Questions:**

1. Based on a C–C distance of 139 pm, what is the side-to-side dimension of a planar, $C_6$ ring?
2. If a graphene sheet has a width of 1.0 micrometer, how many $C_6$ rings are joined across the sheet?
3. Estimate the thickness of a sheet of graphene (in pm). How did you determine this value?

**Answers to these questions are available in Appendix N.**

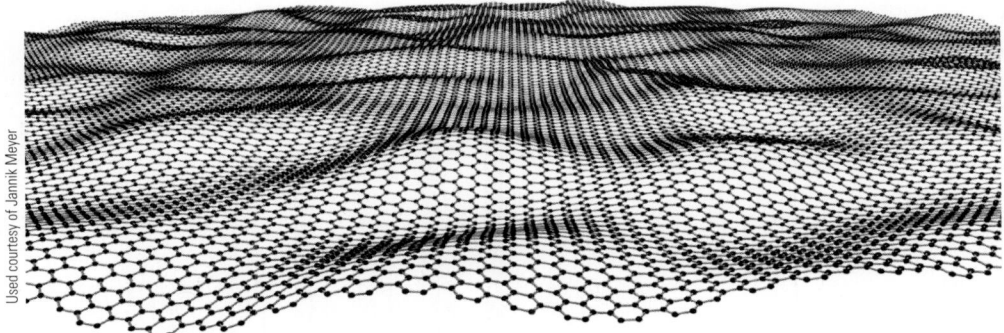

Used courtesy of Jannik Meyer

**Graphene is a single sheet of six-member carbon rings.** This latest material in the world of carbon chemistry is a faster conductor of electrons than any other material.

are associated with high enthalpies of fusion. Figure 13.19 shows the enthalpies of fusion for the metals of the fourth through the sixth periods. Here we see that transition metals have high enthalpies of fusion, with many of those in the sixth period being extraordinarily high. This trend parallels the trend seen with the melting points for these elements. Tungsten, which has the highest melting point of all the known elements except for carbon, also has the highest enthalpy of fusion among

**Table 13.3 Melting Points and Enthalpies of Fusion of Some Elements and Compounds**

| Element or Compound | Melting Point (°C) | Enthalpy of Fusion (kJ/mol) | Type of Interparticle Forces |
|---|---|---|---|
| *Metals* | | | |
| Hg | −39 | 2.29 | Metal bonding. |
| Na | 98 | 2.60 | |
| Al | 660 | 10.7 | |
| Ti | 1668 | 20.9 | |
| W | 3422 | 35.2 | |
| *Molecular Solids: Nonpolar Molecules* | | | |
| $O_2$ | −219 | 0.440 | Dispersion forces only. |
| $F_2$ | −220 | 0.510 | |
| $Cl_2$ | −102 | 6.41 | |
| $Br_2$ | −7.2 | 10.8 | |
| *Molecular Solids: Polar Molecules* | | | |
| HCl | −114 | 1.99 | All three HX molecules have dipole–dipole forces. Dispersion forces increase with size and molar mass. |
| HBr | −87 | 2.41 | |
| HI | −51 | 2.87 | |
| $H_2O$ | 0 | 6.01 | Hydrogen bonding, dispersion forces. |
| *Ionic Solids* | | | |
| NaF | 996 | 33.4 | All ionic solids have extended ion–ion interactions. Note the general trend is the same as for lattice energies (see Section 13.4 and Figure 13.15). |
| NaCl | 801 | 28.2 | |
| NaBr | 747 | 26.1 | |
| NaI | 660 | 23.6 | |

**FIGURE 13.19**
**Enthalpy of fusion of fourth-, fifth-, and sixth-period metals.** Enthalpies of fusion range from 2–5 kJ/mol for Group 1A elements to 35.2 kJ/mol for tungsten. Notice that enthalpies of fusion generally increase for group 4B–8B metals on descending the periodic table.

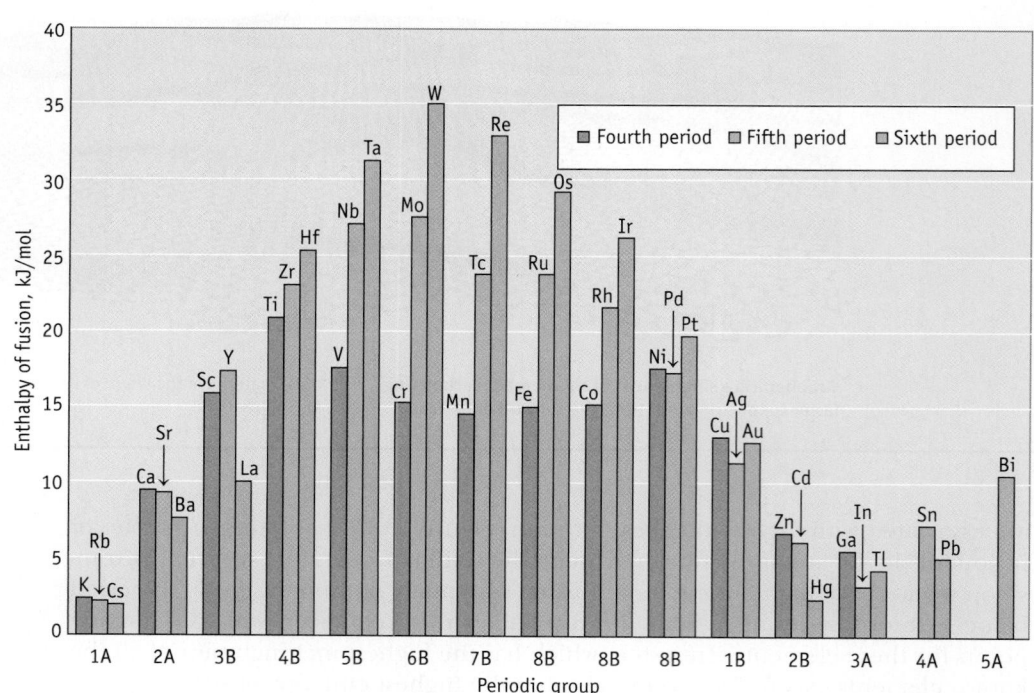

the transition metals. This is the reason tungsten is used for the filaments in incandescent lightbulbs; no other material has been found to work better since the invention of the lightbulb in 1908.

Table 13.3 presents some data for several basic types of substances: metals, polar and nonpolar molecules, and ionic solids. In general, nonpolar substances that form molecular solids have low melting points. Melting points increase within a series of related molecules, however, as the size and molar mass increase. This happens because London dispersion forces are generally larger when the molar mass is larger. Thus, increasing amounts of energy are required to break down the intermolecular forces in the solid, a principle that is reflected in an increasing enthalpy of fusion.

The ionic compounds in Table 13.3 have higher melting points and higher enthalpies of fusion than the molecular solids. This property is due to the strong ion–ion forces present in ionic solids, forces that are reflected in high lattice energies. Because ion–ion forces depend on ion size (as well as ion charge), there is a good correlation between lattice energy and the position of the metal or halogen in the periodic table. For example, the data in Table 13.3 show a decrease in melting point and enthalpy of fusion for sodium salts as the halide ion increases in size. This parallels the decrease in lattice energy seen with increasing ion size.

© Cengage Learning/
Charles D. Winters

**LED lights.** Incandescent lights, with a tungsten filament, may soon be a thing of the past. They can be replaced by LED (light-emitting diode) lamps with a much lower energy consumption. The LED element is a semiconductor that releases light energy when electrons recombine with holes.

## Sublimation: Conversion of Solid into Vapor

Molecules can escape directly from the solid to the gas phase by sublimation (Figure 13.20).

$$\text{Solid} \rightarrow \text{gas} \qquad \text{Energy required as heat} = \Delta_{\text{sublimation}}H$$

Sublimation, like fusion and evaporation, is an endothermic process. The energy required as heat is called the **enthalpy of sublimation**. Water, which has a molar enthalpy of sublimation of 51 kJ/mol, can be converted from solid ice to water vapor quite readily. A good example of this phenomenon is the sublimation of frost from grass and trees as night turns to day on a cold morning in the winter.

---

**REVIEW & CHECK FOR SECTION 13.6**

1. Which of the following Group 1A halides is expected to have the highest enthalpy of fusion?

   (a) NaCl          (b) KCl          (c) NaBr          (d) KBr

2. Suppose you wanted to cool 100. g of water from 20 °C to 0 °C using dry ice, $CO_2(s)$. The enthalpy of sublimation of $CO_2(s)$ is 25.2 kJ/mol. What mass of dry ice should you need?

   (a)  0.33 g          (b)  15 g          (c)  3.5 g          (d)  150 g

---

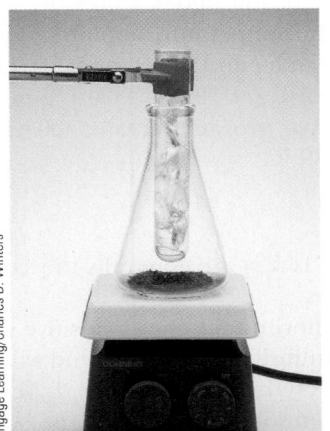

© Cengage Learning/Charles D. Winters

Iodine sublimes
when heated. →

© Cengage Learning/Charles D. Winters

**FIGURE 13.20 Sublimation.** Sublimation is the conversion of a solid directly to its vapor. Here, iodine ($I_2$) sublimes when warmed. If an ice-filled test tube is inserted into the flask, the vapor deposits on the cold surface.

## 13.7  Phase Diagrams

Depending on the conditions of temperature and pressure, a substance can exist as a gas, a liquid, or a solid. In addition, under certain specific conditions, two (or even three) states can coexist in equilibrium. It is possible to summarize this information in the form of a graph called a **phase diagram**. Phase diagrams are used to illustrate the relationship between phases of matter and the pressure and temperature.

### Water

Figure 13.21 illustrates the phase diagram for water. The lines in a phase diagram identify the conditions under which two phases exist at equilibrium. Conversely, all points that do not fall on the lines in the figure represent conditions under which there is only one state that is stable. Line *A–B* represents conditions for solid-vapor equilibrium, and line *A–C* for liquid–solid equilibrium. The line from point *A* to point *D*, representing the temperature and pressure combination at which the liquid and vapor phases are in equilibrium, is the same curve plotted for water vapor pressure in Figure 12.17. Recall that the normal boiling point, 100 °C in the case of water, is the temperature at which the equilibrium vapor pressure is 760 mm Hg.

Point *A*, appropriately called the **triple point**, indicates the conditions under which all three phases coexist in equilibrium. For water, the triple point is at $P = 4.6$ mm Hg and $T = 0.01$ °C.

The line *A–C* shows the conditions of pressure and temperature at which solid–liquid equilibrium exists. (Because no vapor pressure is involved here, the pressure referred to is the external pressure on the liquid.) For water, this line has a negative slope; the change for water is approximately −0.01 °C for each one-atmosphere increase in pressure. That is, the higher the external pressure, the lower the melting point.

The negative slope of the water solid–liquid equilibrium line can be explained from our knowledge of the structure of water and ice. When the pressure on an object increases, common sense tells us that the volume of the object will become smaller, giving the substance a higher density. Because ice is less dense than liquid water (due to the open lattice structure of ice, Figure 12.8), ice and water in equilibrium respond to increased pressure (at constant *T*) by melting ice to form more water because the same mass of liquid water requires less volume.

### Phase Diagrams and Thermodynamics

Let us explore the water phase diagram further by correlating phase changes with thermodynamic data. Suppose we begin with ice at −10 °C and under a pressure of 500 mm Hg (point *a* on Figure 13.21). As ice is heated (at constant *P*), it absorbs about 2.1 J/g · K in warming from point *a* to point *b* at a temperature between 0 °C and 0.01 °C. At this point, the solid is in equilibrium with liquid water. Solid-liquid equilibrium is maintained until 333 J/g has been transferred to the sample and it has become liquid water at this temperature. If the liquid, still under a pressure of 500 mm Hg, absorbs 4.184 J/g · K, it warms to point *c*. The temperature at point *c* is about 89 °C, and equilibrium is established between liquid water and water vapor. The equilibrium vapor pressure of the liquid water is 500 mm Hg. If about 2300 J/g is transferred to the liquid–vapor sample, the equilibrium vapor pressure remains 500 mm Hg until the liquid is completely converted to vapor at 89 °C.

### Carbon Dioxide

The features of the phase diagram for $CO_2$ (Figure 13.22) are generally the same as those for water but with some important differences.

In contrast to water, the $CO_2$ solid–liquid equilibrium line has a positive slope. Once again, increasing pressure on the solid in equilibrium with the liquid will shift the equilibrium to the more dense phase, but for $CO_2$ this will be the solid. Because solid $CO_2$ is denser than the liquid, the newly formed solid $CO_2$ sinks to the bottom in a container of liquid $CO_2$.

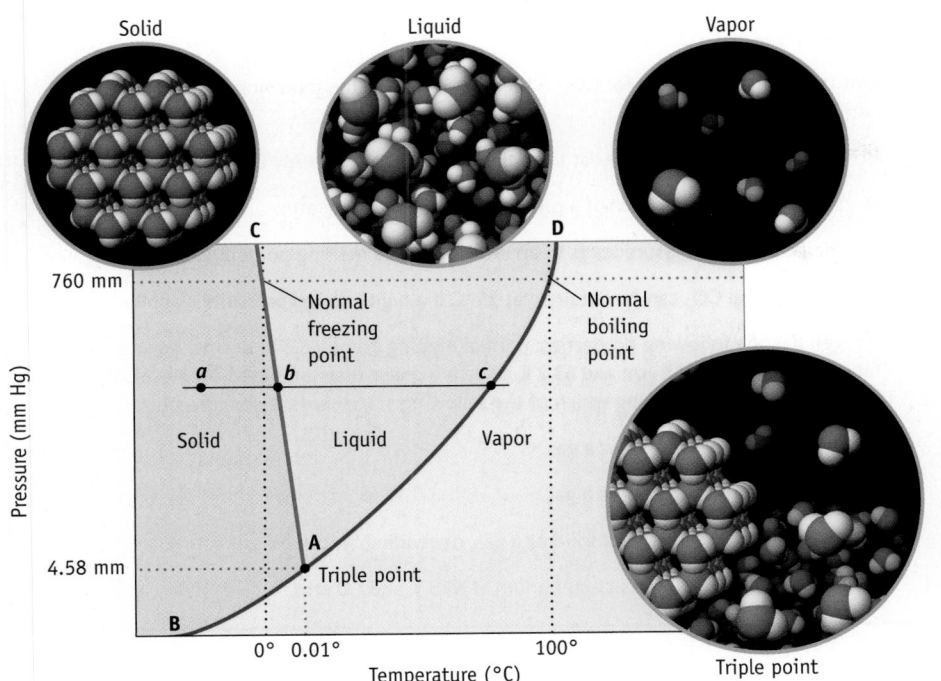

**FIGURE 13.21 Phase diagram for water.** The scale is intentionally exaggerated to be able to show the triple point and the negative slope of the line representing the liquid–solid equilibrium. (Points a, b, and c are discussed in the text.)

Another feature of the $CO_2$ phase diagram is the triple point that occurs at a pressure of 5.19 atm (3940 mm Hg) and 216.6 K ($-56.6$ °C). Carbon dioxide cannot be a liquid at pressures lower than this.

At pressures around normal atmospheric pressure, $CO_2$ will be either a solid or a gas, depending on the temperature. [At a pressure of 1 atm, solid $CO_2$ is in equilibrium with the gas at a temperature of 197.5 K ($-78.7$ °C).] As a result, as solid $CO_2$ warms above this temperature, it sublimes rather than melts. Carbon dioxide is called *dry ice* for this reason; it looks like water ice, but it does not melt.

From the $CO_2$ phase diagram, we can also learn that $CO_2$ gas can be converted to a liquid at room temperature (20–25 °C) by exerting a moderate pressure on the gas. In fact, $CO_2$ is regularly shipped in tanks as a liquid to laboratories and industrial companies.

Finally, the critical pressure and temperature for $CO_2$ are 73 atm and 31 °C, respectively. Because the critical temperature and pressure are easily attained in the laboratory, it is possible to observe the transformation to supercritical $CO_2$ (Figure 12.20).

**FIGURE 13.22 The phase diagram of $CO_2$.** Notice in particular the positive slope of the solid–liquid equilibrium line. (For more on the critical point, see page 573.)

**REVIEW & CHECK FOR SECTION 13.7**

1. Refer to the phase diagram for $CO_2$ in the text. Which of the following statements is *not* true?

    (a) Liquid and gaseous $CO_2$ exist in equilibrium at approximately 0 °C and 12 atm.

    (b) Liquid $CO_2$ can only exist at a pressure greater than 5.19 atm.

    (c) Increasing the pressure leads to an increase in the melting point of $CO_2(s)$.

    (d) Supercritical $CO_2$ can be obtained at 25 °C if a high enough pressure is applied.

2. Nitrogen has the following properties: normal melting point, 63.3 K; normal boiling point, 77.4 K; triple point, 0.123 atm and 63.2 K. Sketch a phase diagram based on these data. Determine from your drawing which of the following statements is *not* correct.

    (a) At 75 K and 0.20 atm $N_2$ is a gas.

    (b) At 66 K and 0.50 atm $N_2$ is a gas.

    (c) At 60 K $N_2$ will be either a solid or a gas, depending on the pressure.

    (d) Solid and liquid coexist at equilibrium at 63.3 K and 1.0 atm.

 and

# CHAPTER GOALS REVISITED

*Now that you have studied this chapter, you should ask whether you have met the chapter goals. In particular, you should be able to:*

### Understand cubic unit cells

a. Describe the three types of cubic unit cells: primitive cubic (pc), body-centered cubic (bcc), and face-centered cubic (fcc) (Section 13.1).

b. Relate atom size and unit cell dimensions. **Study Questions: 7, 8, 10, 38, 39, 41, 44, 46, 48, 61, and Go Chemistry Module 18.**

### Relate unit cells for ionic compounds to formulas

a. Understand the relation of unit cell structure and formula for ionic compounds. (Section 13.2). **Study Questions: 3, 4, 5, 6, 8, 40, and Go Chemistry Module 18.**

### Describe bonding in ionic and metallic solids and the nature of semiconductors.

a. Understand the band theory of bonding in metals and the electrical conductivity of metals. (Section 13.3). **Study Questions: 11, 13.**

b. Understand the nature of semiconductors. (Section 13.3). **Study Questions: 15–18, 51, 53.**

### Describe the properties of solids

a. Understand lattice energy and how it is calculated (Section 13.4). **Study Questions: 19, 21, 22, 24, 50.**

b. Characterize different types of solids: metallic (e.g., copper), ionic (e.g., NaCl and $CaF_2$), molecular (e.g., water and $I_2$), network (e.g., diamond), and amorphous (e.g., glass and many synthetic polymers) (Table 13.1). **Study Questions: 25–30.**

c. Define the processes of melting, freezing, and sublimation and their enthalpies (Sections 13.6 and 13.7). **Study Questions: 31, 32.**

### Interpret phase diagrams

a. Identify the different points (triple point, critical point, normal boiling point, freezing point) and regions (solid, liquid, vapor) of a phase diagram, and use the diagram to evaluate the vapor pressure of a liquid and the relative densities of a liquid and a solid (Section 13.7). **Study Questions: 33–36.**

## Study Questions

**◑WL** Interactive versions of these questions are assignable in OWL.

▲ denotes challenging questions.

Blue-numbered questions have answers in Appendix R and fully worked solutions in the *Student Solutions Manual*.

## Practicing Skills

### Metallic and Ionic Solids
*(See Sections 13.1 and 13.2 and Examples 13.1–13.3.)*

1. Outline a two-dimensional unit cell for the pattern shown here. If the black squares are labeled A and the white squares are B, what is the simplest formula for a "compound" based on this pattern?

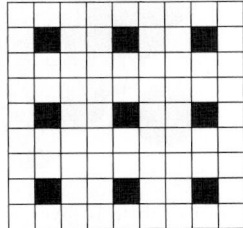

2. Outline a two-dimensional unit cell for the pattern shown here. If the black squares are labeled A and the white squares are B, what is the simplest formula for a "compound" based on this pattern?

3. One way of viewing the unit cell of perovskite was illustrated in Example 13.2. Another way is shown here. Prove that this view also leads to a formula of $CaTiO_3$.

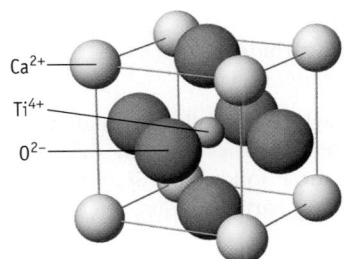

4. Rutile, $TiO_2$, crystallizes in a structure characteristic of many other ionic compounds. How many formula units of $TiO_2$ are in the unit cell illustrated here? (The oxide ions marked by an *x* are wholly within the cell; the others are in the cell faces.)

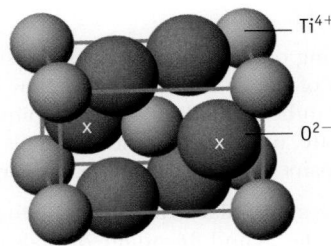

5. Cuprite is a semiconductor. Oxide ions are at the cube corners and in the cube center. Copper ions are wholly within the unit cell.
   (a) What is the formula of cuprite?
   (b) What is the oxidation number of copper?

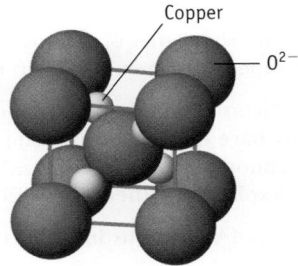

6. The mineral fluorite, which is composed of calcium ions and fluoride ions, has the unit cell shown here.
   (a) What type of unit cell is described by the $Ca^{2+}$ ions?
   (b) Where are the $F^-$ ions located, in octahedral holes or tetrahedral holes?
   (c) Based on this unit cell, what is the formula of fluorite?

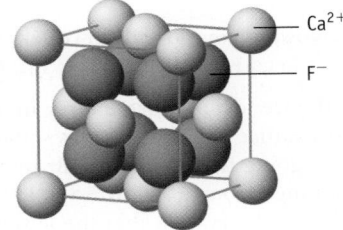

7. Calcium metal crystallizes in a face-centered cubic unit cell. The density of the solid is 1.54 g/cm³. What is the radius of a calcium atom?

8. The density of copper metal is 8.95 g/cm³. If the radius of a copper atom is 127.8 pm, is the copper unit cell primitive, body-centered cubic, or face-centered cubic?

9. Potassium iodide has a face-centered cubic unit cell of iodide ions with potassium ions in octahedral holes. The density of KI is 3.12 g/cm³. What is the length of one side of the unit cell? (Ion sizes are found in Table 7.12.)

10. ▲ A unit cell of cesium chloride is shown on page 590. The density of the solid is 3.99 g/cm³, and the radius of the $Cl^-$ ion is 181 pm. Calculate the radius of the $Cs^+$ ion in the center of the cell. (Assume that the $Cs^+$ ion touches all of the corner $Cl^-$ ions.)

## Metals and Semiconductors
*(See Section 13.3.)*

11. Considering only the molecular orbitals formed by combinations of the 2s atomic orbitals, how many molecular orbitals can be formed by 1000 Li atoms? In the lowest energy state, how many of these orbitals will be populated by pairs of electrons and how many will be empty?

12. How many molecular orbitals will be formed by combination of the 3s and 3p atomic orbitals in 1.0 mol of Mg atoms? At 0 K, what fraction of these orbitals will be occupied by electron pairs (all orbitals filled up to the Fermi level)?

13. Conduction of an electric current is a general property associated with metals. How does the theory for metallic bonding explain conductivity?

14. Most metals are shiny, that is, they reflect light. How does the bonding theory for metals explain this characteristic?

15. Elemental silicon and carbon (in the diamond allotropic form) have the same solid-state structure. However, diamond is an insulator and silicon is a semiconductor. Explain why there is a difference.

16. List the Group 4A elements in order of the size of the band gap.

17. Define the terms intrinsic semiconductor and extrinsic semiconductor. Give an example of each.

18. Explain the conductivity that occurs in an aluminum-doped silicon semiconductor. Is this material a *p*-type or an *n*-type semiconductor?

## Ionic Bonding and Lattice Energy
*(See Section 13.4.)*

19. List the following compounds in order from least negative to most negative lattice energy: LiI, LiF, CaO, RbI.

20. Examine the trends in lattice energy in Table 13.2. The value of the lattice energy becomes somewhat more negative on going from NaI to NaBr to NaCl, and all are in the range from $-700$ to $-800$ kJ/mol. Suggest a reason for the observation that the lattice energy of NaF ($\Delta_{\text{lattice}} U = -926$ kJ/mol) is much more negative than those of the other sodium halides.

21. To melt an ionic solid, energy must be supplied to disrupt the forces between ions so the regular array of ions collapses. If the distance between the anion and the cation in a crystalline solid decreases (but ion charges remain the same), should the melting point decrease or increase? Explain.

22. Which compound in each of the following pairs should have the higher melting point? (See Study Question 21.)
    (a) NaCl or RbCl
    (b) BaO or MgO
    (c) NaCl or MgS

23. Calculate the molar enthalpy of formation, $\Delta_f H°$, of solid lithium fluoride from the lattice energy (Table 13.2) and other thermochemical data. The enthalpy of formation of Li(g), $\Delta_f H°$ [Li(g)] = 159.37 kJ/mol, and other required data can be found in Appendices F and L.

24. Calculate the lattice enthalpy for RbCl. In addition to data in Appendices F and L, you will need the following information:

$$\Delta_f H° \text{ [Rb(g)]} = 80.9 \text{ kJ/mol}$$

$$\Delta_f H° \text{ [RbCl(s)]} = -435.4 \text{ kJ/mol}$$

## Other Types of Solids
*(See Section 13.5.)*

25. A diamond unit cell is shown here.
    (a) How many carbon atoms are in one unit cell?
    (b) The unit cell can be considered as a cubic unit cell of C atoms with other C atoms in holes in the lattice. What type of unit cell is this (pc, bcc, fcc)? In what holes are other C atoms located, octahedral or tetrahedral holes?

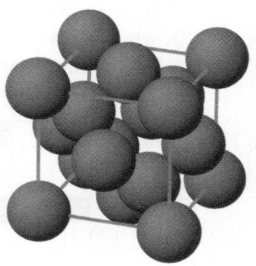

26. The structure of graphite is given in Figure 2.7.
    (a) What type of intermolecular bonding forces exist between the layers of six-member carbon rings?
    (b) Account for the lubricating ability of graphite. That is, why does graphite feel slippery? Why does pencil lead (which is really graphite in clay) leave black marks on paper?

27. We have identified five types of solids (metallic, ionic, molecular, network, amorphous). What particles make up each of these solids and what are the forces of attraction between these particles?

28. List the general properties of each type of solid.

29. Classify each of the following materials as falling into one of the categories listed in Table 13.1. What particles make up these solids and what are the forces of attraction between particles? Give one physical property of each.
    (a) gallium arsenide
    (b) polystyrene
    (c) silicon carbide
    (d) perovskite, $CaTiO_3$

30. Classify each of the following materials as falling into one of the categories listed in Table 13.1. What particles make up these solids, and what are the forces of attraction between particles? Give one physical property of each.
    (a) Si doped with P
    (b) graphite
    (c) benzoic acid, $C_6H_5CO_2H$
    (d) $Na_2SO_4$

## Phase Changes for Solids
*(See Section 13.6.)*

31. Benzene, $C_6H_6$, is an organic liquid that freezes at 5.5 °C (◄ Figure 12.1) to form beautiful, feather-like crystals. How much energy is evolved as heat when 15.5 g of benzene freezes at 5.5 °C? (The enthalpy of fusion of benzene is 9.95 kJ/mol.) If the 15.5-g sample is remelted, again at 5.5 °C, what quantity of energy is required to convert it to a liquid?

32. The specific heat capacity of silver is 0.235 J/g · K. Its melting point is 962 °C, and its enthalpy of fusion is 11.3 kJ/mol. What quantity of energy, in joules, is required to change 5.00 g of silver from a solid at 25 °C to a liquid at 962 °C?

## Phase Diagrams and Phase Changes
*(See Section 13.7.)*

33. Consider the phase diagram of $CO_2$ in Figure 13.22.
    (a) Is the density of liquid $CO_2$ greater or less than that of solid $CO_2$?
    (b) In what phase do you find $CO_2$ at 5 atm and 0 °C?
    (c) Can $CO_2$ be liquefied at 45 °C?

34. Use the phase diagram given here to answer the following questions:

    (a) In what phase is the substance found at room temperature and 1.0 atm pressure?
    (b) If the pressure exerted on a sample is 0.75 atm and the temperature is −114 °C, in what phase does the substance exist?
    (c) If you measure the vapor pressure of a liquid sample and find it to be 380 mm Hg, what is the temperature of the liquid phase?
    (d) What is the vapor pressure of the solid at −122 °C?
    (e) Which is the denser phase—solid or liquid? Explain briefly.

35. Liquid ammonia, $NH_3(\ell)$, was once used in home refrigerators as the heat transfer fluid. The specific heat capacity of the liquid is 4.7 J/g · K and that of the vapor is 2.2 J/g · K. The enthalpy of vaporization is 23.33 kJ/mol at the boiling point. If you heat 12 kg of liquid ammonia from −50.0 °C to its boiling point of −33.3 °C, allow it to evaporate, and then continue warming to 0.0 °C, how much energy must you supply?

36. If your air conditioner is more than several years old, it may use the chlorofluorocarbon $CCl_2F_2$ as the heat transfer fluid. The normal boiling point of $CCl_2F_2$ is −29.8 °C, and the enthalpy of vaporization is 20.11 kJ/mol. The gas and the liquid have molar heat capacities of 117.2 J/mol · K and 72.3 J/mol · K, respectively. How much energy is evolved as heat when 20.0 g of $CCl_2F_2$ is cooled from +40 °C to −40 °C?

## General Questions

*These questions are not designated as to type or location in the chapter. They may combine several concepts.*

37. Construct a phase diagram for $O_2$ from the following information: normal boiling point, 90.18 K; normal melting point, 54.8 K; and triple point, 54.34 K at a pressure of 2 mm Hg. Very roughly estimate the vapor pressure of liquid $O_2$ at −196 °C, the lowest temperature easily reached in the laboratory. Is the density of liquid $O_2$ greater or less than that of solid $O_2$?

38. ▲ Tungsten crystallizes in the unit cell shown here.

316.5 pm

    (a) What type of unit cell is this?
    (b) How many tungsten atoms occur per unit cell?
    (c) If the edge of the unit cell is 316.5 pm, what is the radius of a tungsten atom? (*Hint:* The W atoms touch each other along the diagonal line from one corner of the unit cell to the opposite corner of the unit cell.)

39. Silver crystallizes in a face-centered cubic unit cell. Each side of the unit cell has a length of 409 pm. What is the radius of a silver atom?

40. ▲ The unit cell shown here is for calcium carbide. How many calcium atoms and how many carbon atoms are in each unit cell? What is the formula of calcium carbide? (Calcium ions are silver in color and carbon atoms are gray.)

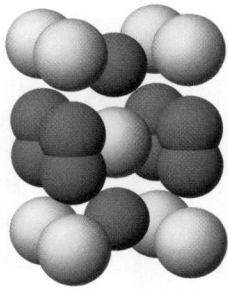

41. The very dense metal iridium has a face-centered cubic unit cell and a density of 22.56 g/cm³. Use this information to calculate the radius of an atom of the element.

42. Vanadium metal has a density of 6.11 g/cm³. Assuming the vanadium atomic radius is 132 pm, is the vanadium unit cell primitive cubic, body-centered cubic, or face-centered cubic?

43. ▲ Calcium fluoride is the well-known mineral fluorite. Each unit cell contains four $Ca^{2+}$ ions and eight $F^-$ ions. The $F^-$ ions fill all the tetrahedral holes in a face-centered cubic lattice of $Ca^{2+}$ ions. The edge of the $CaF_2$ unit cell is $5.46295 \times 10^{-8}$ cm in length. The density of the solid is 3.1805 g/cm³. Use this information to calculate Avogadro's number.

44. ▲ Iron has a body-centered cubic unit cell with a cell dimension of 286.65 pm. The density of iron is 7.874 g/cm³. Use this information to calculate Avogadro's number.

45. ▲ You can get some idea of how efficiently spherical atoms or ions are packed in a three-dimensional solid by seeing how well circular atoms pack in two dimensions. Using the drawings shown here, prove that B is a more efficient way to pack circular atoms than A. The unit cell of A contains portions of four circles and one hole. In B, packing coverage can be calculated by looking at a triangle that contains portions of three circles and one hole. Show that A fills about 80% of the available space, whereas B fills closer to 90% of the available space.

 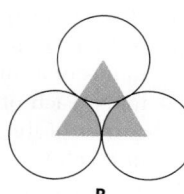

A          B

46. ▲ Assuming that in a primitive cubic unit cell the spherical atoms or ions just touch along the cube's edges, calculate the percentage of empty space within the unit cell. (Recall that the volume of a sphere is $(4/3)\pi r^3$, where $r$ is the radius of the sphere.)

47. ▲ The solid state structure of silicon is shown below.

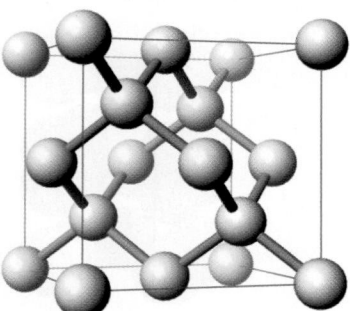

(a) Describe this crystal as pc, bcc, or fcc. What type of holes are occupied in the lattice?

(b) Calculate the density of silicon in g/cm³ (given that the cube edge has a length of 543.1 pm), and estimate the radius of the silicon atom. (*Note:* The Si atoms on the edges do not touch one another.)

48. ▲ The solid state structure of silicon carbide, SiC, is shown below. Knowing that the Si—C bond length is 188.8 pm (and the Si—C—Si bond angle is 109.5°), calculate the density of SiC.

**Unit cell of SiC.**

**Sample of silicon carbide.**

49. Spinels are solids with the general formula $AB_2O_4$ (where $A^{2+}$ and $B^{3+}$ are metal cations of the same or different metals). The best-known example is common magnetite, $Fe_3O_4$ [which you can formulate as $(Fe^{2+})(Fe^{3+})_2O_4$]. Another example is the mineral often referred to as *spinel*, $MgAl_2O_4$.

**A crystal of the spinel MgAl₂O₄.**

The oxide ions of spinels form a face-centered cubic lattice. In a *normal spinel*, cations occupy ⅛ of the tetrahedral sites and ½ of the octahedral sites.

(a) In $MgAl_2O_4$, in what types of holes are the magnesium and aluminum ions found?

(b) The mineral chromite has the formula $FeCr_2O_4$. What ions are involved, and in what types of holes are they found?

**50.** Using the thermochemical data below and an estimated value of $-2481$ kJ/mol for the lattice energy for $Na_2O$, calculate the value for the *second* electron affinity of oxygen $[O^-(g) + e^- \rightarrow O^{2-}(g)]$.

| Quantity | Numerical Value (kJ/mol) |
|---|---|
| Enthalpy of atomization of Na | 107.3 |
| Ionization energy of Na | 495.9 |
| Enthalpy of formation of solid $Na_2O$ | $-418.0$ |
| Enthalpy of formation of $O(g)$ from $O_2$ | 249.1 |
| First electron attachment enthalpy of O | $-141.0$ |

**51.** The band gap in gallium arsenide is 140 kJ/mol. What is the maximum wavelength of light needed to excite an electron to move from the valence band to the conduction band?

**52.** The conductivity of an intrinsic semiconductor increases with increasing temperature. How can this be rationalized?

**53.** Which will show the highest conductivity at 298 K, silicon or germanium?

**54.** Identify the following as either *p*- or *n*-type semiconductors.
(a) Germanium doped with arsenic
(b) Silicon doped with phosphorus
(c) Germanium doped with indium
(d) Germanium doped with antimony

**55.** Diamond-based semiconductors are currently of enormous interest in the research community. Although diamond itself is an insulator, the addition of a dopant will narrow the band gap. One semiconductor system has diamond with boron as a dopant. Is this a *p*- or an *n*-type semiconductor?

**56.** Molecular solids, network solids, and amorphous solids all contain atoms that are joined together by covalent bonds. However, these classes of compounds are very different in overall structure and this leads to different physical properties associated with each group. Describe how the overall structures of these classes of solids differ from each other.

## In the Laboratory

**57.** Like ZnS, lead(II) sulfide, PbS (commonly called *galena*), has a 1:1 empirical formula with a 2+ cation combined with the sulfide anion.

**Unit cell of PbS.**

**Sample of galena.**

Does PbS have the same solid structure as ZnS? If different, how are they different? How is the unit cell of PbS related to its formula?

**58.** $CaTiO_3$, a perovskite, has the structure below.
(a) If the density of the solid is 4.10 g/cm³, what is the length of a side of the unit cell?
(b) Calculate the radius of the $Ti^{4+}$ ion in the center of the unit cell. How well does your calculation agree with a literature value of 75 pm?

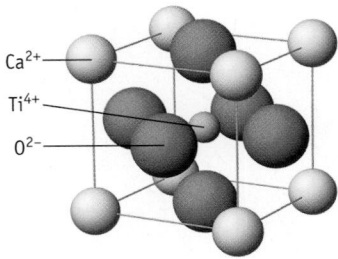

$Ca^{2+}$
$Ti^{4+}$
$O^{2-}$

**Unit cell of the perovskite $CaTiO_3$.**

**A sample of perovskite, $CaTiO_3$.**

# Summary and Conceptual Questions

*The following questions may use concepts from this and previous chapters.*

59. ▲ Boron phosphide, BP, is a semiconductor and a hard, abrasion-resistant material. It is made by reacting boron tribromide and phosphorus tribromide in a hydrogen atmosphere at high temperature (>750 °C).
    (a) Write a balanced chemical equation for the synthesis of BP. (*Hint:* Hydrogen is a reducing agent.)
    (b) Boron phosphide crystallizes in a zinc-blend structure, formed from boron atoms in a face-centered cubic lattice and phosphorus atoms in tetrahedral holes. How many tetrahedral holes are filled with P atoms in each unit cell?
    (c) The length of a unit cell of BP is 478 pm. What is the density of the solid in $g/cm^3$?
    (d) Calculate the closest distance between a B and a P atom in the unit cell. (Assume the B atoms do not touch along the cell edge. The B atoms in the faces touch the B atoms at the corners of the unit cell.)

60. ▲ Why is it not possible for a salt with the formula $M_3X$ ($Na_3PO_4$, for example) to have a face-centered cubic lattice of X anions with M cations in octahedral holes?

61. ▲ Two identical swimming pools are filled with uniform spheres of ice packed as closely as possible. The spheres in the first pool are the size of grains of sand; those in the second pool are the size of oranges. The ice in both pools melts. In which pool, if either, will the water level be higher? (Ignore any differences in filling space at the planes next to the walls and bottom.)

62. Spinels are described in Study Question 49. Consider two normal spinels, $CoAl_2O_4$ and $SnCo_2O_4$. What metal ions are involved in each? What are their electron configurations? Are the metal ions paramagnetic, and if so how many unpaired electrons are involved?

## Applying Chemical Principles

### Tin Disease

Organ pipes in northern European cathedrals have been made of tin for several hundred years. It is believed that the metal improves both the tone and appearance of the pipes. Now organ pipes are made of a tin-lead alloy, in part because many old organ pipes have crumbled over time due to "tin disease." Gray splotches appear on the normally shiny metal and over time the metal crumbles to a gray powder. Although it could be assumed that the tin reacted with other elements or compounds to form this gray substance, chemical analysis shows the substance is pure tin.

What is the cause of "tin disease"? Two allotropes of tin exist at atmospheric pressure. The metallic form, known as white tin (or $\beta$-tin), is stable at temperatures above 13 °C (Figure 1). This metallic form of tin has a tetragonal crystal structure (Figure 2). Below 13 °C, the metal undergoes a phase transition to a cubic crystal structure that is similar to diamond (page 596). The transition occurs slowly, with a rate that depends on the purity of the tin and the temperature, but the final product is gray tin or $\alpha$-tin.

The tetragonal structure of white tin has atoms at each corner as well as an atom in four of its six faces and an atom at the center of the lattice. The cubic crystal lattice structure of gray tin has an atom on each of the six faces and four atoms within the unit cell (in addition to atoms at the corners) as in the diamond structure.

The low temperature transformation of white tin to gray tin has been used to explain some famous disasters in history, one apparently true, the other false.

Early in the 20th century, there was great interest in reaching the South Pole, and many tried. The British explorer Robert Scott mounted a large expedition and reached the Pole in January 1912 with a party of five. It was an enormous accomplishment, but he learned to his great disappointment that the Norwegian Roald Amundsen had beaten him by five weeks. Having reached their goal, the Scott party started the 800-mile journey back across the polar ice to the Ross Sea. Along the journey to the Pole they had left food and fuel for use on their return trip. Both fuel and food were packed in tin cans with tin-soldered joints. Unfortunately, in the extremely low temperature, the tin in the joints turned into gray tin, flaked off, and the fuel leaked out. None was available to use, and all in Scott's party perished.

Another story of tin disease is a myth: the legend of crumbling buttons on the overcoats of French soldiers in 1812. In the winter of 1812, Napoleon's army fought and lost a brutal campaign in Russia. The shiny tin buttons used by the French soldiers are said to have crumbled in the cold Russian climate so they could not keep their clothing around them in the frigid weather. The problem with this story is that the uniform buttons at the time were made of bone.

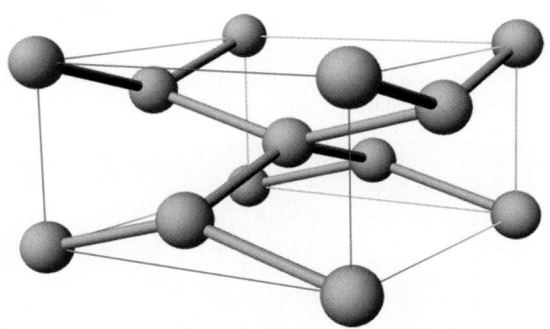

**FIGURE 2** **A tetragonal unit cell of white of $\beta$-tin.** The tetragonal unit cell has 90 angles at each corner. Two of the three sides are equal in length (583 pm) while the third side is shorter (318 pm). (Note that the lines connecting atoms are not bonds. They are meant only to show the spatial relationship of the atoms.)

### Questions:

1. How many tin atoms are contained in the tetragonal crystal lattice unit cell of $\beta$-tin? How many tin atoms are contained in the cubic crystal lattice unit cell of $\alpha$-tin?
2. Using the dimensions of the unit cell and the molar mass of tin, calculate the density of white tin (in g/cm³).
3. The density of gray tin is 5.769 g/cm³. Determine the dimensions (in pm) of the cubic crystal lattice.
4. Determine the percentage of space occupied by tin atoms in both the tetragonal and cubic crystal lattices. The atomic radius of tin is 141 pm.

### References:

1. J. Emsley, *Nature's Building Blocks, An A–Z Guide to the Elements*, Oxford University Press, 2001.
2. P. LeCouteur and J. Burreson, *Napoleon's Buttons*, Penguin Putnam, New York, 2003.

© Cengage Learning/Charles D. Winters

**FIGURE 1** **A sample of white tin.** This common element has a density of 7.31 g/cm³ and a melting point of 232 °C.

# 14 Solutions and Their Behavior

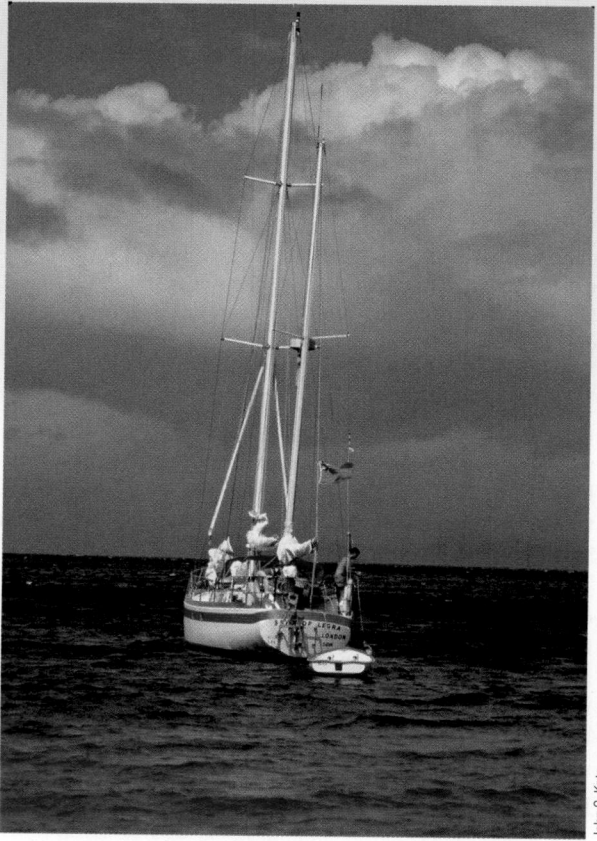

The Seax, an ocean-going yacht, in the Fiji Islands.

Portable reverse osmosis water purifier carried by deep water sailors.

**Survival at Sea** In the late 1980s, Bill and Simone Butler set off from Florida to sail their 38-foot boat around the world. Everything went well as they sailed through the Panama Canal and into the Pacific Ocean. Somewhere west of Costa Rica, however, on June 15, 1989, their boat was attacked by a school of whales in the middle of the night. The boat was holed and was going to sink. They had only enough time to launch their small life raft, grab some fishing line and a few other supplies, and one other important device: a portable water purifier that worked by reverse osmosis.

The Butlers drifted toward the east in their little raft for 66 days. They subsisted on the raw fish they could catch, but most importantly they had fresh water to drink from the reverse osmosis device. The device was able to produce 2–3 L of pure water a day, which saved their lives. Although they lost some weight, they were in good health when they were rescued by Costa Rican fishermen on August 19, 1989.

## Question:

What is the osmotic pressure of seawater at 25 °C with a total dissolved ion concentration of 1.15 M?

**The answer to this question is available in Appendix N.**

## CHAPTER GOALS

*See Chapter Goals Revisited (page 646) for Study Questions keyed to these goals.*

- Calculate and use the solution concentration units molality, mole fraction, and weight percent.

- Understand the solution process.

- Understand and use the colligative properties of solutions.

- Recognize the properties and importance of colloids

**☉WL**

Sign in to OWL at **www.cengage.com/owl** to view tutorials and simulations, develop problem-solving skills, and complete online homework assigned by your professor.

**go** Chemistry

Download mini lecture videos for key concept review and exam prep from OWL or purchase them from **www.cengagebrain.com**

We come into contact with solutions every day: aqueous solutions of ionic salts, gasoline with additives to improve its properties, and household cleaners such as ammonia in water. We purposely make solutions. Adding sugar, flavoring, and sometimes $CO_2$ to water produces a palatable soft drink. Athletes drink commercial beverages with dissolved salts to match salt concentrations in body fluids precisely, thus allowing the fluid to be taken into the body more rapidly. In medicine, saline solutions (aqueous solutions containing NaCl and other soluble salts) are infused into the body to replace lost fluids.

A **solution** is a homogeneous mixture of two or more substances in a single phase. By convention, the component present in largest amount is identified as the **solvent** and the other component(s) as the **solute**(s) (Figure 14.1). Although other types of solutions exist (such as alloys, solid solutions of metals), the objective in this chapter is to develop an understanding of gases, liquids, and solids dissolved in liquid solvents.

Experience tells you that adding a solute to a pure liquid will change the properties of the liquid. Indeed, that is the reason some solutions are made. For instance, adding antifreeze to the water in your car's radiator prevents the coolant from boiling in the summer and freezing in the winter. The changes that occur in the freezing and boiling points when a substance is dissolved in a pure liquid are two observations we want to examine in detail. These properties, as well as the osmotic pressure of a solution and changes in solvent vapor pressure, are examples of colligative properties. **Colligative properties** are properties of solutions that depend only on the number of solute particles per solvent molecule and not on the identity of the solute.

**(a)** Copper(II) chloride, the solute, is added to water, the solvent.

**(b)** Interactions between water molecules and $Cu^{2+}$ and $Cl^-$ ions allow the solid to dissolve. The ions are now sheathed with water molecules.

**FIGURE 14.1** Making a solution of copper(II) chloride (the solute) in water (the solvent). When ionic compounds dissolve in water, each ion is surrounded by water molecules. The number of water molecules depends on ion size and charge.

**FIGURE 14.2 Preparing 0.100 molal and 0.100 molar solutions.** In the flask on the right, 0.100 mol (19.4 g) of $K_2CrO_4$ was mixed with enough water to make 1.000 L of solution. (The volumetric flask was filled to the mark on its neck, indicating that the volume is 1.000 L. Slightly less than 1.00 L of water was added.) If 1.00 kg of water was added to 0.100 mol of $K_2CrO_4$ in the flask on the left, the volume of solution is greater than 1.000 L. (The small pile of yellow solid in front of the flasks is 0.100 mol of $K_2CrO_4$.)

Notice the difference in water levels in the two flasks

0.100 molal solution
Water added to flask = 1.00 kg
Volume of solution > 1.00 L

0.100 molar solution
Water added to flask < 1.00 L
Volume of solution = 1.00 L

© Cengage Learning/Charles D. Winters

## 14.1 Units of Concentration

To analyze the colligative properties of solutions, we need ways of measuring solute concentrations that reflect the number of molecules or ions of solute per molecule of solvent.

Molarity, a concentration unit useful in stoichiometry calculations, is not useful when dealing with most colligative properties. Recall that molarity (M) is defined as the number of moles of solute per liter of solution (◄ page 173), so using molarity does not allow us to identify the exact amount of solvent used to make the solution. This fact is illustrated in Figure 14.2. The flask on the right contains a 0.100 M aqueous solution of potassium chromate. It was made by adding enough water to 0.100 mol of $K_2CrO_4$ to make 1.000 L of solution. The amount of solvent (water) that was actually added is not readily known. If 1.00 kg of water had been added to 0.100 mol of $K_2CrO_4$, as illustrated with the flask on the left in Figure 14.2, the volume of solution would be greater than 1.000 L.

Three concentration units are described here that reflect the number of molecules or ions of solute per solvent molecule: molality, mole fraction, and weight percent.

The **molality**, *m*, of a solution is defined as the amount of solute (mol) per kilogram of solvent.

$$\text{Concentration } (c, \text{ mol/kg}) = \text{molality of solute} = \frac{\text{amount of solute (mol)}}{\text{mass of solvent (kg)}} \quad (14.1)$$

The molality of $K_2CrO_4$ in the flask on the left side of Figure 14.2 is 0.100 mol/kg. It was prepared from 0.100 mol (19.4 g) of $K_2CrO_4$ and 1.00 kg (1.000 L × 1.00 kg/L) of water.

Notice that different quantities of water were used to make the 0.100 M (0.100 molar) and 0.100 *m* (0.100 molal) solutions of $K_2CrO_4$. This means the *molarity and the molality of a given solution cannot be the same*, although the difference may be negligibly small when the solution is quite dilute.

The **mole fraction**, *X*, of a solution component is defined as the amount of that component ($n_A$) divided by the total amount of all of the components of the mixture ($n_A + n_B + n_C + \ldots$). Mathematically it is represented as

• **Mole Fraction and Gases** The mole fraction of a gas in a mixture of gases was defined on page 526.

$$\text{Mole fraction of A } (X_A) = \frac{n_A}{n_A + n_B + n_C + \ldots} \quad (14.2)$$

Consider a solution that contains 1.00 mol (46.1 g) of ethanol, $C_2H_5OH$, in 9.00 mol (162 g) of water. The mole fraction of alcohol is 0.100, and that of water is 0.900.

$$X_{ethanol} = \frac{1.00\ mol\ ethanol}{1.00\ mol\ ethanol + 9.00\ mol\ water} = 0.100$$

$$X_{water} = \frac{9.00\ mol\ water}{1.00\ mol\ ethanol + 9.00\ mol\ water} = 0.900$$

Notice that the sum of the mole fractions of the components in the solution equals 1.000, a relationship that must be true, based on how mole fraction is defined.

**Weight percent** is the mass of one component divided by the total mass of the mixture, multiplied by 100%:

$$Weight\ \%\ A = \frac{mass\ of\ A}{mass\ of\ A + mass\ of\ B + mass\ of\ C + ...} \times 100\% \qquad (14.3)$$

The alcohol–water mixture has 46.1 g of ethanol and 162 g of water, so the total mass of solution is 208 g, and the weight % of alcohol is

$$Weight\ \%\ ethanol = \frac{46.1\ g\ ethanol}{46.1\ g\ ethanol + 162\ g\ water} \times 100\% = 22.2\%$$

Weight percent is a common unit in consumer products (Figure 14.3). Vinegar, for example, is an aqueous solution containing approximately 5% acetic acid and 95% water. The label on a common household bleach lists its active ingredient as 6.00% sodium hypochlorite (NaOCl) and 94.00% inert ingredients.

Naturally occurring solutions are often very dilute. Environmental chemists, biologists, geologists, oceanographers, and others frequently use **parts per million (ppm)** to express their concentrations. The unit ppm refers to relative quantities by mass; 1.0 ppm represents 1.0 g of a substance in a sample with a total mass of 1.0 million g or 1 mg in 1000 g.

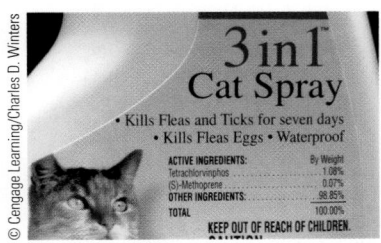
**FIGURE 14.3  Weight percent.** The composition of many common products is often given in terms of weight percent. Here, the label on the cat spray indicates it contains 1.15% active ingredients.

## EXAMPLE 14.1    Calculating Mole Fractions, Molality, and Weight Percent

**Problem**  Assume you add 1.2 kg of ethylene glycol, $HOCH_2CH_2OH$, as an antifreeze to 4.0 kg of water in the radiator of your car. What are the mole fraction, molality, and weight percent of the ethylene glycol?

**What Do You Know?**  You know the identity and masses of solute and solvent.

**Strategy**  The amount of solute and solvent can be calculated using the mass and molar mass of each material. The masses and amounts of solute and solvent can then be combined to calculate the concentration in each of the desired concentration units using Equations 14.1–14.3.

**Solution**  The 1.2 kg of ethylene glycol (molar mass = 62.1 g/mol) is equivalent to 19 mol, and 4.0 kg of water represents 220 mol.

Mole fraction:

$$X_{glycol} = \frac{19\ mol\ ethylene\ glycol}{19\ mol\ ethylene\ glycol + 220\ mol\ water} = 0.080$$

Molality:

$$c_{glycol} = \frac{19\ mol\ ethylene\ glycol}{4.0\ kg\ water} = 4.8\ mol/kg = 4.8\ m$$

Weight percent:

$$Weight\ \% = \frac{1.2 \times 10^3\ g\ ethylene\ glycol}{1.2 \times 10^3 g\ ethylene\ glycol + 4.0 \times 10^3\ g\ water} \times 100\% = 23\%$$

**Commercial antifreeze.** This solution contains ethylene glycol, $HOCH_2CH_2OH$, an organic alcohol that is readily soluble in water. Regulations specify that the weight percent of ethylene glycol in ethylene glycol–based antifreeze must be at least 75%. (The remainder of the solution can be other glycols and water.)

**Think about Your Answer** Although the numerical values are very different, the information contained in these values is similar; each relates to the relative numbers of solvent and solute particles.

**Check Your Understanding**

(a) Mole fraction, molality, and weight percent: If you dissolve 10.0 g (about one heaping teaspoonful) of sugar (sucrose, $C_{12}H_{22}O_{11}$), in a cup of water (250. g), what are the mole fraction, molality, and weight percent of sugar?

(b) Parts per million: Seawater has a sodium ion concentration of $1.08 \times 10^4$ ppm. If the sodium is present in the form of dissolved sodium chloride, what mass of NaCl is in each liter of seawater? Seawater is denser than pure water because of dissolved salts. Its density is 1.05 g/mL.

---

**REVIEW & CHECK FOR SECTION 14.1**

1. You dissolve 1.0 mol of urea ($H_2NCONH_2$) in 270 g of water. The mole fraction of urea is

   (a) $3.7 \times 10^{-3}$     (b) 0.063     (c) 16     (d) 1.0

   and its molality is

   (a) 1.0     (b) 3.7     (c) 0.063     (d) 0.27

2. An aqueous solution has 1.0 g of $CH_3OH$ in 50.0 g of water. Which concentration has the largest numerical value for the methanol content?

   (a) weight percent

   (b) mole fraction

   (c) molality

---

# 14.2 The Solution Process

• **Unsaturated** The term unsaturated is used when referring to solutions with solute concentrations that are less than that of a saturated solution.

If solid $CuCl_2$ is added to a beaker of water, the salt will begin to dissolve (Figure 14.1). The amount of solid diminishes, and the concentrations of $Cu^{2+}$(aq) and $Cl^-$(aq) in the solution increase. If we continue to add $CuCl_2$, however, we will eventually reach a point when no additional $CuCl_2$ seems to dissolve. The concentrations of $Cu^{2+}$(aq) and $Cl^-$(aq) will not increase further, and any additional solid $CuCl_2$ added after this point will remain as a solid at the bottom of the beaker. We say that such a solution is **saturated**.

Although no change is observed on the macroscopic level, it is a different matter on the particulate level. The process of dissolving continues, with $Cu^{2+}$ and $Cl^-$ ions leaving the solid state and entering solution. However, at the same time solid $CuCl_2$(s) is being formed from $Cu^{2+}$(aq) and $Cl^-$(aq). The rates at which $CuCl_2$ is dissolving and reprecipitating are equal in a saturated solution, so that no net change in the concentration of ions is observed on the macroscopic level.

This process is another example of a dynamic equilibrium (◄ page 118), and we can describe the situation in terms of an equation with substances linked by a set of double arrows ($\rightleftharpoons$):

$$CuCl_2(s) \rightleftharpoons Cu^{2+}(aq) + 2\ Cl^-(aq)$$

A saturated solution gives us a way to define precisely the solubility of a solid in a liquid. **Solubility** is the concentration of solute in equilibrium with undissolved solute in a saturated solution. The solubility of $CuCl_2$, for example, is 70.6 g in 100 mL of water at 0 °C. If we add 100.0 g of $CuCl_2$ to 100 mL of water at 0 °C, we can expect 70.6 g to dissolve, and 29.4 g of solid to remain.

**FIGURE 14.4**
**Miscibility.**

Less dense layer of non-polar octane, $C_8H_{18}$.

Solution of $CuSO_4$ in water.

More dense layer of non-polar carbon tetrachloride, $CCl_4$.

Solution of $CuSO_4$ moves to the top.

Homogeneous mixture of nonpolar $CCl_4$ and $C_8H_{18}$ has a greater density than water.

**(a) Before mixing.** The colorless, denser bottom layer is nonpolar carbon tetrachloride, $CCl_4$. The blue middle layer is a solution of $CuSO_4$ in water, and the colorless, less dense top layer is nonpolar octane, $C_8H_{18}$. This mixture was prepared by carefully layering one liquid on top of another, without mixing.

**(b) After mixing.** After stirring the mixture, the two nonpolar liquids form a homogeneous mixture. This layer of mixed liquids is under the water layer because the mixture of $CCl_4$ and $C_8H_{18}$ has a greater density than water.

## Liquids Dissolving in Liquids

If two liquids mix to an appreciable extent to form a solution, they are said to be **miscible**. In contrast, **immiscible** liquids do not mix to form a solution; they exist in contact with each other as separate layers (Figure 14.4).

The polar compounds ethanol ($C_2H_5OH$) and water are miscible in all proportions, as are the nonpolar liquids octane ($C_8H_{18}$) and carbon tetrachloride ($CCl_4$). On the other hand, neither $C_8H_{18}$ nor $CCl_4$ is miscible with water. Observations like these have led to a familiar rule of thumb: *Like dissolves like.* That is, two or more nonpolar liquids frequently are miscible, just as are two or more polar liquids.

What is the molecular basis for the "like dissolves like" guideline? In pure water and pure ethanol, the major force between molecules is hydrogen bonding involving —OH groups. When the two liquids are mixed, hydrogen bonding between ethanol and water molecules also occurs and assists in the solution process. In contrast, molecules of pure octane or pure $CCl_4$, both of which are nonpolar, are held together in the liquid phase by dispersion forces (◀ Section 12.4). The energy associated with these forces of attraction is similar in value to the energy due to the forces of attraction between octane and $CCl_4$ molecules when these nonpolar liquids are mixed. Thus, little or no energy change occurs when octane–octane and $CCl_4$–$CCl_4$ attractive forces are replaced with octane–$CCl_4$ forces. The solution process is expected to be nearly energy neutral. So, why do the liquids mix? The answer lies deeper in thermodynamics. As you shall see in Chapter 19, spontaneous changes, such as the mixing of liquids, are accompanied by an increase in entropy, a thermodynamic function that is a measure of the wider dispersal of the energy of the particles in the mixture relative to the pure liquids (Figure 14.5).

In contrast, polar and nonpolar liquids usually do not mix to an appreciable degree; when placed together in a container, they separate into two distinct layers

● **Entropy and the Solution Process** Although the energetics of solution formation are important, it is generally accepted that entropy is a more important contributor to the solution process. (See Chapter 19 and T. P. Silverstein: "The real reason why oil and water don't mix." *Journal of Chemical Education*, Vol. 75, pp. 116–118, 1998.)

$H_2O$        Separate liquids        $CH_3OH$                                    Mixture

**FIGURE 14.5** Driving the solution process—entropy. When two similar liquids—here water and methanol—are mixed, the molecules intermingle, and the energy of the system is more dispersed than in the two, separate pure liquids. A measure of this energy dispersal is entropy, a thermodynamic function described in more detail in Chapter 19.

## Supersaturated Solutions

Although at first glance it may seem a contradiction, it is possible for a solution to hold more dissolved solute than the amount in a saturated solution. Such solutions are referred to as **supersaturated** solutions. Supersaturated solutions are unstable, and the excess solid eventually crystallizes from the solution until the equilibrium concentration of the solute is reached.

The solubility of substances often decreases if the temperature is lowered. Supersaturated solutions are usually made by preparing a saturated solution at a given temperature and then carefully cooling it. If the rate of crystallization is slow, the solid may not precipitate when the solubility is exceeded. The result is a solution that has more solute than the amount defined by equilibrium conditions; it is supersaturated.

When disturbed in some manner, a supersaturated solution moves toward equilibrium by precipitating solute. This change can occur rapidly, often with the evolution of thermal energy. In fact, supersaturated solutions are used in "heat packs" to apply

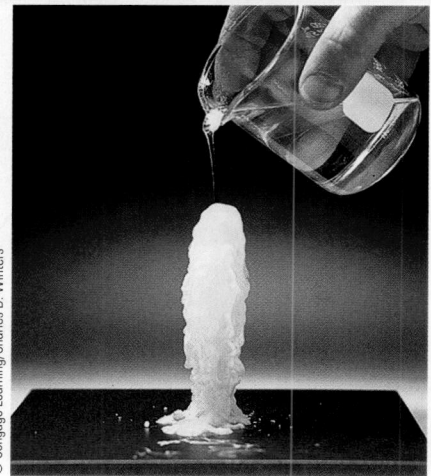

**Supersaturated solutions.** When a supersaturated solution is disturbed, the dissolved salt (here sodium acetate, $NaCH_3CO_2$) rapidly crystallizes.

heat to injured muscles. When crystallization of sodium acetate ($NaCH_3CO_2$) from a supersaturated solution in a heat pack is

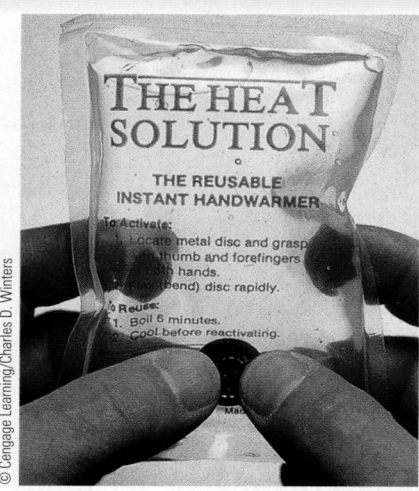

**Heat of crystallization.** A heat pack relies on the heat evolved by the crystallization of sodium acetate.

initiated, the temperature of the heat pack rises to about 50 °C and crystals of solid sodium acetate are detected inside the bag.

---

(Figure 14.4). The explanation is complex and involves the interplay of the enthalpy of mixing and entropy. The enthalpy of mixing is zero or nearly so, but mixing dissimilar liquids leads to a decrease in entropy. As explained in Chapter 19, this means that mixing dissimilar liquids is not thermodynamically favorable.

### Solids Dissolving in Water

The "like dissolves like" guideline also holds for molecular solids dissolving in liquids. Nonpolar solids such as naphthalene, $C_{10}H_8$, dissolve readily in nonpolar solvents such as benzene, $C_6H_6$, and hexane, $C_6H_{14}$. Iodine, $I_2$, a nonpolar inorganic solid, dissolves in water to some extent, but, given a choice, it dissolves to a larger extent in a nonpolar liquid such as $CCl_4$ (Figure 14.6). Sucrose (sugar), a polar molecular solid, is not very soluble in nonpolar solvents but is readily soluble in water, a fact that we know well because of its use to sweeten beverages. The presence of O—H groups in the structure of sugar and other substances such as glucose

**FIGURE 14.6 Solubility of nonpolar iodine in polar water and nonpolar carbon tetrachloride.** When a solution of nonpolar $I_2$ in water (the brown layer on top in the left test tube) is shaken with nonpolar $CCl_4$ (the colorless bottom layer in the left test tube), the $I_2$ transfers preferentially to the nonpolar solvent. Evidence for this is the purple color of the bottom $CCl_4$ layer in the test tube on the right.

Nonpolar $I_2$
Polar $H_2O$

Nonpolar $CCl_4$

Shake the test tube

Polar $H_2O$

Nonpolar $CCl_4$ and $I_2$

Photos © Cengage Learning/Charles D. Winters

**(a)** Dissolving NaOH in water is a strongly exothermic process.

**FIGURE 14.7** Dissolving ionic solids and enthalpy of solution.

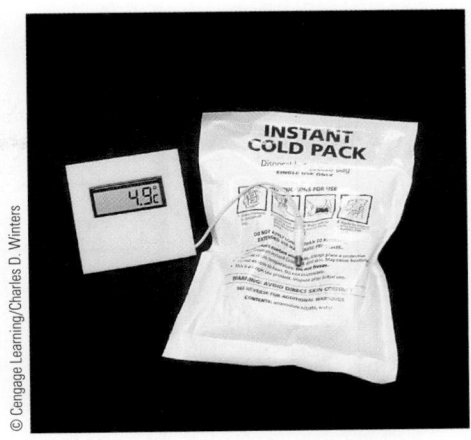

**(b)** A "cold pack" contains solid ammonium nitrate, $NH_4NO_3$, and a package of water. When the water and $NH_4NO_3$ are mixed and the salt dissolves, the temperature of the system drops, owing to the endothermic enthalpy of solution of ammonium nitrate ($\Delta_{soln}H° = +25.7$ kJ/mol).

allows these molecules to interact with polar water molecules through hydrogen bonding.

"Like dissolves like" is a somewhat less effective but still useful guideline when considering the solubility of ionic solids. Thus, we can reasonably predict that ionic compounds, which can be considered extreme examples of polar compounds, will not dissolve in nonpolar solvents. This fact is amply borne out by observation. Sodium chloride, for example, will not dissolve in liquids such as hexane or $CCl_4$, but it does have a significant solubility in water. Many ionic compounds are soluble in water, but, according to the solubility guidelines on page 122, there are many other ionic solids that are not.

Predicting the solubility of ionic compounds in water is complicated. As mentioned earlier, two factors—enthalpy and entropy—together determine the extent to which one substance dissolves in another. For ionic compounds dissolving in water, entropy usually (but not always) favors solution. A favorable enthalpy factor (negative $\Delta H$) generally leads to a compound being soluble. For example, when sodium hydroxide dissolves in water, the solution warms up (Figure 14.7a), and sodium hydroxide dissolves readily in water. An unfavorable enthalpy factor, however, does not guarantee that an ionic compound will not dissolve. When ammonium nitrate dissolves in water, the solution becomes colder (Figure 14.7b), but ammonium nitrate is still very soluble in water.

Network solids, including graphite, diamond, and quartz sand ($SiO_2$), do not dissolve in water. (Where would all the beaches be if sand dissolved in water?) The covalent chemical bonding in network solids is simply too strong to be broken; the lattice remains intact when in contact with water.

## Enthalpy of Solution

To understand the energetics of the solution process, let us view it at the molecular level. We will use the process of dissolving potassium fluoride, KF, in water to illustrate what occurs, and the energy-level diagram in Figure 14.8 will help us to follow the changes.

Solid potassium fluoride has an ionic crystal lattice with alternating $K^+$ and $F^-$ ions held in place by attractive forces due to their opposite charges. In water, these ions are separated from each other and *hydrated*; that is, they are surrounded by water molecules (Figure 14.1). Ion–dipole forces of attraction bind water molecules strongly to each ion. The energy change occurring on going from the

OH group

**Like dissolves like.** Glucose has five —OH groups on each molecule, groups that allow it to form hydrogen bonds with water molecules. As a result, glucose dissolves readily in water.

**FIGURE 14.8 Model for energy changes on dissolving KF.** An estimate of the magnitude of the energy change on dissolving an ionic compound in water is achieved by imagining it as occurring in two steps at the particulate level. Here, KF is first separated into cations and anions in the gas phase with an expenditure of 821 kJ per mol of KF. These ions are then hydrated, with $\Delta_{hydration}H$ estimated to be −837 kJ. Thus, the net energy change is −16 kJ, a slightly exothermic enthalpy of solution.

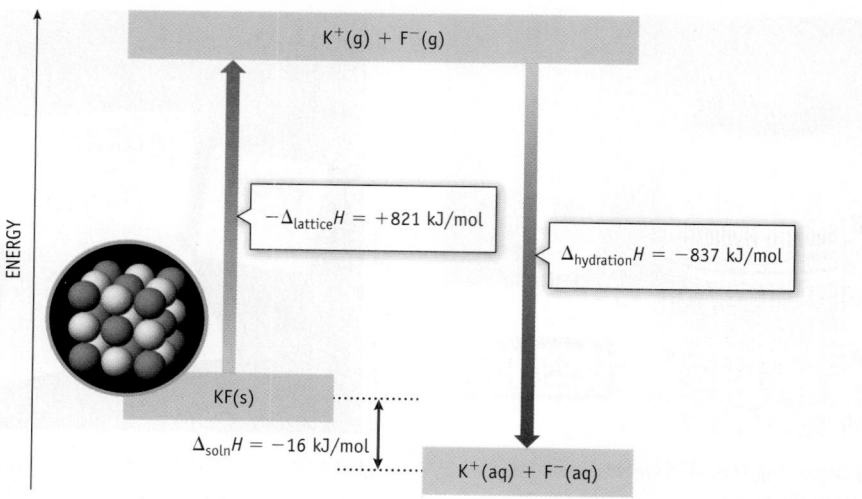

reactant, KF(s), to the products, $K^+(aq)$ and $F^-(aq)$, is the sum of the energies of two individual steps:

1. Energy must be supplied to separate the ions in the lattice against their attractive forces. This is the reverse of the process defining the lattice enthalpy of an ionic compound (◄ page 598), and its value will be equal to $-\Delta_{lattice}H$. Separating the ions from one another is highly endothermic because the attractive forces between ions are strong.

2. Energy is evolved when the individual ions dissolve in water, where each ion becomes surrounded by water molecules. Again, strong forces of attraction (ion–dipole forces) are involved. This process, referred to as **hydration** when water is the solvent, is strongly exothermic.

We can therefore represent the process of dissolving KF in terms of these chemical equations:

Step 1: $KF(s) \longrightarrow K^+(g) + F^-(g)$         $-\Delta_{lattice}H$
Step 2: $K^+(g) + F^-(g) \longrightarrow K^+(aq) + F^-(aq)$     $\Delta_{hydration}H$

The overall reaction is the sum of these two steps. The enthalpy of the overall reaction, called the **enthalpy of solution** ($\Delta_{soln}H$), is the sum of the two enthalpies.

Overall:     $KF(s) \longrightarrow K^+(aq) + F^-(aq)$     $\Delta_{soln}H = -\Delta_{lattice}H + \Delta_{hydration}H$

We can use this equation to estimate the value of $\Delta_{hydration}H$. For example, the lattice energy for KF is −821 kJ/mol [calculated using a Born-Haber cycle calculation (◄ page 600)], and the value of $\Delta_{soln}H$ determined by a calorimetry experiment is −16.4 kJ/mol. From these two values, we can determine $\Delta_{hydration}H$ to be −837 kJ/mol.

As a general rule, to be soluble, an ionic compound will have an enthalpy of solution that is exothermic or only slightly endothermic (Figure 14.9). In the latter instance, it is assumed that the enthalpy-disfavored solution process will be balanced by a favorable entropy of solution. If the enthalpy of solution is very endothermic—because of a low hydration energy, for example—then the compound is unlikely to be soluble. We can reasonably speculate that nonpolar solvents would not solvate ions strongly, and that solution formation would thus be energetically unfavorable. We therefore predict that an ionic compound, such as copper(II) sulfate, is not very soluble in nonpolar solvents such as carbon tetrachloride and octane (Figure 14.4).

It is also important to recognize that the enthalpy of solution is the difference between two very large numbers. Small variations in either lattice energy or hydration enthalpies can determine whether a salt dissolves endothermically or exothermically.

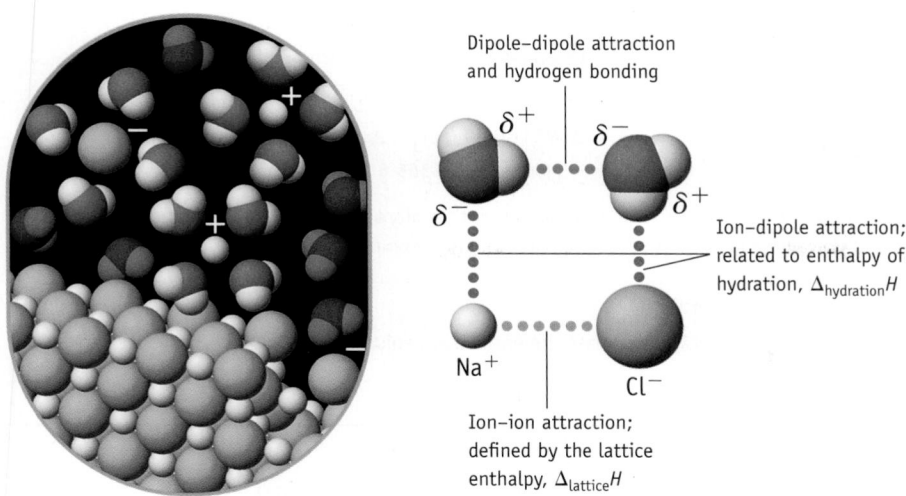

**FIGURE 14.9 Dissolving an ionic solid in water.** This process is a balance of forces. There are intermolecular forces between water molecules, and ion–ion forces are at work in the ionic crystal lattice. To dissolve, the ion–dipole forces between water and the ions (as measured by $\Delta_{hydration}H$) must overcome the ion–ion forces (as measured by $\Delta_{lattice}H$) and the intermolecular forces in water.

Finally, notice that the two energy quantities, $\Delta_{lattice}H$ and $\Delta_{hydration}H$, are both affected by ion sizes and ion charges (◄ pages 551 and 598). A salt composed of smaller ions is expected to have a greater (more negative) lattice enthalpy because the ions can be closer together and experience higher attractive forces. However, the small size will also allow a closer approach of solvent molecules and a greater solvation enthalpy. The net result is that correlations of solubility with structure (ionic radii) or thermodynamic parameters ($\Delta_{lattice}H$) are generally not successful.

## Enthalpy of Solution: Thermodynamic Data

As mentioned earlier, the enthalpy of solution for a salt can be measured using a calorimeter. This is usually done in an open system such as the coffee-cup calorimeter described in Section 5.6. For an experiment run under standard conditions, the resulting measurement produces a value for the standard enthalpy of solution, $\Delta_{soln}H°$, where standard conditions refer to a concentration of 1 molal.

Tables of thermodynamic values often include values for the enthalpies of formation of aqueous solutions of salts. For example, a value of $\Delta_fH°$ for NaCl(aq) of −407.3 kJ/mol is listed in Table 14.1 and Appendix L. This value refers to the formation of a 1 *m* solution of NaCl from the elements. It may be considered to involve the enthalpies of two steps: (1) the formation of NaCl(s) from the elements Na(s) and $Cl_2$(g) in their standard states, and (2) the formation of a 1 *m* solution by dissolving solid NaCl in water:

Formation of NaCl(s):   Na(s) + ½ $Cl_2$(g) ⟶ NaCl(s)   $\Delta_fH° = -411.1$ kJ/mol

Dissolving NaCl:   NaCl(s) ⟶ NaCl(aq, 1 *m*)   $\Delta_{soln}H° = +3.8$ kJ/mol

Net process:   Na(s) + ½ $Cl_2$(g) ⟶ NaCl(aq, 1 *m*)   $\Delta_fH° = -407.3$ kJ/mol

**Table 14.1**
**Data for Calculating Enthalpy of Solution**

| Compound | $\Delta_fH°$(s) (kJ/mol) | $\Delta_fH°$ (aq, 1 *m*) (kJ/mol) |
|---|---|---|
| LiF | −616.9 | −611.1 |
| NaF | −573.6 | −572.8 |
| KF | −568.6 | −585.0 |
| RbF | −557.7 | −583.8 |
| LiCl | −408.7 | −445.6 |
| NaCl | −411.1 | −407.3 |
| KCl | −436.7 | −419.5 |
| RbCl | −435.4 | −418.3 |
| NaOH | −425.9 | −469.2 |
| $NH_4NO_3$ | −365.6 | −339.9 |

## EXAMPLE 14.2   Calculating an Enthalpy of Solution

**Problem** Determine the enthalpy of solution for $NH_4NO_3$, the compound used in cold packs.

**What Do You Know?** The solution process for $NH_4NO_3$ is represented by the equation

$$NH_4NO_3(s) \longrightarrow NH_4NO_3(aq)$$

The enthalpies of formation of $NH_4NO_3$ in the solid state (−365.6 kJ/mol) and in solution (−339.9 kJ/mol) are given in Table 14.1.

**Strategy** Equation 5.6 (page 234) states that the enthalpy change for a process is the difference between the enthalpy of the final state (here the compound in solution) and the initial state (the solid).

**Solution** The enthalpy change for this process is calculated using Equation 5.6 as follows:

$$\Delta_{soln}H° = \Sigma[n\Delta_fH° \text{ (product)}] - \Sigma[n\Delta_fH° \text{ (reactant)}]$$
$$= \Delta_fH° \left[NH_4NO_3(aq)\right] - \Delta_fH° \left[NH_4NO_3(s)\right] \text{ (where } n = 1 \text{ for both)}$$
$$= -339.9 \text{ kJ} - (-365.6 \text{ kJ}) = +25.7 \text{ kJ}$$

**Think about Your Answer** The process is endothermic, as indicated by the fact that $\Delta_{soln}H°$ has a positive value and as verified by the experiment in Figure 14.7b.

**Check Your Understanding**

Use the data in Table 14.1 to calculate the enthalpy of solution for NaOH.

---

**REVIEW & CHECK FOR SECTION 14.2**

Given the enthalpy of formation data below, calculate $\Delta_{soln}H°$ for LiOH.

$$\Delta_fH° \text{ [LiOH(s)]} = -484.93 \text{ kJ/mol} \qquad \Delta_fH° \text{ [LiOH(aq)]} = -508.48 \text{ kJ/mol}$$

(a) +23.55 kJ/mol

(c) −23.55 kJ/mol

(b) +993.41 kJ/mol

(d) −993.41 kJ/mol

---

## 14.3 Factors Affecting Solubility: Pressure and Temperature

**Table 14.2**
**Henry's Law Constants (25 °C)\***

| Gas | $k_H$ (mol/kg · bar) |
|-----|------------------|
| $N_2$ | $6.0 \times 10^{-4}$ |
| $O_2$ | $1.3 \times 10^{-3}$ |
| $CO_2$ | 0.034 |

\*From http://webbook.nist.gov/
chemistry/. *Note:* 1 bar = 0.9869 atm.

Pressure and temperature are two external factors that influence solubility. Both affect the solubility of gases in liquids, whereas only temperature is a factor in the solubility of solids in liquids.

### Dissolving Gases in Liquids: Henry's Law

The solubility of a gas in a liquid is directly proportional to the gas pressure. This is a statement of **Henry's law**,

$$S_g = k_HP_g \tag{14.4}$$

where $S_g$ is the gas solubility (in mol/kg), $P_g$ is the partial pressure of the gaseous solute, and $k_H$ is Henry's law constant (Table 14.2), a constant characteristic of the solute and solvent.

Carbonated soft drinks illustrate how Henry's law works. These beverages are packed under pressure in a chamber filled with carbon dioxide gas, some of which dissolves in the beverage. When the can or bottle is opened, the partial pressure of $CO_2$ above the solution drops, which causes the solubility of $CO_2$ to drop. Gas bubbles out of the solution (Figure 14.10).

Henry's law has important consequences in SCUBA diving. When you dive, the pressure of the air you breathe must be balanced against the external pressure of the water. In deeper dives, the pressure of the gases in the SCUBA gear must be several atmospheres and, as a result, more gas dissolves in the blood. This can lead to a problem. If you ascend too rapidly, you can experience a painful and potentially lethal condition referred to as "the bends," in which nitrogen gas bubbles form in the blood as the solubility of nitrogen decreases with decreasing pressure. In an effort to prevent the bends, divers may use a helium–oxygen mixture (rather than nitrogen–oxygen) because helium is not as soluble in blood as nitrogen.

We can better understand the effect of pressure on solubility by examining the system at the particulate level. The solubility of a gas is defined as the concentration of the dissolved gas in equilibrium with the substance in the gaseous state. At equilibrium, the rate at which solute gas molecules escape the solution and enter the gaseous state equals the rate at which gas molecules reenter the solution. An increase in pressure

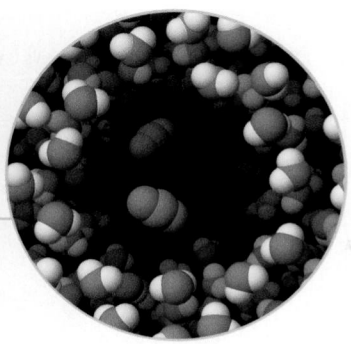

© Cengage Learning/Charles D. Winters

**FIGURE 14.10 Gas solubility and pressure.** Carbonated beverages are bottled under $CO_2$ pressure. When the bottle is opened, the pressure is released, and bubbles of $CO_2$ form within the liquid and rise to the surface. After some time, an equilibrium between dissolved $CO_2$ and atmospheric $CO_2$ is reached. The beverage tastes flat when most of its dissolved $CO_2$ is lost.

results in more molecules of gas striking the surface of the liquid and entering solution in a given time. The solution eventually reaches a new equilibrium when the concentration of gas dissolved in the solvent is high enough that the rate of gas molecules escaping the solution again equals the rate of gas molecules entering the solution.

• **Limitations of Henry's Law** Henry's law holds quantitatively only for gases that do not interact chemically with the solvent. It does not accurately predict the solubility of $NH_3$ in water, for example, because this compound gives small concentrations of $NH_4^+$ and $OH^-$ in water.

## EXAMPLE 14.3    Using Henry's Law

**Problem** What is the concentration of $O_2$ in a freshwater stream in equilibrium with air at 25 °C and 1.0 bar? Express the answer in grams of $O_2$ per kg of solvent.

**What Do You Know?** You know the total air pressure and temperature, and you can look up the Henry's law constant at the indicated temperature ($1.3 \times 10^{-3}$ mol/kg · bar). (Note that 1 bar is approximately 1 atm; page 510.)

**Strategy** Because you are trying to find the solubility of $O_2$, you first must find the partial pressure of $O_2$ from its mole fraction in air (0.21) and the specified atmospheric pressure (1.0 bar). Then use Henry's Law to calculate its molar solubility.

**Solution**

(a)   The mole fraction of $O_2$ in air is 0.21, and, assuming the total pressure is 1.0 bar, the partial pressure of $O_2$ is 0.21 bar.

(b)   Using the $O_2$ partial pressure for $P_g$ in Henry's law, we have:

$$\text{Solubility of } O_2 = k_H P_g = \left( \frac{1.3 \times 10^{-3} \text{ mol}}{\text{kg} \cdot \text{bar}} \right)(0.21 \text{ bar}) = 2.7 \times 10^{-4} \text{ mol/kg}$$

(c)   Calculate the concentration in g/kg from the concentration in mol/kg and the molar mass of $O_2$:

$$\text{Solubility of } O_2 = \left( \frac{2.7 \times 10^{-4} \text{ mol}}{\text{kg}} \right)\left( \frac{32.0 \text{ g}}{\text{mol}} \right) = 0.0087 \text{ g/kg}$$

**Think about Your Answer** The concentration of $O_2$ is 8.7 ppm (8.7 mg/1000 g). This concentration is quite low, but it is sufficient to provide the oxygen required by aquatic life.

**Check Your Understanding**

What is the concentration of $CO_2$ in water at 25 °C when the partial pressure is 0.33 bar? (Although $CO_2$ reacts with water to give traces of $H_3O^+$ and $HCO_3^-$, the reaction occurs to such a small extent that Henry's law is obeyed at low $CO_2$ partial pressures.)

## Temperature Effects on Solubility: Le Chatelier's Principle

The solubility of all gases in water decreases with increasing temperature. You may realize this from everyday observations such as the appearance of bubbles of air as water is heated below the boiling point.

To understand the effect of temperature on the solubility of gases, let us reexamine the enthalpy of solution. Gases that dissolve to an appreciable extent in water usually do so in an exothermic process

$$\text{Gas + liquid solvent} \overset{\Delta_{\text{soln}}H < 0}{\rightleftharpoons} \text{saturated solution + energy}$$

**FIGURE 14.11**
**The temperature dependence of the solubility of some ionic compounds in water.** Most compounds, such as $NH_4Cl$, decrease in solubility with decreasing temperature.

**(a)** Temperature dependence of the solubility of some ionic compounds.

© Cengage Learning/Charles D. Winters

**(b)** $NH_4Cl$ dissolved in water.

© Cengage Learning/Charles D. Winters

**(c)** $NH_4Cl$ precipitates when the solution is cooled in ice.

The reverse process, loss of dissolved gas molecules from a solution, requires energy as heat. At equilibrium, the rates of the two processes are the same.

To understand how temperature affects solubility, we turn to **Le Chatelier's principle**, which states that a change in any of the factors determining an equilibrium causes the system to adjust by shifting in the direction that reduces or counteracts the effect of the change. If a solution of a gas in a liquid is heated, for example, the equilibrium will shift to absorb some of the added energy. That is, the reaction

$$\text{Gas + liquid solvent} \xleftrightarrow{\substack{\text{Exothermic process} \\ \Delta_{soln}H \text{ is negative.}}} \text{saturated solution + energy}$$

Add energy. Equilibrium shifts left.

shifts to the left if the temperature is raised because energy is absorbed in the process that produces free gas molecules and pure solvent. This shift corresponds to less gas dissolved and a lower solubility at higher temperature—the observed result.

The solubility of solids in water is also affected by temperature, but, unlike the situation involving solutions of gases, no general pattern of behavior is observed. In Figure 14.11, the solubilities of several salts are plotted versus temperature. The solubility of many salts increases with increasing temperature, but there are notable exceptions. Predictions based on whether the enthalpy of solution is positive or negative work most of the time, but exceptions do occur.

Chemists take advantage of the variation of solubility with temperature to purify compounds. An impure sample of a compound that is more soluble at higher temperatures is dissolved by heating the solution. The solution is then cooled to decrease the solubility (Figure 14.11c). When the limit of solubility is reached at the lower temperature, crystals of the pure compound form. If the process is done slowly and carefully, it is sometimes possible to obtain very large crystals (Figure 14.12).

Courtesy of Lawrence Livermore National Laboratory

**FIGURE 14.12 Giant crystals of potassium dihydrogen phosphate.** The crystal being measured by this researcher at Lawrence Livermore Laboratory in California weighs 318 kg and measures 66 × 53 × 58 cm. The crystals were grown by suspending a thumbnail-sized seed crystal in a 6-foot tank of saturated $KH_2PO_4$. The temperature of the solution was gradually reduced from 65 °C over a period of about 50 days. The crystals are sliced into thin plates, which are used to convert light from a giant laser from infrared to ultraviolet.

---

**REVIEW & CHECK FOR SECTION 14.3**

Soft drinks are carbonated by adding $CO_2$ under pressure. Assume that $CO_2$ is added to a bottle of soft drink containing 710 g of diet soda. The pressure of $CO_2$ is 4.0 bar. ($CO_2$ obeys Henry's law at pressures up to about 5 bar.) What amount of $CO_2$ is dissolved in 710 g of diet soda?

(a)  0.14 mol          (b)  0.097 mol          (c)  0.034 mol          (d)  0.13 mol

## CASE STUDY

# Exploding Lakes and Diet Cokes

On Thursday, August 21, 1986, people and animals around Lake Nyos in Cameroon, a small nation on the west coast of Africa, suddenly collapsed and died. More than 1700 people and hundreds of animals were dead, but there was no apparent cause—no fire, no earthquake, no storm. What had brought on this disaster?

Some weeks later, the mystery was solved. Lake Nyos and nearby Lake Monoun are crater lakes, which formed when cooled volcanic craters filled with water. Importantly, Lake Nyos contains an enormous amount of dissolved carbon dioxide, which was generated as a result of volcanic activity deep in the earth. Under the high pressure at the bottom of the lake, a very large amount of $CO_2$ dissolved in the water.

But on that evening in 1986, something disturbed the lake. The $CO_2$-saturated water at the bottom of the lake was carried to the surface, where, under lower pressure, the gas was much less soluble. About one cubic kilometer of carbon dioxide was released into the atmosphere, much like the explosive release of $CO_2$ from a can of carbonated beverage that has been shaken. The $CO_2$ shot up about 260 feet; then, because this gas is more dense than air, it hugged the ground and began to move with the prevailing breeze at about 45 miles per hour. When it reached the villages 12 miles away, vital oxygen was displaced. The result was that both people and animals were asphyxiated.

**Lake Nyos in Cameroon (western Africa), the site of a natural disaster.** In 1986, a huge bubble of $CO_2$ escaped from the lake and asphyxiated more than 1700 people.

In most lakes, this situation would not occur because lake water "turns over" as the seasons change. In the autumn, the top layer of water in a lake cools; its density increases; and the water sinks. This process continues, with warmer water coming to the surface and cooler water sinking. Dissolved $CO_2$ at the bottom of a lake would normally be expelled in this turnover process, but geologists found that the lakes in Cameroon are different. The chemocline, the boundary between deep water, rich in gas and minerals, and the upper layer, full of freshwater, stayed intact. As carbon dioxide continued to enter the lake through vents in the bottom of the lake, the water became saturated with this gas. It is presumed that a minor disturbance—perhaps a small earthquake, a strong wind, or an underwater landslide—caused the lake water to turn over and led to the explosive release of $CO_2$.

The explosive release of $CO_2$ that occurred in Lake Nyos is much like what occurs when you drop a candy like a Mentos into a bottle of Diet Coke. Carbonated sodas are bottled under a high pressure of $CO_2$. Some of the gas dissolves in the soda, but some also remains in the small space above the liquid (called the *headspace*). The pressure of the $CO_2$ in the headspace is between 2 and 4 atm. When the bottle cap is removed, the $CO_2$ in the headspace escapes rapidly. Some of the dissolved $CO_2$ also comes out of solution, and you see bubbles of gas rising to the surface. If the bottle remains open, this continues until equilibrium is established with $CO_2$ in the atmosphere (where the partial pressure of $CO_2$ is $3.75 \times 10^{-4}$ atm),

$$CO_2(\text{solution}) \rightleftharpoons CO_2(g)$$

and the soda goes "flat." If the newly opened soda bottle is undisturbed, however, the loss of $CO_2$ from solution is rather slow because bubble formation is not rapid, and your soda keeps its fizz.

To understand how $CO_2$ can be released explosively, you have to understand that impurities in the water or the rough surfaces of an ice cube or bottle or drinking glass can serve as "nucleation sites" on which a bubble can form. The more nucleation sites available, the more rapid the bubble formation. The surface of a Mentos apparently has many such sites and pro-

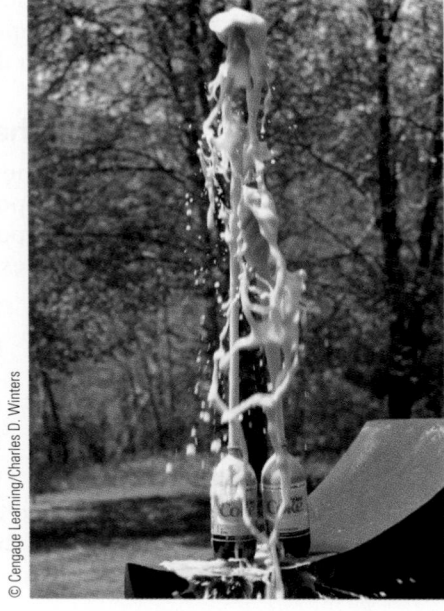

**A Mentos was dropped into large bottles of Diet Coke.** For more information, see J. E. Baur and M. B. Baur, *Journal of Chemical Education,* Vol. 83, pages 577–580, 2006.

motes very rapid bubble formation. In the case of the African lake, perhaps an earthquake or underwater landslide opened up nucleation sites, and the $CO_2$ was released explosively.

### Questions:

1. If the headspace of a soda is 25 mL and the pressure of $CO_2$ in the space is 4.0 atm ($\approx$4.0 bar) at 25 °C, what amount of $CO_2$ is contained in the headspace?

2. If the $CO_2$ in the headspace escapes into the atmosphere where the partial pressure of $CO_2$ is $3.7 \times 10^{-4}$ atm, what volume would the $CO_2$ occupy (at 25 °C)? By what amount did the $CO_2$ expand when it was released?

3. What is the solubility of $CO_2$ in water at 25 °C when the pressure of the gas is $3.7 \times 10^{-4}$ bar?

4. After opening a 1.0 L soda, what mass of the dissolved $CO_2$ is released to the atmosphere in order to reach equilibrium? Assume that the $CO_2$ dissolved in the soda in the sealed bottle was in equilibrium with the $CO_2$ in the headspace at 4.0 bar pressure.

**Answers to these questions are available in Appendix N.**

**Module 19: Colligative Properties**
covers concepts in this section.

## 14.4 Colligative Properties

If you dissolve some salt in water, the vapor pressure of the water over the solution will decrease. In addition, the solution will freeze below 0 °C and boil above 100 °C. These observations refer to the **colligative properties** of the solution, properties that depend on the relative numbers of solute and solvent particles in a solution and not on their identity.

### Changes in Vapor Pressure: Raoult's Law

The equilibrium vapor pressure at a particular temperature is the pressure of the vapor when the liquid and the vapor are in equilibrium (◄ page 568). When the vapor pressure of the solvent over a solution is measured at a given temperature, it is experimentally observed that

- The vapor pressure of the solvent over the solution is lower than the vapor pressure of the pure solvent.
- The vapor pressure of the solvent, $P_{solvent}$, is proportional to the relative number of solvent molecules in the solution; that is, the solvent vapor pressure is proportional to the solvent mole fraction, $P_{solvent} \propto X_{solvent}$.

Because solvent vapor pressure is proportional to the relative number of solvent molecules, we can write the following equation for the equilibrium vapor pressure of the solvent over a solution:

$$P_{solvent} = X_{solvent}\, P°_{solvent} \tag{14.5}$$

This equation, called **Raoult's law**, tells us that the vapor pressure of solvent over a solution ($P_{solvent}$) is some fraction of the pure solvent equilibrium vapor pressure ($P°_{solvent}$). For example, if 95% of the molecules in a solution are solvent molecules ($X_{solvent} = 0.95$), then the vapor pressure of the solvent ($P_{solvent}$) is 95% of $P°_{solvent}$.

*An ideal solution is one that obeys Raoult's law.* However, just as no gas is truly ideal, no solution is ideal. Although Raoult's law describes a simplified model of a solution, it is a good approximation of solution behavior in many instances, especially at low solute concentration.

For Raoult's law to hold, the forces of attraction between solute and solvent molecules must be the same as those between solvent molecules in the pure solvent. This is frequently the case when molecules with similar structures are involved. Solutions of one hydrocarbon in another (hexane, $C_6H_{14}$, dissolved in octane, $C_8H_{18}$, for example) follow Raoult's law quite closely. If solvent–solute interactions are stronger than solvent–solvent interactions, the actual vapor pressure will be lower than calculated by Raoult's law. If the solvent–solute interactions are weaker than solvent–solvent interactions, the vapor pressure will be higher.

### EXAMPLE 14.4   Using Raoult's Law

**Problem**  You dissolve 651 g of ethylene glycol, $HOCH_2CH_2OH$, in 1.50 kg of water. What is the vapor pressure of the water over the solution at 90 °C? Assume ideal behavior for the solution.

**What Do You Know?**  This is a Raoult's law problem where you want to know $P_{solvent}$. To calculate $P_{solvent}$ you need the mole fraction of solvent and the vapor pressure of the pure solvent. You can calculate the mole fraction of solute from the masses of solute and solvent and the molar masses of these species. The vapor pressure of pure water at 90 °C (= 525.8 mm Hg) is found in Appendix G.

**Strategy**  First calculate the mole fraction of the solvent (water) and then combine that with the vapor pressure of pure solvent at the specified temperature using Raoult's law (Equation 14.5).

## Solution

(a) Calculate the amounts of water and ethylene glycol and, from these, the mole fraction of water.

$$\text{Amount of water} = 1.50 \times 10^3 \text{ g} \left( \frac{1 \text{ mol}}{18.02 \text{ g}} \right) = 83.2 \text{ mol water}$$

$$\text{Amount of ethylene glycol} = 651 \text{ g} \left( \frac{1 \text{ mol}}{62.07 \text{ g}} \right) = 10.5 \text{ mol glycol}$$

$$X_{\text{water}} = \frac{83.2 \text{ mol water}}{83.2 \text{ mol water} + 10.5 \text{ mol glycol}} = 0.888$$

(b) Next apply Raoult's law.

$$P_{\text{water}} = X_{\text{water}}P^{\circ}_{\text{water}} = (0.888)(525.8 \text{ mm Hg}) = 467 \text{ mm Hg}$$

**Think about Your Answer** Although a substantial mass of ethylene glycol was added to the water, it led to a decrease in the vapor pressure of the solvent of only 59 mm Hg, or about 11%:

$$\Delta P_{\text{water}} = P_{\text{water}} - P^{\circ}_{\text{water}} = 467 \text{ mm Hg} - 525.8 \text{ mm Hg} = -59 \text{ mm Hg}$$

Ethylene glycol is ideal for use as antifreeze. It dissolves easily in water, is noncorrosive, and is relatively inexpensive. Because of its high boiling point, it will not evaporate readily. It is, however, toxic to animals, so it is being replaced by less toxic propylene glycol.

---

**Check Your Understanding**

Assume you dissolve 10.0 g of sucrose ($C_{12}H_{22}O_{11}$) in 225 mL (225 g) of water and warm the water to 60 °C. What is the vapor pressure of the water over this solution? (Appendix G lists $P^{\circ}(H_2O)$ at various temperatures.)

---

Adding a nonvolatile solute to a solvent lowers the vapor pressure of the solvent (Example 14.4). Raoult's law can be modified to calculate directly the lowering of the vapor pressure, $\Delta P_{\text{solvent}}$, as a function of the mole fraction of the solute.

$$\Delta P_{\text{solvent}} = P_{\text{solvent}} - P^{\circ}_{\text{solvent}}$$

Substituting Raoult's law for $P_{\text{solvent}}$, we have

$$\Delta P_{\text{solvent}} = (X_{\text{solvent}} P^{\circ}_{\text{solvent}}) - P^{\circ}_{\text{solvent}} = -(1 - X_{\text{solvent}})P^{\circ}_{\text{solvent}}$$

In a solution that has only the volatile solvent and one nonvolatile solute, the sum of the mole fraction of solvent and solute must be 1:

$$X_{\text{solvent}} + X_{\text{solute}} = 1$$

Therefore, $1 - X_{\text{solvent}} = X_{\text{solute}}$, and the equation for $\Delta P_{\text{solvent}}$ can be rewritten as

$$\Delta P_{\text{solvent}} = -X_{\text{solute}} P^{\circ}_{\text{solvent}} \qquad (14.6)$$

Thus, the *decrease* in the vapor pressure of the solvent is proportional to the mole fraction (the relative number of particles) of solute.

## Boiling Point Elevation

Suppose you have a solution of a nonvolatile solute in the volatile solvent benzene. If the solute concentration is 0.200 mol in 100. g of benzene ($C_6H_6$) (= 2.00 mol/kg), this means that $X_{\text{benzene}} = 0.865$. Using $X_{\text{benzene}}$ and applying Raoult's law, we can calculate that the vapor pressure of the solvent at 60 °C will drop from 400. mm Hg for the pure solvent to 346 mm Hg for the solution:

$$P_{\text{benzene}} = X_{\text{benzene}} P^{\circ}_{\text{benzene}} = (0.865)(400. \text{ mm Hg}) = 346 \text{ mm Hg}$$

**FIGURE 14.13 Lowering the vapor pressure of benzene by addition of a nonvolatile solute.** The curve drawn in red represents the vapor pressure of pure benzene, and the curve in blue represents the vapor pressure of a solution containing 0.200 mol of a solute dissolved in 0.100 kg of solvent (2.00 *m*). This graph was created by doing a series of calculations such as those shown in the text. As an alternative, the graph could be created by measuring various vapor pressures for the solution in a laboratory experiment.

This point is marked on the vapor pressure graph in Figure 14.13. Now, what is the vapor pressure when the temperature of the solution is raised another 10 °C? The vapor pressure of pure benzene, $P°_{benzene}$, becomes larger with increasing temperature, so $P_{benzene}$ for the solution must also become larger. This new point, and additional ones calculated in the same way for other temperatures, define the vapor pressure curve for the solution (the lower curve in Figure 14.13).

An important observation we can make in Figure 14.13 is that the vapor pressure lowering caused by the nonvolatile solute leads to an increase in the boiling point. The normal boiling point of a liquid is the temperature at which its vapor pressure is equal to 1 atm or 760 mm Hg (◄ page 571). In Figure 14.13, we see that the normal boiling point of pure benzene (at 760 mm Hg) is about 80 °C. Tracing the vapor pressure curve for the solution, we also see that the vapor pressure reaches 760 mm Hg at a temperature about 5 °C higher than this value.

An important question is how the boiling point of the solution varies with solute concentration. In fact, a simple relationship exists: the boiling point elevation, $\Delta T_{bp}$, is directly proportional to the molality of the solute.

$$\text{Elevation in boiling point} = \Delta T_{bp} = K_{bp}m_{solute} \qquad (14.7)$$

In this equation, $K_{bp}$ is a proportionality constant called the **molal boiling point elevation constant**. It has the units of degrees/molal (°C/*m*). Values for $K_{bp}$ are determined experimentally, and different solvents have different values (Table 14.3). Formally, the value of $K_{bp}$ corresponds to the elevation in boiling point for a 1 *m* solution.

**⊘WL  INTERACTIVE EXAMPLE 14.5  Boiling Point Elevation**

**Problem** Eugenol, a compound found in nutmeg and cloves, has the formula $C_{10}H_{12}O_2$. What is the boiling point of a solution containing 0.144 g of this compound dissolved in 10.0 g of benzene?

**What Do You Know?** You know the identify and mass of both the solute and the solvent.

Eugenol, $C_{10}H_{12}O_2$, is an important component in oil of cloves, a commonly used spice.

**Strategy**

- Calculate the solution concentration (molality, *m*, in mol/kg) from the amount of eugenol and the mass of solvent (kg).

- Calculate the change in boiling point using Equation 14.7 (with a value of $K_{bp}$ from Table 14.3).

- Add the change to the boiling temperature of pure benzene to obtain the new boiling point.

**Solution**

(a) Solution concentration

$$0.144 \text{ g eugenol}\left(\frac{1 \text{ mol eugenol}}{164.2 \text{ g}}\right) = 8.77 \times 10^{-4} \text{ mol eugenol}$$

$$c_{eugenol} = \frac{8.77 \times 10^{-4} \text{ mol eugenol}}{0.0100 \text{ kg benzene}} = 8.77 \times 10^{-2} \text{ m}$$

(b) Boiling point elevation

$$\Delta T_{bp} = (2.53 \text{ °C/}m)(0.0877 \text{ }m) = 0.222 \text{ °C}$$

Because the boiling point rises relative to that of the pure solvent, the boiling point of the solution is

$$80.10 \text{ °C} + 0.222 \text{ °C} = \boxed{80.32 \text{ °C}}$$

**Think about Your Answer** Keep in mind that the boiling point elevation is proportional to the solute concentration. At high concentrations, sizable increases in boiling point are possible.

**Check Your Understanding**

What quantity of ethylene glycol, $HOCH_2CH_2OH$, must be added to 125 g of water to raise the boiling point by 1.0 °C? Express the answer in grams.

Strategy Map 14.5

PROBLEM

Calculate **boiling point** of solution.

DATA/INFORMATION
- **Mass** of *compound* and *solvent*
- $K_{bp}$ and $T$(bp solvent) from Table 14.3

STEP 1. Calculate $c_{solute}$ = (mol compound/kg solvent).

**Concentration** of solute (mol/kg)

STEP 2. Use $\Delta T_{bp} = K_{bp}m$.

**Change** in boiling point ($\Delta T_{bp}$)

STEP 3. $\Delta T_{bp}$ = $T$(bp solution) – $T$(bp solvent).

$T$(bp solution)

The elevation of the boiling point of a solvent on adding a solute has many practical consequences. One of them is the summer protection your car's engine receives from "all-season" antifreeze. The main ingredient of commercial antifreeze is ethylene glycol, $HOCH_2CH_2OH$. The car's radiator and cooling system are sealed to keep the coolant under pressure, ensuring that it will not vaporize at normal engine temperatures. When the air temperature is high in the summer, however, the radiator could "boil over" if it were not protected with "antifreeze." By adding this nonvolatile liquid, the solution in the radiator has a higher boiling point than that of pure water.

**Table 14.3 Some Boiling Point Elevation and Freezing Point Depression Constants**

| Solvent | Normal Boiling Point (°C) Pure Solvent | $K_{bp}$ (°C/m) | Normal Freezing Point (°C) Pure Solvent | $K_{fp}$ (°C/m) |
|---|---|---|---|---|
| Water | 100.00 | +0.5121 | 0.0 | −1.86 |
| Benzene | 80.10 | +2.53 | 5.50 | −5.12 |
| Camphor | 207.4 | +5.611 | 179.75 | −39.7 |
| Chloroform ($CHCl_3$) | 61.70 | +3.63 | — | — |

**FIGURE 14.14** Freezing a solution.

solution

pure solvent

**(a)** Adding antifreeze to water prevents the water from freezing. Here, a jar of pure water *(left)* and a jar of water to which automobile antifreeze had been added *(right)* were kept overnight in the freezing compartment of a home refrigerator.

**(b)** When a solution freezes, it is pure solvent that solidifies. To take this photo, a purple dye was dissolved in water, and the solution was frozen slowly. Pure ice formed along the walls of the tube, and the dye stayed in solution. The concentration of the solute increased as more and more solvent was frozen out, and the resulting solution had a lower and lower freezing point. Eventually, the system contains pure, colorless ice that formed along the walls of the tube and a concentrated solution of dye in the center of the tube.

## Freezing Point Depression

● **Why Is the Boiling Point of a Solution Elevated and Its Freezing Point Depressed?** The answer to this question is related to entropy, a thermodynamic function discussed in Chapter 19. You can consult a website that has an *extensive* discussion of entropy (entropysite.oxy.edu) or the specific site at which colligative properties are discussed: http://entropysite.oxy .edu/entropy_is_simple/index.html.

Another consequence of dissolving a solute in a solvent is that the freezing point of the solution is lower than that of the pure solvent (Figure 14.14). For an ideal solution, the depression of the freezing point is given by an equation similar to that for the elevation of the boiling point:

$$\text{Freezing point depression} = \Delta T_{fp} = K_{fp}m_{solute} \qquad (14.8)$$

where $K_{fp}$ is the **freezing point depression constant** in degrees Celsius per molal ($°C/m$). Values of $K_{fp}$ for a few common solvents are given in Table 14.3. The values are negative quantities, so the result of the calculation is a negative value for $\Delta T_{fp}$, signifying a decrease in temperature.

The practical aspects of freezing point changes from pure solvent to solution are similar to those for boiling point elevation. The very name of the liquid you add to the radiator in your car, antifreeze, indicates its purpose (Figure 14.14a). The label on the container of antifreeze tells you, for example, to add 6 qt (5.7 L) of antifreeze to a 12-qt (11.4-L) cooling system to lower the freezing point to −34 °C and to raise the boiling point to +109 °C.

### EXAMPLE 14.6    Freezing Point Depression

**Problem** What mass of ethylene glycol, $HOCH_2CH_2OH$, must be added to 5.50 kg of water to lower the freezing point of the water from 0.0 °C to −10.0 °C?

**What Do You Know?** In some ways this is the reverse of Example 14.5. Here you know the change in freezing point, but wish to know how much solute is needed to produce that value of $\Delta T$.

**Strategy** The solution concentration (molality, $m$) can be calculated from $\Delta T_{fp}$ and $K_{fp}$ (Table 14.3) using Equation 14.8. Combine the concentration with the mass of solvent to obtain the amount of solute and then its mass.

### Solution

(a) Calculate the solute concentration in a solution with a freezing point depression of −10.0 °C.

$$\text{Solute concentration } (m) = \frac{\Delta T_{fp}}{K_{fp}} = \frac{-10.0 \text{ °C}}{-1.86 \text{ °C}/m} = 5.38 \text{ } m$$

(b) Calculate the amount of solute from the concentration and solvent mass.

$$\left(\frac{5.38 \text{ mol glycol}}{1.00 \text{ kg water}}\right)(5.50 \text{ kg water}) = 29.6 \text{ mol glycol}$$

(c) Calculate the mass of the solute, ethylene glycol.

$$29.6 \text{ mol glycol}\left(\frac{62.07 \text{ g}}{1 \text{ mol}}\right) = 1840 \text{ g glycol}$$

**Think about Your Answer** The value of $K_{fp}$ tells us that the freezing point of water goes down by 1.86 °C for a 1 molal solution. In this particular problem, the freezing point depression was −10.0 °C, so a molality around 5 $m$ is reasonable. The density of ethylene glycol is 1.11 kg/L, so the volume of glycol to be added is: (1.84 kg)(1 L/1.11 kg) = 1.66 L.

---

### Check Your Understanding

In the northern United States, summer cottages are usually closed up for the winter. When doing so, the owners "winterize" the plumbing by putting antifreeze in the toilet tanks, for example. Will adding 525 g of $HOCH_2CH_2OH$ to 3.00 kg of water ensure that the water will not freeze at −25 °C?

## Osmotic Pressure

**Osmosis** is the movement of solvent molecules through a semipermeable membrane from a region of lower solute concentration to a region of higher solute concentration. This movement can be demonstrated with a simple experiment. The beaker in Figure 14.15 contains pure water, and the bag and tube hold a concentrated sugar

**FIGURE 14.15** The process of osmosis.

Height of solution column

time

Pure water

5% sugar 95% water

Semi-permeable membrane

**(a)** The bag attached to the tube contains a solution that is 5% sugar and 95% water. The beaker contains pure water. The bag is made of a material that is semipermeable, meaning that it allows water, but not sugar molecules, to pass through.

**(b)** Over time, water flows from the region of low solute concentration (pure water) to the region of higher solute concentration (the sugar solution). Flow continues until the pressure exerted by the column of solution in the tube above the water level in the beaker is great enough to result in equal rates of passage of water molecules in both directions. The height of the column of solution is a measure of the osmotic pressure.

solution. The liquids are separated by a semipermeable membrane, a thin sheet of material (such as a vegetable tissue or cellophane) through which only certain types of molecules can pass. Here, water molecules can pass through the membrane, but larger sugar molecules (or hydrated ions) cannot (Figure 14.16). When the experiment is begun, the liquid levels in the beaker and the tube are the same. Over time, however, the level of the sugar solution inside the tube rises, the level of pure water in the beaker falls, and the sugar solution becomes more dilute. Eventually, no further net change occurs; equilibrium is reached.

From a molecular point of view, the semipermeable membrane does not present a barrier to the movement of water molecules, so they move through the membrane in both directions. Over time, more water molecules pass through the membrane from the pure water side to the solution side than in the opposite direction. The net effect is that water molecules move from regions of low solute concentration to regions of high solute concentration. The same is true for any solvent, as long as the membrane allows solvent molecules but not solute molecules or ions to pass through.

Why does the system eventually reach equilibrium? Clearly, the solution in the tube in Figure 14.15 can never reach zero sugar or salt concentration, which would be required to equalize the number of water molecules moving through the membrane in each direction in a given time. The answer lies in the fact that the solution moves higher and higher in the tube as osmosis continues and water moves into the sugar solution. Eventually, the pressure exerted by this column of solution counterbalances the pressure exerted by the water moving through the membrane from the pure water side, and no further net movement of water occurs. An equilibrium of forces is achieved. The pressure created by the column of solution for the system at equilibrium is called the **osmotic pressure**, $\Pi$. A measure of this pressure is the difference between the height of the solution in the tube and the level of pure water in the beaker.

From experimental measurements on dilute solutions, it is known that osmotic pressure and concentration ($c$) are related by the equation

$$\Pi = cRT \tag{14.9}$$

In this equation, $c$ is the molar concentration (in moles per liter); $R$ is the gas constant; and $T$ is the absolute temperature (in kelvins). Using a value for the gas law constant of 0.082057 L · atm/K · mol allows calculation of the osmotic pressure $\Pi$ in atmospheres. This equation is analogous to the ideal gas law ($PV = nRT$), with $\Pi$ taking the place of $P$ and $c$ being equivalent to $n/V$.

**FIGURE 14.16 Osmosis at the particulate level.** Osmotic flow through a membrane that is selectively permeable (semipermeable) to water. Dissolved substances such as hydrated ions or large sugar molecules cannot diffuse through the membrane.

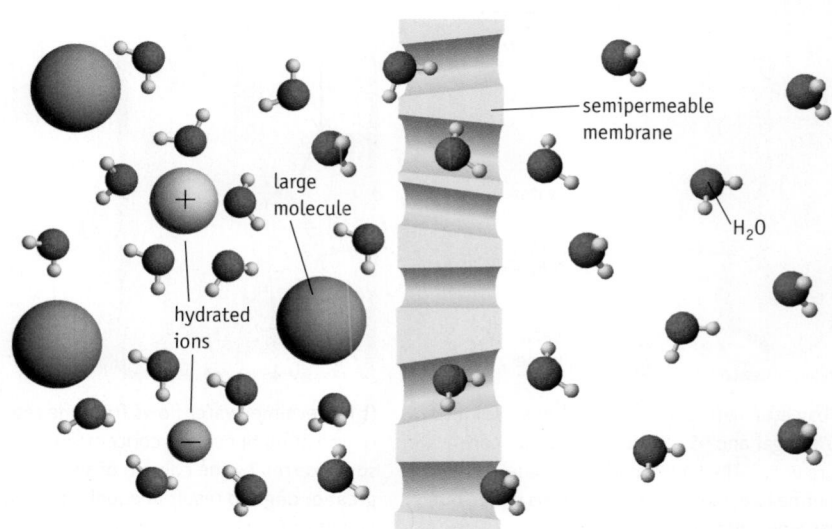

## A CLOSER LOOK

# Reverse Osmosis for Pure Water

Finding sources of freshwater for humans and agriculture has been a constant battle for centuries, and, if we continue using Earth's water at the present rate, those problems may increase. Although the earth has abundant water, 97% of it is too salty to drink or to use on crops. A large portion of the remaining 3% is locked in the form of ice in the polar regions and is not easily obtained.

One of the oldest ways to obtain freshwater from seawater is by evaporation. This

**A reverse osmosis plant.**

is, however, very energy-intensive, and the salt and other materials left behind may not be useful.

*Reverse osmosis* is another method of obtaining freshwater from seawater or groundwater. In this technique a pressure greater than the osmotic pressure of the impure water is applied to force water through a semipermeable membrane from a region of high solute concentration to one of lower solute concentration, that is, in the reverse direction that the water would move by osmosis.

Although reverse osmosis has been known for over 200 years, only in the last few decades has it been exploited. Now some municipalities obtain drinking water that way, and pharmaceutical companies use it to obtain highly purified water. More than 15,000 reverse osmosis plants are in operation or in the planning stage worldwide.

**Reverse osmosis.** Drinking water can be produced from seawater by reverse osmosis. The osmotic pressure of seawater is approximately 22 atm. To obtain freshwater at a reasonable rate, reverse osmosis requires a pressure of about 50 atm. For comparison, bicycle tires usually have an air pressure of 2–3 atm. (See the portable reverse osmosis device on page 616.)

Even solutions with low solute concentrations have a significant osmotic pressure. For example, the osmotic pressure of a $1.00 \times 10^{-3}$ M solution at 298K is 18.5 mm Hg. Such pressures are easily and accurately measured. Because of this, the concentrations of very dilute solutions can be determined using this technique. Compare this to the effect of a solute on freezing point, for example. A dilute aqueous solution of similar concentration, $1.00 \times 10^{-3}$ mol/kg solvent, would be expected to lower the freezing point by about 0.002 °C, too small to measure accurately. For this reason osmosis is a particularly useful technique when dealing with solutions of compounds having a very high molar mass such as polymers and large biomolecules.

Other examples of osmosis are shown in Figure 14.17. In this case, the egg's membrane serves as the semipermeable membrane. Osmosis occurs in one direction if the concentration of solute is greater inside the egg than in the exterior

**(a)** A fresh egg is placed in dilute acetic acid. The acid reacts with the $CaCO_3$ of the shell but leaves the egg membrane intact.

**(b)** If the egg, with its shell removed, is placed in pure water, the egg swells.

**(c)** If the egg, with its shell removed, is placed in a concentrated sugar solution, the egg shrivels.

**FIGURE 14.17 An experiment to observe osmosis.** You can try this experiment in your kitchen. In the first step, use vinegar as a source of acetic acid.

solution and occurs in the other direction if the concentration solution is less inside the egg than it is in the exterior solution. In both cases, solvent flows from the region of low solute concentration to the region of high solute concentration.

### EXAMPLE 14.7    Determining the Osmotic Pressure of a Solution of a Polymer

**Problem** Polyvinyl alcohol is a water soluble polymer with an average molar mass of 28,000. You dissolve 1.844 g of this polymer in water to give 150. mL of solution. What is the osmotic pressure, measured at 27 °C?

**What Do You Know?** Osmotic pressure is calculated by Equation 14.9, $\Pi = cRT$. You are given the mass and molar mass of the polymer and the temperature and will need the gas law constant.

**Strategy** Calculate the concentration of the polymer, $c$, in mol/L. The temperature must be expressed in kelvins. Substitute these values into Equation 14.9 to solve for the osmotic pressure.

**Solution**

$$c = 1.844 \text{ g}(1 \text{ mol}/28{,}000 \text{ g})/(0.150 \text{ L}) = 4.4 \times 10^{-4} \text{ mol/L}$$

$$\Pi = cRT$$

$$\Pi = (4.4 \times 10^{-4} \text{ mol/L})(0.08206 \text{ L atm/mol K})(300 \text{ K})$$

$$\Pi = 0.011 \text{ atm } (= 8.2 \text{ mm Hg})$$

**Think about Your Answer** If the osmotic pressure is measured in a device similar to that shown in Figure 14.15, the height of the column of aqueous solution supported would be about 110 mm (8.2 mm × 13.5 mm H$_2$O/mm Hg = 110 mm). This would be easily measurable in the laboratory.

---

**Check Your Understanding**

Bradykinin is a small peptide (9 amino acids; 1060 g/mol) that lowers blood pressure by causing blood vessels to dilate. What is the osmotic pressure of a solution of this protein at 20 °C if 0.033 g of the peptide is dissolved in water to give 50.0 mL of solution?

## Colligative Properties and Molar Mass Determination

Earlier in this book you learned how to calculate a molecular formula from an empirical formula when given the molar mass. But how do you know the molar mass of an unknown compound? An experiment must be carried out to find this crucial piece of information, and one way to do so is to use a colligative property of a solution of the compound. The strategy map used with Example 14.8 represents the basic approach for each of the colligative properties studied.

### ⦿WL    INTERACTIVE EXAMPLE 14.8    Determining Molar Mass from Boiling Point Elevation

**Problem** A solution prepared from 1.25 g of oil of wintergreen (methyl salicylate) in 99.0 g of benzene has a boiling point of 80.31 °C. Determine the molar mass of methyl salicylate.

**What Do You Know?** The molar mass of a compound is the quotient of the mass of a sample (g) and the amount (mol) represented by that sample. Here you know the mass of the sample (1.25 g), so you need to find the amount that corresponds to this mass.

**Strategy**

- Determine $\Delta T_{bp}$ from the given boiling point of the solution. (The boiling point of pure benzene and $K_{bp}$ for benzene are given in Table 14.3.) Use the equation $\Delta T_{bp} = K_{bp} \cdot m$ to calculate the solution concentration in units of mol/kg.

- Knowing the mass of solvent, calculate the amount of solute (mol).

- Combine the mass and amount of solute to give the molar mass [molar mass = mass (g)/amount (mol)].

## Solution

(a) Use the boiling point elevation to calculate the solution concentration:

$$\text{Boiling point elevation } (\Delta T_{bp}) = 80.31\,°\text{C} - 80.10\,°\text{C} = 0.21\,°\text{C}$$

$$c_{\text{solute}} = \frac{\Delta T_{bp}}{K_{bp}} = \frac{0.21\,°\text{C}}{2.53\,°\text{C}/m} = 0.083\,m$$

(b) Calculate the amount of solute in the solution from the solution concentration:

$$\text{Amount of solute} = \left(\frac{0.083\,\text{mol}}{1.00\,\text{kg}}\right)(0.099\,\text{kg solvent}) = 0.0082\,\text{mol solute}$$

(c) Combine the amount of solute with its mass to obtain its molar mass.

$$\frac{1.25\,\text{g}}{0.0082\,\text{mol}} = 150\,\text{g/mol}$$

**Think about Your Answer** Methyl salicylate has the formula $C_8H_8O_3$ and a molar mass of 152.14 g/mol. Given that $\Delta T$ has only two significant figures, the calculated value is acceptably close to the actual value.

---

**Check Your Understanding**

An aluminum-containing compound has the empirical formula $(C_2H_5)_2AlF$. Find the molecular formula if 0.448 g of the compound dissolved in 23.46 g of benzene has a freezing point of 5.265 °C.

---

**Strategy Map 14.8**

**PROBLEM**

Calculate **molar mass** of unknown.

↓

**DATA/INFORMATION**
- **Mass** of unknown and solvent
- **Boiling point** of solution (80.31 °C)

↓

STEP 1. Use $\Delta T_{bp} = K_{bp}m$.

**Concentration** of solute (mol/kg)

↓

STEP 2. Mol solute = (mol/kg)(kg solvent).

**Amount of solute (mol)**

↓

STEP 3. Molar mass = g solute/mol solute.

**Molar mass** of unknown **(g/mol)**

---

# EXAMPLE 14.9 Osmotic Pressure and Molar Mass

**Problem** Beta-carotene is the most important of the A vitamins. Calculate the molar mass of β-carotene if 10.0 mL of a solution in chloroform containing 7.68 mg of β-carotene has an osmotic pressure of 26.57 mm Hg at 25.0 °C.

**What Do You Know?** As in Example 14.8, the molar mass of a compound is the quotient of the mass of a sample and the amount represented by that sample. Here you know the mass of the sample (7.68 mg), so you need to find the amount equivalent to this mass.

**Strategy**

- Use Equation 14.9 to calculate the solution concentration from the osmotic pressure.

- Use the volume and concentration of the solution to calculate the amount of solute.

- Find the molar mass of the solute from its mass and amount.

**Solution**

(a) Calculate the concentration of β-carotene from Π, R, and T.

$$\text{Concentration (mol/L)} = \frac{\Pi}{RT} = \frac{(26.57\text{ mm Hg})\left(\dfrac{1\text{ atm}}{760\text{ mm Hg}}\right)}{(0.082057\text{ L}\cdot\text{atm/K}\cdot\text{mol})(298.2\text{ K})}$$

$$= 1.429 \times 10^{-3}\text{ mol/L}$$

(b) Calculate the amount of β-carotene dissolved in 10.0 mL of solvent.

$$(1.429 \times 10^{-3}\text{ mol/L})(0.0100\text{ L}) = 1.43 \times 10^{-5}\text{ mol}$$

(c) Combine the amount of solute with its mass to calculate its molar mass:

$$\frac{7.68 \times 10^{-3}\text{ g}}{1.43 \times 10^{-5}\text{ mol}} = 538\text{ g/mol}$$

**Think about Your Answer** Beta-carotene is a hydrocarbon with the formula $C_{40}H_{56}$ (molar mass = 536.9 g/mol).

# Osmosis and Medicine

Osmosis is of practical significance for people in the health professions. Patients who become dehydrated through illness often need to be given water and nutrients intravenously. Water cannot simply be dripped into a patient's vein, however. Rather, the intravenous solution must have the same overall solute concentration as the patient's blood: the solution must be isoosmotic or **isotonic** (Figure B, middle). If pure water was used, the inside of a blood cell would have a higher solute concentration (lower water concentration), and water would flow into the cell. This hypotonic situation would cause the red blood cells to burst (lyse) (Figure B, right). The opposite situation, hypertonicity, occurs if the intravenous solution is more concentrated than the contents of the blood cell (Figure B, left). In this case, the cell would lose water and shrivel up (crenate). To combat this, a dehydrated patient is rehydrated in the hospital with a sterile saline solution that is 0.16 M NaCl, a solution that is isotonic with the cells of the body.

**FIGURE A** **An isotonic saline solution.** This solution has the same molality as body fluids.

**FIGURE B** **Osmosis and living cells.** *(middle)* A cell placed in an isotonic solution. The net movement of water into and out of the cell is zero because the concentration of solutes inside and outside the cell is the same. *(left)* In a hypertonic solution, the concentration of solutes outside the cell is greater than that inside. There is a net flow of water out of the cell, causing the cell to dehydrate, shrink, and perhaps die. *(right)* In a hypotonic solution, the concentration of solutes outside the cell is less than that inside. There is a net flow of water into the cell, causing the cell to swell and perhaps to burst (or lyse).

---

**Check Your Understanding**

A 1.40-g sample of polyethylene, a common plastic, is dissolved in enough organic solvent to give 100.0 mL of solution. What is the average molar mass of the polymer if the measured osmotic pressure of the solution is 1.86 mm Hg at 25 °C?

---

## Colligative Properties of Solutions Containing Ions

In the northern United States, it is common practice to scatter salt on snowy or icy roads or sidewalks. When the sun shines on the snow or patch of ice, a small amount melts, and some salt dissolves in the water. As a result of the dissolved solute, the freezing point of the solution is lower than 0 °C. The solution "eats" its way through the ice, breaking it up, and the icy patch is no longer dangerous for drivers or for people walking.

Salt (NaCl) is the most common substance used on roads because it is inexpensive and dissolves readily in water. Its relatively low molar mass means that the effect per gram is large. In addition, salt is especially effective because it is an electrolyte. That is, it dissolves to give ions in solution:

$$NaCl(s) \rightarrow Na^+(aq) + Cl^-(aq)$$

Recall that colligative properties depend not on what is dissolved but *only on the number of particles of solute per solvent particle*. When 1 mol of NaCl dissolves, 2 mol of ions form, which means that the effect on the freezing point of water should be twice as large as that expected for a mole of sugar. A 0.100 *m* solution of

**Table 14.4  Freezing Point Depressions of Some Ionic Solutions**

| Mass % | $m$ (mol/kg) | $\Delta T_{fp}$ (measured, °C) | $\Delta T_{fp}$ (calculated, °C) | $\dfrac{\Delta T_{fp},\ \text{measured}}{\Delta T_{fp},\ \text{calculated}}$ |
|---|---|---|---|---|
| *NaCl* | | | | |
| 0.00700 | 0.0120 | −0.0433 | −0.0223 | 1.94 |
| 0.500 | 0.0860 | −0.299 | −0.160 | 1.87 |
| 1.00 | 0.173 | −0.593 | −0.322 | 1.84 |
| 2.00 | 0.349 | −1.186 | −0.649 | 1.83 |
| *Na₂SO₄* | | | | |
| 0.00700 | 0.00493 | −0.0257 | −0.00917 | 2.80 |
| 0.500 | 0.0354 | −0.165 | −0.0658 | 2.51 |
| 1.00 | 0.0711 | −0.320 | −0.132 | 2.42 |
| 2.00 | 0.144 | −0.606 | −0.268 | 2.26 |

NaCl really contains two solutes, $0.100\ m$ $Na^+$ and $0.100\ m$ $Cl^-$. What we should use to estimate the freezing point depression is the *total* molality of solute particles:

$$m_{\text{total}} = m(Na^+) + m(Cl^-) = (0.100 + 0.100)\ \text{mol/kg} = 0.200\ \text{mol/kg}$$

$$\Delta T_{fp} = (-1.86\ °C/m)(0.200\ m) = -0.372\ °C$$

To estimate the freezing point depression for an ionic compound, first find the molality of solute from the mass and molar mass of the compound and the mass of the solvent. Then, multiply the molality by the number of ions in the formula: two for NaCl, three for $Na_2SO_4$, four for $LaCl_3$, five for $Al_2(SO_4)_3$, and so on.

Table 14.4 shows that as the concentration of NaCl decreases, $\Delta T_{fp}$ for NaCl approaches but does not quite reach a value that is two times larger than the value determined assuming no dissociation. Likewise, $\Delta T_{fp}$ for $Na_2SO_4$ approaches but does not reach a value that is three times larger. The ratio of the experimentally observed value of $\Delta T_{fp}$ to the value calculated, assuming no dissociation, is called the **van't Hoff factor** after Jacobus Henrikus van't Hoff (1852–1911), who studied this phenomenon. The van't Hoff factor is represented by $i$.

$$i = \frac{\Delta T_{fp},\ \text{measured}}{\Delta T_{fp},\ \text{calculated}} = \frac{\Delta T_{fp},\ \text{measured}}{K_{fp}\ m}$$

or

$$\Delta T_{fp}\ \text{measured} = K_{fp} \times m \times i \qquad (14.10)$$

The numbers in the last column of Table 14.4 are van't Hoff factors. These values can be used in calculations of any colligative property. Vapor pressure lowering, boiling point elevation, freezing point depression, and osmotic pressure are all larger for electrolytes than for nonelectrolytes of the same molality.

The van't Hoff factor approaches a whole number (2, 3, and so on) only with very dilute solutions. In more concentrated solutions, the experimental freezing point depressions indicate that there are fewer ions in solution than expected. This behavior, which is typical of all ionic compounds, is a consequence of the strong attractions between ions. The result is as if some of the positive and negative ions are paired, decreasing the total molality of particles. Indeed, in more concentrated solutions, and especially in solvents less polar than water, ions are extensively associated in ion pairs and in even larger clusters.

## EXAMPLE 14.10 Freezing Point and Ionic Solutions

**Problem** A 0.0200 $m$ aqueous solution of an ionic compound, $Co(NH_3)_4Cl_3$, freezes at $-0.0640$ °C. How many moles of ions does 1 mol of the salt produce on being dissolved in water?

**What Do You Know?** You know the freezing point depression ($-0.0640$ °C), the solution concentration, and $K_{fp}$.

**Strategy** The van't Hoff factor, $i$, is the ratio of the measured $\Delta T_{fp}$ to the calculated freezing point depression. First, calculate $\Delta T_{fp}$ expected for a solution in which no ions are produced. Compare this value with the actual value of $\Delta T_{fp}$. The ratio ($= i$) will reflect the number of ions produced.

**Solution**

(a) Calculate the freezing-point depression expected for a 0.0200 $m$ solution assuming that the salt does not dissociate into ions.

$$\Delta T_{fp} \text{ calculated} = K_{fp}m = (-1.86 \text{ °C})(0.0200 \text{ } m) = -0.0372 \text{ °C}$$

(b) Compare the calculated freezing point depression with the measured depression. This gives the van't Hoff factor:

$$i = \frac{\Delta T_{fp}, \text{ measured}}{\Delta T_{fp}, \text{ calculated}} = \frac{-0.0640 \text{ °C}}{-0.0372 \text{ °C}} = 1.72$$

The $i$ value is much greater that 1 and is approaching 2. Therefore, we assume each molecule affords 2 ions in solution.

**Think about Your Answer** We find $i$ is approaching 2, meaning that the complex dissociates into two ions: $[Co(NH_3)Cl_2]^+$ and $Cl^-$. As you will see in Chapter 22, the cation is a $Co^{3+}$ ion surrounded octahedrally by 4 $NH_3$ molecules and two $Cl^-$ ions.

---

**Check Your Understanding**

Calculate the freezing point of 525 g of water that contains 25.0 g of NaCl. Assume $i$, the van't Hoff factor, is 1.85 for NaCl.

---

### REVIEW & CHECK FOR SECTION 14.4

1. *Vapor pressure:* Arrange the following aqueous solutions in order of increasing vapor pressure at 25 °C: 0.35 $m$ $C_2H_4(OH)_2$ (ethylene glycol, nonvolatile solute); 0.50 $m$ sugar; 0.20 $m$ KBr; and 0.20 $m$ $Na_2SO_4$.

   (a) $C_2H_4(OH)_2 <$ sugar $<$ KBr $<$ $Na_2SO_4$   (c) sugar $<$ $C_2H_4(OH)_2 <$ KBr $<$ $Na_2SO_4$

   (b) $Na_2SO_4 <$ sugar $<$ KBr $<$ $C_2H_4(OH)_2$   (d) KBr $<$ sugar $<$ $Na_2SO_4 <$ $C_2H_4(OH)_2$

2. One gram (1.00 g) of each of the listed substances is dissolved in 50 g of benzene. Which of the solutions has the lowest freezing point?

   (a) buckyballs, $C_{60}$                        (c) trinitrotoluene, $C_7H_5(NO_2)_3$

   (b) acetaminophen, $C_8H_9NO_2$               (d) naphthalene, $C_{10}H_8$

3. Samples of each of the substances listed below are dissolved in 125 g of water. Which of the solutions has the highest boiling point?

   (a) 3.0 g sucrose, $C_{12}H_{22}O_{11}$          (c) 1.0 g propylene glycol, $C_3H_6(OH)_2$

   (b) 1.0 g glycerol, $C_3H_5(OH)_3$             (d) 2.0 g glucose, $C_6H_{12}O_6$

4. *Molar mass:* Erythritol is a compound that occurs naturally in algae and fungi. It is about twice as sweet as sucrose. A solution of 2.50 g of erythritol in 50.0 g of water freezes at $-0.762$ °C. What is the molar mass of the compound?

   (a) 26.9 g/mol                               (c) 122 g/mol

   (b) 35.5 g/mol                               (d) 224 g/mol

# 14.5 Colloids

Earlier in this chapter, we defined a solution broadly as a homogeneous mixture of two or more substances in a single phase. To this definition we should add that, in a true solution, no settling of the solute should be observed and the solute particles should be in the form of ions or relatively small molecules. Thus, NaCl and sugar form true solutions in water. You are also familiar with suspensions, which result, for example, if a handful of fine sand is added to water and shaken vigorously. Sand particles are still visible and gradually settle to the bottom of the beaker or bottle. **Colloidal dispersions**, also called **colloids**, represent a state intermediate between a solution and a suspension (Figure 14.18). Colloids include many of the foods you eat and the materials around you; among them are JELL-O®, milk, fog, and porcelain (Table 14.5).

Around 1860, the British chemist Thomas Graham (1805–1869) found that substances such as starch, gelatin, glue, and albumin from eggs diffused only very slowly when placed in water, compared with sugar or salt. In addition, the former substances differ significantly in their ability to diffuse through a thin membrane: Sugar molecules can diffuse through many membranes, but the very large molecules that make up starch, gelatin, glue, and albumin do not. Moreover, Graham found that he could not crystallize these substances, whereas he could crystallize sugar, salt, and other materials that form true solutions. Graham coined the word "colloid" (from the Greek, meaning "glue") to describe this class of substances that are distinctly different from true solutions and suspensions.

We now know that it is possible to crystallize some colloidal substances, albeit with difficulty, so there really is no sharp dividing line between these classes based on this property. Colloids do, however, have two distinguishing characteristics. First, colloids generally have high molar masses; this is true of proteins such as hemoglobin that have molar masses in the thousands. Second, the particles of a colloid are relatively large (say, 1000 nm in diameter). As a consequence, they exhibit the **Tyndall effect**; they scatter visible light when dispersed in a solvent, making the mixture appear cloudy (Figure 14.19). Third, even though colloidal particles are large, they are not so large that they settle out.

Graham also gave us the words **sol** for a colloidal dispersion of a solid substance in a fluid medium and **gel** for a colloidal dispersion that has a structure that prevents it from being mobile. JELL-O® is a sol when the solid is first mixed with boiling water, but it becomes a gel when cooled. Other examples of gels are the gelatinous precipitates of $Al(OH)_3$, $Fe(OH)_3$, and $Cu(OH)_2$ (Figure 14.20).

Colloidal dispersions consist of finely divided particles that, as a result, have a very high surface area. For example, if you have one millionth of a mole of colloidal particles, each assumed to be a sphere with a diameter of 200 nm, the total surface

**FIGURE 14.18 Gold colloid.** A water-soluble salt of $[AuCl_4]^-$ is reduced to give colloidal gold metal. The colloidal gold gives the dispersion its red color (when the particles have a length or diameter of less than 100 nm). (Similarly, colloidal gold is used to give a beautiful red color to glass.) Since the days of alchemy, some have claimed that drinking a colloidal gold solution "cleared the mind, increased intelligence and willpower, and balanced the emotions."

Dust in the air scatters the light coming through the trees in a forest along the Oregon coast.

A narrow beam of light from a laser is passed through an NaCl solution *(left)* and then a colloidal mixture of gelatin and water *(right)*.

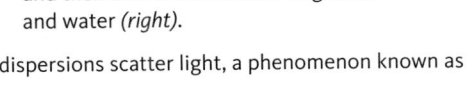

**FIGURE 14.19 The Tyndall effect.** Colloidal dispersions scatter light, a phenomenon known as the Tyndall effect.

**FIGURE 14.20 Gelatinous precipitates.** *(left)* $Al(OH)_3$, *(center)* $Fe(OH)_3$, and *(right)* $Cu(OH)_2$.

**Table 14.5 Types of Colloids**

| Type | Dispersing Medium | Dispersed Phase | Examples |
|------|-------------------|-----------------|----------|
| Aerosol | Gas | Liquid | Fog, clouds, aerosol sprays |
| Aerosol | Gas | Solid | Smoke, airborne viruses, automobile exhaust |
| Foam | Liquid | Gas | Shaving cream, whipped cream |
| Foam | Solid | Gas | Styrofoam, marshmallow |
| Emulsion | Liquid | Liquid | Mayonnaise, milk, face cream |
| Gel | Solid | Liquid | Jelly, JELL-O®, cheese, butter |
| Sol | Liquid | Solid | Gold in water, milk of magnesia, mud |
| Solid sol | Solid | Solid | Milkglass |

area of the particles would be on the order of 200 million cm², or the size of several football fields. It is not surprising, therefore, that many of the properties of colloids depend on the properties of surfaces.

## Types of Colloids

Colloids are classified according to the state of the dispersed phase and the dispersing medium. Table 14.5 lists several types of colloids and gives examples of each.

Colloids with water as the dispersing medium can be classified as **hydrophobic** (from the Greek, meaning "water-fearing") or **hydrophilic** ("water-loving"). A hydrophobic colloid is one in which only weak attractive forces exist between the water and the surfaces of the colloidal particles. Examples include dispersions of metals (Figure 14.18) and of nearly insoluble salts in water. When compounds like AgCl precipitate, the result is often a colloidal dispersion. The precipitation reaction occurs too rapidly for ions to gather from long distances and make large crystals, so the ions aggregate to form small particles that remain suspended in the liquid.

Why don't the particles come together (coagulate) and form larger particles? The answer is that the colloidal particles carry electric charges. To see how this happens, suppose AgCl ion pairs come together to form a tiny particle. If $Ag^+$ ions are still present in substantial concentration in the solution, these positive ions could be attracted to negative $Cl^-$ ions on the surface of the particle. Thus the original clump of AgCl ion pairs becomes positively charged, allowing it to attract a secondary layer of anions. The particles, now surrounded by layers of ions, repel one another and are prevented from coming together to form a precipitate (Figure 14.21).

**FIGURE 14.21 Hydrophobic colloids.** A hydrophobic colloid is stabilized by positive ions absorbed onto each particle and a secondary layer of negative ions. Because the particles bear similar charges, they repel one another, and precipitation is prevented.

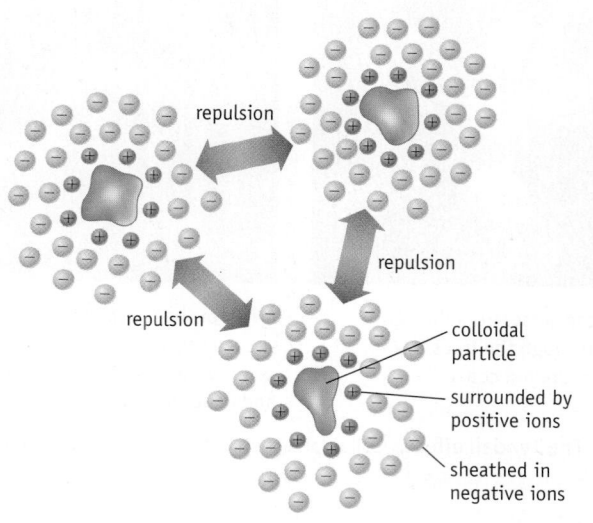

Soil particles are often carried by water in rivers and streams as hydrophobic colloids. When river water carrying large amounts of colloidal particles meets seawater with its high concentration of salts, the particles coagulate to form the silt seen at the mouth of the river (Figure 14.22). Municipal water treatment plants often add salts such as $Al_2(SO_4)_3$ to clarify water. In aqueous solution, aluminum ions exist as $[Al(H_2O)_6]^{3+}$ cations, which neutralize the charge on the hydrophobic colloidal soil particles, causing these particles to aggregate and settle out.

*Hydrophilic colloids* are strongly attracted to water molecules. They often have groups such as —OH and —$NH_2$ on their surfaces. These groups form strong hydrogen bonds to water, thereby stabilizing the colloid. Proteins and starch are important examples of hydrophilic colloids, and homogenized milk is the most familiar example.

**Emulsions** are colloidal dispersions of one liquid in another, such as oil or fat in water. Familiar examples include salad dressing, mayonnaise, and milk. If vegetable oil and vinegar are mixed to make a salad dressing, the mixture quickly separates into two layers because the nonpolar oil molecules do not interact with the polar water and acetic acid ($CH_3CO_2H$) molecules. So why are milk and mayonnaise apparently homogeneous mixtures that do not separate into layers? The answer is that they contain an **emulsifying agent** such as soap or a protein. Lecithin is a phospholipid found in egg yolks, so mixing egg yolks with oil and vinegar stabilizes the colloidal dispersion known as mayonnaise. To understand this process further, let us look into the functioning of soaps and detergents, substances known as surfactants.

## Surfactants

Soaps and detergents are emulsifying agents. Soap is made by heating a fat with sodium or potassium hydroxide, which produces the anions of long chain carboxylic acids, sometimes referred to as fatty acids (◀ page 489). An example is sodium stearate.

$$H_3C(CH_2)_{16}-\underset{\underset{\text{polar head}}{\underbrace{\phantom{C-O}}}}{\overset{\overset{\text{O}}{\underset{\|}{}}}{C}-O^-}\ Na^+$$

$\underbrace{\phantom{H_3C(CH_2)_{16}}}_{\substack{\text{hydrocarbon tail}\\\text{soluble in oil}}}$  $\underbrace{\phantom{C-O^-}}_{\substack{\text{polar head}\\\text{soluble in water}}}$

sodium stearate, a soap

The fatty acid anion has a split personality: It has a nonpolar, hydrophobic hydrocarbon tail that is soluble in other similar hydrocarbons and a polar, hydrophilic head that is soluble in water.

Oil cannot be readily washed away from dishes or clothing with water because oil is nonpolar and thus insoluble in water. Instead, we add soap to the water to clean away the oil. The nonpolar molecules of the oil interact with the nonpolar hydrocarbon tails of the soap molecules, leaving the polar heads of the soap to interact with surrounding water molecules. The oil and water then mix (Figure 14.23).

NASA/Peter Arnold, Inc.

**FIGURE 14.22 Formation of silt.** Silt forms at a river delta as colloidal soil particles come in contact with saltwater in the ocean. Here, the Ashley and Cooper Rivers empty into the Atlantic Ocean at Charleston, South Carolina. The high concentration of ions in seawater causes the colloidal soil particles to coagulate.

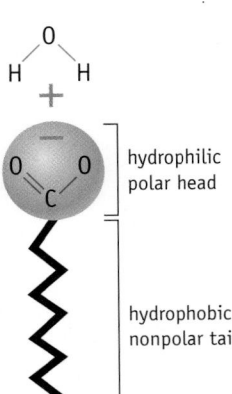

**FIGURE 14.23 The cleaning action of soap.** Soap molecules interact with water through the charged, hydrophilic end of the molecule. The long, hydrocarbon end of the molecule is hydrophobic, but it can bind through dispersion forces with hydrocarbons and other nonpolar substances.

**FIGURE 14.24 Effect of a detergent on the surface tension of water.** Sulfur (density = 2.1 g/cm³) is carefully placed on the surface of water (density, 1.0 g/cm³) *(left)*. The surface tension of the water keeps the denser sulfur afloat. Several drops of detergent are then placed on the surface of the water *(right)*. The surface tension of the water is reduced, and the sulfur sinks to the bottom of the beaker.

add surfactant

• **Soaps and Surfactants** A sodium soap is a solid at room temperature, whereas potassium soaps are usually liquids. About 30 million tons of household and toilet soap, and synthetic and soap-based laundry detergents, are produced annually worldwide.

If the oily material on a piece of clothing or a dish also contains some dirt particles, that dirt can now be washed away.

Substances such as soaps that affect the properties of surfaces, and therefore affect the interaction between two phases, are called surface-active agents, or **surfactants**, for short. A surfactant used for cleaning is called a **detergent**. One function of a surfactant is to lower the surface tension of water, which enhances the cleansing action of the detergent (Figure 14.24).

Many detergents used in the home and industry are synthetic. One example is sodium laurylbenzenesulfonate, a biodegradable compound.

$$CH_3CH_2CH_2CH_2CH_2CH_2CH_2CH_2CH_2CH_2CH_2CH_2 —\!\!\bigcirc\!\!— SO_3^-\ Na^+$$

sodium laurylbenzenesulfonate

In general, synthetic detergents use the sulfonate group, $—SO_3^-$, as the polar head instead of the carboxylate group, $—CO_2^-$. The carboxylate anions form an insoluble precipitate with any $Ca^{2+}$ or $Mg^{2+}$ ions present in water. Because hard water is characterized by high concentrations of these ions, using soaps containing carboxylates produces bathtub rings and telltale gray clothing. The synthetic sulfonate detergents have the advantage that they do not form such precipitates because their calcium salts are more soluble in water.

---

**REVIEW & CHECK FOR SECTION 14.5**

Figure 14.18 illustrates a gold colloid. Assume the colloidal particles are spherical clumps of gold atoms and are 100 nm in diameter. What is the approximate number of gold atoms that could form such a particle? (The radius of a gold atom is 144 pm.)

(a)  300 atoms          (b)  40 million atoms   (c)  2 billion atoms

---

## CHAPTER GOALS REVISITED

*Now that you have studied this chapter, you should ask whether you have met the chapter goals. In particular, you should be able to:*

**Calculate and use the solution concentration units molality, mole fraction, and weight percent**

a.  Define the terms solution, solvent, solute, and colligative properties.

b.  Use the following concentration units: molality, mole fraction, and weight percent (Section 14.1) **Study Questions: 1–12.**

c. Understand the distinctions between saturated, unsaturated, and supersaturated solutions (Section 14.2). **Study Questions: 17, 18, 94.**

d. Define and illustrate the terms *miscible* and *immiscible* (Section 14.2). **Study Questions: 13, 96.**

**Understand the solution process**

a. Describe the process of dissolving a solute in a solvent, including the energy changes that may occur (Section 14.2). **Study Questions: 14–16, 71.**

b. Understand the relationship of lattice enthalpy and enthalpy of hydration to the enthalpy of solution for an ionic solute (Section 14.2). **Study Question: 91.**

c. Describe the effect of pressure and temperature on the solubility of a solute (Section 14.3). **Study Questions: 17, 18.**

d. Use Henry's law to calculate the solubility of a gas in a solvent (Section 14.3). **Study Questions: 19–22, 67, 81, 82.**

e. Apply Le Chatelier's principle to the change in solubility of gases with temperature changes (Section 14.3).

**Understand and use the colligative properties of solutions**

a. Calculate the mole fraction of a solvent ($X_{solvent}$) and the effect of a solute on solvent vapor pressure ($P_{solvent}$) using Raoult's law (Section 14.4). **Study Questions: 23–26, 73, 74, 98.**

b. Calculate the boiling point elevation or freezing point depression caused by a solute in a solvent (Section 14.4). **Study Questions: 27–34, 45, 53, 60, and Go Chemistry Module 19.**

c. Calculate the osmotic pressure ($\Pi$) for solutions (Section 14.4). **Study Questions: 35–38, 78, 88.**

d. Use colligative properties to determine the molar mass of a solute (Section 14.4). **Study Questions: 39–44, 64, 89, 90.**

e. Characterize the effect of ionic solutes on colligative properties (Section 14.4). **Study Questions: 47, 48, 52, 53, 60, 61, 93.**

f. Use the van't Hoff factor, $i$, in calculations involving colligative properties (Section 14.4). **Study Questions: 45, 46, 62, 63, 75, 77, 79, 80, 102.**

**Recognize the properties and importance of colloids (Section 14.5).**

 **and**

Sign in at **www.cengage.com/owl** to:
- View tutorials and simulations, develop problem-solving skills, and complete online homework assigned by your professor.
- For quick review and exam prep, download Go Chemistry mini lecture modules from OWL (or purchase them at **www.cengagebrain.com**)

 Access **How Do I Solve It?** tutorials on how to approach problem solving using concepts in this chapter.

# Key Equations

**Equation 14.1 (page 618)** Molality is defined as the amount of solute per kilogram of solvent.

$$\text{Concentration } (c, \text{ mol/kg}) = \text{molality of solute} = \frac{\text{amount of solute (mol)}}{\text{mass of solvent (kg)}}$$

**Equation 14.2 (page 618)** The mole fraction, $X$, of a solution component is defined as the number of moles of a given component of a mixture ($n_A$, mol) divided by the total number of moles of all of the components of the mixture.

$$\text{Mole fraction of A } (X_A) = \frac{n_A}{n_A + n_B + n_C + \ldots}$$

**Equation 14.3 (page 619)** Weight percent is the mass of one component divided by the total mass of the mixture (multiplied by 100%).

$$\text{Weight \% A} = \frac{\text{mass of A}}{\text{mass of A} + \text{mass of B} + \text{mass of C} + \ldots} \times 100\%$$

**Equation 14.4 (page 626)** Henry's law: The solubility of a gas, $S_g$, is equal to the product of the partial pressure of the gaseous solute ($P_g$) and a constant ($k_H$) characteristic of the solute and solvent.

$$S_g = k_H P_g$$

**Equation 14.5 (page 630)** Raoult's law: The equilibrium vapor pressure of a solvent over a solution at a given temperature, $P_{solvent}$, is the product of the mole fraction of the solvent ($X_{solvent}$) and the vapor pressure of the pure solvent ($P°_{solvent}$).

$$P_{solvent} = X_{solvent} \, P°_{solvent}$$

**Equation 14.6 (page 631)** The decrease in the vapor pressure of the solvent over a solution, $\Delta P_{solvent}$, depends on the mole fraction of the solute ($X_{solute}$) and the vapor pressure of the pure solvent ($P°_{solvent}$).

$$\Delta P_{solvent} = -X_{solute} \, P°_{solvent}$$

**Equation 14.7 (page 632)** The elevation in boiling point of the solvent in a solution, $\Delta T_{bp}$, is the product of the molality of the solute, $m_{solute}$, and a constant characteristic of the solvent, $K_{bp}$.

$$\text{Elevation in boiling point} = \Delta T_{bp} = K_{bp} m_{solute}$$

**Equation 14.8 (page 634)** The depression of the freezing point of the solvent in a solution, $\Delta T_{fp}$, is the product of the molality of the solute, $m_{solute}$, and a constant characteristic of the solvent, $K_{fp}$.

$$\text{Freezing point depression} = \Delta T_{fp} = K_{fp} m_{solute}$$

**Equation 14.9 (page 636)** The osmotic pressure, $\Pi$, is the product of the solute concentration $c$ (in mol/L), the universal gas constant $R$ (0.082057 L · atm/ K · mol), and the temperature $T$ (in kelvins).

$$\Pi = cRT$$

**Equation 14.10 (page 641)** This modified equation for freezing point depression accounts for the possible dissociation of a solute. The van't Hoff factor, $i$, the ratio of the measured freezing point depression and the freezing point depression calculated assuming no solute dissociation, is related to the relative number of particles produced by a dissolved solute.

$$\Delta T_{fp} \text{ measured} = K_{fp} \times m \times i$$

## Study Questions

 WL Interactive versions of these questions are assignable in OWL.

▲ denotes challenging questions.

Blue-numbered questions have answers in Appendix R and fully worked solutions in the *Student Solutions Manual*.

## Practicing Skills

### Concentration
*(See Section 14.1 and Example 14.1.)*

1. Suppose you dissolve 2.56 g of succinic acid, $C_2H_4(CO_2H)_2$, in 500. mL of water. Assuming that the density of water is 1.00 g/cm³, calculate the molality, mole fraction, and weight percent of acid in the solution.

2. Assume you dissolve 45.0 g of camphor, $C_{10}H_{16}O$, in 425 mL of ethanol, $C_2H_5OH$. Calculate the molality, mole fraction, and weight percent of camphor in this solution. (The density of ethanol is 0.785 g/mL.)

3. Fill in the blanks in the table. Aqueous solutions are assumed.

| Compound | Molality | Weight Percent | Mole Fraction |
|---|---|---|---|
| NaI | 0.15 | ___ | ___ |
| $C_2H_5OH$ | ___ | 5.0 | ___ |
| $C_{12}H_{22}O_{11}$ | 0.15 | ___ | ___ |

4. Fill in the blanks in the table. Aqueous solutions are assumed.

| Compound | Molality | Weight Percent | Mole Fraction |
|---|---|---|---|
| $KNO_3$ | ___ | 10.0 | ___ |
| $CH_3CO_2H$ | 0.0183 | ___ | ___ |
| $HOCH_2CH_2OH$ | ___ | 18.0 | ___ |

5. What mass of $Na_2CO_3$ must you add to 125 g of water to prepare 0.200 $m$ $Na_2CO_3$? What is the mole fraction of $Na_2CO_3$ in the resulting solution?

6. You want to prepare a solution that is 0.0512 $m$ in $NaNO_3$. What mass of $NaNO_3$ must be added to 500. g of water? What is the mole fraction of $NaNO_3$ in the solution?

7. You wish to prepare an aqueous solution of glycerol, $C_3H_5(OH)_3$, in which the mole fraction of the solute is 0.093. What mass of glycerol must you add to 425 g of water to make this solution? What is the molality of the solution?

8. You want to prepare an aqueous solution of ethylene glycol, $HOCH_2CH_2OH$, in which the mole fraction of solute is 0.125. What mass of ethylene glycol, in grams, should you combine with 955 g of water? What is the molality of the solution?

9. Hydrochloric acid is sold as a concentrated aqueous solution. If the molarity of commercial HCl is 12.0 and its density is 1.18 g/cm³, calculate the following:
   (a) the molality of the solution
   (b) the weight percent of HCl in the solution

10. Concentrated sulfuric acid has a density of 1.84 g/cm³ and is 95.0% by weight $H_2SO_4$. What is the molality of this acid? What is its molarity?

11. The average lithium ion concentration in seawater is 0.18 ppm. What is the molality of $Li^+$ in seawater?

12. Silver ion has an average concentration of 28 ppb (parts per billion) in U.S. water supplies.
   (a) What is the molality of the silver ion?
   (b) If you wanted $1.0 \times 10^2$ g of silver and could recover it chemically from water supplies, what volume of water in liters, would you have to treat? (Assume the density of water is 1.0 g/cm³.)

**The Solution Process**
*(See Section 14.2 and Example 14.2.)*

13. Which pairs of liquids will be miscible?
   (a) $H_2O$ and $CH_3CH_2CH_2CH_3$
   (b) $C_6H_6$ (benzene) and $CCl_4$
   (c) $H_2O$ and $CH_3CO_2H$

14. Acetone, $CH_3COCH_3$, is quite soluble in water. Explain why this should be so.

$$\overset{\displaystyle O}{\underset{\displaystyle H_3CCCH_3}{\|}}$$

15. Use the data of Table 14.1 to calculate the enthalpy of solution of LiCl.

16. Use the following data to calculate the enthalpy of solution of sodium perchlorate, $NaClO_4$:

$\Delta_fH°(s) = -382.9$ kJ/mol   and
$\Delta_fH°(aq, 1\ m) = -369.5$ kJ/mol

17. You make a saturated solution of NaCl at 25 °C. No solid is present in the beaker holding the solution. What can be done to increase the amount of dissolved NaCl in this solution? (See Figure 14.11.)
   (a) Add more solid NaCl.
   (b) Raise the temperature of the solution.
   (c) Raise the temperature of the solution, and add some NaCl.
   (d) Lower the temperature of the solution, and add some NaCl.

18. Some lithium chloride, LiCl, is dissolved in 100 mL of water in one beaker, and some $Li_2SO_4$ is dissolved in 100 mL of water in another beaker. Both are at 10 °C, and both are saturated solutions; some solid remains undissolved in each beaker. Describe what you would observe as the temperature is raised. The following data are available to you from a handbook of chemistry:

| Compound | Solubility (g/100 mL) | |
| --- | --- | --- |
| | 10 °C | 40 °C |
| $Li_2SO_4$ | 35.5 | 33.7 |
| LiCl | 74.5 | 89.8 |

**Henry's Law**
*(See Section 14.3 and Example 14.3.)*

19. The partial pressure of $O_2$ in your lungs varies from 25 mm Hg to 40 mm Hg. What mass of $O_2$ can dissolve in 1.0 L of water at 25 °C if the partial pressure of $O_2$ is 40 mm Hg?

20. The Henry's law constant for $O_2$ in water at 25 °C is given in Table 14.2. Which of the following is a reasonable constant when the temperature is 50 °C? Explain the reason for your choice.
   (a) $6.7 \times 10^{-4}$ mol/kg · bar   (c) $1.3 \times 10^{-3}$ mol/kg · bar
   (b) $2.6 \times 10^{-3}$ mol/kg · bar   (d) $6.4 \times 10^{-2}$ mol/kg · bar

21. An unopened soda can has an aqueous $CO_2$ concentration of 0.0506 $m$ at 25 °C. What is the pressure of $CO_2$ gas in the can?

22. Hydrogen gas has a Henry's law constant of $7.8 \times 10^{-4}$ mol/kg · bar at 25 °C when dissolving in water. If the total pressure of gas ($H_2$ gas plus water vapor) over water is 1.00 bar, what is the concentration of $H_2$ in the water in grams per milliliter? (See Appendix G for the vapor pressure of water.)

**Raoult's Law**
*(See Section 14.4 and Example 14.4.)*

23. A 35.0-g sample of ethylene glycol, $HOCH_2CH_2OH$, is dissolved in 500.0 g of water. The vapor pressure of water at 32 °C is 35.7 mm Hg. What is the vapor pressure of the water–ethylene glycol solution at 32 °C? (Ethylene glycol is nonvolatile.)

24. Urea, $(NH_2)_2CO$, which is widely used in fertilizers and plastics, is quite soluble in water. If you dissolve 9.00 g of urea in 10.0 mL of water, what is the vapor pressure of the solution at 24 °C? Assume the density of water is 1.00 g/mL.

25. Pure ethylene glycol, $HOCH_2CH_2OH$, is added to 2.00 kg of water in the cooling system of a car. The vapor pressure of the water in the system when the temperature is 90 °C is 457 mm Hg. What mass of glycol was added? (Assume the solution is ideal. See Appendix G for the vapor pressure of water.)

26. Pure iodine (105 g) is dissolved in 325 g of $CCl_4$ at 65 °C. Given that the vapor pressure of $CCl_4$ at this temperature is 531 mm Hg, what is the vapor pressure of the $CCl_4$–$I_2$ solution at 65 °C? (Assume that $I_2$ does not contribute to the vapor pressure.)

**Boiling Point Elevation**
*(See Section 14.4 and Example 14.5.)*

27. Verify that 0.200 mol of a nonvolatile solute in 125 g of benzene ($C_6H_6$) produces a solution whose boiling point is 84.2 °C.

28. What is the boiling point of a solution composed of 15.0 g of urea, $(NH_2)_2CO$, in 0.500 kg of water?

29. What is the boiling point of a solution composed of 15.0 g of $CHCl_3$ and 0.515 g of the nonvolatile solute acenaphthene, $C_{12}H_{10}$, a component of coal tar?

30. A solution of glycerol, $C_3H_5(OH)_3$, in 735 g of water has a boiling point of 104.4 °C at a pressure of 760 mm Hg. What is the mass of glycerol in the solution? What is the mole fraction of the solute?

**Freezing Point Depression**
*(See Section 14.4 and Example 14.6.)*

31. A mixture of ethanol, $C_2H_5OH$, and water has a freezing point of −16.0 °C.
    (a) What is the molality of the alcohol?
    (b) What is the weight percent of alcohol in the solution?

32. Some ethylene glycol, $HOCH_2CH_2OH$, is added to your car's cooling system along with 5.0 kg of water. If the freezing point of the water–glycol solution is −15.0 °C, what mass of $HOCH_2CH_2OH$ must have been added?

33. You dissolve 15.0 g of sucrose, $C_{12}H_{22}O_{11}$, in a cup of water (225 g). What is the freezing point of the solution?

34. Assume a bottle of wine consists of an 11% solution (by weight) of ethanol ($C_2H_5OH$) in water. If the bottle of wine is chilled to −20 °C, will the solution begin to freeze?

**Osmosis**
*(See Section 14.4 and Example 14.7.)*

35. An aqueous solution contains 3.00% phenylalanine ($C_9H_{11}NO_2$) by mass. Assume the phenylalanine is non-ionic and nonvolatile. Find the following:
    (a) the freezing point of the solution
    (b) the boiling point of the solution
    (c) the osmotic pressure of the solution at 25 °C
    In your view, which of these values is most easily measurable in the laboratory?

36. Estimate the osmotic pressure of human blood at 37 °C. Assume blood is isotonic with a 0.154 M NaCl solution, and assume the van't Hoff factor, *i*, is 1.90 for NaCl.

37. An aqueous solution containing 1.00 g of bovine insulin (a protein, not ionized) per liter has an osmotic pressure of 3.1 mm Hg at 25 °C. Calculate the molar mass of bovine insulin.

38. Calculate the osmotic pressure of a 0.0120 M solution of NaCl in water at 0 °C. Assume the van't Hoff factor, *i*, is 1.94 for this solution.

**Colligative Properties and Molar Mass Determination**
*(See Section 14.4 and Examples 14.8 and 14.9.)*

39. You add 0.255 g of an orange, crystalline compound whose empirical formula is $C_{10}H_8Fe$ to 11.12 g of benzene. The boiling point of the benzene rises from 80.10 °C to 80.26 °C. What are the molar mass and molecular formula of the compound?

40. Butylated hydroxyanisole (BHA) is used in margarine and other fats and oils. (It is used as an antioxidant and prolongs the shelf life of the food.) What is the molar mass of BHA if 0.640 g of the compound, dissolved in 25.0 g of chloroform, produces a solution whose boiling point is 62.22 °C?

41. Benzyl acetate is one of the active components of oil of jasmine. If 0.125 g of the compound is added to 25.0 g of chloroform ($CHCl_3$), the boiling point of the solution is 61.82 °C. What is the molar mass of benzyl acetate?

42. Anthracene, a hydrocarbon obtained from coal, has an empirical formula of $C_7H_5$. To find its molecular formula, you dissolve 0.500 g in 30.0 g of benzene. The boiling point of pure benzene is 80.10 °C, whereas the solution has a boiling point of 80.34 °C. What is the molecular formula of anthracene?

43. An aqueous solution contains 0.180 g of an unknown, nonionic solute in 50.0 g of water. The solution freezes at −0.040 °C. What is the molar mass of the solute?

44. The organic compound called *aluminon* is used as a reagent to test for the presence of the aluminum ion in aqueous solution. A solution of 2.50 g of aluminon in 50.0 g of water freezes at −0.197 °C. What is the molar mass of aluminon?

**Colligative Properties of Ionic Compounds**
*(See Section 14.4 and Example 14.10.)*

45. If 52.5 g of LiF is dissolved in 306 g of water, what is the expected freezing point of the solution? (Assume the van't Hoff factor, *i*, for LiF is 2.)

46. To make homemade ice cream, you cool the milk and cream by immersing the container in ice and a concentrated solution of rock salt (NaCl) in water. If you want to have a water–salt solution that freezes at −10. °C, what mass of NaCl must you add to 3.0 kg of water? (Assume the van't Hoff factor, *i*, for NaCl is 1.85.)

47. List the following aqueous solutions in order of increasing melting point. (The last three are all assumed to dissociate completely into ions in water.)
    (a) 0.1 *m* sugar       (c) 0.08 *m* $CaCl_2$
    (b) 0.1 *m* NaCl        (d) 0.04 *m* $Na_2SO_4$

**48.** Arrange the following aqueous solutions in order of decreasing freezing point. (The last three are all assumed to dissociate completely into ions in water.)
(a) 0.20 $m$ ethylene glycol (nonvolatile, nonelectrolyte)
(b) 0.12 $m$ K₂SO₄
(c) 0.10 $m$ MgCl₂
(d) 0.12 $m$ KBr

### Colloids
*(See Section 14.5.)*

**49.** When solutions of BaCl₂ and Na₂SO₄ are mixed, the mixture becomes cloudy. After a few days, a white solid is observed on the bottom of the beaker with a clear liquid above it.
(a) Write a balanced equation for the reaction that occurs.
(b) Why is the solution cloudy at first?
(c) What happens during the few days of waiting?

**50.** The dispersed phase of a certain colloidal dispersion consists of spheres of diameter $1.0 \times 10^2$ nm.
(a) What are the volume ($V = \frac{4}{3}\pi r^3$) and surface area ($A = 4\pi r^2$) of each sphere?
(b) How many spheres are required to give a total volume of 1.0 cm³? What is the total surface area of these spheres in square meters?

## General Questions

*These questions are not designated as to type or location in the chapter. They may combine several concepts.*

**51.** Phenylcarbinol is used in nasal sprays as a preservative. A solution of 0.52 g of the compound in 25.0 g of water has a melting point of −0.36 °C. What is the molar mass of phenylcarbinol?

**52.** (a) Which aqueous solution is expected to have the higher boiling point: 0.10 $m$ Na₂SO₄ or 0.15 $m$ sugar?
(b) For which aqueous solution is the vapor pressure of water higher: 0.30 $m$ NH₄NO₃ or 0.15 $m$ Na₂SO₄?

**53.** Arrange the following aqueous solutions in order of (i) increasing vapor pressure of water and (ii) increasing boiling point.
(a) 0.35 $m$ HOCH₂CH₂OH (a nonvolatile solute)
(b) 0.50 $m$ sugar
(c) 0.20 $m$ KBr (a strong electrolyte)
(d) 0.20 $m$ Na₂SO₄ (a strong electrolyte)

**54.** Making homemade ice cream is one of life's great pleasures. Fresh milk and cream, sugar, and flavorings are churned in a bucket suspended in an ice–water mixture, the freezing point of which has been lowered by adding rock salt. One manufacturer of home ice cream freezers recommends adding 2.50 lb (1130 g) of rock salt (NaCl) to 16.0 lb of ice (7250 g) in a 4-qt freezer. For the solution when this mixture melts, calculate the following:
(a) the weight percent of NaCl
(b) the mole fraction of NaCl
(c) the molality of the solution

**55.** Dimethylglyoxime [DMG, (CH₃CNOH)₂] is used as a reagent to precipitate nickel ion. Assume that 53.0 g of DMG has been dissolved in 525 g of ethanol (C₂H₅OH).

© Cengage Learning/Charles D. Winters

**The red, insoluble compound formed between nickel(II) ion and dimethylglyoxime (DMG) is precipitated when DMG is added to a basic solution of Ni²⁺(aq).**

(a) What is the mole fraction of DMG?
(b) What is the molality of the solution?
(c) What is the vapor pressure of the ethanol over the solution at ethanol's normal boiling point of 78.4 °C?
(d) What is the boiling point of the solution? (DMG does not produce ions in solution.) ($K_{bp}$ for ethanol = +1.22 °C/$m$)

**56.** A 10.7 $m$ solution of NaOH has a density of 1.33 g/cm³ at 20 °C. Calculate the following:
(a) the mole fraction of NaOH
(b) the weight percent of NaOH
(c) the molarity of the solution

**57.** Concentrated aqueous ammonia has a molarity of 14.8 mol/L and a density of 0.90 g/cm³. What is the molality of the solution? Calculate the mole fraction and weight percent of NH₃.

**58.** If you dissolve 2.00 g of Ca(NO₃)₂ in 750 g of water, what is the molality of Ca(NO₃)₂? What is the total molality of ions in solution? (Assume total dissociation of the ionic solid.)

**59.** If you want a solution that is 0.100 $m$ in ions, what mass of Na₂SO₄ must you dissolve in 125 g of water? (Assume total dissociation of the ionic solid.)

**60.** Consider the following aqueous solutions: (i) 0.20 $m$ HOCH₂CH₂OH (nonvolatile, nonelectrolyte); (ii) 0.10 $m$ CaCl₂; (iii) 0.12 $m$ KBr; and (iv) 0.12 $m$ Na₂SO₄.
(a) Which solution has the highest boiling point?
(b) Which solution has the lowest freezing point?
(c) Which solution has the highest water vapor pressure?

**61.** (a) Which solution is expected to have the higher boiling point: 0.20 $m$ KBr or 0.30 $m$ sugar?
(b) Which aqueous solution has the lower freezing point: 0.12 $m$ NH₄NO₃ or 0.10 $m$ Na₂CO₃?

**62.** The solubility of NaCl in water at 100 °C is 39.1 g/100. g of water. Calculate the boiling point of this solution. (Assume $i = 1.85$ for NaCl.)

63. Instead of using NaCl to melt the ice on your sidewalk, you decide to use $CaCl_2$. If you add 35.0 g of $CaCl_2$ to 150. g of water, what is the freezing point of the solution? (Assume $i = 2.7$ for $CaCl_2$.)

64. The smell of ripe raspberries is due to 4-(*p*-hydroxyphenyl)-2-butanone, which has the empirical formula $C_5H_6O$. To find its molecular formula, you dissolve 0.135 g in 25.0 g of chloroform, $CHCl_3$. The boiling point of the solution is 61.82 °C. What is the molecular formula of the solute?

65. Hexachlorophene has been used in germicidal soap. What is its molar mass if 0.640 g of the compound, dissolved in 25.0 g of chloroform, produces a solution whose boiling point is 61.93 °C?

66. The solubility of ammonium formate, $NH_4CHO_2$, in 100. g of water is 102 g at 0 °C and 546 g at 80 °C. A solution is prepared by dissolving $NH_4CHO_2$ in 200. g of water until no more will dissolve at 80 °C. The solution is then cooled to 0 °C. What mass of $NH_4CHO_2$ precipitates? (Assume that no water evaporates and that the solution is not supersaturated.)

67. How much $N_2$ can dissolve in water at 25 °C if the $N_2$ partial pressure is 585 mm Hg?

68. Cigars are best stored in a "humidor" at 18 °C and 55% relative humidity. This means the pressure of water vapor should be 55% of the vapor pressure of pure water at the same temperature. The proper humidity can be maintained by placing a solution of glycerol [$C_3H_5(OH)_3$] and water in the humidor. Calculate the percent by mass of glycerol that will lower the vapor pressure of water to the desired value. (The vapor pressure of glycerol is negligible.)

69. An aqueous solution containing 10.0 g of starch per liter has an osmotic pressure of 3.8 mm Hg at 25 °C.
    (a) What is the average molar mass of starch? (Because not all starch molecules are identical, the result will be an average.)
    (b) What is the freezing point of the solution? Would it be easy to determine the molecular weight of starch by measuring the freezing point depression? (Assume that the molarity and molality are the same for this solution.)

70. Vinegar is a 5% solution (by weight) of acetic acid in water. Determine the mole fraction and molality of acetic acid. What is the concentration of acetic acid in parts per million (ppm)? Explain why it is not possible to calculate the molarity of this solution from the information provided.

71. Calculate the enthalpies of solution for $Li_2SO_4$ and $K_2SO_4$. Are the solution processes exothermic or endothermic? Compare them with LiCl and KCl. What similarities or differences do you find?

| Compound | $\Delta_fH°(s)$ (kJ/mol) | $\Delta_fH°(aq, 1\ m)$ (kJ/mol) |
|---|---|---|
| $Li_2SO_4$ | −1436.4 | −1464.4 |
| $K_2SO_4$ | −1437.7 | −1414.0 |

72. ▲ Water at 25 °C has a density of 0.997 g/cm³. Calculate the molality and molarity of pure water at this temperature.

73. ▲ If a volatile solute is added to a volatile solvent, both substances contribute to the vapor pressure over the solution. Assuming an ideal solution, the vapor pressure of each is given by Raoult's law, and the total vapor pressure is the sum of the vapor pressures for each component. A solution, assumed to be ideal, is made from 1.0 mol of toluene ($C_6H_5CH_3$) and 2.0 mol of benzene ($C_6H_6$). The vapor pressures of the pure solvents are 22 mm Hg and 75 mm Hg, respectively, at 20 °C. What is the total vapor pressure of the mixture? What is the mole fraction of each component in the liquid and in the vapor?

74. A solution is made by adding 50.0 mL of ethanol ($C_2H_5OH$, $d = 0.789$ g/mL) to 50.0 mL of water ($d = 0.998$ g/mL). What is the total vapor pressure over the solution at 20 °C? (See Study Question 73.) The vapor pressure of ethanol at 20 °C is 43.6 mm Hg.

75. A 2.0% (by mass) aqueous solution of novocainium chloride ($C_{13}H_{21}ClN_2O_2$) freezes at −0.237 °C. Calculate the van't Hoff factor, $i$. How many moles of ions are in the solution per mole of compound?

76. A solution is 4.00% (by mass) maltose and 96.00% water. It freezes at −0.229 °C.
    (a) Calculate the molar mass of maltose (which is not an ionic compound).
    (b) The density of the solution is 1.014 g/mL. Calculate the osmotic pressure of the solution.

77. ▲ The following table lists the concentrations of the principal ions in seawater:

| Ion | Concentration (ppm) |
|---|---|
| $Cl^-$ | $1.95 \times 10^4$ |
| $Na^+$ | $1.08 \times 10^4$ |
| $Mg^{2+}$ | $1.29 \times 10^3$ |
| $SO_4^{2-}$ | $9.05 \times 10^2$ |
| $Ca^{2+}$ | $4.12 \times 10^2$ |
| $K^+$ | $3.80 \times 10^2$ |
| $Br^-$ | 67 |

    (a) Calculate the freezing point of seawater.
    (b) Calculate the osmotic pressure of seawater at 25 °C. What is the minimum pressure needed to purify seawater by reverse osmosis?

78. ▲ A tree is exactly 10 m tall.
    (a) What must be the total molarity of the solutes if sap rises to the top of the tree by osmotic pressure at 20 °C? Assume the groundwater outside the tree is pure water and that the density of the sap is 1.0 g/mL. (1 mm Hg = 13.6 mm $H_2O$.)
    (b) If the only solute in the sap is sucrose, $C_{12}H_{22}O_{11}$, what is its percent by mass?

79. A 2.00% solution of $H_2SO_4$ in water freezes at $-0.796$ °C.
    (a) Calculate the van't Hoff factor, $i$.
    (b) Which of the following best represents sulfuric acid in a dilute aqueous solution: $H_2SO_4$, $H_3O^+ + HSO_4^-$, or $2 H_3O^+ + SO_4^{2-}$?

80. A compound is known to be a potassium halide, KX. If 4.00 g of the salt is dissolved in exactly 100 g of water, the solution freezes at $-1.28$ °C. Identify the halide ion in this formula.

81. The Henry's law constant for $N_2O$ is $2.4 \times 10^{-2}$ mol/kg · bar. (Nitrous oxide, $N_2O$, laughing gas, is used as an anesthetic). Determine the mass of $N_2O$ that will dissolve in 500. mL of water, under an $N_2O$ pressure of 1.00 bar. What is the concentration of $N_2O$ in this solution, expressed in ppm ($d$ ($H_2O$) = 1.00 g/mL)?

82. If a carbonated beverage is bottled under 1.5 bar $CO_2$ pressure, what will be the concentration of dissolved $CO_2$ in that beverage? ($k_H$ for $CO_2$ is 0.034 mol/kg bar.) After the pressure is released what fraction of the dissolved gas will escape before equilibrium with the $CO_2$ in the atmosphere is reached?

83. You are given a flask filled with a colored liquid. Suggest several tests that would allow you to determine whether this is a solution or a colloid.

84. If one is very careful, it is possible to float a needle on the surface of water. (If the needle is magnetized, it will turn to point north and south and become a makeshift compass.) What would happen to the needle if a drop of liquid soap is added to the solution? Explain the observation.

## In the Laboratory

85. ▲ A solution of benzoic acid in benzene has a freezing point of 3.1 °C and a boiling point of 82.6 °C. (The freezing point of pure benzene is 5.50 °C, and its boiling point is 80.1 °C.) The structure of benzoic acid is

    What can you conclude about the state of the benzoic acid molecules at the two different temperatures? Recall the discussion of hydrogen bonding in Section 12.3, and see Figure 12.7.

86. ▲ You dissolve 5.0 mg of iodine, $I_2$, in 25 mL of water. You then add 10.0 mL of $CCl_4$ and shake the mixture. If $I_2$ is 85 times more soluble in $CCl_4$ than in $H_2O$ (on a volume basis), what are the masses of $I_2$ in the water and $CCl_4$ layers after shaking? (See Figure 14.6.)

87. ▲ A solution of 5.00 g of acetic acid in 100. g of benzene freezes at 3.37 °C. A solution of 5.00 g of acetic acid in 100. g of water freezes at $-1.49$ °C. Find the molar mass of acetic acid from each of these experiments. What can you conclude about the state of the

acetic acid molecules dissolved in each of these solvents? Recall the discussion of hydrogen bonding in Section 12.3 (and see Figure 12.7), and propose a structure for the species in benzene solution.

88. ▲ In a police forensics lab, you examine a package that may contain heroin. However, you find the white powder is not pure heroin but a mixture of heroin ($C_{21}H_{23}O_5N$) and lactose ($C_{12}H_{22}O_{11}$). To determine the amount of heroin in the mixture, you dissolve 1.00 g of the white powdery mixture in water in a 100.0-mL volumetric flask. You find that the solution has an osmotic pressure of 539 mm Hg at 25 °C. What is the composition of the mixture?

89. A newly synthesized compound containing boron and fluorine is 22.1% boron. Dissolving 0.146 g of the compound in 10.0 g of benzene gives a solution with a vapor pressure of 94.16 mm Hg at 25 °C. (The vapor pressure of pure benzene at this temperature is 95.26 mm Hg.) In a separate experiment, it is found that the compound does not have a dipole moment.
    (a) What is the molecular formula for the compound?
    (b) Draw a Lewis structure for the molecule, and suggest a possible molecular structure. Give the bond angles in the molecule and the hybridization of the boron atom.

90. In chemical research we often send newly synthesized compounds to commercial laboratories for analysis. These laboratories determine the weight percent of C and H by burning the compound and collecting the evolved $CO_2$ and $H_2O$. They determine the molar mass by measuring the osmotic pressure of a solution of the compound. Calculate the empirical and molecular formulas of a compound, $C_xH_yCr$, given the following information:
    (a) The compound contains 73.94% C and 8.27% H; the remainder is chromium.
    (b) At 25 °C, the osmotic pressure of a solution containing 5.00 mg of the unknown dissolved in exactly 100 mL of chloroform solution is 3.17 mm Hg.

## Summary and Conceptual Questions

*The following questions may use concepts from this and previous chapters.*

91. When salts of $Mg^{2+}$, $Ca^{2+}$, and $Be^{2+}$ are placed in water, the positive ion is hydrated (as is the negative ion). Which of these three cations is most strongly hydrated? Which one is least strongly hydrated?

92. Explain why a cucumber shrivels up when it is placed in a concentrated solution of salt.

93. If you dissolve equal molar amounts of NaCl and $CaCl_2$ in water, the $CaCl_2$ lowers the freezing point of the water almost 1.5 times as much as the NaCl. Why?

94. A 100.-gram sample of sodium chloride (NaCl) is added to 100. mL of water at 0 °C. After equilibrium is reached, about 64 g of solid remains undissolved. Describe the equilibrium that exists in this system at the particulate level.

95. Which of the following substances is/are likely to dissolve in water, and which is/are likely to dissolve in benzene ($C_6H_6$)?
    (a) $NaNO_3$
    (b) diethyl ether, $CH_3CH_2OCH_2CH_3$
    (c) naphthalene, $C_{10}H_8$ (see page 454 for structure)
    (d) $NH_4Cl$

96. Account for the fact that alcohols such as methanol ($CH_3OH$) and ethanol ($C_2H_5OH$) are quite miscible with water, whereas an alcohol with a long-carbon chain, such as octanol ($C_8H_{17}OH$), is poorly soluble in water.

97. Starch contains C—C, C—H, C—O, and O—H bonds. Hydrocarbons have only C—C and C—H bonds. Both starch and hydrocarbons can form colloidal dispersions in water. Which dispersion is classified as hydrophobic? Which is hydrophilic? Explain briefly.

98. Which substance would have the greater influence on the vapor pressure of water when added to 1000. g of the liquid: 10.0 g of sucrose ($C_{12}H_{22}O_{11}$) or 10.0 g of ethylene glycol ($HOCH_2CH_2OH$)?

99. Suppose you have two aqueous solutions separated by a semipermeable membrane. One contains 5.85 g of NaCl dissolved in 100. mL of solution, and the other contains 8.88 g of $KNO_3$ dissolved in 100. mL of solution. In which direction will solvent flow: from the NaCl solution to the $KNO_3$ solution, or from $KNO_3$ to NaCl? Explain briefly.

100. A protozoan (single-celled animal) that normally lives in the ocean is placed in freshwater. Will it shrivel or burst? Explain briefly.

101. In the process of distillation, a mixture of two (or more) volatile liquids is first heated to convert the volatile materials to the vapor state. Then the vapor is condensed, reforming the liquid. The net result of this liquid→ vapor→ liquid conversion is to enrich the fraction of a more volatile component in the mixture in the condensate. We can describe how this occurs using Raoult's law. Imagine that you have a mixture of 12% (by weight) ethanol and water (as formed, for example, by fermentation of grapes.)
    (a) What are the mole fractions of ethanol and water in this mixture?
    (b) This mixture is heated to 78.5 °C (the normal boiling point of ethanol). What are the equilibrium vapor pressures of ethanol and water at this temperature, assuming Raoult's law (ideal) behavior? (You will need to derive the equilibrium vapor pressure of water at 78.5 °C from data in Appendix G.)
    (c) What are the mole fractions of ethanol and water in the vapor?
    (d) After this vapor is condensed to a liquid, to what extent has the mole fraction of ethanol been enriched? What is the mass fraction of ethanol in the condensate?

102. Sodium chloride (NaCl) is commonly used to melt ice on roads during the winter. Calcium chloride ($CaCl_2$) is sometimes used for this purpose too. Let us compare the effectiveness of equal masses of these two compounds in lowering the freezing point of water, by

calculating the freezing point depression of solutions containing 200. g of each salt in 1.00 kg of water. (An advantage of $CaCl_2$ is that it acts more quickly because it is hygroscopic, that is, it absorbs moisture from the air to give a solution and begin the process. A disadvantage is that this compound is more costly.)

103. Review the trend in values of the van't Hoff factor $i$ as a function of concentration (Table 14.4). Use the following data to calculate the van't Hoff factor for a NaCl concentration of 5.00% (by weight) (for which $\Delta T = -3.05$ °C) and a $Na_2SO_4$ concentration of 5.00% (by weight) (for which $\Delta T = -1.36$ °C). Are these values in line with your expectations based on the trend in the values given in Table 14.4? Speculate on why this trend is seen.

104. The table below gives experimentally determined values for freezing points of 1.00% solutions (mass %) of a series of acids.
    (a) Calculate the molality of each solution, determine the calculated freezing points, and then calculate the values of the van't Hoff factor $i$. Fill these values into the table.

| Acid (1.00 mass %) | Molality (mol/kg $H_2O$) | $T_{measured}$ (°C) | $T_{calculated}$ (°C) | $i$ |
|---|---|---|---|---|
| $HNO_3$ | _____ | −0.56 | _____ | _____ |
| $CH_3CO_2H$ | _____ | −0.32 | _____ | _____ |
| $H_2SO_4$ | _____ | −0.42 | _____ | _____ |
| $H_2C_2O_4$ | _____ | −0.30 | _____ | _____ |
| $HCO_2H$ | _____ | −0.42 | _____ | _____ |
| $CCl_3CO_2H$ | _____ | −0.21 | _____ | _____ |

(b) Analyze the results, comparing the values of $i$ for the various acids. How does this data relate to acid strengths? (The discussion of strong and weak acids on pages 128–131 will assist you to answer this question.)

105. It is interesting how the Fahrenheit temperature scale was established. One report, given by Fahrenheit in a paper in 1724, stated that the value of 0 °F was established as the freezing temperature of saturated solutions of sea salt. From the literature we find that the freezing point of a 20% by mass solution of NaCl is −16.46 °C (This is the lowest freezing temperature reported for solutions of NaCl.) Does this value lend credence to this story of the establishment of the Fahrenheit scale?

106. The osmotic pressure exerted by seawater at 25 °C is about 27 atm. Calculate the concentration of ions dissolved in seawater that is needed to give an osmotic pressure of this magnitude. (Desalination of seawater is accomplished by reverse osmosis. In this process an applied pressure forces water through a membrane against a concentration gradient. The minimum external force needed for this process will be 27 atm. Actually, to accomplish the process at a reasonable rate, the applied pressure needs to be about twice this value.)

# Applying Chemical Principles

## Distillation

Distillation is a means of separating components of a mixture based upon differences in volatility. Because petroleum consists of a large number of compounds of widely varying volatility, distillation is a key process used to produce gasoline and related products. How does this process work?

If a mixture is composed of one volatile component and one or more nonvolatile components, a complete separation of the volatile component is possible. But, when two or more components in a mixture have nonzero vapor pressures at the mixture's boiling point, the result of a simple distillation is an incomplete separation.

Fractional distillation uses repetitive evaporation-condensation cycles to improve the separation of volatile compounds. When a mixture is boiled, the vapor above the liquid has a higher concentration of the more volatile components than the liquid. If this vapor is condensed, then boiled again, the resulting vapor is further enriched in more volatile material.

The temperature-composition diagram for a hexane–heptane mixture is shown below. The lower curved line indicates the boiling point of the mixture as a function of the mole fraction of the more volatile component, hexane. The upper curve indicates the mole fraction of hexane in the vapor phase above the boiling solution. The blue line represents the change in composition of the mixture in the course of the fractional distillation of a mixture with an initial hexane mole fraction of 0.20.

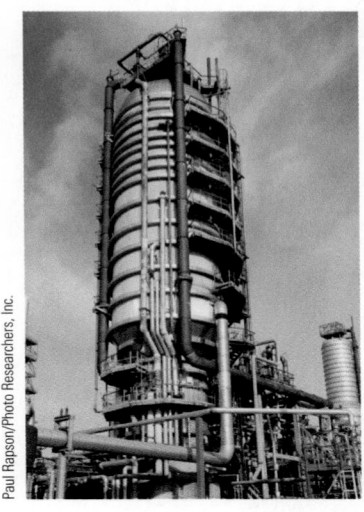

Equipment used for fractional distillation of petroleum in an oil refinery.

Paul Rapson/Photo Researchers, Inc.

The solution may be heated until it reaches its boiling point of 90 °C. At this temperature, the mole fraction of hexane in the vapor phase can be determined by drawing a horizontal line at 90 °C that intersects the top curve. This indicates that the vapor phase has a mole fraction of hexane of 0.38 at this temperature.

The efficiency of a fractional distillation column is expressed in terms of *theoretical plates*. Each evaporation-condensation cycle requires one theoretical plate. The greater the number of theoretical plates, the better the separation for most mixtures.

## Questions:

1. The blue line on the diagram illustrates the effect of using fractional distillation to separate a mixture of hexane ($C_6H_{14}$) and heptane ($C_7H_{16}$). If one starts a fractional distillation with a 0.20 mole fraction of hexane, what is the approximate mole fraction of hexane in the vapor phase after two evaporation-condensation cycles?

2. How many theoretical plates are required to produce a solution with a mole fraction of hexane greater than 0.90?

3. What is the mass percent of hexane in a mixture with heptane if the mole fraction of hexane is 0.20?

4. The vapor pressure of pure heptane is 361.5 mm Hg at 75.0 °C and its normal boiling point is 98.4 °C. Use the Clausius–Clapeyron equation to determine the enthalpy of vaporization of heptane.

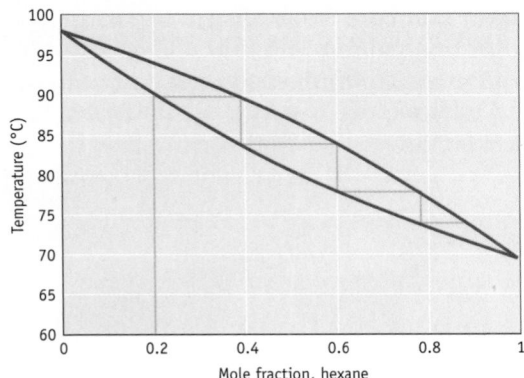

A temperature-composition diagram for hexane ($C_6H_{14}$)-heptane ($C_7H_{16}$) mixtures.

# The Chemistry of Modern Materials

White limestone and the minerals calcite, aragonite, and Iceland spar are all composed of calcium carbonate. So are chalk, eggshells, and seashells. These objects have distinctly different physical characteristics (Figure 1), yet they are composed primarily of the same component ions, $Ca^{2+}$ and $CO_3^{2-}$ ions. What is interesting to chemists, geologists, and biologists is that the differences in the macroscopic characteristics result from small differences in composition (due to the presence of impurities) and in the arrangement of these ions.

**FIGURE 1 Forms of calcium carbonate.** (clockwise from top) The shell of an abalone, a limestone paving block from Europe, crystalline aragonite, common blackboard chalk (CaCO₃ and a binder), and transparent Iceland spar.

As defined by the International Union of Pure and Applied Chemistry (IUPAC) the area of materials chemistry "comprises the application of chemistry to the design, synthesis, characterization, processing, understanding and utilization of materials, particularly those with useful, or potentially useful, physical properties." By studying the composition and structure of synthetic and naturally occurring materials, chemists are able to gain insight into what gives each material its properties and to create new materials that are tailored to particular applications and that have predictable behaviors.

This section explores a variety of common materials—except organic polymers, which were described in Section 10.5—and examines the connection between composition, atomic arrangements, and bulk properties.

## Alloys: Mixtures of Metals

**Alloys**, materials formed by addition of one or more elements to a metal, are among the earliest materials made by humans. The Bronze Age, dating back to 3300 BC, is well established in history, and the use of this alloy of copper and tin for tools and decorations was well known. Smelting of iron ore to form an impure iron containing carbon, among other elements, was introduced about 2000 years later (Figure 2). Mercury amalgams (mixtures of mercury and gold, silver, or tin) were used for centuries for gilding objects; a liquid mixture of gold and mercury, an amalgam, was placed on the surface of a metal object that was then heated, vaporizing the mercury and leaving a surface coating of gold (Figure 2).

● **Fiberoptics.** Fibers made of glass are used increasingly to carry information.

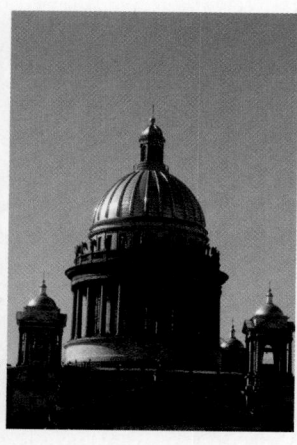

John C. Kotz

John C. Kotz

**FIGURE 2** **Uses of iron and gold.** *(left)* The top of the iron pillar in the Qutub complex in Delhi, India. The 24-foot tall pillar was made in approximately 400 AD. Although there is a thin film of rust on the pillar, it is largely free of corrosion because there is a significant amount of phosphorus (> 0.1%) in the metal. *(right)* The dome of St. Isaac's Cathedral in St. Petersburg, Russia, is covered with 100 kg of gold. An amalgam of gold and mercury was sprayed onto the surface and then heated to evaporate the mercury. Dozens of workers died as a result of mercury poisoning.

Even though the names we give them are the names of the elements, most "metals" we now use are, in fact, alloys (Table 1). Steel is an alloy of iron with carbon and often other elements. Adding elements to iron can greatly change its properties, as we noted earlier when discussing special steels used in cars (page 592). Most aluminum contains small amounts of magnesium or silicon.

Gold and silver alloys are familiar to most of us. For example, sterling silver, commonly used for jewelry, is an alloy composed of 92.5% Ag and 7.5% Cu. Pure silver is soft and easily damaged, but the addition of copper makes the metal more rigid. You can confirm that an article of jewelry

**Table 1** **Some Common Alloys**

| | |
|---|---|
| Sterling silver | 92.5% Ag, 7.5% Cu |
| 18 K "yellow" gold | 75% Au, 12.5% Ag, 12.5% Cu |
| Pewter | 91% Sn, 7.5% Sb, 1.5% Cu |
| Low-alloy steel | 98.6% Fe, 1.0% Mn, 0.4% C |
| Carbon steels | Approximately 99% Fe, 0.2–1.5% C |
| Stainless steel | 72.8% Fe, 17.0% Cr, 7.1% Ni, and approximately 1% each of Al and Mn |
| Alnico magnets | 10% Al, 19% Ni, 12% Co, 6% Cu, remainder Fe |
| Brass | 95–60% Cu, 5–40% Zn |
| Bronze | 90% Cu, 10% Sn |

is sterling silver by looking for the stamp that says "925," which means 92.5% silver.

Gold used in jewelry is rarely pure (24 carat) gold. More often, you will find 18 K, 14 K, or 9 K stamped on a gold object, referring to alloys that are 18/24, 14/24, or 9/24 gold. "Yellow" gold (18 K) is 75% gold, and the remaining 25% is copper and silver. As with sterling silver, the added metals lead to a harder and more rigid material (and one that is less costly).

Alloys fall into three general classes: solid solutions, which are homogeneous mixtures of two or more elements; heterogeneous mixtures; and intermetallic compounds.

In solid solutions, one element is usually considered the "solute" and the other the "solvent." As with solutions in liquids, the solute atoms are dispersed throughout the solvent such that the bulk structure is homogeneous. Unlike liquid solutions, however, there are limitations on the size of solvent and solute atoms. For a solid solution to form, the solute atoms must be incorporated in such a way that the original crystal structure of the solvent metal is preserved. Solid solutions can be achieved in two ways: with solute atoms as **interstitial** atoms or as **substitutional** atoms in the crystalline lattice. In interstitial alloys, the solute atoms occupy the interstices, the small "holes" between solvent atoms (Figure 3a). The solute atoms must be substantially smaller than the metal atoms making up the lattice to fit into these positions. In substitutional alloys, the solute atoms replace one of the solvent atoms in the original crystal structure (Figure 3b). For this to occur, the solute and solvent atoms must be similar in size.

If the size constraints are not met, then the alloy will likely form a heterogeneous mixture. When viewed under a microscope, regions of different composition and crystal structure can be seen in heterogeneous alloys.

For a solid solution to form, the electronegativities of the alloy components must also be similar. When the two metals have different electronegativities, the possibility exists for intermetallic compounds, substances with a definite stoichiometry and formula. Examples of intermetallic compounds include $CuAl_2$, $Mg_2Pb$, and $AuCu_3$. In general, intermetallic compounds are likely when one element is relatively electronegative and the other is more electro-

**(a)** Interstitial atoms    **(b)** Substitutional atoms

**FIGURE 3** **Alloys.** **(a)** The solute atoms may be interstitial atoms, fitting into holes in the crystal lattice. **(b)** The solute atoms can also substitute for one of the lattice atoms.

© Cengage Learning/Charles D. Winters

**FIGURE 4** **Light-emitting diodes (LEDs).** *(left)* A schematic drawing of a typical LED. *(right)* Traffic signs with LED lights require much less energy input than incandescent lights and are now being widely used.

positive. For $Mg_2Pb$, for example, $\chi$ for Pb = 2.3 and $\chi$ for Mg = 1.3 ($\Delta\chi$ = 1.0). (For more on this topic, see the *Applying Chemical Principles* question on the van Arkel triangle on page 1015.)

The macroscopic properties of an alloy will vary, depending on the ratio of the elements in the mixture. For example, "stainless" steel is highly resistant to corrosion and is roughly five times stronger than carbon and low-alloy steels. Melting point, electrical resistance, thermal conductivity, ductility, and other properties can be similarly adjusted by changing the composition of the alloys.

Metals and their alloys are good examples of how changes in the atomic composition and structure of a crystalline substance can have profound effects on its macroscopic chemical and physical characteristics. The same is true for semiconductors, the next class of materials we want to explore.

## Semiconductors

Semiconducting materials are at the heart of all solid-state electronic devices, including such well-known devices as computer chips and diode lasers. Semiconductors will not conduct electricity easily but can be encouraged to do so by the input of energy. This property allows devices made from semiconductors to essentially have "on" and "off" states, which form the basis of the binary logic used in computers. We can understand how semiconductors function by looking at their electronic structure, following the band theory approach used for metals. (◀ Section 13.3, pages 594–598, for a discussion of the mechanism by which metals and semiconductors can conduct an electric current.)

### Applications of Semiconductors: Diodes, LEDs, and Transistors

The combination of *p*- and *n*-type semiconducting materials in a single electronic device launched the microelectronics and computer industries. When a semiconductor is created such that it is *p*-type on one half and *n*-type on the other, a marvelous device known as the *p–n rectifying junction*, or **diode**, results. Diodes, which allow current to flow easily in only one direction when a voltage is applied, are the fundamental building blocks of solid-state electronic devices. They are used for many circuitry applications, such as switching and converting between electromagnetic radiation and electric current.

**LEDs**, or **light-emitting diodes** (Figure 4), are now used in the lights in the dashboards of cars and in their rear warning lights, in traffic lights, and in toys. These semiconducting devices are made by combining elements such as gallium, phosphorus, arsenic, and aluminum. When attached to a low-voltage (say 6–12 V) source, they emit light with a wavelength that depends on their composition. Furthermore, they emit light with a brightness that rivals standard incandescent lights, and the light can be focused using a tiny plastic lens.

An LED has a simple construction. It consists of a *p*-type semiconductor joined to an *n*-type semiconductor (Figure 5). A voltage is applied to the material, perhaps by hooking the positive terminal of a battery to the *p*-type semiconductor and the negative terminal to the *n*-type semiconductor. Electrons move from the *n*-type to the *p*-type, and positive holes move from the *p*-type to the *n*-type. When an electron moves across the *p–n* junction, it can drop from the conduction band into a hole in the valence band of the *p*-type semiconductor, and energy is released as a photon of electromagnetic radiation. (The mechanism of light emission by an LED is similar to that described for excited atoms in Section 6.3.) If the band gap energy is equivalent to the energy of light in the visible region, light can be observed. Because the band gap energy can be adjusted by changing the composition of the doped semiconductor, the wavelength of the light can also be altered, giving light of different colors.

The same device that forms the LED can be run in reverse to convert light into an electrical signal. Solar panel cells work in this manner (Figure 6). They are generally silicon-based *p–n* junction materials that have a band gap corresponding to the energy of visible light. When sunlight falls on these devices, a current is induced. That current can be used either immediately or stored in batteries for later use.

The *p*- and *n*-type semiconductor materials can also be constructed into a sandwich structure of either *p–n–p* or *n–p–n* composition. This arrangement forms a device known as a **transistor**. A transistor amplifies an electrical signal, making it ideal for powering loudspeakers, for ex-

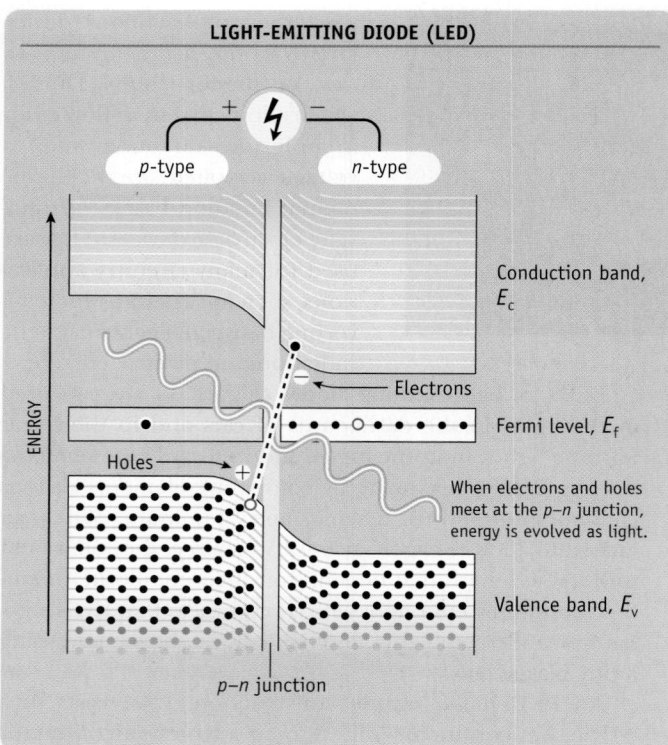

**LIGHT-EMITTING DIODE (LED)**

**FIGURE 5** Mechanism for the emission of light from an LED constructed from *n*- and *p*-type semiconductors. When *p*- and *n*-type semiconductors are joined, the energy levels adjust so that the Fermi levels ($E_f$) are equal. This causes the energy levels of the conduction ($E_c$) and valence ($E_v$) bands to "bend." Also, holes flow from the *p* side to the *n* side, and electrons flow from *n* to *p* until equilibrium is reached. No more charge will flow until a voltage is applied. When an electric field is applied, occasionally electrons in the conduction band will move across the band gap and combine with holes in the valence band. Energy is then evolved as light. The energy of the emitted light is approximately equal to the band gap. Therefore, by adjusting the band gap, the color of the emitted light can be altered. (See pages 594–598 for background information on semiconductors. See also S. M. Condren, G. C. Lisensky, A. B. Ellis, K. J. Nordell, T. F. Kuech, and S. A. Stockman: *Journal of Chemical Education*, Vol. 78, pp. 1033–1040, 2001.)

ample. Transistors can also be used for processing and storing information, a critical function for computer chips. By combining thousands of these transistors and diodes, an integrated circuit can be made that is the basis of what we commonly refer to as computer chips, devices for controlling and storing information (Figure 7).

**FIGURE 6** Silicon photovoltaic panel.

**FIGURE 7** Integrated circuits. *(left)* A wafer on which a large number of integrated circuits have been printed. *(right)* A close-up of a semiconductor chip showing the complex layering of circuits that is now possible.

## Ceramics

Let's go back to our original examples of various forms of $CaCO_3$, including seashells and chalk. Chalk is so soft that it will rub off on the rough surface of a blackboard. In contrast, seashells are inherently tough. They are designed to protect their soft and vulnerable inhabitants from the powerful jaws of sea-borne predators or rough conditions underwater. Chalk, seashells, and the spines of sea urchins (Figure 8) are all ceramics, but they are obviously different from one another. Clearly, there is a great deal of variability in this class of materials.

You may be accustomed to thinking of "ceramics" as the objects that result from high-temperature firing, such as pottery. From a materials chemistry perspective, however,

**FIGURE 8** A sea urchin. The spines of the urchin are composed primarily of $CaCO_3$, but a significant amount of $MgCO_3$ is present as well.

other materials such as clay, which largely consists of hydrated silicates of various compositions, are also considered ceramics. **Ceramics** are solid inorganic compounds typically composed of metallic elements combined with nonmetallic elements, and the bonding between atoms ranges from very ionic to covalent (◄ Section 8.1). In general, ceramics are hard, relatively brittle, and inflexible, and they are usually good thermal insulators. Some ceramics can be electrically conductive, but most are electrical insulators. Some, like glass, another type of ceramic, can be optically transparent, whereas other ceramics are completely opaque.

It is also possible to have ceramics in which impurity atoms are included in the composition. As we saw with metals and semiconductors, impurity atoms can have dramatic effects on the characteristics of a material.

## Glass: A Disordered Ceramic

An amorphous, or noncrystalline, solid material is generally referred to as a **glass** (◄ Section 13.5). As with alloys, there is a long history of glass making. Glass beads have been found dating back to at least 3500 BC in Egypt and Mesopotamia.

Glasses are formed by melting the raw material and then cooling it from the liquid state rapidly so that the component atoms do not have time to crystallize into a regular lattice structure. A wide range of materials, including metals and organic polymers, can be coaxed into a glassy form. However, the best-known glasses are silicate glasses. These are derived from $SiO_2$, which is plentiful, inexpensive, and chemically unreactive. Each silicon atom is linked to four oxygen atoms in the solid structure, with a tetrahedral arrangement around each silicon atom. The $SiO_2$ units are linked together to form a large network of atoms (Figure 9). Over a longer distance, however, the network has no discernible order or pattern.

Glasses can be modified by the presence of alkali metal oxides (such as $Na_2O$ and $K_2O$) or other metal or nonmetal oxides (such as $CaO$, $B_2O_3$, and $Al_2O_3$). The added impurities change the silicate network and alter the properties of

the material. The oxide ions are incorporated into the silicate network structure, and the resultant negative charge is balanced by the interstitial metal cations (Figure 9c). Because the network is changed by such an addition, these network modifiers can dramatically alter the physical characteristics of the material, such as melting point, color, opacity, and strength. Soda-lime glass—made from $SiO_2$, $Na_2O$ (soda), and $CaO$ (lime)—is a common glass used in windows and for containers. The metal oxides lower the melting temperature by about a thousand degrees from that of pure silica. Pyrex glass, also called *borosilicate glass*, incorporates an additional component, boric oxide. The boric oxide raises the softening temperature and minimizes the coefficient of thermal expansion, enabling the glass to better withstand temperature changes. Because of its excellent thermal properties, this type of glass is used for beakers and flasks in chemistry laboratories and for ovenware for the kitchen.

Colors in glass result from the presence of metal ions (Figure 10). Adding small amounts of iron(II) oxide and chromium(III) oxide results in a green glass (used in some wine bottles), whereas cobalt(III) oxide imparts a blue color. Dishes made from yellow-green uranium glass [glass containing uranium(IV) oxide] were popular in the first half of the 20th century. However, because of the radioactivity associated with uranium, this glass is no longer used.

The presence of particulate materials in glass will also result in colors. Nanoscale particles of selenium give glass a deep red color. A notable example is the inclusion of very small silver halide crystals resulting in a photochromic glass (Figure 11). This glass darkens reversibly when exposed to light, a result of the reduction of the silver halide to metallic silver. This technology was used in early versions of self-darkening eyeglasses.

An important characteristic of some glasses is their optical transparency, which allows them to be used as windows and lenses. Glasses can also be reflective. The combination of transparency and reflectivity is controlled by the material's **index of refraction**. All materials have an index of

(a)　　　　(b)

(c)

**FIGURE 9 Representation of glass structure.** Silica glass ($SiO_2$) may have some order over a short distance **(a)** but much less order over a larger portion of the solid **(b)**. **(c)** The $SiO_2$ structure can be modified by adding metal oxides (such as $Na_2O$), which leads to a lower melting temperature and other desirable properties. (In these simple representations, the gray Si atoms are shown at the center of a planar triangle of red O atoms; in reality, each Si atom is surrounded tetrahedrally by O atoms. The structure is not planar but is three dimensional.)

**FIGURE 10 Colored glass.** Small amounts of transition metal ions can give color to glass: blue ($Co_2O_3$); green (FeO or $Cr_2O_3$); purple (NiO or $Co_2O_3$); iridescent green ($U_2O_3$).

**(a)**

$i$ = angle of incidence
$r$ = angle of refraction
$i > r$

**(b)**

**FIGURE 12 Refraction of light. (a)** When light enters a different medium, its velocity changes. This causes the path of a photon to change direction in the material. **(b)** Observing an object in a glass of water illustrates the effect of light refraction.

refraction that determines how much a beam of light will change its velocity when entering the material. The index of refraction is defined relative to the speed of light in a vacuum, which is defined as exactly 1. (The index of refraction = velocity of light in a vacuum/velocity in material.) On this basis, dry air has an index of refraction of 1.0003, and typical values for silicate glasses range from 1.5 to 1.9.

The change in the velocity of the electromagnetic wave once it enters the material causes the beam to bend, or change direction within the material. If light hits a surface at some incident angle relative to the line perpendicular to the surface, some of the light will be reflected at the same angle, and some will be transmitted into the material at a refracted angle (Figure 12). Both the incident angle and the index of refraction will affect how much of the light is reflected and the angle at which it bends in the second material. You can observe this effect by putting an object in a glass of water and looking at the apparent bend that results in the object (Figure 12b).

This combination of the transmission and reflection characteristics of glass allowed scientists and engineers to develop optical fibers (Figure 13). Optical fibers are designed to have a property called *total internal reflection,* whereby all the light that enters at one end of the fiber stays within the fiber through reflections with the interior surface as the light trav-

els from one end of the fiber to the other. Total internal reflection in these fibers is achieved by controlling the ratio of the indices of refraction between the fiber's core and its outside surface. Chemically, the index of refraction is controlled by adjusting the quantity and type of cationic network modifiers that are added to the glass. The index of refraction of a glass fiber can be controlled so that it has one value at the core of the fiber but changes smoothly across the radius of the fiber to a different value at the surface. This is accomplished by an ion-exchange process during fiber production in which, for example, $K^+$ ions are replaced by $Tl^+$ ions.

Optical fibers are transforming the communications industry in an amazing fashion. Instead of transmitting information using electrons traveling through metallic wires, optical fibers allow communication to occur by transmitting photons through glass fiber bundles. Signal transmission by optical fibers, known as *photonics,* is much faster and more economical than transmission using copper wires and cables. For example, the quantity of copper required to carry the equivalent amount of information

**FIGURE 11 Photochromic glass.** Glass with embedded silver halide particles darkens reversibly when exposed to sunlight.

**FIGURE 13 Optical fibers.** Glass fibers transmit light along the axis of the fiber.

**FIGURE 14** **The deep sea sponge, *Euplectella*.** Photographs of sponge's structure at various levels of magnification. **(a)** Photograph of the sponge. **(b)** Fragment of the structure showing the square grid of the lattice with diagonal supports. Scale bar = 1 mm. **(c)** Scanning electron microscope (SEM) image of a single strand showing its ceramic—composite structure. Scale bar = 20 μm. **(d)** SEM image of the surface of a strand showing that it is composed of nanoscale spheres of hydrated silica. Scale bar = 500 nm. **(e)** Scientist Joanna Aizenberg. Dr. Aizenberg's research group at Harvard University also developed the polymeric material shown on the front cover of this book.

transmitted by optical fiber would weigh 300,000 times more than the optical fiber material!

Interestingly, research has led to the discovery that materials with similar structure and optical properties exist in nature. Joanna Aizenberg, now at Harvard University, discovered that a deep sea sponge, made chiefly of silica ($SiO_2$), has a framework with the same characteristics (Figure 14).

### Fired Ceramics for Special Purposes: Cements, Clays, and Refractories

Other classes of ceramics include cements, clays, and refractories. Unlike glasses, these ceramics are processed by shaping, drying, and sometimes firing, without ever melting the solid.

Cements are extremely strong and are commonly used as structural materials. They can be formed into almost any shape. When mixed with water, they produce a paste that can be poured into molds and allowed to dry and harden.

Clays are generally mixtures of hydrated alumina ($Al_2O_3$) and silica ($SiO_2$), but they may also contain other ingredients, such as tricalcium silicate ($3\ CaO \cdot SiO_2$), dicalcium silicate ($2\ CaO \cdot SiO_2$), and MgO. Their composition is irregular, and, because they are powders, their crystallinity extends for only short distances.

Clays have the useful property of becoming very plastic when water is added, a characteristic referred to as **hydroplasticity**. This plasticity, and clay's ability to hold its shape during firing, are very important for the forming processes used to create various objects.

The layered molecular structure of clays results in microscopic platelets that can slide over each other easily when wet. The layers consist of $SiO_4$ tetrahedra joined with $AlO_6$ octahedra (▶ Section 21.7). In addition to these basic silicon- and aluminum-based structures, different cations can be substituted into the framework to change the properties of the clay. Common substituents include $Ca^{2+}$, $Fe^{2+}$, and $Mg^{2+}$. Different clay materials can then be created by varying the combinations of layers and the substituent cations.

**Refractories** constitute a class of ceramics that are capable of withstanding very high temperatures without deforming, in some cases up to 1650 °C (3000 °F), and that are thermally insulating. Because of these properties, refractory bricks are used in applications such as furnace linings and in metallurgical operations. These materials are thermally insulating largely because of the porosity of their structure; that is, holes (or pores) are dispersed evenly within the solid. However, while porosity will make a material more thermally insulating, it will also weaken it. As a consequence, refractories are not as strong as cements.

### Aerogels

It has been called the "world's lightest solid" and the "best thermal insulator." Even though it is 99.98% air and has a density of only about 1.9 mg/cm$^3$, it is a light blue solid that, to the touch, feels much like Styrofoam chips that are used in packaging. It is also strong structurally, able to hold over 2000 times its weight (Figure 15a). "It" is a silica aerogel, a low-density substance derived from a gel in which the liquid has been replaced by air. There are

**FIGURE 15** Aerogel. **(a)** A 2.5-kg brick is supported by a piece of silica aerogel weighing about 2 g. (http://stardust.jpl.nasa.gov/photo/aerogel.html) **(b)** Aerogel as an insulator.

(a)

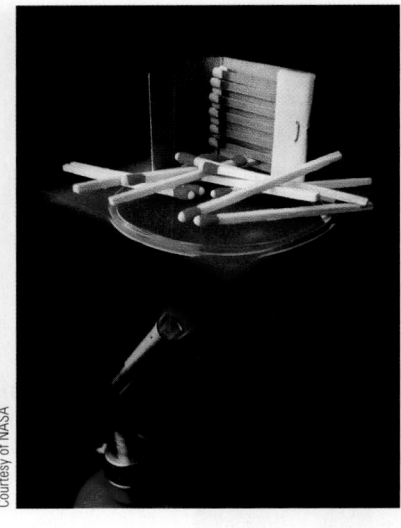

(b)

aerogels based on silicon and carbon as well as aluminum and other metals, but the silicon-based aerogel is the most thoroughly studied. This aerogel is made by polymerizing a compound like $Si(OC_2H_5)_4$ in alcohol. The resulting long-chain molecules form a gel that is bathed in the alcohol. This substance is then placed in supercritical $CO_2$ (page 574), which causes the alcohol in the nanopores in the gel to be replaced by $CO_2$. When the $CO_2$ is vented off as a gas, what remains is a highly porous aerogel with an incredibly low density.

Aerogels have been known for decades but have only recently received a lot of study. They do have amazing properties! Chief among them is their insulating ability, as illustrated in Figure 15b. Aerogels do not allow heat to be conducted through the lattice, and convective heat transfer is also poor because air cannot circulate throughout the lattice. One potential use for these aerogels is in insulating glass. However, before aerogels can be truly useful for this purpose, researchers need to find a way to make one that is completely transparent. (Silica aerogel is very light blue owing to Rayleigh scattering, the same process that makes the sky blue.) Aerogels are also biocompatible and are being studied as possible drug delivery systems.

Aerogel was in the news a few years ago because it was used to catch comet dust in Project Stardust (Figure 16). A spacecraft was sent to intercept a comet in 2004 and returned to Earth in January 2006. On the spacecraft was an array holding blocks of aerogel. As the craft flew through the comet's tail, dust particles impacted the aerogel blocks and were "brought to a standstill as they tunneled through it without much heating or alteration, leaving carrot-shaped tracks." When the spacecraft

was returned to Earth, scientists analyzed the particles and found that there were silicate minerals that seemed to have been formed in the inner regions of the solar system.

## Ceramics with Exceptional Properties

In 1880, Pierre Curie and his brother Jacques worked in a small laboratory in Paris to examine the electrical properties of certain crystalline substances. Using nothing more than tinfoil, glue, wire, and magnets, they were able to confirm the presence of surface charges on samples of materials such as tourmaline, quartz, and topaz when they were subjected to mechanical stresses. This phenomenon, now called **piezoelectricity**, is the property that allows a mechanical distortion (such as a slight bending) to induce an electrical current and, conversely, an electrical current to cause a distortion in the material.

Not all crystalline ceramics exhibit piezoelectricity. Those that do have a specific unit cell structure (◄ Section 13.2)

**FIGURE 16** Aerogel, a networked matrix of $SiO_2$. *(left)* NASA's Peter Tsou holds a piece of aerogel. *(right)* Aerogel was used on a NASA mission to collect the particles in comet dust. The particles entered the gel at a very high velocity, but were slowed gradually. Scientists studied the tracks made by the particles and later retrieved the particles and studied their composition.

that can loosely trap an impurity cation. The ion's position shifts when the unit cell is deformed by mechanical stress. This shift causes an induced dipole (◀ Section 12.3) and, therefore, a potential difference across the material that can be converted to an electrical signal.

Materials that exhibit piezoelectricity—such as lead(II) zirconate ($PbZrO_3$) and ammonium dihydrogen phosphate ($NH_4H_2PO_4$)—have a great many applications, ranging from home gadgets to sophisticated medical and scientific applications. One use with which you may be familiar is the ignition systems on some barbecue grills (Figure 17). All digital watch beepers are based on piezoceramics, as are smoke detector alarms. A less familiar application is found in the sensing lever of some atomic force microscopes (AFMs) and scanning-tunneling microscopes (STMs), instruments that convert mechanical vibrations to electrical signals.

Scientists and engineers are always searching for materials with new and useful properties. Perhaps the most dramatic property that has been observed in newly developed ceramics is superconductivity at relatively high temperatures. **Superconductivity** is a phenomenon in which the electrical resistivity of a material drops to nearly zero at a particular temperature referred to as the **critical temperature**, $T_c$ (Figure 18). Most metals naturally have resistivities that decrease with temperature in a constant manner but still have significant resistivity even at temperatures near 0 K.

A few metals and metal alloys have been found to exhibit superconductivity. For metals, however, the critical temperatures are extremely low, between 0 and 20 K. These temperatures are costly to achieve and difficult to maintain. Recent scientific attention has, therefore, focused on a class of ceramics with superconductive critical temperatures ($T_c$) near

FIGURE 18 **Superconductivity.** Several superconductive disks were cooled in liquid nitrogen (77 K). When a 500 g magnet was brought toward the disks, the magnet induced a magnetic field in the superconductors. The two magnetic fields repelled, causing the magnet to float (or levitate) above the cooled superconductors.

100 K. These materials include $YBa_2Cu_3O_7$, with $T_c = 92$ K (Figure 19), and $HgBa_2Ca_2Cu_2O_3$, with $T_c = 153$ K.

Once again, we see that combining atoms into sometimes complex chemical compositions allows scientists to develop materials with particular properties. In ceramics, which are normally electrically insulating, this includes even the ability to conduct electricity.

## Biomaterials: Learning from Nature

Most of the materials described so far in this chapter come from nonliving sources and, in many cases, are the result of laboratory syntheses. However, an important branch of materials research deals with examining, understanding, and even copying materials produced by living systems.

The study of naturally occurring materials has led to the development of synthetic materials that possess important properties. A good example is rubber (◀ Chapter 10, page 476). This natural polymer was initially obtained from certain trees and chemically modified to convert it to a useful material. It was found to be so useful that chemists eventually achieved the synthesis of a structurally identical material. Research on rubber, which spanned more than 200 years, has had important consequences for humans as evidenced by the myriad applications of rubber today.

Today, scientists continue to look to nature to provide new materials and to provide clues to improve the materials we already use. The sea urchin and its ceramic spines (Figure 8) and the sponge whose skeleton has the characteristics of optical fibers (Figure 14) are just two examples where biomaterials research has focused on sea life in a search for new materials.

Scientists have also examined conch shells to understand their incredible fracture strength. They used scan-

FIGURE 17 **Devices that depend on the piezoelectric effect.** These devices work by using a mechanical stress to produce an electric current. Piezoelectric materials are widely used in ignitors and in devices that convert electric impulses to vibrations, such as in the timing circuit of a wristwatch.

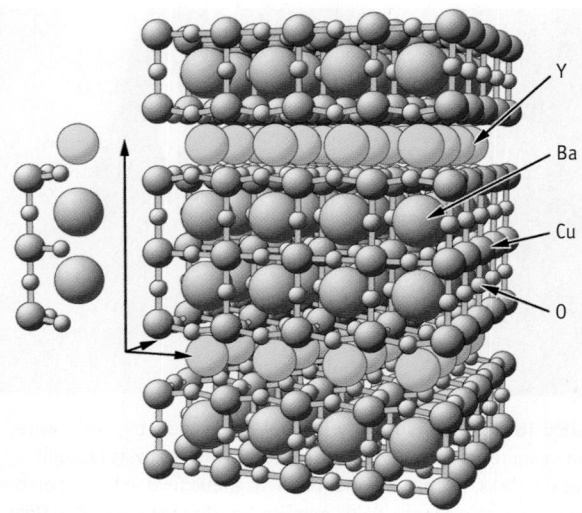

**FIGURE 19** The lattice of $YBa_2Cu_3O_7$, a superconductor. Yttrium ions are yellow; barium ions are red; copper ions are green; and oxygen ions are blue. (Reprinted with permission of Dr. Klaus Hermann of the Fritz Haber Institution.)

© 2000 Nature Publishing Inc. Used courtesy of Dr. Arthur Heuer.

**FIGURE 20** A scanning electron microscope picture of the shell of the conch. (From S. Kamat, X. Su, R. Ballarini, and A. H. Heuer. Structural basis for the fracture toughness of the shell of the conch *Strombus gigas*. *Nature*. Vol. 405, pp. 1036–1040, 2000.)

ning electron microscopy (SEM) to scrutinize the structure of the shell when it was fractured. What they discovered was a criss-crossed, layered structure that is the equivalent of a "ceramic plywood" (Figure 20). This microarchitecture prevents fractures that occur on the outside surface of the shell from being transferred into the inner layers. The discovery has inspired materials engineers to create materials that are significantly strengthened by incorporating a fibrous ceramic matrix, such as SiC (silicon carbide) whiskers.

Research on adhesive materials represents another area in which sea creatures can provide some clues. Getting things to stick together is important in a multitude of applications. The loss of the space shuttle Columbia in early 2003, caused by loss of some ceramic tiles when a piece of insulating foam that fell off during launch hit them, offered a sobering lesson in adhesive failure under extreme conditions of temperature and humidity. If you look around, you will probably find something with an adhesive label, something with an attached plastic part, something with a rubber seal, or perhaps something taped together. Adhesives have also proven useful for medical applications, where specialized glues help doctors seal tissues within the human body. For every type of sticking application, different properties are needed for the adhesive material.

Nature provides numerous examples of adhesion. Geckos and flies that can walk on

glass while completely inverted hold clues to the kind of biologically based adhesion that could be the basis of synthetic analogs (◄ page 548). Marine mussels, which can stick quite well to wood, metal, and rock, also hold great interest for scientists studying adhesion.

Scientists who have researched mussel adhesives have been able to determine that the amino acid 3,4-dihydroxyphenylalanine (DOPA) is the agent primarily responsible for the strength of the adhesion. But DOPA alone cannot explain the incredible strength of the mussel glues. The secret lies in the combination of an $Fe^{3+}$ ion with DOPA to form a cross-linked matrix of the mussel's protein (Figure 21; see also "Green Adhesives" on page 481). The curing process, or hardening of the natural proteinaceous liquid produced by the mussel, is a result of the iron–protein interaction that occurs to form $Fe(DOPA)_3$ cross-links.

## The Future of Materials

The modern tools and techniques of chemistry are making it possible for scientists not only to develop novel materials, but also to proceed in new and unforeseen directions. The

**FIGURE 21** Strong mussels. *(left)* A common blue mussel can cling to almost any surface, including this Teflon sheet, even underwater. *(right)* The adhesive precursor is a protein interlinked with iron(III) ions. An iron(III) ion binds to the hydroxyl groups (–OH) in three side chains of dihydroxyphenylalanine (DOPA) amino acids in the protein chain.

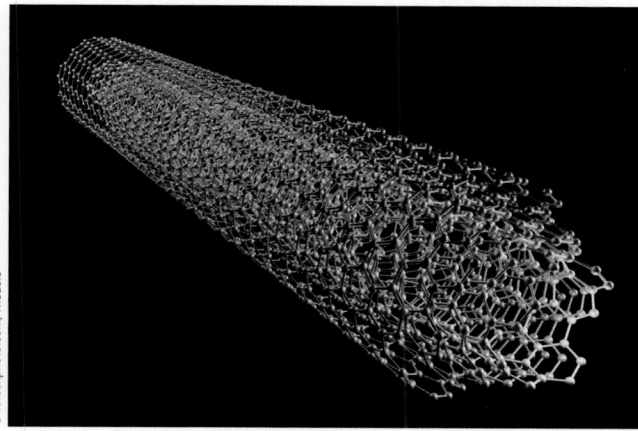

**FIGURE 22 Multi-walled carbon nanotubes (MWNT).** Sheets of six-membered carbon rings close on themselves to form tubes. Multi-walled nanotubes, which are presently more easily produced than single-wall tubes, have tubes within tubes.

field of **nanotechnology** is an example. In nanotechnology, structures with dimensions on the order of nanometers are used to carry out specific functions.

Nanotubes (Figure 22) and graphene (page 603), both allotropes of carbon, are among the best known examples of nanomaterials. If carbon or carbon-based compounds are heated under the right conditions, the carbon atoms assemble into sheets of six-member rings, just as in graphite. However, under the right conditions, the sheets close on themselves to form tubes. Because these tubes are only a nanometer or so in diameter, chemists refer to them as *carbon nanotubes* (CNT). Some are single-walled (SWNT), but multi-walled tubes within tubes (MWNT) are also common. The record for their length (as of 2010) is 18 cm!

There is enormous industrial interest in CNTs for a variety of uses: for displays for computers and televisions, molecular wiring in appliances, biosensors, and drug-delivery systems. Thus far, MWNTs are more easily produced, and prices have fallen from thousands of dollars per gram to a few hundred dollars per kilogram. Companies in Asia, Europe, and the United States are being built to produce up to 3000 metric tons per year.

Chemistry is the key to understanding and developing materials. The atomic compositions and long-range structure of different materials fundamentally determine their properties and characteristics. Chemists can use analytical instruments to determine these structures. They can then exploit this knowledge to manipulate or develop materials to achieve different properties for special functions. In many cases, we can look to nature to provide answers and suggestions on how to proceed.

## SUGGESTED READINGS

1. Materials chemistry: P. Day, L. V. Interrante, and A. R. West, *Pure and Applied Chemistry*, Vol. 81, page 1707, 2009.
2. X. Su, S. Kamat, and A. H. Heuer: "The structure of sea urchin spines, large biogenic single crystals of calcite." *Journal of Materials Science*, Vol. 35, pp. 5545–5551, 2000.
3. M. J. Sever, J. T. Weisser, J. Monahan, S. Srinivasan, and J. J. Wilker: "Metal-mediated cross-linking in the generation of marine mussel adhesive." *Angewandte Chemie International Edition*, Vol. 43, pp. 447–450, 2004.

## STUDY QUESTIONS

Blue-numbered questions have answers in Appendix Q and fully worked solutions in the *Student Solutions Manual*.

1. The degree of magnification is often given when photographing objects with a microscope. Refer to the photos of the skeleton of the sea sponge (Figure 14). What are the degrees of magnification for the pictures in Figures 14b, 14c, and 14d? The length of the scale bar in each figure is 5.0 mm.

2. Which of the following would be good substitutional impurities for an aluminum alloy?
   (a) Sn      (b) P      (c) K      (d) Pb

3. The amount of sunlight striking the surface of the earth (when the sun is directly overhead on a clear day) is approximately 925 watts per square meter ($W/m^2$). The area of a typical solar cell is approximately $1.0 \text{ cm}^2$. If the cell is running at 25% efficiency, what is its energy output per minute?

4. Using the result of the calculation in Question 3, estimate the number of solar cells that would be needed to power a 700-W microwave oven. If the solar cells were assembled into a panel, what would be the approximate area of the panel?

5. Describe how you could calculate the density of pewter (Table 1) from the densities of the component elements, assuming that pewter is a substitutional alloy. Look up the densities of the constituent elements and carry out this calculation. Densities can be found on a website such as www.webelements.com or www.ptable.com.

6. Calculate an approximate value for the density of aerogel using the fact that it is 99.98% air and the remainder is $SiO_2$ (density = $2.63 \text{ g/cm}^3$). What is the mass of a $1.0\text{-cm}^3$ piece of aerogel?

7. Suppose you wish to make a superinsulated window by filling the gap between two sheets of glass with aerogel. What mass of aerogel is needed for a 180-cm × 150-cm window with a gap of 2.0 mm between the glass sheets?

8. Assume that the repeating unit in an aerogel polymer is $OSi(OC_2H_5)_2$. If the polymer is 99.98% air and the density is about $1.9 \text{ mg/cm}^3$, how many silicon atoms are there in $1.0 \text{ cm}^3$ of aerogel?

# 15 Chemical Kinetics: The Rates of Chemical Reactions

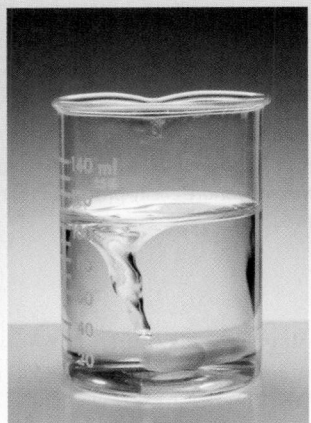

Photos © Cengage Learning/Charles D. Winters

Fading of the color of phenolphthalein with time

(elapsed time about 3 minutes)

## Where Did the Indicator Go?

The indicator phenolphthalein is often used for the titration of a weak acid using a strong base. A change from colorless to pale pink indicates that the equivalence point in the reaction has been reached (◄ page 183). If more base is added to the solution, the color of the indicator intensifies to a bright red color.

If the solution containing phenolphthalein has a pH higher than about 12, another phenomenon is observed. Slowly, the red color fades, and the solution becomes colorless. This is due to a chemical reaction of the anion of phenolphthalein with hydroxide ion, as shown in the equation. The reaction is slow, and it is easy to measure the rate of this reaction by monitoring the intensity of color of the solution.

This chapter is about a fundamental area of chemistry: *chemical kinetics*. This encompasses the study of reaction rates and their interpretation based on reaction mechanisms. In Study Question 75, you will see some data that will allow you to determine how the rate of the phenolphthalein reaction depends on the hydroxide ion concentration, and you will derive an equation that will allow you to predict the results under other conditions.

**The reaction of phenolphthalein and hydroxide ion.**

## CHAPTER GOALS

*See Chapter Goals Revisited (page 706) for Study Questions keyed to these goals.*

- Understand rates of reaction and the conditions affecting rates.

- Derive a rate equation, rate constant, and reaction order from experimental data.

- Use integrated rate laws.

- Understand the collision theory of reaction rates and the role of activation energy.

- Relate reaction mechanisms and rate laws.

When carrying out a chemical reaction, chemists are concerned with two issues: the *rate* at which the reaction proceeds and the *extent* to which the reaction is product-favored at equilibrium. Chapter 5 began to address the second question, and Chapters 16 and 19 will develop that topic further. In this chapter, we turn to the first-mentioned question, **chemical kinetics**, a study of the rates of chemical reactions.

The study of kinetics is divided into two parts. The first part is at the *macroscopic level*, which addresses rates of reactions: what reaction rate means, how to determine a reaction rate experimentally, and how factors such as temperature and the concentrations of reactants influence rates. The second part of this subject considers chemical reactions at the *particulate level*. Here, the concern is with the **reaction mechanism**, the detailed pathway taken by atoms and molecules as a reaction proceeds. The goal is to reconcile data in the macroscopic world of chemistry with an understanding of how and why chemical reactions occur at the particulate level—and then to apply this information to control important reactions.

## 15.1 Rates of Chemical Reactions

You encounter the concept of rates in many nonchemical circumstances. Common examples are the speed of an automobile, given in terms of the distance traveled per unit time (for example, kilometers per hour) and the rate of flow of water from a faucet, given as volume per unit time (perhaps liters per minute). In each case, a change is measured over an interval of time. Similarly, the rate of a chemical reaction refers to the change in concentration of a reactant or product per unit of time.

$$\text{Rate of reaction} = \frac{\text{change in concentration}}{\text{change in time}}$$

Two measurements are made to determine the average speed of an automobile: distance traveled and time elapsed. Average speed is the distance traveled divided by the time elapsed, or $\Delta(\text{distance})/\Delta(\text{time})$. If an automobile travels 3.9 km in 4.5 min (0.075 h), its average speed is (3.9 km/0.075 h), or 52 kph (or 32 mph).

**(a)** A few drops of blue food dye were added to water, followed by a solution of bleach. Initially, the concentration of dye was about $3.4 \times 10^{-5}$ M, and the bleach (NaOCl) concentration was about 0.034 M.

**(b)** The color fades as the dye reacts with the bleach. The absorbance of the solution can be measured at various times using a spectrophotometer (page 188), and these values can be used to determine the concentration of the dye.

**FIGURE 15.1** **An experiment to measure rate of reaction.**

Average rates of chemical reactions can be determined similarly. Two quantities, concentration and time, are measured. Concentrations can be determined in a variety of ways, such as by using a pH meter to determine the concentration of hydronium ion in a solution or by measuring the absorbance of light by a solution, a property that can be related to the concentration of a species in solution (Figure 15.1). The average rate of the reaction is the change in the concentration per unit time—that is, $\Delta(\text{concentration})/\Delta(\text{time})$.

Let's consider the decomposition of $N_2O_5$ in a solvent. This reaction occurs according to the following equation:

$$N_2O_5 \rightarrow 2\ NO_2 + \tfrac{1}{2}\ O_2$$

Concentrations and time elapsed for a typical experiment done at 30.0 °C are presented as a graph in Figure 15.2.

**FIGURE 15.2** **A plot of reactant concentration versus time for the decomposition of $N_2O_5$.** The average rate for a 15-minute interval from 40 to 55 minutes is 0.0080 mol/L · min. The instantaneous rate calculated when $[N_2O_5] = 0.34$ M is 0.0014 mol/L · min.

The rate of this reaction for any interval of time can be expressed as the change in concentration of $N_2O_5$ divided by the change in time:

$$\text{Rate of reaction} = -\frac{\text{change in } [N_2O_5]}{\text{change in time}} = -\frac{\Delta[N_2O_5]}{\Delta t}$$

The minus sign is required because the concentration of $N_2O_5$ decreases with time (that is, $\Delta[N_2O_5] = [N_2O_5](\text{final}) - [N_2O_5](\text{initial})$ is negative), and rate is always expressed as a positive quantity. Using data from Figure 15.2, the rate of disappearance of $N_2O_5$ between 40 and 55 minutes is given by

$$\text{Rate} = -\frac{\Delta[N_2O_5]}{\Delta t} = -\frac{(1.10 \text{ mol/L}) - (1.22 \text{ mol/L})}{55 \text{ min} - 40 \text{ min}} = +\frac{0.12 \text{ mol/L}}{15 \text{ min}}$$

$$\text{Rate} = 0.0080 \frac{\text{mol } N_2O_5 \text{ consumed}}{L \cdot \text{min}}$$

Note the units for reaction rates; if concentration is expressed in mol/L, the units for rate will be mol/L · time.

During a chemical reaction, amounts of reactants decrease with time, and amounts of products increase. For the decomposition of $N_2O_5$, we could also express the rate either as $\Delta[NO_2]/\Delta t$ or as $\Delta[O_2]/\Delta t$. Rates based on changes in concentrations of products will have a positive sign because the concentration is increasing. Furthermore, the numerical values of rates defined in these ways will be different from the value of $\Delta[N_2O_5]/\Delta t$. Note that the rate of decomposition of $N_2O_5$ is one half the rate of formation of $NO_2$ and twice the rate of formation of $O_2$. A rate expression relating all of these rates can be determined by dividing each rate expression by the stoichiometric coefficient of the substance in the balanced chemical equation.

$$\text{Rate of reaction} = -\frac{\Delta[N_2O_5]}{\Delta t} = +\frac{1}{2}\frac{\Delta[NO_2]}{\Delta t} = +2\frac{\Delta[O_2]}{\Delta t}$$

For the 15-minute interval between 40 and 55 minutes, the average rates for the formation of $NO_2$ and $O_2$ are

$$\text{Rate} = \frac{\Delta[NO_2]}{\Delta t} = \frac{0.0080 \text{ mol } N_2O_5 \text{ consumed}}{L \cdot \text{min}} \times \frac{2 \text{ mol } NO_2 \text{ formed}}{1 \text{ mol } N_2O_5 \text{ consumed}}$$

$$= 0.016 \frac{\text{mol } NO_2 \text{ formed}}{L \cdot \text{min}}$$

$$\text{Rate} = \frac{\Delta[O_2]}{\Delta t} = \frac{0.0080 \text{ mol } N_2O_5 \text{ consumed}}{L \cdot \text{min}} \times \frac{\frac{1}{2} \text{ mol } O_2 \text{ formed}}{1 \text{ mol } N_2O_5 \text{ consumed}}$$

$$= 0.0040 \frac{\text{mol } O_2 \text{ formed}}{L \cdot \text{min}}$$

The graph of $[N_2O_5]$ versus time in Figure 15.2 does not give a straight line because, as described in Section 15.3, the rate of the reaction changes during the course of the reaction. The concentration of $N_2O_5$ decreases rapidly at the beginning of the reaction but more slowly near the end. We can verify this by comparing the rate of disappearance of $N_2O_5$ calculated previously (the concentration decreased by 0.12 mol/L in 15 minutes) to the average rate of reaction calculated for the time interval from 6.5 to 9.0 hours (when the concentration drops by 0.12 mol/L in 150 minutes). The average rate in this later stage of this reaction is only one tenth of the previous value.

$$-\frac{\Delta[N_2O_5]}{\Delta t} = -\frac{(0.10 \text{ mol/L}) - (0.22 \text{ mol/L})}{540 \text{ min} - 390 \text{ min}} = +\frac{0.12 \text{ mol/L}}{150 \text{ min}}$$

$$= 0.00080 \frac{\text{mol}}{L \cdot \text{min}}$$

● **Representing Concentrations** Recall that square brackets around a formula indicate its concentrations in mol/L (Section 4.5).

● **Calculating Changes** When calculating a change in a quantity, we always do so by subtracting the initial quantity from the final quantity: $\Delta c = c_{final} - c_{initial}$.

● **Reaction Rates and Stoichiometry** For the general reaction $a\,A + b\,B \rightarrow c\,C + d\,D$, the international convention defines the reaction rate as

$$\text{Reaction rate} = -\frac{1}{a}\frac{\Delta[A]}{\Delta t} = -\frac{1}{b}\frac{\Delta[B]}{\Delta t}$$
$$= +\frac{1}{c}\frac{\Delta[C]}{\Delta t} = +\frac{1}{d}\frac{\Delta[D]}{\Delta t}$$

Note that this gives us the reaction rate on a "per mole of reaction" basis. For more on this topic, see K. T. Quisenberry and J. Tellinghuisen, *Journal of Chemical Education*, Vol. 83, pp. 510–512, 2006.

● **The Slope of a Line** The instantaneous rate in Figure 15.2 can be determined from an analysis of the slope of the line. See pages 41–42 for more on finding the slope of a line.

The procedure we have used to calculate the reaction rate gives the average rate over the chosen time interval.

We might also ask what the instantaneous rate is at a single point in time. In an automobile, the instantaneous rate can be read from the speedometer. For a chemical reaction, we can extract the instantaneous rate from the concentration–time graph by drawing a line tangent to the concentration–time curve at a particular time (Figure 15.2). The instantaneous rate is obtained from the slope of this line. For example, when $[N_2O_5] = 0.34$ mol/L and $t = 5.0$ hours, the rate is

$$\text{Rate when } \left[N_2O_5\right] \text{ is 0.34 M} = -\frac{\Delta\left[N_2O_5\right]}{\Delta t} = +\frac{0.20 \text{ mol/L}}{140 \text{ min}}$$

$$= 0.0014 \frac{\text{mol}}{\text{L} \cdot \text{min}}$$

At that particular moment in time, $(t = 5.0$ hours), $N_2O_5$ is being consumed at a rate of $0.0014$ mol/L $\cdot$ min.

## EXAMPLE 15.1 Relative Rates and Stoichiometry

**Problem** Relate the rates for the disappearance of reactants and formation of products for the following reaction:

$$4 \text{ PH}_3(g) \rightarrow P_4(g) + 6 \text{ H}_2(g)$$

**What Do You Know?** The balanced chemical equation for the reaction is given. The stoichiometric coefficients in this equation will be used to evaluate the relative rates for the disappearance of the starting material and formation of the products.

**Strategy** In this reaction, $PH_3$ disappears, and $P_4$ and $H_2$ are formed. Consequently, the value of $\Delta[PH_3]/\Delta t$ will be negative, whereas $\Delta[P_4]/\Delta t$ and $\Delta[H_2]/\Delta t$ will be positive. To relate the rates to each other, we divide $\Delta[\text{reagent}]/\Delta t$ by its stoichiometric coefficient in the balanced equation.

**Solution** Because four moles of $PH_3$ disappear for every one mole of $P_4$ formed, the numerical value of the rate of formation of $P_4$ is one fourth of the rate of disappearance of $PH_3$. Similarly, $P_4$ is formed at only one sixth of the rate that $H_2$ is formed.

$$\text{Reaction rate} = -\frac{1}{4}\left(\frac{\Delta\left[PH_3\right]}{\Delta t}\right) = +\frac{\Delta\left[P_4\right]}{\Delta t} = +\frac{1}{6}\left(\frac{\Delta\left[H_2\right]}{\Delta t}\right)$$

**Think about Your Answer** A general equation to determine the relative rates of disappearance and formation from a balanced chemical equation is given in the margin on page 671.

### Check Your Understanding

What are the relative rates of appearance or disappearance of each product and reactant, respectively, in the decomposition of nitrosyl chloride, NOCl?

$$2 \text{ NOCl}(g) \rightarrow 2 \text{ NO}(g) + Cl_2(g)$$

## EXAMPLE 15.2 Rate of Reaction

**Problem** Data collected on the concentration of dye as a function of time (Figure 15.1) are given in the graph below. What is the average rate of change of the dye concentration over the first 2 minutes? What is the average rate of change during the fifth minute (from $t = 4.0$ minutes to $t = 5.0$ minutes)? Estimate the instantaneous rate at 4.0 minutes.

**What Do You Know?** The concentration of dye as a function of time is presented as a graph. From this curve you can identify the concentration of dye at specific times.

**Strategy** To find the average rate, calculate the difference in concentration at the beginning and end of a time period ($\Delta c = c_{final} - c_{initial}$) and divide by the elapsed time. To find the instantaneous rate at 4 minutes, draw a line tangent to the graph at the specified time. The negative of the slope of the line is the instantaneous rate.

**Solution** The concentration of dye decreases from $3.4 \times 10^{-5}$ mol/L at $t = 0$ minutes to $1.7 \times 10^{-5}$ mol/L at $t = 2.0$ minutes. The average rate of the reaction in this interval of time is

$$\text{Average rate} = -\frac{\Delta[\text{Dye}]}{\Delta t} = -\frac{(1.7 \times 10^{-5}\ \text{mol/L}) - (3.4 \times 10^{-5}\ \text{mol/L})}{2.0\ \text{min}}$$

$$\text{Average rate} = \frac{8.5 \times 10^{-6}\ \text{mol}}{\text{L} \cdot \text{min}}$$

The concentration of dye decreases from $0.90 \times 10^{-5}$ mol/L at $t = 4.0$ minutes to $0.60 \times 10^{-5}$ mol/L at $t = 5.0$ minutes. The average rate of the reaction in this interval of time is

$$\text{Average rate} = -\frac{\Delta[\text{Dye}]}{\Delta t} = -\frac{(0.60 \times 10^{-5}\ \text{mol/L}) - (0.90 \times 10^{-5}\ \text{mol/L})}{1.0\ \text{min}}$$

$$\text{Average rate} = \frac{3.0 \times 10^{-6}\ \text{mol}}{\text{L} \cdot \text{min}}$$

From the slope of the line tangent to the curve, the instantaneous rate at 4 minutes is found to be $+3.5 \times 10^{-6}$ mol/L · min.

**Think about Your Answer** Notice that the rate of reaction decreases as the concentration of dye decreases. This tells us that the rate of the reaction is related to the concentration of dye. We can also deduce this qualitatively from the fact that graphing concentration vs. time gave a curved line.

**Check Your Understanding**

Sucrose decomposes to fructose and glucose in acid solution. A plot of the concentration of sucrose as a function of time is given in the margin. What is the rate of change of the sucrose concentration over the first 2 hours? What is the rate of change over the last 2 hours? Estimate the instantaneous rate at 4 hours.

**Concentration versus time for the decomposition of sucrose.**

("Check Your Understanding" in Example 15.2.)

**REVIEW & CHECK FOR SECTION 15.1**

1.  Compare the rates of disappearance of NO(g) and $O_2$(g) for the reaction
    $2\ NO(g) + O_2(g) \rightarrow 2\ NO_2(g)$.

    (a) The rates are equal.

    (b) The rate of disappearance of NO(g) is twice the rate of disappearance of $O_2$(g).

    (c) The rate of disappearance of NO(g) is one half the rate of disappearance of $O_2$(g).

    (d) The rates are not related.

2.  Use the graph provided in Example 15.2 to estimate the average rate of disappearance of dye for the period 1-3 minutes.

(a) 0.6 mol/L · min

(c) $0.6 \times 10^{-5}$ mol/L · min

(b) $1.2 \times 10^{-5}$ mol/L · min

(d) 1.2 mol/L · min

## 15.2 Reaction Conditions and Rate

Several factors—reactant concentrations, temperature, and presence of catalysts—affect the rate of a reaction. If the reactant is a solid, the surface area available for reaction is also a factor.

The "iodine clock reaction" (Figure 15.3) illustrates the **effect of concentration and temperature**. The reaction mixture contains hydrogen peroxide ($H_2O_2$), iodide ion ($I^-$), vitamin C (ascorbic acid), and starch (which is an indicator of the presence of iodine, $I_2$). A sequence of reactions begins with the slow oxidation of iodide ion to $I_2$ by $H_2O_2$.

$$H_2O_2(aq) + 2\ I^-(aq) + 2\ H_3O^+(aq) \rightarrow 4\ H_2O(\ell) + I_2(aq)$$

As soon as $I_2$ is formed in the solution, vitamin C rapidly reduces it to $I^-$.

$$2\ H_2O(\ell) + I_2(aq) + C_6H_8O_6(aq) \rightarrow C_6H_6O_6(aq) + 2\ H_3O^+(aq) + 2\ I^-(aq)$$

When all of the vitamin C has been consumed, $I_2$ remains in solution and forms a blue-black complex with starch. The time measured represents how long it has taken for the given amount of vitamin C to react. For the first experiment (A in Figure 15.3) the time required is 51 seconds. When the concentration of iodide ion is smaller (B), the time required for the vitamin C to be consumed is longer, 1 minute 33 seconds. Finally, when the concentrations are again the same as in experiment B but the reaction mixture is heated, the reaction occurs more rapidly (56 seconds). This experiment illustrates two features that are true of most reactions:

*   If the concentration of a reactant is increased, the reaction rate will often increase as well.
*   Chemical reactions occur more rapidly at higher temperatures.

● **Effect of Temperature on Reaction Rate** Cooking involves chemical reactions, and a higher temperature results in foods cooking faster. In the laboratory, reaction mixtures are often heated to make reactions occur faster.

**(a) Initial experiment.**
The blue color of the starch–iodine complex develops in 51 seconds.

**(b) Change concentration.**
The blue color of the starch–iodine complex develops in 1 minute 33 seconds when the solution is less concentrated than A.

**(c) Change temperature.**
The blue color of the starch–iodine complex develops in 56 seconds when the solution is the same concentration as in B but at a higher temperature.

Hot bath

Smaller concentration of $I^-$ than in Experiment A.

Same concentrations as in Experiment B, but at a higher temperature.

Solutions containing vitamin C, $H_2O_2$, $I^-$, and starch are mixed.

**FIGURE 15.3 The iodine clock reaction.** This reaction illustrates the effects of concentration and temperature on reaction rate. (You can do these experiments yourself with reagents available in the supermarket. For details, see S. W. Wright: "The vitamin C clock reaction," *Journal of Chemical Education*, Vol. 79, p. 41, 2002.)

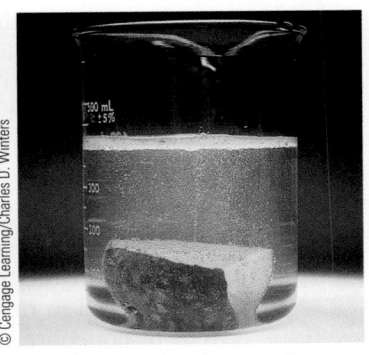

**(a)** The rate of decomposition of hydrogen peroxide is increased by the catalyst $MnO_2$. Here, $H_2O_2$ (as a 30% aqueous solution) is poured onto the black solid $MnO_2$ and rapidly decomposes to $O_2$ and $H_2O$. Steam forms because of the high heat of reaction.

**(b)** A bombardier beetle uses the catalyzed decomposition of $H_2O_2$ as a defense mechanism. The energy involved in the reaction lets the insect eject hot water and other irritating chemicals with explosive force.

**(c)** Enzyme catalysis. Here, the enzyme catalase, found in potatoes, is used to catalyze $H_2O_2$ decomposition, and bubbles of $O_2$ gas are seen rising in the solution.

**FIGURE 15.4** Catalyzed decomposition of $H_2O_2$.

**Catalysts** are substances that accelerate chemical reactions but are not themselves consumed. Consider the effect of a catalyst on the decomposition of hydrogen peroxide, $H_2O_2$, to form water and oxygen.

$$2\ H_2O_2(aq) \rightarrow O_2(g) + 2\ H_2O(\ell)$$

This decomposition is very slow; a solution of $H_2O_2$ can be stored for many months with only minimal change in concentration. Adding manganese(IV) oxide, an iodide-containing salt, or a compound called catalase—an example of a biological catalyst or *enzyme*—causes this reaction to occur rapidly, as shown by vigorous bubbling as gaseous oxygen escapes from the solution (Figure 15.4).

The *surface area* of a solid reactant can also affect the reaction rate. Only molecules at the surface of a solid can come in contact with other reactants. The smaller the particles of a solid, the more molecules are found on the solid's surface. With very small particles, the effect of surface area on rate can be quite dramatic (Figure 15.5). Farmers know that explosions of fine dust particles (suspended in the air in an enclosed silo or at a feed mill) represent a major hazard.

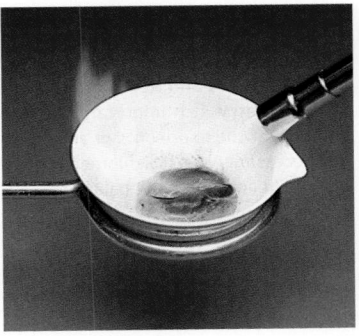

**(a)**

---

**REVIEW & CHECK FOR SECTION 15.2**

Which of the factors listed below affect the rates of chemical reactions?

(a) catalysts

(b) temperature

(c) concentration of reactants

(d) surface area of solid

(e) all of the above

---

**(b)**

**FIGURE 15.5 The combustion of lycopodium powder. (a)** The spores of this common fern burn only with difficulty when piled in a dish. **(b)** If the spores are ground to a fine powder and sprayed into a flame, combustion is rapid.

## 15.3 Effect of Concentration on Reaction Rate

One important goal in studying the kinetics of a reaction is to determine its mechanism; that is, how the reaction occurs at the molecular level. The place to begin is to learn how concentrations of reactants affect the reaction rate.

The effect of concentration can be determined by evaluating how the rate is affected when the concentrations of the reactants are varied (with the temperature held constant). Consider, for example, the decomposition of $N_2O_5$ to $NO_2$ and $O_2$. Figure 15.2 presented data on the concentration of $N_2O_5$ as a function of time. We previously calculated that, when $[N_2O_5] = 0.34$ mol/L, the instantaneous rate of disappearance of $N_2O_5$ is 0.0014 mol/L $\cdot$ min. An evaluation of the instantaneous rate of the reaction when $[N_2O_5] = 0.68$ mol/L reveals a rate of 0.0028 mol/L $\cdot$ min.

That is, doubling the concentration of $N_2O_5$ doubles the reaction rate. A similar exercise shows that if $[N_2O_5]$ is 0.17 mol/L (half of 0.34 mol/L), the reaction rate is also halved. From these results, we know that the rate for this reaction must be directly proportional to the $N_2O_5$ concentration:

$$N_2O_5 \rightarrow 2\ NO_2 + \tfrac{1}{2}\ O_2$$
$$\text{Rate of reaction} \propto [N_2O_5]$$

where the symbol $\propto$ means "proportional to."

Different relationships between reaction rate and reactant concentration are encountered in other reactions. For example, the reaction rate could be independent of concentration, or it may depend on the reactant concentration raised to some power $n$ (that is, $[\text{reactant}]^n$). If the reaction involves several reactants, the reaction rate may depend on the concentrations of each of them or on only one of them. Finally, the concentration of a catalyst or even the concentrations of the products may affect the rate.

## Rate Equations

The relationship between reactant concentration and reaction rate is expressed by an equation called a **rate equation**, or **rate law**. For the decomposition of $N_2O_5$ the rate equation is

$$N_2O_5(g) \rightarrow 2\ NO_2(g) + \tfrac{1}{2}\ O_2$$
$$\text{Rate of reaction} = -\Delta[N_2O_5]/\Delta t = +(1/2)\Delta[NO_2]/\Delta t = +2\Delta[O_2]/\Delta t = k[N_2O_5]$$

where the proportionality constant, $k$, is called the **rate constant**. This rate equation tells us that this reaction rate is proportional to the concentration of the reactant. Based on this equation, we can determine that when $[N_2O_5]$ is doubled, the reaction rate doubles (and we know $[N_2O_5]$ decreases twice as fast as $[O_2]$ increases).

Generally, for a reaction such as

$$a\ \text{A} + b\ \text{B} \rightarrow x\ \text{X}$$

the rate equation has the form

$$\text{Rate of reaction} = k[\text{A}]^m[\text{B}]^n$$

● **Exponents on Reactant Concentrations and Reaction Stoichiometry** It is important to recognize that the exponents $m$ and $n$ are not necessarily the stoichiometric coefficients ($a$ and $b$) for the balanced chemical equation.

The rate equation expresses the fact that the rate of reaction is proportional to the reactant concentrations, each concentration being raised to some power. The exponents in this equation are often positive whole numbers, but they can also be negative numbers, fractions, or zero, and they are determined by experiment.

If a homogeneous catalyst is present, its concentration might also be included in the rate equation, even though the catalytic species in not a product or reactant in the equation for the reaction. Consider, for example, the decomposition of hydrogen peroxide in the presence of a catalyst such as iodide ion.

$$H_2O_2(aq) \xrightarrow{\text{I}^-(aq)} H_2O(\ell) + \tfrac{1}{2}\ O_2(g)$$

Experiments show that this reaction has the following rate equation:

$$\text{Reaction rate} = -\Delta[H_2O_2]/\Delta t = +\Delta[H_2O]/\Delta t = +2\Delta[O_2]/\Delta t = k[H_2O_2][\text{I}^-]$$

● **The Nature of Catalysts** A catalyst does not appear as a reactant in the balanced, overall equation for the reaction, but it may appear in the rate expression. A common practice is to identify catalysts by name or symbol above the reaction arrow, as shown in the example. A homogeneous catalyst is one in the same phase as the reactants. For example, both $H_2O_2$ and $\text{I}^-$ are dissolved in water.

Here, the concentration of $\text{I}^-$ appears in the rate law, even though it is not involved in the balanced equation.

## The Order of a Reaction

The **order** of a reaction with respect to a particular reactant is the exponent of its concentration term in the rate expression, and the **overall reaction order** is the sum of the exponents on all concentration terms. Consider, for example, the reaction of NO and $Cl_2$:

$$2\ NO(g) + Cl_2(g) \rightarrow 2\ NOCl(g)$$

The experimentally determined rate equation for this reaction is

$$\text{Reaction rate} = -(1/2)\Delta[\text{NO}]/\Delta t = -\Delta[\text{Cl}_2]/\Delta t = +(1/2)\Delta[\text{NOCl}]/\Delta t = k[\text{NO}]^2[\text{Cl}_2]$$

This reaction is second order in NO, first order in $Cl_2$, and third order overall. How is this related to the following experimental data for the rate of disappearance of NO?

| Experiment | [NO] mol/L | [Cl₂] mol/L | Rate mol/L · s |
|---|---|---|---|
| 1 | 0.250 | 0.250 | $1.43 \times 10^{-6}$ |
|   | ↓ × 2 | ↓ No change | ↓ × 4 |
| 2 | 0.500 | 0.250 | $5.72 \times 10^{-6}$ |
| 3 | 0.250 | 0.500 | $2.86 \times 10^{-6}$ |
| 4 | 0.500 | 0.500 | $11.4 \times 10^{-6}$ |

- *Compare Experiments 1 and 2:* Here, $[Cl_2]$ is held constant, and [NO] is doubled. The change in [NO] leads to a reaction rate increase by a factor of 4; that is, the rate is proportional to the *square* of the NO concentration.
- *Compare Experiments 1 and 3:* In experiments 1 and 3, [NO] is held constant, and $[Cl_2]$ is doubled, causing the rate to double. That is, the rate is proportional to $[Cl_2]$.
- *Compare Experiments 1 and 4:* Both [NO] and $[Cl_2]$ are doubled from 0.250 M to 0.500 M. From previous experiments, we know that doubling [NO] should cause a four-fold increase, and doubling $[Cl_2]$ causes a two-fold increase. Therefore, doubling both concentrations should cause an eight-fold increase, as is observed [$(1.43 \times 10^{-6} \text{ mol/L} \cdot \text{s}) \times 8 = 11.4 \times 10^{-6} \text{ mol/L} \cdot \text{s}$].

The decomposition of ammonia on a platinum surface at 856 °C is a zero-order reaction.

$$\text{NH}_3(g) \rightarrow \tfrac{1}{2}\,\text{N}_2(g) + \tfrac{3}{2}\,\text{H}_2(g)$$

This means that the reaction rate is independent of $NH_3$ concentration.

$$\text{Reaction rate} = -\Delta[\text{NH}_3]/\Delta t = +2\Delta[\text{N}_2]/\Delta t = +(2/3)\Delta[\text{H}_2]/\Delta t = k[\text{NH}_3]^0 = k$$

Reaction order is important because it gives some insight into the most interesting question of all—how the reaction occurs. This is described further in Section 15.6.

## The Rate Constant, *k*

The rate constant, *k*, is a proportionality constant that relates rate and concentration at a given temperature. It is an important quantity because it enables you to find the reaction rate for a new set of concentrations. To see how to use *k*, consider the substitution of $Cl^-$ ion by water in the cancer chemotherapy agent cisplatin, $Pt(NH_3)_2Cl_2$.

$$\text{Pt(NH}_3)_2\text{Cl}_2(aq) + \text{H}_2\text{O}(\ell) \longrightarrow [\text{Pt(NH}_3)_2(\text{H}_2\text{O})\text{Cl}]^+(aq) + \text{Cl}^-(aq)$$

The rate law for this reaction is

$$\text{Reaction rate} = -\Delta[\text{Pt(NH}_3)_2\text{Cl}_2]\Delta t = k[\text{Pt(NH}_3)_2\text{Cl}_2]$$

and the rate constant, *k*, is 0.27/h at 25 °C. Knowing *k* allows you to calculate the rate at a particular reactant concentration—for example, when $[Pt(NH_3)_2Cl_2] = 0.018$ mol/L:

$$\text{Reaction rate} = (0.27/\text{h})(0.018 \text{ mol/L}) = 0.0049 \text{ mol/L} \cdot \text{h}$$

● **Time and Rate Constants** The time in a rate constant can be seconds, minutes, hours, days, years, or whatever time unit is appropriate. The fraction 1/time can also be written as time$^{-1}$. For example, 1/y is equivalent to $y^{-1}$, and 1/s is equivalent to s$^{-1}$.

● **Some Rate Constants**

| First Order | k (1/s) |
|---|---|
| 2 N₂O₅(g) → 4 NO₂(g) + O₂(g) | $3.38 \times 10^{-5}$ at 25 °C |
| C₂H₆(g) → 2 CH₃(g) | $5.36 \times 10^{-4}$ at 700 °C |
| Sucrose(aq, H₃O⁺) → fructose(aq) + glucose(aq) | $6.0 \times 10^{-5}$ at 25 °C |

| Second Order | k (L/mol · s) |
|---|---|
| 2 NOBr(g) → 2 NO(g) + Br₂(g) | 0.80 at 10 °C |
| H₂(g) + I₂(g) → 2 HI(g) | 0.0242 at 400 °C |

As noted earlier, reaction rates have units of mol/L · time when concentrations are given as moles per liter. Rate constants must have units consistent with the units for the other terms in the rate equation.

- First-order reactions: The units of $k$ are 1/time.
- Second-order reactions: The units of $k$ are L/mol · time.
- Zero-order reaction: The units of $k$ are mol/L · time.

## Determining a Rate Equation

One way to determine a rate equation is by using the "method of initial rates." The initial rate is the instantaneous reaction rate at the start of the reaction (the rate at $t = 0$). An approximate value of the initial rate can be obtained by mixing the reactants and determining the reaction rate after 1% to 2% of the limiting reactant has been consumed. Measuring the rate during the initial stage of a reaction is convenient because initial concentrations are known.

As an example of the determination of a reaction rate by the method of initial rates, let us consider the reaction of sodium hydroxide with methyl acetate to produce acetate ion and methanol.

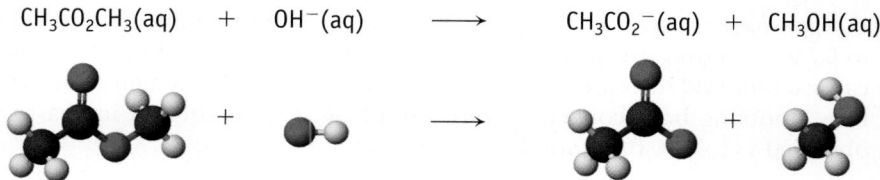

$$CH_3CO_2CH_3(aq) \quad + \quad OH^-(aq) \quad \longrightarrow \quad CH_3CO_2^-(aq) \quad + \quad CH_3OH(aq)$$

Reactant concentrations and initial rates for this reaction for several experiments at 25 °C are collected in the table below.

| Experiment | Initial Concentrations (mol/L) | | Initial Reaction Rate |
|---|---|---|---|
| | $[CH_3CO_2CH_3]$ | $[OH^-]$ | (mol/L · s) at 25 °C |
| 1 | 0.050 | 0.050 | 0.00034 |
| | ↓ no change | ↓ × 2 | ↓ × 2 |
| 2 | 0.050 | 0.10 | 0.00069 |
| | ↓ × 2 | ↓ no change | ↓ × 2 |
| 3 | 0.10 | 0.10 | 0.00137 |

As you can see from the data in the table, when the initial concentration of one reactant (either $CH_3CO_2CH_3$ or $OH^-$) is doubled while the concentration of the other reactant is held constant, the initial reaction rate doubles. This rate doubling shows that the reaction rate is directly proportional to the concentrations of both $CH_3CO_2CH_3$ and $OH^-$; thus, the reaction is first order in each of these reactants and second order overall. The rate law that reflects these experimental observations is

$$\text{Reaction rate} = -\Delta[CH_3CO_2H]/\Delta t = k[CH_3CO_2CH_3][OH^-]$$

Using this equation, we can predict that doubling both concentrations at the same time should cause the rate to go up by a factor of 4. What happens, however, if one concentration is doubled and the other is halved? The rate equation tells us the rate should not change!

If the rate equation is known, the value of $k$, the rate constant, can be found by substituting values for the rate and concentration into the rate equation. Using the data for the methyl acetate/hydroxide ion reaction from the first experiment, we have

$$\text{Reaction rate} = 0.00034 \text{ mol/L} \cdot \text{s} = k(0.050 \text{ mol/L})(0.050 \text{ mol/L})$$

$$k = \frac{0.00034 \text{ mol/L} \cdot \text{s}}{(0.050 \text{ mol/L})(0.050 \text{ mol/L})} = 0.14 \text{ L/mol} \cdot \text{s}$$

# OWL   INTERACTIVE EXAMPLE 15.3   Determining a Rate Equation

**Problem** The rate of the reaction between CO and $NO_2$ at 540 K

$$CO(g) + NO_2(g) \rightarrow CO_2(g) + NO(g)$$

was measured starting with various concentrations of CO and $NO_2$. Determine the rate equation and the value of the rate constant.

| | Initial Concentrations | | Initial Rate |
|---|---|---|---|
| Experiment | [CO], mol/L | $[NO_2]$, mol/L | $(mol/L \cdot h)$ |
| 1 | $5.10 \times 10^{-4}$ | $0.350 \times 10^{-4}$ | $3.4 \times 10^{-8}$ |
| 2 | $5.10 \times 10^{-4}$ | $0.700 \times 10^{-4}$ | $6.8 \times 10^{-8}$ |
| 3 | $5.10 \times 10^{-4}$ | $0.175 \times 10^{-4}$ | $1.7 \times 10^{-8}$ |
| 4 | $1.02 \times 10^{-3}$ | $0.350 \times 10^{-4}$ | $6.8 \times 10^{-8}$ |
| 5 | $1.53 \times 10^{-3}$ | $0.350 \times 10^{-4}$ | $10.2 \times 10^{-8}$ |

**What Do You Know?** The table contains concentrations of the two reactants and initial rates for five experiments.

**Strategy** For a reaction involving several reactants, the general approach is to keep the concentration of one reactant constant and then decide how the rate of reaction changes as the concentration of the other reagent is varied. Because the rate is proportional to the concentration of a reactant, R, raised to some power $n$ (the reaction order)

$$\text{Rate} \propto [R]^n$$

we can write the general equation for the ratio of rates in two experiments

$$\frac{\text{Rate in experiment 2}}{\text{Rate in experiment 1}} = \frac{[R_2]^n}{[R_1]^n} = \left(\frac{[R_2]}{[R_1]}\right)^n$$

If [R] is doubled and the rate doubles from experiment 1 to experiment 2, then $n = 1$. If [R], doubles and the rate goes up by 4, then $n = 2$.

**Solution** In the first three experiments, the concentration of CO is held constant. In the second experiment, the $NO_2$ concentration has been doubled relative to experiment 1, leading to a two-fold increase in the rate. Thus, $n = 1$ and the reaction is first order in $NO_2$.

$$\frac{\text{Rate in experiment 2}}{\text{Rate in experiment 1}} = \frac{6.8 \times 10^{-8} \text{ mol/L} \cdot h}{3.4 \times 10^{-8} \text{ mol/L} \cdot h} = \left(\frac{0.700 \times 10^{-4}}{0.350 \times 10^{-4}}\right)^n$$

$$2 = (2)^n$$

and so $n = 1$.

This finding is confirmed by experiment 3. Decreasing $[NO_2]$ in experiment 3 to half its original value causes the rate to decrease by half.

The data in experiments 1 and 4 (with constant $[NO_2]$) show that doubling [CO] doubles the rate, and the data from experiments 1 and 5 show that tripling the concentration of CO triples the rate. These results mean that the reaction is first order in [CO]. Thus, we now know the rate equation is

$$\text{Reaction rate} = -\Delta[CO]/\Delta t = -\Delta[NO_2]/\Delta t = +\Delta[CO_2]/\Delta t = +\Delta[NO]/\Delta t = k[CO][NO_2]$$

The rate constant, $k$, can be found by inserting data for one of the experiments into the rate equation. Using data from experiment 1, for example,

$$\text{Rate} = 3.4 \times 10^{-8} \text{ mol/L} \cdot h = k(5.10 \times 10^{-4} \text{ mol/L})(0.350 \times 10^{-4} \text{ mol/L})$$

$$k = 1.9 \text{ L/mol} \cdot h$$

**Think about Your Answer** This reaction is first order in each reactant (and second order overall), and you know the value of the rate constant $k$. The same rate law would apply if the reaction were carried out at a different temperature, but the rate constant $k$ would have a different value.

**Strategy Map 15.3**

**PROBLEM**
Derive the **rate equation** and **value of $k$** for a given reaction.

↓

**DATA/INFORMATION**
- **5 experiments** measuring *initial rate* as a function of **reactant concentration**

**STEP 1.** **Compare rates** for two experiments where the concentration of reactant **A** is *constant* and reactant **B** is *varied*.

Gives the **dependence of rate** on one reactant **(B)**

**STEP 2.** **Compare rates** for two experiments where the concentration of reactant **B** is *constant* and reactant **A** is *varied*.

Gives the **dependence of rate** on the other reactant **(A)**

**STEP 3.** Use the *rate dependence* on **A** and **B** to write the **rate equation**.

Rate = $k$ $[A]^n[B]^m$

**STEP 4.** Substitute the **rate data** for one experiment into the **rate equation** to calculate $k$.

**Value** of rate constant $k$

**Check Your Understanding**

The initial rate of the reaction of nitrogen monoxide and oxygen

$$2\ NO(g) + O_2(g) \rightarrow 2\ NO_2(g)$$

was measured for various initial concentrations of NO and $O_2$. Determine the rate equation from these data. What is the value of the rate constant, $k$, and what are its units?

| | Initial Concentrations (mol/L) | | Initial Rate for [NO] |
|---|---|---|---|
| **Experiment** | **[NO]** | **[O₂]** | **(mol NO/L · s)** |
| 1 | 0.020 | 0.010 | 0.028 |
| 2 | 0.020 | 0.020 | 0.057 |
| 3 | 0.020 | 0.040 | 0.114 |
| 4 | 0.040 | 0.020 | 0.227 |
| 5 | 0.010 | 0.020 | 0.014 |

Be sure to note that the reaction rate here is defined as

$$\text{Reaction rate} = -(1/2)\Delta[NO]/\Delta t = -\Delta[O_2]/\Delta t = +(1/2)\Delta[NO_2]/\Delta t = k[NO]^m[O_2]^n$$

## EXAMPLE 15.4 Using a Rate Equation to Determine Rates

**Problem** Using the rate equation and rate constant determined for the reaction of CO and $NO_2$ at 540 K in Example 15.3, determine the initial rate of the reaction when $[CO] = 3.8 \times 10^{-4}$ mol/L and $[NO_2] = 0.650 \times 10^{-4}$ mol/L.

**What Do You Know?** The rate law and the value for the rate constant (1.9 L/mol · h) are both known. The concentrations of the two reactants are given.

**Strategy** A rate equation consists of three parts: a rate, a rate constant ($k$), and the concentration terms. if two of these parts are known (here $k$ and the concentrations), the third can be calculated.

**Solution** Substitute $k$ (= 1.9 L/mol · h) and the concentration of each reactant into the rate law determined in Example 15.3.

$$\text{Reaction rate} = k[CO][NO_2] = (1.9\ \text{L/mol} \cdot h)(3.8 \times 10^{-4}\ \text{mol/L})(0.650 \times 10^{-4}\ m$$

$$\text{Reaction rate} = 4.7 \times 10^{-8}\ \text{mol/L} \cdot h$$

**Think about Your Answer** As a check on the calculated result, it is sometimes useful to make an educated guess at the answer before carrying out the mathematical solution. We know that the reaction here is first order in both reactants. Comparing the concentration values given in this problem with the concentration values in experiment 1 in Example 15.3, we notice that [CO] is about three fourths of the concentration value, whereas [NO₂] is almost twice the value. The effects do not precisely offset each other, but we might predict that the difference in rates between this experiment and experiment 1 will be fairly small, with the rate of this experiment being just a little greater. The calculated value bears this out.

**Check Your Understanding**

The rate constant, $k$, at 25 °C is 0.27/h for the reaction

$$Pt(NH_3)_2Cl_2(aq) + H_2O(\ell) \rightarrow [Pt(NH_3)_2(H_2O)Cl]^+(aq) + Cl^-(aq)$$

and the rate equation is

$$\text{Reaction rate} = k[Pt(NH_3)_2Cl_2]$$

Calculate the rate of reaction when the concentration of $Pt(NH_3)_2Cl_2$ is 0.020 M.

**REVIEW & CHECK FOR SECTION 15.3**

The reaction 2 NO(g) + $Cl_2$(g) → 2 NOCl(g) is first order in $[Cl_2]$ and second order with respect to [NO]. Under a given set of conditions, the initial rate of this reaction is $6.20 \times 10^{-6}$ mol/L · s. What is the rate of this reaction if the concentration of NO is doubled and the concentration of $Cl_2$ is reduced to half the original value?

(a)  $6.20 \times 10^{-6}$ mol/L · s

(b)  $1.24 \times 10^{-5}$ mol/L · s

(c)  $2.48 \times 10^{-5}$ mol/L · s

(d)  $4.96 \times 10^{-5}$ mol/L · s

## 15.4 Concentration–Time Relationships: Integrated Rate Laws

It is often important for a chemist to know how long a reaction must proceed to reach a predetermined concentration of some reactant or product, or what the reactant and product concentrations will be after some time has elapsed. For this reason it would be useful to have a mathematical equation that relates time and concentration—an equation that describes concentration-time curves like the one shown in Figure 15.2—and that can be used to determine this information. With such an equation, we could calculate the concentration at any given time or the length of time needed for a given amount of reactant to react.

**Module 20: Chemical Kinetics** covers concepts in this section.

### First-Order Reactions

Suppose the reaction "R → products" is first order. This means the reaction rate is directly proportional to the concentration of R raised to the first power, or, mathematically,

$$-\frac{\Delta[R]}{\Delta t} = k[R]$$

Using calculus, this relationship can be transformed into a very useful equation called an **integrated rate equation** (because integral calculus is used in its derivation).

$$\ln\frac{[R]_t}{[R]_0} = -kt \qquad (15.1)$$

Here, $[R]_0$ and $[R]_t$ are concentrations of the reactant at time $t = 0$ and at a later time, $t$, respectively. The ratio of concentrations, $[R]_t/[R]_0$, is the fraction of reactant that remains after a given time has elapsed. Notice the negative sign in the equation. The ratio $[R]_t/[R]_0$ is less than 1 because $[R]_t$ is always less than $[R]_0$; the reactant R is consumed during the reaction. This means the logarithm of $[R]_t/[R]_0$ is negative, so the other side of the equation must also bear a negative sign.

Equation 15.1 can be used to carry out the following calculations:

- If $[R]_t/[R]_0$ is measured in the laboratory after some amount of time has elapsed, then $k$ can be calculated.
- If $[R]_0$ and $k$ are known, then the concentration of material remaining after a given amount of time ($[R]_t$) can be calculated.
- If $k$ is known, then the time elapsed until a specific fraction ($[R]_t/[R]_0$) remains can be calculated.

Finally, notice that $k$ for a first-order reaction is independent of concentration; $k$ has units of time$^{-1}$ ($y^{-1}$ or $s^{-1}$, for example). This means we can choose any convenient unit for $[R]_t$ and $[R]_0$: moles per liter, moles, grams, number of atoms, number of molecules, or gas pressure.

● **Initial and Final Time, $t$** The time $t = 0$ does not need to correspond to the actual beginning of the experiment. It can be the time when instrument readings were started, for example, even though the reaction may have already begun.

## EXAMPLE 15.5    The First-Order Rate Equation

**Problem** In the past, cyclopropane, $C_3H_6$, was used in a mixture with oxygen as an anesthetic. (This practice has almost ceased today because the compound is flammable.) When heated, cyclopropane rearranges to propene in a first-order process.

cyclopropane                propene

$$\text{Rate} = k[\text{cyclopropane}] \qquad k = 2.42 \ h^{-1} \text{ at } 500 \ °C$$

If the initial concentration of cyclopropane is 0.050 mol/L, how much time (in hours) must elapse for its concentration to drop to 0.010 mol/L?

**What Do You Know?** The reaction is first order in cyclopropane. You know the rate constant, $k$, and the initial and final concentrations of this reactant, $[R]$ and $[R]_0$.

**Strategy** Use Equation 15.1 to calculate the time ($t$) elapsed to reach a concentration of 0.010 mol/L.

**Solution** Values for $[\text{cyclopropane}]_t$, $[\text{cyclopropane}]_0$, and $k$ are substituted into Equation 15.1; $t$ (time) is the unknown:

$$\ln\frac{[0.010]}{[0.050]} = -(2.42 \ h^{-1})t$$

$$t = \frac{-\ln(0.20)}{2.42 \ h^{-1}} = \frac{-(-1.61)}{2.42 \ h^{-1}} = \boxed{0.665 \ h}$$

**Think about Your Answer** Cycloalkanes with fewer than five carbon atoms are strained because the C—C—C bond angles cannot match the preferred 109.5°. Because of ring strain, the cyclopropane ring opens readily to form propene.

---

**Check Your Understanding**

Sucrose, a sugar, decomposes in acid solution to give glucose and fructose. The reaction is first order in sucrose, and the rate constant at 25 °C is $k = 0.21 \ h^{-1}$. If the initial concentration of sucrose is 0.010 mol/L, what is its concentration after 5.0 h?

---

## EXAMPLE 15.6    Using the First-Order Rate Equation

**Problem** Hydrogen peroxide decomposes in a dilute sodium hydroxide solution at 20 °C in a first-order reaction:

$$H_2O_2(aq) \rightarrow H_2O(\ell) + \tfrac{1}{2} O_2(g)$$
$$\text{Rate} = k[H_2O_2] \text{ with } k = 1.06 \times 10^{-3} \ min^{-1}$$

What is the fraction remaining after 100. min? What is the concentration of $H_2O_2$ after 100. minutes if the initial concentration of $H_2O_2$ is 0.020 mol/L??

**What Do You Know?** This is a first-order reaction. The rate constant $k$, initial concentration of $H_2O_2$, and elapsed time are given.

**Strategy** Because the reaction is first order in $H_2O_2$, we use Equation 15.1. Here, $[H_2O_2]_0$, $k$, and $t$ are known, and we are asked to find the value of the fraction remaining. Recall that

$$\frac{[R]_t}{[R]_0} = \text{fraction remaining}$$

Once this value is known, and knowing $[H_2O_2]_0$, we can calculate $[H_2O_2]_t$.

**Solution**  Substitute the known values into Equation 15.1.

$$\ln \frac{[H_2O_2]_t}{[H_2O_2]_0} = -kt = -(1.06 \times 10^{-3} \text{ min}^{-1})(100. \text{ min})$$

$$\ln \frac{[H_2O_2]_t}{[H_2O_2]_0} = -0.106$$

Taking the antilogarithm of $-0.106$ [i.e., the inverse of the logarithm of $-0.106$ or $e^{-0.106}$], we find the fraction remaining to be 0.90.

$$\text{Fraction remaining} = \frac{[H_2O_2]_t}{[H_2O_2]_0} = 0.90$$

The calculated fraction remaining is 0.90, thus the concentration of $H_2O_2$ remaining is 90% of the initial concentration.

$$[H_2O_2]_t = 0.90 \; [H_2O_2]_0 = 0.90 \; (0.020 \text{ mol/L}) = 0.018 \text{ mol/L}$$

**Think about Your Answer**  Although $H_2O_2$ is unstable, its rate of decomposition is very slow, particularly in a dilute solution. However, sodium hydroxide catalyzes the decomposition. The rate of the reaction can be studied by measuring the volume of $O_2$ gas evolved as a function of time.

**Check Your Understanding**

Gaseous azomethane ($CH_3N_2CH_3$) decomposes to ethane and nitrogen when heated:

$$CH_3N_2CH_3(g) \rightarrow CH_3CH_3(g) + N_2(g)$$

The disappearance of azomethane is a first-order reaction with $k = 3.6 \times 10^{-4} \text{ s}^{-1}$ at 600 K.

(a)  A sample of gaseous $CH_3N_2CH_3$ is placed in a flask and heated at 600 K for 150 seconds. What fraction of the initial sample remains after this time?

(b)  How long must a sample be heated so that 99% of the sample has decomposed?

## Second-Order Reactions

Suppose the reaction "R → products" is second order. The rate equation is

$$-\frac{\Delta[R]}{\Delta t} = k[R]^2$$

Using calculus, this relationship can be transformed into the following equation that relates reactant concentration and time:

$$\frac{1}{[R]_t} - \frac{1}{[R]_0} = kt \tag{15.2}$$

The same symbolism used with first-order reactions applies: $[R]_0$ is the concentration of reactant at the time $t = 0$; $[R]_t$ is the concentration at a later time; and $k$ is the second-order rate constant, which has the units of L/mol · time.

## EXAMPLE 15.7    Using the Second-Order Integrated Rate Equation

**Problem**  The gas-phase decomposition of HI

$$HI(g) \rightarrow \tfrac{1}{2} H_2(g) + \tfrac{1}{2} I_2(g)$$

has the rate equation

$$-\frac{\Delta[HI]}{\Delta t} = k[HI]^2$$

where $k = 30.$ L/mol · min at 443 °C. How much time does it take for the concentration of HI to drop from 0.010 mol/L to 0.0050 mol/L at 443 °C?

**What Do You Know?** Equation 15.2 is used for a second-order reaction. The rate constant, $k$, and the initial and final concentrations of HI are given; the elapsed time is the unknown.

**Strategy** Substitute the values of $[HI]_0$, $[HI]_t$, and $k$ into Equation 15.2, and solve for the unknown, $t$.

**Solution** Here, $[HI]_0 = 0.010$ mol/L and $[HI]_t = 0.0050$ mol/L. Using Equation 15.2, we have

$$\frac{1}{0.0050 \text{ mol/L}} - \frac{1}{0.010 \text{ mol/L}} = (30. \text{ L/mol} \cdot \text{min})t$$

$$(2.0 \times 10^2 \text{ L/mol}) - (1.0 \times 10^2 \text{ L/mol}) = (30. \text{ L/mol} \cdot \text{min})t$$

$$t = 3.3 \text{ minutes}$$

**Think about Your Answer** In the solution of this problem, we kept track of the units for each quantity. This leads to an answer for time elapsed with the unit minutes.

**Check Your Understanding**

Using the rate constant for HI decomposition given in this Example, calculate the concentration of HI after 12 minutes if $[HI]_0 = 0.010$ mol/L.

## Zero-Order Reactions

If a reaction (R → products) is zero order, the rate equation is

$$-\frac{\Delta[R]}{\Delta t} = k[R]^0$$

This equation leads to the integrated rate equation

$$[R]_0 - [R]_t = kt \tag{15.3}$$

where the units of $k$ are mol/L · s.

## Graphical Methods for Determining Reaction Order and the Rate Constant

● **Finding the Slope of a Line** See pages 41–42 for a description of methods for finding the slope of a line.

Chemists find it is convenient to determine the order of a reaction and its rate constant using graphical methods. Equations 15.1, 15.2, and 15.3, if rearranged slightly, have the form $y = mx + b$. This is the equation for a straight line, where $m$ is the slope of the line and $b$ is the y-intercept. In these equations, $x = t$ in each case.

| Zero order | First order | Second order |
|---|---|---|
| $[R]_t = -kt + [R]_0$ | $\ln [R]_t = -kt + \ln [R]_0$ | $\dfrac{1}{[R]_t} = +kt + \dfrac{1}{[R]_0}$ |
| $y \quad\quad mx \quad\quad b$ | $y \quad\quad mx \quad\quad b$ | $y \quad\quad mx \quad\quad b$ |

As an example of the graphical method for determining reaction order, consider the decomposition of azomethane.

$$CH_3N_2CH_3(g) \rightarrow CH_3CH_3(g) + N_2(g)$$

The decomposition of azomethane was followed at 600 K by observing the decrease in its partial pressure with time (Figure 15.6). (Recall from Chapter 11 that pressure is proportional to concentration at a given temperature and volume.) The third column of the data table lists values of $\ln P(CH_3N_2CH_3)$. As shown in Figure 15.6, a graph of $\ln P(CH_3N_2CH_3)$ versus time produces a straight line, which shows that the reaction is first order in $CH_3N_2CH_3$. The slope of the line can be measured, and the negative of the slope equals the rate constant for the reaction, $3.6 \times 10^{-4}$ s$^{-1}$.

| $t(s)$ | $P \times 10^2$ atm | $\ln P$ |
|---|---|---|
| 0 | 8.20 | −2.50 |
| 1000 | 5.72 | −2.86 |
| 2000 | 3.99 | −3.22 |
| 3000 | 2.78 | −3.58 |
| 4000 | 1.94 | −3.94 |

$$\text{Slope} = -k = \frac{(-3.94) - (-2.86)}{(4000 - 1000)s}$$

$$k = 3.6 \times 10^{-4}(s^{-1})$$

**FIGURE 15.6 The decomposition of azomethane, $CH_3N_2CH_3$.** If data for the decomposition of azomethane,

$$CH_3N_2CH_3(g) \rightarrow CH_3CH_3(g) + N_2(g)$$

are plotted as the natural logarithm of the $CH_3N_2CH_3$ pressure versus time, the result is a straight line with a negative slope. This indicates a first-order reaction. The rate constant $k = -$slope.

The decomposition of $NO_2$ is a second-order process.

$$NO_2(g) \rightarrow NO(g) + \tfrac{1}{2} O_2(g)$$

$$\text{Rate} = k[NO_2]^2$$

This fact can be verified by showing that a plot of $1/[NO_2]$ versus time is a straight line (Figure 15.7). Here, the slope of the line is equal to $k$.

For a zero-order reaction (Figure 15.8 on page 686), a plot of concentration versus time gives a straight line with a slope equal to the negative of the rate constant.

Table 15.1 (on page 686) summarizes the relationships between concentration and time for first-, second-, and zero-order processes.

## Half-Life and First-Order Reactions

The **half-life**, $t_{1/2}$, of a reaction is the time required for the concentration of a reactant to decrease to one half its initial value. Half-life is a convenient way to describe the rate at which a reactant is consumed in a chemical reaction: *The longer the half-life, the slower the reaction.* Half-life is used primarily when dealing with first-order processes.

The half-life, $t_{1/2}$, is the time when the fraction of the reactant R remaining is equal to $1/2$.

$$[R]_t = \tfrac{1}{2}[R]_0 \quad \text{or} \quad \frac{[R]_t}{[R]_0} = \tfrac{1}{2}$$

Here, $[R]_0$ is the initial concentration, and $[R]_t$ is the concentration after the reaction is half completed. To evaluate $t_{1/2}$ for a first-order reaction, we substitute $[R]_t/[R]_0 = \tfrac{1}{2}$ and $t = t_{1/2}$ into the integrated first-order rate equation (Equation 15.1),

$$\ln (\tfrac{1}{2}) = -kt_{1/2} \quad \text{or} \quad \ln 2 = kt_{1/2}$$

| Time (min) | $[NO_2]$ (mol/L) | $1/[NO_2]$ (L/mol) |
|---|---|---|
| 0 | 0.020 | 50 |
| 0.50 | 0.015 | 67 |
| 1.0 | 0.012 | 83 |
| 1.5 | 0.010 | 100 |
| 2.0 | 0.0087 | 115 |

**FIGURE 15.7 A second-order reaction.** A plot of $1/[NO_2]$ versus time for the decomposition of $NO_2$,

$$NO_2(g) \rightarrow NO(g) + \tfrac{1}{2} O_2(g)$$

results in a straight line. This confirms this is a second-order reaction. The slope of the line equals the rate constant for this reaction.

**Table 15.1 Characteristic Properties of Reactions of the Type "R ⟶ Products"**

| Order | Rate Equation | Integrated Rate Equation | Straight-Line Plot | Slope | k Units |
|---|---|---|---|---|---|
| 0 | $-\Delta[R]/\Delta t = k[R]^0$ | $[R]_0 - [R]_t = kt$ | $[R]_t$ vs. $t$ | $-k$ | mol/L · time |
| 1 | $-\Delta[R]/\Delta t = k[R]^1$ | $\ln([R]_t/[R]_0) = -kt$ | $\ln[R]_t$ vs. $t$ | $-k$ | 1/time |
| 2 | $-\Delta[R]/\Delta t = k[R]^2$ | $(1/[R]_t) - (1/[R]_0) = kt$ | $1/[R]_t$ vs. $t$ | $k$ | L/mol · time |

● **Half-Life and Radioactivity**
*Half-life* is a term often encountered when dealing with radioactive elements. Radioactive decay is a first-order process, and half-life is commonly used to describe how rapidly a radioactive element decays. See Chapter 23 and Example 15.9.

Rearranging this equation (and calculating that ln 2 = 0.693) provides a useful equation that relates half-life and the first-order rate constant:

$$t_{1/2} = \frac{0.693}{k} \tag{15.4}$$

This equation identifies an important feature of first-order reactions: $t_{1/2}$ is independent of concentration.

To illustrate the concept of half-life, consider again the first-order decomposition of azomethane, $CH_3N_2CH_3$.

$$CH_3N_2CH_3(g) \rightarrow CH_3CH_3(g) + N_2(g)$$
Rate = $k[CH_3N_2CH_3]$ with $k = 3.6 \times 10^{-4}$ s$^{-1}$ at 600 K

● **Half-Life Equations for Other Reaction Orders**
For a zero-order reaction, R → products

$$t_{1/2} = \frac{[R]_0}{2k}$$

For a second-order reaction, R → products

$$t_{1/2} = \frac{1}{k[R]_0}$$

Note that in both cases the half-life depends on the initial concentration.

Given a rate constant of $3.6 \times 10^{-4}$ s$^{-1}$, we calculate a half-life of $1.9 \times 10^3$ s or 32 minutes.

$$t_{1/2} = \frac{0.693}{3.6 \times 10^{-4} \text{ s}^{-1}} = 1.9 \times 10^3 \text{ s (or 32 min)}$$

The partial pressure of azomethane has been plotted as a function of time in Figure 15.9, and this graph shows that *P*(azomethane) decreases by half every 32 minutes. The initial pressure was 820 mm Hg, but it dropped to 410 mm Hg in 32 minutes, and then dropped to 205 mm Hg in another 32 minutes. That is, after two half-lives (64 minutes), the pressure is (½) × (½) = (½)² = ¼ or 25% of the initial pressure. After three half-lives, the pressure has dropped further to 102 mm Hg or 12.5% of the initial value and is equal to (½) × (½) × (½) = (½)³ = ⅛ of the initial value.

It can be hard to visualize whether a reaction is fast or slow from the rate constant value. Can you tell from the rate constant, $k = 3.6 \times 10^{-4}$ s$^{-1}$, whether the

**FIGURE 15.8 Plot of a zero-order reaction.** A graph of the concentration of ammonia, $[NH_3]_t$, against time for the decomposition of $NH_3$.

$$NH_3(g) \rightarrow \tfrac{1}{2} N_2(g) + \tfrac{3}{2} H_2(g)$$

on a metal surface at 856 °C is a straight line, indicating that this is a zero-order reaction. The rate constant, *k*, for this reaction is found from the slope of the line; *k* = −slope. (The points chosen to calculate the slope are given in red.)

**FIGURE 15.9 Half-life of a first-order reaction.** The curve is a plot of the pressure of $CH_3N_2CH_3$ as a function of time. (The compound decomposes to $CH_3CH_3$ and $N_2$ with $k = 3.6 \times 10^{-4}$ s$^{-1}$). The pressure of $CH_3N_2CH_3$ is halved every 1900 seconds (32 minutes). (This plot of pressure versus time is similar in shape to plots of concentration versus time for all other first-order reactions.)

azomethane decomposition will take seconds, hours, or days to reach completion? Probably not, but this can be assessed from the value of the half-life for the reaction (32 minutes). Now we know that we would only have to wait a few hours for the reactant to be essentially consumed.

## EXAMPLE 15.8 Half-Life and a First-Order Process

**Problem** Sucrose, $C_{12}H_{22}O_{11}$, decomposes to fructose and glucose in acid solution with the rate law

$$\text{Rate} = k[C_{12}H_{22}O_{11}] \qquad k = 0.216 \text{ h}^{-1} \text{ at } 25 \text{ °C}$$

(a) What is the half-life of $C_{12}H_{22}O_{11}$ at this temperature?

(b) What amount of time is required for 87.5% of the initial concentration of $C_{12}H_{22}O_{11}$ to decompose?

**What Do You Know?** The decomposition of sucrose is a first-order reaction. The rate constant for the reaction (at 25 °C) is given.

**Strategy** (a) Use Equation 15.4 to calculate the half-life from the rate constant. (b) After 87.5% of the $C_{12}H_{22}O_{11}$ has decomposed, 12.5% (or one eighth of the sample) remains. To reach this point, three half-lives are required.

| Half-Life | Fraction Remaining |
|-----------|--------------------|
| 1         | 0.5                |
| 2         | 0.25               |
| 3         | 0.125              |

Therefore, we multiply the half-life calculated in part (a) by 3.

**Solution**

(a) The half-life for the reaction is

$$t_{1/2} = 0.693/k = 0.693/(0.216 \text{ h}^{-1}) = 3.21 \text{ hours}$$

(b) Three half-lives must elapse before the fraction remaining is 0.125, so

$$\text{Time elapsed} = 3 \times 3.21 \text{ h} = 9.63 \text{ hours}$$

**Think about Your Answer** Half-life is a convenient way to describe the speed of a reaction. In this example, we can quickly see that complete decomposition of a sample of sucrose requires many hours.

**Check Your Understanding**

The catalyzed decomposition of hydrogen peroxide is first order in $[H_2O_2]$. It was found that the concentration of $H_2O_2$ decreased from 0.24 M to 0.060 M over a period of 282 minutes. What is the half-life of $H_2O_2$? What is the rate constant for this reaction? What is the initial rate of decomposition at the beginning of this experiment (when $[H_2O_2] = 0.24$ M)?

**Strategy Map 15.9**

PROBLEM

Find the **final number of atoms** of a radioactive isotope after a **given time period**.

↓

DATA/INFORMATION

- Half-life for decay
- Initial number of atoms
- Time elapsed

↓

STEP 1. Use Equation 15.4 to calculate $k$ from $t_{1/2}$.

Value of $k$

STEP 2. Use Equation 15.1 where $k$, $[R]_0$, and $t$ are known to calculate $[R]_t$.

Value of $[R]_t$, the **final number of atoms** of radioactive isotope after time $t$.

⊙WL     **INTERACTIVE EXAMPLE 15.9**   Half-Life and First-Order
Processes

**Problem** Radioactive radon-222 gas ($^{222}Rn$) occurs naturally as a product of uranium decay. The half-life of $^{222}Rn$ is 3.8 days. Suppose a flask originally contained $4.0 \times 10^{13}$ atoms of $^{222}Rn$. How many atoms of $^{222}Rn$ will remain after one month (30. days)?

**What Do You Know?** All radioactive decay processes follow first-order kinetics. The half-life of $^{222}Rn$ and the number of atoms initially present are known.

**Strategy** First, the rate constant, $k$, must be found from the half-life using Equation 15.4. Then, using Equation 15.1, and knowing the number of atoms at the beginning ($[R]_0$), the elapsed time (30. days), and the rate constant, we can calculate the number of atoms remaining ($[R]_t$).

**Solution** The rate constant, $k$, is

$$k = \frac{0.693}{t_{1/2}} = \frac{0.693}{3.8 \text{ d}} = 0.18 \text{ d}^{-1}$$

Now use Equation 15.1 to calculate the number of atoms remaining after 30. days.

$$\ln \frac{[Rn]_t}{4.0 \times 10^{13} \text{ atoms}} = -(0.18 \text{ d}^{-1})(30.\text{ d}) = -5.5$$

$$\frac{[Rn]_t}{4.0 \times 10^{13} \text{ atoms}} = e^{-5.5} = 0.0042$$

$$[Rn]_t = 2 \times 10^{11} \text{ atoms}$$

**Think about Your Answer** Thirty days is approximately 8 half-lives for this element. This means that the number of atoms present at the end of the month is approximately $(1/2)^8$ or $1/256$th of the original number.

**Check Your Understanding**

Americium is used in smoke detectors and in medicine for the treatment of certain malignancies. One isotope of americium, $^{241}Am$, has a rate constant, $k$, for radioactive decay of 0.0016 $y^{-1}$. In contrast, radioactive iodine-125, which is used for studies of thyroid functioning, has a rate constant for decay of 0.011 $d^{-1}$.

(a)   What are the half-lives of these isotopes?

(b)   Which isotope decays faster?

(c)   If you are given a dose of iodine-125 containing $1.6 \times 10^{15}$ atoms, how many atoms remain after 2.0 days?

**REVIEW & CHECK FOR SECTION 15.4**

1.   The decomposition of $N_2O_5$ is a first-order process. How many half-lives would be required to decompose 99% of the sample?

     (a)  7          (b)  between 6 and 7          (c)  5          (d)  between 5 and 6

2. Which of the following will confirm that the decomposition of $SO_2Cl_2$ (to form $SO_2$ and $Cl_2$) is a first-order process?

    (a) A graph of $[SO_2Cl_2]$ vs. time gives a curved line.

    (b) A graph of $\ln[SO_2Cl_2]$ vs. time gives a curved line.

    (c) A graph of $1/[SO_2Cl_2]$ vs time gives a straight line.

    (d) A graph of $\ln[SO_2Cl_2]$ vs. time gives a straight line.

3. The equation for the decomposition of $NO_2(g)$ at 573 K is $2\ NO_2(g) \rightarrow 2\ NO(g) + O_2(g)$. Using the concentration-time data below, determine the order of the reaction with respect to $[NO_2]$.

| $[NO_2]$, M | time, min |
|---|---|
| 0.20 | 0 |
| 0.095 | 5 |
| 0.063 | 10 |
| 0.047 | 15 |

    (a) first order     (b) second order     (c) zero order

# 15.5 A Microscopic View of Reaction Rates

Throughout this book, we have turned to the particulate level of chemistry to understand chemical phenomena. Rates of reaction are no exception. Looking at the way reactions occur at the atomic and molecular levels can give us some insight into the various influences on rates of reactions.

Let us review the macroscopic observations we have made so far concerning reaction rates. We know that there are wide differences in rates of reactions—from very fast reactions like the explosion that occurs when hydrogen and oxygen are exposed to a spark or flame (◄ Figure 1.16), to slow reactions like the formation of rust that occurs over days, weeks, or years. For a specific reaction, factors that influence reaction rate include the concentrations of the reactants, the temperature of the reaction system, and the presence of catalysts. In this section we want to look at each of these influences in more depth in the context of the **collision theory of reaction rates**, which states that three conditions must be met for a reaction to occur:

1. The reacting molecules must collide with one another.
2. The reacting molecules must collide with sufficient energy to initiate the process of breaking and forming bonds.
3. The molecules must collide in an orientation that can lead to rearrangement of the atoms and the formation of products.

## Collision Theory: Concentration and Reaction Rate

Consider the gas-phase reaction of nitric oxide and ozone, an environmentally important reaction:

$$NO(g) + O_3(g) \rightarrow NO_2(g) + O_2(g)$$

The rate law for this product-favored reaction is first order in each reactant: Rate $= k[NO][O_3]$. How can this reaction have this rate law?

Let us consider the reaction at the particulate level and imagine a flask containing a mixture of NO and $O_3$ molecules in the gas phase. Both kinds of molecules are in rapid and random motion within the flask. They strike the walls of the vessel, but they also collide with other molecules. Thus, it is reasonable to propose that the rate of their reaction should be related to the number of collisions, which is in turn related to their concentrations (Figure 15.10). Doubling the concentration of one reagent in the $NO + O_3$ reaction, say NO, will lead to twice the number of

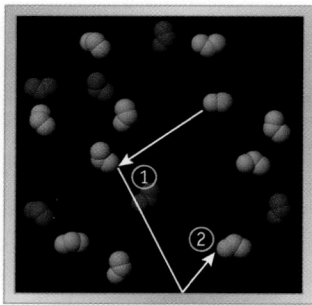

**(a) 1 NO : 16 O₃** − *2 hits/second.*
A single NO molecule, moving among sixteen $O_3$ molecules, is shown colliding with two of them per second.

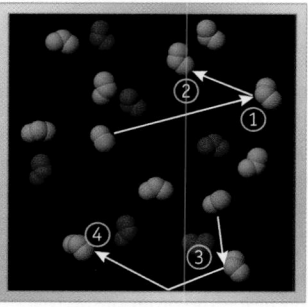

**(b) 2 NO : 16 O₃** − *4 hits/second.*
If two NO molecules move among 16 $O_3$ molecules, we would predict that four NO—$O_3$ collisions would occur per second.

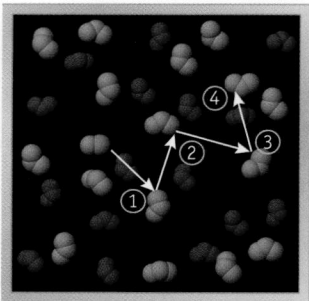

**(c) 1 NO : 32 O₃** − *4 hits/second.*
If the number of $O_3$ molecules is doubled (to 32), the frequency of NO—$O_3$ collisions is also doubled, to four per second.

**FIGURE 15.10** The effect of concentration on the frequency of molecular collisions.

molecular collisions. Figure 15.10a shows a single molecule of one of the reactants (NO) moving randomly among sixteen $O_3$ molecules. In a given time period, it might collide with two $O_3$ molecules. The number of NO—$O_3$ collisions will double, however, if the concentration of NO molecules is doubled (to 2, as shown in Figure 15.10b) or if the number of $O_3$ molecules is doubled (to 32, as in Figure 15.10c). Thus, we can explain the dependence of reaction rate on concentration: The number of collisions between the two reactant molecules is directly proportional to the concentration of each reactant, and the rate of the reaction shows a first-order dependence on each reactant.

## Collision Theory: Temperature and Reaction Rate

In a laboratory or in the chemical industry, a chemical reaction is often carried out at elevated temperatures because this allows the reaction to occur more rapidly. Conversely, it is sometimes desirable to lower the temperature to slow down a chemical reaction (to avoid an uncontrollable reaction or a potentially dangerous explosion). Chemists are very aware of the effect of temperature on the rate of a reaction.

A discussion of the effect of temperature on reaction rate begins with reference to distribution of energies for molecules in a sample of a gas or liquid. Recall from studying gases and liquids that the molecules in a sample have a wide range of energies, described earlier as a Boltzmann distribution of energies (◄ Figure 11.14). In any sample of a gas or liquid, some molecules have very low energies; others have very high energies; but most have some intermediate energy. As the temperature increases, the average energy of the molecules in the sample increases, as does the fraction having higher energies (Figure 15.11).

## Collision Theory: Activation Energy

Molecules require some minimum energy to react. Chemists visualize this as an energy barrier that must be surmounted by the reactants for a reaction to occur (Figure 15.12). The energy required to surmount the barrier is called the **activation energy**, $E_a$. If the barrier is low, the energy required is low, and a high proportion of the molecules in a sample may have sufficient energy to react. In such a case, the reaction will be fast. If the barrier is high, the activation energy is high, and only a few reactant molecules in a sample may have sufficient energy. In this case, the reaction will be slow.

To illustrate an activation energy barrier, consider the high temperature conversion of $NO_2$ and CO to NO and $CO_2$ or the reverse reaction (Figure 15.13). At the molecular level, we imagine that the reaction involves the transfer of an O atom

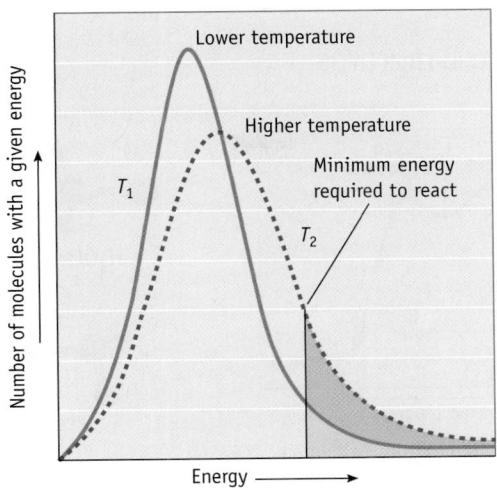

**FIGURE 15.11 Energy distribution curve.** The vertical axis gives the relative number of molecules possessing the energy indicated on the horizontal axis. The graph indicates the minimum energy required for an arbitrary reaction. At a higher temperature, a larger fraction of the molecules have sufficient energy to react. (Recall Figure 11.14, the Boltzmann distribution function, for a collection of gas molecules.)

from an $NO_2$ molecule to a CO molecule (or, in the reverse reaction, the transfer of an O atom from $CO_2$ to NO).

$$NO_2(g) + CO(g) \rightleftharpoons NO(g) + CO_2(g)$$

We can describe this process by using an energy diagram or **reaction coordinate** diagram. The horizontal axis describes the reaction progress as the reaction proceeds, and the vertical axis represents the potential energy of the system during the reaction. When $NO_2$ and CO approach and O atom transfer begins, an N—O bond is being broken, and a C═O bond is forming. Energy input (the activation energy) is required for this to occur. The energy of the system reaches a maximum at the **transition state**. At the transition state, sufficient energy has been concentrated in the appropriate bonds; bonds in the reactants can now break, and new bonds can form to give products. The system is poised to go on to products. Alternatively, it can return to the reactants. Because the transition state is at a maximum in potential energy, it cannot be isolated. Using computer molecular modeling techniques, however, chemists can describe what the transition state must look like.

In the $NO_2$ + CO reaction, 132 kJ/mol is required to reach the transition state; that is, the top of the energy barrier. As the reaction continues toward the products—as the N—O bond is finally broken and a C═O bond forms—the reaction evolves energy, 358 kJ/mol. The net energy change involved in this exothermic reaction is −226 kJ/mol.

$$\Delta U = +132 \text{ kJ/mol} + (-358 \text{ kJ/mol}) = -226 \text{ kJ/mol}$$

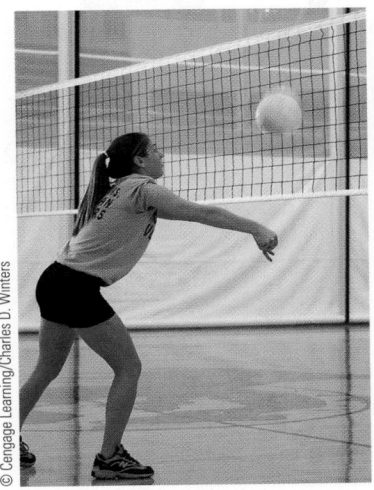

**FIGURE 15.12 An analogy to chemical activation energy.** For the volleyball to go over the net, the player must give it sufficient energy.

**FIGURE 15.13 Activation Energy.** The reaction of $NO_2$ and CO (to give NO and $CO_2$) has an activation energy barrier of 132 kJ/mol. The reverse reaction (NO + $CO_2 \rightarrow NO_2$ + CO) has an activation energy barrier of 358 kJ/mol. The net energy change for the reaction of $NO_2$ and CO is −226 kJ/mol.

# Reaction Coordinate Diagrams

Reaction coordinate diagrams (Figure 15.13) convey a great deal of information. A reaction that would have an energy diagram like that in Figure 15.13 is the substitution of a halogen atom of $CH_3Cl$ by an ion such as $F^-$. Here, the $F^-$ ion attacks the molecule from the side opposite the Cl substituent. As $F^-$ begins to form a bond to carbon, the C—Cl bond weakens, and the $CH_3$ portion of the molecule changes shape. As time progresses, the products $CH_3F$ and $Cl^-$ are formed.

**FIGURE A** A reaction coordinate diagram for a two-step reaction, a process involving an intermediate.

The diagram in Figure A describes a reaction that occurs in two steps. An example of such a reaction is the substitution of the —OH group on methanol by a halide ion in the presence of acid. In the first step, an $H^+$ ion attaches to the O of the C—O—H group in a rapid, reversible reaction. The energy of this protonated species, $CH_3OH_2^+$, a reaction intermediate, is higher than the energies of the reactants and is represented by the dip in the curve shown in Figure A. In the second step, a halide ion, say $Br^-$, attacks the intermediate to produce methyl bromide, $CH_3Br$, and water. There is an activation energy barrier in both the first step and second step.

Notice in Figure A, as in Figure 15.13, that the energy of the products is lower than the energy of the reactants. The reaction is exothermic.

What happens if NO and $CO_2$ are mixed to form $NO_2$ and CO? Now the reaction requires 358 kJ/mol-rxn to reach the transition state, and 132 kJ/mol-rxn is evolved on proceeding to the product, $NO_2$ and CO. The reaction in this direction is endothermic, requiring a net input of +226 kJ/mol-rxn.

## Collision Theory: Activation Energy and Temperature

The conversion of $NO_2$ and CO to products at room temperature is slow because only a small fraction of the molecules have enough energy to reach the transition state. The rate can be increased by heating the sample. Raising the temperature increases the reaction rate by increasing the fraction of molecules with enough energy to surmount the activation energy barrier (Figure 15.11).

## Collision Theory: Effect of Molecular Orientation on Reaction Rate

Having a sufficiently high energy is necessary, but it is not sufficient to ensure that a given collision of reactants will form products. The reactant molecules must also come together in the correct orientation. For the reaction of $NO_2$ and CO, we can imagine that the transition state structure has one of the O atoms of $NO_2$ beginning to bind to the C atom of CO in preparation for O atom transfer (Figure 15.13). The lower the probability of achieving the proper alignment, the smaller the value of $k$, and the slower the reaction.

Imagine what happens when two or more complicated molecules collide. In only a small fraction of the collisions will the molecules come together in exactly the right orientation. Thus, only a tiny fraction of the collisions can be effective. No wonder some reactions are slow. Conversely, it is amazing that so many are fast!

## The Arrhenius Equation

The observation that reaction rates depend on the energy and frequency of collisions between reacting molecules, on the temperature, and on whether the collisions have the correct geometry is summarized by the **Arrhenius equation**:

$$k = \text{rate constant} = Ae^{-E_a/RT}$$

Frequency factor ⟋    ⟍ Fraction of molecules with minimum      **(15.5)**
energy for reaction

● **$E_a$, Reaction Rates, and Temperature** An often-used rule of thumb is that reaction rates double for every 10 °C rise in temperature in the vicinity of room temperature.

In this equation, $k$ is the rate constant, $R$ is the gas constant with a value of $8.314510 \times 10^{-3}$ kJ/K·mol, and $T$ is the kelvin temperature. The parameter $A$ is called the **frequency factor**. It is related to the number of collisions and to the fraction of collisions that have the correct geometry; $A$ is specific to each reaction and is temperature dependent. The factor $e^{-E_a/RT}$ represents *the fraction of molecules having the minimum energy required for reaction*; its value is always less than 1. As the table in the margin shows, this fraction changes significantly with temperature.

The Arrhenius equation is significant because

- it can be used to calculate $E_a$ from the temperature dependence of the rate constant.
- it can be used to calculate the rate constant for a given temperature, if $E_a$ and $A$ are known.

If rate constants of a given reaction are measured at several temperatures then one can apply graphical techniques to determine the activation energy of a reaction. Taking the natural logarithm of each side of Equation 15.5, we have

$$\ln k = \ln A + \left(-\frac{E_a}{RT}\right)$$

Rearranging this expression slightly shows that ln $k$ and $1/T$ are related linearly.

$$\ln k = -\frac{E_a}{R}\left(\frac{1}{T}\right) + \ln A \quad \leftarrow \text{Arrhenius equation} \qquad \textbf{(15.6)}$$

$$\downarrow \qquad \downarrow \qquad \downarrow$$
$$y \quad = \quad mx \quad + b \quad \leftarrow \text{Equation for straight line}$$

This means that, if the natural logarithm of $k$ (ln $k$) is plotted versus $1/T$, the result is a downward-sloping straight line with a slope of $(-E_a/R)$. The activation energy, $E_a$, can be obtained from the slope of this line ($E_a = -R \times$ slope).

● **Interpreting the Arrhenius Equation (a)** The exponential term. This gives the fraction of molecules having sufficient energy for reaction and is a function of $T$.

| Temperature (K) | Value of $e^{-E_a/RT}$ for $E_a =$ 40 kJ/mol-rxn |
|---|---|
| 298 | $9.7 \times 10^{-8}$ |
| 400 | $5.9 \times 10^{-6}$ |
| 600 | $3.3 \times 10^{-4}$ |

**(b)** Significance of $A$. Although a complete understanding of $A$ goes beyond the level of this text, it can be noted that $A$ becomes smaller as the reactants become larger. It reflects the fact that larger molecules have a smaller probability of coming together in the appropriate geometry.

## EXAMPLE 15.10   Determination of $E_a$ from the Arrhenius Equation

**Problem** Using the experimental data shown in the table, calculate the activation energy $E_a$ for the reaction

$$2\ N_2O(g) \rightarrow 2\ N_2(g) + O_2(g)$$

| Experiment | Temperature (K) | $k$ (L/mol·s) |
|---|---|---|
| 1 | 1125 | 11.59 |
| 2 | 1053 | 1.67 |
| 3 | 1001 | 0.380 |
| 4 | 838 | 0.0011 |

**What Do You Know?** The rate constants are given at several temperatures.

**Strategy** To solve this problem graphically, we first need to calculate ln $k$ and $1/T$ for each data point. These data are then plotted, and $E_a$ is calculated from the resulting straight line (slope $= -E_a/R$).

**Solution** First, calculate $1/T$ and ln $k$.

| Experiment | $1/T$ (K$^{-1}$) | ln $k$ |
|---|---|---|
| 1 | $8.889 \times 10^{-4}$ | 2.4501 |
| 2 | $9.497 \times 10^{-4}$ | 0.513 |
| 3 | $9.990 \times 10^{-4}$ | $-0.968$ |
| 4 | $11.9 \times 10^{-4}$ | $-6.81$ |

Plotting these data gives the graph shown in Figure 15.14. Choosing the large blue points on the graph, the slope is found to be

$$\text{Slope} = \frac{\Delta \ln k}{\Delta(1/T)} = \frac{2.0 - (-5.6)}{(9.0 - 11.5)(10^{-4})K^{-1}} = -3.0 \times 10^4 \text{ K}$$

The activation energy is evaluated from the slope.

$$\text{Slope} = -\frac{E_a}{R} = -\frac{E_a}{8.31 \times 10^{-3} \text{ kJ/K} \cdot \text{mol}} = -3.0 \times 10^4 \text{ K}$$

$$E_a = 250 \text{ kJ/mol}$$

**Think about Your Answer** Notice the units of the answer. Using the value for $R = 8.31 \times 10^{-3}$ kJ/mol will give an answer with the units kJ/mol.

---

**Check Your Understanding**

Rate constants were determined for the decomposition of acetaldehyde ($CH_3CHO$) in the temperature range 700 to 1000 K. Use these data to determine $E_a$ for the reaction using a graphical method.

| $T$ (K) | 700 | 760 | 840 | 1000 |
|---|---|---|---|---|
| $k$ (L/mol · s) | 0.011 | 0.105 | 2.17 | 145 |

**FIGURE 15.14** Arrhenius plot. A plot of ln $k$ versus $1/T$ for the reaction $2 N_2O(g) \rightarrow 2 N_2(g) + O_2(g)$. The slope of the line can be used to calculate $E_a$. See Example 15.10.

The activation energy, $E_a$, for a reaction can be obtained algebraically if $k$ is known at two different temperatures. We can write an equation for each set of these conditions:

$$\ln k_1 = -\left(\frac{E_a}{RT_1}\right) + \ln A \quad \text{and} \quad \ln k_2 = -\left(\frac{E_a}{RT_2}\right) + \ln A$$

If one of these equations is subtracted from the other, we have

$$\ln k_2 - \ln k_1 = \ln \frac{k_2}{k_1} = -\frac{E_a}{R}\left[\frac{1}{T_2} - \frac{1}{T_1}\right] \qquad (15.7)$$

Example 15.11 demonstrates the use of this equation.

## EXAMPLE 15.11    Calculating E$_a$ Numerically

**Problem** Use values of $k$ determined at two different temperatures to calculate the value of $E_a$ for the decomposition of HI:

$$2 \text{ HI(g)} \rightarrow H_2(g) + I_2(g)$$

$$k_1 = 2.15 \times 10^{-8} \text{ L/(mol} \cdot \text{s) at } 6.50 \times 10^2 \text{ K } (T_1)$$

$$k_2 = 2.39 \times 10^{-7} \text{ L/(mol} \cdot \text{s) at } 7.00 \times 10^2 \text{ K } (T_2)$$

**What Do You Know?** Values for the rate constant at two temperatures are given.

**Strategy** Substitute values of $k_1$, $k_2$, $T_1$, and $T_2$ into Equation 15.7 and solve for $E_a$.

**Solution**

$$\ln \frac{2.39 \times 10^{-7} \text{ L/(mol} \cdot \text{s)}}{2.15 \times 10^{-8} \text{ L/(mol} \cdot \text{s)}} = -\frac{E_a}{8.315 \times 10^{-3} \text{ kJ/K} \cdot \text{mol}} \times \left[ \frac{1}{7.00 \times 10^2 \text{ K}} - \frac{1}{6.50 \times 10^2 \text{ K}} \right]$$

Solving this equation gives $E_a = 180$ kJ/mol.

**Think about Your Answer** Another way to write the difference in fractions in brackets is

$$\left[ \frac{1}{T_2} - \frac{1}{T_1} \right] = \frac{T_1 - T_2}{T_1 T_2}$$

This expression is sometimes easier to use.

---

**Check Your Understanding**

The colorless gas $N_2O_4$ decomposes to the brown gas $NO_2$ in a first-order reaction.

$$N_2O_4(g) \rightarrow 2\ NO_2(g)$$

The rate constant $k = 4.5 \times 10^3 \text{ s}^{-1}$ at 274 K and $k = 1.00 \times 10^4 \text{ s}^{-1}$ at 283 K. What is the activation energy, $E_a$?

---

## Effect of Catalysts on Reaction Rate

Catalysts are substances that speed up the rate of a chemical reaction. We have seen several examples of catalysts in earlier discussions in this chapter: $MnO_2$, iodide ion, the enzyme catalase in a potato, and hydroxide ion all catalyze the decomposition of hydrogen peroxide (Figure 15.4).

Catalysts are not consumed in a chemical reaction. They are, however, intimately involved in the details of the reaction at the particulate level. Their function is to provide a different pathway with a lower activation energy for the reaction. To illustrate how a catalyst participates in a reaction, let us consider the isomerization of *cis*-2-butene, to the slightly more stable isomer, *trans*-2-butene.

cis-2-butene          Transition state          trans-2-butene

End rotates

π bond breaks

● **Enzymes: Biological Catalysts** Catalase is an enzyme whose function is to speed up the decomposition of hydrogen peroxide. This enzyme ensures that hydrogen peroxide, which is highly toxic, does not build up in the body.

● **Butene Isomerization** Isomerization of *cis*-2-butene is a first-order process with the rate law Rate = $k$[*cis*-2-butene]. It is suggested to occur by rotation around the carbon–carbon double bond. The rate at which a molecule will isomerize is related to the fraction of molecules that have a high enough energy.

The activation energy for the uncatalyzed conversion is relatively large—264 kJ/mol—because the $\pi$ bond must be broken to allow one end of the molecule to rotate into a new position. Because of the high activation energy, this is a slow reaction, and rather high temperatures are required for it to occur at a reasonable rate.

The *cis*- to *trans*-2-butene reaction is greatly accelerated by a catalyst, iodine. In the presence of iodine, this reaction can be carried out at a temperature several hundred degrees lower than for the uncatalyzed reaction. Iodine is not consumed

● **Catalysts and the Economy** "One third of [the] material gross national product in the United States involves a catalytic process somewhere in the production chain." (Quoted in A. Bell, *Science*, Vol. 299, p. 1688, 2003.)

(nor is it a product), and it does not appear in the overall balanced equation. It does appear in the reaction rate law, however; the rate of the reaction depends on the square root of the iodine concentration:

$$\text{Rate} = k[\textit{cis}\text{-2-butene}][I_2]^{1/2}$$

The presence of $I_2$ changes the way the reaction occurs; that is, it changes the mechanism of the reaction (Figure 15.15). The best hypothesis is that iodine molecules first dissociate to form iodine atoms (Step 1). An iodine atom then adds to one of the C atoms of the C=C double bond (Step 2). This converts the double bond between the carbon atoms to a single bond (the $\pi$ bond is broken) and allows the ends of the molecule to twist freely relative to each other (Step 3). If the iodine atom then dissociates from the intermediate, the double bond can re-form in the *trans* configuration (Step 4). The iodine atom catalyzing the rotation is now free to add to another molecule of *cis*-2-butene. The result is a kind of chain reaction, as one molecule of *cis*-2-butene after another is converted to the *trans* isomer. The chain is broken if the iodine atom recombines with another iodine atom to re-form molecular iodine.

An energy profile for the catalyzed reaction (Figure 15.16) shows that the overall energy barrier is much lower than for the uncatalyzed reaction. Five separate steps are identified for the mechanism in the energy profile. This proposed mechanism also includes a series of chemical species called **reaction intermediates**, species formed in one step of the reaction and consumed in a later step. Iodine atoms are intermediates, as are the free radical species formed when an iodine atom adds to *cis*-2-butene.

Five important points are associated with this mechanism:

- Iodine molecules, $I_2$, dissociate to atoms and then re-form. On the macroscopic level, the concentration of $I_2$ is unchanged. Iodine does not appear in the balanced, stoichiometric equation even though it appears in the rate equation. This is generally true of catalysts.
- Both the catalyst $I_2$ and the reactant *cis*-2-butene are in the gas phase. If a catalyst is present in the same phase as the reacting substance, it is called a *homogeneous catalyst*.
- Iodine atoms and the radical species formed by addition of an iodine atom to a 2-butene molecule are intermediates.

**FIGURE 15.15 The mechanism of the iodine-catalyzed isomerization of *cis*-2-butene.** *Cis*-2-butene is converted to *trans*-2-butene in the presence of a catalytic amount of iodine. Catalyzed reactions are often pictured in such diagrams to emphasize what chemists refer to as a "catalytic cycle."

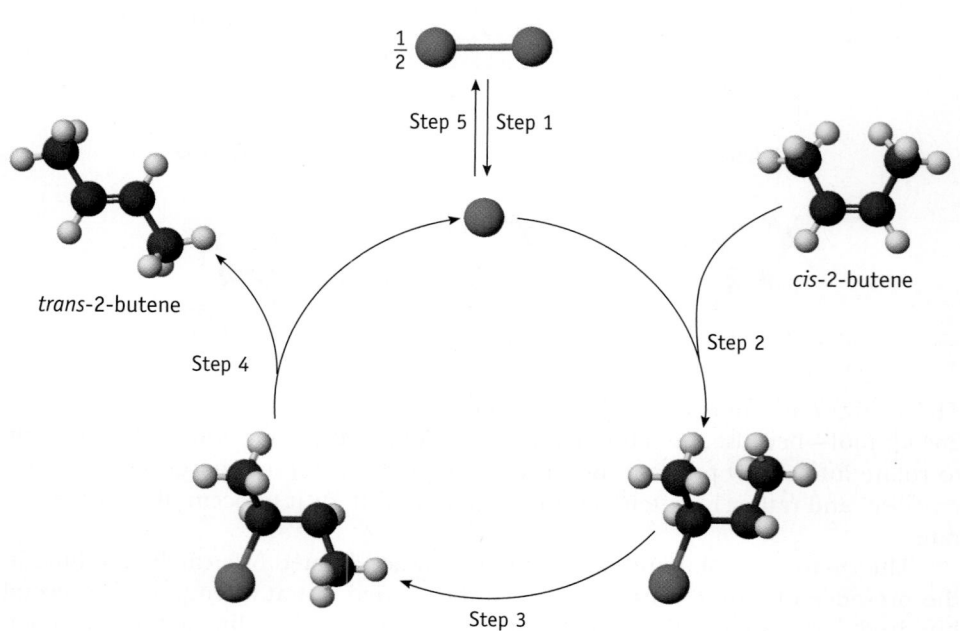

trans-2-butene

cis-2-butene

$\frac{1}{2}$

Step 5    Step 1

Step 2

Step 4

Step 3

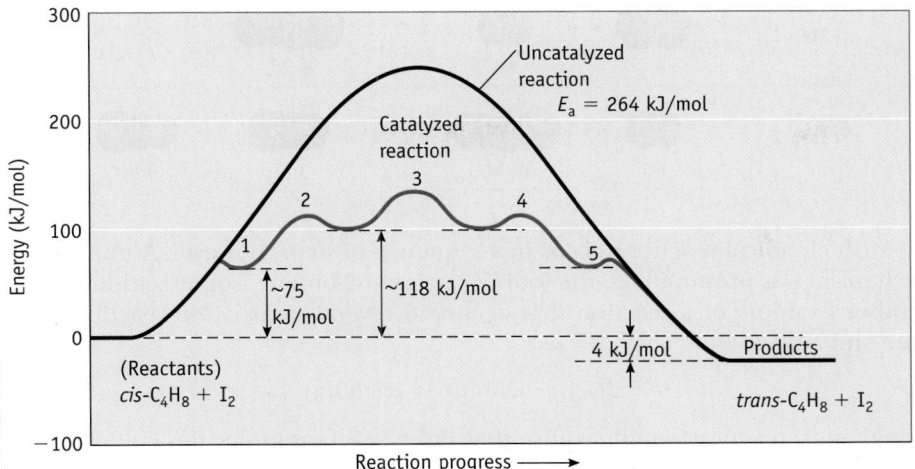

**FIGURE 15.16** **Energy profile for the iodine-catalyzed reaction of** *cis*-2-butene. A catalyst accelerates a reaction by altering the mechanism so that the activation energy is lowered. With a smaller barrier to overcome, more reacting molecules have sufficient energy to surmount the barrier, and the reaction occurs more rapidly. The energy profile for the uncatalyzed conversion of *cis*-2-butene to *trans*-2-butene is shown by the black curve, and that for the iodine-catalyzed reaction is represented by the red curve. Notice that the shape of the barrier has changed because the mechanism has changed.

- The activation energy barrier to reaction is significantly lower because the mechanism changed. Dropping the activation energy from 264 kJ/mol for the uncatalyzed reaction to about 150 kJ/mol for the catalyzed process makes the catalyzed reaction $10^{15}$ times faster!
- The diagram of energy-versus-reaction progress has five energy barriers (five humps appear in the curve). This feature in the diagram means that the reaction occurs in a series of five steps.

What we have described here are two different reaction mechanisms for the isomerization of *cis*-2-butene. The uncatalyzed isomerization reaction is a one-step reaction mechanism, whereas the catalyzed mechanism involves a series of steps. We shall discuss reaction mechanisms in more detail in the next section.

---

**REVIEW & CHECK FOR SECTION 15.5**

1. Which of the following graphs will produce a straight line?

   (a) $k$ vs. $T$       (b) $\ln E_a$ vs. $T$       (c) $\ln k$ vs. $1/T$       (d) $E_a$ vs. $1/T$

2. What is the primary reason that increasing the temperature causes an increase in reaction rate?

   (a) An increase in $T$ lowers the activation energy.

   (b) A higher proportion of reactant molecules exceeds the activation energy.

   (c) In a closed vessel, increasing the temperature results in a higher pressure.

   (d) Increasing the temperature provides other reaction pathways.

---

## 15.6 Reaction Mechanisms

Rate laws help us understand **reaction mechanisms**, the sequence of bond-making and bond-breaking steps that occurs during the conversion of reactants to products. We want to analyze the changes that molecules undergo when they react. We then want to relate this description back to the macroscopic world, to the experimental observations of reaction rates.

Based on the rate equation for a reaction, and by applying chemical intuition, chemists can often make an educated guess about the mechanism for a reaction. In some reactions, the conversion of reactants to products in a single step is envisioned as the logical mechanism. For example, the uncatalyzed isomerization of *cis*-2-butene to *trans*-2-butene is best described as a single-step reaction (Figure 15.16).

**FIGURE 15.17 A reaction mechanism.** A representation of the proposed two-step mechanism by which NO and $Br_2$ are converted to NOBr.

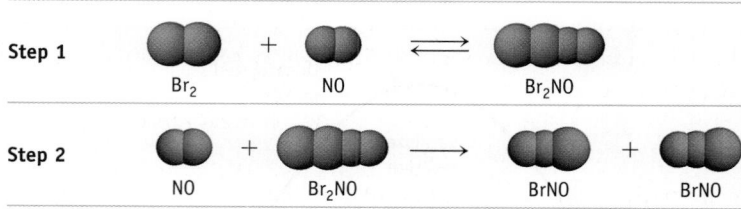

Step 1

$Br_2$    NO    $Br_2NO$

Step 2

NO    $Br_2NO$    BrNO    BrNO

• **Rate Laws and Mechanisms** Rate laws are derived by experiment; they are macroscopic observations. Mechanisms are schemes we propose that speculate on how reactions occur at the particulate level.

Most chemical reactions occur in a sequence of steps, however. A multiple-step mechanism was proposed for the iodine-catalyzed 2-butene isomerization reaction. Another example of a reaction that occurs in several steps is the reaction of bromine and NO:

$$Br_2(g) + 2\,NO(g) \rightarrow 2\,BrNO(g)$$

A single-step reaction would require that three reactant molecules collide simultaneously in just the right orientation. The probability of this occurring is small; thus, it would be reasonable to look for a mechanism that occurs in a series of steps, with each step involving only one or two molecules. In one possible mechanism, $Br_2$ and NO might combine in an initial step to produce an intermediate species, $Br_2NO$ (Figure 15.17). This intermediate would then react with another NO molecule to give the reaction products. The equation for the overall reaction is obtained by adding the equations for these two steps:

Step 1:             $Br_2(g) + NO(g) \rightleftharpoons Br_2NO(g)$

Step 2:             $Br_2NO(g) + NO(g) \rightarrow 2\,BrNO(g)$

Overall Reaction:    $Br_2(g) + 2\,NO(g) \rightarrow 2\,BrNO(g)$

Each step in a multistep reaction sequence is an **elementary step**, defined by a chemical equation that describes a single molecular event such as the formation or rupture of a chemical bond resulting from a molecular collision. Each step has its own activation energy, $E_a$, and rate constant, $k$. Adding the equations for each step must give the balanced equation for the overall reaction, and the time required to complete all of the steps defines the overall reaction rate. The series of steps constitutes a possible reaction mechanism.

## Molecularity of Elementary Steps

Elementary steps are classified by the number of reactant molecules (or ions, atoms, or free radicals) that come together. This whole, positive number is called the **molecularity** of the elementary step. When one molecule is the only reactant in an elementary step, the reaction is a **unimolecular** process. A **bimolecular** elementary process involves two molecules, which may be identical (A + A → products) or different (A + B → products). The mechanism proposed for the decomposition of ozone in the stratosphere illustrates the use of these terms.

Step 1:    Unimolecular    $O_3(g) \rightarrow O_2(g) + O(g)$

Step 2:    Bimolecular    $O_3(g) + O(g) \rightarrow 2\,O_2(g)$

Overall Reaction:            $2\,O_3(g) \rightarrow 3\,O_2(g)$

A **termolecular** elementary step involves three molecules, which could be the same or different (3 A → products; 2 A + B → products; or A + B + C → products). Be aware, however, the simultaneous collision of three molecules has a low probability, unless one of the molecules involved is in high concentration, such as a solvent molecule. In fact, most termolecular processes involve the collision of two reactant molecules and a third, inert molecule. The function of the inert molecule is to absorb the excess energy produced when a new chemical bond is formed by the first two molecules. For example, $N_2$ is unchanged in a termolecular reaction between oxygen molecules and oxygen atoms that produces ozone in the upper atmosphere:

$$O(g) + O_2(g) + N_2(g) \rightarrow O_3(g) + \text{energetic } N_2(g)$$

The probability that four or more molecules will simultaneously collide with sufficient kinetic energy and proper orientation to react is so small that reaction molecularities greater than three are never proposed.

## Rate Equations for Elementary Steps

The experimentally determined rate equation for a reaction cannot be predicted from its overall stoichiometry. In contrast, *the rate equation for any elementary step is defined by the reaction stoichiometry.* The rate equation of an elementary step is given by the product of the rate constant for that step and the concentrations of the reactants in that step. We can therefore write the rate equation for any elementary step, as shown by examples in the following table:

| Elementary Step | Molecularity | Rate Equation |
|---|---|---|
| A → product | Unimolecular | Rate $= k[A]$ |
| A + B → product | Bimolecular | Rate $= k[A][B]$ |
| A + A → product | Bimolecular | Rate $= k[A]^2$ |
| 2 A + B → product | Termolecular | Rate $= k[A]^2[B]$ |

For example, the rate laws for each of the two elementary steps in the decomposition of ozone are

$$\text{Rate for (unimolecular) Step 1} = k[O_3]$$

$$\text{Rate for (bimolecular) Step 2} = k'[O_3][O]$$

When a reaction mechanism consists of two elementary steps, the two steps will likely occur at different rates. The two rate constants ($k$ and $k'$ in this example) are not expected to have the same value (nor the same units, if the two steps have different molecularities).

## Molecularity and Reaction Order

A unimolecular elementary step must be first order; a bimolecular elementary step must be second order; and a termolecular elementary step must be third order. Such a direct relation between molecularity and order is emphatically not true for a multistep reaction. If you learn from an experiment that a reaction is first order, you cannot conclude that it occurs in a single, unimolecular elementary step. Similarly, a second-order rate equation does not imply that the reaction occurs in a single, bimolecular elementary step. An illustration of this is the decomposition of $N_2O_5$:

$$2\ N_2O_5(g) \rightarrow 4\ NO_2(g) + O_2(g)$$

Here, the rate law is "Rate $= k[N_2O_5]$," but chemists are fairly certain the mechanism involves a series of unimolecular and bimolecular steps.

To see how the experimentally observed rate equation for the overall reaction is connected with a possible mechanism or sequence of elementary steps requires some chemical intuition. We will provide only a glimpse of the subject in the next section.

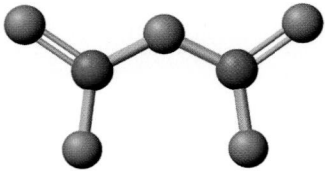

**$N_2O_5$ Decomposition.** The first step in the decomposition of $N_2O_5$ is thought to be the cleavage of one of the N—O bonds in the N—O—N link to give the odd-electron molecules $NO_2$ and $NO_3$. These react further to give the final products.

## EXAMPLE 15.12 Elementary Steps

**Problem** The hypochlorite ion undergoes self-oxidation–reduction to give chlorate, $ClO_3^-$, and chloride ions.

$$3\ ClO^-(aq) \rightarrow ClO_3^-(aq) + 2\ Cl^-(aq)$$

This reaction is thought to occur in two steps:

Step 1: $\qquad ClO^-(aq) + ClO^-(aq) \rightarrow ClO_2^-(aq) + Cl^-(aq)$

Step 2: $\qquad ClO_2^-(aq) + ClO^-(aq) \rightarrow ClO_3^-(aq) + Cl^-(aq)$

What is the molecularity of each step? Write the rate equation for each reaction step. Show that the sum of these reactions gives the equation for the net reaction.

**What Do You Know?** A two-step mechanism for the reaction of $OCl^-$ to form $Cl^-$ and $ClO_3^-$ is proposed.

**Strategy** The molecularity is the number of ions or molecules involved in a reaction step. The rate equation involves the concentration of each ion or molecule in an elementary step, raised to the power of its stoichiometric coefficient.

**Solution** Because two ions are involved in each elementary step, each step is bimolecular. The rate equation for any elementary step involves the product of the concentrations of the reactants. Thus, in this case, the rate equations are

Step 1: Rate $= k[ClO^-]^2$

Step 2: Rate $= k'[ClO_2^-][ClO^-]$

From the equations for the two elementary steps, we see that the $ClO_2^-$ ion is an intermediate, a product of the first step and a reactant in the second step. It therefore cancels out, and we are left with the stoichiometric equation for the overall reaction:

| | |
|---|---|
| Step 1: | $ClO^-(aq) + ClO^-(aq) \rightarrow ClO_2^-(aq) + Cl^-(aq)$ |
| Step 2: | $ClO_2^-(aq) + ClO^-(aq) \rightarrow ClO_3^-(aq) + Cl^-(aq)$ |
| Sum of steps: | $3\ ClO^-(aq) \rightarrow ClO_3^-(aq) + 2\ Cl^-(aq)$ |

**Think about Your Answer** Other mechanisms are possible. The next question to ask is "What is the evidence that will let you decide between several different mechanisms?"

---

**Check Your Understanding**

Nitrogen monoxide is reduced by hydrogen to give nitrogen and water:

$$2\ NO(g) + 2\ H_2(g) \rightarrow N_2(g) + 2\ H_2O(g)$$

One possible mechanism for this reaction is

$$2\ NO(g) \rightarrow N_2O_2(g)$$

$$N_2O_2(g) + H_2(g) \rightarrow N_2O(g) + H_2O(g)$$

$$N_2O(g) + H_2(g) \rightarrow N_2(g) + H_2O(g)$$

What is the molecularity of each of the three steps? What is the rate equation for the third step? Identify the intermediates in this reaction; how many different intermediates are there? Show that the sum of these elementary steps gives the equation for the overall reaction.

## Reaction Mechanisms and Rate Equations

The dependence of rate on concentration is an experimental fact. Mechanisms, by contrast, are constructs of our imagination, intuition, and good "chemical sense." To describe a mechanism, we need to make a guess (a good guess, we hope) about how the reaction occurs at the particulate level. Several mechanisms can always be proposed that correspond to the observed rate equation, and a postulated mechanism can be wrong. A good mechanism is a worthy goal because it allows us to understand the chemistry better. A practical consequence of a good mechanism is that it allows us to predict, for example, how to control a reaction better and how to design new experiments.

One of the important guidelines of kinetics is that *products of a reaction can never be produced at a rate faster than the rate of the slowest step.* If one step in a multistep reaction is slower than the others, then *the rate of the overall reaction is limited by the combined rates of all elementary steps up through the slowest step in the mechanism.* Often the overall reaction rate and the rate of the slow step are nearly the same. If the slow step determines the rate of the reaction, it is called the **rate-determining step**, or rate-limiting step.

Imagine that a reaction takes place with a mechanism involving two sequential steps, and assume that we know the rates of both steps. The first step is slow and the second is fast:

Elementary Step 1:       $A + B \xrightarrow[\text{Slow, } E_a \text{ large}]{k_1} X + M$

Elementary Step 2:       $M + A \xrightarrow[\text{Fast, } E_a \text{ small}]{k_2} Y$

Overall Reaction:        $2A + B \longrightarrow X + Y$

In the first step, A and B come together and slowly react to form one of the products (X) plus another reactive species, M. Almost as soon as M is formed, however, it is rapidly consumed by reacting with another molecule of A to form the second product Y. The rate-determining elementary step in this example is the first step. That is, the rate of the first step is equal to the rate of the overall reaction. This step is bimolecular and so it has the rate equation:

$$\text{Rate} = k_1[A][B]$$

where $k_1$ is the rate constant for that step. The overall reaction is expected to have this same second-order rate equation.

Let us apply these ideas to the mechanism of a real reaction: the second-order reaction of nitrogen dioxide with fluorine.

Overall Reaction:       $2 NO_2(g) + F_2(g) \rightarrow 2 FNO_2(g)$

$$\text{Rate} = k[NO_2][F_2]$$

The rate equation immediately rules out the possibility that the reaction occurs in a single step. If the equation for the reaction represented an elementary step, the rate law would have a second-order dependence on $[NO_2]$. Because a single-step reaction is ruled out, the mechanism must include at least two steps. We can also conclude from the rate law that the rate-determining elementary step must involve $NO_2$ and $F_2$ in a 1:1 ratio. One possible mechanism proposes that molecules of $NO_2$ and $F_2$ first react to produce one molecule of the product ($FNO_2$) plus one F atom. In a second step, the fluorine atom produced in the first step reacts with additional $NO_2$ to give a second molecule of product. If the first, bimolecular step is rate determining, the rate equation would be "Rate = $k_1[NO_2][F_2]$," the same as the experimentally observed rate equation. The experimental rate constant would be the same as $k_1$.

● **Can You Derive a Mechanism?** At this introductory level, you cannot be expected to derive reaction mechanisms. Given a mechanism, however, you can decide whether it agrees with experimental rate laws.

Elementary Step 1:    Slow       $NO_2(g) + F_2(g) \xrightarrow{k_1} FNO_2(g) + F(g)$

Elementary Step 2:    Fast       $NO_2(g) + F(g) \xrightarrow{k_2} FNO_2(g)$

Overall Reaction:        $2 NO_2(g) + F_2(g) \longrightarrow 2 FNO_2(g)$

The fluorine atom formed in the first step of the $NO_2/F_2$ reaction is a reaction intermediate. It does not appear in the equation describing the overall reaction. Reaction intermediates usually have only a fleeting existence, but occasionally they have long enough lifetimes to be observed. The detection and identification of an intermediate are strong evidence for the proposed mechanism.

## CASE STUDY

# Enzymes—Nature's Catalysts

Within any living organism, there are untold numbers of chemical reactions occurring, many of them extremely rapidly. In many cases, enzymes, biological catalysts, speed up reactions that would normally move at a snail's pace from reactants to products. Typically, enzyme-catalyzed reactions are $10^7$ to $10^{14}$ times faster than uncatalyzed reactions.

Enzymes are typically large proteins, often containing metal ions such as $Zn^{2+}$. They are thought to function by bringing the reactants together in just the right orientation in a site where specific bonds can be broken and/or made.

Carbonic anhydrase is one of many enzymes important in biological processes (Figure A). Carbon dioxide dissolves in water to a small extent to produce carbonic acid, which ionizes to give $H_3O^+$ and $HCO_3^-$ ions.

$$CO_2(g) \rightleftharpoons CO_2(aq) \qquad (1)$$

$$CO_2(aq) + H_2O(\ell) \rightleftharpoons H_2CO_3(aq) \qquad (2)$$

$$H_2CO_3(aq) + H_2O(\ell) \rightleftharpoons H_3O^+(aq) + HCO_3^-(aq) \qquad (3)$$

Carbonic anhydrase speeds up reactions 1 and 2. Many of the $H_3O^+$ ions produced by ionization of $H_2CO_3$ (reaction 3) are picked up by hemoglobin in the blood as hemoglobin loses $O_2$. The resulting $HCO_3^-$ ions are transported back to the lungs. When hemoglobin again takes on $O_2$, it releases $H_3O^+$ ions. These ions and $HCO_3^-$ re-form $H_2CO_3$, from which $CO_2$ is liberated and exhaled.

You can do an experiment that illustrates the effect of carbonic anhydrase. First, add a small amount of NaOH to a cold, aqueous solution of $CO_2$. The solution becomes basic immediately because there is not enough $H_2CO_3$ in the solution to use up the NaOH. After some seconds, however, dissolved $CO_2$ slowly produces more $H_2CO_3$, which consumes NaOH, and the solution is again acidic.

Now try the experiment again, this time adding a few drops of blood to the solution (Figure A). Carbonic anhydrase in blood speeds up reactions 1 and 2 by a factor of about $10^7$, as evidenced by the more rapid reaction under these conditions.

In 1913, Leonor Michaelis and Maud L. Menten proposed a general theory of enzyme action based on kinetic observations. They assumed that the substrate, S (the reactant), and the enzyme, E, form a complex, ES. This complex then breaks down, releasing the enzyme and the product, P.

$$E + S \rightleftharpoons ES$$

$$ES \rightarrow P + E$$

When the substrate concentration is low, the rate of the reaction is first order in S (Figure B). As [S] increases, however, the active sites in the enzyme become saturated with substrate, and the rate reaches its maximum value. Now the kinetics are zero order in substrate.

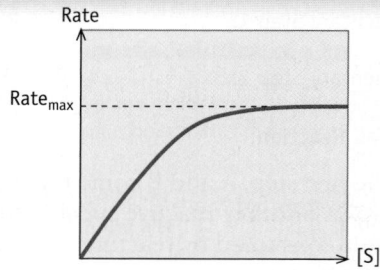

**FIGURE B** **Rate of enzyme-catalyzed reaction.** This plot of substrate concentration [S] versus reaction velocity is typical of reactions catalyzed by enzymes that follow the Michaelis–Menten model.

## Questions:

1. Catalase can decompose hydrogen peroxide to $O_2$ and water about $10^7$ times faster than the uncatalyzed reaction. If the latter requires one year, how much time is required by the enzyme-catalyzed reaction?

2. According to the Michaelis–Menten model, if 1/Rate is plotted versus 1/[S], the intercept of the plot (when 1/[S] = 0) is $1/Rate_{max}$. Find $Rate_{max}$ for a reaction involving carbonic anhydrase.

| [S], mol/L | Rate (millimoles/min) |
|------------|------------------------|
| 2.500 | 0.588 |
| 1.00 | 0.500 |
| 0.714 | 0.417 |
| 0.526 | 0.370 |
| 0.250 | 0.256 |

Answers to these questions are available in Appendix N.

Photos © Cengage Learning/Charles D. Winters

**(a)** $t = 0$ **(b)** $t = 3$ sec **(c)** $t = 15$ sec **(d)** $t = 17$ sec **(e)** $t = 21$ sec

**FIGURE A** **$CO_2$ in water.** **(a)** A few drops of blood are added to a cold solution of $CO_2$ in water. **(b)** A few drops of a dye (bromthymol blue) are added to the solution, the yellow color indicating an acidic solution. **(c, d)** A less-than-stoichiometric amount of sodium hydroxide is added, converting the $H_2CO_3$ to $HCO_3^-$ (and $CO_3^{2-}$). The blue color of the dye indicates a basic solution. **(e)** The blue color begins to fade after some seconds as $CO_2$ forms more $H_2CO_3$. The amount of $H_2CO_3$ formed is finally sufficient to consume the added NaOH, and the solution is again acidic. Blood is a source of the enzyme *carbonic anhydrase*, so the formation of $H_2CO_3$ is noticeably more rapid than the reaction in the absence of blood.

## EXAMPLE 15.13    Elementary Steps and Reaction Mechanisms

**Problem** Oxygen atom transfer from $NO_2$ to CO produces nitrogen monoxide and carbon dioxide (Figure 15.13):

$$NO_2(g) + CO(g) \rightarrow NO(g) + CO_2(g)$$

The rate equation for this reaction at temperatures less than 500 K is Rate = $k[NO_2]^2$. Can this reaction occur in one bimolecular step?

**What Do You Know?** The reaction equation and the rate law for the reaction are given.

**Strategy** Write the rate law based on the equation for the $NO_2$ + CO reaction occurring as if it were an elementary step. If this rate law corresponds to the observed rate law, then a one-step mechanism is possible.

**Solution** If the reaction occurs by the collision of one $NO_2$ molecule with one CO molecule, the rate equation would be

$$Rate = k[NO_2][CO]$$

This does not agree with experiment, so the mechanism must involve more than a single step. In one possible mechanism, the reaction occurs in two bimolecular steps, the first one slow and the second one fast:

Elementary Step 1:    Slow, rate-        $2 NO_2(g) \longrightarrow NO_3(g) + NO(g)$
                      determining

Elementary Step 2:    Fast        $NO_3(g) + CO(g) \longrightarrow NO_2(g) + CO_2(g)$

Overall Reaction:        $NO_2(g) + CO(g) \longrightarrow NO(g) + CO_2(g)$

The first (rate-determining) step has a rate equation that agrees with experiment, so this is a possible mechanism.

**Think about Your Answer** Because the rate equation is second order in $[NO_2]$, the rate-determining step in this multistep reaction must involve the collision of two $NO_2$ molecules.

---

**Check Your Understanding**

The Raschig reaction produces hydrazine, $N_2H_4$, an industrially important reducing agent, from $NH_3$ and $OCl^-$ in basic, aqueous solution. A proposed mechanism is

Step 1: Fast    $NH_3(aq) + OCl^-(aq) \rightarrow NH_2Cl(aq) + OH^-(aq)$

Step 2: Slow    $NH_2Cl(aq) + NH_3(aq) \rightarrow N_2H_5^+(aq) + Cl^-(aq)$

Step 3: Fast    $N_2H_5^+(aq) + OH^-(aq) \rightarrow N_2H_4(aq) + H_2O(\ell)$

(a)   What is the overall equation?

(b)   Which step of the three is rate determining?

(c)   Write the rate equation for the rate-determining elementary step.

(d)   What reaction intermediates are involved?

---

## Reaction Mechanisms Involving an Equilibrium Step

A common two-step reaction mechanism involves an initial fast reaction that produces an intermediate, followed by a slower second step in which the intermediate is converted to the final product. The rate of the reaction is determined by the second step, for which a rate law can be written. The rate of that step, however, depends on the concentration of the intermediate. An intermediate, whose concentration will probably not be measurable, cannot appear as a term in the overall rate equation. We must find a way to replace the expression for the intermediate with another expression in terms of quantities measurable in the lab.

The reaction of nitrogen monoxide and oxygen is an example of a two-step reaction where the first step is fast and the second step is rate determining.

$$2\ NO(g) + O_2(g) \rightarrow 2\ NO_2(g)$$

$$Rate = k[NO]^2[O_2]$$

The experimentally determined rate law shows second-order dependence on NO and first-order dependence on $O_2$. Although this rate law would be correct for a termolecular reaction, experimental evidence indicates that an intermediate is formed in this reaction. A possible two-step mechanism that proceeds through an intermediate is

Elementary Step 1:    Fast, equilibrium        $NO(g) + O_2(g) \underset{k_{-1}}{\overset{k_1}{\rightleftharpoons}} OONO(g)$   intermediate

Elementary Step 2:    Slow, rate-determining      $\underline{NO(g) + OONO(g) \overset{k_2}{\rightarrow} 2\ NO_2(g)}$

Overall Reaction:                          $2\ NO(g) + O_2(g) \rightarrow 2\ NO_2(g)$

The second step of this reaction is the slow step, and the overall rate depends on it. We can write a rate law for the second step:

$$Rate = k_2[NO][OONO]$$

This rate law cannot be compared directly with the experimental rate law because it contains the concentration of an intermediate, OONO. To eliminate the concentration of intermediate from this rate expression, we look at the rapid first step in this reaction sequence that involves an equilibrium between the intermediate species and the reactants.

At the beginning of the reaction, NO and $O_2$ react rapidly and produce the intermediate OONO. The rate of formation can be defined by a rate law with a rate constant $k_1$:

$$\text{Rate of production of OONO} = k_1[NO][O_2]$$

Because the intermediate is consumed only very slowly in the second step, it is possible for the OONO to revert to NO and $O_2$ before it reacts further:

$$\text{Rate of reverse reaction } (OONO \rightarrow NO + O_2) = k_{-1}[OONO]$$

As NO and $O_2$ form OONO, their concentrations drop, so the rate of the forward reaction decreases. At the same time, the concentration of OONO builds up, so the rate of the reverse reaction increases. At equilibrium, the rates of the forward and reverse reactions become the same.

$$\text{Rate of forward reaction} = \text{rate of reverse reaction}$$

$$k_1[NO][O_2] = k_{-1}[OONO]$$

Rearranging this equation, we find

$$\frac{k_1}{k_{-1}} = \frac{[OONO]}{[NO][O_2]} = K$$

Both $k_1$ and $k_{-1}$ are constants (they will change only if the temperature changes). We can define a new constant $K$ equal to the ratio of these two constants and called the **equilibrium constant**, which is equal to the quotient $[OONO]/[NO][O_2]$. From this, we can derive an expression for the concentration of OONO:

$$[OONO] = K[NO][O_2]$$

● **Mechanisms with an Initial Equilibrium** In this mechanism, the forward and reverse reactions in the first elementary step are so much faster than the second elementary step that equilibrium is established before any significant amount of OONO is consumed by NO to give $NO_2$. The state of equilibrium for the first step remains throughout the lifetime of the overall reaction.

## Relating Rate Equations and Reaction Mechanisms

The connection between an experimental rate equation and the proposed reaction mechanism is important in chemistry.

1. Experiments must first be performed to determine the experimental rate equation.
2. A mechanism for the reaction is proposed on the basis of the experimental rate equation, the principles of stoichi-

ometry, molecular structure and bonding, general chemical experience, and intuition.

3. The proposed reaction mechanism is used to derive a rate equation. This rate equation can contain only those species present in the overall chemical reaction. If the derived and experimental rate equations are the same, the postulated

mechanism *may* be a reasonable hypothesis of the reaction sequence.

4. If more than one mechanism can be proposed and they all predict derived rate equations in agreement with experiment, then more experiments must be done.

---

If $K[NO][O_2]$ is substituted for $[OONO]$ in the rate law for the rate-determining elementary step, we have

$$\text{Rate} = k_2[NO][OONO] = k_2[NO]\{K[NO][O_2]\}$$

$$= k_2K[NO]^2[O_2]$$

Because both $k_2$ and $K$ are constants, their product is another constant $k'$, and we have

$$\text{Rate} = k'[NO]^2[O_2]$$

This is exactly the rate law derived from experiment. Thus, the sequence of reactions on which the rate law is based may be a reasonable mechanism for this reaction. It is not the only possible mechanism, however. This rate equation is also consistent with the reaction occurring in a single termolecular step. Another possible mechanism is illustrated in Example 15.14.

● **Equilibrium Constant** The important concept of chemical equilibrium was introduced in Chapter 3 and will be described in more detail in Chapters 16–19.

## EXAMPLE 15.14   Reaction Mechanism Involving an Equilibrium Step

**Problem**  The NO + O$_2$ reaction described in the text could also occur by the following mechanism:

Elementary Step 1: Fast, equilibrium

$$NO(g) + NO(g) \underset{k_{-1}}{\overset{k_1}{\rightleftharpoons}} \underset{\text{intermediate}}{N_2O_2(g)}$$

Elementary Step 2: Slow, rate-determining

$$N_2O_2(g) + O_2(g) \xrightarrow{k_2} 2\,NO_2(g)$$

Overall Reaction: $2\,NO(g) + O_2(g) \longrightarrow 2\,NO_2(g)$

Show that this mechanism leads to the following experimental rate law: Rate = $k[NO]^2[O_2]$.

**What Do You Know?**  A possible mechanism for the reaction of NO and O$_2$ is given.

**Strategy**  The rate law for the rate-determining elementary step is

$$\text{Rate} = k_2[N_2O_2][O_2]$$

The intermediate N$_2$O$_2$ cannot appear in the final derived rate law. However, we can find an expression relating the concentration of the unknown to the concentrations of the reactants, using the equilibrium constant expression for the first step.

**Solution**  $[N_2O_2]$ and $[NO]$ are related by the equilibrium constant.

$$\frac{k_1}{k_{-1}} = \frac{[N_2O_2]}{[NO]^2} = K$$

Solving this equation for $[N_2O_2]$ gives $[N_2O_2] = K[NO]^2$. When this is substituted into the derived rate law

$$\text{Rate} = k_2\{K[NO]^2\}[O_2]$$

the resulting equation is identical with the experimental rate law where $k_2K = k$.

**Think about Your Answer** Three mechanisms have been proposed for the $NO + O_2$ reaction. The challenge for chemists is to decide which is correct. In this case, further experimentation detected the species OONO as a short-lived intermediate, thus providing evidence for the mechanism involving this intermediate.

**Check Your Understanding**

One possible mechanism for the decomposition of nitryl chloride, $NO_2Cl$, is

Elementary Step 1: Fast, equilibrium    $NO_2Cl(g) \underset{k_{-1}}{\overset{k_1}{\rightleftharpoons}} NO_2(g) + Cl(g)$

Elementary Step 2: Slow    $NO_2Cl(g) + Cl(g) \overset{k_2}{\rightarrow} NO_2(g) + Cl_2(g)$

What is the overall reaction? What rate law would be derived from this mechanism? What effect does increasing the concentration of the product $NO_2$ have on the reaction rate?

---

**REVIEW & CHECK FOR SECTION 15.6**

1.  The rate equation for a reaction $A + B \rightarrow C$ was determined by experiment to be Rate $= k[A][B]$. From this we can conclude

    (a)   the reaction occurs in a single elementary step

    (b)   this reaction might occur in a single elementary step

    (c)   this reaction must involve several elementary steps

2.  A reaction is believed to occur by the following mechanism:

    Step 1:  $2\,A \rightleftharpoons I$        (Fast, equilibrium)

    Step 2:  $I + B \rightarrow C$        (Slow)

    Overall:  $2\,A + B \rightarrow C$

    What experimentally determined rate law would lead to this mechanism?

    (a)   Rate $= k[A][B]$          (c)   Rate $= k[A]^2[B]$

    (b)   Rate $= k[A]^2$          (d)   Rate $= k[I][B]$

---

and **go Chemistry**

## CHAPTER GOALS REVISITED

*Now that you have studied this chapter, you should ask whether you have met the chapter goals. In particular, you should be able to:*

### Understand rates of reaction and the conditions affecting rates
a.   Explain the concept of reaction rate (Section 15.1).
b.   Derive the average and instantaneous rates of a reaction from concentration-time data (Section 15.1). **Study Question: 5.**
c.   Describe factors that affect reaction rate (i.e., reactant concentrations, temperature, presence of a catalyst, and the state of the reactants) (Section 15.2). **Study Questions: 8, 9, 10, 66, 80, 81, 85.**

### Derive a rate equation, rate constant, and reaction order from experimental data
a.   Define the various parts of a rate equation (the rate constant and order of reaction), and understand their significance (Section 15.3). **Study Questions: 12–14.**

b. Derive a rate equation from experimental information (Section 15.3). **Study Questions: 11–14, 52, 60.**

## Use integrated rate laws

a. Describe and use the relationships between reactant concentration and time for zero-order, first-order, and second-order reactions (Section 15.4 and Table 15.1). **Study Questions: 15–24, and Go Chemistry Module 20.**

b. Apply graphical methods for determining reaction order and the rate constant from experimental data (Section 15.4 and Table 15.1). **Study Questions: 31–36, 54, 55, 57.**

c. Use the concept of half-life ($t_{1/2}$), especially for first-order reactions (Section 15.4). **Study Questions: 25–30, 64, 75.**

## Understand the collision theory of reaction rates and the role of activation energy

a. Describe the collision theory of reaction rates (Section 15.5).

b. Relate activation energy ($E_a$) to the rate of a reaction (Section 15.5). **Study Question: 40.**

c. Use collision theory to describe the effect of reactant concentration on reaction rate (Section 15.5). **Study Question: 84.**

d. Understand the effect of molecular orientation on reaction rate (Section 15.5).

e. Describe the effect of temperature on reaction rate using the collision theory of reaction rates and the Arrhenius equation (Section 15.5 and Equations 15.5–15.7). **Study Question: 84.**

f. Use Equations 15.5, 15.6, and 15.7 to calculate the activation energy from rate constants at different temperatures (Section 15.5). **Study Questions: 37, 39, 40, 62, 67, 68, 76c.**

g. Understand reaction coordinate diagrams (Section 15.5). **Study Questions: 41, 42, 47, 87.**

## Relate reaction mechanisms and rate laws

a. Describe the functioning of a catalyst and its effect on the activation energy and mechanism of a reaction (Section 15.5). **Study Questions: 82, 88.**

b. Understand the concept of a reaction mechanism (a proposed sequence of bond-making and bond-breaking steps that occurs during the conversion of reactants to products) and the relation of the mechanism to the overall, stoichiometric equation for a reaction (Section 15.6).

c. Describe the elementary steps of a mechanism, and give their molecularity (Section 15.6). **Study Questions: 43–48, 78.**

d. Define the rate-determining step in a mechanism, and identify any reaction intermediates (Section 15.6). **Study Questions: 45, 48, 59, 65, 74, 82, 83.**

# Key Equations

**Equation 15.1 (page 681)** Integrated rate equation for a first-order reaction (in which $-\Delta[R]/\Delta t = k[R]$).

$$\ln\frac{[R]_t}{[R]_0} = -kt$$

Here, $[R]_0$ and $[R]_t$ are concentrations of the reactant at time $t = 0$ and at a later time, $t$. The ratio of concentrations, $[R]_t/[R]_0$, is the fraction of reactant that remains after a given time has elapsed.

**Equation 15.2 (page 683)** Integrated rate equation for a second-order reaction (in which $-\Delta[R]/\Delta t = k[R]^2$).

$$\frac{1}{[R]_t} - \frac{1}{[R]_0} = kt$$

**Equation 15.3 (page 684)** Integrated rate equation for a zero-order reaction (in which $-\Delta[R]/\Delta t = k[R]^0$).

$$[R]_0 - [R]_t = kt$$

**Equation 15.4 (page 686)** The relation between the half-life ($t_{1/2}$) and the rate constant ($k$) for a first-order reaction.

$$t_{1/2} = \frac{0.693}{k}$$

**Equation 15.5 (page 693)** Arrhenius equation in exponential form.

$$k = \text{rate constant} = Ae^{-E_a/RT}$$

Frequency factor ↗        ↖ Fraction of molecules with minimum energy for reaction

$A$ is the frequency factor; $E_a$ is the activation energy; $T$ is the temperature (in kelvins); and $R$ is the gas constant (= $8.314510 \times 10^{-3}$ kJ/K · mol).

**Equation 15.6 (page 693)** Expanded Arrhenius equation in logarithmic form.

$$\ln k = -\frac{E_a}{R}\left(\frac{1}{T}\right) + \ln A \longleftarrow \text{Arrhenius equation}$$

$$\downarrow \qquad\qquad \downarrow \qquad\quad \downarrow$$

$$y \quad = \quad mx \quad + b \longleftarrow \text{Equation for straight line}$$

**Equation 15.7 (page 694)** A version of the Arrhenius equation used to calculate the activation energy for a reaction when you know the values of the rate constant at two temperatures (in kelvins).

$$\ln k_2 - \ln k_1 = \ln \frac{k_2}{k_1} = -\frac{E_a}{R}\left[\frac{1}{T_2} - \frac{1}{T_1}\right]$$

# Study Questions

� WL Interactive versions of these questions are assignable in OWL.

▲ denotes challenging questions.

Blue-numbered questions have answers in Appendix R and fully worked solutions in the *Student Solutions Manual*.

## Practicing Skills

### Reaction Rates
*(See Section 15.1 and Examples 15.1–15.2.)*

1. Give the relative rates of disappearance of reactants and formation of products for each of the following reactions.
   (a) $2 O_3(g) \rightarrow 3 O_2(g)$
   (b) $2 HOF(g) \rightarrow 2 HF(g) + O_2(g)$

2. Give the relative rates of disappearance of reactants and formation of products for each of the following reactions.
   (a) $2 NO(g) + Br_2(g) \rightarrow 2 NOBr(g)$
   (b) $N_2(g) + 3 H_2(g) \rightarrow 2 NH_3(g)$

3. In the reaction $2 O_3(g) \rightarrow 3 O_2(g)$, the rate of formation of $O_2$ is $1.5 \times 10^{-3}$ mol/L · s. What is the rate of decomposition of $O_3$?

4. In the synthesis of ammonia, if $-\Delta[H_2]/\Delta t = 4.5 \times 10^{-4}$ mol/L·min, what is $\Delta[NH_3]/\Delta t$ ?

$$N_2(g) + 3 H_2(g) \rightarrow 2 NH_3(g)$$

5. Experimental data are listed here for the reaction $A \rightarrow 2 B$.

| Time (s) | [B] (mol/L) |
|----------|-------------|
| 0.00 | 0.000 |
| 10.0 | 0.326 |
| 20.0 | 0.572 |
| 30.0 | 0.750 |
| 40.0 | 0.890 |

(a) Prepare a graph from these data; connect the points with a smooth line; and calculate the rate of change of [B] for each 10-second interval from 0.0 to 40.0 seconds. Does the rate of change decrease from one time interval to the next? Suggest a reason for this result.

(b) How is the rate of change of [A] related to the rate of change of [B] in each time interval? Calculate the rate of change of [A] for the time interval from 10.0 to 20.0 seconds.

(c) What is the instantaneous rate, $\Delta[B]/\Delta t$, when [B] = 0.750 mol/L?

**6.** Phenyl acetate, an ester, reacts with water according to the equation

$$CH_3COC_6H_5 + H_2O \longrightarrow CH_3COH + C_6H_5OH$$

phenyl acetate        acetic acid    phenol

The data in the table were collected for this reaction at 5 °C.

| Time (s) | [Phenyl acetate] (mol/L) |
|---|---|
| 0 | 0.55 |
| 15.0 | 0.42 |
| 30.0 | 0.31 |
| 45.0 | 0.23 |
| 60.0 | 0.17 |
| 75.0 | 0.12 |
| 90.0 | 0.085 |

(a) Plot the phenyl acetate concentration versus time, and describe the shape of the curve observed.

(b) Calculate the rate of change of the phenyl acetate concentration during the period 15.0 seconds to 30.0 seconds and also during the period 75.0 seconds to 90.0 seconds. Why is one value smaller than the other?

(c) What is the rate of change of the phenol concentration during the time period 60.0 seconds to 75.0 seconds?

(d) What is the instantaneous rate at 15.0 seconds?

## Concentration and Rate Equations

*(See Section 15.3 and Examples 15.3–15.4.)*

**7.** Using the rate equation "Rate = $k[A]^2[B]$," define the order of the reaction with respect to A and B. What is the total order of the reaction?

**8.** A reaction has the experimental rate equation Rate = $k[A]^2$. How will the rate change if the concentration of A is tripled? If the concentration of A is halved?

**9.** The reaction between ozone and nitrogen dioxide at 231 K is first order in both [NO$_2$] and [O$_3$].

$$2\ NO_2(g) + O_3(g) \longrightarrow N_2O_5(g) + O_2(g)$$

(a) Write the rate equation for the reaction.

(b) If the concentration of NO$_2$ is tripled (and [O$_3$] is not changed), what is the change in the reaction rate?

(c) What is the effect on reaction rate if the concentration of O$_3$ is halved (with no change in [NO$_2$])?

**10.** Nitrosyl bromide, NOBr, is formed from NO and Br$_2$:

$$2\ NO(g) + Br_2(g) \longrightarrow 2\ NOBr(g)$$

Experiments show that this reaction is second order in NO and first order in Br$_2$.

(a) Write the rate equation for the reaction.

(b) How does the initial reaction rate change if the concentration of Br$_2$ is changed from 0.0022 mol/L to 0.0066 mol/L?

(c) What is the change in the initial rate if the concentration of NO is changed from 0.0024 mol/L to 0.0012 mol/L?

**11.** The data in the table are for the reaction of NO and O$_2$ at 660 K. (See "Check Your Understanding" for Example 15.3, page 680.)

$$2\ NO(g) + O_2(g) \longrightarrow 2\ NO_2(g)$$

| Reactant Concentration (mol/L) | | Rate of Disappearance of NO |
|---|---|---|
| [NO] | [O$_2$] | (mol/L · s) |
| 0.010 | 0.010 | $2.5 \times 10^{-5}$ |
| 0.020 | 0.010 | $1.0 \times 10^{-4}$ |
| 0.010 | 0.020 | $5.0 \times 10^{-5}$ |

(a) Determine the order of the reaction for each reactant.

(b) Write the rate equation for the reaction.

(c) Calculate the rate constant.

(d) Calculate the rate (in mol/L · s) at the instant when [NO] = 0.015 mol/L and [O$_2$] = 0.0050 mol/L.

(e) At the instant when NO is reacting at the rate $1.0 \times 10^{-4}$ mol/L · s, what is the rate at which O$_2$ is reacting and NO$_2$ is forming?

**12.** The reaction

$$2\ NO(g) + 2\ H_2(g) \longrightarrow N_2(g) + 2\ H_2O(g)$$

was studied at 904 °C, and the data in the table were collected.

| Reactant Concentration (mol/L) | | Rate of Appearance of N$_2$ |
|---|---|---|
| [NO] | [H$_2$] | (mol/L · s) |
| 0.420 | 0.122 | 0.136 |
| 0.210 | 0.122 | 0.0339 |
| 0.210 | 0.244 | 0.0678 |
| 0.105 | 0.488 | 0.0339 |

(a) Determine the order of the reaction for each reactant.

(b) Write the rate equation for the reaction.

(c) Calculate the rate constant for the reaction.

(d) Find the rate of appearance of N$_2$ at the instant when [NO] = 0.350 mol/L and [H$_2$] = 0.205 mol/L.

13. Data for the reaction $2\ NO(g) + O_2(g) \rightarrow 2\ NO_2(g)$ are given (for a particular temperature) in the table.

| | Concentration (mol/L) | | Initial Rate |
|---|---|---|---|
| **Experiment** | **[NO]** | **[O$_2$]** | **(mol NO/L · h)** |
| 1 | $3.6 \times 10^{-4}$ | $5.2 \times 10^{-3}$ | $3.4 \times 10^{-8}$ |
| 2 | $3.6 \times 10^{-4}$ | $1.04 \times 10^{-2}$ | $6.8 \times 10^{-8}$ |
| 3 | $1.8 \times 10^{-4}$ | $1.04 \times 10^{-2}$ | $1.7 \times 10^{-8}$ |
| 4 | $1.8 \times 10^{-4}$ | $5.2 \times 10^{-3}$ | ? |

(a) What is the rate law for this reaction?
(b) What is the rate constant for the reaction?
(c) What is the initial rate of the reaction in experiment 4?

14. Data for the following reaction are given in the table below.

$$CO(g) + NO_2(g) \rightarrow CO_2(g) + NO(g)$$

| | Concentration (mol/L) | | Initial Rate |
|---|---|---|---|
| **Experiment** | **[CO]** | **[NO$_2$]** | **(mol/L · h)** |
| 1 | $5.0 \times 10^{-4}$ | $0.36 \times 10^{-4}$ | $3.4 \times 10^{-8}$ |
| 2 | $5.0 \times 10^{-4}$ | $0.18 \times 10^{-4}$ | $1.7 \times 10^{-8}$ |
| 3 | $1.0 \times 10^{-3}$ | $0.36 \times 10^{-4}$ | $6.8 \times 10^{-8}$ |
| 4 | $1.5 \times 10^{-3}$ | $0.72 \times 10^{-4}$ | ? |

(a) What is the rate law for this reaction?
(b) What is the rate constant for the reaction?
(c) What is the initial rate of the reaction in experiment 4?

## Concentration–Time Relationships
*(See Section 15.4 and Examples 15.5–15.7.)*

15. The rate equation for the hydrolysis of sucrose to fructose and glucose

$$C_{12}H_{22}O_{11}(aq) + H_2O(\ell) \rightarrow 2\ C_6H_{12}O_6(aq)$$

is $-\Delta[\text{sucrose}]/\Delta t = k[C_{12}H_{22}O_{11}]$. After 27 minutes at 27 °C, the sucrose concentration decreased from 0.0146 M to 0.0132 M. Find the rate constant, $k$.

16. The decomposition of $N_2O_5$ in $CCl_4$ is a first-order reaction. If 2.56 mg of $N_2O_5$ is present initially and 2.50 mg is present after 4.26 minutes at 55 °C, what is the value of the rate constant, $k$?

17. The decomposition of $SO_2Cl_2$ is a first-order reaction:

$$SO_2Cl_2(g) \rightarrow SO_2(g) + Cl_2(g)$$

The rate constant for the reaction is $2.8 \times 10^{-3}$ min$^{-1}$ at 600 K. If the initial concentration of $SO_2Cl_2$ is $1.24 \times 10^{-3}$ mol/L, how long will it take for the concentration to drop to $0.31 \times 10^{-3}$ mol/L?

18. The conversion of cyclopropane to propene (see Example 15.5) occurs with a first-order rate constant of $2.42 \times 10^{-2}$ h$^{-1}$. How long will it take for the concentration of cyclopropane to decrease from an initial concentration of 0.080 mol/L to 0.020 mol/L?

19. Hydrogen peroxide, $H_2O_2(aq)$, decomposes to $H_2O(\ell)$ and $O_2(g)$ in a reaction that is first order in $H_2O_2$ and has a rate constant $k = 1.06 \times 10^{-3}$ min$^{-1}$ at a given temperature.
(a) How long will it take for 15% of a sample of $H_2O_2$ to decompose?
(b) How long will it take for 85% of the sample to decompose?

20. The decomposition of nitrogen dioxide at a high temperature

$$NO_2(g) \rightarrow NO(g) + \tfrac{1}{2}\ O_2(g)$$

is second order in this reactant. The rate constant for this reaction is 3.40 L/mol · min. Determine the time needed for the concentration of $NO_2$ to decrease from 2.00 mol/L to 1.50 mol/L.

21. At 573 K, gaseous $NO_2(g)$ decomposes, forming $NO(g)$ and $O_2(g)$. If a vessel containing $NO_2(g)$ has an initial concentration of $2.8 \times 10^{-2}$ mol/L, how long will it take for 75% of the $NO_2(g)$ to decompose? The decomposition of $NO_2(g)$ is second order in the reactant and the rate constant for this reaction, at 573 K, is 1.1 L/mol · s.

22. The dimerization of butadiene, $C_4H_6$, to form 1,5-cyclooctadiene is a second-order process that occurs when the diene is heated. In an experiment, a sample of 0.0087 mol of $C_4H_6$ was heated in a 1.0-L flask. After 600 seconds, 21% of the butadiene had dimerized. Calculate the rate constant for this reaction.

23. The decomposition of ammonia on a metal surface to form $N_2$ and $H_2$ is a zero-order reaction (Figure 15.8). At 873 °C, the value of the rate constant is $1.5 \times 10^{-3}$ mol/L · s. How long it will take to completely decompose 1.0 g of $NH_3$ in a 1.0-L flask?

24. Hydrogen iodide decomposes when heated, forming $H_2(g)$ and $I_2(g)$. The rate law for this reaction is $-\Delta[\text{HI}]/\Delta t = k[\text{HI}]^2$. At 443 °C, $k$ = 30. L/mol · min. If the initial HI(g) concentration is $3.5 \times 10^{-2}$ mol/L, what concentration of HI(g) will remain after 10. minutes?

## Half-Life
*(See Section 15.4 and Examples 15.8 and 15.9.)*

25. The rate equation for the decomposition of $N_2O_5$ (giving $NO_2$ and $O_2$) is Rate = $k[N_2O_5]$. The value of $k$ is $6.7 \times 10^{-5}$ s$^{-1}$ for the reaction at a particular temperature.
(a) Calculate the half-life of $N_2O_5$.
(b) How long does it take for the $N_2O_5$ concentration to drop to one tenth of its original value?

26. The decomposition of $SO_2Cl_2$

$$SO_2Cl_2(g) \rightarrow SO_2(g) + Cl_2(g)$$

is first order in $SO_2Cl_2$, and the reaction has a half-life of 245 minutes at 600 K. If you begin with $3.6 \times 10^{-3}$ mol of $SO_2Cl_2$ in a 1.0-L flask, how long will it take for the amount of $SO_2Cl_2$ to decrease to $2.00 \times 10^{-4}$ mol?

27. Gaseous azomethane, $CH_3N{=}NCH_3$, decomposes in a first-order reaction when heated:

$$CH_3N{=}NCH_3(g) \rightarrow N_2(g) + C_2H_6(g)$$

The rate constant for this reaction at 600 K is 0.0216 min$^{-1}$. If the initial quantity of azomethane in the flask is 2.00 g, how much remains after 0.0500 hour? What quantity of $N_2$ is formed in this time?

28. The compound $Xe(CF_3)_2$ decomposes in a first-order reaction to elemental Xe with a half-life of 30. minutes. If you place 7.50 mg of $Xe(CF_3)_2$ in a flask, how long must you wait until only 0.25 mg of $Xe(CF_3)_2$ remains?

**29.** The radioactive isotope $^{64}$Cu is used in the form of copper(II) acetate to study Wilson's disease. The isotope has a half-life of 12.70 hours. What fraction of radioactive copper(II) acetate remains after 64 hours?

**30.** Radioactive gold-198 is used in the diagnosis of liver problems. The half-life of this isotope is 2.7 days. If you begin with a 5.6-mg sample of the isotope, how much of this sample remains after 1.0 day?

**Graphical Analysis: Rate Equations and $k$**
*(See Section 15.4.)*

**31.** Data for the decomposition of dinitrogen monoxide

$$N_2O(g) \longrightarrow N_2(g) + \tfrac{1}{2}\,O_2(g)$$

on a gold surface at 900 °C are given below. Verify that the reaction is first order by preparing a graph of ln [$N_2O$] versus time. Derive the rate constant from the slope of the line in this graph. Using the rate law and value of $k$, determine the decomposition rate at 900 °C when [$N_2O$] = 0.035 mol/L.

| Time (min) | [$N_2O$] (mol/L) |
|---|---|
| 15.0 | 0.0835 |
| 30.0 | 0.0680 |
| 80.0 | 0.0350 |
| 120.0 | 0.0220 |

**32.** Ammonia decomposes when heated according to the equation

$$NH_3(g) \longrightarrow NH_2(g) + H(g)$$

The data in the table for this reaction were collected at a high temperature.

| Time (h) | [$NH_3$] (mol/L) |
|---|---|
| 0 | $8.00 \times 10^{-7}$ |
| 25 | $6.75 \times 10^{-7}$ |
| 50 | $5.84 \times 10^{-7}$ |
| 75 | $5.15 \times 10^{-7}$ |

Plot ln [$NH_3$] versus time and 1/[$NH_3$] versus time. What is the order of this reaction with respect to $NH_3$? Find the rate constant for the reaction from the slope.

**33.** Gaseous $NO_2$ decomposes at 573 K.

$$NO_2(g) \longrightarrow NO(g) + \tfrac{1}{2}\,O_2(g)$$

The concentration of $NO_2$ was measured as a function of time. A graph of 1/[$NO_2$] versus time gives a straight line with a slope of 1.1 L/mol · s. What is the rate law for this reaction? What is the rate constant?

**34.** The decomposition of HOF occurs at 25 °C.

$$HOF(g) \longrightarrow HF(g) + \tfrac{1}{2}\,O_2(g)$$

Using the data in the table below, determine the rate law, and then calculate the rate constant.

| [HOF] (mol/L) | Time (min) |
|---|---|
| 0.850 | 0 |
| 0.810 | 2.00 |
| 0.754 | 5.00 |
| 0.526 | 20.0 |
| 0.243 | 50.0 |

**35.** For the reaction $C_2F_4 \longrightarrow \tfrac{1}{2}\,C_4F_8$, a graph of 1/[$C_2F_4$] versus time gives a straight line with a slope of +0.04 L/mol · s. What is the rate law for this reaction?

**36.** Butadiene, $C_4H_6(g)$, dimerizes when heated, forming 1,5-cyclooctadiene, $C_8H_{12}$. The data in the table were collected.

$$H_2C{=}CHCH{=}CH_2 \longrightarrow \tfrac{1}{2}$$

1,3-butadiene

1,5-cyclooctadiene

| [$C_4H_6$] (mol/L) | Time (s) |
|---|---|
| $1.0 \times 10^{-2}$ | 0 |
| $8.7 \times 10^{-3}$ | 200. |
| $7.7 \times 10^{-3}$ | 500. |
| $6.9 \times 10^{-3}$ | 800. |
| $5.8 \times 10^{-3}$ | 1200. |

(a) Use a graphical method to verify that this is a second-order reaction.
(b) Calculate the rate constant for the reaction.

**Kinetics and Energy**
*(See Section 15.5 and Examples 15.10 and 15.11.)*

**37.** Calculate the activation energy, $E_a$, for the reaction

$$2\,N_2O_5(g) \longrightarrow 4\,NO_2(g) + O_2(g)$$

from the observed rate constants: $k$ at 25 °C = $3.46 \times 10^{-5}\ s^{-1}$ and $k$ at 55 °C = $1.5 \times 10^{-3}\ s^{-1}$.

**38.** If the rate constant for a reaction triples when the temperature rises from $3.00 \times 10^2$ K to $3.10 \times 10^2$ K, what is the activation energy of the reaction?

**39.** When heated to a high temperature, cyclobutane, $C_4H_8$, decomposes to ethylene:

$$C_4H_8(g) \longrightarrow 2\,C_2H_4(g)$$

The activation energy, $E_a$, for this reaction is 260 kJ/mol. At 800 K, the rate constant $k = 0.0315\ s^{-1}$. Determine the value of $k$ at 850 K.

**40.** When heated, cyclopropane is converted to propene (see Example 15.5). Rate constants for this reaction at 470 °C and 510 °C are $k = 1.10 \times 10^{-4}\ s^{-1}$ and $k = 1.02 \times 10^{-3}\ s^{-1}$, respectively. Determine the activation energy, $E_a$, from these data.

**41.** The reaction of $H_2$ molecules with F atoms

$$H_2(g) + F(g) \longrightarrow HF(g) + H(g)$$

has an activation energy of 8 kJ/mol and an enthalpy change of −133 kJ/mol. Draw a diagram similar to Figure 15.13 for this process. Indicate the activation energy and enthalpy change on this diagram.

**42.** Answer the following questions based on the diagram below.
(a) Is the reaction exothermic or endothermic?
(b) Does the reaction occur in more than one step? If so, how many?

## Reaction Mechanisms
*(See Section 15.6 and Examples 15.12–15.14.)*

**43.** What is the rate law for each of the following elementary reactions?
(a) $NO(g) + NO_3(g) \rightarrow 2\ NO_2(g)$
(b) $Cl(g) + H_2(g) \rightarrow HCl(g) + H(g)$
(c) $(CH_3)_3CBr(aq) \rightarrow (CH_3)_3C^+(aq) + Br^-(aq)$

**44.** What is the rate law for each of the following elementary reactions?
(a) $Cl(g) + ICl(g) \rightarrow I(g) + Cl_2(g)$
(b) $O(g) + O_3(g) \rightarrow 2\ O_2(g)$
(c) $2\ NO_2(g) \rightarrow N_2O_4(g)$

**45.** Ozone, $O_3$, in the earth's upper atmosphere decomposes according to the equation

$$2\ O_3(g) \rightarrow 3\ O_2(g)$$

The mechanism of the reaction is thought to proceed through an initial fast, reversible step followed by a slow, second step.

Step 1:   Fast, reversible   $O_3(g) \rightleftharpoons O_2(g) + O(g)$

Step 2:   Slow   $O_3(g) + O(g) \rightarrow 2\ O_2(g)$

(a) Which of the steps is rate-determining?
(b) Write the rate equation for the rate-determining step.

**46.** The reaction of $NO_2(g)$ and $CO(g)$ is thought to occur in two steps:

Step 1:   Slow   $NO_2(g) + NO_2(g) \rightarrow NO(g) + NO_3(g)$

Step 2:   Fast   $NO_3(g) + CO(g) \rightarrow NO_2(g) + CO_2(g)$

(a) Show that the elementary steps add up to give the overall, stoichiometric equation.
(b) What is the molecularity of each step?
(c) For this mechanism to be consistent with kinetic data, what must be the experimental rate equation?
(d) Identify any intermediates in this reaction.

**47.** A proposed mechanism for the reaction of $NO_2$ and $CO$ is

Step 1:   Slow, endothermic
$$2\ NO_2(g) \rightarrow NO(g) + NO_3(g)$$

Step 2:   Fast, exothermic
$$NO_3(g) + CO(g) \rightarrow NO_2(g) + CO_2(g)$$

Overall Reaction:   Exothermic
$$NO_2(g) + CO(g) \rightarrow NO(g) + CO_2(g)$$

(a) Identify each of the following as a reactant, product, or intermediate: $NO_2(g)$, $CO(g)$, $NO_3(g)$, $CO_2(g)$, $NO(g)$.
(b) Draw a reaction coordinate diagram for this reaction. Indicate on this drawing the activation energy for each step and the overall enthalpy change.

**48.** The mechanism for the reaction of $CH_3OH$ and $HBr$ is believed to involve two steps. The overall reaction is exothermic.

Step 1: Fast, endothermic
$$CH_3OH + H^+ \rightleftharpoons CH_3OH_2^+$$

Step 2: Slow
$$CH_3OH_2^+ + Br^- \rightarrow CH_3Br + H_2O$$

(a) Write an equation for the overall reaction.
(b) Draw a reaction coordinate diagram for this reaction.
(c) Show that the rate law for this reaction is Rate $= k[CH_3OH][H^+][Br^-]$.

## General Questions

*These questions are not designated as to type or location in the chapter. They may combine several concepts.*

**49.** A reaction has the following experimental rate equation: Rate $= k[A]^2[B]$. If the concentration of A is doubled and the concentration of B is halved, what happens to the reaction rate?

**50.** For a first-order reaction, what fraction of reactant remains after five half-lives have elapsed?

**51.** To determine the concentration dependence of the rate of the reaction

$$H_2PO_3^-(aq) + OH^-(aq) \rightarrow HPO_3^{2-}(aq) + H_2O(\ell)$$

you might measure $[OH^-]$ as a function of time using a pH meter. (To do so, you would set up conditions under which $[H_2PO_3^-]$ remains constant by using a large excess of this reactant.) How would you prove a second-order rate dependence for $[OH^-]$?

**52.** Data for the following reaction are given in the table.

$$2\ NO(g) + Br_2(g) \rightarrow 2\ NOBr(g)$$

| Experiment | [NO] (M) | [Br₂] (M) | Initial Rate (mol/L · s) |
|---|---|---|---|
| 1 | $1.0 \times 10^{-2}$ | $2.0 \times 10^{-2}$ | $2.4 \times 10^{-2}$ |
| 2 | $4.0 \times 10^{-2}$ | $2.0 \times 10^{-2}$ | 0.384 |
| 3 | $1.0 \times 10^{-2}$ | $5.0 \times 10^{-2}$ | $6.0 \times 10^{-2}$ |

What is the order of the reaction with respect to [NO] and [Br₂], and what is the overall order of the reaction?

**53.** Formic acid decomposes at 550 °C according to the equation

$$HCO_2H(g) \rightarrow CO_2(g) + H_2(g)$$

The reaction follows first-order kinetics. In an experiment, it is determined that 75% of a sample of $HCO_2H$ has decomposed in 72 seconds. Determine $t_{1/2}$ for this reaction.

**54.** Isomerization of $CH_3NC$ occurs slowly when $CH_3NC$ is heated.

$$CH_3NC(g) \rightarrow CH_3CN(g)$$

To study the rate of this reaction at 488 K, data on $[CH_3NC]$ were collected at various times. Analysis led to the graph below.

(a) What is the rate law for this reaction?
(b) What is the equation for the straight line in this graph?
(c) Calculate the rate constant for this reaction.
(d) How long does it take for half of the sample to isomerize?
(e) What is the concentration of $CH_3NC$ after $1.0 \times 10^4$ s?

**55.** When heated, tetrafluoroethylene dimerizes to form octafluorocyclobutane.

$$C_2F_4(g) \rightarrow \tfrac{1}{2}\, C_4F_8(g)$$

To determine the rate of this reaction at 488 K, the data in the table were collected. Analysis was done graphically, as shown below:

| $[C_2F_4]$ (M) | Time (s) |
|---|---|
| 0.100 | 0 |
| 0.080 | 56 |
| 0.060 | 150. |
| 0.040 | 335 |
| 0.030 | 520. |

(a) What is the rate law for this reaction?
(b) What is the value of the rate constant?
(c) What is the concentration of $C_2F_4$ after 600 s?
(d) How long will it take until the reaction is 90% complete?

**56.** Data in the table were collected at 540 K for the following reaction:

$$CO(g) + NO_2(g) \rightarrow CO_2(g) + NO(g)$$

(a) Derive the rate equation.
(b) Determine the reaction order with respect to each reactant.
(c) Calculate the rate constant, giving the correct units for $k$.

| Initial Concentration (mol/L) | | Initial Rate |
|---|---|---|
| **[CO]** | **[NO₂]** | **(mol/L · h)** |
| $5.1 \times 10^{-4}$ | $0.35 \times 10^{-4}$ | $3.4 \times 10^{-8}$ |
| $5.1 \times 10^{-4}$ | $0.70 \times 10^{-4}$ | $6.8 \times 10^{-8}$ |
| $5.1 \times 10^{-4}$ | $0.18 \times 10^{-4}$ | $1.7 \times 10^{-8}$ |
| $1.0 \times 10^{-3}$ | $0.35 \times 10^{-4}$ | $6.8 \times 10^{-8}$ |
| $1.5 \times 10^{-3}$ | $0.35 \times 10^{-4}$ | $10.2 \times 10^{-8}$ |

**57.** Ammonium cyanate, $NH_4NCO$, rearranges in water to give urea, $(NH_2)_2CO$.

$$NH_4NCO(aq) \rightarrow (NH_2)_2CO(aq)$$

| Time (min) | [NH₄NCO] (mol/L) |
|---|---|
| 0 | 0.458 |
| $4.50 \times 10^1$ | 0.370 |
| $1.07 \times 10^2$ | 0.292 |
| $2.30 \times 10^2$ | 0.212 |
| $6.00 \times 10^2$ | 0.114 |

Using the data in the table:
(a) Decide whether the reaction is first order or second order.
(b) Calculate $k$ for this reaction.
(c) Calculate the half-life of ammonium cyanate under these conditions.
(d) Calculate the concentration of $NH_4NCO$ after 12.0 hours.

**58.** Nitrogen oxides, $NO_x$ (a mixture of NO and $NO_2$ collectively designated as $NO_x$), play an essential role in the production of pollutants found in photochemical smog. The $NO_x$ in the atmosphere is slowly broken down to $N_2$ and $O_2$ in a first-order reaction. The average half-life of $NO_x$ in the smokestack emissions in a large city during daylight is 3.9 hours.
(a) Starting with 1.50 mg in an experiment, what quantity of $NO_x$ remains after 5.25 hours?
(b) How many hours of daylight must have elapsed to decrease 1.50 mg of $NO_x$ to $2.50 \times 10^{-6}$ mg?

59. At temperatures below 500 K, the reaction between carbon monoxide and nitrogen dioxide

$$CO(g) + NO_2(g) \rightarrow CO_2(g) + NO(g)$$

has the following rate equation: Rate = $k[NO_2]^2$. Which of the three mechanisms suggested here best agrees with the experimentally observed rate equation?

Mechanism 1    Single, elementary step

$$NO_2 + CO \rightarrow CO_2 + NO$$

Mechanism 2    Two steps

Slow        $NO_2 + NO_2 \rightarrow NO_3 + NO$

Fast        $NO_3 + CO \rightarrow NO_2 + CO_2$

Mechanism 3    Two steps

Slow        $NO_2 \rightarrow NO + O$

Fast        $CO + O \rightarrow CO_2$

60. ▲ Nitryl fluoride can be made by treating nitrogen dioxide with fluorine:

$$2\,NO_2(g) + F_2(g) \rightarrow 2\,NO_2F(g)$$

Use the rate data in the table to do the following:
(a) Write the rate equation for the reaction.
(b) Indicate the order of reaction with respect to each component of the reaction.
(c) Find the numerical value of the rate constant, $k$.

| | Initial Concentrations (mol/L) | | | Initial Rate |
|---|---|---|---|---|
| Experiment | [NO₂] | [F₂] | [NO₂F] | (mol F₂/L · s) |
| 1 | 0.001 | 0.005 | 0.001 | $2.0 \times 10^{-4}$ |
| 2 | 0.002 | 0.005 | 0.001 | $4.0 \times 10^{-4}$ |
| 3 | 0.006 | 0.002 | 0.001 | $4.8 \times 10^{-4}$ |
| 4 | 0.006 | 0.004 | 0.001 | $9.6 \times 10^{-4}$ |
| 5 | 0.001 | 0.001 | 0.001 | $4.0 \times 10^{-5}$ |
| 6 | 0.001 | 0.001 | 0.002 | $4.0 \times 10^{-5}$ |

61. The decomposition of dinitrogen pentaoxide

$$N_2O_5(g) \rightarrow 2\,NO_2(g) + \tfrac{1}{2}\,O_2(g)$$

has the following rate equation: Rate = $k[N_2O_5]$. It has been found experimentally that the decomposition is 20.5% complete in 13.0 hours at 298 K. Calculate the rate constant and the half-life at 298 K.

62. The data in the table give the temperature dependence of the rate constant for the reaction $N_2O_5(g) \rightarrow 2\,NO_2(g) + \tfrac{1}{2}\,O_2(g)$. Plot these data in the appropriate way to derive the activation energy for the reaction.

| T(K) | k (s⁻¹) |
|---|---|
| 338 | $4.87 \times 10^{-3}$ |
| 328 | $1.50 \times 10^{-3}$ |
| 318 | $4.98 \times 10^{-4}$ |
| 308 | $1.35 \times 10^{-4}$ |
| 298 | $3.46 \times 10^{-5}$ |
| 273 | $7.87 \times 10^{-7}$ |

63. The decomposition of gaseous dimethyl ether at ordinary pressures is first order. Its half-life is 25.0 minutes at 500 °C:

$$CH_3OCH_3(g) \rightarrow CH_4(g) + CO(g) + H_2(g)$$

(a) Starting with 8.00 g of dimethyl ether, what mass remains (in grams) after 125 minutes and after 145 minutes?
(b) Calculate the time in minutes required to decrease 7.60 ng (nanograms) to 2.25 ng.
(c) What fraction of the original dimethyl ether remains after 150 minutes?

64. The decomposition of phosphine, $PH_3$, proceeds according to the equation

$$PH_3(g) \rightarrow \tfrac{1}{4}\,P_4(g) + \tfrac{3}{2}\,H_2(g)$$

It is found that the reaction has the following rate equation: Rate = $k[PH_3]$. The half-life of $PH_3$ is 37.9 seconds at 120 °C.
(a) How much time is required for three fourths of the $PH_3$ to decompose?
(b) What fraction of the original sample of $PH_3$ remains after 1.00 minute?

65. The ozone in the earth's ozone layer decomposes according to the equation

$$2\,O_3(g) \rightarrow 3\,O_2(g)$$

The mechanism of the reaction is thought to proceed through an initial fast equilibrium and a slow step:

Step 1:  Fast, reversible    $O_3(g) \rightleftharpoons O_2(g) + O(g)$

Step 2:  Slow                $O_3(g) + O(g) \rightarrow 2\,O_2(g)$

Show that the mechanism agrees with this experimental rate law:

$$\text{Rate} = -(1/2)\Delta[O_3]/\Delta t = k\,[O_3]^2/[O_2].$$

66. Hundreds of different reactions can occur in the stratosphere, among them reactions that destroy the earth's ozone layer. The table below lists several (second-order) reactions of Cl atoms with ozone and organic compounds; each is given with its rate constant.

| Reaction | Rate Constant (298 K, cm³/molecule · s) |
|---|---|
| (a) Cl + O₃ → ClO + O₂ | $1.2 \times 10^{-11}$ |
| (b) Cl + CH₄ → HCl + CH₃ | $1.0 \times 10^{-13}$ |
| (c) Cl + C₃H₈ → HCl + C₃H₇ | $1.4 \times 10^{-10}$ |
| (d) Cl + CH₂FCl → HCl + CHFCl | $3.0 \times 10^{-18}$ |

For equal concentrations of Cl and the other reactant, which is the slowest reaction? Which is the fastest reaction?

**67.** Data for the reaction

$$[Mn(CO)_5(CH_3CN)]^+ + NC_5H_5$$
$$\longrightarrow [Mn(CO)_5(NC_5H_5)]^+ + CH_3CN$$

are given in the table. Calculate $E_a$ from a plot of $\ln k$ versus $1/T$.

| $T$(K) | $k$(min$^{-1}$) |
|---|---|
| 298 | 0.0409 |
| 308 | 0.0818 |
| 318 | 0.157 |

**68.** The gas-phase reaction

$$2\,N_2O_5(g) \longrightarrow 4\,NO_2(g) + O_2(g)$$

has an activation energy of 103 kJ/mol, and the rate constant is 0.0900 min$^{-1}$ at 328.0 K. Find the rate constant at 318.0 K.

**69.** ▲ Egg protein albumin is precipitated when an egg is cooked in boiling (100 °C) water. $E_a$ for this first-order reaction is 52.0 kJ/mol. Estimate the time to prepare a 3-minute egg at an altitude at which water boils at 90 °C.

**70.** ▲ Two molecules of 1,3-butadiene ($C_4H_6$) form 1,5-cyclooctadiene, $C_8H_{12}$ at higher temperatures.

$$2\,C_4H_6(g) \longrightarrow C_8H_{12}(g)$$

Use the following data to determine the order of the reaction and the rate constant, $k$. (Note that the total pressure is the pressure of the unreacted $C_4H_6$ at any time and the pressure of the $C_8H_{12}$.)

| Time (min) | Total Pressure (mm Hg) |
|---|---|
| 0 | 436 |
| 3.5 | 428 |
| 11.5 | 413 |
| 18.3 | 401 |
| 25.0 | 391 |
| 32.0 | 382 |
| 41.2 | 371 |

**71.** ▲ Hypofluorous acid, HOF, is very unstable, decomposing in a first-order reaction to give HF and $O_2$, with a half-life of 30. minutes at room temperature:

$$HOF(g) \longrightarrow HF(g) + \tfrac{1}{2}\,O_2(g)$$

If the partial pressure of HOF in a 1.00-L flask is initially $1.00 \times 10^2$ mm Hg at 25 °C, what are the total pressure in the flask and the partial pressure of HOF after exactly 30 minutes? After 45 minutes?

**72.** ▲ We know that the decomposition of $SO_2Cl_2$ is first order in $SO_2Cl_2$,

$$SO_2Cl_2(g) \longrightarrow SO_2(g) + Cl_2(g)$$

with a half-life of 245 minutes at 600 K. If you begin with a partial pressure of $SO_2Cl_2$ of 25 mm Hg in a 1.0-L flask, what is the partial pressure of each reactant and product after 245 minutes? What is the partial pressure of each reactant after 12 hours?

**73.** ▲ Nitramide, $NO_2NH_2$, decomposes slowly in aqueous solution according to the following reaction:

$$NO_2NH_2(aq) \longrightarrow N_2O(g) + H_2O(\ell)$$

The reaction follows the experimental rate law

$$\text{Rate} = \frac{k[NO_2NH_2]}{[H_3O^+]}$$

(a) What is the apparent order of the reaction in a buffered solution?
(b) Which of the following mechanisms is the most appropriate for the interpretation of this rate law? Explain.

Mechanism 1
$$NO_2NH_2 \xrightarrow{k_1} N_2O + H_2O$$

Mechanism 2
$$NO_2NH_2 + H_3O^+ \underset{k_2'}{\overset{k_2}{\rightleftharpoons}} NO_2NH_3^+ + H_2O$$
$$\text{(rapid equilibrium)}$$
$$NO_2NH_3^+ \xrightarrow{k_3} N_2O + H_3O^+ \text{ (rate-limiting step)}$$

Mechanism 3
$$NO_2NH_2 + H_2O \underset{k_4'}{\overset{k_4}{\rightleftharpoons}} NO_2NH^- + H_3O^+$$
$$\text{(rapid equilibrium)}$$
$$NO_2NH^- \xrightarrow{k_5} N_2O + OH^- \text{ (rate-limiting step)}$$
$$H_3O^+ + OH^- \xrightarrow{k_6} 2\,H_2O \text{ (very fast reaction)}$$

(c) Show the relationship between the experimentally observed rate constant, $k$, and the rate constants in the selected mechanism. (Note that when writing the expression for $K$, the equilibrium constant, $[H_2O]$ is not involved. ▶ Chapter 16.)
(d) Show that hydroxide ions catalyze the decomposition of nitramide.

**74.** Many biochemical reactions are catalyzed by acids. A typical mechanism consistent with the experimental results (in which HA is the acid and X is the reactant) is

Step 1: Fast, reversible:   $HA \rightleftharpoons H^+ + A^-$

Step 2: Fast, reversible:   $X + H^+ \rightleftharpoons XH^+$

Step 3: Slow                $XH^+ \longrightarrow$ products

What rate law is derived from this mechanism? What is the order of the reaction with respect to HA? How would doubling the concentration of HA affect the reaction?

## In the Laboratory

**75.** The color change accompanying the reaction of phenolphthalein with strong base is illustrated on page 668. The change in concentration of the dye can be followed by spectrophotometry (page 188), and some data collected by that approach are given below. The initial concentrations were [phenolphthalein] = 0.0050 mol/L and [OH$^-$] = 0.61 mol/L. (Data are taken from review materials for kinetics at chemed.chem.purdue.edu.)

(For more details on this reaction see L. Nicholson, *Journal of Chemical Education*, Vol. 66, p. 725, 1989.)

| Concentration of Phenolphthalein (mol/L) | Time (s) |
|---|---|
| 0.0050 | 0.00 |
| 0.0045 | 10.5 |
| 0.0040 | 22.3 |
| 0.0035 | 35.7 |
| 0.0030 | 51.1 |
| 0.0025 | 69.3 |
| 0.0020 | 91.6 |
| 0.0015 | 120.4 |
| 0.0010 | 160.9 |
| 0.00050 | 230.3 |
| 0.00025 | 299.6 |

(a) Plot the data above as [phenolphthalein] versus time, and determine the average rate from $t = 0$ to $t = 15$ seconds and from $t = 100$ seconds to $t = 125$ seconds. Does the rate change? If so, why?

(b) What is the instantaneous rate at 50 seconds?

(c) Use a graphical method to determine the order of the reaction with respect to phenolphthalein. Write the rate law, and determine the rate constant.

(d) What is the half-life for the reaction?

76. ▲ We want to study the hydrolysis of the beautiful green, cobalt-based complex called *trans*-dichlorobis-(ethylenediamine)cobalt(III) ion,

In this hydrolysis reaction, the green complex ion *trans*–$[Co(en)_2Cl_2]^+$ forms the red complex ion $[Co(en)_2(H_2O)Cl]^{2+}$ as a $Cl^-$ ion is replaced with a water molecule on the $Co^{3+}$ ion (en = $H_2NCH_2CH_2NH_2$).

*trans*–$[Co(en)_2Cl_2]^+(aq) + H_2O(\ell) \rightarrow$
     green
          $[Co(en)_2(H_2O)Cl]^{2+}(aq) + Cl^-(aq)$
               red

The reaction progress is followed by observing the color of the solution. The original solution is green, and the final solution is red, but at some intermediate stage when both the reactant and product are present, the solution is gray.

original solution          intermediate solution

final solution

**Changes in color with time as $Cl^-$ ion is replaced by $H_2O$ in a cobalt(III) complex.** The shape in the middle of the beaker is a vortex that arises because the solutions are being stirred using a magnetic stirring bar in the bottom of the beaker.

Reactions such as this have been studied extensively, and experiments suggest that the initial, slow step in the reaction is the breaking of the Co—Cl bond to give a five-coordinate intermediate. The intermediate is then attacked rapidly by water.

Slow:     *trans*–$[Co(en)_2Cl_2]^+(aq) \rightarrow$
                    $[Co(en)_2Cl]^{2+}(aq) + Cl^-(aq)$

Fast:     $[Co(en)_2Cl]^{2+}(aq) + H_2O(aq) \rightarrow$
                    $[Co(en)_2(H_2O)Cl]^{2+}(aq)$

(a) Based on the reaction mechanism, what is the predicted rate law?

(b) As the reaction proceeds, the color changes from green to red with an intermediate stage where the color is gray. The gray color is reached at the same time, no matter what the concentration of the green starting material (at the same temperature). How does this show the reaction is first order in the green form? Explain.

(c) The activation energy for a reaction can be found by plotting ln $k$ versus $1/T$. However, here we do not need to measure $k$ directly. Instead, because $k = -(1/t)\ln([R]/[R]_0)$, the time needed to achieve the gray color is a measure of $k$. Use the data below to find the activation energy.

| Temperature °C | Time Needed to Achieve Gray Colors (for the Same Initial Concentration) |
|---|---|
| 56 | 156 s |
| 60 | 114 s |
| 65 | 88 s |
| 75 | 47 s |

77. The enzyme chymotrypsin catalyzes the hydrolysis of a peptide containing phenylalanine. Using the data below at a given temperature, calculate the maximum rate of the reaction, Rate$_{max}$. (For more information on enzyme catalysis and the Michaelis–Menten model, see page 702.)

| Peptide Concentration (mol/L) | Reaction Rate (mol/L · min) |
|---|---|
| $2.5 \times 10^{-4}$ | $2.2 \times 10^{-6}$ |
| $5.0 \times 10^{-4}$ | $3.8 \times 10^{-6}$ |
| $10.0 \times 10^{-4}$ | $5.9 \times 10^{-6}$ |
| $15.0 \times 10^{-4}$ | $7.1 \times 10^{-6}$ |

78. The substitution of CO in $Ni(CO)_4$ by another molecule L [where L is an electron-pair donor such as $P(CH_3)_3$] was studied some years ago and led to an understanding of some of the general principles that govern the chemistry of compounds having metal–CO bonds. (See J. P. Day, F. Basolo, and R. G. Pearson: *Journal of the American Chemical Society*, Vol. 90, p. 6927, 1968.) A detailed study of the kinetics of the reaction led to the following mechanism:

Slow        $Ni(CO)_4 \rightarrow Ni(CO)_3 + CO$

Fast        $Ni(CO)_3 + L \rightarrow Ni(CO)_3L$

(a) What is the molecularity of each of the elementary reactions?
(b) Doubling the concentration of $Ni(CO)_4$ increased the reaction rate by a factor of 2. Doubling the concentration of L had no effect on the reaction rate. Based on this information, write the rate equation for the reaction. Does this agree with the mechanism described?
(c) The experimental rate constant for the reaction, when L = $P(C_6H_5)_3$, is $9.3 \times 10^{-3}$ s$^{-1}$ at 20 °C. If the initial concentration of $Ni(CO)_4$ is 0.025 M, what is the concentration of the product after 5.0 minutes?

## Summary and Conceptual Questions

*The following questions may use concepts from this and previous chapters.*

79. Hydrogenation reactions, processes wherein $H_2$ is added to a molecule, are usually catalyzed. An excellent catalyst is a very finely divided metal suspended in the reaction solvent. Tell why finely divided rhodium, for example, is a much more efficient catalyst than a small block of the metal.

80. ▲ Suppose you have 1000 blocks, each of which is 1.0 cm on a side. If all 1000 of these blocks are stacked to give a cube that is 10. cm on a side, what fraction of the 1000 blocks have at least one surface on the outside surface of the cube? Next, divide the 1000 blocks into eight equal piles of blocks and form them into eight cubes, 5.0 cm on a side. What fraction of the blocks now have at least one surface on the outside of the cubes? How does this mathematical model pertain to Study Question 79?

81. The following statements relate to the reaction for the formation of HI:

$$H_2(g) + I_2(g) \rightarrow 2\ HI(g) \qquad Rate = k[H_2][I_2]$$

Determine which of the following statements are true. If a statement is false, indicate why it is incorrect.
(a) The reaction must occur in a single step.
(b) This is a second-order reaction overall.
(c) Raising the temperature will cause the value of $k$ to decrease.
(d) Raising the temperature lowers the activation energy for this reaction.
(e) If the concentrations of both reactants are doubled, the rate will double.
(f) Adding a catalyst in the reaction will cause the initial rate to increase.

82. Chlorine atoms contribute to the destruction of the earth's ozone layer by the following sequence of reactions:

$$Cl + O_3 \rightarrow ClO + O_2$$
$$ClO + O \rightarrow Cl + O_2$$

where the O atoms in the second step come from the decomposition of ozone by sunlight:

$$O_3(g) \rightarrow O(g) + O_2(g)$$

What is the net equation on summing these three equations? Why does this lead to ozone loss in the stratosphere? What is the role played by Cl in this sequence of reactions? What name is given to species such as ClO?

83. Describe each of the following statements as true or false. If false, rewrite the sentence to make it correct.
(a) The rate-determining elementary step in a reaction is the slowest step in a mechanism.
(b) It is possible to change the rate constant by changing the temperature.

(c) As a reaction proceeds at constant temperature, the rate remains constant.

(d) A reaction that is third order overall must involve more than one step.

84. Identify which of the following statements are incorrect. If the statement is incorrect, rewrite it to be correct.

(a) Reactions are faster at a higher temperature because activation energies are lower.

(b) Rates increase with increasing concentration of reactants because there are more collisions between reactant molecules.

(c) At higher temperatures, a larger fraction of molecules have enough energy to get over the activation energy barrier.

(d) Catalyzed and uncatalyzed reactions have identical mechanisms.

85. The reaction cyclopropane → propene occurs on a platinum metal surface at 200 °C. (The platinum is a catalyst.) The reaction is first order in cyclopropane. Indicate how the following quantities change (increase, decrease, or no change) as this reaction progresses, assuming constant temperature.

(a) [cyclopropane]

(b) [propene]

(c) [catalyst]

(d) the rate constant, $k$

(e) the order of the reaction

(f) the half-life of cyclopropane

86. Isotopes are often used as "tracers" to follow an atom through a chemical reaction, and the following is an example. Acetic acid reacts with methanol (Chapter 10).

$$CH_3CO_2H \quad + \quad CH_3OH$$

$$\longrightarrow \qquad CH_3CO_2CH_3 \quad + \quad H_2O$$

Explain how you could use the isotope $^{18}O$ to show whether the oxygen atom in the water comes from the —OH of the acid or the —OH of the alcohol.

87. Examine the reaction coordinate diagram given here.

(a) How many steps are in the mechanism for the reaction described by this diagram?

(b) Is the reaction overall exothermic or endothermic?

88. Draw a reaction coordinate diagram for an exothermic reaction that occurs in a single step. Identify the activation energy and the net energy change for the reaction on this diagram. Draw a second diagram that represents the same reaction in the presence of a catalyst, assuming a single step reaction is involved here also. Identify the activation energy of this reaction and the energy change. Is the activation energy in the two drawings different? Does the energy evolved in the two reactions differ?

## Applying Chemical Principles

### Kinetics and Mechanisms: A 70-Year-Old Mystery Solved

Toward the end of the 19th century, the gas phase reaction of $H_2(g)$ with $I_2(s)$ was shown to be first-order for each reactant.

$$H_2(g) + I_2(g) \rightleftharpoons 2\,HI(g)$$

For approximately 70 years, the accepted mechanism was an elementary bimolecular collision that results in an exchange of atoms.

However, in 1967, John H. Sullivan determined that this single-step mechanism is incorrect. Sullivan provided evidence that the reaction actually occurs in two steps. The first step of the mechanism is the dissociation of elemental iodine into iodine atoms. The dissociation of $I_2$ is a fast equilibrium process that produces a relatively constant concentration of iodine atoms.

Fast equilibrium $\qquad I_2(g) \rightleftharpoons 2\,I(g)$

The second step of the mechanism is a termolecular reaction between two iodine atoms and elemental hydrogen.

Slow $\qquad H_2(g) + 2\,I(g) \rightarrow 2\,HI$

What was Sullivan's evidence for the revised mechanism? First, he worked at temperatures too low to allow thermal decomposition of $I_2$. At these temperatures, little or no hydrogen iodide is formed. Second, he used a technique called *flash photolysis* to create iodine atoms from $I_2$. In this technique a mixture of hydrogen and iodine was irradiated with a strong pulse of light. Sullivan found that the rate of the reaction was dependent on the square of the concentration of iodine atoms created by flash photolysis, which is consistent with the second elementary step in his reaction mechanism.

The story of the mechanism of the hydrogen-iodine reaction is a good lesson: chemists should not trust a proposed mechanism just because it fits with an experimentally determined reaction order. Verifying mechanisms often requires identifying intermediates during the course of a reaction. Sullivan was not only able to identify an intermediate, he controlled its production.

An apparatus for carrying out flash photolysis experiments in the study of kinetics.
(http://www.photophysics.com/chem_react_mech.php)

### Questions:

1. Sullivan used 578 nm light to dissociate $I_2$ molecules to I atoms.
   a) What is the energy (in kJ/mol) of 578 nm light?
   b) Breaking an $I_2$ bond requires 151 kJ/mol of energy. What is the longest wavelength of light that has enough energy to dissociate $I_2$?
2. Show that the two-step mechanism proposed by Sullivan yields the correct (overall second-order) rate law.
3. Why is a termolecular elementary step likely to be the slowest in a mechanism?
4. Determine the activation energy for the reaction of $H_2$ and $I_2$ to produce HI, given the data in the table.

| Temperature (°C) | Rate Constant ($M^{-1}s^{-1}$) |
|---|---|
| 144.7 | $1.40 \times 10^{-12}$ |
| 207.5 | $1.52 \times 10^{-9}$ |
| 246.9 | $5.15 \times 10^{-8}$ |

### Reference:

J. H. Sullivan, *Journal of Chemical Physics*, Vol. 46, pp. 73–77, 1967.

# 16 Principles of Chemical Reactivity: Equilibria

Photos © Cengage Learning/Charles D. Winters

**Solution of cobalt(II) chloride in dilute hydrochloric acid**

Solution in an ice bath

Solution in a boiling water bath

Solution after adding more hydrochloric acid

Solution after adding more water

## Dynamic and Reversible!

Chemical reactions are dynamic, as proved by experiments in which reactants and products can be interconverted by making small changes in the conditions of the reaction. Dissolving cobalt(II) chloride in dilute hydrochloric acid demonstrates this very well.

$$[Co(H_2O)_6]^{2+}(aq) + 4\ Cl^-(aq) \rightleftharpoons [CoCl_4]^{2-}(aq) + 6\ H_2O(\ell)$$

red                        blue

The photo at the top shows a solution that is a mixture of the red cation, $[Co(H_2O)_6]^{2+}$, and the blue anion, $[CoCl_4]^{2-}$. When the solution is placed in ice, the color changes to red, and when it is put in boiling water, the color is blue. Adding more hydrochloric acid also changes the color, as does adding more water.

### Questions:

1. Is the conversion of the red cation to the blue anion by changing the temperature exothermic or endothermic?
2. Account for the effect of adding hydrochloric acid and more water.
3. How do these observations prove the reaction is reversible?

**Answers to these questions are available in Appendix N.**

## CHAPTER GOALS

*See Chapter Goals Revisited (page 746) for Study Questions keyed to these goals.*

- Understand the nature and characteristics of chemical equilibria.

- Understand the significance of the equilibrium constant, $K$, and the reaction quotient, $Q$.

- Understand how to use $K$ in quantitative studies of chemical equilibria.

- Predict how a system at equilibrium will respond if the reaction conditions are changed.

**ÖWL**

Sign in to OWL at **www.cengage.com/ owl** to view tutorials and simulations, develop problem-solving skills, and complete online homework assigned by your professor.

**go Chemistry**

Download mini lecture videos for key concept review and exam prep from OWL or purchase them from **www.cengagebrain.com**

The concept of equilibrium is fundamental in chemistry. The general concept was introduced in Chapter 3, and you have already encountered its importance in explaining phenomena such as solubility, acid–base behavior, and changes of state. These preliminary discussions of equilibrium emphasized the following concepts: that chemical reactions are reversible, that chemical reactions proceed spontaneously in the direction that leads toward equilibrium, that in a closed system a state of equilibrium between reactants and products is achieved eventually, and that outside forces can affect the equilibrium. A major result of our further exploration of chemical equilibria in this and the next two chapters will be an ability to describe chemical equilibria in quantitative terms.

## 16.1 Chemical Equilibrium: A Review

If you mix solutions of $CaCl_2$ and $NaHCO_3$, a chemical reaction is immediately detected: a gas ($CO_2$) bubbles from the mixture, and white solid (insoluble) $CaCO_3$ forms (Figure 16.1a). The reaction occurring is

$$Ca^{2+}(aq) + 2\ HCO_3^-(aq) \rightarrow CaCO_3(s) + CO_2(g) + H_2O(\ell)$$

If you next add pieces of dry ice to the suspension of $CaCO_3$ (or if you bubble gaseous $CO_2$ into the mixture), you will observe that the solid $CaCO_3$ dissolves (Figure 16.1b). This happens because a reaction occurs that is the reverse of the reaction that led to precipitation of $CaCO_3$; that is:

$$CaCO_3(s) + CO_2(g) + H_2O(\ell) \rightarrow Ca^{2+}(aq) + 2\ HCO_3^-(aq)$$

Now imagine what will happen if the solution of $Ca^{2+}$ and $HCO_3^-$ ions is in a *closed* container (unlike the reaction in Figure 16.1, which was done in an open container). As the reaction begins, $Ca^{2+}$ and $HCO_3^-$ react to give products at some rate. As the reactants are depleted, the rate of this reaction slows. At the same time, however, the reaction products ($CaCO_3$, $CO_2$, and $H_2O$) begin to combine to re-form $Ca^{2+}$ and $HCO_3^-$. Eventually, the rate of the forward reaction, the formation of $CaCO_3$, and the rate of the reverse reaction, the redissolving of $CaCO_3$, become equal. With $CaCO_3$ being formed and redissolving at the same rate, no further macroscopic change is observed. Equilibrium has been achieved.

We describe an equilibrium system with an equation that connects reactants and products with double arrows. The double arrows, $\rightleftharpoons$, indicate that the reaction is reversible and that the reaction will be studied using the concepts of chemical equilibria.

$$Ca^{2+}(aq) + 2\ HCO_3^-(aq) \rightleftharpoons CaCO_3(s) + CO_2(g) + H_2O(\ell)$$

● **Cave Chemistry** This same chemistry accounts for stalactites and stalagmites in caves. See page 116.

**(a)** Combining solutions of $NaHCO_3$ and $CaCl_2$ produces solid $CaCO_3$ and $CO_2$ gas.

**(b)** Dry ice (the white solid) is added to the slurry of $CaCO_3$ precipitated in (a).

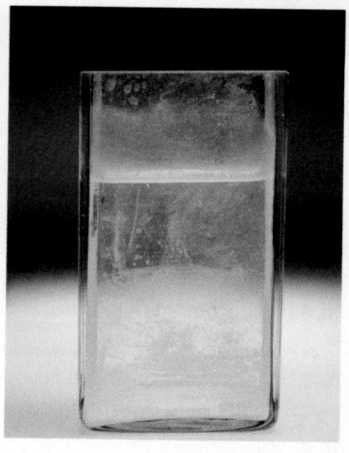

**(c)** The calcium carbonate dissolves on adding sufficient dry ice ($CO_2$) to give $Ca^{2+}(aq)$ and $HCO_3^-(aq)$.

**FIGURE 16.1 Equilibrium in the $CO_2/Ca^{2+}/H_2O$ system.** See Figure 3.5, which shows the same reaction and illustrates the chemistry of the system.

These experiments illustrate an important feature of chemical reactions: *All chemical reactions are reversible, at least in principle.* This was a key point in our earlier discussion of equilibrium (◄ Chapter 3).

Our next step will be to move from a qualitative to a quantitative description of equilibrium systems. Among other things, this will lead us to the subject of product- and reactant-favored reactions (◄ page 118). Recall that a reaction that has a greater concentration of products than reactants once it has reached equilibrium is said to be product-favored. Similarly, a reaction that has a greater concentration of reactants than products at equilibrium is said to be reactant-favored.

---

**REVIEW & CHECK FOR SECTION 16.1**

What would happen in the experiment in Figure 16.1c if you added some additional $Ca^{2+}$ ions (in the form of $CaCl_2$)?

(a)    More $CaCO_3$ would precipitate.          (c)    Nothing would happen.

(b)    Some $CaCO_3$ would dissolve.

---

## 16.2 The Equilibrium Constant and Reaction Quotient

Chemical equilibria can also be described in a quantitative fashion. The concentrations of reactants and products when a reaction has reached equilibrium are related. For the reaction of hydrogen and iodine to produce hydrogen iodide, for example, a very large number of experiments have shown that at equilibrium the ratio of the square of the HI concentration to the product of the $H_2$ and $I_2$ concentrations is a constant.

$$H_2(g) + I_2(g) \rightleftharpoons 2\,HI(g)$$

$$\frac{[HI]^2}{[H_2][I_2]} = \text{constant } (K) \text{ at equilibrium}$$

This constant is always the same within experimental error for all experiments done *at a given temperature.* Suppose, for example, the concentrations of $H_2$ and $I_2$ in a flask are each initially 0.0175 mol/L at 425 °C and no HI is present. Over time, the concentrations of $H_2$ and $I_2$ will decrease, and the concentration of HI will increase until a state of equilibrium is reached (Figure 16.2). If the gases in

$$H_2(g) + I_2(g) \rightleftharpoons 2HI(g)$$

Reactants proceeding toward equilibrium

**FIGURE 16.2 The reaction of $H_2$ and $I_2$ reaches equilibrium.** The final concentrations of $H_2$, $I_2$, and HI depend on the initial concentrations of $H_2$ and $I_2$. If one begins with a different set of initial concentrations, the equilibrium concentrations will be different, but the quotient $[HI]^2/[H_2][I_2]$ will always be the same at a given temperature.

the flask are then analyzed, the observed concentrations would be $[H_2] = [I_2] =$ 0.0037 mol/L and $[HI] = 0.0276$ mol/L. The following table—which we call an **ICE table for initial, change, and equilibrium concentrations**—summarizes these results:

● **ICE Table: Initial, Change, and Equilibrium** Throughout our discussions of chemical equilibria, we shall express the quantitative information for reactions in an amounts table or ICE table (◀ Chapter 4, page 159). These tables show what the initial (*I*) concentrations are, how those concentrations change (*C*) on proceeding to equilibrium, and what the concentrations are at equilibrium (*E*). Some students call these **RICE tables**, where R stands for "reaction."

| Equation | $H_2(g)$ | + | $I_2(g)$ | $\rightleftharpoons$ | 2 HI(g) |
|---|---|---|---|---|---|
| I = Initial concentration (M) | 0.0175 | | 0.0175 | | 0 |
| C = Change in concentration as reaction proceeds to equilibrium (M) | −0.0138 | | −0.0138 | | +0.0276 |
| E = Equilibrium concentration (M) | 0.0037 | | 0.0037 | | 0.0276 |

The second line in the table gives the change in concentration of reactants and products on proceeding to equilibrium. Changes are always equal to the difference between the equilibrium and initial concentrations.

Change in concentration = equilibrium concentration − initial concentration

Putting the equilibrium concentration values from the ICE table into the expression for the constant ($K$) gives a value of 56 (to two significant figures).

$$\frac{[HI]^2}{[H_2][I_2]} = \frac{(0.0276)^2}{(0.0037)(0.0037)} = 56$$

Other experiments can be done on the $H_2/I_2$ reaction with different concentrations of reactants, or done using mixtures of reactants and products. Regardless of the initial amounts, when equilibrium is achieved, the ratio $[HI]^2/[H_2][I_2]$ is always the same, 56, at this temperature.

The observation that the product and reactant concentrations for the $H_2$ and $I_2$ reaction are always in the same ratio can be generalized to other reactions. For the general chemical reaction

$$aA + bB \rightleftharpoons cC + dD$$

we can define the equilibrium constant, $K$.

*When the reaction is at equilibrium*

$$\text{Equilibrium constant} = K = \frac{[C]^c[D]^d}{[A]^a[B]^b} \qquad (16.1)$$

Equation 16.1 is called the **equilibrium constant expression**. If the ratio of products to reactants as defined by Equation 16.1 matches the equilibrium constant value, the system is known to be at equilibrium. Conversely, if the ratio has a

**FIGURE 16.3** Burning sulfur. Elemental sulfur burns in oxygen with a beautiful blue flame to give $SO_2$ gas.

different value, the system is not at equilibrium, and, as you will see later in this section, we can predict in which direction the reaction will proceed to reach equilibrium.

## Writing Equilibrium Constant Expressions

In an equilibrium constant expression,

- all concentrations are equilibrium values.
- product concentrations appear in the numerator, and reactant concentrations appear in the denominator.
- each concentration is raised to the power of its stoichiometric coefficient in the balanced chemical equation.
- the value of the constant $K$ depends on the particular reaction and on the temperature.
- values of $K$ are dimensionless.

### Reactions Involving Solids

The oxidation of solid, yellow sulfur produces colorless sulfur dioxide gas in a product-favored reaction (Figure 16.3).

$$S(s) + O_2(g) \rightleftharpoons SO_2(g)$$

The general principle when writing an equilibrium constant expression is to place product concentrations in the numerator and reactant concentrations in the denominator. In reactions involving solids, however, experiments show that the equilibrium concentrations of other reactants or products—here, $O_2$ and $SO_2$—do not depend on the amount of solid present (as long as some solid is present at equilibrium). Therefore, the concentration of a solid such as sulfur is not included in the equilibrium constant expression.

$$K = \frac{[SO_2]}{[O_2]}$$

In general, *the concentrations of any solid reactants and products are not included in the equilibrium constant expression.*

### Reactions in Solution

There are also special considerations for reactions occurring in solution, particularly aqueous solutions in which water is either a reactant or a product. Consider ammonia, which is a weak base owing to its incomplete reaction with water.

$$NH_3(aq) + H_2O(\ell) \rightleftharpoons NH_4^+(aq) + OH^-(aq)$$

Because the water concentration is very high in a dilute ammonia solution, the concentration of water is essentially unchanged by the reaction. The general rule *for reactions in aqueous solution is that the molar concentration of water is not included in the equilibrium constant expression.* Thus, for aqueous ammonia we write

$$K = \frac{[NH_4^+][OH^-]}{[NH_3]}$$

● $K_c$ **and** $K_p$ The subscript "c" ($K_c$) indicates that the numerical values of concentrations in the equilibrium constant expression have units of mol/L. A subscript "p" ($K_p$) indicates that partial pressures of gaseous reactants and products were used in calculating the equilibrium constant. In this chapter, we will sometimes write simply $K$ for $K_c$ but will always write $K_p$ to indicate that partial pressures were used.

### Reactions Involving Gases: $K_c$ and $K_p$

Concentration data can be used to calculate equilibrium constants for both aqueous and gaseous systems. In these cases, the symbol $K$ is sometimes given the subscript "c" for "concentration," as in $K_c$. For gases, however, equilibrium constant expressions can be written in another way—in terms of partial pressures of reactants and products. If you rearrange the ideal gas law, $[PV = nRT]$, and recognize that the "gas concentration," $(n/V)$, is equivalent to $P/RT$, you see that the partial pressure of a gas is proportional to its concentration $[P = (n/V)RT]$. If reactant and

**A CLOSER LOOK**

## Activities and Units of *K*

In the text we state that "Values of *K* are dimensionless." After all our care in using units, this might seem sloppy. However, advanced thermodynamics informs us that equilibrium constants should really be calculated from the "activities" of reactants and products and not from their concentrations or partial pressures. Activities can be thought of as "effective" concentrations or partial pressures.

The activity of a substance in solution is obtained by calculating the ratio of its concentration, [X], relative to a standard concentration (1 M) and then multiplying this ratio by a correction factor called an *activity coefficient*. Because it involves a ratio of concentrations, the activity is dimensionless. (Likewise, the activity of a gas is obtained from the ratio of its partial pressure, $P_X$, relative to a standard pressure (1 atm or 1 bar) and then multiplying by an activity coefficient.) In general chemistry, we assume all the activity coefficients are equal to 1 and so the activity of a solute or a gas is numerically the same as its concentration or partial pressure, respectively. This assumption is best met for solutes in very dilute solutions or gases at low pressures. Regardless of the values of activity coefficients, values of *K* are properly calculated using dimensionless quantities and so they have no units.

Another consequence of using activities is that the "concentration" of solids does not appear in the *K* expression. This is because the activity of a solid is 1. Similarly, water or other solvent is not included because its activity is 1.

product quantities are given in partial pressures (in atmospheres or in bars), then *K* is given the subscript "p," as in $K_p$.

$$H_2(g) + I_2(g) \rightleftharpoons 2\ HI(g)$$

$$K_p = \frac{P_{HI}^2}{P_{H_2}P_{I_2}}$$

Notice that the basic form of the equilibrium constant expression is the same as for $K_c$. In some cases, the numerical values of $K_c$ and $K_p$ are the same, but they are different when the numbers of moles of gaseous reactants and products are different. *A Closer Look: Equilibrium Constant Expressions for Gases—$K_c$ and $K_p$* shows how $K_c$ and $K_p$ are related and how to convert from one to the other.

## EXAMPLE 16.1    Writing Equilibrium Constant Expressions

**Problem**  Write the equilibrium constant expressions for the following reactions.

(a)  $N_2(g) + 3\ H_2(g) \rightleftharpoons 2\ NH_3(g)$

(b)  $H_2CO_3(aq) + H_2O(\ell) \rightleftharpoons HCO_3^-(aq) + H_3O^+(aq)$

**What Do You Know?**  You have balanced chemical equations, from which you can write the equilibrium constant expressions.

**Strategy**  Product concentrations always appear in the numerator and reactant concentrations appear in the denominator. Each concentration should be raised to a power equal to the stoichiometric coefficient in the balanced equation. In reaction (b), the water concentration does not appear in the equilibrium constant expression.

**Solution**

(a)  $K = \dfrac{[NH_3]^2}{[N_2][H_2]^3}$     (b)  $K = \dfrac{[HCO_3^-][H_3O^+]}{[H_2CO_3]}$

**Think about Your Answer**  Always check to make sure you have the products in the numerator and reactants in the denominator. Confusing these is a common source of student error.

**Check Your Understanding**

Write the equilibrium constant expression for each of the following reactions in terms of concentrations.

(a)  $CO_2(g) + C(s) \rightleftharpoons 2\ CO(g)$

(b)  $[Cu(NH_3)_4]^{2+}(aq) \rightleftharpoons Cu^{2+}(aq) + 4\ NH_3(aq)$

(c)  $CH_3CO_2H(aq) + H_2O(\ell) \rightleftharpoons CH_3CO_2^-(aq) + H_3O^+(aq)$

# Equilibrium Constant Expressions for Gases—$K_c$ and $K_p$

Many metal carbonates, such as limestone, decompose on heating to give the metal oxide and $CO_2$ gas.

$$CaCO_3(s) \rightleftharpoons CaO(s) + CO_2(g)$$

The equilibrium constant for this reaction can be expressed either in terms of the number of moles per liter of $CO_2$, $K_c = [CO_2]$, or in terms of the pressure of $CO_2$, $K_p = P_{CO_2}$. From the ideal gas law, you know that

$$P = (n/V)RT =$$
(concentration in mol/L) $\times RT$

For this reaction, we can therefore say that $P_{CO_2} = [CO_2]RT = K_p$. Because $K_c = [CO_2]$, we find that $K_p = K_c(RT)$. That is, the values of $K_p$ and $K_c$ are not the same; for the decomposition of calcium carbonate, $K_p$ is the product of $K_c$ and the factor $RT$.

Consider the equilibrium constant for the reaction of $N_2$ and $H_2$ to produce ammonia in terms of partial pressures, $K_p$.

$$N_2(g) + 3 H_2(g) \rightleftharpoons 2 NH_3(g)$$

$$K_p = \frac{(P_{NH_3})^2}{(P_{N_2})(P_{H_2})^3}$$

Does $K_c$, the equilibrium constant in terms of concentrations, have the same value as, or a different value than, $K_p$? We can answer this question by substituting for each pressure in $K_p$ the equivalent expression $[C](RT)$. That is,

$$K_p = \frac{\{[NH_3](RT)\}^2}{\{[N_2](RT)\}\{[H_2](RT)\}^3} =$$
$$\frac{[NH_3]^2}{[N_2][H_2]^3} \times \frac{1}{(RT)^2} = \frac{K_c}{(RT)^2}$$

or $K_p = K_c(RT)^{-2}$

Once again, you see that $K_p$ and $K_c$ are not the same but are related by some function of $RT$.

Looking carefully at this example and others, we find that

$$K_p = K_c(RT)^{\Delta n}$$

where $\Delta n$ is the change in the number of moles of gas on going from reactants to products.

$\Delta n$ = total moles of gaseous products − total moles of gaseous reactants

For the decomposition of $CaCO_3$,

$$\Delta n = 1 - 0 = 1$$

whereas the value of $\Delta n$ for the ammonia synthesis is

$$\Delta n = 2 - 4 = -2$$

## The Meaning of the Equilibrium Constant, $K$

Table 16.1 lists a few equilibrium constants for different kinds of reactions. A large value of $K$ means that the concentrations of the products are higher than the concentrations of the reactants at equilibrium. That is, the products are favored over the reactants at equilibrium.

$K > 1$: **Reaction is product-favored at equilibrium.** The concentrations of products are greater than the concentrations of the reactants at equilibrium.

**Table 16.1 Selected Equilibrium Constant Values**

| Reaction | Equilibrium Constant, $K$ (at 25 °C) | Product- or Reactant-Favored at Equilibrium |
|---|---|---|
| *Combination Reaction of Nonmetals* | | |
| $S(s) + O_2(g) \rightleftharpoons SO_2(g)$ | $4.2 \times 10^{52}$ | $K > 1$; product-favored |
| $2 H_2(g) + O_2(g) \rightleftharpoons 2 H_2O(g)$ | $3.2 \times 10^{81}$ | $K > 1$; product-favored |
| $N_2(g) + 3 H_2(g) \rightleftharpoons 2 NH_3(g)$ | $3.5 \times 10^8$ | $K > 1$; product-favored |
| *Ionization of Weak Acids and Bases* | | |
| $HCO_2H(aq) + H_2O(\ell) \rightleftharpoons HCO_2^-(aq) + H_3O^+(aq)$ formic acid | $1.8 \times 10^{-4}$ | $K < 1$; reactant-favored |
| $CH_3CO_2H(aq) + H_2O(\ell) \rightleftharpoons CH_3CO_2^-(aq) + H_3O^+(aq)$ acetic acid | $1.8 \times 10^{-5}$ | $K < 1$; reactant-favored |
| $H_2CO_3(aq) + H_2O(\ell) \rightleftharpoons HCO_3^-(aq) + H_3O^+(aq)$ carbonic acid | $4.2 \times 10^{-7}$ | $K < 1$; reactant-favored |
| $NH_3(aq) + H_2O(\ell) \rightleftharpoons NH_4^+(aq) + OH^-(aq)$ ammonia | $1.8 \times 10^{-5}$ | $K < 1$; reactant-favored |
| *Dissolution of "Insoluble" Solids* | | |
| $CaCO_3(s) \rightleftharpoons Ca^{2+}(aq) + CO_3^{2-}(aq)$ | $3.8 \times 10^{-9}$ | $K < 1$; reactant-favored |
| $AgCl(s) \rightleftharpoons Ag^+(aq) + Cl^-(aq)$ | $1.8 \times 10^{-10}$ | $K < 1$; reactant-favored |

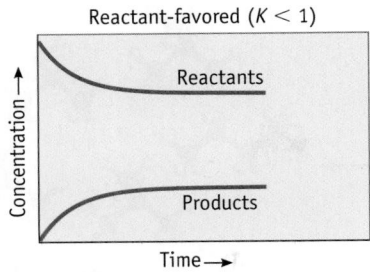

**(a)** The concentrations of products exceeds the concentrations of reactants at equilibrium, and the reaction is product-favored.

**(b)** The reactant concentrations exceed the product concentrations at equilibrium, and the reaction is reactant-favored.

**FIGURE 16.4** The difference between reactions that are product-favored or reactant-favored at equilibrium.

An example is the reaction of nitrogen monoxide and ozone.

$$NO(g) + O_3(g) \rightleftharpoons NO_2(g) + O_2(g)$$

$$K = \frac{[NO_2][O_2]}{[NO][O_3]} = 6 \times 10^{34} \text{ at } 25 \text{ °C}$$

The very large value of $K$ indicates that, at equilibrium, $[NO_2][O_2] \gg [NO][O_3]$. If stoichiometric amounts of NO and $O_3$ are mixed and allowed to come to equilibrium, virtually none of the reactants will be found (Figure 16.4a). Essentially, all will have been converted to $NO_2$ and $O_2$. A chemist would say that "the reaction has gone to completion."

Conversely, a small value of $K$ means that very little of the products exists when equilibrium has been achieved (Figure 16.4b). That is, the reactants are favored over the products at equilibrium.

**$K < 1$: Reaction is reactant-favored at equilibrium.** Concentrations of reactants are greater than concentrations of products at equilibrium.

This is true for the formation of ozone from oxygen.

$$3/2 \, O_2(g) \rightleftharpoons O_3(g)$$

$$K = \frac{[O_3]}{[O_2]^{3/2}} = 2.5 \times 10^{-29} \text{ at } 25 \text{ °C}$$

The very small value of $K$ indicates that, at equilibrium, $[O_3] \ll [O_2]^{3/2}$. If $O_2$ is placed in a flask, very little $O_2$ will have been converted to $O_3$ when equilibrium has been achieved.

When $K$ is close to 1, it may not be immediately clear whether the reactant concentrations are larger than the product concentrations, or vice versa. It will depend on the form of $K$ and thus on the reaction stoichiometry. Calculations of the concentrations will have to be done.

## The Reaction Quotient, Q

The equilibrium constant, $K$, for a reaction has a particular numerical value when the reactants and products are at equilibrium. When the reactants and products in a reaction are not at equilibrium, however, it is convenient to calculate the reaction quotient, $Q$. For the general reaction of A and B to give C and D,

$$aA + bB \rightleftharpoons cC + dD$$

the reaction quotient is defined as

$$\text{Reaction quotient} = Q = \frac{[C]^c[D]^d}{[A]^a[B]^b} \qquad (16.2)$$

**(a)** Not at equilibrium. $Q = 4/3 < K$.

Here, four isobutane molecules and three butane molecules are present. Reaction will proceed to convert butane into isobutane to reach equilibrium.

**(b)** At equilibrium. $Q = 5/2 = K$.

Here, five isobutane molecules and two butane molecules are present. Reaction is at equilibrium.

**(c)** Not at equilibrium. $Q = 6/1 > K$.

Here, six isobutane molecules and one butane molecule are present. Reaction will proceed to convert isobutane into butane to reach equilibrium.

**FIGURE 16.5 The interconversion of isobutane and butane.** Only when the concentrations of isobutane and butane are in the ratio [isobutane]/[butane] = 2.5 is the system at equilibrium (b). With any other ratio of concentrations, there will be a net conversion of one compound into the other until equilibrium is achieved.

This expression appears to be just like the expression for the equilibrium constant, $K$, in Equation 16.1, but it is not. In calculating $K$, the concentrations must be those present *at equilibrium*. The concentrations of reactants and products in the expression for $Q$ are those that occur at any point as the reaction proceeds from reactants to an equilibrium mixture. Only when the system is at equilibrium does $Q = K$. For the reaction of $H_2$ and $I_2$ to give HI (Figure 16.2), any combination of reactant and product concentrations before equilibrium is achieved will give a value of $Q$ different than $K$.

Determining a reaction quotient is useful for two reasons. First, it will tell you whether a system is at equilibrium (when $Q = K$) or is not at equilibrium (when $Q \neq K$). Second, by comparing $Q$ and $K$, we can predict what changes will occur in reactant and product concentrations as the reaction proceeds to equilibrium.

● **Comparing $Q$ and $K$**

| Relative Magnitude | Direction of Reaction |
|---|---|
| $Q < K$ | Reactants → Products |
| $Q = K$ | Reaction at equilibrium |
| $Q > K$ | Reactants ← Products |

- $Q < K$: If $Q$ is less than $K$, some reactants must be converted to products for the reaction to reach equilibrium. This will decrease the reactant concentrations and increase the product concentrations. (This is the case for the system in Figure 16.5a.)
- $Q > K$: If $Q$ is greater than $K$, some products must be converted to reactants for the reaction to reach equilibrium. This will increase the reactant concentrations and decrease the product concentrations (Figure 16.5c).

To illustrate these points, let us consider a reaction such as the transformation of butane to isobutane (2-methylpropane).

Butane  ⇌  Isobutane

$$CH_3CH_2CH_2CH_3 \quad \rightleftharpoons \quad CH_3\overset{\overset{\displaystyle CH_3}{|}}{C}HCH_3$$

$$K_c = \frac{[\text{isobutane}]}{[\text{butane}]} = 2.50 \text{ at } 298 \text{ K}$$

Any mixture of butane and isobutane, whether at equilibrium or not, can be represented by the reaction quotient $Q$ ($=$[isobutane]/[butane]). Suppose you have a mixture composed of 3.0 mol/L of butane and 4.0 mol/L of isobutane (at 298 $K$) (Figure 16.5a). This means that the reaction quotient, $Q$, is

$$Q = \frac{\left[\text{isobutane}\right]}{\left[\text{butane}\right]} = \frac{4.0}{3.0} = 1.3$$

This set of concentrations clearly does not represent an equilibrium system because $Q < K$. To reach equilibrium, some butane molecules must be transformed into molecules of isobutane, thereby lowering [butane] and raising [isobutane]. This transformation will continue until the ratio [isobutane]/[butane] = 2.5; that is, until $Q = K$ (Figure 16.5b).

What happens when there is too much isobutane in the system relative to the amount of butane? Suppose [isobutane] = 6.0 mol/L but [butane] is only 1.0 mol/L (Figure 16.5c). Now the reaction quotient $Q$ is greater than $K$ ($Q > K$), and the system is again not at equilibrium. It will proceed to equilibrium by converting isobutane molecules to butane molecules.

## ✪WL INTERACTIVE EXAMPLE 16.2    The Reaction Quotient

**Problem** The brown gas nitrogen dioxide, $NO_2$, can exist in equilibrium with the colorless gas $N_2O_4$. $K = 170$ at 298 K for the reaction

$$2\ NO_2(g) \rightleftharpoons N_2O_4(g)\quad K = 170$$

Suppose that, at a specific time, the concentration of $NO_2$ is 0.015 M and the concentration of $N_2O_4$ is 0.025 M. Is $Q$ larger than, smaller than, or equal to $K$? If the system is not at equilibrium, in which direction will the reaction proceed to achieve equilibrium?

**What Do You Know?** You are given the balanced chemical equation, the value of the equilibrium constant $K_c$, and concentrations of reactant and product.

**Strategy**

- Write the expression for the reaction quotient, $Q$, from the balanced equation.

- Substitute concentrations of reactant and product into the expression and calculate $Q$.

- Decide if $Q$ is greater than, less than, or equal to $K_c$ and in which direction the reaction will proceed.

**Solution**

$$Q = \frac{[N_2O_4]}{[NO_2]^2} = \frac{(0.025)}{(0.015)^2} = 110$$

The value of $Q$ is less than the value of $K$ ($Q < K$), so the reaction is not at equilibrium. The system proceeds to equilibrium by converting $NO_2$ to $N_2O_4$, increasing [$N_2O_4$], and decreasing [$NO_2$] until $Q = K$.

**Think about Your Answer** When calculating $Q$, make sure that you raise each concentration to the power corresponding to the stoichiometric coefficient.

---

**Check Your Understanding**

Answer the following questions regarding the butane $\rightleftharpoons$ isobutane equilibrium ($K = 2.50$ at 298 K).

(a) Is the system at equilibrium when [butane] = 0.97 M and [isobutane] = 2.18 M? If not, in which direction will the reaction proceed to achieve equilibrium?

(b) Is the system at equilibrium when [butane] = 0.75 M and [isobutane] = 2.60 M? If not, in which direction will the reaction proceed to achieve equilibrium?

---

**Strategy Map 16.2**

**PROBLEM**

Is a reaction at **equilibrium**? If not, which way does it proceed? Calculate **Q**.

↓

**DATA/INFORMATION KNOWN**

- Balanced equation
- Value of **K**
- Concentrations of **reactant** and **product**

STEP 1. Write **Q** expression and calculate **Q**.

Calculated **Q** from reactant and product concentrations

STEP 2. Compare **Q** and **K**.

**Q** (110) < **K** (170)
More product forms from reactant to reach equilibrium.

---

**REVIEW & CHECK FOR SECTION 16.2**

1.  Which of the following is the correct form of the equilibrium constant expression for the reaction below?

$$2 SO_3(g) \rightleftharpoons 2 SO_2(g) + O_2(g)$$

    (a)  $K = [SO_2][O_2]/[SO_3]$               (c)  $K = [SO_3]^2/[SO_2]^2[O_2]$

    (b)  $K = [SO_2]^2[O_2]/[SO_3]^2$            (d)  $K = [SO_2][O_2]^2$

2.  At 2000 K the equilibrium constant for the formation of NO(g) is $4.0 \times 10^{-4}$.

$$N_2(g) + O_2(g) \rightleftharpoons 2 NO(g)$$

You have a flask in which, at 2000 K, the concentration of $N_2$ is 0.50 mol/L, that of $O_2$ is 0.25 mol/L, and that of NO is $4.2 \times 10^{-3}$ mol/L. Is the system at equilibrium?

    (a)  Yes, it is at equilibrium.

    (b)  No, it is not at equilibrium, and the reaction proceeds further to the right.

    (c)  No, it is not at equilibrium, and the reaction proceeds to the left, turning products into reactants.

---

## 16.3 Determining an Equilibrium Constant

When the experimental values of the concentrations of all of the reactants and products are known at equilibrium, an equilibrium constant can be calculated by substituting the data into the equilibrium constant expression. Consider this concept as it applies to the oxidation of sulfur dioxide.

$$2 SO_2(g) + O_2(g) \rightleftharpoons 2 SO_3(g)$$

In an experiment done at 852 K, the equilibrium concentrations are found to be $[SO_2] = 3.61 \times 10^{-3}$ mol/L, $[O_2] = 6.11 \times 10^{-4}$ mol/L, and $[SO_3] = 1.01 \times 10^{-2}$ mol/L. Substituting these data into the equilibrium constant expression, we can calculate the value of $K$.

$$K = \frac{[SO_3]^2}{[SO_2]^2[O_2]} = \frac{(1.01 \times 10^{-2})^2}{(3.61 \times 10^{-3})^2(6.11 \times 10^{-4})} = 1.28 \times 10^4 \text{ at 852 K}$$

(Notice that $K$ has a large value; at equilibrium, the oxidation of sulfur dioxide is product-favored at 852 K.)

More commonly, an experiment will provide information on the initial quantities of reactants and the concentration at equilibrium of only one of the reactants or of one of the products. The equilibrium concentrations of the rest of the reactants and products must then be inferred from the reaction stoichiometry. As an example, again consider the oxidation of sulfur dioxide to sulfur trioxide. Suppose that 1.00 mol of $SO_2$ and 1.00 mol of $O_2$ are placed in a 1.00-L flask, this time at 1000 K. When equilibrium has been achieved, 0.925 mol of $SO_3$ has been formed. Let us use this information to calculate the equilibrium constant for the reaction. After writing the equilibrium constant expression in terms of concentrations, we set up an ICE table (page 723) showing the initial concentrations, the changes in those concentrations on proceeding to equilibrium, and the concentrations at equilibrium.

| Equation | 2 SO₂(g) | + | O₂(g) | ⇌ | 2 SO₃(g) |
|---|---|---|---|---|---|
| Initial (M) | 1.00 | | 1.00 | | 0 |
| Change (M) | $-2x$ | | $-x$ | | $+2x$ |
| Equilibrium (M) | $1.00 - 2x$ | | $1.00 - x$ | | $2x$ |
| | $1.00 - 0.925 = 0.075$ | | $1.00 - 0.925/2 = 0.54$ | | $= 0.925$ |

The quantities in the ICE table result from the following analysis:

- Line 1: Original concentrations.
- Line 2: The amount of $O_2$ consumed is designated as $-x$ mol/L. We give it a minus sign because $O_2$ is consumed. It then follows from the reaction stoichiometry that the amount of $SO_2$ consumed is $-2x$, and the amount of $SO_3$ produced is $+2x$.
- Lines 3 and 4:
  (a) We know from experiment that $[SO_3]$ at equilibrium is 0.925 M. Therefore, $2x = 0.925$ M.
  (b) The equilibrium concentration of $SO_2$ is equal to the initial concentration minus what was consumed. Therefore, $[SO_2]$ is $(1.00 - 2x)$M or 0.075 M.
  (c) The amount of $O_2$ consumed is half of the amount of $SO_3$ produced or $x$ $(= 0.463$ mol/L$)$. Therefore, the equilibrium concentration of $O_2$ is 0.54 M.

With the equilibrium concentrations now known, it is possible to calculate $K$.

$$K = \frac{[SO_3]^2}{[SO_2]^2[O_2]} = \frac{(0.925)^2}{(0.075)^2(0.54)} = 2.8 \times 10^2 \text{ at 1000 K}$$

---

⏺WL   **INTERACTIVE EXAMPLE 16.3**   Calculating an Equilibrium Constant ($K_c$) Using Concentrations

**Problem** In aqueous solution iron(III) ions react with iodide ions to give iron(II) ions and triiodide ions, $I_3^-$. Suppose the initial concentration of $Fe^{3+}$ ions is 0.200 M, the initial $I^-$ ion concentration is 0.300 M, and the equilibrium concentration of $I_3^-$ ions is 0.0866 M. What is the value of $K_c$?

$$2\ Fe^{3+}(aq) + 3\ I^-(aq) \rightleftharpoons 2\ Fe^{2+}(aq) + I_3^-(aq)$$

**What Do You Know?** You are given the balanced equation (from which the equilibrium constant expression can be written), initial concentrations of the reactants, and the concentration of one product ($I_3^-$) after equilibrium has been reached.

**Strategy**

- Set up an ICE table and enter the initial concentrations.

- Decide how each concentration changes. Let us begin by saying that $x$ mol/L of $I_3^-$ ions are produced on proceeding to equilibrium. Based on the reaction stoichiometry, this means that $2x$ mol/L of $Fe^{2+}$ must also be produced, $2x$ mol/L of $Fe^{3+}$ ions are consumed, and $3x$ mol/L of $I^-$ ions are consumed.

- The equilibrium concentration of $I_3^-$ is known (0.0866 M), so this is the quantity $x$.

- Knowing that $x = 0.0866$ M, calculate the equilibrium concentrations for each species.

- Enter the equilibrium concentrations of reactants and products into the equilibrium constant expression and solve for $K_c$.

**Solution** The strategy outlined leads to the ICE table below.

| Equation | 2 Fe³⁺ | + | 3 I⁻ | ⇌ | 2 Fe²⁺ | + | I₃⁻ |
|---|---|---|---|---|---|---|---|
| Initial (M) | 0.200 | | 0.300 | | 0 | | 0 |
| Change (M) | −2x | | −3x | | +2x | | +x |
| Equilibrium (M) | 0.200 − 2(0.0866) | | 0.300 − 3(0.0866) | | 2(0.0866) | | 0.0866 |
| | = 0.027 | | = 0.040 | | = 0.173 | | |

The concentration of each substance at equilibrium is now known, and $K$ can be calculated.

$$K_c = \frac{[Fe^{2+}]^2[I_3^-]}{[Fe^{3+}]^2[I^-]^3} = \frac{(0.173)^2(0.0866)}{(0.027)^2(0.040)^3} = 5.6 \times 10^4$$

**Strategy Map 16.3**

**PROBLEM**

Calculate $K_c$ for reaction of $Fe^{3+}$ with $I^-$ to give $Fe^{2+}$ and $I_3^-$.

**DATA/INFORMATION KNOWN**

- Balanced equation
- **Initial concentrations** of reactants
- **Equilibrium concentration** of one product

STEP 1. Organize information.

Write $K_c$ **expression**, set up **ICE table**, and enter *known concentrations* in the table.

STEP 2. Enter *concentration changes* in ICE table and derive **equilibrium concentrations**.

Complete **ICE table** with equilibrium concentrations known.

STEP 3. Enter **equilibrium concentrations** in $K_c$ expression and solve for $K_c$.

Value of $K_c$

**Think about Your Answer** The key to this problem is that the concentration of one product, $I_3^-$, was known at equilibrium. The concentrations of the other product and of the reactants could be derived from this based on the reaction stoichiometry. Also notice that the calculated $K$ is much greater than one, so the reaction is product-favored at equilibrium. This is consistent with the equilibrium concentrations calculated in the ICE table.

**Check Your Understanding**

A solution is prepared by dissolving 0.050 mol of diiodocyclohexane, $C_6H_{10}I_2$, in the solvent $CCl_4$. The total solution volume is 1.00 L. When the reaction

$$C_6H_{10}I_2 \rightleftharpoons C_6H_{10} + I_2$$

has come to equilibrium at 35 °C, the concentration of $I_2$ is 0.035 mol/L.

(a) What are the concentrations of $C_6H_{10}I_2$ and $C_6H_{10}$ at equilibrium?

(b) Calculate $K_c$, the equilibrium constant.

## EXAMPLE 16.4 Calculating an Equilibrium Constant ($K_p$) Using Partial Pressures

**Problem** Suppose a tank initially contains $H_2S$ at a pressure of 10.00 atm and a temperature of 800 K. When the reaction has come to equilibrium, the partial pressure of $S_2$ vapor is 0.020 atm. Calculate $K_p$.

$$2\,H_2S(g) \rightleftharpoons 2\,H_2(g) + S_2(g)$$

**What Do You Know?** You are given the balanced equation (from which the equilibrium constant expression for $K_p$ can be written), the initial pressure of the reactant ($H_2S$), and the pressure of one product ($S_2$) after equilibrium has been reached.

**Strategy**

• Set up an ICE table and enter the initial pressures of $H_2S$, $H_2$, and $S_2$.

• Define the change in $S_2$ concentration as $+x$.

• From the reaction stoichiometry you know that the change in the partial pressure of $H_2$ is twice that of $S_2$ ($= +2x$ atm) and that the change in $H_2S$ partial pressure is $-2x$.

• The equilibrium partial pressure of $S_2$ is given, so you know that $x = 0.020$ atm. From this calculate the equilibrium partial pressures for $H_2S$ and $H_2$.

• Enter the equilibrium pressures of reactants and products into the equilibrium constant expression and solve for $K_p$.

**Solution** Following the strategy outlined gives the ICE table below.

| Equation | 2 H₂S(g) | ⇌ | 2 H₂(g) | + | S₂(g) |
|---|---|---|---|---|---|
| Initial (atm) | 10.00 | | 0 | | 0 |
| Change (atm) | −2x | | +2x | | +x |
| Equilibrium (atm) | 10.00 − 2x | | 2(0.020) | | 0.020 |
| | 10.00 − 0.040 = 9.96 | | = 0.040 | | |

Now that the partial pressures of all of the reactants and products are known, $K_p$ can be calculated.

$$K_p = \frac{(P_{H_2})^2 P_{S_2}}{(P_{H_2S})^2} = \frac{(0.040)^2(0.020)}{(9.96)^2} = 3.2 \times 10^{-7}$$

**Think about Your Answer** The value of $K_p$ calculated is much less than 1, therefore this reaction is reactant-favored at equilibrium, as also indicated by the concentrations calculated in the ICE table. The value of $K_p$ is the same as the value of $K_c$ only when the number of moles of gaseous reactants is the same as the number of moles of gaseous products. This is not true here, so $K_p \neq K_c$. (See *A Closer Look*, page 726).

**Check Your Understanding**

Pure $PCl_5$ gas is placed in a 2.00-L flask. After heating to 250 °C the pressure of $PCl_5$ is initially 2.000 atm. However, the gas slowly but only partially decomposes to gaseous $PCl_3$ and $Cl_2$. When equilibrium is reached, the partial pressure of $Cl_2$ is 0.814 atm. Calculate $K_p$ for the decomposition.

---

**REVIEW & CHECK FOR SECTION 16.3**

You place 0.010 mol of $N_2O_4(g)$ in a 2.0-L flask at 200 °C. After reaching equilibrium, $[N_2O_4]$ = 0.0042 M. Calculate $K_c$ for the following reaction: $N_2O_4(g) \rightleftharpoons 2\ NO_2(g)$

(a)  1640

(c)  $3.1 \times 10^{-4}$

(b)  $6.1 \times 10^{-4}$

(d)  $8.8 \times 10^{-6}$

---

# 16.4 Using Equilibrium Constants in Calculations

In many cases, the value of $K$ and the initial concentrations of reactants are known, and you want to know the concentrations present at equilibrium. As we look at several examples of this situation, we will again use ICE tables that summarize the initial conditions, the changes occurring on proceeding to equilibrium, and the final conditions.

**⊙WL  INTERACTIVE EXAMPLE 16.5**  Calculating Equilibrium Concentrations

**Problem** The equilibrium constant $K_c$ (= 55.64) for

$$H_2(g) + I_2(g) \rightleftharpoons 2\ HI(g)$$

has been determined at 425 °C. If 1.00 mol each of $H_2$ and $I_2$ is placed in a 0.500-L flask at 425 °C, what are the concentrations of $H_2$, $I_2$, and HI when equilibrium has been achieved?

**What Do You Know?** You are given the balanced equation (from which the equilibrium constant expression can be written), the value of $K$, and the initial amounts of the reactants and the volume of the container (from which initial concentrations of the reactants can be calculated).

**Strategy**

- Write the equilibrium constant expression and set up an ICE table.

- Enter the initial concentrations of $H_2$ and $I_2$ on the first line (I).

- Assign the variable $x$ to represent changes in concentration. Based on the reaction stoichiometry the change in $[H_2]$ and $[I_2]$ is $-x$ and the change in $[HI]$ is $+2x$. Enter these values into the change (C) line of the table.

- Enter the expressions for the final equilibrium concentrations of all three species on the third line (E) of the ICE table, and then transfer these expressions to the equilibrium constant expression and solve for $x$.

- Use the calculated value of $x$ to solve for the final concentration of each species.

**Strategy Map 16.5**

**PROBLEM**

What are the **equilibrium concentrations** of $H_2$, $I_2$, and **HI** in formation of HI from $H_2$ and $I_2$?

↓

**DATA/INFORMATION KNOWN**

- Balanced equation
- Value of $K_c$
- **Initial concentrations** of reactants

↓

STEP 1. Organize information.

Write $K_c$ expression, set up **ICE table**, and enter *known concentrations* in the table.

STEP 2. Enter *concentration changes* in ICE table and derive **equilibrium concentrations** in terms of unknown quantity $x$.

Equilibrium concentrations of $H_2$, $I_2$, and **HI** are defined in terms of the unknown quantity $x$.

STEP 3. Enter **equilibrium concentrations** in $K_c$ expression and solve for $x$.

Value of $x$

↓

STEP 4. Use value of $x$ to derive **equilibrium concentrations**.

Values of equilibrium concentrations

**Module 21: Chemical Equilibrium**
covers concepts in this section.

**Solution** Write the equilibrium constant expression

$$K = \frac{[HI]^2}{[H_2][I_2]} = 55.64$$

and then set up the ICE table as outlined in the Strategy.

| Equation | $H_2(g)$ | + | $I_2(g)$ | $\rightleftharpoons$ | 2 HI(g) |
|---|---|---|---|---|---|
| Initial (M) | 1.00 mol/0.500 L = 2.00 M | | 1.00 mol/0.500 L = 2.00 M | | 0 |
| Change (M) | $-x$ | | $-x$ | | $+2x$ |
| Equilibrium (M) | $2.00 - x$ | | $2.00 - x$ | | $2x$ |

Now the expressions for the equilibrium concentrations can be substituted into the equilibrium constant expression.

$$55.64 = \frac{(2x)^2}{(2.00 - x)(2.00 - x)} = \frac{(2x)^2}{(2.00 - x)^2}$$

In this case, you can solve for the unknown quantity $x$ by taking the square root of both sides of the equation,

$$\sqrt{K} = 7.459 = \frac{2x}{2.00 - x}$$
$$7.459 (2.00 - x) = 14.9 - 7.459x = 2x$$
$$14.9 = 9.459x$$
$$x = 1.58$$

With $x$ known, you can solve for the equilibrium concentrations of the reactants and products.

$$[H_2] = [I_2] = 2.00 - x = 0.42 \text{ M}$$

$$[HI] = 2x = 3.16 \text{ M}$$

**Think about Your Answer** It is always wise to verify the answer by substituting the value of each concentration back into the equilibrium expression to see if your calculated $K$ agrees with the one given in the problem. In this case, $(3.16)^2/(0.42)^2 = 57$. The slight discrepancy with the given value, $K = 55.64$, occurs because we know $[H_2]$ and $[I_2]$ to only two significant figures.

---

**Check Your Understanding**

At some temperature, $K_c = 33$ for the reaction

$$H_2(g) + I_2(g) \rightleftharpoons 2 \text{ HI}(g)$$

Assume the initial concentrations of both $H_2$ and $I_2$ are $6.00 \times 10^{-3}$ mol/L. Find the concentration of each reactant and product at equilibrium.

---

## Calculations Where the Solution Involves a Quadratic Expression

Suppose you are studying the decomposition of $PCl_5$ to form $PCl_3$ and $Cl_2$. You know that $K = 1.20$ at a given temperature.

$$PCl_5(g) \rightleftharpoons PCl_3(g) + Cl_2(g)$$

If the initial concentration of $PCl_5$ is 1.60 M, what will be the concentrations of reactant and products when the system reaches equilibrium? Following the procedures outlined in Example 16.5, you would set up an ICE table to define the equilibrium concentrations of reactants and products.

| Reaction | $PCl_5(g)$ | $\rightleftharpoons$ | $PCl_3(g)$ | + | $Cl_2(g)$ |
|---|---|---|---|---|---|
| Initial (M) | 1.60 | | 0 | | 0 |
| Change (M) | $-x$ | | $+x$ | | $+x$ |
| Equilibrium (M) | $1.60 - x$ | | $x$ | | $x$ |

Substituting into the equilibrium constant expression, we have

$$K = 1.20 = \frac{[PCl_3][Cl_2]}{[PCl_5]} = \frac{(x)(x)}{1.60 - x}$$

Expanding the algebraic expression results in a quadratic equation,

$$x^2 + 1.20x - 1.92 = 0$$

Using the quadratic formula (Appendix A; $a = 1$, $b = 1.20$, and $c = -1.92$), we find two roots to the equation: $x = 0.91$ and $-2.11$. Because a negative value of $x$ (which represents a negative concentration) is not chemically meaningful, the answer is $x = 0.91$. Therefore, at equilibrium we have

$$[PCl_5] = 1.60 - 0.91 = 0.69 \text{ M}$$

$$[PCl_3] = [Cl_2] = 0.91 \text{ M}$$

Although a solution to a quadratic equation can always be obtained using the quadratic formula, in many instances an acceptable answer can be obtained by using a realistic approximation to simplify the equation. To illustrate this, consider another equilibrium, the dissociation of $I_2$ molecules to form I atoms, for which $K = 5.6 \times 10^{-12}$ at 500 K.

$$I_2(g) \rightleftharpoons 2\ I(g)$$

$$K = \frac{[I]^2}{[I_2]} = 5.6 \times 10^{-12}$$

Assuming the initial $I_2$ concentration is 0.45 M and setting up the ICE table in the usual manner, we have

| Reaction | $I_2(g)$ | $\rightleftharpoons$ | $2\ I(g)$ |
|---|---|---|---|
| Initial (M) | 0.45 | | 0 |
| Change (M) | $-x$ | | $+2x$ |
| Equilibrium (M) | $0.45 - x$ | | $2x$ |

For the equilibrium constant expression, we again arrive at a quadratic equation.

$$K = 5.6 \times 10^{-12} = \frac{(2x)^2}{(0.45 - x)}$$

Although we could solve this equation using the quadratic formula, there is a simpler way to reach an answer. Notice that the value of $K$ is very small, indicating that the amount of $I_2$ that will be dissociated ($= x$) is very small. In fact, $K$ is so small that subtracting $x$ from the original reactant concentration (0.45 mol/L) in the denominator of the equilibrium constant expression will leave the denominator essentially unchanged. That is, $(0.45 - x)$ is essentially equal to 0.45. Thus, we drop $x$ in the denominator and have a simpler equation to solve.

$$K = 5.6 \times 10^{-12} = \frac{(2x)^2}{(0.45)}$$

The solution to this equation gives $x = 7.9 \times 10^{-7}$. From this value, we can determine that $[I_2] = 0.45 - x = 0.45$ mol/L and $[I] = 2x = 1.6 \times 10^{-6}$ mol/L. Notice that the answer to the $I_2$ dissociation problem confirms the assumption the dissociation of $I_2$ is so small that $[I_2]$ at equilibrium is essentially equal to the initial concentration.

When is it possible to simplify a quadratic equation? The decision depends on both the value of the initial concentration of the reactant and the value of $x$, which is in turn related to the value of $K$. Consider the general reaction

$$A \rightleftharpoons B + C$$

● **Solving Quadratic Equations**
Quadratic equations are usually solved using the quadratic formula (Appendix A). An alternative is the *method of successive approximations*, also outlined in Appendix A. Most equilibrium expressions can be solved quickly by this method, and you are urged to try it. This will remove the uncertainty of whether $K$ expressions need to be solved exactly. (There are, however, rare cases in which this does not work.)

In most equilibrium calculations, the quantity $x$ may be neglected in the denominator of the equation $K = x^2/([A]_0 - x)$ if $x$ is less than 10% of the quantity of reactant initially present. The guideline presented in the text for making the approximation that $[A]_0 - x = [A]_0$ when $100 \times K < [A]_0$ reflects this fact.

# When Do You Need to Use the Quadratic Equation?

In general, when $K$ is about 1 or greater, the approximation cannot be made. If $K$ is much less than 1 and $100 \times K < [A]_0$ (you will see many such cases in Chapter 17), the approximate expression ($K = x^2/[A]_0$) gives an acceptable answer. If you are not certain, then first make the assumption that the unknown ($x$) is small, and solve the approximate expression ($K = (x)^2/[A]_0$). Next, compare the "approximate" value of $x$ with $[A]_0$. If $x$ has a value equal to or less than 10% of $[A]_0$, then there is no need to solve the full equation using the quadratic formula.

where $K = [B][C]/[A]$. Assume you know $K$ and the initial concentration of A ($= [A]_0$) and wish to find the equilibrium concentrations of B and C ($= x$). The equilibrium constant expression now is

$$K = \frac{[B][C]}{[A]} = \frac{(x)(x)}{[A]_0 - x}$$

When $K$ is very small, the value of $x$ will be much less than $[A]_0$, so $[A]_0 - x \cong [A]_0$. Therefore, we can write the following expression.

$$K = \frac{[B][C]}{[A]} \approx \frac{(x)(x)}{[A]_0} \tag{16.3}$$

If $100 \times K < [A]_0$, the approximate expression will give acceptable values of equilibrium concentrations (to two significant figures). For more about this useful guideline, see *Problem Solving Tip 16.1*.

## Strategy Map 16.6

**PROBLEM**

What are the **equilibrium concentrations** of $N_2$, $O_2$, and **NO** in formation of NO from $N_2$ and $O_2$?

↓

**DATA/INFORMATION KNOWN**

- Balanced equation
- Value of $K_c$
- **Initial concentrations** of reactants

> **STEP 1.** Enter *concentration changes* in ICE table and derive **equilibrium concentrations** in terms of unknown quantity $x$.

**Equilibrium concentrations** of $N_2$, $O_2$, and **NO** are defined in terms of the unknown quantity $x$.

> **STEP 2.** Enter **equilibrium concentrations** in $K_c$ expression and solve for $x$.

Value of $x$

> **STEP 3.** Use value of $x$ to derive **equilibrium concentrations**.

Values of equilibrium concentrations

## ⌾WL   INTERACTIVE EXAMPLE 16.6   Calculating Equilibrium Concentrations Using an Equilibrium Constant

**Problem** The reaction

$$N_2(g) + O_2(g) \rightleftharpoons 2\ NO(g)$$

contributes to air pollution whenever a fuel is burned in air at a high temperature, as in a gasoline engine. At 1500 K, $K = 1.0 \times 10^{-5}$. Suppose a sample of air has $[N_2] = 0.80$ mol/L and $[O_2] = 0.20$ mol/L before any reaction occurs. Calculate the equilibrium concentrations of reactants and products after the mixture has been heated to 1500 K.

**What Do You Know?** As in Example 16.5, you know the value of $K$ and can write the equilibrium expression from the balanced equation. You also know the initial concentrations of the reactants and can define the equilibrium concentrations in terms of the amounts of $N_2$ and $O_2$ consumed ($= x$).

**Strategy** Set up an ICE table, and then substitute the equilibrium concentrations into the equilibrium constant expression. The result will be a quadratic equation. This expression can be solved using the methods outlined in Appendix A or by using the guideline in the text to simplify the calculation.

**Solution** We first set up an ICE table where the amounts of $N_2$ and $O_2$ consumed are designated as $x$.

| Equation | $N_2(g)$ | + | $O_2(g)$ | $\rightleftharpoons$ | $2\ NO(g)$ |
|---|---|---|---|---|---|
| Initial (M) | 0.80 | | 0.20 | | 0 |
| Change (M) | $-x$ | | $-x$ | | $+2x$ |
| Equilibrium (M) | $0.80 - x$ | | $0.20 - x$ | | $2x$ |

Next, the equilibrium concentrations are substituted into the equilibrium constant expression.

$$K = 1.0 \times 10^{-5} = \frac{[NO]^2}{[N_2][O_2]} = \frac{[2x]^2}{(0.80 - x)(0.20 - x)}$$

We refer to the guideline (Equation 16.3) to decide whether an approximate solution is possible. Here, $100 \times K \,(= 1.0 \times 10^{-3})$ is smaller than either of the initial reactant concentrations (0.80 and 0.20). This means we can use the approximate expression

$$K = 1.0 \times 10^{-5} = \frac{[NO]^2}{[N_2][O_2]} = \frac{(2x)^2}{(0.80)(0.20)}$$

Solving this expression, we find

$$1.6 \times 10^{-6} = 4x^2$$

$$x = 6.3 \times 10^{-4}$$

Therefore, the reactant and product concentrations at equilibrium are

$$[N_2] = 0.80 - 6.3 \times 10^{-4} \approx 0.80 \text{ M}$$

$$[O_2] = 0.20 - 6.3 \times 10^{-4} \approx 0.20 \text{ M}$$

$$[NO] = 2x = 1.3 \times 10^{-3} \text{ M}$$

**Think about Your Answer** The value of $x$ obtained using the approximation is the same as that obtained from the quadratic formula. If the full equilibrium constant expression is expanded, we have

$$(1.0 \times 10^{-5})(0.80 - x)(0.20 - x) = 4x^2$$

$$(1.0 \times 10^{-5})(0.16 - 1.00x + x^2) = 4x^2$$

$$\underbrace{(4 - 1.0 \times 10^{-5})x^2}_{ax^2} + \underbrace{(1.0 \times 10^{-5})x}_{bx} - \underbrace{0.16 \times 10^{-5}}_{c} = 0$$

The two roots to this equation are:

$$x = 6.3 \times 10^{-4} \text{ or } x = -6.3 \times 10^{-4}$$

The only meaningful root is identical to the approximate answer obtained above. The approximation is indeed valid in this case.

---

**Check Your Understanding**

The decomposition of $PCl_5(g)$ to form $PCl_3(g)$ and $Cl_2(g)$ has $K_c = 33.3$ at a high temperature. If the initial concentration of $PCl_5$ is 0.1000 M, what are the equilibrium concentrations of the reactants and products?

---

**REVIEW & CHECK FOR SECTION 16.4**

Graphite and carbon dioxide are kept at constant volume at 1000 K until the reaction

$$C(\text{graphite}) + CO_2(g) \rightleftharpoons 2\,CO(g)$$

has come to equilibrium. At this temperature, $K = 0.021$. The initial concentration of $CO_2$ is 0.012 mol/L. Calculate the equilibrium concentration of CO.

(a)  0.012 M

(c)  0.0057 M

(b)  0.011 M

## 16.5 More about Balanced Equations and Equilibrium Constants

Chemical equations can be balanced using different sets of stoichiometric coefficients. For example, the equation for the oxidation of carbon to give carbon monoxide can be written

$$C(s) + \tfrac{1}{2} O_2(g) \rightleftharpoons CO(g)$$

In this case, the equilibrium constant expression would be

$$K_1 = \frac{[CO]}{[O_2]^{1/2}} = 4.6 \times 10^{23} \text{ at } 25 \text{ °C}$$

You can write the chemical equation equally well, however, as

$$2\ C(s) + O_2(g) \rightleftharpoons 2\ CO(g)$$

and the equilibrium constant expression would now be

$$K_2 = \frac{[CO]^2}{[O_2]} = 2.1 \times 10^{47} \text{ at } 25 \text{ °C}$$

When you compare the two equilibrium constant expressions you find that $K_2 = (K_1)^2$; that is,

$$K_2 = \frac{[CO]^2}{[O_2]} = \left\{ \frac{[CO]}{[O_2]^{1/2}} \right\}^2 = K_1^2$$

*When the stoichiometric coefficients of a balanced equation are multiplied by some factor, the equilibrium constant for the new equation ($K_{new}$) is the old equilibrium constant ($K_{old}$) raised to the power of the multiplication factor.*

In the case of the oxidation of carbon, the second equation was obtained by multiplying the first equation by two. Therefore, $K_2$ is the *square* of $K_1$ ($K_2 = K_1^2$).

Let us consider what happens if a chemical equation is reversed. Here, we will compare the value of $K$ for formic acid transferring an $H^+$ ion to water

$$HCO_2H(aq) + H_2O(\ell) \rightleftharpoons HCO_2^-(aq) + H_3O^+(aq)$$

$$K_1 = \frac{[HCO_2^-][H_3O^+]}{[HCO_2H]} = 1.8 \times 10^{-4} \text{ at } 25 \text{ °C}$$

with the opposite reaction, the gain of an $H^+$ ion by the formate ion, $HCO_2^-$.

$$HCO_2^-(aq) + H_3O^+(aq) \rightleftharpoons HCO_2H(aq) + H_2O(\ell)$$

$$K_2 = \frac{[HCO_2H]}{[HCO_2^-][H_3O^+]} = 5.6 \times 10^3 \text{ at } 25 \text{ °C}$$

Here, $K_2 = 1/K_1$.

*The equilibrium constants for a reaction and its reverse are the reciprocals of one another.*

It is often useful to add two equations to obtain the equation for a net process. As an example, consider the reactions that take place when silver chloride dissolves in water (to a *very* small extent) and ammonia is added to the solution. Ammonia reacts with silver ions to form a water-soluble compound, $Ag(NH_3)_2Cl$ (Figure 16.6). Adding the equation for dissolving solid AgCl to the equation for the reaction of $Ag^+$ ions with ammonia gives the equation for the net reaction, dissolving solid AgCl in aqueous ammonia. (All equilibrium constants are given at 25 °C.)

$$AgCl(s) \rightleftharpoons Ag^+(aq) + Cl^-(aq) \qquad K_1 = [Ag^+][Cl^-] = 1.8 \times 10^{-10}$$

$$Ag^+(aq) + 2\ NH_3(aq) \rightleftharpoons [Ag(NH_3)_2]^+(aq) \qquad K_2 = \frac{[Ag(NH_3)_2^+]}{[Ag^+][NH_3]^2} = 1.1 \times 10^7$$

Net equation:

$$AgCl(s) + 2\ NH_3(aq) \rightleftharpoons [Ag(NH_3)_2]^+(aq) + Cl^-(aq)$$

# Balanced Equations and Equilibrium Constants

You should now know

1. how to write an equilibrium constant expression from the balanced equation, recognizing that the concentrations of solids and liquids used as solvents do not appear in the expression.

2. that when the stoichiometric coefficients in a balanced equation are changed by a factor of $n$, $K_{new} = (K_{old})^n$.

3. that when a balanced equation is reversed, $K_{new} = 1/K_{old}$.

4. that when several balanced equations (each with its own equilibrium constant, $K_1$, $K_2$, etc.) are added to obtain a net, balanced equation, $K_{net} = K_1 \times K_2 \times K_3 \times \ldots$ .

**FIGURE 16.6  Dissolving silver chloride in aqueous ammonia.** *(left)* A precipitate of AgCl(s) is suspended in water. *(right)* When aqueous ammonia is added, the ammonia reacts with the trace of silver ion in solution, the equilibrium shifts, and the silver chloride dissolves.

To obtain the equilibrium constant for the net reaction, $K_{net}$, we *multiply* the equilibrium constants for the two reactions, $K_1$ by $K_2$.

$$K_{net} = K_1 \times K_2 = [Ag^+][Cl^-] \times \frac{[Ag(NH_3)_2^+]}{[Ag^+][NH_3]^2} = \frac{[Ag(NH_3)_2^+][Cl^-]}{[NH_3]^2}$$

$$K_{net} = K_1 \times K_2 = 2.0 \times 10^{-3}$$

*When two or more chemical equations are added to produce a net equation, the equilibrium constant for the net equation is the product of the equilibrium constants for the added equations.*

## EXAMPLE 16.7    Balanced Equations and Equilibrium Constants

**Problem**  A mixture of nitrogen, hydrogen, and ammonia is brought to equilibrium. When the equation is written using whole-number coefficients, as follows, the value of $K$ is $3.5 \times 10^8$ at 25 °C.

*Equation 1:*  $\quad\quad\quad N_2(g) + 3\ H_2(g) \rightleftharpoons 2\ NH_3(g) \quad\quad K_1 = 3.5 \times 10^8$

However, the equation can also be written as given in Equation 2. What is the value of $K_2$?

*Equation 2:*  $\quad\quad\quad \frac{1}{2}\ N_2(g) + \frac{3}{2}\ H_2(g) \rightleftharpoons NH_3(g) \quad\quad K_2 = ?$

The decomposition of ammonia to the elements (Equation 3) is the reverse of its formation (Equation 1). What is the value of $K_3$?

*Equation 3:*  $\quad\quad\quad 2\ NH_3(g) \rightleftharpoons N_2(g) + 3\ H_2(g) \quad\quad K_3 = ?$

**What Do You Know?**  You know the value of $K$ for a given balanced equation. You want to know how the value of $K$ changes as the stoichiometric coefficients change or when the equation is reversed.

**Strategy** Determine how the desired reaction is related to the given reaction(s). (Was a given chemical reaction multiplied by a factor? Was a reaction reversed? Were two or more reactions added?) Use the relationships discussed to determine the effect(s) of these transformations on the given $K$ value(s). See also *Problem Solving Tip 16.2*.

**Solution** Equation 2 can be obtained by multiplying Equation 1 by 1/2. Thus $K_2$ is equal to $K_1$ raised to the one-half power, $K_1^{1/2}$. To confirm this relationship between $K_1$ and $K_2$, write the equilibrium constant expressions for these two balanced equations.

$$K_1 = \frac{[NH_3]^2}{[N_2][H_2]^3} \qquad K_2 = \frac{[NH_3]}{[N_2]^{1/2}[H_2]^{3/2}}$$

Writing these expressions makes it clear that $K_2$ is the square root of $K_1$.

$$K_2 = (K_1)^{1/2} = \sqrt{K_1} = \sqrt{3.5 \times 10^8} = 1.9 \times 10^4$$

Equation 3 is the reverse of Equation 1, and its equilibrium constant expression is

$$K_3 = \frac{[N_2][H_2]^3}{[NH_3]^2}$$

In this case, $K_3$ is the reciprocal of $K_1$. That is, $K_3 = 1/K_1$.

$$K_3 = \frac{1}{K_1} = \frac{1}{3.5 \times 10^8} = 2.9 \times 10^{-9}$$

**Think about Your Answer**

Notice that the production of ammonia from the elements has a large equilibrium constant and is product-favored (see Section 16.2). As expected, the reverse reaction, the decomposition of ammonia to its elements, has a small equilibrium constant and is reactant-favored.

**Check Your Understanding**

The conversion of oxygen to ozone has a very small equilibrium constant.

$$3/2\ O_2(g) \rightleftharpoons O_3(g) \qquad K = 2.5 \times 10^{-29}$$

(a) What is the value of $K$ when the equation is written using whole-number coefficients?

$$3\ O_2(g) \rightleftharpoons 2\ O_3(g)$$

(b) What is the value of $K$ for the conversion of ozone to oxygen?

$$2\ O_3(g) \rightleftharpoons 3\ O_2(g)$$

**REVIEW & CHECK FOR SECTION 16.5**

The following equilibrium constants are given at 500 K:

| | |
|---|---|
| $H_2(g) + Br_2(g) \rightleftharpoons 2\ HBr(g)$ | $K_p = 7.9 \times 10^{11}$ |
| $H_2(g) \rightleftharpoons 2\ H(g)$ | $K_p = 4.8 \times 10^{-41}$ |
| $Br_2(g) \rightleftharpoons 2\ Br$ | $K_p = 2.2 \times 10^{-15}$ |

Calculate $K_p$ for the reaction $H + Br \rightarrow HBr$.

(a) $K_p = 8.3 \times 10^{-44}$    (b) $K_p = 7.5 \times 10^{66}$    (c) $K_p = 2.7 \times 10^{33}$

# 16.6 Disturbing a Chemical Equilibrium

The equilibrium between reactants and products may be disturbed in three ways: (1) by changing the temperature, (2) by changing the concentration of a reactant or product, or (3) by changing the volume (for systems involving gases) (Table 16.2).

**Table 16.2  Effects of Disturbances on Equilibrium Composition**

| Disturbance | Change as Mixture Returns to Equilibrium | Effect on Equilibrium | Effect on *K* |
|---|---|---|---|
| *Reactions Involving Solids, Liquids, or Gases* | | | |
| Rise in temperature | Energy is consumed by system | Shift in endothermic direction | Change |
| Drop in temperature | Energy is generated by system | Shift in exothermic direction | Change |
| Addition of reactant* | Some of added reactant is consumed | Product concentration increases | No change |
| Addition of product* | Some of added product is consumed | Reactant concentration increases | No change |
| *Reactions Involving Gases* | | | |
| Decrease in volume, increase in pressure | Pressure decreases | Composition changes to reduce total number of gas molecules | No change |
| Increase in volume, decrease in pressure | Pressure increases | Composition changes to increase total number of gas molecules | No change |

*Does not apply when an insoluble solid reactant or product is added. Recall that their "concentrations" do not appear in the reaction quotient.

*A change in any of the factors that determine the equilibrium conditions of a system will cause the system to change in such a manner as to reduce or counteract the effect of the change.* This statement is often referred to as *Le Chatelier's principle* (◄ page 627). It is a shorthand way of saying how the quantities of reactants and products are adjusted so that equilibrium is restored, that is, so that the reaction quotient is once again equal to the equilibrium constant.

## Effect of the Addition or Removal of a Reactant or Product

If the concentration of a reactant or product is changed from its equilibrium value *at a given temperature,* equilibrium will be reestablished eventually. The new equilibrium concentrations of reactants and products will be different, but the value of the equilibrium constant expression will still equal *K* (Table 16.2). To illustrate this, let us return to the butane/isobutane equilibrium (with $K = 2.5$).

$$CH_3CH_2CH_2CH_3 \rightleftharpoons \underset{\text{isobutane}}{CH_3\overset{\overset{\displaystyle CH_3}{|}}{C}HCH_3} \qquad K = 2.5$$

$$\underset{\text{butane}}{}$$

Suppose the equilibrium mixture consists of two molecules of butane and five molecules of isobutane (Figure 16.7). The reaction quotient, *Q,* is 5/2 (or 2.5/1), the

| Seven isobutane are added. | | The system returns to equilibrium. |
|---|---|---|

$Q = 5/2 = K$

An equilibrium mixture of five isobutane molecules and two butane molecules.

$Q = 12/2 > K$

Seven isobutane molecules are added, so the system is no longer at equilibrium.

$Q = 10/4 = K$

A net of two isobutane molecules has changed to butane molecules, to once again give an equilibrium mixture where the ratio of isobutane to butane is 5:2 (or 2.5:1).

**FIGURE 16.7  Addition of more reactant or product to an equilibrium system.**

value of the equilibrium constant for the reaction. Now we add seven more molecules of isobutane to the mixture to give a ratio of 12 isobutane molecules to two butane molecules. The reaction quotient is now 6/1. This means $Q$ is greater than $K$, and the system will change to reestablish equilibrium. To do so, some molecules of isobutane must be changed into butane molecules, a process that continues until the ratio [isobutane]/[butane] is once again 2.5/1. In this particular case, if two of the 12 isobutane molecules change to butane, the ratio of isobutane to butane is again equal to $K$ (= 10/4 = 2.5/1), and equilibrium is reestablished.

**Strategy Map 16.8**

**PROBLEM**

What are the **equilibrium concentrations** of reactant and product after adding **excess reactant?**

↓

**DATA/INFORMATION KNOWN**

- Balanced equation
- Value of $K_c$
- **Initial concentrations** of **reactant** and **product** and amount of **excess reactant** added

**STEP 1.** Enter **concentration changes** in ICE table and derive **equilibrium concentrations** in terms of unknown quantity **x.**

**Equilibrium concentrations** of **reactant** and **product** are defined in terms of the unknown quantity **x.**

**STEP 2.** Enter **equilibrium concentrations** in $K_c$ **expression** and solve for **x.**

Value of **x**

**STEP 3.** Use value of **x** to derive **equilibrium concentrations.**

Values of equilibrium concentrations

**◉WL  INTERACTIVE EXAMPLE 16.8  Effect of Concentration Changes on Equilibrium**

**Problem**  Assume equilibrium has been established in a 1.00-L flask with [butane] = 0.500 mol/L and [isobutane] = 1.25 mol/L.

$$\text{Butane} \rightleftharpoons \text{Isobutane} \qquad K = 2.50$$

Then 1.50 mol of butane is added. What are the concentrations of butane and isobutane when equilibrium is reestablished?

**What Do You Know?**  Here you know the value of $K$, the balanced equation, the original equilibrium concentrations of reactant and product, and the amount of reactant added to the system at equilibrium.

**Strategy**  After adding excess butane, $Q < K$. To reestablish equilibrium, the concentration of butane must decrease by an amount $x$ and that of isobutane must increase, also by an amount $x$. Use an ICE table to track the changes.

**Solution**  First organize the information in a modified ICE table.

| Equation | Butane | ⇌ | Isobutane |
|---|---|---|---|
| Initial (M) | 0.500 | | 1.25 |
| Concentration immediately on adding butane (M) | 0.500 + 1.50 | | 1.25 |
| Change in concentration to reestablish equilibrium (M) | −x | | +x |
| Equilibrium (M) | 0.500 + 1.50 − x | | 1.25 + x |

The entries in this table were arrived at as follows:

(a)  The concentration of butane when equilibrium is reestablished will be the original equilibrium concentration plus what was added (1.50 mol/L) minus the concentration of butane that is converted to isobutane to reestablish equilibrium. The quantity of butane converted to isobutane is unknown and so is designated as $x$.

(b)  The concentration of isobutane when equilibrium is reestablished is the concentration that was already present (1.25 mol/L) plus the concentration formed ($x$ mol/L) on reestablishing equilibrium.

Having defined [butane] and [isobutane] when equilibrium is reestablished and remembering that $K$ is a constant (= 2.50), we can write

$$K = 2.50 = \frac{[\text{isobutane}]}{[\text{butane}]}$$

We now calculate the new equilibrium composition:

$$2.50 = \frac{1.25 + x}{0.500 + 1.50 - x} = \frac{1.25 + x}{2.00 - x}$$

$$2.50\,(2.00 - x) = 1.25 + x$$

$$x = 1.07 \text{ mol/L}$$

[butane] = 0.500 + 1.50 − x = 0.93 M and [isobutane] = 1.25 + x = 2.32 M

Answer check: new ratio [isobutane]/[butane] = 2.32/0.93 = 2.5

**Think about Your Answer** It is useful to see a graphical solution to this problem because it emphasizes the point that, after adding excess butane, some butane is consumed on proceeding to the new equilibrium mixture and additional isobutane is formed. In the diagram here any mixture of butane and isobutane lying on the equilibrium line represents an equilibrium mixture. Mixtures in the blue portion of the diagram have $Q > K$, whereas those in the tan portion have $Q < K$. In this case, adding butane produced a mixture in the $Q < K$ region of the diagram. As predicted by Le Chatelier's principle, the added "stress" on the system is relieved by converting some butane to isobutane to achieve a new equilibrium mixture when $Q = K$.

A graphical representation of the butane–isobutane problem.

---

**Check Your Understanding**

Equilibrium exists between butane and isobutane when [butane] = 0.20 M and [isobutane] = 0.50 M. An additional 2.00 mol/L of isobutane is added to the mixture. What are the concentrations of butane and isobutane after equilibrium has again been attained?

---

## Effect of Volume Changes on Gas-Phase Equilibria

For a reaction that involves gases, what happens to equilibrium concentrations or pressures if the size of the container is changed? (Such a change occurs, for example, when fuel and air are compressed in an automobile engine.) To answer this question, recall that concentrations are in moles per liter. If the volume of a gas changes, its concentration therefore must also change, and the equilibrium composition can change. As an example, consider the following equilibrium:

$$2\ NO_2(g) \rightleftharpoons N_2O_4(g)$$

    brown gas          colorless gas

$$K_c = \frac{[N_2O_4]}{[NO_2]^2} = 170 \text{ at } 298 \text{ K}$$

What happens to this equilibrium if the volume of the flask holding the gases is suddenly halved? The immediate result is that the concentrations of both gases will double. For example, assume equilibrium is established when $[N_2O_4]$ is 0.0280 mol/L and $[NO_2]$ is 0.0128 mol/L. When the volume is halved, $[N_2O_4]$ becomes 0.0560 mol/L, and $[NO_2]$ is 0.0256 mol/L. The reaction quotient, $Q$, under these circumstances is $(0.0560)/(0.0256)^2 = 85.4$, a value less than $K$. Because $Q$ is less than $K$, the quantity of product must increase at the expense of the reactants to return to equilibrium, and the new equilibrium composition will have a higher concentration of $N_2O_4$ than immediately after the volume change.

$$2\ NO_2(g) \rightleftharpoons N_2O_4(g)$$

         $\xrightarrow{\text{decrease volume of container}}$
         $NO_2$ is converted to $N_2O_4$
         until equilibrium is attained

The concentration of $NO_2$ decreases twice as much as the concentration of $N_2O_4$ increases because one molecule of $N_2O_4$ is formed by consuming two molecules of

$NO_2$. This occurs until the reaction quotient, $Q = [N_2O_4]/[NO_2]^2$, is once again equal to $K$. The net effect of the volume decrease is to decrease the number of molecules in the gas phase.

The conclusions for the $NO_2/N_2O_4$ equilibrium can be generalized:

- For reactions involving gases, the stress of a volume decrease (a pressure increase) will be counterbalanced by a change in the equilibrium composition to one having a smaller number of gas molecules.
- For a volume increase (a pressure decrease), the equilibrium composition will favor the side of the reaction with the larger number of gas molecules.
- For a reaction in which there is no change in the number of gas molecules in proceeding from reactants to products, such as in the reaction of $H_2$ and $I_2$ to produce HI [$H_2(g) + I_2(g) \rightleftharpoons 2\,HI(g)$], a volume change will have no effect.

## Effect of Temperature Changes on Equilibrium Composition

The value of the equilibrium constant for a given reaction varies with temperature. Changing the temperature of a system at equilibrium is therefore different in some ways from the other means we have studied of disturbing a chemical equilibrium because the equilibrium constant itself will be different at the new temperature from what it was at the previous temperature. Predicting the exact changes in equilibrium compositions with temperature is beyond the scope of this text, but you can make a qualitative prediction about the effect if you know whether the reaction is exothermic or endothermic. As an example, consider the endothermic reaction of $N_2$ with $O_2$ to give NO.

$$N_2(g) + O_2(g) \rightleftharpoons 2\,NO(g) \qquad \Delta_r H° = +180.6 \text{ kJ/mol-rxn}$$

$$K = \frac{[NO]^2}{[N_2][O_2]}$$

Le Chatelier's principle allows us to predict how the value of $K$ will vary with temperature. The formation of NO from $N_2$ and $O_2$ is endothermic; that is, energy must be provided as heat for the reaction to occur. We might imagine that heat is a "reactant." If the system is at equilibrium and the temperature then increases, the system will adjust to alleviate this "stress." The way to counteract the energy input is to use up some of the energy added as heat by consuming $N_2$ and $O_2$ and producing more NO as the system returns to equilibrium. This raises the value of the numerator ($[NO]^2$) and lowers the value of the denominator ($[N_2][O_2]$) in the reaction quotient, $Q$, resulting in a higher value of $K$.

This prediction is borne out. The following table lists the equilibrium constant for this reaction at various temperatures. As predicted, the equilibrium constant and thus the proportion of NO in the equilibrium mixture increases with temperature.

| Equilibrium Constant, $K$ | Temperature (K) |
| --- | --- |
| $4.5 \times 10^{-31}$ | 298 |
| $6.7 \times 10^{-10}$ | 900 |
| $1.7 \times 10^{-3}$ | 2300 |

As another example, consider the combination of molecules of the brown gas $NO_2$ to form colorless $N_2O_4$. An equilibrium between these compounds is readily achieved in a closed system (Figure 16.8).

$$2\,NO_2(g) \rightleftharpoons N_2O_4(g) \qquad \Delta_r H° = -57.1 \text{ kJ/mol-rxn}$$

$$K = \frac{[N_2O_4]}{[NO_2]^2}$$

| Equilibrium Constant, $K$ | Temperature (K) |
| --- | --- |
| 1300 | 273 |
| 170 | 298 |

Higher temperature                                                    Lower temperature

**FIGURE 16.8 Effect of temperature on an equilibrium.** The tubes in the photograph both contain gaseous $NO_2$ (brown) and $N_2O_4$ (colorless) at equilibrium. $K$ is larger at the lower temperature because the equilibrium favors colorless $N_2O_4$. This is clearly seen in the tube at the right, where the gas in the ice bath at 0 °C is only slightly brown, which indicates a smaller concentration of the brown gas $NO_2$. At 50 °C (the tube at the left), the equilibrium is shifted toward $NO_2$, as indicated by the darker brown color.

Here, the reaction is exothermic, so we might imagine heat as being a reaction "product." By lowering the temperature of the system, as in Figure 16.8, some energy is removed as heat. The removal of energy can be counteracted if the reaction produces energy as heat by the combination of $NO_2$ molecules to give more $N_2O_4$. Thus, the equilibrium concentration of $NO_2$ decreases; the concentration of $N_2O_4$ increases; and the value of $K$ is larger at lower temperatures.

In summary,

- when the temperature of a system at equilibrium increases, the equilibrium will shift in the direction that absorbs energy as heat (Table 16.2)—that is, in the endothermic direction.
- if the temperature decreases, the equilibrium will shift in the direction that releases energy as heat—that is, in the exothermic direction.
- changing the temperature changes the value of $K$.

---

**REVIEW & CHECK FOR SECTION 16.6**

The formation of ammonia from its elements is an important industrial process.

$$3 H_2(g) + N_2(g) \rightleftharpoons 2 NH_3(g)$$

1. Does the reaction shift to the right or to the left, or does it remain unchanged, when extra $H_2$ is added?

  (a) shift left                              (c) unchanged

  (b) shift right

2. Does the reaction shift to the right or to the left, or does it remain unchanged, when the volume of the system is increased?

  (a) shift left                              (c) unchanged

  (b) shift right

3. For the equilibrium $2 SO_2(g) + O_2(g) \rightleftharpoons 2 SO_3(g)$, $K$ has the following values: $4.0 \times 10^{24}$ at 300 K, $2.5 \times 10^{10}$ at 500 K, and $3.0 \times 10^4$ at 700 K. Is this reaction exothermic or endothermic?

  (a) exothermic                              (b) endothermic

# Applying Equilibrium Concepts—The Haber-Bosch Ammonia Process

Nitrogen-containing substances are used around the world to stimulate the growth of field crops. Farmers from Portugal to Tibet have used animal waste for centuries as a "natural" fertilizer. In the 19th century, industrialized countries imported nitrogen-rich marine bird manure from Peru, Bolivia, and Chile, but the supply of this material was clearly limited. In 1898, William Ramsay (the discoverer of the noble gases, page 109) pointed out that the amount of "fixed nitrogen" in the world was being depleted and predicted that world food shortages would occur by the mid-20th century as a result. That Ramsay's prediction failed to materialize was due in part to the work of Fritz Haber (1868–1934). In about 1908, Haber developed a method to make ammonia directly from the elements,

$$N_2(g) + 3\ H_2(g) \rightleftharpoons 2\ NH_3(g)$$

and, a few years later, Carl Bosch (1874–1940) perfected the industrial scale synthesis. Ammonia is now made for pennies per kilogram and is consistently ranked in the top five chemicals produced in the United States, with 15–20 billion kilograms produced annually. Not only is ammonia used directly as a fertilizer, but it is also a starting material for making nitric acid and ammonium nitrate, among other things.

The manufacture of ammonia (Figure A) is a good example of the role that kinetics and chemical equilibria play in practical chemistry.

The $N_2 + H_2$ reaction is exothermic and product-favored ($K > 1$ at 25 °C).

At 25 °C, $K$ (calc'd value) $= 3.5 \times 10^8$ and $\Delta_r H° = -92.2$ kJ/mol-rxn

Unfortunately, the reaction at 25 °C is slow, so it is carried out at a higher temperature to increase the reaction rate. The problem with this, however, is that the equilibrium constant declines with temperature, as predicted by Le Chatelier's principle.

At 450 °C, $K$ (experimental value) $= 0.16$ and $\Delta_r H° = -111.3$ kJ/mol-rxn

Thus, the yield declines with increasing temperature.

**Figure A** **The Haber-Bosch process for ammonia synthesis.** A mixture of $H_2$ and $N_2$ is pumped over a catalytic surface. The $NH_3$ is collected as a liquid (at $-33$ °C), and unchanged reactants are recycled in the catalytic chamber.

There are two things that can be done. The first is to raise the pressure. This does not change the value of $K$, but an increase in pressure can be compensated by converting 4 mol of reactants to 2 mol of product.

In an industrial ammonia plant, it is necessary to balance reaction rate (improved at higher temperature) with product yield ($K$ is smaller at higher temperatures). Additionally, a catalyst is often used to accelerate the reaction. An effective catalyst for the Haber-Bosch process is $Fe_3O_4$ mixed with KOH, $SiO_2$, and $Al_2O_3$ (all inexpensive chemicals). Because the catalyst is not effective below 400 °C, the process is carried out at 450–500 °C and 250 atm pressure.

## Questions:

1. Anhydrous ammonia is used directly as a fertilizer, but much of it is also converted to other fertilizers, ammonium nitrate and urea.
   (a) How is $NH_3$ converted to ammonium nitrate?

   (b) Urea is formed in the reaction of ammonia and $CO_2$.

   $$2\ NH_3(g) + CO_2(g) \rightleftharpoons (NH_2)_2CO(s) + H_2O(g)$$

   Which would favor urea production, high temperature or high pressure? ($\Delta_f H°$ for solid urea $= -333.1$ kJ/mol-rxn)

2. One important aspect of the Haber-Bosch process is the source of the hydrogen. This is made from natural gas in a process called *steam reforming*.

   $$CH_4(g) + H_2O(g) \rightarrow CO(g) + 3\ H_2(g)$$
   $$CO(g) + H_2O(g) \rightarrow CO_2(g) + H_2(g)$$

   (a) Are the two reactions above endo- or exothermic?
   (b) To obtain the $H_2$ necessary to manufacture 15 billion kilograms of $NH_3$, how much $CH_4$ is required, and what mass of $CO_2$ is produced as a by-product?

   **Answers to these questions are available in Appendix N.**

---

## CHAPTER GOALS REVISITED

*Now that you have studied this chapter, you should ask whether you have met the chapter goals. In particular, you should be able to:*

### Understand the nature and characteristics of chemical equilibria

a. Chemical reactions are reversible and equilibria are dynamic (Section 16.1).

**Understand the significance of the equilibrium constant, *K*, and reaction quotient, *Q*.**

a. Write the reaction quotient, *Q*, for a chemical reaction (Section 16.2). When the system is at equilibrium, the reaction quotient is called the *equilibrium constant expression* and has a constant value called the *equilibrium constant*, which is symbolized by *K* (Equation 16.1). **Study Questions: 1–4.**

b. Recognize that the concentrations of solids, pure liquids, and solvents (e.g., water) are not included in the equilibrium constant expression (Section 16.2).

c. Recognize that a large value of *K* (*K* > 1) means the reaction is product-favored, and the product concentrations are greater than the reactant concentrations at equilibrium. A small value of *K* (*K* < 1) indicates a reactant-favored reaction in which the product concentrations are smaller than the reactant concentrations at equilibrium (Section 16.2). **Study Questions: 66, 68.**

d. Appreciate the fact that equilibrium concentrations may be expressed in terms of reactant and product concentrations (in moles per liter) and that *K* is then sometimes designated as $K_c$. Alternatively, concentrations of gases may be represented by partial pressures, and *K* for such cases is designated $K_p$ (Section 16.2). **Study Questions: 53, 60.**

**Understand how to use *K* in quantitative studies of chemical equilibria**

a. Use the reaction quotient (*Q*) to decide whether a reaction is at equilibrium (*Q* = *K*), or if there will be a net conversion of reactants to products (*Q* < *K*) or products to reactants (*Q* > *K*) to attain equilibrium (Section 16.2). **Study Questions: 3–6, 35, 36.**

b. Calculate an equilibrium constant given the reactant and product concentrations at equilibrium (Section 16.3). **Study Questions: 7–11, 29, 33, 34, 44, 61a.**

c. Use equilibrium constants to calculate the concentration (or pressure) of a reactant or a product at equilibrium (Section 16.4). **Study Questions: 16, 17, 32, 36, 42, 46, 47, 50–54, 56, 59–61, and Go Chemistry Module 21.**

d. Know how *K* changes as different stoichiometric coefficients are used in a balanced equation, if the equation is reversed, or if several equations are added to give a new net equation (Section 16.5). **Study Questions: 19–24, 31, 37.**

**Predict how a system at equilibrium will respond if the reaction conditions are changed.**

a. Know how to predict, using Le Chatelier's principle, the effect of a disturbance on a chemical equilibrium—a change in temperature, a change in concentrations, or a change in volume or pressure for a reaction involving gases (Section 16.6 and Table 16.2). **Study Questions: 25–28, 39, 41, 54, 62.**

# Key Equations

**Equation 16.1 (page 723)** The equilibrium constant expression. At equilibrium, the ratio of products to reactants (each raised to the power corresponding to its stoichiometric coefficient) has a constant value, *K* (at a particular temperature). For the general reaction $aA + bB \rightleftharpoons cC + dD$,

$$\text{Equilibrium constant} = K = \frac{[C]^c[D]^d}{[A]^a[B]^b}$$

**Equation 16.2 (page 727)** For the general reaction $aA + bB \rightleftharpoons cC + dD$, the ratio of product to reactant concentrations at any point in the reaction is the reaction quotient, *Q*.

$$\text{Reaction quotient} = Q = \frac{[C]^c[D]^d}{[A]^a[B]^b}$$

**Equation 16.3 (page 736)** This approximation is used to solve for the equilibrium concentrations of *B* and *C* (= *x*) in the general reaction $A \rightleftharpoons B + C$ when the value of $100 \times K$ is less than the original concentration of $A (= [A]_0)$.

$$K = \frac{[B][C]}{[A]} \approx \frac{(x)(x)}{[A]_0}$$

 **and**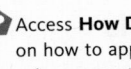

Sign in at **www.cengage.com/owl** to:
- View tutorials and simulations, develop problem-solving skills, and complete online homework assigned by your professor.
- For quick review and exam prep, download Go Chemistry mini lecture modules from OWL (or purchase them at **www.cengagebrain.com**)

❓ Access **How Do I Solve It?** tutorials on how to approach problem solving using concepts in this chapter.

# Study Questions

⭕WL Interactive versions of these questions are assignable in OWL.

▲ denotes challenging questions.

Blue-numbered questions have answers in Appendix R and fully worked solutions in the *Student Solutions Manual*.

## Practicing Skills

### Writing Equilibrium Constant Expressions
*(See Section 16.2 and Example 16.1.)*

1. Write equilibrium constant expressions for the following reactions. For gases, use either pressures or concentrations.
   (a) $2 H_2O_2(g) \rightleftharpoons 2 H_2O(g) + O_2(g)$
   (b) $CO(g) + \frac{1}{2} O_2(g) \rightleftharpoons CO_2(g)$
   (c) $C(s) + CO_2(g) \rightleftharpoons 2 CO(g)$
   (d) $NiO(s) + CO(g) \rightleftharpoons Ni(s) + CO_2(g)$

2. Write equilibrium constant expressions for the following reactions. For gases, use either pressures or concentrations.
   (a) $3 O_2(g) \rightleftharpoons 2 O_3(g)$
   (b) $Fe(s) + 5 CO(g) \rightleftharpoons Fe(CO)_5(g)$
   (c) $(NH_4)_2CO_3(s) \rightleftharpoons 2 NH_3(g) + CO_2(g) + H_2O(g)$
   (d) $Ag_2SO_4(s) \rightleftharpoons 2 Ag^+(aq) + SO_4^{2-}(aq)$

### The Equilibrium Constant and Reaction Quotient
*(See Section 16.2 and Example 16.2.)*

3. $K_c = 5.6 \times 10^{-12}$ at 500 K for the dissociation of iodine molecules to iodine atoms.

   $$I_2(g) \rightleftharpoons 2 I(g)$$

   A mixture has $[I_2] = 0.020$ mol/L and $[I] = 2.0 \times 10^{-8}$ mol/L. Is the reaction at equilibrium (at 500 K)? If not, which way must the reaction proceed to reach equilibrium?

4. The reaction

   $$2 NO_2(g) \rightleftharpoons N_2O_4(g)$$

   has an equilibrium constant, $K_c$, of 170 at 25 °C. If $2.0 \times 10^{-3}$ mol of $NO_2$ is present in a 10.-L flask along with $1.5 \times 10^{-3}$ mol of $N_2O_4$, is the system at equilibrium? If it is not at equilibrium, does the concentration of $NO_2$ increase or decrease as the system proceeds to equilibrium?

5. A mixture of $SO_2$, $O_2$, and $SO_3$ at 1000 K contains the gases at the following concentrations: $[SO_2] = 5.0 \times 10^{-3}$ mol/L, $[O_2] = 1.9 \times 10^{-3}$ mol/L, and $[SO_3] = 6.9 \times 10^{-3}$ mol/L. Is the reaction at equilibrium? If not, which way will the reaction proceed to reach equilibrium?

   $$2 SO_2(g) + O_2(g) \rightleftharpoons 2 SO_3(g) \quad K_c = 279$$

6. The equilibrium constant, $K_c$, for the reaction

   $$2 NOCl(g) \rightleftharpoons 2 NO(g) + Cl_2(g)$$

   is $3.9 \times 10^{-3}$ at 300 °C. A mixture contains the gases at the following concentrations: $[NOCl] = 5.0 \times 10^{-3}$ mol/L, $[NO] = 2.5 \times 10^{-3}$ mol/L, and $[Cl_2] = 2.0 \times 10^{-3}$ mol/L. Is the reaction at equilibrium at 300 °C? If not, in which direction does the reaction proceed to come to equilibrium?

### Calculating an Equilibrium Constant
*(See Section 16.3 and Examples 16.3 and 16.4.)*

7. The reaction

   $$PCl_5(g) \rightleftharpoons PCl_3(g) + Cl_2(g)$$

   was examined at 250 °C. At equilibrium, $[PCl_5] = 4.2 \times 10^{-5}$ mol/L, $[PCl_3] = 1.3 \times 10^{-2}$ mol/L, and $[Cl_2] = 3.9 \times 10^{-3}$ mol/L. Calculate $K_c$ for the reaction.

8. An equilibrium mixture of $SO_2$, $O_2$, and $SO_3$ at a high temperature contains the gases at the following concentrations: $[SO_2] = 3.77 \times 10^{-3}$ mol/L, $[O_2] = 4.30 \times 10^{-3}$ mol/L, and $[SO_3] = 4.13 \times 10^{-3}$ mol/L. Calculate the equilibrium constant, $K_c$, for the reaction.

   $$2 SO_2(g) + O_2(g) \rightleftharpoons 2 SO_3(g)$$

9. The reaction

   $$C(s) + CO_2(g) \rightleftharpoons 2 CO(g)$$

   occurs at high temperatures. At 700 °C, a 2.0-L flask contains 0.10 mol of CO, 0.20 mol of $CO_2$, and 0.40 mol of C at equilibrium.
   (a) Calculate $K_c$ for the reaction at 700 °C.
   (b) Calculate $K_c$ for the reaction, also at 700 °C, if the amounts at equilibrium in the 2.0-L flask are 0.10 mol of CO, 0.20 mol of $CO_2$, and 0.80 mol of C.
   (c) Compare the results of (a) and (b). Does the quantity of carbon affect the value of $K_c$? Explain.

10. Hydrogen and carbon dioxide react at a high temperature to give water and carbon monoxide.

    $$H_2(g) + CO_2(g) \rightleftharpoons H_2O(g) + CO(g)$$

    (a) Laboratory measurements at 986 °C show that there are 0.11 mol each of CO and $H_2O$ vapor and 0.087 mol each of $H_2$ and $CO_2$ at equilibrium in a 1.0-L container. Calculate the equilibrium constant for the reaction at 986 °C.
    (b) Suppose 0.050 mol each of $H_2$ and $CO_2$ are placed in a 2.0-L container. When equilibrium is achieved at 986 °C, what amounts of CO(g) and $H_2O(g)$, in moles, would be present? [Use the value of $K_c$ from part (a).]

11. A mixture of CO and $Cl_2$ is placed in a reaction flask: $[CO] = 0.0102$ mol/L and $[Cl_2] = 0.00609$ mol/L. When the reaction

    $$CO(g) + Cl_2(g) \rightleftharpoons COCl_2(g)$$

has come to equilibrium at 600 K, $[Cl_2]$ = 0.00301 mol/L.

(a) Calculate the concentrations of CO and $COCl_2$ at equilibrium.

(b) Calculate $K_c$.

**12.** You place 3.00 mol of pure $SO_3$ in an 8.00-L flask at 1150 K. At equilibrium, 0.58 mol of $O_2$ has been formed. Calculate $K_c$ for the reaction at 1150 K.

$$2\ SO_3(g) \rightleftharpoons 2\ SO_2(g) + O_2(g)$$

## Using Equilibrium Constants
*(See Section 16.4 and Examples 16.5 and 16.6.)*

**13.** The value of $K_c$ for the interconversion of butane and isobutane is 2.5 at 25 °C.

butane          isobutane

If you place 0.017 mol of butane in a 0.50-L flask at 25 °C and allow equilibrium to be established, what will be the equilibrium concentrations of the two forms of butane?

**14.** Cyclohexane, $C_6H_{12}$, a hydrocarbon, can isomerize or change into methylcyclopentane, a compound of the same formula ($C_5H_9CH_3$) but with a different molecular structure.

cyclohexane     methylcyclopentane

The equilibrium constant has been estimated to be 0.12 at 25 °C. If you had originally placed 0.045 mol of cyclohexane in a 2.8-L flask, what would be the concentrations of cyclohexane and methylcyclopentane when equilibrium is established?

**15.** The equilibrium constant for the dissociation of iodine molecules to iodine atoms

$$I_2(g) \rightleftharpoons 2\ I(g)$$

is $3.76 \times 10^{-3}$ at 1000 K. Suppose 0.105 mol of $I_2$ is placed in a 12.3-L flask at 1000 K. What are the concentrations of $I_2$ and I when the system comes to equilibrium?

**16.** The equilibrium constant, $K_c$, for the reaction

$$N_2O_4(g) \rightleftharpoons 2\ NO_2(g)$$

at 25 °C is 170. Suppose 15.6 g of $N_2O_4$ is placed in a 5.000-L flask at 25 °C. Calculate the following:

(a) the amount of $NO_2$ (mol) present at equilibrium;

(b) the percentage of the original $N_2O_4$ that is dissociated.

**17.** Carbonyl bromide decomposes to carbon monoxide and bromine.

$$COBr_2(g) \rightleftharpoons CO(g) + Br_2(g)$$

$K_c$ is 0.190 at 73 °C. If you place 0.500 mol of $COBr_2$ in a 2.00-L flask and heat it to 73 °C, what are the equilibrium concentrations of $COBr_2$, CO, and $Br_2$? What percentage of the original $COBr_2$ decomposed at this temperature?

**18.** Iodine dissolves in water, but its solubility in a nonpolar solvent such as $CCl_4$ is greater.

Nonpolar $I_2$
Polar $H_2O$

Polar $H_2O$

Shake the test tube

Nonpolar $CCl_4$

Nonpolar $CCl_4$ and $I_2$

Photos © Cengage Learning/Charles D. Winters

**Extracting iodine ($I_2$) from water with the nonpolar solvent $CCl_4$.** $I_2$ is more soluble in $CCl_4$ and, after shaking a mixture of water and $CCl_4$, the $I_2$ has accumulated in the more dense $CCl_4$ layer.

The equilibrium constant is 85.0 for the process

$$I_2(aq) \rightleftharpoons I_2(CCl_4)$$

You place 0.0340 g of $I_2$ in 100.0 mL of water. After shaking it with 10.0 mL of $CCl_4$, how much $I_2$ remains in the water layer?

## Manipulating Equilibrium Constant Expressions
*(See Section 16.5 and Example 16.7.)*

**19.** Which of the following correctly relates the equilibrium constants for the two reactions shown?

$$A + B \rightleftharpoons 2\ C \qquad K_1$$
$$2\ A + 2\ B \rightleftharpoons 4\ C \qquad K_2$$

(a) $K_2 = 2K_1$      (c) $K_2 = 1/K_1$
(b) $K_2 = K_1^2$     (d) $K_2 = 1/K_1^2$

**20.** Which of the following correctly relates the equilibrium constants for the two reactions shown?

$$A + B \rightleftharpoons 2\ C \qquad K_1$$
$$C \rightleftharpoons \tfrac{1}{2}\ A + \tfrac{1}{2}\ B \qquad K_2$$

(a) $K_2 = 1/(K_1)^{1/2}$   (c) $K_2 = K_1^2$
(b) $K_2 = 1/K_1$           (d) $K_2 = -K_1^{1/2}$

**21.** Consider the following equilibria involving $SO_2(g)$ and their corresponding equilibrium constants.

$$SO_2(g) + \tfrac{1}{2}\ O_2(g) \rightleftharpoons SO_3(g) \qquad K_1$$
$$2\ SO_3(g) \rightleftharpoons 2\ SO_2(g) + O_2(g) \qquad K_2$$

Which of the following expressions relates $K_1$ to $K_2$?

(a) $K_2 = K_1^2$      (d) $K_2 = 1/K_1$
(b) $K_2^2 = K_1$      (e) $K_2 = 1/K_1^2$
(c) $K_2 = K_1$

**22.** The equilibrium constant $K$ for the reaction

$$CO_2(g) \rightleftharpoons CO(g) + \text{½} O_2(g)$$

is $6.66 \times 10^{-12}$ at 1000 K. Calculate $K$ for the reaction

$$2 CO(g) + O_2(g) \rightleftharpoons 2 CO_2(g)$$

**23.** Calculate $K$ for the reaction

$$SnO_2(s) + 2 CO(g) \rightleftharpoons Sn(s) + 2 CO_2(g)$$

given the following information:

$$SnO_2(s) + 2 H_2(g) \rightleftharpoons Sn(s) + 2 H_2O(g) \quad K = 8.12$$

$$H_2(g) + CO_2(g) \rightleftharpoons H_2O(g) + CO(g) \quad K = 0.771$$

**24.** Calculate $K$ for the reaction

$$Fe(s) + H_2O(g) \rightleftharpoons FeO(s) + H_2(g)$$

given the following information:

$$H_2O(g) + CO(g) \rightleftharpoons H_2(g) + CO_2(g) \quad K = 1.6$$

$$FeO(s) + CO(g) \rightleftharpoons Fe(s) + CO_2(g) \quad K = 0.67$$

**Disturbing a Chemical Equilibrium**
*(See Section 16.6 and Example 16.8.)*

**25.** Dinitrogen trioxide decomposes to NO and $NO_2$ in an endothermic process ($\Delta_r H° = 40.5$ kJ/mol-rxn).

$$N_2O_3(g) \rightleftharpoons NO(g) + NO_2(g)$$

Predict the effect of the following changes on the position of the equilibrium; that is, state which way the equilibrium will shift (left, right, or no change) when each of the following changes is made.
(a) adding more $N_2O_3(g)$
(b) adding more $NO_2(g)$
(c) increasing the volume of the reaction flask
(d) lowering the temperature

**26.** $K_p$ for the following reaction is 0.16 at 25 °C:

$$2 NOBr(g) \rightleftharpoons 2 NO(g) + Br_2(g)$$

The enthalpy change for the reaction at standard conditions is $+16.3$ kJ/mol-rxn. Predict the effect of the following changes on the position of the equilibrium; that is, state which way the equilibrium will shift (left, right, or no change) when each of the following changes is made.
(a) adding more $Br_2(g)$
(b) removing some $NOBr(g)$
(c) decreasing the temperature
(d) increasing the container volume

**27.** Consider the isomerization of butane with an equilibrium constant of $K = 2.5$. (See Study Question 13.) The system is originally at equilibrium with [butane] = 1.0 M and [isobutane] = 2.5 M.
(a) If 0.50 mol/L of isobutane is suddenly added and the system shifts to a new equilibrium position, what is the equilibrium concentration of each gas?
(b) If 0.50 mol/L of butane is added to the original equilibrium mixture and the system shifts to a new equilibrium position, what is the equilibrium concentration of each gas?

**28.** The decomposition of $NH_4HS$

$$NH_4HS(s) \rightleftharpoons NH_3(g) + H_2S(g)$$

is an endothermic process. Using Le Chatelier's principle, explain how increasing the temperature would affect the equilibrium. If more $NH_4HS$ is added to a flask in which this equilibrium exists, how is the equilibrium affected? What if some additional $NH_3$ is placed in the flask? What will happen to the pressure of $NH_3$ if some $H_2S$ is removed from the flask?

## General Questions

*These questions are not designated as to type or location in the chapter. They may combine several concepts.*

**29.** Suppose 0.086 mol of $Br_2$ is placed in a 1.26-L flask and heated to 1756 K, a temperature at which the halogen dissociates to atoms.

$$Br_2(g) \rightleftharpoons 2 Br(g)$$

If $Br_2$ is 3.7% dissociated at this temperature, calculate $K_c$.

**30.** The equilibrium constant for the reaction

$$N_2(g) + O_2(g) \rightleftharpoons 2 NO(g)$$

is $1.7 \times 10^{-3}$ at 2300 *K*.
(a) What is $K$ for the reaction when written as follows?

$$\text{½} N_2(g) + \text{½} O_2(g) \rightleftharpoons NO(g)$$

(b) What is $K$ for the following reaction?

$$2 NO(g) \rightleftharpoons N_2(g) + O_2(g)$$

**31.** $K_p$ for the formation of phosgene, $COCl_2$, is $6.5 \times 10^{11}$ at 25 °C.

$$CO(g) + Cl_2(g) \rightleftharpoons COCl_2(g)$$

What is the value of $K_p$ for the dissociation of phosgene?

$$COCl_2(g) \rightleftharpoons CO(g) + Cl_2(g)$$

**32.** The equilibrium constant, $K_c$, for the following reaction is 1.05 at 350 K.

$$2 CH_2Cl_2(g) \rightleftharpoons CH_4(g) + CCl_4(g)$$

If an equilibrium mixture of the three gases at 350 K contains 0.0206 M $CH_2Cl_2(g)$ and 0.0163 M $CH_4$, what is the equilibrium concentration of $CCl_4$?

**33.** Carbon tetrachloride can be produced by the following reaction:

$$CS_2(g) + 3 Cl_2(g) \rightleftharpoons S_2Cl_2(g) + CCl_4(g)$$

Suppose 1.2 mol of $CS_2$ and 3.6 mol of $Cl_2$ are placed in a 1.00-L flask. After equilibrium has been achieved, the mixture contains 0.90 mol $CCl_4$. Calculate $K_c$.

**34.** Equal numbers of moles of $H_2$ gas and $I_2$ vapor are mixed in a flask and heated to 700 °C. The initial concentration of each gas is 0.0088 mol/L, and 78.6% of the $I_2$ is consumed when equilibrium is achieved according to the equation

$$H_2(g) + I_2(g) \rightleftharpoons 2\ HI(g)$$

Calculate $K_c$ for this reaction.

**35.** The equilibrium constant for the butane $\rightleftharpoons$ isobutane isomerization reaction is 2.5 at 25 °C. If 1.75 mol of butane and 1.25 mol of isobutane are mixed, is the system at equilibrium? If not, when it proceeds to equilibrium, which reagent increases in concentration? Calculate the concentrations of the two compounds when the system reaches equilibrium.

**36.** At 2300 K the equilibrium constant for the formation of $NO(g)$ is $1.7 \times 10^{-3}$.

$$N_2(g) + O_2(g) \rightleftharpoons 2\ NO(g)$$

(a) Analysis shows that the concentrations of $N_2$ and $O_2$ are both 0.25 M, and that of NO is 0.0042 M under certain conditions. Is the system at equilibrium?
(b) If the system is not at equilibrium, in which direction does the reaction proceed?
(c) When the system is at equilibrium, what are the equilibrium concentrations?

**37.** Which of the following correctly relates the two equilibrium constants for the two reactions shown?

$$NOCl(g) \rightleftharpoons NO(g) + \tfrac{1}{2}\ Cl_2(g) \qquad K_1$$

$$2\ NO(g) + Cl_2(g) \rightleftharpoons 2\ NOCl(g) \qquad K_2$$

(a) $K_2 = -K_1{}^2$     (c) $K_2 = 1/K_1{}^2$
(b) $K_2 = 1/(K_1)^{1/2}$     (d) $K_2 = 2K_1$

**38.** Sulfur dioxide is readily oxidized to sulfur trioxide.

$$2\ SO_2(g) + O_2(g) \rightleftharpoons 2\ SO_3(g) \qquad K_c = 279$$

If we add 3.00 g of $SO_2$ and 5.00 g of $O_2$ to a 1.0-L flask, approximately what quantity of $SO_3$ will be in the flask once the reactants and the product reach equilibrium?
(a) 2.21 g     (c) 3.61 g
(b) 4.56 g     (d) 8.00 g

(*Note:* The full solution to this problem results in a cubic equation. Do not try to solve it exactly. Decide only which of the answers is most reasonable.)

**39.** Heating a metal carbonate leads to decomposition.

$$BaCO_3(s) \rightleftharpoons BaO(s) + CO_2(g)$$

Predict the effect on the equilibrium of each change listed below. Answer by choosing (i) no change, (ii) shifts left, or (iii) shifts right.
(a) add $BaCO_3$     (c) add BaO
(b) add $CO_2$      (d) raise the temperature
(e) increase the volume of the flask containing the reaction

**40.** Carbonyl bromide decomposes to carbon monoxide and bromine.

$$COBr_2(g) \rightleftharpoons CO(g) + Br_2(g)$$

$K_c$ is 0.190 at 73 °C. Suppose you place 0.500 mol of $COBr_2$ in a 2.00-L flask and heat it to 73 °C (see Study Question 17). After equilibrium has been achieved, you add an additional 2.00 mol of CO.
(a) How is the equilibrium mixture affected by adding more CO?
(b) When equilibrium is reestablished, what are the new equilibrium concentrations of $COBr_2$, CO, and $Br_2$?
(c) How has the addition of CO affected the percentage of $COBr_2$ that decomposed?

**41.** Phosphorus pentachloride decomposes at higher temperatures.

$$PCl_5(g) \rightleftharpoons PCl_3(g) + Cl_2(g)$$

An equilibrium mixture at some temperature consists of 3.120 g of $PCl_5$, 3.845 g of $PCl_3$, and 1.787 g of $Cl_2$ in a 1.00-L flask. If you add 1.418 g of $Cl_2$, how will the equilibrium be affected? What will the concentrations of $PCl_5$, $PCl_3$, and $Cl_2$ be when equilibrium is reestablished?

**42.** Ammonium hydrogen sulfide decomposes on heating.

$$NH_4HS(s) \rightleftharpoons NH_3(g) + H_2S(g)$$

If $K_p$ for this reaction is 0.11 at 25 °C (when the partial pressures are measured in atmospheres), what is the total pressure in the flask at equilibrium?

**43.** Ammonium iodide dissociates reversibly to ammonia and hydrogen iodide if the salt is heated to a sufficiently high temperature.

$$NH_4I(s) \rightleftharpoons NH_3(g) + HI(g)$$

Some ammonium iodide is placed in a flask, which is then heated to 400 °C. If the total pressure in the flask when equilibrium has been achieved is 705 mm Hg, what is the value of $K_p$ (when partial pressures are in atmospheres)?

**44.** When solid ammonium carbamate sublimes, it dissociates completely into ammonia and carbon dioxide according to the following equation:

$$(NH_4)(H_2NCO_2)(s) \rightleftharpoons 2\ NH_3(g) + CO_2(g)$$

At 25 °C, experiment shows that the total pressure of the gases in equilibrium with the solid is 0.116 atm. What is the equilibrium constant, $K_p$?

**45.** The equilibrium reaction $N_2O_4(g) \rightleftharpoons 2\ NO_2(g)$ has been thoroughly studied (Figure 16.8).
(a) If the total pressure in a flask containing $NO_2$ and $N_2O_4$ gas at 25 °C is 1.50 atm and the value of $K_p$ at this temperature is 0.148, what fraction of the $N_2O_4$ has dissociated to $NO_2$?
(b) What happens to the fraction dissociated if the volume of the container is increased so that the total equilibrium pressure falls to 1.00 atm?

**46.** In the gas phase, acetic acid exists as an equilibrium of monomer and dimer molecules. (The dimer consists of two molecules linked through hydrogen bonds.)

The equilibrium constant, $K_c$, at 25 °C for the monomer–dimer equilibrium

$$2 \, CH_3CO_2H \rightleftharpoons (CH_3CO_2H)_2$$

has been determined to be $3.2 \times 10^4$. Assume that acetic acid is present initially at a concentration of $5.4 \times 10^{-4}$ mol/L at 25 °C and that no dimer is present initially.

(a) What percentage of the acetic acid is converted to dimer?

(b) As the temperature increases, in which direction does the equilibrium shift? (Recall that hydrogen-bond formation is an exothermic process.)

**47.** Assume 3.60 mol of ammonia is placed in a 2.00-L vessel and allowed to decompose to the elements.

$$2 \, NH_3(g) \rightleftharpoons N_2(g) + 3 \, H_2(g)$$

If the experimental value of $K_c$ is 6.3 for this reaction at the temperature in the reactor, calculate the equilibrium concentration of each reagent. What is the total pressure in the flask?

**48.** The total pressure for a mixture of $N_2O_4$ and $NO_2$ is 1.5 atm. If $K_p = 7.1$ (at 25 °C), calculate the partial pressure of each gas in the mixture.

$$2 \, NO_2(g) \rightleftharpoons N_2O_4(g)$$

**49.** $K_c$ for the decomposition of ammonium hydrogen sulfide is $1.8 \times 10^{-4}$ at 25 °C.

$$NH_4HS(s) \rightleftharpoons NH_3(g) + H_2S(g)$$

(a) When the pure salt decomposes in a flask, what are the equilibrium concentrations of $NH_3$ and $H_2S$?

(b) If $NH_4HS$ is placed in a flask already containing 0.020 mol/L of $NH_3$ and then the system is allowed to come to equilibrium, what are the equilibrium concentrations of $NH_3$ and $H_2S$?

**50.** The equilibrium constant, $K_p$, is 0.14 at 25 °C for the following reaction:

$$N_2O_4(g) \rightleftharpoons 2 \, NO_2(g)$$

If the total pressure of the gas mixture is 2.5 atm at equilibrium, what is the partial pressure of each gas?

**51.** ▲ A 15-L flask at 300 K contains 64.4 g of a mixture of $NO_2$ and $N_2O_4$ in equilibrium. What is the total pressure in the flask? ($K_p$ for 2 $NO_2$ (g) $\rightleftharpoons N_2O_4(g)$ is 7.1.)

**52.** ▲ Lanthanum oxalate decomposes when heated to lanthanum(III) oxide, CO, and $CO_2$.

$$La_2(C_2O_4)_3(s) \rightleftharpoons La_2O_3(s) + 3 \, CO(g) + 3 \, CO_2(g)$$

(a) If, at equilibrium, the total pressure in a 10.0-L flask is 0.200 atm, what is the value of $K_p$?

(b) Suppose 0.100 mol of $La_2(C_2O_4)_3$ was originally placed in the 10.0-L flask. What quantity of $La_2(C_2O_4)_3$ remains unreacted at equilibrium at 373 K?

**53.** ▲ The reaction of hydrogen and iodine to give hydrogen iodide has an equilibrium constant, $K_c$, of 56 at 435 °C.

(a) What is the value of $K_p$?

(b) Suppose you mix 0.45 mol of $H_2$ and 0.45 mol of $I_2$ in a 10.0-L flask at 425 °C. What is the total pressure of the mixture before and after equilibrium is achieved?

(c) What is the partial pressure of each gas at equilibrium?

**54.** Sulfuryl chloride, $SO_2Cl_2$, is used as a reagent in the synthesis of organic compounds. When heated to a sufficiently high temperature, it decomposes to $SO_2$ and $Cl_2$.

$$SO_2Cl_2(g) \rightleftharpoons SO_2(g) + Cl_2(g) \qquad K_c = 0.045 \text{ at } 375 \text{ °C}$$

(a) A 1.00-L flask containing 6.70 g of $SO_2Cl_2$ is heated to 375 °C. What is the concentration of each of the compounds in the system when equilibrium is achieved? What fraction of $SO_2Cl_2$ has dissociated?

(b) What are the concentrations of $SO_2Cl_2$, $SO_2$, and $Cl_2$ at equilibrium in the 1.00-L flask at 375 °C if you begin with a mixture of $SO_2Cl_2$ (6.70 g) and $Cl_2$ (1.00 atm)? What fraction of $SO_2Cl_2$ has dissociated?

(c) Compare the fractions of $SO_2Cl_2$ in parts (a) and (b). Do they agree with your expectations based on Le Chatelier's principle?

**55.** ▲ Hemoglobin (Hb) can form a complex with both $O_2$ and CO. For the reaction

$$HbO_2(aq) + CO(g) \rightleftharpoons HbCO(aq) + O_2(g)$$

at body temperature, $K$ is about 200. If the ratio $[HbCO]/[HbO_2]$ comes close to 1, death is probable. What partial pressure of CO in the air is likely to be fatal? Assume the partial pressure of $O_2$ is 0.20 atm.

**56.** ▲ Limestone decomposes at high temperatures.

$$CaCO_3(s) \rightleftharpoons CaO(s) + CO_2(g)$$

At 1000 °C, $K_p = 3.87$. If pure $CaCO_3$ is placed in a 5.00-L flask and heated to 1000 °C, what quantity of $CaCO_3$ must decompose to achieve the equilibrium pressure of $CO_2$?

**57.** At 1800 K, oxygen dissociates very slightly into its atoms.

$$O_2(g) \rightleftharpoons 2 \, O(g) \qquad K_p = 1.2 \times 10^{-10}$$

If you place 1.0 mol of $O_2$ in a 10.-L vessel and heat it to 1800 K, how many O atoms are present in the flask?

**58.** ▲ Nitrosyl bromide, NOBr, dissociates readily at room temperature.

$$NOBr(g) \rightleftharpoons NO(g) + \tfrac{1}{2}\,Br_2(g)$$

Some NOBr is placed in a flask at 25 °C and allowed to dissociate. The total pressure at equilibrium is 190 mm Hg and the compound is found to be 34% dissociated. What is the value of $K_p$?

**59.** ▲ Boric acid and glycerin form a complex

$$B(OH)_3(aq) + glycerin(aq) \rightleftharpoons B(OH)_3 \cdot glycerin(aq)$$

with an equilibrium constant of 0.90. If the concentration of boric acid is 0.10 M, how much glycerin should be added, per liter, so that 60.% of the boric acid is in the form of the complex?

**60.** ▲ The dissociation of calcium carbonate has an equilibrium constant of $K_p = 1.16$ at 800 °C.

$$CaCO_3(s) \rightleftharpoons CaO(s) + CO_2(g)$$

(a) What is $K_c$ for the reaction?
(b) If you place 22.5 g of $CaCO_3$ in a 9.56-L container at 800 °C, what is the pressure of $CO_2$ in the container?
(c) What percentage of the original 22.5-g sample of $CaCO_3$ remains undecomposed at equilibrium?

**61.** ▲ A sample of $N_2O_4$ gas with a pressure of 1.00 atm is placed in a flask. When equilibrium is achieved, 20.0% of the $N_2O_4$ has been converted to $NO_2$ gas.
(a) Calculate $K_p$.
(b) If the original pressure of $N_2O_4$ is 0.10 atm, what is the percent dissociation of the gas? Is the result in agreement with Le Chatelier's principle?

**62.** ▲ A reaction important in smog formation is

$$O_3(g) + NO(g) \rightleftharpoons O_2(g) + NO_2(g) \qquad K = 6.0 \times 10^{34}$$

(a) If the initial concentrations are $[O_3] = 1.0 \times 10^{-6}$ M, $[NO] = 1.0 \times 10^{-5}$ M, $[NO_2] = 2.5 \times 10^{-4}$ M, and $[O_2] = 8.2 \times 10^{-3}$ M, is the system at equilibrium? If not, in which direction does the reaction proceed?
(b) If the temperature is increased, as on a very warm day, will the concentrations of the products increase or decrease? (*Hint*: You may have to calculate the enthalpy change for the reaction to find out if it is exothermic or endothermic.)

## In the Laboratory

**63.** ▲ The ammonia complex of trimethylborane, $(NH_3)B(CH_3)_3$, dissociates at 100 °C to its components with $K_p = 4.62$ (when the pressures are in atmospheres).

$$(NH_3)B(CH_3)_3(g) \rightleftharpoons B(CH_3)_3(g) + NH_3(g)$$

If $NH_3$ is changed to some other molecule, the equilibrium constant is different.

For $[(CH_3)_3P]B(CH_3)_3$ $\qquad K_p = 0.128$

For $[(CH_3)_3N]B(CH_3)_3$ $\qquad K_p = 0.472$

(a) If you begin an experiment by placing 0.010 mol of each complex in a flask, which would have the largest partial pressure of $B(CH_3)_3$ at 100 °C?
(b) If 0.73 g (0.010 mol) of $(NH_3)B(CH_3)_3$ is placed in a 100.-mL flask and heated to 100 °C, what is the partial pressure of each gas in the equilibrium mixture, and what is the total pressure? What is the percent dissociation of $(NH_3)B(CH_3)_3$?

**64.** The photographs below show what occurs when a solution of potassium chromate is treated with a few drops of concentrated hydrochloric acid. Some of the bright yellow chromate ion is converted to the orange dichromate ion.

$$2\,CrO_4^{2-}(aq) + 2\,H_3O^+(aq) \rightleftharpoons Cr_2O_7^{2-}(aq) + 3\,H_2O(\ell)$$

© Cengage Learning/Charles D. Winters

(a) Explain this experimental observation in terms of Le Chatelier's principle.
(b) What would you observe if you treated the orange solution with sodium hydroxide? Explain your observation.

**65.** The photograph below (a) shows what occurs when a solution of iron(III) nitrate is treated with a few drops of aqueous potassium thiocyanate. The nearly colorless iron(III) ion is converted to a red $[Fe(H_2O)_5SCN]^{2+}$ ion. (This is a classic test for the presence of iron(III) ions in solution.)

$$[Fe(H_2O)_6]^{3+}(aq) + SCN^-(aq) \rightleftharpoons [Fe(H_2O)_5SCN]^{2+}(aq) + H_2O(\ell)$$

Photos © Cengage Learning/Charles D. Winters

**(a) Adding KSCN**          **(b) Adding Ag⁺**

(a) As more KSCN is added to the solution, the color becomes even more red. Explain this observation.
(b) Silver ions form a white precipitate with $SCN^-$ ions. What would you observe on adding a few drops of aqueous silver nitrate to a red solution of $[Fe(H_2O)_5SCN]^+$ ions? Explain your observation.

**66.** ▲ The photographs at the bottom of the page show what occurs when you add ammonia to aqueous nickel(II) nitrate and then add ethylenediamine ($NH_2CH_2CH_2NH_2$) to the intermediate blue-purple solution.

$[Ni(H_2O)_6]^{2+}(aq) + 6\ NH_3(aq)$
green
$$\rightleftharpoons [Ni(NH_3)_6]^{2+}(aq) + 6\ H_2O(\ell) \qquad K_1$$
blue-purple

$[Ni(NH_3)_6]^{2+}(aq) + 3\ NH_2CH_2CH_2NH_2(aq)$
blue-purple
$$\rightleftharpoons [Ni(NH_2CH_2CH_2NH_2)_3]^{2+}(aq) + 6\ NH_3(aq)\ \ K_2$$
violet

(a) Write a chemical equation for the formation of $[Ni(NH_2CH_2CH_2NH_2)_3]^{2+}$ from $[Ni(H_2O)_6]^{2+}$ and ethylenediamine, and relate the value of $K$ for this reaction to $K_1$ and $K_2$.
(b) Which species, $[Ni(NH_2CH_2CH_2NH_2)_3]^{2+}$, $[Ni(NH_3)_6]^{2+}$, or $[Ni(H_2O)_6]^{2+}$ is the most stable? Explain.

## Summary and Conceptual Questions

*The following questions may use concepts from this and previous chapters.*

**67.** Decide whether each of the following statements is true or false. If false, change the wording to make it true.
(a) The magnitude of the equilibrium constant is always independent of temperature.
(b) When two chemical equations are added to give a net equation, the equilibrium constant for the net equation is the product of the equilibrium constants of the summed equations.
(c) The equilibrium constant for a reaction has the same value as $K$ for the reverse reaction.
(d) Only the concentration of $CO_2$ appears in the equilibrium constant expression for the reaction $CaCO_3(s) \rightleftharpoons CaO(s) + CO_2(g)$.
(e) For the reaction $CaCO_3(s) \rightleftharpoons CaO(s) + CO_2(g)$, the value of $K$ is numerically the same, whether the amount of $CO_2$ is expressed as moles/liter or as gas pressure.

**68.** Neither $PbCl_2$ nor $PbF_2$ is appreciably soluble in water. If solid $PbCl_2$ and solid $PbF_2$ are placed in equal amounts of water in separate beakers, in which beaker is the concentration of $Pb^{2+}$ greater? Equilibrium constants for these solids dissolving in water are as follows:

$$PbCl_2(s) \rightleftharpoons Pb^{2+}(aq) + 2\ Cl^-(aq) \qquad K = 1.7 \times 10^{-5}$$

$$PbF_2(s) \rightleftharpoons Pb^{2+}(aq) + 2\ F^-(aq) \qquad K = 3.7 \times 10^{-8}$$

**69.** Characterize each of the following as product- or reactant-favored at equilibrium.
(a) $CO(g) + \frac{1}{2}\ O_2(g) \rightleftharpoons CO_2(g)\ \ K_p = 1.2 \times 10^{45}$
(b) $H_2O(g) \rightleftharpoons H_2(g) + \frac{1}{2}\ O_2(g)\ \ K_p = 9.1 \times 10^{-41}$
(c) $CO(g) + Cl_2(g) \rightleftharpoons COCl_2(g)\ \ K_p = 6.5 \times 10^{11}$

**70.** ▲ The size of a flask containing colorless $N_2O_4(g)$ and brown $NO_2(g)$ at equilibrium is rapidly reduced to half the original volume.

$$N_2O_4(g) \rightleftharpoons 2\ NO_2(g)$$

(a) What color change (if any) is observed immediately upon halving the flask size?
(b) What color change (if any) is observed during the process in which equilibrium is reestablished in the flask?

**71.** Describe an experiment that would allow you to prove that the system $3\ H_2(g) + N_2(g) \rightleftharpoons 2\ NH_3(g)$ is a dynamic equilibrium. (*Hint:* Consider using a stable isotope such as $^{15}N$ or $^2H$.)

**72.** Consider the following equilibrium:

$$COBr_2(g) \rightleftharpoons CO(g) + Br_2(g) \qquad K_c = 0.190\ \text{at}\ 73\ °C$$

(a) A 1.0 mol sample of $COBr_2$ is transferred to a 2.0-L flask and heated until equilibrium is attained. Calculate the equilibrium concentrations of each species.
(b) The volume of the container is decreased to 1.0 L and the system allowed to return to equilibrium. Calculate the new equilibrium concentrations. (*Hint:* The calculation will be easier if you view this as a new problem with the new initial concentration of $COBr_2$ of 1.0 mol/L.)

$[Ni(H_2O)_6]^{2+}$     $\xrightarrow{NH_3}$     $[Ni(NH_3)_6]^{2+}$     Add ethylenediamine $NH_2CH_2CH_2NH_2$     $[Ni(NH_2CH_2CH_2NH_2)_3]^{2+}$

# Applying Chemical Principles

## Trivalent Carbon

The octet rule is a guiding principle in organic chemistry. As a result, when someone discovers a molecule that does not obey the octet rule, organic chemists are always interested. The synthesis of the triphenylmethyl radical, $(C_6H_5)_3C$ was one such event.

The triphenylmethyl radical (**compound 2**), the first known persistent organic free radical, was discovered over 100 years ago by Moses Gomberg, a chemist at the University of Michigan. Gomberg set out to make hexaphenylethane $[(C_6H_5)_3C–C(C_6H_5)_3]$ (**compound 3**). When he combined the reactants $(C_6H_5)_3CCl$ (**compound 1**) and Zn, he obtained a yellow solution that became more intensely yellow when heated and was reactive toward oxygen and halogens. This extreme reactivity led Gomberg to conclude that the yellow color was due to the presence of $(C_6H_5)_3C$ in solution. The existence of the stable free radical was explained by the fact that there are three large phenyl groups around a carbon atom, which prevents the radical from undergoing the expected dimerization to hexaphenylethane.

Actually, the triphenylmethyl radical does dimerize, but not the way Gomberg had expected. A diamagnetic, white solid crystalline dimer (**compound 4**) can be isolated from the solutions containing the radical. The dimerization occurs between a methyl carbon radical on one molecule and the phenyl ring on a second. When redissolved in benzene, the original yellow solution forms.

Studies determined that compounds **4** and **2** exist in solution in equilibrium. The value of $K_c$ for the dimer-monomer equilibrium (**4** $\rightleftharpoons$ **2**) in benzene is $4.1 \times 10^{-4}$ at 20 °C.

Interestingly, Gomberg finished his initial publication with the following statement: "This work will be continued and I wish to reserve the field for myself." In the United States, chemical research is competitive and Gomberg's wish was not respected.

## Questions:

1. Freezing point depression is one means of determining the molar mass of a compound. The freezing point depression constant of benzene is $-5.12$ °C/$m$.
   (a) When a 0.503 g sample of the white crystalline dimer is dissolved in 10.0 g benzene, the freezing point of benzene is decreased by 0.542 °C. Verify that the molar mass of the dimer is 475 g/mol when determined by freezing point depression. Assume no dissociation of the dimer occurs.
   (b) The correct molar mass of the dimer is 487 g/mol. Explain why the dissociation equilibrium causes the freezing point depression calculation to yield a lower molar mass for the dimer.

2. What concentration of the monomer will exist at equilibrium with 0.015 mol/L of the dimer (**2**) in benzene at 20 °C?

3. A 0.64 g sample of the white crystalline dimer (**4**) is dissolved in 25.0 mL of benzene at 20 °C. Use the equilibrium constant to calculate the concentrations of monomer (**2**) and dimer (**4**) in this solution.

4. Predict whether the dissociation of the dimer to the monomer is exothermic or endothermic, based on the fact that at higher temperatures the yellow color of the solution intensifies.

5. Which of the organic species mentioned in this story is paramagnetic?
   (a) triphenylmethyl chloride
   (b) triphenylmethyl radical
   (c) the triphenylmethyl dimer

## Reference:

M. Gomberg, *Journal of the American Chemical Society*, Vol. 22, pp. 757-771, 1900.

# 17 Principles of Chemical Reactivity: The Chemistry of Acids and Bases

© Cengage Learning/Charles D. Winters

## Aspirin Is Over 100 Years Old!

Aspirin is one of the most successful nonprescription drugs ever made. Americans swallow more than 50 million aspirin tablets a day, mostly for the pain-relieving (analgesic) effects of the drug. Aspirin also wards off heart disease and thrombosis (blood clots), and it has even been suggested as a possible treatment for certain cancers and for senile dementia.

Hippocrates (460–370 BC), the ancient Greek physician, recommended an infusion of willow bark to ease the pain of childbirth. It was not until the 19th century that an Italian chemist, Raffaele Piria, isolated salicylic acid, the active compound in the bark. Soon thereafter, it was found that the acid could be extracted from a wild flower, *Spiraea ulmaria*. It is from the name of this plant that the name "aspirin" (a + spiraea) is derived.

Hippocrates's willow bark extract, salicylic acid, is an analgesic, but it is also very irritating to the stomach lining. It was therefore an important advance when chemists at Bayer Chemicals in Germany found, in 1897, that a derivative of salicylic acid, acetylsalicylic acid, was also a useful drug and had fewer side effects. This is the compound we now call "aspirin."

Acetylsalicylic acid slowly reverts to salicylic acid, and acetic acid in the presence of moisture; therefore, if you smell the characteristic odor of acetic acid in an old bottle of aspirin, the tablets are too old and should be discarded.

Aspirin (acetylsalicylic acid ) is a component of various over-the-counter medicines, such as Anacin, Ecotrin, Excedrin, and Alka-Seltzer. The latter is a combination of aspirin with citric acid and sodium bicarbonate. Sodium bicarbonate is a base and reacts with the acid to produce the sodium salt of acetylsalicylic acid, a form of aspirin that is water-soluble and quicker acting.

### Questions:

1. Aspirin has a p$K_a$ of 3.49, and that of acetic acid is 4.74. Which is the stronger acid?
2. Identify the acidic H atom in aspirin.
3. Write an equation for the ionization of aspirin.

**Answers to these questions are available in Appendix N.**

## CHAPTER GOALS

*See Chapter Goals Revisited (page 796) for Study Questions keyed to these goals.*

- Use the Brønsted–Lowry and Lewis theories of acids and bases.
- Apply the principles of chemical equilibrium to acids and bases in aqueous solution.
- Predict the outcome of reactions of acids and bases.
- Understand the influence of structure and bonding on acid–base properties.

**OWL**

Sign in to OWL at **www.cengage.com/owl** to view tutorials and simulations, develop problem-solving skills, and complete online homework assigned by your professor.

Download mini lecture videos for key concept review and exam prep from OWL or purchase them from **www.cengagebrain.com**

Acids and bases are among the most common substances in nature. Amino acids are the building blocks of proteins. The repository of genetic information in your cells is DNA, deoxyribonucleic acid. The pH of the lakes, rivers, and oceans is affected by dissolved acids and bases, and many bodily functions depend on acids and bases. You were introduced to acids and bases and to some of their chemistry in Chapter 3, but this chapter and the next take up the chemistry of this important class of substances in more detail.

## 17.1  Acids and Bases: A Review

In Chapter 3, you were introduced to two definitions of acids and bases: the Arrhenius definition and the Brønsted–Lowry definition. According to the Arrhenius definition, an acid is any substance that, when dissolved in water, increases the concentration of hydrogen ions, $H^+$ (◀ page 128). An Arrhenius base is any substance that increases the concentration of hydroxide ions, $OH^-$, when dissolved in water. Based on the Arrhenius definition, hydrochloric acid is therefore classified as an acid, and sodium hydroxide is classified as a base.

$$HCl(aq) \rightarrow H^+(aq) + Cl^-(aq)$$

$$NaOH(aq) \rightarrow Na^+(aq) + OH^-(aq)$$

Using this definition, reactions between acids and bases involve the combination of $H^+$ and $OH^-$ ions to form water (and a salt).

$$NaOH(aq) + HCl(aq) \rightarrow H_2O(\ell) + NaCl(aq)$$

The Brønsted–Lowry definition of acids and bases is more general and views acid–base behavior in terms of proton transfer from one substance to another. *A Brønsted–Lowry acid is a proton ($H^+$) donor, and a Brønsted–Lowry base is a proton acceptor,* a definition that extends the list of acids and bases and the scope of acid–base reactions. In the following reaction, HCl acts as a Brønsted–Lowry acid, and water acts as a Brønsted–Lowry base because HCl transfers a $H^+$ ion to $H_2O$ to form the hydronium ion, $H_3O^+$.

$$HCl(aq) + H_2O(\ell) \rightleftharpoons H_3O^+(aq) + Cl^-(aq)$$

We will begin this chapter by looking at Brønsted–Lowry acid–base chemistry in more detail.

---

**REVIEW & CHECK FOR SECTION 17.1**

Which of the following is a list of Brønsted–Lowry acids?

(a)   $CH_3CO_2H$, $Al(OH)_3$, $H_3PO_4$

(b)   $NH_4^+$, $NH_3$, HCl

(c)   $H_2CO_3$, $CH_3CO_2H$, $H_3PO_4$

---

## 17.2 The Brønsted–Lowry Concept of Acids and Bases Extended

A wide variety of Brønsted–Lowry acids is known. These include some molecular compounds such as nitric acid,

$$\underset{\text{acid}}{HNO_3(aq)} + H_2O(\ell) \rightleftharpoons NO_3^-(aq) + H_3O^+(aq)$$

cations such as $NH_4^+$,

$$\underset{\text{acid}}{NH_4^+(aq)} + H_2O(\ell) \rightleftharpoons NH_3(aq) + H_3O^+(aq)$$

and anions.

$$H_2PO_4^-(aq) + H_2O(\ell) \rightleftharpoons HPO_4^{2-}(aq) + H_3O^+(aq)$$

Similarly, many different types of species can act as Brønsted–Lowry bases in their reactions with water. These include some molecular compounds,

$$\underset{\text{base}}{NH_3(aq)} + H_2O(\ell) \rightleftharpoons NH_4^+(aq) + OH^-(aq)$$

and anions.

$$CO_3^{2-}(aq) + H_2O(\ell) \rightleftharpoons HCO_3^-(aq) + OH^-(aq)$$

Hydrated metal cations can also function as acids and bases. Some of these ions act as Brønsted–Lowry acids:

$$[Fe(H_2O)_6]^{3+}(aq) + H_2O(\ell) \rightleftharpoons [Fe(H_2O)_5(OH)]^{2+}(aq) + H_3O^+(aq)$$

while others act as Brønsted–Lowry bases.

$$[Al(H_2O)_5(OH)]^{2+}(aq) + H_2O(\ell) \rightleftharpoons [Al(H_2O)_6]^{3+}(aq) + OH^-(aq)$$

Acids such as HF, HCl, $HNO_3$, and $CH_3CO_2H$ (acetic acid) are all capable of donating one proton and so are called **monoprotic acids.** Other acids, called **polyprotic acids** (Table 17.1), are capable of donating two or more protons. Sulfuric acid is a familiar example of a polyprotic acid.

$$H_2SO_4(aq) + H_2O(\ell) \rightleftharpoons HSO_4^-(aq) + H_3O^+(aq)$$

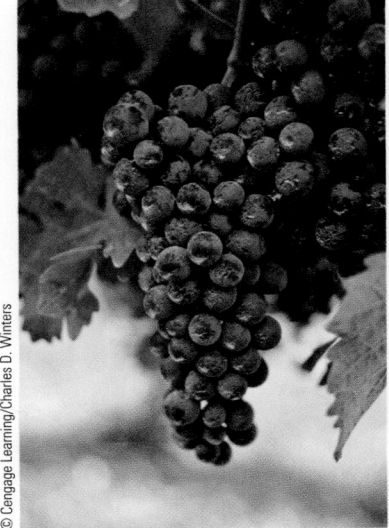

$$HSO_4^-(aq) + H_2O(\ell) \rightleftharpoons SO_4^{2-}(aq) + H_3O^+(aq)$$

Just as there are acids that can donate more than one proton, so there are **polyprotic bases** that can accept more than one proton. The fully deprotonated anions of polyprotic acids are polyprotic bases; examples include $SO_4^{2-}$, $PO_4^{3-}$, $CO_3^{2-}$, and $C_2O_4^{2-}$. The carbonate ion, for example, can accept two protons.

$$CO_3^{2-}(aq) + H_2O(\ell) \rightleftharpoons HCO_3^-(aq) + OH^-(aq)$$
base

$$HCO_3^-(aq) + H_2O(\ell) \rightleftharpoons H_2CO_3(aq) + OH^-(aq)$$
base

Some molecules (such as water) and ions can behave either as Brønsted acids or bases and are referred to as being **amphiprotic** (◄ page 131). An example of an amphiprotic anion that is particularly important in biochemical systems is the dihydrogen phosphate anion (Table 17.1).

$$H_2PO_4^-(aq) + H_2O(\ell) \rightleftharpoons H_3O^+(aq) + HPO_4^{2-}(aq)$$
acid

$$H_2PO_4^-(aq) + H_2O(\ell) \rightleftharpoons H_3PO_4(aq) + OH^-(aq)$$
base

**Tartaric acid, $H_2C_4H_4O_6$, is a naturally occurring diprotic acid.** Tartaric acid and its potassium salt are found in grapes and other fruits. The acidic protons are the H atoms of the $-CO_2H$ or carboxylic acid groups.

Carboxylic acid groups

© Cengage Learning/Charles D. Winters

**Table 17.1 Polyprotic Acids and Bases**

| Acid Form | Amphiprotic Form | Base Form |
|---|---|---|
| $H_2S$ (hydrosulfuric acid or hydrogen sulfide) | $HS^-$ (hydrogen sulfide ion) | $S^{2-}$ (sulfide ion) |
| $H_3PO_4$ (phosphoric acid) | $H_2PO_4^-$ (dihydrogen phosphate ion) <br> $HPO_4^{2-}$ (hydrogen phosphate ion) | $PO_4^{3-}$ (phosphate ion) |
| $H_2CO_3$ (carbonic acid) | $HCO_3^-$ (hydrogen carbonate ion or bicarbonate ion) | $CO_3^{2-}$ (carbonate ion) |
| $H_2C_2O_4$ (oxalic acid) | $HC_2O_4^-$ (hydrogen oxalate ion) | $C_2O_4^{2-}$ (oxalate ion) |

## Conjugate Acid–Base Pairs

The reaction of the hydrogen corbonate ion and water exemplifies a feature of Brønsted acid–base chemistry: a Brønsted acid and base produce a new acid and base.

In the forward direction, $HCO_3^-$ is the Brønsted base because it captures $H^+$ from the Brønsted acid, $H_2O$. The products are a new Brønsted acid and base. In the reverse direction, the $H_2CO_3$ is the acid, and $OH^-$ is the base.

A **conjugate acid–base pair** consists of two species that differ from each other by the presence of one hydrogen ion. Thus, $H_2CO_3$ and $HCO_3^-$ comprise a conjugate acid–base pair. In this pair, $HCO_3^-$ is the conjugate base of the acid $H_2CO_3$, and $H_2CO_3$ is the conjugate acid of the base $HCO_3^-$. There is a second conjugate acid–base pair in this reaction: $H_2O$ and $OH^-$. In fact, *every reaction between a Brønsted acid and a Brønsted base involves two conjugate acid–base pairs* (Table 17.2).

---

**REVIEW & CHECK FOR SECTION 17.2**

1.  $H_3PO_4$, phosphoric acid, can donate two protons to water to form the monohydrogen phosphate ion, $HPO_4^{2-}$. Is the monohydrogen phosphate ion an acid, a base, or amphiprotic?

    (a)  acid          (b)  base          (c)  amphiprotic

2.  The cyanide ion, $CN^-$, accepts a proton from water to form HCN. Is $CN^-$ a Brønsted acid or base or is it amphiprotic?

    (a)  acid          (b)  base          (c)  amphiprotic

3.  In the following reaction, identify the acid on the left and its conjugate base on the right.

    $$HNO_3(aq) + NH_3(aq) \rightleftharpoons NH_4^+(aq) + NO_3^-(aq)$$

    (a)  acid = $NH_3$ and conjugate base = $NH_4^+$

    (b)  acid = $HNO_3$ and conjugate base = $NO_3^-$

    Similarly, identify the base on the left and its conjugate acid on the right.

    (a)  base = $NH_3$ and conjugate acid = $NH_4^+$

    (b)  base = $HNO_3$ and conjugate acid = $NO_3^-$

4.  Identify the conjugate acid/base pairs in the reaction of HF and acetic acid.

    $$HF(aq) + CH_3CO_2^-(aq) \rightleftharpoons F^-(aq) + CH_3CO_2H(aq)$$

    (a)  $HF/CH_3CO_2^-$ and $F^-/CH_3CO_2H$

    (b)  $HF/CH_3CO_2H$ and $F^-/CH_3CO_2^-$

    (c)  $HF/F^-$ and $CH_3CO_2H/CH_3CO_2^-$

---

## 17.3    Water and the pH Scale

Because we generally use aqueous solutions of acids and bases and because the acid–base reactions in your body occur in your aqueous interior, we want to consider the behavior of water in terms of chemical equilibria.

**Table 17.2  Acid–Base Reactions and Conjugate Acid–Base Pairs***

| Name | Acid 1 | | Base 2 | | Base 1 | | Acid 2 |
|---|---|---|---|---|---|---|---|
| Hydrochloric acid | HCl | + | $H_2O$ | ⇌ | $Cl^-$ | + | $H_3O^+$ |
| Nitric acid | $HNO_3$ | + | $H_2O$ | ⇌ | $NO_3^-$ | + | $H_3O^+$ |
| Carbonic acid | $H_2CO_3$ | + | $H_2O$ | ⇌ | $HCO_3^-$ | + | $H_3O^+$ |
| Acetic acid | $CH_3CO_2H$ | + | $H_2O$ | ⇌ | $CH_3CO_2^-$ | + | $H_3O^+$ |
| Hydrocyanic acid | HCN | + | $H_2O$ | ⇌ | $CN^-$ | + | $H_3O^+$ |
| Hydrogen sulfide | $H_2S$ | + | $H_2O$ | ⇌ | $HS^-$ | + | $H_3O^+$ |
| Ammonia | $H_2O$ | + | $NH_3$ | ⇌ | $OH^-$ | + | $NH_4^+$ |
| Carbonate ion | $H_2O$ | + | $CO_3^{2-}$ | ⇌ | $OH^-$ | + | $HCO_3^-$ |
| Water | $H_2O$ | + | $H_2O$ | ⇌ | $OH^-$ | + | $H_3O^+$ |

*Acid 1 and base 1 are a conjugate pair, as are base 2 and acid 2.

## Water Autoionization and the Water Ionization Constant, $K_w$

An acid such as HCl does not need to be present for the hydronium ion to exist in water. In fact, two water molecules can interact with each other to produce a hydronium ion and a hydroxide ion by proton transfer from one water molecule to the other.

$$2\ H_2O(\ell) \rightleftharpoons H_3O^+(aq) + OH^-(aq)$$

This **autoionization** reaction of water was demonstrated a century ago by Friedrich Kohlrausch (1840–1910). He found that, even after water is painstakingly purified, it still conducts electricity to a very small extent. We now know this is because autoionization produces very low concentrations of $H_3O^+$ and $OH^-$ ions. *Water autoionization is the cornerstone of our concepts of aqueous acid–base behavior.*

The water autoionization equilibrium lies far to the left side. In fact, in pure water at 25 °C, only about two out of a billion ($10^9$) water molecules are ionized at any instant. To express this idea more quantitatively, we can write the equilibrium constant expression for autoionization.

$$K_w = [H_3O^+][OH^-] = 1.0 \times 10^{-14} \text{ at } 25\ °C \tag{17.1}$$

There are several important aspects of this equation.

- Based on the rules for writing equilibrium constants, we do not include the concentration of water.
- The equilibrium constant is given a special symbol, $K_w$, and is known as the **autoionization constant for water**.
- Because autoionization is the only source of hydronium and hydroxide ions in pure water, we know that $[H_3O^+]$ must be equal to $[OH^-]$. Electrical conductivity measurements of pure water show that $[H_3O^+] = [OH^-] = 1.0 \times 10^{-7}$ M at 25 °C, so $K_w$ has a value of $1.0 \times 10^{-14}$ at 25 °C.

In pure water, the hydronium ion and hydroxide ion concentrations are equal, and the water is said to be neutral. If some acid or base is added to pure water, however, the equilibrium

$$2\ H_2O(\ell) \rightleftharpoons H_3O^+(aq) + OH^-(aq)$$

● **$K_w$ and Temperature** The equation $K_w = [H_3O^+][OH^-]$ is valid for pure water and for any aqueous solution. The numerical value for $K_w$, however, is temperature dependent. Because the autoionization reaction is endothermic, $K_w$ increases with temperature.

| $T$ (°C) | $K_w$ |
|---|---|
| 10 | $0.29 \times 10^{-14}$ |
| 15 | $0.45 \times 10^{-14}$ |
| 20 | $0.68 \times 10^{-14}$ |
| 25 | $1.01 \times 10^{-14}$ |
| 30 | $1.47 \times 10^{-14}$ |
| 50 | $5.48 \times 10^{-14}$ |

● **The Magnitude of $[H_3O^+]$ in Pure Water** The ionization of two water molecules out of a billion produces a $H_3O^+$ concentration of $1 \times 10^{-7}$ M. To have a sense of this tiny amount, this would be like identifying just 14 people out of the current population of the earth, about 7 billion.

is disturbed. Adding acid raises the concentration of the $H_3O^+$ ions, so the solution is acidic. To oppose this increase, Le Chatelier's principle (◀ Section 16.6) predicts that a small fraction of the $H_3O^+$ ions will react with $OH^-$ ions from water autoionization to form water. This lowers $[OH^-]$ until the product of $[H_3O^+]$ and $[OH^-]$ is again equal to $1.0 \times 10^{-14}$ at 25 °C. Similarly, adding a base to pure water gives a basic solution because the $OH^-$ ion concentration has increased. Le Chatelier's principle predicts that some of the added $OH^-$ ions will react with $H_3O^+$ ions present in the solution from water autoionization, thereby lowering $[H_3O^+]$ until the value of the product of $[H_3O^+]$ and $[OH^-]$ equals $1.0 \times 10^{-14}$ at 25 °C.

Thus, for aqueous solutions at 25 °C, we can say that

> • In a neutral solution, $[H_3O^+] = [OH^-]$.
> Both are equal to $1.0 \times 10^{-7}$ M.
> • In an acidic solution, $[H_3O^+] > [OH^-]$.
> $[H_3O^+] > 1.0 \times 10^{-7}$ M and $[OH^-] < 1.0 \times 10^{-7}$ M.
> • In a basic solution, $[H_3O^+] < [OH^-]$.
> $[H_3O^+] < 1.0 \times 10^{-7}$ M and $[OH^-] > 1.0 \times 10^{-7}$ M.

### EXAMPLE 17.1    Hydronium and Hydroxide Ion Concentrations in a Solution of a Strong Base

**Problem** What are the hydroxide and hydronium ion concentrations in a 0.0012 M solution of NaOH at 25 °C?

**What Do You Know?** You know the concentration of NaOH and that it is a strong base, 100% dissociated into ions in water.

**Strategy** Because NaOH is a strong base we assume that the $OH^-$ ion concentration is the same as the NaOH concentration. The $H_3O^+$ ion concentration can then be calculated using Equation 17.1.

**Solution** The initial concentration of $OH^-$ is 0.0012 M.

$$0.0012 \text{ mol NaOH per liter} \rightarrow 0.0012 \text{ M Na}^+(aq) + 0.0012 \text{ M OH}^-(aq)$$

Substituting the $OH^-$ concentration into Equation 17.1, we have

$$K_w = 1.0 \times 10^{-14} = [H_3O^+][OH^-] = [H_3O^+](0.0012)$$

and so

$$[H_3O^+] = \frac{1.0 \times 10^{-14}}{0.0012} = 8.3 \times 10^{-12} \text{ M}$$

**Think about Your Answer** Why didn't we take into account the ions produced by water autoionization when we calculated the concentration of hydroxide ions? It should add $OH^-$ and $H_3O^+$ ions to the solution. If x *is equal to the concentration of* $OH^-$ *ions generated by the autoionization of water*, then, when equilibrium is achieved,

$$[OH^-] = (0.0012 \text{ M} + OH^- \text{ from water autoionization}) = (0.0012 \text{ M} + x)$$

In pure water, the concentration of $OH^-$ ion generated by autoionization is $1.0 \times 10^{-7}$ M. Le Chatelier's principle (◀ Section 16.6) suggests that the concentration should be even smaller when $OH^-$ ions are already present in solution from NaOH; that is, x should be much less than $1.0 \times 10^{-7}$ M. This means x in the term $(0.0012 + x)$ is insignificant compared with 0.0012. (Following the rules for significant figures, the sum of 0.0012 and a number even smaller than $1.0 \times 10^{-7}$ is 0.0012.) Thus, the equilibrium concentration of $OH^-$ is equivalent to the concentration of NaOH in the solution.

---

**Check Your Understanding**

A solution of the strong acid HCl has $[HCl] = 4.0 \times 10^{-3}$ M. What are the concentrations of $H_3O^+$ and $OH^-$ in this solution at 25 °C? (Recall that because HCl is a strong acid, it is 100% ionized in water.)

## The pH Scale

The **pH** of a solution is defined as the negative of the base-10 logarithm (log) of the hydronium ion concentration (◀ Section 4.6, page 178).

$$pH = -\log[H_3O^+] \qquad \text{(4.3 and 17.2)}$$

In a similar way, we can define the pOH of a solution as the negative of the base-10 logarithm of the hydroxide ion concentration.

$$pOH = -\log[OH^-] \qquad \text{(17.3)}$$

In pure water, the hydronium and hydroxide ion concentrations are both $1.0 \times 10^{-7}$ M. Therefore, for pure water at 25 °C

$$pH = -\log(1.0 \times 10^{-7}) = 7.00$$

In the same way, you can show that the pOH of pure water is also 7.00 at 25 °C.

If we take the negative logarithms of both sides of the expression $K_w = [H_3O^+][OH^-]$, we obtain another useful equation.

$$K_w = 1.0 \times 10^{-14} = [H_3O^+][OH^-]$$
$$-\log K_w = -\log(1.0 \times 10^{-14}) = -\log([H_3O^+][OH^-])$$
$$pK_w = 14.00 = -\log([H_3O^+]) + (-\log[OH^-])$$

$$pK_w = 14.00 = pH + pOH \qquad \text{(17.4)}$$

The sum of the pH and pOH of a solution must be equal to 14.00 at 25 °C.

As illustrated in Figures 4.11 and 17.1, solutions with pH less than 7.00 (at 25 °C) are acidic, whereas solutions with pH greater than 7.00 are basic. Solutions with pH = 7.00 at 25 °C are neutral.

## Calculating pH

The calculation of pH from the hydronium ion concentration, or the concentration of hydronium ion from pH, was introduced in Chapter 4 (◀ page 178). The *Review & Check* questions below review those calculations.

---

**REVIEW & CHECK FOR SECTION 17.3**

1. What is the pH of a 0.0012 M NaOH solution at 25 °C?

   (a) 2.92  (b) 11.08  (c) 8.67

2. The pH of a diet soda is 4.32 at 25 °C. What is the hydronium ion concentration in the soda?

   (a) $4.8 \times 10^{-5}$ M  (b) $2.1 \times 10^{-10}$ M  (c) $2.1 \times 10^{-4}$ M

3. If the pH of a solution containing the strong base $Sr(OH)_2$ is 10.46 at 25 °C, what is the concentration of $Sr(OH)_2$?

   (a) $3.5 \times 10^{-11}$ M  (b) $2.9 \times 10^{-4}$ M  (c) $6.9 \times 10^{-11}$ M  (d) $1.4 \times 10^{-4}$ M

---

• **Working with Logarithms** See Appendix A for more on using logarithms.

| | pH | $[H_3O^+]$ | $[OH^-]$ | pOH |
|---|---|---|---|---|
| Basic | 14.00 | $1.0 \times 10^{-14}$ | $1.0 \times 10^{0}$ | 0.00 |
| | 10.00 | $1.0 \times 10^{-10}$ | $1.0 \times 10^{-4}$ | 4.00 |
| Neutral | 7.00 | $1.0 \times 10^{-7}$ | $1.0 \times 10^{-7}$ | 7.00 |
| Acidic | 4.00 | $1.0 \times 10^{-4}$ | $1.0 \times 10^{-10}$ | 10.00 |
| | 0.00 | $1.0 \times 10^{0}$ | $1.0 \times 10^{-14}$ | 14.00 |

**FIGURE 17.1 pH and pOH.** This figure illustrates the relationship of hydronium ion and hydroxide ion concentrations and of pH and pOH.

## 17.4 Equilibrium Constants for Acids and Bases

In Chapter 3, it was stated that acids and bases can be divided roughly into those that are strong electrolytes (such as HCl, HNO₃, and NaOH) and those that are weak electrolytes (such as CH₃CO₂H and NH₃) (Figure 17.2) (◄ Table 3.1, Common Acids and Bases, page 129). Hydrochloric acid is a strong acid, so 100% of the acid ionizes to produce hydronium and chloride ions. In contrast, acetic acid is a weak electrolyte because it ionizes only to a very small extent in water.

$$CH_3CO_2H(aq) + H_2O(\ell) \rightleftharpoons H_3O^+(aq) + CH_3CO_2^-(aq)$$

The acid, its anion, and the hydronium ion are all present at equilibrium in solution, but the ions are present in very low concentration relative to the acid concentration. For example, in a 0.100 M solution of acetic acid, $[H_3O^+]$ and $[CH_3CO_2^-]$ are each about 0.0013 M whereas that of un-ionized acetic acid, $[CH_3CO_2H]$, is 0.099 M.

Similarly, ammonia is a weak base.

$$NH_3(aq) + H_2O(\ell) \rightleftharpoons NH_4^+(aq) + OH^-(aq)$$

Only about 1% of ammonia molecules in a 0.100 M solution react with water to produce the ammonium and hydroxide ions.

One way to define the relative strengths of a series of acids is to measure the pH of solutions of acids of equal concentration: the lower the pH, the greater the concentration of hydronium ion, the stronger the acid. Similarly, for a series of weak bases, $[OH^-]$ will increase, and the pH will increase as the bases become stronger.

- For a strong monoprotic acid, $[H_3O^+]$ in solution is equal to the original acid concentration. Similarly, for a strong monoprotic base, $[OH^-]$ will be equal to the original base concentration.
- For a weak acid, $[H_3O^+]$ will be much less than the original acid concentration. That is, $[H_3O^+]$ will be smaller than if the acid were a strong acid of the same concentration. Similarly, a weak base will give a smaller $[OH^-]$ than if the base were a strong base of the same concentration.
- For a series of weak monoprotic acids (of the type HA) of the same concentration, $[H_3O^+]$ will increase (and the pH will decline) as the acids become stronger. Similarly, for a series of weak bases, $[OH^-]$ will increase (and the pH will increase) as the bases become stronger.

**Strong Acid**

HCl completely ionizes in aqueous solution.

HCl

**(a)** Hydrochloric acid, a strong acid, is sold for household use as "muriatic acid." The acid completely ionizes in water.

**Weak Acid**

Acetic acid, CH₃CO₂H, ionizes only slightly in water.

CH₃CO₂H

**(b)** Vinegar is a solution of acetic acid, a weak acid that ionizes only to a small extent in water.

**Weak Base**

The weak base ammonia reacts to a small extent with water to give a weakly basic solution.

NH₃

**(c)** Ammonia is a weak base, ionizing to a small extent in water.

**FIGURE 17.2 Strong and weak acids and bases.**

## Strong or Weak?

How can you tell whether an acid or a base is weak? The easiest way is to remember those few that are strong. All others are probably weak.

Common strong acids include the following:

Hydrohalic acids: HCl, HBr, and HI (but not HF)
Nitric acid: $HNO_3$

Sulfuric acid: $H_2SO_4$ (for loss of first $H^+$ only)
Perchloric acid: $HClO_4$

Some common strong bases include the following:

All Group 1A hydroxides: LiOH, NaOH, KOH, RbOH, CsOH

Group 2A hydroxides: $Sr(OH)_2$ and $Ba(OH)_2$. [$Mg(OH)_2$ and $Ca(OH)_2$ are not considered strong bases because they do not dissolve appreciably in water.]

The relative strength of an acid or base can also be expressed quantitatively with an equilibrium constant, often called an **ionization constant**. For the general acid HA, we can write

$$HA(aq) + H_2O(\ell) \rightleftharpoons H_3O^+(aq) + A^-(aq)$$

$$K_a = \frac{[H_3O^+][A^-]}{[HA]} \tag{17.5}$$

where the equilibrium constant, $K$, has a subscript "a" to indicate that it is an equilibrium constant for an acid in water. For weak acids, the value of $K_a$ is less than 1 because the product $[H_3O^+][A^-]$ is less than the equilibrium concentration of the weak acid [HA]. For a series of acids, the acid strength increases as the value of $K_a$ increases.

Similarly, we can write the equilibrium expression for a weak base B in water. Here, we label $K$ with a subscript "b." Its value is less than 1 for weak bases.

$$B(aq) + H_2O(\ell) \rightleftharpoons BH^+(aq) + OH^-(aq)$$

$$K_b = \frac{[BH^+][OH^-]}{[B]} \tag{17.6}$$

Some acids and bases are listed in Table 17.3, each with its value of $K_a$ or $K_b$. The following are important concepts concerning this table.

- Acids are listed in the table at the left, and their conjugate bases are listed on the right.
- A large value of $K$ indicates that ionization products are strongly favored, whereas a small value of $K$ indicates that reactants are favored.
- The strongest acids are at the upper left. They have the largest $K_a$ values. $K_a$ values become smaller on descending the chart as acid strength declines.
- The strongest bases are at the lower right. They have the largest $K_b$ values. $K_b$ values become larger on descending the chart as base strength increases.
- *The weaker the acid, the stronger its conjugate base.* That is, the smaller the value of $K_a$, the larger the value of $K_b$.
- Some acids or bases are listed as having $K_a$ or $K_b$ values that are large or very small. Aqueous acids that are stronger than $H_3O^+$ are completely ionized ($HNO_3$, for example), so their $K_a$ values are "large." Their conjugate bases (such as $NO_3^-$) do not produce meaningful concentrations of $OH^-$ ions, so their $K_b$ values are "very small." Similar arguments follow for strong bases and their conjugate acids.

**Table 17.3** Ionization Constants for Some Acids and Their Conjugate Bases at 25 °C

| Acid Name | Acid | $K_a$ | Base | $K_b$ | Base Name |
|---|---|---|---|---|---|
| Perchloric acid | $HClO_4$ | Large | $ClO_4^-$ | Very small | Perchlorate ion |
| Sulfuric acid | $H_2SO_4$ | Large | $HSO_4^-$ | Very small | Hydrogen sulfate ion |
| Hydrochloric acid | $HCl$ | Large | $Cl^-$ | Very small | Chloride ion |
| Nitric acid | $HNO_3$ | Large | $NO_3^-$ | Very small | Nitrate ion |
| Hydronium ion | $H_3O^+$ | 1.0 | $H_2O$ | $1.0 \times 10^{-14}$ | Water |
| Sulfurous acid | $H_2SO_3$ | $1.2 \times 10^{-2}$ | $HSO_3^-$ | $8.3 \times 10^{-13}$ | Hydrogen sulfite ion |
| Hydrogen sulfate ion | $HSO_4^-$ | $1.2 \times 10^{-2}$ | $SO_4^{2-}$ | $8.3 \times 10^{-13}$ | Sulfate ion |
| Phosphoric acid | $H_3PO_4$ | $7.5 \times 10^{-3}$ | $H_2PO_4^-$ | $1.3 \times 10^{-12}$ | Dihydrogen phosphate ion |
| Hexaaquairon(III) ion | $[Fe(H_2O)_6]^{3+}$ | $6.3 \times 10^{-3}$ | $[Fe(H_2O)_5OH]^{2+}$ | $1.6 \times 10^{-12}$ | Pentaaquahydroxoiron(III) ion |
| Hydrofluoric acid | $HF$ | $7.2 \times 10^{-4}$ | $F^-$ | $1.4 \times 10^{-11}$ | Fluoride ion |
| Nitrous acid | $HNO_2$ | $4.5 \times 10^{-4}$ | $NO_2^-$ | $2.2 \times 10^{-11}$ | Nitrite ion |
| Formic acid | $HCO_2H$ | $1.8 \times 10^{-4}$ | $HCO_2^-$ | $5.6 \times 10^{-11}$ | Formate ion |
| Benzoic acid | $C_6H_5CO_2H$ | $6.3 \times 10^{-5}$ | $C_6H_5CO_2^-$ | $1.6 \times 10^{-10}$ | Benzoate ion |
| Acetic acid | $CH_3CO_2H$ | $1.8 \times 10^{-5}$ | $CH_3CO_2^-$ | $5.6 \times 10^{-10}$ | Acetate ion |
| Propanoic acid | $CH_3CH_2CO_2H$ | $1.3 \times 10^{-5}$ | $CH_3CH_2CO_2^-$ | $7.7 \times 10^{-10}$ | Propanoate ion |
| Hexaaquaaluminum ion | $[Al(H_2O)_6]^{3+}$ | $7.9 \times 10^{-6}$ | $[Al(H_2O)_5OH]^{2+}$ | $1.3 \times 10^{-9}$ | Pentaaquahydroxoaluminum ion |
| Carbonic acid | $H_2CO_3$ | $4.2 \times 10^{-7}$ | $HCO_3^-$ | $2.4 \times 10^{-8}$ | Hydrogen carbonate ion |
| Hexaaquacopper(II) ion | $[Cu(H_2O)_6]^{2+}$ | $1.6 \times 10^{-7}$ | $[Cu(H_2O)_5OH]^+$ | $6.3 \times 10^{-8}$ | Pentaaquahydroxocopper(II) ion |
| Hydrogen sulfide | $H_2S$ | $1 \times 10^{-7}$ | $HS^-$ | $1 \times 10^{-7}$ | Hydrogen sulfide ion |
| Dihydrogen phosphate ion | $H_2PO_4^-$ | $6.2 \times 10^{-8}$ | $HPO_4^{2-}$ | $1.6 \times 10^{-7}$ | Hydrogen phosphate ion |
| Hydrogen sulfite ion | $HSO_3^-$ | $6.2 \times 10^{-8}$ | $SO_3^{2-}$ | $1.6 \times 10^{-7}$ | Sulfite ion |
| Hypochlorous acid | $HClO$ | $3.5 \times 10^{-8}$ | $ClO^-$ | $2.9 \times 10^{-7}$ | Hypochlorite ion |
| Hexaaqualead(II) ion | $[Pb(H_2O)_6]^{2+}$ | $1.5 \times 10^{-8}$ | $[Pb(H_2O)_5OH]^+$ | $6.7 \times 10^{-7}$ | Pentaaquahydroxolead(II) ion |
| Hexaaquacobalt(II) ion | $[Co(H_2O)_6]^{2+}$ | $1.3 \times 10^{-9}$ | $[Co(H_2O)_5OH]^+$ | $7.7 \times 10^{-6}$ | Pentaaquahydroxocobalt(II) ion |
| Boric acid | $B(OH)_3(H_2O)$ | $7.3 \times 10^{-10}$ | $B(OH)_4^-$ | $1.4 \times 10^{-5}$ | Tetrahydroxoborate ion |
| Ammonium ion | $NH_4^+$ | $5.6 \times 10^{-10}$ | $NH_3$ | $1.8 \times 10^{-5}$ | Ammonia |
| Hydrocyanic acid | $HCN$ | $4.0 \times 10^{-10}$ | $CN^-$ | $2.5 \times 10^{-5}$ | Cyanide ion |
| Hexaaquairon(II) ion | $[Fe(H_2O)_6]^{2+}$ | $3.2 \times 10^{-10}$ | $[Fe(H_2O)_5OH]^+$ | $3.1 \times 10^{-5}$ | Pentaaquahydroxoiron(II) ion |
| Hydrogen carbonate ion | $HCO_3^-$ | $4.8 \times 10^{-11}$ | $CO_3^{2-}$ | $2.1 \times 10^{-4}$ | Carbonate ion |
| Hexaaquanickel(II) ion | $[Ni(H_2O)_6]^{2+}$ | $2.5 \times 10^{-11}$ | $[Ni(H_2O)_5OH]^+$ | $4.0 \times 10^{-4}$ | Pentaaquahydroxonickel(II) ion |
| Hydrogen phosphate ion | $HPO_4^{2-}$ | $3.6 \times 10^{-13}$ | $PO_4^{3-}$ | $2.8 \times 10^{-2}$ | Phosphate ion |
| Water | $H_2O$ | $1.0 \times 10^{-14}$ | $OH^-$ | 1.0 | Hydroxide ion |
| Hydrogen sulfide ion* | $HS^-$ | $1 \times 10^{-19}$ | $S^{2-}$ | $1 \times 10^5$ | Sulfide ion |
| Ethanol | $C_2H_5OH$ | Very small | $C_2H_5O^-$ | Large | Ethoxide ion |
| Ammonia | $NH_3$ | Very small | $NH_2^-$ | Large | Amide ion |
| Hydrogen | $H_2$ | Very small | $H^-$ | Large | Hydride ion |

*The values of $K_a$ for $HS^-$ and $K_b$ for $S^{2-}$ are estimates.

*(left margin, bottom to top)* Increasing Acid Strength

*(right margin, bottom to top)* Increasing Base Strength

To illustrate some of these ideas, let us compare some common acids and bases. For example, HF is a stronger acid than HClO, which is in turn stronger than $HCO_3^-$,

Increasing acid strength →

| $HCO_3^-$ | HClO | HF |
|---|---|---|
| $K_a = 4.8 \times 10^{-11}$ | $K_a = 3.5 \times 10^{-8}$ | $K_a = 7.2 \times 10^{-4}$ |

and their conjugate bases become stronger from $F^-$ to $ClO^-$ to $CO_3^{2-}$.

← Increasing base strength

| $CO_3^{2-}$ | $ClO^-$ | $F^-$ |
|---|---|---|
| $K_b = 2.1 \times 10^{-4}$ | $K_b = 2.9 \times 10^{-7}$ | $K_a = 1.4 \times 10^{-11}$ |

Nature abounds in acids and bases (Figure 17.3). Many naturally occurring acids contain the carboxyl group ($-CO_2H$) (see page 759), and a few are illustrated here. Notice that the organic portion of the molecule has an effect on its relative strength (as described further in Section 17.10).

$K_a$ increases; acid strength increases →

propanoic acid, $CH_3CH_2CO_2H$
$K_a = 1.3 \times 10^{-5}$

acetic acid, $CH_3CO_2H$
$K_a = 1.8 \times 10^{-5}$

formic acid, $HCO_2H$
$K_a = 1.8 \times 10^{-4}$

← $K_b$ of conjugate base increases

There are many naturally occurring weak bases as well (Figure 17.3). Ammonia and its conjugate acid, the ammonium ion, are part of the nitrogen cycle in the environment (▶ page 949). Biological systems reduce nitrate ion to $NH_3$ and $NH_4^+$ and incorporate nitrogen into amino acids and proteins. Many bases are derived from $NH_3$ by replacement of the H atoms with organic groups.

ammonia
$K_b = 1.8 \times 10^{-5}$

methylamine
$K_b = 5.0 \times 10^{-4}$

aniline
$K_b = 4.0 \times 10^{-10}$

Ammonia is a weaker base than methylamine ($K_b$ for $NH_3 < K_b$ for $CH_3NH_2$). This means that the conjugate acid of ammonia, $NH_4^+$ ($K_a = 5.6 \times 10^{-10}$), is stronger than the methylammonium ion, the conjugate acid of methylamine, $CH_3NH_3^+$ ($K_a = 2.0 \times 10^{-11}$).

## $K_a$ Values for Polyprotic Acids

Like all polyprotic acids, phosphoric acid ionizes in a series of steps, three in this case.

First ionization step: $K_{a1} = 7.5 \times 10^{-3}$

$$H_3PO_4(aq) + H_2O(\ell) \rightleftharpoons H_2PO_4^-(aq) + H_3O^+(aq)$$

Second ionization step: $K_{a2} = 6.2 \times 10^{-8}$

$$H_2PO_4^-(aq) + H_2O(\ell) \rightleftharpoons HPO_4^{2-}(aq) + H_3O^+(aq)$$

The tartness of lemons and oranges comes from the weak acid citric acid. The acid is found widely in nature and in many consumer products.

Caffeine is a well-known stimulant and a weak base.

Photos © Cengage Learning/Charles D. Winters

**FIGURE 17.3 Natural acids and bases.** Hundreds of acids and bases occur in nature. Our foods contain a wide variety, and biochemically important molecules are often acids and bases.

Third ionization step: $K_{a3} = 3.6 \times 10^{-13}$

$$HPO_4^{2-}(aq) + H_2O(\ell) \rightleftharpoons PO_4^{3-}(aq) + H_3O^+(aq)$$

We observe that the $K_a$ value for each successive step becomes smaller because it is more difficult to remove $H^+$ from a negatively charged ion, such as $H_2PO_4^-$, than from a neutral molecule, such as $H_3PO_4$. Similarly, the larger the negative charge of the anionic acid, the more difficult it is to remove $H^+$. Finally, for many inorganic polyprotic acids, $K_a$ values become smaller by about $10^5$ for each proton removed.

## Logarithmic Scale of Relative Acid Strength, p$K_a$

Many chemists and biochemists use a logarithmic scale to report and compare relative acid strengths.

$$pK_a = -\log K_a \tag{17.7}$$

The p$K_a$ of an acid is the negative log of the $K_a$ value (just as pH is the negative log of the hydronium ion concentration). For example, acetic acid has a p$K_a$ value of 4.74.

$$pK_a = -\log (1.8 \times 10^{-5}) = 4.74$$

The p$K_a$ value becomes smaller as the acid strength increases.

—— Acid strength increases ⟶

| Propanoic acid | Acetic acid | Formic acid |
|---|---|---|
| $CH_3CH_2CO_2H$ | $CH_3CO_2H$ | $HCO_2H$ |
| $K_a = 1.3 \times 10^{-5}$ | $K_a = 1.8 \times 10^{-5}$ | $K_a = 1.8 \times 10^{-4}$ |
| $pK_a = 4.89$ | $pK_a = 4.74$ | $pK_a = 3.74$ |

—— p$K_a$ decreases ⟶

## Relating the Ionization Constants for an Acid and Its Conjugate Base

Let us look again at Table 17.3. From the top of the table to the bottom, the strengths of the acids decline ($K_a$ becomes smaller), and the strengths of their conjugate bases increase (the values of $K_b$ increase). Examining a few cases shows that the product of $K_a$ for an acid and $K_b$ for its conjugate base is equal to a constant, specifically $K_w$.

● **A Relation Among p$K$ Values** A useful relationship for an acid–conjugate base pair follows from Equation 17.8. $pK_w = pK_a + pK_b$

$$K_a \times K_b = K_w \tag{17.8}$$

Consider the specific case of the ionization of a weak acid, say HCN, and the interaction of its conjugate base, $CN^-$, with $H_2O$.

Weak acid:  $HCN(aq) + H_2O(\ell) \rightleftharpoons H_3O^+(aq) + CN^-(aq)$  $\quad K_a = 4.0 \times 10^{-10}$

Conjugate base:  $CN^-(aq) + H_2O(\ell) \rightleftharpoons HCN(aq) + OH^-(aq)$  $\quad K_b = 2.5 \times 10^{-5}$

$\overline{\phantom{CN^-(aq) + H_2O(\ell) }2 H_2O(\ell) \rightleftharpoons H_3O^+(aq) + OH^-(aq)} \quad K_w = 1.0 \times 10^{-14}$

Adding the equations gives the chemical equation for the autoionization of water, and the numerical value is indeed $1.0 \times 10^{-14}$. That is,

$$K_a \times K_b = \left( \frac{[H_3O^+][\cancel{CN^-}]}{[\cancel{HCN}]} \right) \left( \frac{[\cancel{HCN}][OH^-]}{[\cancel{CN^-}]} \right) = [H_3O^+][OH^-] = K_w$$

Equation 17.8 is useful because $K_b$ can be calculated from $K_a$. The value of $K_b$ for the cyanide ion, for example, is

$$K_b \text{ for } CN^- = \frac{K_w}{K_a \text{ for } HCN} = \frac{1.0 \times 10^{-14}}{4.0 \times 10^{-10}} = 2.5 \times 10^{-5}$$

---

**REVIEW & CHECK FOR SECTION 17.4**

Use Table 17.3 to answer the following questions.

1.  Which of the following is the strongest acid?

    (a)  HF  $\quad\quad\quad$ (b)  $H_2S$  $\quad\quad\quad$ (c)  HOCl  $\quad\quad\quad$ (d)  $CH_3CO_2H$

2.  Which acid has the strongest conjugate base?

    (a)  $HNO_2$  $\quad\quad$ (b)  $C_6H_5CO_2H$  $\quad$ (c)  HCN  $\quad\quad\quad$ (d)  HCl

3.  Which of the following has a $pK_a$ value of 4.20?

    (a)  $C_6H_5CO_2H$  $\quad$ (b)  $CH_3CO_2H$  $\quad$ (c)  $HCO_2H$  $\quad$ (d)  HF

4.  What is the $pK_a$ for the conjugate acid of ammonia?

    (a)  4.74  $\quad\quad\quad$ (b)  9.25  $\quad\quad\quad$ (c)  5.60  $\quad\quad\quad$ (d)  7.00

5.  $K_a$ for lactic acid, $CH_3CHOHCO_2H$, is $1.4 \times 10^{-4}$. What is $pK_b$ for the conjugate base of this acid, $CH_3CHOHCO_2^-$?

    (a)  3.85  $\quad\quad\quad$ (b)  7.00  $\quad\quad\quad$ (c)  10.15  $\quad\quad\quad$ (d)  12.60

---

# 17.5 Acid–Base Properties of Salts

A number of the acids and bases listed in Table 17.3 are cations or anions. As described earlier, anions can act as Brønsted bases because they can accept a proton from an acid to form the conjugate acid of the ion.

$$CO_3^{2-}(aq) + H_2O(\ell) \rightleftharpoons HCO_3^-(aq) + OH^-(aq)$$
$$K_b = 2.1 \times 10^{-4}$$

You should also notice that many metal cations in water are Brønsted acids.

$$[Al(H_2O)_6]^{3+}(aq) + H_2O(\ell) \rightleftharpoons [Al(H_2O)_5(OH)]^{2+}(aq) + H_3O^+(aq)$$
$$K_a = 7.9 \times 10^{-6}$$

Table 17.4 summarizes the acid–base properties of some common cations and anions. As you look over this table, notice the following points:

- Anions that are conjugate bases of strong acids (for example, $Cl^-$ and $NO_3^-$) are such weak bases that they have no effect on solution pH.
- There are numerous basic anions (such as $CO_3^{2-}$). All are the conjugate bases of weak acids.
- The acid–base behavior of anions of polyprotic acids depends on the extent of deprotonation. For example, a fully deprotonated anion (such as $CO_3^{2-}$) will be basic. A partially deprotonated anion (such as $HCO_3^-$) is amphiprotic. Its behavior will depend on the other species in the reaction.

● **Hydrolysis Reactions and Hydrolysis Constants** Chemists often say that, when ions interact with water to produce acidic or basic solutions, the ions "hydrolyze" in water, or they undergo "hydrolysis." Thus, some books refer to the $K_a$ and $K_b$ values of ions as "hydrolysis constants," $K_h$.

**Many aqueous metal cations are Brønsted acids.** A pH measurement of a dilute solution of copper(II) sulfate shows that the solution is clearly acidic. Among the common cations, $Al^{3+}$ and transition metal ions form acidic solutions in water.

**Table 17.4  Acid and Base Properties of Some Ions in Aqueous Solution**

| | Neutral | | Basic | | | Acidic |
|---|---|---|---|---|---|---|
| Anions | $Cl^-$  $Br^-$  $I^-$ | $NO_3^-$  $ClO_4^-$ | $CH_3CO_2^-$  $HCO_2^-$  $CO_3^{2-}$  $S^{2-}$  $F^-$ | $CN^-$  $PO_4^{3-}$  $HCO_3^-$  $HS^-$  $NO_2^-$ | $SO_4^{2-}$  $HPO_4^{2-}$  $SO_3^{2-}$  $OCl^-$ | $HSO_4^-$  $H_2PO_4^-$  $HSO_3^-$ |
| Cations | $Li^+$  $Na^+$  $K^+$ | $Ca^{2+}$  $Ba^{2+}$ | $[Al(H_2O)_5(OH)]^{2+}$ (for example) | | | $[Al(H_2O)_6]^{3+}$ and hydrated transition metal cations (such as $[Fe(H_2O)_6]^{3+}$)  $NH_4^+$ |

- Alkali metal and alkaline earth cations have no measurable effect on solution pH.
- Basic cations are conjugate bases of acidic cations such as $[Al(H_2O)_6]^{3+}$.
- Acidic cations fall into two categories: (a) metal cations with 2+ and 3+ charges and (b) ammonium ions (and its organic derivatives). All metal cations are hydrated in water, forming ions such as $[M(H_2O)_6]^{n+}$. However, only when M is a 2+ or 3+ ion, particularly a transition metal ion, does the ion act as an acid.

### ◉WL    INTERACTIVE EXAMPLE 17.2    Acid–Base Properties of Salts

**Problem**  Decide whether each of the following will give rise to an acidic, basic, or neutral solution in water.

(a)  $NaNO_3$

(b)  $K_3PO_4$

(c)  $FeCl_2$

(d)  $NaHCO_3$

(e)  $NH_4F$

**What Do You Know?**  You know the salt formulas and, from Tables 17.3 and 17.4, you know the effect of the constituent ions on pH.

**Strategy**  First, identify the cation and anion in each salt. Next, use Tables 17.3 and 17.4 to describe the acid–base properties of each ion. Finally decide on the overall acid–base properties of the salt.

**Solution**

(a)  $NaNO_3$: This salt gives a neutral, aqueous solution (pH = 7). Neither the sodium ion, $Na^+$, nor the nitrate ion, $NO_3^-$ (the very weak conjugate base of a strong acid), affects the solution pH.

(b)  $K_3PO_4$: An aqueous solution of $K_3PO_4$ should be basic (pH > 7) because $PO_4^{3-}$ is the conjugate base of the weak acid $HPO_4^{2-}$. The $K^+$ ion, like the $Na^+$ ion, does not affect the solution pH.

(c)  $FeCl_2$: An aqueous solution of $FeCl_2$ should be weakly acidic (pH < 7). The $Fe^{2+}$ ion in water, $[Fe(H_2O)_6]^{2+}$, is a Brønsted acid. In contrast, $Cl^-$ is the very weak conjugate base of the strong acid HCl, so it does not contribute excess $OH^-$ ions to the solution.

(d)  $NaHCO_3$: Some additional information is needed concerning salts of amphiprotic anions such as $HCO_3^-$. Because they have an ionizable hydrogen, they can act as acids,

$$HCO_3^-(aq) + H_2O(\ell) \rightleftharpoons CO_3^{2-}(aq) + H_3O^+(aq) \qquad K_a = 4.8 \times 10^{-11}$$

but because they are anions, they can also act as bases and accept an $H^+$ ion from water.

$$HCO_3^-(aq) + H_2O(\ell) \rightleftharpoons H_2CO_3(aq) + OH^-(aq) \qquad K_b = 2.4 \times 10^{-8}$$

**Strategy Map 17.2**

**PROBLEM**

Decide whether a salt is **acidic, basic,** or **neutral.**

↓

**DATA/INFORMATION KNOWN**

- The formula of the salt: $K_3PO_4$

↓

STEP 1. Identify the **cation** and **anion.**

Cation = $K^+$, anion = $PO_4^{3-}$

↓

STEP 2. Identify the nature of the **cation.**

$K^+$ is a **neutral** cation.

↓

STEP 3. Identify the nature of the **anion.**

$PO_4^{3-}$ is a *relatively strong* base.

↓

STEP 4. Decide on the acid–base properties of the salt.

$K_3PO_4$ is **basic.**

## Aqueous Solutions of Salts

Because aqueous solutions of salts are found in our bodies and throughout our economy and environment, it is important to know how to predict their acid and base properties. Information on the pH of an aqueous solution of a salt is summarized in Table 17.4. Consider also the following examples:

| Cation | Anion | pH of the Solution |
|---|---|---|
| From strong base ($Na^+$) | From strong acid ($Cl^-$) | = 7 (neutral) |
| From strong base ($K^+$) | From weak acid ($CH_3CO_2^-$) | > 7 (basic) |
| From weak base ($NH_4^+$) | From strong acid ($Cl^-$) | < 7 (acidic) |
| From any weak base ($BH^+$) | From any weak acid ($A^-$) | Depends on relative acid strength of $BH^+$ and base strength of $A^-$ |

Whether the solution is acidic or basic will depend on the relative magnitude of $K_a$ and $K_b$. In the case of the hydrogen carbonate anion, $K_b$ is larger than $K_a$, so $[OH^-]$ is larger than $[H_3O^+]$, and an aqueous solution of $NaHCO_3$ will be slightly basic.

(e) $NH_4F$: What happens if you have a salt based on an acidic cation and a basic anion? One example is ammonium fluoride. Here, the ammonium ion would decrease the pH, and the fluoride ion would increase the pH.

$$NH_4^+(aq) + H_2O(\ell) \rightleftharpoons H_3O^+(aq) + NH_3(aq) \qquad K_a (NH_4^+) = 5.6 \times 10^{-10}$$

$$F^-(aq) + H_2O(\ell) \rightleftharpoons HF(aq) + OH^-(aq) \qquad K_b (F^-) = 1.4 \times 10^{-11}$$

Because $K_a (NH_4^+) > K_b (F^-)$, the ammonium ion is a stronger acid than the fluoride ion is a base. The resulting solution should be slightly acidic.

**Think about Your Answer** There are several important points here:

- Anions that are conjugate bases of strong acids—such as $Cl^-$ and $NO_3^-$—have no effect on solution pH.

- To determine whether a salt is acidic, basic, or neutral, we must take into account both the cation and the anion. When a salt has an acidic cation and a basic anion, the pH of the solution will be determined by the ion that is the stronger acid or base.

**Check Your Understanding**

For each of the following salts in water, predict whether the pH will be greater than, less than, or equal to 7.

(a) KBr      (b) $NH_4NO_3$      (c) $AlCl_3$      (d) $Na_2HPO_4$

---

**REVIEW & CHECK FOR SECTION 17.5**

1. Adding $NaH_2PO_4$ to water will cause the pH to

   (a) increase      (b) decrease      (c) stay the same

2. Adding KCN to water will cause the pH to

   (a) increase      (b) decrease      (c) stay the same

---

# 17.6 Predicting the Direction of Acid–Base Reactions

According to the Brønsted–Lowry theory, all acid–base reactions can be written as equilibria involving the acid and base and their conjugates.

Acid + base $\rightleftharpoons$ conjugate base of the acid + conjugate acid of the base

In Sections 17.4 and 17.5, we used equilibrium constants to provide information about the relative strengths of acids and bases. Now we want to show how these constants can be used to decide whether a particular acid–base reaction is product- or reactant–favored at equilibrium.

Hydrochloric acid is a strong acid. Its equilibrium constant for reaction with water is very large, with the equilibrium lying completely to the right.

$$HCl(aq) + H_2O(\ell) \rightleftharpoons H_3O^+(aq) + Cl^-(aq)$$

Strong acid ($\approx$ 100% ionized), $K \gg 1$

$[H_3O^+] \approx$ initial concentration of the acid

Of the two acids here, HCl is stronger than $H_3O^+$. Of the two bases, $H_2O$ and $Cl^-$, water is the stronger base and wins out in the competition for the proton. Thus, the equilibrium lies to the side of the chemical equation having the weaker acid and base.

In contrast to HCl and other strong acids, acetic acid, a *weak* acid, ionizes to only a very small extent (Table 17.3).

$$CH_3CO_2H(aq) + H_2O(\ell) \rightleftharpoons H_3O^+(aq) + CH_3CO_2^-(aq)$$

Weak acid ($<$ 100% ionized), $K = 1.8 \times 10^{-5}$

$[H_3O^+] \ll$ initial concentration of the acid

When equilibrium is achieved in a 0.1 M aqueous solution of $CH_3CO_2H$, the concentrations of $H_3O^+(aq)$ and $CH_3CO_2^-(aq)$ are each only about 0.001 M. Approximately 99% of the acetic acid is not ionized.

● **General Principle of Reactivity**
A general principle in chemistry is that more reactive substances react to form less reactive substances. Here you see the result of this for acid–base reactions: The stronger acid and stronger base always react to form the weaker acid and weaker base.

Again, the equilibrium lies toward the side of the reaction having the weaker acid and base.

These two examples of the relative extent of acid–base reactions illustrate a general principle:

> All proton transfer reactions proceed from the stronger acid and base to the weaker acid and base.

Using this principle and Table 17.3, you can predict which reactions are product-favored and which are reactant-favored at equilibrium. Consider the possible reaction of phosphoric acid and acetate ion to give acetic acid and the dihydrogen phosphate ion. Table 17.3 informs us that $H_3PO_4$ is a stronger acid ($K_a = 7.5 \times 10^{-3}$) than acetic acid ($K_a = 1.8 \times 10^{-5}$), and the acetate ion ($K_b = 5.6 \times 10^{-10}$) is a stronger base than the dihydrogen phosphate ion ($K_b = 1.3 \times 10^{-12}$).

Thus, mixing phosphoric acid with sodium acetate will produce a significant amount of dihydrogen phosphate ion and acetic acid. That is, the equilibrium is predicted to lie to the right because the reaction proceeds from the stronger acid–base combination to the weaker acid–base combination.

## EXAMPLE 17.3 Reactions of Acids and Bases

**Problem** Write a balanced, net ionic equation for the reaction that occurs between acetic acid and sodium bicarbonate. Decide whether the equilibrium lies predominantly to the left or to the right.

**What Do You Know?** You know the identity of the acid, and you know that the other reactant, $NaHCO_3$, is a water-soluble salt that forms $Na^+$ and $HCO_3^-$ ions in water. You also know that the $HCO_3^-$ ion is amphiprotic, but it must act as a base toward acetic acid in this reaction. You need to know the ionization constants for acetic acid and the $HCO_3^-$ ion and for their conjugates.

**Strategy**

- Identify the products of the acid–base reaction (which arise by $H^+$ transfer from acetic acid to the base, $HCO_3^-$). That is, identify the conjugate base of acetic acid and the conjugate acid of $HCO_3^-$.

- Write a balanced chemical equation for the equilibrium between the acid and base and their conjugate base and acid.

- Use Table 17.3 to decide which is the weaker of the two acids (or the weaker of the two bases). The equilibrium will favor the weaker acid and base.

**Solution** The conjugate base of acetic acid is the acetate ion, $CH_3CO_2^-$, and the conjugate acid of the base $HCO_3^-$ is $H_2CO_3$. Hydrogen ion transfer from the acid to the base occurs by the following net ionic equation:

$$CH_3CO_2H(aq) + HCO_3^-(aq) \rightleftharpoons CH_3CO_2^-(aq) + H_2CO_3(aq)$$
$$K_a = 1.8 \times 10^{-5} \quad K_b = 2.4 \times 10^{-8} \quad K_b = 5.6 \times 10^{-10} \quad K_a = 4.2 \times 10^{-7}$$

The value of $K_a$ or $K_b$ (from Table 17.3) is given for each reactant and product. The equilibrium constants show that $H_2CO_3$ is a weaker acid than $CH_3CO_2H$, and $CH_3CO_2^-$ is a weaker base than $HCO_3^-$. The reaction favors the side having the weaker acid and base—that is, the right side.

**Think about Your Answer** One product of the reaction of acetic acid and $NaHCO_3$ is $H_2CO_3$, which dissociates into $CO_2$ and $H_2O$. As you can see in the photograph in the margin, $CO_2$ bubbles out of the solution. The equilibrium for the dissociation of $H_2CO_3$ to form $CO_2$ and $H_2O$ lies far to the right.

$$H_2CO_3(aq) \rightleftharpoons CO_2(g) + H_2O(\ell)$$

The loss of a product, $CO_2$, causes the equilibrium to shift further to the right. See the discussion of gas-forming reactions in Chapter 3 and of Le Chatelier's principle in Section 16.6.

**Check Your Understanding**

(a) Which is the stronger Brønsted acid, $HCO_3^-$ or $NH_4^+$? Which has the stronger conjugate base?

(b) Is a reaction between $HCO_3^-$ ions and $NH_3$ product- or reactant-favored at equilibrium?

$$HCO_3^-(aq) + NH_3(aq) \rightleftharpoons CO_3^{2-}(aq) + NH_4^+(aq)$$

(c) You mix solutions of sodium hydrogen phosphate and ammonia. The net ionic equation for a possible reaction is

$$HPO_4^{2-}(aq) + NH_3(aq) \rightleftharpoons PO_4^{3-}(aq) + NH_4^+(aq)$$

Does the equilibrium lie to the left or to the right for this reaction?

**Reaction of vinegar and baking soda.** This reaction involves the weak acid acetic acid and the weak base $HCO_3^-$ from sodium hydrogen carbonate. Based on the values of the equilibrium constants, the reaction is predicted to proceed to the right to produce acetate ion, $CO_2$, and water.

© Cengage Learning/Charles D. Winters

## 17.7  Types of Acid–Base Reactions

The reaction of hydrochloric acid and sodium hydroxide is the classic example of a strong acid–strong base reaction, whereas the reaction of citric acid and bicarbonate ion represents the reaction of a weak acid and weak base (Figure 17.4). These are two of four general types of acid–base reactions (Table 17.5). Because acid–base reactions are among the most important classes of chemical reactions, it is useful for you to know the outcome of the various types of these reactions.

### The Reaction of a Strong Acid with a Strong Base

Strong acids and bases are effectively 100% ionized in solution. Therefore, the complete ionic equation for the reaction of HCl (strong acid) and NaOH (strong base) is

$$H_3O^+(aq) + Cl^-(aq) + Na^+(aq) + OH^-(aq) \rightleftharpoons 2\ H_2O(\ell) + Na^+(aq) + Cl^-(aq)$$

which leads to the following net ionic equation

$$H_3O^+(aq) + OH^-(aq) \rightleftharpoons 2\ H_2O(\ell) \qquad K = 1/K_w = 1.0 \times 10^{14}$$

The net ionic equation for the reaction of any strong acid with any strong base is always simply the reaction of hydronium ion and hydroxide ion to give water (◄ Section 3.6). Because this reaction is the reverse of the autoionization of water, it has an equilibrium constant of $1/K_w$. This very large value of $K$ shows that, for all practical purposes, the reactants are completely consumed to form products. Thus, if equal numbers of moles of NaOH and HCl are mixed, the result is just a solution of NaCl in water. The constituents of NaCl, $Na^+$ and $Cl^-$ ions, which arise from a strong base and a strong acid, respectively, produce a neutral aqueous solution. For this reason, reactions of strong acids and bases are often called "neutralizations."

> Mixing equal amounts (moles) of a strong base and a strong acid produces a neutral solution (pH = 7.00 at 25 °C).

### The Reaction of a Weak Acid with a Strong Base

Consider the reaction of the naturally occurring weak acid formic acid, $HCO_2H$, with sodium hydroxide. The net ionic equation is

$$HCO_2H(aq) + OH^-(aq) \rightleftharpoons H_2O(\ell) + HCO_2^-(aq)$$

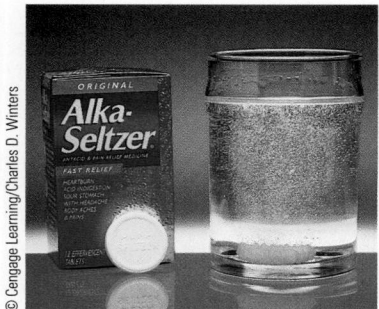

© Cengage Learning/Charles D. Winters

**FIGURE 17.4  Reaction of a weak acid with a weak base.** The bubbles coming from the tablet are carbon dioxide. This arises from the reaction of a weak Brønsted acid (citric acid) with a weak Brønsted base ($HCO_3^-$). The reaction is driven to completion by gas evolution.

● **Formic Acid + NaOH** The equilibrium constant for the reaction of formic acid and sodium hydroxide is $1.8 \times 10^{10}$. Can you confirm this? (See Study Question 17.97.)

Table 17.5  **Characteristics of Acid–Base Reactions**

| Type | Example | Net Ionic Equation | Species Present after Equal Amounts Are Mixed; pH |
|---|---|---|---|
| Strong acid + strong base | HCl + NaOH | $H_3O^+(aq) + OH^-(aq) \rightleftharpoons 2\ H_2O(\ell)$ | $Cl^-$, $Na^+$, pH = 7 |
| Strong acid + weak base | $HCl + NH_3$ | $H_3O^+(aq) + NH_3(aq) \rightleftharpoons NH_4^+(aq) + H_2O(\ell)$ | $Cl^-$, $NH_4^+$, pH < 7 |
| Weak acid + strong base | $HCO_2H + NaOH$ | $HCO_2H(aq) + OH^-(aq) \rightleftharpoons HCO_2^-(aq) + H_2O(\ell)$ | $HCO_2^-$, $Na^+$, pH > 7 |
| Weak acid + weak base | $HCO_2H + NH_3$ | $HCO_2H(aq) + NH_3(aq) \rightleftharpoons HCO_2^-(aq) + NH_4^+(aq)$ | $HCO_2^-$, $NH_4^+$, pH dependent on $K_a$ and $K_b$ of conjugate acid and base |

In the reaction of formic acid with NaOH, $OH^-$ is a much stronger base than $HCO_2^-$ ($K_b = 5.6 \times 10^{-11}$), and the reaction is predicted to proceed to the right. If equal amounts of weak acid and base are mixed, the final solution will contain sodium formate ($NaHCO_2$), a salt that is 100% dissociated in water. The $Na^+$ ion is a Group IA cation and so gives a neutral solution. The formate ion, however, is the conjugate base of a weak acid (Table 17.3), so the solution is basic. This example leads to a useful general conclusion:

> Mixing equal amounts (moles) of a strong base and a weak acid produces a salt whose anion is the conjugate base of the weak acid. The solution is basic, with the pH depending on $K_b$ for the anion.

## The Reaction of a Strong Acid with a Weak Base

The net ionic equation for the reaction of the strong acid HCl and the weak base $NH_3$ is

$$H_3O^+(aq) + NH_3(aq) \rightleftharpoons H_2O(\ell) + NH_4^+(aq)$$

The hydronium ion, $H_3O^+$, is a much stronger acid than $NH_4^+$ ($K_a = 5.6 \times 10^{-10}$), and $NH_3$ is a stronger base ($K_b = 1.8 \times 10^{-5}$) than $H_2O$. Therefore, reaction is predicted to proceed to the right and essentially to completion. Thus, after mixing equal amounts of HCl and $NH_3$, the solution contains the salt ammonium chloride, $NH_4Cl$. The $Cl^-$ ion has no effect on the solution pH (Tables 17.3 and 17.4). However, the $NH_4^+$ ion is the conjugate acid of the weak base $NH_3$, so the solution at the conclusion of the reaction is acidic. In general, we can conclude that

> Mixing equal amounts (moles) of a strong acid and a weak base produces a salt whose cation is the conjugate acid of the weak base. The solution is acidic, with the pH depending on $K_a$ for the cation.

## The Reaction of a Weak Acid with a Weak Base

If acetic acid, a weak acid, is mixed with ammonia, a weak base, the following reaction occurs.

$$CH_3CO_2H(aq) + NH_3(aq) \rightleftharpoons NH_4^+(aq) + CH_3CO_2^-(aq)$$

You know that the reaction is product-favored because $CH_3CO_2H$ is a stronger acid than $NH_4^+$ and $NH_3$ is a stronger base than $CH_3CO_2^-$ (Table 17.3). Thus, if equal amounts of the acid and base are mixed, the resulting solution contains ammonium acetate, $NH_4CH_3CO_2$. Is this solution acidic or basic? On page 771 you learned that this depends on the relative values of $K_a$ for the conjugate acid (here, $NH_4^+$; $K_a = 5.6 \times 10^{-10}$) and $K_b$ for the conjugate base (here, $CH_3CO_2^-$; $K_b = 5.6 \times 10^{-10}$). In this case, the values of $K_a$ and $K_b$ are the same, so the solution is predicted to be neutral.

> Mixing equal amounts (moles) of a weak acid and a weak base produces a salt whose cation is the conjugate acid of the weak base and whose anion is the conjugate base of the weak acid. The solution pH depends on the relative $K_a$ and $K_b$ values.

● **Ammonia + HCl** The equilibrium constant for the reaction of a strong acid with aqueous ammonia is $1.8 \times 10^9$. Can you confirm this? (See Study Question 17.96.)

● ***K* for Reaction of Weak Acid and Weak Base** The equilibrium constant for the reaction between a weak acid and a weak base is $K_{net} = K_w/(K_a \cdot K_b)$. Can you confirm this? (See Study Question 17.121.)

---

**REVIEW & CHECK FOR SECTION 17.7**

1. Equal amounts (moles) of HCl(aq) and NaCN(aq) are mixed. The resulting solution is

   (a) acidic        (b) basic        (c) neutral

2. Equal amounts (moles) of acetic acid(aq) and sodium sulfite, $Na_2SO_3$(aq), are mixed. The resulting solution is

   (a) acidic        (b) basic        (c) neutral

3. Equal amounts (moles) of NaOH(aq) and $NaH_2PO_4$(aq) are mixed. The resulting solution is

   (a) acidic        (b) basic        (c) neutral

© Cengage Learning/Charles D. Winters

**A weak acid reacting with a weak base.** Baking powder contains the weak acid calcium dihydrogen phosphate, $Ca(H_2PO_4)_2$. This can react with the basic $HCO_3^-$ ion in baking soda to give $HPO_4^{2-}$, $CO_2$ gas, and water.

## 17.8 Calculations with Equilibrium Constants

### Determining K from Initial Concentrations and Measured pH

The $K_a$ and $K_b$ values found in Table 17.3 and in the more extensive tables in Appendices H and I were all determined by experiment. There are several experimental methods available, but one approach, illustrated by the following example, is to determine the pH of the solution.

**Strategy Map 17.4**

**PROBLEM**

Calculate $K_a$ for the ionization of **lactic acid**, a weak acid.

⬇

**DATA/INFORMATION KNOWN**

- Acid concentration
- Solution pH

**STEP 1.** Write **balanced equation** and $K_a$ **expression**, and set up **ICE table**.

⬇

$K_a$ expression and ICE table

**STEP 2.** Enter **equilibrium concentrations** in ICE table.

⬇

At equilibrium:
$[H_3O^+] = $ [Conjugate base] $= x$
[Lactic acid] = original conc. $- x$

**STEP 3.** Convert **pH** to **[H₃O⁺]**, and solve for **x**

⬇

Equilibrium concentrations of **lactic acid, hydronium ion**, and **lactate ion**

**STEP 4.** Enter **equilibrium concentrations** into $K_a$ **expression** and solve.

⬇

Value of $K_a$

**ⓌWL INTERACTIVE EXAMPLE 17.4** Calculating a $K_a$ Value from a Measured pH

**Problem** A 0.10 M aqueous solution of lactic acid, $CH_3CHOHCO_2H$, has a pH of 2.43. What is the value of $K_a$ for lactic acid?

**What Do You Know?** To calculate $K_a$, you need to know the equilibrium concentration of each species. The pH of the solution allows you to calculate the equilibrium concentration of $H_3O^+$, and you can derive the other equilibrium concentrations from this.

**Strategy**

- Write the equilibrium constant expression, set up an ICE table, and convert pH to $[H_3O^+]$, the hydronium ion equilibrium concentration.

- Enter the initial concentration of $CH_3CHOHCO_2H$ on the initial (I) line of the ICE table and the equilibrium concentration of $H_3O^+$ on the equilibrium (E) line.

- Assign the variable $x$ to represent changes in concentration. Based on the reaction stoichiometry the change in $[CH_3CHOHCO_2H]$ is $-x$ and the change in $[CH_3CHOHCO_2^-]$ is $+x$. Enter these values in the change (C) line of the table.

- Recognize that the hydronium ion equilibrium concentration, $[H_3O^+]$, is equal to $x$.

- Enter the expressions for the final equilibrium concentrations of all three species on the E line of the ICE table. Using this, determine the values of the other equilibrium concentrations.

- Use the equilibrium concentrations to solve for $K_a$.

**Solution** The equation for the reaction of lactic acid with water and its equilibrium constant expression are

$$CH_3CHOHCO_2H(aq) + H_2O(\ell) \rightleftharpoons CH_3CHOHCO_2^-(aq) + H_3O^+(aq)$$

lactic acid                      lactate ion

$$K_a \text{ (lactic acid)} = \frac{[H_3O^+][CH_3CHOHCO_2^-]}{[CH_3CHOHCO_2H]}$$

Begin by converting the pH to $[H_3O^+]$:

$$[H_3O^+] = 10^{-pH} = 10^{-2.43} = 3.7 \times 10^{-3} \text{ M}$$

Enter in the ICE table the concentrations before equilibrium is established, the change that occurs as the reaction proceeds to equilibrium, and the concentrations when equilibrium has been achieved. (See Examples 16.2–16.5.)

| Equilibrium | $CH_3CHOHCO_2H$ | + | $H_2O$ | $\rightleftharpoons$ | $CH_3CHOHCO_2^-$ | + | $H_3O^+$ |
|---|---|---|---|---|---|---|---|
| Initial (M) | 0.10 | | | | 0 | | 0 |
| Change (M) | $-x$ | | | | $+x$ | | $+x$ |
| Equilibrium (M) | $(0.10 - x)$ | | | | $x$ | | $x$ |

The following points can be made concerning the ICE table.

- The quantity $x$ represents the equilibrium concentrations of hydronium ion and lactate ion. That is, at equilibrium $x = [H_3O^+] = [CH_3CHOHCO_2^-] = 3.7 \times 10^{-3}$ M.

- By stoichiometry, $x$ is also the concentration of acid that ionized on proceeding to equilibrium.

With these points in mind, we can calculate $K_a$ for lactic acid.

$$K_a \text{ (lactic acid)} = \frac{[H_3O^+][CH_3CHOHCO_2^-]}{[CH_3CHOHCO_2H]}$$

$$= \frac{(3.7 \times 10^{-3})(3.7 \times 10^{-3})}{0.10 - 0.0037} = 1.4 \times 10^{-4}$$

Comparing this value of $K_a$ with others in Table 17.3, we see lactic acid is similar to formic acid in its strength.

**Think about Your Answer** Hydronium ion, $H_3O^+$, is present in solution from lactic acid ionization and from water autoionization. Le Chatelier's principle informs us that the $H_3O^+$ from lactic acid will suppress the $H_3O^+$ coming from the water autoionization. Because $[H_3O^+]$ from water must be less than $10^{-7}$ M, the pH is almost completely a reflection of $H_3O^+$ from lactic acid. (See Example 17.1.)

**Check Your Understanding**

A solution prepared from 0.055 mol of butanoic acid dissolved in sufficient water to give 1.0 L of solution has a pH of 2.72. Determine $K_a$ for butanoic acid. The acid ionizes according to the balanced equation

$$CH_3CH_2CH_2CO_2H(aq) + H_2O(\ell) \rightleftharpoons H_3O^+(aq) + CH_3CH_2CH_2CO_2^-(aq)$$

lactic acid, $CH_3CHOHCO_2H$

**Lactic acid, $CH_3CHOHCO_2H$.** Lactic acid is a weak monoprotic acid that occurs naturally in sour milk and arises from metabolism in the human body.

**Module 22: Equilibrium: pH of a Weak Acid** covers concepts in this section.

There is an important point to notice in Example 17.4. The lactic acid concentration at equilibrium was given by $(0.10 - x)$ where $x$ was found from the solution pH to be $3.7 \times 10^{-3}$ M. By the usual rules governing significant figures $(0.10 - 0.0037)$ is equal to 0.10. The acid is weak, so very little of it ionizes (approximately 4%), and the equilibrium concentration of lactic acid is essentially equal to the initial acid concentration. Neglecting to subtract 0.0037 from 0.10 has no effect on the answer, which is known only to two significant figures.

Like lactic acid, most weak acids (HA) are so weak that the equilibrium concentration of the acid, $[HA]$, is effectively its initial concentration ($= [HA]_0$). This leads to the useful conclusion that the denominator in the equilibrium constant expression for dilute solutions of most weak acids is simply $[HA]_0$, the original or initial concentration of the weak acid.

$$HA(aq) + H_2O(\ell) \rightleftharpoons H_3O^+(aq) + A^-(aq)$$

$$K_a = \frac{[H_3O^+][A^-]}{[HA]_0 - [H_3O^+]} \approx \frac{[H_3O^+][A^-]}{[HA]_0}$$

Analysis shows that

> The approximation that
>
> $$[HA]_{equilibrium} = [HA]_0 - [H_3O^+] \approx [HA]_0$$
>
> is valid whenever $[HA]_0$ is greater than or equal to $100 \times K_a$.

This is the same approximation we used in Chapter 16 when deciding whether we needed to solve quadratic equations exactly (◄ Problem Solving Tip 16.1).

## What Is the pH of an Aqueous Solution of a Weak Acid or Base?

Knowing values of the equilibrium constants for weak acids and bases enables us to calculate the pH of a solution of a weak acid or base.

## Strategy Map 17.5

**PROBLEM**

Calculate the **pH** for a weak acid solution knowing the value of $K_a$.

↓

**DATA/INFORMATION KNOWN**

- Acid concentration
- Value of $K_a$

↓

**STEP 1.** Write **balanced equation** and $K_a$ **expression**, and set up **ICE table**.

↓

$K_a$ expression and ICE table

↓

**STEP 2.** Enter **equilibrium concentrations** in ICE table.

↓

At equilibrium:
$[H_3O^+]$ = [conjugate base] = $x$
[acid] = original conc. − $x$

↓

**STEP 3.** Enter **equilibrium concentrations** in $K_a$.

↓

$K_a$ **expression** with equilibrium concentrations in terms of $x$

↓

**STEP 4.** Solve $K_a$ **expression** for $x$.

↓

$x$ = value of $[H_3O^+]$

↓

**STEP 5.** Convert $[H_3O^+]$ to **pH**.

↓

pH of solution

---

**⊍WL   INTERACTIVE EXAMPLE 17.5   Calculating Equilibrium Concentrations and pH from $K_a$**

**Problem** Calculate the pH of a 0.020 M solution of benzoic acid ($C_6H_5CO_2H$) given that $K_a = 6.3 \times 10^{-5}$ for the acid.

$$C_6H_5CO_2H(aq) + H_2O(\ell) \rightleftharpoons H_3O^+(aq) + C_6H_5CO_2^-(aq)$$

**What Do You Know?** You know the value of $K_a$ for the acid and its initial concentration. You need to find the equilibrium concentration of $H_3O^+$ in order to calculate the pH.

**Strategy** This is similar to Examples 16.5 and 16.6, where you wanted to find the concentration of a reaction product. The strategy is the same:

- Write the equilibrium constant expression and set up an ICE table.

- Enter the initial concentration of $C_6H_5CO_2H$ on the initial (I) line of the ICE table.

- The variable $x$ represents changes in concentration, so the change in $[C_6H_5CO_2H]$ is $-x$ and the change in product concentrations is $+x$. Enter these values in the change (C) line of the table.

- Enter the expressions for the final equilibrium concentrations of all three species on the E line of the ICE table, and then transfer these expressions to the equilibrium constant expression and solve for $x$.

- Convert $[H_3O^+]$ ($= x$) to pH.

**Solution** Organize the information in an ICE table.

| Equilibrium | $C_6H_5CO_2H$ | + | $H_2O$ | ⇌ | $C_6H_5CO_2^-$ | + | $H_3O^+$ |
|---|---|---|---|---|---|---|---|
| Initial (M) | 0.020 | | | | 0 | | 0 |
| Change (M) | $-x$ | | | | $+x$ | | $+x$ |
| Equilibrium (M) | $(0.020 - x)$ | | | | $x$ | | $x$ |

According to reaction stoichiometry,

$$[H_3O^+] = [C_6H_5CO_2^-] = x \text{ at equilibrium}$$

the concentration of acid ionized is $x$. Thus, the benzoic acid concentration at equilibrium is

$$[C_6H_5CO_2H] = \text{initial acid concentration} - \text{concentration of acid that ionized}$$

$$[C_6H_5CO_2H] = 0.020 - x$$

Substituting these equilibrium concentrations into the $K_a$ expression, we have

$$K_a = \frac{[H_3O^+][C_6H_5CO_2^-]}{[C_6H_5CO_2H]}$$

$$6.3 \times 10^{-5} = \frac{(x)(x)}{0.020 - x}$$

The value of $x$ is small compared with 0.020 (because $[HA]_0 > 100 \times K_a$; 0.020 M $> 6.3 \times 10^{-3}$). Therefore, you can use the approximate expression.

$$K_a = 6.3 \times 10^{-5} = \frac{x^2}{0.020}$$

Solving for $x$, we have

$$x = \sqrt{K_a \times (0.020)} = 0.0011 \text{ M}$$

and we find that

$$[H_3O^+] = [C_6H_5CO_2^-] = 0.0011 \text{ M}$$

and

$$[C_6H_5CO_2H] = (0.020 - x) = 0.019 \text{ M}$$

Finally, the pH of the solution is found to be

$$pH = -\log (1.1 \times 10^{-3}) = 2.96$$

**Think about Your Answer** We made the approximation that $(0.020 - x) \approx 0.020$. If we do not make the approximation and instead solve the exact expression, $x = [H_3O^+] = 0.0011$ M. This is the same answer to two significant figures that we obtained from the "approximate" expression. Finally, notice that we again ignored any $H_3O^+$ that arises from water ionization.

**Check Your Understanding**

What are the equilibrium concentrations of acetic acid, the acetate ion, and $H_3O^+$ for a 0.10 M solution of acetic acid ($K_a = 1.8 \times 10^{-5}$)? What is the pH of the solution?

## EXAMPLE 17.6    Calculating Equilibrium Concentrations and pH from $K_a$ and Using the Method of Successive Approximations

**Problem** What is the pH of a 0.0010 M solution of formic acid? What is the concentration of formic acid at equilibrium? The acid is moderately weak, with $K_a = 1.8 \times 10^{-4}$.

$$HCO_2H(aq) + H_2O(\ell) \rightleftharpoons HCO_2^-(aq) + H_3O^+(aq)$$

**What Do You Know?** You know the value of $K_a$ for the acid and its initial concentration. You need to find the equilibrium concentration of $H_3O^+$ in order to calculate the pH.

**Strategy** This is similar to Example 17.5, where you wanted to find the concentration of a reaction product, except that an approximate solution will not be possible. The strategy is the same:

*   Write the equilibrium constant expression and set up an ICE table.

*   Enter the initial concentration of $HCO_2H$ on the initial (I) line of the ICE table.

*   The variable $x$ represents changes in concentration, so the change in $[HCO_2H]$ is $-x$ and the change in product concentrations is $+x$. Enter these values in the change (C) line of the table.

*   Enter the expressions for the final equilibrium concentrations of all three species on the E line of the ICE table, and then transfer these expressions to the equilibrium constant expression and solve for $x$.

*   Convert $[H_3O^+]$ ($= x$) to pH.

**Solution** The ICE table is as follows.

| Equilibrium | $HCO_2H + H_2O$ | $\rightleftharpoons$ | $HCO_2^-$ | + | $H_3O^+$ |
|---|---|---|---|---|---|
| Initial (M) | 0.0010 | | 0 | | 0 |
| Change (M) | $-x$ | | $+x$ | | $+x$ |
| Equilibrium (M) | $(0.0010 - x)$ | | $x$ | | $x$ |

Substituting the values in the table into the $K_a$ expression we have

$$K_a = \frac{[H_3O^+][HCO_2^-]}{[HCO_2H]} = 1.8 \times 10^{-4} = \frac{(x)(x)}{0.0010 - x}$$

In this example, $[HA]_0$ ($= 0.0010$ M) is *not* greater than $100 \times K_a$ ($= 1.8 \times 10^{-2}$), so the usual approximation is not reasonable. Thus, we have to find the equilibrium concentrations by solving the "exact" expression. This can be solved with the quadratic formula or by successive approximations (Appendix A). Let us use the successive approximation method here.

To use the **successive approximations approach**, begin by solving the approximate expression for $x$.

$$1.8 \times 10^{-4} = \frac{(x)(x)}{0.0010}$$

Solving this, we find $x = 4.2 \times 10^{-4}$. Put this value into the expression for $x$ in the denominator of the exact expression.

$$1.8 \times 10^{-4} = \frac{(x)(x)}{0.0010 - x} = \frac{(x)(x)}{0.0010 - 4.2 \times 10^{-4}}$$

Solving this equation for $x$, we now find $x = 3.2 \times 10^{-4}$. Again, put this value into the denominator, and solve for $x$.

$$1.8 \times 10^{-4} = \frac{(x)(x)}{0.0010 - x} = \frac{(x)(x)}{0.0010 - 3.2 \times 10^{-4}}$$

Continue this procedure until the value of $x$ does not change from one cycle to the next. In this case, two more cycles give us the result that

$$x = [H_3O^+] = [HCO_2^-] = 3.4 \times 10^{-4} \text{ M}$$

Thus,

$$[HCO_2H] = 0.0010 - x \approx 0.0007 \text{ M}$$

and the pH of the formic acid solution is

$$pH = -\log (3.4 \times 10^{-4}) = 3.47$$

**Think about Your Answer** If we had used the approximate expression to find the $H_3O^+$ concentration, we would have obtained a value of $[H_3O^+] = 4.2 \times 10^{-4}$ M. The simplifying assumption led to a large error, about 24%. The approximate solution fails in this case because (a) the acid concentration is small and (b) the acid is not all that weak.

**Check Your Understanding**

What are the equilibrium concentrations of HF, $F^-$ ion, and $H_3O^+$ ion in a 0.00150 M solution of HF? What is the pH of the solution?

Just as acids can be molecular species or ions, so too can bases be ionic or molecular (Figures 17.3–17.5). Many molecular bases are based on nitrogen, with ammonia being the simplest. Many other nitrogen-containing bases occur naturally; caffeine and nicotine are two that are well known. The anionic conjugate bases of weak acids make up another group of bases. The following example describes the calculation of the pH for a solution of sodium acetate.

© Cengage Learning/Charles D. Winters

Ammonia, $NH_3$
$K_b = 1.8 \times 10^{-5}$

Caffeine, $C_8H_{10}N_4O_2$
$K_b = 2.5 \times 10^{-4}$

Benzoate ion, $C_6H_5CO_2^-$
$K_b = 1.6 \times 10^{-10}$

Phosphate ion, $PO_4^{3-}$
$K_b = 2.8 \times 10^{-2}$

**FIGURE 17.5 Examples of weak bases.** Weak bases in water include molecules having one or more N atoms capable of accepting an $H^+$ ion and anions of weak acids such as benzoate and phosphate.

# ⊙WL   **INTERACTIVE EXAMPLE 17.7**   The pH of a Solution of a Weakly Basic Salt, Sodium Acetate

**Problem** What is the pH of a 0.015 M solution of sodium acetate, $NaCH_3CO_2$?

**What Do You Know?** You know sodium acetate is basic in water because the acetate ion, the conjugate base of a weak acid, acetic acid, reacts with water to form $OH^-$ (Tables 17.3 and 17.4). (You also know that the sodium ion of sodium acetate does not affect the solution pH.) Finally, you know the value of $K_b$ for the acetate ion (Table 17.3) and its initial concentration. You need to find the equilibrium concentration of $H_3O^+$ in order to calculate the pH.

**Strategy** This is similar to Examples 17.5 and 17.6, where you wanted to find the concentration of a reaction product.

- Write the balanced equation and the equilibrium constant expression, and set up an ICE table.

- Enter the initial concentration of $CH_3CO_2^-$ on the initial (I) line of the ICE table.

- The variable $x$ represents changes in concentration, so the change in $[CH_3CO_2^-]$ is $-x$ and the change in product concentrations is $+x$. Enter these values in the change (C) line of the table.

- Enter the expressions for the equilibrium concentrations of all three species on the E line of the ICE table, and then transfer these to the equilibrium constant expression and solve for $x$.

- The value of $x = [OH^-]$. Determine $[H_3O^+]$ from this value using the expression $K_w = [H_3O^+][OH^-]$, then calculate pH from $[H_3O^+]$.

**Solution** The value of $K_b$ for the acetate ion is $5.6 \times 10^{-10}$ (Table 17.3).

$$CH_3CO_2^-(aq) + H_2O(\ell) \rightleftharpoons CH_3CO_2H(aq) + OH^-(aq)$$

Set up an ICE table to summarize the initial and equilibrium concentrations of the species in solution.

| Equilibrium | $CH_3CO_2^-$ | + | $H_2O$ | $\rightleftharpoons$ | $CH_3CO_2H$ | + | $OH^-$ |
|---|---|---|---|---|---|---|---|
| Initial (M) | 0.015 | | | | 0 | | 0 |
| Change (M) | $-x$ | | | | $+x$ | | $+x$ |
| Equilibrium (M) | $(0.015 - x)$ | | | | $x$ | | $x$ |

Next, substitute the values in the table into the $K_b$ expression.

$$K_b = 5.6 \times 10^{-10} = \frac{[CH_3CO_2H][OH^-]}{[CH_3CO_2^-]} = \frac{x^2}{0.015 - x}$$

The acetate ion, a weak base, has a very small value of $K_b$. Therefore, we assume that $x$, the concentration of hydroxide ion generated by reaction of acetate ion with water, is very small, and we use the approximate expression to solve for $x$.

$$K_b = 5.6 \times 10^{-10} = \frac{x^2}{0.015}$$

$$x = [OH^-] = [CH_3CO_2H] = \sqrt{(5.6 \times 10^{-10})(0.015)} = 2.9 \times 10^{-6} \text{ M}$$

To calculate the pH of the solution, we need the hydronium ion concentration. In aqueous solutions, it is always true that, at 25 °C,

$$K_w = 1.0 \times 10^{-14} = [H_3O^+][OH^-]$$

Therefore,

$$[H_3O^+] = \frac{K_w}{[OH^-]} = \frac{1.0 \times 10^{-14}}{2.9 \times 10^{-6}} = 3.5 \times 10^{-9} \text{ M}$$

$$pH = -\log(3.5 \times 10^{-9}) = \boxed{8.46}$$

The acetate ion gives rise to a weakly basic solution as expected for the conjugate base of a weak acid.

---

**Strategy Map 17.7**

**PROBLEM**
Calculate the **pH** for a weak base knowing the value of $K_b$.

↓

**DATA/INFORMATION KNOWN**
- Base concentration
- Value of $K_b$

↓

**STEP 1.** Write **balanced equation** and $K_b$ **expression**, and set up **ICE table**.

$K_b$ expression and ICE table

↓

**STEP 2.** Enter **equilibrium concentrations** in ICE table.

At equilibrium:
$[OH^-] = [\text{conjugate acid}] = x$
$[\text{base}] = \text{original conc.} - x$

↓

**STEP 3.** Enter **equilibrium concentrations** in $K_b$.

$K_b$ **expression** with equilibrium concentrations in terms of $x$

↓

**STEP 4.** Solve $K_b$ **expression** for $x$.

$x$ = value of $[OH^-]$

↓

**STEP 5.** Using $[OH^-]$ and $K_w$, calculate $[H_3O^+]$ and then **pH**.

↓

pH of solution

**Think about Your Answer** The hydroxide ion concentration ($x$) is indeed quite small relative to the initial acetate ion concentration so the approximate expression is appropriate. (Note that $100 \times K_b$ is less than the initial base concentration.)

**Check Your Understanding**

The weak base, $ClO^-$ (hypochlorite ion), is used in the form of NaClO as a disinfectant in swimming pools and water treatment plants. What are the concentrations of HClO and $OH^-$ and the pH of a 0.015 M solution of NaClO?

## Strategy Map 17.8

**PROBLEM**

Calculate **pH** of solution after the reaction of a **weak base** and a **strong acid**.

↓

**DATA/INFORMATION KNOWN**

- Reactant concentrations
- Reactant volumes

**STEP 1.** Write **balanced equation** and solve **stoichiometry problem**.

↓

Know **amounts of reactants** and derive **amount of product**.

**STEP 2.** Decide if product is **weak acid** or **weak base**.

↓

Product is a **weak acid** ($NH_4^+$)

**STEP 3.** Calculate concentration of $NH_4^+$.

↓

Concentration of weak acid whose $K_a$ is known.

**STEP 4.** Solve for $[H_3O^+]$ as in Examples 17.5 - 17.7.

↓

Value of $[H_3O^+]$

**STEP 5.** Convert $[H_3O^+]$ to **pH**.

↓

pH of solution

**⊙WL   INTERACTIVE EXAMPLE 17.8   Calculating the pH after the Reaction of a Weak Base with a Strong Acid**

**Problem** What is the pH of the solution that results from mixing 25 mL of 0.016 M $NH_3$ and 25 mL of 0.016 M HCl?

**What Do You Know?** You know this is an acid–base reaction (HCl + $NH_3$), and you know the amount of each reactant (calculated from the volume and concentration of each). Because equal volumes and concentrations are involved, neither the acid nor the base is in excess, and none will remain after the reaction. To find the pH of the solution after reaction, you need to know the amount of product, whether it is a weak acid or weak base, and its concentration. The final step then involves a weak acid or weak base equilibrium calculation (Examples 17.5–17.7).

**Strategy** This question involves three problems in one:

(a) *Writing a balanced equation:* First write a balanced equation for the reaction that occurs and then decide whether the reaction products are acids or bases. Here, the weak acid $NH_4^+$ is the product of interest.

(b) *Stoichiometry problem:* Finding the "initial" $NH_4^+$ concentration is a stoichiometry problem: What amount of $NH_4^+$ (in moles) is produced in the HCl + $NH_3$ reaction, and in what volume of solution is the $NH_4^+$ ion found?

(c) *Equilibrium problem:* Calculating the pH involves first solving an equilibrium problem. The crucial piece of information needed for this calculation is the "initial" concentration of $NH_4^+$ from part (b).

**Solution** If equal amounts (moles) of base ($NH_3$) and acid (HCl) are mixed, the result should be an acidic solution because the significant species remaining in solution upon completion of the reaction is $NH_4^+$, the conjugate acid of the weak base ammonia (see Tables 17.3 and 17.5).

(a) *Writing balanced equations*

The equation for the product-favored reaction of HCl (the supplier of hydronium ion) with $NH_3$ to give $NH_4^+$:

$$NH_3(aq) + H_3O^+(aq) \rightarrow NH_4^+(aq) + H_2O(\ell)$$

The equation for the reactant-favored reaction of $NH_4^+$, the product, with water:

$$NH_4^+(aq) + H_2O(\ell) \rightleftharpoons H_3O^+(aq) + NH_3(aq)$$

(b) *Stoichiometry problem*

Amount of HCl and $NH_3$ consumed:

$$(0.025 \text{ L HCl})(0.016 \text{ mol/L}) = 4.0 \times 10^{-4} \text{ mol HCl}$$

$$(0.025 \text{ L } NH_3)(0.016 \text{ mol/L}) = 4.0 \times 10^{-4} \text{ mol } NH_3$$

Amount of $NH_4^+$ produced upon completion of the reaction:

$$4.0 \times 10^{-4} \text{ mol } NH_3\left(\frac{1 \text{ mol } NH_4^+}{1 \text{ mol } NH_3}\right) = 4.0 \times 10^{-4} \text{ mol } NH_4^+$$

## What is the pH After Mixing Equal Numbers of Moles of an Acid and a Base

Table 17.5 summarizes the outcome of mixing various types of acids and bases. But how do you calculate a numerical value for the pH, particularly in the case of mixing a weak acid with a strong base or a weak base with a strong acid? The strategy (Example 17.8) is to recognize that this involves two calculations: a stoichiometry calculation and an equilibrium calculation. The key to this is that you need to know the concentration of the weak acid or weak base produced when the acid

and base are mixed. Answering the following questions will guide you to an answer:

(a) What amounts of acid and base are used (in moles)? (This is a stoichiometry problem.)

(b) What is the total volume of the solution after mixing the acid and base solutions?

(c) What is the concentration of the weak acid or base produced on mixing the acid and base solutions?

(d) Using the concentration found in Step (c), what is the hydronium ion concentration in the solution? (This is an equilibrium problem.)

(e) Calculate the pH of the solution from $[H_3O^+]$.

Concentration of $NH_4^+$: Combining 25 mL each of HCl and $NH_3$ gives a total solution volume of 50. mL. Therefore, the concentration of $NH_4^+$ is

$$[NH_4^+] = \frac{4.0 \times 10^{-4} \text{ mol}}{0.050 \text{ L}} = 8.0 \times 10^{-3} \text{ M}$$

(c) *Acid–base equilibrium problem*

With the initial concentration of ammonium ion known, set up an ICE table to find the equilibrium concentration of hydronium ion.

| Equilibrium | $NH_4^+$ | + | $H_2O$ | ⇌ | $NH_3$ | + | $H_3O^+$ |
|---|---|---|---|---|---|---|---|
| Initial (M) | 0.0080 | | | | 0 | | 0 |
| Change (M) | $-x$ | | | | $+x$ | | $+x$ |
| Equilibrium (M) | $(0.0080 - x)$ | | | | $x$ | | $x$ |

Next, substitute the values in the table into the $K_a$ expression for the ammonium ion. Thus, we have

$$K_a = 5.6 \times 10^{-10} = \frac{[H_3O^+][NH_3]}{[NH_4^+]} = \frac{(x)(x)}{0.0080 - x}$$

The ammonium ion is a very weak acid, as reflected by the very small value of $K_a$. Therefore, $x$, the concentration of hydronium ion generated by reaction of ammonium ion with water, is assumed to be very small, and the approximate expression is used to solve for $x$. (Here $100 \times K_a$ is much less than the original acid concentration.)

$$K_a = 5.6 \times 10^{-10} \approx \frac{x^2}{0.0080}$$

$$x = \sqrt{(5.6 \times 10^{-10})(0.0080)}$$

$$= [H_3O^+] = [NH_3] = 2.1 \times 10^{-6} \text{ M}$$

$$pH = -\log(2.1 \times 10^{-6}) = 5.67$$

**Think about Your Answer** As predicted (Table 17.5), the solution after mixing equal amounts of a strong acid and weak base is weakly acidic.

### Check Your Understanding

Calculate the pH after mixing 15 mL of 0.12 M acetic acid with 15 mL of 0.12 M NaOH. What are the major species in solution at equilibrium (besides water), and what are their concentrations?

**CASE STUDY**

# Would You Like Some Belladonna Juice in Your Drink?

The belladonna plant produces black, cherry-sized berries that look good enough to eat. But you should think twice because the plant is also called *deadly nightshade*. The berries contain atropine, a base, which is toxic and has been used by women and men for centuries to eliminate old lovers and political enemies.

The name for the plant, *belladonna*, comes from the Italian meaning "beautiful woman." Courtesans and actresses in Venice in the 16th century would put a drop or two of the juice in their eyes. It would dilate the pupils and give them a "fashionable, doe-like" appearance that could last several days.

Atropine was used for some years by physicians to dilate the eye, and it is used to treat such conditions as bradycardia, an extremely low heart rate. It is also an antidote for sarin, a nerve gas. In fact, victims of a sarin gas attack in Japan in the 1990s were treated with atropine, and soldiers in the first Gulf War in 1990–1991 carried atropine as an antidote in the event of a nerve gas attack.

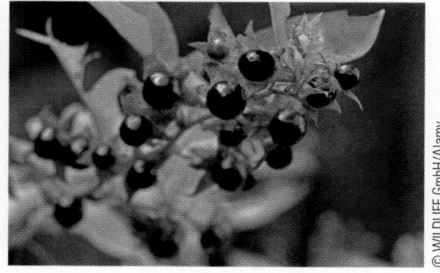

© WILDLIFE GmbH/Alamy

Berries of the belladonna plant, a source of atropine

But atropine is mostly remembered in history as a poison. A fatal dose is around 100 mg. One legend is that Cleopatra at first wanted to commit suicide by taking atropine. She had a slave try it first, but the slave's death was not pleasant, so she opted for the bite of an asp, a deadly snake.

At the height of the Roman Empire, poisoning with atropine and other agents was so often used that a law was passed in 82 BC to "suppress domestic poisoning." It apparently had little effect.

The symptoms of atropine poisoning are well known. Physicians say the patient is "red as a beet" because the blood vessels dilate. Or you can be "blind as a bat" because the pupils are so dilated that vision is blurred. "Dry as a bone" is another symptom arising from the suppression of the salivary glands. In addition, you can be "hot as a hare" because your body temperature goes up and stays up for some hours. Finally, you can be "mad as a hatter" (like the hatter in *Alice in Wonderland*) because you act like a drunk person.

Atropine is not very soluble in water. However, because atropine is a base—like so many other naturally occurring substances such as caffeine, nicotine, morphine, heroin, and amphetamine—it reacts with acids. For example, reaction with sulfuric acid forms the sulfate salt. This salt is so soluble that 1 mL of a saturated solution of this compound contains many times the amount needed for a fatal dose.

If you are interested in the history of atropine as a murder weapon be sure to

read about the attempted murder of Alexandra Agutter by her husband in Scotland in the 1990s. Just like an episode of CSI!

**Atropine, $C_{17}H_{23}NO_3$.**

## Questions:

1.  If a fatal dose of atropine is 100. mg, what amount of compound (moles) is this?
2.  When atropine is added to sulfuric acid, a proton attaches to the molecule. What is the site of attachment?
3.  The $pK_a$ of the conjugate acid of atropine is 4.35. How does this compare with the $pK_a$ values for the conjugate acids of ammonia, methylamine, and aniline (page 767)?
4.  Atropine is chiral. (See Chapter 10.) Which C atom is the site of chirality? (Of the two enantiomers, only one is physiologically active.)

**Answers to these questions are available in Appendix N.**

## Reference:

J. Emsley, *Molecules of Murder*, Royal Society of Chemistry, London, 2008.

---

**REVIEW & CHECK FOR SECTION 17.8**

1.  What is $[H_3O^+]$ in a 0.10 M solution of HCN at 25 °C? ($K_a$ for HCN = $4.0 \times 10^{-10}$)

    (a)  $1.6 \times 10^{-9}$ M

    (b)  $6.3 \times 10^{-6}$ M

    (c)  $2.0 \times 10^{-5}$ M

    (d)  $4.0 \times 10^{-11}$ M

2.  A 0.040 M solution of an acid, HA, has a pH of 3.02 at 25 °C. What is $K_a$ for this acid?

    (a)  $2.3 \times 10^{-5}$

    (b)  $5.7 \times 10^{-4}$

    (c)  $2.4 \times 10^{-2}$

    (d)  $4.3 \times 10^{-10}$

3. What are the pH and ion concentrations in a solution of 0.10 M sodium formate, $NaCHO_2$? $K_b$ for the formate ion, $HCO_2^-$ is $5.6 \times 10^{-11}$.

| | pH | $[Na^+]$ | $[CHO_2^-]$ | $[OH^-]$ |
|---|---|---|---|---|
| (a) | 5.63 | 0.10 | 0.10 | $2.4 \times 10^{-6}$ |
| (b) | 8.37 | 0.10 | 0.10 | $2.4 \times 10^{-6}$ |
| (c) | 8.22 | 0.050 | 0.050 | $1.7 \times 10^{-6}$ |
| (d) | 5.63 | 0.10 | 0.10 | $4.2 \times 10^{-9}$ |

4. You mix 0.40 g of NaOH with 100 mL of 0.10 M acetic acid. What is the pH of the resulting solution?

   (a) less than 7      (b) equal to 7      (c) greater than 7

**A polyprotic acid.** Malic acid $C_4H_4O_4$ is a diprotic acid occurring in apples. It is also classified as an alpha-hydroxy acid because it has an OH group on the C atom next to the $CO_2H$ (in the alpha position). It is one of a large group of natural alpha-hydroxy acids such as lactic acid, citric acid, and ascorbic acid. Alpha-hydroxy acids have been touted as an ingredient in "anti-aging" skin creams. They work by accelerating the natural process by which skin replaces the outer layer of cells with new cells.

# 17.9 Polyprotic Acids and Bases

Because polyprotic acids are capable of donating more than one proton (Table 17.1), they present us with additional challenges when predicting the pH of their solutions. For many inorganic polyprotic acids, such as phosphoric acid, carbonic acid, and hydrosulfuric acid ($H_2S$), the ionization constant for each successive loss of a proton is about $10^4$ to $10^6$ smaller than the previous ionization step. This means that the first ionization step of a polyprotic acid produces up to about a million times more $H_3O^+$ ions than the second step. For this reason, *the pH of many inorganic polyprotic acids depends primarily on the hydronium ion generated in the first ionization step; the hydronium ion produced in the second step can be neglected.* The same principle applies to the fully deprotonated conjugate bases of polyprotic acids. This is illustrated by the calculation of the pH of a solution of carbonate ion, an important base in our environment (Example 17.9).

## EXAMPLE 17.9   Calculating the pH of the Solution of a Polyprotic Base

**Problem** The carbonate ion, $CO_3^{2-}$, is a base in water, forming the hydrogen carbonate ion, which in turn can form carbonic acid.

$$CO_3^{2-}(aq) + H_2O(\ell) \rightleftharpoons HCO_3^-(aq) + OH^-(aq) \qquad K_{b1} = 2.1 \times 10^{-4}$$

$$HCO_3^-(aq) + H_2O(\ell) \rightleftharpoons H_2CO_3(aq) + OH^-(aq) \qquad K_{b2} = 2.4 \times 10^{-8}$$

What is the pH of a 0.10 M solution of $Na_2CO_3$?

**What Do You Know?** You know the balanced equations and the values of $K_b$ for the ions as well as the concentration of the carbonate ion.

**Strategy** The first ionization constant, $K_{b1}$, is much larger than the second, $K_{b2}$, so the hydroxide ion concentration in the solution results almost entirely from the first step. Therefore, you can calculate the $OH^-$ concentration produced in the first ionization step, but we will test the conclusion that $OH^-$ produced in the second step is negligible.

**Solution** Set up an ICE table for the reaction of the carbonate ion (Equilibrium Table 1).

**Equilibrium Table 1—Reaction of $CO_3^{2-}$ Ion**

| Equilibrium | $CO_3^{2-}$ | + | $H_2O$ | $\rightleftharpoons$ | $HCO_3^-$ | + | $OH^-$ |
|---|---|---|---|---|---|---|---|
| Initial (M) | 0.10 | | | | 0 | | 0 |
| Change | $-x$ | | | | $+x$ | | $+x$ |
| Equilibrium (M) | $(0.10 - x)$ | | | | $x$ | | $x$ |

Based on this table, the equilibrium concentration of $OH^-$ ($= x$) can then be calculated.

$$K_{b1} = 2.1 \times 10^{-4} = \frac{[HCO_3^-][OH^-]}{[CO_3^{2-}]} = \frac{x^2}{0.10 - x}$$

**Sodium carbonate, a polyprotic base.** This common substance is a base in aqueous solution. Its primary use is in the glass industry. Although it used to be manufactured, it is now mined as the mineral trona, $Na_2CO_3 \cdot NaHCO_3 \cdot 2\,H_2O$.

Because $K_{b1}$ is relatively small, it is reasonable to make the approximation that $(0.10 - x) \approx 0.10$. Therefore,

$$x = [HCO_3^-] = [OH^-] = \sqrt{(2.1 \times 10^{-4})(0.10)} = 4.6 \times 10^{-3} \text{ M}$$

Using this value of $[OH^-]$, you can calculate the pOH of the solution,

$$pOH = -\log (4.6 \times 10^{-3}) = 2.34$$

and then use the relationship $pH + pOH = 14$ to calculate the pH.

$$pH = 14 - pOH = 11.66$$

Finally, you can conclude that the concentration of the carbonate ion is, to a good approximation, 0.10 M.

$$[CO_3^{2-}] = 0.10 - 0.0046 \approx 0.10 \text{ M}$$

The $HCO_3^-$ ion produced in the first step could acquire another proton to give $H_2CO_3$ and this could affect the pH. But does this occur to a meaningful extent? To test this, set up a second ICE Table.

**Equilibrium Table 2—Reaction of HCO₃⁻ Ion**

| Equilibrium | $HCO_3^-$ | + | $H_2O$ | $\rightleftharpoons$ | $H_2CO_3$ | + | $OH^-$ |
|---|---|---|---|---|---|---|---|
| Initial (M) | $4.6 \times 10^{-3}$ | | | | 0 | | $4.6 \times 10^{-3}$ |
| Change (M) | $-y$ | | | | $+y$ | | $+y$ |
| Equilibrium (M) | $(4.6 \times 10^{-3} - y)$ | | | | $y$ | | $(4.6 \times 10^{-3} + y)$ |

Because $K_{b2}$ is so small, the second step occurs to a much smaller extent than the first step. This means the amount of $H_2CO_3$ and $OH^-$ produced in the second step ($= y$) is much smaller than $10^{-3}$ M. Therefore, it is reasonable that both $[HCO_3^-]$ and $[OH^-]$ are very close to $4.6 \times 10^{-3}$ M.

$$K_{b2} = 2.4 \times 10^{-8} = \frac{[H_2CO_3][OH^-]}{[HCO_3^-]} = \frac{(y)(4.6 \times 10^{-3})}{4.6 \times 10^{-3}}$$

Because $[HCO_3^-]$ and $[OH^-]$ have nearly identical values, they cancel from the expression, and we find that $[H_2CO_3]$ is simply equal to $K_{b2}$.

$$y = [H_2CO_3] = K_{b2} = 2.4 \times 10^{-8} \text{ M}$$

The amount of $OH^-$ produced in this reaction is negligible. The hydroxide ion is essentially all produced in the first equilibrium process.

**Think about Your Answer**  It is almost always the case that the pH of a solution of an inorganic polyprotic acid is due to the hydronium ion generated in the first ionization step. Similarly, the pH of a polyprotic base is due to the $OH^-$ ion produced in the first ionization step.

**Check Your Understanding**

What is the pH of a 0.10 M solution of oxalic acid, $H_2C_2O_4$? What are the concentrations of $H_3O^+$, $HC_2O_4^-$, and the oxalate ion, $C_2O_4^{2-}$? (See Appendix H for $K_a$ values.)

**REVIEW & CHECK FOR SECTION 17.9**

Hydrazine ($N_2H_4$) is like $CO_3^{2-}$ in that it is a polyprotic base ($K_{b1} = 8.5 \times 10^{-7}$ and $K_{b2} = 8.9 \times 10^{-16}$). The two conjugate acids are $N_2H_5^+$ and $N_2H_6^{2+}$. What is the expected pH of a 0.025 M solution of $N_2H_4$?

(a)  3.83          (b)  8.32          (c)  10.16

# 17.10 Molecular Structure, Bonding, and Acid–Base Behavior

One of the most interesting aspects of chemistry is the correlation between a molecule's structure and bonding and its chemical properties. Because so many acids and bases play such a key role in chemistry, it is especially useful to see if there are some general principles governing acid–base behavior.

## Acid Strength of the Hydrogen Halides, HX

Aqueous HF is a weak Brønsted acid in water, whereas the other hydrohalic acids—aqueous HCl, HBr, and HI—are all strong acids. Experiments show that the acid strength increases in the order HF << HCl < HBr < HI. A detailed analysis of the factors that lead to these differences in acid strength in this group is interesting (see *A Closer Look, Acid Strengths and Molecular Structure*, page 788), and predictions about relative acid strength can be made based on the sum of two energy quantities, the energy required to break the H—X bond (the bond dissociation enthalpy, page 383) and the electron attachment enthalpy of the halogen (page 320). That is, when a hydrohalic acid HX ionizes in water,

$$HX(aq) + H_2O(\ell) \rightarrow H_3O^+(aq) + X^-(aq)$$

the sum of the two energy terms

Change in energy $\propto$ HX bond dissociation enthalpy + electron attachment enthalpy of X

should correlate with acid strength. Stronger acids should result when the H—X bond is more easily broken (as signaled by a smaller, positive value of $\Delta H$ for bond dissociation) and a more negative value for the electron attachment enthalpy of X.

The bond dissociation enthalpy and electron attachment enthalpy effects can work together (a weak H—X bond and a large, negative electron attachment enthalpy of the X group) to produce a strong acid, but they can also work in opposite directions. The balance of the two effects is important. Let us examine some data for the Group 7A binary acids, HX.

|  | — Increasing acid strength ⟶ | | | |
|---|---|---|---|---|
|  | **HF** | **HCl** | **HBr** | **HI** |
| $pK_a$ | +3.14 | −7 | −9 | −10 |
| H—X bond strength (kJ/mol) | 565 | 432 | 366 | 299 |
| Electron attachment enthalpy of X (kJ/mol) | −328 | −349 | −325 | −295 |
| Sum (kJ/mol) | 237 | 83 | 41 | 4 |

In this series of acids, the bond enthalpy factor dominates: the weakest acid, HF, has the strongest H—X bond, and the strongest acid, HI, has the weakest H—X bond. However, the electron attachment enthalpy of X is most negative with Cl, less so with F and Br, and much less so with I. A less negative electron attachment enthalpy should lead to a weaker acid, but it is the *sum* of the two effects that leads to the observation that HI is the strongest acid. In Figure 17.6 you see there is a good correlation between an acid's $pK_a$ and the *sum* of the enthalpies for bond dissociation and electron attachment enthalpy.

## Comparing Oxoacids: HNO₂ and HNO₃

Nitrous acid ($HNO_2$) and nitric acid ($HNO_3$) are representative of several series of **oxoacids**. Oxoacids contain an atom (usually a nonmetal atom) bonded to one or more oxygen atoms, some with hydrogen atoms attached. Besides those based on N, you are familiar with the sulfur- and chlorine-based oxoacids (Table 17.6). In all these series of related compounds, the acid strength increases as the number of oxy-

**FIGURE 17.6 The effect of H—X bond enthalpy and X electron attachment enthalpy on acid strength.** Stronger acids have weaker H—X bonds and X atoms with more negative electron attachment enthalpies. (BDE is the bond dissociation enthalpy of the H—X bond, and $\Delta_{EA}H$ is the electron attachment enthalpy of the halogen atom, see page 321.) See M. Moran, *Journal of Chemical Education*, Vol. 83, pp. 800–803, 2006.

**Table 17.6 Oxoacids**

| Acid | $pK_a$ |
|---|---|
| **Cl-Based Oxoacids** | |
| HOCl | 7.46 |
| HOClO ($HClO_2$) | ∼ 2 |
| HOClO₂ ($HClO_3$) | ∼ −3 |
| HOClO₃ ($HClO_4$) | ∼ −8 |
| **S-Based Oxoacids** | |
| (HO)₂SO [$H_2SO_3$] | 1.92, 7.21 |
| (HO)₂SO₂ [$H_2SO_4$] | ∼ −3, 1.92 |

Linus Pauling stated the general relationship that, for oxoacids with the general formula $(HO)_nE(O)_m$, the value of $pK_a$ is about 8–5m. When $n > 1$, the $pK_a$ increases by about 5 for each successive loss of a proton.

## A CLOSER LOOK

# Acid Strengths and Molecular Structure

Although predictions about acid strength in aqueous solution are fairly simple to make, a complete explanation can be complicated.

Acid strength is sometimes correlated with the strength and the polarity of the H—X bond, readily identifiable characteristics derived from the structure of the acid, the reactant in the ionization process. We need to point out, however, that when one is assessing any chemical reaction, it is necessary to consider both reactants and products. Looking only at the reactant when dealing with acid ionization only takes you halfway.

When evaluating the strength of an acid HX(aq), we are looking at the following reaction:

$$HX(aq) + H_2O(\ell) \rightleftharpoons H_3O^+(aq) + X^-(aq)$$

To fully explain the extent of ionization, we must consider characteristics of both the acid and the anion. The ability of the anion to spread out the negative charge across the ion, for example, and the solvation of the anion by the solvent are among the issues that must have some relevance in an explanation of the strength of the acid.

How enthalpy changes contribute to acid strength can be assessed using a thermochemical cycle (such as the one used to evaluate a lattice enthalpy, page 599). Consider the relative acid strengths of the hydrogen halides. The enthalpy change for the ionization of an acid in water can be related to other enthalpy changes as shown in the diagram. The solvation of $H^+$ (Step 5) and the ionization energy of H(g) (Step 3) are common to all of the hydrogen halides and do not contribute to the differences among hydrogen halides, but the four remaining terms are different. For the hydrogen halides, the bond dissociation

STEP 3
IE for H
(endothermic)

H•(g) + X•(g) ⟶ H⁺(g) + X⁻(g)

STEP 4
$\Delta_{EA}H$ for X
(exothermic)

STEP 2
$\Delta_{bond}H°(HX)$
(endothermic)

HX(g)

STEP 5
$\Delta_{solvation}H°(H^+)$
(exothermic)

STEP 6
$\Delta_{solvation}H°(X^-)$
(exothermic)

STEP 1
$-\Delta_{solvation}H°(HX)$
(endothermic)

HX(aq) + H₂O(ℓ) ⟶ H₃O⁺(aq) + X⁻(aq)

enthalpy (Step 2) of HF is much larger than the dissociation enthalpies of the other hydrogen halides. However, it is compensated for significantly by the enthalpy of solvation of the anion (Step 6), which for the fluoride ion is much more exothermic than the solvation energies of the other halide ions. The electron attachment enthalpy is also a contributor to the differences in overall enthalpy changes. Electron attachment enthalpy values vary among the halogens, but to a smaller extent than the variation in bond energy and the enthalpy of solvation of the halide ion. Differences in solvation energy for the molecular species (Step 1) are minimal.

A complete analysis of strengths of acids in aqueous solution will include consideration of both enthalpies and entropies. Entropy has yet to be discussed in this text

in detail (▶ Chapter 19) but we noted earlier (◀ page 622) that entropy plays an important role in solution chemistry, specifically in determining solubilities. It is not surprising that entropy has a role in determining acid strength, too. Indeed, differences in entropy changes are significant in accounting for the differences in acid strength of the hydrogen halides.

Although all of these terms contribute to acid strength, acid strength can often be correlated with a subset of this information, as can be seen by the examples presented in this section. We point out, however, that correlations, while highly useful to a chemist because they can be used to make important predictions, are at best only partial explanations.

gen atoms bonded to the central element increases. Thus, nitric acid ($HNO_3$) is a stronger acid than nitrous acid ($HNO_2$).

HNO₃, strong acid,
$pK_a = -1.4$

HNO₂, weak acid,
$pK_a = +3.35$

Let's apply the bond enthalpy/electron affinity analysis to $HNO_3$ and $HNO_2$.

| | Increasing acid strength ⟶ | |
| --- | :---: | :---: |
| | **HNO$_2$** | **HNO$_3$** |
| p$K_a$ | +3.35 | −1.4 |
| H—O bond strength (kJ/mol) | 328 | 423 |
| Electron attachment enthalpy of X (kJ/mol) | −219 | −377 |
| Sum (kJ/mol) | 109 | 46 |

nitrous acid, HNO$_2$   nitric acid, HNO$_3$

**FIGURE 17.7 Electrostatic potential surfaces for the nitrogen oxoacids.** Both surfaces show the O—H bond is quite polar. More importantly, calculations show that the OH bond becomes more polar as more O atoms are added to N.

**Partial Charges**

| Molecule | H Atom | O Atom of OH | N Atom |
| --- | --- | --- | --- |
| HNO$_2$ | +0.39 | −0.35 | +0.14 |
| HNO$_3$ | +0.41 | −0.47 | +0.76 |

As in the case of the Group 7A acids, we again see that acid strength correlates with the sum of the enthalpies for bond breaking and X group (NO$_2$ or NO$_3$) electron attachment enthalpy.

Our previous analysis of the Group 7A acids showed that, in that series, the H—X bond strength was the more important factor; as the H—X bond became stronger, the acid became weaker. However, the data for HNO$_3$ and HNO$_2$ show this is not true here. The O—H bond is stronger in the stronger acid HNO$_3$. Instead, the electron attachment term is the more important term in this correlation. These same effects are observed for other oxyacids such as the chlorine-based oxoacids HOCl < HOClO < HOClO$_2$ < HOClO$_3$ and the S-based oxoacids (Table 17.6). How is this to be interpreted?

In HNO$_3$, there are two other oxygen atoms bonded to the central nitrogen atom, whereas in HNO$_2$ only one other oxygen is bonded to the nitrogen atom. By attaching more electronegative O atoms to nitrogen, we are increasing the electron affinity of the group attached to hydrogen, and anything that increases the affinity of the X group for an electron should also make HX a stronger acid and X$^-$ a weaker conjugate base. This is another way of saying that if X$^-$ has a way to accommodate and stabilize a negative charge, it will be a weaker conjugate base. In the case of oxoacids, additional oxygen atoms have the effect of stabilizing the anion because the negative charge on the anion can be dispersed over more atoms. In the nitrate ion, for example, the negative charge is shared equally over the three oxygen atoms. This is represented symbolically by the three resonance structures for this ion.

In nitrite ion, only two atoms share the negative charge. Therefore, NO$_2^-$ is a stronger conjugate base than NO$_3^-$. In general, greater stabilization of the products formed by ionizing the acid contributes to increased acidity.

Table 17.7 and Figure 17.7 show that another empirical correlation can be made between the structure of an acid and its acidity: In a series of related acids, the larger the formal charge on the central atom, the stronger the acid (Table 17.7). For example, the N atom formal charge in the weak acid HNO$_2$ is 0, whereas it is +1 in the strong acid HNO$_3$, and these are reflected by the results of theoretical calculations cited in Figure 17.7.

In summary, molecules such as the oxoacids can behave as stronger Brønsted acids when the anion created by loss of H$^+$ is stable and able to accommodate the negative charge. These conditions are promoted by

- the presence of electronegative atoms attached to the central atom.
- the possibility of resonance structures for the anion, which lead to delocalization of the negative charge over the anion and thus to a more stable ion.
- greater positive formal charge of the central atom.

## Why Are Carboxylic Acids Brønsted Acids?

There is a large class of organic acids, typified by acetic acid (CH$_3$CO$_2$H) (Figure 17.8), called *carboxylic acids* because all have the carboxylic acid group, —CO$_2$H (◀ page 467). The arguments used to explain the acidity of oxoacids can

**Table 17.7 Correlation of Atom Formal Charge and pK$_a$**

| | Central Atom Formal Charge | pK$_a$ |
| --- | :---: | :---: |
| :O—H  :O—S—O:  :O—H | +2 | −3 |
| H :O—H  :O—S—O: | +1 | 1.92 |
| :O—Cl—O—H | +1 | 2 |
| :Cl—O—H | 0 | 7.46 |

**FIGURE 17.8 Electrostatic potential surface and partial charges for acetic acid.** The H atoms of the molecule are all positively charged, but the H atom of the OH is much more highly charged. As expected, both of the electronegative O atoms have a partial negative charge. The table below gives some of the computer-calculated partial charges on the acid.

| Atom or Group | Calc'd Partial Charge |
|---|---|
| H of OH | +0.43 |
| O of OH | −0.62 |
| H of CH₃ | +0.23 |

also be applied to carboxylic acids. The O—H bond in these compounds is polar, a prerequisite for ionization.

polar O—H bond broken by interaction of positively charged H atom with hydrogen-bonded H₂O

In addition, carboxylate anions are stabilized by delocalizing the negative charge over the two oxygen atoms.

The simple carboxylic acids, $RCO_2H$ in which R is a hydrocarbon group (◄ Section 10.4), do not differ markedly in acid strength (compare acetic acid, $pK_a = 4.74$, and propanoic acid, $pK_a = 4.89$, Table 17.3). The acidity of carboxylic acids is enhanced, however, if electronegative substituents replace the hydrogens in the alkyl ($-CH_3$ or $-C_2H_5$) group. Compare, for example, the $pK_a$ values of a series of acetic acids in which hydrogen is replaced sequentially by the more electronegative element chlorine.

| Acid | | pK_a Value | |
|---|---|---|---|
| $CH_3CO_2H$ | Acetic acid | 4.74 | |
| $ClCH_2CO_2H$ | Chloroacetic acid | 2.85 | Increasing acid |
| $Cl_2CHCO_2H$ | Dichloroacetic acid | 1.49 | strength |
| $Cl_3CCO_2H$ | Trichloroacetic acid | 0.7 | ↓ |

As in the nitrogen oxoacids, increasingly electronegative substituents lead to an increase in acid strength. One argument is that electronegative substituents stabilize the negative charge of the anion. That is, the $Cl_3CCO_2^-$ anion is more stable than the $H_3CCO_2^-$ anion, so the formation of $Cl_3CCO_2^-$ is more favored than the formation of $CH_3CO_2^-$. Thus, the $Cl_3CCO_2^-$ anion is a weaker base than the $CH_3CO_2^-$ anion.

Finally, why are the C—H hydrogens of carboxylic acids not dissociated as $H^+$ instead of (or in addition to) the O—H hydrogen atom? The calculated partial positive charges listed in Figure 17.8 show that the H atoms of the $CH_3$ group have a much smaller positive partial charge than the O—H hydrogen atom. Furthermore, in carboxylic acids, the C atom of the $CH_3$ group is not sufficiently electronegative to accommodate the negative charge left if the bond breaks as $C—H \rightarrow C:^- + H^+$, and the product anion is not well stabilized.

## Why Are Hydrated Metal Cations Brønsted Acids?

When a coordinate covalent bond is formed between a metal cation and a water molecule, the positive charge of the metal ion and its small size means that the electrons of the $H_2O \rightarrow M^{n+}$ bond are very strongly attracted to the metal (Section 17.11). As a result, the O—H bonds of the bound water molecules are polarized, just as in oxoacids and carboxylic acids. The net effect is that a H atom of a coordinated water molecule is removed as $H^+$ more readily than in an uncoordinated water molecule. Thus, a hydrated metal cation functions as a Brønsted acid or proton donor.

$$[Cu(H_2O)_6]^{2+} + H_2O(\ell) \rightleftharpoons [Cu(H_2O)_5(OH)]^+(aq) + H_3O^+(aq)$$

The acidity of the hydrated metal ion increases with increasing charge. Consulting Table 17.3, you see that the $K_a$ of +3 ions (for example $Al^{3+}$ and $Fe^{3+}$) is greater than for +2 cations ($Cu^{2+}$, $Pb^{2+}$, $Co^{2+}$, $Fe^{2+}$, $Ni^{2+}$). Ions with a single positive charge such as $Na^+$ and $K^+$ are not acidic. (This is similar to the effect of central atom formal charge in a series of related acids. See Table 17.7.)

### Why Are Anions Brønsted Bases?

Anions, particularly oxoanions such as $PO_4^{3-}$, are Brønsted bases. The negatively charged anion interacts with the positively charged H atom of a polar water molecule, and an $H^+$ ion is transferred to the anion.

Hydrogen bond with water. $H^+$ ion moves to phosphate ion.

The data in Table 17.8 show that, in a series of related anions, the basicity of an anionic base increases as the negative charge of the anion increases.

- **Polarization of O—H Bonds** Water molecules attached to a metal cation have strongly polarized O—H bonds.

$$(H_2O)_5M^{n+} \longleftarrow :\overset{\delta-}{\underset{}{O}}—H^{\delta+}$$
$$\overset{H^{\delta+}}{}$$

**Table 17.8 Basic Oxoanions**

| Anion | p$K_b$ |
|---|---|
| $PO_4^{3-}$ | 1.55 |
| $HPO_4^{2-}$ | 6.80 |
| $H_2PO_4^-$ | 11.89 |
| $CO_3^{2-}$ | 3.68 |
| $HCO_3^-$ | 7.62 |
| $SO_3^{2-}$ | 6.80 |
| $HSO_3^-$ | 12.08 |

**REVIEW & CHECK FOR SECTION 17.10**

1. Which of the following is the stronger acid?

   (a) $H_2SeO_4$          (b) $H_2SeO_3$

2. Which of the following should be the stronger acid?

   (a) $[Fe(H_2O)_6]^{2+}$      (b) $[Fe(H_2O)_6]^{3+}$

3. Which of the following should be the stronger acid?

   (a) HOCl          (b) HOBr

## 17.11 The Lewis Concept of Acids and Bases

The concept of acid–base behavior advanced by Brønsted and Lowry in the 1920s works well for reactions involving proton transfer. However, a more general acid–base concept was developed by Gilbert N. Lewis in the 1930s (◄ page 342). This concept is based on the sharing of electrons pairs between an acid and a base.

> A **Lewis acid** is a substance that can accept a pair of electrons from another atom to form a new bond, and a **Lewis base** is a substance that can donate a pair of electrons to another atom to form a new bond.

This means that an acid–base reaction in the Lewis sense occurs when a molecule (or ion) donates a pair of electrons to another molecule (or ion).

$$\begin{array}{ccccc} A & + & B: & \rightarrow & B{\rightarrow}A \\ \text{acid} & & \text{base} & & \text{adduct} \end{array}$$

The product is often called an **acid–base adduct.** In Section 8.5, this type of chemical bond was called a *coordinate covalent bond.*

Formation of a hydronium ion from $H^+$ and water, and the formation of the ammonium ion from $H^+$ and ammonia, are good examples of a Lewis acid–base reaction (Figure 17.9). The $H^+$ ion has no electrons in its valence (1s) shell, and the

**FIGURE 17.9 Protonation of water and ammonia are examples of Lewis acid–base reactions.**

**FIGURE 17.10** **The Lewis acid–base complex ion [Cu(NH₃)₄]²⁺.** Here, aqueous ammonia was added to aqueous CuSO₄ (the light blue solution at the bottom of the beaker). The small concentration of OH⁻ in NH₃(aq) first led to the formation of insoluble blue-white Cu(OH)₂ (the solid in the middle of the beaker). With additional NH₃, however, the deep blue, soluble complex ion formed (the solution at the top of the beaker). The model in the text shows the copper(II)–ammonia complex ion.

water molecule has two unshared pairs of electrons (located in $sp^3$ hybrid orbitals). One of the lone pairs of a water molecule oxygen atom can be shared with an H⁺ ion, thus forming an O—H bond in an $H_3O^+$ ion. A similar interaction occurs between H⁺ and the nitrogen lone pair on ammonia to form the ammonium ion.

Lewis acid–base reactions are very common. In general, they involve Lewis acids that are cations or neutral molecules with an available, empty valence orbital and bases that are anions or neutral molecules with a lone electron pair.

## Cationic Lewis Acids

Just as H⁺ and water form a Lewis acid–base adduct, metal cations interact with water molecules to form hydrated cations (Figure 17.10 and page 551). In these species, coordinate covalent bonds form between the metal cation and a lone pair of electrons on the O atom of each water. For example, an iron(II) ion, $Fe^{2+}$, forms six coordinate covalent bonds to water.

$$Fe^{2+}(aq) + 6\ H_2O(\ell) \rightarrow [Fe(H_2O)_6]^{2+}(aq)$$

Solutions of transition metal cations are generally very colorful (Figures 17.10 and 17.11 and Section 22.3). Chemists call the species formed by coordination of water to a metal ion **complex ions** or, because of the presence of coordinate covalent bonds, **coordination complexes**. Several are listed in Table 17.3 as acids, and their behavior is described further in Chapter 22.

Ammonia is an excellent Lewis base and, like water, it also combines with metal cations to give adducts (complex ions), which are often very colorful. For example, copper(II) ions, light blue in aqueous solution (Figure 17.10), react with ammonia to give a deep blue adduct with four ammonia molecules surrounding each $Cu^{2+}$ ion.

$$Cu^{2+}(aq) + 4\ NH_3(aq) \longrightarrow [Cu(NH_3)_4]^{2+}(aq)$$
light blue                               deep blue

copper–ammonia coordinate covalent bond

Hydroxide ion, OH⁻, is an excellent Lewis base and binds readily to metal cations to give metal hydroxides. An important feature of the chemistry of some metal

$[Fe(H_2O)_6]^{3+}$  $[Ni(H_2O)_6]^{2+}$

$[Co(H_2O)_6]^{2+}$  $[Cu(H_2O)_6]^{2+}$

**(a)** Solutions of the nitrate salts of iron(III), cobalt(II), nickel(II), and copper(II) all have characteristic colors.

**FIGURE 17.11** Metal cations in water.

octahedral
$[M(H_2O)_6]^{n+}$

tetrahedral
$Be^{2+}(aq) + 4\ H_2O(\ell) \longrightarrow [Be(H_2O)_4]^{2+}(aq)$

water–metal ion coordinate covalent bond

**(b)** Models of complex ions (Lewis acid–base adducts) formed between a metal cation and water molecules. Such complexes often have six or four water molecules arranged octahedrally or tetrahedrally around the metal cation.

**Table 17.9 Some Common Amphoteric Metal Hydroxides***

| Hydroxide | Reaction as a Base | Reaction as an Acid |
|---|---|---|
| $Al(OH)_3$ | $Al(OH)_3(s) + 3\,H_3O^+(aq) \rightleftharpoons Al^{3+}(aq) + 6\,H_2O(\ell)$ | $Al(OH)_3(s) + OH^-(aq) \rightleftharpoons [Al(OH)_4]^-(aq)$ |
| $Zn(OH)_2$ | $Zn(OH)_2(s) + 2\,H_3O^+(aq) \rightleftharpoons Zn^{2+}(aq) + 4\,H_2O(\ell)$ | $Zn(OH)_2(s) + 2\,OH^-(aq) \rightleftharpoons [Zn(OH)_4]^{2-}(aq)$ |
| $Sn(OH)_4$ | $Sn(OH)_4(s) + 4\,H_3O^+(aq) \rightleftharpoons Sn^{4+}(aq) + 8\,H_2O(\ell)$ | $Sn(OH)_4(s) + 2\,OH^-(aq) \rightleftharpoons [Sn(OH)_6]^{2-}(aq)$ |
| $Cr(OH)_3$ | $Cr(OH)_3(s) + 3\,H_3O^+(aq) \rightleftharpoons Cr^{3+}(aq) + 6\,H_2O(\ell)$ | $Cr(OH)_3(s) + OH^-(aq) \rightleftharpoons [Cr(OH)_4]^-(aq)$ |

* The aqueous metal cations are best described as $[M(H_2O)_6]^{n+}$.

hydroxides is that they are **amphoteric**. An amphoteric metal hydroxide can behave as an acid or a base (Table 17.9). The chemistry of aluminum hydroxide, $Al(OH)_3$, is one of the best examples of this behavior (Figure 17.12). Adding $OH^-$ to a precipitate of $Al(OH)_3$ produces the water-soluble complex ion $[Al(OH)_4]^-$. In this reaction, $Al(OH)_3$ is acting as a Lewis acid.

$$Al(OH)_3(s) + OH^-(aq) \rightarrow [Al(OH)_4]^-(aq)$$
$$\text{acid} \qquad\quad \text{base}$$

If acid is added to the $Al(OH)_3$ precipitate, it again dissolves. This time, however, aluminum hydroxide is acting as a base.

$$Al(OH)_3(s) + 3\,H_3O^+(aq) \rightarrow Al^{3+}(aq) + 6\,H_2O(\ell)$$
$$\text{base} \qquad\quad \text{acid}$$

Adding a strong base (NaOH) to $Al(OH)_3$ dissolves the precipitate. Here, aluminum hydroxide acts as a Lewis acid toward the Lewis base $OH^-$ and forms the soluble sodium salt of the complex ion $[Al(OH)_4]^-$.

**(b)** Add NaOH(aq)

**(a)** Add $NH_3$(aq)

**(c)** Add HCl(aq)

Adding aqueous ammonia to a soluble salt of $Al^{3+}$ leads to a precipitate of $Al(OH)_3$.

$Al(OH)_3$ dissolves when a strong acid (HCl) is added. In this case, $Al(OH)_3$ acts as a Brønsted base and forms a soluble aluminum salt and water.

**FIGURE 17.12 The amphoteric nature of $Al(OH)_3$.** Aluminum hydroxide is formed by the reaction of aqueous $Al^{3+}$ and ammonia.

$$Al^{3+}(aq) + 3\,NH_3(aq) + 3\,H_2O(\ell) \rightleftharpoons Al(OH)_3(s) + 3\,NH_4^+(aq)$$

Reactions of solid $Al(OH)_3$ with aqueous NaOH and HCl demonstrate that aluminum hydroxide is amphoteric.

## Molecular Lewis Acids

Lewis's acid–base concept also accounts for the fact that oxides of nonmetals such as $CO_2$ and $SO_2$ behave as acids (◄ Section 3.6). Because oxygen is more electronegative than C, the C—O bonding electrons in $CO_2$ are polarized away from carbon and toward oxygen. This causes the carbon atom to be slightly positive, and it is this atom that the negatively charged Lewis base $OH^-$ can attack to give, ultimately, the bicarbonate ion.

● **$CO_2$ in Basic Solution** This reaction of $CO_2$ with $OH^-$ is the first step in the precipitation of $CaCO_3$ when $CO_2$ is bubbled into a solution of $Ca(OH)_2$ (Figure 3.5, page 117).

Similarly, $SO_2$ reacts with aqueous $OH^-$ to form the $HSO_3^-$ ion.

Compounds based on the Group 3A elements boron and aluminum are among the most-studied Lewis acids. One example is a reaction in organic chemistry that is catalyzed by the Lewis acid $AlCl_3$. The mechanism of this important reaction—called the *Friedel-Crafts reaction*—is illustrated here. In the first step, a Lewis base, the $Cl^-$ ion, transfers from the reactant, here $CH_3COCl$, to the Lewis acid to give $[AlCl_4]^-$ and an organic cation. The organic cation attacks a benzene molecule to give a cationic intermediate, and this then interacts with $[AlCl_4]^-$ to produce HCl and the final organic product.

## Molecular Lewis Bases

Ammonia is the parent compound of an enormous number of compounds that behave as Lewis and Brønsted bases (Figure 17.13). These molecules all have an electronegative N atom with a partial negative charge surrounded by three bonds and a lone pair of electrons. Owing to this partially negative N atom, they can extract a proton from water.

Hydrogen bond with water.
$H^+$ ion moves to N atom.

trimethylamine            pyridine                    nicotine                    glycine, an amino acid

**FIGURE 17.13 Nitrogen-based Lewis and Brønsted bases.** All have an N atom surrounded by three bonds and a lone pair of electrons.

In addition, the lone pair can be used to form a coordinate covalent bond to Lewis acids such as a metal cation (◄ page 792).

Ammonia is widely distributed in nature and is involved as a Lewis base in numerous reactions. One example where this is important is in the conversion of ammonia to urea ($NH_2CONH_2$) in natural systems. The process begins with the reaction of bicarbonate ion with ATP (adenosine triphosphate), and a subsequent step in the mechanism is the following:

intermediate

Here, the Lewis base ammonia attacks a carbon atom with a partial positive charge. The dihydrogen phosphate ion is then released, yielding the $NH_2CO_2^-$ ion, which eventually forms urea in another step in this reaction mechanism.

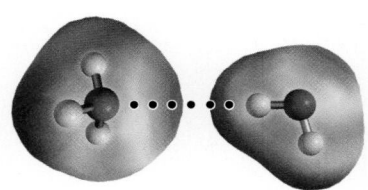

**Electrostatic potential surfaces for $NH_3$ and $H_2O$.** The red or negative region of these surfaces corresponds to the lone pair of electrons on N or the two pairs on O. The N atom of $NH_3$ has a calculated partial charge of −1.0, and the H atoms have a charge of +0.33. The N atom lone pair of $NH_3$ is involved in forming a hydrogen bond with the polar O—H bond of water. The $NH_3$ is both a Lewis and a Brønsted base and can remove the proton from water to form $NH_4^+$ and $OH^-$.

**REVIEW & CHECK FOR SECTION 17.11**

1.  Which of the following can act as a Lewis acid? (*Hint:* In each case, draw the Lewis electron dot structure of the molecule or ion. Are there lone pairs of electrons on the central atom? If so, it can be a Lewis base. Does the central atom lack an electron pair? If so, it can behave as a Lewis acid.)

    (a)  $PH_3$             (c)  $H_2S$

    (b)  $BCl_3$            (d)  $HS^-$

2.  The molecule whose structure is illustrated here is amphetamine, a stimulant. Which description best fits this molecule? (*Note:* There may be more than one answer.)

    (a)  Brønsted acid    (b)  Lewis acid    (c)  Brønsted base    (d)  Lewis base

and

## CHAPTER GOALS REVISITED

*Now that you have studied this chapter, you should ask whether you have met the chapter goals. In particular, you should be able to:*

### Use the Brønsted–Lowry and Lewis theories of acids and bases

a.  Define and use the Brønsted concept of acids and bases (Sections 17.1 and 17.2).

b.  Recognize common monoprotic and polyprotic acids and bases, and write balanced equations for their ionization in water (Section 17.2).

c.  Appreciate when a substance can be amphiprotic (Section 17.2). **Study Questions: 5, 6.**

d.  Recognize the Brønsted acid and base in a reaction, and identify the conjugate partner of each (Section 17.2). **Study Questions: 1–4, 7, 8.**

e.  Use the water ionization constant, $K_w$ (Section 17.3).

f.  Use the pH concept (Section 17.3). **Study Questions: 9–14.**

g.  Identify common strong acids and bases (Tables 3.1 and 17.3).

h.  Recognize some common weak acids and understand that they can be neutral molecules (such as acetic acid), cations ($NH_4^+$ or hydrated metal ions such as $[Fe(H_2O)_6]^{2+}$, or anions (such as $HCO_3^-$) (Table 17.3).

### Apply the principles of chemical equilibrium to acids and bases in aqueous solution

a.  Write equilibrium constant expressions for weak acids and bases (Section 17.4).

b.  Calculate $pK_a$ from $K_a$ (or $K_a$ from $pK_a$), and understand how $pK_a$ is correlated with acid strength (Section 17.4). **Study Questions: 15, 16, 23–28, 104, 106.**

c.  Understand the relationship between $K_a$ for a weak acid and $K_b$ for its conjugate base (Section 17.4). **Study Questions: 17, 18, 29–32.**

d.  Write equations for acid–base reactions, and decide whether they are product- or reactant-favored at equilibrium (Section 17.6 and Table 17.5). **Study Questions: 33–40.**

e.  Calculate the equilibrium constant for a weak acid ($K_a$) or a weak base ($K_b$) from experimental information (such as pH, $[H_3O^+]$, or $[OH^-]$) (Section 17.8 and Example 17.4). **Study Questions: 41–44, 85, 107.**

f.  Use the equilibrium constant and other information to calculate the pH of a solution of a weak acid or weak base (Section 17.8 and Examples 17.5 and 17.6). **Study Questions: 47–56, 65, 66, 89, 91, 99, and Go Chemistry Module 22.**

g.  Describe the acid–base properties of salts, and calculate the pH of a solution of a salt of a weak acid or of a weak base (Section 17.5 and Example 17.7). **Study Questions: 57–60, 84, 92, 93, 103, 121.**

### Predict the outcome of reactions of acids and bases

a.  Recognize the type of acid–base reaction, and describe its result (Section 17.7).

b.  Calculate the pH after an acid–base reaction (Section 17.7 and Example 17.8). **Study Questions: 61–64, 98, 102.**

### Understand the influence of structure and bonding on acid–base properties

a.  Appreciate the connection between the structure of a compound and its acidity or basicity (Section 17.10). **Study Questions: 69–72, 74, 114.**

b.  Characterize a compound as a Lewis base (an electron-pair donor) or a Lewis acid (an electron-pair acceptor) (Section 17.11). **Study Questions: 73–76, 108.**

## Key Equations

**Equation 17.1 (page 761)** Water ionization constant.

$$K_w = [H_3O^+][OH^-] = 1.0 \times 10^{-14} \text{ at 25 °C}$$

**Equation 17.2 (page 763)** Definition of pH (see also Equation 4.3).

$$pH = -\log[H_3O^+]$$

**Equation 17.3 (page 763)** Definition of pOH.

$$pOH = -\log[OH^-]$$

**Equation 17.4 (page 763)** Definition of $pK_w = pH + pOH$ (= 14.00 at 25 °C).

$$pK_w = 14.00 = pH + pOH$$

**Equation 17.5 (page 765)** Equilibrium expression for a general acid, HA, in water.

$$K_a = \frac{[H_3O^+][A^-]}{[HA]}$$

**Equation 17.6 (page 765)** Equilibrium expression for a general base, B, in water.

$$K_b = \frac{[BH^+][OH^-]}{[B]}$$

**Equation 17.7 (page 768)** Definition of $pK_a$.

$$pK_a = -\log K_a$$

**Equation 17.8 (page 768)** Relationship of $K_a$, $K_b$, and $K_w$, where $K_a$ and $K_b$ are for a conjugate acid–base pair.

$$K_a \times K_b = K_w$$

## Study Questions

**OWL** Interactive versions of these questions are assignable in OWL.

▲ denotes challenging questions.

Blue-numbered questions have answers in Appendix R and fully worked solutions in the *Student Solutions Manual*.

## Practicing Skills

### The Brønsted Concept
*(See Sections 17.1 and 17.2.)*

1. Write the formula and give the name of the conjugate base of each of the following acids.
   (a) HCN      (b) $HSO_4^-$      (c) HF

2. Write the formula and give the name of the conjugate acid of each of the following bases.
   (a) $NH_3$      (b) $HCO_3^-$      (c) $Br^-$

3. What are the products of each of the following acid–base reactions? Indicate the acid and its conjugate base and the base and its conjugate acid.
   (a) $HNO_3 + H_2O \rightarrow$
   (b) $HSO_4^- + H_2O \rightarrow$
   (c) $H_3O^+ + F^- \rightarrow$

4. What are the products of each of the following acid–base reactions? Indicate the acid and its conjugate base and the base and its conjugate acid.
   (a) $HClO_4 + H_2O \rightarrow$
   (b) $NH_4^+ + H_2O \rightarrow$
   (c) $HCO_3^- + OH^- \rightarrow$

5. Write balanced equations showing how the hydrogen oxalate ion, $HC_2O_4^-$, can be both a Brønsted acid and a Brønsted base.

6. Write balanced equations showing how the $HPO_4^{2-}$ ion of sodium hydrogen phosphate, $Na_2HPO_4$, can be a Brønsted acid or a Brønsted base.

7. In each of the following acid–base reactions, identify the Brønsted acid and base on the left and their conjugate partners on the right.
   (a) $HCO_2H(aq) + H_2O(\ell) \rightleftharpoons HCO_2^-(aq) + H_3O^+(aq)$
   (b) $NH_3(aq) + H_2S(aq) \rightleftharpoons NH_4^+(aq) + HS^-(aq)$
   (c) $HSO_4^-(aq) + OH^-(aq) \rightleftharpoons SO_4^{2-}(aq) + H_2O(\ell)$

8. In each of the following acid–base reactions, identify the Brønsted acid and base on the left and their conjugate partners on the right.
   (a) $C_5H_5N(aq) + CH_3CO_2H(aq) \rightleftharpoons$
       $C_5H_5NH^+(aq) + CH_3CO_2^-(aq)$
   (b) $N_2H_4(aq) + HSO_4^-(aq) \rightleftharpoons$
       $N_2H_5^+(aq) + SO_4^{2-}(aq)$
   (c) $[Al(H_2O)_6]^{3+}(aq) + OH^-(aq) \rightleftharpoons$
       $[Al(H_2O)_5OH]^{2+}(aq) + H_2O(\ell)$

### pH Calculations
*(See Section 17.3 and Examples 4.8 and 17.1.)*

9. An aqueous solution has a pH of 3.75. What is the hydronium ion concentration of the solution? Is it acidic or basic?

10. A saturated solution of milk of magnesia, $Mg(OH)_2$, has a pH of 10.52. What is the hydronium ion concentration of the solution? What is the hydroxide ion concentration? Is the solution acidic or basic?

11. What is the pH of a 0.0075 M solution of HCl? What is the hydroxide ion concentration of the solution?

12. What is the pH of a $1.2 \times 10^{-4}$ M solution of KOH? What is the hydronium ion concentration of the solution?

13. What is the pH of a 0.0015 M solution of $Ba(OH)_2$?

14. The pH of a solution of $Ba(OH)_2$ is 10.66 at 25 °C. What is the hydroxide ion concentration in the solution? If the solution volume is 125 mL, what mass of $Ba(OH)_2$ must have been dissolved?

## Equilibrium Constants for Acids and Bases
*(See Sections 17.4 and 17.5 and Example 17.2.)*

15. Several acids are listed here with their respective equilibrium constants:

$$C_6H_5OH(aq) + H_2O(\ell) \rightleftharpoons H_3O^+(aq) + C_6H_5O^-(aq)$$
$$K_a = 1.3 \times 10^{-10}$$

$$HCO_2H(aq) + H_2O(\ell) \rightleftharpoons H_3O^+(aq) + HCO_2^-(aq)$$
$$K_a = 1.8 \times 10^{-4}$$

$$HC_2O_4^-(aq) + H_2O(\ell) \rightleftharpoons H_3O^+(aq) + C_2O_4^{2-}(aq)$$
$$K_a = 6.4 \times 10^{-5}$$

(a) Which is the strongest acid? Which is the weakest acid?
(b) Which acid has the weakest conjugate base?
(c) Which acid has the strongest conjugate base?

16. Several acids are listed here with their respective equilibrium constants.

$$HF(aq) + H_2O(\ell) \rightleftharpoons H_3O^+(aq) + F^-(aq)$$
$$K_a = 7.2 \times 10^{-4}$$

$$HPO_4^{2-}(aq) + H_2O(\ell) \rightleftharpoons H_3O^+(aq) + PO_4^{3-}(aq)$$
$$K_a = 3.6 \times 10^{-13}$$

$$CH_3CO_2H(aq) + H_2O(\ell) \rightleftharpoons H_3O^+(aq) + CH_3CO_2^-(aq)$$
$$K_a = 1.8 \times 10^{-5}$$

(a) Which is the strongest acid? Which is the weakest acid?
(b) What is the conjugate base of the acid HF?
(c) Which acid has the weakest conjugate base?
(d) Which acid has the strongest conjugate base?

17. Which of the following ions or compounds has the strongest conjugate base? Briefly explain your choice.
(a) $HSO_4^-$ (b) $CH_3CO_2H$ (c) $HOCl$

18. Which of the following compounds or ions has the strongest conjugate acid? Briefly explain your choice.
(a) $CN^-$ (b) $NH_3$ (c) $SO_4^{2-}$

19. Dissolving $K_2CO_3$ in water gives a basic solution. Write a balanced equation showing how this salt can produce a basic solution.

20. Dissolving ammonium bromide in water gives an acidic solution. Write a balanced equation showing how this can occur.

21. If each of the salts listed here were dissolved in water to give a 0.10 M solution, which solution would have the highest pH? Which would have the lowest pH?
(a) $Na_2S$          (d) $NaF$
(b) $Na_3PO_4$      (e) $NaCH_3CO_2$
(c) $NaH_2PO_4$    (f) $AlCl_3$

22. Which of the following common food additives would give a basic solution when dissolved in water?
(a) $NaNO_3$ (used as a meat preservative)
(b) $NaC_6H_5CO_2$ (sodium benzoate; used as a soft-drink preservative)
(c) $Na_2HPO_4$ (used as an emulsifier in the manufacture of pasteurized cheese)

## p$K_a$: A Logarithmic Scale of Acid Strength

*(See Section 17.4.)*

23. A weak acid has a $K_a$ of $6.5 \times 10^{-5}$. What is the value of p$K_a$ for the acid?

24. If $K_a$ for a weak acid is $2.4 \times 10^{-11}$, what is the value of p$K_a$?

25. Epinephrine hydrochloride has a p$K_a$ value of 9.53. What is the value of $K_a$? Where does the acid fit in Table 17.3?

26. An organic acid has p$K_a$ = 8.95. What is its $K_a$ value? Where does the acid fit in Table 17.3?

27. Which is the stronger of the following two acids?
(a) benzoic acid, $C_6H_5CO_2H$, p$K_a$ = 4.20
(b) 2-chlorobenzoic acid, $ClC_6H_4CO_2H$, p$K_a$ = 2.90

28. Which is the stronger of the following two acids?
(a) acetic acid, $CH_3CO_2H$, $K_a = 1.8 \times 10^{-5}$
(b) chloroacetic acid, $ClCH_2CO_2H$, p$K_a$ = 2.85

## Ionization Constants for Weak Acids and Their Conjugate Bases
*(See Section 17.4.)*

29. Chloroacetic acid ($ClCH_2CO_2H$) has $K_a = 1.41 \times 10^{-3}$. What is the value of $K_b$ for the chloroacetate ion ($ClCH_2CO_2^-$)?

30. A weak base has $K_b = 1.5 \times 10^{-9}$. What is the value of $K_a$ for the conjugate acid?

31. The trimethylammonium ion, $(CH_3)_3NH^+$, is the conjugate acid of the weak base trimethylamine, $(CH_3)_3N$. A chemical handbook gives 9.80 as the p$K_a$ value for $(CH_3)_3NH^+$. What is the value of $K_b$ for $(CH_3)_3N$?

32. The chromium(III) ion in water, $[Cr(H_2O)_6]^{3+}$, is a weak acid with p$K_a$ = 3.95. What is the value of $K_b$ for its conjugate base, $[Cr(H_2O)_5OH]^{2+}$?

## Predicting the Direction of Acid–Base Reactions
*(See Section 17.6 and Example 17.3.)*

33. Acetic acid and sodium hydrogen carbonate, $NaHCO_3$, are mixed in water. Write a balanced equation for the acid–base reaction that could, in principle, occur. Using Table 17.3, decide whether the equilibrium lies predominantly to the right or to the left.

34. Ammonium chloride and sodium dihydrogen phosphate, $NaH_2PO_4$, are mixed in water. Write a balanced equation for the acid–base reaction that could, in principle, occur. Using Table 17.3, decide whether the equilibrium lies predominantly to the right or to the left.

35. For each of the following reactions, predict whether the equilibrium lies predominantly to the left or to the right. Explain your predictions briefly.
(a) $NH_4^+(aq) + Br^-(aq) \rightleftharpoons NH_3(aq) + HBr(aq)$
(b) $HPO_4^{2-}(aq) + CH_3CO_2^-(aq) \rightleftharpoons$
$$PO_4^{3-}(aq) + CH_3CO_2H(aq)$$
(c) $[Fe(H_2O)_6]^{3+}(aq) + HCO_3^-(aq) \rightleftharpoons$
$$[Fe(H_2O)_5(OH)]^{2+}(aq) + H_2CO_3(aq)$$

36. For each of the following reactions, predict whether the equilibrium lies predominantly to the left or to the right. Explain your predictions briefly.
(a) $H_2S(aq) + CO_3^{2-}(aq) \rightleftharpoons HS^-(aq) + HCO_3^-(aq)$
(b) $HCN(aq) + SO_4^{2-}(aq) \rightleftharpoons CN^-(aq) + HSO_4^-(aq)$
(c) $SO_4^{2-}(aq) + CH_3CO_2H(aq) \rightleftharpoons$
$$HSO_4^-(aq) + CH_3CO_2^-(aq)$$

## Types of Acid–Base Reactions
*(See Section 17.7.)*

37. Equal molar quantities of sodium hydroxide and sodium hydrogen phosphate ($Na_2HPO_4$) are mixed.
    (a) Write the balanced, net ionic equation for the acid–base reaction that can, in principle, occur.
    (b) Does the equilibrium lie to the right or left?

38. Equal molar quantities of hydrochloric acid and sodium hypochlorite (NaClO) are mixed.
    (a) Write the balanced, net ionic equation for the acid–base reaction that can, in principle, occur.
    (b) Does the equilibrium lie to the right or left?

39. Equal molar quantities of acetic acid and sodium hydrogen phosphate ($Na_2HPO_4$) are mixed.
    (a) Write a balanced, net ionic equation for the acid–base reaction that can, in principle, occur.
    (b) Does the equilibrium lie to the right or left?

40. Equal molar quantities of ammonia and sodium dihydrogen phosphate ($NaH_2PO_4$) are mixed.
    (a) Write a balanced, net ionic equation for the acid–base reaction that can, in principle, occur.
    (b) Does the equilibrium lie to the right or left?

## Using pH to Calculate Ionization Constants
*(See Section 17.8 and Example 17.4.)*

41. A 0.015 M solution of hydrogen cyanate, HOCN, has a pH of 2.67.
    (a) What is the hydronium ion concentration in the solution?
    (b) What is the ionization constant, $K_a$, for the acid?

42. A 0.10 M solution of chloroacetic acid, $ClCH_2CO_2H$, has a pH of 1.95. Calculate $K_a$ for the acid.

43. A 0.025 M solution of hydroxylamine has a pH of 9.11. What is the value of $K_b$ for this weak base?

    $$H_2NOH(aq) + H_2O(\ell) \rightleftharpoons H_3NOH^+(aq) + OH^-(aq)$$

44. Methylamine, $CH_3NH_2$, is a weak base.

    $$CH_3NH_2(aq) + H_2O(\ell) \rightleftharpoons CH_3NH_3^+(aq) + OH^-(aq)$$

    If the pH of a 0.065 M solution of the amine is 11.70, what is the value of $K_b$?

45. A $2.5 \times 10^{-3}$ M solution of an unknown acid has a pH of 3.80 at 25 °C.
    (a) What is the hydronium ion concentration of the solution?
    (b) Is the acid a strong acid, a moderately weak acid ($K_a$ of about $10^{-5}$), or a very weak acid ($K_a$ of about $10^{-10}$)?

46. A 0.015 M solution of a base has a pH of 10.09.
    (a) What are the hydronium and hydroxide ion concentrations of this solution?
    (b) Is the base a strong base, a moderately weak base ($K_b$ of about $10^{-5}$), or a very weak base ($K_b$ of about $10^{-10}$)?

## Using Ionization Constants
*(See Section 17.8 and Examples 17.5–17.6.)*

47. What are the equilibrium concentrations of hydronium ion, acetate ion, and acetic acid in a 0.20 M aqueous solution of acetic acid?

48. The ionization constant of a very weak acid, HA, is $4.0 \times 10^{-9}$. Calculate the equilibrium concentrations of $H_3O^+$, $A^-$, and HA in a 0.040 M solution of the acid.

49. What are the equilibrium concentrations of $H_3O^+$, $CN^-$, and HCN in a 0.025 M solution of HCN? What is the pH of the solution?

50. Phenol ($C_6H_5OH$), commonly called *carbolic acid,* is a weak organic acid.

    $$C_6H_5OH(aq) + H_2O(\ell) \rightleftharpoons C_6H_5O^-(aq) + H_3O^+(aq)$$
    $$K_a = 1.3 \times 10^{-10}$$

    If you dissolve 0.195 g of the acid in enough water to make 125 mL of solution, what is the equilibrium hydronium ion concentration? What is the pH of the solution?

51. What are the equilibrium concentrations of $NH_3$, $NH_4^+$, and $OH^-$ in a 0.15 M solution of ammonia? What is the pH of the solution?

52. A hypothetical weak base has $K_b = 5.0 \times 10^{-4}$. Calculate the equilibrium concentrations of the base, its conjugate acid, and $OH^-$ in a 0.15 M solution of the base.

53. The weak base methylamine, $CH_3NH_2$, has $K_b = 4.2 \times 10^{-4}$. It reacts with water according to the equation

    $$CH_3NH_2(aq) + H_2O(\ell) \rightleftharpoons CH_3NH_3^+(aq) + OH^-(aq)$$

    Calculate the equilibrium hydroxide ion concentration in a 0.25 M solution of the base. What are the pH and pOH of the solution?

54. Calculate the pH of a 0.12 M aqueous solution of the base aniline, $C_6H_5NH_2$ ($K_b = 4.0 \times 10^{-10}$).

    $$C_6H_5NH_2(aq) + H_2O(\ell) \rightleftharpoons C_6H_5NH_3^+(aq) + OH^-(aq)$$

55. Calculate the pH of a 0.0010 M aqueous solution of HF.

56. A solution of hydrofluoric acid, HF, has a pH of 2.30. Calculate the equilibrium concentrations of HF, $F^-$, and $H_3O^+$, and calculate the amount of HF originally dissolved per liter.

## Acid–Base Properties of Salts
*(See Sections 17.5 and 17.8 and Example 17.7.)*

57. Calculate the hydronium ion concentration and pH in a 0.20 M solution of ammonium chloride, $NH_4Cl$.

58. ▲ Calculate the hydronium ion concentration and pH for a 0.015 M solution of sodium formate, $NaHCO_2$.

59. Sodium cyanide is the salt of the weak acid HCN. Calculate the concentrations of $H_3O^+$, $OH^-$, HCN, and $Na^+$ in a solution prepared by dissolving 10.8 g of NaCN in enough water to make $5.00 \times 10^2$ mL of solution at 25 °C.

60. The sodium salt of propanoic acid, $NaCH_3CH_2CO_2$, is used as an antifungal agent by veterinarians. Calculate the equilibrium concentrations of $H_3O^+$ and $OH^-$, and the pH, for a solution of 0.10 M $NaCH_3CH_2CO_2$.

## pH after an Acid–Base Reaction
*(See Example 17.8.)*

61. Calculate the hydronium ion concentration and pH of the solution that results when 22.0 mL of 0.15 M acetic acid, $CH_3CO_2H$, is mixed with 22.0 mL of 0.15 M NaOH.

62. Calculate the hydronium ion concentration and the pH when 50.0 mL of 0.40 M $NH_3$ is mixed with 50.0 mL of 0.40 M HCl.

63. For each of the following cases, decide whether the pH is less than 7, equal to 7, or greater than 7.
    (a) Equal volumes of 0.10 M acetic acid, $CH_3CO_2H$, and 0.10 M KOH are mixed.
    (b) 25 mL of 0.015 M $NH_3$ is mixed with 25 mL of 0.015 M HCl.
    (c) 150 mL of 0.20 M $HNO_3$ is mixed with 75 mL of 0.40 M NaOH.

64. For each of the following cases, decide whether the pH is less than 7, equal to 7, or greater than 7.
    (a) 25 mL of 0.45 M $H_2SO_4$ is mixed with 25 mL of 0.90 M NaOH.
    (b) 15 mL of 0.050 M formic acid, $HCO_2H$, is mixed with 15 mL of 0.050 M NaOH.
    (c) 25 mL of 0.15 M $H_2C_2O_4$ (oxalic acid) is mixed with 25 mL of 0.30 M NaOH. (Both $H^+$ ions of oxalic acid are removed with NaOH.)

### Polyprotic Acids and Bases
*(See Section 17.9 and Example 17.9.)*

65. Sulfurous acid, $H_2SO_3$, is a weak acid capable of providing two $H^+$ ions.
    (a) What is the pH of a 0.45 M solution of $H_2SO_3$?
    (b) What is the equilibrium concentration of the sulfite ion, $SO_3^{2-}$, in the 0.45 M solution of $H_2SO_3$?

66. Ascorbic acid (vitamin C, $C_6H_8O_6$) is a diprotic acid ($K_{a1} = 6.8 \times 10^{-5}$ and $K_{a2} = 2.7 \times 10^{-12}$). What is the pH of a solution that contains 5.0 mg of acid per milliliter of solution?

ascorbic acid

67. Hydrazine, $N_2H_4$, can interact with water in two steps.

$$N_2H_4(aq) + H_2O(\ell) \rightleftharpoons N_2H_5^+(aq) + OH^-(aq)$$
$$K_{b1} = 8.5 \times 10^{-7}$$

$$N_2H_5^+(aq) + H_2O(\ell) \rightleftharpoons N_2H_6^{2+}(aq) + OH^-(aq)$$
$$K_{b2} = 8.9 \times 10^{-16}$$

    (a) What is the concentration of $OH^-$, $N_2H_5^+$, and $N_2H_6^{2+}$ in a 0.010 M aqueous solution of hydrazine?
    (b) What is the pH of the 0.010 M solution of hydrazine?

68. Ethylenediamine, $H_2NCH_2CH_2NH_2$, can interact with water in two steps, forming $OH^-$ in each step (▶ Appendix I). If you have a 0.15 M aqueous solution of the amine, calculate the concentrations of $[H_3NCH_2CH_2NH_3]^{2+}$ and $OH^-$.

ethylenediamine

### Molecular Structure, Bonding, and Acid–Base Behavior
*(See Section 17.10.)*

69. Which should be the stronger acid, HOCN or HCN? Explain briefly. (In HOCN, the $H^+$ ion is attached to the O atom of the $OCN^-$ ion.)

70. Which should be the stronger Brønsted acid, $[V(H_2O)_6]^{2+}$ or $[V(H_2O)_6]^{3+}$?

71. Explain why benzenesulfonic acid is a Brønsted acid.

benzenesulfonic acid

72. The structure of ethylenediamine is illustrated in Study Question 68. Is this compound a Brønsted acid, a Brønsted base, a Lewis acid, or a Lewis base, or some combination of these?

### Lewis Acids and Bases
*(See Section 17.11.)*

73. Decide whether each of the following substances should be classified as a Lewis acid or a Lewis base.
    (a) $H_2NOH$ in the reaction

    $$H_2NOH(aq) + HCl(aq) \longrightarrow [H_3NOH]Cl(aq)$$

    (b) $Fe^{2+}$
    (c) $CH_3NH_2$ (*Hint:* Draw the electron dot structure.)

74. Decide whether each of the following substances should be classified as a Lewis acid or a Lewis base.
    (a) $BCl_3$ (*Hint:* Draw the electron dot structure.)
    (b) $H_2NNH_2$, hydrazine (*Hint:* Draw the electron dot structure.)
    (c) the reactants in the reaction

    $$Ag^+(aq) + 2 NH_3(aq) \rightleftharpoons [Ag(NH_3)_2]^+(aq)$$

75. Carbon monoxide forms complexes with low-valent metals. For example, $Ni(CO)_4$ and $Fe(CO)_5$ are well known. CO also forms complexes with the iron(II) ion in hemoglobin, which prevents the hemoglobin from acting in its normal way. Is CO a Lewis acid or a Lewis base?

76. Trimethylamine, $(CH_3)_3N$, is a common reagent. It interacts readily with diborane gas, $B_2H_6$. The latter dissociates to $BH_3$, and this forms a complex with the amine, $(CH_3)_3N \rightarrow BH_3$. Is the $BH_3$ fragment a Lewis acid or a Lewis base?

## General Questions

*These questions are not designated as to type or location in the chapter. They may combine several concepts.*

77. About this time, you may be wishing you had an aspirin. Aspirin is an organic acid (page 756) with a $K_a$ of $3.27 \times 10^{-4}$ for the reaction

$$HC_9H_7O_4(aq) + H_2O(\ell) \rightleftharpoons C_9H_7O_4^-(aq) + H_3O^+(aq)$$

If you have two tablets, each containing 0.325 g of aspirin (mixed with a neutral "binder" to hold the tablet together), and you dissolve them in a glass of water to give 225 mL of solution, what is the pH of the solution?

78. Consider the following ions: $NH_4^+$, $CO_3^{2-}$, $Br^-$, $S^{2-}$, and $ClO_4^-$.
    (a) Which of these ions in water gives an acidic solution and which gives a basic solution?
    (b) Which of these anions will have no effect on the pH of an aqueous solution?
    (c) Which ion is the strongest base?
    (d) Write a chemical equation for the reaction of each basic anion with water.

79. A 2.50-g sample of a solid that could be $Ba(OH)_2$ or $Sr(OH)_2$ was dissolved in enough water to make 1.00 L of solution. If the pH of the solution is 12.61, what is the identity of the solid?

80. ▲ In a particular solution, acetic acid is 11% ionized at 25 °C. Calculate the pH of the solution and the mass of acetic acid dissolved to yield 1.00 L of solution.

81. Hydrogen sulfide, $H_2S$, and sodium acetate, $NaCH_3CO_2$, are mixed in water. Using Table 17.3, write a balanced equation for the acid–base reaction that could, in principle, occur. Does the equilibrium lie toward the products or the reactants?

82. For each of the following reactions, predict whether the equilibrium lies predominantly to the left or to the right. Explain your prediction briefly.
    (a) $HCO_3^-(aq) + SO_4^{2-}(aq) \rightleftharpoons$
    $$CO_3^{2-}(aq) + HSO_4^-(aq)$$
    (b) $HSO_4^-(aq) + CH_3CO_2^-(aq) \rightleftharpoons$
    $$SO_4^{2-}(aq) + CH_3CO_2H(aq)$$
    (c) $[Co(H_2O)_6]^{2+}(aq) + CH_3CO_2^-(aq) \rightleftharpoons$
    $$[Co(H_2O)_5(OH)]^+(aq) + CH_3CO_2H(aq)$$

83. A monoprotic acid HX has $K_a = 1.3 \times 10^{-3}$. Calculate the equilibrium concentrations of HX and $H_3O^+$ and the pH for a 0.010 M solution of the acid.

84. Arrange the following 0.10 M solutions in order of increasing pH.
    (a) NaCl          (d) $NaCH_3CO_2$
    (b) $NH_4Cl$      (e) KOH
    (c) HCl

85. *m*-Nitrophenol, a weak acid, can be used as a pH indicator because it is yellow at a pH above 8.6 and colorless at a pH below 6.8. If the pH of a 0.010 M solution of the compound is 3.44, calculate its $pK_a$.

HO
⬡— $NO_2$

*m*-nitrophenol

86. The butylammonium ion, $C_4H_9NH_3^+$, has a $K_a$ of $2.3 \times 10^{-11}$.
    $$C_4H_9NH_3^+(aq) + H_2O(\ell) \rightleftharpoons H_3O^+(aq) + C_4H_9NH_2(aq)$$
    (a) Calculate $K_b$ for the conjugate base, $C_4H_9NH_2$ (butylamine).
    (b) Place the butylammonium ion and its conjugate base in Table 17.3. Name an acid weaker than $C_4H_9NH_3^+$ and a base stronger than $C_4H_9NH_2$.
    (c) What is the pH of a 0.015 M solution of butylammonium chloride?

87. The local anesthetic novocaine is the hydrogen chloride salt of an organic base, procaine.
    $$C_{13}H_{20}N_2O_2(aq) + HCl(aq) \longrightarrow [HC_{13}H_{20}N_2O_2]^+Cl^-(aq)$$
    procaine                                    novocaine
    The $pK_a$ for novocaine is 8.85. What is the pH of a 0.0015 M solution of novocaine?

88. Pyridine is a weak organic base and readily forms a salt with hydrochloric acid.
    $$C_5H_5N(aq) + HCl(aq) \longrightarrow C_5H_5NH^+(aq) + Cl^-(aq)$$
    pyridine                            pyridinium ion
    What is the pH of a 0.025 M solution of pyridinium hydrochloride, $[C_5H_5NH^+]Cl^-$?

89. The base ethylamine ($CH_3CH_2NH_2$) has a $K_b$ of $4.3 \times 10^{-4}$. A closely related base, ethanolamine ($HOCH_2CH_2NH_2$), has a $K_b$ of $3.2 \times 10^{-5}$.
    (a) Which of the two bases is stronger?
    (b) Calculate the pH of a 0.10 M solution of the stronger base.

90. Chloroacetic acid, $ClCH_2CO_2H$, is a moderately weak acid ($K_a = 1.40 \times 10^{-3}$). If you dissolve 94.5 mg of the acid in water to give 125 mL of solution, what is the pH of the solution?

91. Saccharin ($HC_7H_4NO_3S$) is a weak acid with $pK_a = 2.32$ at 25 °C. It is used in the form of sodium saccharide, $NaC_7H_4NO_3S$. What is the pH of a 0.10 M solution of sodium saccharide at 25 °C?

saccharin

92. Given the following solutions:
    (a) 0.1 M $NH_3$          (e) 0.1 M $NH_4Cl$
    (b) 0.1 M $Na_2CO_3$      (f) 0.1 M $NaCH_3CO_2$
    (c) 0.1 M NaCl            (g) 0.1 M $NH_4CH_3CO_2$
    (d) 0.1 M $CH_3CO_2H$

    (i)   Which of the solutions are acidic?
    (ii)  Which of the solutions are basic?
    (iii) Which of the solutions is most acidic?

93. For each of the following salts, predict whether a 0.10 M solution has a pH less than, equal to, or greater than 7.
    (a) $NaHSO_4$
    (b) $NH_4Br$
    (c) $KClO_4$
    (d) $Na_2CO_3$
    (e) $(NH_4)_2S$
    (f) $NaNO_3$
    (g) $Na_2HPO_4$
    (h) LiBr
    (i) $FeCl_3$
    Which solution has the highest pH? The lowest pH?

94. Nicotine, $C_{10}H_{14}N_2$, has two basic nitrogen atoms (page 795), and both can react with water.

$$Nic(aq) + H_2O(\ell) \rightleftharpoons NicH^+(aq) + OH^-(aq)$$

$$NicH^+(aq) + H_2O(\ell) \rightleftharpoons NicH_2^{2+}(aq) + OH^-(aq)$$

$K_{b1}$ is $7.0 \times 10^{-7}$ and $K_{b2}$ is $1.1 \times 10^{-10}$. Calculate the approximate pH of a 0.020 M solution.

95. Oxalic acid is a relatively weak diprotic acid. Calculate the equilibrium constant for the reaction shown below from $K_{a1}$ and $K_{a2}$. (See Appendix H for the required $K_a$ values.)

$$H_2C_2O_4(aq) + 2 H_2O(\ell) \rightleftharpoons C_2O_4^{2-}(aq) + 2 H_3O^+(aq)$$

96. ▲ The equilibrium constant for the reaction of hydrochloric acid and ammonia is $1.8 \times 10^9$ (page 775). Confirm this value.

97. ▲ The equilibrium constant for the reaction of formic acid and sodium hydroxide is $1.8 \times 10^{10}$ (page 774). Confirm this value.

98. ▲ Calculate the pH of the solution that results from mixing 25.0 mL of 0.14 M formic acid and 50.0 mL of 0.070 M sodium hydroxide.

99. ▲ To what volume should $1.00 \times 10^2$ mL of any weak acid, HA, with a concentration 0.20 M be diluted to double the percentage ionization?

100. ▲ The hydrogen phthalate ion, $C_8H_5O_4^-$, is a weak acid with $K_a = 3.91 \times 10^{-6}$.

$$C_8H_5O_4^-(aq) + H_2O(\ell) \rightleftharpoons C_8H_4O_4^{2-}(aq) + H_3O^+(aq)$$

What is the pH of a 0.050 M solution of potassium hydrogen phthalate, $KC_8H_5O_4$? *Note:* To find the pH for a solution of the anion, we must take into account that the ion is amphiprotic. It can be shown that, for most cases of amphiprotic ions, the $H_3O^+$ concentration is

$$[H_3O^+] = \sqrt{K_1 \times K_2}$$

For phthalic acid, $C_8H_6O_4$, $K_1$ is $1.12 \times 10^{-3}$, and $K_2$ is $3.91 \times 10^{-6}$.

101. ▲ You prepare a 0.10 M solution of oxalic acid, $H_2C_2O_4$. What molecules and ions exist in this solution? List them in order of decreasing concentration.

102. ▲ You mix 30.0 mL of 0.15 M NaOH with 30.0 mL of 0.15 M acetic acid. What molecules and ions exist in this solution? List them in order of decreasing concentration.

## In the Laboratory

103. Describe an experiment that will allow you to place the following three bases in order of increasing base strength: NaCN, $CH_3NH_2$, $Na_2CO_3$.

104. The data below compare the strength of acetic acid with a related series of acids, where the H atoms of the $CH_3$ group in acetic acid are successively replaced by Br.

| Acid | $pK_a$ |
|---|---|
| $CH_3CO_2H$ | 4.74 |
| $BrCH_2CO_2H$ | 2.90 |
| $Br_2CHCO_2H$ | 1.39 |
| $Br_3CCO_2H$ | −0.147 |

(a) What trend in acid strength do you observe as H is successively replaced by Br? Can you suggest a reason for this trend?
(b) Suppose each of the acids above was present as a 0.10 M aqueous solution. Which would have the highest pH? The lowest pH?

105. ▲ You have three solutions labeled A, B, and C. You know only that each contains a different cation—$Na^+$, $NH_4^+$, or $H_3O^+$. Each has an anion that does not contribute to the solution pH (e.g., $Cl^-$). You also have two other solutions, Y and Z, each containing a different anion, $Cl^-$ or $OH^-$, with a cation that does not influence solution pH (e.g., $K^+$). If equal amounts of B and Y are mixed, the result is an acidic solution. Mixing A and Z gives a neutral solution, whereas B and Z give a basic solution. Identify the five unknown solutions. (Adapted from D. H. Barouch: *Voyages in Conceptual Chemistry*, Boston, Jones and Bartlett, 1997.)

| | Y | Z |
|---|---|---|
| A | | neutral |
| B | acidic | basic |
| C | | |

106. A hydrogen atom in the organic base pyridine, $C_5H_5N$, can be substituted by various atoms or groups to give $XC_5H_4N$, where X is an atom such as Cl or a group such as $CH_3$. The following table gives $K_a$ values for the conjugate acids of a variety of substituted pyridines.

substituted pyridine (aq) + HCl(aq) ⟶ conjugate acid (aq) + Cl⁻(aq)

| Atom or Group X | $K_a$ of Conjugate Acid |
|---|---|
| $NO_2$ | $5.9 \times 10^{-2}$ |
| Cl | $1.5 \times 10^{-4}$ |
| H | $6.8 \times 10^{-6}$ |
| $CH_3$ | $1.0 \times 10^{-6}$ |

(a) Suppose each conjugate acid is dissolved in sufficient water to give a 0.050 M solution. Which solution would have the highest pH? The lowest pH?

(b) Which of the substituted pyridines is the strongest Brønsted base? Which is the weakest Brønsted base?

107. Nicotinic acid, $C_6H_5NO_2$, is found in minute amounts in all living cells, but appreciable amounts occur in liver, yeast, milk, adrenal glands, white meat, and corn. Whole-wheat flour contains about 60. $\mu$g per gram of flour. One gram (1.00 g) of the acid dissolves in water to give 60. mL of solution having a pH of 2.70. What is the approximate value of $K_a$ for the acid?

nicotinic acid

108. ▲ Equilibrium constants can be measured for the dissociation of Lewis acid–base complexes such as the dimethyl ether complex of $BF_3$, $(CH_3)_2O{\rightarrow}BF_3$. The value of $K$ (here $K_p$) for the reaction is 0.17 at 125 °C.

$$(CH_3)_2O{\rightarrow}BF_3(g) \rightleftharpoons BF_3(g) + (CH_3)_2O(g)$$

(a) Describe each product as a Lewis acid or a Lewis base.

(b) If you place 1.00 g of the complex in a 565-mL flask at 125 °C, what is the total pressure in the flask? What are the partial pressures of the Lewis acid, the Lewis base, and the complex?

109. ▲ Sulfanilic acid, which is used in making dyes, is made by reacting aniline with sulfuric acid.

$$H_2SO_4(aq) + \text{(aniline)} \longrightarrow \text{(sulfanilic acid)} + H_2O(\ell)$$

aniline    sulfanilic acid

(a) Is aniline a Brønsted base, a Lewis base, or both? Explain, using its possible reactions with HCl, $BF_3$, or other acid.

(b) Sulfanilic acid has a $pK_a$ value of 3.23. The sodium salt of the acid, $Na(H_2NC_6H_4SO_3)$, is quite soluble in water. If you dissolve 1.25 g of the salt in water to give 125 mL of solution, what is the pH of the solution?

110. Amino acids are an important group of compounds (◄ page 492). At low pH, both the carboxylic acid group (—$CO_2H$) and the amine group (—$NHR$) are protonated. However, as the pH of the solution increases (say by adding base), the carboxylic acid proton is removed, usually at a pH between 2 and 3. In a middle range of pHs, therefore, the amine group is protonated, but the carboxylic acid group has lost the proton. (This is called a *zwitterion*.) At more basic pH values, the amine proton is dissociated.

alanine
cationic form       zwitterionic form

anionic form

What is the pH of a 0.20 M solution of alanine hydrochloride, $[NH_3CHCH_3CO_2H]Cl$?

## Summary and Conceptual Questions

*The following questions may use concepts from this and previous chapters.*

111. How can water be both a Brønsted base and a Lewis base? Can water be a Brønsted acid? A Lewis acid?

112. The nickel(II) ion exists as $[Ni(H_2O)_6]^{2+}$ in aqueous solution. Why is this solution acidic? As part of your answer, include a balanced equation depicting what happens when $[Ni(H_2O)_6]^{2+}$ interacts with water.

113. The halogens form three stable, weak acids, HOX.

| Acid | $pK_a$ |
|---|---|
| HOCl | 7.46 |
| HOBr | 8.7 |
| HOI | 10.6 |

(a) Which is the strongest of these acids?

(b) Explain why the acid strength changes as the halogen atom is changed.

114. The acidity of the oxoacids was described on page 789, and a larger number of acids are listed in the table below.

| E(OH)$_m$ | $pK_a$ | EO(OH)$_m$ | $pK_a$ | EO$_2$(OH)$_m$ | $pK_a$ | EO$_3$(OH)$_m$ | $pK_a$ |
|---|---|---|---|---|---|---|---|
| **Very weak** | | **Weak** | | **Strong** | | **Very strong** | |
| Cl(OH) | 7.5 | ClO(OH) | 2 | ClO$_2$(OH) | −3 | ClO$_3$(OH) | −10 |
| Br(OH) | 8.7 | NO(OH) | 3.4 | NO$_2$(OH) | −1.4 | | |
| I(OH) | 10.6 | IO(OH) | 1.6 | IO$_2$(OH) | 0.8 | | |
| Si(OH)$_4$ | 9.7 | SO(OH)$_2$ | 1.8 | SO$_2$(OH)$_2$ | −3 | | |
| Sb(OH)$_3$ | 11.0 | SeO(OH)$_2$ | 2.5 | SeO$_2$(OH)$_2$ | −3 | | |
| As(OH)$_3$ | 9.2 | AsO(OH)$_3$ | 2.3 | | | | |
| | | PO(OH)$_3$ | 2.1 | | | | |
| | | HPO(OH)$_2$ | 1.8 | | | | |
| | | H$_2$PO(OH) | 2.0 | | | | |

(a) What general trends do you see in these data?

(b) What has a greater effect on acidity, the number of O atoms bonded directly to the central atom E or the number of OH groups?

(c) Look at the acids based on Cl, N, and S. Is there a correlation of acidity with the formal charge on the central atom, E?

(d) The acid $H_3PO_3$ has a $pK_a$ of 1.8, and this led to some insight into its structure. If the structure of the acid were $P(OH)_3$, what would be its predicted $pK_a$ value? Given that this is a diprotic acid, which H atoms are lost as $H^+$ ions?

**The acid $H_3PO_3$.**

115. Perchloric acid behaves as an acid, even when it is dissolved in sulfuric acid.

(a) Write a balanced equation showing how perchloric acid can transfer a proton to sulfuric acid.

(b) Draw a Lewis electron dot structure for sulfuric acid. How can sulfuric acid function as a base?

116. You purchase a bottle of water. On checking its pH, you find that it is not neutral, as you might have expected. Instead, it is slightly acidic. Why?

117. Iodine, $I_2$, is much more soluble in an aqueous solution of potassium iodide, KI, than it is in pure water. The anion found in solution is $I_3^-$.

(a) Draw an electron dot structure for $I_3^-$.

(b) Write an equation for this reaction, indicating the Lewis acid and the Lewis base.

118. ▲ Uracil is a base found in RNA (◄ page 497). Indicate sites in the molecule where hydrogen bonding is possible or that are sites of Lewis basicity.

uracil

119. Chemists often refer to the *degree of ionization* of a weak acid or base and give it the symbol $\alpha$. The equilibrium constant in terms of $\alpha$ and $C_o$, the initial acid or base concentration, is given by the useful equation

$$K = \frac{\alpha^2 C_o}{(1 - \alpha)}$$

As an example, the degree of ionization for 0.010 M acetic acid is 0.013.

(a) Show how we can arrive at the general equation given above.

(b) Calculate the degree of ionization for the ammonium ion in 0.10 M $NH_4Cl$.

120. ▲ Exploring the degree of ionization equation in Study Question 119:

(a) Calculate the degree of ionization, $\alpha$, for formic acid at the following concentrations: 0.0100 M, 0.0200 M, 0.0400 M, 0.100 M, 0.200 M, 0.400 M, 1.00 M, 2.00 M, and 4.00 M.

(b) Plot the results of the calculation as $\alpha$ versus formic acid concentration. Is there a linear relationship? If not, try plotting the logarithm of $C_o$ versus $\alpha$.

(c) What can you conclude about the relationship of the degree of ionization and the initial acid or base concentration?

121. ▲ Consider a salt of a weak base and a weak acid such as ammonium cyanide. Both the $NH_4^+$ and $CN^-$ ions interact with water in aqueous solution, but the net reaction can be considered as a proton transfer from $NH_4^+$ to $CN^-$.

$$NH_4^+(aq) + CN^-(aq) \rightleftharpoons NH_3(aq) + HCN(aq)$$

(a) Show that the equilibrium constant for this reaction, $K_{net}$, is

$$K_{net} = \frac{K_w}{K_a K_b}$$

where $K_a$ is the ionization constant for the weak acid HCN and $K_b$ is the constant for the weak base $NH_3$.

(b) Calculate $K_{net}$ values for each of the following: $NH_4CN$, $NH_4CH_3CO_2$, and $NH_4F$. Which salt has the largest value of $K_{net}$ and why?

(c) Predict whether a solution of each of the compounds in (b) is acidic or basic. Explain how you made this prediction. (You do not need a calculation to make this prediction.)

## Applying Chemical Principles

### The Leveling Effect, Nonaqueous Solvents, and Superacids

What is the strongest Brønsted acid that can exist in water? The answer is the hydronium ion. Although the common strong acids (HCl, HBr, HI, HNO$_3$, HClO$_4$, and H$_2$SO$_4$) are all stronger acids than H$_3$O$^+$, these acids ionize completely in water. The result is that all Brønsted acids with acidities above a certain value are equally acidic in water and, thus, their acid strength is indistinguishable. This is referred to as the *leveling effect* of water.

Similarly, the strongest base that can exist in water is OH$^-$. Any base that is stronger than OH$^-$ will react completely with water to give OH$^-$. The amide ion, NH$_2^-$, and the oxide ion, O$^{2-}$, both stronger bases than OH$^-$, react completely with water, giving OH$^-$.

Although strong acids behave identically in water, they are not equally strong. One means of differentiating the strengths of these acids is to measure the degree of their ionization in solvents other than water. These solvents, like water, must be Brønsted bases. Additionally, the solvents must be weaker bases than water so that they are not fully protonated by a strong acid. One such solvent is acetic acid. Pure acetic acid—known as *glacial acetic acid*—is similar to water in that it can both donate or accept protons. Dissolution of hydrochloric acid in acetic acid, for example, yields the following chemical reaction:

$$HCl + CH_3CO_2H \rightleftharpoons CH_3CO_2H_2^+ + Cl^-$$

Unlike the ionization of HCl in water, this reaction does not go to completion. The p$K$ value of this reaction is 8.8. Two other important acids, HClO$_4$ and H$_2$SO$_4$ (first proton only), have p$K$ values of 5.3 and 6.8, respectively.

Other acids are even stronger, and are often called *superacids*. One superacid is fluorosulfonic acid (HSO$_3$F), which is about 1000 times stronger than sulfuric acid. Even this acid pales in comparison to a mixture of HSO$_3$F and SbF$_5$, which, depending on the concentrations, may be over 10$^{16}$ times stronger than 100% sulfuric acid. It is sold under a suitable name, "Magic Acid."

### Questions:

1. Convert the p$K$ values to $K$ values for the ionization of HCl, HClO$_4$, and H$_2$SO$_4$ in glacial acetic acid. Rank these acids in order from strongest to weakest.

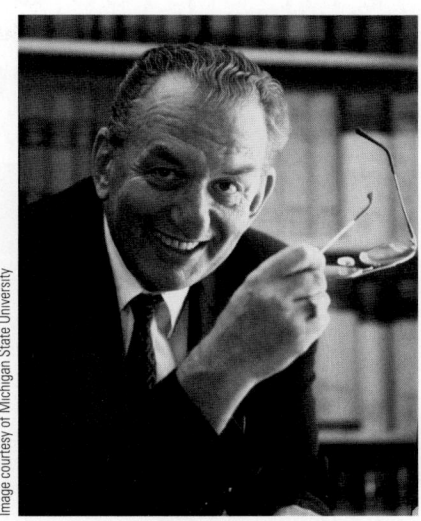

**George Olah (1927-present).** Much of the early research on superacids was done by Olah, and he received the Nobel Prize in chemistry for this work in 1994.

2. Other solvents also undergo autoionization.
   (a) Write a chemical equation for the autoionization of glacial acetic acid.
   (b) The equilibrium constant for the autoionization of glacial acetic acid is $3.2 \times 10^{-15}$ at 25°C. Determine the concentration of $[CH_3CO_2H_2]^+$ in acetic acid at 25°C.

3. Write an equation for the reaction of the amide ion (a stronger base than OH$^-$) and water. Does the equilibrium favor products or reactants?

4. Will a solution of HClO$_4$ in glacial acetic acid be a strong conductor of electricity, a weak conductor, or a nonconductor?

5. To measure the relative strengths of bases stronger than OH$^-$, it is necessary to choose a solvent that is a weaker acid than water. One such solvent is liquid ammonia.
   (a) Write a chemical equation for the autoionization of ammonia.
   (b) What is the strongest acid and base that can exist in liquid ammonia?
   (c) Will a solution of HCl in liquid ammonia be a strong electrical conductor, a weak conductor, or a nonconductor?
   (d) Oxide ion (O$^{2-}$) is a stronger base than the amide ion (NH$_2^-$). Write an equation for the reaction of O$^{2-}$ with NH$_3$ in liquid ammonia. Will the equilibrium favor products or reactants?

# 18 Principles of Chemical Reactivity: Other Aspects of Aqueous Equilibria

© Cengage Learning/Charles D. Winters

Not only does this effectively remove calcium ions from the body, but calcium oxalate crystals can also grow into painful kidney and bladder stones. Because of this, people susceptible to kidney stones are put on a low-oxalic acid diet. Such people also have to be careful of taking too much vitamin C, a compound that can be turned into oxalic acid in the body. People have died from accidentally drinking antifreeze because the ethylene glycol in the antifreeze is converted to oxalic acid in the body. Symptoms of oxalic acid poisoning include nausea, vomiting, abdominal pain, and hemorrhages.

Because oxalic acid also occurs in other edible substances, including cocoa, peanuts, and tea, the average person consumes about 150 mg of oxalic acid a day. But will it kill you? For a person weighing about 145 pounds (65.7 kg), the lethal dose is around 24 grams of pure oxalic acid. You would have to eat a field of rhubarb leaves or drink an ocean of tea to come close to a fatal dose of oxalic acid. What would happen first, however, is that you may have severe diarrhea. Your gut recognizes oxalic acid as something to be eliminated and is stimulated to get rid of it.

In spite of the minor health risk from eating too much rhubarb, this plant and others have been cultivated for thousands of years for their healthful properties. The Chinese particularly have used rhubarb in traditional medicine for centuries. Indeed, it was so important that emperors of China in the 18th and 19th centuries forbade its export. Rhubarb was also cultivated in Russia and later in England. It made first its appearance in the United States in about 1800.

When you enjoy a slice of rhubarb pie, think about the topics in this chapter: the chemistry of acids and bases and of insoluble substances.

**Nature's Acids** Many people grow rhubarb in gardens because the stalks of the plant, when stewed with sugar, make a wonderful dessert or filling for a pie or tart. But the leaves can make you sick! Why?

Rhubarb leaves are a source of at least seven organic acids, among them acetic and citric acids. But the most abundant is oxalic acid, $H_2C_2O_4$.

$$H_2O(\ell) + H_2C_2O_4(aq) \rightleftharpoons H_3O^+(aq) + HC_2O_4^-(aq)$$

$$H_2O(\ell) + HC_2O_4^-(aq) \rightleftharpoons H_3O^+(aq) + C_2O_4^{2-}(aq)$$

Rhubarb leaves contain between 0.1% and 1.4% by weight oxalic acid, while other leafy vegetables such as cabbage, spinach, and beet tops have lesser amounts.

While oxalic acid and other acids give the tart taste many of us enjoy with rhubarb, there is a problem with ingesting it: Oxalic acid interferes with essential elements in the body such as iron, magnesium, and, especially, calcium. The $Ca^{2+}$ ion and oxalic acid react to form insoluble calcium oxalate, $CaC_2O_4$.

$$Ca^{2+}(aq) + H_2C_2O_4(aq) + 2\ H_2O(\ell) \rightarrow CaC_2O_4(s) + 2\ H_3O^+(aq)$$

## Questions:

1. Suppose you eat 28 grams of rhubarb leaves with an oxalic acid content of 1.2% by weight.
   (a) What volume of 0.25 M NaOH is required to titrate completely the oxalic acid in the leaves?
   (b) What mass of calcium oxalate could be formed from the oxalic acid in these leaves?
2. The solubility product constant of calcium oxalate is estimated to be $4 \times 10^{-9}$. What is its solubility in grams per liter?

Answers to these questions are available in Appendix N.

## CHAPTER GOALS

*See Chapter Goals Revisited (page 846) for
Study Questions keyed to these goals.*

- Understand the common ion effect.

- Understand the control of pH in
  aqueous solutions with buffers.

- Evaluate the pH in the course of acid–
  base titrations.

- Apply chemical equilibrium concepts
  to the solubility of ionic
  compounds.

In Chapter 3, we described four fundamental types of chemical reactions: acid–base reactions, precipitation reactions, gas-forming reactions, and oxidation-reduction reactions. In the present chapter, we want to apply the principles of chemical equilibria to a further understanding the first two kinds of reactions.

With regard to acid–base reactions, we are looking for answers to the following questions:

- How can we control the pH in a solution?
- What happens when an acid and base are mixed in any amount?

Precipitation reactions can also be understood in terms of chemical equilibria. The following questions are discussed in this chapter:

- If aqueous solutions of two ionic compounds are mixed, will precipitation occur?
- To what extent does an "insoluble" substance actually dissolve?
- What chemical reactions can be used to dissolve a precipitate?

## 18.1  The Common Ion Effect

In the previous chapter, we looked at the behavior of weak acids and bases in aqueous solution. But what happens to the pH of an acetic acid solution to which you added a significant concentration of its conjugate base, the acetate ion? The answer is that the pH of such a solution—weak acid/conjugate base or weak base/conjugate acid—is different than the pH of a solution of the weak acid or base by itself. The effect on the pH that is produced by having a significant concentration of acetate ion in an acetic acid solution, for example, is called the **common ion effect**. The name comes from the fact that the added acetate ion is "common" to the ionization equilibrium reaction of acetic acid.

$$CH_3CO_2H(aq) + H_2O(\ell) \rightleftharpoons H_3O^+(aq) + CH_3CO_2^-(aq)$$

We want to explore this aspect of acid–base chemistry here because it will be important in understanding *buffer solutions*, as you shall see in Section 18.2.

How does the common ion effect work (Figure 18.1)? If 1.0 L of a 0.25 M acetic acid solution has a pH of 2.67, what is the pH after adding 0.10 mol of sodium acetate? Sodium acetate, $NaCH_3CO_2$, is 100% dissociated into its ions, $Na^+$ and

**OWL**

Sign in to OWL at **www.cengage.com/
owl** to view tutorials and simulations,
develop problem-solving skills, and
complete online homework assigned
by your professor.

Download mini lecture videos for
key concept review and exam prep
from OWL or purchase them from
**www.cengagebrain.com**

**FIGURE 18.1 The common ion effect.** Approximately equal amounts of acetic acid (left flask, pH about 2.7) and sodium acetate, a base (right flask, pH about 9), were mixed in the beaker. The pH meter shows that the resulting solution in the beaker has a lower hydronium ion concentration (a pH of about 5) than the acetic acid solution, owing to the presence of acetate ion, the conjugate base of the acid and an ion common to the ionization reaction of the acid. (The acid and base solutions each had about the same concentration. Each solution contains universal indicator. This dye is red in low pH, yellow in slightly acidic media, and green in neutral to weakly basic media.)

Aqueous acetic acid pH 2.7

Aqueous sodium acetate pH 9

Mixture of acetic acid and sodium acetate

$CH_3CO_2^-$, in water. Sodium ion has no effect on the pH of a solution (◄ Table 17.4 and Example 17.2). Thus, the important components of the solution are the weak acid ($CH_3CO_2H$) and its conjugate base ($CH_3CO_2^-$). Assume the acid ionizes to give $H_3O^+$ and $CH_3CO_2^-$, both in the amount $x$. This means that, relative to their initial concentrations, $CH_3CO_2H$ decreases in concentration slightly (by an amount $x$) and $CH_3CO_2^-$ increases slightly (by an amount $x$).

● **The Common Ion Effect** In this ICE table, the first row (Initial) reflects the assumption that no ionization of the acid (or hydrolysis of the conjugate base) has yet occurred. Ionization of the acid in the presence of the conjugate base then produces $x$ mol/L of hydronium ion and $x$ mol/L more of the conjugate base.

| Equation | $CH_3CO_2H$ | + | $H_2O$ | ⇌ | $H_3O^+$ | + | $CH_3CO_2^-$ |
|---|---|---|---|---|---|---|---|
| Initial (M) | 0.25 | | | | 0 | | 0.10 |
| Change (M) | $-x$ | | | | $+x$ | | $+x$ |
| Equilibrium (M) | $(0.25 - x)$ | | | | $x$ | | $0.10 + x$ |

Because we have been able to define the equilibrium concentrations of acid and conjugate base and we know $K_a$, the hydronium ion concentration ($= x$) can be calculated from the usual equilibrium constant expression.

$$K_a = 1.8 \times 10^{-5} = \frac{[H_3O^+][CH_3CO_2^-]}{[CH_3CO_2H]} = \frac{(x)(0.10 + x)}{0.25 - x}$$

Now, because acetic acid is a weak acid and because it is ionizing in the presence of a significant concentration of its conjugate base, let us assume $x$ is quite small. That is, it is reasonable to assume that $(0.10 + x)M \approx 0.10$ M and that $(0.25 - x)M \approx 0.25$ M. This leads to the "approximate" expression.

$$K_a = 1.8 \times 10^{-5} = \frac{[H_3O^+][CH_3CO_2^-]}{[CH_3CO_2H]} = \frac{(x)(0.10)}{0.25}$$

Solving this, we find that $x = [H_3O^+] = 4.5 \times 10^{-5}$ M and the pH is 4.35.

● **Equilibrium Constants and Temperature** Unless specified otherwise, all equilibrium constants and all calculations in this chapter are at 25 °C.

Without added $NaCH_3CO_2$, which provides the "common ion" $CH_3CO_2^-$, you can calculate that ionization of 0.25 M acetic acid will produce $H_3O^+$ and $CH_3CO_2^-$ ions in a concentration of 0.0021 M (to give a pH of 2.67). Le Chatelier's principle, however, predicts that the added common ion causes the reaction to proceed less far to the right. Hence, as we have found, $x = [H_3O^+]$ is less than 0.0021 M in the presence of added acetate ion. (Finally, note that the simplifying assumptions were valid.)

**⊘WL INTERACTIVE EXAMPLE 18.1** __Reaction of Lactic Acid with a__
__Deficiency of Sodium Hydroxide__

**Problem** What is the pH of the solution that results from adding 25.0 mL of 0.0500 M NaOH to 25.0 mL of 0.100 M lactic acid? ($K_a$ for lactic acid $= 1.4 \times 10^{-4}$)

$$H_3C-\underset{\underset{OH}{|}}{\overset{\overset{H}{|}}{C}}-\overset{\overset{O}{\|}}{C}-O-H(aq) + OH^-(aq) \rightleftharpoons H_2O(\ell) + H_3C-\underset{\underset{OH}{|}}{\overset{\overset{H}{|}}{C}}-\overset{\overset{O}{\|}}{C}-O^-(aq)$$

lactic acid ($HC_3H_5O_3$)
$K_a = 1.4 \times 10^{-4}$
lactate ion ($C_3H_5O_3^-$)

**What Do You Know?** You know the amounts of the acid and base (from the volume and concentration of each), and you know the ionization constant for the weak acid.

**Strategy** There are two parts to this problem: a stoichiometry problem followed by an equilibrium problem.

**Part 1:** *Stoichiometry Problem*

(a) Work a limiting reactant problem (in moles) to determine the amounts of lactic acid and lactate remaining after the reaction between lactic acid and sodium hydroxide.

(b) Calculate the concentrations of lactic acid and lactate ion that are present following the reaction of lactic acid with NaOH.

**Part 2:** *Equilibrium Problem*

(a) Set up an ICE table where the initial acid and conjugate base concentrations are known and the changes in the amount of acid consumed and amount of conjugate base produced are defined as $x$.

(b) Insert the equilibrium concentrations in the $K_a$ expression for lactic acid and solve for $x$.

(c) Calculate the pH from the equilibrium hydronium ion concentration ($= x$).

**Solution**

**Part 1:** *Stoichiometry Problem*

(a) Amounts of NaOH and lactic acid used in the reaction

$$(0.0250 \text{ L NaOH})(0.0500 \text{ mol/L}) = 1.25 \times 10^{-3} \text{ mol NaOH}$$

$$(0.0250 \text{ L lactic acid})(0.100 \text{ mol/L}) = 2.50 \times 10^{-3} \text{ mol lactic acid}$$

(b) Amount of lactate ion produced by the acid–base reaction

Recognizing that NaOH is the limiting reactant, we have

$$(1.25 \times 10^{-3} \text{ mol NaOH})\left(\frac{1 \text{ mol lactate ion}}{1 \text{ mol NaOH}}\right) = 1.25 \times 10^{-3} \text{ mol lactate ion produced}$$

(c) Amount of lactic acid consumed

$$(1.25 \times 10^{-3} \text{ mol NaOH})\left(\frac{1 \text{ mol lactic acid}}{1 \text{ mol NaOH}}\right) = 1.25 \times 10^{-3} \text{ mol lactic acid consumed}$$

(d) Amount of lactic acid remaining when reaction is complete.

$$2.50 \times 10^{-3} \text{ mol lactic acid available} - 1.25 \times 10^{-3} \text{ mol lactic acid consumed}$$

$$= 1.25 \times 10^{-3} \text{ mol lactic acid remaining}$$

(e) Concentrations of lactic acid and lactate ion after reaction. Note that the total solution volume after reaction is 50.0 mL or 0.0500 L.

$$[\text{Lactic acid}] = \frac{1.25 \times 10^{-3} \text{ mol lactic acid}}{0.0500 \text{ L}} = 2.50 \times 10^{-2} \text{ M}$$

---

**Strategy Map 18.1**

**PROBLEM**

Calculate **pH** after combining solutions of **NaOH** and **lactic acid**.

↓

**DATA/INFORMATION KNOWN**

- Solution concentrations
- Solution volumes
- Value of acid $K_a$

**STEP 1.** Stoichiometry problem.

↓

Concentrations of **lactic acid** and **lactate ion** after acid-base reaction

**STEP 2.** Enter **equilibrium concentrations** in ICE table.

↓

At equilibrium:
$[H_3O^+] = x$
$[\text{Lactic acid}] = \text{original conc.} - x$
$[\text{Lactate ion}] = \text{original conc.} + x$

**STEP 3.** Enter **equilibrium concentrations** in $K_a$.

↓

$K_a$ **expression** with equilibrium concentrations in terms of $x$

**STEP 4.** Solve $K_a$ **expression** for $x$.

↓

Value of $[H_3O^+]$

**STEP 5.** Convert $[H_3O^+]$ to **pH**.

↓

pH of solution

Because the amount of lactic acid remaining is the same as the amount of lactate ion produced, we have

$$[\text{Lactic acid}] = [\text{lactate ion}] = 2.50 \times 10^{-2} \text{ M}$$

***Part 2:*** *Equilibrium Problem*

The concentrations just determined are used as the initial concentrations in an ICE table.

| Equilibrium | $HC_3H_5O_3 + H_2O$ | $\rightleftharpoons$ | $H_3O^+$ | $+$ | $C_3H_5O_3^-$ |
|---|---|---|---|---|---|
| Initial (M) | 0.0250 | | 0 | | 0.0250 |
| Change (M) | $-x$ | | $+x$ | | $+x$ |
| Equilibrium (M) | $(0.0250 - x)$ | | $x$ | | $(0.0250 + x)$ |

Substituting the concentrations into the equilibrium expression, we have

$$K_a \text{ (lactic acid)} = 1.4 \times 10^{-4} = \frac{[H_3O^+][C_3H_5O_2^-]}{[HC_3H_5O_2]} = \frac{(x)(0.0250 + x)}{0.0250 - x}$$

Making the assumption that $x$ is small with respect to 0.0250 M, we see that

$$K_a = 1.4 \times 10^{-4} \text{ M} = x = [H_3O^+], \text{ which gives a pH of } 3.85.$$

**Think about Your Answer**  There are several final points to be made:

- Our assumption that $x \ll 0.0250$ is valid.

- By a separate calculation, we can show that a 0.025 M lactic acid solution has a pH of 2.73. The presence of 0.025 M lactate ion (a Brønsted base) in this solution has resulted in an increase of the pH to 3.85

- Here a base was added to the acidic solution. A useful observation is that *adding base to any solution will always result in an increase in pH.*

**Check Your Understanding**

You have a 0.30 M solution of formic acid ($HCO_2H$) and have added enough sodium formate ($NaHCO_2$) to make the solution 0.10 M in the salt. Calculate the pH of the formic acid solution before and after adding solid sodium formate.

---

**REVIEW & CHECK FOR SECTION 18.1**

What is the pH of the solution that results from adding 30.0 mL of 0.100 M NaOH to 45.0 mL of 0.100 M acetic acid?

(a)  2.87            (b)  5.05            (c)  7.00

---

**Module 23: Understanding Acid–Base Buffers** covers concepts in this section.

## 18.2  Controlling pH: Buffer Solutions

The addition of a small quantity of strong acid or base, say 0.010 mol, to a liter of human blood leads to a change in pH of only about 0.1 pH units from the normal pH of about 7.4. In comparison, if you add 0.010 mol of HCl to 1.0 L of pure water, the pH drops from 7 to 2. Addition of 0.010 mol of NaOH to pure water increases the pH from 7 to 12. Blood, and many other body fluids, are said to be buffered. A **buffer** causes solutions to be resistant to a change in pH when a strong acid or base is added (Figure 18.2).

There are two requirements for a buffer:

- Two substances are needed: an acid capable of reacting with added $OH^-$ ions and a base that can consume added $H_3O^+$ ions.
- The acid and base must not react with each another.

**FIGURE 18.2 Buffer solutions.**

Photos © Cengage Learning/Charles D. Winters

**Before**

Buffered | Not buffered

**After adding 0.10 M HCl**

**(a)** The pH electrode is indicating the pH of water that contains a trace of acid (and bromphenol blue acid–base indicator). The solution at the left is a buffer solution with a pH of about 7. (It also contains bromphenol blue dye.)

**(b)** When 5 mL of 0.10 M HCl is added to each solution, the pH of the water drops several units, whereas the pH of the buffer stays essentially constant, as implied by the fact that the indicator color does not change.

These requirements mean a buffer is usually prepared from a conjugate acid–base pair: (1) a weak acid and its conjugate base (acetic acid and acetate ion, for example), or (2) a weak base and its conjugate acid (ammonia and ammonium ion, for example). Some buffers commonly used in the laboratory are given in Table 18.1.

To see how a buffer works, consider an acetic acid/acetate ion buffer. Acetic acid, a weak acid, is needed to consume any added hydroxide ions.

$$CH_3CO_2H(aq) + OH^-(aq) \rightleftharpoons CH_3CO_2^-(aq) + H_2O(\ell) \qquad K = 1.8 \times 10^9$$

The equilibrium constant for the reaction is very large because $OH^-$ is a much stronger base than acetate ion, $CH_3CO_2^-$ (◄ Section 17.6 and Table 17.3). This means that any $OH^-$ entering the solution from an outside source is consumed completely. In a similar way, any hydronium ion added to the solution reacts with the acetate ion present in the buffer.

$$H_3O^+(aq) + CH_3CO_2^-(aq) \rightleftharpoons H_2O(\ell) + CH_3CO_2H(aq) \qquad K = 5.6 \times 10^4$$

The equilibrium constant for this reaction is also quite large because $H_3O^+$ is a much stronger acid than $CH_3CO_2H$.

The next several examples illustrate how to calculate the pH of a buffer solution, how to prepare a buffer, and how a buffer can control the pH of a solution.

● **Buffers and the Common Ion Effect** The common ion effect is observed for an acid (or base) ionizing in the presence of its conjugate base (or acid). A buffer is a solution of an acid, for example, and its conjugate base.

**Table 18.1 Some Commonly Used Buffer Systems**

| Weak Acid | Conjugate Base | Acid $K_a$ (p$K_a$) | Useful pH Range |
|---|---|---|---|
| Phthalic acid, $C_6H_4(CO_2H)_2$ | Hydrogen phthalate ion, $C_6H_4(CO_2H)(CO_2)^-$ | $1.3 \times 10^{-3}$ (2.89) | 1.9–3.9 |
| Acetic acid, $CH_3CO_2H$ | Acetate ion, $CH_3CO_2^-$ | $1.8 \times 10^{-5}$ (4.74) | 3.7–5.8 |
| Dihydrogen phosphate ion, $H_2PO_4^-$ | Hydrogen phosphate ion, $HPO_4^{2-}$ | $6.2 \times 10^{-8}$ (7.21) | 6.2–8.2 |
| Hydrogen phosphate ion, $HPO_4^{2-}$ | Phosphate ion, $PO_4^{3-}$ | $3.6 \times 10^{-13}$ (12.44) | 11.4–13.4 |

**Strategy Map 18.2**

**PROBLEM**

Calculate **pH** of a **buffer solution**.

↓

**DATA/INFORMATION KNOWN**

- Concentration of **weak acid**
- Concentration of **conjugate base**
- Value of acid $K_a$

↓

**STEP 1.** Write **balanced equation** and $K_a$ **expression**, and set up **ICE table**.

$K_a$ expression and ICE table

↓

**STEP 2.** Enter **equilibrium concentrations** in ICE table.

At equilibrium:
$[H_3O^+] = x$
[Weak acid] = original conc. − $x$
[Conjugate base] = original conc. + $x$

↓

**STEP 3.** Enter **equilibrium concentrations** in $K_a$.

$K_a$ **expression** with equilibrium concentrations in terms of $x$

↓

**STEP 4.** Solve $K_a$ **expression** for $x$.

Value of $[H_3O^+]$

↓

**STEP 5.** Convert $[H_3O^+]$ to **pH**.

pH of solution

---

Ⓦ**WL** **INTERACTIVE EXAMPLE 18.2** **pH of a Buffer Solution**

**Problem** What is the pH of an acetic acid/sodium acetate buffer with $[CH_3CO_2H] = 0.700$ M and $[CH_3CO_2^-] = 0.600$ M?

**What Do You Know?** The hydronium ion concentration (and so the pH) of a buffer can be calculated if you know concentrations of the weak acid, its conjugate base, and $K_a$, as is the case here.

**Strategy**

- Write the balanced equation and the equilibrium constant expression.

- Set up an ICE table where the initial concentrations of acid and conjugate base are known, and the change in their concentrations is designated by $x$.

- Use the $K_a$ expression to solve for the hydronium ion concentration (as in Example 17.5).

**Solution**

| Equilibrium | $CH_3CO_2H$ | + | $H_2O$ | ⇌ | $H_3O^+$ | + | $CH_3CO_2^-$ |
|---|---|---|---|---|---|---|---|
| Initial (M) | 0.700 | | | | 0 | | 0.600 |
| Change (M) | −$x$ | | | | +$x$ | | +$x$ |
| Equilibrium (M) | 0.700 − $x$ | | | | $x$ | | 0.600 + $x$ |

The appropriate equilibrium constant expression is

$$K_a = 1.8 \times 10^{-5} = \frac{[H_3O^+][CH_3CO_2^-]}{[CH_3CO_2H]} = \frac{(x)(0.600 + x)}{0.700 - x}$$

As explained on page 808, the value of $x$ will be very small with respect to 0.700 or 0.600, so we can use the "approximate expression" to find $x$, the hydronium ion concentration.

$$K_a = 1.8 \times 10^{-5} = \frac{[H_3O^+][CH_3CO_2^-]}{[CH_3CO_2H]} = \frac{(x)(0.600)}{0.700}$$

$$x = 2.1 \times 10^{-5} \text{ M}$$

$$pH = -\log(2.1 \times 10^{-5}) = 4.68$$

**Think about Your Answer** The pH of the buffer has a value between the pH of 0.700 M acetic acid (2.45) and 0.600 M sodium acetate (9.26).

---

**Check Your Understanding**

What is the pH of a buffer solution composed of 0.50 M formic acid ($HCO_2H$) and 0.70 M sodium formate ($NaHCO_2$)?

---

## General Expressions for Buffer Solutions

In Example 18.2, we found the hydronium ion concentration of the acetic acid/acetate ion buffer solution by solving for $x$ in the equation

$$K_a = 1.8 \times 10^{-5} = \frac{[H_3O^+][CH_3CO_2^-]}{[CH_3CO_2H]} = \frac{(x)(0.600)}{0.700}$$

If this equation is rearranged, we have a useful equation that can help you better understand how a buffer works.

$$[H_3O^+] = \frac{[CH_3CO_2H]}{[CH_3CO_2^-]} \times K_a$$

That is, the hydronium ion concentration in the acetic acid/acetate ion buffer is given by the ratio of the acid and conjugate base concentrations times the acid ionization constant. Indeed, this is true for all solutions of *a weak acid and its conjugate base*.

$$[H_3O^+] = \frac{[acid]}{[conjugate base]} \times K_a \qquad (18.1)$$

It is often convenient to use Equation 18.1 in a different form. If we take the negative logarithm of each side of the equation, we have

$$-\log[H_3O^+] = \left\{-\log\frac{[\text{acid}]}{[\text{conjugate base}]}\right\} + \left(-\log K_a\right)$$

You know that $-\log[H_3O^+]$ is defined as pH, and $-\log K_a$ is defined as $pK_a$ (◀ Sections 17.3 and 17.4). Furthermore, because

$$-\log\frac{[\text{acid}]}{[\text{conjugate base}]} = +\log\frac{[\text{conjugate base}]}{[\text{acid}]}$$

the preceding equation can be rewritten as

$$pH = pK_a + \log\frac{[\text{conjugate base}]}{[\text{acid}]} \qquad (18.2)$$

This equation is known as the **Henderson–Hasselbalch equation.**

Both Equations 18.1 and 18.2 show that *the pH of a buffer solution is controlled by two factors:*

- the strength of the acid (as expressed by $K_a$ or $pK_a$)
- and the relative amounts of acid and conjugate base

The solution pH is established primarily by the value of $K_a$ or $pK_a$, and the pH is fine-tuned by adjusting the acid-to-conjugate base ratio.

When the concentrations of conjugate base and acid are the same in a solution, the ratio [conjugate base]/[acid] is 1. The log of 1 is zero, so $pH = pK_a$ under these circumstances. If there is more of the conjugate base in the solution than acid, for example, then $pH > pK_a$. Conversely, if there is more acid than conjugate base in solution, then $pH < pK_a$.

- **Buffer Solutions** You will find it generally useful to consider all buffer solutions as composed of a weak acid and its conjugate base. Suppose, for example, a buffer is composed of the weak base ammonia and its conjugate acid ammonium ion. The hydronium ion concentration can be found from Equation 18.1 or 18.2 by assuming the buffer is composed of the weak acid $NH_4^+$ and its conjugate base, $NH_3$.

- **$pK_a$ and Using The Henderson–Hasselbalch Equation** Many handbooks of chemistry list acid ionization constants in terms of $pK_a$ values, so the approximate pH values of possible buffer solutions are readily apparent.

## EXAMPLE 18.3  Using the Henderson–Hasselbalch Equation

**Problem** Benzoic acid ($C_6H_5CO_2H$, 2.00 g) and sodium benzoate ($NaC_6H_5CO_2$, 2.00 g) are dissolved in enough water to make 1.00 L of solution. Calculate the pH of the solution using the Henderson–Hasselbalch equation.

**What Do You Know?** You know the masses of weak acid and conjugate base and the volume of solution. (From these you can calculate the concentrations of these reagents, which you need for the Henderson–Hasselbalch equation.) You also know the $K_a$ for the weak acid (Table 17.3 or Appendix H), from which you can calculate the required $pK_a$ for the acid.

**Strategy** Calculate the acid and conjugate base concentrations and substitute these into the Henderson–Hasselbalch equation along with the value of $pK_a$ for the acid.

**Solution**

$K_a$ for benzoic acid is $6.3 \times 10^{-5}$. Therefore, $pK_a = -\log(6.3 \times 10^{-5}) = 4.20$

Next, you need the concentrations of the acid (benzoic acid) and its conjugate base (benzoate ion).

$$2.00 \text{ g benzoic acid} \left(\frac{1 \text{ mol}}{122.1 \text{ g}}\right) = 0.0164 \text{ mol benzoic acid}$$

$$2.00 \text{ g sodium benzoate} \left(\frac{1 \text{ mol}}{144.1 \text{ g}}\right) = 0.0139 \text{ mol sodium benzoate}$$

Because the solution volume is 1.00 L, the concentrations are [benzoic acid] = 0.0164 M and [sodium benzoate] = 0.0139 M. Therefore, using Equation 18.2, you have

$$pH = 4.20 + \log\frac{0.0139}{0.0164} = 4.20 + \log(0.848) = \boxed{4.13}$$

**Think about Your Answer** Notice that the pH is less than the $pK_a$ because the concentration of acid is greater than the concentration of the conjugate base (and so the ratio of conjugate base to acid concentration is less than 1).

**Check Your Understanding**

Use the Henderson–Hasselbalch equation to calculate the pH of 1.00 L of a buffer solution containing 15.0 g of $NaHCO_3$ and 18.0 g of $Na_2CO_3$. (Consider this buffer as a solution of the weak acid $HCO_3^-$ with $CO_3^{2-}$ as its conjugate base.)

## Preparing Buffer Solutions

To be useful, a buffer solution must have two characteristics:

- *pH Control:* It should control the pH at the desired value. The Henderson–Hasselbalch equation shows us how this can be done.

$$pH = pK_a + \log \frac{[\text{conjugate base}]}{[\text{acid}]}$$

First, an acid is chosen whose $pK_a$ (or $K_a$) is near the intended value of pH (or $[H_3O^+]$). Second, the exact value of pH (or $[H_3O^+]$) is then achieved by adjusting the acid-to-conjugate base ratio. (Example 18.4 illustrates this approach.)

- *Buffer capacity:* The buffer should have the ability to keep the pH approximately constant after the addition of reasonable amounts of acid and base. For example, the concentration of acetic acid in an acetic acid/acetate ion buffer must be sufficient to consume all the hydroxide ion that may be added and still control the pH (see Example 18.4). Buffers are usually prepared as 0.10 M to 1.0 M solutions of reagents. However, any buffer will lose its ability to moderate changes if too much strong acid or base is added.

### EXAMPLE 18.4 Preparing a Buffer Solution

**Problem** You wish to prepare 1.0 L of a buffer solution with a pH of 4.30. A list of possible acids (and their conjugate bases) follows:

| Acid | Conjugate Base | $K_a$ | $pK_a$ |
|---|---|---|---|
| $HSO_4^-$ | $SO_4^{2-}$ | $1.2 \times 10^{-2}$ | 1.92 |
| $CH_3CO_2H$ | $CH_3CO_2^-$ | $1.8 \times 10^{-5}$ | 4.74 |
| $HCO_3^-$ | $CO_3^{2-}$ | $4.8 \times 10^{-11}$ | 10.32 |

Which combination should be selected, and what should be the ratio of acid to conjugate base?

**What Do You Know?** You know the desired pH of the buffer, and you have a list of possible acid/conjugate base combinations.

**Strategy** Use either the general equation for a buffer (Equation 18.1) or the Henderson–Hasselbalch equation (Equation 18.2). Equation 18.1 informs you that $[H_3O^+]$ should be close to the acid $K_a$ value, and Equation 18.2 tells you that pH should be close to the acid $pK_a$ value. Either will establish which acid you will use. Having decided which acid to use, convert pH to $[H_3O^+]$ to use Equation 18.1. If you use Equation 18.2, use the $pK_a$ value in the table. Finally, calculate the ratio of acid to conjugate base.

**Solution** The hydronium ion concentration for the buffer is found from the targeted pH.

$$pH = 4.30, \text{ so } [H_3O^+] = 10^{-pH} = 10^{-4.30} = 5.0 \times 10^{-5} \text{ M}$$

Of the acids given, only acetic acid ($CH_3CO_2H$) has a $K_a$ value close to that of the desired [$H_3O^+$] (or a p$K_a$ close to a pH of 4.30). Now you need only to adjust the ratio [$CH_3CO_2H$]/[$CH_3CO_2^-$] to achieve the desired hydronium ion concentration.

$$[H_3O^+] = 5.0 \times 10^{-5} \ M = \frac{[CH_3CO_2H]}{[CH_3CO_2^-]}(1.8 \times 10^{-5})$$

Rearrange this equation to find the ratio [$CH_3CO_2H$]/[$CH_3CO_2^-$].

$$\frac{[CH_3CO_2H]}{[CH_3CO_2^-]} = \frac{[H_3O^+]}{K_a} = \frac{5.0 \times 10^{-5}}{1.8 \times 10^{-5}} = \frac{2.8 \ mol/L}{1.0 \ mol/L}$$

Therefore, if you add 0.28 mol of acetic acid and 0.10 mol of sodium acetate (or any other pair of molar quantities in the ratio 2.8/1) to enough water to prepare 1.0 L of solution, the buffer solution will have a pH of 4.30.

**Think about Your Answer** If you prefer to use the Henderson–Hasselbalch equation, you would have

$$pH = 4.30 = 4.74 + \log\frac{[CH_3CO_2^-]}{[CH_3CO_2H]}$$

$$\log\frac{[CH_3CO_2^-]}{[CH_3CO_2H]} = 4.30 - 4.74 = -0.44$$

$$\frac{[CH_3CO_2^-]}{[CH_3CO_2H]} = 10^{-0.44} = 0.36$$

The ratio of conjugate base to acid, [$CH_3CO_2^-$]/[$CH_3CO_2H$], is 0.36. The reciprocal of this ratio {= [$CH_3CO_2H$]/[$CH_3CO_2^-$] = 1/0.36)} is 2.8/1. This is the same result obtained previously using Equation 18.1.

---

**Check Your Understanding**

Using an acetic acid/sodium acetate buffer solution, what ratio of acid to conjugate base will you need to maintain the pH at 5.00? Describe how you would prepare such a solution.

---

Example 18.4 illustrates several important points concerning buffer solutions. The hydronium ion concentration depends not only on the $K_a$ value of the acid but also on the ratio of acid and conjugate base concentrations. However, even though we write these ratios in terms of reagent concentrations, it is *the relative number of moles of acid and conjugate base that is important in determining the pH of a buffer solution.* Because both reagents are dissolved in the same solution, their concentrations depend on the same solution volume. In Example 18.4, the ratio 2.8/1 for acetic acid and sodium acetate implies that 2.8 times as many moles of acid were dissolved per liter as moles of sodium acetate.

$$\frac{[CH_3CO_2H]}{[CH_3CO_2^-]} = \frac{2.8 \ mol \ CH_3CO_2H/L}{1.0 \ mol \ CH_3CO_2^-/L} = \frac{2.8 \ mol \ CH_3CO_2H}{1.0 \ mol \ CH_3CO_2^-}$$

Notice that on dividing one concentration by the other, the volumes "cancel." This means that we only need to ensure that the ratio of moles of acid to moles of conjugate base is 2.8 to 1 in this example. The acid and its conjugate base could have been dissolved in any reasonable amount of water. This also means that *diluting a buffer solution will not change its pH.* Commercially available buffer solutions are often sold as premixed, dry reagents. To use them, you only need to mix the reagents in some volume of pure water (Figure 18.3).

© Cengage Learning/Charles D. Winters

**FIGURE 18.3 A commercial buffer solution.** The solid acid and conjugate base in the packet are mixed with water to give a solution with the indicated pH. The quantity of water used does not matter because the ratio [acid]/[conjugate base] does not depend on the solution volume. (However, if too much water is added, the acid and conjugate base concentrations will be too low, and the buffer capacity could be exceeded. Again, buffer solutions usually have solute concentrations around 0.1 M to 1.0 M.)

## Buffer Solutions

The following is a summary of important aspects of buffer solutions.

- A buffer resists changes in pH on adding small quantities of acid or base.
- A buffer consists of a weak acid and its conjugate base.
- The hydronium ion concentration of a buffer solution can be calculated from Equation 18.1,

$$[H_3O^+] = \frac{[acid]}{[conjugate\ base]} \times K_a$$

or the pH can be calculated from the Henderson–Hasselbalch equation (Equation 18.2).

$$pH = pK_a + \log \frac{[conjugate\ base]}{[acid]}$$

- The pH depends primarily on the $K_a$ of the weak acid and secondarily on the relative amounts of acid and conjugate base.
- The function of the weak acid of a buffer is to consume added base, and the function of the conjugate base is to consume added acid. Such reactions affect the relative quantities of weak acid and its conjugate base. Because this ratio of acid to its conjugate base has only a secondary effect on the pH, the pH can be maintained relatively constant.
- The buffer must have sufficient capacity to react with reasonable quantities of added acid or base.

## How Does a Buffer Maintain pH?

Now let us explore quantitatively how a given buffer solution can maintain the pH of a solution on adding a small amount of strong acid.

### EXAMPLE 18.5    How Does a Buffer Maintain a Constant pH?

**Problem** What is the change in pH when 1.00 mL of 1.00 M HCl is added to (1) 1.000 L of pure water and to (2) 1.000 L of acetic acid/sodium acetate buffer with $[CH_3CO_2H] = 0.700$ M and $[CH_3CO_2^-] = 0.600$ M? (The pH of this acetic acid/acetate ion buffer is 4.68. See Example 18.2.)

**What Do You Know?** You know HCl is a strong acid and ionizes completely to supply $H_3O^+$ ions. In the first problem, when HCl is added to pure water, the concentration of HCl in the solution determines the pH. In the second problem, the conjugate base of the weak acid will react with the added HCl. Therefore, you need to perform a stoichiometry calculation to determine the new weak acid/conjugate base concentrations before you can calculate the pH.

**Strategy**

**Part 1:** *involves two steps:*

- Find the $H_3O^+$ concentration when adding 1.00 mL of acid to 1.000 L of pure water.

- Convert the value of $[H_3O^+]$ for the dilute solution to pH.

**Part 2:** *involves three steps:*

- A stoichiometry calculation to find how the concentrations of acid and conjugate base change on adding $H_3O^+$

- An equilibrium calculation to find $[H_3O^+]$ for a buffer solution where the concentrations of $CH_3CO_2H$ and $CH_3CO_2^-$ are slightly altered owing to the reaction of $CH_3CO_2^-$ with added $H_3O^+$

- Conversion of $[H_3O^+]$ to pH

**Solution**

**Part 1:** *Adding Acid to Pure Water*

1.00 mL of 1.00 M HCl represents 0.00100 mol of acid. If this is added to 1.000 L of pure water, the $H_3O^+$ concentration of the water changes from $10^{-7}$ to almost $10^{-3}$,

$$c_1 \times V_1 = c_2 \times V_2$$

$$(1.00\ M)(0.00100\ L) = c_2 \times (1.001\ L)$$

$$c_2 = [H_3O^+]\ in\ diluted\ solution = 9.99 \times 10^{-4}\ M$$

and so the pH falls from 7.00 to 3.00.

***Part 2:*** *Adding Acid to an Acetic Acid/Acetate Buffer Solution*

HCl is a strong acid that is 100% ionized in water and supplies $H_3O^+$, which reacts completely with the base (acetate ion) in the buffer solution according to the following equation:

$$H_3O^+(aq) + CH_3CO_2^-(aq) \rightleftharpoons H_2O(\ell) + CH_3CO_2H(aq)$$

|  | $H_3O^+$ from Added HCl | $CH_3CO_2^-$ from Buffer | $CH_3CO_2H$ from Buffer |
|---|---|---|---|
| Initial amount of acid or base (mol = $c \times V$) | 0.00100 | 0.600 | 0.700 |
| Change (mol) | −0.00100 | −0.00100 | +0.00100 |
| After reaction (mol) | 0 | 0.599 | 0.701 |
| Concentrations after reaction ($c$ = mol/V) | 0 | 0.598 | 0.700 |

Because the added HCl reacts completely with acetate ion to produce acetic acid, the solution after this reaction (with $V$ = 1.001 L) is once again a buffer containing only the weak acid and its salt. Now you only need to use Equation 18.1 (or the Henderson–Hasselbalch equation) to find $[H_3O^+]$ and the pH in the buffer solution as in Examples 18.2 and 18.3.

| Equilibrium | $CH_3CO_2H$ | + | $H_2O$ | $\rightleftharpoons$ | $H_3O^+$ | + | $CH_3CO_2^-$ |
|---|---|---|---|---|---|---|---|
| Initial (M) | 0.700 | | | | 0 | | 0.598 |
| Change (M) | −x | | | | +x | | +x |
| Equilibrium (M) | 0.700 − x | | | | x | | 0.598 +x |

As usual, you can make the approximation that x, the concentration of $H_3O^+$ formed by ionizing acetic acid in the presence of acetate ion, is very small compared with 0.700 M or 0.598 M. Using Equation 18.1, you should get a pH of 4.68.

$$[H_3O^+] = x = \frac{[CH_3CO_2H]}{[CH_3CO_2^-]} \times K_a = \left(\frac{0.700 \text{ mol}}{0.598 \text{ mol}}\right)(1.8 \times 10^{-5}) = 2.1 \times 10^{-5} \text{ M}$$

$$pH = 4.68$$

**Think about Your Answer** Within the number of significant figures allowed, the pH of the buffer solution does not change after adding this amount of HCl. The buffer solution contains the conjugate base of the weak acid, and the base consumed the added HCl. In contrast, the pH changed by 4 units when the same amount of HCl was added to 1.0 L of pure water.

**Check Your Understanding**

Calculate the pH of 0.500 L of a buffer solution composed of 0.50 M formic acid ($HCO_2H$) and 0.70 M sodium formate ($NaHCO_2$) before and after adding 10.0 mL of 1.0 M HCl.

---

**REVIEW & CHECK FOR SECTION 18.2**

1. Which choice would be a good buffer solution?

   (a)  0.20 M HCN and 0.10 M KCN          (c)  0.20 M $CH_3CO_2H$ and 0.10 M $HCO_2H$

   (b)  0.20 M HCl and 0.10 M KOH          (d)  0.10 HCl and 0.010 M KCl

2. If an acetic acid/sodium acetate buffer solution is prepared from 100. mL of 0.10 M acetic acid, what volume of 0.10 M sodium acetate must be added to have a pH of 4.00.

   (a)  100. mL          (b)  50. mL          (c)  36 mL          (d)  18 mL

3. What is the pH of a buffer composed of 100. mL of 0.20 M $NH_4Cl$ and 200. mL of 0.10 M $NH_3$?

   (a)  4.85          (c)  7.00          (e)  10.05

   (b)  9.25          (d)  5.65

4. To prepare a buffer containing $CH_3CO_2H$ and $NaCH_3CO_2$ and having a pH of 5, the ratio of the concentration of $CH_3CO_2H$ to that of $NaCH_3CO_2$ should be about

    (a)  1/1          (b)  1.8/1          (c)  1/1.8          (d)  5.0/1

## 18.3  Acid–Base Titrations

A titration is one of the most useful ways of determining accurately the quantity of an acid, a base, or some other substance in a mixture or of ascertaining the purity of a substance. You learned how to perform the stoichiometry calculations involved in titrations in Chapter 4 (◄ Section 4.7). In Chapter 17, we described the following points regarding acid–base reactions (◄ Section 17.7):

- The pH at the equivalence point of a strong acid–strong base titration is 7. The solution at the equivalence point is truly "neutral" *only* when a strong acid is titrated with a strong base and vice versa.

● **Equivalence Point** The equivalence point for a reaction is the point at which one reactant has been completely consumed by addition of another reactant. See page 183.

- If the substance being titrated is a weak acid or base, then the pH at the equivalence point is not 7 (◄ Table 17.5).
    (a) A weak acid titrated with strong base leads to pH > 7 at the equivalence point due to the conjugate base of the weak acid.
    (b) A weak base titrated with strong acid leads to pH < 7 at the equivalence point due to the conjugate acid of the weak base.

A knowledge of buffer solutions and how they work will now allow us to understand more fully how the pH changes in the course of an acid–base reaction.

● **Weak Acid–Weak Base Titrations** Titrations combining a weak acid and weak base are generally not done because the equivalence point often cannot be accurately judged.

### Titration of a Strong Acid with a Strong Base

Figure 18.4 illustrates what happens to the pH as 0.100 M NaOH is slowly added to 50.0 mL of 0.100 M HCl.

$$HCl(aq) + NaOH(aq) \rightarrow NaCl(aq) + H_2O(\ell)$$

Net ionic equation: $H_3O^+(aq) + OH^-(aq) \rightarrow 2\ H_2O(\ell)$

Let us focus on four regions on this plot.

- pH of the initial solution
- pH as NaOH is added to the HCl solution before the equivalence point
- pH at the equivalence point
- pH after the equivalence point

Before beginning the titration, the 0.100 M solution of HCl has a pH of 1.00. As NaOH is added to the acid solution, the amount of HCl declines, and the acid remaining is dissolved in an ever-increasing volume of solution. Thus, [H₃O⁺] decreases,

**FIGURE 18.4  The change in pH as a strong acid is titrated with a strong base.**  In this case, 50.0 mL of 0.100 M HCl is titrated with 0.100 M NaOH. The pH at the equivalence point is 7.0 for the reaction of a strong acid with a strong base.

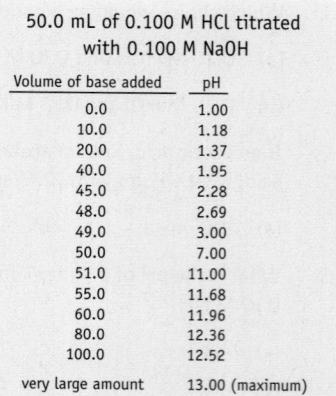

| 50.0 mL of 0.100 M HCl titrated with 0.100 M NaOH | |
|---|---|
| Volume of base added | pH |
| 0.0 | 1.00 |
| 10.0 | 1.18 |
| 20.0 | 1.37 |
| 40.0 | 1.95 |
| 45.0 | 2.28 |
| 48.0 | 2.69 |
| 49.0 | 3.00 |
| 50.0 | 7.00 |
| 51.0 | 11.00 |
| 55.0 | 11.68 |
| 60.0 | 11.96 |
| 80.0 | 12.36 |
| 100.0 | 12.52 |
| very large amount | 13.00 (maximum) |

## CASE STUDY

## Take a Deep Breath

Maintenance of pH is vital to the cells of all living organisms because enzyme activity is influenced by pH. The primary protection against harmful pH changes in cells is provided by buffer systems, which maintain the intracellular pH of most cells between 6.9 and 7.4. Two important biological buffer systems control pH in this range: the bicarbonate/carbonic acid system ($HCO_3^-/H_2CO_3$) and the phosphate system ($HPO_4^{2-}/H_2PO_4^-$).

The bicarbonate/carbonic acid buffer is important in blood plasma, where three equilibria are important.

$$CO_2(g) \rightleftharpoons CO_2(dissolved)$$

$$CO_2(dissolved) + H_2O(\ell) \rightleftharpoons H_2CO_3(aq)$$

$$H_2CO_3(aq) + H_2O(\ell) \rightleftharpoons H_3O^+(aq) + HCO_3^-(aq)$$

The overall equilibrium for the second and third steps has $pK_{overall} = 6.3$ at 37 °C, the temperature of the human body. Thus,

$$7.4 = 6.3 + \log\frac{[HCO_3^-]}{[CO_2(dissolved)]}$$

Although the value of $pK_{overall}$ is about 1 pH unit away from the blood pH, the natural partial pressure of $CO_2$ in the alveoli of the lungs (about 40 mm Hg) is sufficient to keep [$CO_2$(dissolved)] at about $1.2 \times 10^{-3}$ M and [$HCO_3^-$] at about $1.5 \times 10^{-2}$ M as required to maintain this pH.

If blood pH rises above about 7.45, you can suffer from a condition called *alkalosis*. *Respiratory alkalosis* can arise from hyperventilation when a person breathes quickly to expel $CO_2$ from the lungs. This has the effect of lowering the $CO_2$ concentration, which in turn leads to a lower $H_3O^+$ concentration and a higher pH. This same condition can also arise from severe anxiety or from an oxygen deficiency at high altitude. It can

© Cengage Learning/Charles D. Winters

ultimately lead to overexcitability of the central nervous system, muscle spasms, convulsions, and death. One way to treat acute respiratory alkalosis is to breathe into a paper bag. The $CO_2$ you exhale is recycled. This raises the blood $CO_2$ level and causes the equilibria above to shift to the right, thus raising the hydronium ion concentration and lowering the pH.

*Metabolic alkalosis* can occur if you take large amounts of sodium bicarbonate to treat stomach acid (which is mostly HCl at a pH of about 1 to 2). It also commonly occurs when a person vomits profusely. This depletes the body of hydrogen ions, which leads to an increase in bicarbonate ion concentration.

Athletes can use the $H_2CO_3/HCO_3^-$ equilibrium to enhance their performance. Strenuous activity produces high levels of lactic acid, and this can lower blood pH and cause muscle cramps. To counteract this, athletes will prepare before a race by hyperventilating for some seconds to raise blood

pH, thereby helping to neutralize the acidity from the lactic acid.

*Acidosis* is the opposite of alkalosis. There was a case of a toddler who came to the hospital with viral gastroenteritis and *metabolic acidosis*. He had severe diarrhea, was dehydrated, and had a high rate of respiration. One function of the bicarbonate ion is to neutralize stomach acid in the intestines. However, because of his diarrhea, the toddler was losing bicarbonate ions in his stool, and his blood pH was too low. To compensate, the toddler was breathing rapidly and blowing off $CO_2$ through the lungs (the effect of which is to lower [$H_3O^+$] and raise the pH).

*Respiratory acidosis* results from a buildup of $CO_2$ in the body. This can be caused by pulmonary problems, by head injuries, or by drugs such as anesthetics and sedatives. It can be reversed by breathing rapidly and deeply. Doubling the breathing rate increases the blood pH by about 0.23 units.

**Questions:**

Phosphate ions are abundant in cells, both as the ions themselves and as important substituents on organic molecules. Most importantly, the $pK_a$ for the $H_2PO_4^-$ ion is 7.20, which is very close to the high end of the normal pH range in the body.

$$H_2PO_4^-(aq) + H_2O(\ell) \rightleftharpoons H_3O^+(aq) + HPO_4^{2-}(aq)$$

1. What should the ratio [$HPO_4^{2-}$]/[$H_2PO_4^-$] be to control the pH at 7.4?
2. A typical total phosphate concentration in a cell, [$HPO_4^{2-}$] + [$H_2PO_4^-$], is $2.0 \times 10^{-2}$ M. What are the concentrations of $HPO_4^{2-}$ and $H_2PO_4^-$ at pH 7.4?

**Answers to these questions are available in Appendix N.**

---

and the pH slowly increases. As an example, let us find the pH of the solution after 10.0 mL of 0.100 M NaOH has been added to 50.0 mL of 0.100 M HCl. Here, we set up a table to list the amounts of acid and base before reaction, the changes in those amounts, and the amounts remaining after reaction. Be sure to notice that the volume of the solution after reaction is the sum of the combined volumes of NaOH and HCl (60.0 mL or 0.0600 L in this case).

|  | $H_3O^+(aq)$ | + | $OH^-(aq)$ | → | $2 H_2O(\ell)$ |
|---|---|---|---|---|---|
| Initial amount (mol = $c \times V$) | 0.00500 | | 0.00100 | | |
| Change (mol) | −0.00100 | | −0.00100 | | |
| After reaction (mol) | 0.00400 | | 0 | | |
| After reaction ($c$ = mol/V) | 0.00400 mol/0.0600 L = 0.0667 M | | 0 | | |

● **Titrations, Stoichiometry, and Limiting Reactants** In the titration of an acid with a base (as in Figure 18.4) the limiting reactant is the base before the equivalence point. After the equivalence point it will be the acid.

After addition of 10.0 mL of NaOH, the final solution has a hydronium ion concentration of 0.0667 M, and so the pH is

$$pH = -\log[H_3O^+] = -\log(0.0667) = 1.176$$

After 49.5 mL of base has been added—that is, just before the equivalence point—we can use the same approach to show that the pH is 3.3. The solution being titrated is still quite acidic, even very close to the equivalence point.

*The pH of the equivalence point in an acid–base titration is the value at the steepest point in the vertical portion of the pH versus volume of titrant curve.* (The **titrant** is the substance being added during the titration.) In the HCl/NaOH titration illustrated in Figure 18.4, you see that the pH increases very rapidly near the equivalence point. In fact, in this case the pH rises 7 units (the $H_3O^+$ concentration decreases by a factor of 10 million!) when only a drop or two of the NaOH solution is added, and the steepest point of the vertical portion of the curve is at a pH of 7.00.

> The pH of the solution at the equivalence point in a monoprotic strong acid–strong base reaction is always 7.00 (at 25 °C) because the solution contains a neutral salt.

After all of the HCl has been consumed and the slightest excess of NaOH has been added, the solution will be basic, and the pH will continue to increase as more NaOH is added (and the solution volume increases). For example, if we calculate the pH of the solution after 55.0 mL of 0.100 M NaOH has been added to 50.0 mL of 0.100 M HCl, we find

|  | $H_3O^+$(aq) | + | $OH^-$(aq) | → | $2 H_2O(\ell)$ |
|---|---|---|---|---|---|
| Initial amount (mol = $c \times V$) | 0.00500 | | 0.00550 | | |
| Change (mol) | −0.00500 | | −0.00500 | | |
| After reaction (mol) | 0 | | 0.00050 | | |
| After reaction ($c$ = mol/$V$) | 0 | | 0.00050 mol/0.1050 L = 0.0048 M | | |

At this point, the solution has a hydroxide ion concentration of 0.0048 M. Calculate the pOH from this value, then use this to calculate pH.

$$pOH = -\log[OH^-] = -\log(0.0048) = 2.32$$

$$pH = 14.00 - pOH = 11.68$$

## Titration of a Weak Acid with a Strong Base

The titration of a weak acid with a strong base is somewhat different from the strong acid–strong base titration. Look carefully at the curve for the titration of 100.0 mL of 0.100 M acetic acid with 0.100 M NaOH (Figure 18.5),

$$CH_3CO_2H(aq) + NaOH(aq) \rightarrow NaCH_3CO_2(aq) + H_2O(\ell)$$

and focus on three points on this curve:

- *The pH before titration begins.* The pH before any base is added can be calculated from the weak acid $K_a$ value and the acid concentration (◄ Example 17.5).
- *The pH at the equivalence point.* At the equivalence point, the solution contains only sodium acetate, the $CH_3CO_2H$ and NaOH having been consumed. The pH is controlled by the acetate ion, the conjugate base of acetic acid.
- *The pH at the halfway point (half-equivalence point) of the titration.* Here, the pH is equal to the p$K_a$ of the weak acid, a conclusion discussed in more detail in following paragraphs.

As NaOH is added to acetic acid, the base is consumed and sodium acetate is produced. Thus, at every point between the beginning of the titration (when only acetic acid is present) and the equivalence point (when only sodium acetate is present), the solution contains both acetic acid and its salt, sodium acetate. These are

**FIGURE 18.5** **The change in pH during the titration of a weak acid with a strong base.**
Here, 100.0 mL of 0.100 M acetic acid is titrated with 0.100 M NaOH. Note especially the following:
**(a) Before titration.** A 0.100 M solution of acetic acid has a pH of 2.87. **(b) Halfway point.** The pH at
the point at which half the acid has reacted with base is equal to the $pK_a$ for the acid (pH = $pK_a$ = 4.74).
**(c) Equivalence point.** The solution contains the acetate ion, a weak base. Therefore, the solution is
basic, with a pH of 8.72.

the components of a *buffer solution,* and the hydronium ion concentration can be
calculated from Equation 18.3 or 18.4.

$$[H_3O^+] = \frac{[\text{weak acid remaining}]}{[\text{conjugate base produced}]} \times K_a \qquad (18.3)$$

or

$$pH = pK_a + \log \frac{[\text{conjugate base produced}]}{[\text{weak acid remaining}]} \qquad (18.4)$$

The fact that a buffer is present for most of the region between the beginning of the
titration and the equivalence point is the reason that the pH of the solution only
rises slowly after a few milliliters of titrant has been added.

What happens to the pH when *exactly* half of the acid has been consumed by
base? Half of the acid ($CH_3CO_2H$) has been converted to the conjugate base
($CH_3CO_2^-$), and half remains. Therefore, the concentration of weak acid remaining is equal to the concentration of conjugate base produced ([$CH_3CO_2H$] =
[$CH_3CO_2^-$]). Using Equations 18.3 or 18.4, we see that

$$[H_3O^+] = (1) \times K_a \qquad \text{or} \qquad pH = pK_a + \log(1)$$

Because $\log(1) = 0$, we come to the following general conclusion:

At the halfway point in the titration of a weak acid with a strong base

$$[H_3O^+] = K_a \text{ and pH} = pK_a \qquad (18.5)$$

In the particular case of the titration of acetic acid with a strong base, [$H_3O^+$] =
$1.8 \times 10^{-5}$ M at the halfway point, and so the pH is 4.74. This is equal to the $pK_a$ of
acetic acid.

● **Acid–Base Titrations** See Problem Solving Tip 18.2 on page 826: Calculating the pH at Various Stages in an Acid–Base Titration.

⃝WL **INTERACTIVE EXAMPLE 18.6** Titration of Acetic Acid with
### Sodium Hydroxide

**Problem** Consider the titration of 100.0 mL of 0.100 M acetic acid with 0.100 M NaOH (see Figure 18.5).

$$CH_3CO_2H(aq) + OH^-(aq) \rightarrow CH_3CO_2^-(aq) + H_2O(\ell)$$

(a) What is the pH of the solution when 90.0 mL of 0.100 M NaOH has been added to 100.0 mL of 0.100 M acetic acid?

(b) What is the pH at the equivalence point?

(c) What is the pH after 110.0 mL of NaOH has been added?

**What Do You Know?** You know the concentrations and volumes of the acid and base and the balanced equation for the reaction. For part (a) you know $K_a$ of acetic acid and for part (b) you know $K_b$ for the acetate ion (◀ Table 17.3). You might also recognize that part (a) is like Example 18.1.

**Strategy** Each part of the problem has at least two steps:

(1) The first step in each part involves a limiting-reactant stoichiometry calculation to determine the amounts of acetic acid, sodium hydroxide, and acetate ion present after the acid–base reaction has gone to completion.

(2) **Part (a):** Before the equivalence point, do an equilibrium calculation to find $[H_3O^+]$ for a buffer solution where the amounts of $CH_3CO_2H$ and $CH_3CO_2^-$ are known from the stoichiometry calculation. (See Example 18.1.)

**Part (b):** Only the acetate ion remains at the equivalence point. (See Example 17.7.) Determine the concentration of this ion after the acid–base reaction goes to completion. Using the balanced equation for the reaction of the acetate ion with water and its corresponding $K_b$, determine the equilibrium hydroxide ion concentration. Convert this to the equilibrium hydronium ion concentration and calculate the pH.

**Part (c):** After the equivalence point, the solution contains both the acetate ion and excess NaOH, but the latter controls the pH. Determine the concentration of excess NaOH (and $[OH^-]$), and then convert $[OH^-]$ to pH.

**Solution**

***Part (a):*** *pH before the Equivalence Point*

First calculate the amounts of reactants before reaction (= concentration × volume) and then use the principles of stoichiometry to calculate the amounts of reactants and products after reaction. The limiting reactant is NaOH, so some $CH_3CO_2H$ remains along with the product, $CH_3CO_2^-$.

| Equation | $CH_3CO_2H$ | + | $OH^-$ | ⇌ | $CH_3CO_2^-$ | + | $H_2O$ |
|---|---|---|---|---|---|---|---|
| Initial (mol) | 0.0100 | | 0.00900 | | 0 | | |
| Change (mol) | −0.00900 | | −0.00900 | | +0.00900 | | |
| After reaction (mol) | 0.0010 | | 0 | | 0.00900 | | |

The ratio of amounts (moles) of acid to conjugate base is the same as the ratio of their concentrations. Therefore, we can use the amounts of weak acid remaining and conjugate base formed to find the pH from Equation 18.3.

$$[H_3O^+] = \frac{mol\ CH_3CO_2H}{mol\ CH_3CO_2^-} \times K_a = \left(\frac{0.0010\ mol}{0.0090\ mol}\right)(1.8 \times 10^{-5}) = 2.0 \times 10^{-6}\ M$$

$$pH = -\log(2.0 \times 10^{-6}) = 5.70$$

The pH is 5.70, in agreement with Figure 18.5. Notice that this pH is appropriate for a point after the halfway point (4.74) but before the equivalence point (8.72).

**Part (b):** *pH at the Equivalence Point*

To reach the equivalence point, 0.0100 mol of NaOH has been added to 0.0100 mol of $CH_3CO_2H$ and 0.0100 mol of $CH_3CO_2^-$ has been formed.

| Equation | $CH_3CO_2H$ | + | $OH^-$ | ⇌ | $CH_3CO_2^-$ | + | $H_2O$ |
|---|---|---|---|---|---|---|---|
| Initial (mol) | 0.0100 | | 0.0100 | | 0 | | |
| Change (mol) | −0.0100 | | −0.0100 | | +0.0100 | | |
| After reaction (mol) | 0 | | 0 | | 0.0100 | | |

Because two solutions, each with a volume of 100.0 mL, have been combined, the concentration of $CH_3CO_2^-$ at the equivalence point is (0.0100 mol/0.200 L) = 0.0500 M. Next, set up an ICE table for the reaction of this weak base with water,

| Equation | $CH_3CO_2^-$ | + | $H_2O$ | ⇌ | $CH_3CO_2H$ | + | $OH^-$ |
|---|---|---|---|---|---|---|---|
| Initial (M) | 0.0500 | | | | 0 | | 0 |
| Change (M) | −x | | | | +x | | +x |
| After reaction (M) | 0.0500 − x | | | | x | | x |

and calculate the concentration of $OH^-$ ion using $K_b$ for the weak base.

$$K_b \text{ for } CH_3CO_2^- = 5.6 \times 10^{-10} = \frac{[CH_3CO_2H][OH^-]}{[CH_3CO_2^-]} = \frac{(x)(x)}{0.0500 - x}$$

Making the usual assumption that x is small with respect to 0.0500 M,

$$x = [OH^-] = 5.3 \times 10^{-6} \text{ M and so the pOH} = 5.28$$

$$pH = 14.00 - 5.28 = 8.72$$

**Part (c):** *pH after the Equivalence Point*

Now the limiting reactant is $CH_3CO_2H$, and the solution contains excess $OH^-$ ion from the unused NaOH as well as from the hydrolysis of $CH_3CO_2^-$.

| Equation | $CH_3CO_2H$ | + | $OH^-$ | ⇌ | $CH_3CO_2^-$ | + | $H_2O$ |
|---|---|---|---|---|---|---|---|
| Initial (mol) | 0.0100 | | 0.0110 | | 0 | | |
| Change (mol) | −0.0100 | | −0.0100 | | +0.0100 | | |
| After reaction (mol) | 0 | | 0.0010 | | 0.0100 | | |

The amount of $OH^-$ produced by $CH_3CO_2^-$ hydrolysis is very small [see part (b)], so the pH of the solution after the equivalence point is determined by the excess NaOH (in 210 mL of solution).

$$[OH^-] = 0.0010 \text{ mol}/0.210 \text{ L} = 4.8 \times 10^{-3} \text{ M (pOH} = 2.32)$$

$$pH = 14.00 - 2.32 = 11.68$$

**Think about Your Answer** The pH at the equivalence point (8.72) indicates the solution is mildly basic, as expected for a solution of the conjugate base of a weak acid. As more NaOH is added past the equivalence point the solution becomes substantially more basic (pH = 11.68).

**Check Your Understanding**

The titration of 0.100 M acetic acid with 0.100 M NaOH is described in the text. What is the pH of the solution when 35.0 mL of the base has been added to 100.0 mL of 0.100 M acetic acid?

**Strategy Map 18.6**

PROBLEM — *Part (b)*
Calculate **pH** at the *equivalence point* for a titration of **acetic acid** with **NaOH**.

↓

DATA/INFORMATION KNOWN
- Solution concentrations
- Solution volumes
- Value of conjugate base $K_b$

STEP 1. Stoichiometry problem

Concentration of **acetate ion** at *equivalence point* of acid-base titration

STEP 2. Enter **equilibrium concentrations** in ICE table.

At equilibrium:
$[OH^-]$ = [Acetic acid] = x
[Acetate ion] = original conc. − x

STEP 3. Enter **equilibrium concentrations** in $K_b$.

$K_b$ **expression** with equilibrium concentrations in terms of **x**

STEP 4. Solve $K_b$ **expression** for **x**.

Value of $[OH^-]$

STEP 5. Convert $[OH^-]$ to **pH**.

pH of solution

**FIGURE 18.6 Titration curve for a diprotic acid.** The curve for the titration of 100.0 mL of 0.100 M oxalic acid ($H_2C_2O_4$, a weak diprotic acid) with 0.100 M NaOH. The first equivalence point (at 100 mL) occurs when the first hydrogen ion of $H_2C_2O_4$ is titrated, and the second (at 200 mL) occurs at the completion of the reaction. The curve for pH versus volume of NaOH added shows an initial rise at the first equivalence point and then another rise at the second equivalence point.

## Titration of Weak Polyprotic Acids

The titrations illustrated thus far have been for the reaction of a monoprotic acid (HA) with a base such as NaOH. It is possible to extend the discussion of titrations to polyprotic acids such as oxalic acid, $H_2C_2O_4$.

$$H_2C_2O_4(aq) + H_2O(\ell) \rightleftharpoons HC_2O_4^-(aq) + H_3O^+(aq) \qquad K_{a1} = 5.9 \times 10^{-2}$$

$$HC_2O_4^-(aq) + H_2O(\ell) \rightleftharpoons C_2O_4^-(aq) + H_3O^+(aq) \qquad K_{a2} = 6.4 \times 10^{-5}$$

Figure 18.6 illustrates the curve for the titration of 100 mL of 0.100 M oxalic acid with 0.100 M NaOH. The first significant rise in pH is experienced when 100 mL of base has been added, indicating that the first proton of the acid has been titrated.

$$H_2C_2O_4(aq) + OH^-(aq) \rightleftharpoons HC_2O_4^-(aq) + H_2O(aq)$$

When the second proton of oxalic acid is titrated, the pH again rises significantly.

$$HC_2O_4^-(aq) + OH^-(aq) \rightleftharpoons C_2O_4^{2-}(aq) + H_2O(\ell)$$

The pH at this second equivalence point is controlled by the oxalate ion, $C_2O_4^{2-}$.

$$C_2O_4^{2-}(aq) + H_2O(\ell) \rightleftharpoons HC_2O_4^-(aq) + OH^-(aq)$$

$$K_b = K_w/K_{a2} = 1.6 \times 10^{-10}$$

Calculation of the pH at the equivalence point indicates that it should be about 8.4, as observed.

## Titration of a Weak Base with a Strong Acid

Finally, it is useful to consider the titration of a weak base with a strong acid. Figure 18.7 illustrates the pH curve for the titration of 100.0 mL of 0.100 M $NH_3$ with 0.100 M HCl.

$$NH_3(aq) + H_3O^+(aq) \rightleftharpoons NH_4^+(aq) + H_2O(\ell)$$

The initial pH for a 0.100 M $NH_3$ solution is 11.13. As the titration progresses, the important species in solution are the weak acid $NH_4^+$ and its conjugate base, $NH_3$.

$$NH_4^+(aq) + H_2O(\ell) \rightleftharpoons NH_3(aq) + H_3O^+(aq) \qquad K_a = 5.6 \times 10^{-10}$$

**FIGURE 18.7** Titration of a weak base with a strong acid. The change in pH during the titration of a weak base (100.0 mL of 0.100 M $NH_3$) with a strong acid (0.100 M HCl). The pH at the half-neutralization point is equal to the p$K_a$ for the conjugate acid ($NH_4^+$) of the weak base ($NH_3$) (pH = p$K_a$ = 9.25). At the equivalence point, the solution contains the $NH_4^+$ ion, a weak acid, so the pH is about 5.

At the halfway point, the concentrations of $NH_4^+$ and $NH_3$ are the same, so

$$[H_3O^+] = \frac{[NH_4^+]}{[NH_3]} \times K_a = 5.6 \times 10^{-10}$$

$$[H_3O^+] = K_a$$

$$pH = pK_a = -\log(5.6 \times 10^{-10}) = 9.25$$

As the addition of HCl to $NH_3$ continues, the pH declines slowly because of the buffering action of the $NH_3/NH_4^+$ combination. Near the equivalence point, however, the pH drops rapidly. At the equivalence point, the solution contains only ammonium chloride, a weak Brønsted acid, and the solution is weakly acidic.

## EXAMPLE 18.7    Titration of Ammonia with HCl

**Problem**  What is the pH of the solution at the equivalence point in the titration of 100.0 mL of 0.100 M ammonia with 0.100 M HCl (see Figure 18.7)?

**What Do You Know?**  This problem resembles part (b) of Example 18.6, although here you are titrating a weak base with a strong acid. In both examples you know the quantities of reagents and want to know the pH at the equivalence point. Here you need to know the $K_a$ value for $NH_4^+$, the conjugate acid of the weak base, $NH_3$.

**Strategy**  As in Example 18.6, this problem has two steps: (a) a stoichiometry calculation to find the concentration of $NH_4^+$ at the equivalence point, and (b) an equilibrium calculation to find $[H_3O^+]$ for a solution of the weak acid $NH_4^+$.

**Solution**

***Part 1:*** *Stoichiometry Problem*

Here, we are titrating 0.0100 mol of $NH_3$ (= $c \times V$), so 0.0100 mol of HCl is required. Thus, 100.0 mL of 0.100 M HCl (= 0.0100 mol HCl) must be used in the titration.

| Equation | $NH_3$ | + | $H_3O^+$ | $\rightleftharpoons$ | $NH_4^+$ | + | $H_2O$ |
|---|---|---|---|---|---|---|---|
| Initial (mol = $c \times V$) | 0.0100 | | 0.0100 | | 0 | | |
| Change on reaction (mol) | −0.0100 | | −0.0100 | | +0.0100 | | |
| After reaction (mol) | 0 | | 0 | | 0.0100 | | |
| Concentration (M) | 0 | | 0 | | 0.0100 mol (in 0.200L) = 0.0500 M | | |

**PROBLEM SOLVING TIP 18.2**

## Calculating the pH at Various Stages in an Acid–Base Titration

Finding the pH at or before the equivalence point for an acid–base reaction always involves several calculation steps. There are no shortcuts. Consider the *titration of a weak base, B, with a strong acid* as in Example 18.7. (The same principles apply to other acid–base reactions.)

$$H_3O^+(aq) + B(aq) \rightleftharpoons BH^+(aq) + H_2O(\ell)$$

**A: Determining the pH before the equivalence point.**

**Step 1.** *Solve the stoichiometry problem.* Up to the equivalence point, acid is consumed completely to leave a solution containing some base (B) and its conjugate acid (BH$^+$).

Use the principles of stoichiometry to calculate (a) the amount of acid added, (b) the amount of base remaining, and (c) the amount of conjugate acid (BH$^+$) formed.

**Step 2.** Calculate the concentrations of B and BH$^+$. Recognize that the volume of the solution at any point is the sum of the original volume of base solution plus the volume of acid solution added.

**Step 3.** *Calculate the pH.* At any point before the equivalence point, the solution is a buffer solution because both B and BH$^+$ are present. Calculate [H$_3$O$^+$] using the concentra-

tions of Step 2 and the value of $K_a$ for the conjugate acid of the weak base.

**B: Determining the pH at the equivalence point.**

Calculate the concentration of the conjugate acid using the procedure of Part A. Use the value of $K_a$ for the conjugate acid of the weak base and the procedure outlined in Example 18.7. (For a titration of a weak acid with a strong base, use the value of $K_b$ for the conjugate base of the acid and follow the procedure outlined in Example 18.6.)

---

*Part 2: Equilibrium Problem*

When the equivalence point is reached, the solution consists of 0.0500 M NH$_4^+$. The pH is determined by the hydrolysis of this weak acid.

| Equation | NH$_4^+$ | + | H$_2$O | $\rightleftharpoons$ | NH$_3$ | + | H$_3$O$^+$ |
|---|---|---|---|---|---|---|---|
| Initial (M) | 0.0500 | | | | 0 | | 0 |
| Change (M) | $-x$ | | | | $+x$ | | $+x$ |
| Equilibrium (M) | 0.0500 $- x$ | | | | $x$ | | $x$ |

Using $K_a$ for the weak acid NH$_4^+$, we have

$$K_a = 5.6 \times 10^{-10} = \frac{[NH_3][H_3O^+]}{[NH_4^+]} = \frac{x^2}{0.0500 - x}$$

$$\text{Simplifying, } x = [H_3O^+] = \sqrt{(5.6 \times 10^{-10})(0.0500)} = 5.3 \times 10^{-6} \text{ M}$$

$$\boxed{pH = 5.28}$$

**Think about Your Answer** The pH at the equivalence point (5.28) indicates the solution is mildly acidic, as expected for a solution of the conjugate acid of a weak base.

---

**Check Your Understanding**

Calculate the pH after 75.0 mL of 0.100 M HCl has been added to 100.0 mL of 0.100 M NH$_3$. See Figure 18.7.

**(a)  (b)  (c)  (d)  (e)**

**Roses are a natural indicator.**
**(a)** The pigment in red rose petals was extracted with ethanol; the extract was a faint red. **(b)** After adding one drop of 6 M HCl, the color changed to a vivid red. **(c)** Adding two drops of 6 M NH$_3$ produced a green color, and **(d)** adding 1 drop each of HCl and NH$_3$ (to give a buffer solution) gave a blue solution. **(e)** Finally, adding a few milligrams of Al(NO$_3$)$_3$ turned the solution deep purple. (The deep purple color with aluminum ions was so intense that the solution had to be diluted significantly to take the photo.)

## pH Indicators

Many organic compounds, both natural and synthetic, have a color that changes with pH (Figure 18.8). Not only does this add beauty and variety to our world, but it is also a useful property in chemistry.

You may have done an acid–base titration in the laboratory, and, before starting the titration, you added an **indicator**. The acid–base indicator is usually an organic compound that is itself a weak acid or weak base (as are many compounds that give flowers their colors). In aqueous solution, the acid form is in equilibrium with its conjugate base. Abbreviating the indicator's acid formula as HInd and the formula of its conjugate base as Ind$^-$, we can write the equilibrium equation

$$HInd(aq) + H_2O(\ell) \rightleftharpoons H_3O^+(aq) + Ind^-(aq)$$

OH

Phenolphthalein, Brønsted acid, colorless

HO

(aq) + 2 H$_2$O($\ell$) $\rightleftharpoons$ 2 H$_3$O$^+$(aq) +

O

O

O$^-$

Conjugate base of phenolphthalein, Brønsted base, pink

CO$_2^-$ (aq)

O

**FIGURE 18.8 Phenolphthalein, a common acid–base indicator.** Phenolphthalein, a weak acid, is colorless. As the pH increases, the pink conjugate base form predominates, and the color of the solution changes. The change in color is most noticeable around pH 9. The dye is commonly used for strong acid + strong base or weak acid + strong base titrations because the pH changes from about 3 to about 10 in these cases. For other suitable indicator dyes, see Figure 18.10.

Photos © Cengage Learning/Charles D. Winters

The important characteristic of acid–base indicators is that the acid form of the compound (HInd) has one color and the conjugate base (Ind$^-$) has another. To see how such compounds can be used as equivalence point indicators, let us write the usual equilibrium constant expressions for the dependence of hydronium ion concentration or pH on the indicator's ionization constant ($K_a$) and on the relative quantities of the acid and conjugate base.

$$[H_3O^+] = \frac{[HInd]}{[Ind^-]} \times K_a \quad \text{or} \quad pH = pK_a + \log\frac{[Ind^-]}{[HInd]}$$

These equations inform us that

- when the hydronium ion concentration is equivalent to the value of $K_a$ (or when pH = p$K_a$), then [HInd] = [Ind$^-$]
- when [H$_3$O$^+$] > $K_a$ (or pH < p$K_a$), then [HInd] > [Ind$^-$]
- when [H$_3$O$^+$] < $K_a$ (or pH > p$K_a$), then [HInd] < [Ind$^-$]

Now let us apply these conclusions to, for example, the titration of an acid with a base using an indicator whose p$K_a$ value is nearly the same as the pH at the equivalence point (Figure 18.9). At the beginning of the titration, the pH is low and [H$_3$O$^+$] is high; the acid form of the indicator (HInd) predominates, so its color is the one observed. As the titration progresses and the pH increases ([H$_3$O$^+$] decreases), less of the acid HInd and more of its conjugate base exist in solution. Finally, just after we reach the equivalence point, [Ind$^-$] is much larger than [HInd], and the color of [Ind$^-$] is observed.

Several obvious questions remain to be answered. If you are trying to analyze for an acid and add an indicator that is a weak acid, won't this affect the analysis? Recall that you use only a tiny amount of an indicator in a titration. Although the acidic indicator molecules also react with the base as the titration progresses, so little indicator is present that any error is not significant.

Another question is whether you could accurately determine the pH by observing the color change of an indicator. In practice, your eyes are not quite that good. Usually, you see the color of HInd when [HInd]/[Ind$^-$] is about 10/1, and the

**FIGURE 18.9** Indicator color changes in the course of a titration when the p$K_a$ of the indicator HInd is about 8.

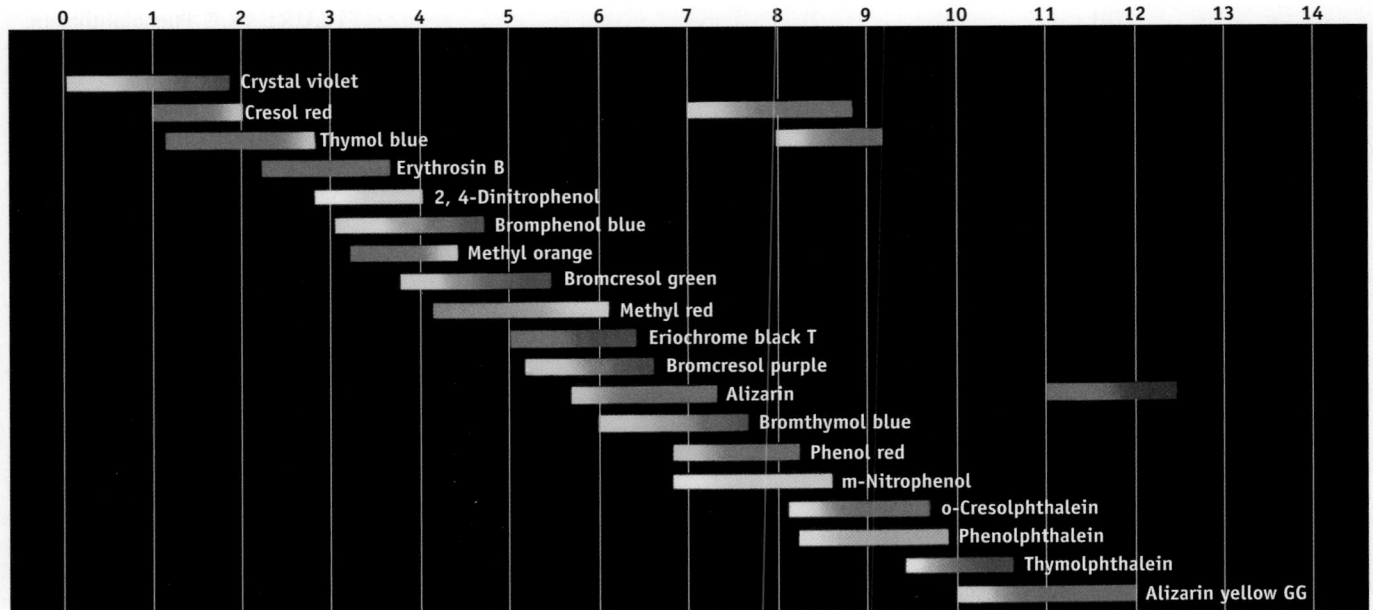

**FIGURE 18.10 Common acid–base indicators.** The color changes occur over a range of pH values. Notice that a few indicators have color changes over two different pH ranges.

color of $Ind^-$ when $[HInd]/[Ind^-]$ is about 1/10. This means the color change is observed over a hydronium ion concentration interval of about 2 pH units. However, as you can see in Figures 18.4–18.7, on passing through the equivalence point of these titrations, the pH changes by as many as 7 units.

As Figure 18.10 shows, a variety of indicators is available, each changing color in a different pH range. If you are analyzing a weak acid or base by titration, you must choose an indicator that changes color in a range that includes the pH to be observed at the equivalence point. This means that an indicator that changes color in the pH range $7 \pm 1$ should be used for a strong acid–strong base titration. On the other hand, the pH at the equivalence point in the titration of a weak acid with a strong base is greater than 7, and you should choose an indicator that changes color at a pH near the anticipated equivalence point.

---

**REVIEW & CHECK FOR SECTION 18.3**

1. What is the pH after 25.0 mL of 0.100 M NaOH has been added to 50.0 mL of 0.100 M HCl?

   (a)  1.00      (b)  1.48      (c)  7.00      (d)  13.00

2. What is the pH at the equivalence point in the titration of 25.0 mL of 0.090 M phenol $(K_a = 1.3 \times 10^{-10})$ with 0.108 M NaOH?

   (a)  7.00      (b)  5.65      (c)  8.98      (d)  11.29

3. Use Figure 18.10 to decide which indicator is best to use in the titration of $NH_3$ with HCl shown in Figure 18.7.

   (a)  crystal violet    (b)  thymol blue    (c)  methyl red    (d)  phenolphthalein

---

## 18.4 Solubility of Salts

Precipitation reactions (◄ Section 3.5) are exchange reactions in which one of the products is a water-insoluble compound such as $CaCO_3$,

$$CaCl_2(aq) + Na_2CO_3(aq) \rightarrow CaCO_3(s) + 2\ NaCl(aq)$$

that is, a compound having a water solubility of less than about 0.01 mol of dissolved material per liter of solution (Figure 18.11).

Crocoite, lead(II) chromate, $PbCrO_4$

Rhodochrosite, manganese(II) carbonate, $MnCO_3$

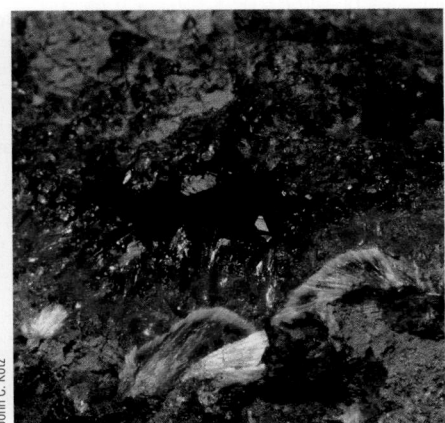

Copper(II) minerals: green malachite, $CuCO_3 \cdot Cu(OH)_2$, and blue azurite, $2\,CuCO_3 \cdot Cu(OH)_2$

**FIGURE 18.11 Some insoluble substances.**

How do you know when to predict an insoluble compound as the product of a reaction? In Chapter 3, we listed some guidelines for predicting solubility (◄ Figure 3.10) and mentioned a few important minerals that are insoluble in water. Now we want to make our estimates of solubility more quantitative and to explore conditions under which some compounds precipitate and others do not.

## The Solubility Product Constant, $K_{sp}$

Silver bromide, AgBr, is used in photographic film. If some AgBr is placed in pure water, a tiny amount of the compound dissolves, and an equilibrium is established.

$$AgBr(s) \rightleftharpoons Ag^+(aq, 7.35 \times 10^{-7}\ M) + Br^-(aq, 7.35 \times 10^{-7}\ M)$$

When sufficient AgBr has dissolved and equilibrium is attained, the solution is said to be **saturated** (◄ Section 14.2), and experiments show that the concentrations of the silver and bromide ions in the solution are each about $7.35 \times 10^{-7}$ M at 25 °C. The extent to which an insoluble salt dissolves can be expressed in terms of the equilibrium constant for the dissolving process. In this case, the appropriate expression is

$$K_{sp} = [Ag^+][Br^-]$$

The equilibrium constant that reflects the solubility of a compound is often referred to as its **solubility product constant**. Chemists frequently use the notation $K_{sp}$ for such constants, the subscript "sp" denoting a "solubility product."

The water solubility of a compound, and thus its $K_{sp}$ value, can be estimated by determining the concentration of the cation or anion when the compound dissolves. For example, if we find that AgBr dissolves to give a silver ion concentration of $7.35 \times 10^{-7}$ mol/L, we know that $7.35 \times 10^{-7}$ mol of AgBr must have dissolved per liter of solution (and that the bromide ion concentration also equals $7.35 \times 10^{-7}$ M). Therefore, the calculated value of the equilibrium constant for AgBr is

$$K_{sp} = [Ag^+][Br^-] = (7.35 \times 10^{-7})(7.35 \times 10^{-7}) = 5.40 \times 10^{-13}\ (\text{at } 25\ °C)$$

Equilibrium constants for dissolving other insoluble salts can be calculated in the same manner.

The solubility product constant, $K_{sp}$, for any salt always has the form

$$A_xB_y(s) \rightleftharpoons x\ A^{y+}(aq) + y\ B^{x-}(aq) \qquad K_{sp} = [A^{y+}]^x[B^{x-}]^y \qquad (18.6)$$

For example,

$$CaF_2(s) \rightleftharpoons Ca^{2+}(aq) + 2\ F^-(aq) \qquad K_{sp} = [Ca^{2+}][F^-]^2 = 5.3 \times 10^{-11}$$

$$Ag_2SO_4(s) \rightleftharpoons 2\ Ag^+(aq) + SO_4^{2-}(aq) \qquad K_{sp} = [Ag^+]^2[SO_4^{2-}] = 1.2 \times 10^{-5}$$

The numerical values of $K_{sp}$ for a few salts are given in Table 18.2, and more values are collected in Appendix J.

● **Writing Equilibrium Constant Expressions** Solids are not included in these equations. See page 724.

**Table 18.2 Some Common Insoluble Compounds and Their $K_{sp}$ Values***

| Formula | Name | $K_{sp}$ (25 °C) | Common Names/Uses |
|---------|------|------------------|-------------------|
| $CaCO_3$ | Calcium carbonate | $3.4 \times 10^{-9}$ | Calcite, iceland spar |
| $MnCO_3$ | Manganese(II) carbonate | $2.3 \times 10^{-11}$ | Rhodochrosite (forms rose-colored crystals) |
| $FeCO_3$ | Iron(II) carbonate | $3.1 \times 10^{-11}$ | Siderite |
| $CaF_2$ | Calcium fluoride | $5.3 \times 10^{-11}$ | Fluorite (source of HF and other inorganic fluorides) |
| $AgCl$ | Silver chloride | $1.8 \times 10^{-10}$ | Chlorargyrite |
| $AgBr$ | Silver bromide | $5.4 \times 10^{-13}$ | Used in photographic film |
| $CaSO_4$ | Calcium sulfate | $4.9 \times 10^{-5}$ | Hydrated form is commonly called *gypsum* |
| $BaSO_4$ | Barium sulfate | $1.1 \times 10^{-10}$ | Barite (used in "drilling mud" and as a component of paints) |
| $SrSO_4$ | Strontium sulfate | $3.4 \times 10^{-7}$ | Celestite |
| $Ca(OH)_2$ | Calcium hydroxide | $5.5 \times 10^{-5}$ | Slaked lime |

* The values in this table were taken from *Lange's Handbook of Chemistry,* 15th edition, McGraw-Hill Publishers, New York, NY (1999). Additional $K_{sp}$ values are given in Appendix J.

Do not confuse the *solubility* of a compound with its *solubility product constant.* The *solubility* of a salt is the quantity present in some volume of a saturated solution, expressed in moles per liter, grams per 100 mL, or other units. The *solubility product constant* is an equilibrium constant. Nonetheless, there is a connection between them: If one is known, the other can, in principle, be calculated.

## Relating Solubility and $K_{sp}$

Solubility product constants are determined by careful laboratory measurements of the concentrations of ions in solution.

### Strategy Map 18.8

**PROBLEM**

Calculate $K_{sp}$ of **$CaF_2$** from its **solubility**.

**DATA/INFORMATION KNOWN**

- Concentration of $Ca^{2+}$
- Form of $K_{sp}$
- Balanced equation

STEP 1. Calculate **$F^-$ concentration**.

$[F^-] = 2 \times [Ca^{2+}]$

STEP 2. Enter **equilibrium concentrations** in $K_{sp}$ expression and calculate $K_{sp}$.

Value of $K_{sp}$

### ⓦWL INTERACTIVE EXAMPLE 18.8 $K_{sp}$ from Solubility Measurements

**Problem** Calcium fluoride, the main component of the mineral fluorite, dissolves to a slight extent in water.

$$CaF_2(s) \rightleftharpoons Ca^{2+}(aq) + 2 F^-(aq) \qquad K_{sp} = [Ca^{2+}][F^-]^2$$

Calculate the $K_{sp}$ value for $CaF_2$ if the calcium ion concentration has been found to be $2.3 \times 10^{-4}$ mol/L.

**What Do You Know?** You know the balanced equation for the process, $Ca^{2+}$ concentration, and the $K_{sp}$ expression.

**Strategy**

- Calculate the fluoride ion concentration from $[Ca^{2+}]$ and stoichiometry.

- Insert the values for $[F^-]$ and $[Ca^{2+}]$ into the $K_{sp}$ expression and calculate the value of $K_{sp}$.

**Solution** When $CaF_2$ dissolves in water, the balanced equation shows that the concentration of $F^-$ ion must be twice the $Ca^{2+}$ ion concentration.

$$\text{If } [Ca^{2+}] = 2.3 \times 10^{-4} \text{ M, then } [F^-] = 2 \times [Ca^{2+}] = 4.6 \times 10^{-4} \text{ M}$$

This means the solubility product constant is

$$K_{sp} = [Ca^{2+}][F^-]^2 = (2.3 \times 10^{-4})(4.6 \times 10^{-4})^2 = 4.9 \times 10^{-11}$$

**Think about Your Answer** A common student error is to forget the reaction stoichiometry. Be sure to notice that for every $Ca^{2+}$ ion in solution there are two $F^-$ ions.

**Check Your Understanding**

The barium ion concentration, $[Ba^{2+}]$, in a saturated solution of barium fluoride is $3.6 \times 10^{-3}$ M. Calculate the value of the $K_{sp}$ for $BaF_2$.

$$BaF_2(s) \rightleftharpoons Ba^{2+}(aq) + 2 F^-(aq)$$

## A CLOSER LOOK

# Minerals and Gems—The Importance of Solubility

Minerals and gems are among nature's most beautiful creations. Many, such as rubies, are metal oxides, and the various types of quartz are based on silicon dioxide. Another large class of gemstones consists largely of metal silicates. These include emerald, topaz, aquamarine, and tourmaline.

Yet another large class of minerals and of a few gemstones is carbonates. Rhodochrosite, one of the most beautiful red stones, is manganese(II) carbonate. And one of the most abundant minerals on earth is limestone, calcium carbonate, which is also a major component of sea shells and corals.

Hydroxides are represented by azurite, which is a mixed carbonate/hydroxide with the formula $Cu_3(OH)_2(CO_3)_2$. Turquoise is a mixed hydroxide/phosphate based on copper(II), the source of the blue color of turquoise.

Among the most common minerals are sulfides such as golden iron pyrite ($FeS_2$), black stibnite ($Sb_2S_3$), red cinnabar (HgS), and yellow orpiment ($As_2S_3$).

Other smaller classes of minerals exist; one of the smallest is the class based on the halides, and the best example is fluorite. Fluorite, $CaF_2$, exhibits a wide range of colors from purple to green to yellow.

What do all of these minerals and gems have in common? They are all insoluble or poorly soluble in water. If they were more soluble, they would be dissolved in the world's lakes and oceans.

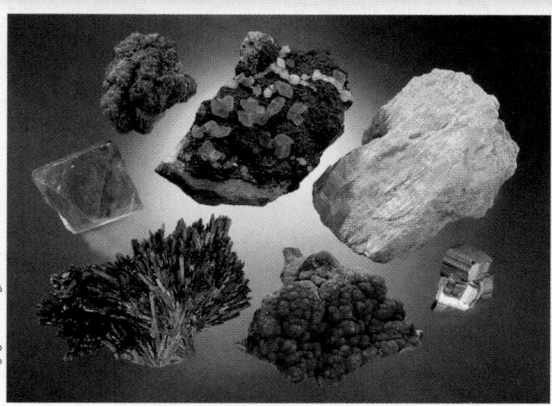

**Mineral samples (clockwise from the top center): red rhodochrosite, yellow orpiment, golden iron pyrite, green-blue turquoise, black stibnite, purple fluorite, and blue azurite.** Formulas are in the text. See also Figure 18.11.

$K_{sp}$ values for insoluble salts can be used to estimate the solubility of a solid salt or to determine whether a solid will precipitate when solutions of its anion and cation are mixed. Let us first look at an example of the estimation of the solubility of a salt from its $K_{sp}$ value.

## OWL    INTERACTIVE EXAMPLE 18.9    Solubility from $K_{sp}$

**Problem** The $K_{sp}$ for the mineral barite ($BaSO_4$, Figure 18.12) is $1.1 \times 10^{-10}$ at 25 °C. Calculate the solubility of barium sulfate in pure water in (a) moles per liter and (b) grams per liter.

**What Do You Know?** You know the formula for the mineral and its $K_{sp}$ value.

**Strategy** When $BaSO_4$ dissolves, equimolar amounts of $Ba^{2+}$ ions and $SO_4^{2-}$ ions are produced. Thus, the solubility of $BaSO_4$ can be estimated by calculating the equilibrium concentration of either $Ba^{2+}$ or $SO_4^{2-}$ from the solubility product constant.

- Write the balanced equation and the $K_{sp}$ expression.

- Set up an ICE table, designating the unknown concentrations of $Ba^{2+}$ and $SO_4^{2-}$ in solution as $x$.

- Using $x$ for $[Ba^{2+}]$ and $[SO_4^{2-}]$ in the $K_{sp}$ expression, solve for $x$.

**Solution** The equation for the solubility of $BaSO_4$ and its $K_{sp}$ expression are

$$BaSO_4(s) \rightleftharpoons Ba^{2+}(aq) + SO_4^{2-}(aq) \qquad K_{sp} = [Ba^{2+}][SO_4^{2-}] = 1.1 \times 10^{-10}$$

Denote the solubility of $BaSO_4$ (in mol/L) by $x$; that is, $x$ moles of $BaSO_4$ dissolve per liter. Therefore, both $[Ba^{2+}]$ and $[SO_4^{2-}]$ must also equal $x$ at equilibrium.

| Equation | $BaSO_4(s)$ | $\rightleftharpoons$ | $Ba^{2+}(aq)$ | + | $SO_4^{2-}(aq)$ |
|---|---|---|---|---|---|
| Initial (M) | | | 0 | | 0 |
| Change (M) | | | +x | | +x |
| Equilibrium (M) | | | x | | x |

Because $K_{sp}$ is the product of the barium ion and sulfate ion concentrations, $K_{sp}$ is the square of the solubility, $x$,

$$K_{sp} = [Ba^{2+}][SO_4^{2-}] = 1.1 \times 10^{-10} = (x)(x) = x^2$$

**Strategy Map 18.9**

PROBLEM
Calculate **solubility** of $BaSO_4$ from $K_{sp}$.

DATA/INFORMATION KNOWN
- $K_{sp}$ for $BaSO_4$
- Balanced equation

STEP 1. Write the **balanced equation** and $K_{sp}$ **expression**, and set up **ICE table**.

At equilibrium:
$[Ba^{2+}] = [SO_4^{2-}] = x$

STEP 2. Enter **equilibrium concentrations** in $K_{sp}$ expression.

$K_{sp}$ **expression** with equilibrium concentrations in terms of $x$

STEP 3. Solve $K_{sp}$ **expression** for $x$.

$x$ = Solubility = $[Ba^{2+}] = [SO_4^{2-}]$

**(a)** A sample of the mineral barite, which is mostly barium sulfate. "Drilling mud," used in drilling oil wells, consists of clay, barite, and calcium carbonate.

**(b)** Barium sulfate is opaque to x-rays, so it is used by physicians to examine the digestive tract. A patient drinks a "cocktail" containing $BaSO_4$, and the progress of the $BaSO_4$ through the digestive organs can be followed by x-ray analysis. This photo is an x ray of the gastrointestinal tract after a person ingested barium sulfate.

**FIGURE 18.12  Barium sulfate.** Barium sulfate, a white solid, is quite insoluble in water ($K_{sp} = 1.1 \times 10^{-10}$) (see Example 18.9).

and so the value of $x$ is

$$x = [Ba^{2+}] = [SO_4^{2-}] = \sqrt{K_{sp}} = \sqrt{1.1 \times 10^{-10}} = 1.0 \times 10^{-5} \text{ M}$$

The solubility of $BaSO_4$ in pure water is $1.0 \times 10^{-5}$ mol/L. To find its solubility in g/L, we only need to multiply by the molar mass of $BaSO_4$.

$$\text{Solubility in g/L} = (1.0 \times 10^{-5} \text{ mol/L})(233 \text{ g/mol}) = 0.0024 \text{ g/L}$$

**Think about Your Answer**  As noted in Figure 18.12, $BaSO_4$ is used to investigate the digestive track. It is fortunate the compound is so insoluble, because water- and acid-soluble barium salts are toxic.

---

**Check Your Understanding**

Calculate the solubility of AgCN in moles per liter and grams per liter. $K_{sp}$ for AgCN is $6.0 \times 10^{-17}$.

---

## EXAMPLE 18.10  Solubility from $K_{sp}$

**Problem**  Knowing that the $K_{sp}$ value for $MgF_2$ is $5.2 \times 10^{-11}$, calculate the solubility of the salt in (a) moles per liter and (b) grams per liter.

**What Do You Know?**  You know the formula for magnesium fluoride and its $K_{sp}$ value.

**Strategy**  The solubility must be defined in terms that will allow you to solve the $K_{sp}$ expression for this value. From stoichiometry, we can say that if $x$ mol of $MgF_2$ dissolves, then $x$ mol of $Mg^{2+}$ and $2x$ mol of $F^-$ appear in solution. This means the $MgF_2$ solubility (in moles dissolved per liter) is equivalent to the concentration of $Mg^{2+}$ ions in the solution.

- Write the balanced equation and the $K_{sp}$ expression.

- Set up an ICE table, designating the unknown concentrations of $Mg^{2+}$ and $F^-$ in solution as $x$ and $2x$, respectively.

- Using $x$ for $[Mg^{2+}]$ and $2x$ for $[F^-]$ in the $K_{sp}$ expression, solve for $x$.

**Solution**

$$MgF_2(s) \rightleftharpoons Mg^{2+}(aq) + 2\ F^-(aq) \qquad K_{sp} = [Mg^{2+}][F^-]^2 = 5.2 \times 10^{-11}$$

| Equation | $MgF_2(s)$ | $\rightleftharpoons$ | $Mg^{2+}(aq)$ | + | $2\ F^-(aq)$ |
|---|---|---|---|---|---|
| Initial (M) | | | 0 | | 0 |
| Change (M) | | | $+x$ | | $+2x$ |
| Equilibrium (M) | | | $x$ | | $2x$ |

## A CLOSER LOOK

# Solubility Calculations

The $K_{sp}$ value reported for lead(II) chloride, $PbCl_2$, is $1.7 \times 10^{-5}$. If we assume the appropriate equilibrium in solution is

$$PbCl_2(s) \rightleftharpoons Pb^{2+}(aq) + 2\,Cl^-(aq)$$

the calculated solubility of $PbCl_2$ is 0.016 M. The experimental value for the solubility of the salt, however, is 0.036 M, more than twice the calculated value! What is the problem? One is that the chemical behavior is sometimes much more complicated than the equation defining $K_{sp}$, as illustrated below.

The main problem in the lead(II) chloride case, and in many others, is that the compound dissolves but is not 100% dissociated into its constituent ions. Instead, it dissolves as the undissociated salt or forms ion pairs.

Other problems that lead to discrepancies between calculated and experimental solubilities are the reactions of ions (particularly anions) with water and complex ion formation. An example of the former effect is the product-favored reaction of sulfide ion with water, that is, *hydrolysis*.

$$S^{2-}(aq) + H_2O(\ell) \rightleftharpoons HS^-(aq) + OH^-(aq)$$

This means that the solubility of a metal sulfide is better described by a chemical equation such as

$$NiS(s) + H_2O(\ell) \rightleftharpoons Ni^{2+}(aq) + HS^-(aq) + OH^-(aq)$$

Complex ion formation is illustrated by the fact that lead chloride is more soluble in the presence of excess chloride ion, owing to the formation of the complex ion $PbCl_4^{2-}$.

$$PbCl_2(s) + 2\,Cl^-(aq) \rightleftharpoons PbCl_4^{2-}(aq)$$

Hydrolysis and complex ion formation are discussed further on pages 837–838 and 843–846, respectively.

**References:**
- L. Meites, J. S. F. Pode, and H. C. Thomas: *Journal of Chemical Education,* Vol. 43, pp. 667–672, 1966.
- S. J. Hawkes: *Journal of Chemical Education,* Vol. 75, pp. 1179–1181, 1998.
- R. W. Clark and J. M. Bonicamp: *Journal of Chemical Education,* Vol. 75, pp. 1182–1185, 1998.
- R. J. Myers: *Journal of Chemical Education,* Vol. 63, pp. 687–690, 1986.

$PbCl_2(aq)$ $\xrightleftharpoons{K = 0.63}$ $PbCl^+(aq) + Cl^-(aq)$
undissociated salt dissolved in water          ion pairs

$K = 0.0011$          $K = 0.026$

$PbCl_2(s)$ $\xrightleftharpoons{K_{sp} = 1.7 \times 10^{-5}}$ $Pb^{2+}(aq) + 2\,Cl^-(aq)$
slightly soluble salt          100% dissociated into ions

---

Substituting the equilibrium concentrations for $[Mg^{2+}]$ and $[F^-]$ into the $K_{sp}$ expression, you find

$$K_{sp} = [Mg^{2+}][F^-]^2 = (x)(2x)^2 = 4x^3$$

Solving the equation for $x$,

$$x = \sqrt[3]{\frac{K_{sp}}{4}} = \sqrt[3]{\frac{5.2 \times 10^{-11}}{4}} = 2.4 \times 10^{-4}$$

you find that $2.4 \times 10^{-4}$ moles of $MgF_2$ dissolve per liter. The solubility of $MgF_2$ in grams per liter is

$$(2.4 \times 10^{-4}\ \text{mol/L})(62.3\ \text{g/mol}) = 0.015\ \text{g MgF}_2/\text{L}$$

**Think about Your Answer** Problems like this one might provoke our students to ask the question, "Aren't you counting things twice when you multiply $x$ by 2 and then square it as well?" in the expression $K_{sp} = (x)(2x)^2$. The answer is no. The 2 in the $2x$ term is based on the stoichiometry of the compound. The exponent of 2 on the $F^-$ ion concentration arises from the rules for writing equilibrium expressions.

---

**Check Your Understanding**

Calculate the solubility of $Ca(OH)_2$ in moles per liter and grams per liter using the value of $K_{sp}$ in Appendix J.

---

The *relative* solubilities of salts can often be deduced by comparing values of solubility product constants, but you must be careful! For example, the $K_{sp}$ for silver chloride is

$$AgCl(s) \rightleftharpoons Ag^+(aq) + Cl^-(aq) \qquad K_{sp} = 1.8 \times 10^{-10}$$

whereas that for silver chromate is

$$Ag_2CrO_4(s) \rightleftharpoons 2\ Ag^+(aq) + CrO_4^{2-}(aq) \qquad K_{sp} = 9.0 \times 10^{-12}$$

In spite of the fact that $Ag_2CrO_4$ has a smaller numerical $K_{sp}$ value than AgCl, the chromate salt is about 10 times *more* soluble than the chloride salt. If you determine solubilities from $K_{sp}$ values as in the examples above, you would find the solubility of AgCl is $1.3 \times 10^{-5}$ mol/L, whereas that of $Ag_2CrO_4$ is $1.3 \times 10^{-4}$ mol/L. From this example and countless others, we conclude that

> Direct comparisons of the solubility of two salts on the basis of their $K_{sp}$ values can be made only for salts having the same cation-to-anion ratio.

This means, for example, that you can directly compare solubilities of 1:1 salts such as the silver halides by comparing their $K_{sp}$ values.

$$AgI\ (K_{sp} = 8.5 \times 10^{-17}) < AgBr\ (K_{sp} = 5.4 \times 10^{-13}) < AgCl\ (K_{sp} = 1.8 \times 10^{-10})$$
$$\xrightarrow{\quad\text{increasing } K_{sp} \text{ and increasing solubility}\quad}$$

Similarly, you could compare 1:2 salts such as the lead halides,

$$PbI_2\ (K_{sp} = 9.8 \times 10^{-9}) < PbBr_2\ (K_{sp} = 6.6 \times 10^{-6}) < PbCl_2\ (K_{sp} = 1.7 \times 10^{-5})$$
$$\xrightarrow{\quad\text{increasing } K_{sp} \text{ and increasing solubility}\quad}$$

but you cannot directly compare a 1:1 salt (AgCl) with a 2:1 salt ($Ag_2CrO_4$).

## Solubility and the Common Ion Effect

The test tube on the left in Figure 18.13 contains a precipitate of silver acetate, $AgCH_3CO_2$, in water. The solution is saturated, and the silver ions and acetate ions in the solution are in equilibrium with solid silver acetate.

$$AgCH_3CO_2(s) \rightleftharpoons Ag^+(aq) + CH_3CO_2^-(aq)$$

But what would happen if the silver ion concentration is increased, say by adding silver nitrate? Le Chatelier's principle (◀ Section 16.6) suggests—and we observe—that more silver acetate precipitate should form because a product ion has been added, causing the equilibrium to shift to form more silver acetate.

The ionization of weak acids and bases is affected by the presence of an ion common to the equilibrium process (Section 18.1), and the effect of adding silver ions to a saturated silver acetate solution is another example of the common ion effect. Adding a common ion to a saturated solution of a salt will lower the salt solubility (unless a complex ion can form; see *A Closer Look*, page 833).

**FIGURE 18.13 The common ion effect.** The tube at the *left* contains a saturated solution of silver acetate, $AgCH_3CO_2$. When 1.0 M $AgNO_3$ is added to the tube *(right)*, more solid silver acetate forms.

# EXAMPLE 18.11   The Common Ion Effect and Salt Solubility

**Problem**  If solid AgCl is placed in 1.00 L of 0.55 M NaCl, what mass of AgCl will dissolve?

**What Do You Know?**  You know the formula of the insoluble compound, its $K_{sp}$ (Table 18.2 and Appendix J), and its molar mass. You also know that the presence of an ion common to the equilibrium ($Cl^-$) suppresses the solubility of AgCl.

**Strategy**  To determine the solubility of AgCl in the presence of excess $Cl^-$, calculate the concentration of the $Ag^+$ ion.

- Write the balanced equation and the $K_{sp}$ expression for AgCl.

- Set up an ICE table, and enter 0.55 M as the initial concentration of the common ion, $Cl^-$.

- Define the solubility of AgCl as $x$. This is the increase in the concentration of $Ag^+$ and $Cl^-$ in solution as AgCl dissolves. Enter this information on the change (C) line in the ICE table.

- Fill in the last line (E) of the ICE table with $x$ for $[Ag^+]$ and $(0.55 + x)$ for $[Cl^-]$. Solve the $K_{sp}$ expression for $x$.

**Solution**  Set up an ICE table to show the concentrations of $Ag^+$ and $Cl^-$ when equilibrium is attained.

| Equation | AgCl(s) | $\rightleftharpoons$ | Ag⁺(aq) | + | Cl⁻(aq) |
|---|---|---|---|---|---|
| Initial (M) | | | 0 | | 0.55 |
| Change (M) | | | $+x$ | | $+x$ |
| Equilibrium (M) | | | $x$ | | $0.55 + x$ |

The equilibrium concentrations from the table are substituted into the $K_{sp}$ expression,

$$K_{sp} = 1.8 \times 10^{-10} = [Ag^+][Cl^-] = (x)(0.55 + x)$$

This is a quadratic equation and can be solved by the methods in Appendix A. An easier approach, however, is to make the approximation that $x$ is very small with respect to 0.55 [and so $(0.55 + x) \approx 0.55$]. This is a reasonable assumption because we know that the solubility is very small without the common ion $Cl^-$ and that it will be even smaller in the presence of added $Cl^-$. Therefore,

$$K_{sp} = 1.8 \times 10^{-10} = (x)(0.55)$$

$$x = [Ag^+] = 3.3 \times 10^{-10} \text{ M}$$

The solubility in grams per liter is then

$$(3.3 \times 10^{-10} \text{ mol/L})(143 \text{ g/mol}) = 4.7 \times 10^{-8} \text{ g/L}$$

As predicted by Le Chatelier's principle, the solubility of AgCl in the presence of added $Cl^-$ is less ($3.3 \times 10^{-10}$ M) than in pure water ($1.3 \times 10^{-5}$ M).

**Think about Your Answer**  The approximation we made here is similar to the approximations we make in acid–base equilibrium problems. However, as a final step, we should check its validity by substituting the calculated value of $x$ into the exact expression $K_{sp} = (x)(0.55 + x)$. If the product $(x)(0.55 + x)$ is the same as the given value of $K_{sp}$, the approximation is valid.

$$K_{sp} = (x)(0.55 + x) = (3.3 \times 10^{-10})(0.55 + 3.3 \times 10^{-10}) = 1.8 \times 10^{-10}$$

**Check Your Understanding**

Calculate the solubility of $BaSO_4$ (a) in pure water and (b) in the presence of 0.010 M $Ba(NO_3)_2$. $K_{sp}$ for $BaSO_4$ is $1.1 \times 10^{-10}$.

## EXAMPLE 18.12 The Common Ion Effect and Salt Solubility

**Problem** Calculate the solubility of silver chromate, $Ag_2CrO_4$, at 25 °C in the presence of 0.0050 M $K_2CrO_4$ solution.

$$Ag_2CrO_4(s) \rightleftharpoons 2\ Ag^+(aq) + CrO_4^{2-}(aq)$$

$$K_{sp} = [Ag^+]^2[CrO_4^{2-}] = 9.0 \times 10^{-12}$$

For comparison, the solubility of $Ag_2CrO_4$ in pure water is $1.3 \times 10^{-4}$ mol/L.

**What Do You Know?** You know the formula and $K_{sp}$ value for $Ag_2CrO_4$.

**Strategy** In the presence of chromate ion from the water-soluble salt $K_2CrO_4$, the concentration of $Ag^+$ ions produced by $Ag_2CrO_4$ will be less than in pure water. Assume the solubility of $Ag_2CrO_4$ is $x$ mol/L. This means the concentration of $Ag^+$ ions will be $2x$ mol/L, whereas the concentration of $CrO_4^{2-}$ ions will be $x$ mol/L plus the concentration of $CrO_4^{2-}$ already in the solution.

- Write the balanced equation and the $K_{sp}$ expression for $Ag_2CrO_4$.

- Set up an ICE table, and enter 0.0050 M as the initial concentration of the common ion, $CrO_4^{2-}$.

- Designate the increase in the concentration of the $CrO_4^{2-}$ ion in solution as $x$ and the increase in $[Ag^+]$ as $2x$.

- Using $2x$ for $[Ag^+]$ and $(0.0050 + x)$ for $[CrO_4^{2-}]$ in the $K_{sp}$ expression, solve for $x$.

**Solution**

| Equation | $Ag_2CrO_4(s)$ | $\rightleftharpoons$ | $2\ Ag^+(aq)$ | $+$ | $CrO_4^{2-}(aq)$ |
|---|---|---|---|---|---|
| Initial (M) | | | 0 | | 0.0050 |
| Change (M) | | | $+2x$ | | $+x$ |
| Equilibrium (M) | | | $2x$ | | $0.0050 + x$ |

Substituting the equilibrium concentrations into the $K_{sp}$ expression, we have

$$K_{sp} = 9.0 \times 10^{-12} = [Ag^+]^2[CrO_4^{2-}]$$

$$K_{sp} = (2x)^2(0.0050 + x)$$

As in Example 18.11, you can make the approximation that $x$ is very small with respect to 0.0050, and so $(0.0050 + x) \approx 0.0050$. Therefore, the approximate expression is

$$K_{sp} = 9.0 \times 10^{-12} = [Ag^+]^2[CrO_4^{2-}] \approx (2x)^2(0.0050)$$

Solving, we find $x$, the solubility of silver chromate in the presence of excess chromate ion, is

$$x = \text{Solubility of } Ag_2CrO_4 = 2.1 \times 10^{-5}\ M$$

**Think about Your Answer** The silver ion concentration in the presence of the common ion is

$$[Ag^+] = 2x = 4.2 \times 10^{-5}\ M$$

This silver ion concentration is indeed less than its value in pure water ($2.6 \times 10^{-4}$ M), owing to the presence of an ion "common" to the equilibrium.

---

**Check Your Understanding**

Calculate the solubility of $Zn(CN)_2$ at 25 °C (a) in pure water and (b) in the presence of 0.10 M $Zn(NO_3)_2$. $K_{sp}$ for $Zn(CN)_2$ is $8.0 \times 10^{-12}$.

---

There are two important general ideas from Examples 18.11 and 18.12:

- The solubility of a salt will be reduced by the presence of a common ion, in accordance with Le Chatelier's principle.
- We made the approximation that the amount of common ion added to the solution was very large in comparison with the amount of that ion coming from the insoluble salt, and this allowed us to simplify our calculations. This is almost always the case, but you should check to be sure.

## The Effect of Basic Anions on Salt Solubility

The next time you are tempted to wash a supposedly insoluble salt down the kitchen or laboratory drain, stop and consider the consequences. Many metal ions such as lead, chromium, and mercury are toxic in the environment. Even if a so-called insoluble salt of one of these cations does not appear to dissolve, its solubility in water may be greater than you think, in part owing to the possibility that the anion of the salt is a weak base or the cation is a weak acid.

Lead(II) sulfide, PbS, which is found in nature as the mineral galena (Figure 18.14), provides an example of the effect of the acid–base properties of an ion on salt solubility. When placed in water, a trace amount dissolves,

$$PbS(s) \rightleftharpoons Pb^{2+}(aq) + S^{2-}(aq)$$

and one product of the reaction is the sulfide ion, which is itself a strong base.

$$S^{2-}(aq) + H_2O(\ell) \rightleftharpoons HS^-(aq) + OH^-(aq) \qquad K_b = 1 \times 10^5$$

This ion undergoes extensive hydrolysis (reaction with water) (◄ Table 17.3), which decreases its concentration, and the equilibrium process for dissolving PbS shifts to the right. Thus, the lead ion concentration in solution is greater than expected from the simple dissociation of the salt.

The lead(II) sulfide example leads to the following general observation:

> Any salt containing an anion that is the conjugate base of a weak acid will dissolve in water to a greater extent than given by $K_{sp}$.

This means that salts of phosphate, acetate, carbonate, and cyanide, as well as sulfide, can be affected, because all of these anions undergo the general hydrolysis reaction

$$X^-(aq) + H_2O(\ell) \rightleftharpoons HX(aq) + OH^-(aq)$$

The observation that ions from insoluble salts can undergo hydrolysis is related to another useful, general conclusion:

> Insoluble salts in which the anion is the conjugate base of a weak acid dissolve in strong acids.

Insoluble salts containing anions such as acetate, carbonate, hydroxide, phosphate, and sulfide dissolve in strong acids. For example, you know that if a strong acid is added to a water-insoluble metal carbonate such as $CaCO_3$, the salt dissolves (◄ Section 3.7).

$$CaCO_3(s) + 2 H_3O^+(aq) \rightarrow Ca^{2+}(aq) + 3 H_2O(\ell) + CO_2(g)$$

You can think of this as the result of a series of reactions.

$$CaCO_3(s) \rightleftharpoons Ca^{2+}(aq) + CO_3{}^{2-}(aq) \qquad K_{sp} = 3.4 \times 10^{-9}$$

$$CO_3{}^{2-}(aq) + H_3O^+(aq) \rightleftharpoons HCO_3{}^-(aq) + H_2O(\ell) \qquad 1/K_{a2} = 1/4.8 \times 10^{-11} = 2.1 \times 10^{10}$$

$$HCO_3{}^-(aq) + H_3O^+(aq) \rightleftharpoons H_2CO_3(aq) + H_2O(\ell) \qquad 1/K_{a1} = 1/4.2 \times 10^{-7} = 2.4 \times 10^6$$

Overall: $CaCO_3(s) + 2 H_3O^+(aq) \rightleftharpoons Ca^{2+}(aq) + 2 H_2O(\ell) + H_2CO_3(aq)$

$$K_{net} = (K_{sp})(1/K_{a2})(1/K_{a1}) = 1.7 \times 10^8$$

Carbonic acid, a product of this reaction, is not stable,

$$H_2CO_3(aq) \rightleftharpoons CO_2(g) + H_2O(\ell) \qquad K \approx 10^5$$

and you see $CO_2$ bubbling out of the solution, a process that moves the $CaCO_3 + H_3O^+$ equilibrium even further to the right. Calcium carbonate dissolves completely in strong acid!

Many metal sulfides are also soluble in strong acids

$$FeS(s) + 2 H_3O^+(aq) \rightleftharpoons Fe^{2+}(aq) + H_2S(aq) + 2 H_2O(\ell)$$

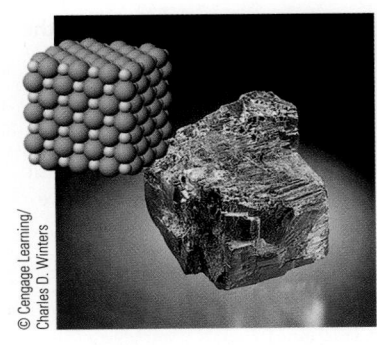

© Cengage Learning/Charles D. Winters

**FIGURE 18.14 Lead(II) sulfide (galena).** This and other metal sulfides dissolve in water to a greater extent than expected because the sulfide ion reacts with water to form the very stable species $HS^-$ and $OH^-$.

$$PbS(s) + H_2O(\ell) \rightleftharpoons Pb^{2+}(aq) + HS^-(aq) + OH^-(aq)$$

The model of PbS shows that the unit cell is cubic, a feature reflected by the cubic crystals of the mineral galena.

● **Metal Sulfide Solubility** The true solubility of a metal sulfide is better represented by a modified solubility product constant, $K_{spa}$, which is defined as follows:

$$MS(s) \rightleftharpoons M^{2+}(aq) + S^{2-}(aq)$$
$$K_{sp} = [M^{2+}][S^{2-}]$$

$$S^{2-}(aq) + H_2O(\ell) \rightleftharpoons HS^-(aq) + OH^-(aq)$$
$$K_b = [HS^-][OH^-]/[S^{2-}]$$

Net reaction:

$$MS(s) + H_2O(\ell) \rightleftharpoons HS^-(aq) + M^{2+}(aq) + OH^-(aq)$$
$$K_{spa} = [M^{2+}][HS^-][OH^-] = K_{sp} \times K_b$$

Values for $K_{spa}$ for several metal sulfides are included in Appendix J.

**FIGURE 18.15 The effect of the anion on salt solubility in acid.**
*(left)* A precipitate of AgCl (white) and Ag₃PO₄ (yellow). *(right)* Adding a strong acid (HNO₃) dissolves Ag₃PO₄ (and leaves insoluble AgCl). The basic anion PO₄³⁻ reacts with acid to give H₃PO₄, whereas Cl⁻ is too weakly basic to form HCl.

Add strong acid.

precipitate of
AgCl and Ag₃PO₄

precipitate of
AgCl

as are metal phosphates (Figure 18.15),

$$Ag_3PO_4(s) + 3\ H_3O^+(aq) \rightleftharpoons 3\ Ag^+(aq) + H_3PO_4(aq) + 3\ H_2O(\ell)$$

and metal hydroxides.

$$Mg(OH)_2(s) + 2\ H_3O^+(aq) \rightleftharpoons Mg^{2+}(aq) + 4\ H_2O(\ell)$$

In general, the solubility of a salt containing the conjugate base of a weak acid is increased by addition of a stronger acid to the solution. In contrast, salts are not soluble in strong acid if the anion is the conjugate base of a strong acid. For example, AgCl is not soluble in strong acid

$$AgCl(s) \rightleftharpoons Ag^+(aq) + Cl^-(aq) \qquad\qquad K_{sp} = 1.8 \times 10^{-10}$$

$$H_3O^+(aq) + Cl^-(aq) \rightleftharpoons HCl(aq) + H_2O(\ell) \qquad K << 1$$

because Cl⁻ is a very weak base (◄ Table 17.3), and so its concentration is not lowered by a reaction with the strong acid H₃O⁺ (Figure 18.15). This same conclusion would also apply to insoluble salts of Br⁻ and I⁻.

---

**REVIEW & CHECK FOR SECTION 18.4**

1.  What is the $K_{sp}$ expression for silver carbonate?

    (a)  $K_{sp} = [Ag^+][CO_3^{2-}]$        (c)  $K_{sp} = [Ag^+][CO_3^{2-}]^2$

    (b)  $K_{sp} = [Ag^+]^2[CO_3^{2-}]$

2.  Using $K_{sp}$ values, predict which salt in each pair is more soluble in water.

    (a)  AgCl ($K_{sp} = 1.8 \times 10^{-10}$) or AgCN ($K_{sp} = 6.0 \times 10^{-17}$)

    (b)  Mg(OH)₂ ($K_{sp} = 5.6 \times 10^{-12}$) or Ca(OH)₂ ($K_{sp} = 5.5 \times 10^{-5}$)

    (c)  Ca(OH)₂ ($K_{sp} = 5.5 \times 10^{-5}$) or CaSO₄ ($K_{sp} = 4.9 \times 10^{-5}$)

3.  What is the solubility of PbSO₄ in water at 25 °C? ($K_{sp}$ for PbSO₄ = $2.5 \times 10^{-8}$)

    (a)  $2.5 \times 10^{-8}$ M    (b)  $1.6 \times 10^{-4}$ M    (c)  $6.3 \times 10^{-16}$ M

4.  What is the solubility of PbSO₄ in water at 25 °C if the solution already contains 0.25 M Na₂SO₄? ($K_{sp}$ for PbSO₄ = $2.5 \times 10^{-8}$)

    (a)  $1.0 \times 10^{-7}$ M    (b)  $1.6 \times 10^{-4}$ M    (c)  $6.3 \times 10^{-9}$ M

5.  Which compound should be more soluble in 0.1 M HCl?

    (a)  FeCO₃ ($K_{sp} = 3.1 \times 10^{-11}$)        (b)  AgCl ($K_{sp} = 1.8 \times 10^{-10}$)

## 18.5 Precipitation Reactions

Metal-bearing ores contain the metal in the form of an insoluble salt (Figure 18.16), and, to complicate matters, ores often contain several such metal salts. Many industrial methods for separating metals from their ores involve dissolving metal salts to obtain the metal ion or ions in solution. The solution is then concentrated in some manner, and a precipitating agent is added to precipitate selectively only one type of metal ion as an insoluble salt. In the case of nickel, for example, the $Ni^{2+}$ ion can be precipitated as insoluble nickel(II) sulfide or nickel(II) carbonate.

$$Ni^{2+}(aq) + HS^-(aq) + H_2O(\ell) \rightleftharpoons NiS(s) + H_3O^+(aq) \qquad K = 1.7 \times 10^{18}$$

$$Ni^{2+}(aq) + CO_3^{2-}(aq) \rightleftharpoons NiCO_3(s) \qquad K = 7.1 \times 10^6$$

After separating the insoluble salt, the final step in obtaining the metal itself is to reduce the metal cation to the metal either chemically or electrochemically (▶ Chapter 20).

Our immediate goal is to work out methods to determine whether a precipitate will form under a given set of conditions. For example, if $Ag^+$ and $Cl^-$ are present at some given concentrations, will AgCl precipitate from the solution?

**FIGURE 18.16 Minerals.** Minerals are insoluble salts. The minerals shown here are light purple fluorite (calcium fluoride), black hematite [iron(III) oxide], and rust brown goethite, a mixture of iron(III) oxide and iron(III) hydroxide.

### $K_{sp}$ and the Reaction Quotient, $Q$

Silver chloride, like silver bromide, is used in photographic films. It dissolves to a very small extent in water and has a correspondingly small value of $K_{sp}$.

$$AgCl(s) \rightleftharpoons Ag^+(aq) + Cl^-(aq) \qquad K_{sp} = [Ag^+][Cl^-] = 1.8 \times 10^{-10}$$

But look at the problem from the other direction: If a solution contains $Ag^+$ and $Cl^-$ ions at some concentration, will AgCl precipitate from solution? This is the same question we asked in Section 16.2 when we wanted to know if a given mixture of reactants and products was an equilibrium mixture, if the reactants continued to form products, or if products would revert to reactants. The procedure there was to calculate the reaction quotient, $Q$.

For silver chloride, the expression for the reaction quotient, $Q$, is

$$Q = [Ag^+][Cl^-]$$

Recall that *the difference between $Q$ and $K$ is that the concentrations in the reaction quotient expression, $Q$, may or may not be those at equilibrium.* For the case of a slightly soluble salt such as AgCl, we can reach the following conclusions (◀ Section 16.2).

1. If $Q = K_{sp}$, the solution is saturated.

When $Q = K_{sp}$ the ion concentrations have reached their maximum value.

2. If $Q < K_{sp}$, the solution is not saturated.

This can mean either of two things: (i) If solid AgCl is present, more will dissolve until equilibrium is achieved (when $Q = K_{sp}$). (ii) If solid AgCl is not already present, more $Ag^+(aq)$ or more $Cl^-(aq)$ (or both) could be added to the solution until precipitation of solid AgCl begins (when $Q > K_{sp}$).

3. If $Q > K_{sp}$, the solution is oversaturated and precipitation will occur.

The concentrations of $Ag^+$ and $Cl^-$ in solution are too high, and AgCl will precipitate until $Q = K_{sp}$.

## CASE STUDY

## Chemical Equilibria in the Oceans

Although there is continuing debate about the issue of global warming, the matter of the amount of $CO_2$ in Earth's atmosphere seems settled: There has been a significant increase since the beginning of the Industrial Revolution in the 18th century. Along with this increase in atmospheric $CO_2$, there has also been a documented increase in the amount of $CO_2$ absorbed by the world's oceans. Indeed, over the last 200 years the oceans have absorbed about 550 billion tons of $CO_2$ (currently about 22 million tons per day). The author of a recent paper in *Nature* stated that "If you took all of the man-made carbon in the ocean and released it into the air, atmospheric levels of $CO_2$ would be 20% higher." If the oceans had not absorbed that much $CO_2$, earth's temperature is predicted to be 2 °C warmer, a point at which significant climate change would occur. The absorption of $CO_2$ by the oceans has prevented much of this gas from entering the atmosphere, but there is evidence that the oceans are becoming a less efficient sink. And that is not the only problem.

When $CO_2$ dissolves in the ocean, it forms carbonic acid, a weak acid in equilibrium with hydronium ions and bicarbonate ions (as well as a small concentration of carbonate ions).

$$CO_2(g) + H_2O(\ell) \rightleftharpoons H_2CO_3(aq)$$

$$H_2CO_3(aq) + H_2O(\ell) \rightleftharpoons H_3O^+(aq) + HCO_3^-(aq)$$

$$HCO_3^-(aq) + H_2O(\ell) \rightleftharpoons H_3O^+(aq) + CO_3^{2-}(aq)$$

John C. Kotz

**Aragonite, a form of CaCO₃.**

Carbonate ions are required by many marine organisms such as plankton, shellfish, and fish to produce shells, made of $CaCO_3$, and skeletons. There are two naturally occurring forms of calcium carbonate: calcite and aragonite. Most mollusk shells are made of aragonite, and, as the $K_{sp}$ values show, aragonite ($K_{sp} = 6.0 \times 10^{-9}$) is slightly more soluble than calcite ($K_{sp} = 3.4 \times 10^{-9}$).

Because carbonate ions are central to the life of marine organisms, any change in the calcium carbonate equilibrium

$$CaCO_3(s) \rightleftharpoons Ca^{2+}(aq) + CO_3^{2-}(aq)$$

can lead to significant changes in marine life. If, for example, the carbonate ion concentration in the oceans drops below the saturation level, calcium carbonate will dissolve. A paper published in the journal *Science* in 2009 reports that that is indeed happening, espe-

cially in the Arctic Ocean. (The pH of ocean surface water is now about 8.1, a drop from 8.2 in the 18th century.) Hydronium ions from dissolved $CO_2$ react with carbonate ions to produce bicarbonate ions, thus disrupting the calcium carbonate equilibrium and affecting the shells of marine creatures (page 128). This trend is exacerbated by the fact that northern rivers and melting sea ice are introducing increasing amounts of fresh water into the Arctic Ocean, which lowers the $CO_3^{2-}$ concentration and allows aragonite to dissolve.

The chemistry of the oceans is a delicate equilibrium, and anthropogenic and natural effects can cause serious disruption in the chemistry. In fact a marine geochemist said in 2009 that "High-latitude oceans may already be at a tipping point for carbonate shell builders."

### Question:

How much more soluble is aragonite than calcite? Compare the solubility of $CaCO_3$ from these two sources on a gram per liter basis.

**The answer to this question is available in Appendix N.**

### References:

1. S. Khatiwala, *Nature*, 2009, *462*, 346.
2. M. Yamamoto-Kawai, F. A. McLaughlin, E. C. Carmack, S. Nishino, and K. Shimada, *Science*, 2009, *326*, 1098–1100, and references therein.
3. R. Petkewich, *Chemical & Engineering News*, February 23, 2009, pp. 56–58.

---

**⬤WL   INTERACTIVE EXAMPLE 18.13   Solubility and the Reaction Quotient**

**Problem** Solid AgCl has been placed in a beaker of water. After some time, the concentrations of $Ag^+$ and $Cl^-$ are each $1.2 \times 10^{-5}$ mol/L. Has the system reached equilibrium? If not, will more AgCl dissolve?

**What Do You Know?** You know the balanced equation for dissolving the AgCl, its value of $K_{sp}$, and the $Ag^+$ and $Cl^-$ concentrations.

**Strategy**

- Write the balanced equation for dissolving the salt and then write the expression for the reaction quotient, $Q$.

- Use the experimental ion concentrations to calculate the reaction quotient $Q$. Compare $Q$ and $K_{sp}$ to decide if the system is at equilibrium (if $Q = K_{sp}$).

**Solution**

$$AgCl(s) \rightleftharpoons Ag^+(aq) + Cl^-(aq) \qquad K_{sp} = [Ag^+][Cl^-] = 1.8 \times 10^{-10}$$

$$Q = [Ag^+][Cl^-] = (1.2 \times 10^{-5})(1.2 \times 10^{-5}) = 1.4 \times 10^{-10}$$

Here, $Q$ is less than $K_{sp}$ ($1.8 \times 10^{-10}$). The solution is not yet saturated, and AgCl will continue to dissolve until $Q = K_{sp}$, at which point $[Ag^+] = [Cl^-] = 1.3 \times 10^{-5}$ M. That is, an additional $0.1 \times 10^{-5}$ mol of AgCl will dissolve per liter.

**Think about Your Answer** Dissolving is often a fairly slow process. If you measure the ion concentrations at a particular time, they may not have yet reached an equilibrium value, as is the case here. In contrast, acid–base reactions generally proceed rapidly to equilibrium.

**Check Your Understanding**

Solid $PbI_2$ ($K_{sp} = 9.8 \times 10^{-9}$) is placed in a beaker of water. After a period of time, the lead(II) concentration is measured and found to be $1.1 \times 10^{-3}$ M. Has the system reached equilibrium? That is, is the solution saturated? If not, will more $PbI_2$ dissolve?

## $K_{sp}$, the Reaction Quotient, and Precipitation Reactions

Using the reaction quotient and the solubility product constant, we can decide (1) if a precipitate will form when the ion concentrations are known or (2) what concentrations of ions are required to begin the precipitation of an insoluble salt.

Suppose the concentration of magnesium ion in an aqueous solution is $1.5 \times 10^{-6}$ M. If enough NaOH is added to make the solution $1.0 \times 10^{-4}$ M in hydroxide ion, $OH^-$, will precipitation of $Mg(OH)_2$ occur ($K_{sp} = 5.6 \times 10^{-12}$)? If not, will it occur if the concentration of $OH^-$ is increased to $1.0 \times 10^{-2}$ M?

Our strategy is similar to that in Example 18.13. That is, use the ion concentrations to calculate the value of $Q$ and then compare $Q$ with $K_{sp}$ to decide if the system is at equilibrium. We begin with the equation for the dissolution of $Mg(OH)_2$.

$$Mg(OH)_2(s) \rightleftharpoons Mg^{2+}(aq) + 2\ OH^-(aq)$$

When the concentrations of magnesium and hydroxide ions are the first ones stated above, we find that $Q$ is less than $K_{sp}$.

$$Q = [Mg^{2+}][OH^-]^2 = (1.5 \times 10^{-6})(1.0 \times 10^{-4})^2 = 1.5 \times 10^{-14}$$

$$Q\ (1.5 \times 10^{-14}) < K_{sp}\ (5.6 \times 10^{-12})$$

This means the solution is not yet saturated, and precipitation does not occur.

When $[OH^-]$ is increased to $1.0 \times 10^{-2}$ M, the reaction quotient is $1.5 \times 10^{-10}$,

$$Q = (1.5 \times 10^{-6})(1.0 \times 10^{-2})^2$$

$$Q = 1.5 \times 10^{-10} > K_{sp}\ (5.6 \times 10^{-12})$$

and the reaction quotient is now *larger* than $K_{sp}$. Precipitation of $Mg(OH)_2$ occurs and will continue until the $Mg^{2+}$ and $OH^-$ ion concentrations have decreased to the point where their product is equal to $K_{sp}$.

Now let us turn to a similar problem: deciding how much of the precipitating agent is required to begin the precipitation of an ion at a given concentration level.

## ◉WL   INTERACTIVE EXAMPLE 18.14   Ion Concentrations Required to Begin Precipitation

**Problem** The concentration of barium ion, $Ba^{2+}$, in a solution is 0.010 M.

(a)   What concentration of sulfate ion, $SO_4^{2-}$, is required to begin the precipitation of $BaSO_4$?

(b)   When the concentration of sulfate ion in the solution reaches 0.015 M, what concentration of barium ion will remain in solution?

**What Do You Know?** There are three terms in the $K_{sp}$ expression: $K_{sp}$ and the anion and cation concentrations. Here, you know $K_{sp}$ ($1.1 \times 10^{-10}$) and one of the ion concentrations. You can then calculate the other ion concentration.

---

**Strategy Map 18.13**

**PROBLEM**

Does **AgCl** precipitate at specified values of $[Ag^+]$ and $[Cl^-]$?

↓

**DATA/INFORMATION KNOWN**

- $K_{sp}$ value for AgCl
- $Ag^+$ concentration
- $Cl^-$ concentration

↓

**STEP 1.** Write expression for $Q$, the reaction quotient.

↓

$$Q = [Ag^+][Cl^-]$$

**STEP 2.** Enter concentrations in $Q$ expression and solve.

↓

$Q < K_{sp}$, so more AgCl will dissolve.

**Strategy Map 18.14**

PROBLEM

What concentration of $SO_4^{2-}$ is required to begin precipitation of $BaSO_4$?

↓

DATA/INFORMATION KNOWN

• $K_{sp}$ value for $BaSO_4$
• Initial [$Ba^{2+}$]

↓

STEP 1. Write **expression** for $K_{sp}$.

↓

$K_{sp} = [Ba^{2+}][SO_4^{2-}]$

↓

STEP 2. Enter **$Ba^{2+}$ concentration** and solve for [$SO_4^{2-}$].

↓

$BaSO_4$ begins to precipitate when [$SO_4^{2-}$] exceeds calculated value.

**Strategy**

• Write the balanced equation for dissolving $BaSO_4$ and the $K_{sp}$ expression.

• **Part (a):** Use the $K_{sp}$ expression to calculate [$SO_4^{2-}$] when [$Ba^{2+}$] = 0.010 M.

• **Part (b):** Use the $K_{sp}$ expression to calculate [$Ba^{2+}$] when [$SO_4^{2-}$] = 0.015 M.

**Solution**

$$BaSO_4(s) \rightleftharpoons Ba^{2+}(aq) + SO_4^{2-}(aq) \qquad K_{sp} = [Ba^{2+}][SO_4^{2-}] = 1.1 \times 10^{-10}$$

(a) When the product of the ion concentrations exceeds the $K_{sp}$ (= $1.1 \times 10^{-10}$)—that is, when $Q > K_{sp}$—precipitation will occur. The $Ba^{2+}$ ion concentration is known (0.010 M), so the $SO_4^{2-}$ ion concentration necessary for precipitation can be calculated.

$$[SO_4^{2-}] = \frac{K_{sp}}{[Ba^{2+}]} = \frac{1.1 \times 10^{-10}}{0.010} = 1.1 \times 10^{-8} \text{ M}$$

The result tells us that if the sulfate ion concentration is just slightly greater than $1.1 \times 10^{-8}$ M, $BaSO_4$ will begin to precipitate.

(b) If the sulfate ion concentration is increased to 0.015 M, the maximum concentration of $Ba^{2+}$ ion that can exist in solution (in equilibrium with $BaSO_4$) is

$$[Ba^{2+}] = \frac{K_{sp}}{[SO_4^{2-}]} = \frac{1.1 \times 10^{-10}}{0.015} = 7.3 \times 10^{-9} \text{ M}$$

**Think about Your Answer** The fact that the barium ion concentration is so small when [$SO_4^{2-}$] = 0.015 M means that the $Ba^{2+}$ ion has been essentially removed from solution. (It began at 0.010 M and has decreased by a factor of about 1 million.)

---

**Check Your Understanding**

What is the minimum concentration of $I^-$ that can cause precipitation of $PbI_2$ from a 0.050 M solution of $Pb(NO_3)_2$? $K_{sp}$ for $PbI_2$ is $9.8 \times 10^{-9}$. What concentration of $Pb^{2+}$ ions remains in solution when the concentration of $I^-$ is 0.0015 M?

---

## EXAMPLE 18.15    $K_{sp}$ and Precipitations

**Problem** Suppose you mix 100.0 mL of 0.0200 M $BaCl_2$ with 50.0 mL of 0.0300 M $Na_2SO_4$. Will $BaSO_4$ ($K_{sp} = 1.1 \times 10^{-10}$) precipitate?

**What Do You Know?** You know the concentration of two different compounds in solutions of differing volumes and so you can calculate the amount (moles) of each substance. You also know that $BaCl_2$ and $Na_2SO_4$ will combine to give a precipitate, $BaSO_4$, if they are mixed in sufficient concentration. You also know the $K_{sp}$ value for $BaSO_4$.

**Strategy** Here, you mix two solutions, one containing $Ba^{2+}$ ions and the other $SO_4^{2-}$ ions, both with known concentration and volume, and insoluble $BaSO_4$ may be formed.

• Find the concentration of each of these ions after mixing.

• Knowing the ion concentrations in the combined solution, calculate $Q$ and compare it with the $K_{sp}$ value for $BaSO_4$ to decide if $BaSO_4$ will precipitate under these circumstances.

**Solution** First, use the equation $c_1V_1 = c_2V_2$ (◀ Section 4.5) to calculate $c_2$, the concentration of the $Ba^{2+}$ and $SO_4^{2-}$ ions after mixing, to give a new solution with a volume of 150.0 mL (= $V_2$).

$$[Ba^{2+}] \text{ after mixing} = \frac{(0.0200 \text{ mol/L})(0.1000 \text{ L})}{0.1500 \text{ L}} = 0.0133 \text{ M}$$

$$[SO_4^{2-}] \text{ after mixing} = \frac{(0.0300 \text{ mol/L})(0.0500 \text{ L})}{0.1500 \text{ L}} = 0.0100 \text{ M}$$

The equilibrium governing the reaction that can occur is

$$BaSO_4(s) \rightleftharpoons Ba^{2+}(aq) + SO_4^{2-}(aq) \qquad K_{sp} = [Ba^{2+}][SO_4^{2-}] = 1.1 \times 10^{-10}$$

Now the reaction quotient can be calculated.

$$Q = [Ba^{2+}][SO_4^{2-}] = (0.0133)(0.0100) = 1.33 \times 10^{-4}$$

$Q$ is much larger than $K_{sp}$, so $BaSO_4$ precipitates.

**Think about Your Answer** The $K_{sp}$ value for $BaSO_4$ is very small, so mixing solutions with $Ba^{2+}$ and $SO_4^{2-}$ ions, even in very low concentration, can lead to the precipitation of $BaSO_4$.

**Check Your Understanding**

You have 100.0 mL of 0.0010 M silver nitrate. Will AgCl precipitate if you add 5.0 mL of 0.025 M HCl?

---

**REVIEW & CHECK FOR SECTION 18.5**

Will $SrSO_4$ precipitate from a solution containing $2.5 \times 10^{-4}$ M strontium ion, $Sr^{2+}$, if enough of the soluble salt $Na_2SO_4$ is added to make the solution $2.5 \times 10^{-4}$ M in $SO_4^{2-}$? $K_{sp}$ for $SrSO_4$ is $3.4 \times 10^{-7}$.

(a)   yes          (b)   no          (c)   can't decide

---

## 18.6 Equilibria Involving Complex Ions

Metal ions exist in aqueous solution as complex ions (◄Section 17.11) (Figure 18.17). Complex ions consist of the metal ion and other molecules or ions bound into a single entity. In water, metal ions are always surrounded by water molecules, with the negative end of the polar water molecule, the oxygen atom, attracted to the positive metal ion. In the case of $Ni^{2+}$, the ion exists as $[Ni(H_2O)_6]^{2+}$ in water. On adding ammonia, water molecules are displaced successively, and in the presence of a high enough concentration of ammonia, the complex ion $[Ni(NH_3)_6]^{2+}$ exists. Many organic molecules also form complex ions with metal ions, one example being the complex with the dimethylglyoximate ion in Figure 18.17.

   The molecules or ions that bind to metal ions are called **ligands** (► Chapter 22). In aqueous solution, metal ions and ligands exist in equilibrium, and the equilibrium constants for these reactions are referred to as **formation constants**, $K_f$ (Appendix K). For example,

| | |
|---|---|
| $Cu^{2+}(aq) + NH_3(aq) \rightleftharpoons [Cu(NH_3)]^{2+}(aq)$ | $K_{f1} = 2.0 \times 10^4$ |
| $[Cu(NH_3)]^{2+}(aq) + NH_3(aq) \rightleftharpoons [Cu(NH_3)_2]^{2+}(aq)$ | $K_{f2} = 4.7 \times 10^3$ |
| $[Cu(NH_3)_2]^{2+}(aq) + NH_3(aq) \rightleftharpoons [Cu(NH_3)_3]^{2+}(aq)$ | $K_{f3} = 1.1 \times 10^3$ |
| $[Cu(NH_3)_3]^{2+}(aq) + NH_3(aq) \rightleftharpoons [Cu(NH_3)_4]^{2+}(aq)$ | $K_{f4} = 2.0 \times 10^2$ |

In these reactions, $Cu^{2+}$ begins as $[Cu(H_2O)_4]^{2+}$, but ammonia successively displaces the water molecules. Overall, the formation of the tetraammine copper(II) complex ion has an equilibrium constant of $2.1 \times 10^{13}$ ($= K_{f1} \times K_{f2} \times K_{f3} \times K_{f4}$).

$$Cu^{2+}(aq) + 4 \ NH_3(aq) \rightleftharpoons [Cu(NH_3)_4]^{2+}(aq) \qquad K_f = 2.1 \times 10^{13}$$

Dimethylglyoximate complex of $Ni^{2+}$ ion

$[Ni(NH_3)_6]^{2+}$

$[Ni(H_2O)_6]^{2+}$

© Cengage Learning/Charles D. Winters

**FIGURE 18.17 Complex ions.** The green solution contains soluble $Ni(H_2O)_6^{2+}$ ions in which water molecules are bound to $Ni^{2+}$ ions by ion–dipole forces. This complex ion gives the solution its green color. The $Ni^{2+}$-ammonia complex ion is purple. The red, insoluble solid is the dimethylglyoximate complex of the $Ni^{2+}$ ion $[Ni(C_4H_7O_2N_2)_2]$ (model at top). Formation of this beautiful red insoluble compound is the classical test for the presence of the aqueous $Ni^{2+}$ ion.

## EXAMPLE 18.16 Complex Ion Equilibria

**Problem** What is the concentration of $Cu^{2+}$ ions in a solution prepared by adding 0.00100 mol of $Cu(NO_3)_2$ to 1.00 L of 1.50 M $NH_3$? $K_f$ for the copper-ammonia complex ion $[Cu(NH_3)_4]^{2+}$ is $2.1 \times 10^{13}$.

**What Do You Know?** Here you know the concentration of the species that form the complex ion ($Cu^{2+}$ and $NH_3$), and you know the formation constant for the ion.

**Strategy** The formation constant for the complex ion is very large, so you start with the assumption that all of the $Cu^{2+}$ ions react with $NH_3$ to form $[Cu(NH_3)_4]^{2+}$. That is, the initial concentration of the complex ion, $[Cu(NH_3)_4]^{2+}$ is 0.00100 M. This cation then dissociates to produce $Cu^{2+}$ ions and additional $NH_3$ in solution. The equilibrium constant for the dissociation of $[Cu(NH_3)_4]^{2+}$ is the reciprocal of $K_f$ because the dissociation of the ion is the reverse of its formation.

- Write a balanced equation for the dissociation of the complex ion that formed in solution and set up an ICE table.

- Assume that all of the $Cu^{2+}$ ions in the solution are in the form of $[Cu(NH_3)_4]^{2+}$ (0.00100 M). This means that $[NH_3]$ = original concentration − 4 × 0.00100 M.

- Assume the concentration of complex ion dissociated at equilibrium is $x$, so $x$ mol/L of $Cu^{2+}$ are released to solution as are $4x$ mol/L of $NH_3$.

- Use the equilibrium concentrations of the ions in the expression for $K_{dissociation}$ ($= 1/K_f$) and solve for $x$ (which is the concentration of $Cu^{2+}$ at equilibrium).

**Solution** Set up an ICE table for the dissociation of $[Cu(NH_3)_4]^{2+}$.

| Equation | $[Cu(NH_3)_4]^{2+}(aq)$ | $\rightleftharpoons$ | $Cu^{2+}(aq)$ | + | $4\,NH_3(aq)$ |
|---|---|---|---|---|---|
| Initial (M) | 0.00100 | | 0 | | 1.50 − 0.00400 M |
| Change (M) | −$x$ | | +$x$ | | +$4x$ |
| Equilibrium (M) | 0.00100 − $x \approx$ 0.00100 | | $x$ | | 1.50 − 0.00400 + $4x \approx$ 1.50 |

Here we assume that $x$ is so small that the concentration of the complex ion is very nearly 0.00100 M and that the $NH_3$ concentration at equilibrium is essentially what was there originally.

$$K_{dissociation} = \frac{1}{K_f} = \frac{1}{2.1 \times 10^{13}} = \frac{[Cu^{2+}][NH_3]^4}{\{[Cu(NH_3)_4]^{2+}\}} = \frac{(x)(1.50)^4}{0.00100}$$

$$x = [Cu^{2+}] = \boxed{9.4 \times 10^{-18} \text{ M}}$$

**Think about Your Answer** Make sure to test your assumption that $x$ is so small it can neglected in determining the equilibrium concentrations of $[Cu(NH_3)_4]^{2+}$ and $NH_3$. It certainly is in this case.

**Check Your Understanding**

Silver nitrate (0.0050 mol) is added to 1.00 L of 1.00 M $NH_3$. What is the concentration of $Ag^+$ ions at equilibrium?

$$Ag^+(aq) + 2\,NH_3(aq) \rightleftharpoons [Ag(NH_3)_2]^+(aq) \qquad K_f = 1.1 \times 10^7$$

---

**REVIEW & CHECK FOR SECTION 18.6**

Iron(II) chloride (0.0025 mol) is added to 1.00 L of 0.500 M NaCN. What is the concentration of $Fe^{2+}$ ions at equilibrium? $K_f$ for $[Fe(CN)_6]^{4-}$ is $1.0 \times 10^{35}$.

(a) $1.0 \times 10^{-35}$ M      (b) $1.9 \times 10^{-36}$ M      (c) $5.2 \times 10^{-38}$ M

## 18.7 Solubility and Complex Ions

Silver chloride does not dissolve either in water or in strong acid, but it does dissolve in ammonia because it forms a water-soluble complex ion, $[Ag(NH_3)_2]^+$ (Figure 18.18).

$$AgCl(s) + 2\,NH_3(aq) \rightleftharpoons [Ag(NH_3)_2]^+(aq) + Cl^-(aq)$$

We can view dissolving AgCl(s) as a two-step process. First, AgCl dissolves minimally in water, giving $Ag^+(aq)$ and $Cl^-(aq)$ ion. Then, the $Ag^+(aq)$ ion combines with $NH_3$ to give the ammonia complex. Lowering the $Ag^+(aq)$ concentration through complexation with $NH_3$ shifts the solubility equilibrium to the right, and more solid AgCl dissolves.

$$AgCl(s) \rightleftharpoons Ag^+(aq) + Cl^-(aq) \qquad K_{sp} = 1.8 \times 10^{-10}$$

$$Ag^+(aq) + 2\ NH_3(aq) \rightleftharpoons [Ag(NH_3)_2]^+(aq) \qquad K_f = 1.1 \times 10^7$$

This is an example of combining or "coupling" two (or more) equilibria where one is a product-favored reaction and the other is reactant-favored.

The large value of the formation constant for $[Ag(NH_3)_2]^+$ means that the equilibrium lies well to the right, and AgCl can dissolve in the presence of $NH_3$. If you combine $K_f$ with $K_{sp}$, you obtain the net equilibrium constant for the interaction of AgCl and aqueous ammonia.

$$K_{net} = K_{sp} \times K_f = (1.8 \times 10^{-10})(1.1 \times 10^7) = 2.0 \times 10^{-3}$$

$$K_{net} = 2.0 \times 10^{-3} = \frac{\{[Ag(NH_3)_2]^+\}[Cl^-]}{[NH_3]^2}$$

Even though the value of $K_{net}$ seems small, if you use a large concentration of $NH_3$, the concentration of $[Ag(NH_3)_2]^+$ in solution can be appreciable. Silver chloride is thus much more soluble in the presence of ammonia than in pure water.

The stabilities of various complex ions involving silver(I) can be compared by comparing values of their formation constants.

| Formation Equilibrium | $K_f$ |
|---|---|
| $Ag^+(aq) + 2\ Cl^-(aq) \rightleftharpoons [AgCl_2]^-(aq)$ | $1.1 \times 10^5$ |
| $Ag^+(aq) + 2\ S_2O_3{}^{2-}(aq) \rightleftharpoons [Ag(S_2O_3)_2]^{3-}(aq)$ | $2.9 \times 10^{13}$ |
| $Ag^+(aq) + 2\ CN^-(aq) \rightleftharpoons [Ag(CN)_2]^-(aq)$ | $1.3 \times 10^{21}$ |

The formation of all three silver complexes is strongly product-favored. The cyanide complex ion $[Ag(CN)_2]^-$ is the most stable of the three.

Figure 18.18 shows what happens as complex ions are formed. Beginning with a precipitate of AgCl, adding aqueous ammonia dissolves the precipitate to give the

● **Complex Ions** Complex ions are prevalent in chemistry and are the basis of such biologically important substances as hemoglobin and vitamin B₁₂. They are described in more detail in Chapter 22.

AgCl(s),
$K_{sp} = 1.8 \times 10^{-10}$

**(a)** AgCl precipitates on adding NaCl(aq) to AgNO₃(aq).

NH₃(aq) →

$[Ag(NH_3)_2]^+(aq)$

**(b)** The precipitate of AgCl dissolves on adding aqueous NH₃ to give water-soluble $[Ag(NH_3)_2]^+$.

NaBr(aq) →

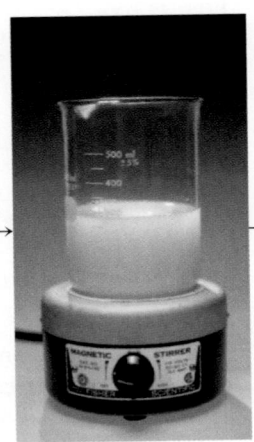

AgBr(s),
$K_{sp} = 5.4 \times 10^{-13}$

**(c)** The silver-ammonia complex ion is changed to insoluble AgBr on adding NaBr(aq).

Na₂S₂O₃(aq) →

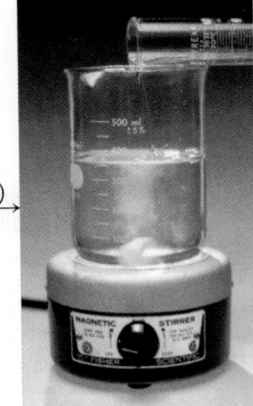

$[Ag(S_2O_3)_2]^{3-}(aq)$

**(d)** Solid AgBr is dissolved on adding Na₂S₂O₃(aq). The product is the water-soluble complex ion $[Ag(S_2O_3)_2]^{3-}$.

Photos © Cengage Learning/Charles D. Winters

**FIGURE 18.18 Forming and dissolving precipitates.** Insoluble compounds often dissolve upon addition of a complexing agent.

soluble complex ion $[Ag(NH_3)_2]^+$. Silver bromide is even more stable than $[Ag(NH_3)_2]^+$, so AgBr ($K_{sp} = 5.4 \times 10^{-13}$) forms in preference to the complex ion on adding bromide ion. If thiosulfate ion, $S_2O_3^{2-}$, is then added, AgBr dissolves due to the formation of $[Ag(S_2O_3)_2]^{3-}$, a complex ion with a large formation constant ($2.9 \times 10^{13}$).

## EXAMPLE 18.17 Complex Ions and Solubility

**Problem** What is the value of the equilibrium constant, $K_{net}$, for dissolving AgBr in a solution containing the thiosulfate ion, $S_2O_3^{2-}$ (Figure 18.18)? Does AgBr dissolve readily on adding aqueous sodium thiosulfate to the solid?

**What Do You Know?** There are two equilibria here. One is for dissolving AgBr in water to give $Ag^+$ and $Br^-$ ions, and its equilibrium constant is $K_{sp}$. The other is the formation of $[Ag(S_2O_3)_2]^{3-}$ ions from $Ag^+$ and $S_2O_3^{2-}$ ions; its equilibrium constant is $K_f$.

**Strategy** Summing several equilibrium processes gives the net chemical equation. $K_{net}$ is the product of the values of $K$ of the summed chemical equations (◀ Section 16.5).

**Solution** The overall reaction for dissolving AgBr in the presence of the thiosulfate anion is the sum of two equilibrium processes.

$$AgBr(s) \rightleftharpoons Ag^+(aq) + Br^-(aq) \qquad\qquad K_{sp} = 5.0 \times 10^{-13}$$

$$Ag^+(aq) + 2\ S_2O_3^{2-}(aq) \rightleftharpoons [Ag(S_2O_3)_2]^{3-}(aq) \qquad K_f = 2.9 \times 10^{13}$$

Net chemical equation:

$$AgBr(aq) + 2\ S_2O_3^{2-}(aq) \rightleftharpoons [Ag(S_2O_3)_2]^{3-}(aq) + Br^-(aq) \qquad K_{net} = K_{sp} \times K_f = 15$$

AgBr is predicted to dissolve readily in aqueous $Na_2S_2O_3$, as observed (Figure 18.18).

**Think about Your Answer** The value of $K_{net}$ is greater than 1, indicating a product-favored reaction at equilibrium.

### Check Your Understanding

Calculate the value of the equilibrium constant, $K_{net}$, for dissolving $Cu(OH)_2$ in aqueous ammonia (to form the complex ion $[Cu(NH_3)_4]^{2+}$) (◀ Figure 17.10).

---

**REVIEW & CHECK FOR SECTION 18.7**

What is the equilibrium constant for the process of dissolving AgI by the addition of aqueous NaCN? $K_{sp}$ for AgI is $8.5 \times 10^{-17}$, and $K_f$ for $[Ag(CN)_2]^-$ is $1.3 \times 10^{21}$.

(a) $6.5 \times 10^{-4}$      (b) $8.7 \times 10^4$      (c) $1.1 \times 10^5$

---

**OWL** and **go Chemistry**

## CHAPTER GOALS REVISITED

*Now that you have studied this chapter, you should ask whether you have met the chapter goals. In particular, you should be able to:*

### Understand the common ion effect

a. Predict the effect of the addition of a "common ion" on the pH of the solution of a weak acid or base (Section 18.1). **Study Questions: 1–4, 109.**

### Understand the control of pH in aqueous solutions with buffers

a. Describe the functioning of buffer solutions. (Section 18.2). **Go Chemistry Module 23.**

b. Use the Henderson–Hasselbalch equation (Equation 18.2) to calculate the pH of a buffer solution of given composition. **Study Questions: 5–8, 11–14.**

c. Describe how a buffer solution of a given pH can be prepared. **Study Questions: 9, 10, 15–18, 83, 90, 101, 102, 109.**

d. Calculate the pH of a buffer solution before and after adding acid or base. **Study Questions: 19–22.**

**Evaluate the pH in the course of acid–base titrations**

a.  Predict the pH of an acid–base reaction at its equivalence point (Section 18.3; see also Sections 17.6 and 17.7). **Study Questions: 24–30, 74, 76, 98, 108.**

| Acid | Base | pH at Equivalence Point |
|------|------|------------------------|
| Strong | Strong | = 7 (neutral) |
| Strong | Weak | < 7 (acidic) |
| Weak | Strong | > 7 (basic) |

b.  Understand the differences between the titration curves for a strong acid–strong base titration and titrations in which one of the substances is weak.

c.  Describe how an indicator functions in an acid–base titration. **Study Questions: 31, 97–99.**

**Apply chemical equilibrium concepts to the solubility of ionic compounds**

a.  Write the equilibrium constant expression—relating concentrations of ions in solutions to $K_{sp}$—for any insoluble salt (Section 18.4). **Study Questions: 37, 38.**

b.  Calculate $K_{sp}$ values from experimental data (Section 18.4). **Study Questions: 39–44.**

c.  Estimate the solubility of a salt from the value of $K_{sp}$ (Section 18.4). **Study Questions: 45–48, 96, 105.**

d.  Calculate the solubility of a salt in the presence of a common ion (Section 18.4). **Study Questions: 53–56.**

e.  Understand how hydrolysis of basic anions affects the solubility of a salt (Section 18.4). **Study Questions: 57, 58, 112.**

f.  Decide if a precipitate will form when the ion concentrations are known Section 18.5). **Study Questions: 59–62, 73, 80, 88, 89.**

g.  Calculate the ion concentrations that are required to begin the precipitation of an insoluble salt (Section 18.5). **Study Questions: 63, 78, 87–89.**

h.  Understand that the formation of a complex ion can increase the solubility of an insoluble salt (Sections 18.6 and 18.7). **Study Questions: 65–70, 86, 92.**

# Key Equations

**Equation 18.1 (page 812)** Hydronium ion concentration in a buffer solution composed of a weak acid and its conjugate base.

$$[H_3O^+] = \frac{[acid]}{[conjugate\ base]} \times K_a$$

**Equation 18.2 (page 813)** Henderson–Hasselbalch equation. To calculate the pH of a buffer solution composed of a weak acid and its conjugate base.

$$pH = pK_a + \log\frac{[conjugate\ base]}{[acid]}$$

**Equation 18.3 (page 821)** Equation to calculate the hydronium ion concentration before the equivalence point in the titration of a weak acid with a strong base. See also Equation 18.4 for the version of the equation based on the Henderson–Hasselbalch equation.

$$[H_3O^+] = \frac{[weak\ acid\ remaining]}{[conjugate\ base\ produced]} \times K_a$$

**Equation 18.5 (page 821)** The relationship between the pH of the solution and the $pK_a$ of the weak acid (or $[H_3O^+]$ and $K_a$) at the halfway or half-neutralization point in the titration of a weak acid with a strong base (or of a weak base with a strong acid).

$$[H_3O^+] = K_a \text{ and } pH = pK_a$$

**Equation 18.6 (page 829)** The general equilibrium constant expression, $K_{sp}$ (solubility constant) for dissolving a poorly soluble salt, $A_xB_y$.

$$A_xB_y(s) \rightleftharpoons x\ A^{y+}(aq) + y\ B^{x-}(aq) \qquad K_{sp} = [A^{y+}]^x[B^{x-}]^y$$

# Study Questions

**⊙WL** Interactive versions of these questions are assignable in OWL.

▲ denotes challenging questions.

Blue-numbered questions have answers in Appendix R and fully worked solutions in the *Student Solutions Manual*.

## Practicing Skills

### The Common Ion Effect and Buffer Solutions
*(See Section 18.1 and 18.2 and Examples 18.1 and 18.2.)*

1. Does the pH of the solution increase, decrease, or stay the same when you
   (a) add solid ammonium chloride to a dilute aqueous solution of $NH_3$?
   (b) add solid sodium acetate to a dilute aqueous solution of acetic acid?
   (c) add solid NaCl to a dilute aqueous solution of NaOH?

2. Does the pH of the solution increase, decrease, or stay the same when you
   (a) add solid sodium oxalate, $Na_2C_2O_4$, to 50.0 mL of 0.015 M oxalic acid, $H_2C_2O_4$?
   (b) add solid ammonium chloride to 75 mL of 0.016 M HCl?
   (c) add 20.0 g of NaCl to 1.0 L of 0.10 M sodium acetate, $NaCH_3CO_2$?

3. What is the pH of a solution that consists of 0.20 M ammonia, $NH_3$, and 0.20 M ammonium chloride, $NH_4Cl$?

4. What is the pH of 0.15 M acetic acid to which 1.56 g of sodium acetate, $NaCH_3CO_2$, has been added?

5. What is the pH of the solution that results from adding 30.0 mL of 0.015 M KOH to 50.0 mL of 0.015 M benzoic acid?

6. What is the pH of the solution that results from adding 25.0 mL of 0.12 M HCl to 25.0 mL of 0.43 M $NH_3$?

7. What is the pH of the buffer solution that contains 2.2 g of $NH_4Cl$ in 250 mL of 0.12 M $NH_3$? Is the final pH lower or higher than the pH of the 0.12 M ammonia solution?

8. Lactic acid ($CH_3CHOHCO_2H$) is found in sour milk, in sauerkraut, and in muscles after activity. ($K_a$ for lactic acid = $1.4 \times 10^{-4}$.)
   (a) If 2.75 g of $NaCH_3CHOHCO_2$, sodium lactate, is added to $5.00 \times 10^2$ mL of 0.100 M lactic acid, what is the pH of the resulting buffer solution?
   (b) Is the pH of the buffered solution lower or higher than the pH of the lactic acid solution?

9. What mass of sodium acetate, $NaCH_3CO_2$, must be added to 1.00 L of 0.10 M acetic acid to give a solution with a pH of 4.50?

10. What mass of ammonium chloride, $NH_4Cl$, must be added to exactly $5.00 \times 10^2$ mL of 0.10 M $NH_3$ solution to give a solution with a pH of 9.00?

### Using the Henderson–Hasselbalch Equation
*(See Section 18.2 and Example 18.3.)*

11. Calculate the pH of a solution that has an acetic acid concentration of 0.050 M and a sodium acetate concentration of 0.075 M.

12. Calculate the pH of a solution that has an ammonium chloride concentration of 0.050 M and an ammonia concentration of 0.045 M.

13. A buffer is composed of formic acid and its conjugate base, the formate ion.
    (a) What is the pH of a solution that has a formic acid concentration of 0.050 M and a sodium formate concentration of 0.035 M?
    (b) What must the ratio of acid to conjugate base be to have a pH value 0.50 units higher than the value calculated in part (a)?

14. A buffer solution is composed of 1.360 g of $KH_2PO_4$ and 5.677 g of $Na_2HPO_4$.
    (a) What is the pH of the buffer solution?
    (b) What mass of $KH_2PO_4$ must be added to decrease the buffer solution pH by 0.50 unit from the value calculated in part (a)?

### Preparing a Buffer Solution
*(See Section 18.2 and Example 18.4.)*

15. Which of the following combinations would be the best to buffer the pH of a solution at approximately 9?
    (a) HCl and NaCl
    (b) $NH_3$ and $NH_4Cl$
    (c) $CH_3CO_2H$ and $NaCH_3CO_2$

16. Which of the following combinations would be the best to buffer the pH of a solution at approximately 7?
    (a) $H_3PO_4$ and $NaH_2PO_4$
    (b) $NaH_2PO_4$ and $Na_2HPO_4$
    (c) $Na_2HPO_4$ and $Na_3PO_4$

17. Describe how to prepare a buffer solution from $NaH_2PO_4$ and $Na_2HPO_4$ to have a pH of 7.5.

18. Describe how to prepare a buffer solution from $NH_3$ and $NH_4Cl$ to have a pH of 9.5.

### Adding an Acid or a Base to a Buffer Solution
*(See Section 18.2 and Example 18.5.)*

19. A buffer solution was prepared by adding 4.95 g of sodium acetate, $NaCH_3CO_2$, to $2.50 \times 10^2$ mL of 0.150 M acetic acid, $CH_3CO_2H$.
    (a) What is the pH of the buffer?
    (b) What is the pH of $1.00 \times 10^2$ mL of the buffer solution if you add 82 mg of NaOH to the solution?

20. You dissolve 0.425 g of NaOH in 2.00 L of a buffer solution that has $[H_2PO_4^-] = [HPO_4^{2-}] = 0.132$ M. What is the pH of the solution before adding NaOH? After adding NaOH?

21. A buffer solution is prepared by adding 0.125 mol of ammonium chloride to $5.00 \times 10^2$ mL of 0.500 M solution of ammonia.
    (a) What is the pH of the buffer?
    (b) If 0.0100 mol of HCl gas is bubbled into $5.00 \times 10^2$ mL of the buffer, what is the new pH of the solution?

22. What is the pH change when 20.0 mL of 0.100 M NaOH is added to 80.0 mL of a buffer solution consisting of 0.169 M $NH_3$ and 0.183 M $NH_4Cl$?

### More about Acid–Base Reactions: Titrations
*(See Section 18.3 and Examples 18.6 and 18.7.)*

23. Phenol, $C_6H_5OH$, is a weak organic acid. Suppose 0.515 g of the compound is dissolved in enough water to make 125 mL of solution. The resulting solution is titrated with 0.123 M NaOH.

    $$C_6H_5OH(aq) + OH^-(aq) \rightleftharpoons C_6H_5O^-(aq) + H_2O(\ell)$$

    (a) What is the pH of the original solution of phenol?
    (b) What are the concentrations of all of the following ions at the equivalence point: $Na^+$, $H_3O^+$, $OH^-$, and $C_6H_5O^-$?
    (c) What is the pH of the solution at the equivalence point?

24. Assume you dissolve 0.235 g of the weak acid benzoic acid, $C_6H_5CO_2H$, in enough water to make $1.00 \times 10^2$ mL of solution and then titrate the solution with 0.108 M NaOH.

    $$C_6H_5CO_2H(aq) + OH^-(aq) \rightleftharpoons$$
    $$C_6H_5CO_2^-(aq) + H_2O(\ell)$$

    (a) What was the pH of the original benzoic acid solution?
    (b) What are the concentrations of all of the following ions at the equivalence point: $Na^+$, $H_3O^+$, $OH^-$, and $C_6H_5CO_2^-$?
    (c) What is the pH of the solution at the equivalence point?

25. You require 36.78 mL of 0.0105 M HCl to reach the equivalence point in the titration of 25.0 mL of aqueous ammonia.
    (a) What was the concentration of $NH_3$ in the original ammonia solution?
    (b) What are the concentrations of $H_3O^+$, $OH^-$, and $NH_4^+$ at the equivalence point?
    (c) What is the pH of the solution at the equivalence point?

26. A titration of 25.0 mL of a solution of the weak base aniline, $C_6H_5NH_2$, requires 25.67 mL of 0.175 M HCl to reach the equivalence point.

    $$C_6H_5NH_2(aq) + H_3O^+(aq) \rightleftharpoons$$
    $$C_6H_5NH_3^+(aq) + H_2O(\ell)$$

    (a) What was the concentration of aniline in the original solution?
    (b) What are the concentrations of $H_3O^+$, $OH^-$, and $C_6H_5NH_3^+$ at the equivalence point?
    (c) What is the pH of the solution at the equivalence point?

### Titration Curves and Indicators
*(See Section 18.3 and Figures 18.4–18.10.)*

27. Without doing detailed calculations, sketch the curve for the titration of 30.0 mL of 0.10 M NaOH with 0.10 M HCl. Indicate the approximate pH at the beginning of the titration and at the equivalence point. What is the total solution volume at the equivalence point?

28. Without doing detailed calculations, sketch the curve for the titration of 50 mL of 0.050 M pyridine, $C_5H_5N$ (a weak base), with 0.10 M HCl. Indicate the approximate pH at the beginning of the titration and at the equivalence point. What is the total solution volume at the equivalence point?

29. You titrate 25.0 mL of 0.10 M $NH_3$ with 0.10 M HCl.
    (a) What is the pH of the $NH_3$ solution before the titration begins?
    (b) What is the pH at the equivalence point?
    (c) What is the pH at the halfway point of the titration?
    (d) What indicator in Figure 18.10 could be used to detect the equivalence point?
    (e) Calculate the pH of the solution after adding 5.00, 15.0, 20.0, 22.0, and 30.0 mL of the acid. Combine this information with that in parts (a)–(c) and plot the titration curve.

30. Construct a rough plot of pH versus volume of base for the titration of 25.0 mL of 0.050 M HCN with 0.075 M NaOH.
    (a) What is the pH before any NaOH is added?
    (b) What is the pH at the halfway point of the titration?
    (c) What is the pH when 95% of the required NaOH has been added?
    (d) What volume of base, in milliliters, is required to reach the equivalence point?
    (e) What is the pH at the equivalence point?
    (f) What indicator would be most suitable for this titration? (See Figure 18.10.)
    (g) What is the pH when 105% of the required base has been added?

31. Using Figure 18.10, suggest an indicator to use in each of the following titrations:
    (a) The weak base pyridine is titrated with HCl.
    (b) Formic acid is titrated with NaOH.
    (c) Ethylenediamine, a weak diprotic base, is titrated with HCl.

32. Using Figure 18.10, suggest an indicator to use in each of the following titrations.
    (a) $NaHCO_3$ is titrated to $CO_3^{2-}$ with NaOH.
    (b) Hypochlorous acid is titrated with NaOH.
    (c) Trimethylamine is titrated with HCl.

### Solubility Guidelines
*(See Sections 3.4 and 3.5, Figure 3.10, and Example 3.2.)*

33. Name two insoluble salts of each of the following ions.
    (a) $Cl^-$
    (b) $Zn^{2+}$
    (c) $Fe^{2+}$

34. Name two insoluble salts of each of the following ions.
    (a) $SO_4^{2-}$
    (b) $Ni^{2+}$
    (c) $Br^-$

35. Using the solubility guidelines (◄ Figure 3.10), predict whether each of the following is insoluble or soluble in water.
    (a) $(NH_4)_2CO_3$
    (b) $ZnSO_4$
    (c) $NiS$
    (d) $BaSO_4$

36. Predict whether each of the following is insoluble or soluble in water.
    (a) $Pb(NO_3)_2$
    (b) $Fe(OH)_3$
    (c) $ZnCl_2$
    (d) $CuS$

**Writing Solubility Product Constant Expressions**
*(See Section 18.4.)*

37. For each of the following insoluble salts, (1) write a balanced equation showing the equilibrium occurring when the salt is added to water, and (2) write the $K_{sp}$ expression.
    (a) $AgCN$
    (b) $NiCO_3$
    (c) $AuBr_3$

38. For each of the following insoluble salts, (1) write a balanced equation showing the equilibrium occurring when the salt is added to water, and (2) write the $K_{sp}$ expression.
    (a) $PbSO_4$
    (b) $BaF_2$
    (c) $Ag_3PO_4$

**Calculating $K_{sp}$**
*(See Section 18.4 and Example 18.8.)*

39. When 1.55 g of solid thallium(I) bromide is added to 1.00 L of water, the salt dissolves to a small extent.

    $$TlBr(s) \rightleftharpoons Tl^+(aq) + Br^-(aq)$$

    The thallium(I) and bromide ions in equilibrium with TlBr each have a concentration of $1.9 \times 10^{-3}$ M. What is the value of $K_{sp}$ for TlBr?

40. At 20 °C, a saturated aqueous solution of silver acetate, $AgCH_3CO_2$, contains 1.0 g of the silver compound dissolved in 100.0 mL of solution. Calculate $K_{sp}$ for silver acetate.

    $$AgCH_3CO_2(s) \rightleftharpoons Ag^+(aq) + CH_3CO_2^-(aq)$$

41. When 250 mg of $SrF_2$, strontium fluoride, is added to 1.00 L of water, the salt dissolves to a very small extent.

    $$SrF_2(s) \rightleftharpoons Sr^{2+}(aq) + 2 F^-(aq)$$

    At equilibrium, the concentration of $Sr^{2+}$ is found to be $1.03 \times 10^{-3}$ M. What is the value of $K_{sp}$ for $SrF_2$?

42. Calcium hydroxide, $Ca(OH)_2$, dissolves in water to the extent of 1.78 g per liter. What is the value of $K_{sp}$ for $Ca(OH)_2$?

    $$Ca(OH)_2(s) \rightleftharpoons Ca^{2+}(aq) + 2 OH^-(aq)$$

43. You add 0.979 g of $Pb(OH)_2$ to 1.00 L of pure water at 25 °C. The pH is 9.15. Estimate the value of $K_{sp}$ for $Pb(OH)_2$.

44. You place 1.234 g of solid $Ca(OH)_2$ in 1.00 L of pure water at 25 °C. The pH of the solution is found to be 12.68. Estimate the value of $K_{sp}$ for $Ca(OH)_2$.

**Estimating Salt Solubility from $K_{sp}$**
*(See Section 18.4 and Examples 18.9 and 18.10.)*

45. Estimate the solubility of silver iodide in pure water at 25 °C (a) in moles per liter and (b) in grams per liter.

    $$AgI(s) \rightleftharpoons Ag^+(aq) + I^-(aq)$$

46. What is the molar concentration of $Au^+(aq)$ in a saturated solution of AuCl in pure water at 25 °C?

    $$AuCl(s) \rightleftharpoons Au^+(aq) + Cl^-(aq)$$

47. Estimate the solubility of calcium fluoride, $CaF_2$, (a) in moles per liter and (b) in grams per liter of pure water.

    $$CaF_2(s) \rightleftharpoons Ca^{2+}(aq) + 2 F^-(aq)$$

48. Estimate the solubility of lead(II) bromide (a) in moles per liter and (b) in grams per liter of pure water.

49. The $K_{sp}$ value for radium sulfate, $RaSO_4$, is $4.2 \times 10^{-11}$. If 25 mg of radium sulfate is placed in $1.00 \times 10^2$ mL of water, does all of it dissolve? If not, how much dissolves?

50. If 55 mg of lead(II) sulfate is placed in 250 mL of pure water, does all of it dissolve? If not, how much dissolves?

51. Use $K_{sp}$ values to decide which compound in each of the following pairs is more soluble. (► Appendix J.)
    (a) $PbCl_2$ or $PbBr_2$
    (b) HgS or FeS
    (c) $Fe(OH)_2$ or $Zn(OH)_2$

52. Use $K_{sp}$ values to decide which compound in each of the following pairs is more soluble. (► Appendix J.)
    (a) AgBr or AgSCN
    (b) $SrCO_3$ or $SrSO_4$
    (c) $AgI$ or $PbI_2$
    (d) $MgF_2$ or $CaF_2$

**The Common Ion Effect and Salt Solubility**
*(See Section 18.4 and Examples 18.11 and 18.12.)*

53. Calculate the molar solubility of silver thiocyanate, AgSCN, in pure water and in water containing 0.010 M NaSCN.

54. Calculate the solubility of silver bromide, AgBr, in moles per liter, in pure water. Compare this value with the molar solubility of AgBr in 225 mL of water to which 0.15 g of NaBr has been added.

55. Compare the solubility, in milligrams per milliliter, of silver iodide, AgI, (a) in pure water and (b) in water that is 0.020 M in $AgNO_3$.

56. What is the solubility, in milligrams per milliliter, of $BaF_2$, (a) in pure water and (b) in water containing 5.0 mg/mL KF?

**The Effect of Basic Anions on Salt Solubility**
*(See pages 837–838.)*

57. Which insoluble compound in each pair should be more soluble in nitric acid than in pure water?
    (a) $PbCl_2$ or PbS
    (b) $Ag_2CO_3$ or AgI
    (c) $Al(OH)_3$ or AgCl

58. Which compound in each pair is more soluble in water than is predicted by a calculation from $K_{sp}$?
    (a) AgI or $Ag_2CO_3$
    (b) $PbCO_3$ or $PbCl_2$
    (c) AgCl or AgCN

**Precipitation Reactions**
*(See Section 18.5 and Examples 18.13–18.15.)*

59. You have a solution that has a lead(II) ion concentration of 0.0012 M. If enough soluble chloride-containing salt is added so that the $Cl^-$ concentration is 0.010 M, will $PbCl_2$ precipitate?

60. Sodium carbonate is added to a solution in which the concentration of $Ni^{2+}$ ion is 0.0024 M. Will precipitation of $NiCO_3$ occur (a) when the concentration of the carbonate ion is $1.0 \times 10^{-6}$ M or (b) when it is 100 times greater ($1.0 \times 10^{-4}$ M)?

61. If the concentration of $Zn^{2+}$ in 10.0 mL of water is $1.63 \times 10^{-4}$ M, will zinc hydroxide, $Zn(OH)_2$, precipitate when 4.0 mg of NaOH is added?

62. You have 95 mL of a solution that has a lead(II) concentration of 0.0012 M. Will $PbCl_2$ precipitate when 1.20 g of solid NaCl is added?

63. If the concentration of $Mg^{2+}$ ion in seawater is 1350 mg/L, what $OH^-$ concentration is required to precipitate $Mg(OH)_2$?

64. Will a precipitate of $Mg(OH)_2$ form when 25.0 mL of 0.010 M NaOH is combined with 75.0 mL of a 0.10 M solution of magnesium chloride?

**Equilibria Involving Complex Ions**
*(See Sections 18.6 and 18.7 and Examples 18.16 and 18.17.)*

65. Zinc hydroxide is amphoteric (◄ page 793). Use equilibrium constants to show that, given sufficient $OH^-$, $Zn(OH)_2$ can dissolve in NaOH.

66. Solid silver iodide, AgI, can be dissolved by adding aqueous sodium cyanide. Calculate $K_{net}$ for the following reaction.

$$AgI(s) + 2\ CN^-(aq) \rightleftharpoons [Ag(CN)_2]^-(aq) + I^-(aq)$$

67. ▲ What amount of ammonia (moles) must be added to dissolve 0.050 mol of AgCl suspended in 1.0 L of water?

68. Can you dissolve 15.0 mg of AuCl in 100.0 mL of water if you add 15.0 mL of 6.00 M NaCN?

69. What is the solubility of AgCl (a) in pure water and (b) in 1.0 M $NH_3$?

70. The chemistry of silver(I) cyanide:
    (a) Calculate the solubility of AgCN(s) in water from the $K_{sp}$ value.
    (b) Calculate the value of the equilibrium constant for the reaction

$$AgCN(s) + CN^-(aq) \rightleftharpoons [Ag(CN)_2]^-(aq)$$

   from $K_{sp}$ and $K_f$ values and predict from this value whether AgCN(s) would dissolve in KCN(aq).
    (c) Determine the equilibrium constant for the reaction

$$AgCN(s) + 2\ S_2O_3{}^{2-}(aq) \\ \rightleftharpoons [Ag(S_2O_3)_2]^{3-}(aq) + CN^-(aq)$$

   Calculate the solubility of AgCN in a solution containing 0.10 M $S_2O_3{}^{2-}$ and compare the value to the solubility in water [part (a)].

## General Questions

*These questions are not designated as to type or location in the chapter. They may combine several concepts.*

71. In each of the following cases, decide whether a precipitate will form when mixing the indicated reagents, and write a balanced equation for the reaction.
    (a) NaBr(aq) + $AgNO_3$(aq)
    (b) KCl(aq) + $Pb(NO_3)_2$(aq)

72. In each of the following cases, decide whether a precipitate will form when mixing the indicated reagents, and write a balanced equation for the reaction.
    (a) $Na_2SO_4$(aq) + $Mg(NO_3)_2$(aq)
    (b) $K_3PO_4$(aq) + $FeCl_3$(aq)

73. If you mix 48 mL of 0.0012 M $BaCl_2$ with 24 mL of $1.0 \times 10^{-6}$ M $Na_2SO_4$, will a precipitate of $BaSO_4$ form?

74. Calculate the hydronium ion concentration and the pH of the solution that results when 20.0 mL of 0.15 M acetic acid, $CH_3CO_2H$, is mixed with 5.0 mL of 0.17 M NaOH.

75. Calculate the hydronium ion concentration and the pH of the solution that results when 50.0 mL of 0.40 M $NH_3$ is mixed with 25.0 mL of 0.20 M HCl.

76. For each of the following cases, decide whether the pH is less than 7, equal to 7, or greater than 7.
    (a) Equal volumes of 0.10 M acetic acid, $CH_3CO_2H$, and 0.10 M KOH are mixed.
    (b) 25 mL of 0.015 M $NH_3$ is mixed with 12 mL of 0.015 M HCl.
    (c) 150 mL of 0.20 M $HNO_3$ is mixed with 75 mL of 0.40 M NaOH.
    (d) 25 mL of 0.45 M $H_2SO_4$ is mixed with 25 mL of 0.90 M NaOH.

77. Rank the following compounds in order of increasing solubility in water: $Na_2CO_3$, $BaCO_3$, $Ag_2CO_3$.

78. A sample of hard water contains about $2.0 \times 10^{-3}$ M $Ca^{2+}$. A soluble fluoride-containing salt such as NaF is added to "fluoridate" the water (to aid in the prevention of dental cavities). What is the maximum concentration of $F^-$ that can be present without precipitating $CaF_2$?

**Dietary sources of fluoride ion.** Adding fluoride ion to drinking water (or toothpaste) prevents the formation of dental cavities.

79. What is the pH of a buffer solution prepared from 5.15 g of $NH_4NO_3$ and 0.10 L of 0.15 M $NH_3$? What is the new pH if the solution is diluted with pure water to a volume of $5.00 \times 10^2$ mL?

80. If you place 5.0 mg of $SrSO_4$ in 1.0 L of pure water, will all of the salt dissolve before equilibrium is established, or will some salt remain undissolved?

Celestite, $SrSO_4$
Strontium sulfate

$SO_4{}^{2-}$

81. Describe the effect on the pH of the following actions and explain why there is not an effect:
   (a) Adding sodium acetate, $NaCH_3CO_2$, to 0.100 M $CH_3CO_2H$
   (b) Adding $NaNO_3$ to 0.100 M $HNO_3$

82. What volume of 0.120 M NaOH must be added to 100. mL of 0.100 M $NaHC_2O_4$ to reach a pH of 4.70?

83. ▲ A buffer solution is prepared by dissolving 1.50 g each of benzoic acid, $C_6H_5CO_2H$, and sodium benzoate, $NaC_6H_5CO_2$, in 150.0 mL of solution.
   (a) What is the pH of this buffer solution?
   (b) Which buffer component must be added, and in what quantity, to change the pH to 4.00?
   (c) What quantity of 2.0 M NaOH or 2.0 M HCl must be added to the buffer to change the pH to 4.00?

84. What volume of 0.200 M HCl must be added to 500.0 mL of 0.250 M $NH_3$ to have a buffer with a pH of 9.00?

85. What is the equilibrium constant for the following reaction?

$$AgCl(s) + I^-(aq) \rightleftharpoons AgI(s) + Cl^-(aq)$$

Does the equilibrium lie predominantly to the left or to the right? Will AgI form if iodide ion, $I^-$, is added to a saturated solution of AgCl?

86. Calculate the equilibrium constant for the following reaction.

$$Zn(OH)_2(s) + 2\ CN^-(aq) \rightleftharpoons$$
$$Zn(CN)_2(s) + 2\ OH^-(aq)$$

Does the equilibrium lie predominantly to the left or to the right?

87. ▲ In principle, the ions $Ba^{2+}$ and $Ca^{2+}$ can be separated by the difference in solubility of their fluorides, $BaF_2$ and $CaF_2$. If you have a solution that is 0.10 M in both $Ba^{2+}$ and $Ca^{2+}$, $CaF_2$ will begin to precipitate first as fluoride ion is added slowly to the solution.
   (a) What concentration of fluoride ion will precipitate the maximum amount of $Ca^{2+}$ ion without precipitating $BaF_2$?
   (b) What concentration of $Ca^{2+}$ remains in solution when $BaF_2$ just begins to precipitate?

88. ▲ A solution contains 0.10 M iodide ion, $I^-$, and 0.10 M carbonate ion, $CO_3^{2-}$.
   (a) If solid $Pb(NO_3)_2$ is slowly added to the solution, which salt will precipitate first, $PbI_2$ or $PbCO_3$?
   (b) What will be the concentration of the first ion that precipitates ($CO_3^{2-}$ or $I^-$) when the second, more soluble salt begins to precipitate?

**Lead(II) iodide ($K_{sp} = 9.8 \times 10^{-9}$) is a bright yellow solid.**

89. ▲ A solution contains $Ca^{2+}$ and $Pb^{2+}$ ions, both at a concentration of 0.010 M. You wish to separate the two ions from each other as completely as possible by precipitating one but not the other using aqueous $Na_2SO_4$ as the precipitating agent.
    (a) Which will precipitate first as sodium sulfate is added, $CaSO_4$ or $PbSO_4$?
    (b) What will be the concentration of the first ion that precipitates ($Ca^{2+}$ or $Pb^{2+}$) when the second, more soluble salt begins to precipitate?

90. Buffer capacity is defined as the number of moles of a strong acid or strong base that is required to change the pH of 1 L of the buffer solution by one unit. What is the buffer capacity of a solution that is 0.10 M in acetic acid and 0.10 M in sodium acetate?

91. The $Ca^{2+}$ ion in hard water can be precipitated as $CaCO_3$ by adding soda ash, $Na_2CO_3$. If the calcium ion concentration in hard water is 0.010 M and if the $Na_2CO_3$ is added until the carbonate ion concentration is 0.050 M, what percentage of the calcium ions has been removed from the water? (You may neglect carbonate ion hydrolysis.)

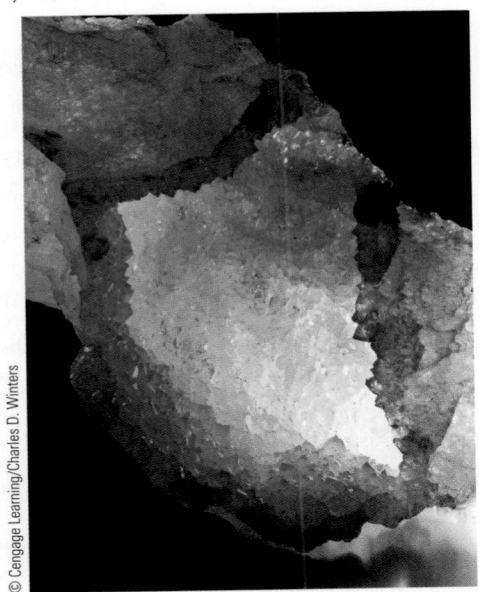

© Cengage Learning/Charles D. Winters

**This sample of calcium carbonate ($K_{sp} = 3.4 \times 10^{-9}$) was deposited in a cave formation.**

92. Some photographic film is coated with crystals of AgBr suspended in gelatin. Some of the silver ions are reduced to silver metal on exposure to light. Unexposed AgBr is then dissolved with sodium thiosulfate in the "fixing" step.

    $$AgBr(s) + 2\,S_2O_3^{2-}(aq) \rightleftharpoons$$
    $$[Ag(S_2O_3)_2]^{3-}(aq) + Br^-(aq)$$

    (a) What is the equilibrium constant for this reaction?
    (b) What mass of $Na_2S_2O_3$ must be added to dissolve 1.00 g of AgBr suspended in 1.00 L of water?

## In the Laboratory

93. Each pair of ions below is found together in aqueous solution. Using the table of solubility product constants in Appendix J, devise a way to separate these ions by adding a reagent to precipitate one of the ions as an insoluble salt and leaving the other in solution.
    (a) $Ba^{2+}$ and $Na^+$
    (b) $Ni^{2+}$ and $Pb^{2+}$

94. Each pair of ions below is found together in aqueous solution. Using the table of solubility product constants in Appendix J, devise a way to separate these ions by adding a reagent to precipitate one of the ions as an insoluble salt and leave the other in solution.
    (a) $Cu^{2+}$ and $Ag^+$
    (b) $Al^{3+}$ and $Fe^{3+}$

95. ▲ The cations $Ba^{2+}$ and $Sr^{2+}$ can be precipitated as very insoluble sulfates.
    (a) If you add sodium sulfate to a solution containing these metal cations, each with a concentration of 0.10 M, which is precipitated first, $BaSO_4$ or $SrSO_4$?
    (b) What will be the concentration of the first ion that precipitates ($Ba^{2+}$ or $Sr^{2+}$) when the second, more soluble salt begins to precipitate?

96. ▲ You will often work with salts of $Fe^{3+}$, $Pb^{2+}$, and $Al^{3+}$ in the laboratory. (All are found in nature, and all are important economically.) If you have a solution containing these three ions, each at a concentration of 0.10 M, what is the order in which their hydroxides precipitate as aqueous NaOH is slowly added to the solution?

97. Aniline hydrochloride, $(C_6H_5NH_3)Cl$, is a weak acid. (Its conjugate base is the weak base aniline, $C_6H_5NH_2$.) The acid can be titrated with a strong base such as NaOH.

    $$C_6H_5NH_3^+(aq) + OH^-(aq) \rightleftharpoons$$
    $$C_6H_5NH_2(aq) + H_2O(\ell)$$

    Assume 50.0 mL of 0.100 M aniline hydrochloride is titrated with 0.185 M NaOH. ($K_a$ for aniline hydrochloride is $2.4 \times 10^{-5}$.)
    (a) What is the pH of the $(C_6H_5NH_3)Cl$ solution before the titration begins?
    (b) What is the pH at the equivalence point?
    (c) What is the pH at the halfway point of the titration?
    (d) Which indicator in Figure 18.10 could be used to detect the equivalence point?
    (e) Calculate the pH of the solution after adding 10.0, 20.0, and 30.0 mL of base.
    (f) Combine the information in parts (a), (b), (c), and (e), and plot an approximate titration curve.

**98.** The weak base ethanolamine, $HOCH_2CH_2NH_2$, can be titrated with HCl.

$$HOCH_2CH_2NH_2(aq) + H_3O^+(aq) \rightleftharpoons$$
$$HOCH_2CH_2NH_3^+(aq) + H_2O(\ell)$$

Assume you have 25.0 mL of a 0.010 M solution of ethanolamine and titrate it with 0.0095 M HCl. ($K_b$ for ethanolamine is $3.2 \times 10^{-5}$.)

(a) What is the pH of the ethanolamine solution before the titration begins?

(b) What is the pH at the equivalence point?

(c) What is the pH at the halfway point of the titration?

(d) Which indicator in Figure 18.10 would be the best choice to detect the equivalence point?

(e) Calculate the pH of the solution after adding 5.00, 10.0, 20.0, and 30.0 mL of the acid.

(f) Combine the information in parts (a), (b), (c), and (e), and plot an approximate titration curve.

**99.** For the titration of 50.0 mL of 0.150 M ethylamine, $C_2H_5NH_2$, with 0.100 M HCl, find the pH at each of the following points, and then use that information to sketch the titration curve and decide on an appropriate indicator.

(a) At the beginning, before HCl is added

(b) At the halfway point in the titration

(c) When 75% of the required acid has been added

(d) At the equivalence point

(e) When 10.0 mL more HCl has been added than is required

(f) Sketch the titration curve.

(g) Suggest an appropriate indicator for this titration.

**100.** A buffer solution with a pH of 12.00 consists of $Na_3PO_4$ and $Na_2HPO_4$. The volume of solution is 200.0 mL.

(a) Which component of the buffer is present in a larger amount?

(b) If the concentration of $Na_3PO_4$ is 0.400 M, what mass of $Na_2HPO_4$ is present?

(c) Which component of the buffer must be added to change the pH to 12.25? What mass of that component is required?

**101.** To have a buffer with a pH of 2.50, what volume of 0.150 M NaOH must be added to 100. mL of 0.230 M $H_3PO_4$?

**102.** ▲ What mass of $Na_3PO_4$ must be added to 80.0 mL of 0.200 M HCl to obtain a buffer with a pH of 7.75?

**103.** You have a solution that contains $AgNO_3$, $Pb(NO_3)_2$, and $Cu(NO_3)_2$. Devise a separation method that results in having $Ag^+$ in one test tube, $Pb^{2+}$ in another, and $Cu^{2+}$ in a third test tube. Use solubility guidelines and $K_{sp}$ and $K_f$ values.

**104.** Once you have separated the three salts in Study Question 103 into three test tubes, you now need to confirm their presence.

(a) For $Pb^{2+}$ ion, one way to do this is to treat a precipitate of $PbCl_2$ with $K_2CrO_4$ to produce the bright yellow insoluble solid, $PbCrO_4$. Using $K_{sp}$ values, confirm that the chloride salt should be converted to the chromate salt.

White $PbCl_2$ is converted to yellow $PbCrO_4$ on adding $K_2CrO_4$.

(b) Suggest a method for confirming the presence of $Ag^+$ and $Cu^{2+}$ ions using complex ions.

## Summary and Conceptual Questions

*The following questions may use concepts from this and previous chapters.*

**105.** Suggest a method for separating a precipitate consisting of a mixture of solid CuS and solid $Cu(OH)_2$.

**106.** Which of the following barium salts should dissolve in a strong acid such as HCl: $Ba(OH)_2$, $BaSO_4$, or $BaCO_3$?

**107.** Explain why the solubility of $Ag_3PO_4$ can be greater in water than is calculated from the $K_{sp}$ value of the salt.

**108.** Two acids, each approximately 0.01 M in concentration, are titrated separately with a strong base. The acids show the following pH values at the equivalence point: HA, pH = 9.5, and HB, pH = 8.5.

(a) Which is the stronger acid, HA or HB?

(b) Which of the conjugate bases, $A^-$ or $B^-$, is the stronger base?

109. Composition diagrams, commonly known as "alpha plots," are often used to visualize the species in a solution of an acid or base as the pH is varied. The diagram for 0.100 M acetic acid is shown here.

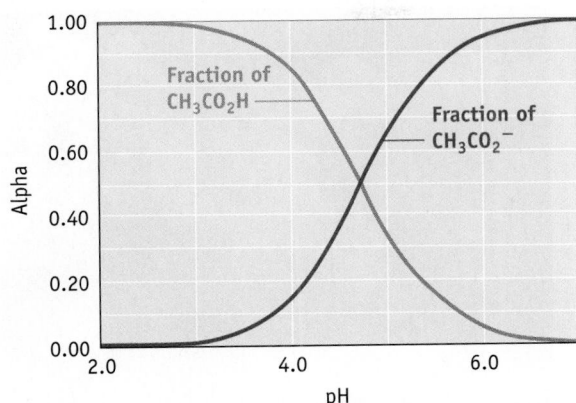

The plot shows how the fraction [alpha ($\alpha$)] of acetic acid in solution,

$$\alpha = \frac{[CH_3CO_2H]}{[CH_3CO_2H] + [CH_3CO_2^-]}$$

changes as the pH increases (blue curve). (The red curve shows how the fraction of acetate ion, $CH_3CO_2^-$, changes as the pH increases.) Alpha plots are another way of viewing the relative concentrations of acetic acid and acetate ion as a strong base is added to a solution of acetic acid in the course of a titration.

(a) Explain why the fraction of acetic acid declines and that of acetate ion increases as the pH increases.

(b) Which species predominates at a pH of 4, acetic acid or acetate ion? What is the situation at a pH of 6?

(c) Consider the point where the two lines cross. The fraction of acetic acid in the solution is 0.5, and so is that of acetate ion. That is, the solution is half acid and half conjugate base; their concentrations are equal. At this point, the graph shows the pH is 4.74. Explain why the pH at this point is 4.74.

110. The composition diagram, or alpha plot, for the important acid–base system of carbonic acid, $H_2CO_3$, is illustrated below. (See Study Question 109 for more information on such diagrams.)

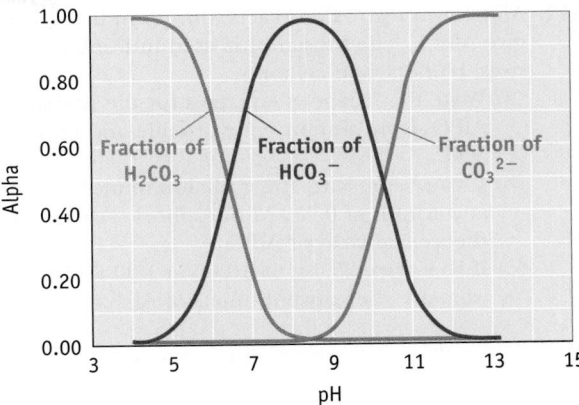

(a) Explain why the fraction of bicarbonate ion, $HCO_3^-$, rises and then falls as the pH increases.

(b) What is the composition of the solution when the pH is 6.0? When the pH is 10.0?

(c) If you wanted to buffer a solution at a pH of 11.0, what should be the ratio of $HCO_3^-$ to $CO_3^{2-}$?

111. The chemical name for aspirin is acetylsalicylic acid. It is believed that the analgesic and other desirable properties of aspirin are due not to the aspirin itself but rather to the simpler compound salicylic acid, $C_6H_4(OH)CO_2H$, which results from the breakdown of aspirin in the stomach.

salicylic acid

(a) Give approximate values for the following bond angles in the acid: (i) C—C—C in the ring; (ii) O—C=O; (iii) either of the C—O—H angles; and (iv) C—C—H.

(b) What is the hybridization of the C atoms of the ring? Of the C atom in the —$CO_2H$ group?

(c) Experiment shows that 1.00 g of the acid will dissolve in 460 mL of water. If the pH of this solution is 2.4, what is $K_a$ for the acid?

(d) If you have salicylic acid in your stomach and if the pH of gastric juice is 2.0, calculate the percentage of salicylic acid that will be present in the stomach in the form of the salicylate ion, $C_6H_4(OH)CO_2^-$.

(e) Assume you have 25.0 mL of a 0.014 M solution of salicylic acid and titrate it with 0.010 M NaOH. What is the pH at the halfway point of the titration? What is the pH at the equivalence point?

**112.** Aluminum hydroxide reacts with phosphoric acid to give $AlPO_4$. The substance is used industrially in adhesives, binders, and cements.

(a) Write the balanced equation for the preparation of $AlPO_4$ from aluminum hydroxide and phosphoric acid.

(b) If you begin with 152 g of aluminum hydroxide and 3.00 L of 0.750 M phosphoric acid, what is the theoretical yield of $AlPO_4$?

(c) If you place 25.0 g of $AlPO_4$ in 1.00 L of water, what are the concentrations of $Al^{3+}$ and $PO_4^{3-}$ at equilibrium? (Neglect hydrolysis of aqueous $Al^{3+}$ and $PO_4^{3-}$ ions.) $K_{sp}$ for $AlPO_4$ is $1.3 \times 10^{-20}$.

(d) Does the solubility of $AlPO_4$ increase or decrease on adding HCl? Explain.

This is a sample of hydrated aluminum phosphate, a mineral known as augelite.

© Cengage Learning/Charles D. Winters

## Applying Chemical Principles

### Everything That Glitters . . .

For thousands of years gold has been used in jewelry and for currency. Gold does not tarnish, and it can be drawn into wires or hammered into sheets. In modern society, the most important application of this element may be in electronics, where its high conductivity and resistance to corrosion make it invaluable for wires and connectors.

Gold mining evokes images of miners panning for gold in mountain streams or chopping rocks with pick axes. However, the percentage of gold in most deposits is too low for these extraction methods to be feasible. Today's miners blast and crush enormous quantities of gold-bearing ore and then dissolve gold from the ore using a chemical process involving cyanide ion and oxygen.

$$4\ Au(s) + 8\ NaCN(aq) + O_2(g) + 2\ H_2O(\ell) \rightarrow$$
$$4\ NaAu(CN)_2(aq) + 4\ NaOH(aq)$$

The solution containing the soluble $[Au(CN)_2]^-$ ion is filtered to separate it from the solids. Metallic gold is then recovered by reacting the cyanide complex with zinc. The zinc reduces the gold(I) complex to elemental gold and then joins with the cyanide to form $[Zn(CN)_4]^{2-}$.

Large volumes of 0.035% aqueous sodium cyanide are used for gold extraction. Unfortunately, unsafe disposal and accidental discharges have resulted in environmental disasters. In 2000, the collapse of dams in Baia Mare, Romania, resulted in millions of liters of cyanide waste entering the Tisza and Danube river. All aquatic life for miles downstream was killed. Although research into safer extraction methods is ongoing, extraction by cyanide ion is still the primary means of obtaining gold.

**Using gold.** *(left)* Much of current gold use today is in electronic devices. The microprocessor connector pins are coated with a thin film of gold. *(right)* The dome of St. Isaac's Cathedral in St. Petersburg, Russia, is covered with 100 kg of pure gold. (It was completed in 1858.)

### Questions:

1. Approximately 0.10 g of sodium cyanide is fatal to humans. What volume (in mL) of 0.035 mass percent NaCN solution contains a fatal dose of sodium cyanide? Assume the density of the solution is 1.0 g/mL.

2. What is the minimum volume of 0.0071 M NaCN(aq) necessary to dissolve the gold from 1.0 metric ton (1000 kg) of ore if the ore contains 0.012% gold?

3. Use the formation constant of $[Au(CN)_2]^-$ in Appendix K to determine the equilibrium concentration of $Au^+(aq)$ in a solution that is 0.0071 M $CN^-$ and $1.1 \times 10^{-4}$ M $[Au(CN)_2]^-$. Is it reasonable to conclude that 100% of the gold in solution is present as the $[Au(CN)_2]^-$ complex ion? Explain.

4. Silver undergoes similar reactions as those shown for gold. Both metals react with cyanide ion in the presence of oxygen to form soluble complexes, and both are reduced by zinc. The reaction of $Ag^+$ with cyanide ion may be viewed as two sequential steps:

   (1)  $Ag^+(aq) + CN^-(aq) \rightleftharpoons AgCN(s)$
   (2)  $AgCN(s) + CN^-(aq) \rightleftharpoons [Ag(CN)_2]^-(aq)$
   _____
   $Ag^+(aq) + 2\ CN^-(aq) \rightleftharpoons [Ag(CN)_2]^-(aq)$
   $K_f = 1.3 \times 10^{21}$

   (a) Use the solubility product equilibrium constant (Appendix J) of AgCN(s) to determine the equilibrium constant for step 1.

   (b) Use the equilibrium constants from Step 1 and the overall reaction to determine the equilibrium constant for Step 2.

   (c) Excess AgCN(s) is combined with 1.0 L of 0.0071 M $CN^-(aq)$ and allowed to equilibrate. Calculate the equilibrium concentrations of $CN^-$ and $[Ag(CN)_2]^-$ using the equilibrium constant for step 2. Assume no change in volume occurs.

5. Write a balanced chemical equation for the reaction of $NaAu(CN)_2(aq)$ and $Zn(s)$.

# 19 Principles of Chemical Reactivity: Entropy and Free Energy

**The Combustion of Hydrogen Gas.** The exothermic reaction of hydrogen with oxygen to form water. (A hydrogen-filled balloon was ignited with a candle.)

© Cengage Learning/Charles D. Winters

## Hydrogen for the Future?

In Chapter 5, you learned that the first law of thermodynamics states that energy is conserved in the universe. In this chapter, you will learn about the second law of thermodynamics. Two of the key concepts involved in the second law are (1) energy goes from being more concentrated to being more dispersed in the universe and (2) it is not possible to have 100% of the energy in a process be transferred as work. Energy is at the forefront of discussions of public policy today, and these fundamental laws of thermodynamics are key to understanding these issues.

One of the best energy sources for the future could be hydrogen. One could imagine a cycle in which water is decomposed by running an electric current through it to produce hydrogen and oxygen, and then the hydrogen and oxygen are recombined in a very exothermic process to yield water. Based on the first law of thermodynamics, however,

the best that we could hope for is to get the same exact amount of energy back from the process as we had to put in to decompose the water. The second law of thermodynamics makes things even worse. Because we cannot transform 100% of the energy released into useful work, the energy that we could use from the combustion step would be less than what would be needed to generate the hydrogen in the first place.

Is there a way around this problem? One widely used way to produce hydrogen is the reaction of carbon or methane with steam, for which there is a net release of energy when we account for both the energy needed to obtain the hydrogen and the energy released when the hydrogen is burned. Another potential solution is to use a renewable energy source such as solar or wind energy to decompose water. The laws of thermodynamics still apply but it is not as important in such a case that less energy is obtained than was needed because the input of energy came from an abundant and renewable energy resource.

Scientists are actively seeking ways to make hydrogen a useful, economical, and safe fuel for the future. Underlying this search, chemistry and the laws of thermodynamics play essential roles.

### Questions:

1. Calculate $\Delta_r H°$, $\Delta_r S°$, and $\Delta_r G°$ for the reaction (at 298.15 K)
   $2\ H_2O(\ell) \rightarrow 2\ H_2(g) + O_2(g)$
2. Calculate $\Delta_r H°$, $\Delta_r S°$ and $\Delta_r G°$ for the reaction (at 298.15 K)
   $CH_4(g) + H_2O(g) \rightarrow 3\ H_2(g) + CO(g)$

**Answers to these questions are available in Appendix N.**

## CHAPTER GOALS

*See Chapter Goals Revisited (page 884) for Study Questions keyed to these goals.*

- Understand the concept of entropy and its relationship to reaction spontaneity.

- Calculate the change in entropy for a system, its surroundings, and the universe to determine whether a process is spontaneous under standard conditions.

- Understand and use the Gibbs free energy.

**⊙WL**

Sign in to OWL at **www.cengage.com/owl** to view tutorials and simulations, develop problem-solving skills, and complete online homework assigned by your professor.

**go** Chemistry

Download mini lecture videos for key concept review and exam prep from OWL or purchase them from **www.cengagebrain.com**

Change is central to chemistry, so it is important to understand the factors that determine whether a change will occur. In chemistry, we encounter many examples of chemical change (chemical reactions) and physical change (the formation of mixtures, expansion of gases, and changes of state, to name a few). Chemists use the term **spontaneous** to represent a change that occurs without outside intervention. *Spontaneous changes occur only in the direction that leads to equilibrium.* Whether or not the process is spontaneous does not tell us anything about the rate of the change or the extent to which a process will occur before equilibrium is reached. It says only that the change will occur in a specific direction (toward equilibrium) and will occur naturally and unaided.

If a piece of hot metal is placed in a beaker of cold water, energy is transferred as heat spontaneously from the hot metal to the cooler water (Figure 19.1), and energy transfer will continue until the two objects are at the same temperature and thermal equilibrium is attained. Similarly, chemical reactions proceed spontaneously until equilibrium is reached, regardless of whether the position of the equilibrium favors products or reactants. We readily recognize that, starting with pure reactants, all product-favored reactions must be spontaneous, such as the formation of water from gaseous hydrogen and oxygen and the neutralization of $H_3O^+(aq)$ and $OH^-(aq)$. Be aware, though, that reactant-favored reactions are also spontaneous until equilibrium is achieved. Even though the dissolution of $CaCO_3$ is reactant-favored at equilibrium, if you place a handful of $CaCO_3$ in water, the process of dissolving will proceed spontaneously until equilibrium is reached.

*Systems never change spontaneously in a direction that takes them farther from equilibrium.* Given two objects at the same temperature, in contact but thermally isolated from their surroundings, it will never happen that one will heat up while the other becomes colder. Gas molecules will never spontaneously congregate at one end of a flask. Similarly, once equilibrium is established, the small amount of dissolved $CaCO_3$ in equilibrium with solid $CaCO_3$ will not spontaneously precipitate from solution, nor will a greater amount of $CaCO_3$ spontaneously dissolve.

The factors that determine the directionality and extent of change are among the topics of this chapter.

## 19.1 Spontaneity and Energy Transfer as Heat

We can readily recognize many chemical reactions that are spontaneous, such as hydrogen and oxygen combining to form water, methane burning to give $CO_2$ and $H_2O$, Na and $Cl_2$ reacting to form NaCl, and HCl(aq) and NaOH(aq) reacting to

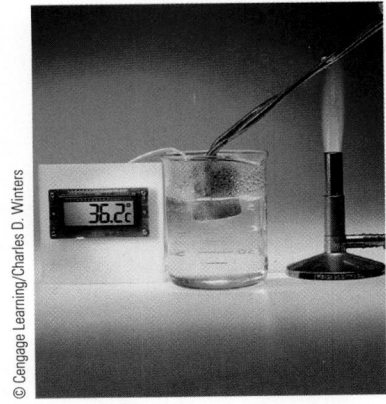

**FIGURE 19.1 A spontaneous process.** The heated metal cylinder is placed in water. Energy transfers as heat spontaneously from the metal to water, that is, from the hotter object to the cooler object.

© Cengage Learning/Charles D. Winters

To understand the thermodynamic concepts introduced in this chapter, be sure to review the ideas of Chapter 5.

*System:* The part of the universe under study.

*Surroundings:* The rest of the universe exclusive of the system, capable of exchanging energy and/or matter with the system.

*Exothermic:* Energy transfers as heat from the system to the surroundings.

*Endothermic:* Energy transfers as heat from the surroundings to the system.

## A Review of Concepts of Thermodynamics

*First law of thermodynamics:* The law of conservation of energy; energy cannot be created or destroyed. The change in internal energy of a system is the sum of energy transferred into or out of the system as heat and/or as work, $\Delta U = q + w$.

*Enthalpy change:* The energy transferred as heat under conditions of constant pressure.

*State function:* A quantity whose value depends only on the state of the system;

changes in a state function can be calculated by taking into account the initial and final states of a system.

*Standard conditions:* Pressure of 1 bar (1 bar = 0.98692 atm) and solution concentration of 1 m.

*Standard enthalpy of formation, $\Delta_f H°$:* The enthalpy change occurring when 1 mol of a compound is formed from its elements in their standard states.

---

● **Spontaneous Processes** A spontaneous physical or chemical change proceeds to equilibrium without outside intervention. Such a process may or may not be product-favored at equilibrium.

form $H_2O$ and NaCl(aq). A common feature of these reactions is that they are exothermic, so it would be tempting to conclude that evolution of energy as heat is the criterion that determines whether a reaction or process is spontaneous. Further inspection, however, reveals significant flaws in this reasoning. This is especially evident with the inclusion of some common spontaneous changes that are endothermic or energy neutral:

- *Dissolving $NH_4NO_3$.* The ionic compound $NH_4NO_3$ dissolves spontaneously in water. The process is endothermic ($\Delta_r H° = +25.7$ kJ/mol).
- *Expansion of a gas into a vacuum.* A system is set up with two flasks connected by a valve (Figure 19.2). One flask is filled with a gas, and the other is evacuated. When the valve is opened, the gas will flow spontaneously from one flask to the other until the pressure is the same throughout. The expansion of an ideal gas is energy neutral (although expansion of most real gases is endothermic).
- *Phase changes.* Melting of ice is an endothermic process. Above 0 °C, the melting of ice is spontaneous. Below 0 °C, melting of ice is not spontaneous. At 0 °C, no net change will occur; liquid water and ice coexist at equilibrium. This example illustrates that temperature can have a role in determining spontaneity and that equilibrium is somehow an important aspect of the problem.
- *Energy transfer as heat.* The temperature of a cold soft drink sitting in a warm environment will rise until the beverage reaches the ambient temperature. The energy required for this process comes from the surroundings. Energy transfer as heat from a hotter object (the surroundings) to a cooler object (the soft drink) is spontaneous.
- The reaction of $H_2$ and $I_2$ to form HI is endothermic, and the reverse reaction, the decomposition of HI to form $H_2$ and $I_2$, is exothermic. If $H_2$(g) and $I_2$(g) are mixed, a reaction forming HI will occur [$H_2$(g) + $I_2$(g) $\rightleftharpoons$ 2 HI(g)] until equilibrium is reached. Furthermore, if HI(g) is placed in a container, there will also be a reaction, but in the reverse direction, until equilibrium is achieved. Notice that approach to equilibrium occurs spontaneously from either direction.

On further reflection, it is logical to conclude that evolution of heat cannot be a sufficient criterion in determining spontaneity. The first law of thermodynamics tells us that in any process energy must be conserved. If energy is transferred out of a system, then the same amount of energy must be transferred to the surroundings. Exothermicity of the system is always accompanied by an endothermic change in the surroundings. If energy evolution were the only factor determining whether a change is spontaneous, then for every spontaneous process there would be a corresponding nonspontaneous change in the surroundings. We must search further than the first law of thermodynamics to determine whether a change is spontaneous.

gas-filled flask      evacuated flask

↓ open valve

When the valve is opened the gas expands irreversibly to fill both flasks.

**FIGURE 19.2** Spontaneous expansion of a gas.

# 19.2  Dispersal of Energy: Entropy

We have shown that we cannot use energy itself as an indicator of spontaneity because energy is conserved in any process; we always end up with the same amount of energy as we had at the beginning. Imagine dropping this book on the floor. (But don't actually drop it!) It would fall spontaneously. The initial potential energy it has from being a certain distance above the floor is converted to kinetic energy. When the book hits the floor, the kinetic energy of the book is converted into other forms of kinetic energy: acoustic energy and thermal energy of the book, floor, and air, since these are all heated up somewhat. This example leads to two important points. First, the total energy is conserved. Second, there is a directionality to this process. The book will spontaneously fall to the ground, but we will not observe a book on its own jump spontaneously from the floor up to a desk. Is there a way to predict this directionality?

Let us consider the initial and final states for this process. Initially, the energy is concentrated in the book—the book has a certain potential energy as it is held above the floor. At the end of the process, this energy has been dispersed to the air, floor, and book. The energy has gone from being concentrated to being more dispersed. This is the indicator for which we have been searching. *In a spontaneous process, energy goes from being more concentrated to being more dispersed.*

There is a state function (◀ Section 5.4) called **entropy (S)** that allows us to quantify this. The **second law of thermodynamics** states that *a spontaneous process is one that results in an increase of the entropy of the universe.* In a spontaneous process $\Delta S$(universe) is greater than zero; this corresponds to energy being dispersed in the process.

Because thermal energy is caused by the random motion of particles, potential energy is dispersed when it is converted to thermal energy. This conversion occurs when energy is transferred as heat, $q$. It is therefore not surprising that $q$ is a part of the mathematical definition of $\Delta S$. In addition, the effect of a given quantity of energy transferred as heat on energy dispersal is different at different temperatures. It turns out that a given $q$ has a greater effect on $\Delta S$ at a lower temperature than at a higher temperature; that is, the extent of energy dispersal is inversely proportional to the temperature.

Our proposed definition for $\Delta S$ is thus $q/T$, but this is still not quite correct. We must be a little more specific about $q$. The value of $q$ used in the calculation of an entropy change must be the energy transferred as heat under what are called *reversible conditions*, which we symbolize as $q_{rev}$ (see *A Closer Look: Reversible and Irreversible Processes*, page 862). Our mathematical definition of $\Delta S$ is therefore $q_{rev}$ divided by the absolute (Kelvin) temperature:

$$\Delta S = \frac{q_{rev}}{T} \qquad \textbf{(19.1)}$$

As expected from this equation, the units for entropy are J/K.

● **Entropy** For a more complete discussion of entropy, see the papers by F. L. Lambert, such as "Entropy Is Simple, Qualitatively," *Journal of Chemical Education*, Vol. 79, pp. 1241–1246, 2002, and references therein. See also Lambert's site: **entropysite.oxy.edu**

● **Second Law of Thermodynamics** For a spontaneous process, $\Delta S$ (universe) > 0.

# Reversible and Irreversible Processes

To determine entropy changes experimentally, the energy transferred by heating and cooling must be measured for a reversible process. But what is a reversible process?

The test for reversibility is that after carrying out a change along a given path (for example, energy added as heat), it must be possible to return to the starting point by the same path (energy taken away as heat) without altering the surroundings. Melting of ice and freezing of water at 0 °C are examples of reversible processes. Given a mixture of ice and water at equilibrium, adding energy as heat in small increments will convert ice to water; removing energy as heat in small increments will convert water back to ice.

Reversibility is closely associated with equilibrium. Assume that we have a system at equilibrium. Reversible changes can be made by very slightly perturbing the equilibrium and letting the system readjust.

Spontaneous processes are often not reversible. Suppose a gas is allowed to expand into a vacuum. No work is done in this process because there is no force to resist expansion. To return the system to its original state, it is necessary to compress the gas. Doing so means doing work on the system, however, because the system will not return to its original state on its own. In this process, the energy content of the surroundings decreases by the amount of work

expended by the surroundings. The system can be restored to its original state, but the surroundings will be altered in the process.

In summary, there are two important points concerning reversibility:
- At every step along a reversible pathway between two states, the system remains at equilibrium.
- Spontaneous processes often follow irreversible pathways and involve nonequilibrium conditions.

To determine the entropy change for a process, it is necessary to identify a reversible pathway. Only then can an entropy change for the process be calculated from $q_{rev}$ and the Kelvin temperature.

---

**REVIEW & CHECK FOR SECTION 19.2**

1. In a spontaneous process, $\Delta S$(universe) is

    (a) $< 0$          (b) $= 0$          (c) $> 0$

2. Which of the following is true for a spontaneous process but not for a nonspontaneous process? Energy in the universe is

    (a) concentrated    (b) conserved    (c) dispersed    (d) not conserved

3. For a particular system, $q_{rev}$ at 25 °C is equal to + 950. J. What is its value of $\Delta S$?

    (a) 38 J/K      (b) 3.19 J/K      (c) −3.19 J/K      (d) −38 J/K

---

## 19.3 Entropy: A Microscopic Understanding

Entropy is a measure of the extent of energy dispersal. In all spontaneous physical and chemical processes, energy changes from being localized or concentrated to being more dispersed or spread out. In a spontaneous process, the change in entropy, $\Delta S$, of the universe indicates the extent to which energy is dispersed in a process carried out at a temperature $T$. So far, however, we have not explained why dispersal of energy occurs, nor have we given an equation for entropy itself. In order to do this, we will need to consider energy in its quantized form and matter on the atomic level.

### Dispersal of Energy

We can explore the dispersal of energy using a simple example: energy being transferred as heat between hot and cold gaseous atoms. Consider an experiment involving two containers, one holding hot atoms and the other with cold atoms. Because they have translational energy, the atoms move randomly in each container and collide with the walls. When the containers are in contact, energy is transferred through the container walls. Eventually, both containers will be at the same temperature; the energy originally localized in the hotter atoms is distributed over a greater number of atoms; and the atoms in each container will have the same distribution of energies.

For further insight, we shall use a statistical explanation to show why energy is dispersed in a system. With statistical arguments, systems must include large

Possible distribution of energy packets

1,1    1,2    1,3    1,4    2,2

2,4    2,3    4,4    3,4    3,3

**FIGURE 19.3 Energy dispersal.** Possible ways of distributing two packets of energy among four atoms. To keep our analysis simple, we assume that initially there is one atom with two quanta of energy (1) and three atoms (2, 3 and 4) with no energy. There are 10 different ways to distribute the two quanta of energy among the four atoms.

numbers of particles for the arguments to be accurate. It will be easiest, however, if we look first at simple examples to understand the underlying concept and then extrapolate our conclusions to larger systems.

Consider a simple system in which, initially, there is one atom (1) with two discrete packets, or quanta, of energy and three other atoms (2, 3, and 4) with no energy (Figure 19.3). When these four atoms are brought together, the total energy in the system is 2 quanta. Collisions among the atoms allow energy to be transferred so that, over time, all distributions of the two packets of energy over the four atoms are seen. There are 10 different ways to distribute these 2 quanta of energy over the four atoms. Each of these 10 different ways to distribute the energy is called a **microstate**. In only one of these microstates do the 2 quanta remain on atom 1. In fact, only in 4 of the 10 microstates [1,1; 2,2; 3,3; and 4,4] is the energy concentrated on a single atom. In the majority of cases, 6 out of 10, the energy is distributed to two different atoms. Even in this small sample (four atoms) with only two packets of energy, it is more likely that at any given time the energy will be distributed to two atoms rather than concentrated on a single atom. There is a distinct preference that the energy will be dispersed over a greater number of atoms.

Let us now add more atoms to our system. We again begin with one atom (1) having 2 quanta of energy but now have five other atoms (2, 3, 4, 5, and 6) with no energy. Collisions let the energy be transferred between the atoms, and we now find there are 21 possible microstates (Figure 19.4). There are six microstates in which the energy is concentrated on one atom, including one in which the energy is still on atom 1, but there are now 15 out of 21 microstates (or 71.4%) in which the energy is present on two different atoms. As the number of particles increases, therefore, the number of microstates available increases dramatically, and the fraction of microstates in which the energy is concentrated rather than dispersed goes down dramatically. It is much more likely that the energy will be dispersed rather than concentrated.

| Number of Microstates | Distribution of 2 Quanta of Energy Among Six Atoms | | | | | |
|---|---|---|---|---|---|---|
| 6 | 1:1 | 2:2 | 3:3 | 4:4 | 5:5 | 6:6 |
| 5 | 1:2 | 2:3 | 3:4 | 4:5 | 5:6 | |
| 4 | 1:3 | 2:4 | 3:5 | 4:6 | | |
| 3 | 1:4 | 2:5 | 3:6 | | | |
| 2 | 1:5 | 2:6 | | | | |
| 1 | 1:6 | | | | | |

**FIGURE 19.4 Distributing 2 quanta of energy among six atoms.** (Atoms are labeled 1 to 6.) There are 21 ways—21 microstates—of distributing 2 quanta of energy among six atoms.

Now let us return to an example using a total of four atoms but increase the quantity of energy from 2 quanta to 6 quanta. Assume that we start with two atoms having 3 quanta of energy each. The other two atoms initially have zero energy (Figure 19.5). Through collisions, energy can be transferred to achieve different distributions of energy among the four atoms. In all, there are 84 microstates, falling into nine basic patterns. For example, one possible arrangement has one atom with 3 quanta of energy, and three atoms with 1 quantum each. There are four

**FIGURE 19.5 Energy dispersal.** Possible ways of distributing 6 quanta of energy among four atoms. A total of 84 microstates is possible.

(a) Initially, four particles are separated from each other. Two particles each have 3 quanta of energy, and the other two have none. A total of 6 quanta of energy will be distributed once the four particles interact.

Number of different ways to achieve this arrangement

(b) Once the particles begin to interact, there are nine ways to distribute the 6 available quanta. Each of these arrangements will have multiple ways of distributing the energy among the four atoms. Part (c) shows how the arrangement on the right can be achieved four ways.

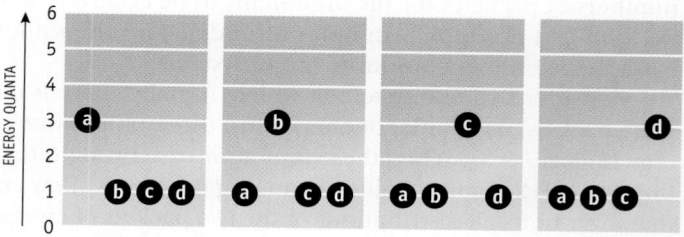

(c) There are four different ways to have four particles (a, b, c, and d) such that one particle has 3 quanta of energy and the other three each have 1 quantum of energy.

**Ludwig Boltzmann (1844–1906).** Engraved on his tombstone in Vienna, Austria, is his equation defining entropy. The constant $k$ is now known as Boltzmann's constant.

● **How Many Microstates?** To give you a sense of the number of microstates available to a substance, consider a mole of ice at 273 K, where $S° = 41.3$ J/K · mol. Using Boltzmann's equation, we find that $W = 10^{1,299,000,000,000,000,000,000,000}$. That is, there are many, many more microstates for 1 mol of ice than there are atoms in the universe (about $10^{80}$).

microstates in which this is true (Figure 19.5c). Increasing the number of quanta from 2 to 6 with the same number of atoms increased the number of possible microstates from 10 to 84. In this case, increasing the amount of energy that is dispersed resulted in an increase in the number of microstates.

Statistical analyses for larger aggregates of atoms and energy quanta become increasingly complex, but the conclusions are even more compelling. As the number of particles and/or quanta increases, the number of energy microstates grows rapidly. A larger number of microstates allows the extent to which the energy is dispersed and/or the amount of the energy dispersed to increase. Ludwig Boltzmann proposed that the entropy of a system (the dispersal of energy at a given temperature) results from the number of microstates available. *As the number of microstates increases, so does the entropy of the system.* He expressed this idea in the equation

$$S = k \ln W \tag{19.2}$$

which states that the entropy of a system, $S$, is proportional to the natural logarithm of the number of accessible microstates, $W$, that belong to a given energy of a system or substance. (The proportionality constant, $k$, is now known as **Boltzmann's constant** and has a value of $1.381 \times 10^{-23}$ J/K.) Within these microstates, it turns out that those states that disperse energy over the largest number of atoms are vastly more probable than the others.

## Dispersal of Matter: Dispersal of Energy Revisited

In many processes, it appears that the dispersal of matter also contributes to spontaneity. We shall see, however, that these effects can also be explained in terms of energy dispersal. Let us examine a specific case. Matter dispersal was illustrated in Figure 19.2 by the expansion of a gas into a vacuum. How is this spontaneous expansion of a gas related to energy dispersal and entropy?

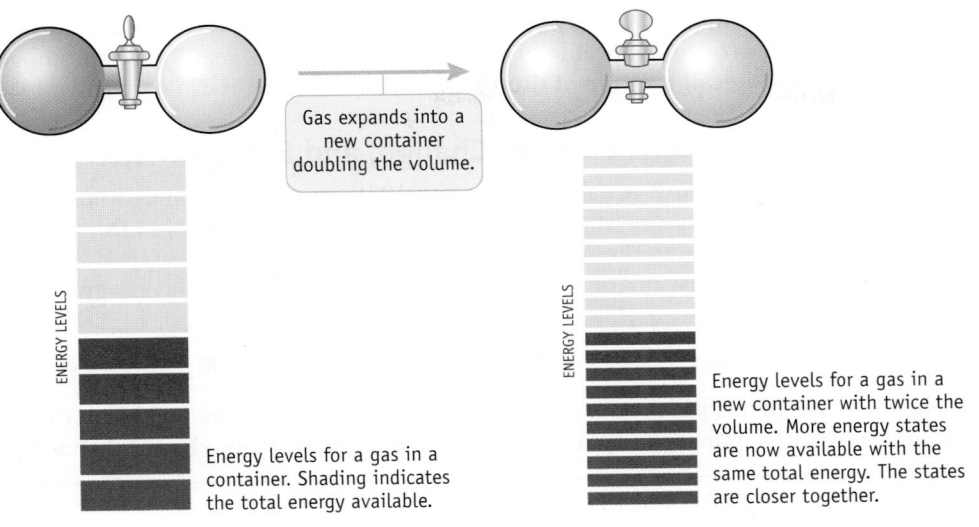

**FIGURE 19.6 Energy (and matter) dispersal.** As the size of the container for the chemical or physical change increases, the number of microstates accessible to the atoms or molecules of the system increases, and the density of states increases. A consequence of the distribution of molecules over a greater number of microstates is an increase in entropy.

Note that for a gas in a container of the size likely to be found in a laboratory, the energy levels are so closely spaced that we do not usually think in terms of quantization of energy levels. For most purposes, the system can be regarded as having a continuum of energy levels.

We begin with the premise that all energy is quantized and that this applies to any system, including gas molecules in a room or in a reaction flask. You know from the previous discussion of kinetic-molecular theory that the molecules in a gas sample have a distribution of energies (◄ Figure 11.14) (often referred to as a *Boltzmann distribution*). The molecules are assigned to (or "occupy") quantized microstates, most of them in states near the average energy of the system, but fewer of them in states of high or low energy. (For a gas in a laboratory-sized container, the energy levels are so closely spaced that, for most purposes, there is a continuum of energy states.)

When the gas expands to fill a larger container, the average energy of the sample and the energy for the particles in a given energy range are constant. However, quantum mechanics shows (for now, you will have to take our word for it) that as a consequence of having a larger volume in which the molecules can move in the expanded state, there is an increase in the number of microstates and that those microstates are even more closely spaced than before (Figure 19.6). The result of this greater density of microstates is that the number of microstates available to the gas particles increases when the gas expands. Gas expansion, a dispersal of matter, leads to the dispersal of energy over a larger number of microstates and thus to an increase in entropy.

The logic applied to the expansion of a gas into a vacuum can be used to rationalize the mixing of two gases, the mixing of two liquids, or the dissolution of a solid in a liquid (Figure 19.7). For example, if flasks containing $O_2$ and $N_2$ are connected (in an experimental setup like that in Figure 19.6), the two gases diffuse together, eventually leading to a mixture in which $O_2$ and $N_2$ molecules are evenly distributed throughout the total volume. A mixture of $O_2$ and $N_2$ will never separate into samples of each component of its own accord. The gases spontaneously move toward a situation in which each gas and its energy are maximally dispersed. The energy of the system is dispersed over a larger number of microstates, and the entropy of the

● **Statistical Thermodynamics** The arguments presented here come from a branch of chemistry called *statistical thermodynamics*. See H. Jungermann, *Journal of Chemical Education*, Vol. 83, pp. 1686–1694, 2006.

**FIGURE 19.7 Dissolving KMnO₄ in water.** A small quantity of solid, purple $KMnO_4$ is added to water *(left)*. With time, the solid dissolves, and the highly colored $MnO_4^-$ ions (and the $K^+$ ions) become dispersed throughout the solution. Entropy makes a large contribution to the mixing of liquids and solutions (page 621).

system increases. Indeed, this is a large part of the explanation for the fact that similar liquids (such as oil and gasoline or water and ethanol) will readily form homogeneous solutions. Recall the rule of thumb that "like dissolves like" (◄ Chapter 14).

## A Summary: Entropy, Entropy Change, and Energy Dispersal

● **Entropy Change on Gas Expansion** The entropy change for a gas expansion can be calculated from

$$\Delta S = nR\ln(V_{final}/V_{initial})$$

At a given temperature, $V$ is proportional to the number of microstates, so the equation is related to $k \ln(W_{final}/W_{initial})$.

According to Boltzmann's equation (Equation 19.2), entropy is proportional to the number of ways that energy can be dispersed in a substance, that is, to the number of microstates available to the system *(W)*. Thus, there will be a change in entropy, $\Delta S$, if there is a change in the number of microstates over which energy can be dispersed.

$$\Delta S = S_{final} - S_{initial} = k \ (\ln W_{final} - \ln W_{initial}) = k \ln(W_{final}/W_{initial})$$

Our focus as chemists is on $\Delta S$, and we shall be mainly concerned with the dispersion of energy in systems and surroundings during a physical or chemical change.

---

**REVIEW & CHECK FOR SECTION 19.3**

1. As the number of microstates over which energy can be distributed in a system increases, its entropy

   (a) decreases      (b) increases      (c) remains constant

2. Calculate the change in entropy for a system in going from a condition with 5 accessible microstates to 30 accessible microstates.

   (a) $-2.5 \times 10^{-23}$ J/K    (b) $9.4 \times 10^{-24}$ J/K    (c) $2.5 \times 10^{-23}$ J/K    (d) $8.3 \times 10^{-23}$ J/K

---

## 19.4 Entropy Measurement and Values

For any substance under a given set of conditions, a numerical value for entropy can be determined. The greater the dispersal of energy, the greater the entropy and the larger the value of $S$. The point of reference for entropy values is established by the **third law of thermodynamics**. Defined by Ludwig Boltzmann, the third law states that *a perfect crystal at 0 K has zero entropy; that is, $S = 0$*. The entropy of an element or compound under any other set of conditions is the entropy gained by converting the substance from 0 K to those conditions. To determine the value of $S$, it is necessary to measure the energy transferred as heat under reversible conditions for the conversion from 0 K to the defined conditions and then to use Equation 19.1 ($\Delta S = q_{rev}/T$). Because it is necessary to add energy as heat to raise the temperature, *all substances have positive entropy values at temperatures above 0 K*. Negative values of entropy cannot occur. Recognizing that entropy is directly related to energy added as heat allows us to predict several general features of entropy values:

- Raising the temperature of a substance corresponds to adding energy as heat. Thus, the entropy of a substance will increase with an increase in temperature.
- Conversions from solid to liquid and from liquid to gas typically require large inputs of energy as heat. Consequently, there is a large increase in entropy in conversions involving changes of state (Figure 19.8).

## Standard Entropy Values, *S°*

● **Negative Entropy Values** A glance at thermodynamic tables indicates that ions in aqueous solution can and do have negative entropy values listed. However, these are not absolute entropies. For ions, the entropy of $H^+(aq)$ is arbitrarily assigned a standard entropy of zero.

We introduced the concept of standard states into the earlier discussion of enthalpy (◄ Chapter 5), and we can similarly define the entropy of any substance in its standard state. The **standard molar entropy**, $S°$, of a substance is the entropy gained by converting 1 mol of it from a perfect crystal at 0 K to standard state conditions (1 bar, 1 molal for a solution) at the specified temperature. The units for standard molar entropy values are J/K · mol. Generally, values of $S°$ found in tables of data refer to a temperature of 298 K. Appendix L lists many standard molar entropies at 298 K. More extensive lists of $S°$ values can be found in standard reference sources such as the NIST tables (**webbook.nist.gov**).

**(a)**

The entropy of liquid bromine, $Br_2(\ell)$, is 152.2 J/K · mol, and that for bromine vapor is 245.47 J/K · mol.

**(b)**

The entropy of ice, which has a highly ordered molecular arrangement, is smaller than the entropy of liquid water.

**FIGURE 19.8 Entropy and states of matter.**

Scanning a list of standard entropies (such as those in Appendix L) will show that *large molecules generally have larger entropies than small molecules.* With a larger molecule, there are more ways for the molecule to rotate and vibrate, which provides a larger number of energy microstates over which energy can be distributed. As an example, consider the standard entropies for methane ($CH_4$), ethane ($C_2H_6$), and propane ($C_3H_8$), whose values are 186.3, 229.2, and 270.3 J/K · mol, respectively. Also, *molecules with more complex structures have larger entropies than molecules with simpler structures.* The effect of molecular structure can also be seen when comparing atoms or molecules of similar molar mass: Gaseous argon, $CO_2$, and $C_3H_8$ have entropies of 154.9, 213.7, and 270.3 J/K · mol, respectively.

Tables of entropy values also show that *entropies of gases are larger than those for liquids, and entropies of liquids are larger than those for solids.* In a solid, the particles have fixed positions in the solid lattice. When a solid melts, these particles have more freedom to assume different positions, resulting in an increase in the number of microstates available and an increase in entropy. When a liquid evaporates, constraints due to forces between the particles nearly disappear, the volume increases greatly, and a large entropy increase occurs. For example, the standard entropies of $I_2(s)$, $Br_2(\ell)$, and $Cl_2(g)$ are 116.1, 152.2, and 223.1 J/K · mol, respectively.

Finally, as illustrated in Figure 19.8, *for a given substance, a large increase in entropy accompanies changes of state,* reflecting the relatively large energy transfer as heat required to carry out these processes (as well as the dispersion of energy over a larger number of available microstates). For example, the entropies of liquid and gaseous water are 65.95 and 188.84 J/K · mol.

**Entropy Values at 25 °C for some Hydrocarbons**

| | $S°$ (J/K · mol) |
|---|---|
| methane | 186.3 |
| ethane | 229.2 |
| propane | 270.3 |

## EXAMPLE 19.1 Entropy Comparisons

**Problem** Which substance has the higher entropy under standard conditions at 25 °C? Explain your reasoning. Check your answer against data in Appendix L.

(a) $NO_2(g)$ or $N_2O_4(g)$

(b) $I_2(g)$ or $I_2(s)$

**What Do You Know?** Entropy decreases in the order gas > liquid > solid, and larger molecules of related substances have greater entropies than smaller molecules.

**Strategy** For each part, identify the difference between the two substances and relate this to the general rules for entropy given above.

**Solution**

(a) Both $NO_2$ and $N_2O_4$ are gases. $N_2O_4$ is a larger molecule than $NO_2$ and so is expected to have the higher standard entropy.

(b) For a given substance, gases have higher entropies than solids, so $I_2(g)$ is expected to have the greater standard entropy.

**Think about Your Answer** $S°$ values in Appendix L confirm these predictions. At 25 °C, $S°$ for $NO_2(g)$ is 240.04 J/K · mol, and $S°$ for $N_2O_4(g)$ is 304.38 J/K · mol. $S°$ for $I_2(g)$ is 260.69 J/K · mol; $S°$ for $I_2(s)$ is 116.135 J/K · mol.

---

**Check Your Understanding**

Predict which substance in each par has the higher entropy and explain your reasoning.

(a) $O_2(g)$ or $O_3(g)$

(b) $SnCl_4(\ell)$ or $SnCl_4(g)$

---

## Determining Entropy Changes in Physical and Chemical Processes

It is possible to use standard molar entropy values quantitatively to calculate the change in entropy that occurs in various processes under standard conditions. The standard entropy change for a reaction ($\Delta_r S°$) is the sum of the standard molar entropies of the products, each multiplied by its stoichiometric coefficient, minus the sum of the standard molar entropies of the reactants, each multiplied by its stoichiometric coefficient.

$$\Delta_r S° = \Sigma n S°(\text{products}) - \Sigma n S°(\text{reactants}) \qquad (19.3)$$

This equation allows us to calculate entropy changes for a *system* in which reactants are completely converted to products, under standard conditions. To illustrate, let us calculate $\Delta_r S°$ for the oxidation of NO with $O_2$.

$$2\ NO(g) + O_2(g) \rightarrow 2\ NO_2(g)$$

$\Delta_r S° = (2\ \text{mol}\ NO_2/\text{mol-rxn})\ S°[NO_2(g)] -$
$\qquad \{(2\ \text{mol}\ NO(g)/\text{mol-rxn})\ S°[NO(g)] + (1\ \text{mol}\ O_2/\text{mol-rxn})\ S°[O_2(g)]\}$

$= (2\ \text{mol}\ NO_2/\text{mol-rxn})(240.0\ \text{J/K} \cdot \text{mol}) -$
$\qquad [(2\ \text{mol}\ NO(g)/\text{mol-rxn})(210.8\ \text{J/K} \cdot \text{mol}) + (1\ \text{mol}\ O_2/\text{mol-rxn})(205.1\ \text{J/K} \cdot \text{mol})]$

$= -146.7\ \text{J/K} \cdot \text{mol-rxn}$

The entropy of the system decreases, as is generally observed when some number of gaseous reactants has been converted to fewer molecules of gaseous products.

**The reaction of NO with $O_2$.** The entropy of the system decreases when two molecules of gas are produced from three molecules of gaseous reactants.

### ⬤WL **INTERACTIVE EXAMPLE 19.2** Predicting and Calculating $\Delta_r S°$ for a Reaction

**Problem** Calculate the standard entropy changes for the following processes.

(a) Evaporation of 1.00 mol of liquid ethanol to ethanol vapor:

$$C_2H_5OH(\ell) \rightarrow C_2H_5OH(g)$$

(b) Formation of ammonia from hydrogen and nitrogen based on the following equation:

$$N_2(g) + 3\ H_2(g) \rightarrow 2\ NH_3(g)$$

**What Do You Know?** For each part, you are given a balanced chemical equation and asked to determine the standard entropy change for the reaction ($\Delta_r S°$). Values of standard molar entropies for the substances can be found in Appendix L.

**Strategy Map 19.2**

**PROBLEM**

Calculate $\Delta_r S°$ for a reaction.

↓

**DATA/INFORMATION**

- Balanced chemical equation
- $S°$ values (Appendix L)

↓

STEP 1. Calculate $\Delta_r S°$ using Equation 19.3.

↓

$\Delta_r S°$ for the reaction

**Strategy** Entropy changes for each system can be calculated from values of standard entropies (Appendix L) using Equation 19.3.

**Solution**

(a)  Evaporation of ethanol

$\Delta_r S° = \Sigma nS°(\text{products}) - \Sigma nS°(\text{reactants})$

= (1 mol $C_2H_5OH$(g)/mol-rxn) $S°[C_2H_5OH$(g)] − (1 mol $C_2H_5OH$(ℓ)/mol-rxn) $S°[C_2H_5OH$(ℓ)]

= (1 mol $C_2H_5OH$(g)/mol-rxn)(282.70 J/K · mol) − (1 mol $C_2H_5OH$(ℓ)/ mol-rxn)(160.7 J/K · mol)

= +122.0 J/K · mol-rxn

(b)  Formation of ammonia

$\Delta_r S° = \Sigma nS°(\text{products}) - \Sigma nS°(\text{reactants})$

= (2 mol $NH_3$(g)/mol-rxn) $S°[NH_3$(g)] −
    {(1 mol $N_2$(g)/mol-rxn) $S°[N_2$(g)] + (3 mol $H_2$(g)/mol-rxn) $S°[H_2$(g)]}

= (2 mol $NH_3$(g)/mol-rxn)(192.77 J/K · mol) −
    [(1 mol $N_2$(g)/mol-rxn)(191.56 J/K · mol) + (3 mol $H_2$(g)/mol-rxn)(130.7 J/K · mol)]

= −198.12 J/K · mol-rxn

**Think about Your Answer** Predictions for the signs of these entropy changes can be made using the guidelines given in the text. In part (a), a large positive value for the entropy change is expected because the process converts ethanol from a liquid to a vapor. In part (b), a decrease in entropy is predicted because the number of moles of gases decreases from four to two.

**Check Your Understanding**

Calculate the standard entropy changes for the following processes using the entropy values in Appendix L. Are the signs of the calculated values of $\Delta_r S°$ in accord with predictions?

(a)  Dissolving 1 mol of $NH_4Cl$(s) in water: $NH_4Cl$(s) → $NH_4Cl$(aq)

(b)  Oxidation of ethanol: $C_2H_5OH$(g) + 3 $O_2$(g) → 2 $CO_2$(g) + 3 $H_2O$(g)

- **Amount of Substance and Thermodynamic Calculations** In the calculation here and in all others in this chapter, when we write, for example,

  282.70 J/K · mol

  for the standard entropy of ethanol at 298 K, we mean

  282.70 J/K · mol $C_2H_5OH$(ℓ)

  The identifying formula has been left off for the sake of simplicity.

**REVIEW & CHECK FOR SECTION 19.4**

1.  Without doing any calculations, identify which of the following lists the materials in order of increasing entropy.

    (a)  $H_2O$(ℓ) < NaCl(s) < $NH_3$(g)      (c)  NaCl(s) < $H_2O$(ℓ) < $NH_3$(g)

    (b)  $H_2O$(ℓ) < $NH_3$(g) < NaCl(s)      (d)  $NH_3$(g) < $H_2O$(ℓ) < NaCl(s)

2.  Without doing any calculations, predict the sign of $\Delta_r S°$ for the following reaction:

    Zn(s) + 2 HCl(aq) → $ZnCl_2$(aq) + $H_2$(g)

    (a)  $\Delta_r S° < 0$      (b) $\Delta_r S° = 0$      (c)  $\Delta_r S° > 0$

3.  Calculate $\Delta_r S°$ for the following reaction at 25 ° C.

    2 $H_2$(g) + $O_2$(g) → 2 $H_2O$(ℓ)

    (a)  −326.6 J/K · mol-rxn      (c)  139.9 J/K · mol-rxn

    (b)  −139.9 J/K · mol-rxn      (d)  326.6 J/K · mol-rxn

# 19.5  Entropy Changes and Spontaneity

As illustrated by Example 19.2, the standard entropy change *for the system* in a physical or chemical change can be either positive (evaporation of ethanol) or negative (synthesis of ammonia from nitrogen and hydrogen). How does this information contribute to determining the spontaneity of the process?

The discussion to this point allows the listing of several general principles involving entropy changes:

- The entropy of a substance will increase in going from a solid to a liquid to a gas.
- The entropy of any substance increases as the temperature is raised. Energy

## A List of Common Entropy-Favored Processes

must be added to a system to increase its temperature (that is, $q > 0$), so $q_{rev}/T$ is necessarily positive.

- The entropy of a gas increases with an increase in volume. A larger volume pro-

vides a larger number of energy states over which to disperse energy.

- Reactions that increase the number of moles of gases in a system are accompanied by an increase in entropy.

---

As discussed previously (page 861), spontaneity is determined by the *second law of thermodynamics*, which states that *a spontaneous process is one that results in an increase of entropy in the universe*. The universe has two parts: the system and its surroundings (◄ Section 5.1), and so it makes sense that the entropy change for the universe is the sum of the entropy changes for the system and the surroundings. Under standard conditions, the entropy change for the universe, $\Delta S°$(universe) is

$$\Delta S°(\text{universe}) = \Delta S°(\text{system}) + \Delta S°(\text{surroundings}) \qquad (19.4)$$

The calculation in Example 19.2 gave us the entropy change under standard conditions for a system, only half of the information needed. Now we will have to determine how the change being studied affects the entropy of the surroundings so that we can then find the entropy change for the universe.

The value of $\Delta S°$(universe) calculated from Equation 19.4 is the entropy change when reactants are converted *completely* to products, with all species at standard conditions. *A process is spontaneous under standard conditions if $\Delta S°$ (universe) is greater than zero.* As an example of the determination of reaction spontaneity, let us calculate $\Delta S°$(universe) for the reaction currently used to manufacture methanol, $CH_3OH$.

$$CO(g) + 2\ H_2(g) \rightarrow CH_3OH(\ell)$$

If $\Delta S°$(universe) is positive, the conversion of 1 mol of $CO(g)$ and 2 mol of $H_2(g)$ to 1 mol of $CH_3OH(\ell)$ will be spontaneous under standard conditions.

● **Using $\Delta S°$(universe)** For a process that is spontaneous under standard conditions:

$$\Delta S°(\text{universe}) > 0$$

For a process at equilibrium under standard conditions:

$$\Delta S°(\text{universe}) = 0$$

For a process that is not spontaneous under standard conditions:

$$\Delta S°(\text{universe}) < 0$$

Note that these conclusions refer to the *complete* conversion of reactants to products.

**Calculating $\Delta S°$(system)** To calculate $\Delta S°$(system), we start by defining the system to include the reactants and products. This means that $\Delta S°$(system) corresponds to the entropy change for the reaction, $\Delta_r S°$. Calculation of this entropy change follows the procedure given in Example 19.2.

$$\Delta S°(\text{system}) = \Delta_r S° = \Sigma n S°(\text{products}) - \Sigma n S°(\text{reactants})$$

$$= (1\ \text{mol } CH_3OH(\ell)/\text{mol-rxn})\ S°[CH_3OH(\ell)] -$$
$$\{(1\ \text{mol } CO(g)/\text{mol-rxn})\ S°[CO(g)] + (2\ \text{mol } H_2(g)/\text{mol-rxn})\ S°[H_2(g)]\}$$

$$= (1\ \text{mol } CH_3OH(\ell)/\text{mol-rxn})(127.2\ \text{J/K} \cdot \text{mol}) -$$
$$[(1\ \text{mol } CO(g)/\text{mol-rxn})(197.7\ \text{J/K} \cdot \text{mol}) +$$
$$(2\ \text{mol } H_2(g)/\text{mol-rxn})(130.7\ \text{J/K} \cdot \text{mol})]$$

$$= -331.9\ \text{J/K} \cdot \text{mol-rxn}$$

A decrease in entropy for the system is expected because three moles of gaseous reactants are converted to one mole of a liquid product.

**Calculating $\Delta S°$(surroundings)** We now need to calculate the entropy change for the surroundings. Recall from Equation 19.1 that for a reversible change, $\Delta S$ is equal to $q_{rev}/T$. Under constant pressure conditions and assuming a reversible process, the entropy change in the surroundings results from the fact that the enthalpy change for the reaction ($q_{rev} = \Delta_r H$) affects the surroundings. That is, the energy associated with an exothermic chemical reaction is dispersed into the surroundings. Recognizing that $\Delta H°$(surroundings) $= -\Delta_r H°$(system), the entropy change for the surroundings can be calculated by the equation

$$\Delta S°(\text{surroundings}) = \Delta H°(\text{surroundings})/T = -\Delta_r H°(\text{system})/T$$

For the synthesis of methanol by the reaction given, the enthalpy change can be calculated from enthalpy of formation data using Equation 5.6 (page 234).

$$\Delta H°(\text{system}) = \Sigma n \Delta_f H°(\text{products}) - \Sigma n \Delta_f H°(\text{reactants})$$

$$= (1 \text{ mol CH}_3\text{OH}(\ell)/\text{mol-rxn}) \Delta_f H°[\text{CH}_3\text{OH}(\ell)] -$$
$$\{(1 \text{ mol CO}(g)/\text{mol-rxn}) \Delta_f H°[\text{CO}(g)] +$$
$$(2 \text{ mol H}_2(g)/\text{mol-rxn}) \Delta_f H°[\text{H}_2(g)]\}$$

$$= (1 \text{ mol CH}_3\text{OH}(\ell)/\text{mol-rxn})(-238.4 \text{ kJ/mol}) -$$
$$[(1 \text{ mol CO}(g)/\text{mol-rxn})(-110.5 \text{ kJ/mol}) +$$
$$(2 \text{ mol H}_2(g)/\text{mol-rxn})(0 \text{ kJ/ mol})]$$

$$= -127.9 \text{ kJ/mol-rxn}$$

Assuming that the process is reversible and occurs at a constant temperature and pressure, the entropy change for the surroundings in the methanol synthesis is +429.2 J/K · mol-rxn, calculated as follows.

$$\Delta S°(\text{surroundings}) = -\Delta_r H°(\text{system})/T$$

$$= -[(-127.9 \text{ kJ/mol-rxn})/298 \text{ K})](1000 \text{ J/kJ})$$

$$= +429.2 \text{ J/K} \cdot \text{mol-rxn}$$

## Calculating $\Delta S°$(universe), the Entropy Change for the System and Surroundings

The pieces are now in place to calculate the entropy change in the universe. For the formation of $CH_3OH(\ell)$ from $CO(g)$ and $H_2(g)$, $\Delta S°$(universe) is

$$\Delta S°(\text{universe}) = \Delta S°(\text{system}) + \Delta S°(\text{surroundings})$$

$$= -331.9 \text{ J/K} \cdot \text{mol-rxn} + 429.2 \text{ J/K} \cdot \text{mol-rxn}$$

$$= +97.3 \text{ J/K} \cdot \text{mol-rxn}$$

The positive value indicates an increase in the entropy of the universe. It follows from the second law of thermodynamics that this reaction is spontaneous.

## OWL INTERACTIVE EXAMPLE 19.3 Determining Whether a Process Is Spontaneous

**Problem** Calculate $\Delta S°$(universe) for the process of dissolving NaCl in water at 298 K.

**What Do You Know?** The process occurring is NaCl(s) → NaCl(aq). $\Delta S°$(universe) is equal to the sum of $\Delta S°$(system) and $\Delta S°$(surroundings). Values of $S°$ and $\Delta_f H°$ for NaCl(s) and NaCl(aq) are given in Appendix L.

**Strategy** The entropy change for the system, $\Delta S°$(system), can be calculated from values of $S°$ for the two species using Equation 19.3. $\Delta_r H°$ can be calculated from values of $\Delta_f H°$ for the two species using Equation 5.6 (page 234). $\Delta S°$(surroundings) is determined by dividing $-\Delta_r H°$ for the process by the Kelvin temperature. The sum of $\Delta S°$(system) and $\Delta S°$(surroundings) is $\Delta S°$(universe). If this value is positive, then the process is spontaneous under standard conditions.

**Solution**

*Calculate $\Delta S°$(system)*

$$\Delta S°(\text{system}) = \Sigma n S°(\text{products}) - \Sigma n S°(\text{reactants})$$

$$= (1 \text{ mol NaCl}(aq)/\text{mol-rxn}) S°[\text{NaCl}(aq)] - (1 \text{ mol NaCl}(s)/\text{mol-rxn}) S°[\text{NaCl}(s)]$$

$$= (1 \text{ mol NaCl}(aq)/\text{mol-rxn})(115.5 \text{ J/K} \cdot \text{mol}) - (1 \text{ mol NaCl}(s)/\text{mol-rxn})(72.11 \text{ J/K} \cdot \text{mol})$$

$$= +43.4 \text{ J/K} \cdot \text{mol-rxn}$$

*Calculate $\Delta S°$(surroundings)*

$$\Delta_r H°(\text{system}) = \Sigma n \Delta_f H°(\text{products}) - \Sigma n \Delta_f H°(\text{reactants})$$

$$= (1 \text{ mol NaCl}(aq)/\text{mol-rxn}) \Delta_f H°[\text{NaCl}(aq)] - (1 \text{ mol NaCl}(s)/\text{mol-rxn}) \Delta_f H°[\text{NaCl}(s)]$$

$$= (1 \text{ mol NaCl}(aq)/\text{mol-rxn})(-407.27 \text{ kJ/mol}) - (1 \text{ mol NaCl}(s)/\text{mol-rxn})(-411.12 \text{ kJ/mol})$$

$$= +3.85 \text{ kJ/mol-rxn}$$

**Strategy Map 19.3**

**PROBLEM**
Determine the value of $\Delta S°$(universe) for a chemical reaction.

**KNOWN DATA/INFORMATION**
- Balanced chemical equation
- Temperature
- Values of $S°$, $\Delta_f H°$ (Appendix L)

STEP 1. Calculate $\Delta_r S°$ using Equation 19.3.

$\Delta S°$(system)

STEP 2. Calculate $\Delta_r H°$ using Equation 5.6.
Change the sign of $\Delta_r H°$ and divide this by $T$ (in K).

$\Delta S°$(surroundings)

STEP 3. Add $\Delta S°$(system) and $\Delta S°$(surroundings).

$\Delta S°$(universe)

The entropy change of the surroundings is determined by dividing $-\Delta_rH°$(system) by the Kelvin temperature.

$$\Delta S°(\text{surroundings}) = -\Delta_rH°(\text{system})/T$$

$$= [(-3.85 \text{ kJ/mol-rxn}/298 \text{ K})](1000 \text{ J/1 kJ})$$

$$= -12.9 \text{ J/K} \cdot \text{mol-rxn}$$

*Calculate $\Delta S°$(universe)*

The overall entropy change—the change of entropy in the universe—is the sum of the values for the system and the surroundings.

$$\Delta S°(\text{universe}) = \Delta S°(\text{system}) + \Delta S°(\text{surroundings})$$

$$= (+43.4 \text{ J/K} \cdot \text{mol-rxn}) + (-12.9 \text{ J/K} \cdot \text{mol-rxn})$$

$$= +30.5 \text{ J/K} \cdot \text{mol-rxn}$$

**Think about Your Answer** The sum of the two entropy quantities is positive, indicating that the entropy in the universe increases; thus, the process is spontaneous under standard conditions. Notice that the spontaneity of the process results from $\Delta S°$(system) and not from $\Delta S°$(surroundings).

---

**Check Your Understanding**

Is the reaction of hydrogen and chlorine to give hydrogen chloride gas predicted to be spontaneous under standard conditions (at 298 K)?

$$H_2(g) + Cl_2(g) \rightarrow 2 \text{ HCl}(g)$$

Predict the spontaneity of the reaction based on $\Delta_rH°$ and $\Delta_rS°$, and then calculate $\Delta S°$(universe) to verify your prediction.

---

● **$\Delta S°$(universe), Spontaneity, and Standard Conditions** It is important to reiterate that $\Delta H°$ and $\Delta S°$ values for a reaction are for the *complete* conversion of reactants to products under standard conditions. If $\Delta S°$(universe) is > 0, the reaction as written is spontaneous *under standard conditions*. However, one can calculate values for $\Delta S$(universe) (without the superscript zero) for *nonstandard* conditions. If $\Delta S$(universe) is > 0, the reaction is spontaneous under those conditions. However, it is possible that this same reaction under standard conditions is not spontaneous [$\Delta S°$(universe) < 0]. We will return to this point on pages 875–877.

## In Summary: Spontaneous or Not?

In the preceding examples, predictions about the spontaneity of a process under standard conditions were made using values of $\Delta S°$(system) and $\Delta H°$(system) calculated from tables of thermodynamic data. It will be useful to look at all possibilities that result from the interplay of these two quantities. There are four possible outcomes when these two quantities are paired (Table 19.1). In two, $\Delta H°$(system) and $\Delta S°$(system) work in concert (Types 1 and 4 in Table 19.1). In the other two, the two quantities are opposed (Types 2 and 3).

Processes in which both the standard enthalpy and entropy changes favor energy dispersal (Type 1) are always spontaneous under standard conditions. Processes disfavored by both their standard enthalpy and entropy changes in the system (Type 4) can *never* be spontaneous under standard conditions. Let us consider examples that illustrate each situation.

**Table 19.1  Predicting Whether a Reaction Will Be Spontaneous Under Standard Conditions**

| Reaction Type | $\Delta H°$(system) | $\Delta S°$(system) | Spontaneous Process? (Standard Conditions) |
|---|---|---|---|
| 1 | Exothermic, < 0 | Positive, > 0 | Spontaneous at all temperatures. $\Delta S°$(universe) > 0. |
| 2 | Exothermic, < 0 | Negative, < 0 | Depends on relative magnitudes of $\Delta H°$ and $\Delta S°$. Spontaneous at lower temperatures. |
| 3 | Endothermic, > 0 | Positive, > 0 | Depends on relative magnitudes of $\Delta H°$ and $\Delta S°$. Spontaneous at higher temperatures. |
| 4 | Endothermic, > 0 | Negative, < 0 | Not spontaneous at any temperature. $\Delta S°$(universe) < 0. |

Combustion reactions are always exothermic and often produce a larger number of gaseous product molecules from a few reactant molecules. They are Type 1 reactions. The equation for the combustion of butane is an example.

$$2 \ C_4H_{10}(g) + 13 \ O_2(g) \rightarrow 8 \ CO_2(g) + 10 \ H_2O(g)$$

For this reaction, $\Delta_r H° = -5315.1$ kJ/mol · rxn, and $\Delta_r S° = 312.4$ J/K · mol-rxn. Both contribute to this reaction being spontaneous under standard conditions.

Hydrazine, $N_2H_4$, is used as a high-energy rocket fuel. Synthesis of $N_2H_4$ from gaseous $N_2$ and $H_2$ would be attractive because these reactants are inexpensive.

$$N_2(g) + 2 \ H_2(g) \rightarrow N_2H_4(\ell)$$

However, this reaction fits into the Type 4 category. The reaction is endothermic ($\Delta_r H° = +50.63$ kJ/mol-rxn), and the entropy change is negative ($\Delta_r S° = -331.4$ J/K·mol-rxn) (1 mol of liquid is produced from 3 mol of gases), so the reaction is not spontaneous under standard conditions, and complete conversion of reactants to products will not occur without outside intervention.

In the two other possible outcomes, entropy and enthalpy changes oppose each other. A process could be favored by the enthalpy change but disfavored by the entropy change (Type 2), or vice versa (Type 3). In either instance, whether a process is spontaneous depends on which factor is more important.

Temperature also influences the value of $\Delta S°$(universe). Because the enthalpy change for the surroundings is divided by the temperature to obtain $\Delta S°$(surroundings), the numerical value of $\Delta S°$(surroundings) will be smaller (either less positive or less negative) at higher temperatures. In contrast, $\Delta S°$(system) and $\Delta H°$(system) do not vary much with temperature. Thus, the effect of $\Delta S°$(surroundings) relative to $\Delta S°$(system) is diminished at higher temperature. Stated another way, at higher temperature, the enthalpy change becomes a less important factor in determining the overall entropy change. Consider the two cases where $\Delta H°$(system) and $\Delta S°$(system) are in opposition (Table 19.1):

- Type 2: Exothermic processes with $\Delta S°$(system) < 0. Such processes become less favorable with an increase in temperature.
- Type 3: Endothermic processes with $\Delta S°$(system) > 0. These processes become more favorable as the temperature increases.

The effect of temperature is illustrated by two examples. The first is the reaction of $N_2$ and $H_2$ to form $NH_3$. The reaction is exothermic, and thus it is favored by energy dispersal to the surroundings. The entropy change for the system is unfavorable, however, because the reaction, $N_2(g) + 3 \ H_2(g) \rightarrow 2 \ NH_3(g)$, converts four moles of gaseous reactants to two moles of gaseous products. The favorable enthalpy effect [$\Delta_r S°$(surroundings) = $-\Delta_r H°$(system)$/T$] becomes less important at higher temperatures. It is therefore reasonable to expect that the reaction will not be spontaneous if the temperature is high enough.

The second example considers the thermal decomposition of $NH_4Cl$ (Figure 19.9). At room temperature, $NH_4Cl$ is a stable, white, crystalline salt. When heated strongly, it decomposes to $NH_3(g)$ and $HCl(g)$. The reaction is endothermic (enthalpy-disfavored) but entropy-favored because of the formation of two moles of gas from one mole of a solid reactant. The reaction is increasingly favored at higher temperatures.

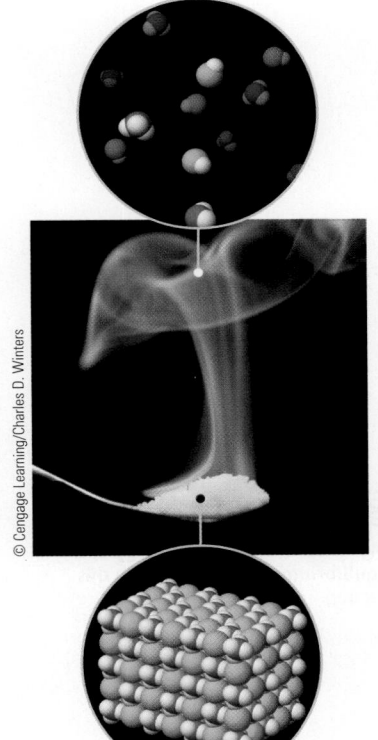

© Cengage Learning/Charles D. Winters

**FIGURE 19.9 Thermal decomposition of NH$_4$Cl(s).** White, solid ammonium chloride, $NH_4Cl(s)$, is heated in a spoon. At high temperatures, decomposition to form $NH_3(g)$ and $HCl(g)$ is spontaneous. At lower temperatures, the reverse reaction, forming $NH_4Cl(s)$, is spontaneous. As gaseous $HCl(g)$ and $NH_3(g)$ cool, they recombine to form solid $NH_4Cl$, the white "smoke" seen in this photo.

---

**REVIEW & CHECK FOR SECTION 19.5**

1. Calculate $\Delta_r S°$ for the following reaction at 25 °C:

$$N_2(g) + 2 \ O_2(g) \rightarrow 2 \ NO_2(g)$$

(a) −480.1 J/K · mol-rxn

(b) −121.6 J/K · mol-rxn

(c) 121.6 J/K · mol-rxn

(d) 480.1 J/K · mol-rxn

2. Calculate $\Delta S°$(universe) for the following reaction at 25.0 °C:

$$C(graphite) + O_2(g) \rightarrow CO_2(g)$$

(a) −1317 J/K · mol-rxn      (c) 4.4 J/K · mol-rxn

(b) 3.1 J/K · mol-rxn      (d) 1320 J/K · mol-rxn

3. If $\Delta_rH° = +467.9$ kJ/mol-rxn and $\Delta_rS° = +560.7$ J/K · mol-rxn for the following reaction

$$2\ Fe_2O_3(s) + 3\ C(graphite) \rightarrow 4\ Fe(s) + 3\ CO_2(g)$$

then, under standard conditions, this reaction will be spontaneous

(a) at all temperatures      (c) at lower temperatures

(b) at higher temperatures      (d) at no temperature

## 19.6 Gibbs Free Energy

The method used so far to determine whether a process is spontaneous required evaluation of two quantities, $\Delta S°$(system) and $\Delta S°$(surroundings). Wouldn't it be convenient to have a single thermodynamic function that serves the same purpose? A function associated with the system only—one that does not require assessment of the surroundings—would be even better. Such a function exists. It is called the **Gibbs free energy**, with the name honoring J. Willard Gibbs (1839–1903). Gibbs free energy, $G$, often referred to simply as "free energy," is defined mathematically as

$$G = H - TS$$

where $H$ is enthalpy, $T$ is the Kelvin temperature, and $S$ is entropy. In this equation, $G$, $H$, and $S$ all refer to the system. Because enthalpy and entropy are state functions (◀ Section 5.4), free energy is also a state function.

Every substance possesses free energy, but the actual quantity is seldom known. Instead, just as with enthalpy ($H$) and internal energy ($U$), we are concerned with *changes* in free energy, $\Delta G$, that occur in chemical and physical processes.

Let us first see how to use free energy as a way to determine whether a reaction is spontaneous. We can then ask further questions about the meaning of the term "free energy" and its use in deciding whether a reaction is product- or reactant-favored.

### The Change in the Gibbs Free Energy, $\Delta G$

Recall the equation defining the entropy change for the universe:

$$\Delta S(\text{universe}) = \Delta S(\text{surroundings}) + \Delta S(\text{system})$$

The entropy change of the surroundings equals the negative of the change in enthalpy of the system divided by $T$. Thus,

$$\Delta S(\text{universe}) = -\Delta H(\text{system})/T + \Delta S(\text{system})$$

Multiplying through this equation by $-T$, gives the equation

$$-T\Delta S(\text{universe}) = \Delta H(\text{system}) - T\Delta S(\text{system})$$

Gibbs defined the free energy function so that $\Delta G(\text{system}) = -T\Delta S(\text{universe})$. Thus, the general expression relating changes in free energy to the enthalpy and entropy changes in the system is the following.

$$\Delta G = \Delta H - T\Delta S$$

Under standard conditions, we can rewrite this, the Gibbs free energy equation, as

$$\Delta G° = \Delta H° - T\Delta S° \tag{19.5}$$

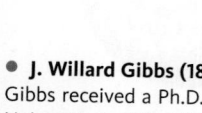

**Module 24: Gibbs Free Energy and Equilibrium** covers concepts in this section.

**J. Willard Gibbs (1839–1903)** Gibbs received a Ph.D. from Yale University in 1863. His was the first Ph.D. in science awarded from an American university.

## Gibbs Free Energy, Spontaneity, and Chemical Equilibrium

Because $\Delta_r G°$ is related directly to $\Delta S°$(universe), the Gibbs free energy can be used as a criterion of spontaneity for physical and chemical changes. As shown earlier, the signs of $\Delta_r G°$ and $\Delta S°$(universe) will be opposites [$\Delta_r G°$(system) = $-T\Delta S°$(universe)]. Therefore, we find the following relationships:

$\Delta_r G° < 0$    The process is spontaneous in the direction written under standard conditions.

$\Delta_r G° = 0$    The process is at equilibrium under standard conditions.

$\Delta_r G° > 0$    The process is not spontaneous in the direction written under standard conditions.

To better understand the Gibbs function, let us examine the diagrams in Figure 19.10. The free energy of pure reactants is plotted on the left, and the free energy of the pure products on the right. The extent of reaction, plotted on the x-axis, goes from zero (pure reactants) to one (pure products). In both cases in Figure 19.10, the free energy initially declines as reactants begin to form products; it reaches a minimum at equilibrium and then increases again as we move from the equilibrium position to pure products. *The free energy at equilibrium, where there is a mixture of reactants and products, is always lower than the free energy of the pure reactants and of the pure products. A reaction proceeds spontaneously toward the minimum in free energy, which corresponds to equilibrium.*

$\Delta_r G°$ *is the change in free energy accompanying the chemical reaction in which the reactants are converted completely to the products under standard conditions.* Mathematically, it is the difference in free energy between the products and the reactants under standard conditions. If the free energy of the products is less than that of the reactants, then $\Delta_r G° < 0$, and the reaction is spontaneous under standard conditions (Figure 19.10a). Conversely, if the free energy of the products is greater than that of the reactants, then $\Delta_r G°$ is positive ($\Delta_r G° > 0$), and the reaction is not spontaneous under standard conditions (Figure 19.10b).

Notice that in Figure 19.10a, the equilibrium position occurs closer to the product side than to the reactant side. This is a product-favored reaction at equilibrium. In Figure 19.10b, we find the opposite. The reaction is reactant-favored at equilibrium. It is no accident that the reaction with a negative $\Delta_r G°$ is product-favored, whereas the one with the positive $\Delta_r G°$ is reactant-favored at equilibrium. It turns out that this is always true as the discussion below will show.

**FIGURE 19.10 Free energy changes in the course of a reaction.** The difference in free energy between the pure reactants in their standard states and the pure products in their standard states is $\Delta_r G°$. Here, Q is the reaction quotient, and K is the equilibrium constant.

Now let us consider what happens to the instantaneous slope of the curve in Figure 19.10 as the reaction proceeds. Initially, this slope is negative, corresponding to a negative $\Delta G$ in moving from point to point. Eventually, however, the free energy reaches a minimum. At this point, the instantaneous slope of the graph is zero ($\Delta G = 0$) and the reaction has reached equilibrium. If we move past the equilibrium point, the instantaneous slope is positive ($\Delta G > 0$); proceeding further to products is not spontaneous. In fact, the reverse reaction will occur spontaneously; the reaction will once again proceed toward equilibrium.

The relationship of $\Delta_r G°$ (the value of $\Delta_r G$ under standard conditions) and the value of $\Delta_r G$ under nonstandard conditions is given by Equation 19.6:

$$\Delta_r G = \Delta_r G° + RT \ln Q \qquad (19.6)$$

where $R$ is the universal gas constant, $T$ is the temperature in kelvins, and $Q$ is the reaction quotient (◀ Section 16.2).

$$Q = \frac{[C]^c[D]^d}{[A]^a[B]^b} \text{ for } aA + bB \rightarrow cC + dD$$

Equation 19.6 informs us that, at a given temperature, $\Delta_r G$ is determined by the values of $\Delta_r G°$ and $Q$. When the system reaches equilibrium, no further net change in concentration of reactants and products will occur, and $\Delta_r G = 0$ and $Q = K$. Substituting these values into Equation 19.6 gives

$$0 = \Delta_r G° + RT \ln K \text{ (at equilibrium)}$$

Rearranging this equation leads to a useful relationship between the standard free energy change for a reaction and the equilibrium constant, $K$, Equation 19.7:

$$\Delta_r G° = -RT \ln K \qquad (19.7)$$

From this equation, we learn that, when $\Delta_r G°$ is negative, $K$ is greater than 1, and we say the reaction is *product-favored at equilibrium*. The more negative the value of $\Delta_r G°$, the larger the equilibrium constant. This makes sense because, as described in Chapter 16, large equilibrium constants are associated with product-favored reactions. The converse is also true: For *reactant-favored* reactions, $\Delta_r G°$ is positive, and $K$ is less than 1. Finally, if $K = 1$ (a special set of conditions), then $\Delta_r G° = 0$.

Let us now see that Equation 19.6 can yield the relationsips between $Q$ and $K$ that we have been using since Chapter 16.

$$\Delta_r G = \Delta_r G° + RT \ln Q$$

Substituting $-RT \ln K$ for $\Delta_r G°$ (Equation 19.7) gives

$$\Delta_r G = -RT \ln K + RT \ln Q$$

This equation can be rearranged as follows:

$$\Delta_r G = RT (\ln Q - \ln K)$$

$$\Delta_r G / RT = \ln Q - \ln K$$

Furthermore, as long as the reaction is "descending" from the free energy of the pure reactants to the equilibrium position, $\Delta_r G$ is negative, implying that the reaction is spontaneous in the forward direction. Because $\Delta_r G$ is negative, we can write:

$$\text{When } \Delta_r G < 0, \text{ then } \ln Q - \ln K < 0$$

$$\text{Therefore, } \ln Q < \ln K$$

$$\text{and } Q < K$$

This means that for a reaction to be spontaneous, $\Delta_r G$ must be negative (a spontaneous reaction), and $Q$ must be less than $K$ ($Q < K$), just as has been stated earlier. A similar analysis shows that if $\Delta_r G$ is positive, then $Q > K$.

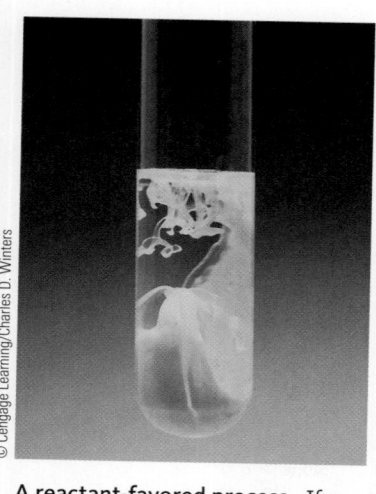

© Cengage Learning/Charles D. Winters

**A reactant-favored process.** If a sample of yellow lead(II) iodide is placed in pure water, a small amount of the compound will dissolve spontaneously ($\Delta_r G < 0$ and $Q < K$) until equilibrium is reached. Because $PbI_2$ is quite insoluble ($K_{sp} = 9.8 \times 10^{-9}$), however, the process of dissolving the compound is reactant-favored at equilibrium. We may conclude, therefore, that the value of $\Delta_r G°$ is positive.

# A Summary: Gibbs Free Energy ($\Delta_r G$ and $\Delta_r G°$), the Reaction Quotient ($Q$) and Equilibrium Constant ($K$), and Reaction Favorability

Let us summarize the relationships among $\Delta_r G°$, $\Delta_r G$, $Q$, and $K$.

- In Figure 19.10, you see that free energy decreases to a minimum as a system approaches equilibrium. The free energy of the mixture of reactants and products at equilibrium is always lower than the free energy of the pure reactants or of the pure products.
- When $\Delta_r G < 0$, the reaction is proceeding spontaneously toward equilibrium and $Q < K$.
- When $\Delta_r G > 0$, the reaction is beyond the equilibrium point and is not spontaneous in the forward direction. It will be spontaneous in the reverse direction; $Q > K$.
- When $\Delta_r G = 0$, the reaction is at equilibrium; $Q = K$.
- When $\Delta_r G° < 0$, the reaction is *spontaneous under standard conditions*. The system will proceed to an equilibrium position at which point the products will dominate in the reaction mixture because $K > 1$. That is, the reaction is *product-favored* at equilibrium.
- When $\Delta_r G° > 0$, the reaction is *not spontaneous under standard conditions*. The system will proceed to the equilibrium position at which point the reactants will dominate in the equilibrium mixture because $K < 1$. That is, the reaction is *reactant-favored* at equilibrium.
- For the special condition where $\Delta_r G° = 0$, the reaction is at equilibrium at standard conditions, with $K = 1$.

## What Is "Free" Energy?

The term *free energy* was not arbitrarily chosen. In any given process, the free energy represents the maximum energy available to do useful work (mathematically, $\Delta G = w_{max}$). In this context, the word *free* means "available."

To illustrate the reasoning behind this relationship, consider a reaction carried out under standard conditions and in which energy is evolved as heat ($\Delta_r H° < 0$) and entropy decreases ($\Delta_r S° < 0$).

$$2\ H_2(g) + O_2(g) \rightarrow 2\ H_2O(g)$$

$$\Delta_r H° = -483.6\ \text{kJ/mol-rxn and } \Delta_r S° = -88.8\ \text{J/K} \cdot \text{mol-rxn}$$

$$\Delta_r G° = -483.6\ \text{kJ/mol-rxn} - (298\ \text{K})(-0.0888\ \text{kJ/mol-rxn}) = -457.2\ \text{kJ/mol-rxn}$$

At first glance, it might seem reasonable that all the energy released as heat ($-483.6$ kJ/mol-rxn) would be available. This energy could be transferred to the surroundings and would thus be available to do work. This is not the case, however. A negative entropy change in this reaction means that energy is less dispersed in the products than in the reactants. A portion of the energy released from the reaction must be used to reverse energy dispersal in the system; that is, to concentrate energy in the product. The energy left over is "free," or available to perform work. Here, the free energy change amounts to $-457.2$ kJ/mol-rxn.

---

**REVIEW & CHECK FOR SECTION 19.6**

1. For a reaction to be spontaneous, $\Delta G$ will be _____ than zero and $Q$ will be _____ than $K$

   (a) greater, greater    (b) greater, less    (c) less, greater    (d) less, less

2. A reaction that is spontaneous under standard conditions is also

   (a) product-favored at equilibrium    (b) reactant-favored at equilibrium

3. A process that has $\Delta G° < 0$ can never be spontaneous in the forward direction. This statement is

   (a) true    (b) false

## 19.7 Calculating and Using Free Energy

### Standard Free Energy of Formation

The standard free energy of formation of a compound, $\Delta_f G°$, is the free energy change that occurs to form one mole of the compound from the component elements, with products and reactants in their standard states. By defining $\Delta_f G°$ in this way, *the free energy of formation of an element in its standard state is zero.*

Just as the standard enthalpy or entropy change for a reaction can be calculated using values of $\Delta_f H°$ (Equation 5.6) or $S°$ (Equation 19.3), the standard free energy change for a reaction can be calculated from values of $\Delta_f G°$ using a similar equation, where $n$ represents the stoichiometric coefficient of the material in the balanced chemical equation under consideration:

$$\Delta_r G° = \Sigma n \Delta_f G°(\text{products}) - \Sigma n \Delta_f G°(\text{reactants}) \qquad (19.8)$$

### Calculating $\Delta_r G°$, the Free Energy Change for a Reaction Under Standard Conditions

The free energy change for a reaction under standard conditions can be calculated from thermodynamic data in two ways, either from standard enthalpy and entropy changes using values of $\Delta_f H°$ and $S°$ (as we did on the previous page for the formation of $H_2O$) or directly from values of $\Delta_f G°$ found in tables. These calculations are illustrated in the following two examples.

### EXAMPLE 19.4 Calculating $\Delta_r G°$ from $\Delta_r H°$ and $\Delta_r S°$

**Problem** Calculate the standard free energy change, $\Delta_r G°$, for the formation of methane from carbon and hydrogen at 298 K, using tabulated values of $\Delta_f H°$ and $S°$. Is the reaction spontaneous under standard conditions? Is it product-favored or reactant-favored at equilibrium?

$$C(\text{graphite}) + 2\,H_2(g) \rightarrow CH_4(g)$$

**What Do You Know?** You are given a balanced chemical equation and asked to determine the standard free energy change for the reaction ($\Delta_r G°$). Values of standard molar enthalpies of formation and standard molar entropies for the substances can be found in Appendix L.

**Strategy** The values of $\Delta_f H°$ *and* $S°$ are first combined to find $\Delta_r H°$ and $\Delta_r S°$. With these values known, $\Delta_r G°$ can be calculated using Equation 19.5. When doing the calculation, remember that $S°$ values are given in units of J/K · mol, whereas $\Delta_f H°$ values are given in units of kJ/mol.

**Solution**

|  | C(graphite) | + | 2 H₂(g) | → | CH₄(g) |
|---|---|---|---|---|---|
| $\Delta_f H°$ (kJ/mol) | 0 | | 0 | | −74.9 |
| $S°$ (J/K·mol) | +5.6 | | +130.7 | | +186.3 |

From these values, we can find both $\Delta_r H°$ and $\Delta_r S°$ for the reaction:

$\Delta_r H° = \Sigma n \Delta_f H°(\text{products}) - \Sigma n \Delta_f H°(\text{reactants})$

$= (1\text{ mol }CH_4(g)/\text{mol-rxn})\,\Delta_f H°[CH_4(g)] - \{(1\text{ mol }C(\text{graphite})/\text{mol-rxn})\,\Delta_f H°[C(\text{graphite})] + (2\text{ mol }H_2(g)/\text{mol-rxn})\,\Delta_f H°[H_2(g)]\}$

$= (1\text{ mol }CH_4(g)/\text{mol-rxn})(-74.9\text{ kJ/mol}) - [(1\text{ mol }C(\text{graphite})/\text{mol-rxn})(0\text{ kJ/mol}) + (2\text{ mol }H_2(g)/\text{mol-rxn})(0\text{ kJ/mol})]$

$= -74.9\text{ kJ/mol-rxn}$

$\Delta_r S° = \Sigma n S°(\text{products}) - \Sigma n S°(\text{reactants})$

$= (1\text{ mol }CH_4(g)/\text{mol-rxn})\,S°[CH_4(g)] - \{(1\text{ mol }C(\text{graphite})/\text{mol-rxn})\,S°[C(\text{graphite})] + (2\text{ mol }H_2(g)/\text{mol-rxn})\,S°[H_2(g)]\}$

$= (1\text{ mol }CH_4(g)/\text{mol-rxn})(186.3\text{ J/K · mol}) - [1\text{ mol }C(\text{graphite})/\text{mol-rxn}](5.6\text{ J/K · mol}) + (2\text{ mol }H_2(g)/\text{mol-rxn})(130.7\text{ J/K · mol})]$

$= -80.7\text{ J/K · mol-rxn}$

Combining the values of $\Delta_r H°$ and $\Delta_r S°$ using Equation 19.5 gives $\Delta_r G°$.

$\Delta_r G° = \Delta_r H° - T\Delta_r S°$

$= -74.9 \text{ kJ/mol-rxn} - [(298 \text{ K})(-80.7 \text{ J/K} \cdot \text{mol-rxn})](1 \text{ kJ/1000 J})$

$= -50.9 \text{ kJ/mol-rxn}$

$\Delta_r G°$ is negative at 298 K, so the reaction is predicted to be spontaneous under standard conditions at this temperature. It is also predicted to be product-favored at equilibrium.

**Think about Your Answer**  One of the most common mistakes students make is to forget to make sure that $\Delta_r H$ and $\Delta_r S$ are both in terms of the same energy unit (in this case, kJ). In this example, the product $T\Delta_r S°$ is negative ($-24.0$ J/mol-rxn) and disfavors the reaction. However, the entropy change is relatively small, and $\Delta_r H° = -74.9$ kJ/mol-rxn is the dominant term. Chemists call this an *enthalpy-driven reaction*.

---

**Check Your Understanding**

Using values of $\Delta_f H°$ and $S°$ to find $\Delta_r H°$ and $\Delta_r S°$, calculate the free energy change, $\Delta_r G°$, for the formation of 2 mol of $NH_3(g)$ from the elements at standard conditions and 25 °C.

$$N_2(g) + 3 \text{ H}_2(g) \rightarrow 2 \text{ NH}_3(g)$$

---

## ⬛WL  INTERACTIVE EXAMPLE 19.5   Calculating $\Delta_r G°$ Using Free Energies of Formation

**Problem**  Calculate the standard free energy change for the combustion of one mole of methane using values for standard free energies of formation of the products and reactants. Is the reaction spontaneous under standard conditions? Is it product-favored or reactant-favored at equilibrium?

**What Do You Know?**  You are asked to determine the standard free energy change for a reaction ($\Delta_r G°$). Values of standard molar free energies of formation for the substances involved in the reaction can be found in Appendix L.

**Strategy**  Write a balanced equation for the reaction. Then, use Equation 19.8 with values of $\Delta_f G°$ obtained from Appendix L.

**Solution**  The balanced equation and values of $\Delta_f G°$ for each reactant and product are

$$CH_4(g) + 2 \text{ O}_2(g) \rightarrow 2 \text{ H}_2O(g) + CO_2(g)$$

| $\Delta_f G°$ (kJ/mol) | | | |
|---|---|---|---|
| $-50.8$ | $0$ | $-228.6$ | $-394.4$ |

These values can then be substituted into Equation 19.8.

$\Delta_r G° = \Sigma n\Delta_f G°(\text{products}) - \Sigma n\Delta_f G°(\text{reactants})$

$= \{(2 \text{ mol H}_2O(g)/\text{mol-rxn}) \Delta_f G°[\text{H}_2O(g)] + (1 \text{ mol CO}_2(g)/\text{mol-rxn}) \Delta_f G°[\text{CO}_2(g)]\}$
$\quad - \{(1 \text{ mol CH}_4(g)/\text{mol-rxn}) \Delta_f G°[\text{CH}_4(g)] + (2 \text{ mol O}_2(g)/\text{mol-rxn}) \Delta_f G°[\text{O}_2(g)]\}$

$= [(2 \text{ mol H}_2O(g)/\text{mol-rxn})(-228.6 \text{ kJ/mol}) + (1 \text{ mol CO}_2(g)/\text{mol-rxn})(-394.4 \text{ kJ/mol})]$
$\quad - [(1 \text{ mol CH}_4(g)/\text{mol-rxn})(-50.8 \text{ kJ/mol}) + (2 \text{ mol O}_2(g)/\text{mol-rxn})(0 \text{ kJ/mol})]$

$= -800.8 \text{ kJ/mol-rxn}$

The large negative value of $\Delta_r G°$ indicates that the reaction is spontaneous under standard conditions and that it is product-favored at equilibrium.

**Think about Your Answer**  Common errors made by students in this calculation are (1) overlooking the stoichiometric coefficients in the equation and (2) confusing the signs for the terms when using Equation 19.8.

---

**Check Your Understanding**

Calculate the standard free energy change for the oxidation of 1.00 mol of $SO_2(g)$ to form $SO_3(g)$ using values of $\Delta_f G°$.

**Strategy Map 19.5**

**PROBLEM**

Calculate $\Delta_r G°$ for a reaction.

**KNOWN DATA/INFORMATION**

- Description of chemical reaction
- $\Delta_f G°$ values (Appendix L)

**STEP 1.** Write a **balanced chemical equation.**

Balanced chemical equation

**STEP 2.** Calculate $\Delta_r G°$ using Equation 19.8.

$\Delta_r G°$

## Free Energy and Temperature

The definition of free energy, $G = H - TS$, informs us that free energy is a function of temperature, so $\Delta_r G°$ will change as the temperature changes (Figure 19.11). A consequence of this dependence on temperature is that, in certain instances, reactions can be product-favored at equilibrium at one temperature and reactant-favored at another. Those instances arise when the $\Delta_r H°$ and $T\Delta_r S°$ terms work in opposite directions:

- Processes that are entropy-favored ($\Delta_r S° > 0$) and enthalpy-disfavored ($\Delta_r H° > 0$)
- Processes that are enthalpy-favored ($\Delta_r H° < 0$) and entropy-disfavored ($\Delta_r S° < 0$)

Let us explore the relationship of $\Delta G°$ and $T$ further and illustrate how it can be used to advantage.

Calcium carbonate is the primary component of limestone, marble, and seashells. Heating $CaCO_3$ produces lime, $CaO$, an important chemical, along with gaseous $CO_2$. The data below from Appendix L are at 298 K (25 °C).

| | $CaCO_3(s)$ | $\rightarrow$ | $CaO(s)$ | + | $CO_2(g)$ |
|---|---|---|---|---|---|
| $\Delta_f G°$ (kJ/mol) | −1129.16 | | −603.42 | | −394.36 |
| $\Delta_f H°$ (kJ/mol) | −1207.6 | | −635.09 | | −393.51 |
| $S°$ (J/K · mol) | 91.7 | | 38.2 | | 213.74 |

For the conversion of 1 mol of $CaCO_3(s)$ to 1 mol of $CaO(s)$ under standard conditions, $\Delta_r G° = +131.38$ kJ, $\Delta_r H° = +179.0$ kJ, and $\Delta_r S° = +160.2$ J/K. Although the reaction is entropy-favored, the large positive and unfavorable enthalpy change dominates at 298 K. Thus, the standard free energy change is positive at 298 K and 1 bar, indicating that the reaction is not spontaneous under standard conditions and is therefore reactant-favored at equilibrium.

The temperature dependence of $\Delta_r G°$ provides a means to turn the $CaCO_3$ decomposition into a product-favored reaction. Notice that the entropy change in the

Reaction of potassium with water is favorable at all temperatures.

$\Delta G° > 0$

0

$\Delta G° < 0$

**Increasing Temperature**

$\Delta H° < 0$
$\Delta S° > 0$

$\Delta H° < 0$ and $\Delta S° > 0$.
Product-favored at all temperatures.

Dehydration of $CuSO_4 · 5 H_2O$ and other hydrates is favorable only at higher temperatures.

$\Delta G° > 0$

0

$\Delta G° < 0$

**Increasing Temperature**

$\Delta H° < 0$
$\Delta S° < 0$

$\Delta H° > 0$
$\Delta S° > 0$

Blue line: $\Delta H° < 0$ and $\Delta S° < 0$.
Favored at low $T$. Red line: $\Delta H° > 0$ and $\Delta S° > 0$. Favored at high $T$.

$\Delta G° > 0$

0

$\Delta G° < 0$

**Increasing Temperature**

$\Delta S° < 0$
$\Delta H° > 0$

Reactant-favored reactions
$\Delta G° = \Delta H° - T\Delta S° > 0$

Product-favored reactions
$\Delta G° = \Delta H° - T\Delta S° < 0$

$\Delta H° > 0$ and $\Delta S° < 0$.
Reactant-favored at all temperatures.

Photos © Cengage Learning/Charles D. Winters

**FIGURE 19.11** The variation in $\Delta_r G°$ with temperature.

## CASE STUDY

# Thermodynamics and Living Things

The laws of thermodynamics apply to all chemical reactions. It should come as no surprise, therefore, that issues of spontaneity and calculations involving $\Delta G$ also arise in studies of biochemical reactions. For biochemical processes, however, a different standard state is often used. Most of the usual definition is retained: 1 bar pressure for gases and 1 $m$ concentration for aqueous solutes with the exception of one very important solute. Rather than using a standard state of 1 molal for hydronium ions (corresponding to a pH of about 0), biochemists use a hydronium concentration of $1 \times 10^{-7}$ M, corresponding to a pH of 7. This pH is much more useful for biochemical reactions. When biochemists use this as the standard state, they write the symbol ' next to the thermodynamic function. For example, they would write $\Delta G°'$ (pronounced *delta G zero prime*).

Living things require energy to perform their many functions. One of the main reactions involved in providing this energy is that of adenosine triphosphate (ATP) with water, a reaction for which $\Delta_r G°' = -30.5$ kJ/mol–rxn (◀ *The Chemistry of Life: Biochemistry*).

John C. Kotz

ATP, adenosine triphosphate

One of the key functions of the process of respiration is to produce molecules of ATP for our bodies to use. ATP is produced in the reaction of adenosine diphosphate (ADP) with hydrogen phosphate ($HP_i = HPO_4{}^{2-}$),

$$ADP + HP_i + H^+ \rightarrow ATP + H_2O$$
$$\Delta_r G°' = +30.5 \text{ kJ/mol-rxn}$$

a reaction that is not spontaneous under standard conditions and thus reactant-favored at equilibrium. How then do our bodies get this reaction to occur? The answer is to couple the production of ATP with another reaction that is even more product-favored than ATP production is reactant-favored. For example, organisms carry out the oxidation of carbohydrates in a multistep process, producing energy. One of the compounds produced in the process called *glycolysis* is phosphoenolpyruvate (PEP).

PEP, phosphoenolpyruvate

Its reaction with water is product-favored at equilibrium

$$PEP + H_2O \rightarrow Pyruvate + HP_i$$
$$\Delta_r G°' = -61.9 \text{ kJ/mol-rxn}$$

This reaction and ATP formation are linked through the $HP_i$ that is produced in the PEP reaction. If both reactions are carried out, we obtain the following:

$$PEP + H_2O \rightarrow Pyruvate + HP_i$$
$$\Delta_r G°' = -61.9 \text{ kJ/mol-rxn}$$

$$ADP + HP_i + H^+ \rightarrow ATP + H_2O$$

$$\Delta_r G°' = +30.5 \text{ kJ/mol-rxn}$$

---

$$PEP + ADP + H^+ \rightarrow Pyruvate + ATP$$
$$\Delta_r G°' = -31.4 \text{ kJ/mol-rxn}$$

The overall reaction has a negative value for $\Delta_r G°'$ and thus is product-favored at equilibrium. ATP is formed in this process.

The coupling of reactions to produce a system that is product-favored is used in a multitude of reactions that occur in our bodies.

## Questions:

1. Consider the hydrolysis reactions of creatine phosphate and adenosine-5′-monophosphate.

   Creatine Phosphate + $H_2O$
   $$\rightarrow \text{Creatine} + HP_i$$
   $$\Delta_r G°' = -43.3 \text{ kJ/mol-rxn}$$

   Adenosine-5′-Monophosphate + $H_2O$
   $$\rightarrow \text{Adenosine} + HP_i$$
   $$\Delta_r G°' = -9.2 \text{ kJ/mol-rxn}$$

   Which of the following combinations produces a reaction that is product-favored at equilibrium: for creatine phosphate to transfer phosphate to adenosine or for adenosine-5′-monophosphate to transfer phosphate to creatine?

2. Assume the reaction A(aq) + B(aq) → C(aq) + $H_3O^+$(aq) produces one hydronium ion. What is the mathematical relationship between $\Delta G°'$ and $\Delta G°$ at 25 °C? (*Hint:* Use the equation $\Delta G = \Delta G° + RT \ln Q$ and substitute $\Delta G°'$ for $\Delta G$.)

**Answers to these questions are available in Appendix N.**

---

reaction is positive as a result of the formation of $CO_2$ gas in the reaction. Thus, raising the temperature results in the value of $T\Delta_r S°$ becoming increasingly large. At a high enough temperature, $T\Delta_r S°$ will outweigh the enthalpy effect, and the process will become product-favored at equilibrium.

How high must the temperature be for this reaction to become product-favored? An estimate of the temperature can be obtained using Equation 19.5, by

● **CaCO₃ Decomposition** Experiments show that the pressure of $CO_2$ in an equilibrium system [$CaCO_3(s) \rightleftharpoons CaO(s) + CO_2(g)$] is 1 bar at about 900 °C ($K = 1$ and $\Delta G° = 0$), close to our estimated temperature.

calculating the temperature at which $\Delta_r G° = 0$. Above that temperature, $\Delta_r G°$ will have a negative value.

$$\Delta_r G° = \Delta_r H° - T\Delta_r S°$$

$$0 = (179.0 \text{ kJ/mol-rxn})(1000 \text{ J/kJ}) - T(160.2 \text{ J/K} \cdot \text{mol-rxn})$$

$$T = 1117 \text{ K (or 844 °C)}$$

How accurate is this result? As noted earlier, this answer is only an estimate of the temperature needed. One source of error is the assumption that $\Delta_r H°$ and $\Delta S°$ do not vary with temperature, an assumption that is not strictly true. There is always a small variation in these values when the temperature changes—not large enough to be important if the temperature range is narrow, but potentially a problem over wider temperature ranges such as seen in this example. As an estimate, however, a temperature in the range of 850 °C for this reaction is reasonable.

**Strategy Map 19.6**

**PROBLEM**

Determine the **temperature** above which a chemical reaction is **product-favored** at **equilibrium**.

↓

**KNOWN DATA/INFORMATION**

● Balanced chemical equation
● Temperature
● Values of $\Delta_f H°$ and $S°$

**STEP 1.** Calculate $\Delta_r H°$ using Equation 5.6.

$\Delta_r H°$

**STEP 2.** Calculate $\Delta_r S°$ using Equation 19.3.

$\Delta_r S°$

**STEP 3.** Use the equation $\Delta_r G° = \Delta_r H° - T\Delta_r S°$ to determine the temperature at which $\Delta_r G° = 0$.

**Temperature** above which the reaction is **product-favored** at **equilibrium**.

**◎WL** **INTERACTIVE EXAMPLE 19.6** **Effect of Temperature on $\Delta_r G°$**

**Problem** The decomposition of liquid $Ni(CO)_4$ to produce nickel metal and carbon monoxide has a $\Delta_r G°$ value of 40 kJ/mol-rxn at 25 °C.

$$Ni(CO)_4(\ell) \rightarrow Ni(s) + 4 CO(g)$$

Use values of $\Delta_f H°$ and $S°$ for the reactant and products to estimate the temperature at which the reaction becomes product-favored at equilibrium.

**What Do You Know?** You are given a balanced chemical equation. Values of standard molar enthalpies of formation and standard molar entropies for the substances can be found in the chemical literature. You also know that the key temperature to determine is that at which $\Delta_r G°$ is zero.

**Strategy** The reaction is reactant-favored at equilibrium at 298 K. However, if the entropy change is positive for the reaction and the reaction is endothermic (with a positive value of $\Delta_r H°$), then a higher temperature may allow the reaction to become product-favored at equilibrium. Therefore, we first find $\Delta_r H°$ and $\Delta_r S°$ to see if their values meet our criteria for spontaneity at a higher temperature, and then we calculate the temperature at which the following condition is met: $0 = \Delta_r H° - T\Delta_r S°$.

**Solution** Values for $\Delta_f H°$ and $S°$ are obtained from the chemical literature for the substances involved.

| | $Ni(CO)_4(\ell)$ | → | $Ni(s)$ | + | $4 CO(g)$ |
|---|---|---|---|---|---|
| $\Delta_f H°$(kJ/mol) | −632.0 | | 0 | | −110.525 |
| $S°$(J/K · mol) | 320.1 | | 29.87 | | 197.67 |

For a process in which 1 mol of liquid $Ni(CO)_4$ is converted to 1 mol of $Ni(s)$ and 4 mol of $CO(g)$, we find

$$\Delta_r H° = +189.9 \text{ kJ/mol-rxn}$$

$$\Delta_r S° = +500.5 \text{ J/K mol-rxn}$$

We use these values of $\Delta_r H°$ and $\Delta_r S°$ to find the temperature at which $\Delta_r G° = 0$.

$$\Delta_r G° = \Delta_r H° - T\Delta_r S°$$

$$0 = (189.9 \text{ kJ/mol-rxn})(1000 \text{ J/kJ}) - T(500.5 \text{ J/K} \cdot \text{mol-rxn})$$

$$T = 379.4 \text{ K (or 106.2 °C)}$$

**Think about Your Answer** At 298 K, the reaction is reactant-favored at equilibrium largely because it is quite endothermic. However, the positive entropy change allows the reaction to be product-favored at equilibrium at a higher temperature.

**Check Your Understanding**

Oxygen was first prepared by Joseph Priestley (1733–1804) by heating HgO. Use data in Appendix L to estimate the temperature required to decompose HgO(s) into Hg(ℓ) and $O_2(g)$.

## Using the Relationship between $\Delta_r G°$ and $K$

Equation 19.7 provides a direct route to determine the standard free energy change from experimentally determined equilibrium constants. Alternatively, it allows calculation of an equilibrium constant from thermochemical data contained in tables or obtained from an experiment.

### ✪WL  INTERACTIVE EXAMPLE 19.7    Calculating $K_p$ from $\Delta_r G°$

**Problem** Determine the standard free energy change, $\Delta_r G°$, for the formation of 1.00 mol of $NH_3(g)$ from nitrogen and hydrogen, and use this value to calculate the equilibrium constant for this reaction at 25 °C.

**What Do You Know?** You are given enough information so you can write a balanced chemical equation for the desired chemical reaction. Values of $\Delta_f G°$ are given in Appendix L.

**Strategy** The free energy of formation of ammonia represents the free energy change to form 1.00 mol of $NH_3(g)$ from the elements. The equilibrium constant for this reaction is calculated from $\Delta_r G°$ using Equation 19.7. Because the reactants and products are gases, the calculated value will be $K_p$.

**Solution** Begin by specifying a balanced equation for the chemical reaction under investigation.

$$\tfrac{1}{2} N_2(g) + \tfrac{3}{2} H_2(g) \rightleftharpoons NH_3(g)$$

The free energy change for this reaction is $-16.37$ kJ/mol-rxn ($\Delta_r G° = \Delta_f G°$ for $NH_3(g)$; Appendix L). In a calculation of $K_p$ using Equation 19.7, we will need consistent units. If we use the gas constant, $R$, in units of 8.3145 J/K · mol, then the value of $\Delta_r G°$ must be in J/mol-rxn (and not kJ/mol-rxn). The temperature is 25 °C (298.15 K).

$$\Delta_r G° = -RT \ln K$$

$$-16{,}370 \text{ J/mol-rxn} = (-8.3145 \text{ J/K} \cdot \text{mol-rxn})(298.15 \text{ K}) \ln K_p$$

$$\ln K_p = 6.604$$

$$\boxed{K_p = 738}$$

**Think about Your Answer** The value of $\Delta_r G°$ is less than zero, indicating that this reaction is spontaneous under standard conditions and therefore product-favored at equilibrium. The value of $K_p$ calculated is greater than 1 as it should be for such a process. This example illustrates how to calculate equilibrium constants from thermodynamic data. In fact, many equilibrium constants you find in the chemical literature are not experimentally determined but are instead calculated from thermodynamic data in this way.

**Check Your Understanding**
Determine the value of the equilibrium constant, $K_p$, for the decomposition of calcium carbonate to calcium oxide and carbon dioxide gas at 298.15 K.

### EXAMPLE 19.8    Calculating $\Delta_r G°$ from $K_{sp}$ for an Insoluble Solid

**Problem** The value of $K_{sp}$ for AgCl(s) at 25 °C is $1.8 \times 10^{-10}$. Determine $\Delta_r G°$ for the process $Ag^+(aq) + Cl^-(aq) \rightleftharpoons AgCl(s)$ at 298.15 K.

**What Do You Know** You are given the value of $K_{sp}$. The process of interest is the reverse of the chemical equation for $K_{sp}$. You also know the temperature.

**Strategy** The chemical equation given is the opposite of the equation used to define $K_{sp}$; therefore, the equilibrium constant for this reaction is $1/K_{sp}$. This value is used in Equation 19.7 to calculate $\Delta_r G°$.

**Solution**

For $Ag^+(aq) + Cl^-(aq) \rightleftharpoons AgCl(s)$,

$$K = 1/K_{sp} = 1/\ 1.8 \times 10^{-10} = 5.6 \times 10^9$$

$$\Delta_r G° = -RT \ln K = -(8.3145 \text{ J/K} \cdot \text{mol-rxn})(298.15 \text{ K}) \ln(5.6 \times 10^9)$$

$$= \boxed{-56 \text{ kJ/mol-rxn}}$$

**Strategy Map 19.7**

**PROBLEM**

Determine the **equilibrium constant** for a reaction using **thermodynamic data.**

↓

**KNOWN DATA/INFORMATION**
- Information to write a balanced chemical equation
- The values of $\Delta_f G°$
- Temperature

↓

STEP 1. Write the **balanced chemical equation.**

Balanced chemical equation

↓

STEP 2. Calculate $\Delta_r G°$ using values of $\Delta_f G°$ in Equation 19.8.

$\Delta_r G°$

↓

STEP 3. Use the equation $\Delta_r G° = -RT \ln K$ to determine the value of $K$.

Equilibrium constant, $K$

**Think about Your Answer**  The negative value of $\Delta_r G°$ indicates that the precipitation of AgCl from $Ag^+(aq)$ and $Cl^-(aq)$ is product-favored at equilibrium.

**Check Your Understanding**

Determine the value of $\Delta_r G°$ for the reaction $C(s) + CO_2(g) \rightleftharpoons 2\,CO(g)$ from data in Appendix L. Use this result to calculate the equilibrium constant.

---

## REVIEW & CHECK FOR SECTION 19.7

1.  Given that $\Delta_r H° = -2219$ kJ/mol-rxn and that $\Delta_r S° = -216$ J/K · mol-rxn at 25 °C, determine the value of $\Delta_r G°$ at 25 °C for the reaction

    $$C_3H_8(g) + 5\,O_2(g) \rightarrow 3\,CO_2(g) + 4\,H_2O(\ell)$$

    (a)  $-2283$ kJ/mol-rxn        (c)  $-2155$ kJ/mol-rxn

    (b)  $-2214$ kJ/mol-rxn        (d)  $6.218 \times 10^4$ kJ/mol-rxn

2.  Using values of $\Delta_f G°$, determine the value of $\Delta_r G°$ at 25 °C for the reaction

    $$2\,KClO_3(s) \rightarrow 2\,KCl(s) + 3\,O_2(g)$$

    (a)  $-225$ kJ/mol-rxn        (c)  $112$ kJ/mol-rxn

    (b)  $-112$ kJ/mol-rxn        (d)  $225$ kJ/mol-rxn

3.  The value of $K_p$ for the following reaction at 425 °C is 0.018. What is the value of $\Delta_r G°$ at this temperature?

    $$2\,HI(g) \rightleftharpoons H_2(g) + I_2(g)$$

    (a)  $1.0 \times 10^1$ kJ/mol-rxn       (c)  $23$ kJ/mol-rxn

    (b)  $-14$ kJ/mol-rxn        (d)  $240$ kJ/mol-rxn

---

## CHAPTER GOALS REVISITED

*Now that you have studied this chapter, you should ask whether you have met the chapter goals. In particular, you should be able to:*

### Understand the concept of entropy and its relationship to reaction spontaneity

a.  Understand that entropy is a measure of energy dispersal (Section 19.2). **Study Questions: 1, 2.**

b.  Recognize that an entropy change is the energy transferred as heat for a reversible process divided by the Kelvin temperature. (*A Closer Look*, Section 19.2 and Equation 19.1) **Study Questions: 40–42.**

c.  Identify common processes that are entropy-favored (Section 19.4). **Study Question: 3.**

### Calculate the change in entropy for a system, its surroundings, and the universe to determine whether a process is spontaneous under standard conditions

a.  Calculate entropy changes from tables of standard entropy values (Section 19.4). **Study Questions: 4–8.**

b.  Use standard entropy and enthalpy changes to predict whether a reaction will be spontaneous under standard conditions (Section 19.5 and Table 19.1). **Study Questions: 9–12.**

c.  Recognize how temperature influences whether a reaction is spontaneous (Section 19.5). **Study Questions: 13, 14, 23–26.**

## Understand and use the Gibbs free energy

a. Understand the connection between enthalpy and entropy changes and the Gibbs free energy change for a process (Section 19.6). **Study Questions: 15, 16.**

b. Understand the relationship of $\Delta_r G$, $\Delta_r G°$, $Q$, $K$, reaction spontaneity, and product- or reactant-favorability (Section 19.6).

| $Q$ | $\Delta G$ | Spontaneous? |
|-----|-----|-----|
| $Q < K$ | $\Delta G < 0$ | Spontaneous to the right as the equation is written |
| $Q = K$ | $\Delta G = 0$ | Reaction is at equilibrium |
| $Q > K$ | $\Delta G > 0$ | Not spontaneous to the right; spontaneous to the left |

| $K$ | $\Delta G°$ | Reactant-Favored or Product-Favored at Equilibrium? | Spontaneous Under Standard Conditions? |
|-----|-----|-----|-----|
| $K >> 1$ | $\Delta G° < 0$ | Product-favored | Spontaneous under standard conditions |
| $K = 1$ | $\Delta G° = 0$ | $[C]^c[D]^d = [A]^a[B]^b$ at equilibrium | At equilibrium under standard conditions |
| $K << 1$ | $\Delta G° > 0$ | Reactant-favored | Not spontaneous under standard conditions |

c. Describe and use the relationship between the free energy change under standard conditions and equilibrium constants, and calculate $K$ from $\Delta_r G°$ (Sections 19.6 and 19.7). **Study Questions: 27–30, 44, 48, 50, 61, and Go Chemistry Module 24.**

d. Calculate the change in free energy at standard conditions for a reaction from the enthalpy and entropy changes under standard conditions or from the standard free energy of formation of reactants and products ($\Delta_f G°$) (Section 19.7). **Study Questions: 15–20, 46, 55, 56, 75, 79.**

e. Know how free energy changes with temperature (Section 19.7). **Study Questions: 23–26, 57, 59, 70.**

# Key Equations

**Equation 19.1 (page 861)** Calculate the entropy change from the energy transferred as heat for a reversible process and the temperature at which it occurs.

$$\Delta S = \frac{q_{rev}}{T}$$

**Equation 19.2 (page 864)** The Boltzmann equation: The entropy of a system, $S$, is proportional to the number of accessible microstates, $W$, belonging to a given energy of a system or substance.

$$S = k \ln W$$

**Equation 19.3 (page 868)** Calculate the standard entropy change under standard conditions for a process from the tabulated entropies of the products and reactants and the stoichiometric coefficients ($n$) of the substances in the balanced chemical equation for the reaction.

$$\Delta_r S° = \Sigma n S°(\text{products}) - \Sigma n S°(\text{reactants})$$

**Equation 19.4 (page 870)** Calculate the total entropy change for a system and its surroundings, to determine whether a process is spontaneous under standard conditions.

$$\Delta S°(\text{universe}) = \Delta S°(\text{system}) + \Delta S°(\text{surroundings})$$

**Equation 19.5 (page 874)** Calculate the free energy change for a process from enthalpy and entropy changes.

$$\Delta G° = \Delta H° - T\Delta S°$$

**Equation 19.6 (page 876)** Relates the free energy change under nonstandard conditions ($\Delta_r G$) to the standard free energy change ($\Delta_r G°$) and the reaction quotient $Q$.

$$\Delta_r G = \Delta_r G° + RT \ln Q$$

**Equation 19.7 (page 876):** Relates the standard free energy change for a reaction and its equilibrium constant.

$$\Delta_r G° = -RT \ln K$$

**Equation 19.8 (page 878):** Calculate the standard free energy change for a reaction using tabulated values of $\Delta_f G°$ and the stoichiometric coefficients ($n$) of the substances in the balanced chemical equation for the reaction.

$$\Delta_r G° = \Sigma n \Delta_f G°(\text{products}) - \Sigma n \Delta_f G°(\text{reactants})$$

# Study Questions

⏻**WL** Interactive versions of these questions are assignable in OWL.

▲ denotes challenging questions.

Blue-numbered questions have answers in Appendix R and fully worked solutions in the *Student Solutions Manual*.

## Practicing Skills

**Entropy**
*(See Sections 19.2–19.4 and Examples 19.1 and 19.2.)*

1. Which substance has the higher entropy?
   (a) dry ice (solid $CO_2$) at $-78$ °C or $CO_2(g)$ at 0 °C
   (b) liquid water at 25 °C or liquid water at 50 °C
   (c) pure alumina, $Al_2O_3(s)$, or ruby (ruby is $Al_2O_3$ in which some $Al^{3+}$ ions in the crystalline lattice are replaced with $Cr^{3+}$ ions)
   (d) one mole of $N_2(g)$ at 1 bar pressure or one mole of $N_2(g)$ at 10 bar pressure (both at 298 K)

2. Which substance has the higher entropy?
   (a) a sample of pure silicon (to be used in a computer chip) or a piece of silicon containing a trace of another element such as boron or phosphorus
   (b) $O_2(g)$ at 0 °C or $O_2(g)$ at $-50$ °C
   (c) $I_2(s)$ or $I_2(g)$, both at room temperature
   (d) one mole of $O_2(g)$ at 1 bar pressure or one mole of $O_2(g)$ at 0.01 bar pressure (both at 298 K)

3. Use $S°$ values to calculate the standard entropy change, $\Delta_r S°$, for each of the following processes and comment on the sign of the change.
   (a) $KOH(s) \rightarrow KOH(aq)$
   (b) $Na(g) \rightarrow Na(s)$
   (c) $Br_2(\ell) \rightarrow Br_2(g)$
   (d) $HCl(g) \rightarrow HCl(aq)$

4. Use $S°$ values to calculate the standard entropy change, $\Delta_r S°$, for each of the following processes, and comment on the sign of the change.
   (a) $NH_4Cl(s) \rightarrow NH_4Cl(aq)$
   (b) $CH_3OH(\ell) \rightarrow CH_3OH(g)$
   (c) $CCl_4(g) \rightarrow CCl_4(\ell)$
   (d) $NaCl(s) \rightarrow NaCl(g)$

5. Calculate the standard entropy change for the formation of 1.0 mol of the following compounds from the elements at 25 °C.
   (a) $HCl(g)$          (b) $Ca(OH)_2(s)$

6. Calculate the standard entropy change for the formation of 1.0 mol of the following compounds from the elements at 25 °C.
   (a) $H_2S(g)$          (b) $MgCO_3(s)$

7. Calculate the standard entropy change for the following reactions at 25 °C. Comment on the sign of $\Delta_r S°$.
   (a) $2\,Al(s) + 3\,Cl_2(g) \rightarrow 2\,AlCl_3(s)$
   (b) $2\,CH_3OH(\ell) + 3\,O_2(g) \rightarrow 2\,CO_2(g) + 4\,H_2O(g)$

8. Calculate the standard entropy change for the following reactions at 25 °C. Comment on the sign of $\Delta_r S°$.
   (a) $2\,Na(s) + 2\,H_2O(\ell) \rightarrow 2\,NaOH(aq) + H_2(g)$
   (b) $Na_2CO_3(s) + 2\,HCl(aq) \rightarrow 2\,NaCl(aq) + H_2O(\ell) + CO_2(g)$

**$\Delta_r S°$(universe) and Spontaneity**
*(See Sections 19.2–19.5 and Example 19.3.)*

9. Is the reaction $Si(s) + 2\,Cl_2(g) \rightarrow SiCl_4(g)$ spontaneous under standard conditions at 298 K? Answer this question by calculating $\Delta S°$(system), $\Delta S°$(surroundings), and $\Delta S°$(universe). (Define reactants and products as the system.)

10. Is the reaction $Si(s) + 2\,H_2(g) \rightarrow SiH_4(g)$ spontaneous under standard conditions at 298 K? Answer this question by calculating calculating $\Delta S°$(system), $\Delta S°$(surroundings), and $\Delta S°$(universe). (Define reactants and products as the system.)

11. Calculate $\Delta S°$(universe) for the decomposition of 1 mol of liquid water to form gaseous hydrogen and oxygen. Is this reaction spontaneous under these conditions at 25 °C? Explain your answer briefly.

12. Calculate $\Delta S°$(universe) for the formation of 1 mol $HCl(g)$ from gaseous hydrogen and chlorine. Is this reaction spontaneous under these conditions at 25 °C? Explain your answer briefly.

13. Classify each of the reactions according to one of the four reaction types summarized in Table 19.1.
   (a) $Fe_2O_3(s) + 2\,Al(s) \rightarrow 2\,Fe(s) + Al_2O_3(s)$

   $\Delta_r H° = -851.5$ kJ/mol-rxn
   $\Delta_r S° = -375.2$ J/K · mol-rxn

   (b) $N_2(g) + 2\,O_2(g) \rightarrow 2\,NO_2(g)$

   $\Delta_r H° = 66.2$ kJ/mol-rxn
   $\Delta_r S° = -121.6$ J/K · mol-rxn

**14.** Classify each of the reactions according to one of the four reaction types summarized in Table 19.1.

(a) $C_6H_{12}O_6(s) + 6 O_2(g) \rightarrow 6 CO_2(g) + 6 H_2O(\ell)$

$\Delta_r H° = -673 \text{ kJ/mol-rxn}$
$\Delta_r S° = 60.4 \text{ J/K} \cdot \text{mol-rxn}$

(b) $MgO(s) + C(\text{graphite}) \rightarrow Mg(s) + CO(g)$

$\Delta_r H° = 490.7 \text{ kJ/mol-rxn}$
$\Delta_r S° = 197.9 \text{ J/K} \cdot \text{mol-rxn}$

## Gibbs Free Energy
*(See Section 19.6 and 19.7 and Example 19.4.)*

**15.** Using values of $\Delta_f H°$ and $S°$, calculate $\Delta_r G°$ for each of the following reactions at 25 °C.

(a) $2 Pb(s) + O_2(g) \rightarrow 2 PbO(s)$
(b) $NH_3(g) + HNO_3(aq) \rightarrow NH_4NO_3(aq)$

Which of these reactions is (are) predicted to be product-favored at equilibrium? Are the reactions enthalpy- or entropy-driven?

**16.** Using values of $\Delta_f H°$ and $S°$, calculate $\Delta_r G°$ for each of the following reactions at 25 °C.

(a) $2 Na(s) + 2 H_2O(\ell) \rightarrow 2 NaOH(aq) + H_2(g)$
(b) $6 C(\text{graphite}) + 3 H_2(g) \rightarrow C_6H_6(\ell)$

Which of these reactions is (are) predicted to be product-favored at equilibrium? Are the reactions enthalpy- or entropy-driven?

**17.** Using values of $\Delta_f H°$ and $S°$, calculate the standard molar free energy of formation, $\Delta_f G°$, for each of the following compounds:

(a) $CS_2(g)$
(b) $NaOH(s)$
(c) $ICl(g)$

Compare your calculated values of $\Delta_f G°$ with those listed in Appendix L. Which of these formation reactions are predicted to be spontaneous under standard conditions at 25 °C?

**18.** Using values of $\Delta_f H°$ and $S°$, calculate the standard molar free energy of formation, $\Delta_f G°$, for each of the following:

(a) $Ca(OH)_2(s)$
(b) $Cl(g)$
(c) $Na_2CO_3(s)$

Compare your calculated values of $\Delta_f G°$ with those listed in Appendix L. Which of these formation reactions are predicted to be spontaneous under standard conditions at 25 °C?

## Free Energy of Formation
*(See Sections 19.6 and 19.7 and Example 19.5.)*

**19.** Using values of $\Delta_f G°$, calculate $\Delta_r G°$ for each of the following reactions at 25 °C. Which are product-favored at equilibrium?

(a) $2 K(s) + Cl_2(g) \rightarrow 2 KCl(s)$
(b) $2 CuO(s) \rightarrow 2 Cu(s) + O_2(g)$
(c) $4 NH_3(g) + 7 O_2(g) \rightarrow 4 NO_2(g) + 6 H_2O(g)$

**20.** Using values of $\Delta_f G°$, calculate $\Delta_r G°$ for each of the following reactions at 25 °C. Which are product-favored at equilibrium?

(a) $HgS(s) + O_2(g) \rightarrow Hg(\ell) + SO_2(g)$
(b) $2 H_2S(g) + 3 O_2(g) \rightarrow 2 H_2O(g) + 2 SO_2(g)$
(c) $SiCl_4(g) + 2 Mg(s) \rightarrow 2 MgCl_2(s) + Si(s)$

**21.** For the reaction $BaCO_3(s) \rightarrow BaO(s) + CO_2(g)$, $\Delta_r G° = +219.7 \text{ kJ}$. Using this value and other data available in Appendix L, calculate the value of $\Delta_f G°$ for $BaCO_3(s)$.

**22.** For the reaction $TiCl_2(s) + Cl_2(g) \rightarrow TiCl_4(\ell)$, $\Delta_r G° = -272.8 \text{ kJ}$. Using this value and other data available in Appendix L, calculate the value of $\Delta_f G°$ for $TiCl_2(s)$.

## Effect of Temperature on ΔG
*(See Section 19.7 and Example 19.6.)*

**23.** Determine whether the reactions listed below are entropy-favored or disfavored under standard conditions. Predict how an increase in temperature will affect the value of $\Delta_r G°$.

(a) $N_2(g) + 2 O_2(g) \rightarrow 2 NO_2(g)$
(b) $2 C(s) + O_2(g) \rightarrow 2 CO(g)$
(c) $CaO(s) + CO_2(g) \rightarrow CaCO_3(s)$
(d) $2 NaCl(s) \rightarrow 2 Na(s) + Cl_2(g)$

**24.** Determine whether the reactions listed below are entropy-favored or disfavored under standard conditions. Predict how an increase in temperature will affect the value of $\Delta_r G°$.

(a) $I_2(g) \rightarrow 2 I(g)$
(b) $2 SO_2(g) + O_2(g) \rightarrow 2 SO_3(g)$
(c) $SiCl_4(g) + 2 H_2O(\ell) \rightarrow SiO_2(s) + 4 HCl(g)$
(d) $P_4(s, \text{white}) + 6 H_2(g) \rightarrow 4 PH_3(g)$

**25.** Heating some metal carbonates, among them magnesium carbonate, leads to their decomposition.

$$MgCO_3(s) \rightarrow MgO(s) + CO_2(g)$$

(a) Calculate $\Delta_r G°$ and $\Delta_r S°$ for the reaction.
(b) Is the reaction spontaneous under standard conditions at 298 K?
(c) Is the reaction predicted to be spontaneous at higher temperatures?

**26.** Calculate $\Delta_r H°$ and $\Delta_r S°$ for the reaction of tin(IV) oxide with carbon.

$$SnO_2(s) + C(s) \rightarrow Sn(s) + CO_2(g)$$

(a) Is the reaction spontaneous under standard conditions at 298 K?
(b) Is the reaction predicted to be spontaneous at higher temperatures?

## Free Energy and Equilibrium Constants
*(See Section 19.7 and Example 19.7.)*

**27.** The standard free energy change, $\Delta_r G°$, for the formation of $NO(g)$ from its elements is $+86.58 \text{ kJ/mol}$ at 25 °C. Calculate $K_p$ at this temperature for the equilibrium

$$\tfrac{1}{2} N_2(g) + \tfrac{1}{2} O_2(g) \rightleftharpoons NO(g)$$

Comment on the sign of $\Delta G°$ and the magnitude of $K_p$.

**28.** The standard free energy change, $\Delta_r G°$, for the formation of $O_3(g)$ from $O_2(g)$ is $+163.2 \text{ kJ/mol}$ at 25 °C. Calculate $K_p$ at this temperature for the equilibrium

$$3 O_2(g) \rightleftharpoons 2 O_3(g)$$

Comment on the sign of $\Delta G°$ and the magnitude of $K_p$.

29. Calculate $\Delta_r G°$ at 25 °C for the formation of 1.00 mol of $C_2H_6(g)$ from $C_2H_4(g)$ and $H_2(g)$. Use this value to calculate $K_p$ for the equilibrium.

$$C_2H_4(g) + H_2(g) \rightleftharpoons C_2H_6(g)$$

Comment on the sign of $\Delta_r G°$ and the magnitude of $K_p$.

30. Calculate $\Delta_r G°$ at 25 °C for the formation of 1.00 mol of $C_2H_5OH(g)$ from $C_2H_4(g)$ and $H_2O(g)$. Use this value to calculate $K_p$ for the equilibrium.

$$C_2H_4(g) + H_2O(g) \rightleftharpoons C_2H_5OH(g)$$

Comment on the sign of $\Delta_r G°$ and the magnitude of $K_p$.

## General Questions

*These questions are not designated as to type or location in the chapter. They may combine several concepts.*

31. Compare the compounds in each set below and decide which is expected to have the higher entropy. Assume all are at the same temperature. Check your answers using data in Appendix L.
    (a) $HF(g)$, $HCl(g)$, or $HBr(g)$
    (b) $NH_4Cl(s)$ or $NH_4Cl(aq)$
    (c) $C_2H_4(g)$ or $N_2(g)$ (two substances with the same molar mass)
    (d) $NaCl(s)$ or $NaCl(g)$

32. Using standard entropy values, calculate $\Delta_r S°$ for the formation of 1.0 mol of $NH_3(g)$ from $N_2(g)$ and $H_2(g)$ at 25 °C.

33. About 5 billion kilograms of benzene, $C_6H_6$, is made each year. Benzene is used as a starting material for many other compounds and as a solvent (although it is also a carcinogen, and its use is restricted). One compound that can be made from benzene is cyclohexane, $C_6H_{12}$.

$$C_6H_6(\ell) + 3 H_2(g) \rightarrow C_6H_{12}(\ell)$$

$$\Delta_r H° = -206.7 \text{ kJ}; \ \Delta_r S° = -361.5 \text{ J/K}$$

Is this reaction predicted to be product-favored at equilibrium at 25 °C? Is the reaction enthalpy- or entropy-driven?

34. Hydrogenation, the addition of hydrogen to an organic compound, is an industrially important reaction. Calculate $\Delta_r H°$, $\Delta_r S°$, and $\Delta_r G°$ for the hydrogenation of octene, $C_8H_{16}$, to give octane, $C_8H_{18}$, at 25 °C. Is the reaction product- or reactant-favored at equilibrium?

$$C_8H_{16}(g) + H_2(g) \rightarrow C_8H_{18}(g)$$

Along with data in Appendix L, the following information is needed for this calculation.

| Compound | $\Delta_f H°$ (kJ/mol) | $S°$ (J/K · mol) |
|---|---|---|
| Octene | −82.93 | 462.8 |
| Octane | −208.45 | 463.639 |

35. Is the combustion of ethane, $C_2H_6$, product-favored at equilibrium at 25 °C?

$$C_2H_6(g) + \tfrac{7}{2} O_2(g) \rightarrow 2 CO_2(g) + 3 H_2O(g)$$

Answer the question by calculating the value of $\Delta S°$ (universe) at 298 K, using values of $\Delta_f H°$ and $S°$ in Appendix L. Does the answer agree with your preconceived idea of this reaction?

36. Write a balanced equation that depicts the formation of 1 mol of $Fe_2O_3(s)$ from its elements. What is the standard free energy of formation of 1.00 mol of $Fe_2O_3(s)$? What is the value of $\Delta G°$ when 454 g (1 lb) of $Fe_2O_3(s)$ is formed from the elements?

37. When vapors from hydrochloric acid and aqueous ammonia come in contact, they react, producing a white "cloud" of solid $NH_4Cl$ (Figure 19.9).

$$HCl(g) + NH_3(g) \rightleftharpoons NH_4Cl(s)$$

Defining the reactants and products as the system under study:
(a) Predict whether $\Delta S°$(system), $\Delta S°$(surroundings), $\Delta S°$(universe), $\Delta_r H°$, and $\Delta_r G°$ (at 298 K) are greater than zero, equal to zero, or less than zero; and explain your prediction. Verify your predictions by calculating values for each of these quantities.
(b) Calculate the value of $K_p$ for this reaction at 298 K.

38. Calculate $\Delta S°$(system), $\Delta S°$(surroundings), and $\Delta S°$(universe) for each of the following processes at 298 K, and comment on how these systems differ.
    (a) $HNO_3(g) \rightarrow HNO_3(aq)$
    (b) $NaOH(s) \rightarrow NaOH(aq)$

39. Methanol is now widely used as a fuel in race cars. Consider the following reaction as a possible synthetic route to methanol.

$$C(graphite) + \tfrac{1}{2} O_2(g) + 2 H_2(g) \rightleftharpoons CH_3OH(\ell)$$

Calculate $K_p$ for the formation of methanol at 298 K using this reaction. Would this reaction be more product-favored at a different temperature?

40. The enthalpy of vaporization of liquid diethyl ether, $(C_2H_5)_2O$, is 26.0 kJ/mol at the boiling point of 35.0 °C. Calculate $\Delta S°$ for a vapor-to-liquid transformation at 35.0 °C.

41. Calculate the entropy change, $\Delta S°$, for the vaporization of ethanol, $C_2H_5OH$, at its normal boiling point, 78.0 °C. The enthalpy of vaporization of ethanol is 39.3 kJ/mol.

42. Using thermodynamic data, estimate the normal boiling point of ethanol. (Recall that liquid and vapor are in equilibrium at 1.0 atm pressure at the normal boiling point.) The actual normal boiling point is 78 °C. How well does your calculated result agree with the actual value?

43. The following reaction is reactant-favored at equilibrium at room temperature.

$$COCl_2(g) \rightarrow CO(g) + Cl_2(g)$$

Will raising or lowering the temperature make it product-favored?

44. When calcium carbonate is heated strongly, $CO_2$ gas is evolved. The equilibrium pressure of $CO_2$ is 1.00 bar at 897 °C, and $\Delta_r H°$ at 298 K is 179.0 kJ.

$$CaCO_3(s) \rightarrow CaO(s) + CO_2(g)$$

Estimate the value of $\Delta_r S°$ at 897 °C for the reaction.

45. Sodium reacts violently with water according to the equation

$$Na(s) + H_2O(\ell) \rightarrow NaOH(aq) + \tfrac{1}{2} H_2(g)$$

Without doing calculations, predict the signs of $\Delta_r H°$ and $\Delta_r S°$ for the reaction. Verify your prediction with a calculation.

**46.** Yeast can produce ethanol by the fermentation of glucose $(C_6H_{12}O_6)$, which is the basis for the production of most alcoholic beverages.

$$C_6H_{12}O_6(aq) \rightarrow 2\ C_2H_5OH(\ell) + 2\ CO_2(g)$$

Calculate $\Delta_r H°$, $\Delta_r S°$, and $\Delta_r G°$ for the reaction at 25 °C. Is the reaction product- or reactant-favored? In addition to the thermodynamic values in Appendix L, you will need the following data for $C_6H_{12}O_6(aq)$:

$\Delta_f H° = -1260.0$ kJ/mol; $S° = 289$ J/K · mol; and $\Delta_f G° = -918.8$ kJ/mol.

**47.** Elemental boron, in the form of thin fibers, can be made by reducing a boron halide with $H_2$.

$$BCl_3(g) + \tfrac{3}{2}\ H_2(g) \rightarrow B(s) + 3\ HCl(g)$$

Calculate $\Delta_r H°$, $\Delta_r S°$, and $\Delta_r G°$ at 25 °C for this reaction. Is the reaction predicted to be product-favored at equilibrium at 25 °C? If so, is it enthalpy- or entropy-driven? [$S°$ for B(s) is 5.86 J/K · mol.]

**48.** ▲ Estimate the vapor pressure of ethanol at 37 °C using thermodynamic data. Express the result in millimeters of mercury.

**49.** The equilibrium constant, $K_p$, for $N_2O_4(g) \rightleftharpoons$ $2\ NO_2(g)$ is 0.14 at 25 °C. Calculate $\Delta_r G°$ for the conversion of $N_2O_4(g)$ to $NO_2(g)$ from this constant, and compare this value with that determined from the $\Delta_f G°$ values in Appendix L.

**50.** ▲ Estimate the boiling point of water in Denver, Colorado (where the altitude is 1.60 km and the atmospheric pressure is 630 mm Hg or 0.840 bar).

**51.** The equilibrium constant for the butane $\rightleftharpoons$ isobutane equilibrium at 25 °C is 2.50. Calculate $\Delta_r G°$ at this temperature in units of kJ/mol.

butane        $\rightleftharpoons$        isobutane

$$CH_3CH_2CH_2CH_3 \quad \rightleftharpoons \quad CH_3CHCH_3$$

with $CH_3$ group

$$K_c = \frac{[\text{isobutane}]}{[\text{butane}]} = 2.50 \text{ at } 298 \text{ K}$$

**52.** A crucial reaction for the production of synthetic fuels is the production of $H_2$ by the reaction of coal with steam. The chemical reaction is

$$C(s) + H_2O(g) \rightarrow CO(g) + H_2(g)$$

(a) Calculate $\Delta_r G°$ for this reaction at 25 °C, assuming C(s) is graphite.
(b) Calculate $K_p$ for the reaction at 25 °C.
(c) Is the reaction predicted to be product-favored at equilibrium at 25 °C? If not, at what temperature will it become so?

**53.** Calculate $\Delta_r G°$ for the decomposition of sulfur trioxide to sulfur dioxide and oxygen.

$$2\ SO_3(g) \rightleftharpoons 2\ SO_2(g) + O_2(g)$$

(a) Is the reaction product-favored at equilibrium at 25 °C?
(b) If the reaction is not product-favored at 25 °C, is there a temperature at which it will become so? Estimate this temperature.
(c) Estimate the equilibrium constant for the reaction at 1500 °C.

**54.** Methanol can be made by partial oxidation of methane by $O_2(g)$.

$$CH_4(g) + \tfrac{1}{2}\ O_2(g) \rightleftharpoons CH_3OH(\ell)$$

(a) Determine $\Delta S°$(system), $\Delta S°$(surroundings), and $\Delta S°$(universe) for this process.
(b) Is this reaction product-favored at equilibrium at 25 °C?

**55.** A cave in Mexico was recently discovered to have some interesting chemistry. Hydrogen sulfide, $H_2S$, reacts with oxygen in the cave to give sulfuric acid, which drips from the ceiling in droplets with a pH less than 1. The reaction occurring is

$$H_2S(g) + 2\ O_2(g) \rightarrow H_2SO_4(\ell)$$

Calculate $\Delta_r H°$, $\Delta_r S°$, and $\Delta_r G°$. Is the reaction product-favored at equilibrium at 25 °C? Is it enthalpy- or entropy-driven?

**56.** Wet limestone is used to scrub $SO_2$ gas from the exhaust gases of power plants. One possible reaction gives hydrated calcium sulfite:

$$CaCO_3(s) + SO_2(g) + \tfrac{1}{2}\ H_2O(\ell) \rightleftharpoons$$
$$CaSO_3 \cdot \tfrac{1}{2}\ H_2O(s) + CO_2(g)$$

Another reaction gives hydrated calcium sulfate:

$$CaCO_3(s) + SO_2(g) + \tfrac{1}{2}\ H_2O(\ell) + \tfrac{1}{2}\ O_2(g) \rightleftharpoons$$
$$CaSO_4 \cdot \tfrac{1}{2}\ H_2O(s) + CO_2(g)$$

(a) Which is the more product-favored reaction? Use the data in the table below and any other information needed in Appendix L to calculate $\Delta_r G°$ for each reaction at 25 °C.

|  | $CaSO_3 \cdot \tfrac{1}{2}\ H_2O(s)$ | $CaSO_4 \cdot \tfrac{1}{2}\ H_2O(s)$ |
|---|---|---|
| $\Delta_f H°$ (kJ/mol) | −1311.7 | −1574.65 |
| $S°$ (J/K · mol) | 121.3 | 134.8 |

(b) Calculate $\Delta_r G°$ for the reaction

$$CaSO_3 \cdot \tfrac{1}{2}\ H_2O(s) + \tfrac{1}{2}\ O_2(g) \rightleftharpoons CaSO_4 \cdot \tfrac{1}{2}\ H_2O(s)$$

Is this reaction product- or reactant-favored at equilibrium?

**57.** Sulfur undergoes a phase transition between 80 and 100 °C.

$$S_8(\text{rhombic}) \rightarrow S_8(\text{monoclinic})$$

$\Delta_r H° = 3.213$ kJ/mol-rxn    $\Delta_r S° = 8.7$ J/K · mol-rxn

(a) Estimate $\Delta_r G°$ for the transition at 80.0 °C and 110.0 °C. What do these results tell you about the stability of the two forms of sulfur at each of these temperatures?
(b) Calculate the temperature at which $\Delta_r G° = 0$. What is the significance of this temperature?

58. Calculate the entropy change for dissolving HCl gas in water at 25 °C. Is the sign of $\Delta S°$ what you expected? Why or why not?

## In the Laboratory

59. Some metal oxides can be decomposed to the metal and oxygen under reasonable conditions. Is the decomposition of silver(I) oxide product-favored at 25 °C?

$$2 \, Ag_2O(s) \rightarrow 4 \, Ag(s) + O_2(g)$$

If not, can it become so if the temperature is raised? At what temperature does the reaction become product-favored?

60. Copper(II) oxide, CuO, can be reduced to copper metal with hydrogen at higher temperatures.

$$CuO(s) + H_2(g) \rightarrow Cu(s) + H_2O(g)$$

Is this reaction product- or reactant-favored at equilibrium at 298 K?

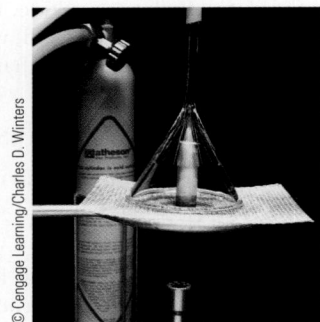

**If copper metal is heated in air, a black film of CuO forms on the surface.** In this photo, the heated bar, covered with a black CuO film, has been bathed in hydrogen gas. Black, solid CuO is reduced rapidly to copper at higher temperatures.

61. Calculate $\Delta_f G°$ for HI(g) at 350 °C, given the following equilibrium partial pressures: $P(H_2) = 0.132$ bar, $P(I_2) = 0.295$ bar, and $P(HI) = 1.61$ bar. At 350 °C and 1 bar, $I_2$ is a gas.

$$\tfrac{1}{2} \, H_2(g) + \tfrac{1}{2} \, I_2(g) \rightleftharpoons HI(g)$$

62. Calculate the equilibrium constant for the formation of NiO at 1627 °C. Can the reaction proceed in the forward direction if the initial pressure of $O_2$ is below 1.00 mm Hg? {$\Delta_f G°$ [NiO(s)] = −72.1 kJ/mol at 1627 °C}

$$Ni(s) + \tfrac{1}{2} \, O_2(g) \rightleftharpoons NiO(s)$$

63. Titanium(IV) oxide is converted to titanium carbide with carbon at a high temperature.

$$TiO_2(s) + 3 \, C(s) \rightarrow 2 \, CO(g) + TiC(s)$$

| Compound | Free Energies of Formation at 727 °C, kJ/mol |
|---|---|
| $TiO_2(s)$ | −757.8 |
| $TiC(s)$ | −162.6 |
| $CO(g)$ | −200.2 |

(a) Calculate $\Delta_r G°$ and $K$ at 727 °C
(b) Is the reaction product-favored at equilibrium at this temperature?
(c) How can the reactant or product concentrations be adjusted for the reaction to be spontaneous at 727 °C?

64. Cisplatin [cis-diamminedichloroplatinum(II)] is a potent treatment for certain types of cancers, but the *trans* isomer is not effective. What is the equilibrium constant at 298 K for the transformation of the *cis* to the *trans* isomer? Which is the favored isomer at 298 K, the *cis* or the *trans* isomer?

| Compound | $\Delta_f H°$ (kJ/mol, 298 K) | $\Delta_f G°$ (kJ/mol, 298 K) |
|---|---|---|
| *Cis*-Pt(NH$_3$)$_2$Cl$_2$ | −467.4 | −228.7 |
| *Trans*-Pt(NH$_3$)$_2$Cl$_2$ | −480.3 | −222.8 |

## Summary and Conceptual Questions

*The following questions may use concepts from this and previous chapters.*

65. ▲ Mercury vapor is dangerous because breathing it brings this toxic element into the lungs. We wish to estimate the vapor pressure of mercury at two different temperatures from the following data:

| | $\Delta_f H°$ (kJ/mol) | $S°$ (J/K · mol) | $\Delta_f G°$ (kJ/mol) |
|---|---|---|---|
| Hg($\ell$) | 0 | 76.02 | 0 |
| Hg(g) | 61.38 | 174.97 | 31.88 |

Estimate the temperature at which $K_p$ for the process Hg($\ell$) $\rightleftharpoons$ Hg(g) is equal to 1.00 (and the vapor pressure of Hg is 1.00 bar). Next, estimate the temperature at whch the vapor pressure is (1/760) bar. (Experimental vapor pressures are 1.00 mm Hg at 126.2 °C and 1.00 bar at 356.6 °C.) (*Note:* The temperature at which $P = 1.00$ bar can be calculated from thermodynamic data. To find the other temperature, you will need to use the temperature for $P = 1.00$ bar and the Clausius–Clapeyron equation on page 570.)

66. Explain why each of the following statements is incorrect.
(a) Entropy increases in all spontaneous reactions.
(b) Reactions with a negative free energy change ($\Delta_r G° < 0$) are product-favored and occur with rapid transformation of reactants to products.
(c) All spontaneous processes are exothermic.
(d) Endothermic processes are never spontaneous.

67. Decide whether each of the following statements is true or false. If false, rewrite it to make it true.
(a) The entropy of a substance increases on going from the liquid to the vapor state at any temperature.
(b) An exothermic reaction will always be spontaneous.
(c) Reactions with a positive $\Delta_r H°$ and a positive $\Delta_r S°$ can never be product-favored.
(d) If $\Delta_r G°$ for a reaction is negative, the reaction will have an equilibrium constant greater than 1.

68. Under what conditions is the entropy of a pure substance 0 J/K · mol? Could a substance at standard conditions have a value of 0 J/K · mol? A negative entropy value? Are there any conditions under which a substance will have negative entropy? Explain your answer.

69. In Chapter 14, you learned that entropy, as well as enthalpy, plays a role in the solution process. If $\Delta H°$ for the solution process is zero, explain how the process can be driven by entropy.

70. ▲ Consider the formation of NO(g) from its elements.

$$N_2(g) + O_2(g) \rightleftharpoons 2\ NO(g)$$

(a) Calculate $K_p$ at 25 °C. Is the reaction product-favored at this temperature?

(b) Assuming $\Delta_r H°$ and $\Delta_r S°$ are nearly constant with temperature, calculate $\Delta_r G°$ at 700 °C. Estimate $K_p$ from the new value of $\Delta_r G°$ at 700 °C. Is the reaction product-favored at 700 °C?

(c) Using $K_p$ at 700 °C, calculate the equilibrium partial pressures of the three gases if you mix 1.00 bar each of $N_2$ and $O_2$.

71. Write a chemical equation for the oxidation of $C_2H_6(g)$ by $O_2(g)$ to form $CO_2(g)$ and $H_2O(g)$. Defining this as the system:

(a) Predict whether the signs of $\Delta S°$ (system), $\Delta S°$ (surroundings), and $\Delta S°$ (universe) will be greater than zero, equal to zero, or less than zero. Explain your prediction.

(b) Predict the signs of $\Delta_r H°$ and $\Delta_r G°$. Explain how you made this prediction.

(c) Will the value of $K_p$ be very large, very small, or near 1? Will the equilibrium constant, $K_p$, for this system be larger or smaller at temperatures greater than 298 K? Explain how you made this prediction.

72. The normal melting point of benzene, $C_6H_6$, is 5.5 °C. For the process of melting, what is the sign of each of the following?

(a) $\Delta H°$      (c) $\Delta G°$ at 5.5 °C      (e) $\Delta G°$ at 25.0 °C
(b) $\Delta S°$      (d) $\Delta G°$ at 0.0 °C

73. Calculate the standard molar entropy change, $\Delta_r S°$, for each of the following reactions at 25 °C:

1.  $C(s) + 2\ H_2(g) \rightarrow CH_4(g)$
2.  $CH_4(g) + \frac{1}{2}\ O_2(g) \rightarrow CH_3OH(\ell)$
3.  $C(s) + 2\ H_2(g) + \frac{1}{2}\ O_2(g) \rightarrow CH_3OH(\ell)$

Verify that these values are related by the equation $\Delta_r S°(1) + \Delta_r S°(2) = \Delta_r S°(3)$. What general principle is illustrated here?

74. For each of the following processes, predict the algebraic sign of $\Delta_r H°$, $\Delta_r S°$, and $\Delta_r G°$. No calculations are necessary; use your common sense.

(a) The decomposition of liquid water to give gaseous oxygen and hydrogen, a process that requires a considerable amount of energy.

(b) Dynamite is a mixture of nitroglycerin, $C_3H_5N_3O_9$, and diatomaceous earth. The explosive decomposition of nitroglycerin gives gaseous products such as water, $CO_2$, and others; much heat is evolved.

(c) The combustion of gasoline in the engine of your car, as exemplified by the combustion of octane.

$$2\ C_8H_{18}(g) + 25\ O_2(g) \rightarrow 16\ CO_2(g) + 18\ H_2O(g)$$

75. "Heater Meals" are food packages that contain their own heat source. Just pour water into the heater unit, wait a few minutes, and voilà! You have a hot meal.

$$Mg(s) + 2\ H_2O(\ell) \rightarrow Mg(OH)_2(s) + H_2(g)$$

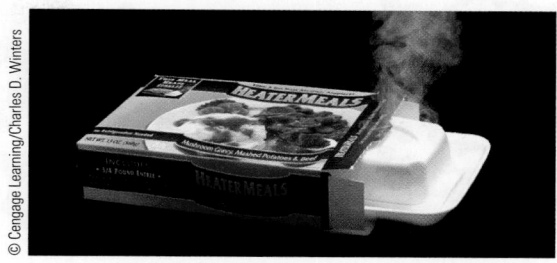

© Cengage Learning/Charles D. Winters

**The heat for the heater unit is produced by the reaction of magnesium with water.**

(a) Confirm that this is a spontaneous reaction under standard conditions.

(b) What mass of magnesium is required to produce sufficient energy to heat 225 mL of water (density = 0.995 g/mL) from 25 °C to the boiling point?

76. Use values of $\Delta_f G°$ for solid and gaseous iodine at 25 °C (Appendix L) to calculate the equilibrium vapor pressure of iodine at this temperature.

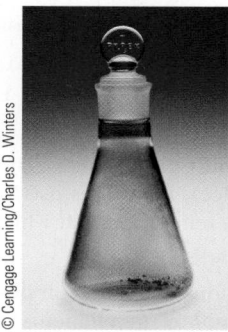

© Cengage Learning/Charles D. Winters

**Iodine, $I_2$, readily sublimes at room temperature.**

77. Oxygen dissolved in water can cause corrosion in hot-water heating systems. To remove oxygen, hydrazine ($N_2H_4$) is often added. Hydrazine reacts with dissolved $O_2$ to form water and $N_2$.

(a) Write a balanced chemical equation for the reaction of hydrazine and oxygen. Identify the oxidizing and reducing agents in this redox reaction.

(b) Calculate $\Delta_r H°$, $\Delta_r S°$, and $\Delta_r G°$ for this reaction involving 1 mol of $N_2H_4$ at 25 °C.

(c) Because this is an exothermic reaction, energy is evolved as heat. What temperature change is expected in a heating system containing $5.5 \times 10^4$ L of water? (Assume no energy is lost to the surroundings.)

(d) The mass of a hot-water heating system is $5.5 \times 10^4$ kg. What amount of $O_2$ (in moles) would be present in this system if it is filled with water saturated with $O_2$? (The solubility of $O_2$ in water at 25 °C is 0.000434 g per 100 g of water.)

(e) Assume hydrazine is available as a 5.0% solution in water. What mass of this solution should be added to totally consume the dissolved $O_2$ [described in part (d)]?

(f) Assuming the $N_2$ escapes as a gas, calculate the volume of $N_2(g)$ (measured at 273 K and 1.00 atm) that will be produced.

**78.** The formation of diamond from graphite is a process of considerable importance.

graphite                                diamond

(a) Using data in Appendix L, calculate $\Delta_r S°$, $\Delta_r H°$, and $\Delta_r G°$ for this process at 25 °C.

(b) The calculations will suggest that this process is not possible at any temperature. However, the synthesis of diamonds by this reaction is a commercial process. How can this contradiction be rationalized? (*Note:* In the industrial synthesis, high pressure and high temperatures are used.)

**79.** Iodine, $I_2$, dissolves readily in carbon tetrachloride. For this process, $\Delta H° = 0$ kJ/mol.

$$I_2(s) \rightarrow I_2 \text{ (in } CCl_4 \text{ solution)}$$

What is the sign of $\Delta_r G°$? Is the dissolving process entropy-driven or enthalpy-driven? Explain briefly.

**80.** Write an equation for the reaction of $Fe_2O_3(s)$ and $C(s)$ to give $Fe(s)$ and $CO(g)$ (one of the reactions occurring in a blast furnace). How does $\Delta_r G°$ vary with temperature? Is there a temperature at which the reaction is spontaneous?

**81.** Write an equation for the decomposition of 1.0 mol of gaseous methanol to the elements in their standard states.

(a) Does the spontaneity of the decomposition of $CH_3OH$ change as the temperature increases?

(b) Is there a temperature between 400 K and 1000 K at which the decomposition is spontaneous?

**82.** Consider the reaction of NO and $Cl_2$ to produce NOCl.

(a) What is $\Delta S°$ (system) for this reaction?

(b) Does $\Delta S°$ (system) change with temperature?

(c) Does $\Delta S°$ (surroundings) change with temperature?

(d) Does $\Delta S°$ (universe) always change with an increase in temperature?

(e) Do exothermic reactions always lead to positive values of $\Delta S°$ (universe)?

(f) Is the NO + $Cl_2$ reaction spontaneous at 298 K? At 700 K?

**83.** ▲ The Haber–Bosch process for the production of ammonia is one of the key industrial processes in developed countries.

$$N_2(g) + 3 H_2(g) \rightleftharpoons 2 NH_3(g)$$

(a) Calculate $\Delta_r G°$ for the reaction at 298 K, 800 K, and 1300 K. Data at 298 K are given in Appendix L. Data for the other temperatures are as follows:

| Temperature | $\Delta_r H°$ (kJ/mol) | $\Delta_r S°$ (J/K · mol) |
|---|---|---|
| 800 K | −107.4 | −225.4 |
| 1300 K | −112.4 | −228.0 |

How does the free energy change for the reaction change with temperature?

(b) Calculate the equilibrium constant for the reaction at 298 K, 800 K, and 1300 K.

(c) Calculate the mole fraction of ammonia in the equilibrium mixture at each of the temperatures. At what temperature is the mole fraction of $NH_3$ the largest?

**84.** ▲ Muscle cells need energy to contract. One biochemical pathway for energy transfer is the breakdown of glucose to pyruvate in a process called *glycolysis*. In the presence of sufficient oxygen in the cell, pyruvate is oxidized to $CO_2$ and $H_2O$ to make further energy available. However, under extreme conditions not enough oxygen can be supplied to the cells, so muscle cells produce lactate ion according to the reaction

$$H_3C-\overset{\overset{O}{\|}}{C}-\overset{\overset{O}{\|}}{C}-O^- + NADH + H^+$$

pyruvate

$$\xrightarrow[\text{dehydrogenase}]{\text{lactate}} H_3C-\overset{OH}{\underset{H}{C}}-\overset{\overset{O}{\|}}{C}-O^- + NAD^+$$

lactate

where $\Delta_r G°' = -25.1$ kJ/mol. In living cells, the pH value is about 7. The hydronium ion concentration is constant and is included in $\Delta G°$, which is then called $\Delta_r G°'$ (as explained on page 881). (*This problem is taken from the problems for the 36th International Chemistry Olympiad for high school students held in Kiel, Germany, in 2004.*)

(a) Calculate $\Delta_r G°$ for the reaction at 25 °C.

(b) Calculate the equilibrium constant $K'$. (The hydronium ion concentration is included in the constant. That is, $K' = K \cdot [H_3O^+]$ for the reaction at 25 °C and pH = 7.0.)

(c) $\Delta_r G°'$ is the free energy change under standard conditions; that is, the concentrations of all reactants (except $H_3O^+$) are 1.00 mol/L. Calculate $\Delta_r G'$ at 25 °C, assuming the following concentrations in the cell: pyruvate, 380 $\mu$mol/L; NADH, 50 $\mu$mol/L; lactate ion, 3700 $\mu$mol/L; and $NAD^+$ ion, 540 $\mu$mol/L.

# Applying Chemical Principles

## Are Diamonds Forever?

Natural diamonds are created over 150 kilometers beneath the Earth's surface. At these depths, enormous pressures and high temperatures convert graphite, the more stable allotrope of carbon at lower pressure, into diamond. It is believed that volcanic eruptions push diamonds to the Earth's surface. If a diamond is pushed to the surface quickly, it will cool before it has a chance to revert to graphite. Although diamonds are thermodynamically unstable at room temperature, the activation barrier for conversion is too high for the process to occur.

Diamonds have been synthesized in laboratories since the 1950s by duplicating the conditions that exist deep underground. To produce a synthetic diamond, a seed crystal of diamond is combined with graphite and nickel (or chromium), then subjected to pressures greater than 50,000 atmospheres and temperatures around 1500 °C. The nickel, now molten, simultaneously acts as a solvent for carbon and a catalyst for the formation of diamond. If conditions are maintained near the equilibrium line between diamond and graphite (Figure 1), single crystals of synthetic diamonds may be grown to sizes larger than one carat in approximately three days. Synthetic diamonds may be produced in a variety of colors. One of the most common colors is yellow, which results from a small amount of nitrogen replacing carbon in diamond's lattice. Is this a problem? Probably not. Natural yellow diamonds are extremely rare and sell for high prices.

Currently, a technique known as *chemical vapor deposition* (CVD) is being used to grow diamonds in a vacuum and at lower temperatures (800 °C). In CVD, methane and hydrogen gases are atomized above a diamond seed crystal. Hydrogen atoms bond with carbon atoms on the diamond's surface, preventing the carbon atoms from forming double bonds with its neighbors. Carbon radicals, from the decomposed methane, slowly replace the

**FIGURE 2 Diamond wafers.** The chemical vapor deposition (CVD) technique allows the synthesis of diamond in the shape of extended disks or wafers. Under optimized growth conditions the properties of these disks approach those of perfect diamond single crystals.

hydrogen atoms on the diamond's surface, building a larger diamond, one atom layer at a time. In addition to gemstones, the CVD method may be used to create diamond windows or thin diamond films over a variety of substrates (Figure 2).

## Questions:

1. The decomposition of diamond to graphite [C(diamond) → C(graphite)] is thermodynamically favored, but occurs slowly at room temperature.
   (a) Use $\Delta_f G°$ values from Appendix L to calculate $\Delta_r G°$ and $K_{eq}$ for the reaction under standard conditions and 298.15 K.
   (b) Use $\Delta_f H°$ and $S°$ values from Appendix L to calculate $\Delta_r G°$ and $K_{eq}$ for the reaction at 1000 K. Assume that enthalpy and entropy values are valid at these temperatures. Does heating shift the equilibrium toward the formation of diamond or graphite?
   (c) Why is the formation of diamond favored at high pressures?
   (d) The phase diagram shows that diamond is thermodynamically favored over graphite at 20,000 atmospheres pressure at room temperature. Why is this conversion actually done at much higher temperatures and pressures?

2. It has been demonstrated that buckminsterfullerene ($C_{60}$), another allotrope of carbon (page 63), may be converted into diamond at room temperature and 20,000 atmospheres pressure (about 2 GPa). The standard enthalpy of formation, $\Delta_f H°$, for buckminsterfullerene is 2320 kJ/mol at 298.2 K.
   (a) Calculate $\Delta_r H°$ for the conversion of $C_{60}$ to diamond at standard state conditions and 298.2 K.
   (b) Assuming that the standard entropy per mole of carbon in both $C_{60}$ and diamond is comparable (both about 2.3 J/K mol), is the conversion of $C_{60}$ to diamond product-favored at room temperature?

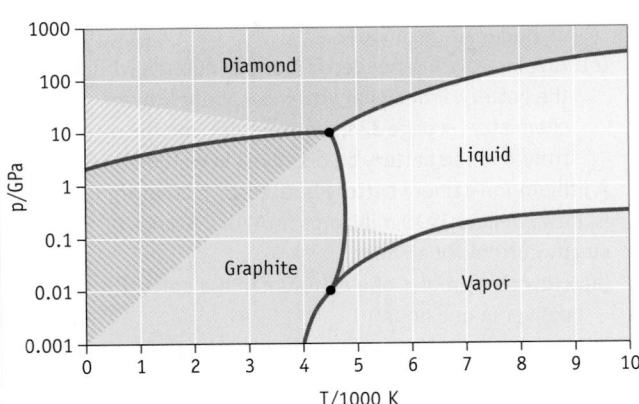

**FIGURE 1 Phase diagram for carbon.** The hatched areas are regions where the two phases can coexist. Pressures are in gigapascals (where 1 GPa is about 9900 atm).

# 20 Principles of Chemical Reactivity: Electron Transfer Reactions

Courtesy General Motors/Orlando Sentinel/MCT

## Battery Power
The 20th century was the century of the use and abuse of petroleum. The 21st century has to be the century of the discovery and use of alternative energy sources. Many of these will involve electrochemistry, the use of chemical reactions to produce electricity (batteries), or the use of electricity to produce chemical change (electrolysis).

The lithium-ion battery in your laptop computer or your phone, or the nickel-metal hydride battery in your hybrid car, works because redox reactions release chemical energy. (When you recharge the battery, you use electric energy to rejuvenate the chemicals in the battery.) But don't for a moment think that everything is understood about batteries or how to make them smaller, cheaper, or more efficient. One of the most important areas of research today is in battery technology, especially lithium-based batteries. Companies and universities around the world are searching for new battery designs that are lightweight, inexpensive, safe, environmentally kind, and that produce sufficient energy.

**Electric vehicles.** The forthcoming Chevrolet Volt will use lithium-ion batteries for propulsion. (For more on lithium-ion batteries see page 582.)

### Questions:

1. The simplest way to write the reaction for discharge in a lithium-ion battery is

    $$\text{Li(on carbon)(s)} + CoO_2(s) \rightarrow 6\ C(s) + LiCoO_2(s)$$

    (a) What are the oxidation numbers for cobalt in the two substances in the battery?
    (b) In such a battery, what reaction occurs at the cathode? At the anode?
    (c) An electrolyte is needed for ion conduction within the battery. From what you know about lithium chemistry (◄ page 324, for example), can the electrolyte in the battery be dissolved in water?

2. A lithium-ion camera battery is rated at 7500 mAh. That is, it can deliver 7500 milliamps (mA) or 7.5 amps of steady current for an hour.

    (a) How many moles of electrons can the battery deliver in one hour?
    (b) What mass of lithium is oxidized under these conditions in 1 hour?

**Answers to these questions are available in Appendix N.**

894

# CHAPTER OUTLINE

# CHAPTER GOALS

*See Chapter Goals Revisited (page 935) for Study Questions keyed to these goals.*

- Balance equations for oxidation–reduction reactions in acidic or basic solutions using the half-reaction approach.

- Understand the principles underlying voltaic cells.

- Understand how to use electrochemical potentials.

- Explore electrolysis, the use of electrical energy to produce chemical change.

Let us introduce you to electrochemistry and electron transfer reactions with a simple experiment. Place a piece of copper in an aqueous solution of silver nitrate. After a short time, metallic silver deposits on the copper, and the solution takes on the blue color typical of aqueous $Cu^{2+}$ ions (Figure 20.1). The following oxidation–reduction (redox) reaction has occurred:

$$Cu(s) + 2\ Ag^+(aq) \rightarrow Cu^{2+}(aq) + 2\ Ag(s)$$

At the particulate level, $Ag^+$ ions in solution come into direct contact with the copper surface where the transfer of electrons occurs. Two electrons are transferred from a Cu atom to two $Ag^+$ ions. Copper ions, $Cu^{2+}$, enter the solution, and silver

**OWL**

Sign in to OWL at **www.cengage.com/owl** to view tutorials and simulations, develop problem-solving skills, and complete online homework assigned by your professor.

**go Chemistry**

Download mini lecture videos for key concept review and exam prep from OWL or purchase them from **www.cengagebrain.com**

A clean piece of copper wire will be placed in a solution of silver nitrate, $AgNO_3$.

With time, the copper reduces $Ag^+$ ions to silver metal crystals, and the copper metal is oxidized to copper ions, $Cu^{2+}$.

The blue color of the solution is due to the presence of aqueous copper(II) ions.

Add $AgNO_3(aq)$

After several days

$Cu^{2+}$

Silver ions in solution

Surface of copper wire

Photos © Cengage Learning/Charles D. Winters

**FIGURE 20.1 The oxidation of copper by silver ions.** Note that water molecules are not shown for clarity.

atoms are deposited on the copper surface. This product-favored reaction continues until one or both of the reactants is consumed.

Can we use the reaction between copper metal and silver ions to generate an electric current? When the reactants, Cu(s) and Ag⁺(aq), are in direct contact, electrons are transferred directly from copper atoms to silver ions, and an increase in temperature (heating) rather than electrical work results. Instead, we can run the reaction in an apparatus that allows electrons to be transferred from one reactant to the other through an electrical circuit. The movement of electrons through the circuit constitutes an electric current that can be used to light a light bulb or to run a motor.

Devices that use chemical reactions to produce an electric current are called **voltaic cells** or **galvanic cells**, names honoring Count Alessandro Volta (1745–1827) and Luigi Galvani (1737–1798). All voltaic cells work in the same general way: They use product-favored redox reactions, and the electrons produced by the reducing agent are transferred through an electric circuit to the oxidizing agent.

A voltaic cell converts chemical energy to electrical energy. The opposite process, the use of electric energy to effect a chemical change, occurs in **electrolysis**. An example is the electrolysis of water (◀ Figure 1.10), in which electrical energy is used to split water into its component elements, hydrogen and oxygen. Electrolysis is also used to electroplate one metal onto another, to obtain aluminum from its common ore (bauxite, mostly $Al_2O_3$), and to prepare important chemicals such as chlorine.

Electrochemistry is the field of chemistry that considers chemical reactions that produce or are caused by electrical energy. Because all electrochemical reactions are oxidation–reduction (redox) reactions, we begin our exploration of this subject by first describing electron transfer reactions in more detail.

- **Two Types of Electrochemical Processes**
- Chemical change can produce an electric current in a voltaic cell.
- Electric energy can cause chemical change in the process of electrolysis.

- **Oxidation Numbers** Oxidation numbers (page 139) can be used to determine whether a substance is oxidized or reduced. An element is oxidized if its oxidation number increases. The oxidation number decreases in a reduction.

## 20.1 Oxidation–Reduction Reactions

In an oxidation–reduction reaction, electron transfer occurs between a reducing agent and an oxidizing agent (◀ Section 3.8). The essential features of all electron transfer reactions are as follows:

- One reactant is oxidized, and one is reduced.
- The extent of oxidation and reduction must balance.
- The oxidizing agent (the chemical species causing oxidation) is reduced.
- The reducing agent (the chemical species causing reduction) is oxidized.

These aspects of oxidation–reduction or redox reactions are illustrated for the reaction of copper metal and silver ion (Figure 20.1).

Cu oxidized, oxidation number increases;
Cu is the reducing agent.

$$Cu(s) + 2\ Ag^+(aq) \longrightarrow Cu^{2+}(aq) + 2\ Ag(s)$$

Ag⁺ reduced, oxidation number decreases;
Ag⁺ is the oxidizing agent.

**go Chemistry**

**Module 25: Oxidation–Reduction Reactions** covers concepts in this section.

## Balancing Oxidation–Reduction Equations

All equations for oxidation–reduction reactions must be balanced for both mass and charge. The same number of atoms appear in the products and reactants of an equation, and the sum of electric charges of all the species on each side of the equation arrow must be the same. Charge balance guarantees that the number of electrons produced in oxidation equals the number of electrons consumed in reduction.

Balancing some redox equations can be complicated, but fortunately some systematic procedures can be used in these cases. Here, we describe the **half-reaction method**, a procedure that involves writing separate, balanced equations for the oxidation and reduction processes. One half-reaction describes the oxidation part of the reaction, and a second half-reaction describes the reduction part.

When a reaction has been determined to involve oxidation and reduction (by noting, for example, that oxidation state changes have occurred), the equation is separated into two half-reactions, which are then balanced for mass and charge. The equation for the overall reaction is then the sum of these two balanced half-reactions, after adjustments have been made (if necessary) in one or both half-reaction equations so that the numbers of electrons transferred from reducing agent to oxidizing agent balance. For example, the half-reactions for the reaction of copper metal with silver ions are

Reduction half-reaction:    $Ag^+(aq) + e^- \rightarrow Ag(s)$

Oxidation half-reaction:    $Cu(s) \rightarrow Cu^{2+}(aq) + 2\,e^-$

Notice that the equations for the half-reactions are themselves balanced for mass and charge. In the copper half-reaction, there is one Cu atom on each side of the equation (mass balance). The electric charge on the right side of the equation is 0 (the sum of +2 for the ion and −2 for two electrons), as it is on the left side (charge balance).

To produce the net chemical equation, we will add the two half-reactions. First, however, we must multiply the silver half-reaction by 2.

$$2\,Ag^+(aq) + 2\,e^- \rightarrow 2\,Ag(s)$$

Each mole of copper atoms produces two moles of electrons, and two moles of $Ag^+$ ions are required to consume those electrons.

Finally, adding the two half-reactions and canceling electrons from both sides leads to the net ionic equation for the reaction.

Reduction half-reaction:    $2\,[Ag^+(aq) + e^- \rightarrow Ag(s)]$

Oxidation half-reaction:    $Cu(s) \rightarrow Cu^{2+}(aq) + 2\,e^-$

Net ionic equation    $Cu(s) + 2\,Ag^+(aq) \rightarrow Cu^{2+}(aq) + 2\,Ag(s)$

The resulting net ionic equation is balanced for mass and charge.

## ⬤WL    INTERACTIVE EXAMPLE 20.1    Balancing Oxidation–Reduction Equations

**Problem**  Balance the following net ionic equation

$$Al(s) + Cu^{2+}(aq) \rightarrow Al^{3+}(aq) + Cu(s)$$

Identify the oxidizing agent, the reducing agent, the substance oxidized, and the substance reduced. Write balanced half-reactions and the balanced net ionic equation. See Figure 20.2 for photographs of this reaction.

**(a)** A ball of aluminum foil is added to a solution of $Cu(NO_3)_2$ and NaCl.

**(b)** A coating of copper is soon seen on the surface of the aluminum, and the reaction generates a significant amount of energy as heat.

**FIGURE 20.2  Reduction of $Cu^{2+}$ by Al.** Aluminum always has a thin coating of $Al_2O_3$ on the surface, which protects the metal from further reaction. However, in the presence of $Cl^-$ ion, the coating is breached, and reaction occurs. See Example 20.1.

Photos © Cengage Learning/Charles D. Winters

## Strategy Map 20.1

**PROBLEM**

**Balance the equation** for the reaction of **Al** and **$Cu^{2+}$**.

↓

**KNOWN DATA/INFORMATION**

- Products
- Reactants

> **STEP 1.** Identify reaction as **redox**.

↓

Oxidation numbers change, so this is a redox reaction.

> **STEP 2.** Write half-reactions.

↓

Reduction half-reaction
Oxidation half-reaction

> **STEP 3. Balance** each half-reaction for **mass**.

↓

Half-reactions balanced for mass

> **STEP 4.** Use electrons for **charge balance**.

↓

Half-reactions balanced for charge.

> **STEP 5. Multiply** each half-reaction by a factor so **red. agent** supplies as many electrons as **ox. agent** acquires.

↓

Half-reactions balanced for **mass** and **charge**

> **STEP 6. Add** half-reactions.

↓

Overall **balanced equation**

> **STEP 7.** Simplify, and **check for balance**.

↓

Final balanced equation checked for correctness.

**What Do You Know?** You know that Al is producing $Al^{3+}$ ions, and copper(II) ions are producing copper metal.

**Strategy**

- Make sure the reaction is an oxidation–reduction reaction by checking each element to see whether the oxidation numbers change.

- Separate the equation into half-reactions, identifying what has been reduced (oxidizing agent) and what has been oxidized (reducing agent). (You may wish to review oxidation numbers and oxidation–reduction reactions in Section 3.8.)

- Balance the half-reactions, first for mass and then for charge.

- Add the two half-reactions, after ensuring that the reducing agent half-reaction involves the same number of moles of electrons as the oxidizing agent half-reaction.

**Solution**

***Step 1.*** *Recognize the Reaction as an Oxidation–Reduction Reaction.*

Here, the oxidation number for aluminum changes from 0 to +3, and the oxidation number of copper changes from +2 to 0. Aluminum is oxidized and serves as the reducing agent. Copper(II) ions are reduced, and $Cu^{2+}$ is the oxidizing agent.

***Step 2.*** *Separate the Process into Half-Reactions.*

Reduction: $Cu^{2+}(aq) \rightarrow Cu(s)$
(Oxidation number of Cu decreases.)

Oxidation: $Al(s) \rightarrow Al^{3+}(aq)$
(Oxidation number of Al increases.)

***Step 3.*** *Balance Each Half-Reaction for Mass.*

Both half-reactions are already balanced for mass.

***Step 4.*** *Balance Each Half-Reaction for Charge.*

To balance the equations for charge, add electrons to the more positive side of each half-reaction to bring the charge on that side of the equation down to the same value as is present on the other side.

Reduction: $2\ e^- + Cu^{2+}(aq) \rightarrow Cu(s)$
(Each $Cu^{2+}$ ion requires two electrons.)

Oxidation: $Al(s) \rightarrow Al^{3+}(aq) + 3\ e^-$
(Each Al atom releases three electrons.)

***Step 5.*** *Multiply Each Half-Reaction by an Appropriate Factor.*

The reducing agent must donate as many electrons as the oxidizing agent acquires. Three $Cu^{2+}$ ions are required to take on the six electrons produced by two Al atoms. Thus, we multiply the $Cu^{2+}/Cu$ half-reaction by 3 and the $Al/Al^{3+}$ half-reaction by 2.

Reduction: $3[2\ e^- + Cu^{2+}(aq) \rightarrow Cu(s)]$

Oxidation: $2[Al(s) \rightarrow Al^{3+}(aq) + 3\ e^-]$

***Step 6.*** *Add the Half-Reactions to Produce the Overall Balanced Equation.*

Reduction: $6\ e^- + 3\ Cu^{2+}(aq) \rightarrow 3\ Cu(s)$

Oxidation: $2\ Al(s) \rightarrow 2\ Al^{3+}(aq) + 6\ e^-$

Net ionic equation: $3\ Cu^{2+}(aq) + 2\ Al(s) \rightarrow 3\ Cu(s) + 2\ Al^{3+}(aq)$

***Step 7.*** *Simplify by Eliminating Reactants and Products That Appear on Both Sides.*

This step is not required here.

**Think about Your Answer** You should always check the overall equation to ensure there is mass and charge balance. In this case, three Cu atoms and two Al atoms appear on each side. The net electric charge on each side is $+6$. The equation is balanced.

**Check Your Understanding**

Aluminum reacts with nonoxidizing acids to give $Al^{3+}(aq)$ and $H_2(g)$. The (unbalanced) equation is

$$Al(s) + H^+(aq) \rightarrow Al^{3+}(aq) + H_2(g)$$

Write balanced equations for the half-reactions and the balanced net ionic equation. Identify the oxidizing agent, the reducing agent, the substance oxidized, and the substance reduced.

## Balancing Equations in Acid Solution

When balancing equations for redox reactions in aqueous solution, it is sometimes necessary to add water molecules ($H_2O$) and either $H^+(aq)$ in acidic solution or $OH^-(aq)$ in basic solution to the equation. Equations that include oxoanions such as $SO_4^{2-}$, $NO_3^-$, $ClO^-$, $CrO_4^{2-}$, and $MnO_4^-$ and organic compounds fall into this category. The process is outlined in Example 20.2 for the reduction of an oxocation in acid solution and in Example 20.3 for a reaction in basic solution.

● **Balancing Equations in Acid Solution** To simplify equations, we shall use $H^+$ instead of $H_3O^+$ when balancing equations in acid solution.

⏻WL    **INTERACTIVE EXAMPLE 20.2**   Balancing Equations
for Oxidation–Reduction Reactions in Acid Solution

**Problem** Balance the net ionic equation for the reaction of the dioxovanadium(V) ion, $VO_2^+$, with zinc in acid solution to form $VO^{2+}$ (Figure 20.3).

$$VO_2^+(aq) + Zn(s) \rightarrow VO^{2+}(aq) + Zn^{2+}(aq)$$

**What Do You Know?** You know that the $VO_2^+$ ions produce $VO^{2+}$ ions, and Zn metal produces $Zn^{2+}$ ions. You need to know how $H^+$ ions and water are used to balanced the O atoms involved in the reaction.

**Strategy** Follow the strategy outlined in the text and Example 20.1. Note that water and $H^+$ ions will appear as product and reactant, respectively, in the half-reaction for the reduction of $VO_2^+$ ion.

The $VO_2^+$ ion is yellow in acid solution.

Zn added. With time, the yellow $VO_2^+$ ion is reduced to blue $VO^{2+}$ ion.

With time, the blue $VO^{2+}$ ion is further reduced to green $V^{3+}$ ion.

Finally, green $V^{3+}$ ion is reduced to violet $V^{2+}$ ion.

Add Zn

$VO_2^+$          $VO^{2+}$          $V^{3+}$          $V^{2+}$

**FIGURE 20.3 Reduction of vanadium(V) with zinc.** See Example 20.2 for the balanced equation for the first stage of the reaction.

**Strategy Map 20.2**

PROBLEM

**Balance** the equation for the reaction of **Zn** and **VO₂⁺** in acid solution.

↓

KNOWN DATA/INFORMATION
- Products
- Reactants

STEP 1. Identify reaction as **redox**.

↓

Oxidation numbers change, so this is a redox reaction.

STEP 2. **Write** half-reactions.

↓

Reduction half-reaction
Oxidation half-reaction

STEP 3. **Balance** each half-reaction for **mass**. Use **H⁺** and **H₂O** as reactants or products if necessary for mass balance.

↓

Half-reactions **balanced for mass.** May include H⁺ and H₂O in addition to original reactants and products.

STEP 4. Use electrons for **charge balance.**

↓

Half-reactions balanced for charge.

STEP 5. **Multiply** each half-reaction by a factor so **red. agent** supplies as many electrons as **ox. agent** acquires.

↓

Half-reactions balanced for **mass** and **charge.**

STEP 6. **Add** half-reactions.

↓

Overall **balanced equation**

STEP 7. Simplify and **check for balance.**

↓

**Final equation** checked for correctness.

**Solution**

**Step 1.** *Recognize the Reaction as an Oxidation–Reduction Reaction.*

The oxidation number of V changes from +5 in $VO_2^+$ to +4 in $VO^{2+}$. The oxidation number of Zn changes from 0 in the metal to +2 in $Zn^{2+}$.

**Step 2.** *Separate the Process into Half-Reactions.*

Oxidation:    $Zn(s) \rightarrow Zn^{2+}(aq)$
(Zn(s) is oxidized and is the reducing agent.)

Reduction:    $VO_2^+(aq) \rightarrow VO^{2+}(aq)$
($VO_2^+(aq)$ is reduced and is the oxidizing agent.)

**Step 3.** *Balance the Half-Reactions for Mass.*

Begin by balancing all atoms except H and O. (These atoms are always the last to be balanced because they often appear in more than one reactant or product.)

Zinc half-reaction:    $Zn(s) \rightarrow Zn^{2+}(aq)$

This half-reaction is already balanced for mass.

Vanadium half-reaction:    $VO_2^+(aq) \rightarrow VO^{2+}(aq)$

The V atoms in this half-reaction are already balanced. An oxygen-containing species must be added to the right side of the equation to achieve an O atom balance, however.

$$VO_2^+(aq) \rightarrow VO^{2+}(aq) + (\text{need 1 O atom})$$

In acid solution, add $H_2O$ to the side requiring O atoms, one $H_2O$ molecule for each O atom required.

$$VO_2^+(aq) \rightarrow VO^{2+}(aq) + H_2O(\ell)$$

There are now two unbalanced H atoms on the right. Because the reaction occurs in an acidic solution, $H^+$ ions are present. Therefore, a mass balance for H can be achieved by adding $H^+$ to the side of the equation deficient in H atoms. Here, two $H^+$ ions are added to the left side of the equation.

$$2\,H^+(aq) + VO_2^+(aq) \rightarrow VO^{2+}(aq) + H_2O(\ell)$$

**Step 4.** *Balance the Half-Reactions for Charge by Adding Electrons to the More Positive Side to Make the Charges Equal on Both Sides.*

Two electrons are added to the right side of the zinc half-reaction to bring its charge down to the same value as is present on the left side (in this case, zero).

Zinc half-reaction:    $Zn(s) \rightarrow Zn^{2+}(aq) + 2\,e^-$

The mass-balanced $VO_2^+$ equation has a net charge of 3+ on the left side and 2+ on the right. Therefore, $1\,e^-$ is added to the more positive left side.

Vanadium half-reaction:    $e^- + 2\,H^+(aq) + VO_2^+(aq) \rightarrow VO^{2+}(aq) + H_2O(\ell)$

As a check on your work, notice that the vanadium atom changes in oxidation number from +5 to +4 and so needs to acquire one electron for each vanadium atom reduced.

**Step 5.** *Multiply the Half-Reactions by Appropriate Factors so That the Reducing Agent Donates as Many Electrons as the Oxidizing Agent Consumes.*

Here, the oxidation half-reaction supplies 2 mol of electrons per mol of Zn, and the reduction half-reaction consumes 1 mol of electrons per mol of $VO_2^+$. Therefore, the reduction half-reaction must be multiplied by 2. Now 2 mol of the oxidizing agent ($VO_2^+$) consumes the 2 mol of electrons provided per mol of the reducing agent (Zn).

$$Zn(s) \rightarrow Zn^{2+}(aq) + 2\,e^-$$

$$2[e^- + 2\,H^+(aq) + VO_2^+(aq) \rightarrow VO^{2+}(aq) + H_2O(\ell)]$$

**Step 6.** *Add the Half-Reactions to Give the Balanced, Overall Equation.*

Oxidation half-reaction: $Zn(s) \rightarrow Zn^{2+}(aq) + 2\ e^-$

Reduction half-reaction: $2\ e^- + 4\ H^+(aq) + 2\ VO_2^+(aq) \rightarrow 2\ VO^{2+}(aq) + 2\ H_2O(\ell)$

Net ionic equation:     $Zn(s) + 4\ H^+(aq) + 2\ VO_2^+(aq) \rightarrow Zn^{2+}(aq) + 2\ VO^{2+}(aq) + 2\ H_2O(\ell)$

**Step 7.** *Simplify by Eliminating Reactants and Products That Appear on Both Sides.*

This step is not required here.

**Think about Your Answer** Check the overall equation to ensure that there is a mass and charge balance.

Mass balance:          1 Zn, 2 V, 4 H, and 4 O

Charge balance:        Each side has a net charge of +6.

**Check Your Understanding**

1.  The yellow dioxovanadium(V) ion, $VO_2^+(aq)$, is reduced by zinc metal in three steps. The first step reduces it to blue $VO^{2+}(aq)$. This ion is further reduced to green $V^{3+}(aq)$ in the second step, and $V^{3+}$ can be reduced to violet $V^{2+}(aq)$ in a third step. In each step, zinc is oxidized to $Zn^{2+}(aq)$. Write balanced net ionic equations for Steps 2 and 3. (This reduction sequence is shown in Figure 20.3.)

2.  A common laboratory analysis for iron is to titrate aqueous iron(II) ion with a solution of potassium permanganate of precisely known concentration. Use the half-reaction method to write the balanced net ionic equation for the reaction in acid solution.

    $$MnO_4^-(aq) + Fe^{2+}(aq) \rightarrow Mn^{2+}(aq) + Fe^{3+}(aq)$$

    Identify the oxidizing agent, the reducing agent, the substance oxidized, and the substance reduced. See Figure 20.4.

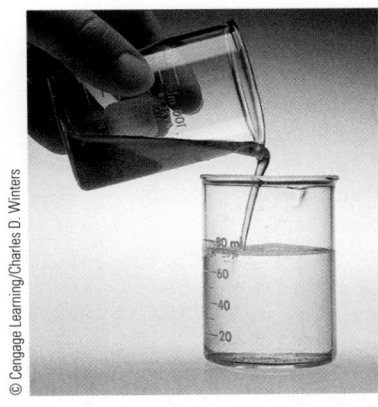

**FIGURE 20.4** The reaction of purple permanganate ion ($MnO_4^-$) with iron(II) ions in acid solution. The products are the nearly colorless $Mn^{2+}$ and $Fe^{3+}$ ions.

© Cengage Learning/Charles D. Winters

## Balancing Equations in Basic Solution

Example 20.2 illustrates the technique of balancing equations for redox reactions involving oxocations and oxoanions that occur in acid solution. Under these conditions, $H^+$ ion or the $H^+/H_2O$ pair can be used to achieve a balanced equation if required. Conversely, in basic solution, only $OH^-$ ion or the $OH^-/H_2O$ pair can be used.

## EXAMPLE 20.3    Balancing Equations for Oxidation–Reduction Reactions in Basic Solution

**Problem** Aluminum metal is oxidized in aqueous base, with water serving as the oxidizing agent. The products of the reaction are $[Al(OH)_4]^-(aq)$ and $H_2(g)$. Write a balanced net ionic equation for this reaction.

**What Do You Know?** You know the reactants and products. Here the reaction is in basic solution, so $OH^-$ ions may be involved and perhaps water as well.

**Strategy** The strategy is basically that of Examples 20.1 and 20.2 with the exception that you will need to decide if $OH^-$ ions are involved and if $H_2O$ is also included in the half-reactions.

**Solution**

**Step 1.** *Recognize the Reaction as an Oxidation–Reduction Reaction.*

The unbalanced equation is

$$Al(s) + H_2O(\ell) \rightarrow [Al(OH)_4]^-(aq) + H_2(g)$$

Here, aluminum is oxidized, with its oxidation number changing from 0 to +3. Hydrogen is reduced, with its oxidation number decreasing from +1 to zero.

**Step 2.** *Separate the Process into Half-Reactions.*

> Oxidation half-reaction:     $Al(s) \rightarrow [Al(OH)_4]^-(aq)$
> (Al oxidation number increased from 0 to +3.)

> Reduction half-reaction:     $H_2O(\ell) \rightarrow H_2(g)$
> (H oxidation number decreased from +1 to 0.)

**Step 3.** *Balance the Half-Reactions for Mass.*

Addition of $OH^-$ or $OH^-$ and $H_2O$ is required for mass balance in both half-reactions. In the case of the aluminum half-reaction, we simply add $OH^-$ ions to the left side.

> Oxidation half-reaction:     $Al(s) + 4\ OH^-(aq) \rightarrow [Al(OH)_4]^-(aq)$

To balance the half-reaction for water reduction, notice that an oxygen-containing species must appear on the right side of the equation. Because $H_2O$ is a reactant, we use $OH^-$, which is present in this basic solution, as the other product.

> Reduction half-reaction:     $2\ H_2O(\ell) \rightarrow H_2(g) + 2\ OH^-(aq)$

**Step 4.** *Balance the Half-Reactions for Charge.*

Electrons are added to balance charge.

> Oxidation half-reaction:     $Al(s) + 4\ OH^-(aq) \rightarrow [Al(OH)_4]^-(aq) + 3\ e^-$

> Reduction half-reaction:     $2\ H_2O(\ell) + 2\ e^- \rightarrow H_2(g) + 2\ OH^-(aq)$

**Step 5.** *Multiply the Half-Reactions by Appropriate Factors so That the Reducing Agent Donates as Many Electrons as the Oxidizing Agent Consumes.*

Here, electron balance is achieved by using 2 mol of Al to provide 6 mol of $e^-$, which are then acquired by 6 mol of $H_2O$.

> Oxidation half-reaction:     $2[Al(s) + 4\ OH^-(aq) \rightarrow [Al(OH)_4]^-(aq) + 3\ e^-]$

> Reduction half-reaction:     $3[2\ H_2O(\ell) + 2\ e^- \rightarrow H_2(g) + 2\ OH^-(aq)]$

**Step 6.** *Add the Half-Reactions.*

$$2\ Al(s) + 8\ OH^-(aq) \rightarrow 2\ [Al(OH)_4]^-(aq) + 6\ e^-$$

$$6\ H_2O(\ell) + 6\ e^- \rightarrow 3\ H_2(g) + 6\ OH^-(aq)$$

> Net equation:     $2\ Al(s) + 8\ OH^-(aq) + 6\ H_2O(\ell) \rightarrow 2\ [Al(OH)_4]^-(aq) + 3\ H_2(g) + 6\ OH^-(aq)$

**Step 7.** *Simplify by Eliminating Reactants and Products That Appear on Both Sides.*

Six $OH^-$ ions can be canceled from the two sides of the equation:

$$2\ Al(s) + 2\ OH^-(aq) + 6\ H_2O(\ell) \rightarrow 2\ [Al(OH)_4]^-(aq) + 3\ H_2(g)$$

**Think about Your Answer** The final equation is balanced for mass and charge.

> Mass balance:     2 Al, 14 H, and 8 O

> Charge balance: There is a net $-2$ charge on each side.

---

**Check Your Understanding**

Voltaic cells based on the reduction of sulfur are under development. One such cell involves the reaction of sulfur with aluminum under basic conditions.

$$Al(s) + S(s) \rightarrow Al(OH)_3(s) + HS^-(aq)$$

(a)   Balance this equation, showing each balanced half-reaction.

(b)   Identify the oxidizing and reducing agents, the substance oxidized, and the substance reduced.

**PROBLEM SOLVING TIP 20.1**

## Balancing Oxidation–Reduction Equations—A Summary

- Hydrogen balance can be achieved only with $H^+/H_2O$ (in acid) or $OH^-/H_2O$ (in base). Never add H or $H_2$ to balance hydrogen.
- Use $H_2O$ or $OH^-$ as appropriate to balance oxygen. Never add O atoms, $O^{2-}$ ions, or $O_2$ for O balance.
- Never include $H^+(aq)$ and $OH^-(aq)$ in the same equation. A solution can be either acidic or basic, never both.

- The number of electrons in a half-reaction reflects the change in oxidation number of the element being oxidized or reduced.
- Electrons are always a component of half-reactions but should never appear in the overall equation.

- Include charges in the formulas for ions. Omitting the charge, or writing the charge incorrectly, is one of the most common errors seen on student papers.
- The best way to become competent in balancing redox equations is to practice, practice, practice.

---

### REVIEW & CHECK FOR SECTION 20.1

1. Copper(II) sulfide reacts with nitric acid according to the balanced equation:

$$3 \text{ CuS(s)} + 8 \text{ H}^+(aq) + 2 \text{ NO}_3^-(aq) \rightarrow 3 \text{ Cu}^{2+}(aq) + 3 \text{ S(s)} + 4 \text{ H}_2O(\ell) + 2 \text{ NO(g)}$$

The substance oxidized is

   (a) CuS       (b) $H^+$       (c) $NO_3^-$

2. The balanced half-reaction for $NO_3^- \rightarrow NO$ in acid solution is

   (a) $NO_3^- \rightarrow NO + e^-$

   (b) $2 \text{ H}^+ + e^- + NO_3^- \rightarrow NO + 2 \text{ H}_2O$

   (c) $NO_3^- \rightarrow NO + O^{2-} + e^-$

   (d) $4 \text{ H}^+ + 3 e^- + NO_3^- \rightarrow NO + 2 \text{ H}_2O$

3. The balanced half-reaction for $Br_2 \rightarrow BrO_3^-$ in basic solution is

   (a) $3 \text{ OH}^- + Br_2 \rightarrow 2 \text{ BrO}_3^- + H_2O + e^-$

   (b) $12 \text{ OH}^- + Br_2 \rightarrow 2 \text{ BrO}_3^- + 6 \text{ H}_2O + 10 e^-$

   (c) $e^- + OH^- + Br_2 \rightarrow 2 \text{ BrO}_3^- + H_2O$

   (d) $10 e^- + Br_2 + 6 \text{ H}_2O \rightarrow 2 \text{ BrO}_3^- + 6 \text{ OH}^-$

---

## 20.2 Simple Voltaic Cells

Let us use the reaction of copper metal and silver ions (Figure 20.1) as the basis of a voltaic cell. To do so, we place the components of the two half-reactions in separate compartments (Figure 20.5). This prevents the copper metal from transferring electrons directly to silver ions. Instead, electrons will be transferred through an external circuit, and useful work can potentially be done.

---

**PROBLEM SOLVING TIP 20.2**

## An Alternative Method of Balancing Equations in Basic Solution

Balancing redox equations in basic solution, which may require you to use $OH^-$ ions and $H_2O$, can sometimes be more challenging than balancing equations in acidic solution. Rather than learn a separate method for balancing equations in basic solution, some find it easier to first balance an equation in basic solution as if it were in acidic solution and then add enough $OH^-$ ions to both sides of the equation so that $H^+$ ions are converted to water. Let us show how this works for balancing the reaction of hypochlorite ion with manganese(IV) oxide to form chloride ion and permanganate ion.

(a) Balance the equation as if the reaction were carried out in acid by following Steps 1–7 in Example 20.2:

$$3 \text{ ClO}^-(aq) + H_2O(\ell) + 2 \text{ MnO}_2(s) \rightarrow$$
$$3 \text{ Cl}^-(aq) + 2 \text{ MnO}_4^-(aq) + 2 \text{ H}^+(aq)$$

(b) To adjust for the fact that this reaction is carried out in base rather than in acid, we will add the same number of hydroxide ions to both sides of the equation as there are $H^+(aq)$ ions. On the side that

had the $H^+(aq)$ ions, the $H^+(aq)$ ions and $OH^-(aq)$ ions will form $H_2O(\ell)$.

$$3 \text{ ClO}^-(aq) + H_2O(\ell) + 2 \text{ MnO}_2(s) + 2 \text{ OH}^-(aq) \rightarrow$$
$$3 \text{ Cl}^-(aq) + 2 \text{ MnO}_4^-(aq) + 2 \text{ H}^+(aq) + 2 \text{ OH}^-(aq)$$

$$3 \text{ ClO}^-(aq) + H_2O(\ell) + 2 \text{ MnO}_2(s) + 2 \text{ OH}^-(aq) \rightarrow$$
$$3 \text{ Cl}^-(aq) + 2 \text{ MnO}_4^-(aq) + 2 \text{ H}_2O(\ell)$$

(c) Simplify

$$3 \text{ ClO}^-(aq) + 2 \text{ MnO}_2(s) + 2 \text{ OH}^-(aq) \rightarrow$$
$$3 \text{ Cl}^-(aq) + 2 \text{ MnO}_4^-(aq) + H_2O(\ell)$$

The copper half-cell (on the left in Figure 20.5) consists of copper metal that serves as one electrode and a solution containing copper(II) ions. The half-cell on the right uses a silver electrode and a solution containing silver(I) ions. Important features of this simple cell are as follows:

- *The two half-cells are connected with a* **salt bridge** *that allows cations and anions to move between the two half-cells.* The electrolyte chosen for the salt bridge should contain ions that will not react with chemical reagents in both half-cells. In the example in Figure 20.5, $NaNO_3$ is used.
- *In all electrochemical cells, the* **anode** *is the electrode at which oxidation occurs. The electrode at which reduction occurs is always the* **cathode**. (In Figure 20.5, the copper electrode is the anode, and the silver electrode is the cathode.)
- *A negative sign can be assigned to the anode in a voltaic cell, and the cathode is marked with a positive sign.* The chemical oxidation occurring at the anode, which produces electrons, gives it a negative charge.
- *In all electrochemical cells, electrons flow in the external circuit from the anode to the cathode.* Electric current in the external circuit of a voltaic cell consists of electrons moving from the negative to the positive electrode.

The chemistry occurring in the cell pictured in Figure 20.5 is summarized by the following half-reactions and net ionic equation:

| | |
|---|---|
| Cathode, reduction: | $2\,Ag^+(aq) + 2\,e^- \rightarrow 2\,Ag(s)$ |
| Anode, oxidation: | $Cu(s) \rightarrow Cu^{2+}(aq) + 2\,e^-$ |
| Net ionic equation: | $Cu(s) + 2\,Ag^+(aq) \rightarrow Cu^{2+}(aq) + 2\,Ag(s)$ |

The salt bridge is required in a voltaic cell for the reaction to proceed. In the $Cu/Ag^+$ voltaic cell, anions move in the salt bridge toward the copper half-cell, and cations move toward the silver half-cell (Figure 20.5). As $Cu^{2+}(aq)$ ions are formed in the copper half-cell by oxidation of copper metal, negative ions enter that cell from the salt bridge (and positive ions leave the cell), so that the numbers of positive and negative charges in the half-cell compartment remain in balance. The silver half-cell originally contained $AgNO_3$, so, as $Ag^+(aq)$ ions are

● **Salt Bridges** A simple salt bridge can be made by adding gelatin to a solution of an electrolyte. Gelatin makes the contents semi-rigid so that the salt bridge is easier to handle. Porous glass disks and ion-permeable membranes are alternatives to a salt bridge. These devices allow ions to traverse from one half-cell to the other while keeping the two solutions from mixing.

Net reaction: $Cu(s) + 2\,Ag^+(aq) \longrightarrow Cu^{2+}(aq) + 2\,Ag(s)$

**FIGURE 20.5  A voltaic cell using $Cu(s)\,|\,Cu^{2+}(aq)$ and $Ag(s)\,|\,Ag^+(aq)$ half-cells.** The cell is set up using 1.0 M $Cu(NO_3)_2$(aq) and 1.0 M $AgNO_3$(aq) solutions. Under these conditions, the cell will generate 0.46 volts at 25 °C.

Voltmeter

$(-)$ Direction of electron flow $\longrightarrow$ $(+)$

Electrode $(-)$

Electrode $(+)$

Salt bridge

Electrolyte: ions in solution

$e^-$

Reduced species

Oxidized species

Oxidized species

Reduced species

$\longleftarrow$ Anions

Cations $\longrightarrow$

$e^-$

ANODE compartment
OXIDATION occurs

CATHODE compartment
REDUCTION occurs

**FIGURE 20.6 Summary of terms used in a voltaic cell.** Electrons move from the anode, the site of oxidation, through the external circuit to the cathode, the site of reduction. Charge balance in each half-cell is achieved by migration of ions through the salt bridge. Negative ions move from the reduction half-cell to the oxidation half-cell and positive ions move in the opposite direction.

reduced to silver metal, negative ions ($NO_3^-$) move out of the half-cell into the salt bridge, and positive ions move into the cell. A complete circuit is required for current to flow. If the salt bridge is removed, reactions at the electrodes will cease.

In Figure 20.5, the electrodes are connected by wires to a voltmeter. In an alternative setup, the connections might be to a light bulb or other device that uses electricity. Electrons are produced by oxidation of copper, and $Cu^{2+}(aq)$ ions enter the solution. The electrons traverse the external circuit to the silver electrode, where they reduce $Ag^+(aq)$ ions to silver metal. To balance the extent of oxidation and reduction, two $Ag^+(aq)$ ions are reduced for every $Cu^{2+}(aq)$ ion formed. The main features of this and of all other voltaic cells are summarized in Figure 20.6.

## EXAMPLE 20.4  Electrochemical Cells

**Problem**  Describe how to set up a voltaic cell to generate an electric current using the reaction

$$Fe(s) + Cu^{2+}(aq) \rightarrow Cu(s) + Fe^{2+}(aq)$$

Which electrode is the anode, and which is the cathode? In which direction do electrons flow in the external circuit? In which direction do the positive and negative ions flow in the salt bridge? Write equations for the half-reactions that occur at each electrode.

**What Do You Know?**  You are told the reaction proceeds in the direction written. You also know that the half-reaction occurring in one half-cell will involve an iron electrode and a solution of an iron(II) salt such as $Fe(NO_3)_2$. The other half-cell contains a copper electrode and a soluble copper(II) salt such as $Cu(NO_3)_2$.

**Strategy**  First, identify the two different half-cells that make up the cell. These two half-cells are linked together with a salt bridge and an external circuit, as diagrammed in Figure 20.5. The description of the cell (anode, cathode), its chemistry (oxidizing and reducing agents, substances oxidized and reduced), and the movement of electrons in the external circuit and ions through the salt bridge will be similar to the features of the $Cu/Cu^{2+}$ and $Ag^+/Ag$ voltaic cell discussed in the text.

**Solution**  This voltaic cell is similar to the one diagrammed in Figure 20.5. Here we assume the two half-cells are linked with a salt bridge containing $KNO_3$ as the electrolyte.

Iron is oxidized, so the iron electrode is the anode:

Oxidation, anode: $\qquad Fe(s) \rightarrow Fe^{2+}(aq) + 2\ e^-$

Because copper(II) ions are reduced, the copper electrode is the cathode. The cathodic half-reaction is

Reduction, cathode: $Cu^{2+}(aq) + 2\,e^- \rightarrow Cu(s)$

In the external circuit, electrons flow from the iron electrode (anode) to the copper electrode (cathode). In the salt bridge, negative ions flow toward the iron/iron(II) half-cell, and positive ions flow in the opposite direction.

**Think about Your Answer** A good strategy is to focus on the movement of the negative species in the cell (electron flow in the external circuit and anion flow in the salt bridge). These species always move in a circular fashion: electrons from anode to cathode, and anions in the salt bridge in the opposite direction. If you establish which reactant is oxidized (provides electrons), you then know which electrode is the anode, in which direction electrons move in the external circuit, and in which direction anions flow in the salt bridge. (That said, don't ignore the fact that cations flow in the opposite direction to the anions in the salt bridge.)

**Check Your Understanding**

Describe how to set up a voltaic cell using the following half-reactions:

Reduction half-reaction: $Ag^+(aq) + e^- \rightarrow Ag(s)$

Oxidation half-reaction: $Ni(s) \rightarrow Ni^{2+}(aq) + 2\,e^-$

Which is the anode, and which is the cathode? What is the overall cell reaction? What is the direction of electron flow in an external wire connecting the two electrodes? Describe the ion flow in a salt bridge (with $NaNO_3$) connecting the cell compartments.

## Voltaic Cells with Inert Electrodes

In the half-cells described so far, the metal used as an electrode is also a reactant or a product in the redox reaction. Not all half-reactions involve a metal as a reactant or product, however. With the exception of carbon in the form of graphite, most nonmetals are unsuitable as electrode materials because they do not conduct electricity. It is not possible to make an electrode from a gas, a liquid (except mercury), or a solution. Ionic solids do not make satisfactory electrodes because the ions are locked tightly in a crystal lattice, and these materials do not conduct electricity.

In situations where reactants and products cannot serve as the electrode material, an inert or chemically unreactive electrode must be used. Such electrodes are made of materials that conduct an electric current but that are neither oxidized nor reduced in the cell.

Consider constructing a voltaic cell to accommodate the following product-favored reaction:

$$2\,Fe^{3+}(aq) + H_2(g) \rightarrow 2\,Fe^{2+}(aq) + 2\,H^+(aq)$$

Reduction half-reaction: $Fe^{3+}(aq) + e^- \rightarrow Fe^{2+}(aq)$

Oxidation half-reaction: $H_2(g) \rightarrow 2\,H^+(aq) + 2\,e^-$

Neither the reactants nor the products can be used as an electrode material. Therefore, the two half-cells are set up so that the reactants and products come in contact with an electrode where they can accept or give up electrons. Graphite is a commonly used electrode material: It is a conductor of electricity, and it is inexpensive (essential in commercial cells) and not readily oxidized under the conditions encountered in most cells. Mercury is used in certain types of cells. Platinum and gold are also commonly used because both are chemically inert under most circumstances, but they are generally too costly for commercial cells.

The *hydrogen electrode* is particularly important in the field of electrochemistry because it is used as a reference in assigning cell voltages (see Section 20.4) (Figure 20.7). The electrode material is platinum, chosen because hydrogen adsorbs on the metal's surface. In this half-cell's operation, hydrogen is bubbled over the electrode, and a large surface area maximizes the contact of the gas and the electrode. The aqueous solution contains $H^+(aq)$. The half-reactions involving $H^+(aq)$ and $H_2(g)$

$$2\ H^+(aq) + 2\ e^- \rightarrow H_2(g) \quad \text{or} \quad H_2(g) \rightarrow 2\ H^+(aq) + 2\ e^-$$

take place at the electrode surface, and the electrons involved in the reaction are conducted to or from the reaction site by the metal electrode.

A half-cell using the reduction of $Fe^{3+}(aq)$ to $Fe^{2+}(aq)$ can also be set up with a platinum electrode. In this case, the solution surrounding the electrode contains iron ions in two different oxidation states. Transfer of electrons to or from the reactant occurs at the electrode surface.

A voltaic cell involving the reduction of $Fe^{3+}(aq, 1.0\ M)$ to $Fe^{2+}(aq, 1.0\ M)$ with $H_2$ gas is illustrated in Figure 20.8. In this cell, the hydrogen electrode is the anode ($H_2$ is oxidized to $H^+$), and the iron-containing compartment is the cathode ($Fe^{3+}$ is reduced to $Fe^{2+}$). The cell produces 0.77 V.

## Electrochemical Cell Notations

Chemists often use a shorthand notation to simplify cell descriptions. For example, the cell involving the reduction of silver ion with copper metal is written as

$$Cu(s)\,|\,Cu^{2+}(aq,\ 1.0\ M)\,||\,Ag^+(aq,\ 1.0\ M)\,|\,Ag(s)$$

Anode information        Cathode information

**FIGURE 20.7 Hydrogen electrode.** Hydrogen gas is bubbled over a platinum electrode in a solution containing $H^+$ ions. Such electrodes function best if they have a large surface area. Often, platinum wires are woven into a gauze, or the metal surface is roughened either by abrasion or by chemical treatment to increase the surface area.

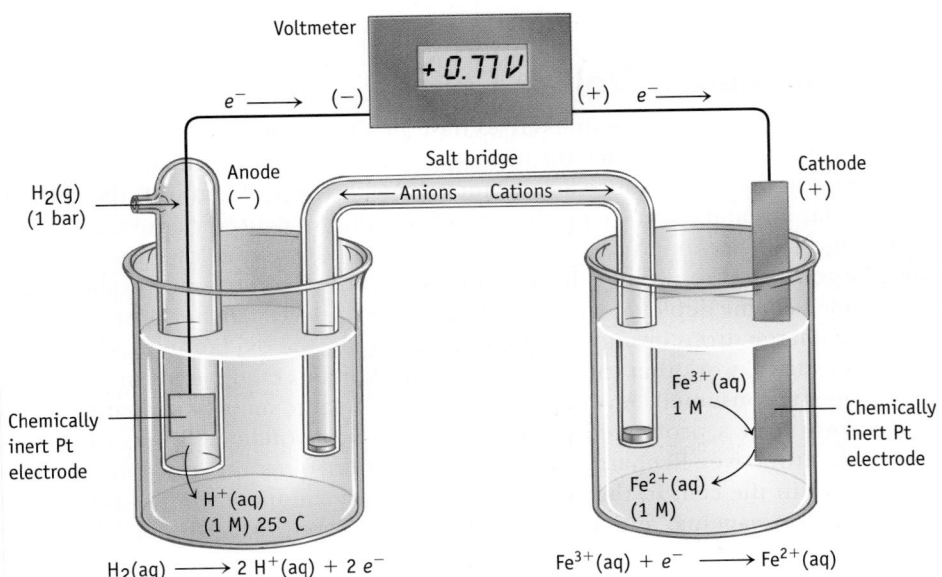

Net reaction: $2\ Fe^{3+}(aq) + H_2(aq) \longrightarrow 2\ Fe^{2+}(aq) + 2\ H^+(aq)$

**FIGURE 20.8 A voltaic cell with a hydrogen electrode.** This cell has $Fe^{2+}(aq, 1.0\ M)$ and $Fe^{3+}(aq, 1.0\ M)$ in the cathode compartment and $H_2(g)$ and $H^+(aq, 1.0\ M)$ in the anode compartment. At 25 °C, the cell generates 0.77 V. (The hydrogen electrode in the anode compartment in this illustration is a simplified schematic. See Figure 20.7 for a photograph of a commercial hydrogen electrode.)

The cell using $H_2$ gas to reduce $Fe^{3+}$ ions is written as

$$Pt \mid H_2(P = 1\ bar) \mid H^+(aq,\ 1.0\ M) \mid\mid Fe^{3+}(aq,\ 1.0\ M),\ Fe^{2+}(aq,\ 1.0\ M) \mid Pt$$

Anode information           Cathode information

By convention, on the left we write the anode and information with respect to the solution with which it is in contact. A single vertical line (|) indicates a phase boundary, and double vertical lines (||) indicate a salt bridge.

---

**REVIEW & CHECK FOR SECTION 20.2**

Answer the questions based on the cell below in which the following reaction occurs:

$$Ni^{2+}(aq) + Cd(s) \rightarrow Ni(s) + Cd^{2+}(aq)$$

1.  Electron transfer:

    (a)  Electrons transfer from Ni to Cd          (b)  Electrons transfer from Cd to Ni

2.  Electrodes:

    (a)  Cd is the anode and is negative           (c)  Cd is the cathode and is negative

    (b)  Cd is the anode and is positive           (d)  Cd is the cathode and is positive

3.  Salt bridge (which contains $K^+$ and $NO_3^-$ ions):

    (a)  $NO_3^-$ ions move from the Cd half-cell to the Ni half-cell and $K^+$ ions move from the Ni half-cell to the Cd half-cell.

    (b)  $NO_3^-$ ions move from the Ni half-cell to the Cd half-cell and $K^+$ ions move from the Cd half-cell to the Ni half-cell.

---

## 20.3 Commercial Voltaic Cells

The cells described so far are unlikely to have practical use. They are neither compact nor robust, high priorities for most applications. In most situations, it is also important that the cell produce a constant voltage, but a problem with the cells described so far is that the voltage produced varies as the concentrations of ions in solution change (see Section 20.5). Also, the current production is low. Attempting to draw a large current results in a drop in voltage because the ion concentrations near the cathode become depleted if current is drawn too quickly. Furthermore, the negative anode charge drops owing to a build up of cations, the oxidation product.

The electrical work that can be drawn from a voltaic cell depends on the quantity of reagents consumed. A voltaic cell must have a large mass of reactants to produce current over a prolonged period. In addition, a voltaic cell that can be recharged is attractive. Recharging a cell means returning the reagents to their original sites in the cell. In the cells described so far, the movement of ions in the cell mixes the reagents, and they cannot be "unmixed" after the cell has been running.

Batteries can be classified as primary and secondary. **Primary batteries** cannot be returned to their original state by recharging, so when the reactants are

**FIGURE 20.9 Some commercial voltaic cells.** Commercial voltaic cells provide energy for a wide range of devices, come in a myriad of sizes and shapes, and produce different voltages. Some are rechargeable; others are discarded after use. One might think that there is nothing further to learn about batteries, but this is not true. Research on these devices is actively pursued in the chemical community.

consumed, the battery is "dead" and must be discarded. **Secondary batteries** are often called **storage batteries** or **rechargeable batteries**. The reactions in these batteries can be reversed, so the batteries can be recharged.

Years of development have led to many different commercial voltaic cells to meet specific needs (Figure 20.9), and several common ones are described below. All adhere to the principles that have been developed in earlier discussions.

## Primary Batteries: Dry Cells and Alkaline Batteries

If you buy an inexpensive flashlight battery or dry cell battery, it might be a modern version of a voltaic cell invented by George LeClanché in 1866 (Figure 20.10). Zinc serves as the anode, and the cathode is a graphite rod placed down the center of the device. These cells are often called "dry cells" because there is no visible liquid phase. However, the cell contains a moist paste of $NH_4Cl$, $ZnCl_2$, and $MnO_2$, so water is present. The moisture is necessary because the ions present must be able to migrate from one electrode to the other. The cell generates a potential of 1.5 V using the following half-reactions:

Cathode, reduction:     $2\ NH_4^+(aq) + 2\ e^- \rightarrow 2\ NH_3(g) + H_2(g)$

Anode, oxidation:     $Zn(s) \rightarrow Zn^{2+}(aq) + 2\ e^-$

The products at the cathode are gases, which could build up pressure in the cell and cause it to rupture. The problem is avoided, however, by two other reactions that take place in the cell. Ammonia molecules bind to $Zn^{2+}$ ions, and hydrogen gas is oxidized by $MnO_2$ to water.

$$Zn^{2+}(aq) + 2\ NH_3(g) + 2\ Cl^-(aq) \rightarrow Zn(NH_3)_2Cl_2(s)$$

$$2\ MnO_2(s) + H_2(g) \rightarrow Mn_2O_3(s) + H_2O(\ell)$$

Zinc-carbon dry cells were widely used because of their low cost, but they have several disadvantages. If current is drawn from the battery rapidly, the gaseous products cannot be consumed rapidly enough, so the cell resistance rises, and the voltage drops. In addition, the zinc electrode and ammonium ions are in contact in the cell, and these chemicals react slowly. Recall that zinc reacts with acid to form hydrogen. The ammonium ion, $NH_4^+(aq)$, is a weak Brønsted acid and reacts slowly with zinc. Because of this reaction, these voltaic cells cannot be stored indefinitely, a fact you may have learned from experience. When the zinc outer shell deteriorates, the battery can leak acid and perhaps damage the appliance in which it is contained.

At the present time, you are more likely to use **alkaline batteries** in your camera or flashlight because they generate current up to 50% longer than a dry cell of the

● **Batteries** The word *battery* has become part of our common language, designating any self-contained device that generates an electric current. The term battery has a more precise scientific meaning, however. It refers to a collection of two or more voltaic cells. For example, the 12-volt battery used in automobiles is made up of six voltaic cells. Each voltaic cell develops a voltage of 2 volts. Six cells connected in series produce 12 volts.

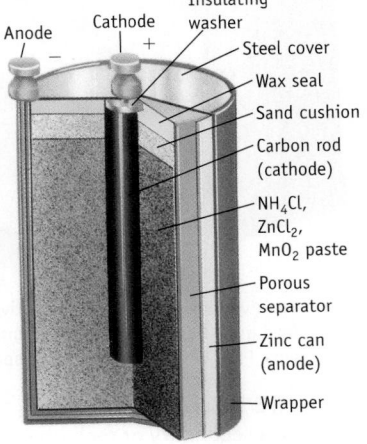

**FIGURE 20.10 The common dry cell battery.** Sometimes called the *zinc-carbon battery.*

same size. The chemistry of alkaline cells is quite similar to that in a zinc-carbon dry cell, except that the material inside the cell is basic (alkaline). Alkaline cells use the oxidation of zinc and the reduction of $MnO_2$ to generate a current, but NaOH or KOH is used in the cell instead of the acidic salt $NH_4Cl$.

Cathode, reduction: $2\ MnO_2(s) + H_2O(\ell) + 2\ e^- \rightarrow Mn_2O_3(s) + 2\ OH^-(aq)$

Anode, oxidation: $Zn(s) + 2\ OH^-(aq) \rightarrow ZnO(s) + H_2O(\ell) + 2\ e^-$

Alkaline cells, which produce 1.54 V (approximately the same voltage as the zinc-carbon dry cell), have the further advantage that the cell potential does not decline under high current loads because no gases are formed.

Prior to 2000, mercury-containing batteries were widely used in calculators, cameras, watches, heart pacemakers, and other devices. However, these small batteries were banned in the United States in the 1990s because of environmental problems. They have been replaced by several other types of batteries, such as silver oxide batteries and zinc-oxygen batteries. Both operate under alkaline conditions, and both have zinc anodes. In the silver oxide battery, which produces a voltage of about 1.5 V, the cell reactions are

Cathode, reduction: $Ag_2O(s) + H_2O(\ell) + 2\ e^- \rightarrow 2\ Ag(s) + 2\ OH^-(aq)$

Anode, oxidation: $Zn(s) + 2\ OH^-(aq) \rightarrow ZnO(s) + H_2O(\ell) + 2\ e^-$

The zinc-oxygen battery, which produces about 1.15–1.35 V, is unique in that atmospheric oxygen and not a metal oxide is the oxidizing agent.

Cathode, reduction: $O_2(g) + 2\ H_2O(\ell) + 4\ e^- \rightarrow 4\ OH^-(aq)$

Anode, oxidation: $Zn(s) + 2\ OH^-(aq) \rightarrow ZnO(s) + H_2O(\ell) + 2\ e^-$

These batteries are used in hearing aids, pagers, and medical devices.

## Secondary or Rechargeable Batteries

When a zinc-carbon dry cell or an alkaline cell ceases to produce a usable electric current, it is discarded. In contrast, some types of cells can be recharged, often hundreds of times. Recharging requires applying an electric current from an external source to restore the cell to its original state. There are a number of well known types of secondary batteries in common use.

### Lead Storage Battery

An automobile battery—the lead storage battery—is probably the best-known rechargeable battery (Figure 20.11). The 12-V version of this battery contains six voltaic cells, each generating about 2 V. The lead storage battery can produce a large initial current, an essential feature when starting an automobile engine.

The anode of a lead storage battery is metallic lead. The cathode is also made of lead, but it is covered with a layer of compressed, insoluble lead(IV) oxide, $PbO_2$. The electrodes, arranged alternately in a stack and separated by thin fiberglass sheets, are immersed in aqueous sulfuric acid. When the cell supplies electrical energy, the lead anode is oxidized to lead(II) sulfate, an insoluble substance that adheres to the electrode surface. The two electrons produced per lead atom move through the external circuit to the cathode, where $PbO_2$ is reduced to $Pb^{2+}$ ions that, in the presence of $H_2SO_4$, also form lead(II) sulfate.

Anode

Cathode

Positive plates: lead grids filled with $PbO_2$

Negative plates: lead grids filled with spongy lead

**FIGURE 20.11 Lead storage battery, a secondary or rechargeable battery.** Each cell of the battery generates 2 V.

Cathode, reduction: $PbO_2(s) + 4\ H^+(aq) + SO_4{}^{2-}(aq) + 2\ e^- \rightarrow PbSO_4(s) + 2\ H_2O(\ell)$

Anode, oxidation: $Pb(s) + SO_4{}^{2-}(aq) \rightarrow PbSO_4(s) + 2\ e^-$

Net ionic equation: $Pb(s) + PbO_2(s) + 2\ H_2SO_4(aq) \rightarrow 2\ PbSO_4(s) + 2\ H_2O(\ell)$

When current is generated, sulfuric acid is consumed and water is formed. Because water is less dense than sulfuric acid, the density of the solution decreases during this process. Therefore, one way to determine whether a lead storage battery needs to be recharged is to measure the density of the solution.

A lead storage battery is recharged by supplying electrical energy. The $PbSO_4$ coating the surfaces of the electrodes is converted back to metallic lead and $PbO_2$, and sulfuric acid is regenerated. Recharging this battery is possible because the reactants and products remain attached to the electrode surface. The lifetime of a lead storage battery is limited, however, because, with time, the coatings of $PbO_2$ and $PbSO_4$ flake off of the surface and fall to the bottom of the battery case.

Scientists and engineers would like to find an alternative to lead storage batteries, especially for use in cars. Lead storage batteries have the disadvantage of being large and heavy. In addition, lead and its compounds are toxic and their disposal adds a further complication. Nevertheless, at this time, the advantages of lead storage batteries often outweigh their disadvantages.

**Tesla Motors Roadster, an all-electric car.** This limited edition sports car (cost is over $100,000) is powered by a rechargeable nickel-metal hydride battery that will last for over 200 miles of driving.

### Nickel-Cadmium Batteries

Nickel-cadmium ("Ni-cad") batteries, used in a variety of cordless appliances such as telephones, video camcorders, and cordless power tools, are lightweight and rechargeable. The chemistry of the cell is based on the oxidation of cadmium and the reduction of nickel(III) oxide under basic conditions. As with the lead storage battery, the reactants and products formed when producing a current are solids that adhere to the electrodes.

Cathode, reduction: $NiO(OH)(s) + H_2O(\ell) + e^- \rightarrow Ni(OH)_2(s) + OH^-(aq)$

Anode, oxidation: $Cd(s) + 2\ OH^-(aq) \rightarrow Cd(OH)_2(s) + 2\ e^-$

Ni-cad batteries produce a nearly constant voltage. However, their cost is relatively high, and there are restrictions on their disposal because cadmium compounds are toxic and present an environmental hazard.

### Nickel-Metal Hydride

Rechargeable nickel-metal hydride batteries (NiMH) are now in common use. You may have them in your camera or portable music player. Their most important use, however, is in electric or hybrid cars.

In the nickel-metal hydride battery, electrons are generated when H atoms interact with $OH^-$ ions at the metal alloy anode.

$$Alloy(H) + OH^- \rightarrow Alloy + H_2O + e^-$$

The reaction at the cathode is the same as in Ni-cad batteries.

$$NiO(OH) + H_2O + e^- \rightarrow Ni(OH)_2 + OH^-$$

The "alloy" in NiMH batteries is generally a mixture of a rare earth metal such as lanthanum, cerium, or neodymium and another metal such as nickel, cobalt, manganese or aluminum.

### Lithium Batteries

As we introduced on page 894 (and in Chapter 13, page 582), much of the battery research now focuses on lithium batteries, and there are two types in common use: lithium-ion and a variant, lithium-ion polymer batteries. The chemistry of both is the same.

Cathode, reduction: $Li_{1-x}CoO_2(s) + x\ Li^+ + x\ e^- \rightarrow LiCoO_2(s)$

Anode, oxidation: $Li_xC_6(s) \rightarrow x\ Li^+ + x\ e^- + 6\ C(s)$

Lithium-ion polymer batteries are popular because they can be made in any shape and so fit into products such as Amazon's Kindle and Apple's portable

● **Be Alert: Children Can Ingest Lithium Batteries!** Very small lithium batteries are used in many devices such as toys, musical greeting cards, and appliances. Unfortunately, because they are small and shiny, children put them in their mouths and can swallow them. In 2010 the *New York Times* (June 1, 2010, page D5) reported that an increasing number of children have died from reactions induced by the battery's current when the battery was swallowed.

devices. They also deliver a higher current density than lithium-ion batteries and can be charged and discharged through many cycles.

Finally, an important reason for the development of lithium-based batteries is their light weight. Lithium has a much lower density (0.53 g/cm³) than cadmium (8.69 g/cm³), nickel (8.91 g/cm³), or lead (11.34 g/cm³). This is important not only in portable devices where people do not want to carry around heavy objects but also in the automobile industry. A lighter weight for a battery in a car results in more of the energy going into moving the rest of the car and less being used simply to transport the battery.

The importance of lithium-based batteries in our 21st-century economy cannot be overstated. Most of the current development and manufacture is being done in Japan, South Korea, and China, but much of the basic technology of lithium batteries was developed in the United States, and investment is increasing.

## Fuel Cells

An advantage of voltaic cells is that they are small and portable, but their size is also a limitation. The amount of electric current produced is limited by the quantity of reagents contained in the cell. When one of the reactants is completely consumed, the cell will no longer generate a current. Fuel cells avoid this limitation because the reactants (fuel and oxidant) can be supplied continuously to the cell from an external reservoir.

Although the first fuel cells were first constructed more than 150 years ago, little was done to develop this technology until the space program rekindled interest in these devices. Hydrogen-oxygen fuel cells have been used in NASA's Gemini, Apollo, and Space Shuttle programs. Not only are they lightweight and efficient, but they also have the added benefit that they generate drinking water for the ship's crew.

In a hydrogen-oxygen fuel cell (Figure 20.12), hydrogen is pumped onto the anode of the cell, and $O_2$ (or air) is directed to the cathode where the following reactions occur:

Cathode, reduction:    $O_2(g) + 2 H_2O(\ell) + 4 e^- \rightarrow 4 OH^-(aq)$

Anode, oxidation:    $H_2(g) \rightarrow 2 H^+(aq) + 2 e^-$

The two halves of the cell are separated by a special material called a proton exchange membrane (PEM). Protons, $H^+(aq)$, formed at the anode traverse the PEM and react with the hydroxide ions produced at the cathode, forming water. The net reaction in the cell is thus the formation of water from $H_2$ and $O_2$. Cells currently in use run at temperatures of 70–140 °C and produce about 0.9 V.

Hydrogen-oxygen fuel cells operate at 40–60% efficiency and meet most of the requirements for use in automobiles: They operate at room temperature or slightly

● **Energy for Automobiles** Energy available from systems that can be used to power an automobile.

| Chemical System | W · h/kg* (1 W · h = 3600 J) |
|---|---|
| Lead-acid battery | 18–56 |
| Nickel-cadmium battery | 33–70 |
| Sodium-sulfur battery | 80–140 |
| Lithium polymer battery | 150 |
| Gasoline-air combustion engine | 12,200 |

* watt-hour/kilogram

**FIGURE 20.12  Fuel cell design.** Hydrogen gas is oxidized to $H^+(aq)$ at the anode surface. On the other side of the proton exchange membrane (PEM), oxygen gas is reduced to $OH^-(aq)$. The $H^+(aq)$ ions travel through the PEM and combine with $OH^-(aq)$, forming water.

above, start rapidly, and develop a high current density. However, cost is a serious problem as is the absence of a carbon-free way of making hydrogen. These faults, and the cost and difficulty of building a nationwide infrastructure for distributing hydrogen, remain major stumbling blocks that would need to be overcome before hydrogen fuel cells could be adopted for widespread use in automobiles.

---

**REVIEW & CHECK FOR SECTION 20.3**

1. The following half-reaction occurs in an automobile lead-acid battery:

$$PbO_2(s) + 4\ H^+(aq) + SO_4^{2-}(aq) + 2\ e^- \rightarrow PbSO_4(s) + 2\ H_2O(\ell)$$

   (a) Lead(IV) oxide is oxidized.

   (b) Lead(IV) oxide is reduced.

   (c) Hydrogen ions are oxidized.

   (d) Hydrogen ions are reduced.

2. You can determine if a lead-based battery is no longer working by checking the density of the solution in the battery. If the density is low, then the battery is "dead." This works because

   (a) $PbO_2$ is consumed.

   (b) Sulfuric acid is consumed.

   (c) Water evaporates.

   (d) Lead is consumed.

---

# 20.4 Standard Electrochemical Potentials

Different electrochemical cells produce different potentials: 1.5 V for alkaline cells, about 3.7 V for a lithium-ion battery, and about 2.0 V for the individual cells in a lead storage battery. In this section, we want to identify some of the factors affecting cell voltages and develop ways to calculate the expected potential of a cell based on the chemistry in the cell and the conditions used.

## Electromotive Force

Electrons generated at the anode of an electrochemical cell move through the external circuit toward the cathode, and the force needed to move the electrons arises from a difference in the potential energy of electrons at the two electrodes. This difference in potential energy per electrical charge is called the **electromotive force** or **emf**, for which the literal meaning is "force causing electrons to move." Emf has units of volts (V); 1 volt is the potential difference needed to impart one joule of energy to an electric charge of one coulomb (1 J = 1 V × 1 C). *One coulomb is the quantity of charge that passes a point in an electric circuit when a current of 1 ampere flows for 1 second (1 C = 1 A × 1 s).*

● **Electrochemical Units**
• The coulomb (abbreviated C) is the standard (SI) unit of electrical charge (Appendix C, Table 6).
• 1 joule = 1 volt × 1 coulomb.
• 1 coulomb = 1 ampere × 1 second.

## Measuring Standard Potentials

Imagine you planned to study cell voltages in a laboratory with two objectives: (1) to understand the factors that affect these values and (2) to be able to predict the potential of a voltaic cell. You might construct a number of different half-cells, link them together in various combinations to form voltaic cells (as in Figure 20.13), and measure the cell potentials. After a few experiments, it would become apparent that cell potentials depend on a number of factors: the half-cells used (i.e., the reaction in each half-cell and the overall or net reaction in the cell), the concentrations of reactants and products in solution, the pressure of gaseous reactants, and the temperature.

To simplify matters for now, let us consider only cell potentials measured under **standard conditions**:

• Reactants and products are present in their standard states.
• Solutes in aqueous solution have a concentration of 1.0 M.
• Gaseous reactants or products have a pressure of 1.0 bar.

A cell potential measured under these conditions is called the **standard potential** and is denoted by $E°_{cell}$. Unless otherwise specified, all values of $E°_{cell}$ refer to measurements at 298 K (25 °C).

**FIGURE 20.13 A voltaic cell using Zn | Zn²⁺(aq, 1.0 M) and H₂ | H⁺(aq, 1.0 M) half-cells.**

- When zinc and acid are combined in an electrochemical cell, the cell generates a potential of 0.76 V under standard conditions.
- The electrode in the H₂ | H⁺(aq, 1.0 M) half-cell is the cathode, and the Zn electrode is the anode.
- Electrons flow in the external circuit to the hydrogen half-cell from the zinc half-cell.
- The positive sign of the measured voltage indicates that the hydrogen electrode is the cathode or positive electrode.

© Cengage Learning/Charles D. Winters

**(a)** The product-favored reaction of aqueous hydrogen ions with zinc produces H₂(g) and Zn²⁺ ions.

$$Zn(s) \longrightarrow Zn^{2+}(aq) + 2\ e^-$$

$$2\ H^+(aq) + 2\ e^- \longrightarrow H_2(g)$$

Net reaction: $Zn(s) + 2\ H^+(aq) \longrightarrow H_2(g) + Zn^{2+}(aq)$

**(b)** A voltaic cell that makes use of the product-favored reduction of aqueous hydrogen ions by zinc.

Suppose you set up a number of standard half-cells and connect each in turn to a **standard hydrogen electrode (SHE)**. Your apparatus would look like the voltaic cell in Figure 20.13b. For now, we will concentrate on three aspects of this cell:

1. *The reaction that occurs.* The reaction occurring in the cell pictured in Figure 20.13 could be *either* the reduction of Zn²⁺ ions with H₂ gas

$$Zn^{2+}(aq) + H_2(g) \rightarrow Zn(s) + 2\ H^+(aq)$$

Zn²⁺(aq) is the oxidizing agent, and H₂ is the reducing agent.
*Standard hydrogen electrode would be the anode (negative electrode).*

*or* the reduction of H⁺(aq) ions by Zn(s).

$$Zn(s) + 2\ H^+(aq) \rightarrow Zn^{2+}(aq) + H_2(g)$$

Zn is the reducing agent, and H⁺(aq) is the oxidizing agent.
*Standard hydrogen electrode would be the cathode (positive electrode).*

The reaction that actually occurs is the one that is product-favored at equilibrium and thus is spontaneous under standard conditions. In this case we know the product-favored reaction is the reduction of H⁺ ions by zinc metal (Figure 20.13a).

2. *Direction of electron flow in the external circuit.* In a voltaic cell, electrons always flow from the anode (negative electrode) to the cathode (positive electrode). We can tell the direction of electron movement—and therefore which is the anode and which is the cathode—by placing a voltmeter in the circuit. A positive potential is observed if the voltmeter terminal with a plus sign (+) is connected to the positive electrode or cathode [and the terminal with the minus sign (−) is connected to the negative electrode or anode]. Connected in the opposite way (plus to minus and minus to plus), the voltmeter will indicate a negative potential.

3. *Cell potential.* In Figure 20.13, the voltmeter is hooked up with its positive terminal connected to the hydrogen half-cell, and a reading of +0.76 V is observed. The hydrogen electrode is thus the positive electrode or cathode, and the reactions occurring in this cell must be

| | |
|---|---|
| Reduction, cathode: | $2\ H^+(aq) + 2\ e^- \rightarrow H_2(g)$ |
| Oxidation, anode: | $Zn(s) \rightarrow Zn^{2+}(aq) + 2\ e^-$ |
| Net cell reaction: | $Zn(s) + 2\ H^+(aq) \rightarrow Zn^{2+}(aq) + H_2(g)$ |

## A CLOSER LOOK

# EMF, Cell Potential, and Voltage

Electromotive force (emf) and cell potential ($E_{cell}$) are often used synonymously, but the two are subtly different. $E_{cell}$ is a measured quantity, so its value is affected by how the measurement is made. To understand this point, consider as an analogy water in a pipe under pressure. Water pressure can be viewed as analogous to emf; it represents a force that will cause water in the pipe to move. If we open a faucet, water will flow. Opening the faucet will, however, decrease the pressure in the system.

Emf is the potential difference when no current flows. To measure $E_{cell}$, a voltmeter is placed in the external circuit. Although voltmeters have high internal resistance to minimize current flow, a small current flows nonetheless. As a result, the value of $E_{cell}$ will be slightly different than the emf.

Finally, there is a difference between a *potential* and a *voltage*. The voltage of a cell has a magnitude but no sign. In contrast, the potential of a half-reaction or a cell has a sign (+ or −) and a magnitude.

---

This is an important result. All of the species are present in the cell at standard conditions, so the reaction can, in principle, proceed in either direction. The product-favored reaction, however, proceeds from left to right as written. This shows us that, of the two reducing agents present, zinc is better than $H_2$, and $H^+$ ions are a better oxidizing agent than zinc ions.

The potential of +0.76 V measured for the oxidation of zinc with hydrogen ions also reflects the difference in potential energy of an electron at each electrode. From the direction of flow of electrons in the external circuit (Zn electrode → $H_2$ electrode), we conclude that the potential energy of an electron at the zinc electrode is higher than the potential energy of the electron at the hydrogen electrode.

Hundreds of electrochemical cells like that shown in Figure 20.13 can be set up, allowing us to determine the relative oxidizing or reducing ability of various chemical species and to determine the electrical potential generated by the reaction under standard conditions. A few results are given in Figure 20.14, where half-reactions are listed as reductions. That is, the chemical species on the left are oxidizing agents and are listed in descending oxidizing ability.

● **$E°$ Values** An extensive listing of $E°$ values is found in Appendix M, and still larger tables of data can be found in chemistry reference books. A common convention, used in Appendix M, lists standard reduction potentials in two groups, one for acid and neutral solutions and the other for basic solutions.

**FIGURE 20.14 A potential ladder for reduction half-reactions.**
- The position of a half-reaction on this potential ladder reflects the relative ability of the species at the left to act as an oxidizing agent.
- The higher the compound or ion is in the list, the better it is as an oxidizing agent. Conversely, the atoms or ions on the right are reducing agents. The lower they are in the list, the better they are as a reducing agent.
- The potential for each half-reaction is given with its standard reduction potential, $E°_{reduction}$.
- For more information see J. R. Runo and D. G. Peters, *Journal of Chemical Education*, Vol 70, p. 708, 1993.

## Standard Reduction Potentials

By doing experiments such as that illustrated by Figure 20.13, we not only have a notion of the relative oxidizing and reducing abilities of various chemical species, but we can also rank them quantitatively.

If $E°_{cell}$ is a measure of the standard potential for the cell, then $E°_{cathode}$ and $E°_{anode}$ can be taken as measures of electrode potential. Because $E°_{cell}$ reflects the difference in electrode potentials, $E°_{cell}$ must be the difference between $E°_{cathode}$ and $E°_{anode}$.

$$E°_{cell} = E°_{cathode} - E°_{anode} \tag{20.1}$$

> **Equation 20.1** Equation 20.1 is another example of calculating a change from $X_{final} - X_{initial}$. Electrons move to the cathode (the "final" state) from the anode (the "initial" state). Thus, Equation 20.1 resembles equations you have seen previously in this book (such as Equations 5.6 and 6.5).

Here, $E°_{cathode}$ and $E°_{anode}$ are the standard *reduction* potentials for the half-cell reactions that occur at the cathode and anode, respectively. Equation 20.1 is important for three reasons:

- If you have values for $E°_{cathode}$ and $E°_{anode}$, you can calculate the standard potential, $E°_{cell}$, for a voltaic cell.
- *When the calculated value of $E°_{cell}$ is positive, the reaction as written is predicted to be product-favored at equilibrium.* Conversely, if the calculated value of $E°_{cell}$ is negative, the reaction is predicted to be reactant-favored at equilibrium. Such a reaction will be product-favored at equilibrium in a direction opposite to the way it is written.
- If you measure $E°_{cell}$ and know either $E°_{cathode}$ or $E°_{anode}$, you can calculate the other value. This value would tell you how one half-cell reaction compares with others in terms of relative oxidizing or reducing ability.

But here is a dilemma. You cannot measure individual half-cell potentials. Just as values for $\Delta_f H°$ and $\Delta_f G°$ were established by choosing a reference point (the elements in their standard states), scientists have selected a reference point for half-reactions. We assign a potential of exactly 0 V to the half-reaction that occurs at a standard hydrogen electrode (SHE).

$$2\,H^+(aq,\,1\,M) + 2\,e^- \rightarrow H_2(g,\,1\,bar)\ E° = 0.00\,V$$

With this standard, we can now determine $E°$ values for half-cells by measuring $E°_{cell}$ in experiments such as those described in Figures 20.8 and 20.13, where one of the electrodes is the standard hydrogen electrode. We can then quantify the information with reduction potential tables such as Figure 20.14 and use these values to make predictions about $E°_{cell}$ for new voltaic cells.

## Tables of Standard Reduction Potentials

The experimental approach just described leads to lists of $E°$ values such as seen in Figure 20.14, Table 20.1, and Appendix M. Let us list some important points concerning these tables and then illustrate them in the discussion and examples that follow.

1. The half-reactions are written as "oxidized form + electrons → reduced form." The species on the left side of the reaction arrow is an oxidizing agent, and the species on the right side of the reaction arrow is a reducing agent. Therefore, *all potentials are for reduction reactions*, and the potentials (in volts vs. SHE) are called *standard reduction potentials.*
2. The more positive the value of $E°$ for the reactions in Figure 20.14, Table 20.1, and similar tables, the better the oxidizing ability of the ion or compound on the left side of the reaction. This means *$F_2(g)$ is the best oxidizing agent in the table.* Lithium ion at the lower-left corner of Table 20.1 is the poorest oxidizing agent because its $E°$ value is the most negative.
3. The more negative the value of the reduction potential, $E°$, the less likely the half-reaction will occur as a reduction, and the more likely the reverse

half-reaction will occur (as an oxidation). Thus, Li(s) is the strongest reducing agent in the table, and $F^-$ is the weakest reducing agent. The reducing agents in the table (the ions, elements, and compounds at the right) increase in strength from the top to the bottom.

4. The reaction between any substance on the left in this table (an oxidizing agent) with any substance *lower* than it on the right (a reducing agent) is product-favored at equilibrium. This has been called the *northwest–southeast rule*.

**Table 20.1 Standard Reduction Potentials in Aqueous Solution at 25 °C\***

| Reduction Half-Reaction | | $E°$ (V) |
|---|---|---|
| $F_2(g) + 2 e^-$ | $\rightarrow 2 F^-(aq)$ | +2.87 |
| $H_2O_2(aq) + 2 H^+(aq) + 2 e^-$ | $\rightarrow 2 H_2O(\ell)$ | +1.77 |
| $PbO_2(s) + SO_4^{2-}(aq) + 4 H^+(aq) + 2 e^-$ | $\rightarrow PbSO_4(s) + 2 H_2O(\ell)$ | +1.685 |
| $MnO_4^-(aq) + 8 H^+(aq) + 5 e^-$ | $\rightarrow Mn^{2+}(aq) + 4 H_2O(\ell)$ | +1.51 |
| $Au^{3+}(aq) + 3 e^-$ | $\rightarrow Au(s)$ | +1.50 |
| $Cl_2(g) + 2 e^-$ | $\rightarrow 2 Cl^-(aq)$ | +1.36 |
| $Cr_2O_7^{2-}(aq) + 14 H^+(aq) + 6 e^-$ | $\rightarrow 2 Cr^{3+}(aq) + 7 H_2O(\ell)$ | +1.33 |
| $O_2(g) + 4 H^+(aq) + 4 e^-$ | $\rightarrow 2 H_2O(\ell)$ | +1.229 |
| $Br_2(\ell) + 2 e^-$ | $\rightarrow 2 Br^-(aq)$ | +1.08 |
| $NO_3^-(aq) + 4 H^+(aq) + 3 e^-$ | $\rightarrow NO(g) + 2 H_2O(\ell)$ | +0.96 |
| $OCl^-(aq) + H_2O(\ell) + 2 e^-$ | $\rightarrow Cl^-(aq) + 2 OH^-(aq)$ | +0.89 |
| $Hg^{2+}(aq) + 2 e^-$ | $\rightarrow Hg(\ell)$ | +0.855 |
| $Ag^+(aq) + e^-$ | $\rightarrow Ag(s)$ | +0.799 |
| $Hg_2^{2+}(aq) + 2 e^-$ | $\rightarrow 2 Hg(\ell)$ | +0.789 |
| $Fe^{3+}(aq) + e^-$ | $\rightarrow Fe^{2+}(aq)$ | +0.771 |
| $I_2(s) + 2 e^-$ | $\rightarrow 2 I^-(aq)$ | +0.535 |
| $O_2(g) + 2 H_2O(\ell) + 4 e^-$ | $\rightarrow 4 OH^-(aq)$ | +0.40 |
| $Cu^{2+}(aq) + 2 e^-$ | $\rightarrow Cu(s)$ | +0.337 |
| $Sn^{4+}(aq) + 2 e^-$ | $\rightarrow Sn^{2+}(aq)$ | +0.15 |
| $2 H^+(aq) + 2 e^-$ | $\rightarrow H_2(g)$ | 0.00 |
| $Sn^{2+}(aq) + 2 e^-$ | $\rightarrow Sn(s)$ | −0.14 |
| $Ni^{2+}(aq) + 2 e^-$ | $\rightarrow Ni(s)$ | −0.25 |
| $V^{3+}(aq) + e^-$ | $\rightarrow V^{2+}(aq)$ | −0.255 |
| $PbSO_4(s) + 2 e^-$ | $\rightarrow Pb(s) + SO_4^{2-}(aq)$ | −0.356 |
| $Cd^{2+}(aq) + 2 e^-$ | $\rightarrow Cd(s)$ | −0.40 |
| $Fe^{2+}(aq) + 2 e^-$ | $\rightarrow Fe(s)$ | −0.44 |
| $Zn^{2+}(aq) + 2 e^-$ | $\rightarrow Zn(s)$ | −0.763 |
| $2 H_2O(\ell) + 2 e^-$ | $\rightarrow H_2(g) + 2 OH^-(aq)$ | −0.8277 |
| $Al^{3+}(aq) + 3 e^-$ | $\rightarrow Al(s)$ | −1.66 |
| $Mg^{2+}(aq) + 2 e^-$ | $\rightarrow Mg(s)$ | −2.37 |
| $Na^+(aq) + e^-$ | $\rightarrow Na(s)$ | −2.714 |
| $K^+(aq) + e^-$ | $\rightarrow K(s)$ | −2.925 |
| $Li^+(aq) + e^-$ | $\rightarrow Li(s)$ | −3.045 |

Increasing strength of oxidizing agents →

Increasing strength of reducing agents →

\* In volts (V) versus the standard hydrogen electrode.

Product-favored reactions will always involve a reducing agent that is "southeast" of the proposed oxidizing agent.

*Reduction Half-Reaction*

$$I_2(s) + 2\ e^- \longrightarrow 2\ I^-(aq)$$
$$Cu^{2+}(aq) + 2\ e^- \longrightarrow Cu(s)$$
$$2\ H^+(aq) + 2\ e^- \longrightarrow H_2(g)$$
$$Fe^{2+}(aq) + 2\ e^- \longrightarrow Fe(s)$$
$$Zn^{2+}(aq) + 2\ e^- \longrightarrow Zn(s)$$

*The northwest–southeast rule: The reducing agent always lies to the southeast of the oxidizing agent in a product-favored reaction.*

For example, Zn can reduce $Fe^{2+}$, $H^+$, $Cu^{2+}$, and $I_2$, but, of the species on this list, Cu can reduce only $I_2$.

5. The algebraic sign of the half-reaction reduction potential is the sign of the electrode when it is attached to the $H_2/H^+$ standard cell (see Figures 20.8 and 20.13).

6. Electrochemical potentials depend on the nature of the reactants and products and their concentrations, not on the quantities of material used. Therefore, changing the stoichiometric coefficients for a half-reaction does not change the value of $E°$. For example, the reduction of $Fe^{3+}$ has an $E°$ of $+0.771$ V, whether the reaction is written as

$$Fe^{3+}(aq,\ 1\ M) + e^- \rightarrow Fe^{2+}(aq,\ 1\ M) \qquad E° = +0.771\ V$$

or as

$$2\ Fe^{3+}(aq,\ 1\ M) + 2\ e^- \rightarrow 2\ Fe^{2+}(aq,\ 1\ M) \qquad E° = +0.771\ V$$

## Using Tables of Standard Reduction Potentials

Tables or "ladders" of standard reduction potentials are very useful. They allow you to predict the potential of a new voltaic cell, provide information that can be used to balance redox equations, and help predict which redox reactions are product-favored.

### Calculating Standard Cell Potentials, $E°_{cell}$

The standard reduction potentials for half-reactions were obtained by measuring cell potentials. It makes sense, therefore, that these values can be combined to give the potential of some new cell.

The net reaction occurring in a voltaic cell using silver and copper half-cells is

$$2\ Ag^+(aq) + Cu(s) \rightarrow 2\ Ag(s) + Cu^{2+}(aq)$$

The silver electrode is the cathode, and the copper electrode is the anode. We know this because silver ion is reduced (to silver metal) and copper metal is oxidized (to $Cu^{2+}$ ions). (Recall that oxidations always occur at the anode and reductions at the cathode.) Also notice that the $Cu^{2+}|Cu$ half-reaction is "southeast" of the $Ag^+|Ag$ half-reaction in the potential ladder (Figure 20.14 and Table 20.1).

$E°_{cathode} = +0.799\ V \qquad Ag^+(aq) + e^- \longrightarrow Ag(s)$

"Distance" from $E°_{cathode}$ to $E°_{anode}$ is $0.799\ V - 0.337\ V$ $= 0.462\ V$.

Cu is "southeast" of $Ag^+$

$E°_{anode} = +0.337\ V \qquad Cu^{2+}(aq) + 2\ e^- \longrightarrow Cu(s)$

The potential for the voltaic cell is the difference between the standard reduction potentials for the two half-reactions.

$$E°_{cell} = E°_{cathode} - E°_{anode}$$

$$E°_{cell} = (+0.799\ V) - (+0.337\ V)$$

$$E°_{cell} = +0.462\ V$$

Notice that the value of $E°_{cell}$ is related to the "distance" between the cathode and anode reactions on the potential ladder. The products have a lower potential energy than the reactants, and the cell potential, $E°_{cell}$, has a positive value.

A positive potential calculated for the $Ag^+|Ag$ and $Cu^{2+}|Cu$ cell ($E°_{cell} = +0.462$ V) confirms that the reduction of silver ions in water with copper metal is product-favored at equilibrium (Figure 20.1). We might ask, however, about the value of $E°_{cell}$ if a reactant-favored equation had been selected. For example, what is $E°_{cell}$ for the reduction of copper(II) ions with silver metal?

| | |
|---|---|
| Cathode, reduction: | $Cu^{2+}(aq) + 2\ e^- \rightarrow Cu(s)$ |
| Anode, oxidation: | $2\ Ag(s) \rightarrow 2\ Ag^+(aq) + 2\ e^-$ |
| Net ionic equation: | $2\ Ag(s) + Cu^{2+}(aq) \rightarrow 2\ Ag^+(aq) + Cu(s)$ |

### Cell Voltage Calculation

$$E°_{cathode} = +0.337 \text{ V and } E°_{anode} = +0.799 \text{ V}$$

$$E°_{cell} = E°_{cathode} - E°_{anode} = (+0.337 \text{ V}) - (0.799 \text{ V})$$

$$E°_{cell} = -0.462 \text{ V}$$

The negative sign for $E°_{cell}$ indicates that the reaction as written is reactant-favored at equilibrium. The products of the reaction ($Ag^+$ and $Cu$) have a higher potential energy than the reactants ($Ag$ and $Cu^{2+}$). For the indicated reaction to occur, a potential of at least 0.462 V would have to be imposed on the system by an external source of electricity (see Section 20.7).

## Relative Strengths of Oxidizing and Reducing Agents

Five half-reactions, selected from Appendix M, are arranged from the half-reaction with the highest (most positive) $E°$ value to the one with the lowest (most negative) value.

| $E°$, V | | Reduction Half-Reaction |
|---|---|---|
| +1.36 | | $Cl_2(g) + 2\ e^- \longrightarrow 2\ Cl^-(aq)$ |
| +0.80 | | $Ag^+(aq) + e^- \longrightarrow Ag(s)$ |
| +0.00 | | $2\ H^+(aq) + 2\ e^- \longrightarrow H_2(g)$ |
| −0.25 | | $Ni^{2+}(aq) + 2\ e^- \longrightarrow Ni(s)$ |
| −0.76 | | $Zn^{2+}(aq) + 2\ e^- \longrightarrow Zn(s)$ |

(Increasing strength as oxidizing agents ↑)

- The list on the left is headed by $Cl_2$, an element that is a strong oxidizing agent and thus is easily reduced. At the bottom of the list is $Zn^{2+}(aq)$, an ion not easily reduced and thus a poor oxidizing agent.
- On the right, the list is headed by $Cl^-(aq)$, an ion that can be oxidized to $Cl_2$ only with difficulty. It is a very poor reducing agent. At the bottom of the list is zinc metal, which is readily oxidized and is a good reducing agent.

By arranging these half-reactions based on $E°$ values, we have also arranged the chemical species on the two sides of the equation in order of their strengths as oxidizing or reducing agents. In this list, from strongest to weakest, the order is

Oxidizing agents: $Cl_2 > Ag^+ > H^+ > Ni^{2+} > Zn^{2+}$
strong ⟶ weak

Reducing agents: $Zn > Ni > H_2 > Ag > Cl^-$
strong ⟶ weak

Finally, notice that the value of $E°_{cell}$ is greater the farther apart the oxidizing and reducing agents are on the potential ladder. For example,

$$Zn(s) + Cl_2(g) \rightarrow Zn^{2+}(aq) + 2\ Cl^-(aq) \qquad E° = +2.12 \text{ V}$$

is more strongly product-favored than the reduction of hydrogen ions with nickel metal

$$Ni(s) + 2 H^+(aq) \rightarrow Ni^{2+}(aq) + H_2(g) \qquad E° = +0.25 \text{ V}$$

## EXAMPLE 20.5    Ranking Oxidizing and Reducing Agents

**Problem**  Use the table of standard reduction potentials (Table 20.1) to do the following:

(a)    Rank the halogens in order of their strength as oxidizing agents.

(b)    Decide whether hydrogen peroxide ($H_2O_2$) in acid solution is a stronger oxidizing agent than $Cl_2$.

(c)    Decide which of the halogens is capable of oxidizing gold metal to $Au^{3+}(aq)$.

**What Do You Know?**  A table of electrode potentials, such as Table 20.1 or Appendix M, contains the information needed to answer these questions.

**Strategy**  The ability of a species on the left side of a reduction potential table to function as an oxidizing agent declines on descending the list (see points 2 and 3, pages 916–917).

**Solution**

(a)    Ranking halogens according to oxidizing ability: The halogens ($F_2$, $Cl_2$, $Br_2$, and $I_2$) appear in the upper-left portion Table 20.1, with $F_2$ being highest, followed in order by the other three species. Their strengths as oxidizing agents are $F_2 > Cl_2 > Br_2 > I_2$. (The ability of bromine to oxidize iodide ions to molecular iodine is illustrated in Figure 20.15.)

(b)    Comparing hydrogen peroxide and chlorine: $H_2O_2$ lies just below $F_2$ but well above $Cl_2$ in the potential ladder (Table 20.1). Thus, $H_2O_2$ is a weaker oxidizing agent than $F_2$ but a stronger one than $Cl_2$. (Note that the $E°$ value for $H_2O_2$ refers to an acidic solution and standard conditions.)

(c)    Which halogen will oxidize gold metal to gold(III) ions? The $Au^{3+} | Au$ half-reaction is listed below the $F_2 | F^-$ half-reaction and just above the $Cl_2 | Cl^-$ half-reaction. This tells us that, among the halogens, only $F_2$ is capable of oxidizing Au to $Au^{3+}$ under standard conditions. That is, for the reaction of Au and $F_2$,

| | |
|---|---|
| Oxidation, anode: | $2[Au(s) \rightarrow Au^{3+}(aq) + 3\ e^-]$ |
| Reduction, cathode: | $3[F_2(g) + 2\ e^- \rightarrow 2\ F^-(aq)]$ |
| Net ionic equation: | $3\ F_2(g) + 2\ Au(s) \rightarrow 6\ F^-(aq) + 2\ Au^{3+}(aq)$ |

$$E°_{cell} = E°_{cathode} - E°_{anode} = +2.87 \text{ V} - (+1.50 \text{ V}) = +1.37 \text{ V}$$

$F_2$ is a stronger oxidizing agent than $Au^{3+}$, so the reaction proceeds from left to right as written. (This is confirmed by a positive value of $E°_{cell}$.) For the reaction of $Cl_2$ and Au, Table 20.1 shows us that $Cl_2$ is a weaker oxidizing agent than $Au^{3+}$, so the reaction would be expected to proceed in the opposite direction under standard conditions.

| | |
|---|---|
| Oxidation, anode: | $2[Au(s) \rightarrow Au^{3+}(aq) + 3\ e^-]$ |
| Reduction, cathode: | $3[Cl_2(aq) + 2\ e^- \rightarrow 2\ Cl^-(aq)]$ |
| Net ionic equation: | $3\ Cl_2(aq) + 2\ Au(s) \rightarrow 6\ Cl^-(aq) + 2\ Au^{3+}(aq)$ |

$$E°_{cell} = E°_{cathode} - E°_{anode} = +1.36 \text{ V} - (+1.50 \text{ V}) = -0.14 \text{ V}$$

This is confirmed by the negative value for $E°_{cell}$.

**Think about Your Answer**  In part (c), we calculated $E°_{cell}$ for two reactions. To achieve a balanced net ionic equation, we added the half-reactions, but only after multiplying the gold half-reaction by 2 and the halogen half-reaction by 3. (This means 6 mol of electrons were transferred from 2 mol Au to 3 mol $Cl_2$.) Notice that this multiplication does not change the value of $E°$ for the half-reactions because cell potentials do not depend on the quantity of material.

**Check Your Understanding**

(a)    Rank the following metals in their ability to function as reducing agents: Hg, Sn, and Pb.

(b)    Which halogens will oxidize mercury to mercury(II)?

The test tube contains an aqueous solution of KI (top layer) and immiscible $CCl_4$ (bottom layer).

Add $Br_2$ to solution of KI, and shake.

After adding a few drops of $Br_2$ in water, the $I_2$ produced collects in the bottom $CCl_4$ layer and gives it a purple color. (The top layer contains excess $Br_2$ in water.)

The presence of $I_2$ in the bottom layer indicates that the added $Br_2$ was able to oxidize the iodide ions originally present to molecular iodine ($I_2$).

**FIGURE 20.15 The reaction of bromine and iodide ion.**  This experiment proves that $Br_2$ is a better oxidizing agent than $I_2$.

**A CLOSER LOOK**

## An Electrochemical Toothache

It was reported a few years ago that a 66-year-old woman had intense pain that was traced to her dental work (*New England Journal of Medicine*, Vol. 342, p. 2000, 2003). A root canal procedure had moved a mercury amalgam filling on one tooth slightly closer to a gold alloy crown on an adjacent tooth. Eating acidic foods caused her intense pain. When dental amalgams of dissimilar metals come in contact with saliva, a voltaic cell is formed that generates potentials up to several hundred millivolts—and you feel it! You can do it, too, if you chew an aluminum foil gum wrapper with teeth that have been filled with a dental amalgam. Ouch!

---

**REVIEW & CHECK FOR SECTION 20.4**

1.  The net reaction that occurs in a voltaic cell is $Zn(s) + 2\,Ag^+(aq) \rightarrow Zn^{2+}(aq) + 2\,Ag(s)$.

    Calculate a potential for the cell assuming standard conditions.

    (a)  1.562 V          (b)  0.0360 V          (c)  2.361 V

2.  Which metal in the following list is easiest to oxidize: Fe, Ag, Zn, Mg, Au?

    (a)  Fe          (c)  Zn          (e)  Au

    (b)  Ag          (d)  Mg

3.  Determine which of the following redox equations are product-favored at equilibrium.

    (i)   $Ni^{2+}(aq) + H_2(g) \rightarrow Ni(s) + 2\,H^+(aq)$

    (ii)  $2\,Fe^{3+}(aq) + 2\,I^-(aq) \rightarrow 2\,Fe^{2+}(aq) + I_2(s)$

    (iii) $Br_2(\ell) + 2\,Cl^-(aq) \rightarrow 2\,Br^-(aq) + Cl_2(g)$

    (iv)  $Cr_2O_7{}^{2-}(aq) + 6\,Fe^{2+}(aq) + 14\,H^+(aq) \rightarrow 2\,Cr^{3+}(aq) + 6\,Fe^{3+}(aq) + 7\,H_2O(\ell)$

    (a)  ii and iv          (b)  i and iii          (c)  iv only          (d)  all

---

# 20.5 Electrochemical Cells under Nonstandard Conditions

Electrochemical cells seldom operate under standard conditions in the real world. Even if the cell is constructed with all dissolved species at 1 M, reactant concentrations decrease and product concentrations increase in the course of the reaction. Changing concentrations of reactants and products, as well as the temperature, will affect the cell voltage. Thus, we need to ask what happens to cell potentials under nonstandard conditions.

## The Nernst Equation

Based on both theory and experimental results, it has been determined that cell potentials are related to concentrations of reactants and products and to temperature, as follows:

$$E = E° - (RT/nF)\,\ln Q \qquad\qquad (20.2)$$

In this equation, which is known as the **Nernst equation**, $R$ is the gas constant (8.314472 J/K · mol); $T$ is the temperature (K); and $n$ is the number of moles of electrons transferred between oxidizing and reducing agents (as determined by the balanced equation for the reaction). The symbol $F$ represents the **Faraday constant** (9.6485338 × 10⁴ C/mol). *One Faraday is the quantity of electric charge carried by one mole of electrons.* The term $Q$ is the reaction quotient (◄ Equation 16.2, Section 16.2).

# Manganese in the Oceans

Manganese is a key component of some oxidation–reduction cycles in the oceans. According to an article in the journal *Science*, it "can perform this role because it exists in multiple oxidation states and is recycled rapidly between these states by bacterial processes."

Figure A shows how this cycle is thought to work. Manganese(II) ions in subsurface water are oxidized to form manganese(IV) oxide, $MnO_2$. Particles of this insoluble solid sink toward the ocean floor. However, some encounter hydrogen sulfide, which is produced in the ocean depths, rising toward the surface. Another redox reaction occurs, producing sulfur and manganese(II) ions. The newly formed $Mn^{2+}$ ions diffuse upward, where they are again oxidized.

The manganese cycle had been thought to involve only the +2 and +4 oxidation states of manganese, and analyses of water samples assumed the dissolved manganese existed only as $Mn^{2+}$ ions. One reason for this is that the intermediate oxidation state, $Mn^{3+}$, is not predicted to be stable in water. It should disproportionate to the +2 and +4 states.

$$2\ Mn^{3+}(aq) + 2\ H_2O(\ell) \rightarrow$$
$$Mn^{2+}(aq) + MnO_2(s) + 4\ H^+(aq)$$

It is known, however, that $Mn^{3+}$ can exist when complexed with species such as pyrophosphate ions, $P_2O_7^{4-}$.

Several years ago, geochemists suggested that $Mn^{3+}$ ions could exist in natural water. They could be produced by bacterial action and stabilized by phosphate from ATP or ADP. They speculated that the $Mn^{3+}$ ion could play an important part in the natural manganese cycle.

Now, other researchers have indeed discovered that, in oxygen-poor waters, the manganese(III) ion, $Mn^{3+}$, can persist. These ions were found in anoxic zones (zones without dissolved oxygen) below 100 m in the Black Sea and below about 15 m in the Chesapeake Bay. It is now clear that $Mn^{3+}$ ions, which had previously been known only in the laboratory, can exist in natural waters under the right circumstances and that the manganese cycle may have to be revised.

**Questions:**

1. Given the following reduction potentials, show that $Mn^{3+}$ should disproportionate to $Mn^{2+}$ and $MnO_2$ at standard conditions.

$$4\ H^+(aq) + MnO_2(s) + e^- \rightarrow$$
$$Mn^{3+}(aq) + 2\ H_2O(\ell)$$

$$E° = 0.95\ V$$

$$Mn^{3+}(aq) + e^- \rightarrow Mn^{2+}(aq)$$

$$E° = 1.50\ V$$

2. Balance the following equations in acid solution.
   (a) Reduction of $MnO_2$ with $HS^-$ to $Mn^{2+}$ and S
   (b) Oxidation of $Mn^{2+}$ with $O_2$ to $MnO_2$
3. Calculate $E°$ for the oxidation of $Mn^{2+}$ with $O_2$ to $MnO_2$.

**Answers to these questions are available in Appendix N.**

**FIGURE A  Manganese chemistry in the oceans.** Relative concentrations of important species as a function of depth in the oceans. See K. S. Johnson, *Science*, Vol. 313, p. 1896, 2006 and R. E. Trouwborst, B. G. Clement, B. M. Tebor, B. T. Glazer, and G. W. Luther, III, *Science*, Vol. 313, pp. 1955–1957, 2006.

---

Substituting values for the constants in Equation 20.2, and using 298 K as the temperature, gives

$$E = E° - \frac{0.0257}{n}\ln Q \quad \text{at 25 °C} \qquad (20.3)$$

or, in a commonly used form using base-10 logarithms,

$$E = E° - \frac{0.0592}{n}\log Q$$

In essence, the term $(RT/nF)\ln Q$ "corrects" the standard potential $E°$ for nonstandard conditions or concentrations.

**◆WL   INTERACTIVE EXAMPLE 20.6   Using the Nernst Equation**

**Problem**  A voltaic cell is set up at 25 °C with the half-cells: $Al^{3+}(0.0010\ M)\,|\,Al$ and $Ni^{2+}(0.50\ M)\,|\,Ni$. Write an equation for the reaction that occurs when the cell generates an electric current, and determine the cell potential.

**What Do You Know?**  You know the temperature and the identity and concentrations of the reactants and products.

## Strategy

- Determine which substance is oxidized (Al or Ni) by looking at the appropriate half-reactions in Table 20.1 and deciding which is the better reducing agent (Example 20.5).

- Add the half-reactions to determine the net ionic equation, and calculate $E°_{cell}$.

- Use the Nernst equation to calculate $E$, the potential under nonstandard conditions.

**Solution** Aluminum metal is a stronger reducing agent than Ni metal. (Conversely, $Ni^{2+}$ is a better oxidizing agent than $Al^{3+}$.) Therefore, Al is oxidized, and the $Al^{3+} \mid Al$ compartment is the anode.

Cathode, reduction:   $3 [Ni^{2+}(aq) + 2 e^- \rightarrow Ni(s)]$

Anode, oxidation:   $2 [Al(s) \rightarrow Al^{3+}(aq) + 3 e^-]$

Net ionic equation:   $\overline{2 Al(s) + 3 Ni^{2+}(aq) \rightarrow 2 Al^{3+}(aq) + 3 Ni(s)}$

$$E°_{cell} = E°_{cathode} - E°_{anode}$$

$$E°_{cell} = (-0.25 \text{ V}) - (-1.66 \text{ V}) = 1.41 \text{ V}$$

The expression for $Q$ is written based on the cell reaction. In the net reaction, $Al^{3+}(aq)$ has a coefficient of 2, so this concentration is squared. Similarly, $[Ni^{2+}(aq)]$ is cubed. Solids are not included in the expression for $Q$ (◄ Section 16.2).

$$Q = \frac{[Al^{3+}]^2}{[Ni^{2+}]^3}$$

The net equation requires transfer of six electrons from two Al atoms to three $Ni^{2+}$ ions, so $n = 6$, and the Nernst equation gives

$$E_{cell} = E°_{cell} - \frac{0.0257}{n} \ln \frac{[Al^{3+}]^2}{[Ni^{2+}]^3}$$

$$= +1.41 \text{ V} - \frac{0.0257}{6} \ln \frac{[0.0010]^2}{[0.50]^3}$$

$$= +1.41 \text{ V} - 0.00428 \ln(8.0 \times 10^{-6})$$

$$= +1.41 \text{ V} - 0.00428 (-11.74)$$

$$= \boxed{1.46 \text{ V}}$$

**Think about Your Answer** The concentrations of $Al^{3+}$ and $Ni^{2+}$ both affect the cell potential. Analysis of the $\ln Q$ term in the Nernst equation shows that if $[Ni^{2+}] = 1$ M but $[Al^{3+}] < 1$ M, then $E_{cell} > E°_{cell}$. The reaction is more product-favored in this situation. The reverse situation (with $[Ni^{2+}] < 1$ M and $[Al^{3+}] = 1$ M) would lead to $E_{cell} < E°_{cell}$. In this example, the very low value of $[Al^{3+}]$ has the greater effect, and $E_{cell}$ is greater than $E°_{cell}$.

---

### Check Your Understanding

A voltaic cell is set up with an aluminum electrode in a 0.025 M $Al(NO_3)_3$(aq) solution and an iron electrode in a 0.50 M $Fe(NO_3)_2$(aq) solution. Determine the cell potential, $E_{cell}$, at 298 K.

---

**Strategy Map 20.6**

**PROBLEM**

Write an equation for the reaction involving **Al** and **$Al^{3+}$** with **Ni** and **$Ni^{2+}$**. Calculate $E_{cell}$.

↓

**KNOWN DATA/INFORMATION**

- Concentrations of $Al^{3+}$ and $Ni^{2+}$
- Look up $E°$ values for the half-reactions.

**STEP 1.** Decide which half-reactions occur at the **anode** and **cathode** based on $E°$ values.

**Cathode reaction** (reduction of $Ni^{2+}$) and **anode reaction** (oxidation of Al)

**STEP 2.** Add half-reactions to obtain **net cell reaction**.

**Net cell reaction**

**STEP 3.** Calculate $E°_{cell}$.

$E°_{cell} = E°_{cathode} - E°_{anode}$

**STEP 4.** Use **Nernst equation** with known ion concentrations, calculated $E°_{cell}$, and $n$ value to calculate $E_{cell}$.

$E_{cell}$ under nonstandard conditions

---

Example 20.6 demonstrates the calculation of a cell potential if concentrations are known. It is also useful to apply the Nernst equation in the opposite sense, using a measured cell potential to determine an unknown concentration. A device that does just this is the pH meter (Figure 20.16). In an electrochemical cell in which $H^+$(aq) is a reactant or product, the cell voltage will vary predictably with the hydrogen ion concentration. The cell voltage is measured and the value used to calculate pH. Example 20.7 illustrates how $E_{cell}$ varies with the hydrogen ion concentration in a simple cell.

**FIGURE 20.16  Measuring pH.**

Measuring pH with a portable pH meter that can be used in the field.

A schematic diagram of a glass electrode.

## EXAMPLE 20.7    Variation of $E_{cell}$ with Concentration

**Problem**  A voltaic cell is set up with copper and hydrogen half-cells. Standard conditions are employed in the copper half-cell, $Cu^{2+}$(aq, 1.00 M) | Cu(s). The hydrogen gas pressure is 1.00 bar, and [$H^+$(aq)] in the hydrogen half-cell is the unknown. A value of 0.490 V is recorded for $E_{cell}$ at 298 K. Determine the pH of the solution.

**What Do You Know?**  You know the temperature, the identity of the reactants and products, the concentration of the $Cu^{2+}$ ion, the partial pressure of $H_2$, and $E_{cell}$.

**Strategy**

- Determine which is the better oxidizing and reducing agent in order to decide what net reaction is occurring in the cell. Write a balanced equation for the reaction.

- Calculate $E°_{cell}$.

- Use the Nernst equation with the given $Cu^{2+}$ ion concentration to calculate the hydrogen ion concentration.

- Calculate the pH.

**Solution**  Based on their positions in a table of standard reduction potentials, hydrogen is a better reducing agent than copper metal, so Cu(s) | $Cu^{2+}$(aq, 1.00 M) is the cathode, and $H_2$(g, 1.00 bar) | $H^+$(aq, ? M) is the anode.

| | |
|---|---|
| Cathode, reduction: | $Cu^{2+}(aq) + 2\ e^- \rightarrow Cu(s)$ |
| Anode, oxidation: | $H_2(g) \rightarrow 2\ H^+(aq) + 2\ e^-$ |
| Net ionic equation: | $H_2(g) + Cu^{2+}(aq) \rightarrow Cu(s) + 2\ H^+(aq)$ |

$$E°_{cell} = E°_{cathode} - E°_{anode}$$

$$E°_{cell} = (+0.337\ V) - (0.00\ V) = +0.337\ V$$

The reaction quotient, $Q$, is derived from the balanced net ionic equation.

$$Q = \frac{[H^+]^2}{[Cu^{2+}]P_{H_2}}$$

The net equation requires the transfer of two electrons, so $n = 2$. The value of $[Cu^{2+}]$ is 1.00 M, but $[H^+]$ is unknown. Substitute this information into the Nernst equation (and don't overlook the fact that $[H^+]$ is squared in the expression for Q).

$$E = E° - \frac{0.0257}{n} \ln \frac{[H^+]^2}{[Cu^{2+}]P_{H_2}}$$

$$0.490 \text{ V} = 0.337 \text{ V} - \frac{0.0257}{2} \ln \frac{[H^+]^2}{(1.00)(1.00)}$$

$$-11.9 = \ln[H^+]^2$$

$$[H^+] = 3 \times 10^{-3} \text{ M}$$

$$pH = 2.6$$

**Think about Your Answer**  Be sure to write the balanced equation. Without it you may not have the correct exponents in the term for Q in the Nernst equation.

**Check Your Understanding**

The half-cells $Fe^{2+}(aq, 0.024 \text{ M}) | Fe(s)$ and $H^+(aq, 0.056 \text{ M}) | H_2(1.0 \text{ bar})$ are linked by a salt bridge to create a voltaic cell. Determine the cell potential, $E_{cell}$, at 298 K.

In the real world, using a hydrogen electrode in a pH meter is not practical. The apparatus is clumsy; it is anything but robust; and platinum (for the electrode) is costly. Common pH meters use a glass electrode, so called because it contains a thin glass membrane separating the cell from the solution whose pH is to be measured (Figure 20.16). Inside the glass electrode is a silver wire coated with AgCl and a solution of HCl; outside is the solution of unknown pH to be evaluated. A Ag/AgCl or calomel electrode—the latter a common reference electrode using a mercury(I)–mercury redox couple ($Hg_2Cl_2 | Hg$)—serves as the second electrode of the cell. The potential across the glass membrane depends on $[H^+]$. Common pH meters give a direct readout of pH.

---

**REVIEW & CHECK FOR SECTION 20.5**

Calculate $E_{cell}$ at 298 K for a cell involving Sn and Cu and their ions:

$$Sn(s) | Sn^{2+}(aq, 0.25 \text{ M}) || Cu^{2+}(aq, 0.10 \text{ M}) | Cu(s)$$

(a)  0.47 V          (b)  0.49 V          (c)  0.50 V

---

# 20.6 Electrochemistry and Thermodynamics

## Work and Free Energy

The first law of thermodynamics states that the internal energy change in a system ($\Delta U$) is related to two quantities, heat ($q$) and work ($w$): $\Delta U = q + w$ [Section 5.4]. This equation also applies to chemical changes that occur in a voltaic cell. As current flows, energy is transferred from the system (the voltaic cell) to the surroundings.

In a voltaic cell, the decrease in internal energy in the system will manifest itself ideally as electrical work done on the surroundings by the system. In practice, however, some energy is usually evolved as heat by the voltaic cell. The maximum work done by an electrochemical system (ideally, assuming no heat is generated) is proportional to the potential difference (volts) and the quantity of charge (coulombs):

$$w_{max} = nFE \qquad\qquad (20.4)$$

In this equation, $E$ is the cell voltage, and $nF$ is the quantity of electric charge transferred from anode to cathode.

The free energy change for a process is, by definition, the maximum amount of work that can be obtained [Section 19.6]. Because the maximum work and the cell potential are related, $E°$ and $\Delta_r G°$ can be related mathematically (taking care to assign signs correctly). The maximum work done on the surroundings when electricity is produced by a voltaic cell is $+nFE$, with the positive sign denoting an increase in energy in the surroundings. The energy content of the cell decreases by this amount. Thus, $\Delta_r G$ for the voltaic cell has the opposite sign.

$$\Delta_r G = -nFE \tag{20.5}$$

Under standard conditions, the appropriate equation is

$$\Delta_r G° = -nFE° \tag{20.6}$$

● **Units in Equation 20.6** $n$ has units of mol $e^-$, and $F$ has units of (C/mol $e^-$). Therefore, $nF$ has units of coulombs (C). Because 1 J = 1 C · V, the product $nFE$ will have units of energy (J).

This expression shows that, the more positive the value of $E°$, the more negative the value of $\Delta_r G°$ for the reaction. Also, because of the relationship between $\Delta_r G°$ and $K$, the farther apart the half-reactions are on the potential ladder, the more strongly product-favored the reaction is at equilibrium.

## EXAMPLE 20.8 Relating $E°$ and $\Delta_r G°$

**Problem** The standard cell potential, $E°_{cell}$, for the reduction of silver ions with copper metal (Figure 20.5) is +0.462 V at 25 °C. Calculate $\Delta_r G°$ for this reaction.

**What Do You Know?** You know the cell potential under standard conditions and therefore know to use Equation 20.6 to calculate the change in free energy. In this equation $F$ is a known constant, but $n$ has to be determined. However, you can write the balanced equation for the cell reaction, and so obtain $n$ from that.

**Strategy** Use Equation 20.6 where $E°_{cell}$ and $F$ are known. The value of $n$, the number of moles of electrons transferred between copper metal and silver ions, comes from the balanced equation.

**Solution** In this cell, copper is the anode, and silver is the cathode. The overall cell reaction is

$$Cu(s) + 2\ Ag^+(aq) \rightarrow Cu^{2+}(aq) + 2\ Ag(s)$$

which means that each mole of copper transfers 2 mol of electrons to 2 mol of $Ag^+$ ions. That is, $n = 2$. Now use Equation 20.6.

$$\Delta_r G° = -nFE° = -(2\ \text{mol } e^-)(96{,}485\ \text{C/mol } e^-)(0.462\ \text{V}) = -89{,}200\ \text{C} \cdot \text{V}$$

Because 1 C · V = 1 J, we have

$$\Delta_r G° = -89{,}200\ \text{J or} -89.2\ \text{kJ}$$

**Think about Your Answer** This example demonstrates an effective method of obtaining thermodynamic values from electrochemical experiments. Keep in mind that a positive $E°$ implies a negative $\Delta_r G°$.

**Check Your Understanding**

The following reaction has an $E°$ value of −0.76 V:

$$H_2(g) + Zn^{2+}(aq) \rightarrow Zn(s) + 2\ H^+(aq)$$

Calculate $\Delta_r G°$ for this reaction. Is the reaction product- or reactant-favored at equilibrium?

## $E°$ and the Equilibrium Constant

When a voltaic cell produces an electric current, the reactant concentrations decrease, and the product concentrations increase. The cell voltage also changes. As reactants are converted to products, the value of $E_{cell}$ decreases and the cell potential eventually reaches zero; no further net reaction occurs, and equilibrium is achieved.

This situation can be analyzed using the Nernst equation. When $E_{cell} = 0$, the reactants and products are at equilibrium, and the reaction quotient, $Q$, is equal to the equilibrium constant, $K$. Substituting the appropriate symbols and values into the Nernst equation,

$$E = 0 = E° - \frac{0.0257}{n} \ln K$$

and collecting terms gives an equation that relates the cell potential and equilibrium constant:

$$\ln K = \frac{nE°}{0.0257} \quad \text{at 25 °C (298 K)} \quad \quad (20.7)$$

Equation 20.7 can be used to determine values for equilibrium constants, as illustrated in Example 20.9.

## ⓦWL  INTERACTIVE EXAMPLE 20.9  *E° and Equilibrium Constants*

**Problem**  Calculate the equilibrium constant for the reaction at 298 K:

$$Fe(s) + Cd^{2+}(aq) \rightleftharpoons Fe^{2+}(aq) + Cd(s)$$

**What Do You Know?**  You have the balanced chemical equation and know that Equation 20.7 is required. You need to know $E°$ and $n$, the number of electrons transferred.

**Strategy**  First, determine $E°_{cell}$ from $E°$ values for the two half-reactions (see Example 20.5) and from those the value of $n$, the other parameter required in Equation 20.7.

**Solution**  The half-reactions and $E°$ values are

Cathode, reduction:  $Cd^{2+}(aq) + 2\ e^- \rightarrow Cd(s)$

Anode, oxidation:  $Fe(s) \rightarrow Fe^{2+}(aq) + 2\ e^-$

Net ionic equation:  $\underline{Fe(s) + Cd^{2+}(aq) \rightleftharpoons Fe^{2+}(aq) + Cd(s)}$

$$E°_{cell} = E°_{cathode} - E°_{anode}$$

$$E°_{cell} = (-0.40\ V) - (-0.44\ V) = +0.04\ V$$

Now substitute $n = 2$ and $E°_{cell}$ into Equation 20.7.

$$\ln K = \frac{nE°}{0.0257} = \frac{(2)(0.04\ V)}{0.0257} = 3.1$$

$$K = 20$$

**Think about Your Answer**  The relatively small positive voltage (0.04 V) for the cell indicates that the cell reaction is only mildly product-favored. A value of 20 for the equilibrium constant is in accord with this observation.

### Check Your Understanding

Calculate the equilibrium constant at 25 °C for the reaction

$$2\ Ag^+(aq) + Hg(\ell) \rightleftharpoons 2\ Ag(s) + Hg^{2+}(aq)$$

**Strategy Map 20.9**

**PROBLEM**

Calculate an **equilibrium constant** using *electrochemical data*.

↓

**KNOWN DATA/INFORMATION**

- Balanced equation

**STEP 1.** Decide which half-reactions occur at **anode** and **cathode** based on $E°$ **values** and calculate $E°_{cell}$.

$E°_{cell} = E°_{cathode} - E°_{anode}$

**STEP 2.** Use Equation 20.7 with calculated $E°_{cell}$, and $n$ **value** to calculate $\ln K$.

Calculated $\ln K$

**STEP 3.** Convert $\ln K$ to $K$.

↓

Equilibrium constant, $K$

The relationships between $E°$, $K$, and $\Delta_r G°$, which are summarized in Table 20.2. Values of $E°$ can be used to obtain equilibrium constants for many different chemical systems. One example is the determination of solubility product constants, $K_{sp}$. Let us begin with an electrode in which an insoluble ionic compound, AgCl, is a component of a half-cell. Figure 20.17 illustrates how the potential for the reduction of AgCl in the presence of $Cl^-$ ion (1.00 M) can be determined.

$$AgCl(s) + e^- \rightarrow Ag(s) + Cl^-(aq) \quad \quad E° = +0.222\ V$$

**Table 20.2 Summary of the Relationship of $K$, $\Delta_r G°$, and $E°$**

| $K$ | $\Delta_r G°$ | $E°$ | Reactant-Favored or Product-Favored at Equilibrium? | Spontaneous under Standard Conditions? |
|---|---|---|---|---|
| $K \gg 1$ | $\Delta_r G° < 0$ | $E° > 0$ | Product-favored | Spontaneous under standard conditions |
| $K = 1$ | $\Delta_r G° = 0$ | $E° = 0$ | $[C]^c[D]^d = [A]^a[B]^b$ at equilibrium | At equilibrium under standard conditions |
| $K \ll 1$ | $\Delta_r G° > 0$ | $E° < 0$ | Reactant-favored | Not spontaneous under standard conditions |

When paired with the standard hydrogen electrode, the standard reduction potential for the AgCl|Ag half-cell is +0.222 V. If this half-reaction is then paired with that for a standard silver electrode in a hypothetical voltaic cell, the cell reactions could be written as

Cathode, reduction:  $AgCl(s) + e^- \rightarrow Ag(s) + Cl^-(aq)$

Anode, oxidation:  $Ag(s) \rightarrow Ag^+(aq) + e^-$

Net ionic equation:  $AgCl(s) \rightarrow Ag^+(aq) + Cl^-(aq)$

The equation for the net reaction represents the equilibrium of solid AgCl and its ions. The cell potential is negative,

$$E°_{cell} = E°_{cathode} - E°_{anode} = (+0.222\ V) - (+0.799\ V) = -0.577\ V$$

indicating a reactant-favored process, as would be expected based on the low solubility of AgCl. Using Equation 20.7, the value of $K_{sp}$ can then be obtained from $E°_{cell}$.

$$\ln K = \frac{nE°}{0.0257} = \frac{(1)(-0.577\ V)}{0.0257} = -22.5$$

$$K_{sp} = e^{-22.5} = 2 \times 10^{-10}$$

**FIGURE 20.17** Measurement of the standard electrode potential for the Ag|AgCl electrode.

# 20.7 Electrolysis: Chemical Change Using Electrical Energy

Thus far, we have described electrochemical cells that use product-favored redox reactions to generate an electric current. Equally important, however, is the opposite process, **electrolysis**, the use of electrical energy to bring about chemical change.

Electrolysis of water is a classic chemistry experiment, and the electroplating of metals is another example of electrolysis (Figure 20.18). In electroplating, an electric current is passed through a solution containing a salt of the metal to be plated. The object to be plated is the cathode. When metal ions in solution are reduced, the metal deposits on the object's surface.

Electrolysis is also important because it is widely used in the refining of metals such as aluminum and in the production of chemicals such as chlorine.

## Electrolysis of Molten Salts

All electrolysis experiments are set up in a similar manner. The material to be electrolyzed, either a molten salt or a solution, is contained in an electrolysis cell. As was the case with voltaic cells, ions must be present in the liquid or solution for a current

(a) Electrolysis of water produces hydrogen (at the cathode) and oxygen gas (at the anode).

**FIGURE 20.18** Electrolysis.

(b) Electroplating adds a layer of metal to the surface of an object (*left*), either to protect the object from corrosion or to improve its physical appearance. The procedure uses an electrolysis cell, set up with the object to be plated as the cathode and a solution containing a salt of the metal to be plated (*right*).

**FIGURE 20.19** **The preparation of sodium and chlorine by the electrolysis of molten NaCl.** In the molten state, sodium ions migrate to the negative cathode, where they are reduced to sodium metal. Chloride ions migrate to the positive anode, where they are oxidized to elemental chlorine.

© Cengage Learning/Charles D. Winters

| Sodium ion migrates to cathode. | Reduced to sodium metal. | Chloride migrates to anode. | Oxidized to chlorine |

to flow as it is the movement of ions within the cell that constitutes the electric current. The cell has two electrodes that are connected to a source of DC (direct-current) voltage. If the applied voltage is high enough, chemical reactions occur at the two electrodes. Reduction occurs at the negatively charged cathode, with electrons being transferred from that electrode to a chemical species in the cell. Oxidation occurs at the positive anode, with electrons from a chemical species being transferred to that electrode.

Let us focus our attention first on the chemical reactions that occur at each electrode in the electrolysis of a molten salt. Sodium chloride melts at about 800 °C, and in the molten state sodium ions ($Na^+$) and chloride ions ($Cl^-$) are freed from their rigid arrangement in the crystalline lattice. Therefore, if a potential is applied to the electrodes, sodium ions are attracted to the negative electrode, and chloride ions are attracted to the positive electrode (Figure 20.19). If the potential is high enough, chemical reactions occur at each electrode. At the negative cathode, $Na^+$ ions accept electrons and are reduced to sodium metal (a liquid at this temperature). Simultaneously, at the positive anode, chloride ions give up electrons and form elemental chlorine.

Cathode (−), reduction:     $2\ Na^+ + 2\ e^- \rightarrow 2\ Na(\ell)$

Anode (+), oxidation:     $2\ Cl^- \rightarrow Cl_2(g) + 2\ e^-$

Net ionic equation:     $2\ Na^+ + 2\ Cl^- \rightarrow 2\ Na(\ell) + Cl_2(g)$

Electrons move through the external circuit under the force exerted by the applied potential, and the movement of positive and negative ions in the molten salt

---

**PROBLEM SOLVING TIP 20.3**

## Electrochemical Conventions: Voltaic Cells and Electrolysis Cells

Whether you are describing a voltaic cell or an electrolysis cell, the terms *anode* and *cathode* always refer to the electrodes at which oxidation and reduction occur, respectively. The polarity of the electrodes is reversed, however.

| Type of Cell | Electrode | Function | Polarity |
|---|---|---|---|
| Voltaic | Anode | Oxidation | − |
| | Cathode | Reduction | + |
| Electrolysis | Anode | Oxidation | + |
| | Cathode | Reduction | − |

constitutes the current within the cell. Finally, it is important to recognize that the reaction is not spontaneous. The energy required for this reaction to occur has been provided by the electric current.

## Electrolysis of Aqueous Solutions

Sodium ions ($Na^+$) and chloride ions ($Cl^-$) are the primary species present in molten NaCl. Only chloride ions can be oxidized, and only sodium ions can be reduced. Electrolysis of a substance in aqueous solution is more complicated than the electrolysis of a molten salt, however, because water is now present. Water is an *electroactive* substance; that is, it can be oxidized or reduced in an electrochemical process.

Consider the electrolysis of aqueous sodium iodide (Figure 20.20). In this experiment, the electrolysis cell contains $Na^+(aq)$, $I^-(aq)$, and $H_2O$ molecules. Possible *reduction reactions* at the *negative cathode* include

$$Na^+(aq) + e^- \rightarrow Na(s)$$

$$2\,H_2O(\ell) + 2\,e^- \rightarrow H_2(g) + 2\,OH^-(aq)$$

Possible *oxidation reactions* at the *positive anode* are

$$2\,I^-(aq) \rightarrow I_2(aq) + 2\,e^-$$

$$2\,H_2O(\ell) \rightarrow O_2(g) + 4\,H^+(aq) + 4\,e^-$$

In the electrolysis of aqueous NaI, $H_2(g)$ and $OH^-(aq)$ are formed by water reduction at the cathode, and iodine is formed at the anode. Thus, the overall cell process can be summarized by the following equations:

Cathode (−), reduction:     $2\,H_2O(\ell) + 2\,e^- \rightarrow H_2(g) + 2\,OH^-(aq)$

Anode (+), oxidation:     $2\,I^-(aq) \rightarrow I_2(aq) + 2\,e^-$

Net ionic equation:     $2\,H_2O(\ell) + 2\,I^-(aq) \rightarrow H_2(g) + 2\,OH^-(aq) + I_2(aq)$

where $E°_{cell}$ has a negative value.

$$E°_{cell} = E°_{cathode} - E°_{anode} = (-0.8277\ V) - (+0.621\ V) = -1.449\ V$$

This process is not spontaneous under standard conditions, and a potential of *at least* 1.45 V must be *applied* to the cell for these reactions to occur. If the process had involved the oxidation of water instead of iodide ion at the anode, the required

A drop of phenolphthalein has been added to the solution in this experiment so that the formation of $OH^-(aq)$ can be detected (by the pink color of the indicator in basic solution).

Cathode (−): $2\,e^- + 2\,H_2O(\ell) \longrightarrow H_2(g) + 2\,OH^-(aq)$

Cathode

A solution of NaI(aq) is electrolyzed, a potential applied using an external source of electricity.

Iodine forms at the anode, and $H_2$ and $OH^-$ form at the cathode.

Anode (+): $2\,I^-(aq) \longrightarrow I_2(aq) + 2\,e^-$

**FIGURE 20.20** Electrolysis of aqueous NaI.

Photos © Cengage Learning/Charles D. Winters

potential would be $-2.057$ V $[E°_{cathode} - E°_{anode} = (-0.8277 \text{ V}) - (+1.229 \text{ V})]$, and if the reaction involving the reduction of $Na^+$ and the oxidation of $I^-$ had occurred, the required potential would be $-3.335$ V $[E°_{cathode} - E°_{anode} = (-2.714 \text{ V}) - (+0.621 \text{ V})]$. The reaction occurring is the one requiring the smaller applied potential, so the net cell reaction in the electrolysis of NaI(aq) is the oxidation of iodide and reduction of water.

What happens if an aqueous solution of some other metal halide such as $SnCl_2$ is electrolyzed? Consult Appendix M, and consider all possible half-reactions. In this case, aqueous $Sn^{2+}$ ion is much more easily reduced ($E° = -0.14$ V) than water ($E° = -0.83$ V) at the cathode, so tin metal is produced. At the anode, two oxidations are possible: $Cl^-$(aq) to $Cl_2$(g) or $H_2O$ to $O_2$(g). Experiments show that chloride ion is oxidized in preference to water, so the reactions occurring on electrolysis of aqueous tin(II) chloride are (Figure 20.21)

| | | |
|---|---|---|
| Cathode (−), reduction: | $Sn^{2+}$(aq) + 2 $e^-$ → Sn(s) | |
| Anode (+), oxidation: | 2 $Cl^-$(aq) → $Cl_2$(g) + 2 $e^-$ | |
| Net ionic equation: | $Sn^{2+}$(aq) + 2 $Cl^-$(aq) → Sn(s) + $Cl_2$(g) | |

$$E°_{cell} = E°_{cathode} - E°_{anode} = (-0.14 \text{ V}) - (+1.36 \text{ V}) = -1.50 \text{ V}$$

Formation of $Cl_2$ at the anode in the electrolysis of $SnCl_2$(aq) is contrary to a prediction based on $E°$ values. If the electrode reactions were

| | |
|---|---|
| Cathode (−), reduction: | $Sn^{2+}$(aq) + 2 $e^-$ → Sn(s) |
| Anode (+), oxidation: | 2 $H_2O(\ell)$ → $O_2$(g) + 4 $H^+$(aq) + 4 $e^-$ |

$$E°_{cell} = (-0.14 \text{ V}) - (+1.23 \text{ V}) = -1.37 \text{ V}$$

a smaller applied potential would seemingly be required. To explain the formation of chlorine instead of oxygen, we must take into account rates of reaction. The oxidation of $Cl^-$(aq) is much more rapid than the oxidation of $H_2O$.

This "problem" is used to advantage in the commercially important electrolysis of aqueous NaCl, where a voltage high enough to oxidize both $Cl^-$ and $H_2O$ is used. However, because chloride ion is oxidized much faster than $H_2O$, $Cl_2$ is the major product in this electrolysis. This is the predominant means by which chlorine is produced for commercial use.

Another instance in which rates are important concerns electrode materials. Graphite, commonly used to make inert electrodes, can be oxidized. For the half-reaction $CO_2$(g) + 4 $H^+$(aq) + 4 $e^-$ → C(s) + 2 $H_2O(\ell)$, $E°$ is $+0.20$ V, indicating that carbon is slightly easier to oxidize than copper ($E° = +0.34$ V). Based on this value, oxidation of a graphite electrode might reasonably be expected to occur during an electrolysis. And indeed it does, albeit slowly; graphite electrodes used in electrolysis cells slowly deteriorate and eventually have to be replaced.

• **Overvoltage** Voltages higher than the minimum are typically used to speed up reactions that would otherwise be slow. The term *overvoltage* is often used and refers to the voltage needed to make a reaction occur at a reasonable rate.

**FIGURE 20.21 Electrolysis of aqueous tin(II) chloride.** Tin metal collects at the negative cathode. Chlorine gas is formed at the positive anode. Elemental chlorine is formed in the cell, in spite of the fact that the potential for the oxidation of $Cl^-$ is more negative than that for oxidation of water. (That is, chlorine should be less easily oxidized than water.) This is the result of chemical kinetics and illustrates the complexity of some aqueous electrochemistry.

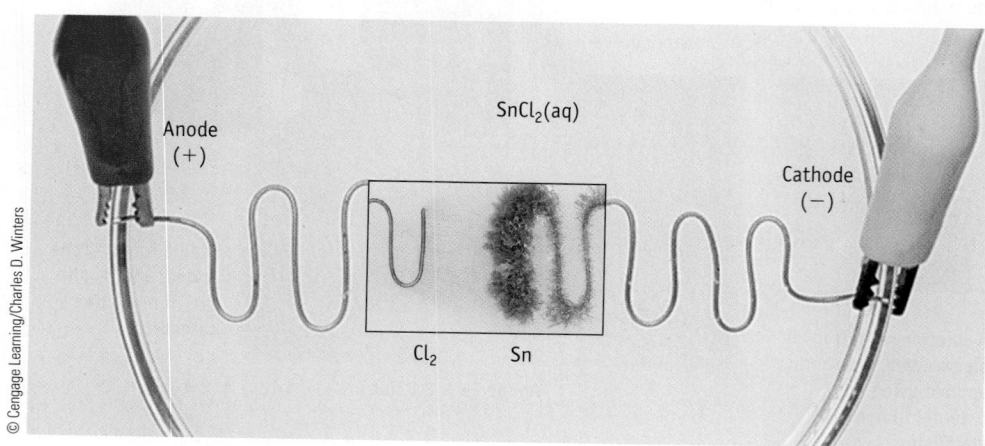

© Cengage Learning/Charles D. Winters

One other factor—the concentration of electroactive species in solution—must be taken into account when discussing electrolyses. As shown in Section 20.6, the potential at which a species in solution is oxidized or reduced depends on concentration. Unless standard conditions are used, predictions based on $E°$ values are merely qualitative. In addition, the rate of a half-reaction depends on the concentration of the electroactive substance at the electrode surface. At a very low concentration, the rate of the redox reaction may depend on the rate at which an ion diffuses from the solution to the electrode surface.

## EXAMPLE 20.10  Electrolysis of Aqueous Solutions

**Problem**  Predict how products of the electrolysis of aqueous solutions of NaF, NaCl, NaBr, and NaI are likely to be different and predict $E°_{cell}$ for each electrolysis. (The electrolysis of NaI is illustrated in Figure 20.20.)

**What Do You Know?**  You know the identity of the compounds to be electrolyzed, but you will need to know the $E°$ values for their half-reactions and for water electrolysis.

**Strategy**  The main criterion used to predict the chemistry in an electrolytic cell should be the ease of oxidation and reduction, an assessment based on $E°$ values.

**Solution**  The cathode reaction presents no problem: Water is reduced to hydroxide ion and $H_2$ gas in preference to reduction of $Na^+(aq)$ (as in the electrolysis of aqueous NaI). Thus, the primary cathode reaction in all cases is

$$2\ H_2O(\ell) + 2\ e^- \rightarrow H_2(g) + 2\ OH^-(aq)$$

$$E°_{cathode} = -0.83\ V$$

At the anode, you need to assess the ease of oxidation of the halide ions relative to water. Based on $E°$ values, this should be $I^-(aq) > Br^-(aq) > Cl^-(aq) >> F^-(aq)$. Fluoride ion is much more difficult to oxidize than water, and electrolysis of an aqueous solution containing this ion results exclusively in $O_2$ formation. That is, the primary anode reaction for NaF(aq) is

$$2\ H_2O(\ell) \rightarrow O_2(g) + 4\ H^+(aq) + 4\ e^-$$

$$E°_{anode} = +1.23\ V$$

Therefore, in this case,

$$E°_{cell} = (-0.83\ V) - (+1.23\ V) = -2.06\ V$$

Recall that chlorine is the primary product at the anode in the electrolysis of aqueous solutions of chloride salts (as in Figure 20.20). Therefore, the primary anode reaction in NaCl(ag) is

$$2\ Cl^-(aq) \rightarrow Cl_2(g) + 2\ e^-$$

$$E°_{cell} = (-0.83\ V) - (+1.36\ V) = -2.19\ V$$

Bromide ions are considerably easier to oxidize than chloride ions, so $Br_2$ may be expected as the primary product in the electrolysis of aqueous NaBr. For NaBr(aq), the primary anode reaction is

$$2\ Br^-(aq) \rightarrow Br_2(\ell) + 2\ e^-$$

so $E°_{cell}$ is

$$E°_{cell} = (-0.83\ V) - (+1.08\ V) = -1.91\ V$$

Thus, the electrolysis of NaBr resembles that of NaI (Figure 20.19) in producing the halogen, hydrogen gas, and hydroxide ion. The half-reactions and the cell potential for aqueous NaI were given on page 931.

**Think about Your Answer**  As described above, you would predict from $E°$ values the ease of oxidation of halide ions is $I^-(aq) > Br^-(aq) > Cl^-(aq) >> F^-(aq)$. This is confirmed by the results.

**Check Your Understanding**

Predict the chemical reactions that will occur at the two electrodes in the electrolysis of an aqueous sodium hydroxide solution. What is the minimum voltage needed to cause this reaction to occur?

# Electrochemistry and Michael Faraday

The terms *anion, cation, electrode,* and *electrolyte* originated with Michael Faraday (1791–1867), one of the most influential people in the history of chemistry. Faraday was apprenticed to a bookbinder in London when he was 13. This situation suited him perfectly, as he enjoyed reading the books sent to the shop for binding. By chance, one of these volumes was a small book on chemistry, which whetted his appetite for science, and he began performing experiments on electricity. In 1812, a patron of the shop invited Faraday to accompany him to the Royal Institute to attend a lecture by one of the most famous chemists of the day, Sir Humphry Davy. Faraday was intrigued by Davy's lecture and wrote to ask Davy for a position as an assistant. He was

accepted and began work in 1813. Faraday was so talented that his work proved extraordinarily fruitful, and only 12 years later he was made the director of the laboratory of the Royal Institute.

It has been said that Faraday's contributions were so enormous that, had there been Nobel Prizes when he was alive, he would have received at least six. These could have been awarded for discoveries such as the following:

- Electromagnetic induction, which led to the first transformer and electric motor
- The laws of electrolysis (the effect of electric current on chemicals)
- The magnetic properties of matter

- Benzene and other organic chemicals (which led to important chemical industries)
- The "Faraday effect" (the rotation of the plane of polarized light by a magnetic field)
- The introduction of the concept of electric and magnetic fields

**Michael Faraday (1791–1867)**

In addition to making discoveries that had profound effects on science, Faraday was an educator. He wrote and spoke about his work in memorable ways, especially in lectures to the general public that helped to popularize science.

---

**REVIEW & CHECK FOR SECTION 20.7**

You have a solution containing several metal ions, $K^+$, $Fe^{2+}$, $Al^{3+}$, $Ag^+$. Which ion will require the lowest potential to plate out on the cathode?

(a) $K^+$   (b) $Fe^{2+}$   (c) $Al^{3+}$   (d) $Ag^+$

## 20.8 Counting Electrons

Metallic silver is produced at the cathode in the electrolysis of aqueous $AgNO_3$ in which one mole of electrons is required to produce one mole of silver. In contrast, two moles of electrons are required to produce one mole of tin (Figure 20.21):

$$Sn^{2+}(aq) + 2\ e^- \rightarrow Sn(s)$$

It follows that if the number of moles of electrons flowing through the electrolysis cell could be measured, the number of moles of silver or tin produced could be calculated. Conversely, if the amount of silver or tin produced is known, then the number of moles of electrons moving through the circuit could be calculated.

The number of moles of electrons consumed or produced in an electron transfer reaction is obtained by measuring the current flowing in the external electric circuit in a given time. The **current** flowing in an electrical circuit is the amount of charge (in units of coulombs, C) per unit time, and the usual unit for current is the ampere (A). One ampere equals the passage of one coulomb of charge per second.

$$\text{Current (amperes, A)} = \frac{\text{electric charge (coulombs, C)}}{\text{time, } t \text{ (seconds, s)}} \qquad (20.8)$$

● **Faraday Constant** The Faraday constant is the charge carried by 1 mol of electrons: $9.6485338 \times 10^4$ C/mol $e^-$.

The current passing through an electrochemical cell and the time for which the current flows are easily measured quantities. Therefore, the charge (in coulombs) that passes through a cell can be obtained by multiplying the current (in amperes) by the time (in seconds). Knowing the charge and using the Faraday constant as a conversion factor, we can calculate the number of moles of electrons that passed through an electrochemical cell. In turn, we can use this quantity to calculate the quantities of reactants and products. The following example illustrates this type of calculation.

WL    **INTERACTIVE EXAMPLE 20.11**  Using the Faraday Constant

**Problem** A current of 2.40 A is passed through a solution containing $Cu^{2+}(aq)$ for 30.0 minutes, with copper metal being deposited at the cathode. What mass of copper, in grams, is deposited?

**What Do You Know?** You know the current passed through the cell and the time over which it was passed.

**Strategy** The current and time can be used to calculate the amount of charge that passed through the cell. The Faraday constant can then be used to relate this to the amount (moles) of electrons that were used. This in turn can be related to the amount of copper metal deposited and finally to the mass of copper.

**Solution**

1.  Calculate the charge (number of coulombs) passing through the cell in 30.0 minutes.

$$\text{Charge (C)} = \text{current (A)} \times \text{time (s)}$$

$$= (2.40 \text{ A})(30.0 \text{ min})(60.0 \text{ s/min})$$

$$= 4.32 \times 10^3 \text{ C}$$

2.  Calculate the number of moles of electrons (i.e., the number of Faradays of electricity).

$$(4.32 \times 10^3 \text{ C})\left(\frac{1 \text{ mol } e^-}{96,485 \text{ C}}\right) = 4.48 \times 10^{-2} \text{ mol } e^-$$

3.  Calculate the amount of copper and, from this, the mass of copper.

$$\text{mass of copper} = (4.48 \times 10^{-2} \text{ mol } e^-)\left(\frac{1 \text{ mol Cu}}{2 \text{ mol } e^-}\right)\left(\frac{63.55 \text{ g Cu}}{1 \text{ mol Cu}}\right) = 1.42 \text{ g}$$

**Think about Your Answer** The key relation in this calculation is "current = charge/time." Most situations will involve knowing two of these three quantities from experiment and calculating the third.

**Check Your Understanding**

1.  Calculate the mass of $O_2$ produced in the electrolysis of water, using a current of 0.445 A for a period of 45 minutes.

2.  In the commercial production of sodium by electrolysis, the cell operates at 7.0 V and a current of $25 \times 10^3$ A. What mass of sodium can be produced in 1 hour?

---

**Strategy Map 20.11**

**PROBLEM**
Calculate the **mass of copper** deposited in electrolysis cell.

↓

**KNOWN DATA/INFORMATION**
- Current in cell
- Time

↓

STEP 1. Use **current × time** to calculate **charge**.

**Charge** passing through cell (in **coulombs**)

↓

STEP 2. Use **Faraday constant** to calculate **moles of electrons** passed.

**Moles** of electrons passed in **given time**

↓

STEP 3. Relate moles of **electrons** to moles of **metal**.

**Amount** of metal **(mol)** produced

↓

STEP 4. Convert **amount** to **mass**.

**Mass** of metal **(g)** produced

---

**REVIEW & CHECK FOR SECTION 20.8**

If you wish to convert 0.0100 mol of $Au^{3+}(aq)$ ions into $Au(s)$ in a "gold-plating" process, how long must you electrolyze a solution if the current passing through the circuit is 2.00 amps?

(a)  483 seconds                    (c)  965 seconds

(b)  $4.83 \times 10^4$ seconds              (d)  1450 seconds

---

## CHAPTER GOALS REVISITED

*Now that you have studied this chapter, you should ask whether you have met the chapter goals. In particular, you should be able to:*

**Balance equations for oxidation–reduction reactions in acidic or basic solutions using the half-reaction approach** Study Questions: 1–6, 15, 16, 49, 50, 84, 85, and Go Chemistry Module 25.

**Understand the principles underlying voltaic cells**

a.  In a voltaic cell, identify the half-reactions occurring at the anode and the cathode, the polarity of the electrodes, the direction of electron flow in the external circuit, and the direction of ion flow in the salt bridge (Section 20.2). Study Questions: 7–10, 51.

WL and go Chemistry

Sign in at **www.cengage.com/owl** to:
- View tutorials and simulations, develop problem-solving skills, and complete online homework assigned by your professor.
- For quick review and exam prep, download Go Chemistry mini lecture modules from OWL (or purchase them at **www.cengagebrain.com**)

❓ Access **How Do I Solve It?** tutorials on how to approach problem solving using concepts in this chapter.

b.  Appreciate the chemistry and advantages and disadvantages of dry cells, alkaline batteries, lead storage batteries, lithium batteries, and Ni-cad batteries (Section 20.3). **Study Questions: 11, 12.**

c.  Understand how fuel cells work, and recognize the difference between batteries and fuel cells (Section 20.3). **Study Question: 101.**

**Understand how to use electrochemical potentials**

a.  Understand the process by which standard reduction potentials are determined, and identify standard conditions as applied to electrochemistry (Section 20.4).

b.  Describe the standard hydrogen electrode ($E° = 0.00$ V), and explain how it is used as the standard to determine the standard potentials of half-reactions (Section 20.4).

c.  Know how to use standard reduction potentials to determine cell voltages for cells under standard conditions (Equation 20.1). **Study Questions: 13–16.**

d.  Know how to use a table of standard reduction potentials (Table 20.1 and Appendix M) to rank the strengths of oxidizing and reducing agents, to predict which substances can reduce or oxidize another species, and to predict whether redox reactions will be product-favored or reactant-favored (Section 20.4). **Study Questions: 17–24, 55, 56.**

e.  Use the Nernst equation (Equations 20.2 and 20.3) to calculate the cell potential under nonstandard conditions (Section 20.5). **Study Questions: 25–28, 75–79.**

f.  Explain how cell voltage allows the determination of pH (Section 20.5) and other ion concentrations. **Study Questions: 29, 30, 77.**

g.  Use the relationships between cell voltage ($E°_{cell}$) and free energy ($\Delta_r G°$) (Equations 20.5 and 20.6) and between $E°_{cell}$ and an equilibrium constant for the cell reaction (Equation 20.7) (Section 20.6 and Table 20.2). **Study Questions: 31–36, 60, 61, 63, 78, 82.**

**Explore electrolysis, the use of electrical energy to produce chemical change**

a.  Describe the chemical processes occurring in an electrolysis. Recognize the factors that determine which substances are oxidized and reduced at the electrodes (Section 20.7). **Study Questions: 37–42, 74.**

b.  Relate the amount of a substance oxidized or reduced to the amount of current and the time the current flows (Section 20.8). **Study Questions: 43–48, 59, 64–66.**

# Key Equations

**Equation 20.1 (page 915)** Calculating a standard cell potential, $E°_{cell}$, from standard half-cell potentials.

$$E°_{cell} = E°_{cathode} - E°_{anode}$$

**Equation 20.2 (page 921)** The Nernst equation, the relationship of the cell potential under nonstandard conditions ($E$) to that under standard conditions ($E°$). $R$ is the gas constant (8.314472 J/K · mol); $T$ is the temperature (K); and $n$ is the number of moles of electrons transferred between oxidizing and reducing agents. $F$ is the **Faraday constant** ($9.6485338 \times 10^4$ C/mol of $e^-$), and $Q$ is the reaction quotient.

$$E = E° - (RT/nF) \ln Q$$

**Equation 20.3 (page 922)** Nernst equation (at 298 K).

$$E = E° - \frac{0.0257}{n} \ln Q$$

**Equation 20.4 (page 925)** The amount of work done (w) by an electrochemical system.

$$w_{max} = nFE$$

**Equations 20.5 and 20.6 (page 926)** Relationship between free energy change and the cell potential under nonstandard or standard conditions, respectively.

$$\Delta G = -nFE \text{ or } \Delta G° = -nFE°$$

**Equation 20.7 (page 927)** Relationship between the equilibrium constant and the standard cell potential for a reaction (at 298 K).

$$\ln K = \frac{nE°}{0.0257}$$

**Equation 20.8 (page 934)** Relationship between current, electric charge, and time.

$$\text{Current (amperes, A)} = \frac{\text{electric charge (coulombs, C)}}{\text{time, } t \text{ (seconds, s)}}$$

# Study Questions

⊙WL Interactive versions of these questions are assignable in OWL.

▲ denotes challenging questions.

Blue-numbered questions have answers in Appendix R and fully worked solutions in the *Student Solutions Manual*.

## Practicing Skills

### Balancing Equations for Oxidation–Reduction Reactions
*(See Section 20.1 and Examples 20.1–20.3.)*

*When balancing the following redox equations, it may be necessary to add $H^+$ (aq) or $H^+$ (aq) plus $H_2O$ for reactions in acid, and $OH^-$ (aq) or $OH^-$ (aq) plus $H_2O$ for reactions in base.*

1. Write balanced equations for the following half-reactions. Specify whether each is an oxidation or reduction.
   (a) $Cr(s) \rightarrow Cr^{3+}(aq)$ (in acid)
   (b) $AsH_3(g) \rightarrow As(s)$ (in acid)
   (c) $VO_3^-(aq) \rightarrow V^{2+}(aq)$ (in acid)
   (d) $Ag(s) \rightarrow Ag_2O(s)$ (in base)

2. Write balanced equations for the following half-reactions. Specify whether each is an oxidation or reduction.
   (a) $H_2O_2(aq) \rightarrow O_2(g)$ (in acid)
   (b) $H_2C_2O_4(aq) \rightarrow CO_2(g)$ (in acid)
   (c) $NO_3^-(aq) \rightarrow NO(g)$ (in acid)
   (d) $MnO_4^-(aq) \rightarrow MnO_2(s)$ (in base)

3. Balance the following redox equations. All occur in acid solution.
   (a) $Ag(s) + NO_3^-(aq) \rightarrow NO_2(g) + Ag^+(aq)$
   (b) $MnO_4^-(aq) + HSO_3^-(aq) \rightarrow$
   $$Mn^{2+}(aq) + SO_4^{2-}(aq)$$
   (c) $Zn(s) + NO_3^-(aq) \rightarrow Zn^{2+}(aq) + N_2O(g)$
   (d) $Cr(s) + NO_3^-(aq) \rightarrow Cr^{3+}(aq) + NO(g)$

4. Balance the following redox equations. All occur in acid solution.
   (a) $Sn(s) + H^+(aq) \rightarrow Sn^{2+}(aq) + H_2(g)$
   (b) $Cr_2O_7^{2-}(aq) + Fe^{2+}(aq) \rightarrow Cr^{3+}(aq) + Fe^{3+}(aq)$
   (c) $MnO_2(s) + Cl^-(aq) \rightarrow Mn^{2+}(aq) + Cl_2(g)$
   (d) $CH_2O(aq) + Ag^+(aq) \rightarrow HCO_2H(aq) + Ag(s)$

5. Balance the following redox equations. All occur in basic solution.
   (a) $Al(s) + H_2O(\ell) \rightarrow Al(OH)_4^-(aq) + H_2(g)$
   (b) $CrO_4^{2-}(aq) + SO_3^{2-}(aq) \rightarrow Cr(OH)_3(s) + SO_4^{2-}(aq)$
   (c) $Zn(s) + Cu(OH)_2(s) \rightarrow [Zn(OH)_4]^{2-}(aq) + Cu(s)$
   (d) $HS^-(aq) + ClO_3^-(aq) \rightarrow S(s) + Cl^-(aq)$

6. Balance the following redox equations. All occur in basic solution.
   (a) $Fe(OH)_3(s) + Cr(s) \rightarrow Cr(OH)_3(s) + Fe(OH)_2(s)$
   (b) $NiO_2(s) + Zn(s) \rightarrow Ni(OH)_2(s) + Zn(OH)_2(s)$
   (c) $Fe(OH)_2(s) + CrO_4^{2-}(aq) \rightarrow$
   $$Fe(OH)_3(s) + [Cr(OH)_4]^-(aq)$$
   (d) $N_2H_4(aq) + Ag_2O(s) \rightarrow N_2(g) + Ag(s)$

### Constructing Voltaic Cells
*(See Section 20.2 and Example 20.4.)*

7. A voltaic cell is constructed using the reaction of chromium metal and iron(II) ions.

$$2 Cr(s) + 3 Fe^{2+}(aq) \rightarrow 2 Cr^{3+}(aq) + 3 Fe(s)$$

Complete the following sentences: Electrons in the external circuit flow from the ___ electrode to the ___ electrode. Negative ions move in the salt bridge from the ___ half-cell to the ___ half-cell. The half-reaction at the anode is ___, and that at the cathode is ___.

8. A voltaic cell is constructed using the reaction

$$Mg(s) + 2 H^+(aq) \rightarrow Mg^{2+}(aq) + H_2(g)$$

   (a) Write equations for the oxidation and reduction half-reactions.
   (b) Which half-reaction occurs in the anode compartment, and which occurs in the cathode compartment?
   (c) Complete the following sentences: Electrons in the external circuit flow from the ___ electrode to the ___ electrode. Negative ions move in the salt bridge from the ___ half-cell to the ___ half-cell. The half-reaction at the anode is ___, and that at the cathode is ___.

9. The half-cells $Fe^{2+}(aq)|Fe(s)$ and $O_2(g)|H_2O$ (in acid solution) are linked to create a voltaic cell.
   (a) Write equations for the oxidation and reduction half-reactions and for the overall (cell) reaction.
   (b) Which half-reaction occurs in the anode compartment, and which occurs in the cathode compartment?
   (c) Complete the following sentences: Electrons in the external circuit flow from the ___ electrode to the ___ electrode. Negative ions move in the salt bridge from the ___ half-cell to the ___ half-cell.

10. The half-cells $Sn^{2+}(aq)|Sn(s)$ and $Cl_2(g)|Cl^-(aq)$ are linked to create a voltaic cell.
    (a) Write equations for the oxidation and reduction half-reactions and for the overall (cell) reaction.
    (b) Which half-reaction occurs in the anode compartment, and which occurs in the cathode compartment?
    (c) Complete the following sentences: Electrons in the external circuit flow from the ___ electrode to the ___ electrode. Negative ions move in the salt bridge from the ___ half-cell to the ___ half-cell.

**Commercial Electrochemical Cells**
*(See Section 20.3.)*

11. What are the similarities and differences between dry cells, alkaline batteries, and Ni-cad batteries?

12. What reactions occur when a lead storage battery is recharged?

**Standard Electrochemical Potentials**
*(See Section 20.4 and Example 20.5.)*

13. Calculate the value of $E°$ for each of the following reactions. Decide whether each is product-favored in the direction written.
    (a) $2 I^-(aq) + Zn^{2+}(aq) \rightarrow I_2(s) + Zn(s)$
    (b) $Zn^{2+}(aq) + Ni(s) \rightarrow Zn(s) + Ni^{2+}(aq)$
    (c) $2 Cl^-(aq) + Cu^{2+}(aq) \rightarrow Cu(s) + Cl_2(g)$
    (d) $Fe^{2+}(aq) + Ag^+(aq) \rightarrow Fe^{3+}(aq) + Ag(s)$

14. Calculate the value of $E°$ for each of the following reactions. Decide whether each is product-favored in the direction written. [Reaction (d) is carried out in basic solution.]
    (a) $Br_2(\ell) + Mg(s) \rightarrow Mg^{2+}(aq) + 2 Br^-(aq)$
    (b) $Zn^{2+}(aq) + Mg(s) \rightarrow Zn(s) + Mg^{2+}(aq)$
    (c) $Sn^{2+}(aq) + 2 Ag^+(aq) \rightarrow Sn^{4+}(aq) + 2 Ag(s)$
    (d) $2 Zn(s) + O_2(g) + 2 H_2O(\ell) + 4 OH^-(aq) \rightarrow$
    $2 [Zn(OH)_4]^{2-}(aq)$

15. Balance each of the following unbalanced equations; then calculate the standard potential, $E°$, and decide whether each is product-favored as written. (All reactions are carried out in acid solution.)
    (a) $Sn^{2+}(aq) + Ag(s) \rightarrow Sn(s) + Ag^+(aq)$
    (b) $Al(s) + Sn^{4+}(aq) \rightarrow Sn^{2+}(aq) + Al^{3+}(aq)$
    (c) $ClO_3^-(aq) + Ce^{3+}(aq) \rightarrow Cl_2(g) + Ce^{4+}(aq)$
    (d) $Cu(s) + NO_3^-(aq) \rightarrow Cu^{2+}(aq) + NO(g)$

16. Balance each of the following unbalanced equations; then calculate the standard potential, $E°$, and decide whether each is product-favored as written. (All reactions are carried out in acid solution.)
    (a) $I_2(s) + Br^-(aq) \rightarrow I^-(aq) + Br_2(\ell)$
    (b) $Fe^{2+}(aq) + Cu^{2+}(aq) \rightarrow Cu(s) + Fe^{3+}(aq)$
    (c) $Fe^{2+}(aq) + Cr_2O_7^{2-}(aq) \rightarrow Fe^{3+}(aq) + Cr^{3+}(aq)$
    (d) $MnO_4^-(aq) + HNO_2(aq) \rightarrow Mn^{2+}(aq) + NO_3^-(aq)$

**Ranking Oxidizing and Reducing Agents**
*(See Section 20.4 and Example 20.5. Use a table of standard reduction potentials [Table 20.1 or Appendix M] to answer Study Questions 17–24.)*

17. Consider the following half-reactions:

| Half-Reaction | $E°(V)$ |
|---|---|
| $Cu^{2+}(aq) + 2 e^- \rightarrow Cu(s)$ | +0.34 |
| $Sn^{2+}(aq) + 2 e^- \rightarrow Sn(s)$ | −0.14 |
| $Fe^{2+}(aq) + 2 e^- \rightarrow Fe(s)$ | −0.44 |
| $Zn^{2+}(aq) + 2 e^- \rightarrow Zn(s)$ | −0.76 |
| $Al^{3+}(aq) + 3 e^- \rightarrow Al(s)$ | −1.66 |

   (a) Based on $E°$ values, which metal is the most easily oxidized?
   (b) Which metals on this list are capable of reducing $Fe^{2+}(aq)$ to $Fe(s)$?
   (c) Write a balanced chemical equation for the reaction of $Fe^{2+}(aq)$ with $Sn(s)$. Is this reaction product-favored or reactant-favored?
   (d) Write a balanced chemical equation for the reaction of $Zn^{2+}(aq)$ with $Sn(s)$. Is this reaction product-favored or reactant-favored?

18. Consider the following half-reactions:

| Half-Reaction | $E°(V)$ |
|---|---|
| $MnO_4^-(aq) + 8 H^+(aq) + 5 e^- \rightarrow Mn^{2+}(aq) + 4 H_2O(\ell)$ | +1.51 |
| $BrO_3^-(aq) + 6 H^+(aq) + 6 e^- \rightarrow Br^-(aq) + 3 H_2O(\ell)$ | +1.47 |
| $Cr_2O_7^{2-}(aq) + 14 H^+(aq) + 6 e^- \rightarrow 2 Cr^{3+}(aq) + 7 H_2O(\ell)$ | +1.33 |
| $NO_3^-(aq) + 4 H^+(aq) + 3 e^- \rightarrow NO(g) + 2 H_2O(\ell)$ | +0.96 |
| $SO_4^{2-}(aq) + 4 H^+(aq) + 2 e^- \rightarrow SO_2(g) + 2 H_2O(\ell)$ | +0.20 |

   (a) Choosing from among the reactants in these half-reactions, identify the strongest and weakest oxidizing agents.
   (b) Which of the oxidizing agents listed is (are) capable of oxidizing $Br^-(aq)$ to $BrO_3^-(aq)$ (in acid solution)?
   (c) Write a balanced chemical equation for the reaction of $Cr_2O_7^{2-}(aq)$ with $SO_2(g)$ in acid solution. Is this reaction product-favored or reactant-favored?
   (d) Write a balanced chemical equation for the reaction of $Cr_2O_7^{2-}(aq)$ with $Mn^{2+}(aq)$. Is this reaction product-favored or reactant-favored?

19. Which of the following elements is the best reducing agent under standard conditions?
    (a) Cu          (d) Ag
    (b) Zn          (e) Cr
    (c) Fe

20. From the following list, identify those elements that are easier to oxidize than $H_2(g)$.
    (a) Cu
    (b) Zn
    (c) Fe
    (d) Ag
    (e) Cr

21. Which of the following ions is most easily reduced?
    (a) $Cu^{2+}(aq)$
    (b) $Zn^{2+}(aq)$
    (c) $Fe^{2+}(aq)$
    (d) $Ag^+(aq)$
    (e) $Al^{3+}(aq)$

22. From the following list, identify the ions that are more easily reduced than $H^+(aq)$.
    (a) $Cu^{2+}(aq)$
    (b) $Zn^{2+}(aq)$
    (c) $Fe^{2+}(aq)$
    (d) $Ag^+(aq)$
    (e) $Al^{3+}(aq)$

23. (a) Which halogen is most easily reduced in acidic solution: $F_2$, $Cl_2$, $Br_2$, or $I_2$?
    (b) Identify the halogens that are better oxidizing agents in acidic solution than $MnO_2(s)$.

24. (a) Which ion is most easily oxidized to the elemental halogen in acidic solution: $F^-$, $Cl^-$, $Br^-$, or $I^-$?
    (b) Identify the halide ions that are more easily oxidized in acidic solution than $H_2O(\ell)$.

## Electrochemical Cells under Nonstandard Conditions
*(See Section 20.5 and Examples 20.6 and 20.7.)*

25. Calculate the potential delivered by a voltaic cell using the following reaction if all dissolved species are $2.5 \times 10^{-2}$ M and the pressure of $H_2$ is 1.0 bar.
$$Zn(s) + 2 H_2O(\ell) + 2 OH^-(aq) \rightarrow [Zn(OH)_4]^{2-}(aq) + H_2(g)$$

26. Calculate the potential developed by a voltaic cell using the following reaction if all dissolved species are 0.015 M.
$$2 Fe^{2+}(aq) + H_2O_2(aq) + 2 H^+(aq) \rightarrow 2 Fe^{3+}(aq) + 2 H_2O(\ell)$$

27. One half-cell in a voltaic cell is constructed from a silver wire electrode in a 0.25 M solution of $AgNO_3$. The other half-cell consists of a zinc electrode in a 0.010 M solution of $Zn(NO_3)_2$. Calculate the cell potential.

28. One half-cell in a voltaic cell is constructed from a copper wire electrode in a $4.8 \times 10^{-3}$ M solution of $Cu(NO_3)_2$. The other half-cell consists of a zinc electrode in a 0.40 M solution of $Zn(NO_3)_2$. Calculate the cell potential.

29. One half-cell in a voltaic cell is constructed from a silver wire electrode in a $AgNO_3$ solution of unknown concentration. The other half-cell consists of a zinc electrode in a 1.0 M solution of $Zn(NO_3)_2$. A potential of 1.48 V is measured for this cell. Use this information to calculate the concentration of $Ag^+(aq)$.

30. One half-cell in a voltaic cell is constructed from an iron electrode in an $Fe(NO_3)_2$ solution of unknown concentration. The other half-cell is a standard hydrogen electrode. A potential of 0.49 V is measured for this cell. Use this information to calculate the concentration of $Fe^{2+}(aq)$.

## Electrochemistry, Thermodynamics, and Equilibrium
*(See Section 20.6 and Examples 20.8 and 20.9.)*

31. Calculate $\Delta_r G°$ and the equilibrium constant for the following reactions.
    (a) $2 Fe^{3+}(aq) + 2 I^-(aq) \rightleftharpoons 2 Fe^{2+}(aq) + I_2(aq)$
    (b) $I_2(aq) + 2 Br^-(aq) \rightleftharpoons 2 I^-(aq) + Br_2(\ell)$

32. Calculate $\Delta_r G°$ and the equilibrium constant for the following reactions.
    (a) $Zn^{2+}(aq) + Ni(s) \rightleftharpoons Zn(s) + Ni^{2+}(aq)$
    (b) $Cu(s) + 2 Ag^+(aq) \rightleftharpoons Cu^{2+}(aq) + 2 Ag(s)$

33. Use standard reduction potentials (Appendix M) for the half-reactions $AgBr(s) + e^- \rightarrow Ag(s) + Br^-(aq)$ and $Ag^+(aq) + e^- \rightarrow Ag(s)$ to calculate the value of $K_{sp}$ for AgBr.

34. Use the standard reduction potentials (Appendix M) for the half-reactions $Hg_2Cl_2(s) + 2 e^- \rightarrow 2 Hg(\ell) + 2 Cl^-(aq)$ and $Hg_2^{2+}(aq) + 2 e^- \rightarrow 2 Hg(\ell)$ to calculate the value of $K_{sp}$ for $Hg_2Cl_2$.

35. Use the standard reduction potentials (Appendix M) for the half-reactions $[AuCl_4]^-(aq) + 3 e^- \rightarrow Au(s) + 4 Cl^-(aq)$ and $Au^{3+}(aq) + 3 e^- \rightarrow Au(s)$ to calculate the value of $K_{formation}$ for the complex ion $[AuCl_4]^-(aq)$.

36. Use the standard reduction potentials (Appendix M) for the half-reactions $[Zn(OH)_4]^{2-}(aq) + 2 e^- \rightarrow Zn(s) + 4 OH^-(aq)$ and $Zn^{2+}(aq) + 2 e^- \rightarrow Zn(s)$ to calculate the value of $K_{formation}$ for the complex ion $[Zn(OH)_4]^{2-}$.

## Electrolysis
*(See Section 20.7 and Example 20.10.)*

37. Diagram the apparatus used to electrolyze molten NaCl. Identify the anode and the cathode. Trace the movement of electrons through the external circuit and the movement of ions in the electrolysis cell.

38. Diagram the apparatus used to electrolyze aqueous $CuCl_2$. Identify the reaction products, the anode, and the cathode. Trace the movement of electrons through the external circuit and the movement of ions in the electrolysis cell.

39. Which product, $O_2$ or $F_2$, is more likely to form at the anode in the electrolysis of an aqueous solution of KF? Explain your reasoning.

40. Which product, Ca or $H_2$, is more likely to form at the cathode in the electrolysis of $CaCl_2$? Explain your reasoning.

41. An aqueous solution of KBr is placed in a beaker with two inert platinum electrodes. When the cell is attached to an external source of electrical energy, electrolysis occurs.
    (a) Hydrogen gas and hydroxide ion form at the cathode. Write an equation for the half-reaction that occurs at this electrode.
    (b) Bromine is the primary product at the anode. Write an equation for its formation.

**42.** An aqueous solution of $Na_2S$ is placed in a beaker with two inert platinum electrodes. When the cell is attached to an external battery, electrolysis occurs.

(a) Hydrogen gas and hydroxide ion form at the cathode. Write an equation for the half-reaction that occurs at this electrode.

(b) Sulfur is the primary product at the anode. Write an equation for its formation.

**Counting Electrons**

*(See Section 20.8 and Example 20.11.)*

**43.** In the electrolysis of a solution containing $Ni^{2+}(aq)$, metallic $Ni(s)$ deposits on the cathode. Using a current of 0.150 A for 12.2 minutes, what mass of nickel will form?

**44.** In the electrolysis of a solution containing $Ag^+(aq)$, metallic $Ag(s)$ deposits on the cathode. Using a current of 1.12 A for 2.40 hours, what mass of silver forms?

**45.** Electrolysis of a solution of $CuSO_4(aq)$ to give copper metal is carried out using a current of 0.66 A. How long should electrolysis continue to produce 0.50 g of copper?

**46.** Electrolysis of a solution of $Zn(NO_3)_2(aq)$ to give zinc metal is carried out using a current of 2.12 A. How long should electrolysis continue in order to prepare 2.5 g of zinc?

**47.** A voltaic cell can be built using the reaction between Al metal and $O_2$ from the air. If the Al anode of this cell consists of 84 g of aluminum, how many hours can the cell produce 1.0 A of electricity, assuming an unlimited supply of $O_2$?

**48.** Assume the specifications of a Ni-Cd voltaic cell include delivery of 0.25 A of current for 1.00 hour. What is the minimum mass of the cadmium that must be used to make the anode in this cell?

# General Questions

*These questions are not designated as to type or location in the chapter. They may combine several concepts.*

**49.** Write balanced equations for the following half-reactions.

(a) $UO_2^+(aq) \rightarrow U^{4+}(aq)$      (acid solution)

(b) $ClO_3^-(aq) \rightarrow Cl^-(aq)$      (acid solution)

(c) $N_2H_4(aq) \rightarrow N_2(g)$      (basic solution)

(d) $ClO^-(aq) \rightarrow Cl^-(aq)$      (basic solution)

**50.** Balance the following equations.

(a) $Zn(s) + VO^{2+}(aq) \rightarrow$
$Zn^{2+}(aq) + V^{3+}(aq)$    (acid solution)

(b) $Zn(s) + VO_3^-(aq) \rightarrow$
$V^{2+}(aq) + Zn^{2+}(aq)$    (acid solution)

(c) $Zn(s) + ClO^-(aq) \rightarrow$
$Zn(OH)_2(s) + Cl^-(aq)$ (basic solution)

(d) $ClO^-(aq) + [Cr(OH)_4]^-(aq) \rightarrow$
$Cl^-(aq) + CrO_4^{2-}(aq)$ (basic solution)

**51.** Magnesium metal is oxidized, and silver ions are reduced in a voltaic cell using $Mg^{2+}(aq, 1\ M)|Mg$ and $Ag^+(aq, 1\ M)|Ag$ half-cells.

(a) Label each part of the cell.

(b) Write equations for the half-reactions occurring at the anode and the cathode, and write an equation for the net reaction in the cell.

(c) Trace the movement of electrons in the external circuit. Assuming the salt bridge contains $NaNO_3$, trace the movement of the $Na^+$ and $NO_3^-$ ions in the salt bridge that occurs when a voltaic cell produces current. Why is a salt bridge required in a cell?

**52.** You want to set up a series of voltaic cells with specific cell potentials. A $Zn^{2+}(aq, 1.0\ M)|Zn(s)$ half-cell is in one compartment. Identify several half-cells that you could use so that the cell potential will be close to (a) 1.1 V and (b) 0.50 V. Consider cells in which the zinc cell can be either the cathode or the anode.

**53.** You want to set up a series of voltaic cells with specific cell potentials. The $Ag^+(aq, 1.0\ M)|Ag(s)$ half-cell is one of the compartments. Identify several half-cells that you could use so that the cell potential will be close to (a) 1.7 V and (b) 0.50 V. Consider cells in which the silver cell can be either the cathode or the anode.

**54.** Which of the following reactions is (are) product-favored?

(a) $Zn(s) + I_2(s) \rightarrow Zn^{2+}(aq) + 2\ I^-(aq)$

(b) $2\ Cl^-(aq) + I_2(s) \rightarrow Cl_2(g) + 2\ I^-(aq)$

(c) $2\ Na^+(aq) + 2\ Cl^-(aq) \rightarrow 2\ Na(s) + Cl_2(g)$

(d) $2\ K(s) + 2\ H_2O(\ell) \rightarrow$
$2\ K^+(aq) + H_2(g) + 2\ OH^-(aq)$

**55.** In the table of standard reduction potentials, locate the half-reactions for the reductions of the following metal ions to the metal: $Sn^{2+}(aq)$, $Au^+(aq)$, $Zn^{2+}(aq)$, $Co^{2+}(aq)$, $Ag^+(aq)$, $Cu^{2+}(aq)$. Among the metal ions and metals that make up these half-reactions:

(a) Which metal ion is the weakest oxidizing agent?

(b) Which metal ion is the strongest oxidizing agent?

(c) Which metal is the strongest reducing agent?

(d) Which metal is the weakest reducing agent?

(e) Will $Sn(s)$ reduce $Cu^{2+}(aq)$ to $Cu(s)$?

(f) Will $Ag(s)$ reduce $Co^{2+}(aq)$ to $Co(s)$?

(g) Which metal ions on the list can be reduced by $Sn(s)$?

(h) What metals can be oxidized by $Ag^+(aq)$?

56. ▲ In the table of standard reduction potentials, locate the half-reactions for the reductions of the following nonmetals: $F_2$, $Cl_2$, $Br_2$, $I_2$ (reduction to halide ions), and $O_2$, S, Se (reduction to $H_2X$ in aqueous acid). Among the elements, ions, and compounds that make up these half-reactions:
    (a) Which element is the weakest oxidizing agent?
    (b) Which ion or $H_2X$ is the weakest reducing agent?
    (c) Which of the elements listed is (are) capable of oxidizing $H_2O$ to $O_2$?
    (d) Which of these elements listed is (are) capable of oxidizing $H_2S$ to S?
    (e) Is $O_2$ capable of oxidizing $I^-$ to $I_2$, in acid solution?
    (f) Is S capable of oxidizing $I^-$ to $I_2$?
    (g) Is the reaction $H_2S(aq) + Se(s) \rightarrow H_2Se(aq) + S(s)$ product-favored?
    (h) Is the reaction $H_2S(aq) + I_2(s) \rightarrow 2\,H^+(aq) + 2\,I^-(aq) + S(s)$ product-favored?

57. Four voltaic cells are set up. In each, one half-cell contains a standard hydrogen electrode. The second half-cell is one of the following:
    (i) $Cr^{3+}(aq, 1.0\,M)\,|\,Cr(s)$
    (ii) $Fe^{2+}(aq, 1.0\,M)\,|\,Fe(s)$
    (iii) $Cu^{2+}(aq, 1.0\,M)\,|\,Cu(s)$
    (iv) $Mg^{2+}(aq, 1.0\,M)\,|\,Mg(s)$.
    (a) In which of the voltaic cells does the hydrogen electrode serve as the cathode?
    (b) Which voltaic cell produces the highest potential? Which produces the lowest potential?

58. The following half-cells are available:
    (i) $Ag^+(aq, 1.0\,M)\,|\,Ag(s)$
    (ii) $Zn^{2+}(aq, 1.0\,M)\,|\,Zn(s)$
    (iii) $Cu^{2+}(aq, 1.0\,M)\,|\,Cu(s)$
    (iv) $Co^{2+}(aq, 1.0\,M)\,|\,Co(s)$.

    Linking any two half-cells makes a voltaic cell. Given four different half-cells, six voltaic cells are possible. These are labeled, for simplicity, Ag-Zn, Ag-Cu, Ag-Co, Zn-Cu, Zn-Co, and Cu-Co.
    (a) In which of the voltaic cells does the copper electrode serve as the cathode? In which of the voltaic cells does the cobalt electrode serve as the anode?
    (b) Which combination of half-cells generates the highest potential? Which combination generates the lowest potential?

59. The reaction occurring in the cell in which $Al_2O_3$ and aluminum salts are electrolyzed is $Al^{3+}(aq) + 3\,e^- \rightarrow Al(s)$. If the electrolysis cell operates at 5.0 V and $1.0 \times 10^5$ A, what mass of aluminum metal can be produced in a 24-hour day?

60. ▲ A cell is constructed using the following half-reactions:

    $Ag^+(aq) + e^- \rightarrow Ag(s)$

    $Ag_2SO_4(s) + 2\,e^- \rightarrow$
    $\qquad\qquad 2\,Ag(s) + SO_4^{2-}(aq) \quad E° = 0.653\,V$

    (a) What reactions should be observed at the anode and cathode?
    (b) Calculate the solubility product constant, $K_{sp}$, for $Ag_2SO_4$.

61. ▲ A potential of 0.142 V is recorded (under standard conditions) for a voltaic cell constructed using the following half reactions:

    Cathode:  $Pb^{2+}(aq) + 2\,e^- \rightarrow Pb(s)$
    Anode:    $PbCl_2(s) + 2\,e^- \rightarrow Pb(s) + 2\,Cl^-(aq)$
    Net:      $Pb^{2+}(aq) + 2\,Cl^-(aq) \rightarrow PbCl_2(s)$

    (a) What is the standard reduction potential for the anode reaction?
    (b) Calculate the solubility product, $K_{sp}$, for $PbCl_2$.

62. What is the value of $E°$ for the following half-reaction?

    $$Ag_2CrO_4(s) + 2\,e^- \rightarrow 2\,Ag(s) + CrO_4^{2-}(aq)$$

63. The standard potential, $E°$, for the reaction of $Zn(s)$ and $Cl_2(g)$ is +2.12 V. What is the standard free energy change, $\Delta_r G°$, for the reaction?

64. ▲ An electrolysis cell for aluminum production operates at 5.0 V and a current of $1.0 \times 10^5$ A. Calculate the number of kilowatt-hours of energy required to produce 1 metric ton ($1.0 \times 10^3$ kg) of aluminum. (1 kWh = $3.6 \times 10^6$ J and 1 J = 1 C · V)

65. ▲ Electrolysis of molten NaCl is done in cells operating at 7.0 V and $4.0 \times 10^4$ A. What mass of $Na(s)$ and $Cl_2(g)$ can be produced in 1 day in such a cell? What is the energy consumption in kilowatt-hours? (1 kWh = $3.6 \times 10^6$ J and 1 J = 1 C · V)

66. ▲ A current of 0.0100 A is passed through a solution of rhodium sulfate, causing reduction of the metal ion to the metal. After 3.00 hours, 0.038 g of Rh has been deposited. What is the charge on the rhodium ion, $Rh^{n+}$? What is the formula for rhodium sulfate?

67. ▲ A current of 0.44 A is passed through a solution of ruthenium nitrate causing reduction of the metal ion to the metal. After 25.0 minutes, 0.345 g of Ru has been deposited. What is the charge on the ruthenium ion, $Ru^{n+}$? What is the formula for ruthenium nitrate?

68. The total charge that can be delivered by a large dry cell battery before its voltage drops too low is usually about 35 amp-hours. (One amp-hour is the charge that passes through a circuit when 1 A flows for 1 hour.) What mass of Zn is consumed when 35 amp-hours are drawn from the cell?

69. Chlorine gas is obtained commercially by electrolysis of brine (a concentrated aqueous solution of NaCl). If the electrolysis cells operate at 4.6 V and $3.0 \times 10^5$ A, what mass of chlorine can be produced in a 24-hour day?

70. Write equations for the half-reactions that occur at the anode and cathode in the electrolysis of *molten* KBr. What are the products formed at the anode and cathode in the electrolysis of *aqueous* KBr?

71. The products formed in the electrolysis of aqueous $CuSO_4$ are $Cu(s)$ and $O_2(g)$. Write equations for the anode and cathode reactions.

72. Predict the products formed in the electrolysis of an aqueous solution of $CdSO_4$.

73. In the electrolysis of $HNO_3(aq)$, hydrogen is produced at the cathode. According to a table of reduction potentials, $NO_3^-(aq)$ is easier to reduce than $H^+(aq)$. Suggest a possible reason why $H_2$ formed rather than NO. What is the product formed at the anode? Write an equation for the anode reaction.

74. The metallurgy of aluminum involves electrolysis of $Al_2O_3$ dissolved in molten cryolyte ($Na_3AlF_6$) at about 950 °C. Aluminum metal is produced at the cathode. Predict the anode product and write equations for the reactions occurring at both electrodes.

75. Two half-cells, $Pt\,|\,Fe^{3+}$ (aq, 0.50 M), $Fe^{2+}$ (aq, $1.0 \times 10^{-5}$ M) and $Hg^{2+}$ (aq, 0.020 M) $|\,Hg$, are constructed and then linked together to form a voltaic cell. Which electrode is the anode? What will be the potential of the voltaic cell at 298 K?

76. A voltaic cell is set up utilizing the reaction

    $$Cu(s) + 2\,Ag^+(aq) \rightarrow Cu^{2+}(aq) + 2\,Ag(s)$$

    $$Cu(s)\,|\,Cu^{2+}(aq, 1.0\ M)\,||\,Ag^+(aq, 0.001\ M)\,|\,Ag(s)$$

    Under standard conditions, the expected potential is 0.45 V. Predict whether the potential for the voltaic cell will be higher, lower, or the same as the standard potential. Verify your prediction by calculating the new cell potential.

77. Calculate the cell potential for the following cell:

    $$Pt\,|\,H_2(P = 1\ bar)\,|\,H^+(aq, 1.0\ M)\,||$$
    $$Fe^{3+}(aq, 1.0M), Fe^{2+}(aq, 1.0M)\,|\,Pt$$

    Will this reaction be more or less favorable at lower pH? To determine this, calculate the cell potential for a reaction in which $[H^+(aq)]$ is $1.0 \times 10^{-7}$ M.

78. A voltaic cell set up utilizing the reaction

    $$Cu(s) + 2\,Ag^+(aq) \rightarrow Cu^{2+}(aq) + 2\,Ag(s)$$

    has a cell potential of 0.45 at 298 K. Describe how the potential of this cell will change as the cell is discharged. At what point does the cell potential reach a constant value? Explain your answer.

79. Two $Ag^+(aq)\,|\,Ag$ half-cells are constructed. The first has $[Ag^+] = 1.0$ M, the second has $[Ag^+] = 1.0 \times 10^{-5}$ M. When linked together with a salt bridge and external circuit, a cell potential is observed. (This kind of voltaic cell is referred to as a *concentration cell*.)
    (a) Draw a picture of this cell, labeling all components. Indicate the cathode and the anode, and indicate in which direction electrons flow in the external circuit.
    (b) Calculate the cell potential at 298 K.

80. Calculate equilibrium constants for the following reactions at 298 K. Indicate whether the equilibrium as written is reactant- or product-favored.
    (a) $Co(s) + Ni^{2+}(aq) \rightleftharpoons Co^{2+}(aq) + Ni(s)$
    (b) $Fe^{3+}(aq) + Cr^{2+}(aq) \rightleftharpoons Cr^{3+}(aq) + Fe^{2+}(aq)$

81. Calculate equilibrium constants for the following reactions at 298 K. Indicate whether the equilibrium as written is reactant- or product-favored.
    (a) $2\,Cl^-(aq) + Br_2(\ell) \rightleftharpoons Cl_2(aq) + 2\,Br^-(aq)$
    (b) $Fe^{2+}(aq) + Ag^+(aq) \rightleftharpoons Fe^{3+}(aq) + Ag(s)$

82. Use the table of standard reduction potentials (Appendix M) to calculate $\Delta_r G°$ for the following reactions at 298 K.
    (a) $ClO_3^-(aq) + 5\,Cl^-(aq) + 6\,H^+(aq) \rightarrow$
    $$3\,Cl_2(g) + 3\,H_2O(\ell)$$
    (b) $AgCl(s) + Br^-(aq) \rightarrow AgBr(s) + Cl^-(aq)$

83. Use the table of standard reduction potentials (Appendix M) to calculate $\Delta_r G°$ for the following reactions at 298 K.
    (a) $3\,Cu(s) + 2\,NO_3^-(aq) + 8\,H^+(aq) \rightarrow$
    $$3\,Cu^{2+}(aq) + 2\,NO(g) + 4\,H_2O(\ell)$$
    (b) $H_2O_2(aq) + 2\,Cl^-(aq) + 2\,H^+(aq) \rightarrow$
    $$Cl_2(g) + 2\,H_2O(\ell)$$

84. ▲ Write balanced equations for the following reduction half-reactions involving organic compounds.
    (a) $HCO_2H \rightarrow CH_2O$        (acid solution)
    (b) $C_6H_5CO_2H \rightarrow C_6H_5CH_3$   (acid solution)
    (c) $CH_3CH_2CHO \rightarrow CH_3CH_2CH_2OH$  (acid solution)
    (d) $CH_3OH \rightarrow CH_4$          (acid solution)

85. ▲ Balance the following equations involving organic compounds.
    (a) $Ag^+(aq) + C_6H_5CHO(aq) \rightarrow$
    $$Ag(s) + C_6H_5CO_2H(aq) \quad \text{(acid solution)}$$
    (b) $CH_3CH_2OH + Cr_2O_7^{2-}(aq) \rightarrow$
    $$CH_3CO_2H(aq) + Cr^{3+}(aq) \quad \text{(acid solution)}$$

86. A voltaic cell is constructed in which one half-cell consists of a silver wire in an aqueous solution of $AgNO_3$. The other half-cell consists of an inert platinum wire in an aqueous solution containing $Fe^{2+}(aq)$ and $Fe^{3+}(aq)$.
    (a) Calculate the cell potential, assuming standard conditions.
    (b) Write the net ionic equation for the reaction occurring in the cell.
    (c) Which electrode is the anode and which is the cathode?
    (d) If $[Ag^+]$ is 0.10 M, and $[Fe^{2+}]$ and $[Fe^{3+}]$ are both 1.0 M, what is the cell potential? Is the net cell reaction still that used in part (a)? If not, what is the net reaction under the new conditions?

87. An expensive but lighter alternative to the lead storage battery is the silver-zinc battery.

    $$Ag_2O(s) + Zn(s) + H_2O(\ell) \rightarrow Zn(OH)_2(s) + 2\,Ag(s)$$

    The electrolyte is 40% KOH, and silver–silver oxide electrodes are separated from zinc–zinc hydroxide electrodes by a plastic sheet that is permeable to hydroxide ions. Under normal operating conditions, the battery has a potential of 1.59 V.
    (a) How much energy can be produced per gram of reactants in the silver-zinc battery? Assume the battery produces a current of 0.10 A.

(b) How much energy can be produced per gram of reactants in the standard lead storage battery? Assume the battery produces a current of 0.10 A at 2.0 V.

(c) Which battery (silver-zinc or lead storage) produces the greater energy per gram of reactants?

**88.** The specifications for a lead storage battery include delivery of a steady 1.5 A of current for 15 hours.

(a) What is the minimum mass of lead that will be used in the anode?

(b) What mass of $PbO_2$ must be used in the cathode?

(c) Assume that the volume of the battery is 0.50 L. What is the minimum molarity of $H_2SO_4$ necessary?

**89.** Manganese may play an important role in chemical cycles in the oceans (page 922). Two reactions involving manganese (in acid solution) are the reduction of nitrate ions (to NO) with $Mn^{2+}$ ions and the oxidation of ammonium ions (to $N_2$) with $MnO_2$.

(a) Write balanced chemical equations for these reactions (in acid solution).

(b) Calculate $E°_{cell}$ for the reactions. (One half-reaction potential you need is for the reduction of $N_2$ to $NH_4^+$, $E° = -0.272$ V.)

**90.** ▲ You want to use electrolysis to plate a cylindrical object (radius = 2.50 and length = 20.00 cm) with a coating of nickel metal, 4.0 mm thick. You place the object in a bath containing a salt ($Na_2SO_4$). One electrode is impure nickel, and the other is the object to be plated. The electrolyzing potential is 2.50 V.

(a) Which is the anode and which is the cathode in the experiment? What half-reaction occurs at each electrode?

(b) Calculate the number of kilowatt-hours (kWh) of energy required to carry out the electrolysis. (1 kWh = $3.6 \times 10^6$ J and 1 J = 1 C × 1 V)

**91.** ▲ Iron(II) ion undergoes a disproportionation reaction to give Fe(s) and the iron(III) ion. That is, iron(II) ion is both oxidized and reduced within the same reaction.

$$3\ Fe^{2+}(aq) \rightleftharpoons Fe(s) + 2\ Fe^{3+}(aq)$$

(a) What two half-reactions make up the disproportionation reaction?

(b) Use the values of the standard reduction potentials for the two half-reactions in part (a) to determine whether this disproportionation reaction is product-favored.

(c) What is the equilibrium constant for this reaction?

**92.** ▲ Copper(I) ion disproportionates to copper metal and copper(II) ion. (See Study Question 91.)

$$2\ Cu^+(aq) \rightleftharpoons Cu(s) + Cu^{2+}(aq)$$

(a) What two half-reactions make up the disproportionation reaction?

(b) Use values of the standard reduction potentials for the two half-reactions in part (a) to determine whether this disproportionation reaction is spontaneous.

(c) What is the equilibrium constant for this reaction? If you have a solution that initially contains 0.10 mol of $Cu^+$ in 1.0 L of water, what are the concentrations of $Cu^+$ and $Cu^{2+}$ at equilibrium?

## In the Laboratory

**93.** Consider an electrochemical cell based on the half-reactions $Ni^{2+}(aq) + 2\ e^- \rightarrow Ni(s)$ and $Cd^{2+}(aq) + 2\ e^- \rightarrow Cd(s)$.

(a) Diagram the cell, and label each of the components (including the anode, cathode, and salt bridge).

(b) Use the equations for the half-reactions to write a balanced, net ionic equation for the overall cell reaction.

(c) What is the polarity of each electrode?

(d) What is the value of $E°_{cell}$?

(e) In which direction do electrons flow in the external circuit?

(f) Assume that a salt bridge containing $NaNO_3$ connects the two half-cells. In which direction do the $Na^+(aq)$ ions move? In which direction do the $NO_3^-(aq)$ ions move?

(g) Calculate the equilibrium constant for the reaction.

(h) If the concentration of $Cd^{2+}$ is reduced to 0.010 M and $[Ni^{2+}] = 1.0$ M, what is the value of $E_{cell}$? Is the net reaction still the reaction given in part (b)?

(i) If 0.050 A is drawn from the battery, how long can it last if you begin with 1.0 L of each of the solutions and each was initially 1.0 M in dissolved species? Each electrode weighs 50.0 g in the beginning.

**94.** An old method of measuring the current flowing in a circuit was to use a "silver coulometer." The current passed first through a solution of $Ag^+(aq)$ and then into another solution containing an electroactive species. The amount of silver metal deposited at the cathode was weighed. From the mass of silver, the number of atoms of silver was calculated. Since the reduction of a silver ion requires one electron, this value equaled the number of electrons passing through the circuit. If the time was noted, the average current could be calculated. If, in such an experiment, 0.052 g of Ag is deposited during 450 s, what was the current flowing in the circuit?

**95.** A "silver coulometer" (Study Question 94) was used in the past to measure the current flowing in an electrochemical cell. Suppose you found that the current flowing through an electrolysis cell deposited 0.089 g of Ag metal at the cathode after exactly 10 min. If this same current then passed through a cell containing gold(III) ion in the form of $[AuCl_4]^-$, how much gold was deposited at the cathode in that electrolysis cell?

**96.** ▲ Four metals, A, B, C, and D, exhibit the following properties:

(i) Only A and C react with 1.0 M hydrochloric acid to give $H_2(g)$.

(ii) When C is added to solutions of the ions of the other metals, metallic B, D, and A are formed.

(iii) Metal D reduces $B^{n+}$ to give metallic B and $D^{n+}$.

Based on this information, arrange the four metals in order of increasing ability to act as reducing agents.

97. ▲ A solution of KI is added dropwise to a pale blue solution of $Cu(NO_3)_2$. The solution changes to a brown color, and a precipitate of CuI forms. In contrast, no change is observed if solutions of KCl and KBr are added to aqueous $Cu(NO_3)_2$. Consult the table of standard reduction potentials to explain the dissimilar results seen with the different halides. Write an equation for the reaction that occurs when solutions of KI and $Cu(NO_3)_2$ are mixed.

98. ▲ The amount of oxygen, $O_2$, dissolved in a water sample at 25 °C can be determined by titration. The first step is to add solutions of $MnSO_4$ and NaOH to the water to convert the dissolved oxygen to $MnO_2$. A solution of $H_2SO_4$ and KI is then added to convert the $MnO_2$ to $Mn^{2+}$, and the iodide ion is converted to $I_2$. The $I_2$ is then titrated with standardized $Na_2S_2O_3$.
    (a) Balance the equation for the reaction of $Mn^{2+}$ ions with $O_2$ in basic solution.
    (b) Balance the equation for the reaction of $MnO_2$ with $I^-$ in acid solution.
    (c) Balance the equation for the reaction of $S_2O_3^{2-}$ with $I_2$.
    (d) Calculate the amount of $O_2$ in 25.0 mL of water if the titration requires 2.45 mL of 0.0112 M $Na_2S_2O_3$ solution.

## Summary and Conceptual Questions

*The following questions may use concepts from this and previous chapters.*

99. Fluorinated organic compounds are used as herbicides, flame retardants, and fire-extinguishing agents, among other things. A reaction such as

    $$CH_3SO_2F + 3 \ HF \rightarrow CF_3SO_2F + 3 \ H_2$$

    is carried out electrochemically in liquid HF as the solvent.
    (a) If you electrolyze 150 g of $CH_3SO_2F$, what mass of HF is required, and what mass of each product can be isolated?
    (b) Is $H_2$ produced at the anode or the cathode of the electrolysis cell?
    (c) A typical electrolysis cell operates at 8.0 V and 250 A. How many kilowatt-hours of energy does one such cell consume in 24 hours?

100. ▲ The free energy change for a reaction, $\Delta_r G°$, is the maximum energy that can be extracted from the process, whereas $\Delta_r H°$ is the total chemical potential energy change. The efficiency of a fuel cell is the ratio of these two quantities.

    $$\text{Efficiency} = \frac{\Delta_r G°}{\Delta_r H°} \times 100\%$$

Consider the hydrogen-oxygen fuel cell, where the net reaction is

$$H_2(g) + \tfrac{1}{2} \ O_2(g) \rightarrow H_2O(\ell)$$

(a) Calculate the efficiency of the fuel cell under standard conditions.
(b) Calculate the efficiency of the fuel cell if the product is water vapor instead of liquid water.
(c) Does the efficiency depend on the state of the reaction product? Why or why not?

101. A hydrogen-oxygen fuel cell operates on the simple reaction

$$H_2(g) + \tfrac{1}{2} \ O_2(g) \rightarrow H_2O(\ell)$$

If the cell is designed to produce 1.5 A of current and if the hydrogen is contained in a 1.0-L tank at 200 atm pressure at 25 °C, how long can the fuel cell operate before the hydrogen runs out? (Assume there is an unlimited supply of $O_2$.)

102. ▲ (a) Is it easier to reduce water in acid or base? To evaluate this, consider the half-reaction

$$2 \ H_2O(\ell) + 2 \ e^- \rightarrow 2 \ OH^-(aq) + H_2(g)$$
$$E° = -0.83 \ V$$

(b) What is the reduction potential for water for solutions at pH = 7 (neutral) and pH = 1 (acid)? Comment on the value of $E°$ at pH = 1.

103. ▲ Living organisms derive energy from the oxidation of food, typified by glucose.

$$C_6H_{12}O_6(aq) + 6 \ O_2(g) \rightarrow 6 \ CO_2(g) + 6 \ H_2O(\ell)$$

Electrons in this redox process are transferred from glucose to oxygen in a series of at least 25 steps. It is instructive to calculate the total daily current flow in a typical organism and the rate of energy expenditure (power). (See T. P. Chirpich: *Journal of Chemical Education*, Vol. 52, p. 99, 1975.)
(a) The molar enthalpy of combustion of glucose is $-2800$ kJ/mol-rxn. If you are on a typical daily diet of 2400 Cal (kilocalories), what amount of glucose (in moles) must be consumed in a day if glucose is the only source of energy? What amount of $O_2$ must be consumed in the oxidation process?
(b) How many moles of electrons must be supplied to reduce the amount of $O_2$ calculated in part (a)?
(c) Based on the answer in part (b), calculate the current flowing, per second, in your body from the combustion of glucose.
(d) If the average standard potential in the electron transport chain is 1.0 V, what is the rate of energy expenditure in watts?

# Applying Chemical Principles

## Sacrifice!

In the latter half of the 18th century the British sheathed the hulls of their naval fleet with copper to protect the hulls from deterioration. Unfortunately, the copper corroded in sea water, so the navy called upon Sir Humphry Davy to determine the cause of the corrosion and to find a cure. Although Davy initially assumed that impurities in the copper caused the corrosion, he soon learned that high-purity copper corroded faster. Turning his attention to the sea water, Davy determined that the copper is oxidized by oxygen in the sea water. The overall reaction,

$$Cu(s) + \tfrac{1}{2} O_2(g) + H_2O(\ell) \rightarrow Cu(OH)_2(s)$$

produces copper(II) hydroxide which falls from the hull to the sea floor.

Davy, a pioneer in the field of electrochemistry, quickly determined that the corrosion of copper can be prevented by attaching small pieces of a more easily oxidized metal (such as zinc, tin, or iron) to the copper sheathing. The quantity of the metal may be small in comparison to the copper, but, to be effective, the metal must be positioned below the water line and in direct electrical contact with the copper.

Why is corrosion prevented by attaching a small piece of metal, such as zinc, to the copper? When the two different metals are submerged in sea water they form a galvanic cell. The copper serves as the cathode and the zinc as a "sacrificial" anode. The zinc anode is oxidized instead of the copper. Although the zinc anodes corrode over time and must be replaced, the cost is cheaper than replacing the copper on an entire ship's hull.

In modern fleets, copper-sheathed hulls have given way to steel hulls. Though surface coatings, such as paint, provide some protection against corrosion, sacrificial anodes are still used to protect the steel from corrosion. In addition, sacrificial anodes are now used to protect the steel in underground pipes, as well as in home water heaters, outboard motors, and boilers.

## Questions:

1. If an electrically insulating material, such as paint, is placed between the zinc and the copper, the zinc will still corrode in seawater, but it will not protect the copper from corrosion. Explain.

2. Use standard reduction potentials to determine which of the following metals could serve as a sacrificial anode on a copper-sheathed hull. Indicate all correct responses.
   (a) tin      (c) iron      (e) chromium
   (b) silver      (d) nickel

**Sacrificial anodes attached to a steel-hulled ship.** The "patches" are zinc blocks. Sacrificial anodes of aluminum or magnesium are also used in domestic hot-water heaters to prevent corrosion in the heater.

Cliverivers/Alamy

3. Use standard reduction potentials to determine which of the following metals could serve as a sacrificial anode on a steel hull. Assume the standard reduction potential for steel is the same as that of iron. Indicate all correct responses.
   (a) tin      (c) iron      (e) chromium
   (b) silver      (d) nickel

4. The overall reaction for the production of $Cu(OH)_2$ from Cu in oxygenated water can be broken into three steps: an oxidation half-reaction, a reduction half-reaction, and a precipitation reaction.
   (a) Complete and balance the two missing half-reactions to give the overall equation for the oxidation of copper in seawater.
   1. Oxidation half-reaction: ?
   2. Reduction half-reaction: ?
   3. Precipitation: $Cu^{2+}(aq) + 2\, OH^-(aq) \rightarrow Cu(OH)_2(s)$
   4. Overall: $Cu(s) + \tfrac{1}{2} O_2(g) + H_2O(\ell) \rightarrow Cu(OH)_2(s)$
   (b) Determine the equilibrium constant for the overall reaction at 25 °C using standard reduction potentials and the solubility product constant ($K_{sp}$) of $Cu(OH)_2(s)$.

5. Assume the following electrochemical cell simulates the galvanic cell formed by copper and zinc in seawater at pH 7.90 and 25 °C.

$$Zn\,|\,Zn(OH)_2(s)\,|\,OH^-(aq)\,|\,Cu(OH)_2(s)\,|\,Cu(s)$$

   (a) Write a balanced equation for the reaction that occurs at the cathode.
   (b) Write a balanced equation for the reaction that occurs at the anode.
   (c) Write a balanced chemical equation for the overall reaction.
   (d) Determine the potential (in volts) of the cell.

# The Chemistry of the Environment

Planet Earth can be discussed from many points of view: geological, political, historical, and environmental. The last of these has now become a main topic of concern. If we are to understand why this is so, we need to understand the chemical composition of our environment and the way it is changing.

Land, sea, air—continents, oceans, atmosphere—solid, liquid, gas. These are the three main components of the environment, and each is governed by the laws of chemistry that we associate with these physical states. Look a little closer at the continents, and we can see more and more space being devoted to human occupation and farming. We may classify the water on the planet as seawater, fresh water, or estuarine water, but how do we get from one to the other? We know the atmosphere is a mixture of gases and vapors and is restlessly in motion, sometimes violently so, but what will happen if its composition changes? Understanding the environment is crucial, but without a chemical perspective we are floundering.

In this interchapter, we look particularly at those parts of the environment that are most susceptible to change: the atmosphere and the aqua sphere (water). What humans are doing to the atmosphere appears to be leading to significant climate change. The water of the planet is also of concern: We often pollute it, and we need to purify it. Nature can supply water in abundance as rain, rivers, and lakes but not necessarily where it is most needed. While many in the developed world have a seemingly abundant supply of pure, fresh water, others obtain water only with difficulty—and even then it may not be fit to drink. As the world's population increases, many more people will find themselves having to rely on seawater for their supply of freshwater. Seawater, of course, is not drinkable, but chemistry can make it so.

If we are to understand atmospheric pollution and its effects on climate and water supplies and ways to make them drinkable, then we need to understand the chemistry that is involved.

## The Atmosphere

The atmosphere may be the least weighty part of the environment, but this does not mean it has the least effect. In fact, it has a disproportionately large influence on our standard of living. We know it is changing because of what we are adding to it, and we fear the consequences of that change.

Earth has changed dramatically over the billions of years the planet has existed, and so has the atmosphere. The first atmosphere is thought to have been mainly ammonia, water vapor, and carbon dioxide. Today, it is mainly nitrogen, oxygen, and argon. At some stage, most of the water condensed onto the surface of the planet, and seas were formed. It was in the seas that life probably emerged, and life had to adapt to conditions as they changed. Sometimes the changes were so great that many species could not adapt and were wiped out. But, despite these mass extinctions, there were always a few survivors.

Table 1 gives the composition of the atmosphere in terms of the gases it contains. The values in the table are for dry air at sea level. Normally, air also contains water vapor, which can vary considerably from place to place and from day to day. It can be as high as 40,000 ppm (parts per million) but is generally about half this value.

In fact, there are many more components of the atmosphere than those listed in Table 1. There are trace amounts of chemicals emitted by plants, animals, and microbes, as well as those released by human activity. Our additions to

John C. Katz

● **Sunrise over the Atlantic Ocean,** Sunday, April 4, 2010.

**Table 1  The Gases of the Atmosphere***

| Gases | Concentration (ppm) |
|---|---|
| Nitrogen ($N_2$) | 780,840 |
| Oxygen ($O_2$) | 209,460 |
| Argon (Ar) | 9340 |
| Carbon dioxide ($CO_2$) | 385 |
| Neon (Ne) | 18 |
| Helium (He) | 5.2 |
| Methane ($CH_4$) | 1.7 |
| Krypton (Kr) | 1.1 |
| Dinitrogen monoxide (nitrous oxide) ($N_2O$) | 0.55 |
| Hydrogen ($H_2$) | 0.5 |
| Ozone ($O_3$) | 0.4 |
| Carbon monoxide (CO) | 0.25 |
| Xenon (Xe) | 0.086 |
| Radon (Rn) | traces |

*Data on gas concentrations refer to relative numbers of particles in dry air (and hence are related to mole fractions).

the atmosphere come from burning fuels to generate electricity, from vehicle exhausts, from industry, and from our day-to-day activities. The atmosphere is changing, and we need to understand what this means for the future.

We might imagine that air is a homogeneous mixture of gases and particles because it is constantly being stirred by the motion of the planet and the heat of the sun. In fact, this mixing is far from complete. There is relatively little exchange of air between the north and south regions of the planet, and there are distinct layers in the atmosphere (◄ page 528). As far as humans are concerned, the most important layer is the lower layer in which we live—the troposphere, which goes up to around 7 km at the poles and 17 km at the equator. Above the troposphere is the stratosphere; this extends to about 30 km, getting thinner and thinner as we rise to higher altitudes. There are even higher regions, but there the air is very thin, although not so thin it cannot interact with incoming space debris or vehicles like the Space Shuttle and cause them to glow red hot. In this interchapter, we concern ourselves only with the troposphere and the stratosphere.

The total mean mass of the atmosphere is estimated to be around $5.15 \times 10^{18}$ kg ($5.15 \times 10^{15}$ metric tons, or $5.15 \times 10^6$ gigatons). (Gigatons are often used in environmental studies because the masses we are discussing are so large. A *metric ton* is 1000 kg, but a gigaton is a billion metric tons, that is, $10^9$ metric tons.) Three quarters of the mass of the atmosphere is in the troposphere, and there its aver-

age temperature is 14 °C (but that is an average of a wide range of temperatures). It can be as low as −89 °C, the lowest temperature ever recorded, in Antarctica in 1983, or as high as 58 °C, the highest temperature ever recorded, in North Africa in 1922. After temperature, the next most obvious property of the atmosphere is the pressure it exerts, which at sea level is around 101 kPa (1 atmosphere).

Some of the gases of the atmosphere are unreactive and never change chemically. These are the noble gases: helium, neon, argon, krypton, and xenon. Two of these, namely, helium and argon, are being added continuously to the atmosphere because they are products of radioactive decay—helium comes from alpha particles emitted by elements such as uranium, and argon is produced by decay of $^{40}K$, a long-lived radioactive isotope of potassium.

The other gases of the atmosphere, namely, oxygen, nitrogen, and carbon dioxide, are chemically reactive and can be changed into other molecules by reactions driven by lightning, ultraviolet rays from the sun, or the influence of living things, and especially the actions of humans.

## Nitrogen and Nitrogen Oxides

The nitrogen of the atmosphere arose from the out-gassing of Earth when it was simply a molten mass. Even today, some nitrogen escapes when volcanoes erupt. Nitrogen gas is relatively unreactive, but every living thing on the planet needs to incorporate nitrogen into its cells as, among other compounds, amino acids, the building blocks of proteins. The process by which nitrogen gas is converted to useful nitrogen-containing compounds, such as ammonia ($NH_3$) and nitrate ions ($NO_3^-$), is known as **nitrogen fixation** (Figure 1). Bacteria in the soil and algae in the oceans are the primary "fixers" of nitrogen. On a global scale, the conversion of nitrogen to various compounds is accomplished to the extent of around 50% by biological processes, 10% by fertilizer manufacture, 10% by lightning, and 30% from the burning of fossil fuels. Once nitrogen is "fixed" it is incorporated into living things, passes through many other life forms, and ends up in the soil, which contains significant amounts of nitrogen-containing compounds such as ammonium salts, nitrates, and nitrites. The two anions ($NO_3^-$ and $NO_2^-$) are converted back to nitrogen gas or to $N_2O$ and returned to the atmosphere.

Dinitrogen monoxide (nitrous oxide), $N_2O$, is only one of several nitrogen oxides important in our environment. Others are nitrogen monoxide (nitric oxide), NO, and nitrogen dioxide, $NO_2$. Because they are readily interconverted, they are referred to collectively as $NO_x$ compounds. There are a number of sources of $NO_x$ compounds.

- NO produced from the combination of $N_2$ and $O_2$ when air is heated in an automobile engine or is sparked by a bolt of lighting

**FIGURE 1 The nitrogen cycle.** The nitrogen cycle involves nitrogen fixation by soil bacteria or, in aquatic environments, by cyanobacteria. The $NH_4^+$ ions produced are converted to nitrate ions, the main form of nitrogen absorbed by plants. Nitrogen is returned to the atmosphere by denitrifying bacteria, which convert nitrate ions to $N_2$.

- NO and $NO_2$ produced by the photochemical oxidation of $N_2O$ in the atmosphere
- Oxidation of $NH_3$ in the atmosphere
- Production of NO and $N_2O$ in soil by microbial processes

In addition, fossil fuel burning and biomass combustion by humans produce about 65% of the $NO_x$ in the atmosphere.

The most abundant nitrogen oxide is dinitrogen monoxide because it is the least reactive. Most of this oxide comes from microbes in the soil. Ten million tons of $N_2O$ are released each year, some from human activity.

The other nitrogen oxides make up only 0.00005 ppm of the atmosphere. While 100 million tons of $NO_x$ come each year from vehicle exhaust, it is quickly washed out of the atmosphere by rain (and thus contributes to "acid rain"). When $NO_x$ compounds do linger, particularly over cities in sunny climates, they can react with hydrocarbons in the atmosphere, such as traces of unburnt fuel, to produce irritating photochemical smog. Among the most polluting components of smog are PANs, peroxyacyl nitrates, represented here by peroxyacetyl nitrate.

One route to its formation is as follows:

(a) Organic compounds called *aldehydes* (such as $CH_3CHO$) are produced by complex reactions in smog. These molecules react with hydroxyl radicals ($OH\cdot$), which are also the result of photochemical reactions in the atmosphere (◀ page 363). Their interaction produces another radical species $CH_3CO\cdot$.

$$CH_3CHO + OH\cdot \rightarrow CH_3CO\cdot + H_2O$$

(b) The newly produced radical reacts with oxygen to produce the peroxyacetyl radical.

$$CH_3CO\cdot + O_2 \rightarrow CH_3COOO\cdot$$

(c) The peroxyacetyl radical reacts with $NO_2$ in polluted air to give peroxyacetyl nitrate.

$$CH_3COOO\cdot + NO_2 \rightarrow CH_3COOONO_2$$

PANs are toxic and irritating. At low concentrations, they irritate the eyes, but at higher concentrations they can cause more serious damage to both animals and vegetation. They are relatively stable, dissociating only slowly into radicals and $NO_2$. Thus, it is possible that they can travel some distance from where they are formed before dissociating into harmful radicals.

## Oxygen

Plant life had a dramatic effect on the early atmosphere, changing it from a reducing to an oxidizing one, that is, from there being no oxygen present to one where this reactive gas is the second most abundant species present in the atmosphere. This change meant life had to change. Those species that could not live in the presence of this reactive gas either died out or were relegated to regions where oxygen is blocked out. The percent of oxygen in the air is now midway between two extremes that would make life on Earth impossible for humans: below 17% we would suffocate, and above 25% all organic material would burn easily.

The total mass of oxygen in the atmosphere is a million gigatons. Even though the burning of 7 gigatons of fossil fuel carbon per year uses up 18 gigatons of oxygen, this makes almost no discernible difference to the amount of oxygen in the atmosphere. Oxygen is also moderately soluble in water (◀ page 626), which makes life in rivers, lakes, and oceans possible.

Oxygen is a by-product of plant **photosynthesis**. Carbon dioxide is the source of the carbon that plants need and which they capture from the air and turn into carbohydrates such as glucose ($C_6H_{12}O_6$) by photosynthesis. The overall chemical reaction is

$$6\ CO_2 + 6\ H_2O \rightarrow C_6H_{12}O_6 + 6\ O_2$$

and the net result is the release of an oxygen molecule back into the atmosphere for each $CO_2$ absorbed. Oxygen

**FIGURE 2 Cyanobacteria.** Cyanobacteria, also known as blue-green algae, obtain their energy by photosynthesis. The name comes from the color of the material. Their importance lies in their production of oxygen by photosynthesis and their participation in the nitrogen-fixation cycle.

molecules released by photosynthesis remain in the atmosphere, on average, for around 3000 years before being reabsorbed.

Blue-green algae, or cyanobacteria (Figure 2), first began producing oxygen as long ago as 3.5 billion years. But, mysteriously, hundreds of millions of years elapsed before a significant amount of oxygen was present in the atmosphere. Astrobiologists are not at all certain why this occurred, but it does seem plausible that the oxygen first produced did not remain in the atmosphere because it reacted with metals, especially converting abundant iron(II) ions to iron(III) ions. This process continued for about a billion years, but then the level of oxygen in the atmosphere began to rise 2 billion years ago, and about 500 million years ago it rose relatively rapidly to around 20% when the first land plants started to appear.

There are three naturally occurring isotopes of oxygen: oxygen-16 accounts for 99.76% of O atoms, oxygen-17 for a mere 0.04%, and oxygen-18 for 0.2%. Because oxygen-18 is 12% heavier than oxygen-16, it can influence the behavior of water in the environment. The ratio of oxygen-18 to oxygen-16 in the world's oceans has varied slightly over geological time, and this has left an imprint on parts of the environment, providing evidence of past climates. When the world is in a cooler period, water molecules with oxygen-16 evaporate more easily from the oceans than their heavier oxygen-18 counterpart. Thus, snow is slightly richer in oxygen-16, and the water that remains in the oceans is slightly richer in oxygen-18. Marine creatures therefore lay down shells that have more oxygen-18 than expected, and these are preserved in sediments. Analyzing the ratio of the two isotopes in such deposits reveals the cycle of global cooling and warming that has characterized the past half million years with its five ice ages.

## Ozone

Ozone ($O_3$) plays a key role for life on this planet, but it is also a threat. In the troposphere, it is a pollutant, while in the stratosphere it acts as a shield, protecting the planet from damaging ultraviolet rays from the sun. This shield is known as the **ozone layer** (Figure 3).

There is a natural low level of ozone in the air we breathe, about 0.02 ppm (parts per million), but in summer this can increase to 0.1 ppm or more as a result of sunlight acting on the nitrogen dioxide emitted by vehicles. In the presence of sunlight, $NO_2$ dissociates to NO and O atoms, and the O atoms can react with $O_2$ (in the presence of a third molecule acting as an energy "sink") to produce ozone.

$$NO_2 + \text{energy } (\lambda < 240 \text{ nm}) \rightarrow NO + O$$

$$O + O_2 \rightarrow O_3$$

Because ozone damages the lungs, the legal limit for exposure to ozone in the workplace is 0.1 ppm. Some growing plants are also susceptible to the gas, and even though they do not show visible signs of stress, their growth is reduced in proportion to the level of ozone in the air.

In contrast with ozone in the troposphere, $O_3$ in the stratosphere is vital to the planet because the molecules absorb ultraviolet radiation before it reaches Earth's surface. Radiation with wavelengths shorter than 240 nm interacts with $O_2$ molecules and cleaves them into two O

**FIGURE 3 The ozone layer.** Substantial concentrations of ozone exist between the 10 and 50 km above the Earth's surface (see page 528). About 90% of the ozone in the atmosphere is contained in the stratosphere (roughly 15–50 km above the surface). Concentrations range from 2 to 8 parts per million.

atoms. Each O atom combines with another $O_2$ molecule to produce an ozone molecule.

$$O_2 + energy \rightarrow O + O$$

$$O + O_2 \rightarrow O_3$$

Ozone in turn absorbs ultraviolet radiation with wavelengths less than 320 nm, and the $O_3$ is decomposed to $O_2$ and O atoms.

$$O_3 + energy\ (\lambda < 320\ nm) \rightarrow O_2 + O$$

$$O + O_3 \rightarrow 2\ O_2$$

Without the ozone layer, dangerous radiation capable of harming living cells would penetrate to Earth's surface and could cause numerous human health and environmental effects. These effects include increased incidence of skin cancer and cataracts and suppression of the human immune response system. Damage to crops and marine phytoplankton and weathering of plastics are also caused by increased levels of ultraviolet radiation.

## Chlorofluorocarbons and Ozone

From the late 1800s until about 1930 ammonia ($NH_3$), chloromethane ($CH_3Cl$), and sulfur dioxide ($SO_2$) were widely used as refrigerants. However, leakage from refrigerators caused several fatal accidents in the 1920s, so three American corporations, Frigidaire, General Motors, and DuPont, collaborated on the search for a less dangerous fluid. In 1928, Thomas Midgley, Jr., and his coworkers discovered a "miracle compound" as a substitute. This compound, dichlorodifluoromethane ($CCl_2F_2$), is a member of a large family of compounds called chlorofluorocarbons (CFCs). The two compounds shown here are CFC-114 ($C_2Cl_2F_4$) and CFC-12 ($CCl_2F_2$).

dichlorotetrafluoroethane          dichlorodifluoromethane

These compounds had exactly the physical and chemical properties needed for a refrigerant: appropriate critical temperatures and pressures, no toxicity, and apparent chemical inertness.

The uses of CFCs grew dramatically, not only in air conditioning and refrigeration equipment but also in applications such as propellants for aerosol cans, foaming agents in the production of expanded plastic foams, and inhalers for asthma sufferers.

Unfortunately, as the world has often learned about other "miracle compounds," the properties that made CFCs so useful also led to environmental problems. CFCs are unreactive in Earth's troposphere, which allows them to remain in the troposphere for hundreds of years. Over time, however, they slowly diffuse into the stratosphere where, as proposed by Sherwood Rowland and Mario Molina in 1974, solar radiation leads to their decomposition.

$$CF_2Cl_2(g) + UV\ radiation \rightarrow CF_2Cl(g) + Cl(g)$$

They also proposed that the Cl atoms released in the decomposition of CFCs and other chlorine-containing compounds can destroy large numbers of ozone molecules. In this mechanism, Cl atoms react with $O_3$ molecules to produce the radical species ClO. This in turn intercepts O atoms from the decomposition of $O_2$ molecules, to produce Cl atoms, which then continue the cycle.

$$O_3(g) + Cl(g) \rightarrow ClO(g) + O_2(g)$$

$$O(g) + ClO(g) \rightarrow Cl(g) + O_2(g)$$

Net reaction:   $O_3(g) + O(g) \rightarrow O_2(g) + O_2(g)$

The two equations above represent steps of a *chain reaction*, which, when repeated over and over, means that the formation of one Cl atom can lead to the destruction of many ozone molecules.

In 1985 three British scientists of the British Antarctic Survey discovered that there was a significant reduction in the ozone concentration over the Antarctic continent, which has since been referred to as the "ozone hole" (Figure 4). In 1986, Susan Solomon and a team from the

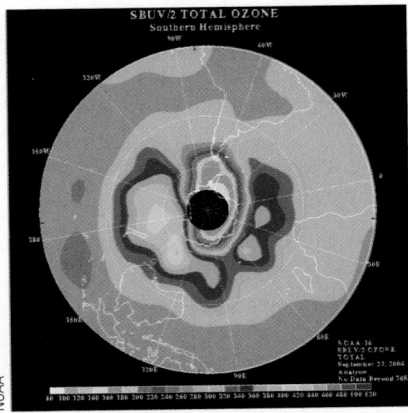

**FIGURE 4** **The "ozone hole" over the Antarctic continent.** During the Antarctic winter, when there are 24 hours of darkness, aerosols of HCl and $ClONO_2$ freeze and accumulate in the polar stratospheric clouds. During the Antarctic spring, these crystals melt, and Cl and ClO radicals are rapidly formed and lead to a depletion of stratospheric ozone over the continent.

National Center for Atmospheric Research went to Antarctica to investigate the "hole" and found that there were indeed higher levels of ClO than expected in the stratosphere.

Because of the damage caused to the stratospheric ozone layer, apparently by CFCs and related compounds, the United States banned the use of CFCs as aerosol propellants in 1978, and 68 nations followed suit in 1987 by signing the Montreal Protocol. This protocol called for an immediate reduction in nonessential uses of CFCs. In 1990, 100 nations met in London and decided to ban the production of CFCs. The United States and 140 other countries agreed to a complete halt in CFC manufacture as of December 31, 1995, and Rowland and Molina received the Nobel Prize for their work in that same year.

## Carbon Dioxide

No element is more essential to life than carbon, and the reason is that only carbon has the ability to form long chains and rings of atoms that are stable. This is the basis of the structures for many compounds that comprise the living cell, of which the most important is DNA (◄ page 388). The food we eat—carbohydrates, oils, proteins, and fiber—is made up of compounds of carbon, and this carbon eventually returns to the atmosphere as $CO_2$ as part of the natural cycle. This cycle moves carbon between various compartments of the terrestrial ecosphere and so rules the tempo of life on Earth. The carbon cycle turns over 200 gigatons of carbon every year, and the amounts of carbon residing in the various compartments are, in order of increasing amounts:

- 40 gigatons in living things in the oceans
- 725 gigatons as $CO_2$ in the atmosphere
- 2000 gigatons in living things on land
- 39,000 gigatons as carbonate ions ($CO_3^{2-}$) dissolved in the oceans
- 20,000,000 gigatons as reduced carbon in fossil fuel deposits
- 100,000,000+ gigatons as carbonate minerals such as limestone

Reduced carbon in Earth's crust comes in various forms such as natural gas, which is largely $CH_4$; oil, which approximates to $CH_2$; and coal, a complex material with a carbon–hydrogen ratio corresponding to CH. Known reserves of these fossil fuels amount to a vast 1 trillion tons of coal, 160 billion tons of oil, and 180 trillion cubic meters of natural gas. A much larger amount of carbon in Earth's crust is also present but is too widely dispersed and inaccessible to be regarded as a potential energy source. Human use of fossil fuels each year releases around 25 gigatons of $CO_2$ into the atmosphere.

## Climate Change

The *Intergovernmental Panel on Climate Change* (IPCC) was set up in 1988 by members of the United Nations Environment Program and the World Meteorological Organization. To date, it has issued four Assessment Reports describing **global warming**. This term refers to the gradual warming of the surface air and oceans of the Earth. The best estimate is that the surface temperature of the Earth has increased $0.74 \pm 0.18$ °C during the last century and that it is continuing to increase.

Earth began to emerge from a cold period around 150 years ago. Will the natural cycle of temperature change create a warm period like those at the time of the Roman Empire and during the Middle Ages? Or has the increase in human population and its burning of fossil fuels, which increases the level of $CO_2$ in the atmosphere, made an additional contribution that will result in a much warmer period than those earlier ages experienced?

In the first three of the IPCC Assessment Reports, the authors warned that human activity might be partly responsible for raising the global temperature. While some heeded the IPCC warnings, little was done to check the use of fossil fuels, although some effort is now being directed into generating electricity by sustainable means such as wind power and solar panels. In 2007, the IPCC issued its *Fourth Assessment Report*. This report went further by saying that there is now little doubt the planet is warming and that additions of greenhouse gases to the atmosphere by humans are having a noticeable effect. (A fifth report is being prepared. To obtain the reports, see www.ipcc.ch.)

## Greenhouse Gases

The greenhouse effect is the process by which radiation from the sun warms Earth's surface (◄ page 259). This is vital to life on Earth because the surface temperature is about 35 °C warmer than it would be without the effect.

The greenhouse effect is caused by certain gases in the troposphere. These gases are small molecules whose bonds vibrate with frequencies in the infrared region of the electromagnetic spectrum. Such a gas can trap infrared radiation, thus retaining energy that would otherwise be radiated into space.

Which gases can act as greenhouse gases depends solely on their chemistry. Gases that are single atoms, like argon, have no chemical bonds and so cannot interact with infrared light. Homonuclear diatomic molecules such as nitrogen ($N_2$) and oxygen ($O_2$) also do not absorb infrared radiation. Since these three gases make up 99% of the atmosphere, it is clearly beneficial for us that they are not greenhouse gases.

On the other hand, molecules with bonds between different atoms, such as water ($H_2O$) and carbon dioxide ($CO_2$), are greenhouse gases and allow Earth to warm more than it would have based solely on its distance from the sun. (Water vapor is the main greenhouse gas and accounts for most of the observed effect.) In this respect, these gases are vital. If Earth did not retain some energy supplied by the sun, the average temperature would be like that of the moon, too hot when feeling the full glare of the sun and too cold when in shadow. Life would be impossible.

Other gases in the atmosphere can also act as greenhouse gases. Methane ($CH_4$) is a greenhouse gas much more powerful than $CO_2$. Nitrous oxide ($N_2O$) is also very powerful at retaining heat energy. These come partly from natural sources but in amounts too small to pose a threat. Methane is released by anaerobic bacteria (that is, those that do not use oxygen). Some anaerobic bacteria live at the bottom of lakes and swamps, some in termite mounds, and some in the guts of animals such as cows and humans. Human activities can also release large amounts of these gases. For example, methane is the natural gas we use in vast amounts, and some of this escapes from leaking pipelines. It also leaks from landfill sites and coal mines, as well as from agricultural sites such as rice fields. Nitrous oxide is released as a by-product of our abundant use of ammonium nitrate fertilizers.

The methane concentration in the atmosphere is now around 1.7 ppm, which is about double the "natural" level. The concentration of $N_2O$ is around 0.55 ppm instead of 0.27 ppm. More significantly, the carbon dioxide concentration increased from around 280 ppm in 1750 to 388 in 2010 (Figure 5). The fourth IPCC report states that "Today's $CO_2$ concentration has not been exceeded during the past 420,000 years and likely not during the past 20 million years. The rate of increase over the past century is unprecedented, at least during the past 20,000 years."

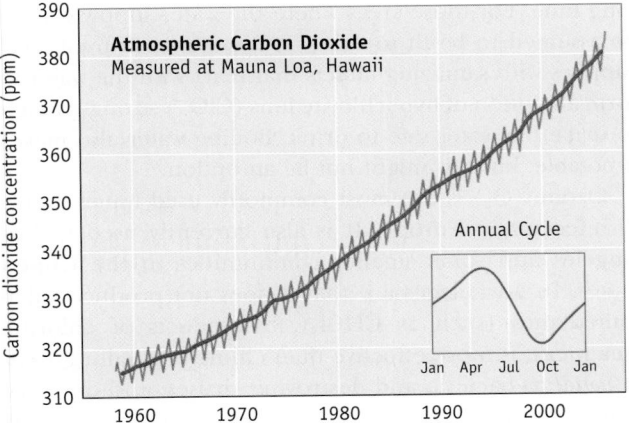

**FIGURE 5** Mean monthly concentrations of $CO_2$ at Mauna Loa, Hawaii.

Industry has added new greenhouse gases to the atmosphere such as the many CFCs and various chemicals known as *volatile organic compounds* (VOCs). Although VOCs, especially isoprene and terpenes, are given off by trees, VOCs are also given off by paints, adhesives, plastics, air fresheners, and cosmetics. The family of CFCs has been replaced by a new generation of hydrofluorocarbon (HFC) compounds such as $F_3C–CH_2F$, also called HFC-134a, a compound now commonly used in air conditioners and refrigerators. Although HFCs behave as greenhouse gases, they are much less persistent in the atmosphere than the long-lived CFCs.

The IPCC estimates that in the past 100 years the atmosphere has warmed by $0.74 \pm 0.18$ °C, and this might well have been higher had it not been offset by the release of soot and other chemicals into the atmosphere. These cause a certain amount of "global dimming."

So how much hotter will the world become if we continue to rely on fossil fuels? The IPCC has considered several predictions and reports two possible scenarios. One of these predicts a relatively low level warming, between 1.8 and 2.9 °C. The other predicts an increase of between 4 and 6.4 °C and is much more worrisome. The lower scenario would lead to sea level rises of 18–38 cm; the higher range would cause a rise of 26–59 cm. While advanced nations could protect vulnerable areas against such rises—the Dutch have been living below sea level for hundreds of years thanks to massive dikes—less-developed nations and especially those that occupy large river deltas in Asia and small island states would literally be swamped by the sea. We still have time to decide what action to take, but the longer we continue with our heavy reliance on natural gas, oil, and coal, the worse the risk becomes.

Some believe we can offset the amount of carbon dioxide we release into the atmosphere by planting trees to reabsorb the $CO_2$. The trees would be paid for by a levy assessed on those who drive cars or travel by plane. Therefore, our journeys would be "carbon-neutral." In fact, very large areas around the world have been planted with trees. Unfortunately, it now appears that trees planted in temperate regions and especially those at higher latitudes might actually contribute to climate warming by absorbing more heat from the sun than the land they occupy would otherwise absorb. However, trees planted in the tropics do have the desired effect and absorb carbon dioxide while not contributing to this heating effect.

## The Aqua Sphere (Water)

Most of the planet is covered by water, and for centuries humans have treated it as an inexhaustible source of food and the easiest place to dump our waste. That is now changing. The aqua sphere is a major asset but will remain so only if we treat it with respect.

## The Oceans

The quantity of minerals dissolved in the oceans is vast, and, even when the concentration is low (Table 2), the total can still be quite surprising. For example, though something may be present at only 5 ppm in seawater, its total mass is almost 7 trillion tons (7000 gigatons.) The lure of vast amounts of dissolved metals has tantalized people through the ages, and the amount of gold in the sea particularly so. At a concentration of only 10 parts per trillion (or 10 g in 1 trillion g of water), even this amounts to more than 13 million tons. Although some have tried, no method has been found by which it can be extracted profitably.

Water has fascinated scientists through the ages, in part because water has some unusual features that are of critical importance to the environment. For example, when it freezes it expands in volume unlike most other materials that shrink as they solidify (◄ page 556). This is why ice floats instead of sinking. In fact, this was essential for the emergence of early forms of life. Because water freezes from the top down, it actually protects the creatures that live underneath the ice; otherwise, only a few microbes that can exist in ice would have survived.

The fact that ice is less dense than water also means that when it melts the volume of water it creates is smaller than the volume of ice. For example, if the North Polar ice melts, it will not raise sea level because this ice is already floating in water and will take up less space in the liquid state than in the solid state. On the other hand, ice stacked on land, such as that in Greenland, will cause an increase in sea level if it melts because its water will be added to the oceans. Thankfully, the ice at the South Pole is not melting (yet), and computer models show that this part of the planet is not likely to be affected by global warming to the same extent as the Northern Hemisphere.

#### Table 2 Concentrations of Some Cations and Anions in Seawater

| Element | Dissolved Species | Concentrations (mmol/L) |
|---|---|---|
| Chlorine | $Cl^-$ | 550 |
| Sodium | $Na^+$ | 460 |
| Magnesium | $Mg^{2+}$ | 52 |
| Calcium | $Ca^{2+}$ | 10 |
| Potassium | $K^+$ | 10 |
| Carbon | $HCO_3^-$, $CO_3^{2-}$ | 30 |
| Phosphorus | $HPO_4^{2-}$ | <1 |

## Drinking Water

Water is as vital to life as food; indeed, you can survive for weeks without anything to eat, but you would not last a week if you had no water to drink. People in developed countries have clean, safe water supplied to their homes by pipe (although curiously many prefer to buy it in small bottles). Sadly, a large number of our fellow humans, generally in less-developed countries, have to make do with whatever water they can find, taking it from a well or even from a river, and then they are at risk of contracting a water-borne disease such as cholera, typhoid, gastroenteritis, or meningitis. More than 5000 people per day are thought to die from diseases from the water they drink.

### Water Purification

Water purification began with the ancient Egyptians 3500 years ago. They discovered that when alum—potassium aluminum sulfate, $KAl(SO_4)_2$—was dissolved in water, all visible impurities were removed. This salt forms a voluminous precipitate of insoluble aluminum hydroxide, $Al(OH)_3$, which carries down any cloudiness as it settles. This is still the way that modern treatment plants produce crystal-clear water (Figure 6). Adding a small amount of *slaked lime* (CaO, calcium hydroxide) to raise the pH slightly and then a solution of aluminum sulfate creates a *floc* of $Al(OH)_3$, which removes many impurities as it precipitates. The water is then filtered through sand to remove any trace of the floc.

After treatment with alum and subsequent settling and filtration, the water is crystal clear and ready to be disinfected to destroy any pathogens that are still present. This can be done with a powerful oxidizing agent such as chlorine, sodium hypochlorite (NaClO), or ozone. Chlorine and hypochlorite have an advantage over ozone in that they are more persistent, meaning that the water will still be fit to drink even when it has been standing in a pipe for a long time. For those areas where the water supply cannot be assumed to be fit to drink, it is possible to treat local supplies with sanitizing tablets that react with the water to form a solution of hypochlorite ions ($ClO^-$) strong enough to make the water safe to drink. Boiling water also makes it potable, but this might not be an option.

Ozone ($O_3$) is the most commonly used water supply disinfectant in Europe. It is also currently used in Los Angeles and some smaller communities in the United States. Its advantages are that it does not produce trihalomethanes (such as $CHCl_3$), by-products of chlorine treatment; is more effective than chlorine at killing *Cryptosporidium* bacteria and destroying viruses; and does not leave a residual "chlorine" taste. However, due to its reactivity, ozone must be generated on site and is therefore more expensive. Also, it does not provide residual disinfection in the distribution system.

**FIGURE 6** **A municipal water treatment plant.** The general steps in this process are (1) the removal of turbidity, (2) softening, (3) sedimentation and filtration, and (4) disinfection. The removal of turbidity (by addition of alum) and the disinfection of water are discussed in the text.

Ultraviolet (UV) light has been used to disinfect food products, such as milk, for some time. Wavelengths ranging from 200 to 295 nm are used, with maximum disinfection occurring at 253.7 nm (Figure 7). UV units are less expensive to install than ozone generators and have the advantage of requiring short contact times for disinfection. In addition, UV radiation disinfection is not pH or temperature dependent, and it leaves no toxic residues. Although no residual disinfection is left in the water distribution system, small amounts of chlorine can be added to address this issue.

In the United States, tap water from a municipality must meet standards at least as strict as those for bottled water. All municipalities publish annual reports of the water quality, many of them on the internet. Check the quality of the tap water in your municipality.

### Reverse Osmosis for Water Purification

Pure water can also be obtained from undrinkable water in other ways. The one most used in areas with access to

**FIGURE 7** Ultraviolet light (UV) is used to disinfect drinking water using this equipment in a large water treatment plant in Beijing, China.

seawater is desalination by **reverse osmosis**. Osmosis is the process whereby water in one solution moves across a membrane in such a way as to dilute a solution with a higher concentration (◄ page 635). The osmotic pressure can be measured by seeing to what extent water will continue to pass across a membrane, even when it has to push against a resisting pressure on the other side. Eventually, the pressure is such that the process of osmosis stops and can be reversed if even more pressure is applied. This is the basis of reverse osmosis, and it is the way that some cities near the sea get their water supplies (◄ page 637).

Chemistry is an important part of the reverse osmosis desalination apparatus because of the membranes that allow the passage of water molecules but not of dissolved salts. The membranes are made of polymers such as polyvinylidene fluoride and polypropylene with ultrafine pores. They have to withstand the high pumping pressures that are needed to force water against the osmotic pressure gradient. The cost is not excessive, and a cubic meter of water (1000 L) produced this way need cost only $1. Desalination systems are now a $1 billion per year industry and growing at a rate of 7% per year. And not only seawater can be purified this way; any waste water from a suspect source can be treated.

### Diminishing Water Supplies

People also want water for washing themselves, their clothing, and their bed linens, or for watering the garden and flushing the lavatory. In developed countries with adequate rainfall, water can be collected and stored in vast reservoirs above or below ground. But such is the increase in global population that even those regions may one day have to conserve supplies; there are times when water use is restricted, and such restrictions are likely to increase as the effects of global warming come into play this century. Already 500 million people worldwide are affected by water shortages. Even in the Great Plains of

# Chlorination of Water Supplies

Chlorination is the oldest and most commonly used water disinfection method in the United States. Originally, chlorine gas was dissolved in water to yield hypochlorous acid (HClO),

$$Cl_2(g) + H_2O(\ell) \rightarrow HClO(aq) + HCl(aq)$$

which dissociates to yield the hypochlorite ion (ClO⁻).

$$HClO(aq) + H_2O(\ell) \rightleftharpoons H_3O^+(aq) + ClO^-(aq)$$
$$K_a = 3.5 \times 10^{-8}$$

Two of the chemical species formed by chlorine in water—hypochlorous acid and the hypochlorite ion—are known to environmental engineers as **free available chlorine**, meaning they are available for disinfection. Because chlorine gas is quite toxic and can easily escape from damaged containers, many water treatment facilities are now switching to solid hypochlorite salts such as sodium or calcium hypochlorite [NaClO and Ca(ClO)$_2$, respectively].

Hypochlorous acid and hypochlorite ion are effective in killing bacteria. However, they will also oxidize reduced inorganic ions such as iron(II), manganese(II), and nitrite ion, as well as organic impurities. These compounds are collectively known as the **chlorine demand**. To be available to kill bacteria, sufficient chlorine must be added to exceed the chlorine demand.

The advantages of chlorination include its relatively low cost and simple application as well as its ability to maintain residual disinfection throughout the distribution system. However, there are also disadvantages. Chlorine can react with dissolved, naturally occurring organic compounds in the source water to form carcinogenic compounds such as trihalomethanes (of which chloroform, CHCl$_3$, is one example). Chlorination has also been blamed for causing an unpleasant taste and odor in some drinking water.

In 1998, the Disinfection Byproducts Rule (DBR), which restricts the presence of chlorinated organic compounds in water, was implemented in the United States. One way to comply with the DBR is to add ammonia to the water, and about 30% of major U.S. water companies currently use this technique. Ammonia and hypochlorous acid react to form chloramines such as NH$_2$Cl:

$$HClO(aq) + NH_3(aq) \rightarrow NH_2Cl(aq) + H_2O(\ell)$$

Chloramines are called **combined available chlorine**. Like free available chlorine, combined available chlorine is retained as a disinfectant throughout the water distribution system, but it is a weaker disinfectant overall. Combined available chlorine, however, has the advantage that it is less likely to lead to chlorinated organic compounds.

Recently, however, chemists in Washington, D.C., which uses the ammonia/chlorine method of water treatment, found increased lead levels in the drinking water in area homes. [Several hundred homes had lead levels of 300 parts per billion (ppb), whereas the allowed level is 15 ppb.] Water treated with only chlorine is highly oxidizing, and lead in the water is oxidized to lead(IV) oxide. This insoluble oxide is

Chlorine tanks in the water treatment plant of a small city.

trapped in the mineral scale that inevitably forms inside water pipes, and lead is thus removed from the water system. However, switching to the less-oxidizing ammonia/chlorine method apparently means lead ions are not removed by oxidation.

Yet another effective disinfectant is the odd-electron molecule chlorine dioxide (ClO$_2$). The primary advantage of ClO$_2$ is that it completely oxidizes organic compounds (forming CO$_2$ and H$_2$O) and therefore does not produce trihalomethanes. However, ClO$_2$ provides no residual disinfection in the distribution system. Also, ClO$_2$ must be generated on site because it is explosive when exposed to air.

---

the United States the underground sources of water, known as *aquifers,* are becoming seriously depleted, and lakes such as Lake Mead, which was created by the Hoover Dam (on the Colorado River on the border between Nevada and Arizona), that were once full to overflowing are now around 20 meters (60 feet) below the level of water they held in the 1980s.

## Water Pollution

Water has been polluted by many things, mainly from activities such as farming, mining, papermaking, inadequate or nonexistent sewage treatment facilities, and the chemical industry. Protecting natural bodies of water is now high on the agenda of most developed societies, and this has been achieved mainly by banning the use of dangerous chemicals and by installing better sewage treatment facilities.

## Phosphates

In the past, phosphate pollution on a massive scale was an environmental problem, such as that which afflicted Lake Erie, one of the Great Lakes, in the 1960s when it appeared it was no longer capable of supporting life owing to a lack of dissolved oxygen. This was due in part to an excess of nutrients, primarily phosphates, supplied by the rivers that drained into the lake. Where did these phosphates come from? While sewage treatment plants draining into the rivers removed most undesirables in water, they were not removing phosphates that had become a major component of household detergents. Phosphate fertilizers were also being used by farmers, and these also found their way into the surface water. Similar problems were being experienced in other parts of the world, notably in Europe.

Campaigns to control the use of phosphates were successful. These chemicals were taken out of household products, and phosphate was extracted at sewage plants before the waste water was released to rivers. The result was to discourage the growth of algae, and slowly Lake Erie and other lakes began to regenerate. In fact, phosphate was not entirely to blame for the pollution. Lack of zooplankton, which feed on algae, also contributed. These creatures were being killed by traces of pesticides and heavy metals. Without the zooplankton, the algae could breed unchecked.

## Heavy Metals

Some metals, such as cadmium, mercury, lead, and chromium, can be highly toxic even in small amounts. Therefore, the United States Environmental Protection Agency (EPA) places limits on the amount of many metals allowed in drinking water and in foods. This also explains why there are sometimes warnings about eating fish from certain areas due to toxic levels of mercury.

Lead is a cumulative poison that has been linked to learning disabilities and may still be found in the water of older houses due to leaching from lead plumbing. Lead levels in water in the United States are currently required to be no more than 50 μg/L (or 50 ppb).

Knowledge of heavy metal toxicity even made its way to Hollywood. The movie "Erin Brockovich" is centered around water pollution from hexavalent chromium ($Cr^{6+}$, generally in the form of ions such as $CrO_4^{2-}$ or $Cr_2O_7^{2-}$) (Figure 8). For chemists, chromium presents a good example of the importance of knowing the oxidation state of an element; chromium(VI) compounds are toxic whereas chromium(III) is an essential trace element that plays a role in human metabolism.

## Emerging Pollutants

A pollutant is "any substance, as certain chemicals or waste products, that renders the air, soil, water, or other natural resource harmful or unsuitable for a specific purpose." However, what would you say if you were told that over-the-counter drugs or your favorite hand sanitizer may be a source of pollution? These compounds and many others termed *pharmaceutical and personal care products* (PPCPs) are present in some natural waters at high enough concentrations to affect the reproductive systems of fish and other aquatic life. Many of these PPCPs are categorized as endocrine disruptors and are the focus of much recent environmental research. Although the impact of these emerging pollutants on human health is not yet clear, their presence in human breast milk

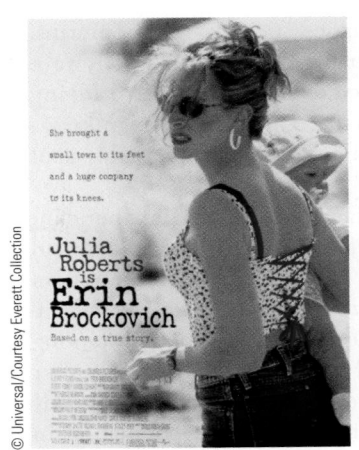

**FIGURE 8** Erin Brockovich. The movie, which came out in 2000, portrayed the campaign of Erin Brockovich, a law office clerk who built a case against a large electric utility for contaminating the water supply with chromium(VI) compounds. (The source of the chromium was compounds used to combat corrosion in cooling towers.) The lawsuit resulted in a large judgment against the utility. The real Erin Brockovich has remained an environmental activist.

has been documented, and some drugs have been shown to increase the growth rate of cancer cells.

There is much work to be done in this area of environmental research and in fact the EPA will require municipalities to begin monitoring certain PPCPs by 2012.

## Arsenic in Drinking Water

Even when drinking water appears to be safe, it may harbor unsuspected dangers acquired from the environment. One example is the occurrence of arsenic-containing compounds in water supplies in the Lagunera region of Mexico, the Antofagasta region of northern Chile, the Codoban region of Argentina, and especially in the West Bengal region of India and the neighboring country of Bangladesh. The effects of arsenic in drinking water can be very serious, and it is very unfortunate that this contamination often went unnoticed for many years.

In Taiwan, an epidemiological study in the 1960s showed that the prevalence of skin cancer was related to the amount of arsenic in water. In one region where the level of arsenic was 500 micrograms per liter (500 ppb), 10% of people aged 60 or over had cancers, mainly on their skin. Thankfully, these types of cancers are not usually fatal and can be removed. Internal cancers, however, are not as easy to diagnose or treat. In one part of Taiwan where the level of arsenic was 800 ppb, there was a high incidence of bladder cancer. Unfortunately, even when measures are taken to purify the water, the incidence of cancer can continue to be high for many years because of the long latency period before the disease appears.

The largest mass poisoning by arsenic involved more than 30 million people (Figure 9). People in West Bengal, India, and in Bangladesh got their drinking water from tube wells that were drilled in the 1970s. The wells were installed by the United Nations Children's Fund (UNICEF) to provide safe drinking water for a population that had traditionally taken its water from contaminated streams, rivers, and ponds and which had suffered accordingly from water-borne diseases such as gastroenteritis, typhoid, and cholera. Eventually, 5 million such wells were drilled, and they indeed served the purpose of bringing cholera under control. In its place, however, they unknowingly brought low-level arsenic poisoning to large areas of Bangladesh.

Tube wells are 5 cm in diameter and tap the abundant ground water about 200 meters below the surface. A few had been installed in Bangladesh in the 1930s when the region was part of the British Empire. Those villages that had installed them showed a decrease in illness, especially among children. UNICEF continued to support the program after independence, and by 1997 it could report that it had already surpassed its goal of providing 80% of the population in those regions with "safe" water. Such had been the success of the program that many villagers installed private wells. Then doctors began to notice a worrying increase in skin cancer and suspected that arsenic was the cause. Analysis of the water from the wells showed that more than 20 million people were drinking water containing arsenic at the 50 ppb level, and as many as 5 million were drinking water containing 300 ppb arsenic. It does appear, though, that 80% of the Bangladeshi population has access to safe drinking water.

In 1997, the Bangladesh government instituted a Rapid Action Program that focused on a group of villages where contamination was severe. Almost two thirds of the tube wells in these villages were delivering water with arsenic in excess of 100 ppb. A team from the Dhaka Community Hospital visited 18 affected areas and examined 2000 adults and children; they concluded that more than half had skin lesions due to arsenic.

So what can the people of this region do? One answer is to dig wells that go deeper than 200 meters or shallower wells that reach down only 20 meters. In this way, the contaminated layer of ground water can be avoided. Once people have access to uncontaminated water, the arsenic in their bodies is quickly lost.

Remediation steps have to be taken when drinking water is contaminated, and yet it is a problem that can be costly to solve. When half a million people in New Mexico were exposed to high arsenic levels in their drinking water, action was taken but at a cost of $100 million. Taking similar action in Bangladesh would be beyond the ability of that country to pay. Even replacing a shallow well with one that draws water from the lower, safer, water table costs $1000. (Shallow tube wells cost only $100 to drill, which is why they have proved so popular.) The alternative is to remove the arsenic from the water. Various simple and cheap devices have been designed by chemists for doing this, such as passing the water through layers of sand, pieces of iron, and charcoal. The inorganic arsenic, which is present as arsenite ions, $AsO_3^{3-}$, sticks to the pieces of iron while the organic forms of arsenic are absorbed into the charcoal.

## Fluoride in Drinking Water

It is generally acknowledged that a little fluoride in drinking water strengthens tooth enamel and prevents decay, and to this end many public water supplies are fluoridated to a level of 1 ppm. Nevertheless, there are dangers in drinking water that has much higher levels, and in some localities the level of fluoride is naturally high. Humans, as well as animals, can be affected and suffer from *fluorosis* (Figure 10), which is a hardening of the bones leading to a deformed skeleton. In certain parts of India, such as the Punjab, the condition is endemic, especially where villagers drink water from wells with high levels of fluoride, up to 15 ppm. About 25 million Indians suffer a mild form of fluorosis, with many thousands showing skeletal deformities.

## Green Chemistry

Our environment is a complex chemical system but not one that is so complex that we can never understand it. It is also a robust system that may be capable of being healed when it is damaged. (One example seems to be the slow reversal of

FIGURE 9 A Bangladesh villager shows his hands affected by arsenic contamination in the water supply.

FIGURE 10 Fluorosis. Here, the teeth have whitish patches, indicating mild fluorosis. Teeth and bones are hydroxyapatite, $Ca_5(OH)(PO_4)_3$. If you drink water with a high $F^-$ ion concentration, the $OH^-$ ion in apatite can be replaced by the $F^-$ ion. This can have the beneficial effect of hardening the surface of teeth, but in excess it can lead to mottling. And in very high concentrations, skeletal deformities can result.

the Antarctic ozone hole when CFC production was stopped.) Our stewardship of Earth demands a good knowledge of chemistry and sensible behavior. Nothing less will suffice.

One way chemists have responded to environmental problems is by practicing **green chemistry**, which is also called "sustainable chemistry." You were introduced to its concepts in Chapter 1 (page 6), and you have seen examples of green chemistry in use throughout the book. The United States EPA has a Green Chemistry Program, which includes research, education, and outreach efforts as well as the Presidential Green Chemistry Challenge Awards, an annual program recognizing innovations in "cleaner, cheaper, smarter chemistry." The American Chemical Society actively promotes green chemistry, and the Royal Society of Chemistry in England publishes the research journal *Green Chemistry*. Some universities now offer degrees in green chemistry.

If we assume the word "green" means environmentally sound or friendly, how can chemistry be green? People have many different opinions concerning chemistry and chemicals. Some use the word "chemical" as a synonym for a toxic substance. Others believe that all our problems can be solved through research in chemistry and other sciences. Chemists realize that all *matter*, including our food, water, and bodies as well as toxic compounds, is composed of chemicals. The practice of chemistry, like most aspects of life, has created problems at times, but chemistry has also solved many, many others.

## SUGGESTED READINGS

1. J. Emsley: *Nature's Building Blocks*. England: Oxford University Press, 2001.
2. S. Manahan, editor: *Environmental Chemistry*, 9th ed. Boca Raton: CRC Press, 2009.
3. Safe Drinking Water Act, including a list of current maximum contaminant levels: www.epa.gov/safewater/sdwa/sdwa.html
4. Green Chemistry Program: www.epa.gov/greenchemistry
5. To check on the quality of air in your community: airnow.gov; see also www.arl.noaa.gov/
6. Intergovernmental Panel on Climate Change: www.ipcc.ch/

## STUDY QUESTIONS

Blue-numbered questions have answers in Appendix Q and fully worked solutions in the *Student Solutions Manual*.

1. Use the data in Table 2 (page 954) to calculate the molar concentrations of $Na^+$ and $Cl^-$ in seawater. Which amount is larger?

2. Using the data in Table 2, estimate the minimum mass of solid that would remain after evaporation of 1.0 L of seawater.

3. What mass of NaCl could be obtained by evaporating 1.0 L of seawater? (*Note:* The amount of $Na^+$ ions in seawater limits the amount of NaCl that can be obtained; see Question 1.)

4. In any solution, there must be a balance between the positive and negative charges of the ions that are present. Use the data in Table 2 to determine how close to a balance of charge is achieved for the ions in seawater. (The table lists only the major ions in seawater, and the balance between positive and negative charge will only be approximate.)

5. In the discussion on the composition of air, mention is made of the fact that water vapor may have a concentration as high as 40,000 ppm. Calculate the pressure exerted by water vapor at this concentration. Assume that this represents a situation with 100% humidity. What temperature would be needed to achieve this value? (See Appendix G.)

6. Although there are a number of magnesium-containing minerals, the commercial source of this metal is seawater. Treatment of seawater with $Ca(OH)_2$ gives solid insoluble $Mg(OH)_2$. This reacts with HCl to produce $MgCl_2$, which is dried, and Mg is obtained by electrolysis of the molten salt. Write balanced net ionic equations for the three reactions described here.

7. Calculate the mass of Mg that could be obtained by the process described in Question 6 from 1.0 L of seawater. To prepare 100. kg of Mg, what volume of seawater would be needed? (The density of seawater is $1.025$ $g/cm^3$.)

8. Assume the average $CO_2$ concentration in the atmosphere is 385 ppm. The actual concentration of $CO_2$ at different sites will vary. Speculate on whether the concentration of $CO_2$ would be expected to be higher, lower, or the same as this average value in a typical large city.

9. Imagine the following experiment. You have a large graduated cylinder containing 100. mL of liquid water at 0 °C. You drop an ice cube with a volume of 25 $cm^3$ into the cylinder. Ice has a density of 0.92 $g/cm^3$, less than the density of liquid water, so it floats with 92% being under water.
   (a) To what level will the water in the graduated cylinder rise after adding the ice?
   (b) Allow the ice to melt. What volume will now be occupied by the liquid water? (One consequence of global warming will be a rise in sea level as ice in the northern and southern regions of the planet melts. However, the effect relates only to melting of ice on land. Melting of floating ice will have no effect on sea levels.)

## ACKNOWLEDGMENT

This article was originally written for the previous edition by Dr. John Emsley of the University of Cambridge, England. It has been revised and reorganized for this edition by the authors and Dr. Trudy Thomas-Smith.

# 21 The Chemistry of the Main Group Elements

**Quartz (SiO$_2$), dry ice (solid CO$_2$), and pure silicon.**

© Cengage Learning/Charles D. Winters

## Carbon and Silicon

Carbon and silicon are both significant elements in the earth's crust. Mendeleev placed them in the same periodic group based on the similarity in stoichiometry of their simple compounds such as their oxides (CO$_2$ and SiO$_2$). We know now that carbon is the backbone of millions of organic compounds. As we will see in this chapter, silicon, the second most abundant element in the earth's crust, is vitally important in the structures of a large number of minerals.

Probe a bit further into silicon chemistry, however, and what emerges are the surprising differences between these elements. We get a hint of this when we compare the two oxides, CO$_2$, a gas above −78 °C and 1 atm pressure, and SiO$_2$, a rock hard solid with a very high melting point. Another interesting contrast can be made between the reactions of the two simple hydrogen compounds, CH$_4$ and SiH$_4$, with water. The reaction of methane with water is reactant-favored, whereas silane will explode on contact with water.

In this chapter, we will evaluate and summarize the inorganic chemistry of the main group elements and explore the similarities and differences between elements in each periodic group.

## Questions:

1. Write balanced chemical equations for the reactions of H$_2$O($\ell$) with CH$_4$ (forming CO$_2$ and H$_2$) and SiH$_4$ (forming SiO$_2$ and H$_2$).
2. Using thermodynamic data, calculate the standard free energy change for the reactions in Question 1. Is either reaction product-favored at equilibrium?
3. Look up the electronegativities of carbon, silicon, and hydrogen. What conclusion can you draw concerning the polarity of C—H and Si—H bonds?
4. Carbon and silicon compounds with the formulas (CH$_3$)$_2$CO (acetone) and [(CH$_3$)$_2$SiO]$_n$ (a silicone polymer) also have quite different structures (Chapter 10). Draw Lewis structures for these species. This difference, along with the difference between structures of CO$_2$ and SiO$_2$, suggests a general observation about silicon compounds. Based on that observation, do you expect that a silicon compound with a structure similar to ethene (C$_2$H$_4$) exists?

**Answers to these questions are available in Appendix N.**

## CHAPTER GOALS

*See Chapter Goals Revisited (page 1006) for Study Questions keyed to these goals.*

- Relate the formulas and properties of compounds to the periodic table.

- Describe the chemistry of the main group or A-Group elements, particularly H; Na and K; Mg and Ca; B and Al; Si; N and P; O and S; and F and Cl.

- Apply the principles of stoichiometry, thermodynamics, and electrochemistry to the chemistry of the main group elements.

The main group or A-Group elements occupy an important place in the world of chemistry. Eight of the 10 most abundant elements on the earth are in these groups. Likewise, the top 10 chemicals produced by the U.S. chemical industry are all main group elements or their compounds.

Because main group elements and their compounds are economically important—and because they have interesting chemistries—we devote this chapter to a brief survey of these elements.

### OWL

Sign in to OWL at **www.cengage.com/owl** to view tutorials and simulations, develop problem-solving skills, and complete online homework assigned by your professor.

## 21.1   Element Abundances

The abundance of the first 18 elements in the solar system is plotted against their atomic numbers in Figure 21.1. Hydrogen and helium are the most abundant by a wide margin because most of the mass of the solar system resides in the sun, and these elements are the sun's primary components. Lithium, beryllium, and boron

### go Chemistry

Download mini lecture videos for key concept review and exam prep from OWL or purchase them from **www.cengagebrain.com**

**FIGURE 21.1** Abundance of elements 1–18 in the solar system. Li, Be, and B have relatively low abundances because they are circumvented when elements are made in stars. The common elements such as C, O, and Ne are made in stars by the accretion of alpha particles (helium nuclei). Helium has an atomic number of 2. If three He atoms combine, they produce an atom with atomic number 6 (carbon). Adding yet another He atom gives an atom with atomic number 8 (oxygen), and so on. (Notice that the vertical axis uses a logarithmic scale. This means, for example, there are $10^{12}$ H atoms for every 100 B atoms.)

**Table 21.1 The 10 Most Abundant Elements in Earth's Crust**

| Rank | Element | Abundance (ppm)* |
|------|---------|------------------|
| 1 | Oxygen | 474,000 |
| 2 | Silicon | 277,000 |
| 3 | Aluminum | 82,000 |
| 4 | Iron | 56,300 |
| 5 | Calcium | 41,000 |
| 6 | Sodium | 23,600 |
| 7 | Magnesium | 23,300 |
| 8 | Potassium | 21,000 |
| 9 | Titanium | 5600 |
| 10 | Hydrogen | 1520 |

*ppm = g per 1000 kg. Most abundance data taken from J. Emsley: *The Elements*, New York, Oxford University Press, 3rd edition, 1998.

are low in abundance, but carbon's abundance is very high. From this point on, with the exception of iron and nickel, elemental abundances gradually decline as the atomic number increases.

Ten elements account for 99% of the aggregate mass of the earth's crust (Table 21.1), and oxygen, silicon, and aluminum represent more than 80% of this mass. Oxygen and nitrogen are the primary components of the atmosphere, and oxygen-containing water is highly abundant on the surface, underground, and as a vapor in the atmosphere. Many common minerals also contain these elements, including limestone ($CaCO_3$) and quartz or sand ($SiO_2$, ◀ Figure 2.8). Aluminum and silicon occur together in many minerals; among the more common ones are feldspar, granite, and clay.

## 21.2 The Periodic Table: A Guide to the Elements

The similarities in the properties of certain elements guided Mendeleev when he created the first periodic table (◀ page 59). He placed elements in groups based partly on the composition of their common compounds with oxygen and hydrogen (Table 21.2). We now understand that the elements are grouped according to the arrangements of their valence electrons.

Recall that the metallic character of the elements declines on moving from left to right in the periodic table. Elements in Group 1A, the alkali metals, are the most metallic elements in the periodic table. Elements on the far right are nonmetals, and in between are the metalloids. Metallic character also increases from the top of a group to the bottom. This is especially well illustrated by Group 4A. Carbon, at the top of the group, is a nonmetal; silicon and germanium are metalloids; and tin and lead are metals (Figure 21.2). The significance of metallic character in a discussion of the chemistry of the elements is readily apparent; metals typically form ionic compounds, whereas compounds composed only of nonmetals are covalent. Typically, ionic compounds are crystalline solids that have high melting points and conduct electricity in the molten state. Covalent compounds, on the other hand, can be gases, liquids, or solids and have low melting and boiling points.

### Valence Electrons

The $ns$ and $np$ electrons are the valence electrons for main group elements (where $n$ is the period in which the element is found) (◀ Section 7.3). The chemical behavior of an element is determined by the valence electrons.

When considering electronic structure, a useful reference point is the noble gases (Group 8A). Helium has an electron configuration of $1s^2$; the other noble gases have $ns^2np^6$ valence electron configurations. The dominant characteristic of the noble gases is their lack of reactivity. Indeed, the first two elements in the group do not form any compounds that can be isolated. The other four elements are now known to have limited chemistry, however, and the discovery of xenon compounds in the 1960s ranks as one of the most interesting developments in modern chemistry.

### Ionic Compounds of Main Group Elements

Ions of main group elements having filled $s$ and $p$ subshells are common—justifying the often-seen statement that elements react in ways that achieve a "noble gas configuration." The elements in Groups 1A and 2A form 1+ and 2+ ions with electron

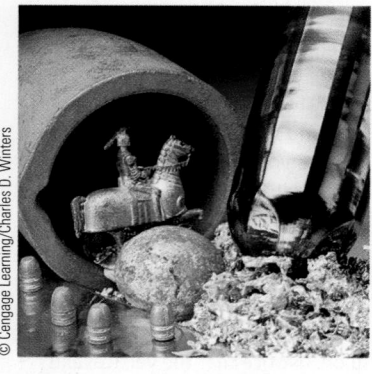

**FIGURE 21.2 Group 4A elements.** A nonmetal, carbon (graphite crucible); a metalloid, silicon (round, lustrous bar); and metals tin (chips of metal) and lead (a bullet, a toy, and a sphere).

**Table 21.2 Similarities within Periodic Groups***

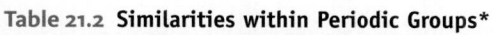

| Group | 1A | 2A | 3A | 4A | 5A | 6A | 7A |
|-------|----|----|----|----|----|----|----|
| Common oxide | $M_2O$ | $MO$ | $M_2O_3$ | $EO_2$ | $E_4O_{10}$ | $EO_3$ | $E_2O_7$ |
| Common hydride | $MH$ | $MH_2$ | $MH_3$ | $EH_4$ | $EH_3$ | $EH_2$ | $EH$ |
| Highest oxidation state | $+1$ | $+2$ | $+3$ | $+4$ | $+5$ | $+6$ | $+7$ |
| Common oxoanion | | | $BO_3^{3-}$ | $CO_3^{2-}$ | $NO_3^-$ | $SO_4^{2-}$ | $ClO_4^-$ |
| | | | | $SiO_4^{4-}$ | $PO_4^{3-}$ | | |

*M denotes a metal and E denotes a nonmetal or metalloid.

configurations that are the same as those for the previous noble gases. All common compounds of these elements (e.g., NaCl, CaCO₃) are ionic. The metallic elements in Group 3A (aluminum, gallium, indium, and thallium, but not the metalloid boron) form compounds containing 3+ ions.

Elements of Groups 6A and 7A can achieve a noble gas configuration by adding electrons. The Group 7A elements (halogens) form anions with a 1− charge (the halide ions, $F^-$, $Cl^-$, $Br^-$, $I^-$), and the Group 6A elements form anions with a 2− charge ($O^{2-}$, $S^{2-}$, $Se^{2-}$, $Te^{2-}$). In Group 5A chemistry, 3− ions with a noble gas configuration (such as the nitride ion, $N^{3-}$) are also known. The energy required to form highly charged anions is large, however, which means that other types of chemical behavior will usually take precedence.

## EXAMPLE 21.1 Reactions of Group 1A–3A Elements

**Problem** Give the formula and name for the product in each of the following reactions. Write a balanced chemical equation for the reaction.

(a) $Ca(s) + S_8(s)$

(b) $Rb(s) + I_2(s)$

(c) lithium and chlorine

(d) aluminum and oxygen

**What Do You Know?** The reactions listed are between metals in periodic groups 1A, 2A, and 3A and nonmetals in periodic groups 6A and 7A. The products formed will be ionic compounds made up of cations formed from metals by loss of electrons and anions formed from nonmetals by the gain of electrons. Remember that equations must be balanced.

**Strategy** Predictions are based on the assumption that ions are formed with the electron configuration of the nearest noble gas. Group 1A elements form 1+ ions; Group 2A elements form 2+ ions; and metals in Group 3A form 3+ ions. In their reactions with metals, halogen atoms typically add a single electron to give anions with a 1− charge; Group 6A elements add two electrons to form anions with a 2− charge. For names of products, refer to the nomenclature discussion on page 75.

**Solution**

| Balanced Equation | Product Name |
|---|---|
| (a) $8 Ca(s) + S_8(s) \rightarrow 8 CaS(s)$ | Calcium sulfide |
| (b) $2 Rb(s) + I_2(s) \rightarrow 2 RbI(s)$ | Rubidium iodide |
| (c) $2 Li(s) + Cl_2(g) \rightarrow 2 LiCl(s)$ | Lithium chloride |
| (d) $4 Al(s) + 3 O_2(g) \rightarrow 2 Al_2O_3(s)$ | Aluminum oxide |

**Think about Your Answer** It will be useful to review the formulas and names of common ions. These were given earlier in the text (Section 2.7).

**Check Your Understanding**
Write balanced chemical equations for the reactions forming the following compounds from the elements.

(a) NaBr    (b) CaSe    (c) PbO    (d) AlCl₃

## Molecular Compounds of Main Group Elements

Many avenues of reactivity are open to nonmetallic main group elements. Reactions with metals generally result in formation of ionic compounds, whereas compounds containing only metalloids and nonmetallic elements are generally molecular in nature.

Molecular compounds are encountered with the Group 3A element boron (Figure 21.3), and the chemistry of carbon in Group 4A is dominated by molecular

**FIGURE 21.3 Boron halides.** Liquid BBr₃ (left) and solid BI₃ (right). Formed from a metalloid and a nonmetal, both are molecular compounds. Both are sealed in glass ampules to prevent these boron compounds from reacting with H₂O in the air.

© Cengage Learning/Charles D. Winters

**Table 21.3 Fluorine Compounds Formed by Main Group Elements**

| Group | Compound | Bonding |
|-------|----------|---------|
| 1A | NaF | Ionic |
| 2A | $MgF_2$ | Ionic |
| 3A | $AlF_3$ | Ionic |
| 4A | $SiF_4$ | Covalent |
| 5A | $PF_5$ | Covalent |
| 6A | $SF_6$ | Covalent |
| 7A | $IF_7$ | Covalent |
| 8A | $XeF_4$ | Covalent |

compounds with covalent bonds (◀ Chapters 8 and 10). Similarly, nitrogen chemistry is dominated by molecular compounds. Consider ammonia, $NH_3$; the various nitrogen oxides (such as "laughing gas," $N_2O$); and nitric acid, $HNO_3$. In each of these species, nitrogen bonds covalently to another nonmetallic element. Also in Group 5A, phosphorus reacts with chlorine to produce the molecular compound $PCl_3$ (◀ page 111).

The valence electron configuration of an element determines the composition of its molecular compounds. Involving all the valence electrons in the formation of a compound is a frequent occurrence in main group element chemistry. We should not be surprised to discover compounds in which the central element has the highest possible oxidation number (such as P in $PF_5$). The highest oxidation number is readily predictable: it equals the group number. Thus, the highest (and only) oxidation number of sodium in its compounds is +1; the highest oxidation number of C is +4; and the highest oxidation number of phosphorus is +5 (Tables 21.2 and 21.3).

## EXAMPLE 21.2     Predicting Formulas for Compounds of Main Group Elements

**Problem** Predict the formula for each of the following:

(a)   The product of the reaction between germanium and excess oxygen

(b)   The product of the reaction of arsenic and excess fluorine

(c)   A compound formed from phosphorus and excess chlorine

(d)   The fully deprotonated anion of selenic acid

**What Do You Know?** You know the symbol and location of each of the elements in the periodic table.

**Strategy** You can predict that in each reaction the element bonded to the halogen or oxygen in the product will achieve its most positive oxidation number, a value equal to the number of its periodic group.

**Solution**

(a)   The Group 4A element germanium should have a maximum oxidation number of +4. Thus, its oxide has the formula $GeO_2$.

(b)   Arsenic, in Group 5A, reacts vigorously with fluorine to form $AsF_5$, in which arsenic has an oxidation number of +5.

(c)   $PCl_5$ is formed when the Group 5A element phosphorus reacts with excess chlorine.

(d)   The chemistries of S and Se are similar. Sulfur, in Group 6A, has a maximum oxidation number of +6, so it forms $SO_3$ and sulfuric acid, $H_2SO_4$. Selenium, also in Group 6A, has analogous chemistry, forming $SeO_3$ and selenic acid, $H_2SeO_4$. The fully deprotonated anion of this acid is the selenate ion, $SeO_4^{2-}$.

**Think about Your Answer** Notice that in several questions the use of excess oxidizing agent was specified. This is important because, for most of the nonmetals, several different products were possible. For example, the oxidation of carbon can produce either $CO_2$ or CO depending on whether there is an excess or a deficiency of oxygen. You will learn more about this in later sections of this chapter.

**Check Your Understanding**

Write the formula for each of the following:

(a)   hydrogen telluride

(b)   sodium arsenate

(c)   selenium hexachloride

(d)   perbromic acid

There are many similarities among elements in the same periodic table group. This means you can use compounds of more common elements as examples when you encounter compounds of elements with which you are not familiar. For example, water, $H_2O$, is the simplest hydrogen compound of oxygen. You can reasonably expect the hydrogen compounds of other Group 6A elements to be $H_2S$, $H_2Se$, and $H_2Te$; all are well known.

## EXAMPLE 21.3    Predicting Formulas

**Problem** Predict the formula for each of the following:

(a)  A compound of hydrogen and phosphorus

(b)  The hypobromite ion

(c)  Germane (the simplest hydrogen compound of germanium)

(d)  Two oxides of tellurium

**What Do You Know?** We expect the elements in a periodic group to behave similarly in their chemistry, in most instances. Thus, we can use known examples from the more common elements found early in the periodic table and extrapolate to predict the behavior of the less common elements found in the same group.

**Strategy** Recall as examples some of the compounds of lighter elements in a group, and then assume other elements in that group will form analogous compounds.

**Solution**

(a)  Phosphine, $PH_3$, has a composition analogous to ammonia, $NH_3$.

(b)  Hypobromite ion, $BrO^-$, is similar to the hypochlorite ion, $ClO^-$, the anion of hypochlorous acid (HClO).

(c)  $GeH_4$ is analogous to $CH_4$ and $SiH_4$, other Group 4A hydrogen compounds.

(d)  Te and S are in Group 6A. $TeO_2$ and $TeO_3$ are analogs of the oxides of sulfur, $SO_2$ and $SO_3$.

**Think about Your Answer** Keep in mind that there can be differences between elements within a periodic group. One difference is that second-period elements generally obey the octet rule, whereas in the third period and below, compounds with expanded octets can form (Section 8.5). For example, in reactions with fluorine, nitrogen forms $NF_3$ whereas phosphorus forms both $PF_3$ and $PF_5$.

**Check Your Understanding**

Identify a compound or ion based on a second-period element that has a formula and Lewis structure analogous to each of the following:

(a)  $PH_4^+$             (b)  $S_2^{2-}$             (c)  $P_2H_4$             (d)  $PF_3$

## EXAMPLE 21.4    Recognizing Incorrect Formulas

**Problem** One formula is incorrect in each of the following groups. Pick out the incorrect formula, and indicate why it is incorrect.

(a)  $CsSO_4$, KCl, $NaNO_3$, $Li_2O$

(b)  MgO, $CaI_2$, $BaPO_4$, $CaCO_3$

(c)  CO, $CO_2$, $CO_3$

(d)  $PF_5$, $PF_4^+$, $PF_7$, $PF_6^-$

**What Do You Know?** One formula in each set of four is wrong. You can determine which by applying the rules for oxidation states set forth in this section.

**Strategy** Look for errors such as incorrect charges on ions or an oxidation number exceeding the maximum possible for the periodic group.

**Solution**

(a)  CsSO$_4$. Sulfate ion has a 2− charge, so this formula would require a Cs$^{2+}$ ion. Cesium, in Group 1A, forms only 1+ ions. The formula of cesium sulfate is Cs$_2$SO$_4$.

(b)  BaPO$_4$. This formula implies a Ba$^{3+}$ ion (because the phosphate anion is PO$_4^{3-}$). The cation charge does not equal the group number. The formula of barium phosphate is Ba$_3$(PO$_4$)$_2$.

(c)  CO$_3$. Given that O has an oxidation number of −2, carbon would have to have an oxidation number of +6. Carbon is in Group 4A, however, and can have a maximum oxidation number of +4.

(d)  PF$_7$. The formula implies P has an oxidation state of +7, whereas +5 is expected for the maximum possible P oxidation state.

**Think about Your Answer**  There are a lot of facts to learn in chemistry. Fortunately, many can be organized in ways that make learning easier. Using the periodic table to predict the chemistry of each element, and recognizing similarities among elements in groups, is one of the essential aspects of chemistry. This has been the goal of this section of the chapter.

**Check Your Understanding**

Explain why compounds with the following formulas would not be expected to exist: Na$_2$Cl, CaCH$_3$CO$_2$, Mg$_2$O.

---

**REVIEW & CHECK FOR SECTION 21.2**

1.  Which of the following formulas is incorrect?

    (a)  CaH$_2$        (b)  CaI$_2$        (c)  CaS        (d)  Ca$_2$O$_3$

2.  What is the name of the product of the reaction between elemental phosphorus and excess oxygen, P$_4$O$_{10}$?

    (a)  phosphorus oxide              (c)  phosphoric acid

    (b)  phosphorus decaoxide          (d)  tetraphosphorus decaoxide

3.  Like sulfur, selenium forms compounds in several different oxidation states. Which of the following is not likely to be an oxidation state of selenium in its compounds?

    (a)  −2        (b)  +3        (c)  +6        (d)  +4

4.  What is the highest oxidation state that antimony can have in its compounds?

    (a)  0        (b)  +1        (c)  +3        (d)  +5

---

## 21.3  Hydrogen

### Chemical and Physical Properties of Hydrogen

Hydrogen has three isotopes, two of them stable (protium and deuterium) and one radioactive (tritium).

**Isotopes of Hydrogen**

| Isotope Mass (u) | Symbol | Name |
|---|---|---|
| 1.0078 | $^1$H (H) | Hydrogen (protium) |
| 2.0141 | $^2$H (D) | Deuterium |
| 3.0160 | $^3$H (T) | Tritium |

Of the three isotopes, only H and D are found in nature in significant quantities. Tritium, which is produced by cosmic ray bombardment of nitrogen in the atmosphere, is found to the extent of 1 atom per 10$^{18}$ atoms of ordinary hydrogen. Tritium has a half-life of 12.26 years.

## A CLOSER LOOK

# Hydrogen, Helium, and Balloons

In 1783, Jacques Charles first used hydrogen to fill a balloon large enough to float above the French countryside (◄ page 518). In World War I, hydrogen-filled observation balloons were used. The Graf Zeppelin, a passenger-carrying dirigible built in Germany in 1928, was also filled with hydrogen. It carried more than 13,000 people between Germany and the United States until 1937, when it was replaced by the Hindenburg. The Hindenburg was designed to be filled with helium. At that time, World War II was approaching, and the United States, which has much of the world's supply of helium, would not sell the gas to Germany. As a consequence, the Hindenburg had to use hydrogen. The Hindenburg exploded and burned when landing in Lakehurst, New Jersey, in May 1937. Of the 62 people on board, only about half escaped uninjured. As a result of this disaster, hydrogen has acquired a reputation as being a very dangerous substance. Actually, it is as safe to handle as many other fuels.

**The Hindenburg.** This hydrogen-filled dirigible crashed in Lakehurst, New Jersey, in May 1937. Some have speculated that the aluminum paint coating the skin of the dirigible was involved in sparking the fire.

Mary Evans Picture Library/Photo Researchers, Inc.

---

Under standard conditions, hydrogen is a colorless gas. Its very low boiling point, 20.7 K, reflects its nonpolar character and low molar mass. As the least dense gas known, it is ideal for filling lighter-than-air craft.

Deuterium compounds have been the subject of much research. One important observation is that, because D has twice the mass of H, reactions involving D atom transfer are slightly slower than those involving H atoms. This knowledge led to a way to produce $D_2O$ or "heavy water." Hydrogen can be produced, albeit expensively, by electrolysis of water (Figure 21.4).

$$2 \, H_2O(\ell) + \text{electrical energy} \rightarrow 2 \, H_2(g) + O_2(g)$$

Any sample of natural water always contains a tiny concentration of $D_2O$. When electrolyzed, $H_2O$ is electrolyzed more rapidly than $D_2O$. Thus, as the electrolysis proceeds, the liquid remaining is enriched in $D_2O$. Repeating this process many times will eventually give pure $D_2O$, often called "heavy water." Large amounts of $D_2O$ are now produced because this compound is used as a moderator in some nuclear reactors that are used for power generation.

Hydrogen combines chemically with virtually every other element, except the noble gases. There are three different types of binary hydrogen-containing compounds.

*Ionic metal hydrides* are formed in the reaction of $H_2$ with a Group 1A or 2A metal.

$$2 \, Na(s) + H_2(g) \rightarrow 2 \, NaH(s)$$

$$Ca(s) + H_2(g) \rightarrow CaH_2(s)$$

These compounds contain the hydride ion, $H^-$, in which hydrogen has a $-1$ oxidation number.

*Molecular compounds* (such as $H_2O$, HF, and $NH_3$) are generally formed by direct combination of hydrogen with nonmetallic elements (Figure 21.5). The oxidation number of the hydrogen atom in these compounds is $+1$, but covalent bonds to hydrogen are the rule.

$$N_2(g) + 3 \, H_2(g) \rightarrow 2 \, NH_3(g)$$

$$F_2(g) + H_2(g) \rightarrow 2 \, HF(g)$$

© Cengage Learning/Charles D. Winters

**FIGURE 21.4 Electrolysis of water.** Electrolysis of water (containing dilute $H_2SO_4$ as an electrolyte) gives $O_2$ *(left)* and $H_2$ *(right)*.

**FIGURE 21.5 The reaction of H₂ and Br₂.** Hydrogen gas burns in an atmosphere of bromine vapor to give hydrogen bromide.

Hydrogen is absorbed by many metals to form *interstitial hydrides,* the third general class of hydrogen compounds. This name refers to the structures of these species, in which the hydrogen atoms reside in the spaces between the metal atoms (called *interstices*) in the crystal lattice. Palladium metal, for example, can soak up 1000 times its volume of hydrogen (at STP). Most interstitial hydrides are non-stoichiometric; that is, the ratio of metal and hydrogen is not a whole number. When interstitial metal hydrides are heated, H₂ is driven out. This phenomenon allows these materials to store H₂, just as a sponge can store water. It suggests one way to store hydrogen for use in automobiles (◀ page 912).

## Preparation of Hydrogen

About 300 billion liters (STP) of hydrogen gas are produced annually worldwide, and virtually all is used immediately in the manufacture of ammonia (▶ Section 21.8), methanol (◀ Section 10.4), or other chemicals.

Some hydrogen is made from coal and steam, a reaction that has been used for more than 100 years.

$$C(s) + H_2O(g) \longrightarrow \underbrace{H_2(g) + CO(g)}_{\text{water gas or synthesis gas}}$$

$$\Delta_r H° = +131 \text{ kJ/mol-rxn}$$

The reaction is carried out by injecting water into a bed of red-hot coke. The mixture of gases produced, called *water gas* or *synthesis gas,* was used until about 1950 as a fuel for cooking, heating, and lighting. However, it has serious drawbacks. It produces only about half as much heat as an equal amount of methane does, and the flame is nearly invisible. Moreover, because it contains carbon monoxide, water gas is toxic.

The largest quantity of hydrogen is now produced by the *catalytic steam reformation of hydrocarbons* such as methane in natural gas (Figure 21.6). Methane reacts with steam at high temperature to give H₂ and CO.

$$CH_4(g) + H_2O(g) \rightarrow 3 H_2(g) + CO(g) \qquad \Delta_r H° = +206 \text{ kJ/mol-rxn}$$

The reaction is rapid at 900–1000 °C and goes nearly to completion. More hydrogen can be obtained in a second step in which the CO formed in the first step reacts with more water. This so-called *water gas shift reaction* is run at 400–500 °C and is slightly exothermic.

$$H_2O(g) + CO(g) \rightarrow H_2(g) + CO_2(g) \qquad \Delta_r H° = -41 \text{ kJ/mol-rxn}$$

The CO₂ formed in the process is removed by reaction with CaO (to give solid CaCO₃), leaving fairly pure hydrogen.

Perhaps the cleanest way to make hydrogen on a relatively large scale is the electrolysis of water (Figure 21.4). This approach provides not only hydrogen gas but also high-purity O₂. Because electricity is quite expensive, however, this method is not generally used commercially.

Table 21.4 and Figure 21.7 give examples of reactions used to produce H₂ gas in the laboratory. The most often used method is the reaction of a metal with an acid. Alternatively, the reaction of aluminum with aqueous NaOH (Figure 21.7b) also generates hydrogen. During World War II, this reaction was used to obtain hydrogen to inflate small balloons for weather observation and to raise radio antennas. Metallic aluminum was plentiful at the time because it came from damaged aircraft.

The combination of a metal hydride and water (Figure 21.7c) is an efficient but expensive way to synthesize H₂ in the laboratory. The reaction is commonly used in laboratories to dry organic solvents because the metal hydride reacts with traces of water present in the solvent.

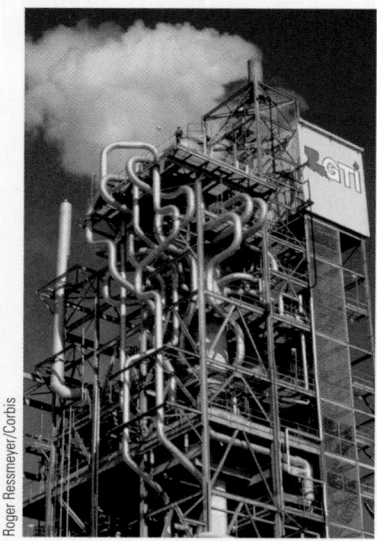

**FIGURE 21.6 Production of water gas.** Water gas, also called *synthesis gas,* is a mixture of CO and H₂. It is produced by treating coal, coke, or a hydrocarbon like methane with steam at high temperatures in plants such as that pictured here. Methane has the advantage that it gives more total H₂ per gram than other hydrocarbons, and the ratio of the by-product CO₂ to H₂ is lower.

**Table 21.4  Methods for Preparing H$_2$ in the Laboratory**

1.  Metal + Acid → metal salt + H$_2$

    Mg(s) + 2 HCl(aq) → MgCl$_2$(aq) + H$_2$(g)

2.  Metal + H$_2$O → metal hydroxide or oxide + H$_2$

    2 Na(s) + 2 H$_2$O($\ell$) → 2 NaOH(aq) + H$_2$(g)

    2 Fe(s) + 3 H$_2$O($\ell$) → Fe$_2$O$_3$(s) + 3 H$_2$(g)

    2 Al(s) + 2 KOH(aq) + 6 H$_2$O($\ell$) → 2 K[Al(OH)$_4$](aq) + 3 H$_2$(g)

3.  Metal hydride + H$_2$O → metal hydroxide + H$_2$

    CaH$_2$(s) + 2 H$_2$O($\ell$) → Ca(OH)$_2$(s) + 2 H$_2$(g)

**REVIEW & CHECK FOR SECTION 21.3**

1.  Which of the following elements does not react with hydrogen?

    (a) neon          (b) nitrogen          (c) potassium          (d) fluorine

2.  Which of the methods below is the most suitable for the preparation of large quantities of hydrogen (such as the amounts needed as a reagent for the synthesis of compounds such as ammonia)?

    (a)  Electrolysis of water

    (b)  The reaction of metal hydrides with water

    (c)  The high temperature reaction of methane and water

    (d)  The reaction of zinc and hydrochloric acid

## 21.4  The Alkali Metals, Group 1A

Sodium and potassium are, respectively, the sixth and eighth most abundant elements in the earth's crust by mass. In contrast, lithium is relatively rare, as are rubidium and cesium. Only traces of radioactive francium occur in nature. Its longest-lived isotope ($^{223}$Fr) has a half-life of only 22 minutes.

The Group 1A elements are metals, and all are highly reactive with oxygen, water, and other oxidizing agents (◄ Figure 7.13, page 324). In all cases, compounds

**Group 1A**
*Alkali metals*

| |
|---|
| Lithium<br>3<br>**Li**<br>20 ppm |
| Sodium<br>11<br>**Na**<br>23,600 ppm |
| Potassium<br>19<br>**K**<br>21,000 ppm |
| Rubidium<br>37<br>**Rb**<br>90 ppm |
| Cesium<br>55<br>**Cs**<br>0.0003 ppm |
| Francium<br>87<br>**Fr**<br>trace |

*Element abundances are in* **parts per million** *in the earth's crust.*

**FIGURE 21.7**
**Producing hydrogen gas.**

**(a)** The reaction of magnesium and acid. The products are hydrogen gas and a magnesium salt.

**(b)** The reaction of aluminum and NaOH. The products of this reaction are hydrogen gas and a solution of Na[Al(OH)$_4$].

**(c)** The reaction of CaH$_2$ and water. The products are hydrogen gas and Ca(OH)$_2$.

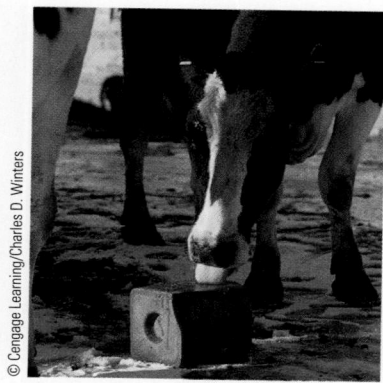

**FIGURE 21.8 The importance of salt.** All animals, including humans, need a certain amount of salt in their diet. Sodium ions are important in maintaining electrolyte balance and in regulating osmotic pressure. For an interesting account of the importance of salt in society, culture, history, and economy, see *Salt, A World History*, by M. Kurlansky, New York, Penguin Books, 2003.

of the Group 1A metals contain the element as a 1+ ion. The free metal is never found in nature. Most sodium and potassium compounds are water-soluble (◄ solubility guidelines, Figure 3.10), so it is not surprising that sodium and potassium compounds are found either in the oceans or in underground deposits that are the residue of ancient seas. To a much smaller extent, these elements are also found in minerals, such as Chile saltpeter ($NaNO_3$).

Despite the fact that sodium is only slightly more abundant than potassium on the earth, sea water contains significantly more sodium than potassium (2.8% NaCl versus 0.8% KCl). Why the great difference? Most compounds of both elements are water-soluble, so why didn't rain dissolve Na- and K-containing minerals over the centuries and carry them down to the sea, so that they appear in the same proportions in the oceans as on land? The answer lies in the fact that potassium is an important factor in plant growth. Most plants contain four to six times as much combined potassium as sodium. Thus, most of the potassium ions in groundwater from dissolved minerals are taken up preferentially by plants, whereas sodium salts continue on to the oceans. (Because plants require potassium, commercial fertilizers usually contain a significant amount of potassium salts.)

Some NaCl is essential in the diet of humans and other animals because many biological functions are controlled by the concentrations of $Na^+$ and $Cl^-$ ions (Figure 21.8). The fact that salt has long been recognized as important is evident in surprising ways. For example, we are paid a "salary" for work done. This word is derived from the Latin *salarium*, which meant "salt money" because Roman soldiers were paid in salt.

## Preparation of Sodium and Potassium

Sodium is produced by reducing sodium ions in sodium salts. However, because common chemical reducing agents are not powerful enough to convert sodium ions to sodium metal, the metal is usually prepared by electrolysis.

The English chemist Sir Humphry Davy first isolated sodium in 1807 by the electrolysis of molten sodium carbonate. However, the element remained a laboratory curiosity until 1824, when it was found sodium could be used to reduce aluminum chloride to aluminum metal. At that time, metallic aluminum was rare and very valuable, so this discovery inspired considerable interest in manufacturing sodium. By 1886, a practical method of sodium production had been devised (the reduction of NaOH with carbon). Unfortunately for sodium producers, in this same year Charles Hall and Paul Heroult invented the electrolytic method for aluminum production (► page 981), thereby eliminating this market for sodium.

Sodium is currently produced by the electrolysis of molten NaCl (◄ Section 20.7). The Downs cell for the electrolysis of molten NaCl operates at 7 to 8 V with currents of 25,000 to 40,000 amps (Figure 21.9). The cell is filled with a mixture of dry NaCl, $CaCl_2$, and $BaCl_2$. Adding other salts to NaCl lowers the melting point from that of pure NaCl (800.7 °C) to about 600 °C. [Recall that solutions have lower melting points than pure solvents (Chapter 14).] Sodium is produced at a copper or iron cathode that surrounds a circular graphite anode. Directly over the cathode is an inverted trough in which the low-density, molten sodium (melting point, 97.8 °C) collects. Chlorine, a valuable by-product, collects at the anode.

Potassium can also be made by electrolysis. Molten potassium is soluble in molten KCl, however, making separation of the metal difficult. The preferred method for preparation of potassium uses the reaction of sodium vapor with molten KCl, with potassium being continually removed from the equilibrium mixture.

$$Na(g) + KCl(\ell) \rightleftharpoons K(g) + NaCl(\ell)$$

## Properties of Sodium and Potassium

Sodium and potassium are silvery metals that are soft and easily cut with a knife (◄ Figure 2.6). They are just a bit less dense than water. Their melting points are quite low, 97.8 °C for sodium and 63.7 °C for potassium.

● **Alkali Metals React with Water— Thermodynamics and Kinetics** The alkali metals all react vigorously with water, and it is easily observed that the violence of the reaction increases with atomic number. This seems counter to the argument presented in *A Closer Look* (page 972) that lithium is the best reducing agent. However, the reducing ability of a metal is a thermodynamic property, whereas the violence of the reaction is mainly a consequence of reaction rate.

**FIGURE 21.9  A Downs cell for preparing sodium.** A circular iron cathode is separated from the graphite anode by an iron screen. At the temperature of the electrolysis, about 600 °C, sodium is a liquid. It rises to the top and is drawn off periodically. Chlorine gas is produced at the anode and collected inside the inverted cone in the center of the cell.

All of the alkali metals are highly reactive. When exposed to moist air, the metal surface quickly becomes coated with a film of oxide or hydroxide. Consequently, the metals must be stored in a way that avoids contact with air, typically by placing them in kerosene or mineral oil.

The high reactivity of Group 1A metals is exemplified by their reaction with water, which generates an aqueous solution of the metal hydroxide and hydrogen gas (◀ Figure 7.13, page 324),

$$2\ Na(s) + 2\ H_2O(\ell) \rightarrow 2\ Na^+(aq) + 2\ OH^-(aq) + H_2(g)$$

and their reaction with any of the halogens to yield a metal halide (◀ Figure 1.2),

$$2\ Na(s) + Cl_2(g) \rightarrow 2\ NaCl(s)$$

$$2\ K(s) + Br_2(\ell) \rightarrow 2\ KBr(s)$$

Chemistry often produces surprises. Group 1A metal oxides, $M_2O$, are known, but they are not the principal products of reactions between the Group 1A elements and oxygen. Instead, the primary product of the reaction of sodium and oxygen is sodium *peroxide*, $Na_2O_2$, whereas the principal product from the reaction of potassium and oxygen is $KO_2$, potassium *superoxide*.

$$2\ Na(s) + O_2(g) \rightarrow Na_2O_2(s)$$

$$K(s) + O_2(g) \rightarrow KO_2(s)$$

Both $Na_2O_2$ and $KO_2$ are ionic compounds. The Group 1A cation is paired with either the peroxide ion ($O_2^{2-}$) or the superoxide ion ($O_2^-$). These compounds are not merely laboratory curiosities. They are used in oxygen-generation devices in places where people are confined, such as submarines, aircraft, and spacecraft, or when an emergency supply is needed. When a person breathes, 0.82 L of $CO_2$ is exhaled for every 1 L of $O_2$ inhaled. Thus, a requirement of an $O_2$-generation system is that it should produce a larger volume of $O_2$ than the volume of $CO_2$ taken in. This requirement is met with superoxides (Figure 21.10). With $KO_2$ the reaction is

$$4\ KO_2(s) + 2\ CO_2(g) \rightarrow 2\ K_2CO_3(s) + 3\ O_2(g)$$

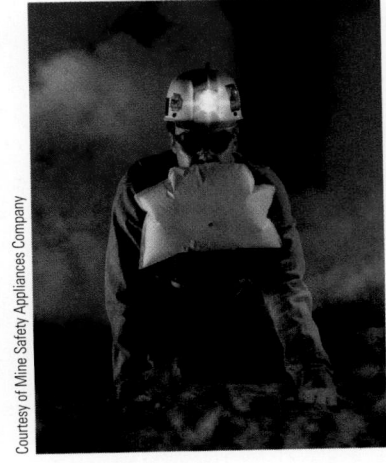

**FIGURE 21.10  A closed-circuit breathing apparatus that generates its own oxygen.** One source of oxygen is potassium superoxide ($KO_2$). Both carbon dioxide and moisture exhaled by the wearer into the breathing tube react with the $KO_2$ to generate oxygen. Because the rate of the chemical reaction is determined by the quantity of moisture and carbon dioxide exhaled, the production of oxygen is regulated automatically. With each exhalation, more oxygen is produced by volume than is required by the user.

# The Reducing Ability of the Alkali Metals

The uses of the Group 1A metals depend on their reducing ability. The values of $E°$ reveal that Li is the best reducing agent in the group, whereas Na is the poorest; the remainder of these metals have roughly comparable reducing abilities.

**Reduction Potential**

| Element | $E°$ (V) |
|---|---|
| $Li^+(aq) + e^- \rightarrow Li(s)$ | −3.045 |
| $Na^+(aq) + e^- \rightarrow Na(s)$ | −2.714 |
| $K^+(aq) + e^- \rightarrow K(s)$ | −2.925 |
| $Rb^+(aq) + e^- \rightarrow Rb(s)$ | −2.925 |
| $Cs^+(aq) + e^- \rightarrow Cs(s)$ | −2.92 |

Analysis of $E°$ is a thermodynamic problem, and to understand it better we can break the process of metal oxidation, $M(s) \rightarrow M^+(aq) + e^-$, into a series of steps. Here, we imagine that the metal sublimes to vapor, an electron is removed to form the gaseous cation, and the cation is hydrated. The first two steps require energy, but the last is exothermic. From Hess's law (page 230), we

$$M(g) \xrightarrow{IE \ (ionization\ energy)} M^+(g) + e^-$$

$$\Delta_{sub}H \uparrow \qquad \qquad \downarrow \Delta_{hyd}H$$

$$M(s) \xrightarrow{\Delta_r H_{net}} M^+(aq) + e^-$$

know that the overall energy change should be

$$\Delta_r H_{net} = \Delta_{sub}H + IE + \Delta_{hyd}H$$

The element that is the best reducing agent should have the most negative (or least positive) value of $\Delta_r H$. Because it is exothermic, the hydration enthalpy serves to offset the energy of the endothermic steps ($\Delta_{sub}H$ and $IE$). Thus, a more exothermic hydration enthalpy leads to a more negative $\Delta_r H$. For the alkali metals, enthalpies of hydration range from −506 kJ/mol for $Li^+$ to −180 kJ/mol for $Cs^+$. The fact that $\Delta_{hyd}H$ is so much more exothermic for $Li^+$ than for $Cs^+$ largely

accounts for the difference in reducing ability.

While this analysis of the problem gives us a reasonable explanation for the great reducing ability of lithium, recall that $E°$ is directly related to $\Delta_r G°$ and not to $\Delta H°$. However, $\Delta_r G°$ is largely determined by $\Delta_r H°$ for these reactions, so it is possible to relate variations in $E°$ to variations in $\Delta_r H°$.

**Potassium is a very good reducing agent and reacts vigorously with water.**

## Important Lithium, Sodium, and Potassium Compounds

Electrolysis of aqueous sodium chloride (*brine*) is the basis of one of the largest chemical industries in the United States.

$$2 \ NaCl(aq) + 2 \ H_2O(\ell) \rightarrow Cl_2(g) + 2 \ NaOH(aq) + H_2(g)$$

Two of the products from this process—chlorine and sodium hydroxide—give the industry its name: the *chlor-alkali industry*. More than 10 billion kilograms of $Cl_2$ and NaOH is produced annually in the United States.

Sodium carbonate, $Na_2CO_3$, is another commercially important compound of sodium. It is also known by two common names, *soda ash* and *washing soda*. In the past, it was largely manufactured by combining NaCl, ammonia, and $CO_2$ in the *Solvay process* (which remains the method of choice in many countries). In the United States, however, sodium carbonate is obtained from naturally occurring deposits of the mineral *trona*, $Na_2CO_3 \cdot NaHCO_3 \cdot 2 \ H_2O$ (Figure 21.11).

The chlor-alkali process has long used electrolysis cells with mercury cathodes. However, because of the environmental dangers of mercury, this process is largely being phased out, and there is considerable interest in the manufacture of sodium hydroxide by other methods. One approach is a revival of the old "soda-lime process," which produces NaOH from inexpensive lime (CaO) and soda ash ($Na_2CO_3$).

$$Na_2CO_3(aq) + CaO(s) + H_2O(\ell) \rightarrow 2 \ NaOH(aq) + CaCO_3(s)$$

The insoluble calcium carbonate by-product is filtered off and then heated (calcining) to convert it to lime, which is recycled into the reaction system.

$$CaCO_3(s) \rightarrow CaO(s) + CO_2(g)$$

Sodium bicarbonate, $NaHCO_3$, also known as *baking soda*, is another common compound of sodium. Not only is $NaHCO_3$ used in cooking, but it is also added in

(a) *(above)* A mine in California. The mineral trona is taken from a mine 1600 feet deep.

(b) *(right)* Blocks of trona are cut from the face of the mine.

**FIGURE 21.11 Producing soda ash.** Trona mined in Wyoming and California is processed into soda ash ($Na_2CO_3$) and other sodium-based chemicals. Soda ash is the ninth most widely used chemical in the United States. Domestically, about half of all soda ash production is used in making glass. The remainder goes to make chemicals such as sodium silicate, sodium phosphate, and sodium cyanide. Some is also used to make detergents, in the pulp and paper industry, and in water treatment.

small amounts to table salt. NaCl is often contaminated with small amounts of $MgCl_2$. The magnesium salt is hygroscopic; that is, it picks water up from the air and, in doing so, causes the NaCl to clump. Adding $NaHCO_3$ converts $MgCl_2$ to magnesium carbonate, a nonhygroscopic salt.

$$MgCl_2(s) + 2\ NaHCO_3(s) \rightarrow MgCO_3(s) + 2\ NaCl(s) + H_2O(\ell) + CO_2(g)$$

Large deposits of sodium nitrate, $NaNO_3$, are found in Chile, which explains its common name of "Chile saltpeter." These deposits are thought to have formed by bacterial action on organisms in shallow seas. The initial product was ammonia, which was subsequently oxidized to nitrate ion; combination with sea salt led to sodium nitrate. Because nitrates in general, and alkali metal nitrates in particular, are highly water-soluble, deposits of $NaNO_3$ are found only in areas with very little rainfall.

Sodium nitrate is important because it can be converted to potassium nitrate by an exchange reaction.

$$NaNO_3(aq) + KCl(aq) \rightleftharpoons KNO_3(aq) + NaCl(s)$$

Equilibrium favors the products here because, of the four salts involved in this reaction, NaCl is least soluble in hot water. Sodium chloride precipitates, and the $KNO_3$ that remains in solution can be recovered by evaporating the water.

Potassium nitrate has been used for centuries as the oxidizing agent in gunpowder (page 251). A mixture of $KNO_3$, charcoal, and sulfur will react when ignited.

$$2\ KNO_3(s) + 4\ C(s) \rightarrow K_2CO_3(s) + 3\ CO(g) + N_2(g)$$

$$2\ KNO_3(s) + 2\ S(s) \rightarrow K_2SO_4(s) + SO_2(g) + N_2(g)$$

Notice that both reactions (which are doubtless more complex than those written here) produce gases. These gases propel the bullet from a gun or cause a firecracker to explode.

In the past several years lithium has become a significant commodity because of its use in lithium ion batteries. In fact, there is some concern that shortages of lithium will arise if the use of lithium ion batteries in cars becomes widespread (◄ page 911). Currently, most lithium is obtained from concentrated brines in Chile and Bolivia, from which $Li_2CO_3$ is extracted. There are also ores from which lithium can be obtained. Similar to the other alkali metals, lithium metal is obtained from its compounds by molten salt electrolysis.

● **Gunpowder** Gunpowder was developed well over 1000 years ago by the Chinese. One of the three ingredients is $KNO_3$, commonly called *saltpeter*. Although there are places in the world where it is prevalent and can be mined, for centuries it was obtained by mixing manure or human waste with wood ashes. Animal and human waste contain ammonia, which is converted by bacterial oxidation to nitrates. Wood ashes contain potash, potassium carbonate, the source of potassium in $KNO_3$. Sodium nitrate will also work in gunpowder, but it is hygroscopic and the powder is not effective when damp. See *Gunpowder* by J. Kelly, Basic Books, 2004.

Group **2A**
*Alkaline earths*

Beryllium
4
**Be**
2.6 ppm

Magnesium
12
**Mg**
23,300 ppm

Calcium
20
**Ca**
41,000 ppm

Strontium
38
**Sr**
370 ppm

Barium
56
**Ba**
500 ppm

Radium
88
**Ra**
$6 \times 10^{-7}$ ppm

*Element
abundances are in*
**parts per million**
*in the earth's crust.*

## 21.5    The Alkaline Earth Elements, Group 2A

The "earth" part of the name alkaline earth dates back to the days of medieval alchemy. To alchemists, any solid that did not melt and was not changed by fire into another substance was called an "earth." Compounds of the Group 2A elements, such as CaO, were alkaline according to experimental tests conducted by the alchemists: They had a bitter taste and neutralized acids. With very high melting points, these compounds were unaffected by fire.

Calcium and magnesium rank fifth and eighth, respectively, in abundance on the earth. Both elements form many commercially important compounds, and we shall focus our attention on these species.

Like the Group 1A elements, the Group 2A elements are very reactive, so they are found in nature as compounds. Unlike most of the compounds of the Group 1A metals, however, many compounds of the Group 2A elements have low water-solubility, which explains their occurrence in various minerals (Figure 21.12). Calcium minerals include limestone ($CaCO_3$), gypsum ($CaSO_4 \cdot 2 H_2O$), and fluorite ($CaF_2$). Magnesite ($MgCO_3$), talc or soapstone ($3 MgO \cdot 4 SiO_2 \cdot H_2O$), and asbestos ($3 MgO \cdot 4 SiO_2 \cdot 2 H_2O$) are common magnesium-containing minerals. The mineral dolomite, $MgCa(CO_3)_2$, contains both magnesium and calcium.

Limestone, a sedimentary rock, is found widely on the earth's surface. Many of these deposits contain the fossilized remains of marine life. Other forms of calcium carbonate include marble and Icelandic spar, the latter occurring as large, clear crystals with the interesting optical property of birefringence (Figure 21.12).

Limestone
$CaCO_3$

Gypsum
$CaSO_4 \cdot 2 H_2O$

Fluorite
$CaF_2$

Common minerals of Group 2A elements.

**Icelandic spar.** This mineral, one of a number of crystalline forms of $CaCO_3$, displays birefringence, a property in which a double image is formed when light passes through the crystal.

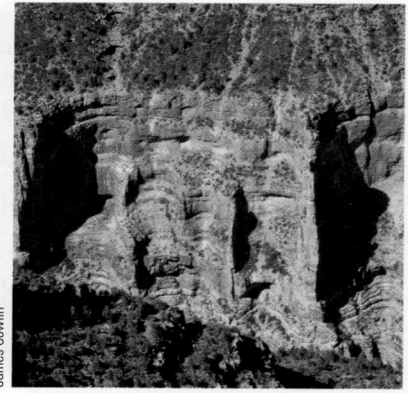

The walls of Arizona's Grand Canyon are largely limestone or dolomite.

**FIGURE 21.12 Various minerals containing calcium and magnesium.**

## Properties of Calcium and Magnesium

Calcium and magnesium are fairly high-melting, silvery metals. The chemical properties of these elements present few surprises. They are oxidized by a wide range of oxidizing agents to form ionic compounds that contain the $M^{2+}$ ion. For example, these elements combine with halogens to form $MX_2$, with oxygen or sulfur to form $MO$ or $MS$, and with water to form hydrogen and the metal hydroxide, $M(OH)_2$ (Figure 21.13). With acids, hydrogen is evolved (Figure 21.7), and a salt of the metal cation and the anion of the acid results.

## Metallurgy of Magnesium

Several hundred thousand tons of magnesium are produced annually, largely for use in lightweight alloys. (Magnesium has a very low density, $1.74$ g/cm³.) Most aluminum used today contains about 5% magnesium to improve its mechanical properties and to make it more resistant to corrosion. Other alloys having more magnesium than aluminum are used when a high strength-to-weight ratio is needed and when corrosion resistance is important, such as in aircraft and automotive parts and in lightweight tools.

Interestingly, magnesium-containing minerals are not the source of this element. Most magnesium is obtained from sea water, in which $Mg^{2+}$ ion is present in a concentration of about 0.05 M. To obtain magnesium metal, magnesium ions in sea water are first precipitated (Figure 21.14) as the relatively insoluble hydroxide [$K_{sp}$ for $Mg(OH)_2 = 5.6 \times 10^{-12}$]. Calcium hydroxide, the source of $OH^-$ in this reaction, is prepared in a sequence of reactions beginning with $CaCO_3$, which may be in the form of seashells. Heating $CaCO_3$ gives $CO_2$ and $CaO$, and addition of water to $CaO$ gives calcium hydroxide. When $Ca(OH)_2$ is added to sea water, $Mg(OH)_2$ precipitates:

$$Mg^{2+}(aq) + Ca(OH)_2(s) \rightleftharpoons Mg(OH)_2(s) + Ca^{2+}(aq)$$

Magnesium hydroxide is isolated by filtration and then converted to magnesium chloride by reaction with hydrochloric acid.

$$Mg(OH)_2(s) + 2\ HCl(aq) \rightarrow MgCl_2(aq) + 2\ H_2O(\ell)$$

After evaporating the water, anhydrous magnesium chloride remains. Solid $MgCl_2$ melts at 714 °C, and the molten salt is electrolyzed to give the metal and chlorine.

$$MgCl_2(\ell) \rightarrow Mg(s) + Cl_2(g)$$

**FIGURE 21.13 The reaction of calcium and warm water.** Hydrogen bubbles are seen rising from the metal surface. The other reaction product is $Ca(OH)_2$. The inset is a model of hexagonal close-packed calcium metal (◀ page 586).

© Cengage Learning/Charles D. Winters

**FIGURE 21.14 The process used to produce magnesium metal from the magnesium in sea water.**

## A CLOSER LOOK

# Alkaline Earth Metals and Biology

Plants and animals derive energy from the oxidation of a sugar, glucose, with oxygen. Plants are unique, however, in being able to synthesize glucose from $CO_2$ and $H_2O$ using sunlight as an energy source. This process is initiated by *chlorophyll*, a very large, magnesium-based molecule.

In your body, the alkaline earth metal ions $Mg^{2+}$ and $Ca^{2+}$ serve regulatory functions. Although the two metal ions are required by living systems, the other Group 2A elements are toxic. Beryllium compounds are carcinogenic, and soluble barium salts are poisons. You may be concerned if your physician asks you to drink a "barium cocktail" to check the condition of your digestive tract. Don't be afraid, because the "cocktail" contains very insoluble $BaSO_4$ ($K_{sp} = 1.1 \times 10^{-10}$), so it passes through your digestive tract without a significant amount being absorbed. Barium sulfate is opaque to x-rays, so its path through your organs appears on the developed x-ray image.

**A molecule of chlorophyll.** Magnesium is its central element.

Susan Leavines/Science Source/ Photo Researchers, Inc.

**X-ray of a gastrointestinal tract using $BaSO_4$ to make the organs visible.**

The calcium-containing compound *hydroxyapatite* is the main component of tooth enamel. Cavities in your teeth form when acids (such as soft drinks) decompose the weakly basic hydroxyapatite coating.

$$Ca_5(OH)(PO_4)_3(s) + 4\ H_3O^+(aq) \rightarrow$$
$$5\ Ca^{2+}(aq) + 3\ HPO_4^{2-}(aq) + 5\ H_2O(\ell)$$

This reaction can be prevented by converting hydroxyapatite to the much more acid-resistant coating of fluoroapatite.

$$Ca_5(OH)(PO_4)_3(s) + F^-(aq) \rightarrow$$
$$Ca_5F(PO_4)_3(s) + OH^-(aq)$$

The source of the fluoride ion can be sodium fluoride or sodium monofluorophosphate ($Na_2FPO_3$, commonly known as MFP) in your toothpaste.

# Calcium Minerals and Their Applications

The most common calcium minerals are the fluoride, phosphate, and carbonate salts of the element. Fluorite, $CaF_2$, and fluoroapatite, $Ca_5F(PO_4)_3$, are important as commercial sources of fluorine. Almost half of the $CaF_2$ mined is used in the steel industry, where it is added to the mixture of materials that is melted to make crude iron. The $CaF_2$ acts to remove some impurities and improves the separation of molten metal from silicates and other by-products resulting from the reduction of iron ore to the metal (Chapter 22). A second major use of fluorite is in the manufacture of hydrofluoric acid by a reaction of the mineral with concentrated sulfuric acid.

$$CaF_2(s) + H_2SO_4(\ell) \rightarrow 2\ HF(g) + CaSO_4(s)$$

Hydrofluoric acid is used to make cryolite, $Na_3AlF_6$, a material needed in aluminum production (▶ Section 21.6) and in the manufacture of fluorocarbons such as tetrafluoroethylene, the precursor to Teflon (Table 10.12).

Apatites have the general formula $Ca_5X(PO_4)_3$ (X = F, Cl, OH). More than 100 million tons of apatite is mined annually, with Florida alone accounting for about one third of the world's output. Most of this material is converted to phosphoric acid by reaction with sulfuric acid. Phosphoric acid is needed in the manufacture of a multitude of products, including fertilizers and detergents, baking powder, and various food products (▶ Section 21.8.).

Calcium carbonate and calcium oxide (*lime*) are of special interest. The thermal decomposition of $CaCO_3$ to give lime (and $CO_2$) is one of the oldest chemical reactions known. Lime is one of the top 10 industrial chemicals produced today, with about 20 billion kilograms produced annually.

Limestone, which consists mostly of calcium carbonate, has been used in agriculture for centuries. It is spread on fields to neutralize acidic compounds in the soil and to supply $Ca^{2+}$, an essential nutrient. Because magnesium carbonate is often present in limestone, "liming" a field also supplies $Mg^{2+}$, another important nutrient for plants.

For several thousand years, lime has been used in *mortar* (a lime, sand, and water paste) to secure stones to one another in building houses, walls, and roads. The

© Cengage Learning/ Charles D. Winters

**Apatite.** The mineral has the general formula of $Ca_5X(PO_4)_3$ (X = F, Cl, OH). (The apatite is the elongated crystal in the center of a matrix of other rock.)

## A CLOSER LOOK

# Of Romans, Limestone, and Champagne

The stones of the Appian Way in Italy, a road conceived by the Roman senate in about 310 BC, are cemented with mortar made from limestone. The Appian Way was intended to serve as a military road linking Rome to seaports from which soldiers could embark to Greece and other Mediterranean countries. The road stretches 560 kilometers (350 miles) from Rome to Brindisi on the Adriatic Sea (at the heel of the Italian "boot"). It took almost 200 years to construct. The road had a standard width of 14 Roman feet, approximately 6 meters, large enough to allow two chariots to pass, and featured two sidewalks of 1.2 m each. Every 16 km or so, there were horse-changing stations with taverns, shops, and *latrinae*, the famous Roman restrooms.

All over the Roman Empire, buildings, temples, and aqueducts were constructed of blocks of limestone and marble, and the mortar to cement the blocks was made by heating the chips from stone cutting (to give CaO). In central France, the Romans dug chalk (also $CaCO_3$) from the ground for cementing sandstone blocks. This activity created huge caves that remain to this day and are used for aging and storing champagne.

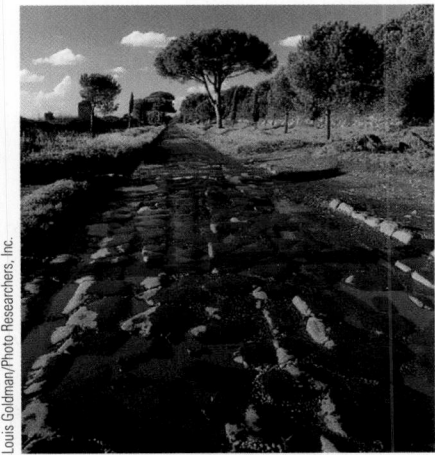

The Appian Way in Italy.

Champagne in a limestone cave in France.

Chinese used it to set stones in the Great Wall. The Romans perfected its use, and the fact that many of their constructions still stand today is testament both to their skill and to the usefulness of lime. The famous Roman road, the Appian Way, used lime mortar between several layers of its stones.

The utility of mortar depends on some simple chemistry. Mortar consists of one part lime to three parts sand, with water added to make a thick paste. The first reaction, referred to as *slaking*, occurs after the solids are mixed with water. This produces a slurry containing calcium hydroxide, which is known as *slaked lime*.

$$CaO(s) + H_2O(\ell) \rightleftharpoons Ca(OH)_2(s)$$

When the wet mortar mix is placed between bricks or stone blocks, it slowly reacts with $CO_2$ from the air, and the slaked lime is converted to calcium carbonate.

$$Ca(OH)_2(s) + CO_2(g) \rightleftharpoons CaCO_3(s) + H_2O(\ell)$$

The sand grains are bound together by the particles of calcium carbonate.

---

### REVIEW & CHECK FOR SECTION 21.5

1. Which of the following insoluble calcium compounds does not dissolve in hydrochloric acid?

   (a) limestone, $CaCO_3$

   (b) slaked lime, $Ca(OH)_2$

   (c) gypsum, $CaSO_4 \cdot 2H_2O$

   (d) hydroxyapatite, $Ca_5(OH)(PO_4)_3$

2. Calcium minerals are the raw materials for a variety of large-scale industrial processes. Which of the following is not an industrial process?

   (a) Converting limestone, $CaCO_3$, to lime

   (b) Converting fluorite, $CaF_2$, to HF

   (c) Converting slaked lime, $Ca(OH)_2$, to lime

   (d) Converting apatite minerals to phosphate fertilizers

# Hard Water

No, hard water doesn't refer to ice. It is the name given to water containing high concentrations of $Ca^{2+}(aq)$ and, in some instances, $Mg^{2+}(aq)$ and other divalent metal cations. Accompanying these cations will be various anions, including in particular the hydrogen carbonate anion, $HCO_3^-(aq)$.

Water obtained from reservoirs that store rainwater does not usually contain high concentrations of these ions, and so is not classified as being "hard water." In many parts of the country, however, the municipal water supply is obtained from aquifers deep underground. If rainwater, containing some dissolved $CO_2$, has to percolate down through layers of limestone ($CaCO_3$) to get into the aquifer, a small amount of the solid will dissolve because of the following equilibrium:

$$CaCO_3(s) + CO_2(aq) + H_2O(\ell) \rightleftharpoons$$
$$Ca^{2+}(aq) + 2\ HCO_3^-(aq)$$

If hard water containing $Ca^{2+}(aq)$ and $HCO_3^-(aq)$ is heated, or even if it is left to stand in an open vessel, $CO_2$ will be expelled, and the equilibrium will shift, precipitating $CaCO_3(s)$ (◄ page 117). This can be a small problem in a teakettle but a bigger problem in an industrial setting, where the solid $CaCO_3$ can clog pipes. Another consequence of hard water is the formation of a scum when soaps are added to water. Soap is made by hydrolysis of fats, which produces long chain carboxylic acids. Soap scum is a precipitate of the calcium salt of these acids.

To avoid the problems associated with hard water, chemists and engineers have devised ways to soften water, that is, to decrease the concentration of the offending cations. In a water treatment plant for a municipality or a large industrial facility, most of the water hardness will be removed chemically, mainly by treatment with calcium oxide (lime, CaO). If $HCO_3^-$ ions are present along with $Ca^{2+}$ and/or $Mg^{2+}$, the following reactions occur:

$$Ca^{2+}(aq) + 2\ HCO_3^-(aq) + CaO(s) \rightarrow$$
$$2\ CaCO_3(s) + H_2O(\ell)$$

$$Mg^{2+}(aq) + 2\ HCO_3^-(aq) + CaO(s) \rightarrow$$
$$CaCO_3(s) + MgCO_3(s) + H_2O(\ell)$$

Although it seems odd to add CaO to remove calcium ions, notice that adding one mole of CaO leads to the precipitation of two moles of $Ca^{2+}$ as $CaCO_3$.

Calcium ions and magnesium ions in untreated water

Calcium and magnesium ions adsorbed onto resin bead, replacing sodium ions

Ion exchange resin

Sodium ions adsorbed onto resin bead

Sodium ions in treated water

**The general operation of an ion-exchange resin.** The ion exchange material is usually a polymeric material formed into small beads.

**Water softening by ion exchange in the home.**

On a smaller scale, most home water purification systems use *ion exchange* to soften water (Figure). This process involves the replacement of an ion adsorbed onto a solid ion exchange resin by an ion in solution. Zeolites (► page 987), naturally occurring aluminosilicate minerals, were at one time used as ion exchange materials. Now, synthetic organic polymers with negatively charged functional groups (such as carboxylate groups, $-CO_2^-$) are the most commonly used resins for this purpose. Sodium ions, $Na^+$, are present in the resin to balance the negative charges of the carboxylate groups. The affinity of a surface for multicharged cations is greater than for monovalent cations. Therefore, when a solution of hard water is passed over the surface of the ion exchange resin, $Ca^{2+}$ and $Mg^{2+}$ (and other divalent ions if present) readily replace $Na^+$ ions in an ion exchange column. This process can be illustrated in a general way by the equilibrium

$$2\ NaX + Ca^{2+}(aq) \rightleftharpoons CaX_2 + 2\ Na^+(aq)$$

where X represents an adsorption site on the ion exchange resin. The equilibrium favors adsorption of $Ca^{2+}$ and release of $Na^+$. However, the equilibrium is reversed if $Na^+(aq)$ ions are present in high concentration, and this allows regeneration of the ion exchange resin. A solution containing a high concentration of $Na^+$ (usually from salt, NaCl) is passed through the resin to convert the resin back to its initial form.

## Questions:

1. Assume that a sample of hard water contains 50. mg/L of $Mg^{2+}$ and 150 mg/L of $Ca^{2+}$, with $HCO_3^-$ as the accompanying anion. What mass of CaO should be added to 1.0 L of this aqueous solution to cause all of this $Mg^{2+}$ and $Ca^{2+}$ to precipitate as $CaCO_3$ and $MgCO_3$? What is the total mass of the two solids formed?

2. One way to remove the calcium carbonate residue in a teakettle is to add vinegar (a dilute solution of acetic acid). Write a chemical equation to explain this process. What kind of a reaction is this?

**Answers to these questions are available in Appendix N.**

# 21.6 Boron, Aluminum, and the Group 3A Elements

With Group 3A, we see the first evidence of a change from metallic behavior of the elements at the left side of the periodic table to nonmetal behavior on the right side of the table. Boron is a metalloid, whereas all the other elements of Group 3A are metals.

The elements of Group 3A vary widely in their relative abundances on earth. Aluminum is the third most abundant element in the earth's crust (82,000 ppm), whereas the other elements of the group are relatively rare, and, except for boron, their compounds have limited commercial uses.

## Chemistry of the Group 3A Elements

It is generally recognized that a chemical similarity exists between some elements diagonally situated in the periodic table. This diagonal relationship means that lithium and magnesium share some chemical properties, as do Be and Al, and B and Si. For example:

- Boric oxide, $B_2O_3$, and boric acid, $B(OH)_3$, are weakly acidic, as are $SiO_2$ and its acid, orthosilicic acid ($H_4SiO_4$). Boron–oxygen compounds, borates, are often chemically similar to silicon–oxygen compounds, silicates.
- Both $Be(OH)_2$ and $Al(OH)_3$ are amphoteric, dissolving in a strong base such as aqueous NaOH (◄ page 793).
- Chlorides, bromides, and iodides of boron and silicon (such as $BCl_3$ and $SiCl_4$) react vigorously with water.
- The hydrides of boron and silicon are simple, molecular species; are volatile and flammable; and react readily with water.
- Beryllium hydride and aluminum hydride are colorless, nonvolatile solids that are extensively polymerized through Be—H—Be and Al—H—Al three-center, two-electron bonds (◄ page 427).

Finally, the Group 3A elements are characterized by electron configurations of the type $ns^2np^1$. This means that each may lose three electrons to have a +3 oxidation number, although the heavier elements, especially thallium, also form compounds with an oxidation number of +1.

## Boron Minerals and Production of the Element

Although boron has a low abundance on earth, its minerals are found in concentrated deposits. Large deposits of borax, $Na_2B_4O_7 \cdot 10\ H_2O$, are currently mined in the Mojave Desert near the town of Boron, California (Figure 21.15).

Group **3A**

| Boron |
| 5 |
| **B** |
| 10 ppm |

| Aluminum |
| 13 |
| **Al** |
| 82,000 ppm |

| Gallium |
| 31 |
| **Ga** |
| 18 ppm |

| Indium |
| 49 |
| **In** |
| 0.05 ppm |

| Thallium |
| 81 |
| **Tl** |
| 0.6 ppm |

*Element abundances are in* **parts per million** *in the earth's crust.*

Diagonal Relationship

| 1A | 2A | 3A | 4A |
| Li | Be | B | |
| | Mg | Al | Si |

● **Diagonal Relationship** The chemistries of elements diagonally situated in the periodic table are often quite similar.

(a) A borax mine near the town of Boron, California.

© George Gerster/Photo Researchers, Inc.

(b) The mineral named ulexite, a form of crystalline borax, $Na_2B_4O_7 \cdot 10\ H_2O$.

© Cengage Learning/Charles D. Winters

(c) All four allotropes of elemental boron have an icosahedron (a 20-sided polyhedron) of 12 covalently linked boron atoms as a structural element.

**FIGURE 21.15** Boron.

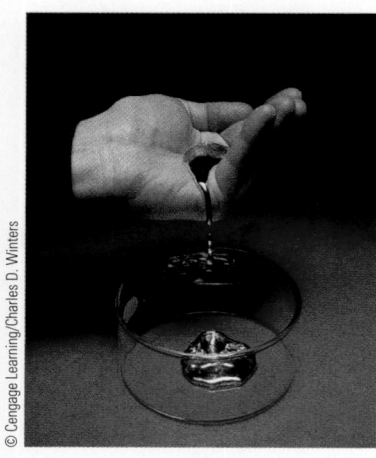

**Gallium.** Gallium, with a melting point of 29.8 °C, is one of the few metals that can be a liquid at or near room temperature. (Others are Hg and Cs.)

● **Boron, a Strange Element**
Within 1 week in 1808 three chemists claimed to have discovered boron: Sir Humphry Davy, J. Gay-Lussac, and L-J. Thenard. They had not; all were impure samples. One hundred years would pass before pure boron was finally isolated. But then the mystery began. What is its structure? Until recently three forms were known, but a fourth was discovered in 2009. The molecular structure of each of the forms has an icosahedron of twelve boron atoms (Figure 21.15).

Isolation of pure, elemental boron from boron-containing minerals is extremely difficult and is done in small quantities. Like most metals and metalloids, boron can be obtained by chemically or electrolytically reducing an oxide or halide. Magnesium has often been used for chemical reductions, but the product of this reaction is a noncrystalline boron of low purity.

$$B_2O_3(s) + 3\ Mg(s) \rightarrow 2\ B(s) + 3\ MgO(s)$$

Boron has several allotropes, all characterized by having an icosahedron of boron atoms as one structural element (Figure 21.15c). Partly as a result of extended covalent bonding, elemental boron is a very hard and refractory (resistant to heat) semiconductor. In this regard, it differs from the other Group 3A elements; Al, Ga, In, and Tl are all relatively low-melting, rather soft metals with high electrical conductivity.

## Metallic Aluminum and Its Production

The low cost of aluminum and the excellent characteristics of its alloys with other metals (low density, strength, ease of handling in fabrication, and inertness toward corrosion, among others), have led to its widespread use. You know it best in the form of aluminum foil, aluminum cans, and parts of aircraft.

Pure aluminum is soft and weak; moreover, it loses strength rapidly at temperatures higher than 300 °C. What we call "aluminum" is actually aluminum alloyed with small amounts of other elements to strengthen the metal and improve its properties. A typical alloy may contain about 4% copper with smaller amounts of silicon, magnesium, and manganese. Softer, more corrosion-resistant alloys for window frames, furniture, highway signs, and cooking utensils may include only manganese.

The standard reduction potential of aluminum $[Al^{3+}(aq) + 3\ e^- \rightarrow Al(s);$ $E° = -1.66\ V]$ tells you that aluminum is easily oxidized. From this, we might expect aluminum to be highly susceptible to corrosion but, in fact, it is quite resistant. Aluminum's corrosion resistance is due to the formation of a thin, tough, and transparent skin of $Al_2O_3$ that adheres to the metal surface. An important feature of the protective oxide layer is that it rapidly self-repairs. If you penetrate the surface coating by scratching it or using some chemical agent, the exposed metal surface immediately reacts with oxygen (or another oxidizing agent) to form a new layer of oxide over the damaged area (Figure 21.16).

Aluminum was first prepared by reducing AlCl₃ using sodium or potassium. This was a costly process, and, in the 19th century, aluminum was a precious metal.

**FIGURE 21.16** Corrosion of aluminum.

**(a)** A ball of aluminum foil is added to a solution of copper(II) nitrate and sodium chloride. Normally, the coating of chemically inert $Al_2O_3$ on the surface of aluminum protects the metal from further oxidation.

**(b)** In the presence of the Cl⁻ ion, the coating of $Al_2O_3$ is breached, and aluminum reduces copper(II) ions to copper metal. The reaction is rapid and so exothermic that the water can boil on the surface of the foil. [The blue color of aqueous copper(II) ions will fade as these ions are consumed in the reaction.]

At the 1855 Paris Exposition, in fact, a sample of aluminum was exhibited along with the crown jewels of France. In an interesting coincidence, in 1886 Frenchman Paul Heroult (1863–1914) and American Charles Hall (1863–1914) simultaneously and independently conceived of the electrochemical method used today. The Hall–Heroult method bears the names of the two discoverers.

Aluminum is found in nature as aluminosilicates, minerals such as clay that are based on aluminum, silicon, and oxygen. As these minerals weather, they break down to various forms of hydrated aluminum oxide, $Al_2O_3 \cdot n\,H_2O$, called *bauxite*. Mined in huge quantities, bauxite is the raw material from which aluminum is obtained. The first step is to purify the ore, separating $Al_2O_3$ from iron and silicon oxides. This is done by the *Bayer process*, which relies on the amphoteric, basic, or acidic nature of the various oxides. (Silica, $SiO_2$, is an acidic oxide, whereas $Al_2O_3$ is amphoteric, and $Fe_2O_3$ is a basic oxide.) Silica and $Al_2O_3$ dissolve in a hot concentrated solution of caustic soda (NaOH), leaving insoluble $Fe_2O_3$ to be filtered out.

$$Al_2O_3(s) + 2\,NaOH(aq) + 3\,H_2O(\ell) \rightarrow 2\,Na[Al(OH)_4](aq)$$

$$SiO_2(s) + 2\,NaOH(aq) + 2\,H_2O(\ell) \rightarrow Na_2[Si(OH)_6](aq)$$

If a solution containing aluminate and silicate anions is treated with $CO_2$, $Al_2O_3$ precipitates, and the silicate ion remains in solution. Recall that $CO_2$ is an acidic oxide that forms the weak acid $H_2CO_3$ in water, so the $Al_2O_3$ precipitation in this step is an acid–base reaction.

$$H_2CO_3(aq) + 2\,Na[Al(OH)_4](aq) \rightarrow Na_2CO_3(aq) + Al_2O_3(s) + 5\,H_2O(\ell)$$

Metallic aluminum is obtained from purified bauxite by electrolysis (Figure 21.17). Bauxite is first mixed with cryolite, $Na_3AlF_6$, to give a lower-melting mixture (melting temperature = 980 °C) that is electrolyzed in a cell with graphite electrodes. The cell operates at a relatively low voltage (4.0–5.5 V) but with an extremely high current (50,000–150,000 A). Aluminum is produced at the cathode and oxygen at the anode. To produce 1 kg of aluminum requires 13 to 16 kilowatt-hours of energy plus the energy required to maintain the high temperature.

● **Charles Martin Hall (1863–1914)** Hall was only 22 years old when he worked out the electrolytic process for extracting aluminum from $Al_2O_3$ in a woodshed behind the family home in Oberlin, Ohio. He went on to found a company that eventually became ALCOA, the Aluminum Corporation of America.

Oesper Collection in the History of Chemistry/ University of Cincinnati

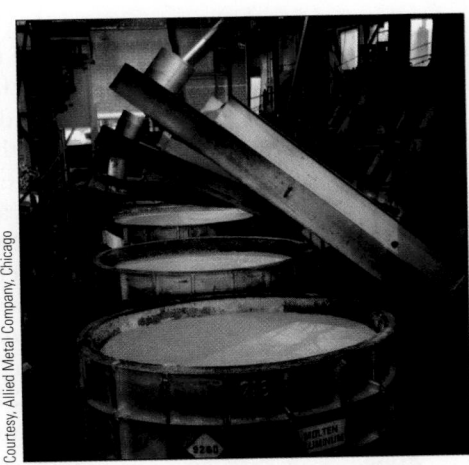

(a) Purified aluminum-containing ore (bauxite) is essentially $Al_2O_3$. In the Hall–Heroult process this is mixed with cryolite ($Na_3AlF_6$) and other fluorides such as $AlF_3$. (The additives serve to lower the melting point of the mixture and increase the conductivity). The aluminum-containing substances are reduced at a graphite cathode to give molten aluminum. Oxygen is produced at a graphite anode, and the gas reacts slowly with the carbon to give $CO_2$, leading to eventual destruction of the electrode.

(b) Molten aluminum alloy, produced from recycled metal, at 760 °C, in $1.6 \times 10^4$-kg capacity crucibles.

**FIGURE 21.17** Industrial production of aluminum.

B atom surrounded by 4 electron pairs

B atom surrounded by 3 electron pairs

**The borate ion of borax, $[B_4O_5(OH)_4]^{2-}$.**

● **Borax in Fire Retardants** The second largest use for boric acid and borates is as a flame retardant for cellulose home insulation. Such insulation is often made of scrap paper, which is inexpensive but flammable. To control the flammability, 5%–10% of the weight of the insulation is boric acid.

# Boron Compounds

Borax, $Na_2B_4O_7 \cdot 10\ H_2O$, is the most important boron–oxygen compound and is the form of the element most often found in nature. It has been used for centuries in metallurgy because of the ability of molten borax to dissolve other metal oxides. That is, borax is used as a *flux* that cleans the surfaces of metals to be joined and permits a good metal-to-metal contact.

The formula for borax gives little information about its structure. The anion is better described by the formula $[B_4O_5(OH)_4]^{2-}$, the structure of which illustrates two commonly observed structural features in inorganic chemistry. First, many minerals consist of $MO_n$ groups that share O atoms. Second, the sharing of O atoms between two metals or metalloids often leads to MO rings.

After refinement, borax can be treated with sulfuric acid to produce boric acid, $B(OH)_3$.

$$Na_2B_4O_7 \cdot 10\ H_2O(s) + H_2SO_4(aq) \rightarrow 4\ B(OH)_3(aq) + Na_2SO_4(aq) + 5\ H_2O(\ell)$$

The chemistry of boric acid incorporates both Lewis and Brønsted acid behavior. Hydronium ions are produced by a Lewis acid–base interaction between boric acid and water.

$$K_a = 7.3 \times 10^{-10}$$

Because of its weak acid properties and slight biological activity, boric acid has been used for many years as an antiseptic. Furthermore, because boric acid is a weak acid, salts of borate ions, such as the $[B_4O_5(OH)_4]^{2-}$ ion in borax, are weak bases.

Boric acid is dehydrated to boric oxide when strongly heated.

$$2\ B(OH)_3(s) \rightarrow B_2O_3(s) + 3\ H_2O(\ell)$$

By far the largest use for the oxide is in the manufacture of borosilicate glass (the type of glass used in most laboratory glassware). This type of glass is composed of 76% $SiO_2$, 13% $B_2O_3$, and much smaller amounts of $Al_2O_3$ and $Na_2O$. The presence of boric oxide gives the glass a higher softening temperature, imparts a better resistance to attack by acids, and makes the glass expand less on heating.

Like its metalloid neighbor silicon, boron forms a series of molecular compounds with hydrogen. Because boron is slightly less electronegative than hydrogen, these compounds are described as hydrides, in which the H atoms bear a partial negative charge. More than 20 neutral boron hydrides, or boranes, with the general formula $B_xH_y$ are known. The simplest of these is diborane, $B_2H_6$, where $x$ is 2 and $y$ is 6. This colorless, gaseous compound has a boiling point of $-92.6\ °C$. This molecule is described as electron deficient because there are apparently not enough electrons to attach all of the atoms using two-electron bonds. Instead, the description of bonding uses three-center two-electron bonds in the B—H—B bridges (◀ page 427).

Diborane has an endothermic enthalpy of formation ($\Delta_f H° = +41.0$ kJ/mol), which contributes to the high exothermicity of oxidation of the compound. Diborane burns in air to give boric oxide and water vapor in an extremely exothermic reaction. It is not surprising that diborane and other boron hydrides were once considered as possible rocket fuels.

$$B_2H_6(g) + 3\ O_2(g) \rightarrow B_2O_3(s) + 3\ H_2O(g) \qquad \Delta_r H° = -2038\ \text{kJ/mol-rxn}$$

Diborane can be synthesized from sodium borohydride, $NaBH_4$, the only B—H compound produced in ton quantities.

$$2\ NaBH_4(s) + I_2(s) \rightarrow B_2H_6(g) + 2\ NaI(s) + H_2(g)$$

133 pm

119 pm

97°  122°

**The structure of diborane, $B_2H_6$, the simplest member of a family of boron hydrides.** See also page 427.

Sodium borohydride, $NaBH_4$, a white, crystalline, water-soluble solid, is made from NaH and borate esters such as $B(OCH_3)_3$.

$$4 \text{ NaH(s)} + B(OCH_3)_3(g) \rightarrow NaBH_4(s) + 3 \text{ NaOCH}_3(s)$$

The main use of $NaBH_4$ is as a reducing agent in organic synthesis. We previously encountered its use to reduce aldehydes, carboxylic acids, and ketones in Chapter 10.

## Aluminum Compounds

Aluminum is an excellent reducing agent, so it reacts readily with hydrochloric acid. In contrast, it does not react with nitric acid, a stronger oxidizing agent than hydrochloric acid. It turns out that nitric acid does rapidly oxidize the surface of aluminum, but the resulting film of $Al_2O_3$ that is produced protects the metal from further attack. In fact, this protection allows nitric acid to be shipped in aluminum tanks.

Various salts of aluminum dissolve in water, giving the hydrated $Al^{3+}$(aq) ion. These solutions are acidic (◀ Table 17.3, page 766) because the hydrated ion is a weak Brønsted acid.

$$[Al(H_2O)_6]^{3+}(aq) + H_2O(\ell) \rightleftharpoons [Al(H_2O)_5(OH)]^{2+}(aq) + H_3O^+(aq)$$

Adding acid shifts the equilibrium to the left, whereas adding base causes the equilibrium to shift to the right. Addition of sufficient hydroxide ion results ultimately in precipitation of the hydrated oxide $Al_2O_3 \cdot 3 \text{ H}_2O$.

Aluminum oxide, $Al_2O_3$, formed by dehydrating the hydrated oxide, is quite insoluble in water and generally resistant to chemical attack. In the crystalline form, aluminum oxide is known as *corundum*. This material is extraordinarily hard, a property that leads to its use as an abrasive in grinding wheels, "sandpaper," and toothpaste.

Some gems are impure aluminum oxide. Rubies, beautiful red crystals prized for jewelry and used in some lasers, are composed of $Al_2O_3$ contaminated with a small amount of $Cr^{3+}$ (Figure 21.18 and page 300). The $Cr^{3+}$ ions replacing some of the $Al^{3+}$ ions in the crystal lattice are the source of the red color. Synthetic rubies were first made in 1902, and the worldwide capacity is now about 200,000 kg/year; much of this production is used for jewel bearings in watches and instruments. Blue sapphires consist of $Al_2O_3$ with $Fe^{2+}$ and $Ti^{4+}$ impurities in place of $Al^{3+}$ ions.

Boron forms halides such as gaseous $BF_3$ and $BCl_3$ that have the expected trigonal planar molecular geometry of halogen atoms surrounding an $sp^2$ hybridized boron atom. In contrast, the aluminum halides are all solids and have more interesting structures. Aluminum bromide, which is made by the very exothermic reaction of aluminum metal and bromine (◀ Figure 2.12, page 67),

$$2 \text{ Al(s)} + 3 \text{ Br}_2(\ell) \rightarrow Al_2Br_6(s)$$

is composed of two units of $AlBr_3$. That is, $Al_2Br_6$ is a dimer of $AlBr_3$ units. The structure resembles that of diborane in that bridging atoms appear between the two Al atoms. However, $Al_2Br_6$ is not electron deficient; the bridge is formed when a Br atom on one $AlBr_3$ uses a lone pair to form a coordinate covalent bond to a neighboring tetrahedral, $sp^3$-hybridized aluminum atom.

**The structure of $Al_2Br_6$.** The bonding in $Al_2Br_6$ is not unique to the aluminum halides. Metal–halogen–metal bridges are found in many other metal–halogen compounds.

Both aluminum bromide and aluminum iodide have this structure. Aluminum chloride has a different solid state structure, but it exists as dimeric molecules in the vapor state.

© Cengage Learning/Charles D. Winters

**Aluminum does not react with nitric acid.** Nitric acid, a strongly oxidizing acid, reacts vigorously with copper *(left)*, but aluminum *(right)* is untouched.

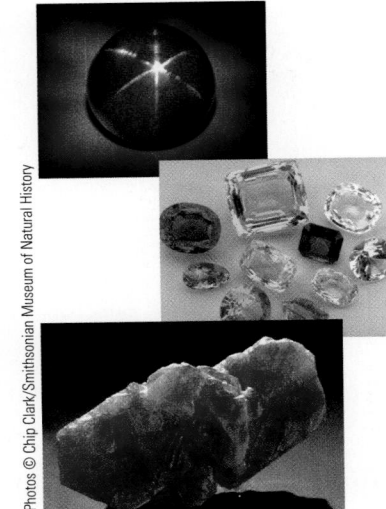

Photos © Chip Clark/Smithsonian Museum of Natural History

**FIGURE 21.18 Forms of corundum.** Corundum is a crystalline form of aluminum oxide. Both rubies and sapphires are a form of corundum in which a few $Al^{3+}$ ions have been replaced by ions such as $Cr^{3+}$, $Fe^{2+}$, or $Ti^{4+}$. *(top)* The Star of Asia sapphire. *(middle)* Various sapphires. *(bottom)* Uncut corundum.

Aluminum chloride can react with a chloride ion to form the anion $[AlCl_4]^-$. Aluminum fluoride, in contrast, can accommodate three additional $F^-$ ions to form an octahedral $[AlF_6]^{3-}$ ion. This anion is found in cryolite, $Na_3AlF_6$, the compound added to aluminum oxide in the electrolytic production of aluminum metal. Apparently, the $Al^{3+}$ ion can bind to six of the smaller $F^-$ ions, whereas only four of the larger $Cl^-$, $Br^-$, or $I^-$ ions can surround an $Al^{3+}$ ion.

---

### REVIEW & CHECK FOR SECTION 21.6

1.   In terms of abundance of the elements in the earth's crust, aluminum ranks

   (a)   first          (b)   second          (c)   third          (d)   fourth

2.   The element below aluminum in Group 3A is gallium, and there are numerous similarities in the chemistry of these two elements. For example, the hydroxides of both elements are amphoteric. A consequence of this is that both gallium hydroxide and aluminum hydroxide

   (a)   are insoluble                         (c)   dissolve only in base

   (b)   dissolve only in acid                 (d)   dissolve in acid and in base

---

## 21.7   Silicon and the Group 4A Elements

Carbon is a nonmetal; silicon and germanium are classified as metalloids; and tin and lead are metals. As a result, the elements of Group 4A have a broad range of chemical behavior.

The Group 4A elements are characterized by half-filled valence shells with two electrons in the $ns$ orbital and two electrons in $np$ orbitals. The bonding in carbon and silicon compounds is largely covalent and involves sharing four electron pairs with neighboring atoms. In germanium compounds, the $+4$ oxidation state is common ($GeO_2$ and $GeCl_4$), but some $+2$ oxidation state compounds exist ($GeI_2$). Oxidation numbers of both $+2$ and $+4$ are common in compounds of tin and lead (such as $SnCl_2$, $SnCl_4$, $PbO$, and $PbO_2$). Oxidation numbers two units less than the group number are often encountered for heavier elements in Groups 3A–7A.

### Silicon

Silicon is second after oxygen in abundance in the earth's crust, so it is not surprising that we are surrounded by silicon-containing materials: bricks, pottery, porcelain, lubricants, sealants, computer chips, and solar cells. The computer revolution is based on the semiconducting properties of silicon.

Reasonably pure silicon can be made in large quantities by heating pure silica sand with purified coke to approximately 3000 °C in an electric furnace.

$$SiO_2(s) + 2\ C(s) \rightarrow Si(\ell) + 2\ CO(g)$$

The molten silicon is drawn off the bottom of the furnace and allowed to cool to a shiny blue-gray solid. Because extremely high-purity silicon is needed for the electronics industry, purifying raw silicon requires several steps. First, the silicon in the impure sample is allowed to react with chlorine to convert the silicon to liquid silicon tetrachloride.

$$Si(s) + 2\ Cl_2(g) \rightarrow SiCl_4(\ell)$$

Silicon tetrachloride (boiling point of 57.6 °C) is carefully purified by distillation and then reduced to silicon using magnesium.

$$SiCl_4(g) + 2\ Mg(s) \rightarrow 2\ MgCl_2(s) + Si(s)$$

The magnesium chloride is washed out with water, and the silicon is remelted and cast into bars. A final purification is carried out by zone refining, a process in which a special heating device is used to melt a narrow segment of the silicon rod. The heater is moved slowly down the rod. Impurities contained in the silicon tend to

Group **4A**

Carbon
6
**C**
480 ppm

Silicon
14
**Si**
277,000 ppm

Germanium
32
**Ge**
1.8 ppm

Tin
50
**Sn**
2.2 ppm

Lead
82
**Pb**
14 ppm

*Element abundances are in* **parts per million** *in the earth's crust.*

remain in the liquid phase because the melting point of a mixture is lower than that of the pure element (Chapter 14). The silicon that crystallizes above the heated zone is therefore of a higher purity (Figure 21.19).

## Silicon Dioxide

The simplest oxide of silicon is $SiO_2$, commonly called *silica*, a constituent of many rocks such as granite and sandstone. Quartz is a pure crystalline form of silica, but impurities in quartz produce gemstones such as amethyst (Figure 21.20).

Silica and $CO_2$ are oxides of two elements in the same chemical group, so similarities between them might be expected. In fact, $SiO_2$ is a high-melting solid (quartz melts at 1610 °C), whereas $CO_2$ is a gas at room temperature and 1 atm. This great disparity arises from the different structures of the two oxides. Carbon dioxide is a molecular compound, with the carbon atom linked to each oxygen atom by a double bond. In contrast, $SiO_2$ is a network solid, which is the preferred structure because the bond energy of two Si=O double bonds is much less than the bond energy of four Si—O single bonds. The contrast between $SiO_2$ and $CO_2$ is an example of a more general phenomenon. Multiple bonds, often encountered between second-period elements, are rare among elements in the third period and beyond. There are many compounds with multiple bonds to carbon but very few compounds featuring multiple bonds to silicon.

Quartz crystals are used to control the frequency of radio and television transmissions. Because these and related applications use so much quartz, there is not enough natural quartz to fulfill demand, and quartz is therefore synthesized. Non-crystalline, or vitreous, quartz, made by melting pure silica sand, is placed in a steel "bomb," and dilute aqueous NaOH is added. A "seed" crystal is placed in the mixture, just as you might use a seed crystal in a hot sugar solution to grow rock candy. When the mixture is heated above the critical temperature of water (above 400 °C and 1700 atm) over a period of days, pure quartz crystallizes.

Silicon dioxide is resistant to attack by all acids except HF, with which it reacts to give $SiF_4$ and $H_2O$.

$$SiO_2(s) + 4\ HF(\ell) \rightarrow SiF_4(g) + 2\ H_2O(\ell)$$

Silicon dioxide also dissolves slowly in hot, molten NaOH or $Na_2CO_3$ to give $Na_4SiO_4$, sodium silicate.

$$SiO_2(s) + 2\ Na_2CO_3(\ell) \rightarrow Na_4SiO_4(s) + 2\ CO_2(g)$$

After the molten mixture has cooled, hot water under pressure is added. This partially dissolves the material to give a solution of sodium silicate. After filtering off insoluble sand or glass, the solvent is evaporated to leave sodium silicate, called *water glass*. The biggest single use of this material is in household and industrial detergents, in which it is included because a sodium silicate solution maintains pH by its

**FIGURE 21.19** **Pure silicon.** The manufacture of very pure silicon begins with producing the volatile liquid silanes $SiCl_4$ or $SiHCl_3$. After carefully purifying these by distillation, they are reduced to elemental silicon with extremely pure Mg or Zn. The resulting spongy silicon is purified by zone refining. The end result is a cylindrical rod of ultrapure silicon such as those seen in this photograph. Thin wafers of silicon are cut from the bars and are the basis for the semiconducting chips in computers and other devices.

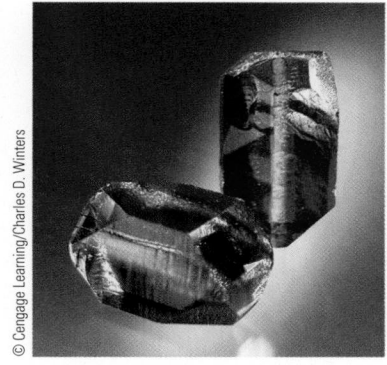

**Synthetic quartz.** These crystals were grown from silica in sodium hydroxide. The colors come from added $Co^{2+}$ ions (blue) or $Fe^{2+}$ ions (brown).

**FIGURE 21.20** **Various forms of quartz.**

**(a)** Pure quartz is colorless, but the presence of small amounts of impurities adds color. Purple amethyst and brown citrine crystals are quartz with iron impurities.

**(b)** Quartz is a network solid in which each Si atom is bound tetrahedrally to four O atoms, each O atom linked to another Si atom.

**Silica gel.** Silica gel is solid, noncrystalline $SiO_2$. Packages of the material are often used to keep electronic equipment dry when stored. Silica gel is also used to clarify beer; passing beer through a bed of silica gel removes minute particles that would otherwise make the brew cloudy. Yet another use is in kitty litter.

buffering ability. Additionally, sodium silicate is used in various adhesives and binders, especially for gluing corrugated cardboard boxes.

If sodium silicate is treated with acid, a gelatinous precipitate of $SiO_2$ called *silica gel* is obtained. Washed and dried, silica gel is a highly porous material with many uses. It is a drying agent, readily absorbing up to 40% of its own weight of water. Small packets of silica gel are often placed in packing boxes of merchandise during storage. The material is frequently stained with $(NH_4)_2CoCl_4$, a humidity detector that is pink when hydrated and blue when dry.

## Silicate Minerals with Chain and Ribbon Structures

The structure and chemistry of silicate minerals is an enormous topic in geology and chemistry. Although all silicates are built from tetrahedral $SiO_4$ units, they have different properties and a wide variety of structures because of the way these tetrahedral $SiO_4$ units link together.

The simplest silicates, *orthosilicates*, contain $SiO_4^{4-}$ anions. The 4− charge of the anion is balanced by four $M^+$ ions, two $M^{2+}$ ions, or a combination of ions. Olivine, an important mineral in the earth's mantle, contains $Mg^{2+}$ and $Fe^{2+}$, with the $Fe^{2+}$ ion giving the mineral its characteristic olive color, and gem-like zircons are $ZrSiO_4$. Calcium orthosilicate, $Ca_2SiO_4$, is a component of Portland cement, the most common type of cement used in many parts of the world. (It consists mostly of a mixture of CaO and $SiO_2$ with the remainder largely aluminum and iron oxides.)

A group of minerals called *pyroxenes* have as their basic structural unit a chain of $SiO_4$ tetrahedra.

If two such chains are linked together by sharing oxygen atoms, the result is an *amphibole*, of which the asbestos minerals are one example. The molecular chain results in asbestos being a fibrous material.

## Silicates with Sheet Structures and Aluminosilicates

Linking many silicate chains together produces a sheet of $SiO_4$ tetrahedra (Figure 21.21). This sheet is the basic structural feature of some of the earth's most important minerals, particularly the clay minerals (such as china clay), mica, talc, and

**FIGURE 21.21 Mica, a sheet silicate.** The sheet-like molecular structure of mica explains its physical appearance. As in the pyroxenes, each silicon is bonded to four oxygen atoms, but the Si and O atoms form a sheet of six-member rings of Si atoms with O atoms in each edge. The ratio of Si to O in this structure is 1 to 2.5. A formula of $SiO_{2.5}$ requires a positive ion, such as $Na^+$, to counterbalance the charge. Thus, mica and other sheet silicates, and aluminosilicates such as talc and many clays, have positive ions between the sheets. The sheet structure leads to the characteristic feature of mica, that it is often found as "books" of thin, silicate sheets. Mica is used in furnace windows and as insulation, and flecks of mica give the glitter to "metallic" paints.

the chrysotile form of asbestos. However, these minerals do not contain just silicon and oxygen. Rather, they are often referred to as *aluminosilicates* because they frequently have $Al^{3+}$ ions in place of $Si^{4+}$ (which means that other positive ions such as $Na^+$, $K^+$, and $Mg^{2+}$ must also be present in the lattice to balance the net negative and positive charges). In kaolinite clay, for example, the sheet of $SiO_4$ tetrahedra is bonded to a sheet of $AlO_6$ octahedra. In addition, some $Si^{4+}$ ions can be replaced by $Al^{3+}$ atoms. Another example is muscovite, a form of mica. Aluminum ions have replaced some $Si^{4+}$ ions, and there are charge-balancing $K^+$ ions, so it is best represented by the formula $KAl_2(OH)_2(Si_3AlO_{10})$.

There are some interesting uses of clays, one being in medicine (Figure 21.22). In certain cultures, clay is eaten for medicinal purposes. Several remedies for the relief of upset stomach contain highly purified clays that absorb excess stomach acid as well as potentially harmful bacteria and their toxins by exchanging the intersheet cations in the clays for the toxins, which are often organic cations.

Other aluminosilicates include the feldspars, common minerals that make up about 60% of the earth's crust, and zeolites (Figure 21.22). Both materials are composed of $SiO_4$ tetrahedra in which some of the Si atoms have been replaced by Al atoms, along with alkali and alkaline earth metal ions for charge balance. The main feature of zeolite structures is their regularly shaped tunnels and cavities. Hole diameters are between 300 and 1000 pm, and small molecules such as water can fit into the cavities of the zeolite structure. As a result, zeolites can be used as drying agents to selectively absorb water from air or a solvent. Small amounts of zeolites are often sealed into multipane windows to keep the air dry between the panes.

Zeolites are also used as catalysts. ExxonMobil, for example, has patented a process in which methanol, $CH_3OH$, is converted to gasoline in the presence of specially tailored zeolites. In addition, zeolites are added to detergents, where they function as water-softening agents because the sodium ions of the zeolite can be exchanged for $Ca^{2+}$ ions in hard water, effectively removing $Ca^{2+}$ ions from the water.

**Kaolinite clay.** The basic structural feature of many clays, and kaolinite in particular, is a sheet of $SiO_4$ tetrahedra (black and red spheres) bonded to a sheet of $AlO_6$ octahedra (gray and green spheres).

## Silicone Polymers

Silicon and chloromethane ($CH_3Cl$) react at 300 °C in the presence of a catalyst, Cu powder. The primary product of this reaction is $(CH_3)_2SiCl_2$.

$$Si(s) + 2\ CH_3Cl(g) \rightarrow (CH_3)_2SiCl_2(\ell)$$

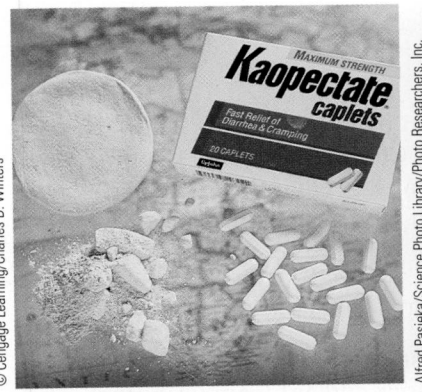

**(a) Remedies for stomach upset.** One of the ingredients in Kaopectate is kaolin, one form of clay. The off-white objects are pieces of clay purchased in a market in Ghana, West Africa. This clay was made to be eaten as a remedy for stomach ailments. Eating clay is widespread among the world's different cultures.

**(b) The stucture of a zeolite.** Zeolites, which have Si, Al, and O linked in a polyhedral framework, are often portrayed in drawings like this. Each edge consists of an Si—O—Si, Al—O—Si, or Al—O—Al bond. The channels in the framework can selectively capture small molecules or ions or act as catalytic sites.

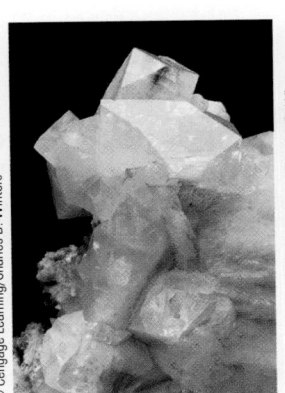

**(c) Apophyllite**, a crystalline zeolite.

**(d) Consumer products** that remove odor-causing molecules from the air often contain zeolites.

**FIGURE 21.22.** Aluminosilicates.

# Lead, Beethoven, and a Mystery Solved

Lead anchors the bottom of Group 4A. One of a handful of elements known since ancient times, it has a variety of modern uses. It ranks fifth among metals in usage behind iron, copper, aluminum, and zinc. The major uses of the metal and its compounds are in storage batteries (page 910), pigments, ammunition, solders, plumbing, and bearings.

Unfortunately, lead and its compounds are cumulative poisons, particularly in children. At a blood level as low as 50 ppb (parts per billion), blood pressure is elevated; intelligence is affected at 100 ppb; and blood levels higher than 800 ppb can lead to coma and possible death. Health experts believe that more than 200,000 children become ill from lead poisoning annually, a problem caused chiefly by children eating paint containing lead-based pigments. Older homes often contain lead-based paint because white lead [2 $PbCO_3 \cdot Pb(OH)_2$] was the pigment used in white paint until about 40 years ago, when it was replaced by $TiO_2$. Lead salts have a sweet taste, which may contribute to the tendency of children to chew on painted objects.

The symptoms of lead poisoning include nausea, abdominal pain, irritability, headaches, and excess lethargy or hyperactivity. Indeed, these describe some of the symptoms of the illness that affected Ludwig van Beethoven. As a child, he was recognized as a musical prodigy and was thought to be the greatest pianist in Europe by the time he was 19. But then he fell ill, and, by the time he was 29, he wrote to his brother to say he

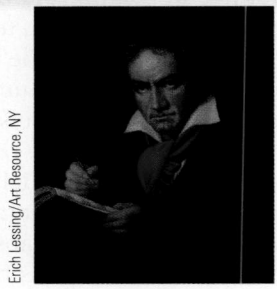

Erich Lessing/Art Resource, NY

**Ludwig van Beethoven (1770–1827).**

was considering suicide. By the time he died in 1827 at the age of 56, his belly, arms, and legs were swollen, and he complained constantly of pain in his joints and in his big toe. It is said he wandered the streets of Vienna with long, uncombed hair, dressed in a top hat and long coat, and scribbling in a notebook.

An autopsy at the time showed he died of kidney failure. Kidney stones had destroyed his kidneys, stones that presumably came from gout, the buildup of uric acid in his body. (Gout leads to joint pain, among other things.) But why did he have gout?

It was well known in the time of the Roman Empire that lead and its salts are toxic. The Romans drank wine sweetened with a very concentrated grape juice syrup that was prepared by boiling the juice in a

lead kettle. The resulting syrup, called *Sapa*, had a very high concentration of lead, and many Romans contracted gout. So, if Beethoven enjoyed drinking wine, which was often kept in lead-glass decanters, he could have contracted gout and lead poisoning. One scientist has also noted that he may have been one of a small number of people who have a "metal metabolism disorder," a condition that prevents the excretion of toxic metals like lead.

In 2005, scientists at Argonne National Laboratory examined fragments of Beethoven's hair and skull and found both were extremely high in lead. The hair sample, for example, had 60 ppm lead, about 100 times higher than normal.

The mystery of what caused Beethoven's death has been solved. But what remains a mystery is how he contracted lead poisoning.

**Questions:**

1. If blood contains 50. ppb lead, how many atoms of lead are there in 1.0 L of blood? (Assume $d$(blood) = 1.0 g/mL.)
2. Research has found that port wine stored for a year in lead-glass decanters contains 2000 ppm lead. If the decanter contains 750 mL of wine ($d$ = 1.0 g/mL), what mass of lead has been extracted into the wine?

**Answers to these questions are available in Appendix N.**

---

Halides of Group 4A elements other than carbon hydrolyze readily. Thus, the reaction of $(CH_3)_2SiCl_2$ with water initially produces $(CH_3)_2Si(OH)_2$. On standing, these molecules combine to form a condensation polymer by eliminating water. The polymer is called polydimethylsiloxane, a member of the *silicone* family of polymers.

$$(CH_3)_2SiCl_2 + 2\ H_2O \rightarrow (CH_3)_2Si(OH)_2 + 2\ HCl$$

$$n\ (CH_3)_2Si(OH)_2 \rightarrow [\text{---}(CH_3)_2SiO\text{---}]_n + n\ H_2O$$

Silicone polymers are nontoxic and have good stability to heat, light, and oxygen; they are chemically inert and have valuable antistick and antifoam properties. They can take the form of oils, greases, and resins. Some have rubber-like properties ("Silly Putty," for example, is a silicone polymer). More than 1 million tons of silicone polymers is made worldwide annually. These materials are used in a wide variety of products: lubricants, peel-off labels, lipstick, suntan lotion, car polish, and building caulk.

© Cengage Learning/Charles D. Winters

**Silicone.** Some examples of products containing silicones, polymers with repeating —$R_2Si$—O— units.

# 21.8 Nitrogen, Phosphorus, and the Group 5A Elements

Group 5A elements are characterized by the $ns^2np^3$ configuration with its half-filled $np$ subshell. In compounds of the Group 5A elements, the primary oxidation numbers are +3 and +5, although common nitrogen compounds display a range of oxidation numbers from −3 to +5. Once again, as in Groups 3A and 4A, the most positive oxidation number is less common for the heavier elements. In many arsenic, antimony, and bismuth compounds, the element has an oxidation number of +3. Not surprisingly, compounds of these elements with oxidation numbers of +5 are powerful oxidizing agents.

This part of our tour of the main group elements will concentrate on the chemistries of nitrogen and phosphorus. Nitrogen is found primarily as $N_2$ in the atmosphere, where it constitutes 78.1% by volume (75.5% by weight). In contrast, phosphorus occurs in the earth's crust in solids. More than 200 different phosphorus-containing minerals are known; all contain the tetrahedral phosphate ion, $PO_4^{3-}$, or a derivative of this ion. By far, the most abundant phosphorus-containing minerals are apatites (◀ page 976).

Nitrogen and its compounds play a key role in our economy, with ammonia making a particularly notable contribution. Phosphoric acid is an important commodity chemical, and it finds its greatest use in producing fertilizers.

Both phosphorus and nitrogen are part of every living organism. Phosphorus is contained in nucleic acids and phospholipids, and nitrogen occurs in proteins and nucleic acids (◀ *The Chemistry of Life: Biochemistry*, page 490).

## Properties of Nitrogen and Phosphorus

Nitrogen ($N_2$) is a colorless gas that liquifies at 77 K (−196 °C) (◀ Figure 12.1, page 550). Its most notable feature is its reluctance to react with other elements or compounds because the N≡N triple bond has a large bond dissociation enthalpy (945 kJ/mol) and because the molecule is nonpolar. Nitrogen does, however, react with hydrogen to give ammonia in the presence of a catalyst (◀ Case Study, page 746) and with a few metals (notably lithium and magnesium) to give metal nitrides, compounds containing the $N^{3-}$ ion.

$$3\ Mg(s) + N_2(g) \longrightarrow Mg_3N_2(s)$$
$$\text{magnesium nitride}$$

Elemental nitrogen is a very useful material. Because of its lack of reactivity, it is used to provide a nonoxidizing atmosphere for packaged foods and wine and to pressurize electric cables and telephone wires. Liquid nitrogen is valuable as a coolant in freezing biological samples such as blood and semen, in freeze-drying food, and for other applications that require extremely low temperatures.

Group **5A**

| Nitrogen |
|---|
| 7 |
| **N** |
| 25 ppm |

| Phosphorus |
|---|
| 15 |
| **P** |
| 1000 ppm |

| Arsenic |
|---|
| 33 |
| **As** |
| 1.5 ppm |

| Antimony |
|---|
| 51 |
| **Sb** |
| 0.2 ppm |

| Bismuth |
|---|
| 83 |
| **Bi** |
| 0.048 ppm |

*Element abundances are in* **parts per million** *in the earth's crust.*

Simon Fraser/MRC Unit, Newcastle General Hospital/Science Photo Library/Photo Researchers, Inc.

**Liquid nitrogen.** Biological samples—such as embryos or semen from animals or humans—can be stored in liquid nitrogen (at −196 °C) for long periods of time.

The red and white allotropes of phosphorus.

Elemental phosphorus was first derived from human waste (see *A Closer Look: Making Phosphorus,* page 993), but it is now produced by the reduction of phosphate minerals in an electric furnace.

$$2\ Ca_3(PO_4)_2(s) + 10\ C(s) + 6\ SiO_2(s) \rightarrow P_4(g) + 6\ CaSiO_3(s) + 10\ CO(g)$$

The phosphorus vapor can then be cooled under water, preventing its spontaneous combustion, and eventually yielding the solid forms of phosphorus present at room temperature. Waxy white phosphorus is the most common allotrope of phosphorus, but paradoxically it is the least stable thermodynamically. Rather than occurring as a diatomic molecule with a triple bond, like its second-period relative nitrogen ($N_2$), phosphorus is made up of tetrahedral $P_4$ molecules in which each P atom is joined to three others via single bonds. Red phosphorus is a polymer of $P_4$ units.

white phosphorus, $P_4$          polymeric red phosphorus

## Nitrogen Compounds

A notable feature of the chemistry of nitrogen is the wide diversity of its compounds. Compounds with nitrogen in all oxidation numbers between $-3$ and $+5$ are known (Figure 21.23).

### Hydrogen Compounds of Nitrogen: Ammonia and Hydrazine

Ammonia is a gas at room temperature and pressure. It has a very penetrating odor and condenses to a liquid at $-33$ °C under 1 atm of pressure. Solutions in water, often referred to as ammonium hydroxide, are basic due to the reaction of ammonia with water (◄ Section 17.4 and Figure 3.14).

$$NH_3(aq) + H_2O(\ell) \rightleftharpoons NH_4^+(aq) + OH^-(aq)\quad K_b = 1.8 \times 10^{-5}\text{ at 25 °C}$$

Ammonia is a major industrial chemical and is prepared by the Haber process (◄ page 746), largely for use as a fertilizer.

Hydrazine, $N_2H_4$, is a colorless, fuming liquid with an ammonia-like odor (mp, 2.0 °C; bp, 113.5 °C). Almost 1 million kilograms of hydrazine is produced annually by the Raschig process—the oxidation of ammonia with alkaline sodium hypochlorite in the presence of gelatin (which is added to suppress metal-catalyzed side reactions that lower the yield of hydrazine).

$$2\ NH_3(aq) + NaClO(aq) \rightleftharpoons N_2H_4(aq) + NaCl(aq) + H_2O(\ell)$$

Hydrazine, like ammonia, is also a base,

$$N_2H_4(aq) + H_2O(\ell) \rightleftharpoons N_2H_5^+(aq) + OH^-(aq) \qquad\qquad K_b = 8.5 \times 10^{-7}$$

and it is a strong reducing agent, as reflected in the reduction potential for the following half-reaction in basic solution:

$$N_2(g) + 4\ H_2O(\ell) + 4\ e^- \rightarrow N_2H_4(aq) + 4\ OH^-(aq) \qquad\qquad E° = -1.15\text{ V}$$

Hydrazine's reducing ability is exploited in its use in wastewater treatment for chemical plants. It removes oxidizing ions such as $CrO_4^{2-}$ by reducing them, thus preventing them from entering the environment. A related use is the treatment of water boilers in large electric-generating plants. Oxygen dissolved in the water presents a serious problem in these plants because the dissolved gas can oxidize (corrode) the metal of the boiler and pipes. Hydrazine reduces the amount of dissolved oxygen in water.

$$N_2H_4(aq) + O_2(g) \rightarrow N_2(g) + 2\ H_2O(\ell)$$

Compound and Oxidation
Number of N

Ammonia, $-3$

Hydrazine, $-2$

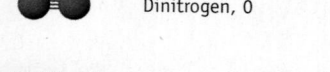
Dinitrogen, 0

Dinitrogen monoxide, $+1$

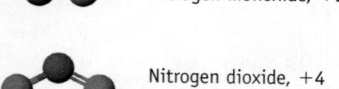
Nitrogen monoxide, $+2$

Nitrogen dioxide, $+4$

Nitric acid, $+5$

**FIGURE 21.23 Compounds and oxidation numbers for nitrogen.** In its compounds, the N atom can have oxidation states ranging from $-3$ to $+5$.

# A Healthy Saltwater Aquarium and the Nitrogen Cycle

*by Jeffrey Keaffaber, University of Florida*

Large saltwater aquariums like those at Sea World in Florida, the Shedd Aquarium in Chicago, and the new Georgia Aquarium in Atlanta, are a continual source of enjoyment. So are smaller aquariums in your home. Maintaining these facilities is not trivial, however; a healthy environment for its marine inhabitants is essential. For this, chemistry plays an important role.

A key part of aquarium maintenance involves control of the concentrations of various dissolved nitrogen-containing species, including ammonia, nitrite ion, and nitrate ion, all of which are stressful to fish at low concentrations and toxic in higher concentrations. The chemistry that relates to maintaining proper balance among these species is called the *nitrogen cycle*.

© Avico Ltd/Alamy

## Nitrification

The nitrogen cycle begins with the production of ammonia (and, in acid solution, its conjugate acid, the ammonium ion, $NH_4^+$), a fundamental waste product of protein metabolism in an aquarium habitat. Unless removed, the ammonia concentration will build up over time. To remove it, the aquarium water is cycled through sand filters infused with aerobic, oxygen-loving bacteria. These bacteria utilize enzymes that catalyze the oxidation of ammonia and ammonium ion by $O_2$ to form first nitrite ion and then nitrate ion. The overall process is called *nitrification*, and the saltwater bacteria that mediate each oxidation step are *Nitrosococcus sp.* and *Nitrococcus sp.*, respectively. Half-reactions representing this chemistry are as follows:

### Oxidation half-reactions

$$NH_4^+(aq) + 8\ OH^-(aq) \rightarrow NO_2^-(aq) + 6\ H_2O(\ell) + 6\ e^-$$

$$NO_2^-(aq) + 2\ OH^-(aq) \rightarrow NO_3^-(aq) + H_2O(\ell) + 2\ e^-$$

### Reduction half-reaction

$$O_2(aq) + 2\ H_2O(\ell) + 4\ e^- \rightarrow 4\ OH^-(aq)$$

When setting up an aquarium at home, it is appropriate to monitor the concentrations of various nitrogen species. Initially, the $NH_3/NH_4^+$ concentration rises, but then it begins to fall as oxidation occurs. With time, the nitrite ion concentration builds up, peaks, and then decreases, with an accompanying increase in nitrate ion concentration. To reach a stable situation, as much as 6 weeks may be required.

## Denitrification

Nitrate is much less toxic than ammonia and the nitrite ion, but its buildup must also be limited. In a small aquarium, nitrate ion concentration can be controlled by partial exchange of water. However, because of environmental restrictions this is not possible for large aquariums; they must use a closed water treatment process.

To remedy the buildup of the nitrate ion, another biologically catalyzed process is used that reduces the nitrate ion to nitrogen gas, $N_2$. A reducing agent is required, and early designs of denitrifying filters utilized methanol, $CH_3OH$, as the reducing agent. Among naturally occurring saltwater bacteria capable of nitrate reduction under low oxygen (anoxic) conditions, *Pseudomonas sp.* is commonly used. The bacteria, utilizing enzymes to catalyze reaction of nitrate and methanol to form $N_2$ and $CO_2$, are introduced to sand filters where methanol is added.

A stable pH is also important to the health of aquarium fish. Therefore, the marine environment in a saltwater aquarium is maintained at a relatively constant pH of 8.0–8.2. To aid in this, the $CO_2$ produced by methanol oxidation remains dissolved in solution, and increases the buffer capacity of the seawater.

## Questions:

1. Write a balanced net ionic equation for the oxidation of $NH_4^+$ by $O_2$ to produce $H_2O$ and $NO_2^-$.
2. Write half-reactions for the reduction of $NO_3^-$ to $N_2$ and for the oxidation of $CH_3OH$ to $CO_2$ in basic solution. Then, combine these half-reactions to obtain the balanced equation for the reduction of $NO_3^-$ by $CH_3OH$.
3. Consider the carbon-containing species $CO_2$, $H_2CO_3$, $HCO_3^-$, and $CO_3^{2-}$. Which one is present in largest concentration at the pH conditions of the aquarium? Give a short explanation. $K_a$ of $H_2CO_3 = 4.2 \times 10^{-7}$ and $K_a$ of $HCO_3^- = 4.8 \times 10^{-11}$. (See Study Question 18.110.)
4. A large, $2.2 \times 10^7$ L, aquarium contains $1.7 \times 10^4$ kg of dissolved $NO_3^-$. Calculate concentrations in ppm (mg/L) N, ppm $NO_3^-$, and the molar concentration of $NO_3^-$.

**Answers to these questions are available in Appendix N.**

## Oxides and Oxoacids of Nitrogen

Nitrogen is unique among all elements in the number of binary oxides it forms (Table 21.5). All are thermodynamically unstable with respect to decomposition to $N_2$ and $O_2$; that is, all have positive $\Delta_f G°$ values. Most are slow to decompose, however, and so are described as kinetically stable.

*Dinitrogen monoxide*, $N_2O$, commonly called *nitrous oxide*, is a nontoxic, odorless, and tasteless gas in which nitrogen has the lowest oxidation number (+1) among the nitrogen oxides. It can be made by the careful decomposition of ammonium nitrate at 250 °C.

$$NH_4NO_3(s) \rightarrow N_2O(g) + 2\ H_2O(g)$$

It is used as an anesthetic in minor surgery and has been called "laughing gas" because of its euphoriant effects. Because it is soluble in vegetable fats, the largest commercial use of $N_2O$ is as a propellant and aerating agent in cans of whipped cream.

*Nitrogen monoxide*, NO, is an odd-electron molecule. It has 11 valence electrons, giving it one unpaired electron and making it a free radical. The compound has recently been the subject of intense research because it has been found to be important in a number of biochemical processes.

*Nitrogen dioxide*, $NO_2$, is the brown gas you see when a bottle of nitric acid is allowed to stand in the sunlight.

$$2\ HNO_3(aq) \rightarrow 2\ NO_2(g) + H_2O(\ell) + \tfrac{1}{2}\ O_2(g)$$

Nitrogen dioxide is also a culprit in air pollution (◄ page 948). Nitrogen monoxide forms when atmospheric nitrogen and oxygen are heated in internal combustion engines. Released into the atmosphere, NO rapidly reacts with $O_2$ to form $NO_2$.

$$2\ NO(g) + O_2(g) \rightarrow 2\ NO_2(g)$$

**Table 21.5 Some Oxides of Nitrogen**

| Formula | Name | Structure | Nitrogen Oxidation Number | Description |
|---------|------|-----------|---------------------------|-------------|
| $N_2O$ | Dinitrogen monoxide (nitrous oxide) | :N≡N—O: <br> linear | +1 | Colorless gas (laughing gas) |
| NO | Nitrogen monoxide (nitric oxide) | * | +2 | Colorless gas; odd-electron molecule (paramagnetic) |
| $N_2O_3$ | Dinitrogen trioxide | O N—N O: O: <br> planar | +3 | Blue solid (mp, −100.7 °C); reversibly dissociates to NO and $NO_2$ above its mp. |
| $NO_2$ | Nitrogen dioxide | N O O | +4 | Brown, paramagnetic gas; odd-electron molecule |
| $N_2O_4$ | Dinitrogen tetraoxide | O N—N O O O <br> planar | +4 | Colorless liquid/gas; dissociates to $NO_2$ (◄ Figure 16.8) |
| $N_2O_5$ | Dinitrogen pentaoxide | O O O N N O: O: | +5 | Colorless solid |

*It is not possible to draw a Lewis structure that accurately represents the electronic structure of NO. ◄ Chapter 8. Also note that only one resonance structure is shown for each structure.

## Making Phosphorus

*He stoked his small furnace with more charcoal and pumped the bellows until his retort glowed red hot. Suddenly something strange began to happen. Glowing fumes filled the vessel and from the end of the retort dripped a shining liquid that burst into flames.*

J. Emsley: *The 13th Element*, p. 5. New York, John Wiley, 2000.

John Emsley begins his story of phosphorus, its discovery, and its uses, by imagining what the German alchemist Hennig Brandt must have seen in his laboratory that day in 1669. (See page 334 for an artist's conception of the discovery of phosphorus by Brandt.) He was in search of the philosopher's stone, the magic elixir that would turn the crudest substance into gold. (Some may recall that the first Harry Potter novel was titled *Harry Potter and the Philosopher's Stone* when it was published in Great Britain.)

Brandt was experimenting with urine, which had served as the source of useful chemicals since Roman times. It is not surprising that phosphorus could be extracted from this source. Humans consume much more phosphorus, in the form of phosphate, than they require, and the excess phosphorus (about 1.4 g per day) is excreted in the urine. It is nonetheless extraordinary that Brandt was able to isolate the element. According to an 18th-century chemistry book, about 30 g of phosphorus could be obtained from 60 gallons of urine. And the process was not simple. Another 18th-century recipe states that "50 or 60 pails full" of urine was to be used. "Let it lie steeping . . . till it putrefy and breed worms." The chemist was then to reduce the whole to a paste and finally to heat the paste very strongly in a retort. After some days, phosphorus distilled from the mixture and was

collected in water. (We know now that carbon from the organic compounds in the urine would have reduced the phosphate to phosphorus.) Phosphorus was made in this manner for more than 100 years.

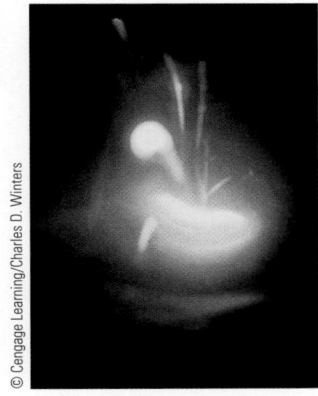

© Cengage Learning/Charles D. Winters

**The glow of phosphorus burning in air.**

---

Nitrogen dioxide has 17 valence electrons, so it is also an odd-electron molecule. Because the odd electron largely resides on the N atom, two $NO_2$ molecules can combine, forming an N—N bond and producing $N_2O_4$, *dinitrogen tetraoxide*.

$$2\ NO_2(g) \longrightarrow N_2O_4(g)$$

deep brown          colorless
gas                (mp, −11.2 °C)

Solid $N_2O_4$ is colorless and consists entirely of $N_2O_4$ molecules. However, as the solid melts and the temperature increases to the boiling point, the color darkens as $N_2O_4$ dissociates to form brown $NO_2$. At the normal boiling point (21.5 °C), the distinctly brown gas consists of 15.9% $NO_2$ and 84.1% $N_2O_4$.

When $NO_2$ is bubbled into water, nitric acid and nitrous acid form.

$$2\ NO_2(g) + H_2O(\ell) \rightarrow HNO_3(aq) + HNO_2(aq)$$

nitric acid     nitrous acid

Nitric acid has been known for centuries and has become an important compound in our modern economy. The oldest way to make the acid is to treat $NaNO_3$ with sulfuric acid (Figure 21.24).

$$2\ NaNO_3(s) + H_2SO_4(\ell) \rightarrow 2\ HNO_3(\ell) + Na_2SO_4(s)$$

Enormous quantities of nitric acid are now produced industrially by the oxidation of ammonia in the multistep *Ostwald process*. The acid has many applications, but by far the greatest amount is turned into ammonium nitrate (for use as a fertilizer) by the reaction of nitric acid and ammonia.

Nitric acid is a powerful oxidizing agent, as the large, positive $E°$ values for the following half-reactions illustrate:

$$NO_3{}^-(aq) + 4\ H_3O^+(aq) + 3\ e^- \rightarrow NO(g) + 6\ H_2O(\ell) \qquad E° = +0.96\ V$$

$$NO_3{}^-(aq) + 2\ H_3O^+(aq) + e^- \rightarrow NO_2(g) + 3\ H_2O(\ell) \qquad E° = +0.80\ V$$

© Cengage Learning/Charles D. Winters

**Nitrous oxide, $N_2O$.** This oxide readily dissolves in fats, so the gas is added, under pressure, to cans of cream. When the valve is opened, the gas expands, whipping the cream. $N_2O$ is also an anesthetic and is considered safe for medical uses. However, significant dangers arise from using it as a recreational drug. Long-term use can induce nerve damage and cause problems such as weakness and loss of feeling.

**FIGURE 21.24 The preparation and properties of nitric acid.**

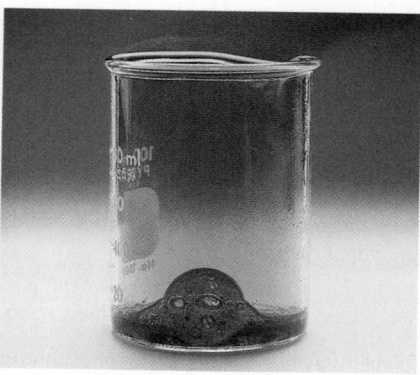

**(a)** Nitric acid is prepared by the reaction of sulfuric acid and sodium nitrate. (Here the reactants were heated in the flask on the right, and $HNO_3$ was distilled and collected in the flask cooled with ice on the left.) Pure $HNO_3$ is colorless, but samples of the acid are often brown because of $NO_2$ formed by decomposition of the acid. In this photo this gas fills the apparatus and colors the liquid in the distillation flask.

**(b)** When concentrated nitric acid reacts with copper, the metal is oxidized to copper(II) ions, and $NO_2$ gas is a reaction product.

Concentrated nitric acid attacks and oxidizes most metals. (Aluminum is an exception; see page 983.) In this process, the nitrate ion is reduced to one of the nitrogen oxides. Which oxide is formed depends on the metal and on reaction conditions. In the case of copper, for example, either NO or $NO_2$ is produced, depending on the concentration of the acid (Figure 21.24b).

In dilute acid:

$$3\ Cu(s) + 8\ H_3O^+(aq) + 2\ NO_3^-(aq) \rightarrow 3\ Cu^{2+}(aq) + 12\ H_2O(\ell) + 2\ NO(g)$$

In concentrated acid:

$$Cu(s) + 4\ H_3O^+(aq) + 2\ NO_3^-(aq) \rightarrow Cu^{2+}(aq) + 6\ H_2O(\ell) + 2\ NO_2(g)$$

Four metals (Au, Pt, Rh, and Ir) that are not attacked by nitric acid are often described as the "noble metals." The alchemists of the 14th century, however, knew that if they mixed $HNO_3$ with HCl in a ratio of about 1:3, this aqua regia, or "kingly water," would attack even gold, the noblest of metals.

$$10\ Au(s) + 6\ NO_3^-(aq) + 40\ Cl^-(aq) + 36\ H_3O^+(aq) \rightarrow$$
$$10\ [AuCl_4]^-(aq) + 3\ N_2(g) + 54\ H_2O(\ell)$$

## Hydrogen Compounds of Phosphorus and Other Group 5A Elements

The phosphorus analog of ammonia, phosphine ($PH_3$), is a poisonous, highly reactive gas with a faint garlic-like odor. Industrially, it is made by the reaction of white phosphorus and aqueous NaOH.

$$P_4(s) + 3\ KOH(aq) + 3\ H_2O(\ell) \rightarrow PH_3(g) + 3\ KH_2PO_2(aq)$$

The other hydrides of the heavier Group 5A elements are also toxic and become more unstable as the atomic number of the element increases. Nonetheless, arsine ($AsH_3$) is used in the semiconductor industry as a starting material in the preparation of gallium arsenide (GaAs) semiconductors.

## Phosphorus Oxides and Sulfides

The most important compounds of phosphorus are those with oxygen, and there are at least six simple binary compounds containing just phosphorus and oxygen. All of them can be thought of as being derived structurally from the $P_4$ tetrahedron

Photos © Cengage Learning/Charles D. Winters

**FIGURE 21.25 Phosphorus oxides.** Other binary P—O compounds have formulas between $P_4O_6$ and $P_4O_{10}$. They are formed by starting with $P_4O_6$ and adding O atoms successively to the P atom vertices.

of white phosphorus. For example, if $P_4$ is carefully oxidized, $P_4O_6$ is formed; an O atom has been placed into each P—P bond in the tetrahedron (Figure 21.25).

The most common and important phosphorus oxide is $P_4O_{10}$, a fine white powder commonly called *phosphorus pentaoxide* because its empirical formula is $P_2O_5$. In $P_4O_{10}$, each phosphorus atom is surrounded tetrahedrally by O atoms.

Phosphorus also forms a series of compounds with sulfur. Of these, the most important is $P_4S_3$. In this phosphorus sulfide, S atoms are placed into only three of the P—P bonds. The principal use of $P_4S_3$ is in "strike anywhere" matches, the kind that light when you rub the head against a rough object. The active ingredients are $P_4S_3$ and the powerful oxidizing agent potassium chlorate, $KClO_3$. The "safety match" is now more common than the "strike anywhere" match. In safety matches, the head is predominantly $KClO_3$, and the material on the match book is red phosphorus (about 50%), $Sb_2S_3$, $Fe_2O_3$, and glue.

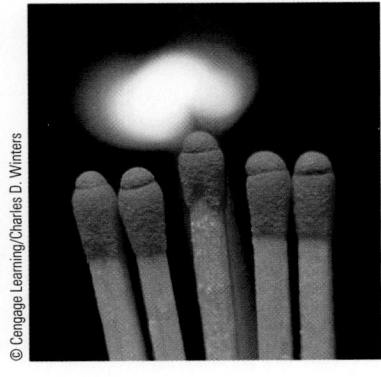

**Matches.** The head of a "strike anywhere" match contains $P_4S_3$ and the oxidizing agent $KClO_3$. (Other components are ground glass, $Fe_2O_3$, ZnO, and glue.) Safety matches have sulfur (3–5%) and $KClO_3$ (45–55%) in the match head and red phosphorus in the striking strip.

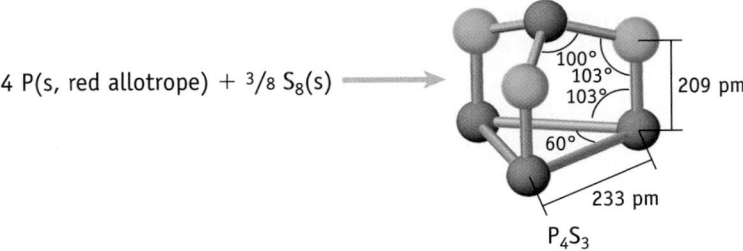

Enormous quantities of phosphorus compounds are used around the world, and most of this begins with phosphate rock, which is largely $Ca_3(PO_4)_2$ or apatite. As outlined in Figure 21.26, phosphate rock is converted to impure phosphoric acid and then to other products, or to elemental phosphorus, from which pure acid and other products are made.

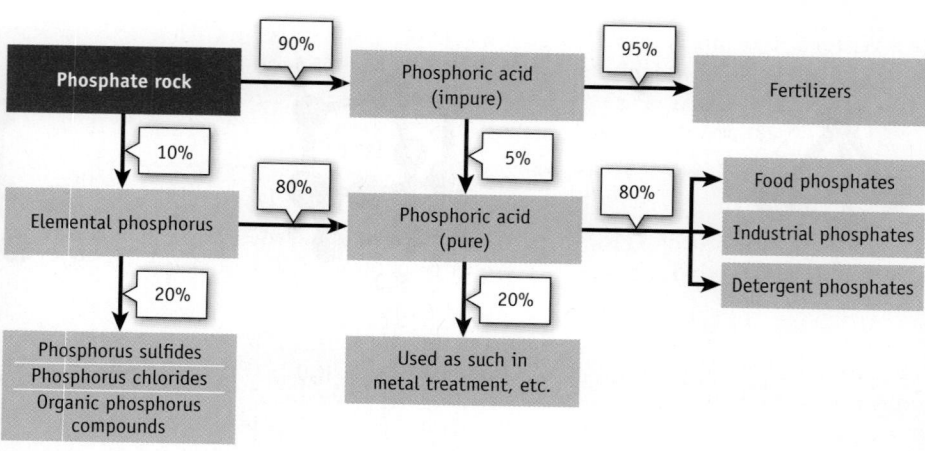

**(a) Mining phosphate rock.** Phosphate rock is primarily $Ca_3(PO_4)_2$, and most mined in the United States comes from Florida.

**(b) Uses of phosphorus and phosphoric acid.**

**FIGURE 21.26** Uses of phosphate rock, phosphorus, and phosphoric acid.

## Phosphorus Oxoacids and Their Salts

A few of the many known phosphorus oxoacids are illustrated in Table 21.6. Indeed, there are so many acids and their salts in this category that structural principles have been developed to organize and understand them.

(a) All P atoms in the oxoacids and their anions (conjugate bases) are four-coordinate and tetrahedral.

(b) All the P atoms in the acids have at least one P—OH group (and this occurs often in the anions as well). In every case, the H atom is ionizable as $H^+$.

(c) Some oxoacids have one or more P—H bonds. These H atoms are not ionizable as $H^+$.

(d) Polymerization can occur by P—O—P bond formation to give both linear and cyclic species. Two P atoms are never joined by more than one P—O—P bridge.

### Table 21.6 Phosphorus Oxoacids

| Formula | Name | Structure | $pK_a$ |
|---|---|---|---|
| $H_3PO_4$ | Orthophosphoric acid | | 2.21, 7.21, 12.67 |
| $H_4P_2O_7$ | Pyrophosphoric acid (diphosphoric acid) | | 0.85, 1.49, 5.77, 8.22 |
| $(HPO_3)_3$ | Metaphosphoric acid | | |
| $H_3PO_3$ | Phosphorous acid (phosphonic acid) | | 2.00, 6.59 |
| $H_3PO_2$ | Hypophosphorous acid (phosphinic acid) | | 1.24 |

(e) When a P atom is surrounded only by O atoms (as in $H_3PO_4$), its oxidation number is +5. For each P—OH that is replaced by P—H, the oxidation number drops by 2 (because P is considered more electronegative than H). For example, the oxidation number of P in $H_3PO_2$ is +1.

Orthophosphoric acid, $H_3PO_4$, and its salts are far more important commercially than other P—O acids. Millions of tons of phosphoric acid are made annually, some using white phosphorus as the starting material. The element is burned in oxygen to give $P_4O_{10}$, and the oxide reacts with water to produce the acid (Figure 21.27).

$$P_4O_{10}(s) + 6\ H_2O(\ell) \rightarrow 4\ H_3PO_4(aq)$$

This approach gives a pure product, so it is used to make phosphoric acid for use in food products in particular. The acid is nontoxic, and it gives the tart or sour taste to carbonated "soft drinks," such as various colas (about 0.05% $H_3PO_4$) or root beer (about 0.01% $H_3PO_4$).

A major use for phosphoric acid is to impart corrosion resistance to metal objects such as nuts and bolts, tools, and car-engine parts by plunging the object into a hot acid bath. Car bodies are similarly treated with phosphoric acid containing metal ions such as $Zn^{2+}$, and aluminum trim is "polished" by treating it with the acid.

The reaction of $H_3PO_4$ with strong bases produces salts such as $NaH_2PO_4$, $Na_2HPO_4$, and $Na_3PO_4$. In industry, the monosodium and disodium salts are produced using $Na_2CO_3$ as the base, but an excess of the stronger (and more expensive) base NaOH is required to remove the third proton to give $Na_3PO_4$.

Sodium phosphate ($Na_3PO_4$) is used in scouring powders and paint strippers because the anion $PO_4^{3-}$ is a relatively strong base in water ($K_b = 2.8 \times 10^{-2}$). Sodium monohydrogen phosphate, $Na_2HPO_4$, which has a less basic anion than $PO_4^{3-}$, is widely used in food products. Kraft has patented a process using the salt in the manufacture of pasteurized cheese, for example. Thousands of tons of $Na_2HPO_4$ are still used for this purpose, even though the function of the salt in this process is not completely understood. In addition, a small amount of $Na_2HPO_4$ in pudding mixes enables the mix to gel in cold water, and the basic anion raises the pH of cereals to provide "quick-cooking" breakfast cereal. (The $OH^-$ ion from $HPO_4^{2-}$ hydrolysis accelerates the breakdown of the cellulose material in the cereal.)

Calcium phosphates are used in a broad spectrum of products. For example, the weak acid $Ca(H_2PO_4)_2 \cdot H_2O$ is used as the acid leavening agent in baking powder. A typical baking powder contains (along with inert ingredients) 28% $NaHCO_3$, 10.7% $Ca(H_2PO_4)_2 \cdot H_2O$, and 21.4% $NaAl(SO_4)_2$ (also a weak acid). The weak acids react with sodium bicarbonate to produce $CO_2$ gas. For example,

$$Ca(H_2PO_4)_2 \cdot H_2O(s) + 2\ NaHCO_3(aq) \rightarrow 2\ CO_2(g) + 3\ H_2O(\ell) + Na_2HPO_4(aq) + CaHPO_4(aq)$$

Finally, calcium monohydrogen phosphate, $CaHPO_4$, is used as an abrasive and polishing agent in toothpaste.

**FIGURE 21.27 Reaction of $P_4O_{10}$ and water.** The white solid oxide reacts vigorously with water to give orthophosphoric acid, $H_3PO_4$. (The heat generated vaporizes the water, so steam is visible.)

---

**REVIEW & CHECK FOR SECTION 21.8**

1. Construct Lewis structures for the several resonance forms of $N_2O$. What is the predicted N—N bond order?

   (a) 1          (b) 2          (c) between 2 and 3     (d) 3

2. Which statement about ammonia is *not correct?*

   (a) Ammonia can be made by a direct reaction of the elements.

   (b) Solutions of ammonia are acidic.

   (c) Ammonia is a gas at room temperature and atmospheric pressure.

   (d) Ammonia is used as a reactant in the synthesis of nitric acid.

3. What is the oxidation state of phosphorus in phosphorous acid, $HPO(OH)_2$?

   (a) 0          (b) +1          (c) +3          (d) +5

Group **6A**

| Oxygen |
| 8 |
| **O** |
| 474,000 ppm |

| Sulfur |
| 16 |
| **S** |
| 260 ppm |

| Selenium |
| 34 |
| **Se** |
| 0.5 ppm |

| Tellurium |
| 52 |
| **Te** |
| 0.005 ppm |

| Polonium |
| 84 |
| **Po** |
| trace |

*Element abundances are in* **parts per million** *in the earth's crust.*

# 21.9 Oxygen, Sulfur, and the Group 6A Elements

Oxygen is by far the most abundant element in the earth's crust, representing slightly less than 50% of it by weight. It is present as elemental oxygen in the atmosphere and is combined with other elements in water and in many minerals. Scientists believe that elemental oxygen did not appear on this planet until about 3.5 billion years ago, when it was formed on the planet by plants through the process of photosynthesis.

Sulfur, seventeenth in abundance in the earth's crust, is also found in its elemental form in nature, but only in certain concentrated deposits. Sulfur-containing compounds occur in natural gas, coal, and oil. In minerals, sulfur occurs as the sulfide ion (for example, in cinnabar, HgS, and galena, PbS), as the disulfide ion (in iron pyrite, $FeS_2$, or "fool's gold"), and as sulfate ion (e.g., in gypsum, $CaSO_4 \cdot 2 H_2O$). Sulfur oxides ($SO_2$ and $SO_3$) also occur in nature, primarily as products of volcanic activity (Figure 21.28).

In the United States, sulfur—several million tons per year—is obtained from deposits of the element found along the Gulf of Mexico. These deposits occur typically at a depth of 150 to 750 m below the surface in layers about 30 m thick. They are thought to have been formed by anaerobic ("without elemental oxygen") bacteria acting on sedimentary sulfate deposits such as gypsum.

## Preparation and Properties of the Elements

Pure oxygen is obtained by the fractional distillation of air and is among the top five industrial chemicals produced in the United States. Oxygen can be made in the laboratory by electrolysis of water (Figure 21.4) and by the catalyzed decomposition of metal chlorates such as $KClO_3$.

$$2\ KClO_3(s) \xrightarrow{\text{catalyst}} 2\ KCl(s) + 3\ O_2(g)$$

At room temperature and pressure, oxygen is a colorless gas, but it is pale blue when condensed to a liquid at $-183\ °C$ (◄ Figure 9.12). As described in Section 9.3, diatomic oxygen is paramagnetic because it has two unpaired electrons.

An allotrope of oxygen, ozone ($O_3$), is a blue, diamagnetic gas with an odor so strong that it can be detected in concentrations as low as 0.05 ppm. Ozone is synthesized by passing $O_2$ through an electric discharge or by irradiating $O_2$ with ultraviolet light. It is often in the news because of the realization that the earth's protective layer of ozone in the stratosphere is being disrupted by chlorofluorocarbons and other chemicals (◄ page 951).

Sulfur has numerous allotropes. The most common and most stable allotrope is the yellow, orthorhombic form, which consists of $S_8$ molecules with the sulfur atoms arranged in a crown-shaped ring (Figure 21.29a). Less stable allotropes are known that have rings of 6 to 20 sulfur atoms. Another form of sulfur, called plastic sulfur, has a molecular structure with chains of sulfur atoms (Figure 21.29b).

Selenium and tellurium are comparatively rare on earth, having abundances about the same as those of silver and gold, respectively. Because their chemistry is similar to that of sulfur, they are often found in minerals associated with the sulfides of copper, silver, iron, and arsenic, and they are recovered as by-products of the industries devoted to those elements.

Selenium has a range of uses, including in glass making. A cadmium sulfide/selenide mixture is added to glass to give it a brilliant red color (Figure 21.30a). The most familiar use of selenium is in xerography, a word meaning "dry printing" and a process at the heart of the modern copy machine. Most photocopy machines use an aluminum plate or roller coated with selenium. Light coming from the imaging lens selectively discharges a static electric charge on the selenium surface, and the black toner sticks only on the areas that remain charged. A copy is made when the toner is transferred to a sheet of plain paper.

The heaviest element of Group 6A, polonium, is radioactive and found only in trace amounts on earth. It was discovered in Paris, France, in 1898 by Marie Sklodowska Curie (1867–1934) and her husband Pierre Curie (1859–1906). The Curies painstakingly separated this element from a large quantity of pitchblende, a uranium-containing ore.

**FIGURE 21.28** Sulfur spewing from a volcano in Indonesia.

Photos © Cengage Learning/ Charles D. Winters

(a)                                                        (b)

**FIGURE 21.29 Sulfur allotropes.**
**(a)** At room temperature, sulfur exists as a bright yellow solid composed of $S_8$ rings. **(b)** When heated, the rings break open and eventually form chains of S atoms in a material described as "plastic sulfur."

## Sulfur Compounds

Hydrogen sulfide, $H_2S$, has a bent molecular geometry, like water. Unlike water, however, $H_2S$ is a gas under standard conditions (mp, −85.6 °C; bp, −60.3 °C) because its intermolecular forces are weak compared with the strong hydrogen bonding in water (◄ Figure 12.6). Hydrogen sulfide is poisonous, comparable in toxicity to hydrogen cyanide, but fortunately it has a terrible odor and is detectable in concentrations as low as 0.02 ppm. You must be careful with $H_2S$, though. Because it has an anesthetic effect, your nose rapidly loses its ability to detect it. Death occurs at $H_2S$ concentrations of 100 ppm.

Sulfur is often found as the sulfide ion in conjunction with metals because all metal sulfides (except those based on Group 1A metals) are insoluble. The recovery of metals from their sulfide ores usually begins by heating the ore in air.

$$2\ PbS(s) + 3\ O_2(g) \rightarrow 2\ PbO(s) + 2\ SO_2(g)$$

Here, lead(II) sulfide is converted to lead(II) oxide, and this is then reduced to lead using carbon or carbon monoxide in a blast furnace.

$$PbO(s) + CO(g) \rightarrow Pb(\ell) + CO_2(g)$$

● **Bad Breath** Halitosis or "bad breath" is due to three sulfur-containing compounds: $H_2S$, $CH_3SH$ (methyl mercaptan), and $(CH_3)_2S$ (dimethyl sulfide). All three can be detected in very tiny concentrations. For example, your nose knows if as little as 0.2 microgram of $CH_3SH$ is present per liter of air. The compounds result from bacteria's attack on the sulfur-containing amino acids cysteine and methionine in food particles in the mouth.

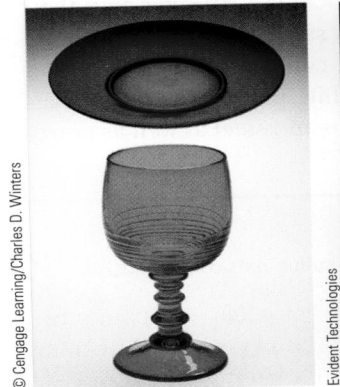

© Cengage Learning/Charles D. Winters

**(a)** Glass takes on a brilliant red color when a mixture of cadmium sulfide/selenide (CdS, CdSe) is added to it.

Evident Technologies

**(b)** These sample bottles hold suspensions of quantum dots, nanometer-sized crystals of CdSe dispersed in a polymer matrix. The crystals emit light in the visible range when excited by ultraviolet light. Light emission at different wavelengths is achieved by changing the particle size. Crystals of PbS and PbSe can be made that emit light in the infrared range.

**FIGURE 21.30 Uses of selenium.**

© Cengage Learning/Charles D. Winters

**Common household products containing sulfur or sulfur-based compounds.**

Alternatively, the oxide can be reduced to elemental lead by combining it with fresh lead sulfide.

$$2\ PbO(s) + PbS(s) \rightarrow 3\ Pb(s) + SO_2(g)$$

H₂S       SO₂       SO₃       H₂SO₄

Models of some common sulfur-containing molecules: $H_2S$, $SO_2$, $SO_3$, and $H_2SO_4$.

Sulfur dioxide ($SO_2$), a colorless, toxic gas with a sharp odor, is produced on an enormous scale by the combustion of sulfur and by roasting sulfide ores in air. The combustion of sulfur in sulfur-containing coal and fuel oil creates particularly large environmental problems. It has been estimated that about $2.0 \times 10^8$ tons of sulfur oxides (primarily $SO_2$) are released into the atmosphere each year by human activities; this is more than half of the total emitted by all other natural sources of sulfur in the environment.

Sulfur dioxide readily dissolves in water. The most important reaction of this gas is its oxidation to $SO_3$.

$$SO_2(g) + \tfrac{1}{2}\ O_2(g) \rightarrow SO_3(g) \qquad \Delta_r H° = -98.9\ \text{kJ/mol-rxn}$$

Sulfur trioxide is almost never isolated but is converted directly to sulfuric acid by reaction with water in the "contact process."

The largest use of sulfur is the production of sulfuric acid, $H_2SO_4$, the compound produced in largest quantity by the chemical industry (◄ page 133). In the United States, roughly 70% of the acid is used to manufacture superphosphate fertilizer from phosphate rock. Plants need a soluble form of phosphorus for growth, but calcium phosphate and apatite [$Ca_5X(PO_4)_3$, X = F, OH, Cl] are insoluble. Treating phosphate-containing minerals with sulfuric acid produces a mixture of soluble phosphates. The balanced equation for the reaction of excess sulfuric acid and calcium phosphate, for example, is

$$Ca_3(PO_4)_2(s) + 3\ H_2SO_4(\ell) \rightarrow 2\ H_3PO_4(\ell) + 3\ CaSO_4(s)$$

but it does not tell the whole story. Concentrated superphosphate fertilizer is actually mostly $CaHPO_4$ or $Ca(H_2PO_4)_2$ plus some $H_3PO_4$ and $CaSO_4$. (Notice that the chemical principle behind this reaction is that sulfuric acid is a stronger acid than $H_3PO_4$ (◄ Table 17.3), so the $PO_4^{3-}$ ion is protonated by sulfuric acid.)

Smaller amounts of sulfuric acid are used in the conversion of ilmenite, a titanium-bearing ore, to $TiO_2$, which is then used as a white pigment in paint, plastics, and paper. The acid is also used to manufacture iron and steel as well as petroleum products, synthetic polymers, and paper.

---

**REVIEW & CHECK FOR SECTION 21.9**

1.  Which of the following is not a common oxidation number for sulfur in its compounds?

    (a)   −2          (b)   +6          (c)   +3          (d)   +4

2.  Which statement about oxygen is *not* true?

    (a)   Liquid oxygen is attracted to a magnet.

    (b)   The allotropes of oxygen are $O_2$ and $O_3$.

    (c)   Oxygen is the most abundant element in the earth's crust.

    (d)   All electrons in $O_2$ are paired.

## Snot-tites and Sulfur Chemistry

Sulfur chemistry can be important in cave formation, as a spectacular example in the jungles of southern Mexico amply demonstrates. Toxic hydrogen sulfide gas spews from the Cueva de Villa Luz along with water that is milky white with suspended sulfur particles. The cave can be followed downward to a large underground stream and a maze of actively enlarging cave passages. Water rises into the cave from underlying sulfur-bearing strata, releasing hydrogen sulfide at concentrations up to 150 ppm. Yellow sulfur crystallizes on the cave walls around the inlets. The sulfur and sulfuric acid are produced by the following reactions:

$$2 \ H_2S(g) + O_2(g) \rightarrow 2 \ S(s) + 2 \ H_2O(\ell)$$

$$2 \ S(s) + 2 \ H_2O(\ell) + 3 \ O_2(g) \rightarrow$$
$$2 \ H_2SO_4(aq)$$

The cave atmosphere is poisonous to humans, so gas masks are essential for would-be explorers. But surprisingly, the cave is teeming with life. Several species of bacteria thrive on sulfur compounds in acidic environments. The chemical energy released in their metabolism is used to obtain carbon for their bodies from calcium carbonate and carbon dioxide, both of which are abundant in the cave. One result is that bacterial filaments hang from the walls and ceilings in bundles. Because the filaments look like something coming from a runny nose, cave explorers refer to them as "snot-tites." Other microbes feed on the bacteria, and so on up the food chain—which includes spiders, gnats, and pygmy snails—all the way to sardine-like fish that swim in the cave stream. This entire ecosystem is supported by reactions involving sulfur within the cave.

**Snot-tites.** Filaments of sulfur-oxidizing bacteria (dubbed "snot-tites") hang from the ceiling of a Mexican cave containing an atmosphere rich in hydrogen sulfide. The bacteria thrive on the energy released by oxidation of the hydrogen sulfide, forming the base of a complex food chain. Droplets of sulfuric acid on the filaments have an average pH of 1.4, with some as low as zero! Drops that landed on explorers in the cave burned their skin and disintegrated their clothing.

*Arthur N. Palmer*

## 21.10  The Halogens, Group 7A

Fluorine and chlorine are the most abundant halogens in the earth's crust, with fluorine somewhat more abundant than chlorine. If their abundance in sea water is measured, however, the situation is quite different. Chlorine has an abundance in sea water of 18,000 ppm, whereas the abundance of fluorine in the same source is only 1.3 ppm. This variation is a result of the differences in the solubility of their salts and plays a role in the methods used to recover the elements themselves.

### Preparation of the Elements

#### Fluorine

The water-insoluble mineral fluorspar (calcium fluoride, $CaF_2$) is one of the many sources of fluorine. Because the mineral was originally used as a flux in metalworking, its name comes from the Latin word meaning "to flow." In the 17th century, it was discovered that solid $CaF_2$ would emit light when heated, and the phenomenon was called *fluorescence*. In the early 1800s, when it was recognized that a new element was contained in fluorspar, A. M. Ampère (1775–1836) suggested that the element be called fluorine.

Although fluorine was recognized as an element by 1812, it was not until 1886 that it was isolated by the French chemist Henri Moisson (1852–1907) in elemental form as a very pale yellow gas by the electrolysis of KF dissolved in anhydrous HF. Indeed, because $F_2$ is such a powerful oxidizing agent, chemical oxidation of $F^-$ to $F_2$ is not feasible, and electrolysis is the only practical way to obtain gaseous $F_2$ (Figure 21.31).

Fluorine is still prepared by the Moisson method, but the preparation is difficult because $F_2$ is so reactive. It corrodes the equipment and reacts violently with traces of grease or other contaminants. Furthermore, the products of electrolysis,

**Group 7A**
*Halogens*

| |
|---|
| Fluorine<br>9<br>**F**<br>950 ppm |
| Chlorine<br>17<br>**Cl**<br>130 ppm |
| Bromine<br>35<br>**Br**<br>0.37 ppm |
| Iodine<br>53<br>**I**<br>0.14 ppm |
| Astatine<br>85<br>**At**<br>trace |

*Element abundances are in* **parts per million** *in the earth's crust.*

**FIGURE 21.31 Schematic of an electrolysis cell for producing fluorine.**

$F_2$ and $H_2$, can recombine explosively, so they must not be allowed to come into contact with each other. (Compare with the reaction of $H_2$ and $Br_2$ in Figure 21.5.) Current U.S. production of fluorine is approximately 5000 metric tons per year.

## Chlorine

Chlorine is a strong oxidizing agent, and to prepare this element from chloride ion by a chemical reaction requires an even stronger oxidizing agent. In the laboratory permanganate ions or dichromate ions in acid solution will serve this purpose (Figure 21.32). Elemental chlorine was first made by the Swedish chemist Karl Wilhelm Scheele (1742–1786) in 1774, who combined sodium chloride with an oxidizing agent in an acidic solution.

Industrially, chlorine is made by electrolysis of brine (concentrated aqueous NaCl). The other product of the electrolysis, NaOH, is also a valuable industrial chemical. About 80% of the chlorine produced is made using an electrochemical cell similar to the one depicted in Figure 21.33. Oxidation of chloride ion to $Cl_2$ gas occurs at the anode and reduction of water occurs at the cathode.

Anode reaction (oxidation): $\qquad$ $2\ Cl^-(aq) \rightarrow Cl_2(g) + 2\ e^-$

Cathode reaction (reduction): $\qquad$ $2\ H_2O(\ell) + 2\ e^- \rightarrow H_2(g) + 2\ OH^-(aq)$

Activated titanium is used for the anode, and stainless steel or nickel is preferred for the cathode. The anode and cathode compartments are separated by a membrane that is not permeable to water but allows $Na^+$ ions to pass to maintain the charge balance. Thus, the membrane functions as a "salt" bridge between the anode and cathode compartments. The energy consumption of these cells is in the range of 2000–2500 kWh per ton of NaOH produced.

## Bromine

The standard reduction potentials of the halogens indicate that their strength as oxidizing agents decreases going from $F_2$ to $I_2$.

| Half-Reaction | Reduction Potential ($E°$, V) |
|---|---|
| $F_2(g) + 2\ e^- \rightarrow 2\ F^-(aq)$ | 2.87 |
| $Cl_2(g) + 2\ e^- \rightarrow 2\ Cl^-(aq)$ | 1.36 |
| $Br_2(\ell) + 2\ e^- \rightarrow 2\ Br^-(aq)$ | 1.08 |
| $I_2(s) + 2\ e^- \rightarrow 2\ I^-(aq)$ | 0.535 |

This means that $Cl_2$ will oxidize $Br^-$ ions to $Br_2$ in aqueous solution, for example.

$$Cl_2(aq) + 2\ Br^-(aq) \rightarrow 2\ Cl^-(aq) + Br_2(aq)$$

$$E°_{net} = E°_{cathode} - E°_{anode} = 1.36\ V - (1.08\ V) = +0.28\ V$$

In fact, this is the commercial method of preparing bromine when NaBr is obtained from natural brine wells in Arkansas and Michigan.

## Iodine

Iodine is a lustrous, purple-black solid, easily sublimed at room temperature and atmospheric pressure (◄ Figure 13.20). The element was first isolated in 1811 from seaweed and kelp, extracts of which had long been used for treatment of goiter, the enlargement of the thyroid gland. It is now known that the thyroid gland produces a growth-regulating hormone (thyroxine) that contains iodine. Consequently, most table salt in the United States has 0.01% NaI added to provide the necessary iodine in the diet.

A laboratory method for preparing $I_2$ is illustrated in Figure 21.34. The commercial preparation depends on the source of $I^-$ and its concentration. One method is interesting because it involves some chemistry described earlier in this book. Iodide ions are first precipitated with silver ions to give insoluble AgI.

$$I^-(aq) + Ag^+(aq) \rightarrow AgI(s)$$

**FIGURE 21.32 Chlorine preparation.** Chlorine is prepared by oxidation of chloride ion using a strong oxidizing agent. Here, oxidation of NaCl is accomplished using $K_2Cr_2O_7$ in $H_2SO_4$. (The $Cl_2$ gas is bubbled into water in a receiving flask.)

**FIGURE 21.33 A membrane cell for the production of NaOH and Cl₂ gas from a saturated, aqueous solution of NaCl (brine).** Here, the anode and cathode compartments are separated by a water-impermeable but ion-conducting membrane. A widely used membrane is made of Nafion, a fluorine-containing polymer that is a relative of polytetrafluoroethylene (Teflon). Brine is fed into the anode compartment and dilute sodium hydroxide or water into the cathode compartment. Overflow pipes carry the evolved gases and NaOH away from the chambers of the electrolysis cell.

This is reduced by clean scrap iron to give iron(II) iodide and metallic silver.

$$2 \, AgI(s) + Fe(s) \rightarrow FeI_2(aq) + 2 \, Ag(s)$$

The silver is recycled by oxidizing it with nitric acid (forming silver nitrate) which is then reused. Finally, iodide ion from water-soluble FeI₂ is oxidized to iodine with chlorine [with iron(III) chloride as a by-product].

$$2 \, FeI_2(aq) + 3 \, Cl_2(aq) \rightarrow 2 \, I_2(s) + 2 \, FeCl_3(aq)$$

## Fluorine Compounds

Fluorine is the most reactive of all of the elements, forming compounds with every element except He and Ne. In most cases, the elements combine directly, and some reactions can be so vigorous as to be explosive. This reactivity can be explained by at least two features of fluorine chemistry: the relatively weak F—F bond compared with chlorine and bromine, and, in particular, the relatively strong bonds formed by

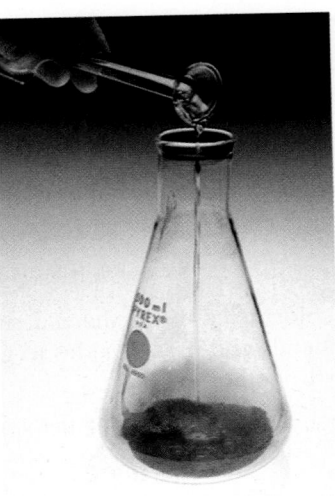

**FIGURE 21.34 The preparation of iodine.** A mixture of sodium iodide and manganese(IV) oxide was placed in the flask *(left)*. On adding concentrated sulfuric acid *(right)*, brown iodine vapor is evolved.

$$2 \, NaI(s) + 2 \, H_2SO_4(aq) + MnO_2(s) \rightarrow \\ Na_2SO_4(aq) + MnSO_4(aq) \\ + 2 \, H_2O(\ell) + I_2(g)$$

**Bond Dissociation Enthalpies of Some Halogen Compounds (kJ/mol)**

| X | X—X | H—X | C—X (in CX$_4$) |
|---|---|---|---|
| F | 155 | 565 | 485 |
| Cl | 242 | 432 | 339 |
| Br | 193 | 366 | 285 |
| I | 151 | 299 | 213 |

fluorine to other elements. This is illustrated by the table of bond dissociation enthalpies in the margin.

In addition to its oxidizing ability, another notable characteristic of fluorine is its small size. These properties lead to the formation of compounds where a number of F atoms can be bonded to a central element in a high oxidation state. Examples include $PtF_6$, $UF_6$, $IF_7$, and $XeF_4$.

Hydrogen fluoride is an important industrial chemical. More than 1 million tons of hydrogen fluoride is produced annually worldwide, almost all by the action of concentrated sulfuric acid on fluorspar.

$$CaF_2(s) + H_2SO_4(\ell) \rightarrow CaSO_4(s) + 2\ HF(g)$$

The U.S. capacity for HF production is approximately 210,000 metric tons, but demand often exceeds supply for this chemical. Anhydrous HF is used in a broad range of industries: in the production of refrigerants, herbicides, pharmaceuticals, high-octane gasoline, aluminum, plastics, electrical components, and fluorescent lightbulbs.

The fluorspar used to produce HF must be very pure and free of $SiO_2$ because HF reacts readily with silicon dioxide.

$$SiO_2(s) + 4\ HF(aq) \rightarrow SiF_4(g) + 2\ H_2O(\ell)$$

$$SiF_4(g) + 2\ HF(aq) \rightarrow H_2SiF_6(aq)$$

This series of reactions explains why HF can be used to etch or frost glass (such as the inside of fluorescent light bulbs). It also explains why HF is not shipped in glass containers (unlike HCl, for example).

The aluminum industry consumes about 10–40 kg of cryolite, $Na_3AlF_6$, per metric ton of aluminum produced. The reason is that cryolite is added to aluminum oxide to produce a lower-melting mixture that can be electrolyzed. Cryolite is found in only small quantities in nature, so it is made in various ways, among them the following reaction:

$$6\ HF(aq) + Al(OH)_3(s) + 3\ NaOH(aq) \rightarrow Na_3AlF_6(s) + 6\ H_2O(\ell)$$

About 3% of the hydrofluoric acid produced is used in uranium fuel production. To separate uranium isotopes in a gas centrifuge (▶ page 1079), the uranium must be in the form of a volatile compound. Naturally occurring uranium is processed to give $UO_2$. This oxide is treated with hydrogen fluoride to give $UF_4$, which is then reacted with $F_2$ to produce the volatile solid $UF_6$.

$$UO_2(s) + 4\ HF(aq) \rightarrow UF_4(s) + 2\ H_2O(\ell)$$

$$UF_4(s) + F_2(g) \rightarrow UF_6(s)$$

This last step consumes 70%–80% of the fluorine produced annually.

## Chlorine Compounds
### Hydrogen Chloride

Hydrochloric acid, an aqueous solution of hydrogen chloride, is a valuable industrial chemical. Hydrogen chloride gas can be prepared by the reaction of hydrogen and chlorine, but the rapid, exothermic reaction is difficult to control. The classical method of making HCl in the laboratory uses the reaction of NaCl and sulfuric acid, a procedure that takes advantage of the facts that HCl is a gas and that $H_2SO_4$ will not oxidize the chloride ion.

$$2\ NaCl(s) + H_2SO_4(\ell) \rightarrow Na_2SO_4(s) + 2\ HCl(g)$$

Hydrogen chloride gas has a sharp, irritating odor. Both gaseous and aqueous HCl react with metals and metal oxides to give metal chlorides and, depending on the reactant, hydrogen or water.

$$Mg(s) + 2\ HCl(aq) \rightarrow MgCl_2(aq) + H_2(g)$$

$$ZnO(s) + 2\ HCl(aq) \rightarrow ZnCl_2(aq) + H_2O(\ell)$$

## Oxoacids of Chlorine

Oxoacids of chlorine range from HClO, in which chlorine has an oxidation number of +1, to $HClO_4$, in which the oxidation number is equal to the group number, +7. All are strong oxidizing agents.

**Oxoacids of Chlorine**

| Acid | Name | Anion | Name |
|------|------|-------|------|
| HClO | Hypochlorous | $ClO^-$ | Hypochlorite |
| $HClO_2$ | Chlorous | $ClO_2^-$ | Chlorite |
| $HClO_3$ | Chloric | $ClO_3^-$ | Chlorate |
| $HClO_4$ | Perchloric | $ClO_4^-$ | Perchlorate |

Hypochlorous acid, HClO, forms when chlorine dissolves in water. In this reaction, half of the chlorine is oxidized to hypochlorite ion and half is reduced to chloride ion in a **disproportionation reaction**.

$$Cl_2(g) + 2 H_2O(\ell) \rightleftharpoons H_3O^+(aq) + HClO(aq) + Cl^-(aq)$$

If $Cl_2$ is dissolved in cold aqueous NaOH instead of in pure water, hypochlorite ion and chloride ion form.

$$Cl_2(g) + 2 OH^-(aq) \rightleftharpoons ClO^-(aq) + Cl^-(aq) + H_2O(\ell)$$

● **Disproportionation** A reaction in which an element or compound is simultaneously oxidized and reduced is called a disproportionation reaction. Here, $Cl_2$ is oxidized to $ClO^-$ and reduced to $Cl^-$.

Under basic conditions, the equilibrium lies far to the right. The resulting alkaline solution is the "liquid bleach" used in home laundries. The bleaching action of this solution is a result of the oxidizing ability of $ClO^-$. Most dyes are colored organic compounds, and hypochlorite ion oxidizes dyes to colorless products.

When calcium hydroxide is combined with $Cl_2$, solid $Ca(ClO)_2$ is the product. This compound is easily handled and is the "chlorine" that is sold for swimming pool disinfection.

When a basic solution of hypochlorite ion is heated, another disproportionation occurs, forming chlorate ion and chloride ion:

$$3 ClO^-(aq) \rightarrow ClO_3^-(aq) + 2 Cl^-(aq)$$

Sodium and potassium chlorates are made in large quantities this way. The sodium salt can be reduced to $ClO_2$, a compound used for bleaching paper pulp. Some $NaClO_3$ is also converted to potassium chlorate, $KClO_3$, the preferred oxidizing agent in fireworks and a component of safety matches.

Perchlorates, salts containing $ClO_4^-$, are powerful oxidants. Pure perchloric acid, $HClO_4$, is a colorless liquid that explodes if shocked. It explosively oxidizes organic materials and rapidly oxidizes silver and gold. Dilute aqueous solutions of the acid are safe to handle, however.

Perchlorate salts of most metals are usually relatively stable, albeit unpredictable. Great care should be used when handling any perchlorate salt. Ammonium perchlorate, for example, bursts into flame if heated above 200 °C.

$$2 NH_4ClO_4(s) \rightarrow N_2(g) + Cl_2(g) + 2 O_2(g) + 4 H_2O(g)$$

The strong oxidizing ability of the ammonium salt accounts for its use as the oxidizer in the solid booster rockets for the Space Shuttle. The solid propellant in these rockets is largely $NH_4ClO_4$, the remainder being the reducing agent, powdered aluminum. Each launch requires about 750 tons of ammonium perchlorate, and more than half of the sodium perchlorate currently manufactured is converted to the ammonium salt. The process for making this conversion is an exchange reaction that takes advantage of the fact that ammonium perchlorate is less soluble in water than sodium perchlorate:

$$NaClO_4(aq) + NH_4Cl(aq) \rightleftharpoons NaCl(aq) + NH_4ClO_4(s)$$

**Use of a perchlorate salt.** The solid-fuel booster rockets of the Space Shuttle utilize a mixture of $NH_4ClO_4$ (oxidizing agent) and Al powder (reducing agent).

**REVIEW & CHECK FOR SECTION 21.10**

1.    Which halogen has the highest bond dissociation enthalpy?

(a)    $F_2$          (b)    $Cl_2$          (c)    $Br_2$          (d)    $I_2$

2.    Which of the following statements is *not* correct?

(a)    The ease of oxidation of the halide ions is $F^- < Cl^- < Br^- < I^-$.

(b)    Fluorine is the most abundant halogen in the earth's crust.

(c)    $F_2$ is prepared industrially by electrolysis of aqueous NaF.

(d)    HF is used to etch glass.

Sign in at **www.cengage.com/owl** to:
• View tutorials and simulations, develop problem-solving skills, and complete online homework assigned by your professor.
• For quick review and exam prep, download Go Chemistry mini lecture modules from OWL (or purchase them at **www.cengagebrain.com**)

 Access **How Do I Solve It?** tutorials on how to approach problem solving using concepts in this chapter.

## CHAPTER GOALS REVISITED

*Now that you have studied this chapter, you should ask whether you have met the chapter goals. In particular, you should be able to:*

**Relate the formulas and properties of compounds to the periodic table**

a.    Predict several chemical reactions of the Group A elements (Section 21.2). **Study Questions: 13, 14.**

b.    Predict similarities and differences among the elements in a given group, based on periodic properties (Section 21.2). **Study Questions: 22, 64, 65.**

c.    Know which reactions produce ionic compounds, and predict formulas for common ions and common ionic compounds based on electron configurations (Section 21.2). **Study Questions: 5, 6, 16.**

d.    Recognize when a formula is incorrectly written, based on general principles governing electron configurations (Section 21.2).

**Describe the chemistry of the main group or A-Group elements, particularly H; Na and K; Mg and Ca; B and Al; Si; N and P; O and S; and F and Cl**

a.    Identify the most abundant elements, know how they are obtained, and list some of their common chemical and physical properties.

b.    Be able to summarize briefly a series of facts about the most common compounds of main group elements (ionic or covalent bonding, color, solubility, simple reaction chemistry) (Sections 21.3–21.10).

c.    Identify uses of common elements and compounds, and understand the chemistry that relates to their usage (Sections 21.3–21.10).

**Apply the principles of stoichiometry, thermodynamics, and electrochemistry to the chemistry of the main group elements** Study Questions: 18, 24, 29, 32, 34, 43, 48, 50, 54, 58, 61, 75, 92, 94.

## Study Questions

⏻WL Interactive versions of these questions are assignable in OWL.

▲ denotes challenging questions.

Blue-numbered questions have answers in Appendix R and fully worked solutions in the *Student Solutions Manual*.

## Practicing Skills

### Properties of the Elements
*(See Sections 21.1 and 21.2.)*

1. Give examples of two basic oxides. Write equations illustrating the formation of each oxide from its component elements. Write another chemical equation that illustrates the basic character of each oxide.

2. Give examples of two acidic oxides. Write equations illustrating the formation of each oxide from its component elements. Write another chemical equation that illustrates the acidic character of each oxide.

3. Give the name and symbol of each element having the valence configuration [noble gas] $ns^2np^1$.

4. Give symbols and names for four monatomic ions that have the same electron configuration as argon.

5. Select one of the alkali metals, and write a balanced chemical equation for its reaction with chlorine. Is the reaction likely to be exothermic or endothermic? Is the product ionic or molecular?

6. Select one of the alkaline earth metals and write a balanced chemical equation for its reaction with oxygen. Is the reaction likely to be exothermic or endothermic? Is the product ionic or molecular?

7. For the product of the reaction you selected in Study Question 5, predict the following physical properties: color, state of matter (s, ℓ, or g), solubility in water.

8. For the product of the reaction you selected in Study Question 6, predict the following physical properties: color, state of matter (s, ℓ, or g), solubility in water.

9. Would you expect to find calcium occurring naturally in the earth's crust as a free element? Why or why not?

10. Which of the first 10 elements in the periodic table are found as free elements in the earth's crust? Which elements in this group occur in the earth's crust only as part of a chemical compound?

11. Place the following oxides in order of increasing basicity: $CO_2$, $SiO_2$, $SnO_2$.

12. Place the following oxides in order of increasing basicity: $Na_2O$, $Al_2O_3$, $SiO_2$, $SO_3$.

13. Complete and balance the equations for the following reactions. [Assume an excess of oxygen for (d).]
    (a) $Na(s) + Br_2(\ell) \rightarrow$
    (b) $Mg(s) + O_2(g) \rightarrow$
    (c) $Al(s) + F_2(g) \rightarrow$
    (d) $C(s) + O_2(g) \rightarrow$

14. Complete and balance the equations for the following reactions:
    (a) $K(s) + I_2(g) \rightarrow$
    (b) $Ba(s) + O_2(g) \rightarrow$
    (c) $Al(s) + S_8(s) \rightarrow$
    (d) $Si(s) + Cl_2(g) \rightarrow$

### Hydrogen
*(See Section 21.3.)*

15. Write balanced chemical equations for the reaction of hydrogen gas with oxygen, chlorine, and nitrogen.

16. Write an equation for the reaction of potassium and hydrogen. Name the product. Is it ionic or covalent? Predict one physical property and one chemical property of this compound.

17. Write a balanced chemical equation for the preparation of $H_2$ (and CO) by the reaction of $CH_4$ and water. Using data in Appendix L, calculate $\Delta_r H°$, $\Delta_r G°$, and $\Delta_r S°$ for this reaction at 298 K.

18. Using data in Appendix L, calculate $\Delta_r H°$, $\Delta_r G°$, and $\Delta_r S°$ for the reaction of carbon and water to give CO and $H_2$ at 298 K.

19. A method recently suggested for the preparation of hydrogen (and oxygen) from water proceeds as follows:
    (a) Sulfuric acid and hydrogen iodide are formed from sulfur dioxide, water, and iodine.
    (b) The sulfuric acid from the first step is decomposed by heat to water, sulfur dioxide, and oxygen.
    (c) The hydrogen iodide from the first step is decomposed with heat to hydrogen and iodine.

    Write a balanced equation for each of these steps, and show that their sum is the decomposition of water to form hydrogen and oxygen.

20. Compare the mass of $H_2$ expected from the reaction of steam ($H_2O$) per mole of methane, petroleum, and coal. (Assume complete reaction in each case. Use $CH_2$ and CH as representative formulas for petroleum and coal, respectively.)

### Alkali Metals
*(See Section 21.4.)*

21. Write equations for the reaction of sodium with each of the halogens. Predict at least two physical properties that are common to all of the alkali metal halides.

22. Write balanced equations for the reaction of lithium, sodium, and potassium with $O_2$. Specify which metal forms an oxide, which forms a peroxide, and which forms a superoxide.

23. The electrolysis of aqueous NaCl gives NaOH, $Cl_2$, and $H_2$.
    (a) Write a balanced equation for the process.
    (b) In the United States, $1.19 \times 10^{10}$ kg of NaOH and $1.14 \times 10^{10}$ kg of $Cl_2$ were produced in a recent year. Does the ratio of masses of NaOH and $Cl_2$ produced agree with the ratio of masses expected from the balanced equation? If not, what does this tell you about the way in which NaOH and $Cl_2$ are actually produced? Is the electrolysis of aqueous NaCl the only source of these chemicals?

24. (a) Write equations for the half-reactions that occur at the cathode and the anode when an aqueous solution of KCl is electrolyzed. Which chemical species is oxidized, and which chemical species is reduced in this reaction?
    (b) Predict the products formed when an aqueous solution of CsI is electrolyzed.

## Alkaline Earth Elements
*(See Section 21.5.)*

25. When magnesium burns in air, it forms both an oxide and a nitride. Write balanced equations for the formation of both compounds.

26. Calcium reacts with hydrogen gas at 300–400 °C to form a hydride. This compound reacts readily with water, so it is an excellent drying agent for organic solvents.
    (a) Write a balanced equation showing the formation of calcium hydride from Ca and $H_2$.
    (b) Write a balanced equation for the reaction of calcium hydride with water (Figure 21.7).

27. Name three uses of limestone. Write a balanced equation for the reaction of limestone with $CO_2$ in water.

28. Explain what is meant by "hard water." What causes hard water, and what problems are associated with it?

29. Calcium oxide, CaO, is used to remove $SO_2$ from power plant exhaust. These two compounds react to give solid $CaSO_3$. What mass of $SO_2$ can be removed using $1.2 \times 10^3$ kg of CaO?

30. $Ca(OH)_2$ has a $K_{sp}$ of $5.5 \times 10^{-5}$, whereas $K_{sp}$ for $Mg(OH)_2$ is $5.6 \times 10^{-12}$. Calculate the equilibrium constant for the reaction

    $$Ca(OH)_2(s) + Mg^{2+}(aq) \rightleftharpoons Ca^{2+}(aq) + Mg(OH)_2(s)$$

    Explain why this reaction can be used in the commercial isolation of magnesium from sea water.

## Boron and Aluminum
*(See Section 21.6.)*

31. Draw a possible structure for the cyclic anion in the salt $K_3B_3O_6$ and the anion in $Ca_2B_2O_5$.

32. The boron trihalides (except $BF_3$) hydrolyze completely to boric acid and the acid HX.
    (a) Write a balanced equation for the reaction of $BCl_3$ with water.
    (b) Calculate $\Delta_r H°$ for the hydrolysis of $BCl_3$ using data in Appendix L and the following information: $\Delta_f H° [BCl_3(g)] = -403$ kJ/mol; $\Delta_f H° [B(OH)_3(s)] = -1094$ kJ/mol.

33. When boron hydrides burn in air, the reactions are very exothermic.
    (a) Write a balanced equation for the combustion of $B_5H_9(g)$ in air to give $B_2O_3(s)$ and $H_2O(g)$.
    (b) Calculate the enthalpy of combustion for $B_5H_9(g)$ ($\Delta_f H° = 73.2$ kJ/mol), and compare it with the enthalpy of combustion of $B_2H_6$ on page 982. (The enthalpy of formation of $B_2O_3(s)$ is $-1271.9$ kJ/mol.)
    (c) Compare the enthalpy of combustion of $C_2H_6(g)$ with that of $B_2H_6(g)$. Which transfers more energy as heat per gram?

34. Diborane can be prepared by the reaction of $NaBH_4$ and $I_2$. Which substance is oxidized, and which is reduced?

35. Write balanced equations for the reactions of aluminum with HCl(aq), $Cl_2$, and $O_2$.

36. (a) Write a balanced equation for the reaction of Al and $H_2O(\ell)$ to produce $H_2$ and $Al_2O_3$.
    (b) Using thermodynamic data in Appendix L, calculate $\Delta_r H°$, $\Delta_r S°$, and $\Delta_r G°$ for this reaction. Do these data indicate that the reaction should favor the products?
    (c) Why is aluminum metal unaffected by water?

37. Aluminum dissolves readily in hot aqueous NaOH to give the aluminate ion, $[Al(OH)_4]^-$, and $H_2$. Write a balanced equation for this reaction. If you begin with 13.2 g of Al, what volume (in liters) of $H_2$ gas is produced when the gas is measured at 22.5 °C and a pressure of 735 mm Hg?

38. Alumina, $Al_2O_3$, is amphoteric. Among examples of its amphoteric character are the reactions that occur when $Al_2O_3$ is heated strongly or "fused" with acidic oxides and basic oxides.
    (a) Write a balanced equation for the reaction of alumina with silica, an acidic oxide, to give aluminum metasilicate, $Al_2(SiO_3)_3$.
    (b) Write a balanced equation for the reaction of alumina with the basic oxide CaO to give calcium aluminate, $Ca(AlO_2)_2$.

39. Aluminum sulfate is the most commercially important aluminum compound, after aluminum oxide and aluminum hydroxide. It is produced from the reaction of aluminum oxide and sulfuric acid. What masses (in kilograms) of aluminum oxide and sulfuric acid must be used to manufacture 1.00 kg of aluminum sulfate?

40. "Aerated" concrete bricks are widely used building materials. They are obtained by mixing gas-forming additives with a moist mixture of lime, cement, and possibly sand. Industrially, the following reaction is important:

$$2\ Al(s) + 3\ Ca(OH)_2(s) + 6\ H_2O(\ell) \rightarrow$$
$$3\ CaO \cdot Al_2O_3 \cdot 6\ H_2O(s) + 3\ H_2(g)$$

Assume the mixture of reactants contains 0.56 g of Al (as well as excess calcium hydroxide and water) for each brick. What volume of hydrogen gas do you expect at 26 °C and a pressure of 745 mm Hg?

## Silicon
*(See Section 21.7.)*

41. Describe the structure of pyroxenes (see page 986). What is the ratio of silicon to oxygen in this type of silicate?

42. Describe how ultrapure silicon can be produced from sand.

43. Silicate structures: Draw a structure, and give the charge for a silicate anion with the formula $[Si_6O_{18}]^{n-}$.

44. Silicates often have chain, ribbon, or sheet structures. One of the simpler ribbon structures is $[Si_2O_5{}^{2-}]_n$. Draw a structure for this anionic material.

## Nitrogen and Phosphorus
*(See Section 21.8.)*

45. Consult the data in Appendix L. Are any of the nitrogen oxides listed there stable with respect to decomposition to $N_2$ and $O_2$?

46. Use data in Appendix L to calculate the enthalpy and free energy change for the reaction

$$2\ NO_2(g) \rightarrow N_2O_4(g)$$

Is this reaction exothermic or endothermic? Is the reaction product- or reactant-favored?

47. Use data in Appendix L to calculate the enthalpy and free energy change for the reaction

$$2\ NO(g) + O_2(g) \rightarrow 2\ NO_2(g)$$

Is this reaction exothermic or endothermic? Is the reaction product- or reactant-favored at equilibrium?

48. The overall reaction involved in the industrial synthesis of nitric acid is

$$NH_3(g) + 2\ O_2(g) \rightarrow HNO_3(aq) + H_2O(\ell)$$

Calculate $\Delta_r G°$ for this reaction and its equilibrium constant at 25 °C.

49. A major use of hydrazine, $N_2H_4$, is in steam boilers in power plants.
    (a) The reaction of hydrazine with $O_2$ dissolved in water gives $N_2$ and water. Write a balanced equation for this reaction.
    (b) $O_2$ dissolves in water to the extent of 0.0044 g in 100. mL of water at 20 °C. What mass of $N_2H_4$ is needed to consume all of the dissolved $O_2$ in $3.00 \times 10^4$ L of water (enough to fill a small swimming pool)?

50. Before hydrazine came into use to remove dissolved oxygen in the water in steam boilers, $Na_2SO_3$ was commonly used for this purpose:

$$2\ Na_2SO_3(aq) + O_2(aq) \rightarrow 2\ Na_2SO_4(aq)$$

What mass of $Na_2SO_3$ is required to remove $O_2$ from $3.00 \times 10^4$ L of water as outlined in Study Question 49?

51. Review the structure of phosphorous acid in Table 21.6.
    (a) What is the oxidation number of the phosphorus atom in this acid?
    (b) Draw the structure of diphosphorous acid, $H_4P_2O_5$. What is the maximum number of ionizable protons in a molecule of this acid?

52. Unlike carbon, which can form extended chains of atoms, nitrogen can form chains of very limited length. Draw the Lewis electron dot structure of the azide ion, $N_3^-$. Is the ion linear or bent?

## Oxygen and Sulfur
*(See Section 21.9.)*

53. In the "contact process" for making sulfuric acid, sulfur is first burned to $SO_2$. Environmental restrictions allow no more than 0.30% of this $SO_2$ to be vented to the atmosphere.
    (a) If enough sulfur is burned in a plant to produce $1.80 \times 10^6$ kg of pure, anhydrous $H_2SO_4$ per day, what is the maximum amount of $SO_2$ that is allowed to be exhausted to the atmosphere?
    (b) One way to prevent any $SO_2$ from reaching the atmosphere is to "scrub" the exhaust gases with slaked lime, $Ca(OH)_2$:

$$Ca(OH)_2(s) + SO_2(g) \rightarrow CaSO_3(s) + H_2O(\ell)$$
$$2\ CaSO_3(s) + O_2(g) \rightarrow 2\ CaSO_4(s)$$

What mass of $Ca(OH)_2$ (in kilograms) is needed to remove the $SO_2$ calculated in part (a)?

54. A sulfuric acid plant produces an enormous amount of heat. To keep costs as low as possible, much of this heat is used to make steam to generate electricity. Some of the electricity is used to run the plant, and the excess is sold to the local electrical utility. Three reactions are important in sulfuric acid production: (1) burning S to $SO_2$; (2) oxidation of $SO_2$ to $SO_3$; and (3) reaction of $SO_3$ with $H_2O$:

$$SO_3(g) + H_2O\ (in\ 98\%\ H_2SO_4) \rightarrow H_2SO_4(\ell)$$

The enthalpy change of the third reaction is −130 kJ/mol. Estimate the enthalpy change when 1.00 mol of S is used to produce 1.00 mol of $H_2SO_4$. How much energy is produced per metric ton (1000 kg exactly) of $H_2SO_4$?

55. Sulfur forms anionic chains of S atoms called polysulfides. Draw a Lewis electron dot structure for the $S_2{}^{2-}$ ion. The $S_2{}^{2-}$ ion is the disulfide ion, an analogue of the peroxide ion. It occurs in iron pyrites, $FeS_2$.

**56.** Sulfur forms a range of compounds with fluorine. Draw Lewis electron dot structures for $S_2F_2$ (connectivity is FSSF), $SF_2$, $SF_4$, $SF_6$, and $S_2F_{10}$. What is the oxidation number of sulfur in each of these compounds?

**Fluorine and Chlorine**
*(See Section 21.10.)*

**57.** The halogen oxides and oxoanions are good oxidizing agents. For example, the reduction of bromate ion has an $E°$ value of 1.44 V in acid solution:

$$2\ BrO_3^-(aq) + 12\ H^+(aq) + 10\ e^- \rightarrow$$
$$Br_2(aq) + 6\ H_2O(\ell)$$

Is it possible to oxidize aqueous 1.0 M $Mn^{2+}$ to aqueous $MnO_4^-$ with 1.0 M bromate ion?

**58.** The hypohalite ions, $XO^-$, are the anions of weak acids. Calculate the pH of a 0.10 M solution of NaClO. What is the concentration of HClO in this solution?

**59.** Bromine is obtained from brine wells. The process involves treating water containing bromide ion with $Cl_2$ and extracting the $Br_2$ from the solution using an organic solvent. Write a balanced equation for the reaction of $Cl_2$ and $Br^-$. What are the oxidizing and reducing agents in this reaction? Using the table of standard reduction potentials (Appendix M), verify that this is a product-favored reaction.

**60.** To prepare chlorine from chloride ion a strong oxidizing agent is required. The dichromate ion, $Cr_2O_7^{2-}$, is one example (Figure 21.32). Consult the table of standard reduction potentials (Appendix M), and identify several other oxidizing agents that may be suitable. Write balanced equations for the reactions of these substances with chloride ion.

**61.** If an electrolytic cell for producing $F_2$ (Figure 21.31) operates at $5.00 \times 10^3$ A (at 10.0 V), what mass of $F_2$ can be produced per 24-hour day? Assume the conversion of $F^-$ to $F_2$ is 100%.

**62.** Halogens combine with one another to produce *interhalogens* such as $BrF_3$. Sketch a possible molecular structure for this molecule, and decide if the F—Br—F bond angles will be less than or greater than ideal.

## General Questions

*The questions are not designated as to type or location in the chapter. They may combine several concepts.*

**63.** For each of the third-period elements (Na through Ar), identify the following:
(a) whether the element is a metal, nonmetal, or metalloid
(b) the color and appearance of the element
(c) the state of the element (s, ℓ, or g) under standard conditions

**64.** Consider the chemistries of C, Si, Ge, and Sn.
(a) Write a balanced chemical equation to depict the reaction of each element with elemental chlorine.
(b) Describe the bonding in each of the products of the reactions with chlorine as ionic or covalent.
(c) Compare the reactions, if any, of some Group 4A chlorides —$CCl_4$, $SiCl_4$, and $SnCl_4$— with water.

**65.** Consider the chemistries of the elements potassium, calcium, gallium, germanium, and arsenic.
(a) Write a balanced chemical equation depicting the reaction of each element with elemental chlorine.
(b) Describe the bonding in each of the products of the reactions with chlorine as ionic or covalent.
(c) Draw Lewis electron dot structures for the products of the reactions of gallium and arsenic with chlorine. What are their electron-pair and molecular geometries?

**66.** When $BCl_3$ gas is passed through an electric discharge, small amounts of the reactive molecule $B_2Cl_4$ are produced. (The molecule has a B—B covalent bond.)
(a) Draw a Lewis electron dot structure for $B_2Cl_4$.
(b) Describe the hybridization of the B atoms in the molecule and the geometry around each B atom.

**67.** Complete and balance the following equations.
(a) $KClO_3$ + heat →
(b) $H_2S(g)$ + $O_2(g)$ →
(c) $Na(s)$ + $O_2(g)$ →
(d) $P_4(s)$ + $KOH(aq)$ + $H_2O(\ell)$ →
(e) $NH_4NO_3(s)$ + heat →
(f) $In(s)$ + $Br_2(\ell)$ →
(g) $SnCl_4(\ell)$ + $H_2O(\ell)$ →

**68.** (a) Heating barium oxide in pure oxygen gives barium peroxide. Write a balanced equation for this reaction.
(b) Barium peroxide is an excellent oxidizing agent. Write a balanced equation for the reaction of iron with barium peroxide to give iron(III) oxide and barium oxide.

**69.** Worldwide production of silicon carbide, SiC, is several hundred thousand tons annually. If you want to produce $1.0 \times 10^5$ metric tons of SiC, what mass (metric tons) of silicon sand ($SiO_2$) will you use if 70% of the sand is converted to SiC? (A metric ton is exactly 1000 kg.)

**70.** To store 2.88 kg of gasoline with an energy equivalence of $1.43 \times 10^8$ J requires a volume of 4.1 L. In comparison, 1.0 kg of $H_2$ has the same energy equivalence. What volume is required if this quantity of $H_2$ is to be stored at 25 °C and 1.0 atm of pressure?

**71.** Using data in Appendix L, calculate $\Delta_r G°$ values for the decomposition of $MCO_3$ to MO and $CO_2$ where M = Mg, Ca, Ba. What is the relative tendency of these carbonates to decompose?

**72.** Ammonium perchlorate is used as the oxidizer in the solid-fuel booster rockets of the Space Shuttle. Assume that one launch requires 700. tons ($6.35 \times 10^5$ kg) of the salt, and the salt decomposes according to the equation on page 1005.
(a) What mass of water is produced? What mass of $O_2$ is produced?
(b) If all the $O_2$ produced is assumed to react with the powdered aluminum present in the rocket engine, what mass of aluminum is required to use up all of the $O_2$?
(c) What mass of $Al_2O_3$ is produced?

73. ▲ Metals react with hydrogen halides (such as HCl) to give the metal halide and hydrogen:

$$M(s) + n\,HX(g) \rightarrow MX_n(s) + \tfrac{1}{2}n\,H_2(g)$$

The free energy change for the reaction is $\Delta_r G° = \Delta_f G°(MX_n) - n\,\Delta_f G°[HX(g)]$.
   (a) $\Delta_f G°$ for HCl(g) is $-95.1$ kJ/mol. What must be the value for $\Delta_f G°$ for $MX_n$ for the reaction to be product-favored?
   (b) Which of the following metals is (are) predicted to have product-favored reactions with HCl(g): Ba, Pb, Hg, Ti?

74. Halogens form polyhalide ions. Sketch Lewis electron dot structures and molecular structures for the following ions:
   (a) $I_3^-$
   (b) $BrCl_2^-$
   (c) $ClF_2^+$
   (d) An iodide ion and two iodine molecules form the $I_5^-$ ion. Here, the ion has five I atoms in a row, but the ion is not linear. Draw the Lewis dot structure for the ion, and propose a structure for the ion.

75. The standard enthalpy of formation of $OF_2$ gas is $+24.5$ kJ/mol. Calculate the average O—F bond enthalpy.

76. Calcium fluoride can be used in the fluoridation of municipal water supplies. If you want to achieve a fluoride ion concentration of $2.0 \times 10^{-5}$ M, what mass of $CaF_2$ must you use for $1.0 \times 10^6$ L of water? ($K_{sp}$ for $CaF_2$ is $5.3 \times 10^{-11}$.)

77. The steering rockets in the Space Shuttle use $N_2O_4$ and a derivative of hydrazine, 1,1-dimethylhydrazine (page 245). This mixture is called a *hypergolic fuel* because it ignites when the reactants come into contact:

$$H_2NN(CH_3)_2(\ell) + 2\,N_2O_4(\ell) \rightarrow$$
$$3\,N_2(g) + 4\,H_2O(g) + 2\,CO_2(g)$$

   (a) Identify the oxidizing agent and the reducing agent in this reaction.
   (b) The same propulsion system was used by the Lunar Lander on moon missions in the 1970s. If the Lander used 4100 kg of $H_2NN(CH_3)_2$, what mass (in kilograms) of $N_2O_4$ was required to react with it? What mass (in kilograms) of each of the reaction products was generated?

78. ▲ Liquid HCN is dangerously unstable with respect to trimer formation—that is, formation of $(HCN)_3$ with a cyclic structure.
   (a) Propose a structure for this cyclic trimer.
   (b) Estimate the energy of the trimerization reaction using bond dissociation enthalpies (◀ Table 8.9).

79. Use $\Delta_f H°$ data in Appendix L to calculate the enthalpy change of the reaction

$$2\,N_2(g) + 5\,O_2(g) + 2\,H_2O(\ell) \rightarrow 4\,HNO_3(aq)$$

Speculate on whether such a reaction could be used to "fix" nitrogen. Would research to find ways to accomplish this reaction be a useful endeavor?

80. ▲ Phosphorus forms an extensive series of oxoanions.
   (a) Draw a structure, and give the charge for an oxophosphate anion with the formula $[P_4O_{13}]^{n-}$. How many ionizable H atoms should the completely protonated acid have?
   (b) Draw a structure, and give the charge for an oxophosphate anion with the formula $[P_4O_{12}]^{n-}$. How many ionizable H atoms should the completely protonated acid have?

81. ▲ Boron and hydrogen form an extensive family of compounds, and the diagram below shows how they are related by reaction.

The following table gives the weight percent of boron in each of the compounds. Derive the empirical and molecular formulas of compounds A–E.

| Substance | State (at STP) | Mass Percent B | Molar Mass (g/mol) |
|---|---|---|---|
| A | Gas | 78.3 | 27.7 |
| B | Gas | 81.2 | 53.3 |
| C | Liquid | 83.1 | 65.1 |
| D | Liquid | 85.7 | 63.1 |
| E | Solid | 88.5 | 122.2 |

82. ▲ In 1774, C. Scheele obtained a gas by reacting pyrolusite ($MnO_2$) with sulfuric acid. The gas, which had been obtained that same year by Joseph Priestley by a different method, was an element, A.
   (a) What is the element isolated by Scheele and Priestley?
   (b) Element A combines with almost all other elements. For example, with cesium it gives a compound in which the mass percent of A is 19.39%. The element combines with hydrogen to give a compound with a mass percent of element A of 94.12%. Determine the formulas of the cesium and hydrogen compounds.
   (c) The compounds of cesium and hydrogen with element A react with one another. Write a balanced equation for the reaction.

83. What current must be used in a Downs cell operating at 7.0 V to produce 1.00 metric ton (exactly 1000 kg) of sodium per day? Assume 100% efficiency.

84. The chemistry of gallium:
    (a) Gallium hydroxide, like aluminum hydroxide, is amphoteric. Write a balanced equation to show how this hydroxide can dissolve in both HCl(aq) and NaOH(aq).
    (b) Gallium ion in water, $Ga^{3+}$(aq), has a $K_a$ value of $1.2 \times 10^{-3}$. Is this ion a stronger or a weaker acid than $Al^{3+}$(aq)?

85. Silicon-oxygen rings are a common structural feature in silicate chemistry. Draw the structure for the anion $[Si_3O_9]^{6-}$, which is found in minerals such as benitoite. Is the ring expected to be planar?

86. Using enthalpy of formation data in Appendix L, determine whether the decomposition of $NH_4NO_3$(s) to give $N_2O$(g) and $H_2O$(g) is endothermic or exothermic.

87. Metal sulfides roasted in air produce metal oxides.

    $$2\ ZnS(s) + 3\ O_2(g) \rightarrow 2\ ZnO(s) + 2\ SO_2(g)$$

    Use thermodynamics to decide if the reaction is product- or reactant-favored at equilibrium at 298 K. Will the reaction be more or less product-favored at a high temperature?

88. Metals generally react with hydrogen halides to give the metal halide and hydrogen. Determine whether this is true for silver by calculating $\Delta_r G°$ for the reaction with each of the hydrogen halides.

    $$Ag(s) + HX(g) \rightarrow AgX(s) + \tfrac{1}{2}\ H_2(g)$$

    The required free energies of formation are:

    | HX | $\Delta_f G°$(kJ/mol) | AgX | $\Delta_f G°$(kJ/mol) |
    |-----|-----|-----|-----|
    | HF | 273.2 | AgF | 193.8 |
    | HCl | 95.09 | AgCl | 109.76 |
    | HBr | 53.45 | AgBr | 96.90 |
    | HI | 1.56 | AgI | 66.19 |

## In the Laboratory

89. One material needed to make silicones is dichlorodimethylsilane, $(CH_3)_2SiCl_2$. It is made by treating silicon powder at about 300 °C with $CH_3Cl$ in the presence of a copper-containing catalyst.
    (a) Write a balanced equation for the reaction.
    (b) Assume you carry out the reaction on a small scale with 2.65 g of silicon. To measure the $CH_3Cl$ gas, you fill a 5.60-L flask at 24.5 °C. What pressure of $CH_3Cl$ gas must you have in the flask to have the stoichiometrically correct amount of the compound?
    (c) What mass of $(CH_3)_2SiCl_2$ can be produced from 2.65 g of Si and excess $CH_3Cl$?

90. Sodium borohydride, $NaBH_4$, reduces many metal ions to the metal.
    (a) Write a balanced equation for the reaction of $NaBH_4$ with $AgNO_3$ in water to give silver metal, $H_2$ gas, boric acid, and sodium nitrate. (The chemistry of $NaBH_4$ is described on pages 982–983.)
    (b) What mass of silver can be produced from 575 mL of 0.011 M $AgNO_3$ and 13.0 g of $NaBH_4$?

91. A common analytical method for hydrazine involves its oxidation with iodate ion, $IO_3^-$, in acid solution. In the process, hydrazine acts as a four-electron reducing agent.

    $$N_2(g) + 5\ H_3O^+(aq) + 4\ e^- \rightarrow$$
    $$N_2H_5^+(aq) + 5\ H_2O(\ell) \qquad E° = -0.23\ V$$

    Write the balanced equation for the reaction of hydrazine in acid solution ($N_2H_5^+$) with $IO_3^-$(aq) to give $N_2$ and $I_2$. Calculate $E°$ for this reaction.

92. When 1.00 g of a white solid A is strongly heated, you obtain another white solid, B, and a gas. An experiment is carried out on the gas, showing that it exerts a pressure of 209 mm Hg in a 450-mL flask at 25 °C. Bubbling the gas into a solution of $Ca(OH)_2$ gives another white solid, C. If the white solid B is added to water, the resulting solution turns red litmus paper blue. Addition of aqueous HCl to the solution of B and evaporation of the resulting solution to dryness yield 1.055 g of a white solid D. When D is placed in a Bunsen burner flame, it colors the flame green. Finally, if the aqueous solution of B is treated with sulfuric acid, a white precipitate, E, forms. Identify the lettered compounds in the reaction scheme.

© Cengage Learning/Charles D. Winters

**The salts $CaCl_2$, $SrCl_2$, and $BaCl_2$ were suspended in methanol.** When the methanol is set ablaze, the heat of combustion causes the salts to emit light of characteristic wavelengths: Calcium salts are yellow; strontium salts are red; and barium salts are green-yellow.

93. ▲ In 1937, R. Schwartz and M. Schmiesser prepared a yellow-orange bromine oxide ($BrO_2$) by treating $Br_2$ with ozone in a fluorocarbon solvent. Many years later, J. Pascal found that, on heating, this oxide decomposed to two other oxides, a less volatile golden yellow oxide (A) and a more volatile deep brown oxide (B). Oxide B was later identified as $Br_2O$. To determine the formula for oxide A, a sample was treated with sodium iodide. The reaction liberated iodine, which was titrated to an equivalence point with 17.7 mL of 0.065 M sodium thiosulfate.

$$I_2(aq) + 2\ S_2O_3^{2-}(aq) \rightarrow 2\ I^-(aq) + S_4O_6^{2-}(aq)$$

Compound A was also treated with $AgNO_3$, and 14.4 mL of 0.020 M $AgNO_3$ was required to completely precipitate the bromine from the sample.

(a) What is the formula of the unknown bromine oxide A?

(b) Draw Lewis structures for A and $Br_2O$. Speculate on their molecular geometry.

94. A mixture of $PCl_5$ (12.41 g) and excess $NH_4Cl$ was heated at 145 °C for 6 hours. The two reacted in equimolar amounts and evolved 5.14 L of HCl (at STP). Three substances (A, B, and C) were isolated from the reaction mixture. The three substances had the same elemental composition but differed in their molar mass. Substance A had a molar mass of 347.7 g/mol and B had a molar mass of 463.5 g/mol. Give the empirical and molecular formulas for A and B and draw a reasonable Lewis structure for A.

## Summary and Conceptual Questions

*The following questions may use concepts from this and previous chapters.*

95. Dinitrogen trioxide, $N_2O_3$, has the structure shown here.

The oxide is unstable, decomposing to NO and $NO_2$ in the gas phase at 25 °C.

$$N_2O_3(g) \rightarrow NO(g) + NO_2(g)$$

(a) Explain why one N—O bond distance in $N_2O_3$ is 114.2 pm, whereas the other two bonds are longer (121 pm) and nearly equal to each other.

(b) For the decomposition reaction, $\Delta_r H° = +40.5$ kJ/mol and $\Delta_r G° = -1.59$ kJ/mol. Calculate $\Delta S°$ and $K$ for the reaction at 298 K.

(c) Calculate $\Delta_f H°$ for $N_2O_3(g)$.

96. ▲ The density of lead is 11.350 g/cm³, and the metal crystallizes in a face-centered cubic unit cell. Estimate the radius of a lead atom.

97. You have a 1.0-L flask that contains a mixture of argon and hydrogen. The pressure inside the flask is 745 mm Hg, and the temperature is 22 °C. Describe an experiment that you could use to determine the percentage of hydrogen in this mixture.

98. The boron atom in boric acid, $B(OH)_3$, is bonded to three —OH groups. In the solid state, the —OH groups are in turn hydrogen-bonded to —OH groups in neighboring molecules.

(a) Draw the Lewis structure for boric acid.

(b) What is the hybridization of the boron atom in the acid?

(c) Sketch a picture showing how hydrogen bonding can occur between neighboring molecules.

99. How would you extinguish a sodium fire in the laboratory? What is the worst thing you could do?

100. Tin(IV) oxide, cassiterite, is the main ore of tin. It crystallizes in a rutile-like unit cell (Question 4, page 609).

(a) How many tin(IV) ions and oxide ions are there per unit cell of this oxide?

(b) Is it thermodynamically feasible to transform solid $SnO_2$ into liquid $SnCl_4$ by reaction of the oxide with gaseous HCl? What is the equilibrium constant for this reaction at 25 °C?

101. You are given a stoppered flask that contains hydrogen, nitrogen, or oxygen. Suggest an experiment you could do to identify the gas.

102. The structure of nitric acid is illustrated on page 990.

(a) Why are the N—O bonds the same length, and why are both shorter than the N—OH bond length?

(b) Rationalize the bond angles in the molecule.

(c) What is the hybridization of the central N atom? Which orbitals overlap to form the N—O π bond?

103. Assume an electrolysis cell that produces chlorine from aqueous sodium chloride operates at 4.6 V (with a current of $3.0 \times 10^5$ A). Calculate the number of kilowatt-hours of energy required to produce 1.00 kg of chlorine (1 kWh = 1 kilowatt-hour = $3.6 \times 10^6$ J).

104. Sodium metal is produced by electrolysis of molten sodium chloride. The cell operates at 7.0 V with a current of $25 \times 10^3$ A.

(a) What mass of sodium can be produced in 1 hour?

(b) How many kilowatt-hours of electricity are used to produce 1.00 kg of sodium metal (1 kWh = $3.6 \times 10^6$ J)?

105. The reduction potentials for the Group 3A metals, $E°$, are given below. What trend or trends do you observe in these data? What can you learn about the chemistry of the Group 3A elements from these data?

| Half-Reaction | Reduction Potential ($E°$, V) |
|---|---|
| $Al^{3+}(aq) + 3\ e^- \longrightarrow Al(s)$ | −1.66 |
| $Ga^{3+}(aq) + 3\ e^- \longrightarrow Ga(s)$ | −0.53 |
| $In^{3+}(aq) + 3\ e^- \longrightarrow In(s)$ | −0.338 |
| $Tl^{3+}(aq) + 3\ e^- \longrightarrow Tl(s)$ | +0.72 |

**106.** (a) Magnesium is obtained from sea water. If the concentration of $Mg^{2+}$ in sea water is 0.050 M, what volume of sea water (in liters) must be treated to obtain 1.00 kg of magnesium metal? What mass of lime (CaO; in kilograms) must be used to precipitate the magnesium in this volume of sea water?

(b) When $1.2 \times 10^3$ kg of molten $MgCl_2$ is electrolyzed to produce magnesium, what mass (in kilograms) of metal is produced at the cathode? What is produced at the anode? What is the mass of this product? What is the total number of Faradays of electricity used in the process?

(c) One industrial process has an energy consumption of 18.5 kWh/kg of Mg. How many joules are required per mole (1 kWh = 1 kilowatt-hour = $3.6 \times 10^6$ J)? How does this energy compare with the energy of the following process?

$$MgCl_2(s) \rightarrow Mg(s) + Cl_2(g)$$

# Applying Chemical Principles

## van Arkel Triangles and Bonding

Two types of bonding, covalent and ionic, involve localized electrons. On one extreme are nonpolar covalent bonds, where electrons are equally shared between two atoms. On the other extreme are ionic bonds, where no sharing of electrons occurs. However, there are many bonds that fall between these extremes, and predictions of the extent of the polarity of a bond can be made using the electronegativity of the individual atoms. And finally, there is a third bonding type: metallic bonding, This raises the question of whether it is possible to develop an integrated picture wherein all three types of bonding, and their variations, can be represented. The answer is that it is possible, at least for binary compounds.

The first efforts in this direction were made by A. E. van Arkel in 1941 and modified later by J. A. A. Ketalaar. They summarized their findings in diagrams such as that shown in the Figure. Referred to now as van Arkel–Ketalaar triangles, the current version of this diagram portrays a wide variety of compounds composed of two different atoms within the boundary of an equilateral triangle. The corners represent the three types of bonding: metallic bonding at the lower left, covalent bonding on the lower right, and ionic bonding at the top. The least electronegative element (Cs), the most electronegative element (F), and the ionic compound formed from these elements are located at the corners of the triangle. All other binary compounds can be positioned inside the triangle.

Different versions of the van Arkel triangle have been developed, each using different scales on the axes. The one chosen for the Figure uses electronegativity values. Here, the x-axis is defined as the average of the electronegativities of the two atoms; as such, the x-axis is a measure of the localization of bonding electrons. The bonding electrons are completely delocalized in cesium, whereas the bonding electrons are completely localized in fluorine. The y-axis is defined as the difference in electronegativities. The greater the value in the y-axis, the greater the ionic character of the compound. With these parameters, the position of each binary compound can be assigned, associating the bond between elements with the degree of ionic/covalent/metallic character.

## Questions:

1. Use electronegativity values (◄ Figure 8.11) to place the compounds GaAs, SBr$_2$, Mg$_3$N$_2$, BP, C$_3$N$_4$, CuZn, and SrBr$_2$ on the van Arkel diagram and use the results to answer the following questions:

**FIGURE** A van Arkel–Ketalaar diagram. The four regions of this triangle represent the locations of metallic (blue), semiconducting (green), ionic (red), and covalent (orange) compounds

(a) Which of the compounds are metallic?

(b) Which of the compounds are semiconductors? Are either (or both) element(s) in these compounds metalloid(s)?

(c) Which of the compounds are ionic? Are the compounds composed of a metal and a nonmetal?

(d) Carbon nitride (C$_3$N$_4$) is predicted to be harder than diamond (which is currently the hardest known substance), but too little has been synthesized to enable a comparison. What type of bonding is predicted for C$_3$N$_4$?

(d) Which of the compounds are covalent? Are both elements in these compounds nonmetallic?

2. High boiling points are one characteristic of ionic compounds. For example, magnesium chloride boils at 1412 °C. Beryllium chloride, on the other hand, vaporizes at 520 °C. The boiling point of BeCl$_2$ is far lower than expected for an ionic compound, yet large for a covalent one. Determine where BeCl$_2$ lies on the van Arkel diagram.

## Reference:

W. B. Jensen, *Journal of Chemical Education*, Vol. 72, pp. 395–398, 1995.

# 22 The Chemistry of the Transition Elements

NASA/Science Source/Photo Researchers, Inc.

Martensite — Ni — Austenite

$x$, $y$, and $z$ are not equal, $\gamma$ about 96°

CsCl structure
$x = y = z$
$\alpha = \beta = \gamma = 90°$

**Two phases of nitinol.** The austenite form has a structure like CsCl.

**Nitinol frames for glasses.** Can you do this with your eye glasses? If you can, it is likely they are made of nitinol, a nickel–titanium alloy. They snap back to the proper fit even after they are twisted like a pretzel.

**Memory Metal** In the 1960s, William J. Buehler, an engineer at the Naval Ordnance Laboratory in Maryland, was looking for a material for use in the nose cone of a Navy missile. It was important that the material be impact- and heat-resistant and not lose these properties when it was bent and shaped. He prepared long, thin strips of an alloy of nickel and titanium to demonstrate that they could be folded and unfolded many times without breaking. At a meeting to discuss this material, one of his associates held a cigarette lighter to a folded-up piece of metal and was amazed to observe that the metal strip immediately unfolded and assumed its original shape. Thus, memory metal was discovered. This unusual alloy is now called *nitinol*, a name constructed out of "nickel," "titanium," and "Naval Ordnance Laboratory."

Memory metal is an alloy with roughly the same number of Ni and Ti atoms. When the atoms are arranged in the highly symmetrical austenite phase, the alloy is relatively rigid. In this phase a specific shape is established that will be "remembered." If the alloy is cooled below its "phase transition temperature," it enters a less symmetrical but flexible phase (martensite). Below this transition temperature, the metal is fairly soft and may be bent and twisted out of shape. When warmed above the phase transition temperature, nitinol returns to its original shape. The temperature at which the change in shape occurs varies with small differences in the nickel-to-titanium ratio.

Besides eye glasses frames, nitinol is now used in stents to reinforce blood vessels and in orthodontics.

**Questions:**

1. What are the dimensions of the austenite unit cell? Assume the Ti and Ni atoms are just touching along the unit cell diagonal. (Atom radii: Ti = 145 pm; Ni = 125 pm.)
2. Calculate the density of nitinol based on the austenite unit cell parameters. Does the calculated density of the austenite unit cell agree with the reported density of 6.5 g/cm$^3$?
3. Are Ti and Ni atoms paramagnetic or diamagnetic?

**Answers to these questions are available in Appendix N.**

# CHAPTER OUTLINE

**22.1** Properties of the Transition Elements

**22.2** Metallurgy

**22.3** Coordination Compounds

**22.4** Structures of Coordination Compounds

**22.5** Bonding in Coordination Compounds

**22.6** Colors of Coordination Compounds

**22.7** Organometallic Chemistry: Compounds with Metal–Carbon Bonds

# CHAPTER GOALS

*See Chapter Goals Revisited (page 1051) for Study Questions keyed to these goals.*

- Identify and explain the chemical and physical properties of the transition elements.

- Understand the composition, structure, and bonding in coordination compounds.

- Relate ligand field theory to the magnetic and spectroscopic properties of the complexes.

- Apply the effective atomic number (EAN) rule to simple organometallic compounds of the transition metals.

The transition elements are the large block of elements in the central portion of the periodic table. All are metals and bridge the *s*-block elements at the left and the *p*-block elements on the right (Figure 22.1). The transition elements are often divided into two groups, depending on the valence electrons involved in their chemistry. The first group are the **d-block elements**, because their occurrence in the periodic table coincides with the filling of the *d* orbitals. The second group are the **f-block elements**, characterized by filling of the *f* orbitals. Contained within this group of elements are two subgroups: the *lanthanides*, elements that occur between La and Hf, and the *actinides*, elements that occur between Ac and Rf.

This chapter focuses primarily on the *d*-block elements, and within this group we concentrate mainly on the elements in the fourth period, that is, the elements of the first transition series, scandium to zinc.

**OWL**

Sign in to OWL at **www.cengage.com/owl** to view tutorials and simulations, develop problem-solving skills, and complete online homework assigned by your professor.

**go Chemistry**

Download mini lecture videos for key concept review and exam prep from OWL or purchase them from **www.cengagebrain.com**

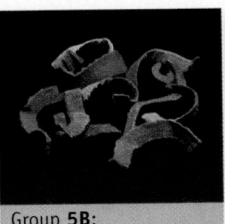
Group **4B**: Titanium (Ti)

Group **5B**: Vanadium (V)

Group **6B**: Chromium (Cr)

Group **7B**: Manganese (Mn)

**FIGURE 22.1**
**The transition metals.** The *d*-block elements and *f*-block elements (the transition elements) are highlighted in a darker shade of blue.

Group **8B**: Iron (Fe)

Group **8B**: Cobalt (Co)

Group **8B**: Nickel (Ni)

Group **1B**: Copper (Cu)

Group **2B**: Zinc (Zn)

Photos © Cengage Learning/Charles D. Winters

## 22.1 Properties of the Transition Elements

The *d*-block metals include elements with a wide range of properties. They encompass the most common metal used in construction and manufacturing (iron), metals that are valued for their beauty (gold, silver, and platinum), and metals used in coins (nickel, copper, and zinc). There are metals used in modern technology (titanium) and metals known and used in early civilizations (copper, silver, gold, and iron). The *d*-block contains the densest elements (osmium, $d = 22.49$ g/cm$^3$, and iridium, $d = 22.41$ g/cm$^3$), the metals with the highest and lowest melting points (tungsten, mp = 3410 °C, and mercury, mp = $-38.9$ °C), and one of only two elements with atomic numbers less than 83 that have only radioactive isotopes [technetium (Tc), atomic number 43; promethium (Pm), atomic number 61, in the *f*-block].

With the exception of mercury, the transition elements are solids, often with high melting and boiling points. They have a metallic sheen and conduct electricity and heat. They react with various oxidizing agents to give ionic compounds. There is considerable variation in such reactions among the elements, however. Because silver, gold, and platinum resist oxidation, for example, they are used for jewelry and decorative items.

Certain *d*-block elements are particularly important in living organisms. Cobalt is the crucial element in vitamin B$_{12}$, which is part of a catalyst essential for several biochemical reactions. Hemoglobin and myoglobin, oxygen-carrying and storage proteins, contain iron (see page 1032). Molybdenum and iron, together with sulfur, form the reactive portion of nitrogenase, a biological catalyst used by nitrogen-fixing organisms to convert atmospheric nitrogen into ammonia.

Many transition metal compounds are highly colored, which makes them useful as pigments in paints and dyes (Figure 22.2). Prussian blue, $Fe_4[Fe(CN)_6]_3 \cdot 14\,H_2O$, is a "bluing agent" used in engineering blueprints and in the laundry to brighten yellowed white cloth. A common pigment (artist's cadmium yellow) contains cadmium sulfide (CdS), and the white in most white paints is titanium(IV) oxide, $TiO_2$.

The presence of transition metal ions in crystalline silicates or alumina transforms these common materials into gemstones. Iron(II) ions produce the yellow color in citrine, and chromium(III) ions produce the red color of a ruby. Transition metal compounds in small quantities add color to glass. Blue glass contains a small amount of a cobalt(III) oxide, and addition of chromium(III) oxide to glass gives a green color. Old window panes sometimes take on a purple color over time as a consequence of oxidation of traces of manganese(II) ion present in the glass to permanganate ion ($MnO_4^-$).

**Prussian blue.** When $Fe^{3+}$ ions are added to $[Fe(CN)_6]^{4-}$ ions in water (or $Fe^{2+}$ ions are added to $[Fe(CN)_6]^{3-}$ ions), a deep blue compound called Prussian blue forms. The formula of the compound is $Fe_4[Fe(CN)_6]_3 \cdot 14\,H_2O$. The color arises from electron transfer between the Fe(II) and Fe(III) ions in the compound.

**(a)** Paint pigments: yellow, CdS; green, $Cr_2O_3$; white, $TiO_2$ and ZnO; purple, $Mn_3(PO_4)_2$; blue, $Co_2O_3$ and $Al_2O_3$; ochre, $Fe_2O_3$.

**(b)** Small amounts of transition metal compounds are used to color glass: blue, $Co_2O_3$; green, copper or chromium oxides; purple, nickel or cobalt oxides; red, copper oxide; iridescent green, uranium oxide.

**(c)** Traces of transition metal ions are responsible for the colors of green jade (iron), red corundum (chromium), blue azurite, blue-green turquoise (copper), and purple amethyst (iron).

**FIGURE 22.2 Colorful chemistry.** Transition metal compounds are often colored, a property that leads to specific uses.

In the next few pages, we will examine the properties of the transition elements, concentrating on the underlying principles that govern these properties.

## Electron Configurations

Because chemical behavior is related to electron structure, it is important to know the electron configurations of the *d*-block elements (Table 22.1) and their common ions (◄ Section 7.4). Recall that the configuration of these metals has the general form [noble gas core]$(n - 1)d^b ns^a$; that is, valence electrons for the transition elements reside in the *ns* and $(n - 1)d$ subshells.

## Oxidation and Reduction

A characteristic chemical property of all metals is that they undergo oxidation by a wide range of oxidizing agents such as oxygen, the halogens, and aqueous acids. Standard reduction potentials for the elements of the first transition series can be used to predict which elements will be oxidized by a given oxidizing agent. For example, all of these metals except vanadium and copper are oxidized by aqueous HCl (Table 22.2). This feature, which dominates the chemistry of these elements, is sometimes highly undesirable (see *A Closer Look: Corrosion of Iron*, page 1021).

When a transition metal is oxidized, the outermost *s* electrons are removed, followed by one or more *d* electrons. With a few exceptions, transition metal ions have the electron configuration [noble gas core]$(n - 1)d^x$. In contrast to ions formed by main group elements, transition metal cations often possess unpaired electrons, resulting in paramagnetism (◄ page 289). They are frequently colored as well, due to the absorption of light in the visible region of the electromagnetic spectrum. Color and magnetism figure prominently in a discussion of the properties and bonding of these elements, as you shall see shortly.

In the first transition series, the most commonly encountered metal ions have oxidation numbers of +2 and +3 (Table 22.2). With iron, for example, oxidation converts Fe($[Ar]3d^6 4s^2$) to either Fe$^{2+}$($[Ar]3d^6$) or Fe$^{3+}$($[Ar]3d^5$). Iron reacts with chlorine to give FeCl$_3$, and it reacts with aqueous acids to produce Fe$^{2+}$(aq) and H$_2$ (Figure 22.3). Despite the preponderance of 2+ and 3+ ions in compounds of the first transition metal series, the range of possible oxidation states for these compounds is broad (Figure 22.4). Earlier in this text, we encountered chromium with a +6 oxidation number (CrO$_4^{2-}$, Cr$_2$O$_7^{2-}$), manganese with an oxidation number of +7 (MnO$_4^-$), silver and copper as 1+ ions, and vanadium oxidation numbers that can range from +5 to +2 (◄ Figure 20.3).

**Table 22.1 Electron Configurations of the Fourth-Period Transition Elements**

| | *spdf* Configuration | Box Notation 3*d* | 4*s* |
|---|---|---|---|
| Sc | [Ar]$3d^1 4s^2$ | ↑ ☐ ☐ ☐ ☐ | ↑↓ |
| Ti | [Ar]$3d^2 4s^2$ | ↑ ↑ ☐ ☐ ☐ | ↑↓ |
| V | [Ar]$3d^3 4s^2$ | ↑ ↑ ↑ ☐ ☐ | ↑↓ |
| Cr | [Ar]$3d^5 4s^1$ | ↑ ↑ ↑ ↑ ↑ | ↑ |
| Mn | [Ar]$3d^5 4s^2$ | ↑ ↑ ↑ ↑ ↑ | ↑↓ |
| Fe | [Ar]$3d^6 4s^2$ | ↑↓ ↑ ↑ ↑ ↑ | ↑↓ |
| Co | [Ar]$3d^7 4s^2$ | ↑↓ ↑↓ ↑ ↑ ↑ | ↑↓ |
| Ni | [Ar]$3d^8 4s^2$ | ↑↓ ↑↓ ↑↓ ↑ ↑ | ↑↓ |
| Cu | [Ar]$3d^{10} 4s^1$ | ↑↓ ↑↓ ↑↓ ↑↓ ↑↓ | ↑ |
| Zn | [Ar]$3d^{10} 4s^2$ | ↑↓ ↑↓ ↑↓ ↑↓ ↑↓ | ↑↓ |

**Table 22.2 Products from Reactions of the Elements in the First Transition Series with O$_2$, Cl$_2$, or Aqueous HCl**

| Element | Reaction with O$_2$* | Reaction with Cl$_2$ | Reaction with Aqueous HCl |
|---|---|---|---|
| Scandium | Sc$_2$O$_3$ | ScCl$_3$ | Sc$^{3+}$(aq) |
| Titanium | TiO$_2$ | TiCl$_4$ | Ti$^{3+}$(aq) |
| Vanadium | V$_2$O$_5$ | VCl$_4$ | NR$^\dagger$ |
| Chromium | Cr$_2$O$_3$ | CrCl$_3$ | Cr$^{2+}$(aq) |
| Manganese | MnO$_2$ | MnCl$_2$ | Mn$^{2+}$(aq) |
| Iron | Fe$_2$O$_3$ | FeCl$_3$ | Fe$^{2+}$(aq) |
| Cobalt | Co$_2$O$_3$ | CoCl$_2$ | Co$^{2+}$(aq) |
| Nickel | NiO | NiCl$_2$ | Ni$^{2+}$(aq) |
| Copper | CuO | CuCl$_2$ | NR$^\dagger$ |
| Zinc | ZnO | ZnCl$_2$ | Zn$^{2+}$(aq) |

\* Product obtained with excess oxygen.

$^\dagger$ NR = no reaction.

**FIGURE 22.3** **Typical reactions of transition metals.** These metals react with oxygen, with halogens, and with acids under appropriate conditions.

**(a)** Steel wool reacts with $O_2$.

**(b)** Steel wool reacts with chlorine gas, $Cl_2$.

**(c)** Iron chips react with aqueous HCl.

Higher oxidation numbers are more common in compounds of the elements in the second and third transition series. For example, the naturally occurring sources of molybdenum and tungsten are the ores molybdenite ($MoS_2$) and wolframite ($WO_3$). This general trend is carried over in the *f*-block. The lanthanides form primarily 3+ ions. In contrast, actinide elements usually have higher oxidation numbers in their compounds; +4 and even +6 are typical. For example, $UO_3$ is a common oxide of uranium, and $UF_6$ is a compound important in processing uranium fuel for nuclear reactors [▶ Section 23.6].

## Periodic Trends in the *d*-Block: Size, Density, Melting Point

The periodic table is the most useful single reference source for a chemist. Not only does it provide data that have everyday use, but it also organizes the elements with respect to their chemical and physical properties. Let us look at three physical properties of the transition elements that vary periodically: atomic radii, density, and melting point.

**(a)** The most common oxidation states are indicated with *red squares;* less common oxidation states are indicated with *blue dots.*

**(b)** Aqueous solutions of chromium compounds with two different oxidation numbers: +3 in $Cr(NO_3)_3$ (violet) and $CrCl_3$ (green), and +6 in $K_2CrO_4$ (yellow) and $K_2Cr_2O_7$ (orange). The two Cr(III) species have different colors in solution because there are different complex ions in solution. The complex ion in the purple solution is $[Cr(H_2O)_6]^{3+}$; the complex ion in the green solution is $[Cr(H_2O)_4Cl_2]^+$.

**FIGURE 22.4** **Oxidation states of the transition elements in the first transition series.**

# A CLOSER LOOK

## Corrosion of Iron

It is hard not to be aware of corrosion. Those of us who live in the northern part of the United States are well aware of the problems of rust on our automobiles. It is estimated that 20% of iron production each year goes solely to replace iron that has rusted away.

Qualitatively, we describe corrosion as the deterioration of metals by a product-favored oxidation reaction. The corrosion of iron, for example, converts iron metal to red-brown rust, which is hydrated iron(III) oxide, $Fe_2O_3 \cdot H_2O$. This process requires both air and water, and it is enhanced if the water contains dissolved ions and if the metal is stressed (e.g., if it has dents, cuts, and scrapes on the surface).

The corrosion process occurs in what is essentially a small electrochemical cell. There is an anode and a cathode, an electrical connection between the two (the metal itself), and an electrolyte in contact with both anode and cathode. When a metal corrodes, the metal is oxidized on anodic areas of the metal surface.

Anode, oxidation    $M(s) \longrightarrow M^{n+} + n\, e^-$

The electrons are consumed by several possible half-reactions in cathodic areas.

Cathode, reduction

$$2\, H_3O^+(aq) + 2\, e^- \longrightarrow H_2(g) + 2\, H_2O(\ell)$$

$$2\, H_2O(\ell) + 2\, e^- \longrightarrow H_2(g) + 2\, OH^-(aq)$$

$$O_2(g) + 2\, H_2O(\ell) + 4\, e^- \longrightarrow 4\, OH^-(aq)$$

The rate of iron corrosion is controlled by the rate of the cathodic process. Of the three possible cathodic reactions, the one that is fastest is determined by acidity and the amount of oxygen present. If little or no oxygen is present—as when a piece of iron is buried in soil such as moist clay—hydronium ions or water are reduced, and $H_2(g)$ and hydroxide ions are the products. Iron(II) hydroxide is relatively insoluble and will precipitate on the metal surface, inhibiting the further formation of $Fe^{2+}$.

| | |
|---|---|
| Anode | $Fe(s) \longrightarrow Fe^{2+}(aq) + 2\, e^-$ |
| Cathode | $2\, H_2O(\ell) + 2\, e^- \longrightarrow H_2(g) + 2\, OH^-(aq)$ |
| Precipitation | $Fe^{2+}(aq) + 2\, OH^-(aq) \longrightarrow Fe(OH)_2(s)$ |
| Net reaction | $Fe(s) + 2\, H_2O(\ell) \longrightarrow H_2(g) + Fe(OH)_2(s)$ |

If both water and $O_2$ are present, the chemistry of iron corrosion is somewhat different, and the corrosion reaction is about 100 times faster than without oxygen.

| | |
|---|---|
| Anode | $2\, Fe(s) \longrightarrow 2\, Fe^{2+}(aq) + 4\, e^-$ |
| Cathode | $O_2(g) + 2\, H_2O(\ell) + 4\, e^- \longrightarrow 4\, OH^-(aq)$ |
| Precipitation | $2\, Fe^{2+}(aq) + 4\, OH^-(aq) \longrightarrow 2\, Fe(OH)_2(s)$ |
| Net reaction | $2\, Fe(s) + 2\, H_2O(\ell) + O_2(g) \longrightarrow 2\, Fe(OH)_2(s)$ |

If oxygen is present but not in excess, further oxidation of the iron(II) hydroxide leads to the formation of magnetic iron oxide $Fe_3O_4$, (which can be thought of as a mixed oxide of $Fe_2O_3$ and FeO).

$$6\, Fe(OH)_2(s) + O_2(g) \longrightarrow 2\, Fe_3O_4 \cdot H_2O(s) + 4\, H_2O(\ell)$$
green hydrated magnetite

$$Fe_3O_4 \cdot H_2O(s) \longrightarrow H_2O(\ell) + Fe_3O_4(s)$$
black magnetite

It is the black magnetite that you find coating an iron object that has corroded by resting in moist soil.

If the iron object has free access to oxygen and water, as in the open or in flowing water, red-brown iron(III) oxide will form.

$$4\, Fe(OH)_2(s) + O_2(g) \longrightarrow 2\, Fe_2O_3 \cdot H_2O(s) + 2\, H_2O(\ell)$$
red-brown

This is the familiar rust you see on cars and buildings and the substance that colors the water red in some mountain streams or in your home.

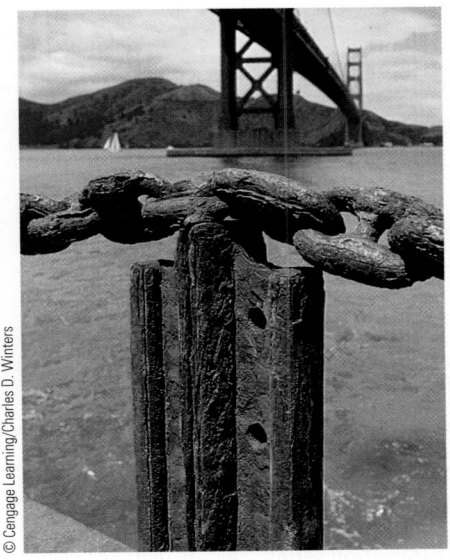

**The corrosion or rusting of iron results in major economic loss.**

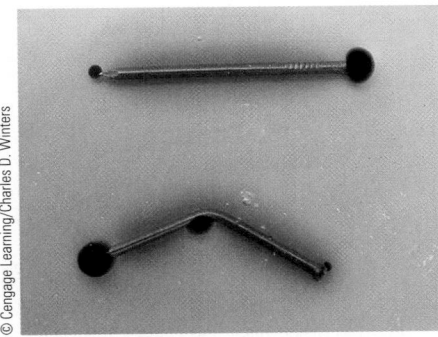

**Anode and cathode reactions in iron corrosion.** Two iron nails were placed in an agar gel that contains phenolphthalein and $K_3[Fe(CN)_6]$. Iron(II) ion, formed at the tip and where the nail is bent, reacts with $[Fe(CN)_6]^{3-}$ to form blue-green $Fe_4[Fe(CN)_6]_3 \cdot 14\, H_2O$ (Prussian blue). Hydrogen and $OH^-(aq)$ are formed at the other parts of the surface of the nail, the latter being detected by the pink color of the acid–base indicator. In this electrochemical cell, regions of stress—the ends and the bent region of the nail—act as anodes, and the remainder of the surface serves as the cathode.

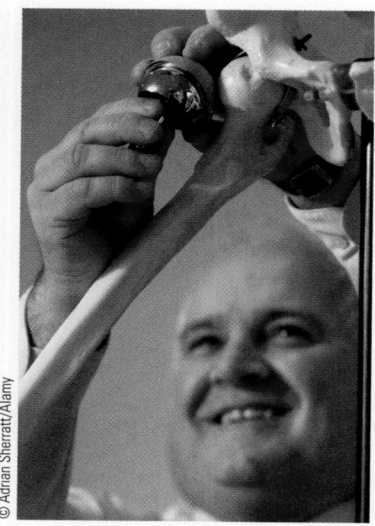

**Titanium, a versatile element.** Titanium takes it name from the Titans, a race of powerful gods in Greek mythology. It is the least dense metal in the *d*-block elements and is resistant to corrosion. For this reason it is used in aircraft and jet engines, not to mention golf clubs. Because it is also nonallergenic, it is used in jewelry and in artificial hip joints (shown here). It also forms many compounds, such as $TiO_2$. Titanium(IV) oxide is in the paper on which this book is printed. It prevents the type and figures on one side of the paper from being seen on the other side.

## Metal Atom Radii

The variation in atomic radii for the transition elements in the fourth, fifth, and sixth periods is illustrated in Figure 7.9. The radii of the transition elements vary over a fairly narrow range, with a small decrease to a minimum being observed around the middle of this group of elements. This similarity of radii can be understood based on electron configurations. Atom size is determined by the electrons in the outermost orbital, which for these elements is the *ns* orbital (*n* = 4, 5, or 6). Progressing from left to right in the periodic table, the size decline expected from increasing the number of protons in the nucleus is mostly canceled out by an opposing effect, repulsion from additional electrons in the (*n* − 1)*d* orbitals.

The radii of the *d*-block elements in the fifth and sixth periods in each group are almost identical. The reason is that the lanthanide elements immediately precede the third series of *d*-block elements. The filling of 4*f* orbitals is accompanied by a steady contraction in size, consistent with the general trend of decreasing size from left to right in the periodic table. At the point where the 5*d* orbitals begin to fill again, the radii have decreased to a size similar to that of elements in the previous period. The decrease in size that results from the filling of the 4*f* orbitals is called the **lanthanide contraction**.

The similar sizes of the second and third series *d*-block elements have significant consequences for their chemistry. For example, the "platinum group metals" (Ru, Os, Rh, Ir, Pd, and Pt) form similar compounds. Thus, it is not surprising that minerals containing these metals are found in the same geological zones on earth. Nor is it surprising that it is difficult to separate these elements from one another.

## Density

The variation in metal radii causes the densities of the transition elements to first increase and then decrease across a period (Figure 22.5). Although the overall change in radii among these elements is small, the effect is magnified because the volume is actually changing with the cube of the radius [$V = (4/3)\pi r^3$].

The lanthanide contraction explains why elements in the sixth period have the highest density. The relatively small radii of sixth-period transition metals, combined with the fact that their atomic masses are considerably larger than their counterparts in the fifth period, causes sixth-period metal densities to be very large.

## Melting Point

The melting point of any substance reflects the forces of attraction between the atoms, molecules, or ions that compose the solid. With transition elements, the

**FIGURE 22.5 Periodic properties in the transition series.** Density *(left)* and melting point *(right)* of the *d*-block elements.

melting points rise to a maximum around the middle of the series (Figure 22.5), then descend. Again, these elements' electron configurations provide us with an explanation. The variation in melting point indicates that the strongest metallic bonds occur when the *d* subshell is about half filled. This is also the point at which the largest number of electrons occupy the bonding molecular orbitals in the metal. (See the discussion of bonding in metals in Section 13.3.)

---

**REVIEW & CHECK FOR SECTION 22.1**

1. What is the maximum oxidation number that manganese can exhibit in its compounds?

   (a) +3        (b) +4        (c) +5        (d) +6        (e) +7

2. The "lanthanide contraction" is often given as an explanation for the fact that the sixth period transition elements have

   (a) densities smaller than that of the fifth period transition elements

   (b) atomic radii that are similar to the fifth period transition elements

   (c) melting points that are lower than the fifth period transition elements

---

## 22.2 Metallurgy

A few metals occur in nature as the free elements. This group includes copper (Figure 22.6), silver, and gold. Most metals, however, are found as oxides, sulfides, halides, carbonates, or other ionic compounds (Figure 22.7). Some metal-containing mineral deposits have little economic value, either because the concentration of the metal is too low or because the metal is difficult to separate from impurities. The relatively few minerals from which elements can be obtained profitably are called *ores* (Figure 22.7). **Metallurgy** is the general name given to the process of obtaining metals from their ores.

Very few ores are chemically pure substances. Instead, the desired mineral is usually mixed with large quantities of impurities such as sand and clay, called **gangue** (pronounced "gang"). Generally, the first step in a metallurgical process is to separate the mineral from the gangue. Then the ore is converted to the metal, a reduction process. Pyrometallurgy and hydrometallurgy are two methods of recovering metals from their ores. As the names imply, **pyrometallurgy** involves high temperatures and **hydrometallurgy** uses aqueous solutions (and thus is limited to the relatively low temperatures at which water is a liquid). Iron and copper metallurgy illustrate these two methods of metal production.

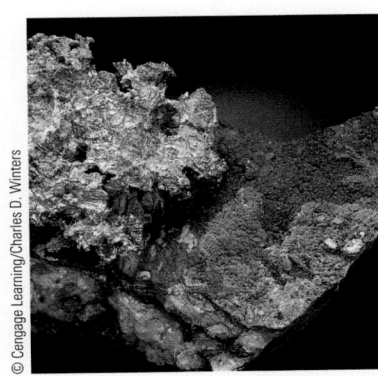

**FIGURE 22.6 Naturally occurring copper.** Copper occurs as the metal (native copper) and as minerals such as blue azurite [2 $CuCO_3 \cdot Cu(OH)_2$] and green malachite [$CuCO_3 \cdot Cu(OH)_2$].

| | | | | | | | | | | | | | | | | H | He |
|---|---|---|---|---|---|---|---|---|---|---|---|---|---|---|---|---|---|
| Li | Be | | | | | | | | | | | B | C | N | O | F | Ne |
| Na | Mg | | | | | | | | | | | Al | Si | P | S | Cl | Ar |
| K | Ca | Sc | Ti | V | Cr | Mn | Fe | Co | Ni | Cu | Zn | Ga | Ge | As | Se | Br | Kr |
| Rb | Sr | Y | Zr | Nb | Mo | | Ru | Rh | Pd | Ag | Cd | In | Sn | Sb | Te | I | Xe |
| Cs | Ba | La | Hf | Ta | W | Re | Os | Ir | Pt | Au | Hg | Tl | Pb | Bi | | | Rn |

| Lathanides | Ce | Pr | Nd | | Sm | Eu | Gd | Tb | Dy | Ho | Er | Tm | Yb | Lu |
|---|---|---|---|---|---|---|---|---|---|---|---|---|---|---|

Key

Sulfides | Oxides | Can occur uncombined | Halide salts | Phosphates | Silicates | C from coal, B from borax | Carbonates

**FIGURE 22.7 Sources of the elements.** A few transition metals, such as copper and gold, occur naturally as the metal. Most other elements are found naturally as oxides, sulfides, or other salts.

**FIGURE 22.8** A blast furnace.
The largest modern furnaces have hearths 14 meters in diameter. They can produce as much as 10,000 tons of iron per day.

- **Coke: A Reducing Agent** Coke is made by heating coal in a tall, narrow oven that is sealed to keep out oxygen. Heating drives off volatile chemicals, including benzene and ammonia. What remains is nearly pure carbon.

## Pyrometallurgy: Iron Production

The production of iron from its ores is carried out in a blast furnace (Figure 22.8). The furnace is charged with a mixture of ore (usually hematite, $Fe_2O_3$), coke (which is primarily carbon), and limestone ($CaCO_3$). A blast of hot air forced in at the bottom of the furnace causes the coke to burn with such an intense heat that the temperature at the bottom is almost 1500 °C. The quantity of air input is controlled so that carbon monoxide is the primary product. Both carbon and carbon monoxide participate in the reduction of iron(III) oxide to give impure metal.

$$Fe_2O_3(s) + 3\ C(s) \longrightarrow 2\ Fe(\ell) + 3\ CO(g)$$

$$Fe_2O_3(s) + 3\ CO(g) \longrightarrow 2\ Fe(\ell) + 3\ CO_2(g)$$

Much of the carbon dioxide formed in the reduction process (and from heating the limestone) is reduced on contact with unburned coke and produces more reducing agent.

$$CO_2(g) + C(s) \longrightarrow 2\ CO(g)$$

The molten iron flows down through the furnace and collects at the bottom, where it is tapped off through an opening in the side. This impure iron is called *cast iron* or *pig iron*. Usually, the impure metal is either brittle or soft (undesirable properties for most uses) due to the presence of impurities such as elemental carbon, phosphorus, and sulfur.

Iron ores generally contain silicate minerals and silicon dioxide. Lime (CaO), formed when limestone is heated, reacts with these materials to give calcium silicate.

$$SiO_2(s) + CaO(s) \longrightarrow CaSiO_3(\ell)$$

This is an acid–base reaction because CaO is a basic oxide and $SiO_2$ is an acidic oxide. The calcium silicate, molten at the temperature of the blast furnace and less dense than molten iron, floats on the iron. Other nonmetal oxides dissolve in this layer and the mixture, called *slag*, is easily removed.

Pig iron from the blast furnace may contain as much as 4.5% carbon, 0.3% phosphorus, 0.04% sulfur, 1.5% silicon, and some other elements as well. The impure iron must be purified to remove these nonmetal components. Several processes are available to accomplish this task, but the most important uses the *basic oxygen furnace* (Figure 22.9). The process in the furnace removes much of the carbon and all of the phosphorus, sulfur, and silicon. Pure oxygen is blown into the molten pig iron and oxidizes phosphorus to $P_4O_{10}$, sulfur to $SO_2$, and carbon to $CO_2$. These nonmetal oxides either escape as gases or react with basic oxides such as CaO that are added or are used to line the furnace. For example,

$$P_4O_{10}(g) + 6\ CaO(s) \longrightarrow 2\ Ca_3(PO_4)_2(\ell)$$

The result is ordinary *carbon steel*. Almost any degree of flexibility, hardness, strength, and malleability can be achieved in carbon steel by reheating and cooling in a process called *tempering*. (See *Case Study: High Strength Steels and Unit Cells*, page 592.) The resulting material can then be used in a wide variety of applications. The major disadvantages of carbon steel are that it corrodes easily and that it loses its properties when heated strongly.

Other transition metals, such as chromium, manganese, and nickel, can be added during the steel-making process, giving *alloys* (solid solutions of two or more metals) that have specific physical, chemical, and mechanical properties. One well-known alloy is stainless steel, which contains 18% to 20% Cr and 8% to 12% Ni. Stainless steel is much more resistant to corrosion than carbon steel. Another alloy of iron is alnico V. Used in loudspeaker magnets because of its permanent magnetism, it contains five elements: Al (8%), Ni (14%), Co (24%), Cu (3%), and Fe (51%).

## Hydrometallurgy: Copper Production

In contrast to iron ores, which are mostly oxides, most copper minerals are sulfides. Copper-bearing minerals include chalcopyrite ($CuFeS_2$), chalcocite ($Cu_2S$), and covellite (CuS). Because ores containing these minerals generally have a very low percentage of copper, enrichment is necessary. This step is carried out by a process known as *flotation*. First, the ore is finely powdered. Next, oil is added and the mixture is agitated with soapy water in a large tank (Figure 22.10). At the same time, compressed air is forced through the mixture, so that the lightweight, oil-covered copper sulfide particles are carried to the top as a frothy mixture. The heavier gangue settles to the bottom of the tank, and the copper-laden froth is skimmed off.

Hydrometallurgy can be used to obtain copper from an enriched ore. In one method, enriched chalcopyrite ore is treated with a solution of copper(II) chloride. A reaction ensues that leaves copper in the form of solid, insoluble CuCl, which is easily separated from the iron that remains in solution as aqueous $FeCl_2$.

$$CuFeS_2(s) + 3\ CuCl_2(aq) \longrightarrow 4\ CuCl(s) + FeCl_2(aq) + 2\ S(s)$$

Aqueous NaCl is then added, and CuCl dissolves because of the formation of the complex ion $[CuCl_2]^-$.

$$CuCl(s) + Cl^-(aq) \longrightarrow [CuCl_2]^-(aq)$$

Copper(I) compounds in solution are unstable with respect to Cu(0) and Cu(II). Thus, $[CuCl_2]^-$ disproportionates to the metal and $CuCl_2$, and the latter is used to treat further ore.

$$2\ [CuCl_2]^-(aq) \longrightarrow Cu(s) + Cu^{2+}(aq) + 4\ Cl^-(aq)$$

Approximately 10% of the copper produced in the United States is obtained with the aid of bacteria. Acidified water is sprayed onto copper-mining wastes that contain low levels of copper. As the water trickles down through the crushed rock, the bacterium *Thiobacillus ferrooxidans* breaks down the iron sulfides in the rock and

**FIGURE 22.9** Molten iron being poured from a basic oxygen furnace.

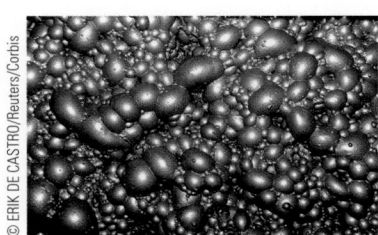

**FIGURE 22.10** Enriching copper ore by the flotation process. The less dense particles of $Cu_2S$ are trapped in the soap bubbles and float. The denser gangue settles to the bottom.

**FIGURE 22.11 Electrolytic refining of copper. (a)** Slabs of impure copper, called *blister copper*, form the anode, and pure copper is deposited at the cathode. **(b)** The electrolysis cells at a copper refinery.

(a)

Thin sheets of pure copper

Solution of CuSO₄ and H₂SO₄

Slabs of impure copper

(b)

Simon Fraser/Northumbria Circuits/Science Photo Library/Photo Researchers, Inc.

converts iron(II) to iron(III). Iron(III) ions oxidize the sulfide ion of copper sulfide to sulfate ions, leaving copper(II) ions in solution. Then the copper(II) ion is reduced to metallic copper by reaction with iron.

$$Cu^{2+}(aq) + Fe(s) \longrightarrow Cu(s) + Fe^{2+}(aq)$$

The purity of the copper obtained via these metallurgical processes is about 99%, but this is not acceptable because even traces of impurities greatly diminish the electrical conductivity of the metal. Consequently, a further purification step is needed—one involving electrolysis (Figure 22.11). Thin sheets of pure copper metal and slabs of impure copper are immersed in a solution containing $CuSO_4$ and $H_2SO_4$. The pure copper sheets serve as the cathode of an electrolysis cell, and the impure slabs are the anode. Copper in the impure sample is oxidized to copper(II) ions at the anode, and copper(II) ions in solution are reduced to pure copper at the cathode.

---

**REVIEW & CHECK FOR SECTION 22.2**

1.  In the reaction between $CuFeS_2(s)$ and $CuCl_2(aq)$, what element is reduced and what element is oxidized?

    (a) Sulfur is reduced, iron is oxidized.

    (c) Sulfur is reduced, copper is oxidized.

    (b) Copper is reduced, sulfur is oxidized.

    (d) This is not a redox reaction.

2.  What is the most common form in which iron is found in the earth's crust?

    (a) Iron is found in elemental form

    (c) Iron sulfide

    (b) Iron oxide

    (d) Iron silicate

---

## 22.3 Coordination Compounds

When metal salts dissolve, water molecules cluster around the ions (page 551). The negative end of each polar water molecule is attracted to the positively charged metal ion, and the positive end of the water molecule is attracted to the anion. As noted earlier (◄ Section 12.2), the energy of the ion–solvent interaction (solvation energy) is an important aspect of the solution process. But there is much more to this story.

### Complexes and Ligands

A green solution formed by dissolving nickel(II) chloride in water contains $Ni^{2+}(aq)$ and $Cl^-(aq)$ ions (Figure 22.12). If the solvent is removed, a green crystalline solid is obtained. The formula of this solid is often written as $NiCl_2 \cdot 6\,H_2O$, and the compound is called nickel(II) chloride hexahydrate. Addition of ammonia to

**FIGURE 22.12 Coordination compounds of Ni²⁺ ion.** The transition metals and their ions form a wide range of compounds, often with beautiful colors and interesting structures. One purpose of this chapter is to explore some commonly observed structures and explain how these compounds can be so colorful.

Add NH₃

$[Ni(H_2O)_6]^{2+}$

Add NaOH

$[Ni(NH_3)_6]^{2+}$

Insoluble Ni(OH)₂

Add
ethylenediamine
NH₂CH₂CH₂NH₂

Add
dimethylglyoxime
(dmg)

$[Ni(NH_2CH_2CH_2NH_2)_3]^{2+}$

Ni(dmg)₂

Sum of metal ion
and ligand charges

Coordination complex

Coordinated
metal ion

Ligand

$[Ni(NH_3)_6]^{2+}$

**FIGURE 22.13 A coordination complex.** In the $[Ni(NH_3)_6]^{2+}$ ion, the ligands are $NH_3$ molecules. Because the metal has a 2+ charge and the ligands have no charge, the charge on the complex ion is 2+.

● **Ligands Are Lewis Bases** Ligands are Lewis bases because they furnish the electron pair; the metal ion is a Lewis acid because it accepts electron pairs (◀ Section 17.11). Thus, the coordinate covalent bond between ligand and metal can be viewed as a Lewis acid–Lewis base interaction.

● **Bidentate Ligands** All common bidentate ligands bind to *adjacent* sites on the metal.

**FIGURE 22.14 Common bidentate ligands.** Coordination of these bidentate ligands to a transition metal ion results in five- or six-member metal-containing rings and no ring strain. (Only one resonance structure each of the acetylacetonate ion and phenanthroline are shown.)

the aqueous nickel(II) chloride solution gives a lilac-colored solution from which another compound, $NiCl_2 \cdot 6\,NH_3$, can be isolated. This formula looks very similar to the formula for the hydrate, with ammonia substituted for water.

What are these two nickel species? The formulas identify the compositions of the compounds but fail to give information about their structures. Because properties of compounds derive from their structures, we need to evaluate the structures in more detail. Typically, metal compounds are ionic, and solid ionic compounds have structures with cations and anions arranged in a regular array. The structure of hydrated nickel chloride contains cations with the formula $[Ni(H_2O)_6]^{2+}$ and chloride anions. The structure of the ammonia-containing compound is similar to the hydrate; it is made up of $[Ni(NH_3)_6]^{2+}$ cations and chloride anions.

Ions such as $[Ni(H_2O)_6]^{2+}$ and $[Ni(NH_3)_6]^{2+}$, in which a metal ion and either water or ammonia molecules compose a single structural unit, are examples of **coordination complexes**, also known as **complex ions** (Figure 22.13). Compounds containing a coordination complex as part of the structure are called **coordination compounds**, and their chemistry is known as **coordination chemistry**. Although the older "hydrate" formulas are still used, the preferred method of writing the formula for coordination compounds places the metal atom or ion and the molecules or anions directly bonded to it within brackets to show that it is a single structural entity. Thus, the formula for the nickel(II)–ammonia compound is better written as $[Ni(NH_3)_6]Cl_2$.

All coordination complexes contain a metal atom or ion as the central part of the structure. Bonded to the metal are molecules or ions called **ligands** (from the Latin verb *ligare*, meaning "to bind"). In the preceding examples, water and ammonia are the ligands. The number of ligand atoms attached to the metal defines the **coordination number** of the metal. The geometry described by the attached ligands is called the **coordination geometry**. In the nickel complex ion $[Ni(NH_3)_6]^{2+}$ (Figure 22.12), the six ligands are arranged in a regular octahedral geometry around the central metal ion.

Ligands can be either neutral molecules or anions (or, in rare instances, cations). The characteristic feature of a ligand is that it contains a lone pair of electrons. In the classic description of bonding in a coordination complex, the lone pair of electrons on a ligand is shared with the metal ion. The attachment is a coordinate covalent bond (◀ Section 8.5), because the electron pair being shared was originally on the ligand. The name "coordination complex" derives from the name given to this kind of bonding.

The net charge on a coordination complex is the sum of the charges on the metal and its attached groups. Complexes can be cations (as in the two nickel complexes used as examples here), anions, or uncharged.

Ligands such as $H_2O$ and $NH_3$, which coordinate to the metal via a single Lewis base atom, are termed **monodentate**. The word "dentate" comes from the Latin *dentis*, meaning "tooth," so $NH_3$ is a "one-toothed" ligand. Some ligands attach to the metal with more than one donor atom. These ligands are called **polydentate**. Ethylenediamine (1,2-diaminoethane), $H_2NCH_2CH_2NH_2$, often abbreviated as en; oxalate ion, $C_2O_4^{2-}$ ($ox^{2-}$); and phenanthroline, $C_{12}H_8N_2$ (phen), are examples of the wide variety of **bidentate** ligands (Figure 22.14). Structures and examples of some complex ions with bidentate ligands are shown in Figure 22.15.

**(a)** $H_2NCH_2CH_2NH_2$, en
ethylenediamine

**(b)** $C_2O_4^{2-}$, ox
oxalate ion

**(c)** $CH_3COCHCOCH_3^-$, acac⁻
acetylacetonate ion

**(d)** $C_{12}H_8N_2$, phen
phenanthroline

**FIGURE 22.15 Complex ions with bidentate ligands.** See Figure 22.14 for abbreviations.

$[Fe(C_2O_4)_3]^{3-}$          $[Co(en)_3]^{3+}$          $Cr(acac)_3$

Polydentate ligands are also called **chelating ligands**, or just *chelates* (pronounced "key-lates"). The name derives from the Greek *chele*, meaning "claw." Because two or more bonds are broken to separate the ligand from the metal, complexes with chelated ligands often have greater stability than those with monodentate ligands. Chelated complexes are important in everyday life. One way to clean the rust out of water-cooled automobile engines and steam boilers is to add a solution of oxalic acid. Iron(III) oxide reacts with oxalic acid to give a water-soluble iron oxalate complex ion:

$$3\ H_2O(\ell) + Fe_2O_3(s) + 6\ H_2C_2O_4(aq) \longrightarrow 2\ [Fe(C_2O_4)_3]^{3-}(aq) + 6\ H_3O^+(aq)$$

Ethylenediaminetetraacetate ion ($EDTA^{4-}$), a hexadentate ligand, is an excellent chelating ligand (Figure 22.16). It can wrap around a metal ion, encapsulating it. Salts of this anion are often added to commercial salad dressings to remove traces of free metal ions from solution; otherwise, these metal ions can act as catalysts for the oxidation of the oils in the dressing. Without $EDTA^{4-}$, the dressing would quickly become rancid. Another use is in bathroom cleansers. The $EDTA^{4-}$ ion removes deposits of $CaCO_3$ and $MgCO_3$ left by hard water by coordinating to $Ca^{2+}$ or $Mg^{2+}$ to create soluble complex ions.

Complexes with polydentate ligands play particularly important roles in biochemistry, one example of which is described in *A Closer Look: Hemoglobin*, page 1032.

## Formulas of Coordination Compounds

It is useful to be able to predict the formula of a coordination complex, given the metal ion and ligands, and to derive the oxidation number of the coordinated metal ion, given the formula of a coordination compound. The following examples explore these issues.

**(a)** ethylenediaminetetraacetate, $EDTA^{4-}$

**(b)** $[Co(EDTA)]^-$

**FIGURE 22.16** $EDTA^{4-}$, a hexadentate ligand. **(a)** Ethylenediaminetetraacetate, $EDTA^{4-}$. **(b)** $[Co(EDTA)]^-$. Notice the five-member rings created when this ligand bonds to the metal.

## EXAMPLE 22.1 Formulas of Coordination Complexes

**Problem** Give the formulas of the following coordination complexes:

(a) A $Ni^{2+}$ ion is bound to two water molecules and two bidentate oxalate ions.

(b) A $Co^{3+}$ ion is bound to one $Cl^-$ ion, one ammonia molecule, and two bidentate ethylenediamine (en) molecules.

**What Do You Know?** The composition of the coordination complex is given for each part of the question.

**Strategy** The problem requires determining the net charge, which equals the sum of the charges of the various component parts of the complex ion. With that information, the metal and ligands can be assembled in the formula, which is placed in brackets, and the net charge indicated.

**Solution**

(a) This complex ion is constructed from two neutral $H_2O$ molecules, two $C_2O_4{}^{2-}$ ions, and one $Ni^{2+}$ ion, so the net charge on the complex is $2-$. The formula for the complex ion is

$$[Ni(C_2O_4)_2(H_2O)_2]^{2-}$$

(b) This cobalt(III) complex ion combines two en molecules and one $NH_3$ molecule, both having no charge, as well as one $Cl^-$ ion and a $Co^{3+}$ ion. The net charge is $2+$. The formula for this complex (writing out the entire formula for ethylenediamine) is

$$[Co(H_2NCH_2CH_2NH_2)_2(NH_3)Cl]^{2+}$$

**Think about Your Answer** Enclosing the formula of a complex in brackets is done to designate that this is a single unit. Species shown outside the brackets are counterions (when shown).

**Check Your Understanding**

(a) What is the formula of a complex ion composed of one $Co^{3+}$ ion, three ammonia molecules, and three $Cl^-$ ions?

(b) What is the formula for the coordination complex of iron (II) having two ethylenediamine ligands and two bromide ion ligands?

## EXAMPLE 22.2 Coordination Compounds

**Problem** In each of the following coordination complexes, determine the metal's oxidation number and coordination number.

(a) $[Co(en)_2(NO_2)_2]Cl$

(b) $Pt(NH_3)_2(C_2O_4)$

(c) $Pt(NH_3)_2Cl_4$

(d) $[Co(NH_3)_5Cl]SO_4$

**What Do You Know?** You are given the formulas of compounds involving complex ions. The oxidation number is the charge that must be present on the metal. The coordination number is the number of ligand attachments to the metal. Remember that bidentate ligands coordinate in two positions.

**Strategy** Each formula consists of a complex ion or molecule made up of the metal ion, neutral, and anionic ligands. Counterions (shown outside the square brackets) may also be present. The oxidation number of the metal is the charge necessary to balance the sum of the negative charges associated with the anionic ligands and counterion. The coordination number is the number of donor atoms in the ligands that are bonded to the metal. Remember that the bidentate ligands in these examples (en, oxalate ion) attach to the metal at two sites and that any counterions present are not part of the complex ion—that is, they are not ligands.

**Solution**

(a)  A chloride ion with a 1− charge is outside the brackets, showing that the charge on the complex ion must be 1+. There are two nitrite ions ($NO_2^-$) and two neutral bidentate ethylenediamine ligands in the complex. To give a 1+ charge on the complex ion, the cobalt ion must have a charge of 3+; that is, the sum of 2− (two nitrites), 0 (two en ligands), and 3+ (the cobalt ion) equals 1+. Each en ligand fills two coordination positions, and the two nitrite ions fill two more positions. The coordination number of the metal is 6.

(b)  There is an oxalate ion ($C_2O_4^{2-}$) and two neutral ammonia ligands. To balance the charge on the oxalate ion, platinum must have a 2+ charge; that is, it has an oxidation number of +2. The coordination number is 4, with an oxalate ligand filling two coordination positions and each ammonia molecule filling one.

(c)  There are four chloride ions ($Cl^-$) and two neutral ammonia ligands. In this complex, the oxidation number of the metal is +4, and the coordination number is 6.

(d)  A sulfate ion with a 2− charge is outside the brackets, showing that the charge on the complex ion must be 2+. There is one chloride ion ($Cl^-$) and five neutral ammonia ligands in the complex ion. To give a 2+ charge on the complex ion, the cobalt must be 3+; the sum of 1− (one chloride), zero (five $NH_3$ ligands), and 3+ (the cobalt ion) equals 2+. The oxidation number of the metal is +3 and the coordination number is 6 (sulfate is not coordinated to the metal).

**Think about Your Answer**  Knowing the oxidation state of the metal in a coordination compound is important. From this, you can determine the electron configuration of the metal. As we shall see in Section 22.5, this information will be needed to determine important properties of a complex such as magnetism and color.

---

**Check Your Understanding**

(a)  Determine the metal's oxidation number and coordination number in (i) $K_3[Co(NO_2)_6]$ and in (ii) $Mn(NH_3)_4Cl_2$.

(b)  Determine the oxidation number and coordination number of cobalt in the complex $NH_4[Co(edta)]$.

---

# Naming Coordination Compounds

Coordination compounds are named according to an established system. The three compounds below are named according to the rules that follow.

| Compound | Systematic Name |
|---|---|
| $[Ni(H_2O)_6]SO_4$ | Hexaaquanickel(II) sulfate |
| $[Cr(en)_2(CN)_2]Cl$ | Dicyanobis(ethylenediamine)chromium(III) chloride |
| $K[Pt(NH_3)Cl_3]$ | Potassium amminetrichloroplatinate(II) |

1.  In naming a coordination compound that is a salt, name the cation first and then the anion. (This is how all salts are commonly named.)
2.  When giving the name of the complex ion or molecule, name the ligands first, in alphabetical order, followed by the name of the metal. (When determining alphabetical order, any prefix is not considered part of the name.)
3.  Ligands and their names:
    (a) If a ligand is an anion whose name ends in *-ite* or *-ate*, the final *e* is changed to *o* (sulfate ⟶ sulfato or nitrite ⟶ nitrito).
    (b) If the ligand is an anion whose name ends in *-ide*, the ending is changed to *o* (chloride ⟶ chloro, cyanide ⟶ cyano).
    (c) If the ligand is a neutral molecule, its common name is usually used with several important exceptions: Water as a ligand is referred to as *aqua*; ammonia is called *ammine*; and CO is called *carbonyl*.

**Common Monodentate Ligands and Their Names**

| Ligand | Name |
|---|---|
| $F^-$ | fluoro |
| $Cl^-$ | chloro |
| $Br^-$ | bromo |
| $I^-$ | iodo |
| $H_2O$ | aqua |
| $NH_3$ | ammine |
| $CO$ | carbonyl |
| $CN^-$ | cyano |
| $OH^-$ | hydroxo |
| $-NO_2^-$ | nitro |

**A CLOSER LOOK**

# Hemoglobin

Metal-containing coordination compounds figure prominently in many biochemical reactions. Perhaps the best-known example is hemoglobin, the chemical in the blood responsible for $O_2$ transport. It is also one of the most thoroughly studied bioinorganic compounds.

As described in *The Chemistry of Life: Biochemistry* (page 493), hemoglobin (Hb) is a large iron-containing protein. It includes four polypeptide segments, each containing an iron(II) ion locked inside a porphyrin ring system and coordinated to a nitrogen atom from another part of the protein. A sixth site is available to attach to oxygen.

One segment of the hemoglobin molecule resembles the myoglobin structure shown below. (Myoglobin, the oxygen-storage protein in muscle, has only one polypeptide chain with an enclosed heme group.) In myoglobin, the heme group (the name given to the metal and porphyrin ring system) is enclosed within a polypeptide chain. The iron ion in the porphyrin ring is shown in Figure B. The first and sixth coordination positions are taken up by nitrogen atoms from amino acids of the polypeptide chain.

Hemoglobin functions by reversibly adding oxygen to the sixth coordination position of each iron, giving a complex called *oxyhemoglobin*.

Because hemoglobin features four iron centers, a maximum of four molecules of oxygen can bind to the molecule. The binding to oxygen is cooperative; that is, binding one molecule enhances the tendency to bind the second, third, and fourth molecules. Formation of the oxygenated complex is favored, but not too highly, because oxy-

gen must also be released by the molecule to body tissues. Interestingly, an increase in acidity leads to a decrease in the stability of the oxygenated complex. This phenomenon is known as the *Bohr effect*, named for Christian Bohr, Niels Bohr's father (page 342). Release of oxygen in tissues is facilitated by an increase in acidity that results from the presence of $CO_2$ formed by metabolism.

Among the notable properties of hemoglobin is its ability to form a complex with carbon monoxide. This complex is very stable, with the equilibrium constant for the following reaction being about 200 (where Hb is hemoglobin):

$$HbO_2(aq) + CO(g) \rightleftharpoons HbCO(aq) + O_2(g)$$

When CO complexes with iron, the oxygen-carrying capacity of hemoglobin is lost. Consequently, CO (and the isoelectronic $CN^-$ ion) is highly toxic to humans. Exposure to even small amounts greatly reduces the capacity of the blood to transport oxygen.

Hemoglobin abnormalities are well known. One of the most common abnormalities causes sickle cell anemia and was described on page 494.

**FIGURE A  Porphyrin ring of the heme group.** The tetradentate ligand surrounding the iron(II) ion in hemoglobin is a dianion of a substituted molecule called a *porphyrin*. Because of the double bonds in this structure, all of the carbon and nitrogen atoms in the dianion of the porphyrin lie in a plane. In addition, the nitrogen lone pairs are directed toward the center of the molecule, and the molecular dimensions are such that a metal ion may fit nicely into the cavity.

porphyrin

$-2\ H^+$

porphyrin$^{2-}$

Heme group with iron cation
Protein chain

Myoglobin (Mb)

**FIGURE B  The heme group in myoglobin.** This protein is a close relative of hemoglobin. The heme group with its iron ion is shown.

120°

Fe

Base from protein

**FIGURE C  Oxygen binding.** Oxygen binds to the iron of the heme group in oxyhemoglobin (and in myoglobin). Interestingly, the Fe—O—O angle is bent.

(d) When there is more than one of a particular monodentate ligand with a simple name, the number of ligands is designated by the appropriate prefix: *di, tri, tetra, penta,* or *hexa.* If the ligand name is complicated, the prefix changes to *bis, tris, tetrakis, pentakis,* or *hexakis,* followed by the ligand name in parentheses.

4.  If the coordination complex is an anion, the suffix *-ate* is added to the metal name.

5.  Following the name of the metal, the oxidation number of the metal is given in Roman numerals.

## EXAMPLE 22.3 Naming Coordination Compounds

**Problem** Name the following compounds:

(a) $[Cu(NH_3)_4]SO_4$

(c) $Co(phen)_2Cl_2$

(b) $K_2[CoCl_4]$

(d) $[Co(en)_2(H_2O)Cl]Cl_2$

**What Do You Know?** Formulas of each compound are given.

**Strategy** Apply the rules for nomenclature given above.

**Solution**

(a) The complex ion (in square brackets) is composed of four $NH_3$ molecules (named *ammine* in a complex) and the copper ion. To balance the $2-$ charge on the sulfate counterion, copper must have a $2+$ charge. The compound's name is

> tetraamminecopper(II) sulfate

(b) The complex ion $[CoCl_4]^{2-}$ has a $2-$ charge. With four $Cl^-$ ligands, the cobalt ion must have a $2+$ charge, so the sum of charges is $2-$. The name of the compound is

> potassium tetrachlorocobaltate(II)

(c) This is a neutral coordination compound. The ligands include two $Cl^-$ ions and two neutral bidentate *phen* (phenanthroline) ligands (page 1028). The metal ion must have a $2+$ charge ($Co^{2+}$). The name, listing ligands in alphabetical order, is

> dichlorobis(phenanthroline)cobalt(II)

(d) The complex ion has a $2+$ charge because it is paired with two uncoordinated $Cl^-$ ions. The cobalt ion is $Co^{3+}$ because it is bonded to two neutral en ligands, one neutral water, and one $Cl^-$. The name is

> aquachlorobis(ethylenediamine)cobalt(III) chloride

**Think about Your Answer** The earliest studies of coordination compounds created a colorful array of names, and a few of these are still used (Prussian Blue, mentioned earlier, and Zeise's salt, $K[Pt(C_2H_4)Cl_3]$, are two examples). However, a systematic nomenclature is essential to communication among scientists working in the area. The rules of nomenclature make it possible for any scientist to derive a formula from the name, or to name a compound if given its formula.

**Check Your Understanding**

Name the following coordination compounds.

(a) $[Ni(H_2O)_6]SO_4$     (b) $[Cr(en)_2(CN)_2]Cl$    (c) $K[Pt(NH_3)Cl_3]$     (d) $K[CuCl_2]$

---

**REVIEW & CHECK FOR SECTION 22.3**

1. What is the coordination number for the metal in the compound tetraaquaoxalatoiron(III) chloride?

    (a) 4       (b) 6       (c) 7       (d) 2

2. What is the oxidation number of the metal in $(NH_4)_3[Fe(CN)_6]$?

    (a) 0       (b) $+1$       (c) $+2$       (d) $+3$

3. Which of the following is a complex ion based on an iron(II) ion?

    (a) $[Fe(H_2O)_4Cl_2]ClO_4$

    (c) $Fe(acac)_3$

    (b) $Na_4[Fe(C_2O_4)_3]$

    (d) $[Fe(NH_3)_5Cl]SO_4$

4.    In which of the following complexes is the metal 6-coordinate?

(a)    lithium tetrachlorocobaltate(II)

(b)    pentaamminehydroxochromium(III) chloride

(c)    bis(ethylenediamine)silver(I) chloride

(d)    diamminedichlorozinc(II)

## 22.4 Structures of Coordination Compounds
### Common Coordination Geometries

The geometry of a coordination complex is defined by the arrangement of donor atoms of the ligands around the central metal ion. Metal ions in coordination compounds can have coordination numbers ranging from 2 to 12. Only complexes with coordination numbers of 2, 4, and 6 are common, however, so we will concentrate on species such as $[ML_2]^{n\pm}$, $[ML_4]^{n\pm}$, and $[ML_6]^{n\pm}$, where M is the metal ion and L is a *monodentate* ligand. Within these stoichiometries, the following geometries are encountered:

- All $[ML_2]^{n\pm}$ complexes are linear. The two ligands are on opposite sides of the metal, and the L—M—L bond angle is 180°. Common examples include $[Ag(NH_3)_2]^+$ and $[CuCl_2]^-$.
- Tetrahedral geometry occurs in many $[ML_4]^{n\pm}$ complexes. Examples include $TiCl_4$, $[CoCl_4]^{2-}$, $[NiCl_4]^{2-}$, and $[Zn(NH_3)_4]^{2+}$.
- Some $[ML_4]^{n\pm}$ complexes can have square planar geometry. This geometry is most often seen with metal ions that have eight $d$ electrons. Examples include $Pt(NH_3)_2Cl_2$, $[Ni(CN)_4]^{2-}$, and the nickel complex with the dimethylglyoximate ($dmg^-$) ligand in Figure 22.12.
- Octahedral geometry is found in complexes with the stoichiometry $[ML_6]^{n\pm}$ (Figure 22.12).

### Isomerism

Isomerism is one of the most interesting aspects of molecular structure. Recall that the chemistry of organic compounds is greatly enlivened by the multitude of isomeric compounds that are known.

Isomers are classified as follows:

- *Structural isomers* have the same molecular formula but different bonding arrangements of atoms.
- *Stereoisomers* have the same atom-to-atom bonding sequence, but the atoms differ in their arrangement in space. There are two types of stereoisomers: geometric isomers (such as *cis* and *trans* alkenes, page 449) and optical isomers (nonsuperimposable mirror images that have the unique property that they rotate the plane of plane-polarized light, page 442).

All three types of isomerism—structural, geometric, and optical—are encountered in coordination chemistry.

### Structural Isomerism

The two most important types of structural isomerism in coordination chemistry are coordination isomerism and linkage isomerism. **Coordination isomerism** occurs when it is possible to exchange a coordinated ligand and the uncoordinated counterion. For example, dark violet $[Co(NH_3)_5Br]SO_4$ and red $[Co(NH_3)_5SO_4]Br$ are coordination isomers. In the first compound, bromide ion is a ligand and sulfate is a counterion; in the second, sulfate is a ligand and bromide is the counterion. A diagnostic test for this kind of isomer is often made based on chemical reactions. For example, these two compounds can be distinguished by precipitation reactions.

linear

$[Ag(NH_3)_2]^+$

square planar

$Pt(NH_3)_2Cl_2$

tetrahedral

$[NiCl_4]^{2-}$

octahedral

$[Ni(H_2O)_6]^{2+}$

**Common Coordination Geometries**

**FIGURE 22.17 Linkage isomers, [Co(NH₃)₅ONO]²⁺ and [Co(NH₃)₅NO₂]²⁺.** These complex ions, whose systematic names are pentaamminenitritocobalt(III) and pentaamminenitrocobalt(III), respectively, were the first known examples of this type of isomerism. (Each compound has a Cl⁻ as a counterion.)

Addition of $Ba^{2+}$(aq) to a solution of $[Co(NH_3)_5Br]SO_4$ gives a precipitate of $BaSO_4$, indicating the presence of sulfate ion in solution. In contrast, no reaction occurs if $Ba^{2+}$(aq) is added to a solution of $[Co(NH_3)_5SO_4]Br$. In this complex, sulfate ion is attached to $Co^{3+}$ and is not a free ion in solution.

$$[Co(NH_3)_5Br]SO_4 + Ba^{2+}(aq) \longrightarrow BaSO_4(s) + [Co(NH_3)_5Br]^{2+}(aq)$$

$$[Co(NH_3)_5SO_4]Br + Ba^{2+}(aq) \longrightarrow \text{no reaction}$$

**Linkage isomerism** occurs when it is possible to attach a ligand to the metal through different atoms. The two most common ligands with which linkage isomerism arises are thiocyanate, $SCN^-$, and nitrite, $NO_2^-$. The Lewis structure of the thiocyanate ion shows that there are lone pairs of electrons on sulfur and nitrogen. The ligand can attach to a metal either through sulfur (called *S-bonded thiocyanate*) or through nitrogen (called *N-bonded thiocyanate*). Nitrite ion can attach either at oxygen or at nitrogen. The former are called nitrito complexes; the latter are nitro complexes (Figure 22.17).

*Ligands forming linkage isomers*

:S̈—C≡N:        :Ö—N—Ö:   ← Bind to metal ion
                            using either lone
                            pair.

Bind to metal ion
using either lone pair.

## Geometric Isomerism

Geometric isomerism results when the atoms bonded directly to the metal have a different spatial arrangement. The simplest example of geometric isomerism in coordination chemistry is *cis–trans* isomerism, which occurs in both square-planar and octahedral complexes. An example of *cis–trans* isomerism is seen in the square-planar complex $Pt(NH_3)_2Cl_2$ (Figure 22.18a). In this complex, the two $Cl^-$ ions can be either adjacent to each other (*cis*) or on opposite sides of the metal (*trans*). The

● **Cis–Trans Isomerism** *Cis–trans* isomerism is not possible for tetrahedral complexes. All L—M—L angles are 109.5°, and all positions are equivalent in this three-dimensional structure.

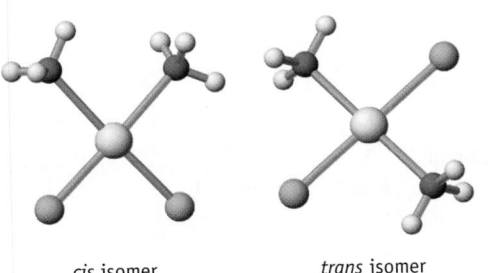

*cis* isomer          *trans* isomer

**(a)** The square-planar complex $Pt(NH_3)_2Cl_2$ can exist in two geometries, *cis* and *trans*.

*cis* isomer, purple          *trans* isomer, green

**(b)** *Cis* and *trans* octahedral isomers are possible for $[Co(en)_2Cl_2]^+$.

**FIGURE 22.18 *Cis–trans* isomers.**

*fac* isomer

*mer* isomer

**FIGURE 22.19** *Fac* and *mer* isomers of Cr(NH$_3$)$_3$Cl$_3$. In the *fac* isomer, the three chloride ligands (and the three ammonia ligands) are arranged at the corners of a triangular face. In the *mer* isomer, the three similar ligands follow a meridian.

*cis* isomer is effective in the treatment of testicular, ovarian, bladder, and osteogenic sarcoma cancers, but the *trans* isomer has no effect on these diseases.

*Cis–trans* isomerism in an octahedral complex is illustrated by a complex ion with two bidentate ethylenediamine ligands and two chloride ligands, [Co(H$_2$NCH$_2$CH$_2$NH$_2$)$_2$Cl$_2$]$^+$. In this complex, the two Cl$^-$ ions occupy positions that are either adjacent (the purple *cis* isomer) or opposite (the green *trans* isomer) (Figure 22.18b).

Another common type of geometric isomerism occurs for octahedral complexes with the general formula MX$_3$Y$_3$. A *fac* isomer has three identical ligands lying at the corners of a triangular face of an octahedron defined by the ligands (*fac* = facial), whereas the ligands follow a meridian in the *mer* isomer (*mer* = meridional). *Fac* and *mer* isomers of Cr(NH$_3$)$_3$Cl$_3$ are shown in Figure 22.19.

### Optical Isomerism

Optical isomerism (chirality) occurs for octahedral complexes when the metal ion coordinates to three bidentate ligands or when the metal ion coordinates to two bidentate ligands and two monodentate ligands in a *cis* position. The complexes [Co(en)$_3$]$^{3+}$ and *cis*-[Co(en)$_2$Cl$_2$]$^+$, illustrated in Figure 22.20, are examples of chiral complexes. The diagnostic test for chirality is met with both species: Mirror images of these molecules are not superimposable (page 442). Solutions of the optical isomers rotate plane-polarized light in opposite directions.

### EXAMPLE 22.4    Isomerism in Coordination Chemistry

**Problem** For which of the following compounds or complex ions do isomers exist? If isomers are possible, identify the type of isomerism (structural, geometric, or optical).

(a)  [Co(NH$_3$)$_4$Cl$_2$]$^+$

(b)  Pt(NH$_3$)$_2$(CN)$_2$ (square-planar)

(c)  Co(NH$_3$)$_3$Cl$_3$

(d)  K$_3$[Fe(C$_2$O$_4$)$_3$]

(e)  Zn(NH$_3$)$_2$Cl$_2$ (tetrahedral)

(f)  [Co(NH$_3$)$_5$SCN]$^{2+}$

**What Do You Know?** From the formulas, which are given, you can infer coordination number and geometry. Structural isomers are those for which there are different attachments of atoms; geometric isomers are those where the spatial arrangement of atoms is different. Complexes that are optically active have nonsuperimposable mirror images.

**Strategy** Determine the number of ligands attached to the metal and decide whether the ligands are monodentate or bidentate. Knowing how many donor atoms are coordinated to the metal (the coordination number) will allow you to establish the metal geometry. At that point, it is necessary to recall the possible types of isomers for each geometry. The only isomerism possible for square-planar complexes is geometric (*cis* and *trans*). Tetrahedral complexes do not have geometric or optical isomers. Six-coordinate complexes of the formula MA$_4$B$_2$ can be either *cis* or *trans*. *Mer* and *fac* isomers are possible with a stoichiometry of MA$_3$B$_3$. Optical activity arises for metal complexes of the formula *cis*-M(bidentate)$_2$X$_2$ and M(bidentate)$_3$ (among others). Drawing pictures of the molecules will help you visualize the isomers.

[Co(en)$_3$]$^{3+}$

[Co(en)$_3$]$^{3+}$ mirror image

*cis*-[Co(en)$_2$Cl$_2$]$^+$

*cis*-[Co(en)$_2$Cl$_2$]$^+$ mirror image

**FIGURE 22.20 Chiral metal complexes.** Both [Co(en)$_3$]$^{3+}$ and *cis*-[Co(en)$_2$Cl$_2$]$^+$ are chiral. Notice that the mirror images of the two compounds are not superimposable.

**Solution**

(a) Two geometric isomers can be drawn for octahedral complexes with a formula of $MA_4B_2$. One isomer has two $Cl^-$ ions in *cis* positions (adjacent positions, at a 90° angle), and the other isomer has the $Cl^-$ ligands in *trans* positions (with a 180° angle between the ligands). Optical isomers are not possible.

*cis* isomer        *trans* isomer

(b) In this square-planar complex, the two $NH_3$ ligands (and the two $CN^-$ ligands) can be either *cis* or *trans*. These are geometric isomers. Optical isomers are not possible.

*cis* isomer        *trans* isomer

● **Optical Isomerism** Square-planar complexes are incapable of optical isomerism based at the metal center; mirror images are always superimposable. Chiral tetrahedral complexes are possible, but examples of complexes with a metal bonded tetrahedrally to four different monodentate ligands are rare.

(c) Two geometric isomers of this octahedral complex, with chloride ligands either *fac* or *mer*, are possible. In the *fac* isomer, the three $Cl^-$ ligands are all at 90° to each other; in the *mer* isomer, two $Cl^-$ ligands are at 180°, and the third is 90° from the other two. Optical isomers are not possible.

*fac* isomer        *mer* isomer

(d) Ignore the counterions, $K^+$. The anion is an octahedral complex. Remember that the bidentate oxalate ion occupies two coordination sites of the metal, and that three oxalate ligands means that the metal has a coordination number of 6. Mirror images of complexes of the stoichiometry $M(bidentate)_3$ are not superimposable; therefore, two optical isomers are possible. (Here the ligands, $C_2O_4^{2-}$, are drawn abbreviated as O—O.)

nonsuperimposable mirror images of $[Fe(ox)_3]^{3-}$

(e) Only a single structure is possible for tetrahedral complexes such as $Zn(NH_3)_2Cl_2$.

(f) Only linkage isomerism (structural isomerism) is possible for this octahedral cobalt complex. Either the sulfur or the nitrogen of the $SCN^-$ anion can be attached to the cobalt(III) ion in this complex.

S-bonded $SCN^-$        N-bonded $SCN^-$

**Think about Your Answer** More complex situations occur when a complex has three or more different ligands. In those instances it is important to be able to visualize the three dimensional molecule and to organize your approach.

**Check Your Understanding**

What types of isomers are possible for the following compounds or complex ions?

(a)  K[Co(NH₃)₂Cl₄]

(c)  [Co(NH₃)₅Cl]²⁺

(e)  Na₂[MnCl₄] (tetrahedral)

(b)  Pt(en)Cl₂ (square-planar)

(d)  [Ru(phen)₃]Cl₃

(f)  [Co(NH₃)₅NO₂]²⁺

---

**REVIEW & CHECK FOR SECTION 22.4**

1.  Which of the following complexes cannot exist as *cis–trans* isomers?

   (a)  Fe(NH₃)₄Cl₂

   (c)  Square-planar [PtCl₂(CN)₂]²⁻

   (b)  Ni(H₂O)₄(C₂O₄)   (C₂O₄²⁻ = oxalate)

   (d)  Mn(en)₂Cl₂ (en = ethylenediamine)

2.  Which of the following complexes can exist as optical isomers?

   (a)  Square-planar Pt(NH₃)(H₂O)(CN)Cl

   (c)  Fe(NH₃)₄Cl₂

   (b)  Fe(en)₂(CN)₂ (en = ethylenediamine)

   (d)  Cr(NH₃)₃Cl₃

3.  Which statement best describes the isomers for the complex Fe(en)₂Cl₂? (en = ethylenediamine)

   (a)  Only a single structure can be drawn.

   (b)  There are two geometric isomers, one of which has an optical isomer.

   (c)  The compound exists as a pair of optical isomers.

   (d)  This compound exists as two structural isomers.

4.  How many geometric isomers are possible for Fe(en)(NH₃)₂Cl₂? (To answer this question, try to draw out possible structures in an organized manner. Start by placing the bidentate ethylenediamine ligand in two coordination sites, then add chloride and ammonia ligands into the remaining positions in various ways.)

   (a)  0          (b)  1          (c)  2          (d)  3

---

## 22.5  Bonding in Coordination Compounds

Metal–ligand bonding in a coordination complex was described earlier in this chapter as being covalent, resulting from the sharing of an electron pair between the metal and the ligand donor atom. Although frequently used, this description is not capable of explaining the color and magnetic behavior of these complexes. As a consequence, the covalent bonding picture has now largely been superseded by two other bonding models: molecular orbital theory and ligand field theory.

The bonding model based on molecular orbital theory assumes that the metal and the ligand bond through the molecular orbitals formed by atomic orbital overlap between metal and ligand. The **ligand field model**, in contrast, focuses on repulsion (and destabilization) of electrons in the metal coordination sphere. The ligand field model also assumes that the positive metal ion and the negative ligand lone pair are attracted electrostatically; that is, the bond arises when a positively charged metal ion attracts a negative ion or the negative end of a polar molecule. For the most part, the molecular orbital and ligand field models predict similar, qualitative results regarding color and magnetic behavior. Here, we will focus on the ligand field approach and illustrate how it explains color and magnetism of transition metal complexes.

### The *d* Orbitals: Ligand Field Theory

To understand ligand field theory, it is necessary to look at the *d* orbitals, particularly with regard to their orientation relative to the positions of ligands in a metal complex.

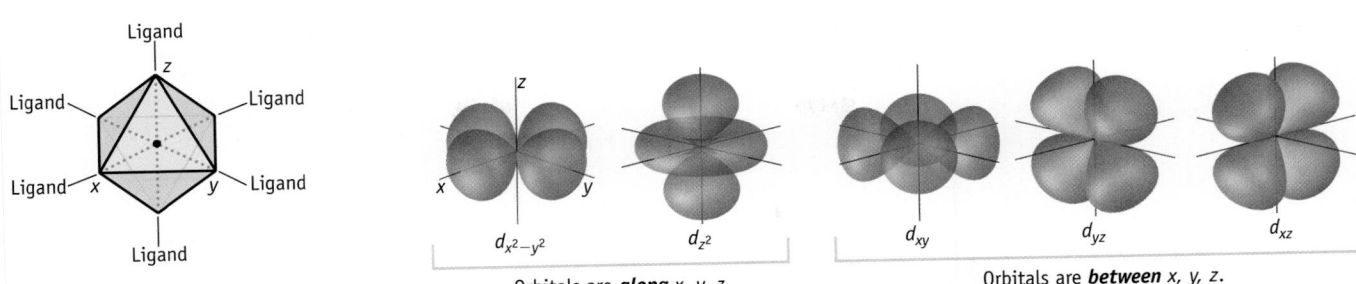

$d_{x^2-y^2}$   $d_{z^2}$
Orbitals are **along** $x$, $y$, $z$.

$d_{xy}$   $d_{yz}$   $d_{xz}$
Orbitals are **between** $x$, $y$, $z$.

**FIGURE 22.21 The $d$ orbitals.** The five $d$ orbitals and their spatial relation to the ligands on the $x$-, $y$-, and $z$-axes.

We look first at octahedral complexes. Assume the ligands in an octahedral complex lie along the $x$-, $y$-, and $z$-axes. This results in the five $d$ orbitals (Figure 22.21) being subdivided into two sets: the $d_{x^2-y^2}$ and $d_{z^2}$ orbitals in one set and the $d_{xy}$, $d_{xz}$, and $d_{yz}$ orbitals in the second. The $d_{x^2-y^2}$ and $d_{z^2}$ orbitals are directed along the $x$-, $y$-, and $z$-axes, whereas the orbitals of the second group are aligned between these axes.

In an isolated atom or ion, the five $d$ orbitals have the same energy. For a metal atom or ion in a coordination complex, however, the $d$ orbitals have different energies. According to the ligand field model, repulsion between $d$ electrons on the metal and electron pairs of the ligands destabilizes electrons that reside in the $d$ orbitals; that is, it causes their energy to increase. Electrons in the various $d$ orbitals are not affected equally, however, because of their different orientations in space relative to the position of the ligand lone pairs (Figure 22.22). Electrons in the $d_{x^2-y^2}$ and $d_{z^2}$ orbitals experience a larger repulsion because these orbitals point directly at the incoming ligand electron pairs. A smaller repulsive effect is experienced by electrons in the $d_{xy}$, $d_{xz}$, and $d_{yz}$ orbitals. The difference in degree of repulsion means that an energy difference exists between the two sets of orbitals in an octahedral complex. This difference, called the **ligand field splitting** and denoted by the symbol $\Delta_0$, is a function of the metal and the ligands and varies predictably from one complex to another.

A different splitting pattern is encountered with square-planar complexes (Figure 22.23). Assume that the four ligands are along the $x$- and $y$-axes. The $d_{x^2-y^2}$ orbital also points along these axes, so it has the highest energy. The $d_{xy}$ orbital (which also lies in the $xy$-plane, but does not point at the ligands) is next highest in energy, followed by the $d_{z^2}$ orbital. The $d_{xz}$ and $d_{yz}$ orbitals, both of which partially point in the $z$-direction, have the lowest energy.

The $d$-orbital splitting pattern for a tetrahedral complex is the reverse of the pattern observed for octahedral complexes. Three orbitals ($d_{xz}$, $d_{xy}$, $d_{yz}$) are higher in energy, whereas the $d_{x^2-y^2}$ and $d_{z^2}$ orbitals are below them in energy (Figure 22.23).

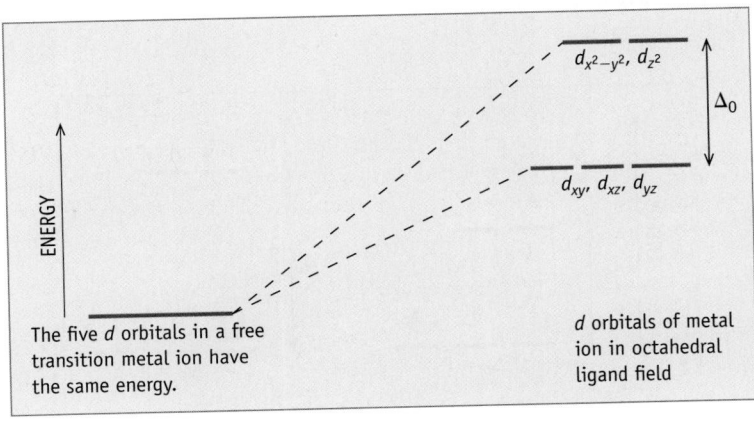

ENERGY

$d_{x^2-y^2}$, $d_{z^2}$

$\Delta_0$

$d_{xy}$, $d_{xz}$, $d_{yz}$

The five $d$ orbitals in a free transition metal ion have the same energy.

$d$ orbitals of metal ion in octahedral ligand field

**FIGURE 22.22 Ligand field splitting for an octahedral complex.** The $d$-orbital energies increase as the ligands approach the metal along the $x$-, $y$-, and $z$-axes. The $d_{xy}$, $d_{xz}$, and $d_{yz}$ orbitals, not pointed toward the ligands, are less destabilized than the $d_{x^2-y^2}$ and $d_{z^2}$ orbitals. Thus, the $d_{xy}$, $d_{xz}$, and $d_{yz}$ orbitals are at lower energy. ($\Delta_0$ stands for the splitting in an octahedral ligand field.)

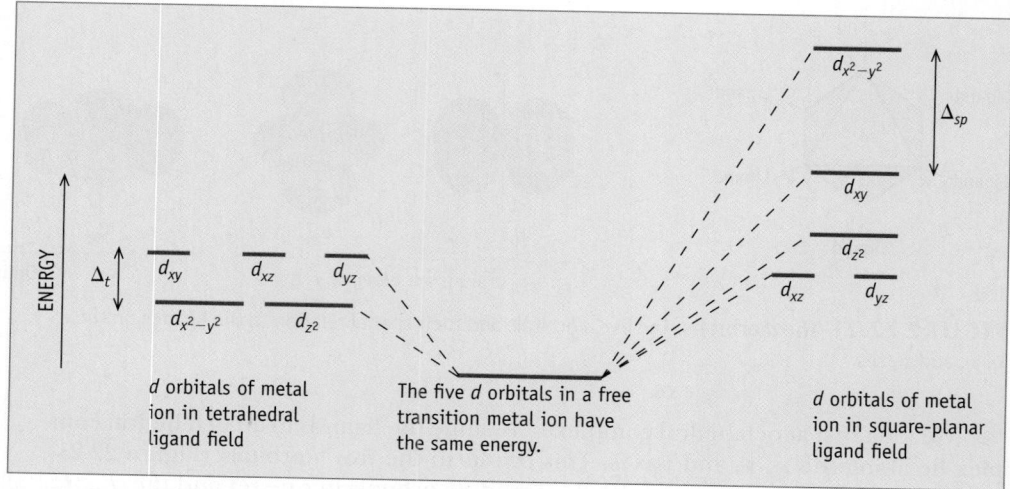

**FIGURE 22.23** **Splitting of the *d* orbitals in *(left)* tetrahedral and *(right)* square-planar geometries.** ($\Delta_t$ and $\Delta_{sp}$ are, respectively, the splitting in tetrahedral and square-planar ligand fields.)

## Electron Configurations and Magnetic Properties

The *d*-orbital splitting in coordination complexes provides the means to explain both the magnetic behavior and the color of these complexes. To understand this explanation, however, we must first understand how to assign electrons to the various orbitals in each geometry.

A gaseous $Cr^{2+}$ ion has the electron configuration $[Ar]3d^4$. The term *gaseous* in this context is used to denote a single, isolated atom or ion with all other particles located an infinite distance away. In this situation, the five $3d$ orbitals have the same energy. The four electrons reside singly in different *d* orbitals, according to Hund's rule, and the $Cr^{2+}$ ion has four unpaired electrons.

Cr(II) electron configuration

$Cr^{2+}$ $[Ar]3d^4$ ⬛⬛⬛⬛⬛ ☐

$\phantom{Cr^{2+} [Ar]3d^4}$ $3d$ $\phantom{xxxx}$ $4s$

When the $Cr^{2+}$ ion is part of an octahedral complex, the five *d* orbitals do not have identical energies. As illustrated in Figure 22.22, these orbitals divide into two sets, with the $d_{xy}$, $d_{xz}$, and $d_{yz}$ orbitals having a lower energy than the $d_{x^2-y^2}$ and $d_{z^2}$ orbitals. Having two sets of orbitals means that two different electron configurations are possible (Figure 22.24). Three of the four *d* electrons in $Cr^{2+}$ are assigned to the lower-energy $d_{xy}$, $d_{xz}$, and $d_{yz}$ orbitals. The fourth electron either can be assigned to an orbital in the higher-energy $d_{x^2-y^2}$ and $d_{z^2}$ set or can pair up with an electron already in the lower-energy set. The first arrangement is called **high spin**, because it has the maximum number of unpaired electrons, four in the case of $Cr^{2+}$. The second arrangement is called **low spin**, because it has the minimum number of unpaired electrons possible.

**FIGURE 22.24** **High- and low-spin cases for an octahedral chromium(II) complex.** *(left, high spin)* If the ligand field splitting ($\Delta_0$) is smaller than the pairing energy (P), the electrons are placed in different orbitals, and the complex has four unpaired electrons. *(right, low spin)* If the splitting is larger than the pairing energy, all four electrons will be in the lower-energy orbital set. This requires pairing two electrons in one of the orbitals, so the complex will have two unpaired electrons.

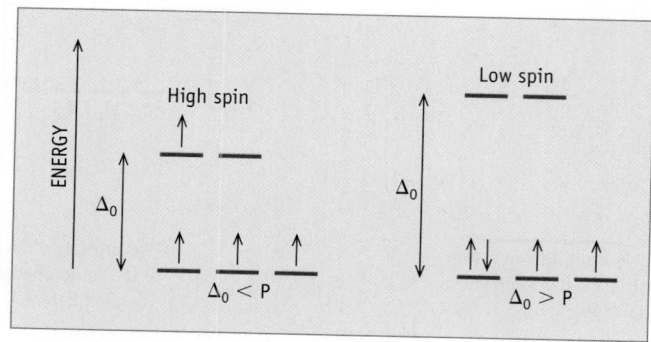

**FIGURE 22.25** **High- and low-spin octahedral complexes.** $d$-Orbital occupancy for octahedral complexes of metal ions. Only the $d^4$ through $d^7$ cases have both high- and low-spin configurations.

At first glance, a high-spin configuration appears to contradict conventional thinking. It seems logical that the most stable situation would occur when electrons occupy the lowest-energy orbitals. A second factor intervenes, however. Because electrons are negatively charged, repulsion increases when they are assigned to the same orbital. This destabilizing effect bears the name **pairing energy (P)**. The preference for an electron to be in the lowest-energy orbital and the pairing energy have opposing effects (Figure 22.24). Low-spin complexes arise when the splitting of the $d$ orbitals by the ligand field is large—that is, when $\Delta_0$ has a large value. The energy gained by putting all of the electrons in the lowest-energy level is the dominant effect when $\Delta_0 > P$. In contrast, high-spin complexes occur if the value of $\Delta_0$ is smaller than the energy required to pair electrons ($\Delta_0 < P$).

For octahedral complexes, high- and low-spin complexes can occur only for configurations $d^4$ through $d^7$ (Figure 22.25). Complexes of the $d^6$ metal ion, $Fe^{2+}$, for example, can have either high spin or low spin. The complex formed when the $Fe^{2+}$ ion is placed in water, $[Fe(H_2O)_6]^{2+}$, is high spin, whereas the $[Fe(CN)_6]^{4-}$ complex ion is low spin.

Electron configuration for $Fe^{2+}$ in an octahedral complex

It is possible to tell whether a complex is high or low spin by examining its magnetic behavior. The high-spin complex $[Fe(H_2O)_6]^{2+}$ has four unpaired electrons and is *paramagnetic* (attracted by a magnet), whereas the low-spin $[Fe(CN)_6]^{4-}$ complex has no unpaired electrons and is *diamagnetic* (repelled by a magnet) (◀ page 289).

Most complexes of $Pd^{2+}$ and $Pt^{2+}$ ions are square-planar, the electron configuration of these metals being [noble gas]$(n-1)d^8$. In a square-planar complex, there are four sets of orbitals (Figure 22.23). For square-planar $d^8$ complexes, all except the highest-energy orbital are filled, and all electrons are paired, resulting in diamagnetic (low-spin) complexes.

Nickel, which is found above palladium in the periodic table, forms both square-planar and tetrahedral complexes (as well as octahedral complexes). For example, the complex ion $[Ni(CN)_4]^{2-}$ is square-planar, whereas the $[NiCl_4]^{2-}$ ion is tetrahedral. Magnetism allows us to differentiate between these two geometries. Based on the ligand field splitting pattern, the cyanide complex is expected to be diamagnetic, whereas the chloride complex is paramagnetic with two unpaired electrons.

**Nickel(II) complexes and magnetism.** The anion $[NiCl_4]^{2-}$ is a paramagnetic tetrahedral complex. In contrast, $[Ni(CN)_4]^{2-}$ is a diamagnetic square-planar complex.

## EXAMPLE 22.5    High- and Low-Spin Complexes and Magnetism

**Problem**  Give the electron configuration for the metal ion in each of the following complexes. How many unpaired electrons are present in each? Are the complexes paramagnetic or diamagnetic?

(a)   Low-spin $[Co(NH_3)_6]^{3+}$                    (b)   High-spin $[CoF_6]^{3-}$

**What Do You Know?**  From their formulas, we know that these have six ligands and we can presume that they have octahedral geometry. Both are complexes of cobalt(III), a metal ion with a $d^6$ configuration. One complex is low spin, the other high spin.

**Strategy**  Set up an energy-level diagram for an octahedral complex. In low-spin complexes, the electrons are added preferentially to the lower-energy set of orbitals. In high-spin complexes, the first five electrons are added singly to each of the five orbitals, then additional electrons are paired with electrons in orbitals in the lower-energy set.

**Solution**

(a)   The six electrons of the $Co^{3+}$ ion fill the lower-energy set of orbitals entirely. This $d^6$ complex ion has no unpaired electrons and is diamagnetic.

(b)   To obtain the electron configuration in high-spin $[CoF_6]^{3-}$, place one electron in each of the five $d$ orbitals, and then place the sixth electron in one of the lower-energy orbitals. The complex has four unpaired electrons and is paramagnetic.

Electron configuration of low-spin, octahedral $[Co(NH_3)_6]^{3+}$

(a)

Electron configuration of high-spin, octahedral $[CoF_6]^{3-}$

(b)

**Think about Your Answer**  The two complexes have different magnetic properties; low-spin $[Co(NH_3)_6]^{3+}$ is diamagnetic and high-spin $[CoF_6]^{3-}$ is paramagnetic. As expected, the low-spin complex has fewer unpaired electrons than the high-spin complex.

**Check Your Understanding**

For each of the following complex ions, give the oxidation number of the metal, depict possible low- and high-spin configurations, give the number of unpaired electrons in each configuration, and tell whether each is paramagnetic or diamagnetic.

(a)   $[Ru(H_2O)_6]^{2+}$                    (b)   $[Ni(NH_3)_6]^{2+}$

---

**REVIEW & CHECK FOR SECTION 22.5**

1.   Which of the following complexes has the greatest number of unpaired electrons?

    (a)   Low-spin $[Fe(CN)_6]^{4-}$                    (c)   $[V(H_2O)_6]^{3+}$

    (b)   High-spin $[Mn(NH_3)_6]^{2+}$                (d)   $[Ni(en)_3]^{2+}$ (en = ethylenediamine)

2.   Which of the following complexes is diamagnetic?

    (a)   Square-planar $[PtCl_4]^{2-}$                    (c)   $[Fe(H_2O)_6]^{3+}$

    (b)   Tetrahedral $[NiCl_4]^{2-}$                    (d)   High-spin $[CoF_6]^{3-}$

$Fe^{3+}(aq)$     $Co^{2+}(aq)$     $Ni^{2+}(aq)$     $Cu^{2+}(aq)$     $Zn^{2+}(aq)$

# 22.6 Colors of Coordination Compounds

The range of colors observed for compounds of the transition elements is one of their most interesting features (Figure 22.26). In contrast, compounds of main group metals are usually colorless. The underlying reason for this difference is that the color of transition metal compounds results from *d*-orbital splitting. Before discussing how *d*-orbital splitting is involved, however, we need to look more closely at what we mean by color.

## Color

Visible light, consisting of radiation with wavelengths from 400 to 700 nm (◄ Section 6.1), represents a very small portion of the electromagnetic spectrum. Within this region are all the colors you see when white light passes through a prism: red, orange, yellow, green, blue, indigo, and violet (ROY G BIV). Each color is identified with a portion of the wavelength range.

Isaac Newton did experiments with light and established that the mind's perception of color requires only three colors! When we see white light, we are seeing a mixture of all of the colors—in other words, the superposition of red, green, and blue. If one or more of these colors is absent, the light of the other colors that reaches your eyes is interpreted by your mind as color.

Figure 22.27 will help you in analyzing perceived colors. This color wheel shows the three primary colors—red, green, and blue—as overlapping disks arranged in a triangle. The secondary colors—cyan, magenta, and yellow—appear where two disks overlap. The overlap of all three disks in the center produces white light.

The colors we perceive are determined as follows:

- Light of a single primary color is perceived as that color: Red light is perceived as red, green light as green, blue light as blue.
- Light made up of two primary colors is perceived as the color shown where the disks in Figure 22.27 overlap: Red and green light together appear yellow, green and blue light together are perceived as cyan; and red and blue light are perceived as magenta.
- Light made up of the three primary colors is white (colorless).

In discussing the color of a substance such as a coordination complex *in solution*, these guidelines are turned around because the color we see is the color of light *not* absorbed by the solution.

- Red color is the result of the absence of green and blue light from white light.
- Green color results if red and blue light are absent from white light.
- Blue color results if red and green light are absent.

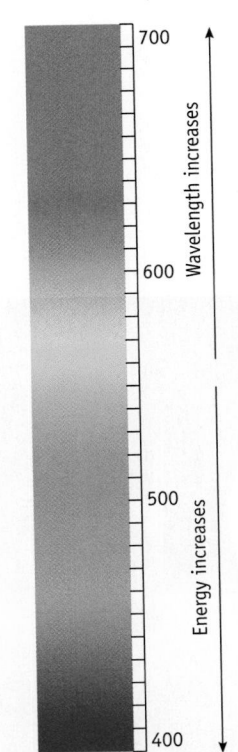

λ (nm)

700

Wavelength increases

600

500

Energy increases

400

**The ROY G BIV spectrum of colors of visible light.** The colors used in printing this book are cyan, magenta, yellow, and black. The blue in ROY G BIV is actually cyan, according to color industry standards. Magenta doesn't have its own wavelength region. Rather, it is a mixture of blue and red.

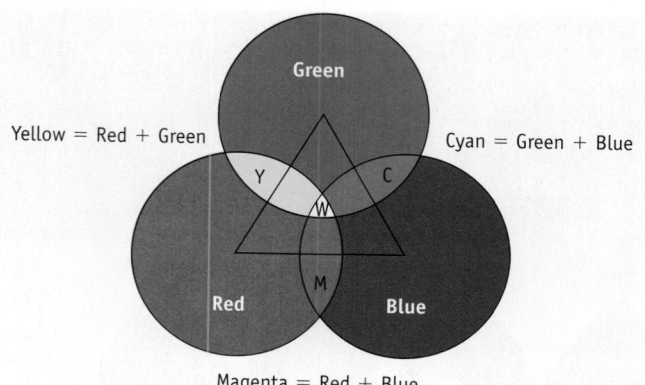

**FIGURE 22.27 Using color disks to analyze colors.** The three primary colors are red, green, and blue. Adding light of two primary colors gives the secondary colors yellow (= red + green), cyan (= green + blue), and magenta (= red + blue). Adding all three primary colors results in white light.

The secondary colors are rationalized similarly. Absorption of blue light gives yellow (the color across from it in Figure 22.27); absorption of red light results in cyan; and absorption of green light results in magenta.

Now we can apply these ideas to explain colors in transition metal complexes. Focus on what kind of light is *absorbed*. A solution of $[Ni(H_2O)_6]^{2+}$ is green. Green light is the result of removing red and blue light from white light. As white light passes through an aqueous solution of $Ni^{2+}$, red and blue light are absorbed, and green light is allowed to pass (Figure 22.28). Similarly, the $[Co(NH_3)_6]^{3+}$ ion is yellow because blue light has been absorbed and red and green light pass through.

## The Spectrochemical Series

Recall that atomic spectra are obtained when electrons are excited from one energy level to another (◄ Section 6.3). The energy of the light absorbed or emitted is related to the energy levels of the atom or ion under study. The concept that light is absorbed when electrons move from lower to higher energy levels applies to all substances, not just atoms. It is the basic premise for the absorption of light for transition metal coordination complexes.

In coordination complexes, the splitting between *d* orbitals often corresponds to the energy of visible light, so light in the visible region of the spectrum is absorbed when electrons move from a lower-energy *d* orbital to a higher-energy *d* orbital. This change, as an electron moves between two orbitals having different energies in a complex, is called a **d-to-d transition**. Qualitatively, such a transition for $[Co(NH_3)_6]^{3+}$ might be represented using an energy-level diagram such as that shown here.

**FIGURE 22.28 Light absorption and color.** The color of a solution is due to the color of the light *not* absorbed by the solution. Here, a solution of $Ni^{2+}$ ion in water absorbs red and blue light and so appears green. See also Figures 4.15–4.19.

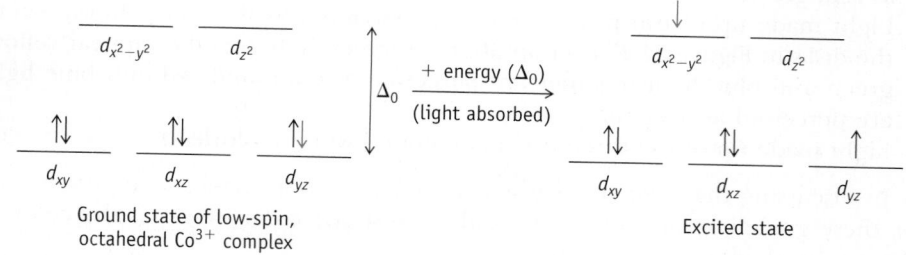

Experiments with coordination complexes reveal that, for a given metal ion, some ligands cause a small energy separation of the *d* orbitals, whereas others cause a large separation. In other words, some ligands create a small ligand field, and

© Cengage Learning/Charles D. Winters

**Table 22.3 The Colors of Some $Co^{3+}$ Complexes\***

| Complex Ion | Wavelength of Light Absorbed (nm) | Color of Light Absorbed | Color of Complex |
|---|---|---|---|
| $[CoF_6]^{3-}$ | 700 | Red | Blue |
| $[Co(C_2O_4)_3]^{3-}$ | 600, 420 | Yellow, violet | Dark green |
| $[Co(H_2O)_6]^{3+}$ | 600, 400 | Yellow, violet | Blue-green |
| $[Co(NH_3)_6]^{3+}$ | 475, 340 | Blue, ultraviolet | Yellow-orange |
| $[Co(en)_3]^{3+}$ | 470, 340 | Blue, ultraviolet | Yellow-orange |
| $[Co(CN)_6]^{3-}$ | 310 | Ultraviolet | Pale yellow |

\*The complex with fluoride ion, $[CoF_6]^{3-}$, is high spin and has one absorption band. The other complexes are low spin and have two absorption bands. In all but one case, one of these absorptions occurs in the visible region of the spectrum. The wavelengths are measured at the top of that absorption band.

others create a large one. An example is seen in the spectroscopic data for several cobalt(III) complexes presented in Table 22.3.

- Both $[Co(NH_3)_6]^{3+}$ and $[Co(en)_3]^{3+}$ are yellow-orange, because they absorb light in the blue portion of the visible spectrum. These compounds have very similar spectra, to be expected because both have six amine-type donor atoms ($H—NH_2$ or $R—NH_2$).
- Although $[Co(CN)_6]^{3-}$ does not have an absorption band whose maximum falls in the visible region, it is pale yellow. The peak of the absorption band occurs in the ultraviolet region, but the absorption band is broad and extends minimally into the visible (blue) region.
- $[Co(C_2O_4)_3]^{3-}$ and $[Co(H_2O)_6]^{3+}$ have similar absorptions, in the yellow and violet regions. Their colors are shades of green with a small difference due to the relative amount of light of each color being absorbed.

The wavelength of maximum absorption among the listed complexes ranges from 700 nm for $[CoF_6]^{3-}$ to 310 nm for $[Co(CN)_6]^{3-}$. The ligands change from member to member of this series, and we can conclude that the energy of the light absorbed by the complex is related to the different ligand field splittings, $\Delta_0$, caused by the different ligands. Fluoride ion causes the smallest splitting of the $d$ orbitals among the complexes listed in Table 22.3, whereas cyanide causes the largest splitting.

Spectra of complexes of other metals provide similar results. Based on this information, ligands can be listed in order of their ability to split the $d$ orbitals. This list is called the **spectrochemical series** because it was determined by spectroscopy. A short list, with some of the more common ligands, follows:

$$F^-, Cl^-, Br^-, I^- < C_2O_4{}^{2-} < H_2O < NH_3 = en < phen < CN^-$$

small orbital splitting                                large orbital splitting
small $\Delta_0$                                            large $\Delta_0$

The spectrochemical series is applicable to a wide range of metal complexes. Indeed, the ability of ligand field theory to explain the differences in the colors of the transition metal complexes is one of the strengths of this theory.

Based on the relative position of a ligand in the series, predictions can be made about a compound's magnetic behavior. Recall that $d^4$, $d^5$, $d^6$, and $d^7$ complexes can be high or low spin, depending on the ligand field splitting, $\Delta_0$. Complexes formed with ligands near the left end of the spectrochemical series are expected to have small $\Delta_0$ values and, therefore, are likely to be high spin. In contrast, complexes with ligands near the right end are expected to have large $\Delta_0$ values and low-spin configurations. The complex $[CoF_6]^{3-}$ is high spin, whereas $[Co(NH_3)_6]^{3+}$ and the other complexes in Table 22.3 are low spin.

# Ligand Field Theory

This summary of the concepts of ligand field theory may help you to keep the broader picture in mind.

- Ligand–metal bonding results from the electrostatic attraction between a metal cation and either an anion or a polar molecule.
- The ligands define a coordination geometry. Common geometries are linear (coordination number = 2), tetrahedral and square-planar (coordination number = 4), and octahedral (coordination number = 6).
- The placement of the ligands around the metal causes the $d$ orbitals on the metal

to have different energies. In an octahedral complex, for example, the $d$ orbitals divide into two groups: a higher-energy group ($d_{x^2-y^2}$ and $d_{z^2}$) and a lower-energy group ($d_{xy}$, $d_{xz}$, and $d_{yz}$).
- Electrons are placed in the metal $d$ orbitals in a manner that leads to the lowest total energy. Two competing features determine the placement: the relative energy of the sets of orbitals and the electron pairing energy.
- For the electron configurations of $d^4$, $d^5$, $d^6$, and $d^7$ in octahedral complexes, two electron configurations are possible:

high spin, which occurs when the orbital splitting is small, and low spin, which occurs with a large orbital splitting. To determine whether a complex is high spin or low spin, measure its magnetism to determine the number of unpaired electrons.
- The $d$-orbital splitting (the energy difference between the metal $d$-orbital energies) often corresponds to the energy associated with visible light. As a consequence, many metal complexes absorb visible light and thus are colored.

## EXAMPLE 22.6    Spectrochemical Series

**Problem**  An aqueous solution of $[Fe(H_2O)_6]^{2+}$ is light blue-green. Do you expect the $d^6$ $Fe^{2+}$ ion in this complex to have a high- or low-spin configuration? How could you test your prediction experimentally?

**What Do You Know?**  This is an octahedral complex of $Fe^{2+}$, an ion with a $d^6$ configuration. The blue-green color is the result of the absorption of visible light due to a $d$-to-$d$ transition. The complex could be either low spin (no unpaired electrons) or high spin (four unpaired electrons).

**Strategy**  Use the color wheel in Figure 22.27 to determine what color light is transmitted and therefore what color of light has been absorbed. Based on the energy of the light absorbed, determine if $\Delta_o$ is high or low. If it is low, then the complex is high spin. If it is high, then the complex is low spin.

**Solution**  In this case, the blue-green color of the solution indicates that blue and green light is transmitted. This implies that red light was absorbed. The low energy of the light absorbed suggests that $[Fe(H_2O)_6]^{2+}$ is likely to be a high-spin complex. If the complex is high spin, it will have four unpaired electrons and be paramagnetic; if, contrary to our prediction, it is low spin, it will have no unpaired electrons and be diamagnetic. Thus, identifying the presence of four unpaired electrons by measuring the compound's magnetism can be used to verify the high-spin configuration experimentally.

**Think about Your Answer**  The spectrochemical series was generated by measuring the absorptions for a series of complexes of a given metal, varying the ligands. As in the example here, the spectrochemical series is useful because it allows you to predict whether a complex is likely to be high or low spin. The more definitive evidence for high or low spin comes from information on the magnetism of the complex.

**Check Your Understanding**

1.  The complex $[Co(NH_3)_5OH]^{2+}$ has an absorption maximum at 500 nm. What color of light is absorbed and what color is the complex?

2.  Figure 22.17 shows a sample of yellow $[Co(NH_3)_5NO_2]^{2+}$. What color of light is absorbed by this complex? Predict whether this is a high-spin or low-spin complex.

---

**REVIEW & CHECK FOR SECTION 22.6**

Solutions of each of the following complexes absorb light in the visible region of the spectrum. Predict which complex will absorb light of the longest wavelength.

(a)  $[Cr(H_2O)_6]^{3+}$        (b)  $[Cr(NH_3)_6]^{3+}$        (c)  $[CrF_6]^{3-}$        (d)  $[Cr(CN)_6]^{3-}$

## Accidental Discovery of a Chemotherapy Agent

There are many naturally occurring metal-based molecules such as heme, vitamin $B_{12}$, and the enzyme involved in fixing nitrogen (nitrogenase). Chemists have also synthesized various metal-based compounds for medical purposes. One of these, *cisplatin* [$PtCl_2(NH_3)_2$], was known for many years, but it was discovered serendipitously to be effective in treatment of certain kinds of cancers.

In 1965, Barnett Rosenberg, a biophysicist at Michigan State University, set out to study the effect of electric fields on living cells, but the results of his experiments were very different from his expectations. He and his students had placed an aqueous suspension of live *Escherichia coli* bacteria in an electric field between supposedly inert platinum electrodes. Much to their surprise, they found that cell growth was significantly affected. After careful experimentation, the effect on cell division was found to be due to a trace of a complex of platinum, ammonia, and chloride ion formed by an electrolytic process involving the platinum electrode in the presence of ammonia in the growth medium.

To follow up on this interesting discovery, Rosenberg and his students tested the effect of *cis*- and *trans*-$PtCl_2(NH_3)_2$ on cell growth and found that only the *cis* isomer

was effective. This led Rosenberg and others to study the effect of so-called *cisplatin* on cancer cell growth, and the result is that cisplatin and similar compounds are now used to treat genitourinary tumors. In fact, testicular cancer in particular is now considered largely curable because of cisplatin chemotherapy.

The chemistry of cisplatin has now been thoroughly studied and illustrates many of the principles of transition metal coordination chemistry. It has been found that cisplatin has a half-life of 2.5 hours for the replacement of a $Cl^-$ ligand by water at 310 K (in a first order reaction) and that the replacement of a second $Cl^-$ ligand by water is slightly faster.

The aqua species are acidic and damaging to the kidneys, so cisplatin is generally used in a saline solution to prevent the hydrolysis reactions. It has been found that, in blood plasma at pH 7.4 and with a $Cl^-$ ion concentration of about $1.04 \times 10^{-5}$ M, $PtCl_2(NH_3)_2$

$k = 7.6 \times 10^{-5}$ s$^{-1}$  $pK_a = 6.6$  $k = 2.3 \times 10^{-4}$ s$^{-1}$  $pK_a = 5.5$  $pK_a = 7.3$

and $PtCl(OH)(NH_3)_2$ are the dominant species. In the cell nucleus, however, the $Cl^-$ ion concentration is lower, and the aqua species are present in higher concentration.

**Question:**
If a patient is given 10.0 mg of cisplatin, what quantity remains as cisplatin at 24 hours?

**The answer to this question is available in Appendix N.**

# 22.7 Organometallic Chemistry: Compounds with Metal–Carbon Bonds

One of the largest and most active areas of chemistry over the past half-century has been the field of organometallic chemistry, the study of molecules having metal–carbon bonds. Thousands of such compounds have been made and characterized, and much of the activity has involved transition metals. Many have unique bonding modes and structures. In recent years, organometallic compounds have also found particularly widespread use as reagents in organic synthesis and as catalysts for economically important chemical reactions.

## Carbon Monoxide Complexes of Metals

In the earlier discussion of hemoglobin (page 1032), you learned that the iron in this biologically important complex binds not only to $O_2$ but also to CO. Our understanding of metal–CO complexes, however, emerged from the solution to a problem in industrial chemistry at the end of the 19th century.

The synthesis of sodium carbonate from NaCl, $CO_2$, $NH_3$, and $H_2O$ by the Solvay process was an important chemical industry in the late 19th century (and remains so today in some parts of the world; page 972). In the late 1800s, a Solvay plant in England had a problem: The valves used to conduct the gaseous reactants and products rapidly corroded. A German chemist, Ludwig Mond (1839–1909), traced this problem to a small quantity of CO in the gas stream. Carbon monoxide gas reacted with nickel metal in the valves to form $Ni(CO)_4$ (Figure 22.29), tetracarbonyl nickel, a volatile liquid with a low boiling point (bp 47 °C). The

**FIGURE 22.29 Metals carbonyls.** $Ni(CO)_4$ is a tetrahedral molecule. Pentacarbonyliron(O) [$Fe(CO)_5$] is trigonal bipyramidal, whereas $Mo(CO)_6$ is octahedral, and the geometry around the manganese atom in $Mn_2(CO)_{10}$ is likewise octahedral (with the sixth position being an Mn—Mn bond).

Ni(CO)₄          Fe(CO)₅          Mo(CO)₆          Mn₂(CO)₁₀

deterioration of the valves occurred when the gaseous $Ni(CO)_4$ that formed was carried away in the effluent gas stream.

$$Ni(s) + 4\ CO(g) \rightleftharpoons Ni(CO)_4(g)$$

Mond determined that the reaction forming $Ni(CO)_4$ is reversible; at moderate temperatures or at low pressures, CO is liberated, and nickel metal re-forms. He then exploited the formation and decomposition reactions in a process to obtain pure nickel. Nickel and cobalt are generally found together in nature. Because of this, the two metals are obtained together when ores are refined, and they are difficult to separate. However, if a mixture of the metals is exposed to CO, nickel is converted to $Ni(CO)_4$ whereas cobalt is unchanged. Volatile $Ni(CO)_4$ is easily separated from solid cobalt metal. The $Ni(CO)_4$ can then be decomposed to give pure nickel. The Mond process, as it is now known, was the preferred procedure to obtain pure nickel for the first half of the 20th century.

Nickel is unique among metals in its facile reaction with CO, but many other transition metal carbonyl compounds are now known and can be synthesized by a variety of procedures. One of the most common is reductive carbonylation, in which a metal salt is reduced in the presence of CO, usually under high pressure. In effect, reduction of the metal salt gives metal atoms. Before these very reactive atoms aggregate to form the unreactive bulk metal, however, they react with CO. Metal carbonyls of most of the transition metals can be made by this route. Simple examples include hexacarbonyls of the Group 6B metals [$Cr(CO)_6$, $Mo(CO)_6$, and $W(CO)_6$,] as well as $Fe(CO)_5$ and $Mn_2(CO)_{10}$ (Figure 22.29).

• **Terminology in Organometallic Chemistry** The standard terminology of coordination chemistry applies to metal carbonyls. In tetracarbonylnickel(0), for example, the metal is formally zerovalent, and CO molecules are ligands. The metal has a coordination number of 4 and a tetrahedral coordination geometry.

## The Effective Atomic Number Rule and Bonding in Organometallic Compounds

An important observation has guided researchers studying these metal–CO complexes and other organometallic compounds. The **effective atomic number (EAN) rule**, now often referred to as the **18-electron rule**, states that compounds in which the sum of the metal valence electrons plus the electrons donated by the ligand groups totals 18 are likely to be stable. Thus, the 18-electron rule predicts the stoichiometry of a number of compounds. Iron(0), for example, which has eight valence electrons, would be expected to coordinate to five CO ligands. Each CO donates two electrons for a total of 10; adding these to the eight valence electrons on the metal gives 18 electrons around the Fe atom (Figure 22.30). We now recognize that the 18-electron rule is similar to the octet rule in main group chemistry, in that it defines the likely number of bonds to an element.

The bonding in traditional coordination compounds is described as being due to attractive forces between a positively charged metal ion and a polar molecule or an anion, and the properties of these species are in accord with substantial ionic character to the metal–ligand bond. In metal carbonyls, the zerovalent metal lacks a charge, and CO is only slightly polar. Both features argue against ionic bonding. The best model for these species instead describes the bonding between the metal and CO as covalent. Each CO donates a C-atom lone pair to the metal atom to form a sigma bond (Figure 22.31). However, carbon monoxide is a very poor donor, and this alone would not lead to these species being stable. Rather, in conjunction with

5 **CO** ligands donate a total of **10** electrons.

Each **CO** donates **2** electrons.

The **Fe** atom has **8** valence electrons.

**FIGURE 22.30 The EAN rule and Fe(CO)₅.** The EAN or 18-electron rule states that stable organometallic compounds frequently have 18 valence electrons around the central metal. (There are also many 16-electron molecules, particularly of the heavier transition metals. See Study Question 22.34.) Here, the zerovalent Fe atom has the configuration [Ar]3d⁶4s², so eight valence electrons are available for bonding.

Ligand to metal sigma bonding.
Donation of **CO** lone pair to empty orbital on **M**.

Metal to ligand pi bonding.
Donation of electrons from filled **M** $d$ orbital to empty $\pi^*$ antibonding orbital on **CO**.

**FIGURE 22.31 Bonding in metal carbonyls.** The current understanding is that the CO ligand donates a lone pair of electrons to the low-valent metal to form a sigma bond. The electron-rich metal then donates electrons from a $d$ orbital to the antibonding $\pi^*$ orbital of the CO. There is a "synergistic" effect; the sigma and pi bonds complement each other.

the sigma bond, the electron-rich metal donates a pair of electrons to form a $\pi$ bond formed by overlap of a $d$ orbital of the metal and a $\pi^*$ antibonding orbital of CO. The latter interaction is described as $d\pi$–$p\pi$ bonding. Based on this model of bonding, carbon monoxide in these compounds is best described as a $\sigma$ donor and $\pi$ acceptor ligand.

## Ligands in Organometallic Compounds

The bonding model for metal–CO complexes leads to important conclusions: Only metals of low charge and with filled or partially filled $d$ orbitals can form stable bonds to CO, and only ligands capable of forming $\pi$ bonds with the metal are capable of forming low-valent metal compounds. Thus, this area is dominated by low-valent metals and special types of ligands that are capable of $\pi$ bonding.

Some of the most common ligands in coordination chemistry cannot engage in $\pi$ bonding and thus cannot form low-valent compounds with transition metals. For example, low-valent metal complexes with $NH_3$ or amines (such as $N(CH_3)_3$) do not exist, but phosphine complexes of zerovalent metals are well known. Phosphines, such as $P(CH_3)_3$, are the phosphorus analogs of amines and so have a lone pair of electrons on the P atom. Thus, phosphines can donate this lone pair to a metal to form a sigma bond. In addition, phosphorus atoms have empty $3d$ orbitals, and these can overlap with the filled $d$ orbitals of a low-valent metal. Ammonia, with no empty valence orbitals to overlap with a filled metal $d$ orbitals cannot form such $\pi$ bonds.

Yet another class of molecules that can serve as ligands in organometallic compounds are organic species such as ethylene ($C_2H_4$) and benzene ($C_6H_6$). For example, in the anion of Zeise's salt, ethylene binds to a $Pt^{2+}$ ion through donation of the two $\pi$ electrons of the double bond (Figure 22.32). As in metal carbonyls, there is also a metal-to-ligand $\pi$ bond formed by overlap of filled metal $d$ orbitals with the antibonding $\pi$ orbitals from the ligand. This combination of bonding modes strengthens the metal–ligand bond.

Benzene can be thought of as a tridentate ligand capable of donating three $\pi$ electron pairs to a metal atom (which then donates $d$ electrons back to the ligand in a $\pi$-type interaction). Such molecules also obey the 18-electron rule. For example, in dibenzenechromium (Figure 22.33), the Cr(0) atom with six valence electrons is bound to two ligands, each donating six $\pi$ electrons.

Dibenzenechromium is one of many organometallic compounds often referred to as "sandwich" compounds. (See *Case Study: Ferrocene—The Beginning of a Chemical Revolution*, page 1051.) These are molecular compounds in which a low-valent metal atom is "sandwiched" between two organic ligands. In addition, they are often referred to as $\pi$ complexes because the $\pi$ electrons of the ligand are involved in bonding. Modern terminology uses the Greek letter eta ($\eta$) to indicate this type of attachment, so dibenzenechromium is properly symbolized as $Cr(\eta^6\text{-}C_6H_6)_2$ (where the superscript 6 indicates the number of carbon atoms involved in bonding on each ligand).

Zeise's salt $[(C_2H_4)PtCl_3]^-$

Electron density transferred from $\pi$ bonding MO of $C_2H_4$ to $Pt^{2+}$ $C_2H_4$ $\pi_{2p}$ $Pt^{2+}$

Electron density transferred from $Pt^{2+}$ to $\pi$ antibonding MO of $C_2H_4$ $C_2H_4$ $\pi^*_{2p}$ $Pt^{2+}$

**FIGURE 22.32 Bonding in the anion of Zeise's salt.**

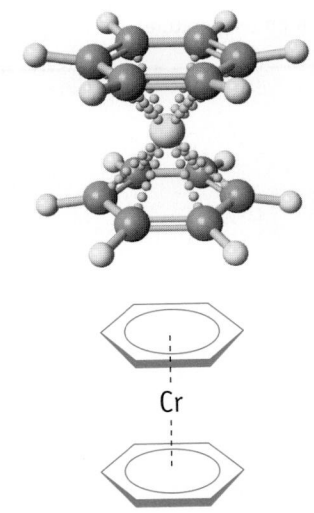

Cr

**FIGURE 22.33 Dibenzenechromium.** Two views of the molecule. *(top)*: A computer-generated model. *(bottom)*: A line drawing typically used by chemists.

# Ferrocene—The Beginning of a Chemical Revolution

Unexpected discoveries open up new areas of science. One example was the synthesis of compounds of Xe (page 400), a result that destroyed the myth that the noble gases were unreactive and led to a rich chemistry of these elements. At approximately the same time, another discovery, the synthesis of ferrocene, $Fe(C_5H_5)_2$, set the stage for the rapid and exciting growth of organometallic chemistry, the chemistry of compounds containing metal–carbon bonds. This destroyed another common myth of the time, that metal–carbon bonds are inherently unstable. Xenon compounds and ferrocene spearheaded a renaissance in inorganic chemistry that continues to this day.

The synthesis of ferrocene in two quite dissimilar research laboratories was accidental and unexpected. The first report, from an academic laboratory, described the reaction of the cyclopentadienide anion, $[C_5H_5]^-$ with $FeCl_2$. This reaction was intended to provide a precursor to an elusive organic compound fulvalene, $(C_5H_4)_2$ but a completely new substance—ferrocene—was obtained instead.

$2 C_5H_5MgCl + FeCl_2 \rightarrow Fe(\eta^5\text{-}C_5H_5)_2 + 2 MgCl_2$
(in diethyl ether)

The second report, from an industrial laboratory, described a high-temperature process in which cyclopentadiene was passed over a catalyst that contained, among other things, iron(II) oxide.

$2 C_5H_6(g) + FeO(s) \rightarrow$
$\qquad Fe(\eta^5\text{-}C_5H_5)_2(s) + H_2O(g)$
(at high temperature)

The properties of ferrocene were unexpected. Ferrocene is a diamagnetic orange solid, has a relatively low melting point (mp 173 °C), and is soluble in organic solvents but not in water. Most striking is its thermal and oxidative stability. Ferrocene is unaffected by oxygen, water, aqueous bases and nonoxidizing acids under ambient conditions, and can be heated to over 450 °C without decomposing. These observations contradicted conventional wisdom that held that metal–carbon bonds were weak and unstable, hard to make, and reactive.

The structure of ferrocene was quickly established by x-ray crystallography. Like dibenzenechromium (Figure 22.33), ferrocene is a molecular "sandwich" compound, containing an iron atom sandwiched between two planar hydrocarbon rings (Figure). Iron(II), a $d^6$ metal ion, is in its low-spin configuration. The cyclopentadienyl anions can be thought of as tridentate ligands with the six $\pi$ electrons (three pairs) of each organic ring being donated to the metal ion.

Once the structure of ferrocene was known, the race was on to make other complexes with unsaturated hydrocarbon ligands. Synthesis of cyclopentadienyl compounds of other metals soon followed, and now hundreds are known in combination with CO, benzene, ethylene, and many other carbon-containing compounds. The discovery of ferrocene was one of the keys that unlocked the field of organometallic chemistry.

**The structure of ferrocene, $Fe(\eta^5\text{-}C_5H_5)_2$**

**Questions:**
1. Rationalize ferrocene's diamagnetism.
2. Dibenzenechromium is also a "sandwich" compound. What is the oxidation state of chromium in this compound? Is it diamagnetic or paramagnetic?
3. Do ferrocene and dibenzenechromium obey the 18-electron rule (page 1048)?
4. Ferrocene can be oxidized to form the ferrocenium cation, $[Fe(\eta\text{-}C_5H_5)_2]^+$. The standard reduction potential for the ferrocenium–ferrocene half-reaction is 0.400 V. Identify several oxidizing agents in Appendix M that are capable of oxidizing ferrocene. Is elemental chlorine, $Cl_2$, a sufficiently strong oxidizing agent to carry out this oxidation?
5. Write an equation for one way to synthesize nickelocene, $Ni(\eta^5\text{-}C_5H_5)_2$. Nickelocene is paramagnetic. Predict the number of unpaired electrons in this compound.

**Answers to these questions are available in Appendix N.**

## EXAMPLE 22.7 The Effective Atomic Number Rule

**Problem** Show that each of the following molecules or ions satisfies the EAN rule.

(a) $[Fe(CO)_2(\eta^5\text{-}C_5H_5)]^-$ (b) $[Mn(CO)_5]^-$ (c) $Co(C_2H_4)_2(\eta^5\text{-}C_5H_5)$

**What Do You Know?** The formulas of the several complexes are given. Recognize that CO and $C_2H_4$ are both two-electron donors and that the $C_5H_5^-$ ion is a six-electron donor.

**Strategy** A complex obeys the EAN rule if the total number of electrons around the metal (valence electrons from the metal plus electrons donated by the ligands) equals 18. For the metal center, take its total number of valence electrons, and add or subtract electrons as necessary to adjust for negative or positive charges.

**Solution**

(a) The overall charge is 1−, which is equal to the charge on the $C_5H_5^-$ group. Thus, the Fe atom must have no charge.

6 electrons for $C_5H_5^-$ + 8 electrons for Fe + 4 electrons for 2 CO groups = 18 electrons

(b) Because CO is neutral the Mn center must have a negative charge. This means the manganese center has effectively eight valence electrons. Together with the five CO groups, each donating two electrons, the total is 18 electrons.

(c) This is a neutral molecule, so the negative charge on the $C_5H_5^-$ group must be balanced by a positive charge on Co. The $Co^+$ ion has eight valence electrons. Each $C_2H_4$ molecule donates two electrons.

6 electrons for $C_5H_5^-$ + 8 electrons for $Co^+$ + 4 electrons for 2 $C_2H_4$ molecules = 18 electrons

**Think about Your Answer** The octet rule and the 18-electron rule have similar rationales. According to the octet rule, 8 electrons (4 pairs) are required to fill all the bonding and nonbonding orbitals for main group elements. By analogy, complexes obeying the 18-electron rule will have 18 electrons (9 pairs) filling all the bonding and nonbonding orbitals for *d*-block elements.

**Check Your Understanding**

What must the charge of the metal in each species be for the species to satisfy the EAN rule?

---

**REVIEW & CHECK FOR SECTION 22.7**

Which of the following formulas does not obey the 18-electron rule?

(a) $Mn(CO)_5H$

(b) $[V(CO)_6]^-$

(c) $[Co(\eta^5{-}C_5H_5)_2]^+$

(d) The anion in Zeise's salt, $[Pt(\eta^2{-}C_2H_4)Cl_3]^-$

---

# CHAPTER GOALS REVISITED

*Now that you have studied this chapter, you should ask whether you have met the chapter goals. In particular, you should be able to:*

**Identify and explain the chemical and physical properties of the transition elements**

a. Identify the general classes of transition elements (Section 22.1).

b. Identify the transition metals from their symbols and positions in the periodic table, and recall some physical and chemical properties (Section 22.1).

c. Understand the electrochemical nature of corrosion (Section 22.1).

d. Describe the metallurgy of iron and copper (Section 22.2).

**Understand the composition, structure, and bonding in coordination compounds**

a. Given the formula for a coordination complex, identify the metal and its oxidation state, the ligands, the coordination number and coordination geometry, and the overall charge on the complex (Section 22.3). Relate names and formulas of complexes. **Study Questions: 9–18, 48, 49, 57.**

b. Given the formula for a complex, be able to recognize whether isomers will exist, and draw their structures (Section 22.4). **Study Questions: 41, 44, 45, 47, 48.**

c. Describe the bonding in coordination complexes (Section 22.5). **Study Question: 42.**

d. Apply the principles of stoichiometry, thermodynamics, and equilibrium to transition metal compounds. **Study Questions: 64, 67, 68, 70.**

**Relate ligand field theory to the magnetic and spectroscopic properties of the complexes**

a. Understand why substances are colored (Section 22.6). **Study Questions: 31, 32, 43.**

b. Understand the relationship between the ligand field splitting, magnetism, and color of complexes (Sections 22.5–22.6). **Study Questions: 23–30, 36, 37, 44, 45, 52, 55, 56, 60, 63.**

**Apply the effective atomic number (EAN) rule to simple organometallic compounds of the transition metals**

a. Apply the EAN rule to molecules containing a low-valent metal and ligands such as $C_6H_6$, $C_2H_4$, and CO (Section 22.7). **Study Questions: 33, 34, 68, 71.**

# Study Questions

⏻WL Interactive versions of these questions are assignable in OWL.

▲ denotes challenging questions.

Blue-numbered questions have answers in Appendix R and fully worked solutions in the *Student Solutions Manual*.

## Practicing Skills

### Properties of Transition Elements
*(See Section 22.1 and Example 7.3.)*

1. Give the electron configuration for each of the following ions, and tell whether each is paramagnetic or diamagnetic.
   (a) $Cr^{3+}$    (b) $V^{2+}$    (c) $Ni^{2+}$    (d) $Cu^+$

2. Identify two transition metal cations with each of the following electron configurations.
   (a) $[Ar]3d^6$  (b) $[Ar]3d^{10}$  (c) $[Ar]3d^5$  (d) $[Ar]3d^8$

3. Identify a cation of a first series transition metal that is isoelectronic with each of the following.
   (a) $Fe^{3+}$    (b) $Zn^{2+}$    (c) $Fe^{2+}$    (d) $Cr^{3+}$

4. Match up the isoelectronic ions on the following list.
   $$Cu^+ \; Mn^{2+} \; Fe^{2+} \; Co^{3+} \; Fe^{3+} \; Zn^{2+} \; Ti^{2+} \; V^{3+}$$

5. The following equations represent various ways of obtaining transition metals from their compounds. Balance each equation.
   (a) $Cr_2O_3(s) + Al(s) \longrightarrow Al_2O_3(s) + Cr(s)$
   (b) $TiCl_4(\ell) + Mg(s) \longrightarrow Ti(s) + MgCl_2(s)$
   (c) $[Ag(CN)_2]^-(aq) + Zn(s) \longrightarrow$
   $$Ag(s) + [Zn(CN)_4]^{2-}(aq)$$
   (d) $Mn_3O_4(s) + Al(s) \longrightarrow Mn(s) + Al_2O_3(s)$

6. Identify the products of each reaction, and balance the equation.
   (a) $CuSO_4(aq) + Zn(s) \longrightarrow$
   (b) $Zn(s) + HCl(aq) \longrightarrow$
   (c) $Fe(s) + Cl_2(g) \longrightarrow$
   (d) $V(s) + O_2(g) \longrightarrow$

### Formulas of Coordination Compounds
*(See Examples 22.1 and 22.2.)*

7. Which of the following ligands is expected to be monodentate, and which might be polydentate?
   (a) $CH_3NH_2$ (d) en
   (b) $CH_3CN$ (e) $Br^-$
   (c) $N_3^-$ (f) phen

8. One of the following nitrogen compounds or ions is not capable of serving as a ligand: $NH_4^+$, $NH_3$, $NH_2^-$. Identify this species, and explain your answer.

9. Give the oxidation number of the metal ion in each of the following compounds.
   (a) $[Mn(NH_3)_6]SO_4$ (c) $[Co(NH_3)_4Cl_2]Cl$
   (b) $K_3[Co(CN)_6]$ (d) $Cr(en)_2Cl_2$

10. Give the oxidation number of the metal ion in each of the following complexes.
    (a) $[Fe(NH_3)_6]^{2+}$ (c) $[Co(NH_3)_5(NO_2)]^+$
    (b) $[Zn(CN)_4]^{2-}$ (d) $[Cu(en)_2]^{2+}$

11. Give the formula of a complex constructed from one $Ni^{2+}$ ion, one ethylenediamine ligand, three ammonia molecules, and one water molecule. Is the complex neutral or is it charged? If charged, give the charge.

12. Give the formula of a complex constructed from one $Cr^{3+}$ ion, two ethylenediamine ligands, and two ammonia molecules. Is the complex neutral or is it charged? If charged, give the charge.

### Naming Coordination Compounds
*(See Example 22.3.)*

13. Write formulas for the following ions or compounds.
    (a) dichlorobis(ethylenediamine)nickel(II)
    (b) potassium tetrachloroplatinate(II)
    (c) potassium dicyanocuprate(I)
    (d) tetraamminediaquairon(II)

14. Write formulas for the following ions or compounds.
    (a) diamminetriaquahydroxochromium(II) nitrate
    (b) hexaammineiron(III) nitrate
    (c) pentacarbonyliron(0) (where the ligand is CO)
    (d) ammonium tetrachlorocuprate(II)

15. Name the following ions or compounds.
    (a) $[Ni(C_2O_4)_2(H_2O)_2]^{2-}$   (c) $[Co(en)_2(NH_3)Cl]^{2+}$
    (b) $[Co(en)_2Br_2]^+$   (d) $Pt(NH_3)_2(C_2O_4)$

16. Name the following ions or compounds.
    (a) $[Co(H_2O)_4Cl_2]^+$   (c) $[Pt(NH_3)Br_3]^-$
    (b) $Co(H_2O)_3F_3$   (d) $[Co(en)(NH_3)_3Cl]^{2+}$

17. Give the name or formula for each ion or compound, as appropriate.
    (a) pentaaquahydroxoiron(III) ion
    (b) $K_2[Ni(CN)_4]$
    (c) $K[Cr(C_2O_4)_2(H_2O)_2]$
    (d) ammonium tetrachloroplatinate(II)

18. Give the name or formula for each ion or compound, as appropriate.
    (a) tetraaquadichlorochromium(III) chloride
    (b) $[Cr(NH_3)_5SO_4]Cl$
    (c) sodium tetrachlorocobaltate(II)
    (d) $[Fe(C_2O_4)_3]^{3-}$

### Isomerism
*(See Example 22.4.)*

19. Draw all possible geometric isomers of the following.
    (a) $Fe(NH_3)_4Cl_2$
    (b) $Pt(NH_3)_2(SCN)(Br)$ ($SCN^-$ is bonded to $Pt^{2+}$ through S)
    (c) $Co(NH_3)_3(NO_2)_3$ ($NO_2^-$ is bonded to $Co^{3+}$ through N)
    (d) $[Co(en)Cl_4]^-$

20. In which of the following complexes are geometric isomers possible? If isomers are possible, draw their structures and label them as *cis* or *trans*, or as *fac* or *mer*.
    (a) $[Co(H_2O)_4Cl_2]^+$   (c) $[Pt(NH_3)Br_3]^-$
    (b) $Co(NH_3)_3F_3$   (d) $[Co(en)_2(NH_3)Cl]^{2+}$

21. Determine whether the following complexes have a chiral metal center.
    (a) $[Fe(en)_3]^{2+}$
    (b) *trans*-$[Co(en)_2Br_2]^+$
    (c) *fac*-$[Co(en)(H_2O)Cl_3]$
    (d) square-planar $Pt(NH_3)(H_2O)(Cl)(NO_2)$

22. Four geometric isomers are possible for $[Co(en)(NH_3)_2(H_2O)Cl]^+$. Draw the structures of all four. (Two of the isomers are chiral, meaning that each has a non-superimposable mirror image.)

### Magnetic Properties of Complexes
*(See Example 22.5.)*

23. The following are low-spin complexes. Use the ligand field model to find the electron configuration of the central metal ion in each ion. Determine which are diamagnetic. Give the number of unpaired electrons for the paramagnetic complexes.
    (a) $[Mn(CN)_6]^{4-}$   (c) $[Fe(H_2O)_6]^{3+}$
    (b) $[Co(NH_3)_6]Cl_3$   (d) $[Cr(en)_3]SO_4$

24. The following are high-spin complexes. Use the ligand field model to find the electron configuration of the central metal ion in each ion. Determine the number of unpaired electrons, if any, in each.
    (a) $K_4[FeF_6]$   (c) $[Cr(H_2O)_6]^{2+}$
    (b) $[MnF_6]^{4-}$   (d) $(NH_4)_3[FeF_6]$

25. Determine the number of unpaired electrons in the following tetrahedral complexes. All tetrahedral complexes are high spin.
    (a) $[FeCl_4]^{2-}$   (c) $[MnCl_4]^{2-}$
    (b) $Na_2[CoCl_4]$   (d) $(NH_4)_2[ZnCl_4]$

26. Determine the number of unpaired electrons in the following tetrahedral complexes. All tetrahedral complexes are high spin.
    (a) $[Zn(H_2O)_4]^{2+}$   (c) $Mn(NH_3)_2Cl_2$
    (b) $VOCl_3$   (d) $[Cu(en)_2]^{2+}$

27. For the high-spin complex $[Fe(H_2O)_6]SO_4$, identify the following:
    (a) the coordination number of iron
    (b) the coordination geometry for iron
    (c) the oxidation number of iron
    (d) the number of unpaired electrons
    (e) whether the complex is diamagnetic or paramagnetic

28. For the low-spin complex $[Co(en)(NH_3)_2Cl_2]ClO_4$, identify the following:
    (a) the coordination number of cobalt
    (b) the coordination geometry for cobalt
    (c) the oxidation number of cobalt
    (d) the number of unpaired electrons
    (e) whether the complex is diamagnetic or paramagnetic
    (f) Draw any geometric isomers.

29. The anion $[NiCl_4]^{2-}$ is paramagnetic, but when $CN^-$ ions are added, the product, $[Ni(CN)_4]^{2-}$, is diamagnetic. Explain this observation.

$$[NiCl_4]^{2-}(aq) + 4\ CN^-(aq) \longrightarrow [Ni(CN)_4]^{2-}(aq) + 4\ Cl^-(aq)$$
paramagnetic                                                                          diamagnetic

30. An aqueous solution of iron(II) sulfate is paramagnetic. If $NH_3$ is added, the solution becomes diamagnetic. Why does the magnetism change?

### Spectroscopy of Complexes
*(See Example 22.6.)*

31. In water, the titanium(III) ion, $[Ti(H_2O)_6]^{3+}$, has a broad absorption band centered at about 500 nm. What color light is absorbed by the ion?

32. In water, the chromium(II) ion, $[Cr(H_2O)_6]^{2+}$, absorbs light with a wavelength of about 700 nm. What color is the solution?

### Organometallic Compounds
*(See Example 22.7.)*

33. Show that the molecules and ions below satisfy the EAN rule.
    (a) $[Mn(CO)_6]^+$   (b)                    (c)

(In (b) $PR_3$ is a phosphine such as $P(C_6H_5)_3$, a two-electron donor ligand.)

34. Many organometallic compounds of the transition metals satisfy the 18-electron rule. However, there also are many other stable molecules that have only 16-valence electrons. These often have the capability of adding more ligands and function as catalysts in chemical reactions (see Study Question 71). (In the molecules below, $PR_3$ is a phosphine such as $P(C_6H_5)_3$, a two-electron donor ligand. For electron counting purposes, the $CH_3$ or methyl group is considered an anion, $(CH_3)^-$, and also a two-electron donor ligand.) Which molecules below have 18-valence electrons and which have 16?

## General Questions

*These questions are not designated as to type or location in the chapter. They may contain several concepts.*

35. Describe an experiment that would determine whether nickel in $K_2[NiCl_4]$ is square-planar or tetrahedral.

36. Which of the following high-spin complexes has the greatest number of unpaired electrons?
    (a) $[Cr(H_2O)_6]^{3+}$
    (c) $[Fe(H_2O)_6]^{2+}$
    (b) $[Mn(H_2O)_6]^{2+}$
    (d) $[Ni(H_2O)_6]^{2+}$

37. How many unpaired electrons are expected for high-spin and low-spin complexes of $Fe^{2+}$?

38. Excess silver nitrate is added to a solution containing 1.0 mol of $[Co(NH_3)_4Cl_2]Cl$. What amount of AgCl (in moles) will precipitate?

39. Which of the following complex ions is (are) square-planar?
    (a) $[Ti(CN)_4]^{2-}$
    (c) $[Zn(CN)_4]^{2-}$
    (b) $[Ni(CN)_4]^{2-}$
    (d) $[Pt(CN)_4]^{2-}$

40. Which of the following complex ions containing the oxalate ion is (are) chiral?
    (a) $[Fe(C_2O_4)Cl_4]^{2-}$
    (b) *cis*-$[Fe(C_2O_4)_2Cl_2]^{2-}$
    (c) *trans*-$[Fe(C_2O_4)_2Cl_2]^{2-}$

41. How many geometric isomers are possible for the square-planar complex ion $[Pt(NH_3)(CN)Cl_2]^-$?

42. For a tetrahedral complex of a metal in the first transition series, which of the following statements concerning energies of the $3d$ orbitals is correct?
    (a) The five $d$ orbitals have the same energy.
    (b) The $d_{x^2-y^2}$ and $d_{z^2}$ orbitals are higher in energy than the $d_{xz}$, $d_{yz}$, and $d_{xy}$ orbitals.
    (c) The $d_{xz}$, $d_{yz}$, and $d_{xy}$ orbitals are higher in energy than the $d_{x^2-y^2}$ and $d_{z^2}$ orbitals.
    (d) The $d$ orbitals all have different energies.

43. A transition metal coordination compound absorbs 425-nm light. What is its color?
    (a) red
    (c) yellow
    (b) green
    (d) blue

44. For the low-spin coordination compound $[Fe(en)_2Cl_2]Cl$, identify the following.
    (a) the oxidation number of iron
    (b) the coordination number for iron
    (c) the coordination geometry for iron
    (d) the number of unpaired electrons per metal atom
    (e) whether the complex is diamagnetic or paramagnetic
    (f) the number of geometric isomers

45. For the high-spin coordination compound $Mn(NH_3)_4Cl_2$, identify the following.
    (a) the oxidation number of manganese
    (b) the coordination number for manganese
    (c) the coordination geometry for manganese
    (d) the number of unpaired electrons per metal atom
    (e) whether the complex is diamagnetic or paramagnetic
    (f) the number of geometric isomers

46. A platinum-containing compound, known as Magnus's green salt, has the formula $[Pt(NH_3)_4][PtCl_4]$ (in which both platinum ions are $Pt^{2+}$). Name the cation and the anion.

47. Early in the 20th century, coordination compounds sometimes were given names based on their colors. Two compounds with the formula $CoCl_3 \cdot 4\ NH_3$ were named praseo-cobalt chloride (*praseo* = green) and violio-cobalt chloride (violet color). We now know that these compounds are octahedral cobalt complexes and that they are *cis* and *trans* isomers. Draw the structures of these two compounds, and name them using systematic nomenclature.

48. Give the formula and name of a square-planar complex of $Pt^{2+}$ with one nitrite ion ($NO_2^-$, which binds to $Pt^{2+}$ through N), one chloride ion, and two ammonia molecules as ligands. Are isomers possible? If so, draw the structure of each isomer, and tell what type of isomerism is observed.

49. Give the formula of the coordination complex formed from one $Co^{3+}$ ion, two ethylenediamine molecules, one water molecule, and one chloride ion. Is the complex neutral or charged? If charged, give the net charge on the ion.

50. ▲ How many geometric isomers of the complex ion $[Cr(dmen)_3]^{3+}$ can exist? (dmen is the bidentate ligand 1,1-dimethylethylenediamine.)

$$(CH_3)_2\ddot{N}CH_2CH_2\ddot{N}H_2$$

**1,1-Dimethylethylenediamine, dmen.**

51. ▲ Diethylenetriamine (dien) is capable of serving as a tridentate ligand.

$$H_2\ddot{N}CH_2CH_2-\underset{\underset{H}{|}}{\ddot{N}}-CH_2CH_2\ddot{N}H_2$$

**Diethylenetriamine, dien.**

(a) Draw the structures of *fac*-Cr(dien)Cl₃ and *mer*-Cr(dien)Cl₃.

(b) Two different geometric isomers of *mer*-Cr(dien) Cl₂Br are possible. Draw the structure for each.

(c) Three different geometric isomers are possible for [Cr(dien)₂]³⁺. Two have the dien ligand in a *fac* configuration, and one has the ligand in a *mer* orientation. Draw the structure of each isomer.

52. From experiment, we know that [CoF₆]³⁻ is paramagnetic and [Co(NH₃)₆]³⁺ is diamagnetic. Using the ligand field model, depict the electron configuration for each ion, and use this model to explain the magnetic property. What can you conclude about the effect of the ligand on the magnitude of $\Delta_o$?

53. Three geometric isomers are possible for [Co(en)(NH₃)₂(H₂O)₂]³⁺. One of the three is chiral; that is, it has a nonsuperimposable mirror image. Draw the structures of the three isomers. Which one is chiral?

54. The square-planar complex Pt(en)Cl₂ has chloride ligands in a *cis* configuration. No *trans* isomer is known. Based on the bond lengths and bond angles of carbon and nitrogen in the ethylenediamine ligand, explain why the *trans* compound is not possible.

55. The complex [Mn(H₂O)₆]²⁺ has five unpaired electrons, whereas [Mn(CN)₆]⁴⁻ has only one. Using the ligand field model, depict the electron configuration for each ion. What can you conclude about the effects of the different ligands on the magnitude of $\Delta_o$?

56. Experiments show that K₄[Cr(CN)₆] is paramagnetic and has two unpaired electrons. The related complex K₄[Cr(SCN)₆] is paramagnetic and has four unpaired electrons. Account for the magnetism of each compound using the ligand field model. Predict where the SCN⁻ ion occurs in the spectrochemical series relative to CN⁻.

57. Give a systematic name or the formula for the following:
(a) (NH₄)₂[CuCl₄]
(b) Mo(CO)₆
(c) tetraaquadichlorochromium(III) chloride
(d) aquabis(ethylenediamine)thiocyanatocobalt(III) nitrate

58. When CrCl₃ dissolves in water, three different species can be obtained.
(a) [Cr(H₂O)₆]Cl₃, violet
(b) [Cr(H₂O)₅Cl]Cl₂, pale green
(c) [Cr(H₂O)₄Cl₂]Cl, dark green
If diethyl ether is added, a fourth complex can be obtained: Cr(H₂O)₃Cl₃ (brown). Describe an experiment that will allow you to differentiate these complexes.

59. ▲ The complex ion [Co(CO₃)₃]³⁻, an octahedral complex with bidentate carbonate ions as ligands, has one absorption in the visible region of the spectrum at 640 nm. From this information,
(a) Predict the color of this complex, and explain your reasoning.
(b) Is the carbonate ion a weak- or strong-field ligand?
(c) Predict whether [Co(CO₃)₃]³⁻ will be paramagnetic or diamagnetic.

60. The glycinate ion, H₂NCH₂CO₂⁻, formed by deprotonation of the amino acid glycine, can function as a bidentate ligand, coordinating to a metal through the nitrogen of the amino group and one of the oxygen atoms.

Glycinate ion, a bidentate ligand

Site of bonding to transition metal ion

A copper complex of this ligand has the formula Cu(H₂NCH₂CO₂)₂(H₂O)₂. For this complex, determine the following:
(a) the oxidation state of copper
(b) the coordination number of copper
(c) the number of unpaired electrons
(d) whether the complex is diamagnetic or paramagnetic

61. ▲ Draw structures for the five possible geometric isomers of Cu(H₂NCH₂CO₂)₂(H₂O)₂. Are any of these species chiral? (See the structure of the ligand in Study Question 60.)

62. Chromium forms two anionic carbonyls, [Cr(CO)₅]ˣ⁻ and [Cr(CO)₄]ʸ⁻. What are the values of $x$ and $y$?

63. Nickel and palladium both form complexes of the general formula M(PR₃)₂Cl₂ (where PR₃ is a phosphine such as P(C₆H₅)₃, triphenylphosphine). The nickel(II) compound is paramagnetic whereas the palladium(II) compound is diamagnetic.
(a) Explain the magnetic properties of these compounds.
(b) How many isomers of each compound are expected?

64. ▲ The transition metals form a class of compounds called metal carbonyls, an example of which is the tetrahedral complex Ni(CO)₄. Given the following thermodynamic data (at 298 K):

|  | $\Delta_f H°$ (kJ/mol) | S° (J/K · mol) |
|---|---|---|
| Ni(s) | 0 | 29.87 |
| CO(g) | −110.525 | +197.674 |
| Ni(CO)₄(g) | −602.9 | +410.6 |

(a) Calculate the equilibrium constant for the formation of Ni(CO)₄(g) from nickel metal and CO gas.
(b) Is the reaction of Ni(s) and CO(g) product- or reactant-favored at equilibrium?
(c) Is the reaction more or less product-favored at higher temperatures? How could this reaction be used in the purification of nickel metal?

# In the Laboratory

**65.** Two different coordination compounds containing one cobalt(III) ion, five ammonia molecules, one bromide ion, and one sulfate ion exist. The dark violet form (A) gives a precipitate upon addition of aqueous $BaCl_2$. No reaction is seen upon addition of aqueous $BaCl_2$ to the violet-red form (B). Suggest structures for these two compounds, and write a chemical equation for the reaction of (A) with aqueous $BaCl_2$.

**66.** Three different compounds of chromium(III) with water and chloride ion have the same composition: 19.51% Cr, 39.92% Cl, and 40.57% $H_2O$. One of the compounds is violet and dissolves in water to give a complex ion with a 3+ charge and three chloride ions. All three chloride ions precipitate immediately as AgCl on adding $AgNO_3$. Draw the structure of the complex ion, and name the compound. Write a net ionic equation for the reaction of this compound with silver nitrate.

**67.** ▲ A 0.213-g sample of uranyl(VI) nitrate, $UO_2(NO_3)_2$, is dissolved in 20.0 mL of 1.0 M $H_2SO_4$ and shaken with Zn. The zinc reduces the uranyl ion, $UO_2^{2+}$, to a uranium ion, $U^{n+}$. To determine the value of $n$, this solution is titrated with $KMnO_4$. Permanganate is reduced to $Mn^{2+}$ and $U^{n+}$ is oxidized back to $UO_2^{2+}$.
  (a) In the titration, 12.47 mL of 0.0173 M $KMnO_4$ was required to reach the equivalence point. Use this information to determine the charge on the ion $U^{n+}$.
  (b) With the identity of $U^{n+}$ now established, write a balanced net ionic equation for the reduction of $UO_2^{2+}$ by zinc (assume acidic conditions).
  (c) Write a balanced net ionic equation for the oxidation of $U^{n+}$ to $UO_2^{2+}$ by $MnO_4^-$ in acid.

**68.** ▲ You have isolated a solid organometallic compound containing manganese, some number of CO ligands, and one or more $CH_3$ ligands. To find the molecular formula of the compound, you burn 0.225 g of the solid in oxygen and isolate 0.283 g of $CO_2$ and 0.0290 g of $H_2O$. The molar mass of the compound is 210 g/mol. Suggest a plausible formula and structure for the molecule. (Make sure it satisfies the EAN rule. The $CH_3$ group can be thought of as a $CH_3^-$ ion, a two-electron donor ligand.)

# Summary and Conceptual Questions

*The following questions may use concepts from this and previous chapters.*

**69.** The stability of analogous complexes $[ML_6]^{n+}$ (relative to ligand dissociation) is in the general order $Mn^{2+} <$ $Fe^{2+} < Co^{2+} < Ni^{2+} < Cu^{2+} > Zn^{2+}$. This order of ions is called the Irving–Williams series. Look up the values of the formation constants for the ammonia complexes of $Co^{2+}$, $Ni^{2+}$, $Cu^{2+}$, and $Zn^{2+}$ in Appendix K, and verify this statement.

**70.** ▲ In this question, we explore the differences between metal coordination by monodentate and bidentate ligands. Formation constants, $K_f$, for $[Ni(NH_3)_6]^{2+}(aq)$ and $[Ni(en)_3]^{2+}(aq)$ are as follows:

$$Ni^{2+}(aq) + 6\ NH_3(aq) \longrightarrow [Ni(NH_3)_6]^{2+}(aq)$$
$$K_f = 10^8$$

$$Ni^{2+}(aq) + 3\ en(aq) \longrightarrow [Ni(en)_3]^{2+}(aq)$$
$$K_f = 10^{18}$$

The difference in $K_f$ between these complexes indicates a higher thermodynamic stability for the chelated complex, caused by the *chelate effect*. Recall that $K$ is related to the standard free energy of the reaction by $\Delta_r G° = -RT \ln K$ and $\Delta_r G° = \Delta_r H° - T\Delta_r S°$. We know from experiment that $\Delta_r H°$ for the $NH_3$ reaction is $-109$ kJ/mol-rxn, and $\Delta_r H°$ for the ethylenediamine reaction is $-117$ kJ/mol-rxn. Is the difference in $\Delta_r H°$ sufficient to account for the $10^{10}$ difference in $K_f$? Comment on the role of entropy in the second reaction.

**71.** As mentioned on page 1047, transition metal organo-metallic compounds have found use as catalysts. One example is Wilkinson's catalyst, a rhodium compound $[RhCl(PR_3)_3]$ used in the hydrogenation of alkenes. The steps involved in the catalytic process are outlined below. Indicate whether the rhodium compounds in each step have 18- or 16-valence electrons. (See Study Question 34.)

Step 1. Addition of $H_2$ to the rhodium center of Wilkinson's catalyst. (For electron-counting purposes H is considered a hydride ion, $H^-$, a two-electron donor.)

Step 2. Loss of a $PR_3$ ligand (a two-electron donor) to open a coordination site. ($PR_3$ is a phosphine such as $P(C_6H_5)_3$, triphenylphosphine.)

Step 3. Addition of the alkene to the open site.

Step 4. Rearrangement to add H to the double bond. (Here the $-CH_2CH_3$ group is a two-electron donor and can be thought of as a $[CH_2CH_3]^-$ anion for electron counting purposes.)

Step 5. Loss of the alkane.

Step 6. Regeneration of the catalyst.

Net reaction: $CH_2{=}CH_2 + H_2 \longrightarrow CH_3CH_3$

## Applying Chemical Principles

### Green Catalysts

You were introduced to "green chemistry" in Chapter 1 and have seen several instances of it throughout the book. The important objective of this field is that a process that creates a useful product must have a negligible impact on the environment. Thus, important goals of green chemistry include eliminating the use of toxic substances as reactants and reducing the quantity of unwanted reaction by-products.

Catalysts can play an important role in green chemistry processes. Catalysts increase reaction rates sufficiently so that reactions can often be run at lower temperatures, thereby reducing energy usage. Catalysts may also improve the reaction specificity, yielding higher percentages of products, often in fewer synthetic steps. A specific area where green catalytic alternatives are needed is in oxidation reactions. At present these are often carried out by environmentally unfriendly compounds such as chlorine or chlorine dioxide.

Terry Collins, Professor of Chemistry at the Carnegie Mellon Institute for Green Chemistry, has designed a family of iron-based coordination complexes that are promising oxidation catalysts. Named Fe-TAML® (where TAML stands for tetraamido-macrocyclic ligand), these complexes catalyze reactions using hydrogen peroxide as an oxidizing agent. Hydrogen peroxide is an environmentally friendly oxidizing agent. However, when $H_2O_2$ decomposes it tends to produce hydroxyl radicals that indiscriminately attack organic molecules when used without a suitable catalyst.

Recently, this catalyst has shown positive results in the treatment of waste water from wood pulp treatment plants. Wood pulp consists of two naturally occurring polymers, cellulose and lignin. Cellulose is used for making white paper, whereas lignin is a dark colored polymer that must be removed. Current practice is to oxidize the lignin with chlorine dioxide before releasing it into waste water. Not all the lignin is destroyed in this process. The remaining lignin darkens the water and affects the quantity of light absorbed by aquatic life. Low concentrations of Fe-TAML (500 nanomolar) combined with small amounts of hydrogen peroxide have been shown to destroy the majority of lignin quickly at room temperature.

### Questions:

Answer the following questions concerning the Fe-TAML catalyst in the Figure.

1. What is the coordination number of the metal in the Fe-TAML catalyst?

The prototype TAML activator or a relative *plus* hydrogen peroxide

**The prototype TAML activator.** A model of hydrogen peroxide is also shown. The central iron cation is coordinated to four nitrogen atoms and a water molecule. The geometry around the central iron atom is square pyramidal geometry. (Model from the Institute for Green Science: www.chem.cmu.edu/groups/collins.)

2. Fe-TAML, as pictured here, is a complex ion of a macrocyclic ligand (with a charge of 4–), a water molecule, and an iron(III) ion. What is the overall charge on the Fe-TAML complex ion?

3. TAML is a tetra_____ macrocyclic ligand, meaning it has four "teeth" than can bond to the metal.

4. What is the geometry of the coordinating atoms around the $Fe^{3+}$ ion in the Fe-TAML complex ion: tetrahedral, square pyramidal, or octahedral?

5. What is the geometry of the coordinating atoms around the $Fe^{3+}$ ion in the Fe-TAML complex ion if the water is removed: tetrahedral, square planar, square pyramidal, or octahedral?

6. Can this metal–ligand complex have any isomers?

### References and Notes:

1. Professor Terry Collins, whose research group developed the Fe-TAML catalyst, received the 1999 Presidential Green Chemistry Award.

2. See an outline of the Twelve Principles of green chemistry on page 6. See also the U. S. Environmental Protection Agency website: www.epa.gov/greenchemistry/pubs/principles.html.

# 23 Nuclear Chemistry

## A Primordial Nuclear Reactor

The natural nuclear reactors in West Africa have been called "one of the greatest natural phenomena that ever occurred." In 1972, a French scientist noticed that the uranium taken from a mine in Oklo, Gabon, was strangely deficient in $^{235}U$. Uranium exists in nature as two principal isotopes, $^{238}U$ (99.275% abundant) and $^{235}U$ (0.72% abundant). It is $^{235}U$ that most readily undergoes nuclear fission and is used to fuel nuclear power plants around the world. But the uranium found in the Oklo mines had an isotope ratio like that of the spent fuel that comes from modern reactors. Based on this and other evidence, scientists concluded that $^{235}U$ at the Oklo mine was once about 3% of the total and that a "natural" fission process occurred in the bed of uranium ore nearly 2 billion years ago.

But intriguing questions remained: Why could fission occur to a significant extent in this natural deposit of uranium and why didn't the "reactor" explode? Apparently, there must have been a moderator of neutron energy and a regulation mechanism. In a modern nuclear power reactor, control rods slow down the neutrons from nuclear fission so that they can induce fission in other $^{235}U$ nuclei; that is, they moderate the neutron energy. Without a moderator, the neutrons just fly off. In the Oklo reactors, water seeping into the bed of uranium ore could have acted as a moderator.

The reason the Oklo reactor did not explode is that water could have also been the regulator. As the fission process heated the water, it boiled off as steam. This caused the fission to stop, but it began again when more water seeped in.

Courtesy of Francois Gauthier-Lafaye

**The natural nuclear reactor in Oklo, Gabon (West Africa).** Nearly 2 billion years ago, a natural formation containing uranium oxide (the yellow material) underwent fission that started and stopped over a period of a million years.

Scientists now believe this natural reactor would turn on for about 30 minutes and then shut down for several hours before turning on again. There is evidence these natural reactors functioned intermittently for about 1 million years, until the concentration of uranium isotopes was too low to keep the reaction going.

**Questions:**

1. How many protons and neutrons are there in the $^{235}U$ and $^{238}U$ nuclei?
2. Although plutonium does not occur naturally on earth now, it is thought to have been produced in the Oklo reactor (and then decayed). Write balanced nuclear equations for:
   (a) the reaction of $^{238}U$ and a neutron to give $^{239}U$
   (b) the decay of $^{239}U$ to $^{239}Np$ and then to $^{239}Pu$ by beta emission
   (c) the decay of $^{239}Pu$ to $^{235}U$ by alpha emission

**Answers to these questions are available in Appendix N.**

## CHAPTER GOALS

*See Chapter Goals Revisited (page 1088) for Study Questions keyed to these goals.*

- Identify radioactive elements, and describe natural and artificial nuclear reactions.
- Calculate the binding energy and binding energy per nucleon for a particular isotope.
- Understand rates of radioactive decay.
- Understand artificial nuclear reactions.
- Understand issues of health and safety with respect to radioactivity.
- Be aware of some uses of radioactive isotopes in science and medicine.

History of science scholars cite areas of study out of which modern chemistry arose: technology, medicine, and alchemy. The third of these pillars, alchemy, was pursued in many cultures on three continents for well over 1000 years. Simply stated, the goal of the ancient alchemists was to turn less valuable materials into gold. We now recognize the futility of these efforts, because this goal is not reachable by chemical processes. But we now also know that their dream of transmuting one element into another can be achieved by means of nuclear reactions. This happens naturally in the decomposition of uranium and other radioactive elements, and scientists can intentionally carry out such reactions in the laboratory. The goal is no longer to make gold, however. Far more important and valuable products of nuclear reactions are possible.

Nuclear chemistry encompasses a wide range of topics that share one thing in common: they involve changes in the nucleus of an atom. While nuclear "chemistry" is a major focus in this chapter, this subject cuts across many areas of science and modern society. Radioactive isotopes are used in medicine. Nuclear power provides a sizable fraction of energy for modern society. And, then there are nuclear weapons. . . .

## 23.1 Natural Radioactivity

In the late 19th century, while studying radiation emanating from uranium and thorium, Ernest Rutherford (1871–1937) stated, "There are present at least two distinct types of radiation—one that is readily absorbed, which will be termed for convenience **α (alpha) radiation**, and the other of a more penetrative character, which will be termed **β (beta) radiation**." Subsequently, charge-to-mass ratio measurements showed that α radiation is composed of helium nuclei ($He^{2+}$) and β radiation is composed of electrons ($e^-$) (Table 23.1).

**OWL**

Sign in to OWL at **www.cengage.com/owl** to view tutorials and simulations, develop problem-solving skills, and complete online homework assigned by your professor.

**go Chemistry**

Download mini lecture videos for key concept review and exam prep from OWL or purchase them from **www.cengagebrain.com**

● **Discovery of Radioactivity** The discovery of radioactivity by Henri Becquerel and the isolation of radium and polonium from pitchblende, a uranium ore, by Marie Curie were described in *Milestones in the Development of Chemistry*, page 338.

Table 23.1  **Characteristics of α, β, and γ Radiation**

| Name | Symbols | Charge | Mass (g/particle) |
|---|---|---|---|
| Alpha | $^4_2He$, $^4_2\alpha$ | 2+ | $6.65 \times 10^{-24}$ |
| Beta | $^0_{-1}e$, $^0_{-1}\beta$ | 1− | $9.11 \times 10^{-28}$ |
| Gamma | $\gamma$ | 0 | 0 |

**FIGURE 23.1 The relative penetrating ability of α, β, and γ radiation.** Highly charged α particles interact strongly with matter and are stopped by a piece of paper. Beta particles, with less mass and a lower charge, interact to a lesser extent with matter and thus can penetrate farther. Gamma radiation is the most penetrating.

• **Common Symbols: α and β**
Symbols used to represent alpha and beta particles do not include a plus or minus superscript, respectively, to show that they have a charge.

Rutherford hedged his bet when he said at least two types of radiation existed. A third type was later discovered by the French scientist Paul Villard (1860–1934); he named it **γ (gamma) radiation**, using the third letter in the Greek alphabet in keeping with Rutherford's scheme. Unlike α and β radiation, γ radiation is not affected by electric and magnetic fields. Rather, it is a form of electromagnetic radiation like x-rays but even more energetic.

Early studies measured the penetrating power of the three types of radiation (Figure 23.1). Alpha radiation is the least penetrating; it can be stopped by several sheets of ordinary paper or clothing. Beta particles can penetrate several millimeters of living bone or tissue, but about 0.5 cm of lead will stop the particles. Gamma radiation is the most penetrating. Thick layers of lead or concrete are required to shield the body from this radiation, and γ-rays can pass completely through the human body.

Alpha and β particles typically possess high kinetic energies. The energy of γ radiation is similarly very high. The energy associated with this radiation is transferred to any material used to stop the particle or absorb the radiation. This fact is important because the damage caused by radiation is related to the energy absorbed (see Section 23.8).

## 23.2 Nuclear Reactions and Radioactive Decay
### Equations for Nuclear Reactions

• **Symbols Used in Nuclear Equations** The mass number is included as a superscript, and the atomic number is included as a subscript preceding the symbols for reactants and products. This is done to facilitate balancing these equations.

In 1903, Rutherford and Frederick Soddy (1877–1956) proposed that radioactivity is the result of a natural change of an isotope of one element into an isotope of a different element. Such processes are called **nuclear reactions**.

Consider a reaction in which radium-226 (the isotope of radium with mass number 226) emits an α particle to form radon-222. The equation for this reaction is

$$^{226}_{88}\text{Ra} \rightarrow {}^{4}_{2}\alpha + {}^{222}_{86}\text{Rn}$$

In a nuclear reaction, the sum of the mass numbers of reacting particles must equal the sum of the mass numbers of products. Furthermore, to maintain nuclear charge balance, the sum of the atomic numbers of the products must equal the sum of the atomic numbers of the reactants. These principles are illustrated using the preceding nuclear equation:

|  | $^{226}_{88}\text{Ra}$ | $\rightarrow$ | $^{4}_{2}\alpha$ | + | $^{222}_{86}\text{Rn}$ |
|---|---|---|---|---|---|
|  | radium-226 | $\rightarrow$ | α particle | + | radon-222 |
| Mass number: (protons + neutrons) | 226 | = | 4 | + | 222 |
| Atomic number: (protons) | 88 | = | 2 | + | 86 |

Alpha-particle emission causes a decrease of two units in atomic number and four units in the mass number.

Similarly, nuclear mass and nuclear charge balance accompany $\beta$-particle emission, as illustrated by the decomposition of uranium-239:

| | $^{239}_{92}U$ | $\rightarrow$ | $^{0}_{-1}\beta$ | + | $^{239}_{93}Np$ |
|---|---|---|---|---|---|
| | uranium-239 | $\rightarrow$ | $\beta$ particle | + | neptunium-239 |
| Mass number: (protons + neutrons) | 239 | = | 0 | + | 239 |
| Atomic number: (protons) | 92 | = | -1 | + | 93 |

The $\beta$ particle has a charge of $1-$. Charge balance requires that the atomic number of the product be one unit greater than the atomic number of the reacting nucleus. The mass number does not change in this process.

How does a nucleus, composed of protons and neutrons, eject an electron? It is a complex process, but the net result is the conversion within the nucleus of a neutron to a proton and an electron.

$$^{1}_{0}n \longrightarrow \, ^{0}_{-1}e \; + \; ^{1}_{1}p$$

$$\text{neutron} \qquad \text{electron} \quad \text{proton}$$

Notice that the mass and charge numbers balance in this equation.

What is the origin of the gamma radiation that accompanies many nuclear reactions? Recall that a photon of visible light is emitted when an atom undergoes a transition from an excited electronic state to a lower energy state (◄ Section 6.3). Gamma radiation originates from transitions between nuclear energy levels. Nuclear reactions often result in the formation of a product nucleus in an excited nuclear state. One option is to return to the ground state by emitting a photon. The energy of $\gamma$ radiation is a measure of the large energy difference between the energy levels in the nucleus.

## Radioactive Decay Series

Several naturally occurring radioactive isotopes decay to form a product that is also radioactive. When this happens, the initial nuclear reaction is followed by a second nuclear reaction; if the situation is repeated, a third and a fourth nuclear reaction occur; and so on. Eventually, a nonradioactive isotope is formed to end the series. Such a sequence of nuclear reactions is called a **radioactive decay series**. In each step of this sequence, the reactant nucleus is called the *parent*, and the product is called the *daughter*.

Uranium-238, the most abundant of three naturally occurring uranium isotopes, heads one of four radioactive decay series. This series begins with the loss of an $\alpha$ particle from $^{238}_{92}U$ to form radioactive $^{234}_{90}Th$. Thorium-234 then decomposes by $\beta$ emission to $^{234}_{91}Pa$, which emits a $\beta$ particle to give $^{234}_{92}U$. Uranium-234 is an $\alpha$ emitter, forming $^{230}_{90}Th$. Further $\alpha$ and $\beta$ emissions follow, until the series ends with formation of the stable, nonradioactive isotope, $^{206}_{82}Pb$. In all, this radioactive decay series converting $^{238}_{92}U$ to $^{206}_{82}Pb$ is made up of 14 reactions, with eight $\alpha$ and six $\beta$ particles being emitted. The series is portrayed graphically by plotting atomic number versus mass number (Figure 23.2). An equation can be written for each step in the sequence. Equations for the first four steps in the uranium-238 radioactive decay series are as follows:

Step 1. $\quad ^{238}_{92}U \rightarrow \, ^{234}_{90}Th + \, ^{4}_{2}\alpha$

Step 2. $\quad ^{234}_{90}Th \rightarrow \, ^{234}_{91}Pa + \, ^{0}_{-1}\beta$

Step 3. $\quad ^{234}_{91}Pa \rightarrow \, ^{234}_{92}U + \, ^{0}_{-1}\beta$

Step 4. $\quad ^{234}_{92}U \rightarrow \, ^{230}_{90}Th + \, ^{4}_{2}\alpha$

Uranium ore contains trace quantities of the radioactive elements formed in the radioactive decay series. A significant development in nuclear chemistry was Marie Curie's discovery in 1898 of radium and polonium as trace components of

**FIGURE 23.2 The uranium-238 radioactive decay series.** The steps in this radioactive decay series are shown graphically in this plot of mass number versus atomic number. Each α-decay step lowers the atomic number by two units and the mass number by four units. Beta-particle emission does not change the mass but raises the atomic number by one unit. Half-lives of the isotopes are included on the chart. Notice that several of the isotopes in this series decompose by two different pathways.

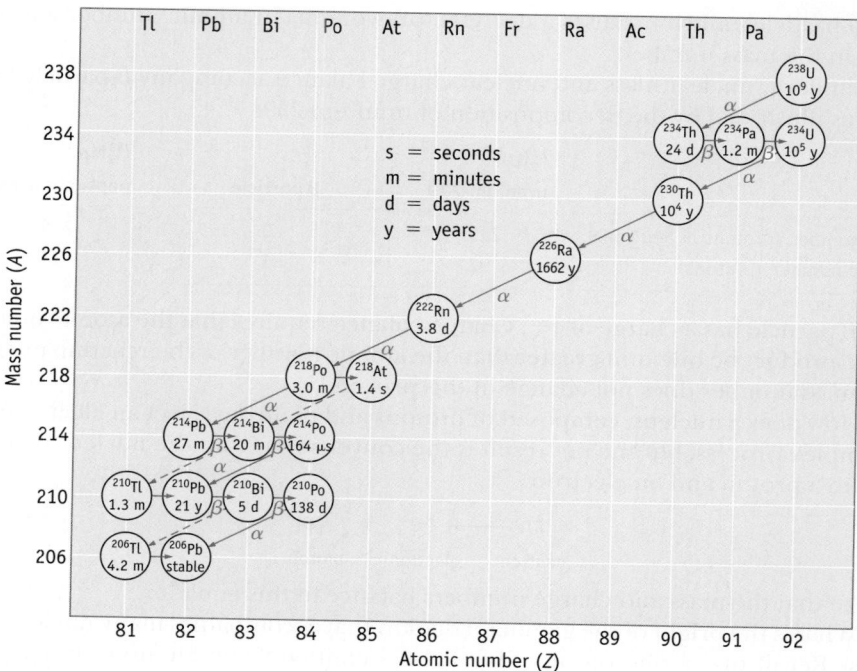

pitchblende, a uranium ore. The amount of each of these elements is small because the isotopes of these elements have short half-lives. Marie Curie isolated only a single gram of radium from 7 tons of ore. It is a credit to her skills as a chemist that she extracted sufficient amounts of radium and polonium from uranium ore to identify these elements.

The uranium-238 radioactive decay series is also the source of the environmental hazard radon. Trace quantities of uranium are often present naturally in the soil and rocks, and radon-222 is being continuously formed. Because radon is chemically inert, it is not trapped by chemical processes in soil or water and is free to seep into mines or into homes through pores in cement block walls, through cracks in the basement floor or walls, or around pipes. Because it is more dense than air, radon tends to collect in low spots, and its concentration can build up in a basement if steps are not taken to remove it.

The major health hazard from radon, when it is inhaled by humans, arises not from radon itself but from its decomposition product, polonium.

$$^{222}_{86}\text{Rn} \rightarrow {}^{218}_{84}\text{Po} + {}^{4}_{2}\alpha \qquad t_{1/2} = 3.82 \text{ days}$$

$$^{218}_{84}\text{Po} \rightarrow {}^{214}_{82}\text{Pb} + {}^{4}_{2}\alpha \qquad t_{1/2} = 3.04 \text{ minutes}$$

Radon does not undergo chemical reactions or form compounds that can be taken up in the body. Polonium, however, is not chemically inert. Polonium-218 can lodge in body tissues, where it undergoes α decay to give lead-214, another radioactive isotope. The range of an α particle in body tissue is quite small, perhaps 0.7 mm. This is approximately the thickness of the epithelial cells of the lungs, however, so α-particle radiation can cause serious damage to lung tissues.

Virtually every home in the United States has some level of radon, and kits can be purchased to test for the presence of this gas. If a significant amount of radon gas is detected in your home, you should take corrective actions such as sealing cracks around the foundation and in the basement. It may be reassuring to know that the health risks associated with radon are low. The likelihood of getting lung cancer from exposure to radon is about the same as the likelihood of dying in an accident in your home.

**Radon detector.** This kit is intended for use in the home to detect radon gas. The small device is placed in the home's basement for a given time period and is then sent to a laboratory to measure the amount of radon that might be present.

## EXAMPLE 23.1 Radioactive Decay Series

**Problem** A second radioactive decay series begins with $^{235}_{92}U$ and ends with $^{207}_{82}Pb$.

(a) How many $\alpha$ and $\beta$ particles are emitted in this series?

(b) The first three steps of this series are (in order) $\alpha$, $\beta$, and $\alpha$ emission. Write an equation for each of these steps.

**What Do You Know?** You are given the starting (long-lived radioactive) isotope and the final (stable) isotope. A series of alpha and beta reactions is the link between these two species.

**Strategy** First, find the total change in atomic number and mass number. A combination of $\alpha$ and $\beta$ particles is required that will decrease the total nuclear mass by 28 (235 − 207) and at the same time decrease the atomic number by 10 (92 − 82). Each equation must give symbols for the parent and daughter nuclei and the emitted particle. In the equations, the sums of the atomic numbers and mass numbers for reactants and products must be equal.

**Solution**

(a) Mass declines by 28 mass units (235 − 207). Because a decrease of 4 mass units occurs with each $\alpha$ emission, 7 $\alpha$ particles must be emitted. Also, for each $\alpha$ emission, the atomic number decreases by 2. Emission of 7 $\alpha$ particles would cause the atomic number to decrease by 14, but the actual decrease in atomic number is 10 (92 − 82). This means that 4 $\beta$ particles must also have been emitted because each $\beta$ emission increases the atomic number of the product by one unit. Thus, the radioactive decay sequence involves emission of 7 $\alpha$ and 4 $\beta$ particles.

(b) Step 1. $^{235}_{92}U \rightarrow {}^{231}_{90}Th + {}^{4}_{2}\alpha$

Step 2. $^{231}_{90}Th \rightarrow {}^{231}_{91}Pa + {}^{0}_{-1}\beta$

Step 3. $^{231}_{91}Pa \rightarrow {}^{227}_{89}Ac + {}^{4}_{2}\alpha$

**Think about Your Answer**

Because the mass number changes in these series only when an alpha particle is lost, all of the mass numbers in a given decay series are some multiple of four less than the first isotope in the series. For the series beginning with U-238, the mass numbers are in the series 238, 234, 230, . . . , 206. This series is sometimes called the $4n + 2$ *series* because each mass number ($M$) fits the equation $4n + 2 = M$, where $n$ is an integer ($n$ is 59 for the first member of this series and 51 for the last member). For the series headed by $^{235}_{92}U$, the mass numbers are 235, 231, 227, . . . , 207; this is the $4n + 3$ *series*.

Two other decay series are possible. One, called the $4n$ *series* and beginning with $^{232}Th$, is found in nature; the other, the $4n + 1$ series, is not. No member of this series has a very long half-life. During the 4.5 billion years since this planet was formed, all radioactive members of this series have completely decayed to the end product of this series, $^{209}Bi$.

---

**Check Your Understanding**

(a) Six $\alpha$ and four $\beta$ particles are emitted in the thorium-232 radioactive decay series before a stable isotope is reached. What is the final product in this series?

(b) The first three steps in the thorium-232 decay series (in order) are $\alpha$, $\beta$, and $\beta$ emission. Write an equation for each step.

## Other Types of Radioactive Decay

Most naturally occurring radioactive elements decay by emission of $\alpha$, $\beta$, and $\gamma$ radiation. Other nuclear decay processes became known, however, when new radioactive elements were synthesized by artificial means. These include **positron ($^{0}_{+1}\beta$) emission** and **electron capture**.

Positrons ($^{0}_{+1}\beta$) and electrons have the same mass but opposite charge. The positron is the antimatter analog to an electron. *Positron emission* by polonium-207, for example, results in the formation of bismuth-207.

• **Positrons** Positrons were discovered by Carl Anderson (1905–1991) in 1932. The positron is one of a group of particles that are known as *antimatter*. If matter and antimatter particles collide, mutual annihilation occurs, with energy being emitted.

| | ${}^{207}_{84}\text{Po}$ | $\rightarrow$ | ${}^{0}_{+1}\beta$ | $+$ | ${}^{207}_{83}\text{Bi}$ |
|---|---|---|---|---|---|
| | polonium-207 | $\rightarrow$ | positron | $+$ | bismuth-207 |
| Mass number: (protons + neutrons) | 207 | $=$ | 0 | $+$ | 207 |
| Atomic number: (protons) | 84 | $=$ | 1 | $+$ | 83 |

To retain charge balance, positron decay results in a decrease in the atomic number.

In *electron capture,* an extranuclear electron is captured by the nucleus. The mass number is unchanged, and the atomic number is reduced by 1. (In an old nomenclature, the innermost electron shell was called the *K shell,* and electron capture was called *K capture.*)

| | ${}^{7}_{4}\text{Be}$ | $+$ | ${}^{0}_{-1}e$ | $\rightarrow$ | ${}^{7}_{3}\text{Li}$ |
|---|---|---|---|---|---|
| | beryllium-7 | $+$ | electron | $\rightarrow$ | lithium-7 |
| Mass number: (protons + neutrons) | 7 | $+$ | 0 | $=$ | 7 |
| Atomic number: (protons) | 4 | $+$ | $-1$ | $=$ | 3 |

In summary, most unstable nuclei decay by one of four paths: $\alpha$ or $\beta$ decay, positron emission, or electron capture. Gamma radiation often accompanies these processes. Section 23.6 introduces a fifth way that nuclei decompose, *fission.*

● **Neutrinos and Antineutrinos** Beta particles having a wide range of energies are emitted. To balance the energy associated with $\beta$ decay, it is necessary to postulate the concurrent emission of another particle, the *antineutrino.* Similarly, neutrino emission accompanies positron emission. Much study has gone into detecting neutrinos and antineutrinos. These massless, chargeless particles are not included when writing nuclear equations.

## EXAMPLE 23.2 Nuclear Reactions

**Problem** Complete the following equations. Give the symbol, mass number, and atomic number of the product species.

(a)  ${}^{37}_{18}\text{Ar} + {}^{0}_{-1}e \rightarrow ?$

(b)  ${}^{11}_{6}\text{C} \rightarrow {}^{11}_{5}\text{B} + ?$

(c)  ${}^{35}_{16}\text{S} \rightarrow {}^{35}_{17}\text{Cl} + ?$

(d)  ${}^{30}_{15}\text{P} \rightarrow {}^{0}_{+1}\beta + ?$

**What Do You Know?** You are given the reactant and one of two products formed in these nuclear reactions. You know that both the masses and charges must balance in a balanced nuclear equation.

**Strategy** The missing product in each reaction can be determined by recognizing that the sums of mass numbers and atomic numbers for products and reactants must be equal. When you know the nuclear mass and nuclear charge of the product, you can identify it with the appropriate symbol.

**Solution**

(a)  This is an electron capture reaction. The product has a mass number of 37 + 0 = 37 and an atomic number of 18 − 1 = 17. Therefore, the symbol for the product is ${}^{37}_{17}\text{Cl}.$

(b)  This missing particle has a mass of zero and a charge of 1+; these are the characteristics of a positron, ${}^{0}_{+1}\beta.$ If this particle is included in the equation, the sums of the atomic numbers (6 = 5 + 1) and the mass numbers (11) on either side of the equation are equal.

(c)  A beta particle, ${}^{0}_{-1}\beta,$ is required to balance the mass numbers (35) and atomic numbers (16 = 17 − 1) in the equation.

(d)  The product nucleus has mass number 30 and atomic number 14. This identifies the unknown as ${}^{30}_{14}\text{Si}.$

**Think about Your Answer** The product in each reaction is a stable isotope. As we will see in the next section, there is a narrow range of neutron-to-proton ratios for stable products. Spontaneous nuclear reactions always occur in a way that moves either into or closer to the narrow range of stable isotopes.

**Check Your Understanding**

Indicate the symbol, the mass number, and the atomic number of the missing product in each of the following nuclear reactions.

(a)  ${}^{13}_{7}\text{N} \rightarrow {}^{13}_{6}\text{C} + ?$    (b)  ${}^{41}_{20}\text{Ca} + {}^{0}_{-1}e \rightarrow ?$    (c)  ${}^{90}_{38}\text{Sr} \rightarrow {}^{90}_{39}\text{Y} + ?$    (d)  ${}^{22}_{11}\text{Na} \rightarrow ? + {}^{0}_{+1}\beta$

## 23.3 Stability of Atomic Nuclei

We can learn something about nuclear stability from Figure 23.3. In this plot, the horizontal axis represents the number of protons, and the vertical axis gives the number of neutrons for known isotopes. Each circle represents an isotope identified by the number of neutrons and protons contained in its nucleus. The black circles represent stable (nonradioactive) isotopes, about 300 in number, and the red circles represent some of the known radioactive isotopes. For example, the three isotopes of hydrogen are $^{1}_{1}$H and $^{2}_{1}$H (neither is radioactive) and $^{3}_{1}$H (tritium, radioactive). For lithium, the third element, isotopes with mass numbers 4, 5, 6, and 7 are known. The isotopes with masses of 6 and 7 (shown in black) are stable, whereas the other two isotopes (in red) are radioactive.

Figure 23.3 contains the following information about nuclear stability:

- Stable isotopes fall in a very narrow range called the **band of stability**. It is remarkable how few isotopes are stable.
- Only two stable isotopes ($^{1}_{1}$H and $^{3}_{2}$He) have more protons than neutrons.
- Up to calcium ($Z = 20$), stable isotopes often have equal numbers of protons and neutrons or only one or two more neutrons than protons.
- Beyond calcium, the neutron-to-proton ratio is always greater than 1. As the mass increases, the band of stable isotopes deviates more and more from a 1:1 neutron-to-proton ratio (the line in Figure 23.3 for which $N/Z = 1$).
- Beyond bismuth (83 protons and 126 neutrons), all isotopes are unstable and radioactive. There is apparently no nuclear "superglue" strong enough to hold heavy nuclei together.
- Isotopes that fall farther from the band of stability tend to have shorter half-lives than do unstable isotopes nearer to the band of stability.
- Elements of even atomic number have more stable isotopes than do those of odd atomic number. More stable isotopes have an even number of neutrons than have an odd number. Roughly 200 isotopes have an even number of neutrons and an even number of protons, whereas only about 120 isotopes have an odd number of either protons or neutrons. Only five stable isotopes ($^{2}_{1}$H, $^{6}_{3}$Li, $^{10}_{5}$B, $^{14}_{7}$N, and $^{180}_{73}$Ta) have odd numbers of both protons and neutrons.

### The Band of Stability and Radioactive Decay

Besides being a criterion for stability, the neutron-to-proton ratio can assist in predicting what type of radioactive decay will be observed. Unstable nuclei decay in a manner that brings them toward a stable neutron-to-proton ratio—that is, toward the band of stability.

**FIGURE 23.3** **Stable and unstable isotopes.** A graph of the number of neutrons ($N$) versus the number of protons ($Z$) for stable (*black circles*) and radioactive (*red circles*) isotopes from hydrogen to bismuth. This graph is used to assess criteria for nuclear stability and to predict modes of decay for unstable nuclei.

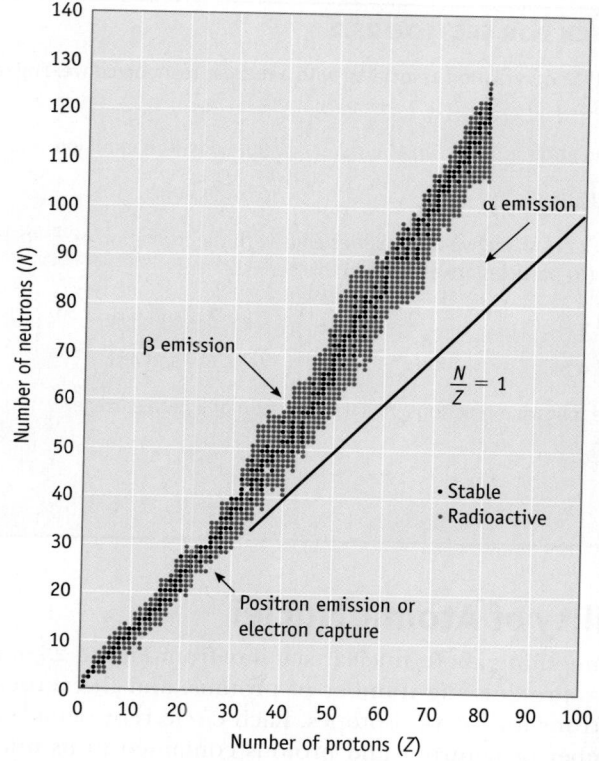

- All elements beyond bismuth ($Z = 83$) are unstable. To reach the band of stability starting with these elements, a process that decreases the atomic number is needed. Alpha emission is an effective way to lower $Z$, the atomic number, because each emission decreases the atomic number by 2. For example, americium, the radioactive element used in smoke detectors, decays by $\alpha$ emission:

$$^{243}_{95}\text{Am} \rightarrow \, ^{4}_{2}\alpha + \, ^{239}_{93}\text{Np}$$

- Beta emission occurs for isotopes that have a high neutron-to-proton ratio—that is, isotopes above the band of stability. With $\beta$ decay, the atomic number increases by 1, and the mass number remains constant, resulting in a lower neutron-to-proton ratio:

$$^{60}_{27}\text{Co} \rightarrow \, ^{0}_{-1}\beta + \, ^{60}_{28}\text{Ni}$$

- Isotopes with a low neutron-to-proton ratio, below the band of stability, decay by positron emission or by electron capture. Both processes lead to product nuclei with a lower atomic number and the same mass number and move the product closer to the band of stability:

$$^{13}_{7}\text{N} \rightarrow \, ^{0}_{+1}\beta + \, ^{13}_{6}\text{C}$$

$$^{41}_{20}\text{Ca} + \, ^{0}_{-1}\text{e} \rightarrow \, ^{41}_{19}\text{K}$$

## EXAMPLE 23.3    Predicting Modes of Radioactive Decay

**Problem** Identify probable mode(s) of decay for each isotope and write an equation for the decay process.

(a)  oxygen-15, $^{15}_{8}\text{O}$

(b)  uranium-234, $^{234}_{92}\text{U}$

(c)  fluorine-20, $^{20}_{9}\text{F}$

(d)  manganese-56, $^{56}_{25}\text{Mn}$

**What Do You Know?** You are given the formulas for four radioactive isotopes. The possible modes of decomposition are $\alpha$, $\beta$, or positron emission and electron capture. The preferred mode will give a more stable isotope and create a nucleus that is closer to the band of stability.

**Strategy** In parts (a), (c), and (d), compare the mass number with the atomic mass. If the mass number of the isotope is higher than the atomic weight, then there are too many neutrons, and $\beta$ emission is likely. If the mass number is lower than the atomic weight, then there are too few neutrons, and positron emission or electron capture is the more likely process. It is not possible to choose between the latter two modes of decay without further information. For part (b), note that isotopes with atomic number greater than 83 are likely to be $\alpha$ emitters.

**Solution**

(a) Oxygen-15 has 7 neutrons and 8 protons, so the neutron-to-proton ($n/p$) ratio is less than 1—too low for $^{15}$O to be stable. Nuclei with too few neutrons are expected to decay by either positron emission or electron capture. In this instance, the process is $^{0}_{+1}\beta$ emission, and the equation is $^{15}_{8}O \rightarrow ^{0}_{+1}\beta + ^{15}_{7}N$.

(b) Alpha emission is a common mode of decay for isotopes of elements with atomic numbers higher than 83. The decay of uranium-234 is one example:

$$^{234}_{92}U \rightarrow ^{230}_{90}Th + ^{4}_{2}\alpha$$

(c) Fluorine-20 has 11 neutrons and 9 protons, a high n/p ratio. The ratio is lowered by $\beta$ emission:

$$^{20}_{9}F \rightarrow ^{0}_{-1}\beta + ^{20}_{10}Ne$$

(d) The atomic weight of manganese is 54.85. The higher mass number, 56, suggests that this radioactive isotope has an excess of neutrons, in which case it would be expected to decay by $\beta$ emission:

$$^{56}_{25}Mn \rightarrow ^{0}_{-1}\beta + ^{56}_{26}Fe$$

**Think about Your Answer** Decomposition can occur by four possible paths, $\alpha$ and $\beta$ emission, positron emission, and electron capture. Whether the decay follows beta emission or positron emission (or electron capture) is predicted by the neutron/proton ratio, relative to the $n/p$ ratio in stable isotopes.

**Check Your Understanding**

Write an equation for the probable mode of decay for each of the following unstable isotopes, and write an equation for that nuclear reaction.

(a) silicon-32, $^{32}_{14}Si$

(b) titanium-45, $^{45}_{22}Ti$

(c) plutonium-239, $^{239}_{94}Pu$

(d) potassium-42, $^{42}_{19}K$

# Nuclear Binding Energy

An atomic nucleus can contain as many as 83 protons and still be stable. For stability, nuclear binding (attractive) forces must be greater than the electrostatic repulsive forces between the closely packed protons in the nucleus. **Nuclear binding energy**, $E_b$, is defined as the energy required to separate the nucleus of an atom into protons and neutrons. For example, the nuclear binding energy for deuterium is the energy required to convert one mole of deuterium ($^{2}_{1}H$) nuclei into one mole of protons and one mole of neutrons.

$$^{2}_{1}H \rightarrow ^{1}_{1}p + ^{1}_{0}n \qquad E_b = 2.15 \times 10^8 \text{ kJ/mol}$$

The positive sign for $E_b$ indicates that energy is required for this process. A deuterium nucleus is more stable than an isolated proton and an isolated neutron, just as the $H_2$ molecule is more stable than two isolated H atoms. Recall, however, that the H—H bond energy is only 436 kJ/mol. The energy holding a proton and a neutron together in a deuterium nucleus, $2.15 \times 10^8$ kJ/mol, is about 500,000 times larger than the typical covalent bond energies.

To further understand nuclear binding energy, we turn to an experimental observation and a theory. The experimental observation is that the mass of a nucleus is always less than the sum of the masses of its constituent protons and neutrons. The theory is that the "missing mass," called the **mass defect**, is equated with the energy that holds the nuclear particles together.

The mass defect for deuterium is the difference between the mass of a deuterium nucleus and the sum of the masses of a proton and a neutron. Mass spectrometric measurements (◀ Section 2.3) give the masses of these particles to a high level of accuracy, providing the numbers needed to carry out calculations of mass defects.

Masses of atomic nuclei are not generally listed in reference tables, but masses of atoms are. Calculation of the mass defect can be carried out using masses of atoms instead of masses of nuclei. By using atomic masses, we are including in this calculation the masses of extranuclear electrons in the reactants and the products. Because the same number of extranuclear electrons appears in products and reactants, this does not affect the result. Thus, for one mole of deuterium nuclei, the mass defect is found as follows:

$$^2_1H \rightarrow {}^1_1H + {}^1_0n$$

$$2.01410 \text{ g/mol} \quad 1.007825 \text{ g/mol} \quad 1.008665 \text{ g/mol}$$

Mass defect = $\Delta m$ = mass of products − mass of reactants

$$= [1.007825 \text{ g/mol} + 1.008665 \text{ g/mol}] - 2.01410 \text{ g/mol}$$

$$= 0.00239 \text{ g/mol}$$

The relationship between mass and energy is contained in Albert Einstein's 1905 theory of special relativity, which holds that mass and energy are different manifestations of the same quantity. Einstein defined the energy–mass relationship: Energy is equivalent to mass times the square of the speed of light; that is, $E = mc^2$. In the case of atomic nuclei, it is assumed that the missing mass (the mass defect, $\Delta m$) is equated with the binding energy holding the nucleus together.

$$E_b = (\Delta m)c^2 \tag{23.1}$$

If $\Delta m$ is given in kilograms and the speed of light is given in meters per second, $E_b$ will have units of joules (because $1 \text{ J} = 1 \text{ kg} \cdot \text{m}^2/\text{s}^2$). For the decomposition of one mole of deuterium nuclei to one mole of protons and one mole of neutrons, we have

$$E_b = (2.39 \times 10^{-6} \text{ kg/mol})(2.998 \times 10^8 \text{ m/s})^2$$

$$= 2.15 \times 10^{11} \text{ J/mol of } {}^2_1H \text{ nuclei } (= 2.15 \times 10^8 \text{ kJ/mol of } {}^2_1H \text{ nuclei})$$

The nuclear stabilities of different elements are compared using the **binding energy per mole of nucleons**. (**Nucleon** is the general name given to nuclear particles—that is, protons and neutrons.) A deuterium nucleus contains two nucleons, so the binding energy per mole of nucleons, $E_b/n$, is $2.15 \times 10^8$ kJ/mol divided by 2, or $1.08 \times 10^8$ kJ/mol nucleon.

$$E_b/n = \left(\frac{2.15 \times 10^8 \text{ kJ}}{\text{mol } {}^2_1H \text{ nuclei}}\right)\left(\frac{1 \text{ mol } {}^2_1H \text{ nuclei}}{2 \text{ mol nucleons}}\right)$$

$$E_b/n = 1.08 \times 10^8 \text{ kJ/mol nucleons}$$

The binding energy per nucleon can be calculated for any atom whose mass is known. Then, to compare nuclear stabilities, we can plot binding energies per nucleon as a function of mass number (Figure 23.4). The greater the binding energy per nucleon, the greater the stability of the nucleus. From the graph in Figure 23.4, the point of maximum nuclear stability occurs at a mass of 56 (i.e., at iron in the periodic table).

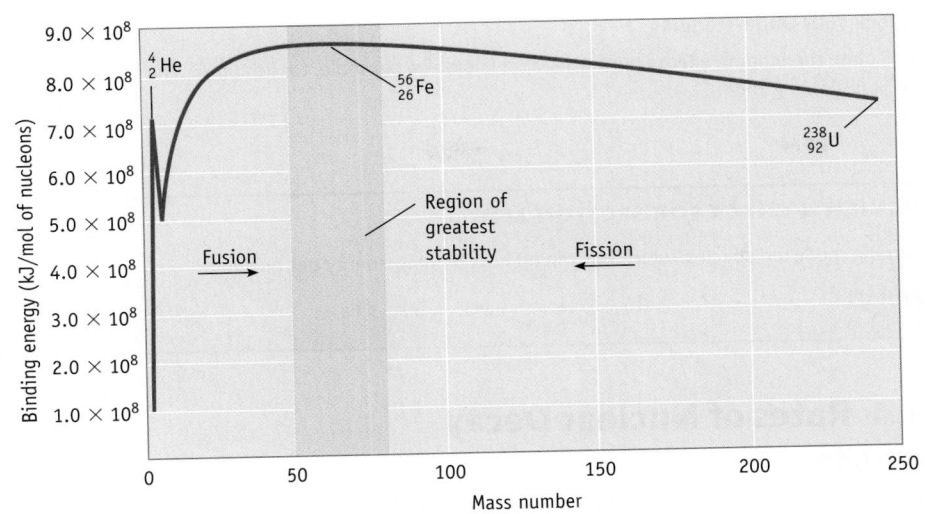

**FIGURE 23.4 Relative stability of nuclei.** Binding energy per nucleon for the most stable isotope of elements between hydrogen and uranium is plotted as a function of mass number. (Fission and fusion are discussed on pages 1078–1081.)

## EXAMPLE 23.4    Nuclear Binding Energy

**Problem** Calculate the binding energy, $E_b$ (in kJ/mol), and the binding energy per nucleon, $E_b/n$ (in kJ/mol nucleon), for carbon-12.

**What Do You Know?** The mass of carbon-12 is, by definition, exactly 12 g/mol. You will need the molar masses of hydrogen atoms ($^1_1H$) and neutrons (1.007825 g/mol and 1.008665 g/mol respectively), to determine the mass defect.

**Strategy** The mass defect is the difference between the mass of carbon-12 and the masses of 6 protons, 6 neutrons, and 6 electrons. The mass of 1 mol of protons and 1 mol of electrons can be taken into account by using the molar mass of $^1_1H$. Use the values given to calculate the mass defect (in g/mol). The binding energy is calculated from the mass defect using Equation 23.1.

**Solution** The mass of $^1_1H$ is 1.007825 g/mol, and the mass of $^1_0n$ is 1.008665 g/mol. Carbon-12, $^{12}_6C$, is the standard for the atomic masses in the periodic table, and its mass is defined as exactly 12 g/mol

$$\Delta m = [(6 \times \text{mass } ^1_1H) + (6 \times \text{mass } ^1_0n)] - \text{mass } ^{12}_6C$$

$$= [(6 \times 1.007825 \text{ g/mol}) + (6 \times 1.008665 \text{ g/mol})] - 12.000000 \text{ g/mol}$$

$$= 9.8940 \times 10^{-2} \text{ g/mol nuclei}$$

The binding energy is calculated using Equation 23.1. Using the mass in kilograms and the speed of light in meters per second gives the binding energy in joules:

$$E_b = (\Delta m)c^2$$

$$= (9.8940 \times 10^{-5} \text{ kg/mol})(2.99792 \times 10^8 \text{ m/s})^2$$

$$= 8.8923 \times 10^{12} \text{ J/mol nuclei} (= 8.8923 \times 10^9 \text{ kJ/mol nuclei})$$

The binding energy per nucleon, $E_b/n$, is determined by dividing the binding energy by 12 (the number of nucleons)

$$\frac{E_b}{n} = \frac{8.8923 \times 10^9 \text{ kJ/mol nuclei}}{12 \text{ mol nucleons/mol nuclei}}$$

$$= 7.4102 \times 10^8 \text{ kJ/mol nucleons}$$

**Think about Your Answer** Be sure that the units of mass and the speed of light are in kg and m/s, respectively, in this calculation. (Note that $1 \text{ kg} \cdot \text{m}^2/\text{s}^2 = 1 \text{ J}$.) The binding energy is a very large quantity of energy compared to those of ordinary chemical reactions. Compare binding energy to the very exothermic reaction of hydrogen and oxygen to form water vapor, for which $\Delta_r H°$ is only $-242$ kJ per mol of water vapor formed at 25 °C.

**Check Your Understanding**

Calculate the binding energy per nucleon, in kilojoules per mole, for lithium-6. The molar mass of $^6_3\text{Li}$ is 6.015125 g/mol.

---

**REVIEW & CHECK FOR SECTION 23.3**

Among the listed species, which has the highest binding energy per nucleon?

(a)  $^2_1\text{D}$        (b)  $^{20}_{10}\text{Ne}$        (c)  $^{56}_{26}\text{Fe}$        (d)  $^{238}_{92}\text{U}$

## 23.4 Rates of Nuclear Decay
### Half-Life

When a new radioactive isotope is identified, its *half-life* is usually measured. Half-life ($t_{1/2}$) is used in nuclear chemistry in the same way it is used when discussing the kinetics of first-order chemical reactions (◀ Section 15.4): It is the time required for half of a sample to decay to products (Figure 23.5). Recall that for first-order kinetics the half-life is independent of the amount of sample.

Half-lives for radioactive isotopes cover a wide range of values. Uranium-238 has one of the longer half-lives, $4.47 \times 10^9$ years, a length of time close to the age of the earth (estimated at $4.5–4.6 \times 10^9$ years). Thus, roughly half of the uranium-238 present when the planet was formed is still around. At the other end of the range of half-lives are isotopes such as the 277 isotope of element 112 (recently named copernicium, $^{277}\text{Cn}$), which has a half-life of 240 microseconds ($1~\mu s = 1 \times 10^{-6}$ s).

Half-life provides an easy way to estimate the time required before a radioactive element is no longer a health hazard. Strontium-90, for example, is a $\beta$ emitter with a half-life of 29.1 years. Significant quantities of strontium-90 were dispersed into the environment in atmospheric nuclear bomb tests in the 1960s and 1970s, and, from the half-life, we know that almost one half is still around. The health problems associated with strontium-90 arise because calcium and strontium have similar chemical properties. Strontium-90 is taken into the body and deposited in bone, taking the place of calcium. Radiation damage by strontium-90 (a $\beta$ emitter) in bone has been directly linked to bone-related cancers.

**FIGURE 23.5 Decay of 20.0 mg of oxygen-15.** After each half-life period of 2.0 minutes, the mass of oxygen-15 decreases by one half. (Oxygen-15 decays by positron emission.)

## EXAMPLE 23.5    Using Half-Life

**Problem** Radioactive iodine-131, used to treat hyperthyroidism, has a half-life of 8.04 days.

(a)   If you have 8.8 $\mu$g (micrograms) of this isotope, what mass remains after 32.2 days?

(b)   How long will it take for a sample of iodine-131 to decay to one eighth of its activity?

(c)   Estimate the length of time necessary for the sample to decay to 10% of its original activity.

**What Do You Know?** The half-life of $^{131}$I, 8.04 days, is given in the problem. Estimates of the masses remaining are made based on this value.

**Strategy** This problem asks you to use half-life to qualitatively assess the rate of decay. After one half-life, half of the sample remains. After another half-life, the amount of sample is again decreased by half to one fourth of its original value. To answer these questions, assess the number of half-lives that have elapsed and use this information to determine the amount of sample remaining.

**Solution**

(a)   The time elapsed, 32.2 days, is 4 half-lives (32.2/8.04 = 4). The amount of iodine-131 has decreased to 1/16 of the original amount [1/2 × 1/2 × 1/2 × 1/2 = (1/2)$^4$ = 1/16]. The amount of iodine remaining is 8.8 $\mu$g × (1/2)$^4$ or 0.55 $\mu$g.

(b)   After 3 half-lives, the amount of iodine-131 remaining is 1/8 [= (1/2)$^3$] of the original amount. The amount remaining is 8.8 $\mu$g × (1/2)$^3$ = 1.1 $\mu$g.

(c)   After 3 half-lives, 1/8 (12.5%) of the sample remains; after 4 half-lives, 1/16 (6.25%) remains. It will take between 3 and 4 half-lives, between 24.15 and 32.2 days, to decrease the amount of sample to 10% of its original value.

**Think about Your Answer** You will find it useful to make approximations as we have done in (c). An exact time can be calculated from the first-order rate law (page 681 and Equation 23.5).

**Check Your Understanding**

Tritium ($^3_1$H), a radioactive isotope of hydrogen, has a half-life of 12.3 years.

(a)   Starting with 1.5 mg of this isotope, what mass (mg) remains after 49.2 years?

(b)   How long will it take for a sample of tritium to decay to one eighth of its activity?

(c)   Estimate the length of time necessary for the sample to decay to 1% of its original activity.

# Kinetics of Nuclear Decay

The rate of nuclear decay is determined from measurements of the **activity** ($A$) of a sample. Activity refers to the number of disintegrations observed per unit of time, a quantity that can be measured readily with devices such as a Geiger–Müller counter (Figure 23.6). *Activity is proportional to the number of radioactive atoms present (N).*

$$A \propto N \qquad (23.2)$$

If the number of radioactive nuclei $N$ is reduced by half, the activity of the sample will be half as large. Doubling $N$ will double the activity. This evidence indicates that the rate of decomposition is first order with respect to $N$. Consequently, the equations describing rates of radioactive decay are the same as those used to describe the kinetics of first-order chemical reactions; the change in the number of radioactive atoms $N$ per unit of time is proportional to $N$:

$$\frac{\Delta N}{\Delta t} = -kN \qquad (23.3)$$

**FIGURE 23.6** **A Geiger–Müller counter.** A charged particle (an $\alpha$ or $\beta$ particle) enters the gas-filled tube (diagram at the *right*) and ionizes the gas. The gaseous ions migrate to electrically charged plates and are recorded as a pulse of electric current. The current is amplified and used to operate a counter. A sample of carnotite, a mineral containing uranium oxide, is also shown in the photograph.

The integrated rate equation can be written in two ways depending on the data used:

$$\ln\left(\frac{N}{N_0}\right) = -kt \tag{23.4}$$

or

$$\ln\left(\frac{A}{A_0}\right) = -kt \tag{23.5}$$

Here, $N_0$ and $A_0$ are the number of atoms and the activity of the sample initially, respectively, and $N$ and $A$ are the number of atoms and the activity of the sample after time $t$, respectively. Thus, $N/N_0$ is the fraction of atoms remaining after a given time ($t$), and $A/A_0$ is the fraction of the activity remaining after the same period. In these equations, $k$ is the rate constant (decay constant) for the isotope in question. The relationship between half-life and the first-order rate constant is the same as seen with chemical kinetics (Equation 15.4, page 686):

$$t_{1/2} = \frac{0.693}{k} \tag{23.6}$$

Equations 23.3–23.6 are useful in several ways:

- If the activity ($A$) or the number of radioactive nuclei ($N$) is measured in the laboratory over some period $t$, then $k$ can be calculated. The decay constant $k$ can then be used to determine the half-life of the sample.
- If $k$ is known, the fraction of a radioactive sample ($N/N_0$) still present after some time $t$ has elapsed can be calculated.
- If $k$ is known, the time required for that isotope to decay to a fraction of the original activity ($A/A_0$) can be calculated.

## EXAMPLE 23.6   Kinetics of Radioactive Decay

**Problem** A sample of radon-222 has an initial $\alpha$-particle activity ($A_0$) of $7.0 \times 10^4$ dps (disintegrations per second). After 6.6 days, its activity ($A$) is $2.1 \times 10^4$ dps. What is the half-life of radon-222?

**What Do You Know?** You are given the initial and final activities of the sample of $^{222}$Rn and the time elapsed.

**Strategy** Values for $A$, $A_0$, and $t$ are given. The problem can be solved using Equation 23.5 with $k$ as the unknown. Once $k$ is found, the half-life can be calculated using Equation 23.6.

**Solution**

$$\ln(2.1 \times 10^4 \text{ dps}/7.0 \times 10^4 \text{ dps}) = -k \text{ (6.6 day)}$$

$$\ln(0.30) = -k(6.6 \text{ day})$$

$$k = 0.18 \text{ days}^{-1}$$

From $k$ we obtain $t_{1/2}$:

$$t_{1/2} = 0.693/0.18 \text{ days}^{-1} = \boxed{3.8 \text{ days}}$$

**Think about Your Answer** Notice that the activity decreased to between one half and one fourth of its original value. The 6.6 days of elapsed time represents one full half-life and part of another half-life.

**Check Your Understanding**

(a) A sample of $Ca_3(PO_4)_2$ containing phosphorus-32 has an activity of $3.35 \times 10^3$ dpm. Exactly 2 days later, the activity is $3.18 \times 10^3$ dpm. Calculate the half-life of phosphorus-32.

(b) A highly radioactive sample of nuclear waste products with a half-life of 200. years is stored in an underground tank. How long will it take for the activity to diminish from an initial activity of $6.50 \times 10^{12}$ dpm to a fairly harmless activity of $3.00 \times 10^3$ dpm?

## Radiocarbon Dating

In certain situations, the age of a material can be determined based on the rate of decay of a radioactive isotope. The best-known example of this procedure is the use of carbon-14 to date historical artifacts.

Naturally occurring carbon is primarily carbon-12 and carbon-13 with isotopic abundances of 98.9% and 1.1%, respectively. In addition, traces of a third isotope, carbon-14, are present to the extent of about 1 in $10^{12}$ atoms in atmospheric $CO_2$ and in living materials. Carbon-14 is a $\beta$ emitter with a half-life of 5730 years. A 1-gram sample of carbon from living material will show about 14 disintegrations per minute, not a lot of radioactivity but nevertheless detectable by modern methods.

Carbon-14 is formed in the upper atmosphere by nuclear reactions initiated by neutrons in cosmic radiation:

$$^{14}_7\text{N} + ^1_0\text{n} \rightarrow ^{14}_6\text{C} + ^1_1\text{H}$$

Once formed, carbon-14 is oxidized to $^{14}CO_2$. This product enters the carbon cycle, circulating through the atmosphere, oceans, and biosphere.

The usefulness of carbon-14 for dating comes about in the following way. Plants absorb $CO_2$ and convert it to organic compounds, thereby incorporating carbon-14 into living tissue. As long as a plant remains alive, this process will continue, and the percentage of carbon that is carbon-14 in the plant will equal the percentage in the atmosphere. When the plant dies, carbon-14 will no longer be taken up. Radioactive decay continues, however, with the carbon-14 activity decreasing over time. After 5730 years, the activity will be 7 dpm/g; after 11,460 years, it will be 3.5 dpm/g; and so on. By measuring the activity of a sample, and knowing the half-life of carbon-14, it is possible to calculate when a plant (or an animal that was eating plants) died.

As with all experimental procedures, carbon-14 dating has limitations. Although the procedure assumes that the amount of carbon-14 in the atmosphere hundreds or thousands of years ago is the same as it is now, in fact the percentage has varied by as much as 10% (Figure 23.7). Furthermore, it is not possible to use carbon-14 to date an object that is less than about 100 years old; the radiation level

**FIGURE 23.7 Variation of atmospheric carbon-14 activity.** The amount of carbon-14 has changed with the variation in cosmic ray activity. To obtain the data for the pre-1990 part of the curve shown in this graph, scientists carried out carbon-14 dating of artifacts for which the age was accurately known (often through written records). Data for this figure were obtained using carbon-14 dating of tree rings.

**Source:** Hans E. Suess, La Jolla Radiocarbon Laboratory

● **Willard Libby (1908–1980)** Libby received the 1960 Nobel Prize in chemistry for developing carbon-14 dating techniques. Carbon-14 dating is widely used in fields such as anthropology.

Oesper Collection in the History of Chemistry, University of Cincinnati

from carbon-14 will not change enough in this short time period to permit accurate detection of a difference from the initial value. In most instances, the accuracy of the measurement is, in fact, only about ±100 years. Finally, it is not possible to determine ages of objects much older than about 40,000 years. By then, after nearly seven half-lives, the radioactivity will have decreased virtually to zero. But for the span of time between 100 and 40,000 years, this technique has provided important information (Figure 23.8).

### EXAMPLE 23.7 Radiochemical Dating

**Problem** To test the concept of carbon-14 dating, J. R. Arnold and W. F. Libby applied this technique to analyze samples of acacia and cyprus wood whose ages were already known. (The acacia wood, which was supplied by the Metropolitan Museum of Art in New York, came from the tomb of Zoser, the first Egyptian pharaoh to be entombed in a pyramid. The cyprus wood was from the tomb of Sneferu.) The average activity based on five determinations on one of these wood samples was 7.04 dpm per gram of carbon. Assume (as Arnold and Libby did) that the original activity of carbon-14, $A_0$, was 12.6 dpm per gram of carbon. Calculate the approximate age of the sample.

**What Do You Know?** You are given the initial and final $^{14}C$ activity. The first-order rate constant can be calculated from the half-life.

**Strategy** First, determine the rate constant for the decay of carbon-14 from its half-life ($t_{1/2}$ for $^{14}C$ is $5.73 \times 10^3$ years). Then, use Equation 23.5.

**Solution**

$$k = 0.693/t_{1/2} = 0.693/5730 \text{ yr}$$

$$= 1.21 \times 10^{-4} \text{ yr}^{-1}$$

$$\ln(A/A_0) = -kt$$

$$\ln\left(\frac{7.04 \text{ dpm/g}}{12.6 \text{ dpm/g}}\right) = (-1.21 \times 10^{-4} \text{ yr}^{-1})t$$

$$t = 4.8 \times 10^3 \text{ yr}$$

The wood is about 4800 years old.

**Think about Your Answer** This problem uses real data from an early research paper in which the carbon-14 dating method was being tested. The age of the wood was known to be 4750 ± 250 years. (See J. R. Arnold and W. F. Libby: *Science*, Vol. 110, p. 678, 1949.)

**FIGURE 23.8 The Iceman.** The world's oldest preserved human remains were discovered in the ice of a glacier high in the Alps. Carbon-14 dating techniques allowed scientists to determine that he lived about 5300 years ago. See pages 58 and 1 for more information on the Iceman.

© JEAN LOUIS PRADELS/PHOTOPOR/ LA DEPECHE DU MIDI/NEWSCOM

**Check Your Understanding**

A sample of the inner part of a redwood tree felled in 1874 was shown to have $^{14}$C activity of 9.32 dpm/g. Calculate the approximate age of the tree when it was cut down. Compare this age with that obtained from tree ring data, which estimated that the tree began to grow in 979 ± 52 BC. Use 13.4 dpm/g for the value of $A_0$.

---

**REVIEW & CHECK FOR SECTION 23.4**

1.  The age of the earth is thought to be 4.5 billion years. Approximately what percentage of $^{232}$Th has decomposed during this period of time? The half-life of $^{232}$Th is $1.4 \times 10^{10}$ years.

    (a) 20%          (b) 40%          (c) 60%          (d) 80%

2.  The half-life of $^{32}$P is 14.3 days. How much $^{32}$P in a sample will remain after 71.5 days have elapsed?

    (a) 1/4          (b) 1/8          (c) 1/16          (d) 1/32

---

# 23.5 Artificial Nuclear Reactions

How many different isotopes are found on earth? All of the stable isotopes occur naturally. A few unstable (radioactive) isotopes that have long half-lives are found in nature; the best-known examples are uranium-235, uranium-238, and thorium-232. Trace quantities of other radioactive isotopes with short half-lives are present because they are being formed continuously by nuclear reactions. They include isotopes of radium, polonium, and radon, along with other elements produced in various radioactive decay series, and carbon-14, formed in a nuclear reaction initiated by cosmic radiation.

Naturally occurring isotopes account for only a very small fraction of the currently known radioactive isotopes, however. The rest—several thousand—have been synthesized via artificial nuclear reactions, sometimes referred to as transmutation.

The first artificial nuclear reaction was identified by Rutherford about 90 years ago. Recall the classic experiment that led to the nuclear model of the atom (◄ *Milestones in the Development of Chemistry*, page 340) in which gold foil was bombarded with α particles. In the years following that experiment, Rutherford and his coworkers bombarded many other elements with α particles. In 1919, one of these experiments led to an unexpected result: When nitrogen atoms were bombarded with α particles, protons were detected among the products. Rutherford correctly concluded that a nuclear reaction had occurred. Nitrogen had undergone a *transmutation* to oxygen:

$$^{4}_{2}\text{He} + {}^{14}_{7}\text{N} \rightarrow {}^{17}_{8}\text{O} + {}^{1}_{1}\text{H}$$

During the next decade, other nuclear reactions were discovered by bombarding other elements with α particles. Progress was slow, however, because in most cases α particles are simply scattered by target nuclei. The bombarding particles cannot get close enough to the nucleus to react because of the strong repulsive forces between the positively charged α particle and the positively charged atomic nucleus.

Two advances were made in 1932 that greatly extended nuclear reaction chemistry. The first involved the use of particle accelerators to create high-energy particles as projectiles. The second was the use of neutrons as the bombarding particles.

The α particles used in the early studies on nuclear reactions came from naturally radioactive materials such as uranium and had relatively low energies, at least by today's standards. Particles with higher energy were needed, so J. D. Cockcroft (1897–1967) and E. T. S. Walton (1903–1995), working in Rutherford's laboratory in Cambridge, England, turned to protons. Protons are formed when hydrogen atoms ionize in a cathode-ray tube, and it was known that they could be accelerated to

● **Discovery of Neutrons** Neutrons had been predicted to exist for more than a decade before they were identified in 1932 by James Chadwick (1891–1974) (page 343). Chadwick produced neutrons in a nuclear reaction between α particles and beryllium: $^{4}_{2}\alpha + {}^{9}_{4}\text{Be} \rightarrow {}^{12}_{6}\text{C} + {}^{1}_{0}\text{n}$.

● **Glenn T. Seaborg (1912–1999)** Seaborg figured out that thorium and the elements that followed it fit under the lanthanides in the periodic table. For this insight, he and Edwin McMillan shared the 1951 Nobel Prize in chemistry. Over a 21-year period, Seaborg and his colleagues synthesized 10 new transuranium elements. To honor Seaborg's scientific contributions, the name "seaborgium" was assigned to element 106. It marked the first time an element was named for a living person.

# The Search for New Elements

By 1936, guided first by Mendeleev's predictions and later by atomic theory, chemists had identified all but two of the elements with atomic numbers between 1 and 92. From this point onward, all new elements to be discovered came from artificial nuclear reactions. Two gaps in the periodic table were filled when radioactive technetium and promethium, the last two elements with atomic numbers less than 92, were identified in 1937 and 1942, respectively. The first success in the search for elements with atomic numbers higher than 92 came with the 1940 discovery of neptunium and plutonium.

Since 1950, laboratories in the United States (Lawrence Berkeley National Laboratory), Russia (Joint Institute for Nuclear Research at Dubna, near Moscow), and Europe (Institute for Heavy Ion Research at Darmstadt, Germany) have competed to make new elements. Syntheses of new transuranium elements use a standard methodology. An element of fairly high atomic number is bombarded with a beam of high-energy particles. Initially, neutrons were used; later, helium nuclei and then larger nuclei such as $^{11}B$ and $^{12}C$ were used; and, more recently, highly charged ions of elements such as calcium, chromium, cobalt, and zinc have been chosen. The bombarding particle fuses with the nucleus of the target atom, forming a new nucleus that lasts for a short time before decomposing. New elements are detected by their decomposition products, a signature of particles with specific masses and energies.

By using bigger particles and higher energies, the list of known elements reached 106 by the end of the 1970s. To further extend the search, Russian scientists used a new idea, matching precisely the energy of the bombarding particle with the energy required to fuse the nuclei. This technique enabled the synthesis of elements 107, 108, and 109 in Darmstadt in the early 1980s, and the synthesis of elements 110, 111, and 112 in the following decade. Lifetimes of these elements were in the millisecond range; copernicium-277, $^{277}_{112}Cn$, for example, has a half-life of 240 $\mu$s.

Yet another breakthrough was needed to extend the list further. Scientists have long known that isotopes with specific so-called *magic numbers* of neutrons and protons are more stable. Elements with 2, 8, 20, 50, and 82 protons are members of this category, as are elements with 126 neutrons. The magic numbers correspond to filled shells in the nucleus. Their significance is analogous to the significance of filled shells for electronic structure. Theory had predicted that the next magic numbers would be 114 protons and 184 neutrons. Using this information, researchers discovered element 114 in early 1999. The Dubna group reporting this discovery found that the mass 289 isotope had an exceptionally long half-life, about 20 seconds.

Work along these lines is continuing and has resulted in the discovery of elements 113, 115, 116 and 118. Then, as we were preparing this edition of the book, the discovery of element 117, Uus, was announced (on April 19, 2010). An international team working at the Flerov Laboratories in Dubna, Russia, described the formation of 6 atoms of this element by bombarding $^{249}Bk$ with $^{48}Ca$ atoms. (The isotopes $^{293}Uus$ and $^{294}Uus$ were detected.) Assuming confirmation of this element from other labs will follow, the periodic table now includes all the elements from 1 to 118!

*Footnote:* Until an official name is chosen for element 117, it will be known by a placeholder name, ununseptium, and the corresponding three-letter symbol Uus. This name simply stands for "one-one-seven," because the atomic number of the element is 117.

Jim Roberto/Department of Energy/ORNL

**Discovery of element 117.** Scientists at the Flerov Laboratories in Dubna, Russia, used radioactive berkelium-249 as the starting material to make two isotopes of element 117. Berkelium-249 is contained in the greenish fluid in the tip of the vial. It was made in the research reactor at Oak Ridge National Laboratory.

higher energy by applying a high voltage. Cockcroft and Walton found that when energetic protons struck a lithium target, the following reaction occurs:

$$^{7}_{3}Li + {}^{1}_{1}p \rightarrow 2\,^{4}_{2}He$$

This was the first example of a reaction initiated by a particle that had been artificially accelerated to high energy. Since this experiment was conducted, the technique has been developed much further, and the use of particle accelerators in nuclear chemistry is now commonplace. Particle accelerators operate on the principle that a charged particle placed between charged plates will be accelerated to a high speed and high energy. Modern examples of this process are seen in the synthesis of the transuranium elements, several of which are described in more detail in *A Closer Look: The Search for New Elements*, on the previous page.

Experiments using neutrons as bombarding particles were first carried out in both the United States and Great Britain in 1932. Nitrogen, oxygen, fluorine, and neon were bombarded with energetic neutrons, and $\alpha$ particles were detected among the products. Using neutrons made sense: Because neutrons have no charge, it was reasoned that these particles would not be repelled by the positively charged nuclear particles. Thus, neutrons did not need high energies to react.

In 1934, Enrico Fermi (1901–1954) and his coworkers showed that nuclear reactions using neutrons are more favorable if the neutrons have low energy. A low-energy neutron is simply captured by the nucleus, giving a product in which the mass number is increased by one unit. Because of the low energy of the bombarding particle, the product nucleus does not have sufficient energy to fragment in these reactions. The new nucleus is produced in an excited state, however; when the nucleus returns to the ground state, a $\gamma$-ray is emitted. Reactions in which a neutron is captured and a $\gamma$-ray is emitted are called **(n, $\gamma$) reactions**.

The (n, $\gamma$) reactions are the source of many of the radioisotopes used in medicine and chemistry. An example is radioactive phosphorus, $^{32}_{15}P$, which is used in chemical studies such as tracing the uptake of phosphorus in the body.

$$^{31}_{15}P + ^{1}_{0}n \rightarrow ^{32}_{15}P + \gamma$$

**Transuranium elements**, elements with an atomic number greater than 92, were first made in a nuclear reaction sequence beginning with an (n, $\gamma$) reaction. Scientists at the University of California at Berkeley bombarded uranium-238 with neutrons. Among the products identified were neptunium-239 and plutonium-239. These new elements were formed when $^{239}U$ decayed by $\beta$ radiation.

$$^{238}_{92}U + ^{1}_{0}n \rightarrow ^{239}_{92}U$$

$$^{239}_{92}U \rightarrow ^{239}_{93}Np + ^{0}_{-1}\beta$$

$$^{239}_{93}Np \rightarrow ^{239}_{94}Pu + ^{0}_{-1}\beta$$

Four years later, a similar reaction sequence was used to make americium-241. Plutonium-239 was found to add two neutrons to form plutonium-241, which decays by $\beta$ emission to give americium-241.

**• Transuranium Elements in Nature** Neptunium, plutonium, and americium were unknown prior to their preparation via these nuclear reactions. Later, these elements were found to be present in trace quantities in uranium ores.

## EXAMPLE 23.8 Nuclear Reactions

**Problem** Write equations for the nuclear reactions described below.

(a) Fluorine-19 undergoes an (n, $\gamma$) reaction to give a radioactive product that decays by $\beta$ emission. (Write equations for both nuclear reactions.)

(b) When an atom of beryllium-9 (the only stable isotope of beryllium) reacts with an alpha particle emitted by a plutonium atom, a neutron is ejected.

**What Do You Know?** Reactants and one of two products are given for each reaction.

**Strategy** The equations are written so that both mass and charge are balanced.

**Solution**

(a) $^{19}_{9}F + ^{1}_{0}n \rightarrow ^{20}_{9}F + \gamma$

$^{20}_{9}F \rightarrow ^{20}_{10}Ne + ^{0}_{-1}\beta$

(b) $^{239}_{94}Pu \rightarrow ^{235}_{92}U + ^{4}_{2}\alpha$

$^{4}_{2}\alpha + ^{9}_{4}Be \rightarrow ^{12}_{6}C + ^{1}_{0}n$

**Think about Your Answer** Both answers deal with neutrons. The equation given for part (a), an (n, γ) reaction, illustrates a process that is easy to carry out. In a lab, the neutrons might be produced in a small device called a *Pu-Be neutron source*. The answer to part (b) of this question describes the nuclear reactions in such a device.

**Check Your Understanding**

Technetium is one of the two elements with atomic numbers less than 83 for which there is no stable isotope (promethium, element 61, is the other). Nevertheless, technetium is a very important element because of its extensive use in medical imaging (page 1085). It is produced in a two-step process. First, $^{98}$Mo undergoes an (n, γ) reaction; then, the resulting unstable isotope decomposes to $^{99}$Tc. Write equations for these two reactions.

---

**REVIEW & CHECK FOR SECTION 23.5**

Which of the following is seldom used as a bombarding particle to initiate a nuclear reaction?

(a) protons      (b) neutrons      (c) electrons      (d) alpha particles

---

## 23.6 Nuclear Fission

● **The Atomic Bomb** In an atomic bomb, each nuclear fission step produces 3 neutrons, which leads to about 3 more fissions and 9 more neutrons, which leads to 9 more fission steps and 27 more neutrons, and so on. The rate of fission depends on the number of neutrons, so the nuclear reaction occurs faster and faster as more and more neutrons are formed, leading to an enormous output of energy in a short time span.

In 1938, two chemists, Otto Hahn (1879–1968) and Fritz Strassman (1902–1980), isolated and identified barium in a sample of uranium that had been bombarded with neutrons. How was barium formed? The answer to that question explained one of the most significant scientific discoveries of the 20th century. The uranium nucleus had split into smaller pieces in the process we now call **nuclear fission**.

The details of nuclear fission were unraveled through the work of a number of scientists. They determined that a uranium-235 nucleus initially captured a neutron to form uranium-236. This isotope underwent nuclear fission to produce two new nuclei, one with a mass number around 140 and the other with a mass around 90, along with several neutrons (Figure 23.9). The nuclear reactions that led to formation of barium when a sample of $^{235}$U was bombarded with neutrons are

$$^{235}_{92}\text{U} + {}^{1}_{0}\text{n} \rightarrow {}^{236}_{92}\text{U}$$

$$^{236}_{92}\text{U} \rightarrow {}^{141}_{56}\text{Ba} + {}^{92}_{36}\text{Kr} + 3\,{}^{1}_{0}\text{n}$$

An important aspect of fission reactions is that they produce more neutrons than are used to initiate the process. Under the right circumstances, these neutrons then serve to continue the reaction. If one or more of these neutrons are captured by another $^{235}$U nucleus, then a further reaction can occur, releasing still more neutrons. This sequence repeats over and over. Such a mechanism, in which each step generates a reactant to continue the reaction, is called a **chain reaction**.

**FIGURE 23.9 Nuclear fission.** Neutron capture by $^{235}_{92}$U produces $^{236}_{92}$U. This isotope undergoes fission, which yields several fragments along with several neutrons. These neutrons initiate further nuclear reactions by adding to other $^{235}_{92}$U nuclei. The process is highly exothermic, producing about $2 \times 10^{10}$ kJ/mol.

A nuclear fission chain reaction has three general steps:

1. *Initiation.* The reaction of a single atom is needed to start the chain. Fission of $^{235}U$ is initiated by the absorption of a neutron.
2. *Propagation.* This part of the process repeats itself over and over, with each step yielding more product. The fission of $^{236}U$ releases neutrons that initiate the fission of other uranium atoms.
3. *Termination.* Eventually, the chain will end. Termination could occur if the reactant ($^{235}U$) is used up, or if the neutrons that continue the chain escape from the sample without being captured by $^{235}U$.

To harness the energy produced in a nuclear reaction, it is necessary to control the rate at which a fission reaction occurs. This is managed by balancing the propagation and termination steps by limiting the number of neutrons available. In a nuclear reactor, this balance is accomplished by using cadmium rods to absorb neutrons. By withdrawing or inserting the rods, the number of neutrons available to propagate the chain can be changed, and the rate of the fission reaction (and the rate of energy production) can be increased or decreased.

Uranium-235 and plutonium-239 are the fissionable isotopes most commonly used in power reactors. Natural uranium contains only 0.72% of uranium-235; more than 99% of the natural element is uranium-238. The percentage of uranium-235 in natural uranium is too small to sustain a chain reaction, however, so the uranium used for nuclear fuel must be enriched in this isotope. One way to do so is by gaseous centrifugation (Figure 23.10). Plutonium, on the other hand, occurs naturally in only trace quantities and so must be made by a nuclear reaction. The raw material for this nuclear synthesis is the more abundant uranium isotope, $^{238}U$. Addition of a neutron to $^{238}U$ gives $^{239}U$, which, as noted earlier, undergoes two $\beta$ emissions to form $^{239}Pu$.

Currently, there are over 100 operating nuclear power plants in the United States and more than 400 worldwide. About 20% of this country's electricity (and 17% of the world's energy) comes from nuclear power (Figure 23.11). Although one might imagine that nuclear energy would be called upon to meet the ever-increasing needs of society, no new nuclear power plants are under construction in the United States. Among other things, the disasters at Chernobyl (in the former Soviet Union) in 1986 and Three Mile Island (in Pennsylvania) in 1979 have sensitized the public to the issue of safety. The cost to construct a nuclear power plant (measured in terms of dollars per kilowatt-hour of power) is considerably more than the cost for a natural gas–powered facility, and there are severe regulatory restrictions for nuclear power. Disposal of highly radioactive nuclear waste is another

● **Lise Meitner (1878–1968)** Meitner's greatest contribution to 20th-century science was her explanation of the process of nuclear fission. She and her nephew, Otto Frisch, also a physicist, published a paper in 1939 that was the first to use the term *nuclear fission*. Element number 109 is named meitnerium to honor Meitner's contributions. The leader of the team that discovered this element said that "She should be honored as the most significant woman scientist of [the 20th] century."

AIP-Emilio Segré Visual Archives, Herzfeld Collection

Oak Ridge National Laboratory

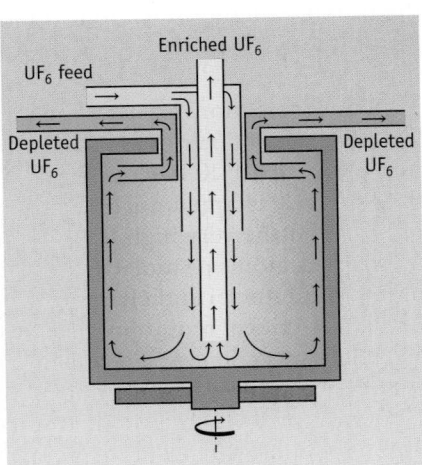

**FIGURE 23.10 Isotope separation.** *(left)* Separation of uranium isotopes for use in atomic weaponry or in nuclear power plants is done with gas centrifuges. *(right)* $UF_6$ gas is injected into the centrifuge from a tube passing down through the center of a tall, spinning cylinder. The heavier $^{238}UF_6$ molecules experience more centrifugal force and move to the outer wall of the cylinder; the lighter $^{235}UF_6$ molecules stay closer to the center. A temperature difference inside the rotor causes the $^{235}UF_6$ molecules to move to the top of the cylinder and the $^{238}UF_6$ molecules to move to the bottom. (See the *New York Times*, page F1, March 23, 2004.)

**FIGURE 23.11 Percentage of electricity generation by nuclear power in various countries.**
This varies from 76.2% in France, to 19.7% in the United States, to a little more than 2% in China and India. (Data from "Energy, Electricity and Nuclear Power Estimates for the Period up to 2030" from the International Atomic Energy Agency, 2009 edition.)

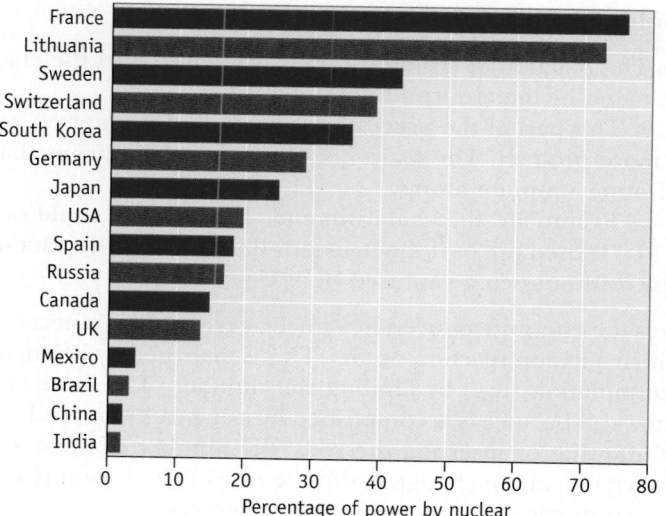

thorny problem, with 20 metric tons of waste being generated per year at each reactor.

In addition to technical problems, nuclear energy production brings with it significant geopolitical security concerns. The process for enriching uranium for use in a reactor is the same process used for generating weapons-grade uranium. Also, some nuclear reactors are designed so that one by-product of their operation is the isotope plutonium-239, which can be removed and used in a nuclear weapon. Despite these problems, nuclear fission is an important part of the energy profile in a number of countries. For example, 76.2% of power production in France and 24.9% in Japan is nuclear generated.

---

**REVIEW & CHECK FOR SECTION 23.6**

Identify the other element generated in this fission reaction: $^{235}_{92}\text{U} + {}^{1}_{0}\text{n} \rightarrow {}^{141}_{55}\text{Cs} + ? + 2\,{}^{1}_{0}\text{n}$

(a) $^{93}_{37}\text{Rb}$        (b) $^{141}_{56}\text{Ba}$        (c) $^{92}_{36}\text{Kr}$

---

## 23.7 Nuclear Fusion

In a **nuclear fusion** reaction, several small nuclei react to form a larger nucleus. Tremendous amounts of energy can be generated by such reactions. An example is the fusion of deuterium and tritium nuclei to form $^{4}_{2}\text{He}$ and a neutron:

$$^{2}_{1}\text{H} + {}^{3}_{1}\text{H} \rightarrow {}^{4}_{2}\text{He} + {}^{1}_{0}\text{n} \qquad \Delta E = -1.7 \times 10^{9} \text{ kJ/mol}$$

Fusion reactions provide the energy of our sun and other stars. Scientists have long dreamed of being able to harness fusion to provide power. To do so, a temperature of $10^{6}$ to $10^{7}$ K, like that in the interior of the sun, would be required to bring the positively charged nuclei together with enough energy to overcome nuclear repulsions. At the very high temperatures needed for a fusion reaction, matter does not exist as atoms or molecules; instead, matter is in the form of a *plasma* made up of unbound nuclei and electrons.

Three critical requirements must be met before nuclear fusion could represent a viable energy source. First, the temperature must be high enough for fusion to occur. The fusion of deuterium and tritium, for example, requires a temperature of $10^{7}$ K or more. Second, the plasma must be confined long enough to release a net output of energy. Third, the energy must be recovered in some usable form.

Harnessing a nuclear fusion reaction for a peaceful use has not yet been achieved. Nevertheless, many attractive features encourage continuing research in this field. The hydrogen used as "fuel" is cheap and available in almost unlimited amounts. As a further benefit, most radioisotopes produced by fusion have short half-lives, so they remain a radiation hazard for only a short time.

## 23.8 Radiation Health and Safety

### Units for Measuring Radiation

Several units of measurement are used to describe levels and doses of radioactivity. Generally the units used in the United States are not the same as the SI units of measurement.

In the United States, the degree of radioactivity is often measured in **curies** (Ci). Less commonly used in the United States is the SI unit, the **becquerel** (Bq). Both units measure the number of disintegrations per second; 1 Ci is $3.7 \times 10^{10}$ dps (disintegrations per second), while 1 Bq represents 1 dps. The curie and the becquerel are used to report the amount of radioactivity when multiple kinds of unstable nuclei are decaying and to report amounts necessary for medical purposes.

By itself, the degree of radioactivity does not provide a good measure of the amount of energy in the radiation or the amount of damage that the radiation can cause to living tissue. Two additional kinds of information are necessary. The first is the amount of energy absorbed; the second is the effectiveness of the particular kind of radiation in causing tissue damage. The amount of energy absorbed by living tissue is measured in **rads**. *Rad* is an acronym for "radiation absorbed dose." One rad represents 0.01 J of energy absorbed per kilogram of tissue. Its SI equivalent is the **gray** (Gy); 1 Gy denotes the absorption of 1 J per kilogram of tissue.

Different forms of radiation cause different amounts of biological damage. The amount of damage depends on how strongly a form of radiation interacts with matter. Alpha particles cannot penetrate the body any farther than the outer layer of skin. If $\alpha$ particles are emitted within the body, however, they will cause between 10 and 20 times the amount of damage done by $\gamma$-rays, which can go entirely through a human body without being stopped. In determining the amount of biological damage to living tissue, differences in damaging power are accounted for using a "quality factor." This quality factor has been set at 1 for $\beta$ and $\gamma$ radiation, 5 for low-energy protons and neutrons, and 20 for $\alpha$ particles or high-energy protons and neutrons.

Biological damage is quantified in a unit called the **rem** (an acronym for "roentgen equivalent man"). A dose of radiation in rem is determined by multiplying the energy absorbed in rads by the quality factor for that kind of radiation. The rad and the rem are very large in comparison to normal exposures to radiation, so it is more common to express exposures in millirems (mrem). The SI equivalent of the rem is the **sievert** (Sv), determined by multiplying the dose in grays by the quality factor.

### Radiation: Doses and Effects

Exposure to a small amount of radiation is unavoidable. Earth is constantly being bombarded with radioactive particles from outer space. There is also some exposure to radioactive elements that occur naturally on earth, including $^{14}C$, $^{40}K$ (a radioactive isotope that occurs naturally in 0.0117% abundance), $^{238}U$, and $^{232}Th$. Radioactive elements in the environment that were created artificially (in the fallout from nuclear bomb tests, for example) also contribute to this exposure. For some people, medical procedures using radioisotopes are a major contributor.

The average dose of background radioactivity to which a person in the United States is exposed is about 200 mrem per year (Table 23.2). Well over half of that amount comes from natural sources over which we have no control. Of the 60–70 mrem per year exposure that comes from artificial sources, nearly 90% is delivered in medical procedures such as x-ray examinations and radiation therapy. Considering the controversy surrounding nuclear power, it is interesting to note that less than 0.5% of the total annual background dose of radiation that the average person receives can be attributed to the nuclear power industry.

● **The Roentgen** The roentgen (R) is an older unit of radiation exposure. It is defined as the amount of x-rays or $\gamma$ radiation that will produce $2.08 \times 10^9$ ions in 1 cm³ of dry air. The roentgen and the rad are similar in size. Wilhelm Roentgen (1845–1923) first produced and detected x radiation. Element 111 has been named roentgenium in his honor.

Table 23.2 **Radiation Exposure of an Individual for One Year from Natural and Artificial Sources**

|  | Millirem/Year | Percentage |
|---|---|---|
| **Natural Sources** | | |
| Cosmic radiation | 50.0 | 25.8 |
| The earth | 47.0 | 24.2 |
| Building materials | 3.0 | 1.5 |
| Inhaled from the air | 5.0 | 2.6 |
| Elements found naturally in human tissue | 21.0 | 10.8 |
| *Subtotal* | **126.0** | **64.9** |
| **Medical Sources** | | |
| Diagnostic x-rays | 50.0 | 25.8 |
| Radiotherapy | 10.0 | 5.2 |
| Internal diagnosis | 1.0 | 0.5 |
| *Subtotal* | **61.0** | **31.5** |
| **Other Artificial Sources** | | |
| Nuclear power industry | 0.85 | 0.4 |
| Luminous watch dials, TV tubes | 2.0 | 1.0 |
| Fallout from nuclear tests | 4.0 | 2.1 |
| *Subtotal* | **6.9** | **3.5** |
| *Total* | **193.9** | **99.9** |

Describing the biological effects of a dose of radiation precisely is not a simple matter. The amount of damage done depends not only on the kind of radiation and the amount of energy absorbed, but also on the particular tissues exposed and the rate at which the dose builds up. A great deal has been learned about the effects of radiation on the human body by studying the survivors of the bombs dropped over Japan in World War II and the workers exposed to radiation from the reactor disaster at Chernobyl. From studies of the health of these survivors, we have learned that the effects of radiation are not generally observable below a single dose of 25 rem. At the other extreme, a single dose of >200 rem will be fatal to about half the population (Table 23.3).

Our information is more accurate when dealing with single, large doses than it is for the effects of chronic, smaller doses of radiation. One current issue of debate in the scientific community is how to judge the effects of multiple smaller doses or long-term exposure (see *A Closer Look: What Is A Safe Exposure?*).

Table 23.3 **Effects of a Single Dose of Radiation**

| Dose (rem) | Effect |
|---|---|
| 0–25 | No effect observed |
| 26–50 | Small decrease in white blood cell count |
| 51–100 | Significant decrease in white blood cell count, lesions |
| 101–200 | Loss of hair, nausea |
| 201–500 | Hemorrhaging, ulcers, death in 50% of population |
| 500 | Death |

## What Is a Safe Exposure?

Is the exposure to natural background radiation totally without effect? Can you equate the effect of a single dose and the effect of cumulative, smaller doses that are spread out over a long period of time? The assumption generally made is that no "safe maximum dose," or level below which absolutely no damage will occur, exists. However, the accuracy of this assumption has come into question. These issues are not testable with human subjects, and tests based on animal studies are not completely reliable because of the uncertainty of species-to-species variations.

The model used by government regulators to set exposure limits assumes that the relationship between exposure to radiation and incidence of radiation-induced problems, such as cancer, anemia, and immune system problems, is linear. Under this assumption, if a dose of 2x rem causes damage in 20% of the population, then a dose of x rem will cause damage in 10% of the population. But is this true? Cells do possess mechanisms for repairing damage. Many scientists believe that this self-repair mechanism renders the human body less susceptible to damage from smaller doses of radiation, because the damage will be repaired as part of the normal course of events. They argue that, at extremely low doses of radiation, the self-repair response results in less damage.

The bottom line is that much still remains to be learned in this area. And the stakes are significant.

**The film badge.** These badges, worn by scientists using radioactive materials, are used to monitor cumulative exposure to radiation.

# 23.9 Applications of Nuclear Chemistry

We tend to think about nuclear chemistry in terms of power plants and bombs. In truth, radioactive elements are now used in many areas of science and medicine, and they are of ever-increasing importance to our lives. Because describing all of their uses would take several books, we have selected just a few examples to illustrate the diversity of applications of radioactivity.

## Nuclear Medicine: Medical Imaging

Diagnostic procedures using nuclear chemistry are essential in medical imaging, which entails the creation of images of specific parts of the body. There are three principal components to constructing a radioisotope-based image:

- A radioactive isotope, administered as the element or incorporated into a compound, that concentrates the radioactive isotope in the tissue to be imaged
- A method of detecting the type of radiation involved
- A computer to assemble the information from the detector into a meaningful image

The choice of a radioisotope and the manner in which it is administered are determined by the tissue in question. A compound containing the isotope must be absorbed more by the target tissue than by the rest of the body. Table 23.4 lists radioisotopes that are commonly used in nuclear imaging processes, their half-lives, and

**Table 23.4 Radioisotopes Used in Medical Diagnostic Procedures**

| Radioisotope | Half-Life (h) | Imaging |
|---|---|---|
| $^{99m}Tc$ | 6.0 | Thyroid, brain, kidneys |
| $^{201}Tl$ | 73.0 | Heart |
| $^{123}I$ | 13.2 | Thyroid |
| $^{67}Ga$ | 78.2 | Various tumors and abscesses |
| $^{18}F$ | 1.8 | Brain, sites of metabolic activity |

# Technetium-99m

Technetium was the first new element to be made artificially. One might think that this element would be a chemical rarity, but this is not so: Its importance in medical imaging has brought a great deal of attention to it. Although all the technetium in the world must be synthesized by nuclear reactions, the element is readily available and even inexpensive; its price is about $60 per gram, only a bit more than gold (in 2010).

Technetium-99m is formed when molybdenum-99 decays by $\beta$ emission. Technetium-99m then decays to its ground state with a half-life of 6.01 hours, giving off a 140-KeV $\gamma$-ray in the process. (Technetium-99 is itself unstable, decaying to stable $^{99}$Ru with a half-life of $2.1 \times 10^5$ years.)

Technetium-99m is produced in hospitals using a molybdenum–technetium generator. Sheathed in lead shielding, the generator contains the artificially synthesized isotope $^{99}$Mo in the form of molybdate ion, $MoO_4^{2-}$, adsorbed on a column of alumina, $Al_2O_3$. The $MoO_4^{2-}$ is continually being converted into the pertechnate ion, $^{99m}TcO_4^-$ by $\beta$ emission. When it is needed, the $^{99m}TcO_4^-$ is washed from the column using a saline solution. Technetium-99m may be used directly as the pertechnate ion or converted into other compounds. The pertechnate ion or radiopharmaceuticals made from it are administered intravenously to the patient. Such small quantities are needed that 1 $\mu$g (microgram) of technetium-99m is sufficient for the average hospital's daily imaging needs.

One use of $^{99m}$Tc is for imaging the thyroid gland. Because $I^-$(aq) and $TcO_4^-$(aq) ions have very similar sizes, the thyroid will (mistakenly) take up $TcO_4^-$(aq) along with iodide ion. This uptake concentrates $^{99m}$Tc in the thyroid and allows a physician to obtain images such as the one shown in the accompanying Figure.

**(a)** Healthy human thyroid gland.

**(b)** Thyroid gland showing effect of hyperthyroidism.

**Thyroid imaging.** Technetium-99m concentrates in sites of high activity. Images of this gland, which is located at the base of the neck, were obtained by recording $\gamma$-ray emission after the patient was given radioactive technetium-99m. Current technology creates a computer color-enhanced scan.

**Technetium-99m generator.** A technician is handling a sample containing the $MoO_4^{2-}$ that will be converted to $^{99m}TcO_4^-$.

the tissues they are used to image. All of the isotopes in Table 23.4 are $\gamma$ emitters; $\gamma$ radiation is preferred for imaging because it is less damaging to the body in small doses than either $\alpha$ or $\beta$ radiation.

Technetium-99m is used in more than 85% of the diagnostic scans done in hospitals each year (see *A Closer Look: Technetium-99m*. The "m" stands for *metastable*, a term used to identify an unstable state that exists for a finite period of time. Recall that atoms in excited electronic states emit visible, infrared, and ultraviolet radiation (◄ Chapter 6). Similarly, a nucleus in an excited state gives up its excess energy, but in this case a much higher energy is involved, and the emission occurs as $\gamma$ radiation. The $\gamma$-rays given off by $^{99m}$Tc are detected to produce the image (Figure 23.12).

Another medical imaging technique based on nuclear chemistry is *positron emission tomography* (PET). In PET, an isotope that decays by positron emission is incorporated into a carrier compound and given to the patient. When emitted, the positron travels no more than a few millimeters before undergoing matter–antimatter annihilation.

$$^{0}_{+1}\beta + {}^{0}_{-1}e \rightarrow 2\gamma$$

The two emitted $\gamma$-rays travel in opposite directions. By determining where high numbers of $\gamma$-rays are being emitted, one can construct a map showing where the positron emitter is located in the body.

An isotope often used in PET is $^{15}O$. A patient is given gaseous $O_2$ that contains $^{15}O$. This isotope travels throughout the body in the bloodstream, allowing images of the brain and bloodstream to be obtained (Figure 23.13). Because positron emitters are typically very short-lived, PET facilities must be located near a cyclotron where the radioactive nuclei are prepared and then immediately incorporated into a carrier compound.

## Nuclear Medicine: Radiation Therapy

To treat most cancers, it is necessary to use radiation that can penetrate the body to the location of the tumor. Gamma radiation from a cobalt-60 source is commonly used. Unfortunately, the penetrating ability of γ-rays makes it virtually impossible to destroy diseased tissue without also damaging healthy tissue in the process. Nevertheless, this technique is a regularly sanctioned procedure, and its successes are well known.

## Analytical Methods: The Use of Radioactive Isotopes as Tracers

Radioactive isotopes can be used to help determine the fate of compounds in the body or in the environment. These studies begin with a compound that contains a radioactive isotope of one of its component elements. In biology, for example, scientists can use radioactive isotopes to measure the uptake of nutrients. Plants take up phosphorus-containing compounds from the soil through their roots. By adding a small amount of radioactive $^{32}P$, a β emitter with a half-life of 14.3 days, to fertilizer and then measuring the rate at which the radioactivity appears in the leaves, plant biologists can determine the rate at which phosphorus is taken up. The outcome can assist scientists in identifying hybrid strains of plants that can absorb phosphorus quickly, resulting in faster-maturing crops, better yields per acre, and more food or fiber at less expense.

To measure pesticide levels, a pesticide can be tagged with a radioisotope and then applied to a test field. By counting the disintegrations of the radioactive tracer, information can be obtained about how much pesticide accumulates in the soil, is taken up by the plant, and is carried off in runoff surface water. After these tests are completed, the radioactive isotope decays to harmless levels in a few days or a few weeks because of the short half-lives of the isotopes used.

## Analytical Methods: Isotope Dilution

Imagine, for the moment, that you wanted to estimate the volume of blood in an animal subject. How might you do this? Obviously, draining the blood and measuring its volume in volumetric glassware is not a desirable option.

One technique uses a method called *isotope dilution*. In this process, a small amount of radioactive isotope is injected into the bloodstream. After a period of time to allow the isotope to become distributed throughout the body, a blood sample is taken and its radioactivity measured. The calculation used to determine the total blood volume is illustrated in the next example.

## EXAMPLE 23.9    Analysis Using Radioisotopes

**Problem**  A 1.00-mL solution containing 0.240 μCi of tritium is injected into a dog's bloodstream. After a period of time to allow the isotope to be dispersed, a 1.00-mL sample of blood is drawn. The radioactivity of this sample is found to be $4.3 \times 10^{-4}$ μCi/mL. What is the total volume of blood in the dog?

**What Do You Know?**  You know the concentration (activity) and volume of a concentrated solution and you then measure the concentration of the dilute solution. The unknown is the volume of the dilute solution.

**Strategy**  In this problem, we relate the activity of the sample (in Ci) to the amount of the radioisotope present. The total amount of solute is 0.240 μCi, and the concentration (measured on the small sample of blood) is $4.3 \times 10^{-4}$ μCi/mL. The unknown is the total volume of blood, *V*.

**FIGURE 23.12  Heart imaging with technetium-99m.**  The radioactive element technetium-99m, a γ emitter, is injected into a patient's vein in the form of the pertechnetate ion ($TcO_4^-$) or as a complex ion with an organic ligand. A series of scans of the γ emissions of the isotope are made while the patient is resting and then again after strenuous exercise. Bright areas in the scans indicate that the isotope is binding to the tissue in that area. The scans in this figure show a normal heart function for one of the authors of this book.

**FIGURE 23.13  PET scans of the brain.**  These scans show the left side of the brain; *red* indicates an area of highest activity. *(upper left) Sight* activates the visual area in the occipital cortex at the back of the brain. *(upper right) Hearing* activates the auditory area in the superior temporal cortex of the brain. *(lower left) Speaking* activates the speech centers in the insula and motor cortex. *(lower right) Thinking* about verbs, and speaking them, generates high activity, including in the hearing, speaking, temporal, and parietal areas.

● **Boron Neutron Capture Therapy (BNCT).** To avoid the side effects associated with more traditional forms of radiation therapy, BNCT is an experimental treatment that has been explored in the last 10 to 15 years. BNCT is unusual in that boron-10, the isotope of boron used as part of the treatment, is not radioactive. This isotope is highly effective in capturing neutrons, however: 2500 times better than boron-11 and eight times better than uranium-235. When the nucleus of a boron-10 atom captures a neutron, the resulting boron-11 nucleus has so much energy that it fragments to form an $\alpha$ particle and a lithium-7 atom. Although the $\alpha$ particles do a great deal of damage, because their penetrating power is so low, the damage remains confined to an area not much larger than one or two cells in diameter.

**Solution** The blood contains a total of 0.240 $\mu$Ci of radioactive material. Exactly 1.00 mL containing this amount was injected. After dilution in the bloodstream, 1.00 mL of blood, representative of the total volume $V$, is found to have an activity of $4.3 \times 10^{-4}$ $\mu$Ci/mL.

$$(0.240 \ \mu\text{Ci/mL})(1.00 \ \text{mL}) = (4.3 \times 10^{-4} \ \mu\text{Ci/mL})(V)$$

$$V = 560 \ \text{mL}$$

**Think about Your Answer** This is solved as a classic dilution problem, by equating $C_{dil} \times V_{dil} = C_{conc} \times V_{conc}$

**Check Your Understanding**

To measure the solubility for $PbCrO_4$ you mix a small amount of a lead(II) salt having radioactive $^{212}Pb$ with a lead salt containing 0.0100 g of lead. To this mixture you add enough $K_2CrO_4$ to completely precipitate the lead(II) ions as $PbCrO_4$. The supernatant solution still contains a trace of lead, of course, and when you evaporate 10.00 mL of this solution to solid $PbCrO_4$, you find a radioactivity that is $4.17 \times 10^{-5}$ of what it is for the pure $^{212}Pb$ salt. Calculate the solubility of $PbCrO_4$ in mol/L. (Adapted from C. E. Housecraft and A. G. Sharpe, *Inorganic Chemistry*, Pearson, 3rd edition, 2008, p. 84.)

## Space Science: Neutron Activation Analysis and the Moon Rocks

The first manned space mission to the moon brought back a number of samples of soil and rock—a treasure trove for scientists. One of their first tasks was to analyze these samples to determine their identity and composition. Most analytical methods require chemical reactions using at least a small amount of material; however, this was not a desirable option, considering that the moon rocks were at the time the most valuable rocks in the world.

A few scientists got a chance to work on this unique project, and one of the analytical tools they used was **neutron activation analysis**. In this nondestructive process, a sample is irradiated with neutrons. Most isotopes add a neutron to form a new isotope that is one mass unit higher in an excited nuclear state. When the nucleus decays to its ground state, it emits a $\gamma$-ray. The energy of the $\gamma$-ray identifies the element, and the number of $\gamma$-rays can be counted to determine the amount of the element in the sample. Using neutron activation analysis, it is possible to analyze for a number of elements in a single experiment (Table 23.5).

Neutron activation analysis has many other uses. This analytical procedure yields a kind of fingerprint that can be used to identify a substance. For example, this technique has been applied in determining whether an art work is real or fraudulent. Analysis of the pigments in paints on a painting can be carried out without damaging the painting to determine whether the composition resembles modern paints or paints used hundreds of years ago.

## Food Science: Food Irradiation

Refrigeration, canning, and chemical additives provide significant protection in terms of food preservation, but in some parts of the world these procedures are unavailable, and stored-food spoilage may claim as much as 50% of the food crop. Irradiation with $\gamma$-rays from sources such as $^{60}Co$ and $^{137}Cs$ is an option for prolonging the shelf life of foods. Relatively low levels of radiation may retard the growth of organisms, such as bacteria, molds, and yeasts, that can cause food spoilage. After irradiation, milk in a sealed container has a minimum shelf life of 3 months without refrigeration. Chicken normally has a 3-day refrigerated shelf life; after irradiation, it may have a 3-week refrigerated shelf life.

Higher levels of radiation, in the 1- to 5-Mrad (1 Mrad = $1 \times 10^6$ rad) range, will kill every living organism. Foods irradiated at these levels will keep indefinitely when sealed in plastic or aluminum-foil packages. Ham, beef, turkey, and corned beef

**Table 23.5 Rare Earth Analysis of Moon Rock Sample 10022 (Fine-Grain Igneous Rock)**

| Element | Concentration (ppm) |
|---------|---------------------|
| La | 26.4 |
| Ce | 68 |
| Nd | 66 |
| Sm | 21.2 |
| Eu | 2.04 |
| Gd | 25 |
| Tb | 4.7 |
| Dy | 31.2 |
| Ho | 5.5 |
| Er | 16 |
| Yb | 17.7 |
| Lu | 2.55 |

*Source:* L. A. Haskin, P. A, Helmke, and R. O. Allen: *Science,* Vol. 167, p. 487, 1970. The concentrations of rare earths in moon rocks were quite similar to the values in terrestrial rocks except that the europium concentration is much depleted. The January 30, 1970, issue of *Science* was devoted to analysis of moon rocks.

## CASE STUDY

# Nuclear Medicine and Hyperthyroidism

The primary function of the thyroid gland, located in your neck, is the production of thyroxine (3,5,3′,5′-tetraiodothyronine) and 3,5,3′-triiodothyronine. These chemical compounds are hormones that help to regulate the rate of metabolism (page 504), a term that refers to all of the chemical reactions that take place in the body. In particular, the thyroid hormones play an important role in the processes that release energy from food.

Abnormally low levels of thyroxine result in a condition known as *hypothyroidism*. Its symptoms include lethargy and feeling cold much of the time. The remedy for this condition is medication, consisting of thyroxine pills. The opposite condition, hyperthyroidism, also occurs in some people. In this condition, the body produces too much of the hormone. Hyperthyroidism is diagnosed by symptoms such as nervousness, heat intolerance, increased appetite, and muscle weakness and fatigue when blood sugar is too rapidly depleted. The standard remedy for hyperthyroidism is to destroy part of the thyroid gland, and one way to do so is to use a compound containing radioactive iodine-123 or iodine-131.

To understand this procedure, you need to know something about iodine in the body. Iodine is an essential element. Some diets provide iodine naturally (seaweed, for example, is a good source of iodine), but in the Western world most iodine taken up by the body comes from iodized salt, NaCl containing a few percent of NaI. An adult man or woman of average size should take in about 150 μg (micrograms) of iodine

**Thyroxine.** The hormone 3,5,3′,5′-tetraiodothyronine (thyroxine) exerts a stimulating effect on metabolism.

(1 μg $= 10^{-6}$ g) in the daily diet. In the body, iodide ion is transported to the thyroid, where it serves as one of the raw materials in making thyroxine.

The fact that iodine concentrates in the thyroid tissue is essential to the procedure for using radioiodine therapy as a treatment for hyperthyroidism. Typically, an aqueous NaI solution is used in which a small fraction of iodide is the radioactive isotope iodine-131 or iodine-123, and the rest is nonradioactive iodine-127. The radioactivity destroys thyroid tissue, resulting in a decrease in thyroid activity.

**Questions:**

1. $^{131}$I decays by beta emission. What is the product of this decay? Write a balanced nuclear equation for this process.
2. The half-life of $^{131}$I is 8.04 days, and that of $^{123}$I is 13.3 hours. If you begin with an equal number of moles of each isotope, at the end of 7 days what are their relative amounts?

**Answers to these questions are available in Appendix N.**

---

sterilized by radiation have been used on many Space Shuttle flights, for example. An astronaut said, "The beautiful thing was that it didn't disturb the taste, which made the meals much better than the freeze-dried and other types of foods we had."

These procedures are not without their opponents, and the public has not fully embraced irradiation of foods. An interesting argument favoring this technique is that radiation is less harmful than other methodologies for food preservation. This type of sterilization offers greater safety to food workers because it lessens chances of exposure to harmful chemicals, and it protects the environment by avoiding contamination of water supplies with toxic chemicals.

Food irradiation is commonly used in European countries, Canada, and Mexico. Its use in the United States is currently regulated by the U.S. Food and Drug Administration (FDA) and Department of Agriculture (USDA). In 1997, the FDA approved the irradiation of refrigerated and frozen uncooked meat to control pathogens and extend shelf-life, and in 2000 the USDA approved the irradiation of eggs to control *Salmonella* infection.

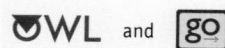 and **go Chemistry**

## CHAPTER GOALS REVISITED

*Now that you have studied this chapter, you should ask whether you have met the chapter goals. In particular, you should be able to:*

### Identify radioactive elements, and describe natural and artificial nuclear reactions

a.  Identify $\alpha$, $\beta$, and $\gamma$ radiation, the three major types of radiation in natural radioactive decay (Section 23.1), and write balanced equations for nuclear reactions (Section 23.2). **Study Questions: 11–16, 32, 41.**

b.  Predict whether a radioactive isotope will decay by $\alpha$ or $\beta$ emission, or by positron emission or electron capture (Sections 23.2 and 23.3). **Study Questions: 17–22.**

### Calculate the binding energy and binding energy per nucleon for a particular isotope

a.  Understand how binding energy per nucleon is defined (Section 23.3) and recognize the significance of a graph of binding energy per nucleon versus mass number (Section 23.3). **Study Questions: 23–28, 52.**

### Understand rates of radioactive decay

a.  Understand and use mathematical equations that characterize the radioactive decay process (Section 23.4). **Study Questions: 29–38, 47, 50, 54, 58.**

### Understand artificial nuclear reactions

a.  Describe nuclear chain reactions, nuclear fission, and nuclear fusion (Sections 23.6 and 23.7). **Study Questions: 39–46.**

### Understand issues of health and safety with respect to radioactivity

a.  Describe the units used to measure intensity, and understand how they pertain to health issues (Sections 23.8 and 23.9).

### Be aware of some uses of radioactive isotopes in science and medicine

## Key Equations

**Equation 23.1 (page 1068):** The equation relating interconversion of mass ($m$) and energy ($E$). This equation is applied in the calculation of binding energy ($E_b$) for nuclei.

$$E_b = (\Delta m)c^2$$

**Equation 23.2 (page 1071):** The activity of a radioactive sample ($A$) is proportional to the number of radioactive atoms ($N$).

$$A \propto N$$

**Equation 23.3 (page 1071):** The change in the number of radioactive elements with time is equal to the product of the rate constant ($k$, decay constant) and number of atoms present ($N$).

$$\Delta N/\Delta t = -kN$$

**Equation 23.4 (page 1072):** The rate law for nuclear decay based on number of radioactive atoms initially present ($N_0$) and the number $N$ after time $t$.

$$\ln(N/N_0) = -kt$$

**Equation 23.5 (page 1072):** The rate law for nuclear decay based on the measured activity of a sample ($A$).

$$\ln(A/A_0) = -kt$$

**Equation 23.6 (page 1072):** The relationship between the half-life and the rate constant for a nuclear decay process.

$$t_{1/2} = 0.693/k$$

# Study Questions

⭘WL Interactive versions of these questions are assignable in OWL.

▲ denotes challenging questions.

Blue-numbered questions have answers in Appendix R and fully worked solutions in the *Student Solutions Manual*.

## Practicing Skills

### Important Concepts

1. Some important discoveries in scientific history that contributed to the development of nuclear chemistry are listed below. Briefly, describe each discovery, identify prominent scientists who contributed to it, and comment on the significance of the discovery to the development of this field.
   (a) 1896, the discovery of radioactivity
   (b) 1898, the identification of radium and polonium
   (c) 1919, the first artificial nuclear reaction
   (d) 1932, $(n, \gamma)$ reactions
   (e) 1939, fission reactions

2. In Chapter 3, the law of conservation of mass was introduced as an important principle in chemistry. The discovery of nuclear reactions forced scientists to modify this law. Explain why, and give an example illustrating that mass is not conserved in a nuclear reaction.

3. A graph of binding energy per nucleon is shown in Figure 23.4. Explain how the data used to construct this graph were obtained.

4. How is Figure 23.3 used to predict the type of decomposition for unstable (radioactive) isotopes?

5. Outline how nuclear reactions are carried out in the laboratory. Describe the artificial nuclear reactions used to make an element with an atomic number greater than 92.

6. What mathematical equations define the rates of decay for radioactive elements?

7. Explain how carbon-14 is used to estimate the ages of archeological artifacts. What are the limitations for use of this technique?

8. Describe how the concept of half-life for nuclear decay is used.

9. What is a radioactive decay series? Explain why radium and polonium are found in uranium ores.

10. The interaction of radiation with matter has both positive and negative consequences. Discuss briefly the hazards of radiation and the way that radiation can be used in medicine.

## Nuclear Reactions

*(See Section 23.2 and Examples 23.1 and 23.2.)*

11. Complete the following nuclear equations. Write the mass number and atomic number for the remaining particle, as well as its symbol.
    (a) $^{54}_{26}\text{Fe} + ^{4}_{2}\text{He} \longrightarrow 2\,^{1}_{0}\text{n} + ?$
    (b) $^{27}_{13}\text{Al} + ^{4}_{2}\text{He} \longrightarrow ^{30}_{15}\text{P} + ?$
    (c) $^{32}_{16}\text{S} + ^{1}_{0}\text{n} \longrightarrow ^{1}_{1}\text{H} + ?$
    (d) $^{96}_{42}\text{Mo} + ^{2}_{1}\text{H} \longrightarrow ^{1}_{0}\text{n} + ?$
    (e) $^{98}_{42}\text{Mo} + ^{1}_{0}\text{n} \longrightarrow ^{99}_{43}\text{Tc} + ?$
    (f) $^{18}_{9}\text{F} \longrightarrow ^{18}_{8}\text{O} + ?$

12. Complete the following nuclear equations. Write the mass number, atomic number, and symbol for the remaining particle.
    (a) $^{9}_{4}\text{Be} + ? \longrightarrow ^{6}_{3}\text{Li} + ^{4}_{2}\text{He}$
    (b) $? + ^{1}_{0}\text{n} \longrightarrow ^{24}_{11}\text{Na} + ^{4}_{2}\text{He}$
    (c) $^{40}_{20}\text{Ca} + ? \longrightarrow ^{40}_{19}\text{K} + ^{1}_{1}\text{H}$
    (d) $^{241}_{95}\text{Am} + ^{4}_{2}\text{He} \longrightarrow ^{243}_{97}\text{Bk} + ?$
    (e) $^{246}_{96}\text{Cm} + ^{12}_{6}\text{C} \longrightarrow 4\,^{1}_{0}\text{n} + ?$
    (f) $^{238}_{92}\text{U} + ? \longrightarrow ^{249}_{100}\text{Fm} + 5\,^{1}_{0}\text{n}$

13. Complete the following nuclear equations. Write the mass number, atomic number, and symbol for the remaining particle.
    (a) $^{111}_{47}\text{Ag} \longrightarrow ^{111}_{48}\text{Cd} + ?$
    (b) $^{87}_{36}\text{Kr} \longrightarrow ^{0}_{-1}\beta + ?$
    (c) $^{231}_{91}\text{Pa} \longrightarrow ^{227}_{89}\text{Ac} + ?$
    (d) $^{230}_{90}\text{Th} \longrightarrow ^{4}_{2}\text{He} + ?$
    (e) $^{82}_{35}\text{Br} \longrightarrow ^{82}_{36}\text{Kr} + ?$
    (f) $? \longrightarrow ^{24}_{12}\text{Mg} + ^{0}_{-1}\beta$

14. Complete the following nuclear equations. Write the mass number, atomic number, and symbol for the remaining particle.
    (a) $^{19}_{10}\text{Ne} \longrightarrow ^{0}_{+1}\beta + ?$
    (b) $^{59}_{26}\text{Fe} \longrightarrow ^{0}_{-1}\beta + ?$
    (c) $^{40}_{19}\text{K} \longrightarrow ^{0}_{-1}\beta + ?$
    (d) $^{37}_{18}\text{Ar} + ^{0}_{-1}\text{e}$ (electron capture) $\longrightarrow ?$
    (e) $^{55}_{26}\text{Fe} + ^{0}_{-1}\text{e}$ (electron capture) $\longrightarrow ?$
    (f) $^{26}_{13}\text{Al} \longrightarrow ^{25}_{12}\text{Mg} + ?$

15. The uranium-235 radioactive decay series, beginning with $^{235}_{92}\text{U}$ and ending with $^{207}_{82}\text{Pb}$, occurs in the following sequence: $\alpha, \beta, \alpha, \beta, \alpha, \alpha, \alpha, \alpha, \beta, \beta, \alpha$. Write an equation for each step in this series.

16. The thorium-232 radioactive decay series, beginning with $^{232}_{90}\text{Th}$ and ending with $^{208}_{82}\text{Pb}$, occurs in the following sequence: $\alpha, \beta, \beta, \alpha, \alpha, \alpha, \alpha, \beta, \beta, \alpha$. Write an equation for each step in this series.

## Nuclear Stability and Nuclear Decay
*(See Section 23.3 and Examples 23.3 and 23.4.)*

17. What particle is emitted in the following nuclear reactions? Write an equation for each reaction.
    (a) Gold-198 decays to mercury-198.
    (b) Radon-222 decays to polonium-218.
    (c) Cesium-137 decays to barium-137.
    (d) Indium-110 decays to cadmium-110.

18. What is the product of the following nuclear decay processes? Write an equation for each process.
    (a) Gallium-67 decays by electron capture.
    (b) Potassium-38 decays with positron emission.
    (c) Technetium-99m decays with $\gamma$ emission.
    (d) Manganese-56 decays by $\beta$ emission.

19. Predict the probable mode of decay for each of the following radioactive isotopes, and write an equation to show the products of decay.
    (a) bromine-80          (c) cobalt-61
    (b) californium-240     (d) carbon-11

20. Predict the probable mode of decay for each of the following radioactive isotopes, and write an equation to show the products of decay.
    (a) manganese-54        (c) silver-110
    (b) americium-241       (d) mercury-197m

21. (a) Which of the following nuclei decay by $_{-1}^{0}\beta$ decay?

    $$^{3}\text{H} \quad ^{16}\text{O} \quad ^{20}\text{F} \quad ^{13}\text{N}$$

    (b) Which of the following nuclei decays by $_{+1}^{0}\beta$ decay?

    $$^{238}\text{U} \quad ^{19}\text{F} \quad ^{22}\text{Na} \quad ^{24}\text{Na}$$

22. (a) Which of the following nuclei decay by $_{-1}^{0}\beta$ decay?

    $$^{1}\text{H} \quad ^{23}\text{Mg} \quad ^{32}\text{P} \quad ^{20}\text{Ne}$$

    (b) Which of the following nuclei decay by $_{+1}^{0}\beta$ decay?

    $$^{235}\text{U} \quad ^{35}\text{Cl} \quad ^{38}\text{K} \quad ^{24}\text{Na}$$

23. Boron has two stable isotopes, $^{10}\text{B}$ and $^{11}\text{B}$. Calculate the binding energies per mole of nucleons of these two nuclei. The required masses (in g/mol) are $_{1}^{1}\text{H} = 1.00783$, $_{0}^{1}\text{n} = 1.00867$, $_{5}^{10}\text{B} = 10.01294$, and $_{5}^{11}\text{B} = 11.00931$.

24. Calculate the binding energy in kilojoules per mole of nucleons of P for the formation of $^{30}\text{P}$ and $^{31}\text{P}$. The required masses (in g/mol) are $_{1}^{1}\text{H} = 1.00783$, $_{0}^{1}\text{n} = 1.00867$, $_{15}^{30}\text{P} = 29.97832$, and $_{15}^{31}\text{P} = 30.97376$.

25. Calculate the binding energy per mole of nucleons for calcium-40, and compare your result with the value in Figure 23.4. Masses needed for this calculation are (in g/mol) $_{1}^{1}\text{H} = 1.00783$, $_{0}^{1}\text{n} = 1.00867$, and $_{20}^{40}\text{Ca} = 39.96259$.

26. Calculate the binding energy per mole of nucleons for iron-56. Masses needed for this calculation (in g/mol) are $_{1}^{1}\text{H} = 1.00783$, $_{0}^{1}\text{n} = 1.00867$, and $_{26}^{56}\text{Fe} = 55.9349$. Compare the result of your calculation to the value for iron-56 in the graph in Figure 23.4.

27. Calculate the binding energy per mole of nucleons for $_{8}^{16}\text{O}$. Masses needed for this calculation are $_{1}^{1}\text{H} = 1.00783$, $_{0}^{1}\text{n} = 1.00867$, and $_{8}^{16}\text{O} = 15.99492$.

28. Calculate the binding energy per mole of nucleons for nitrogen-14. The mass of nitrogen-14 is 14.003074.

## Rates of Radioactive Decay
*(See Section 23.4 and Examples 23.5–23.7.)*

29. Copper(II) acetate containing $^{64}\text{Cu}$ is used to study brain tumors. This isotope has a half-life of 12.7 hours. If you begin with 25.0 $\mu$g of $^{64}\text{Cu}$, what mass remains after 63.5 hours?

30. Gold-198 is used in the diagnosis of liver problems. The half-life of $^{198}\text{Au}$ is 2.69 days. If you begin with 2.8 $\mu$g of this gold isotope, what mass remains after 10.8 days?

31. Iodine-131 is used to treat thyroid cancer.
    (a) The isotope decays by $\beta$-particle emission. Write a balanced equation for this process.
    (b) Iodine-131 has a half-life of 8.04 days. If you begin with 2.4 $\mu$g of radioactive $^{131}\text{I}$, what mass remains after 40.2 days?

32. Phosphorus-32 is used in the form of $\text{Na}_2\text{HPO}_4$ in the treatment of chronic myeloid leukemia, among other things.
    (a) The isotope decays by $\beta$-particle emission. Write a balanced equation for this process.
    (b) The half-life of $^{32}\text{P}$ is 14.3 days. If you begin with 4.8 $\mu$g of radioactive $^{32}\text{P}$ in the form of $\text{Na}_2\text{HPO}_4$, what mass remains after 28.6 days (about one month)?

33. Gallium-67 ($t_{1/2} = 78.25$ hours) is used in the medical diagnosis of certain kinds of tumors. If you ingest a compound containing 0.015 mg of this isotope, what mass (in milligrams) remains in your body after 13 days? (Assume none is excreted.)

34. Iodine-131 ($t_{1/2} = 8.04$ days), a $\beta$ emitter, is used to treat thyroid cancer.
    (a) Write an equation for the decomposition of $^{131}\text{I}$.
    (b) If you ingest a sample of NaI containing $^{131}\text{I}$, how much time is required for the activity to decrease to 35.0% of its original value?

35. Radon has been the focus of much attention recently because it is often found in homes. Radon-222 emits $\alpha$ particles and has a half-life of 3.82 days.
    (a) Write a balanced equation to show this process.
    (b) How long does it take for a sample of $^{222}\text{Rn}$ to decrease to 20.0% of its original activity?

36. Strontium-90 is a hazardous radioactive isotope that resulted from atmospheric testing of nuclear weapons. A sample of strontium carbonate containing $^{90}\text{Sr}$ is found to have an activity of $1.0 \times 10^3$ dpm. One year later, the activity of this sample is 975 dpm.
    (a) Calculate the half-life of strontium-90 from this information.
    (b) How long will it take for the activity of this sample to drop to 1.0% of the initial value?

37. Radioactive cobalt-60 is used extensively in nuclear medicine as a $\gamma$-ray source. It is made by a neutron capture reaction from cobalt-59 and is a $\beta$ emitter; $\beta$ emission is accompanied by strong $\gamma$ radiation. The half-life of cobalt-60 is 5.27 years.
    (a) How long will it take for a cobalt-60 source to decrease to one eighth of its original activity?
    (b) What fraction of the activity of a cobalt-60 source remains after 1.0 year?

**38.** Scandium occurs in nature as a single isotope, scandium-45. Neutron irradiation produces scandium-46, a $\beta$ emitter with a half-life of 83.8 days. If the initial activity is $7.0 \times 10^4$ dpm, draw a graph showing disintegrations per minute as a function of time during a period of 1 year.

## Nuclear Reactions

*(See Section 23.5 and Example 23.9.)*

**39.** Americium-240 is made by bombarding plutonium-239 with $\alpha$ particles. In addition to $^{240}$Am, the products are a proton and two neutrons. Write a balanced equation for this process.

**40.** There are two isotopes of americium, both with half-lives sufficiently long to allow the handling of large quantities. Americium-241, with a half-life of 432 years, is an $\alpha$ emitter. It is used in smoke detectors. The isotope is formed from $^{239}$Pu by absorption of two neutrons followed by emission of a $\beta$ particle. Write a balanced equation for this process.

**41.** The superheavy element $^{287}$Uuq (element 114) was made by firing a beam of $^{48}$Ca ions at $^{242}$Pu. Three neutrons were ejected in the reaction. Write a balanced nuclear equation for the synthesis of $^{287}$Uuq.

**42.** To synthesize the heavier transuranium elements, a nucleus must be bombarded with a relatively large particle. If you know the products are californium-246 and four neutrons, with what particle would you bombard uranium-238 atoms?

**43.** Deuterium nuclei ($^2_1$H) are particularly effective as bombarding particles to carry out nuclear reactions. Complete the following equations:
(a) $^{114}_{48}\text{Cd} + ^2_1\text{H} \longrightarrow ? + ^1_1\text{H}$
(b) $^6_3\text{Li} + ^2_1\text{H} \longrightarrow ? + ^1_0\text{n}$
(c) $^{40}_{20}\text{Ca} + ^2_1\text{H} \longrightarrow ^{38}_{19}\text{K} + ?$
(d) $? + ^2_1\text{H} \longrightarrow ^{65}_{30}\text{Zn} + \gamma$

**44.** Element $^{287}_{114}$Uuq decays by $\alpha$ emission with a half-life of about 5 seconds. Write an equation for this process.

**45.** Boron is an effective absorber of neutrons. When boron-10 is bombarded by neutrons, an $\alpha$ particle is emitted. Write an equation for this nuclear reaction.

**46.** Some of the reactions explored by Ernest Rutherford (page 339) and others are listed below. Identify the unknown species in each reaction.
(a) $^{14}_7\text{N} + ^4_2\text{He} \longrightarrow ^{17}_8\text{O} + ?$
(b) $^9_4\text{Be} + ^4_2\text{He} \longrightarrow ? + ^1_0\text{n}$
(c) $? + ^4_2\text{He} \longrightarrow ^{30}_{15}\text{P} + ^1_0\text{n}$
(d) $^{239}_{94}\text{Pu} + ^4_2\text{He} \longrightarrow ? + ^1_0\text{n}$

## General Questions

*These questions are not designated as to type or location in the chapter. They may combine several concepts.*

**47.** ▲ A technique to date geological samples uses rubidium-87, a long-lived radioactive isotope of rubidium ($t_{1/2} = 4.8 \times 10^{10}$ years). Rubidium-87 decays by $\beta$ emission to strontium-87. If rubidium-87 is part of a rock or mineral, then strontium-87 will remain trapped within the crystalline structure of the rock. The age of the rock dates back to the time when the rock solidified. Chemical analysis of the rock gives the amounts of $^{87}$Rb and $^{87}$Sr. From these data, the fraction of $^{87}$Rb that remains can be calculated. Suppose analysis of a stony meteorite determined that 1.8 mmol of $^{87}$Rb and 1.6 mmol of $^{87}$Sr (the portion of $^{87}$Sr formed by decomposition of $^{87}$Rb) were present. Estimate the age of the meteorite. (*Hint:* The amount of $^{87}$Rb at $t_0$ is moles $^{87}$Rb + moles $^{87}$Sr.)

**48.** Tritium, $^3_1$H, is one of the nuclei used in fusion reactions. This isotope is radioactive, with a half-life of 12.3 years. Like carbon-14, tritium is formed in the upper atmosphere from cosmic radiation, and it is found in trace amounts on earth. To obtain the amounts required for a fusion reaction, however, it must be made via a nuclear reaction. The reaction of $^6_3$Li with a neutron produces tritium and an $\alpha$ particle. Write an equation for this nuclear reaction.

**49.** Phosphorus occurs in nature as a single isotope, phosphorus-31. Neutron irradiation of phosphorus-31 produces phosphorus-32, a $\beta$ emitter with a half-life of 14.28 days. Assume you have a sample containing phosphorus-32 that has a rate of decay of $3.2 \times 10^6$ dpm. Draw a graph showing disintegrations per minute as a function of time during a period of 1 year.

**50.** In June 1972, natural fission reactors, which operated billions of years ago, were discovered in Oklo, Gabon (page 1058). At present, natural uranium contains 0.72% $^{235}$U. How many years ago did natural uranium contain 3.0% $^{235}$U, the amount needed to sustain a natural reactor? ($t_{1/2}$ for $^{235}$U is $7.04 \times 10^8$ years.)

**51.** If a shortage in worldwide supplies of fissionable uranium arose, it would be possible to use other fissionable nuclei. Plutonium, one such fuel, can be made in "breeder" reactors that manufacture more fuel than they consume. The sequence of reactions by which plutonium is made is as follows:
(a) A $^{238}$U nucleus undergoes an (n, $\gamma$) reaction to produce $^{239}$U.
(b) $^{239}$U decays by $\beta$ emission ($t_{1/2} = 23.5$ min) to give an isotope of neptunium.
(c) This neptunium isotope decays by $\beta$ emission to give a plutonium isotope.
(d) The plutonium isotope is fissionable. On collision of one of these plutonium isotopes with a neutron, fission occurs, with at least two neutrons and two other nuclei as products.
Write an equation for each of the nuclear reactions.

**52.** When a neutron is captured by an atomic nucleus, energy is released as $\gamma$ radiation. This energy can be calculated based on the change in mass in converting reactants to products.

For the nuclear reaction $^6_3\text{Li} + ^1_0\text{n} \longrightarrow ^7_3\text{Li} + \gamma$:

(a) Calculate the energy evolved in this reaction (per atom). Masses needed (in g/mol) are $^6_3$Li = 6.01512, $^1_0$n = 1.00867, and $^7_3$Li = 7.01600.
(b) Use the answer in part (a) to calculate the wavelength of the $\gamma$-rays emitted in the reaction.

# In the Laboratory

53. A piece of charred bone found in the ruins of a Native American village has a $^{14}C:^{12}C$ ratio that is 72% of the ratio found in living organisms. Calculate the age of the bone fragment. ($t_{1/2}$ for $^{14}C$ is $5.73 \times 10^3$ years.)

54. A sample of wood from a Thracian chariot found in an excavation in Bulgaria has a $^{14}C$ activity of 11.2 dpm/g. Estimate the age of the chariot and the year it was made. ($t_{1/2}$ for $^{14}C$ is $5.73 \times 10^3$ years, and the activity of $^{14}C$ in living material is 14.0 dpm/g.)

55. The isotope of polonium that was most likely isolated by Marie Curie in her pioneering studies is polonium-210. A sample of this element was prepared in a nuclear reaction. Initially, its activity ($\alpha$ emission) was 7840 dpm. Measuring radioactivity over time produced the data below. Determine the half-life of polonium-210.

| Activity (dpm) | Time (days) |
|---|---|
| 7840 | 0 |
| 7570 | 7 |
| 7300 | 14 |
| 5920 | 56 |
| 5470 | 72 |

56. Sodium-23 (in a sample of NaCl) is subjected to neutron bombardment in a nuclear reactor to produce $^{24}Na$. When removed from the reactor, the sample is radioactive, with $\beta$ activity of $2.54 \times 10^4$ dpm. The decrease in radioactivity over time was studied, producing the following data:

| Activity (dpm) | Time (hours) |
|---|---|
| $2.54 \times 10^4$ | 0 |
| $2.42 \times 10^4$ | 1 |
| $2.31 \times 10^4$ | 2 |
| $2.00 \times 10^4$ | 5 |
| $1.60 \times 10^4$ | 10 |
| $1.01 \times 10^4$ | 20 |

(a) Write equations for the neutron capture reaction and for the reaction in which the product of this reaction decays by $\beta$ emission.
(b) Determine the half-life of sodium-24.

57. The age of minerals can sometimes be determined by measuring the amounts of $^{206}Pb$ and $^{238}U$ in a sample. This determination assumes that all of the $^{206}Pb$ in the sample comes from the decay of $^{238}U$. The date obtained identifies when the rock solidified. Assume that the ratio of $^{206}Pb$ to $^{238}U$ in an igneous rock sample is 0.33. Calculate the age of the rock. ($t_{1/2}$ for $^{238}U$ is $4.5 \times 10^9$ years.)

58. The oldest-known fossil found in South Africa has been dated based on the decay of Rb-87.

$$^{87}Rb \longrightarrow {}^{87}Sr + {}^{0}_{-1}\beta \qquad t_{1/2} = 4.8 \times 10^{10} \text{ years}$$

If the ratio of the present quantity of $^{87}Rb$ to the original quantity is 0.951, calculate the age of the fossil.

# Summary and Conceptual Questions

*The following questions may use concepts from this and previous chapters.*

59. The average energy output of a good grade of coal is $2.6 \times 10^7$ kJ/ton. Fission of 1 mol of $^{235}U$ releases $2.1 \times 10^{10}$ kJ. Find the number of tons of coal needed to produce the same energy as 1 lb of $^{235}U$. (See Appendix C for conversion factors.)

60. Collision of an electron and a positron results in formation of two $\gamma$-rays. In the process, their masses are converted completely into energy.
(a) Calculate the energy evolved from the annihilation of an electron and a positron, in kilojoules per mole.
(b) Using Planck's equation (Equation 6.2), determine the frequency of the $\gamma$-rays emitted in this process.

61. The principle underlying the isotope dilution method of analysis can be applied to many kinds of problems. Suppose that you, a marine biologist, want to estimate the number of fish in a lake. You release 1000 tagged fish, and after allowing an adequate amount of time for the fish to disperse evenly in the lake, you catch 5250 fish and find that 27 of them have tags. How many fish are in the lake?

62. ▲ Radioactive isotopes are often used as "tracers" to follow an atom through a chemical reaction. The following is an example of this process: Acetic acid reacts with methanol, $CH_3OH$, by eliminating a molecule of $H_2O$ to form methyl acetate, $CH_3CO_2CH_3$. Explain how you would use the radioactive isotope $^{15}O$ to show whether the oxygen atom in the water product comes from the —OH of the acid or the —OH of the alcohol.

63. ▲ Radioactive decay series begin with a very long-lived isotope. For example, the half-life of $^{238}U$ is $4.5 \times 10^9$ years. Each series is identified by the name of the long-lived parent isotope of highest mass.
(a) The uranium-238 radioactive decay series is sometimes referred to as the $4n + 2$ series because the masses of all 13 members of this series can be expressed by the equation $m = 4n + 2$, where $m$ is the mass number and $n$ is an integer. Explain why the masses are correlated in this way.
(b) Two other radioactive decay series identified in minerals in the earth's crust are the thorium-232 series and the uranium-235 series. Do the masses of the isotopes in these series conform to a simple mathematical equation? If so, identify the equation.
(c) Identify the radioactive decay series to which each of the following isotopes belongs: $^{226}_{88}Ra$, $^{215}_{86}At$, $^{228}_{90}Th$, $^{210}_{83}Bi$.
(d) Evaluation reveals that one series of elements, the $4n + 1$ series, is not present in the earth's crust. Speculate why.

64. ▲ The thorium decay series includes the isotope $^{228}_{90}Th$. Determine the sequence of nuclei on going from $^{232}_{90}Th$ to $^{228}_{90}Th$.

65. ▲ The last unknown element between bismuth and uranium was discovered by Lise Meitner (1878–1968) and Otto Hahn (1879–1968) in 1918. They obtained $^{231}$Pa by chemical extraction of pitchblende, in which its concentration is about 1 ppm (part per million). This isotope, an α emitter, has a half-life of $3.27 \times 10^4$ years.
    (a) Which radioactive decay series (the uranium-235, uranium-238, or thorium-232 series) contains $^{231}$Pa as a member?
    (b) Suggest a possible sequence of nuclear reactions starting with the long-lived isotope that eventually forms this isotope.
    (c) What quantity of ore would be required to isolate 1.0 g of $^{231}$Pa, assuming 100% yield?
    (d) Write an equation for the radioactive decay process for $^{231}$Pa.

66. ▲ You might wonder how it is possible to determine the half-life of long-lived radioactive isotopes such as $^{238}$U. With a half-life of more than $10^9$ years, the radioactivity of a sample of uranium will not measurably change in your lifetime. In fact, you can calculate the half-life using the mathematics governing first-order reactions.

    It can be shown that a 1.0-mg sample of $^{238}$U decays at the rate of 12 α emissions per second. Set up a mathematical equation for the rate of decay, $\Delta N/\Delta t = -kN$, where $N$ is the number of nuclei in the 1.0-mg sample and $\Delta N/\Delta t$ is 12 dps. Solve this equation for the rate constant for this process, and then relate the rate constant to the half-life of the reaction. Carry out this calculation, and compare your result with the literature value, $4.5 \times 10^9$ years.

67. ▲ Marie and Pierre Curie isolated radium and polonium from uranium ore (pitchblende, which contains $^{238}$U and $^{235}$U). Which of the following isotopes of radium and polonium can be found in the uranium ore? (*Hint:* Consider both the isotope half-lives and the decay series starting with $^{238}$U and $^{235}$U.)

| Isotope | Half-Life |
|---|---|
| $^{226}$Ra | 1620 y |
| $^{225}$Ra | 14.8 d |
| $^{228}$Ra | 6.7 y |
| $^{216}$Po | 0.15 s |
| $^{210}$Po | 138.4 d |

68. To measure the volume of the blood system of an animal, the following experiment was done. A 1.0-mL sample of an aqueous solution containing tritium, with an activity of $2.0 \times 10^6$ dps, was injected into the animal's bloodstream. After time was allowed for complete circulatory mixing, a 1.0-mL blood sample was withdrawn and found to have an activity of $1.5 \times 10^4$ dps. What was the volume of the circulatory system? (The half-life of tritium is 12.3 years, so this experiment assumes that only a negligible amount of tritium has decayed in the time of the experiment.)

# Applying Chemical Principles

## The Age of Meteorites

Meteorites have a significant value for collectors, but they are also of scientific interest. Meteorites are generally regarded as some of the oldest materials in the solar system. And this raises the obvious question: How is the age of a meteorite determined? By age, we are referring to the time since the meteor condensed to a solid, locking the components into a solid matrix so they cannot escape. There are a number of methods to measure the age of a meteor, all involving the decay of long-lived radioactive elements.

One dating procedure involves vaporizing samples of the material and measuring the amounts of $^{86}$Sr, $^{87}$Sr, and $^{87}$Rb by mass spectrometry. Both $^{86}$Sr and $^{87}$Sr are stable isotopes. The rubidium isotope, which decays to $^{87}$Sr, has a half-life of $4.88 \times 10^{10}$ years. The amount of $^{87}$Sr measured includes the amount of $^{87}$Sr initially present ($^{87}$Sr°) when the meteorite was formed plus the amount formed by decay of $^{87}$Rb. The $^{86}$Sr remains constant and is used as a check on the original amounts of the other isotopes. The three measured amounts are related by an equation (which can be derived from the first-order rate law):

$$[^{87}Sr/^{86}Sr] = (e^{kt} - 1)\ [^{87}Rb/^{86}Sr] + [^{87}Sr°/^{86}Sr]$$

The equation has the form of the equation of a straight line, $y = mx + b$. Multiple samples are analyzed from each meteorite. The amounts of each isotope may vary between samples, but a graph of $[^{87}Sr/^{86}Sr]$ versus $[^{87}Rb/^{86}Sr]$ will give a straight line with a slope $m = (e^{kt} - 1)$ and a $y$-intercept of $[^{87}Sr°/^{86}Sr]$. The symbol $k$ refers to the rate constant for the radioactive decomposition. This method is called *isochron dating*.

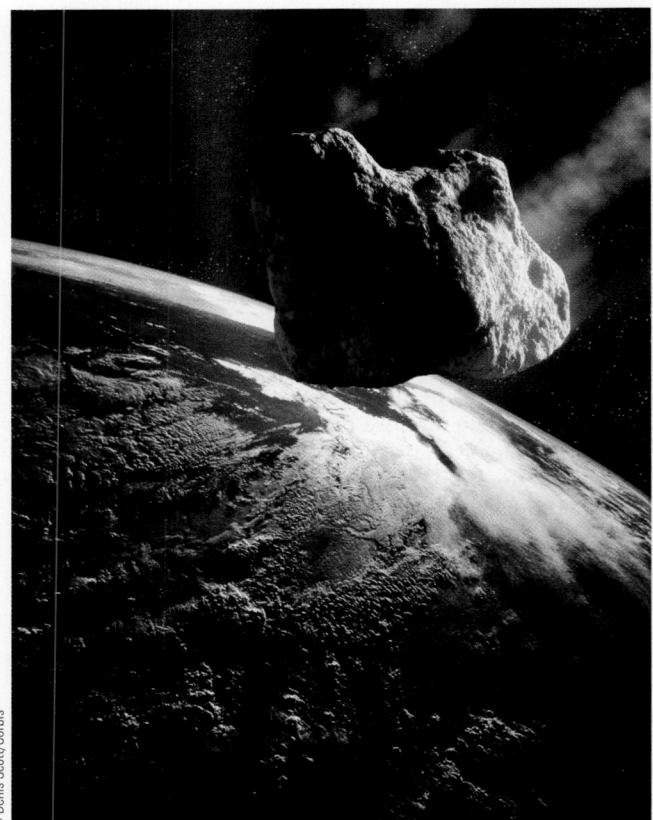

© Denis Scott/Corbis

**Meteorites.** Meteorites are materials that originate in outer space and survive the fall to the earth's surface. They can be large or small, but as they enter Earth's atmosphere they are warmed to a high temperature by friction in the atmosphere and emit light, forming a fireball. They are classified as stony meteorites, which are silicate minerals; iron meteorites, largely composed of iron and nickel; and stony-iron meteorites. (See also the photo of an iron meteorite on page 316.)

## Questions:

1. Write a balanced equation for the radioactive decomposition of $^{87}$Rb.
2. The decomposition of $^{87}$Rb occurs by which of the following processes?
   (a) alpha emission    (d) electron capture
   (b) beta emission    (e) positron emission
   (c) gamma emission
3. Determine the rate constant for the radioactive decay of $^{87}$Rb.
4. The oldest dated meteorites have ages of about 4.5 billion years. What fraction of the initial $^{87}$Rb has decayed?
5. The relative abundances of $^{86}$Sr, $^{87}$Sr, and $^{87}$Rb were measured for four samples of a meteorite; the results were tabulated below. Make a strontium-rubidium isochron plot of these data, then use the slope of the line to determine the age of the meteorite.

### Relative Abundance

| Sample # | $^{86}$Sr | $^{87}$Sr | $^{87}$Rb |
|---|---|---|---|
| 1 | 1.000 | 0.819 | 0.839 |
| 2 | 1.063 | 0.855 | 0.506 |
| 3 | 0.950 | 0.824 | 1.929 |
| 4 | 1.011 | 0.809 | 0.379 |

6. Derive the equation given above for $[^{87}Sr/^{86}Sr]$. (*Hint:* Start with the rate equation in the form $[^{87}Rb°] = [^{87}Rb]\ e^{kt}$.)

# LIST OF APPENDICES

# A  Using Logarithms and Solving Quadratic Equations

An introductory chemistry course requires basic algebra plus a knowledge of (1) exponential (or scientific) notation, (2) logarithms, and (3) quadratic equations. The use of exponential notation was reviewed on pages 33–35, and this appendix reviews the last two topics.

## A.1  Logarithms

Two types of logarithms are used in this text: (1) common logarithms (abbreviated log) whose base is 10 and (2) natural logarithms (abbreviated ln) whose base is $e$ (= 2.71828):

$$\log x = n, \text{ where } x = 10^n$$
$$\ln x = m, \text{ where } x = e^m$$

Most equations in chemistry and physics were developed in natural, or base $e$, logarithms, and we follow this practice in this text. The relation between log and ln is

$$\ln x = 2.303 \log x$$

Despite the different bases of the two logarithms, they are used in the same manner. What follows is largely a description of the use of common logarithms.

A common logarithm is the power to which you must raise 10 to obtain the number. For example, the log of 100 is 2, since you must raise 10 to the second power to obtain 100. Other examples are

$$\begin{aligned}
\log 1000 &= \log (10^3) = 3 \\
\log 10 &= \log (10^1) = 1 \\
\log 1 &= \log (10^0) = 0 \\
\log 0.1 &= \log (10^{-1}) = -1 \\
\log 0.0001 &= \log (10^{-4}) = -4
\end{aligned}$$

To obtain the common logarithm of a number other than a simple power of 10, you must resort to a log table or an electronic calculator. For example,

$$\begin{aligned}
\log 2.10 &= 0.322, \text{ which means that } 10^{0.322} = 2.10 \\
\log 5.16 &= 0.713, \text{ which means that } 10^{0.713} = 5.16 \\
\log 3.125 &= 0.4949, \text{ which means that } 10^{0.4949} = 3.125
\end{aligned}$$

To check this on many calculators, enter the number, and then press the "log" key. You should make sure that you understand how to use your particular calculator.

To obtain the natural logarithm ln of the numbers shown here, use a calculator having this function. Enter each number, and press "ln:"

$$\begin{aligned}
\ln 2.10 &= 0.742, \text{ which means that } e^{0.742} = 2.10 \\
\ln 5.16 &= 1.641, \text{ which means that } e^{1.641} = 5.16
\end{aligned}$$

To find the common logarithm of a number greater than 10 or less than 1 with a log table, first express the number in scientific notation. Then find the log of each part of the number and add the logs. For example,

$$\begin{aligned}
\log 241 &= \log (2.41 \times 10^2) = \log 2.41 + \log 10^2 \\
&= 0.382 + 2 = 2.382 \\
\log 0.00573 &= \log (5.73 \times 10^{-3}) = \log 5.73 + \log 10^{-3} \\
&= 0.758 + (-3) = -2.242
\end{aligned}$$

## Significant Figures and Logarithms

Notice that the mantissa has as many significant figures as the number whose log was found.

## Obtaining Antilogarithms

If you are given the logarithm of a number, and find the number from it, you have obtained the "antilogarithm," or "antilog," of the number. Two common procedures used by electronic calculators to do this are as follows:

| Procedure A | Procedure B |
|---|---|
| 1. Enter the value of the log or ln. | 1. Enter value of the log or ln. |
| 2. Press 2ndF. | 2. Press INV. |
| 3. Press $10^x$ or $e^x$. | 3. Press log or ln x. |

Make sure you can properly perform this operation on your calculator by working the following examples:

1. Find the number whose log is 5.234:

    Recall that log $x = n$, where $x = 10^n$. In this case, $n = 5.234$. Find the value of $10^n$, the antilog. In this case,

    $$10^{5.234} = 10^{0.234} \times 10^5 = 1.71 \times 10^5$$

    Notice that the characteristic (5) sets the decimal point; it is the power of 10 in the exponential form. The mantissa (0.234) gives the value of the number $x$, 1.71 in this case.

2. Find the number whose log is $-3.456$:

    $$10^{-3.456} = 10^{0.544} \times 10^{-4} = 3.50 \times 10^{-4}$$

    Notice here that $-3.456$ is expressed as the sum of $-4$ and $+0.544$.

## Mathematical Operations Using Logarithms

Because logarithms are exponents, operations involving them follow the same rules used for exponents. Thus, multiplying two numbers can be done by adding logarithms:

$$\log xy = \log x + \log y$$

For example, we multiply 563 by 125 by adding their logarithms and finding the antilogarithm of the result:

$$\log 563 = 2.751$$
$$\log 125 = \underline{2.097}$$
$$\log xy = 4.848$$
$$xy = 10^{4.848} = 10^{0.848} \times 10^4 = 7.05 \times 10^4$$

One number ($x$) can be divided by another ($y$) by subtraction of their logarithms:

$$\log \frac{x}{y} = \log x - \log y$$

For example, to divide 125 by 742,

$$\log 125 = 2.097$$
$$-\log 742 = \underline{2.870}$$
$$\log \frac{x}{y} = -0.773$$

$$\frac{x}{y} = 10^{-0.773} = 10^{0.227} \times 10^{-1} = 1.68 \times 10^{-1}$$

● **Logarithms and Nomenclature** The number to the left of the decimal in a logarithm is called the **characteristic**, and the number to the right of the decimal is the **mantissa**.

Similarly, powers and roots of numbers can be found using logarithms.

$$\log x^y = y(\log x)$$

$$\log \sqrt[y]{x} = \log x^{1/y} = \frac{1}{y} \log x$$

As an example, find the fourth power of 5.23. We first find the log of 5.23 and then multiply it by 4. The result, 2.874, is the log of the answer. Therefore, we find the antilog of 2.874:

$$(5.23)^4 = ?$$
$$\log (5.23)^4 = 4 \log 5.23 = 4(0.719) = 2.874$$
$$(5.23)^4 = 10^{2.874} = 748$$

As another example, find the fifth root of $1.89 \times 10^{-9}$:

$$\sqrt[5]{1.89 \times 10^{-9}} = (1.89 \times 10^{-9})^{1/5} = ?$$
$$\log(1.89 \times 10^{-9})^{1/5} = \frac{1}{5}\log(1.89 \times 10^{-9}) = \frac{1}{5}(-8.724) = -1.745$$

The answer is the antilog of $-1.745$:

$$\left(1.89 \times 10^{-9}\right)^{1/5} = 10^{-1.745} = 1.80 \times 10^{-2}$$

## A.2  Quadratic Equations

Algebraic equations of the form $ax^2 + bx + c = 0$ are called **quadratic equations**. The coefficients $a$, $b$, and $c$ may be either positive or negative. The two roots of the equation may be found using the *quadratic formula*:

$$x = \frac{-b \pm \sqrt{b^2 - 4ac}}{2a}$$

As an example, solve the equation $5x^2 - 3x - 2 = 0$. Here $a = 5$, $b = -3$, and $c = -2$. Therefore,

$$x = \frac{3 \pm \sqrt{(-3)^2 - 4(5)(-2)}}{2(5)}$$

$$= \frac{3 \pm \sqrt{9 - (-40)}}{10} = \frac{3 \pm \sqrt{49}}{10} = \frac{3 \pm 7}{10}$$

$$= 1 \text{ and } -0.4$$

How do you know which of the two roots is the correct answer? Mathematically, both roots are possible, but in chemistry problems you have to decide in each case which root has physical significance. It is *usually* true in this course, however, that negative values are not significant.

When you have solved a quadratic expression, you should always check your values by substitution into the original equation. In the previous example, we find that $5(1)^2 - 3(1) - 2 = 0$ and that $5(-0.4)^2 - 3(-0.4) - 2 = 0$.

The most likely place you will encounter quadratic equations is in the chapters on chemical equilibria, particularly in Chapters 16 through 18. Here, you will often be faced with solving an equation such as

$$1.8 \times 10^{-4} = \frac{x^2}{0.0010 - x}$$

This equation can certainly be solved using the quadratic formula (to give $x = 3.4 \times 10^{-4}$). You may find the **method of successive approximations** to be especially convenient, however. Here we begin by making a reasonable approximation of $x$. This approximate value is substituted into the original equation, which is then solved to give what is hoped to be a more correct value of $x$. This process is repeated until the answer converges on a particular value of $x$—that is, until the value of $x$ derived from two successive approximations is the same.

**Step 1:** First, assume that $x$ is so small that $(0.0010 - x) \approx 0.0010$. This means that

$$x^2 = 1.8 \times 10^{-4}\,(0.0010)$$
$$x = 4.2 \times 10^{-4} \text{ (to 2 significant figures)}$$

**Step 2:** Substitute the value of $x$ from Step 1 into the denominator of the original equation, and again solve for $x$:

$$x^2 = 1.8 \times 10^{-4}(0.0010 - 0.00042)$$
$$x = 3.2 \times 10^{-4}$$

**Step 3:** Repeat Step 2 using the value of $x$ found in that step:

$$x = \sqrt{1.8 \times 10^{-4}(0.0010 - 0.00032)} = 3.5 \times 10^{-4}$$

**Step 4:** Continue repeating the calculation, using the value of $x$ found in the previous step:

$$x = \sqrt{1.8 \times 10^{-4}(0.0010 - 0.00035)} = 3.4 \times 10^{-4}$$

**Step 5:** $\qquad x = \sqrt{1.8 \times 10^{-4}(0.0010 - 0.00034)} = 3.4 \times 10^{-4}$

Here, we find that iterations after the fourth step give the same value for $x$, indicating that we have arrived at a valid answer (and the same one obtained from the quadratic formula).

Here are some final thoughts on using the method of successive approximations. First, in some cases the method does not work. Successive steps may give answers that are random or that diverge from the correct value. In Chapters 16 through 18, you confront quadratic equations of the form $K = x^2/(C - x)$. The method of successive approximations works as long as $K < 4C$ (assuming one begins with $x = 0$ as the first guess, that is, $K \approx x^2/C$). This is always going to be true for weak acids and bases (the topic of Chapters 17 and 18), but it may *not* be the case for problems involving gas phase equilibria (Chapter 16), where $K$ can be quite large.

Second, values of $K$ in the equation $K = x^2/(C - x)$ are usually known only to two significant figures. We are therefore justified in carrying out successive steps until two answers are the same to two significant figures.

Finally, we highly recommend this method of solving quadratic equations, especially those in Chapters 17 and 18. If your calculator has a memory function, successive approximations can be carried out easily and rapidly.

# B* Some Important Physical Concepts

## B.1 Matter

The tendency to maintain a constant velocity is called *inertia*. Thus, unless acted on by an unbalanced force, a body at rest remains at rest, and a body in motion remains in motion with uniform velocity. Matter is anything that exhibits inertia; the quantity of matter is its mass.

## B.2 Motion

Motion is the change of position or location in space. Objects can have the following classes of motion:

- Translation occurs when the center of mass of an object changes its location. Example: a car moving on the highway.
- Rotation occurs when each point of a moving object moves in a circle about an axis through the center of mass. Examples: a spinning top, a rotating molecule.
- Vibration is a periodic distortion and then recovery of original shape. Examples: a struck tuning fork, a vibrating molecule.

## B.3 Force and Weight

Force is that which changes the velocity of a body; it is defined as

$$\text{Force} = \text{mass} \times \text{acceleration}$$

The SI unit of force is the **newton**, N, whose dimensions are kilograms times meter per second squared ($kg \cdot m/s^2$). A newton is therefore the force needed to change the velocity of a mass of 1 kilogram by 1 meter per second in a time of 1 second.

Because the earth's gravity is not the same everywhere, the weight (a force) corresponding to a given mass is not a constant. At any given spot on earth, gravity is constant, however, and therefore weight is proportional to mass. When a balance tells us that a given sample (the "unknown") has the same weight as another sample (the "weights," as given by a scale reading or by a total of counterweights), it also tells us that the two masses are equal. The balance is therefore a valid instrument for measuring the mass of an object independently of slight variations in the force of gravity.

## B.4 Pressure†

Pressure is force per unit area. The SI unit, called the *pascal*, Pa, is

$$1 \text{ pascal} = \frac{1 \text{ newton}}{m^2} = \frac{1 \text{ kg} \cdot m/s^2}{m^2} = \frac{1 \text{ kg}}{m \cdot s^2}$$

The International System of Units also recognizes the bar, which is $10^5$ Pa and which is close to standard atmospheric pressure (Table 1).

Chemists also express pressure in terms of the heights of liquid columns, especially water and mercury. This usage is not completely satisfactory because the

---

*Adapted from F. Brescia, J. Arents, H. Meislich, et al.: *General Chemistry*, 5th ed. Philadelphia: Harcourt Brace, 1988.
†See Section 11.1.

**Table 1  Pressure Conversions**

| From | To | Multiply By |
|------|-----|-------------|
| atmosphere | mm Hg | 760 mm Hg/atm (exactly) |
| atmosphere | lb/in² | 14.6960 lb/(in² · atm) |
| atmosphere | kPa | 101.325 kPa/atm |
| bar | Pa | $10^5$ Pa/bar (exactly) |
| bar | lb/in² | 14.5038 lb/(in² · bar) |
| mm Hg | torr | 1 torr/mm Hg (exactly) |

pressure exerted by a given column of a given liquid is not a constant but depends on the temperature (which influences the density of the liquid) and the location (which influences the magnitude of the force exerted by gravity). Such units are therefore not part of the SI, and their use is now discouraged. The older units are still used in books and journals, however, and chemists must be familiar with them.

The pressure of a liquid or a gas depends only on the depth (or height) and is exerted equally in all directions. At sea level, the pressure exerted by the earth's atmosphere supports a column of mercury about 0.76 m (76 cm, or 760 mm) high.

One **standard atmosphere** (atm) is the pressure exerted by exactly 76 cm of mercury at 0 °C (density, 13.5951 g/cm³) and at standard gravity, 9.80665 m/s². The **bar** is equivalent to 0.9869 atm. One **torr** is the pressure exerted by exactly 1 mm of mercury at 0 °C and standard gravity.

## B.5  Energy and Power

The SI unit of energy is the product of the units of force and distance, or kilograms times meter per second squared (kg · m/s²) times meters (× m), which is kg · m²/s²; this unit is called the **joule**, J. The joule is thus the work done when a force of 1 newton acts through a distance of 1 meter.

Work may also be done by moving an electric charge in an electric field. When the charge being moved is 1 coulomb (C) and the potential difference between its initial and final positions is 1 volt (V), the work is 1 joule. Thus,

$$1 \text{ joule} = 1 \text{ coulomb volt (CV)}$$

Another unit of electric work that is not part of the International System of Units but is still in use is the **electron volt**, eV, which is the work required to move an electron against a potential difference of 1 volt. (It is also the kinetic energy acquired by an electron when it is accelerated by a potential difference of 1 volt.) Because the charge on an electron is $1.602 \times 10^{-19}$ C, we have

$$1 \text{ eV} = 1.602 \times 10^{-19} \text{ CV} \times \frac{1 \text{ J}}{1 \text{ CV}} = 1.602 \times 10^{-19} \text{ J}$$

If this value is multiplied by Avogadro's number, we obtain the energy involved in moving 1 mol of electron charges (1 faraday) in a field produced by a potential difference of 1 volt:

$$1 \frac{\text{eV}}{\text{particle}} = \frac{1.602 \times 10^{-19} \text{ J}}{\text{particle}} \times \frac{6.022 \times 10^{23} \text{ particles}}{\text{mol}} \cdot \frac{1 \text{ kJ}}{1000 \text{ J}} = 96.49 \text{ kJ/mol}$$

Power is the amount of energy delivered per unit time. The SI unit is the watt, W, which is 1 joule per second. One kilowatt, kW, is 1000 W. Watt-hours and kilowatt-hours are therefore units of energy (Table 2). For example, 1000 watt-hours, or 1 kilowatt-hour, is

$$1.0 \times 10^3 \text{ W} \cdot \text{h} \times \frac{1 \text{ J}}{1 \text{ W} \cdot \text{s}} \times \frac{3.6 \times 10^3 \text{ s}}{1 \text{ h}} = 3.6 \times 10^6 \text{ J}$$

Table 2 **Energy Conversions**

| From | To | Multiply By |
|---|---|---|
| calorie (cal) | joule | 4.184 J/cal (exactly) |
| kilocalorie (kcal) | cal | $10^3$ cal/kcal (exactly) |
| kilocalorie | joule | $4.184 \times 10^3$ J/kcal (exactly) |
| liter atmosphere (L · atm) | joule | 101.325 J/L · atm |
| electron volt (eV) | joule | $1.60218 \times 10^{-19}$ J/eV |
| electron volt per particle | kilojoules per mole | 96.485 kJ · particle/eV · mol |
| coulomb volt (CV) | joule | 1 CV/J (exactly) |
| kilowatt-hour (kW-h) | kcal | 860.4 kcal/kW-h |
| kilowatt-hour | joule | $3.6 \times 10^6$ J/kW-h (exactly) |
| British thermal unit (BTU) | calorie | 252 cal/BTU |

# C Abbreviations and Useful Conversion Factors

**Table 3  Some Common Abbreviations and Standard Symbols**

| Term | Abbreviation | Term | Abbreviation |
|---|---|---|---|
| Activation energy | $E_a$ | Equilibrium constant | $K$ |
| Ampere | A | Concentration basis | $K_c$ |
| Aqueous solution | aq | Pressure basis | $K_p$ |
| Atmosphere, unit of pressure | atm | Ionization weak acid | $K_a$ |
| Atomic mass unit | u | Ionization weak base | $K_b$ |
| Avogadro's constant | $N$ | Solubility product | $K_{sp}$ |
| Bar, unit of pressure | bar | Formation constant | $K_f$ |
| Body-centered cubic | bcc | Ethylenediamine | en |
| Bohr radius | $a_0$ | Face-centered cubic | fcc |
| Boiling point | bp | Faraday constant | $F$ |
| Celsius temperature | °C | Gas constant | $R$ |
| Charge number of an ion | $z$ | Gibbs free energy | $G$ |
| Coulomb, electric charge | C | Standard free energy | $G°$ |
| Curie, radioactivity | Ci | Standard free energy of formation | $\Delta_f G°$ |
| Cycles per second, hertz | Hz | Standard free energy change for reaction | $\Delta_r G°$ |
| Debye, unit of electric dipole | D | Half-life | $t_{1/2}$ |
| Electron | $e^-$ | Heat | $q$ |
| Electron volt | eV | Hertz | Hz |
| Electronegativity | $\chi$ | Hour | h |
| Energy | $E$ | Joule | J |
| Enthalpy | $H$ | Kelvin | K |
| Standard enthalpy | $H°$ | Kilocalorie | kcal |
| Standard enthalpy of formation | $\Delta_f H°$ | Liquid | $\ell$ |
| Standard enthalpy of reaction | $\Delta_r H°$ | Logarithm, base 10 | log |
| Entropy | $S$ | Logarithm, base $e$ | ln |
| Standard entropy | $S°$ | Millimeters of mercury, unit of pressure | mm Hg |
| Entropy change for reaction | $\Delta_r S°$ | Minute | min |

*(continued)*

**Table 3 Some Common Abbreviations and Standard Symbols (continued)**

| Term | Abbreviation | Term | Abbreviation |
|---|---|---|---|
| Molar | M | Pressure | $P$ |
| Molar mass | $M$ | Proton number | $Z$ |
| Mole | mol | Rate constant | $k$ |
| Osmotic pressure | $\Pi$ | Standard temperature and pressure | STP |
| Pascal, unit of pressure | Pa | Temperature | $T$ |
| Planck's constant | $h$ | Volt | V |
| Pound | lb | Watt | W |
| Primitive cubic (unit cell) | pc | Wavelength | $\lambda$ |

## C.1    Fundamental Units of the SI System

The metric system was begun by the French National Assembly in 1790 and has undergone many modifications. The International System of Units or *Système International* (SI), which represents an extension of the metric system, was adopted by the 11th General Conference of Weights and Measures in 1960. It is constructed from seven base units, each of which represents a particular physical quantity (Table 4).

**Table 4 SI Fundamental Units**

| Physical Quantity | Name of Unit | Symbol |
|---|---|---|
| Length | meter | m |
| Mass | kilogram | kg |
| Time | second | s |
| Temperature | kelvin | K |
| Amount of substance | mole | mol |
| Electric current | ampere | A |
| Luminous intensity | candela | cd |

The first five units listed in Table 4 are particularly useful in general chemistry and are defined as follows:

1.  The *meter* was redefined in 1960 to be equal to 1,650,763.73 wavelengths of a certain line in the emission spectrum of krypton-86.
2.  The *kilogram* represents the mass of a platinum–iridium block kept at the International Bureau of Weights and Measures at Sèvres, France.
3.  The *second* was redefined in 1967 as the duration of 9,192,631,770 periods of a certain line in the microwave spectrum of cesium-133.
4.  The *kelvin* is 1/273.16 of the temperature interval between absolute zero and the triple point of water.
5.  The *mole* is the amount of substance that contains as many entities as there are atoms in exactly 0.012 kg of carbon-12 (12 g of $^{12}$C atoms).

## C.2  Prefixes Used with Traditional Metric Units and SI Units

Decimal fractions and multiples of metric and SI units are designated by using the prefixes listed in Table 5. Those most commonly used in general chemistry appear in italics.

**Table 5  Traditional Metric and SI Prefixes**

| Factor | Prefix | Symbol | Factor | Prefix | Symbol |
|---|---|---|---|---|---|
| $10^{12}$ | tera | T | $10^{-1}$ | *deci* | d |
| $10^{9}$ | giga | G | $10^{-2}$ | *centi* | c |
| $10^{6}$ | mega | M | $10^{-3}$ | *milli* | m |
| $10^{3}$ | *kilo* | k | $10^{-6}$ | micro | $\mu$ |
| $10^{2}$ | hecto | h | $10^{-9}$ | nano | n |
| $10^{1}$ | deka | da | $10^{-12}$ | *pico* | p |
| | | | $10^{-15}$ | femto | f |
| | | | $10^{-18}$ | atto | a |

## C.3  Derived SI Units

In the International System of Units, all physical quantities are represented by appropriate combinations of the base units listed in Table 4. A list of the derived units frequently used in general chemistry is given in Table 6.

**Table 6  Derived SI Units**

| Physical Quantity | Name of Unit | Symbol | Definition |
|---|---|---|---|
| Area | square meter | $m^2$ | |
| Volume | cubic meter | $m^3$ | |
| Density | kilogram per cubic meter | $kg/m^3$ | |
| Force | newton | N | $kg \cdot m/s^2$ |
| Pressure | pascal | Pa | $N/m^2$ |
| Energy | joule | J | $kg \cdot m^2/s^2$ |
| Electric charge | coulomb | C | $A \cdot s$ |
| Electric potential difference | volt | V | $J/(A \cdot s)$ |

**Table 7  Common Units of Mass and Weight**

| **1 pound = 453.39 grams** |
|---|
| 1 kilogram = 1000 grams = 2.205 pounds |
| 1 gram = 1000 milligrams |
| 1 gram = $6.022 \times 10^{23}$ atomic mass units |
| 1 atomic mass unit = $1.6605 \times 10^{-24}$ gram |
| 1 short ton = 2000 pounds = 907.2 kilograms |
| 1 long ton = 2240 pounds |
| 1 metric tonne = 1000 kilograms = 2205 pounds |

### Table 8  Common Units of Length

| 1 inch = 2.54 centimeters (exactly) |
|---|
| 1 mile = 5280 feet = 1.609 kilometers |
| 1 yard = 36 inches = 0.9144 meter |
| 1 meter = 100 centimeters = 39.37 inches = 3.281 feet = 1.094 yards |
| 1 kilometer = 1000 meters = 1094 yards = 0.6215 mile |
| 1 Ångstrom = $1.0 \times 10^{-8}$ centimeter = 0.10 nanometer = 100 picometers = $1.0 \times 10^{-10}$ meter = $3.937 \times 10^{-9}$ inch |

### Table 9  Common Units of Volume

| 1 quart = 0.9463 liter<br>1 liter = 1.0567 quarts |
|---|
| 1 liter = 1 cubic decimeter = 1000 cubic centimeters = 0.001 cubic meter |
| 1 milliliter = 1 cubic centimeter = 0.001 liter = $1.056 \times 10^{-3}$ quart |
| 1 cubic foot = 28.316 liters = 29.924 quarts = 7.481 gallons |

# D Physical Constants

### Table 10 Physical Constants

| Quantity | Symbol | Traditional Units | SI Units |
|---|---|---|---|
| Acceleration of gravity | $g$ | 980.6 cm/s$^2$ | 9.806 m/s$^2$ |
| Atomic mass unit (1/12 the mass of $^{12}$C atom) | u | $1.6605 \times 10^{-24}$ g | $1.6605 \times 10^{-27}$ kg |
| Avogadro's number | $N$ | $6.02214179 \times 10^{23}$ particles/mol | $6.02214179 \times 10^{23}$ particles/mol |
| Bohr radius | $a_0$ | 0.052918 nm $5.2918 \times 10^{-9}$ cm | $5.2918 \times 10^{-11}$ m |
| Boltzmann constant | $k$ | $1.3807 \times 10^{-16}$ erg/K | $1.3807 \times 10^{-23}$ J/K |
| Charge-to-mass ratio of electron | $e/m$ | $1.7588 \times 10^{8}$ C/g | $1.7588 \times 10^{11}$ C/kg |
| Electron rest mass | $m_e$ | $9.1094 \times 10^{-28}$ g 0.00054858 u | $9.1094 \times 10^{-31}$ kg |
| Electronic charge | $e$ | $1.6022 \times 10^{-19}$ C $4.8033 \times 10^{-10}$ esu | $1.6022 \times 10^{-19}$ C |
| Faraday constant | $F$ | 96,485 C/mol e$^-$ 23.06 kcal/V · mol e$^-$ | 96,485 C/mol e$^-$ 96,485 J/V · mol e$^-$ |
| Gas constant | $R$ | $0.082057 \dfrac{L \cdot atm}{mol \cdot K}$ | $8.3145 \dfrac{Pa \cdot dm^3}{mol \cdot K}$ |
| | | $1.987 \dfrac{cal}{mol \cdot K}$ | 8.3145 J/mol · K |
| Molar volume (STP) | $V_m$ | 22.414 L/mol | $22.414 \times 10^{-3}$ m$^3$/mol 22.414 dm$^3$/mol |
| Neutron rest mass | $m_n$ | $1.67493 \times 10^{-24}$ g 1.008665 u | $1.67493 \times 10^{-27}$ kg |
| Planck's constant | $h$ | $6.6261 \times 10^{-27}$ erg · s | $6.6260693 \times 10^{-34}$ J · s |
| Proton rest mass | $m_p$ | $1.6726 \times 10^{-24}$ g 1.007276 u | $1.6726 \times 10^{-27}$ kg |
| Rydberg constant | $R$ $Rhc$ | — | $1.0974 \times 10^{7}$ m$^{-1}$ $2.1799 \times 10^{-18}$ J |
| Velocity of light (in a vacuum) | $c$ | $2.9979 \times 10^{10}$ cm/s (186,282 miles/s) | $2.9979 \times 10^{8}$ m/s |

$\pi = 3.1416$

$e = 2.7183$

$\ln X = 2.303 \log X$

Table 11  **Specific Heats and Heat Capacities for Some Common Substances at 25 °C**

| Substance | Specific Heat (J/g · K) | Molar Heat Capacity (J/mol · K) |
|---|---|---|
| Al(s) | 0.897 | 24.2 |
| Ca(s) | 0.646 | 25.9 |
| Cu(s) | 0.385 | 24.5 |
| Fe(s) | 0.449 | 25.1 |
| Hg($\ell$) | 0.140 | 28.0 |
| $H_2O$(s), ice | 2.06 | 37.1 |
| $H_2O$($\ell$), water | 4.184 | 75.4 |
| $H_2O$(g), steam | 1.86 | 33.6 |
| $C_6H_6$($\ell$), benzene | 1.74 | 136 |
| $C_6H_6$(g), benzene | 1.06 | 82.4 |
| $C_2H_5OH$($\ell$), ethanol | 2.44 | 112.3 |
| $C_2H_5OH$(g), ethanol | 1.41 | 65.4 |
| $(C_2H_5)_2O$($\ell$), diethyl ether | 2.33 | 172.6 |
| $(C_2H_5)_2O$(g), diethyl ether | 1.61 | 119.5 |

Table 12  **Heats of Transformation and Transformation Temperatures of Several Substances**

| Substance | MP (°C) | Heat of Fusion | | BP (°C) | Heat of Vaporization | |
|---|---|---|---|---|---|---|
| | | J/g | kJ/mol | | J/g | kJ/mol |
| Elements* | | | | | | |
| Al | 660 | 395 | 10.7 | 2518 | 12083 | 294 |
| Ca | 842 | 212 | 8.5 | 1484 | 3767 | 155 |
| Cu | 1085 | 209 | 13.3 | 2567 | 4720 | 300 |
| Fe | 1535 | 267 | 13.8 | 2861 | 6088 | 340 |
| Hg | −38.8 | 11 | 2.29 | 357 | 295 | 59.1 |
| Compounds | | | | | | |
| $H_2O$ | 0.00 | 333 | 6.01 | 100.0 | 2260 | 40.7 |
| $CH_4$ | −182.5 | 58.6 | 0.94 | −161.5 | 511 | 8.2 |
| $C_2H_5OH$ | −114 | 109 | 5.02 | 78.3 | 838 | 38.6 |
| $C_6H_6$ | 5.48 | 127.4 | 9.95 | 80.0 | 393 | 30.7 |
| $(C_2H_5)_2O$ | −116.3 | 98.1 | 7.27 | 34.6 | 357 | 26.5 |

*Data for the elements are taken from J. A. Dean: *Lange's Handbook of Chemistry,* 15th ed. New York: McGraw-Hill Publishers, 1999.

# E   A Brief Guide to Naming Organic Compounds

It seems a daunting task to devise a systematic procedure that gives each organic compound a unique name, but that is what has been done. A set of rules was developed to name organic compounds by the International Union of Pure and Applied Chemistry (IUPAC). The IUPAC nomenclature allows chemists to write a name for any compound based on its structure or to identify the formula and structure for a compound from its name. In this book, we have generally used the IUPAC nomenclature scheme when naming compounds.

In addition to the systematic names, many compounds have common names. The common names came into existence before the nomenclature rules were developed, and they have continued in use. For some compounds, these names are so well entrenched that they are used most of the time. One such compound is acetic acid, which is almost always referred to by that name and not by its systematic name, ethanoic acid.

The general procedure for systematic naming of organic compounds begins with the nomenclature for hydrocarbons. Other organic compounds are then named as derivatives of hydrocarbons. Nomenclature rules for simple organic compounds are given in the following section.

## E.1   Hydrocarbons

### Alkanes

The names of alkanes end in "-ane." When naming a specific alkane, the root of the name identifies the longest carbon chain in the compound. Specific substituent groups attached to this carbon chain are identified by name and position.

Alkanes with chains of one to ten carbon atoms are given in Table 10.2. After the first four compounds, the names derive from Greek and Latin numbers—pentane, hexane, heptane, octane, nonane, decane—and this regular naming continues for higher alkanes. For substituted alkanes, the substituent groups on a hydrocarbon chain must be identified both by a name and by the position of substitution; this information precedes the root of the name. The position is indicated by a number that refers to the carbon atom to which the substituent is attached. (Numbering of the carbon atoms in a chain should begin at the end of the carbon chain that allows the substituent groups to have the lowest numbers.)

Names of hydrocarbon substituents are derived from the name of the hydrocarbon. The group —$CH_3$, derived by taking a hydrogen from methane, is called the *methyl group;* the —$C_2H_5$ group is the *ethyl group.* The nomenclature scheme is easily extended to derivatives of hydrocarbons with other substituent groups such as —Cl (chloro), —$NO_2$ (nitro), —CN (cyano), —D (deuterio), and so on (Table 13). If two or more of the same substituent groups occur, the prefixes "di-," "tri-," and "tetra-" are added. When different substituent groups are present, they are generally listed in alphabetical order.

Table 13  **Names of Common Substituent Groups**

| Formula | Name | Formula | Name |
|---|---|---|---|
| —CH$_3$ | methyl | —D | deuterio |
| —C$_2$H$_5$ | ethyl | —Cl | chloro |
| —CH$_2$CH$_2$CH$_3$ | propyl (*n*-propyl) | —Br | bromo |
| —CH(CH$_3$)$_2$ | 1-methylethyl (isopropyl) | —F | fluoro |
| —CH=CH$_2$ | ethenyl (vinyl) | —CN | cyano |
| —C$_6$H$_5$ | phenyl | —NO$_2$ | nitro |
| —OH | hydroxo | | |
| —NH$_2$ | amino | | |

*Example:*

$$\underset{CH_3CH_2\overset{|}{C}HCH_2\overset{|}{C}HCH_2CH_3}{\overset{\overset{CH_3}{|}\qquad\overset{C_2H_5}{|}}{}}$$

| Step | Information to Include | Contribution to Name |
|---|---|---|
| 1 | An alkane | Name will end in "-ane" |
| 2 | Longest chain is 7 carbons | Name as a *heptane* |
| 3 | —CH$_3$ group at carbon 3 | *3-methyl* |
| 4 | —C$_2$H$_5$ group at carbon 5 | *5-ethyl* |
| *Name:* | | 5-ethyl-3-methylheptane |

Cycloalkanes are named based on the ring size and by adding the prefix "cyclo"; for example, the cycloalkane with a six-member ring of carbons is called *cyclohexane.*

## Alkenes

Alkenes have names ending in "-ene." The name of an alkene must specify the length of the carbon chain and the position of the double bond (and when appropriate, the configuration, either *cis* or *trans*). As with alkanes, both identity and position of substituent groups must be given. The carbon chain is numbered from the end that gives the double bond the lowest number.

Compounds with two double bonds are called *dienes,* and they are named similarly—specifying the positions of the double bonds and the name and position of any substituent groups.

For example, the compound H$_2$C=C(CH$_3$)CH(CH$_3$)CH$_2$CH$_3$ has a five-carbon chain with a double bond between carbon atoms 1 and 2 and methyl groups on carbon atoms 2 and 3. Its name using IUPAC nomenclature is **2,3-dimethyl-1-pentene**. The compound CH$_3$CH=CHCCl$_3$ with a *cis* configuration around the double bond is named **1,1,1-trichloro-*cis*-2-butene**. The compound H$_2$C=C(Cl)CH=CH$_2$ is **2-chloro-1,3-butadiene**.

## Alkynes

The naming of alkynes is similar to the naming of alkenes, except that *cis–trans* isomerism isn't a factor. The ending "-yne" on a name identifies a compound as an alkyne.

## Benzene Derivatives

The carbon atoms in the six-member ring are numbered 1 through 6, and the name and position of substituent groups are given. The two examples shown here are **1-ethyl-3-methylbenzene** and **1,4-diaminobenzene**.

1-ethyl-3-methylbenzene          1,4-diaminobenzene

## E.2    Derivatives of Hydrocarbons

The names for alcohols, aldehydes, ketones, and acids are based on the name of the hydrocarbon with an appropriate suffix to denote the class of compound, as follows:

- **Alcohols:** Substitute "-ol" for the final "-e" in the name of the hydrocarbon, and designate the position of the —OH group by the number of the carbon atom. For example, $CH_3CH_2CHOHCH_3$ is named as a derivative of the 4-carbon hydrocarbon butane. The —OH group is attached to the second carbon, so the name is **2-butanol**.

- **Aldehydes:** Substitute "-al" for the final "-e" in the name of the hydrocarbon. The carbon atom of an aldehyde is, by definition, carbon-1 in the hydrocarbon chain. For example, the compound $CH_3CH(CH_3)CH_2CH_2CHO$ contains a 5-carbon chain with the aldehyde functional group being carbon-1 and the —$CH_3$ group at position 4; thus, the name is **4-methylpentanal**.

- **Ketones:** Substitute "-one" for the final "-e" in the name of the hydrocarbon. The position of the ketone functional group (the carbonyl group) is indicated by the number of the carbon atom. For example, the compound $CH_3COCH_2CH(C_2H_5)CH_2CH_3$ has the carbonyl group at the 2 position and an ethyl group at the 4 position of a 6-carbon chain; its name is **4-ethyl-2-hexanone**.

- **Carboxylic acids (organic acids):** Substitute "-oic" for the final "-e" in the name of the hydrocarbon. The carbon atoms in the longest chain are counted beginning with the carboxylic carbon atom. For example, *trans*-$CH_3CH{=}CHCH_2CO_2H$ is named as a derivative of *trans*-3-pentene—that is, ***trans*-3-pentenoic acid**.

An **ester** is named as a derivative of the alcohol and acid from which it is made. The name of an ester is obtained by splitting the formula $RCO_2R'$ into two parts, the $RCO_2$— portion and the —$R'$ portion. The —$R'$ portion comes from the alcohol and is identified by the hydrocarbon group name; derivatives of ethanol, for example, are called *ethyl* esters. The acid part of the compound is named by dropping the "-oic" ending for the acid and replacing it by "-oate." The compound $CH_3CH_2CO_2CH_3$ is named **methyl propanoate**.

Notice that an anion derived from a carboxylic acid by loss of the acidic proton is named the same way. Thus, $CH_3CH_2CO_2^-$ is the **propanoate anion**, and the sodium salt of this anion, $Na(CH_3CH_2CO_2)$, is **sodium propanoate**.

# F Values for the Ionization Energies and Electron Attachment Enthalpies of the Elements

### First Ionization Energies for Some Elements (kJ/mol)

| 1A (1) | 2A (2) | 3B (3) | 4B (4) | 5B (5) | 6B (6) | 7B (7) | 8B (8,9,10) | | | 1B (11) | 2B (12) | 3A (13) | 4A (14) | 5A (15) | 6A (16) | 7A (17) | 8 (18) |
|---|---|---|---|---|---|---|---|---|---|---|---|---|---|---|---|---|---|
| H 1312 | | | | | | | | | | | | | | | | | He 2371 |
| Li 520 | Be 899 | | | | | | | | | | | B 801 | C 1086 | N 1402 | O 1314 | F 1681 | Ne 2081 |
| Na 496 | Mg 738 | | | | | | | | | | | Al 578 | Si 786 | P 1012 | S 1000 | Cl 1251 | Ar 1521 |
| K 419 | Ca 599 | Sc 631 | Ti 658 | V 650 | Cr 652 | Mn 717 | Fe 759 | Co 758 | Ni 757 | Cu 745 | Zn 906 | Ga 579 | Ge 762 | As 947 | Se 941 | Br 1140 | Kr 1351 |
| Rb 403 | Sr 550 | Y 617 | Zr 661 | Nb 664 | Mo 685 | Tc 702 | Ru 711 | Rh 720 | Pd 804 | Ag 731 | Cd 868 | In 558 | Sn 709 | Sb 834 | Te 869 | I 1008 | Xe 1170 |
| Cs 377 | Ba 503 | La 538 | Hf 681 | Ta 761 | W 770 | Re 760 | Os 840 | Ir 880 | Pt 870 | Au 890 | Hg 1007 | Tl 589 | Pb 715 | Bi 703 | Po 812 | At 890 | Rn 1037 |

### Table 14  Electron Attachment Enthalpy Values for Some Elements (kJ/mol)*

| | | | | | | |
|---|---|---|---|---|---|---|
| H −72.77 | | | | | | |
| Li −59.63 | Be 0† | B −26.7 | C −121.85 | N 0 | O −140.98 | F −328.0 |
| Na −52.87 | Mg 0 | Al −42.6 | Si −133.6 | P −72.07 | S −200.41 | Cl −349.0 |
| K −48.39 | Ca 0 | Ga −30 | Ge −120 | As −78 | Se −194.97 | Br −324.7 |
| Rb −46.89 | Sr 0 | In −30 | Sn −120 | Sb −103 | Te −190.16 | I −295.16 |
| Cs −45.51 | Ba 0 | Tl −20 | Pb −35.1 | Bi −91.3 | Po −180 | At −270 |

*Derived from data taken from H. Hotop and W. C. Lineberger: *Journal of Physical Chemistry, Reference Data,* Vol. 14, p. 731, 1985. (This paper also includes data for the transition metals.) Some values are known to more than two decimal places. See also: http://en.wikipedia.org/wiki/Electron_affinity_(data_page)
†Elements with an electron attachment enthalpy of zero indicate that a stable anion A⁻ of the element does not exist in the gas phase.

# G Vapor Pressure of Water at Various Temperatures

**Table 15  Vapor Pressure of Water at Various Temperatures**

| Temperature (°C) | Vapor Pressure (torr) | Temperature (°C) | Vapor Pressure (torr) | Temperature (°C) | Vapor Pressure (torr) | Temperature (°C) | Vapor Pressure (torr) |
|---|---|---|---|---|---|---|---|
| −10 | 2.1 | 21 | 18.7 | 51 | 97.2 | 81 | 369.7 |
| −9 | 2.3 | 22 | 19.8 | 52 | 102.1 | 82 | 384.9 |
| −8 | 2.5 | 23 | 21.1 | 53 | 107.2 | 83 | 400.6 |
| −7 | 2.7 | 24 | 22.4 | 54 | 112.5 | 84 | 416.8 |
| −6 | 2.9 | 25 | 23.8 | 55 | 118.0 | 85 | 433.6 |
| −5 | 3.2 | 26 | 25.2 | 56 | 123.8 | 86 | 450.9 |
| −4 | 3.4 | 27 | 26.7 | 57 | 129.8 | 87 | 468.7 |
| −3 | 3.7 | 28 | 28.3 | 58 | 136.1 | 88 | 487.1 |
| −2 | 4.0 | 29 | 30.0 | 59 | 142.6 | 89 | 506.1 |
| −1 | 4.3 | 30 | 31.8 | 60 | 149.4 | 90 | 525.8 |
| 0 | 4.6 | 31 | 33.7 | 61 | 156.4 | 91 | 546.1 |
| 1 | 4.9 | 32 | 35.7 | 62 | 163.8 | 92 | 567.0 |
| 2 | 5.3 | 33 | 37.7 | 63 | 171.4 | 93 | 588.6 |
| 3 | 5.7 | 34 | 39.9 | 64 | 179.3 | 94 | 610.9 |
| 4 | 6.1 | 35 | 42.2 | 65 | 187.5 | 95 | 633.9 |
| 5 | 6.5 | 36 | 44.6 | 66 | 196.1 | 96 | 657.6 |
| 6 | 7.0 | 37 | 47.1 | 67 | 205.0 | 97 | 682.1 |
| 7 | 7.5 | 38 | 49.7 | 68 | 214.2 | 98 | 707.3 |
| 8 | 8.0 | 39 | 52.4 | 69 | 223.7 | 99 | 733.2 |
| 9 | 8.6 | 40 | 55.3 | 70 | 233.7 | 100 | 760.0 |
| 10 | 9.2 | 41 | 58.3 | 71 | 243.9 | 101 | 787.6 |
| 11 | 9.8 | 42 | 61.5 | 72 | 254.6 | 102 | 815.9 |
| 12 | 10.5 | 43 | 64.8 | 73 | 265.7 | 103 | 845.1 |
| 13 | 11.2 | 44 | 68.3 | 74 | 277.2 | 104 | 875.1 |
| 14 | 12.0 | 45 | 71.9 | 75 | 289.1 | 105 | 906.1 |
| 15 | 12.8 | 46 | 75.7 | 76 | 301.4 | 106 | 937.9 |
| 16 | 13.6 | 47 | 79.6 | 77 | 314.1 | 107 | 970.6 |
| 17 | 14.5 | 48 | 83.7 | 78 | 327.3 | 108 | 1004.4 |
| 18 | 15.5 | 49 | 88.0 | 79 | 341.0 | 109 | 1038.9 |
| 19 | 16.5 | 50 | 92.5 | 80 | 355.1 | 110 | 1074.6 |
| 20 | 17.5 | | | | | | |

# H Ionization Constants for Aqueous Weak Acids at 25 °C

**Table 16  Ionization Constants for Aqueous Weak Acids at 25 °C**

| Acid | Formula and Ionization Equation | $K_a$ |
|---|---|---|
| Acetic | $CH_3CO_2H \rightleftharpoons H^+ + CH_3CO_2^-$ | $1.8 \times 10^{-5}$ |
| Arsenic | $H_3AsO_4 \rightleftharpoons H^+ + H_2AsO_4^-$<br>$H_2AsO_4^- \rightleftharpoons H^+ + HAsO_4^{2-}$<br>$HAsO_4^{2-} \rightleftharpoons H^+ + AsO_4^{3-}$ | $K_1 = 5.8 \times 10^{-3}$<br>$K_2 = 1.1 \times 10^{-7}$<br>$K_3 = 3.2 \times 10^{-12}$ |
| Arsenous | $H_3AsO_3 \rightleftharpoons H^+ + H_2AsO_3^-$<br>$H_2AsO_3^- \rightleftharpoons H^+ + HAsO_3^{2-}$ | $K_1 = 6.0 \times 10^{-10}$<br>$K_2 = 3.0 \times 10^{-14}$ |
| Benzoic | $C_6H_5CO_2H \rightleftharpoons H^+ + C_6H_5CO_2^-$ | $6.3 \times 10^{-5}$ |
| Boric | $H_3BO_3 \rightleftharpoons H^+ + H_2BO_3^-$<br>$H_2BO_3^- \rightleftharpoons H^+ + HBO_3^{2-}$<br>$HBO_3^{2-} \rightleftharpoons H^+ + BO_3^{3-}$ | $K_1 = 7.3 \times 10^{-10}$<br>$K_2 = 1.8 \times 10^{-13}$<br>$K_3 = 1.6 \times 10^{-14}$ |
| Carbonic | $H_2CO_3 \rightleftharpoons H^+ + HCO_3^-$<br>$HCO_3^- \rightleftharpoons H^+ + CO_3^{2-}$ | $K_1 = 4.2 \times 10^{-7}$<br>$K_2 = 4.8 \times 10^{-11}$ |
| Citric | $H_3C_6H_5O_7 \rightleftharpoons H^+ + H_2C_6H_5O_7^-$<br>$H_2C_6H_5O_7^- \rightleftharpoons H^+ + HC_6H_5O_7^{2-}$<br>$HC_6H_5O_7^{2-} \rightleftharpoons H^+ + C_6H_5O_7^{3-}$ | $K_1 = 7.4 \times 10^{-3}$<br>$K_2 = 1.7 \times 10^{-5}$<br>$K_3 = 4.0 \times 10^{-7}$ |
| Cyanic | $HOCN \rightleftharpoons H^+ + OCN^-$ | $3.5 \times 10^{-4}$ |
| Formic | $HCO_2H \rightleftharpoons H^+ + HCO_2^-$ | $1.8 \times 10^{-4}$ |
| Hydrazoic | $HN_3 \rightleftharpoons H^+ + N_3^-$ | $1.9 \times 10^{-5}$ |
| Hydrocyanic | $HCN \rightleftharpoons H^+ + CN^-$ | $4.0 \times 10^{-10}$ |
| Hydrofluoric | $HF \rightleftharpoons H^+ + F^-$ | $7.2 \times 10^{-4}$ |
| Hydrogen peroxide | $H_2O_2 \rightleftharpoons H^+ + HO_2^-$ | $2.4 \times 10^{-12}$ |
| Hydrosulfuric | $H_2S \rightleftharpoons H^+ + HS^-$<br>$HS^- \rightleftharpoons H^+ + S^{2-}$ | $K_1 = 1 \times 10^{-7}$<br>$K_2 = 1 \times 10^{-19}$ |
| Hypobromous | $HOBr \rightleftharpoons H^+ + OBr^-$ | $2.5 \times 10^{-9}$ |
| Hypochlorous | $HOCl \rightleftharpoons H^+ + OCl^-$ | $3.5 \times 10^{-8}$ |
| Nitrous | $HNO_2 \rightleftharpoons H^+ + NO_2^-$ | $4.5 \times 10^{-4}$ |
| Oxalic | $H_2C_2O_4 \rightleftharpoons H^+ + HC_2O_4^-$<br>$HC_2O_4^- \rightleftharpoons H^+ + C_2O_4^{2-}$ | $K_1 = 5.9 \times 10^{-2}$<br>$K_2 = 6.4 \times 10^{-5}$ |
| Phenol | $C_6H_5OH \rightleftharpoons H^+ + C_6H_5O^-$ | $1.3 \times 10^{-10}$ |
| Phosphoric | $H_3PO_4 \rightleftharpoons H^+ + H_2PO_4^-$<br>$H_2PO_4^- \rightleftharpoons H^+ + HPO_4^{2-}$<br>$HPO_4^{2-} \rightleftharpoons H^+ + PO_4^{3-}$ | $K_1 = 7.5 \times 10^{-3}$<br>$K_2 = 6.2 \times 10^{-8}$<br>$K_3 = 3.6 \times 10^{-13}$ |
| Phosphorous | $H_3PO_3 \rightleftharpoons H^+ + H_2PO_3^-$<br>$H_2PO_3^- \rightleftharpoons H^+ + HPO_3^{2-}$ | $K_1 = 1.6 \times 10^{-2}$<br>$K_2 = 7.0 \times 10^{-7}$ |
| Selenic | $H_2SeO_4 \rightleftharpoons H^+ + HSeO_4^-$<br>$HSeO_4^- \rightleftharpoons H^+ + SeO_4^{2-}$ | $K_1 = $ very large<br>$K_2 = 1.2 \times 10^{-2}$ |

**Table 16  Ionization Constants for Aqueous Weak Acids at 25 °C (continued)**

| Acid | Formula and Ionization Equation | $K_a$ |
|---|---|---|
| Selenous | $H_2SeO_3 \rightleftharpoons H^+ + HSeO_3^-$<br>$HSeO_3^- \rightleftharpoons H^+ + SeO_3^{2-}$ | $K_1 = 2.7 \times 10^{-3}$<br>$K_2 = 2.5 \times 10^{-7}$ |
| Sulfuric | $H_2SO_4 \rightleftharpoons H^+ + HSO_4^-$<br>$HSO_4^- \rightleftharpoons H^+ + SO_4^{2-}$ | $K_1 = $ very large<br>$K_2 = 1.2 \times 10^{-2}$ |
| Sulfurous | $H_2SO_3 \rightleftharpoons H^+ + HSO_3^-$<br>$HSO_3^- \rightleftharpoons H^+ + SO_3^{2-}$ | $K_1 = 1.2 \times 10^{-2}$<br>$K_2 = 6.2 \times 10^{-8}$ |
| Tellurous | $H_2TeO_3 \rightleftharpoons H^+ + HTeO_3^-$<br>$HTeO_3^- \rightleftharpoons H^+ + TeO_3^{2-}$ | $K_1 = 2 \times 10^{-3}$<br>$K_2 = 1 \times 10^{-8}$ |

# I Ionization Constants for Aqueous Weak Bases at 25 °C

**Table 17  Ionization Constants for Aqueous Weak Bases at 25 °C**

| Base | Formula and Ionization Equation | $K_b$ |
|------|-------------------------------|-------|
| Ammonia | $NH_3 + H_2O \rightleftharpoons NH_4^+ + OH^-$ | $1.8 \times 10^{-5}$ |
| Aniline | $C_6H_5NH_2 + H_2O \rightleftharpoons C_6H_5NH_3^+ + OH^-$ | $4.0 \times 10^{-10}$ |
| Dimethylamine | $(CH_3)_2NH + H_2O \rightleftharpoons (CH_3)_2NH_2^+ + OH^-$ | $7.4 \times 10^{-4}$ |
| Ethylamine | $C_2H_5NH_2 + H_2O \rightleftharpoons C_2H_5NH_3^+ + OH^-$ | $4.3 \times 10^{-4}$ |
| Ethylenediamine | $H_2NCH_2CH_2NH_2 + H_2O \rightleftharpoons H_2NCH_2CH_2NH_3^+ + OH^-$<br>$H_2NCH_2CH_2NH_3^+ + H_2O \rightleftharpoons H_3NCH_2CH_2NH_3^{2+} + OH^-$ | $K_1 = 8.5 \times 10^{-5}$<br>$K_2 = 2.7 \times 10^{-8}$ |
| Hydrazine | $N_2H_4 + H_2O \rightleftharpoons N_2H_5^+ + OH^-$<br>$N_2H_5^+ + H_2O \rightleftharpoons N_2H_6^{2+} + OH^-$ | $K_1 = 8.5 \times 10^{-7}$<br>$K_2 = 8.9 \times 10^{-16}$ |
| Hydroxylamine | $NH_2OH + H_2O \rightleftharpoons NH_3OH^+ + OH^-$ | $6.6 \times 10^{-9}$ |
| Methylamine | $CH_3NH_2 + H_2O \rightleftharpoons CH_3NH_3^+ + OH^-$ | $5.0 \times 10^{-4}$ |
| Pyridine | $C_5H_5N + H_2O \rightleftharpoons C_5H_5NH^+ + OH^-$ | $1.5 \times 10^{-9}$ |
| Trimethylamine | $(CH_3)_3N + H_2O \rightleftharpoons (CH_3)_3NH^+ + OH^-$ | $7.4 \times 10^{-5}$ |

# J Solubility Product Constants for Some Inorganic Compounds at 25 °C

**Table 18A  Solubility Product Constants at 25 °C**

| Cation | Compound | $K_{sp}$ | Cation | Compound | $K_{sp}$ |
|--------|----------|----------|--------|----------|----------|
| $Ba^{2+}$ | *$BaCrO_4$ | $1.2 \times 10^{-10}$ | $Hg_2^{2+}$ | *$Hg_2Br_2$ | $6.4 \times 10^{-23}$ |
| | $BaCO_3$ | $2.6 \times 10^{-9}$ | | $Hg_2Cl_2$ | $1.4 \times 10^{-18}$ |
| | $BaF_2$ | $1.8 \times 10^{-7}$ | | *$Hg_2I_2$ | $2.9 \times 10^{-29}$ |
| | *$BaSO_4$ | $1.1 \times 10^{-10}$ | | $Hg_2SO_4$ | $6.5 \times 10^{-7}$ |
| $Ca^{2+}$ | $CaCO_3$ (calcite) | $3.4 \times 10^{-9}$ | $Ni^{2+}$ | $NiCO_3$ | $1.4 \times 10^{-7}$ |
| | *$CaF_2$ | $5.3 \times 10^{-11}$ | | $Ni(OH)_2$ | $5.5 \times 10^{-16}$ |
| | *$Ca(OH)_2$ | $5.5 \times 10^{-5}$ | $Ag^+$ | *$AgBr$ | $5.4 \times 10^{-13}$ |
| | $CaSO_4$ | $4.9 \times 10^{-5}$ | | *$AgBrO_3$ | $5.4 \times 10^{-5}$ |
| $Cu^+, Cu^{2+}$ | $CuBr$ | $6.3 \times 10^{-9}$ | | $AgCH_3CO_2$ | $1.9 \times 10^{-3}$ |
| | $CuI$ | $1.3 \times 10^{-12}$ | | $AgCN$ | $6.0 \times 10^{-17}$ |
| | $Cu(OH)_2$ | $2.2 \times 10^{-20}$ | | $Ag_2CO_3$ | $8.5 \times 10^{-12}$ |
| | $CuSCN$ | $1.8 \times 10^{-13}$ | | *$Ag_2C_2O_4$ | $5.4 \times 10^{-12}$ |
| $Au^+$ | $AuCl$ | $2.0 \times 10^{-13}$ | | *$AgCl$ | $1.8 \times 10^{-10}$ |
| $Fe^{2+}$ | $FeCO_3$ | $3.1 \times 10^{-11}$ | | $Ag_2CrO_4$ | $1.1 \times 10^{-12}$ |
| | $Fe(OH)_2$ | $4.9 \times 10^{-17}$ | | *$AgI$ | $8.5 \times 10^{-17}$ |
| $Pb^{2+}$ | $PbBr_2$ | $6.6 \times 10^{-6}$ | | $AgSCN$ | $1.0 \times 10^{-12}$ |
| | $PbCO_3$ | $7.4 \times 10^{-14}$ | | *$Ag_2SO_4$ | $1.2 \times 10^{-5}$ |
| | $PbCl_2$ | $1.7 \times 10^{-5}$ | $Sr^{2+}$ | $SrCO_3$ | $5.6 \times 10^{-10}$ |
| | $PbCrO_4$ | $2.8 \times 10^{-13}$ | | $SrF_2$ | $4.3 \times 10^{-9}$ |
| | $PbF_2$ | $3.3 \times 10^{-8}$ | | $SrSO_4$ | $3.4 \times 10^{-7}$ |
| | $PbI_2$ | $9.8 \times 10^{-9}$ | $Tl^+$ | $TlBr$ | $3.7 \times 10^{-6}$ |
| | $Pb(OH)_2$ | $1.4 \times 10^{-15}$ | | $TlCl$ | $1.9 \times 10^{-4}$ |
| | $PbSO_4$ | $2.5 \times 10^{-8}$ | | $TlI$ | $5.5 \times 10^{-8}$ |
| $Mg^{2+}$ | $MgCO_3$ | $6.8 \times 10^{-6}$ | $Zn^{2+}$ | $Zn(OH)_2$ | $3 \times 10^{-17}$ |
| | $MgF_2$ | $5.2 \times 10^{-11}$ | | $Zn(CN)_2$ | $8.0 \times 10^{-12}$ |
| | $Mg(OH)_2$ | $5.6 \times 10^{-12}$ | | | |
| $Mn^{2+}$ | $MnCO_3$ | $2.3 \times 10^{-11}$ | | | |
| | *$Mn(OH)_2$ | $1.9 \times 10^{-13}$ | | | |

The values reported in this table were taken from J. A. Dean: *Lange's Handbook of Chemistry,* 15th ed. New York: McGraw-Hill Publishers, 1999. Values have been rounded off to two significant figures.

*Calculated solubility from these $K_{sp}$ values will match experimental solubility for this compound within a factor of 2. Experimental values for solubilities are given in R. W. Clark and J. M. Bonicamp: *Journal of Chemical Education,* Vol. 75, p. 1182, 1998.

**Table 18B** $K_{spa}$ **Values\* for Some Metal Sulfides at 25 °C**

| Substance | $K_{spa}$ |
|-----------|-----------|
| HgS (red) | $4 \times 10^{-54}$ |
| HgS (black) | $2 \times 10^{-53}$ |
| $Ag_2S$ | $6 \times 10^{-51}$ |
| CuS | $6 \times 10^{-37}$ |
| PbS | $3 \times 10^{-28}$ |
| CdS | $8 \times 10^{-28}$ |
| SnS | $1 \times 10^{-26}$ |
| FeS | $6 \times 10^{-19}$ |

\*The equilibrium constant value $K_{spa}$ for metal sulfides refers to the equilibrium $MS(s) + H_2O(\ell) \rightleftharpoons M^{2+}(aq) + OH^-(aq) + HS^-(aq)$; see R. J. Myers, *Journal of Chemical Education*, Vol. 63, p. 687, 1986.

# K Formation Constants for Some Complex Ions in Aqueous Solution at 25 °C

**Table 19** **Formation Constants for Some Complex Ions in Aqueous Solution at 25 °C\***

| Formation Equilibrium | $K$ |
|---|---|
| $Ag^+ + 2\ Br^- \rightleftharpoons [AgBr_2]^-$ | $2.1 \times 10^7$ |
| $Ag^+ + 2\ Cl^- \rightleftharpoons [AgCl_2]^-$ | $1.1 \times 10^5$ |
| $Ag^+ + 2\ CN^- \rightleftharpoons [Ag(CN)_2]^-$ | $1.3 \times 10^{21}$ |
| $Ag^+ + 2\ S_2O_3^{2-} \rightleftharpoons [Ag(S_2O_3)_2]^{3-}$ | $2.9 \times 10^{13}$ |
| $Ag^+ + 2\ NH_3 \rightleftharpoons [Ag(NH_3)_2]^+$ | $1.1 \times 10^7$ |
| $Al^{3+} + 6\ F^- \rightleftharpoons [AlF_6]^{3-}$ | $6.9 \times 10^{19}$ |
| $Al^{3+} + 4\ OH^- \rightleftharpoons [Al(OH)_4]^-$ | $1.1 \times 10^{33}$ |
| $Au^+ + 2\ CN^- \rightleftharpoons [Au(CN)_2]^-$ | $2.0 \times 10^{38}$ |
| $Cd^{2+} + 4\ CN^- \rightleftharpoons [Cd(CN)_4]^{2-}$ | $6.0 \times 10^{18}$ |
| $Cd^{2+} + 4\ NH_3 \rightleftharpoons [Cd(NH_3)_4]^{2+}$ | $1.3 \times 10^7$ |
| $Co^{2+} + 6\ NH_3 \rightleftharpoons [Co(NH_3)_6]^{2+}$ | $1.3 \times 10^5$ |
| $Cu^+ + 2\ CN^- \rightleftharpoons [Cu(CN)_2]^-$ | $1.0 \times 10^{24}$ |
| $Cu^+ + 2\ Cl^- \rightleftharpoons [CuCl_2]^-$ | $3.2 \times 10^5$ |
| $Cu^{2+} + 4\ NH_3 \rightleftharpoons [Cu(NH_3)_4]^{2+}$ | $2.1 \times 10^{13}$ |
| $Fe^{2+} + 6\ CN^- \rightleftharpoons [Fe(CN)_6]^{4-}$ | $1.0 \times 10^{35}$ |
| $Hg^{2+} + 4\ Cl^- \rightleftharpoons [HgCl_4]^{2-}$ | $1.2 \times 10^{15}$ |
| $Ni^{2+} + 4\ CN^- \rightleftharpoons [Ni(CN)_4]^{2-}$ | $2.0 \times 10^{31}$ |
| $Ni^{2+} + 6\ NH_3 \rightleftharpoons [Ni(NH_3)_6]^{2+}$ | $5.5 \times 10^8$ |
| $Zn^{2+} + 4\ OH^- \rightleftharpoons [Zn(OH)_4]^{2-}$ | $4.6 \times 10^{17}$ |
| $Zn^{2+} + 4\ NH_3 \rightleftharpoons [Zn(NH_3)_4]^{2+}$ | $2.9 \times 10^9$ |

\*Data reported in this table are taken from J. A. Dean: *Lange's Handbook of Chemistry,* 15th ed. New York: McGraw-Hill Publishers, 1999.

# L    Selected Thermodynamic Values

**Table 20  Selected Thermodynamic Values***

| Species | $\Delta_f H°$ (298.15 K) (kJ/mol) | $S°$ (298.15 K) (J/K · mol) | $\Delta_f G°$ (298.15 K) (kJ/mol) |
|---|---|---|---|
| *Aluminum* | | | |
| Al(s) | 0 | 28.3 | 0 |
| AlCl$_3$(s) | −705.63 | 109.29 | −630.0 |
| Al$_2$O$_3$(s) | −1675.7 | 50.92 | −1582.3 |
| *Barium* | | | |
| BaCl$_2$(s) | −858.6 | 123.68 | −810.4 |
| BaCO$_3$(s) | −1213 | 112.1 | −1134.41 |
| BaO(s) | −548.1 | 72.05 | −520.38 |
| BaSO$_4$(s) | −1473.2 | 132.2 | −1362.2 |
| *Beryllium* | | | |
| Be(s) | 0 | 9.5 | 0 |
| Be(OH)$_2$(s) | −902.5 | 51.9 | −815.0 |
| *Boron* | | | |
| BCl$_3$(g) | −402.96 | 290.17 | −387.95 |
| *Bromine* | | | |
| Br(g) | 111.884 | 175.022 | 82.396 |
| Br$_2$($\ell$) | 0 | 152.2 | 0 |
| Br$_2$(g) | 30.91 | 245.47 | 3.12 |
| BrF$_3$(g) | −255.60 | 292.53 | −229.43 |
| HBr(g) | −36.29 | 198.70 | −53.45 |
| *Calcium* | | | |
| Ca(s) | 0 | 41.59 | 0 |
| Ca(g) | 178.2 | 158.884 | 144.3 |
| Ca$^{2+}$(g) | 1925.90 | — | — |
| CaC$_2$(s) | −59.8 | 70. | −64.93 |
| CaCO$_3$(s, calcite) | −1207.6 | 91.7 | −1129.16 |
| CaCl$_2$(s) | −795.8 | 104.6 | −748.1 |
| CaF$_2$(s) | −1219.6 | 68.87 | −1167.3 |
| CaH$_2$(s) | −186.2 | 42 | −147.2 |
| CaO(s) | −635.09 | 38.2 | −603.42 |
| CaS(s) | −482.4 | 56.5 | −477.4 |
| Ca(OH)$_2$(s) | −986.09 | 83.39 | −898.43 |
| Ca(OH)$_2$(aq) | −1002.82 | — | −868.07 |
| CaSO$_4$(s) | −1434.52 | 106.5 | −1322.02 |

*Most thermodynamic data are taken from the NIST Chemistry WebBook at http://webbook.nist.gov.

**Table 20 Selected Thermodynamic Values (continued)**

| Species | $\Delta_f H°$ (298.15 K) (kJ/mol) | $S°$ (298.15 K) (J/K · mol) | $\Delta_f G°$ (298.15 K) (kJ/mol) |
|---|---|---|---|
| *Carbon* | | | |
| C(s, graphite) | 0 | 5.6 | 0 |
| C(s, diamond) | 1.8 | 2.377 | 2.900 |
| C(g) | 716.67 | 158.1 | 671.2 |
| $CCl_4(\ell)$ | −128.4 | 214.39 | −57.63 |
| $CCl_4(g)$ | −95.98 | 309.65 | −53.61 |
| $CHCl_3(\ell)$ | −134.47 | 201.7 | −73.66 |
| $CHCl_3(g)$ | −103.18 | 295.61 | −70.4 |
| $CH_4$(g, methane) | −74.87 | 186.26 | −50.8 |
| $C_2H_2$(g, ethyne) | 226.73 | 200.94 | 209.20 |
| $C_2H_4$(g, ethene) | 52.47 | 219.36 | 68.35 |
| $C_2H_6$(g, ethane) | −83.85 | 229.2 | −31.89 |
| $C_3H_8$(g, propane) | −104.7 | 270.3 | −24.4 |
| $C_6H_6(\ell$, benzene) | 48.95 | 173.26 | 124.21 |
| $CH_3OH(\ell$, methanol) | −238.4 | 127.19 | −166.14 |
| $CH_3OH$(g, methanol) | −201.0 | 239.7 | −162.5 |
| $C_2H_5OH(\ell$, ethanol) | −277.0 | 160.7 | −174.7 |
| $C_2H_5OH$(g, ethanol) | −235.3 | 282.70 | −168.49 |
| CO(g) | −110.525 | 197.674 | −137.168 |
| $CO_2(g)$ | −393.509 | 213.74 | −394.359 |
| $CS_2(\ell)$ | 89.41 | 151 | 65.2 |
| $CS_2(g)$ | 116.7 | 237.8 | 66.61 |
| $COCl_2(g)$ | −218.8 | 283.53 | −204.6 |
| *Cesium* | | | |
| Cs(s) | 0 | 85.23 | 0 |
| $Cs^+$(g) | 457.964 | — | — |
| CsCl(s) | −443.04 | 101.17 | −414.53 |
| *Chlorine* | | | |
| Cl(g) | 121.3 | 165.19 | 105.3 |
| $Cl^-$(g) | −233.13 | — | — |
| $Cl_2(g)$ | 0 | 223.08 | 0 |
| HCl(g) | −92.31 | 186.2 | −95.09 |
| HCl(aq) | −167.159 | 56.5 | −131.26 |
| *Chromium* | | | |
| Cr(s) | 0 | 23.62 | 0 |
| $Cr_2O_3(s)$ | −1134.7 | 80.65 | −1052.95 |
| $CrCl_3(s)$ | −556.5 | 123.0 | −486.1 |

*(continued)*

Table 20  **Selected Thermodynamic Values (continued)**

| Species | $\Delta_f H°$ (298.15 K) (kJ/mol) | $S°$ (298.15 K) (J/K · mol) | $\Delta_f G°$ (298.15 K) (kJ/mol) |
|---|---|---|---|
| *Copper* | | | |
| $Cu(s)$ | 0 | 33.17 | 0 |
| $CuO(s)$ | −156.06 | 42.59 | −128.3 |
| $CuCl_2(s)$ | −220.1 | 108.07 | −175.7 |
| $CuSO_4(s)$ | −769.98 | 109.05 | −660.75 |
| *Fluorine* | | | |
| $F_2(g)$ | 0 | 202.8 | 0 |
| $F(g)$ | 78.99 | 158.754 | 61.91 |
| $F^-(g)$ | −255.39 | — | — |
| $F^-(aq)$ | −332.63 | — | −278.79 |
| $HF(g)$ | −273.3 | 173.779 | −273.2 |
| $HF(aq)$ | −332.63 | 88.7 | −278.79 |
| *Hydrogen* | | | |
| $H_2(g)$ | 0 | 130.7 | 0 |
| $H(g)$ | 217.965 | 114.713 | 203.247 |
| $H^+(g)$ | 1536.202 | — | — |
| $H_2O(\ell)$ | −285.83 | 69.95 | −237.15 |
| $H_2O(g)$ | −241.83 | 188.84 | −228.59 |
| $H_2O_2(\ell)$ | −187.78 | 109.6 | −120.35 |
| *Iodine* | | | |
| $I_2(s)$ | 0 | 116.135 | 0 |
| $I_2(g)$ | 62.438 | 260.69 | 19.327 |
| $I(g)$ | 106.838 | 180.791 | 70.250 |
| $I^-(g)$ | −197 | — | — |
| $ICl(g)$ | 17.51 | 247.56 | −5.73 |
| *Iron* | | | |
| $Fe(s)$ | 0 | 27.78 | 0 |
| $FeO(s)$ | −272 | — | — |
| $Fe_2O_3(s, hematite)$ | −825.5 | 87.40 | −742.2 |
| $Fe_3O_4(s, magnetite)$ | −1118.4 | 146.4 | −1015.4 |
| $FeCl_2(s)$ | −341.79 | 117.95 | −302.30 |
| $FeCl_3(s)$ | −399.49 | 142.3 | −344.00 |
| $FeS_2(s, pyrite)$ | −178.2 | 52.93 | −166.9 |
| $Fe(CO)_5(\ell)$ | −774.0 | 338.1 | −705.3 |
| *Lead* | | | |
| $Pb(s)$ | 0 | 64.81 | 0 |
| $PbCl_2(s)$ | −359.41 | 136.0 | −314.10 |
| $PbO(s, yellow)$ | −219 | 66.5 | −196 |
| $PbO_2(s)$ | −277.4 | 68.6 | −217.39 |
| $PbS(s)$ | −100.4 | 91.2 | −98.7 |

Table 20  **Selected Thermodynamic Values (continued)**

| Species | $\Delta_f H°$ (298.15 K) (kJ/mol) | $S°$ (298.15 K) (J/K · mol) | $\Delta_f G°$ (298.15 K) (kJ/mol) |
|---|---|---|---|
| *Lithium* | | | |
| Li(s) | 0 | 29.12 | 0 |
| Li$^+$(g) | 685.783 | — | — |
| LiOH(s) | −484.93 | 42.81 | −438.96 |
| LiOH(aq) | −508.48 | 2.80 | −450.58 |
| LiCl(s) | −408.701 | 59.33 | −384.37 |
| *Magnesium* | | | |
| Mg(s) | 0 | 32.67 | 0 |
| MgCl$_2$(s) | −641.62 | 89.62 | −592.09 |
| MgCO$_3$(s) | −1111.69 | 65.84 | −1028.2 |
| MgO(s) | −601.24 | 26.85 | −568.93 |
| Mg(OH)$_2$(s) | −924.54 | 63.18 | −833.51 |
| MgS(s) | −346.0 | 50.33 | −341.8 |
| *Mercury* | | | |
| Hg($\ell$) | 0 | 76.02 | 0 |
| HgCl$_2$(s) | −224.3 | 146.0 | −178.6 |
| HgO(s, red) | −90.83 | 70.29 | −58.539 |
| HgS(s, red) | −58.2 | 82.4 | −50.6 |
| *Nickel* | | | |
| Ni(s) | 0 | 29.87 | 0 |
| NiO(s) | −239.7 | 37.99 | −211.7 |
| NiCl$_2$(s) | −305.332 | 97.65 | −259.032 |
| *Nitrogen* | | | |
| N$_2$(g) | 0 | 191.56 | 0 |
| N(g) | 472.704 | 153.298 | 455.563 |
| NH$_3$(g) | −45.90 | 192.77 | −16.37 |
| N$_2$H$_4$($\ell$) | 50.63 | 121.52 | 149.45 |
| NH$_4$Cl(s) | −314.55 | 94.85 | −203.08 |
| NH$_4$Cl(aq) | −299.66 | 169.9 | −210.57 |
| NH$_4$NO$_3$(s) | −365.56 | 151.08 | −183.84 |
| NH$_4$NO$_3$(aq) | −339.87 | 259.8 | −190.57 |
| NO(g) | 90.29 | 210.76 | 86.58 |
| NO$_2$(g) | 33.1 | 240.04 | 51.23 |
| N$_2$O(g) | 82.05 | 219.85 | 104.20 |
| N$_2$O$_4$(g) | 9.08 | 304.38 | 97.73 |
| NOCl(g) | 51.71 | 261.8 | 66.08 |
| HNO$_3$($\ell$) | −174.10 | 155.60 | −80.71 |
| HNO$_3$(g) | −135.06 | 266.38 | −74.72 |
| HNO$_3$(aq) | −207.36 | 146.4 | −111.25 |

*(continued)*

**Table 20  Selected Thermodynamic Values (continued)**

| Species | $\Delta_f H°$ (298.15 K) (kJ/mol) | $S°$ (298.15 K) (J/K · mol) | $\Delta_f G°$ (298.15 K) (kJ/mol) |
|---|---|---|---|
| *Oxygen* | | | |
| $O_2(g)$ | 0 | 205.07 | 0 |
| $O(g)$ | 249.170 | 161.055 | 231.731 |
| $O_3(g)$ | 142.67 | 238.92 | 163.2 |
| *Phosphorus* | | | |
| $P_4$(s, white) | 0 | 41.1 | 0 |
| $P_4$(s, red) | −17.6 | 22.80 | −12.1 |
| $P(g)$ | 314.64 | 163.193 | 278.25 |
| $PH_3(g)$ | 5.47 | 210.24 | 6.64 |
| $PCl_3(g)$ | −287.0 | 311.78 | −267.8 |
| $P_4O_{10}(s)$ | −2984.0 | 228.86 | −2697.7 |
| $H_3PO_4(\ell)$ | −1279.0 | 110.5 | −1119.1 |
| *Potassium* | | | |
| $K(s)$ | 0 | 64.63 | 0 |
| $KCl(s)$ | −436.68 | 82.56 | −408.77 |
| $KClO_3(s)$ | −397.73 | 143.1 | −296.25 |
| $KI(s)$ | −327.90 | 106.32 | −324.892 |
| $KOH(s)$ | −424.72 | 78.9 | −378.92 |
| $KOH(aq)$ | −482.37 | 91.6 | −440.50 |
| *Silicon* | | | |
| $Si(s)$ | 0 | 18.82 | 0 |
| $SiBr_4(\ell)$ | −457.3 | 277.8 | −443.9 |
| $SiC(s)$ | −65.3 | 16.61 | −62.8 |
| $SiCl_4(g)$ | −662.75 | 330.86 | −622.76 |
| $SiH_4(g)$ | 34.31 | 204.65 | 56.84 |
| $SiF_4(g)$ | −1614.94 | 282.49 | −1572.65 |
| $SiO_2$(s, quartz) | −910.86 | 41.46 | −856.97 |
| *Silver* | | | |
| $Ag(s)$ | 0 | 42.55 | 0 |
| $Ag_2O(s)$ | −31.1 | 121.3 | −11.32 |
| $AgCl(s)$ | −127.01 | 96.25 | −109.76 |
| $AgNO_3(s)$ | −124.39 | 140.92 | −33.41 |
| *Sodium* | | | |
| $Na(s)$ | 0 | 51.21 | 0 |
| $Na(g)$ | 107.3 | 153.765 | 76.83 |
| $Na^+(g)$ | 609.358 | — | — |
| $NaBr(s)$ | −361.02 | 86.82 | −348.983 |
| $NaCl(s)$ | −411.12 | 72.11 | −384.04 |
| $NaCl(g)$ | −181.42 | 229.79 | −201.33 |
| $NaCl(aq)$ | −407.27 | 115.5 | −393.133 |

**Table 20  Selected Thermodynamic Values (continued)**

| Species | $\Delta_f H°$ (298.15 K) (kJ/mol) | $S°$ (298.15 K) (J/K · mol) | $\Delta_f G°$ (298.15 K) (kJ/mol) |
|---|---|---|---|
| *Sodium (continued)* | | | |
| NaOH(s) | −425.93 | 64.46 | −379.75 |
| NaOH(aq) | −469.15 | 48.1 | −418.09 |
| Na$_2$CO$_3$(s) | −1130.77 | 134.79 | −1048.08 |
| *Sulfur* | | | |
| S(s, rhombic) | 0 | 32.1 | 0 |
| S(g) | 278.98 | 167.83 | 236.51 |
| S$_2$Cl$_2$(g) | −18.4 | 331.5 | −31.8 |
| SF$_6$(g) | −1209 | 291.82 | −1105.3 |
| H$_2$S(g) | −20.63 | 205.79 | −33.56 |
| SO$_2$(g) | −296.84 | 248.21 | −300.13 |
| SO$_3$(g) | −395.77 | 256.77 | −371.04 |
| SOCl$_2$(g) | −212.5 | 309.77 | −198.3 |
| H$_2$SO$_4$($\ell$) | −814 | 156.9 | −689.96 |
| H$_2$SO$_4$(aq) | −909.27 | 20.1 | −744.53 |
| *Tin* | | | |
| Sn(s, white) | 0 | 51.08 | 0 |
| Sn(s, gray) | −2.09 | 44.14 | 0.13 |
| SnCl$_4$($\ell$) | −511.3 | 258.6 | −440.15 |
| SnCl$_4$(g) | −471.5 | 365.8 | −432.31 |
| SnO$_2$(s) | −577.63 | 49.04 | −515.88 |
| *Titanium* | | | |
| Ti(s) | 0 | 30.72 | 0 |
| TiCl$_4$($\ell$) | −804.2 | 252.34 | −737.2 |
| TiCl$_4$(g) | −763.16 | 354.84 | −726.7 |
| TiO$_2$(s) | −939.7 | 49.92 | −884.5 |
| *Zinc* | | | |
| Zn(s) | 0 | 41.63 | 0 |
| ZnCl$_2$(s) | −415.05 | 111.46 | −369.398 |
| ZnO(s) | −348.28 | 43.64 | −318.30 |
| ZnS(s, sphalerite) | −205.98 | 57.7 | −201.29 |

# M Standard Reduction Potentials in Aqueous Solution at 25 °C

**Table 21** Standard Reduction Potentials in Aqueous Solution at 25 °C

| Acidic Solution | Standard Reduction Potential $E°$ (volts) |
|---|---|
| $F_2(g) + 2\,e^- \longrightarrow 2\,F^-(aq)$ | 2.87 |
| $Co^{3+}(aq) + e^- \longrightarrow Co^{2+}(aq)$ | 1.82 |
| $Pb^{4+}(aq) + 2\,e^- \longrightarrow Pb^{2+}(aq)$ | 1.8 |
| $H_2O_2(aq) + 2\,H^+(aq) + 2\,e^- \longrightarrow 2\,H_2O$ | 1.77 |
| $NiO_2(s) + 4\,H^+(aq) + 2\,e^- \longrightarrow Ni^{2+}(aq) + 2\,H_2O$ | 1.7 |
| $PbO_2(s) + SO_4^{2-}(aq) + 4\,H^+(aq) + 2\,e^- \longrightarrow PbSO_4(s) + 2\,H_2O$ | 1.685 |
| $Au^+(aq) + e^- \longrightarrow Au(s)$ | 1.68 |
| $2\,HClO(aq) + 2\,H^+(aq) + 2\,e^- \longrightarrow Cl_2(g) + 2\,H_2O$ | 1.63 |
| $Ce^{4+}(aq) + e^- \longrightarrow Ce^{3+}(aq)$ | 1.61 |
| $NaBiO_3(s) + 6\,H^+(aq) + 2\,e^- \longrightarrow Bi^{3+}(aq) + Na^+(aq) + 3\,H_2O$ | $\approx$1.6 |
| $MnO_4^-(aq) + 8\,H^+(aq) + 5\,e^- \longrightarrow Mn^{2+}(aq) + 4\,H_2O$ | 1.51 |
| $Au^{3+}(aq) + 3\,e^- \longrightarrow Au(s)$ | 1.50 |
| $ClO_3^-(aq) + 6\,H^+(aq) + 5\,e^- \longrightarrow \frac{1}{2}\,Cl_2(g) + 3\,H_2O$ | 1.47 |
| $BrO_3^-(aq) + 6\,H^+(aq) + 6\,e^- \longrightarrow Br^-(aq) + 3\,H_2O$ | 1.44 |
| $Cl_2(g) + 2\,e^- \longrightarrow 2\,Cl^-(aq)$ | 1.36 |
| $Cr_2O_7^{2-}(aq) + 14\,H^+(aq) + 6\,e^- \longrightarrow 2\,Cr^{3+}(aq) + 7\,H_2O$ | 1.33 |
| $N_2H_5^+(aq) + 3\,H^+(aq) + 2\,e^- \longrightarrow 2\,NH_4^+(aq)$ | 1.24 |
| $MnO_2(s) + 4\,H^+(aq) + 2\,e^- \longrightarrow Mn^{2+}(aq) + 2\,H_2O$ | 1.23 |
| $O_2(g) + 4\,H^+(aq) + 4\,e^- \longrightarrow 2\,H_2O$ | 1.229 |
| $Pt^{2+}(aq) + 2\,e^- \longrightarrow Pt(s)$ | 1.2 |
| $IO_3^-(aq) + 6\,H^+(aq) + 5\,e^- \longrightarrow \frac{1}{2}\,I_2(aq) + 3\,H_2O$ | 1.195 |
| $ClO_4^-(aq) + 2\,H^+(aq) + 2\,e^- \longrightarrow ClO_3^-(aq) + H_2O$ | 1.19 |
| $Br_2(\ell) + 2\,e^- \longrightarrow 2\,Br^-(aq)$ | 1.08 |
| $AuCl_4^-(aq) + 3\,e^- \longrightarrow Au(s) + 4\,Cl^-(aq)$ | 1.00 |
| $Pd^{2+}(aq) + 2\,e^- \longrightarrow Pd(s)$ | 0.987 |
| $NO_3^-(aq) + 4\,H^+(aq) + 3\,e^- \longrightarrow NO(g) + 2\,H_2O$ | 0.96 |
| $NO_3^-(aq) + 3\,H^+(aq) + 2\,e^- \longrightarrow HNO_2(aq) + H_2O$ | 0.94 |
| $2\,Hg^{2+}(aq) + 2\,e^- \longrightarrow Hg_2^{2+}(aq)$ | 0.920 |
| $Hg^{2+}(aq) + 2\,e^- \longrightarrow Hg(\ell)$ | 0.855 |
| $Ag^+(aq) + e^- \longrightarrow Ag(s)$ | 0.7994 |
| $Hg_2^{2+}(aq) + 2\,e^- \longrightarrow 2\,Hg(\ell)$ | 0.789 |
| $Fe^{3+}(aq) + e^- \longrightarrow Fe^{2+}(aq)$ | 0.771 |

**Table 21  Standard Reduction Potentials in Aqueous Solution at 25 °C (continued)**

| Acidic Solution | Standard Reduction Potential $E°$ (volts) |
|---|---|
| $SbCl_6^-(aq) + 2\,e^- \longrightarrow SbCl_4^-(aq) + 2\,Cl^-(aq)$ | 0.75 |
| $[PtCl_4]^{2-}(aq) + 2\,e^- \longrightarrow Pt(s) + 4\,Cl^-(aq)$ | 0.73 |
| $O_2(g) + 2\,H^+(aq) + 2\,e^- \longrightarrow H_2O_2(aq)$ | 0.682 |
| $[PtCl_6]^{2-}(aq) + 2\,e^- \longrightarrow [PtCl_4]^{2-}(aq) + 2\,Cl^-(aq)$ | 0.68 |
| $I_2(aq) + 2\,e^- \longrightarrow 2\,I^-(aq)$ | 0.621 |
| $H_3AsO_4(aq) + 2\,H^+(aq) + 2\,e^- \longrightarrow H_3AsO_3(aq) + H_2O$ | 0.58 |
| $I_2(s) + 2\,e^- \longrightarrow 2\,I^-(aq)$ | 0.535 |
| $TeO_2(s) + 4\,H^+(aq) + 4\,e^- \longrightarrow Te(s) + 2\,H_2O$ | 0.529 |
| $Cu^+(aq) + e^- \longrightarrow Cu(s)$ | 0.521 |
| $[RhCl_6]^{3-}(aq) + 3\,e^- \longrightarrow Rh(s) + 6\,Cl^-(aq)$ | 0.44 |
| $Cu^{2+}(aq) + 2\,e^- \longrightarrow Cu(s)$ | 0.337 |
| $Hg_2Cl_2(s) + 2\,e^- \longrightarrow 2\,Hg(\ell) + 2\,Cl^-(aq)$ | 0.27 |
| $AgCl(s) + e^- \longrightarrow Ag(s) + Cl^-(aq)$ | 0.222 |
| $SO_4^{2-}(aq) + 4\,H^+(aq) + 2\,e^- \longrightarrow SO_2(g) + 2\,H_2O$ | 0.20 |
| $SO_4^{2-}(aq) + 4\,H^+(aq) + 2\,e^- \longrightarrow H_2SO_3(aq) + H_2O$ | 0.17 |
| $Cu^{2+}(aq) + e^- \longrightarrow Cu^+(aq)$ | 0.153 |
| $Sn^{4+}(aq) + 2\,e^- \longrightarrow Sn^{2+}(aq)$ | 0.15 |
| $S(s) + 2\,H^+ + 2\,e^- \longrightarrow H_2S(aq)$ | 0.14 |
| $AgBr(s) + e^- \longrightarrow Ag(s) + Br^-(aq)$ | 0.0713 |
| $2\,H^+(aq) + 2\,e^- \longrightarrow H_2(g)\,(reference\ electrode)$ | 0.0000 |
| $N_2O(g) + 6\,H^+(aq) + H_2O + 4\,e^- \longrightarrow 2\,NH_3OH^+(aq)$ | −0.05 |
| $Pb^{2+}(aq) + 2\,e^- \longrightarrow Pb(s)$ | −0.126 |
| $Sn^{2+}(aq) + 2\,e^- \longrightarrow Sn(s)$ | −0.14 |
| $AgI(s) + e^- \longrightarrow Ag(s) + I^-(aq)$ | −0.15 |
| $[SnF_6]^{2-}(aq) + 4\,e^- \longrightarrow Sn(s) + 6\,F^-(aq)$ | −0.25 |
| $Ni^{2+}(aq) + 2\,e^- \longrightarrow Ni(s)$ | −0.25 |
| $Co^{2+}(aq) + 2\,e^- \longrightarrow Co(s)$ | −0.28 |
| $Tl^+(aq) + e^- \longrightarrow Tl(s)$ | −0.34 |
| $PbSO_4(s) + 2\,e^- \longrightarrow Pb(s) + SO_4^{2-}(aq)$ | −0.356 |
| $Se(s) + 2\,H^+(aq) + 2\,e^- \longrightarrow H_2Se(aq)$ | −0.40 |
| $Cd^{2+}(aq) + 2\,e^- \longrightarrow Cd(s)$ | −0.403 |
| $Cr^{3+}(aq) + e^- \longrightarrow Cr^{2+}(aq)$ | −0.41 |
| $Fe^{2+}(aq) + 2\,e^- \longrightarrow Fe(s)$ | −0.44 |
| $2\,CO_2(g) + 2\,H^+(aq) + 2\,e^- \longrightarrow H_2C_2O_4(aq)$ | −0.49 |
| $Ga^{3+}(aq) + 3\,e^- \longrightarrow Ga(s)$ | −0.53 |
| $HgS(s) + 2\,H^+(aq) + 2\,e^- \longrightarrow Hg(\ell) + H_2S(g)$ | −0.72 |
| $Cr^{3+}(aq) + 3\,e^- \longrightarrow Cr(s)$ | −0.74 |
| $Zn^{2+}(aq) + 2\,e^- \longrightarrow Zn(s)$ | −0.763 |
| $Cr^{2+}(aq) + 2\,e^- \longrightarrow Cr(s)$ | −0.91 |

*(continued)*

**Table 21  Standard Reduction Potentials in Aqueous Solution at 25 °C (continued)**

| Acidic Solution | Standard Reduction Potential $E°$ (volts) |
|---|---|
| $FeS(s) + 2\,e^- \longrightarrow Fe(s) + S^{2-}(aq)$ | $-1.01$ |
| $Mn^{2+}(aq) + 2\,e^- \longrightarrow Mn(s)$ | $-1.18$ |
| $V^{2+}(aq) + 2\,e^- \longrightarrow V(s)$ | $-1.18$ |
| $CdS(s) + 2\,e^- \longrightarrow Cd(s) + S^{2-}(aq)$ | $-1.21$ |
| $ZnS(s) + 2\,e^- \longrightarrow Zn(s) + S^{2-}(aq)$ | $-1.44$ |
| $Zr^{4+}(aq) + 4\,e^- \longrightarrow Zr(s)$ | $-1.53$ |
| $Al^{3+}(aq) + 3\,e^- \longrightarrow Al(s)$ | $-1.66$ |
| $Mg^{2+}(aq) + 2\,e^- \longrightarrow Mg(s)$ | $-2.37$ |
| $Na^+(aq) + e^- \longrightarrow Na(s)$ | $-2.714$ |
| $Ca^{2+}(aq) + 2\,e^- \longrightarrow Ca(s)$ | $-2.87$ |
| $Sr^{2+}(aq) + 2\,e^- \longrightarrow Sr(s)$ | $-2.89$ |
| $Ba^{2+}(aq) + 2\,e^- \longrightarrow Ba(s)$ | $-2.90$ |
| $Rb^+(aq) + e^- \longrightarrow Rb(s)$ | $-2.925$ |
| $K^+(aq) + e^- \longrightarrow K(s)$ | $-2.925$ |
| $Li^+(aq) + e^- \longrightarrow Li(s)$ | $-3.045$ |

| Basic Solution | Standard Reduction Potential $E°$ (volts) |
|---|---|
| $ClO^-(aq) + H_2O + 2\,e^- \longrightarrow Cl^-(aq) + 2\,OH^-(aq)$ | $0.89$ |
| $OOH^-(aq) + H_2O + 2\,e^- \longrightarrow 3\,OH^-(aq)$ | $0.88$ |
| $2\,NH_2OH(aq) + 2\,e^- \longrightarrow N_2H_4(aq) + 2\,OH^-(aq)$ | $0.74$ |
| $ClO_3^-(aq) + 3\,H_2O + 6\,e^- \longrightarrow Cl^-(aq) + 6\,OH^-(aq)$ | $0.62$ |
| $MnO_4^-(aq) + 2\,H_2O + 3\,e^- \longrightarrow MnO_2(s) + 4\,OH^-(aq)$ | $0.588$ |
| $MnO_4^-(aq) + e^- \longrightarrow MnO_4^{2-}(aq)$ | $0.564$ |
| $NiO_2(s) + 2\,H_2O + 2\,e^- \longrightarrow Ni(OH)_2(s) + 2\,OH^-(aq)$ | $0.49$ |
| $Ag_2CrO_4(s) + 2\,e^- \longrightarrow 2\,Ag(s) + CrO_4^{2-}(aq)$ | $0.446$ |
| $O_2(g) + 2\,H_2O + 4\,e^- \longrightarrow 4\,OH^-(aq)$ | $0.40$ |
| $ClO_4^-(aq) + H_2O + 2\,e^- \longrightarrow ClO_3^-(aq) + 2\,OH^-(aq)$ | $0.36$ |
| $Ag_2O(s) + H_2O + 2\,e^- \longrightarrow 2\,Ag(s) + 2\,OH^-(aq)$ | $0.34$ |
| $2\,NO_2^-(aq) + 3\,H_2O + 4\,e^- \longrightarrow N_2O(g) + 6\,OH^-(aq)$ | $0.15$ |
| $N_2H_4(aq) + 2\,H_2O + 2\,e^- \longrightarrow 2\,NH_3(aq) + 2\,OH^-(aq)$ | $0.10$ |
| $[Co(NH_3)_6]^{3+}(aq) + e^- \longrightarrow [Co(NH_3)_6]^{2+}(aq)$ | $0.10$ |
| $HgO(s) + H_2O + 2\,e^- \longrightarrow Hg(\ell) + 2\,OH^-(aq)$ | $0.0984$ |
| $O_2(g) + H_2O + 2\,e^- \longrightarrow OOH^-(aq) + OH^-(aq)$ | $0.076$ |
| $NO_3^-(aq) + H_2O + 2\,e^- \longrightarrow NO_2^-(aq) + 2\,OH^-(aq)$ | $0.01$ |
| $MnO_2(s) + 2\,H_2O + 2\,e^- \longrightarrow Mn(OH)_2(s) + 2\,OH^-(aq)$ | $-0.05$ |
| $CrO_4^{2-}(aq) + 4\,H_2O + 3\,e^- \longrightarrow Cr(OH)_3(s) + 5\,OH^-(aq)$ | $-0.12$ |
| $Cu(OH)_2(s) + 2\,e^- \longrightarrow Cu(s) + 2\,OH^-(aq)$ | $-0.36$ |
| $S(s) + 2\,e^- \longrightarrow S^{2-}(aq)$ | $-0.48$ |
| $Fe(OH)_3(s) + e^- \longrightarrow Fe(OH)_2(s) + OH^-(aq)$ | $-0.56$ |
| $2\,H_2O + 2\,e^- \longrightarrow H_2(g) + 2\,OH^-(aq)$ | $-0.8277$ |

**Table 21 Standard Reduction Potentials in Aqueous Solution at 25 °C (continued)**

| Basic Solution | Standard Reduction Potential $E°$ (volts) |
|---|---|
| $2\ NO_3^-(aq) + 2\ H_2O + 2\ e^- \longrightarrow N_2O_4(g) + 4\ OH^-(aq)$ | −0.85 |
| $Fe(OH)_2(s) + 2\ e^- \longrightarrow Fe(s) + 2\ OH^-(aq)$ | −0.877 |
| $SO_4^{2-}(aq) + H_2O + 2\ e^- \longrightarrow SO_3^{2-}(aq) + 2\ OH^-(aq)$ | −0.93 |
| $N_2(g) + 4\ H_2O + 4\ e^- \longrightarrow N_2H_4(aq) + 4\ OH^-(aq)$ | −1.15 |
| $[Zn(OH)_4]^{2-}(aq) + 2\ e^- \longrightarrow Zn(s) + 4\ OH^-(aq)$ | −1.22 |
| $Zn(OH)_2(s) + 2\ e^- \longrightarrow Zn(s) + 2\ OH^-(aq)$ | −1.245 |
| $[Zn(CN)_4]^{2-}(aq) + 2\ e^- \longrightarrow Zn(s) + 4\ CN^-(aq)$ | −1.26 |
| $Cr(OH)_3(s) + 3\ e^- \longrightarrow Cr(s) + 3\ OH^-(aq)$ | −1.30 |
| $SiO_3^{2-}(aq) + 3\ H_2O + 4\ e^- \longrightarrow Si(s) + 6\ OH^-(aq)$ | −1.70 |

# N Answers to Chapter Opening Questions and Case Study Questions

## Chapter 1
### Chapter Opening: Gold!

1. $5.2 \times 10^5$ g Au; $19 million

2. Gold = Au; copper = Cu; zinc = Zn

3. 1337 K

4. (a) No, gold is not the most dense element.

   (b) 0.217 cm$^3$ Au

### Case Study: CO$_2$ in the Oceans

1. Carbon dioxide

2. Calcium: Ca; copper: Cu; manganese: Mn; iron: Fe

3. Most dense: copper, least dense: calcium

4. Elements: calcium, carbon, oxygen

   Compound name: calcium carbonate

## Let's Review
### Case Study: Out of Gas!

1. Fuel density in kg/L: (1.77 lb/L) (0.4536 kg/lb) = 0.803 kg/L

2. Mass of fuel already in tank: 7682 L (0.803 kg/L) = 6170 kg

   Mass of fuel needed: 22,300 kg − 6,170 kg = 16,100 kg (answer to three significant figures)

   Volume of fuel needed: 16,130 kg (1 L/0.803 kg) = 20,100 L

## Chapter 2
### Chapter Opening: The Periodic Table, the Central Icon of Chemistry

1. Eka-silicon is germanium. Its atomic weight is 72.61 (predicted 72), and its density is 5.32 g/cm$^3$ (predicted value 5.5 g/cm$^3$).

2. Other elements missing from Mendeleev's periodic table include Sc, Ga, the noble gases (He, Ne, Ar, Kr, Xe), and all of the radioactive elements except Th and U.

### Case Study: Using Isotopes: Ötzi, the Iceman of the Alps

1. $^{18}$O: 18 − 8 = 10 neutrons

   $^{204}$Pb: 204 − 82 = 122 neutrons

   $^{206}$Pb: 206 − 82 = 124 neutrons

2. $^{14}$C: 14 − 6 = 8 neutrons

3. $^{87}$Sr/$^{86}$Sr = 0.710

   The ratio found in the Iceman is slightly higher.

### Case Study: Mummies, Bangladesh, and the Formula of Compound 606

1. Amount As: 19.024 g As × (1 mol As/74.9216 g As) = 0.25392 mol As

   Amount Cu: 48.407 g Cu × (1 mol Cu/63.546 g Cu) = 0.76176 mol Cu

   Amount S: 32.569 g S × (1 mol S/32.066 g S) = 1.0157 mol S

   Mole ratio Cu/As: 0.76176 mol Cu/0.25392 mol As = 3.0000 mol Cu/1 mol As

   Mole ratio S/As: 1.0157 mol S/0.25392 mol As = 4.0001 mol S/1 mol As

   Empirical formula: Cu$_3$AsS$_4$

2. Amount C: 39.37 g C × (1 mol C/12.011 g C) = 3.278 mol C

   Amount H: 3.304 g H × (1 mol H/1.0079 g H) = 3.278 mol H

   Amount O: 8.741 g O × (1 mol O/15.999 g O) = 0.5463 mol O

   Amount N: 7.652 g N × (1 mol N/14.007 g N) = 0.5463 mol N

   Amount As: 40.932 g As × (1 mol As/74.9216 g As) = 0.54633 mol As

   Mole ratio C/O and H/O: 3.278 mol C/0.5463 mol O = 6.000 mol C/1 mol O. A similar calculation yields 6.000 mol H/1 mol O.

Mole ratio N/O and As/O: 0.5463 mol N/ 0.5463 mol O = 1.000 mol N/1 mol O. A similar calculation yields 1.000 mol As/1 mol O.

Empirical formula: $C_6H_6AsNO$

Molar mass of $C_6H_6AsNO$: 183.0 g/mol

Compound 1: 549/183.0 = 3.00; therefore, the molecular formula is $C_{18}H_{18}As_3N_3O_3$.

Compound 2: 915/183.0 = 5.00; therefore, the molecular formula is $C_{30}H_{30}As_5N_5O_5$.

# Chapter 3
## Chapter Opening: Black Smokers and Volcanoes

$Fe^{2+}(aq) + H_2S(aq) + 2 H_2O(\ell) \rightarrow FeS(s) + 2 H_3O^+(aq)$

$2 Bi^{3+}(aq) + 3 H_2S(aq) + 6 H_2O(\ell) \rightarrow Bi_2S_3(s) + 6 H_3O^+(aq)$

$Ca^{2+}(aq) + SO_4^{2-}(aq) \rightarrow CaSO_4(s)$

## Case Study: Killing Bacteria with Silver

1. $100 \times 10^{15}$ $Ag^+$ ions (1 mol/$6.022 \times 10^{23}$ ions) = $2 \times 10^{-7}$ mol $Ag^+$

2. $2 \times 10^{-7}$ mol $Ag^+$ (107.9 g $Ag^+$/1 mol $Ag^+$) = $2 \times 10^{-5}$ g $Ag^+$ ions

# Chapter 4
## Chapter Opening: The Chemistry of Pyrotechnics

1. 1.0 g Fe (1 mol Fe/55.85 g Fe)(2 mol $Fe_2O_3$/ 4 mol Fe)(159.7 g $Fe_2O_3$/1 mol $Fe_2O_3$) = 1.4 g $Fe_2O_3$

2. 10.0 g $Fe_2O_3$ (1 mol $Fe_2O_3$/159.7 g $Fe_2O_3$) (2 mol Al/1 mol $Fe_2O_3$)(26.98 g Al/1 mol Al) = 3.38 g Al

3. 20 g Al (1 mol Al/26.98 g Al) = 0.7 mol Al 10 g $Fe_2O_3$ (1 mol $Fe_2O_3$/159.7 g $Fe_2O_3$) = 0.06 mol $Fe_2O_3$

   Mole ratio from balanced equation: 2 mol Al/ 1 mol $Fe_2O_3$

   Mole ratio actually present: 0.7 mol Al/0.06 mol $Fe_2O_3$ = $1 \times 10^1$ mol Al/1 mol $Fe_2O_3$

   There is an excess of Al compared to what the balanced equation requires, so $Fe_2O_3$ is the limiting reactant.

## Case Study: Green Chemistry and Atom Economy

Reactant molecules contain 5 C, 10 H, 3 O. Combined molar mass = 118.1 g/mol

Desired product (methyl methacrylate) contains 5 C, 8 H, 2 O. Molar mass = 100.1 g/mol

% Atom economy = $(100.1/118.1) \times 100$ = 84.75%

## Case Study: How Much Salt Is There in Seawater?

1. Step 1: Calculate the amount of $Cl^-$ in the diluted solution from titration data.

   Mol $Cl^-$ in 50 mL of dilute solution = mol $Ag^+$ = (0.100 mol/L)(0.02625 L) = $2.63 \times 10^{-3}$ mol $Cl^-$

   Step 2: Calculate the concentration of $Cl^-$ in the dilute solution.

   Concentration of $Cl^-$ in dilute solution = $2.63 \times 10^{-3}$ mol/0.0500 L = $5.25 \times 10^{-2}$ M

   Step 3: Calculate the concentration of $Cl^-$ in seawater.

   Seawater was initially diluted to one hundredth its original concentration. Thus, the concentration of $Cl^-$ in seawater (undiluted) = 5.25 M

## Case Study: Forensic Chemistry: Titrations and Food Tampering

1. Step 1: Calculate the amount of $I_2$ in solution from titration data.

   Amount $I_2$ = (0.0425 mol $S_2O_3^{2-}$/L)(0.0253 L) (1 mol $I_2$/2 mol $S_2O_3^{2-}$) = $5.38 \times 10^{-4}$ mol $I_2$

   Step 2: Calculate the amount of NaClO present based on the amount of $I_2$ formed, and from that value calculate the mass of NaClO.

   Mass NaClO = $5.38 \times 10^{-4}$ mol $I_2$ (1 mol HClO/ 1 mol $I_2$)(1 mol NaClO/1 mol HClO)(74.44 g NaClO/1 mol NaClO) = 0.0400 g NaClO

# Chapter 5
## Chapter Opening: Energy and Your Diet

1. Orange, all commercial varieties (197 kJ) < apple, raw with skin (218 kJ) < potato, flesh and skin, raw (321 kJ) < rice, brown, long grain, uncooked (1548 kJ) < popcorn, unpopped kernels (1568 kJ) < glazed doughnut, yeast-leavened, unenriched (1686 kJ) < peanut M&Ms (2156 kJ) < mixed nuts, dry roasted, with peanuts, with salt (2485 kJ)

2. In the following, we assume water vapor, $H_2O(g)$, is formed upon oxidation.

   Balanced Equation: $C_2H_5OH(\ell) + 3 O_2(g) \rightarrow 2 CO_2(g) + 3 H_2O(g)$

   $\Delta_r H° = $ (2 mol $CO_2$/1 mol-rxn)$[\Delta_f H° CO_2(g)]$ + (3 mol $H_2O$/1 mol-rxn)$[\Delta_f H° H_2O(g)]$ − {(1 mol $C_2H_5OH$/1 mol-rxn)$[\Delta_f H° C_2H_5OH(\ell)]$ + (3 mol $O_2$/1 mol-rxn)$[\Delta_f H° O_2(g)]$}

$\Delta_r H° = $ (2 mol $CO_2$/1 mol-rxn)[−393.5 kJ/mol $CO_2$] + (3 mol $H_2O$/1 mol-rxn)[−241.8 kJ/mol $H_2O$] − {(1 mol $C_2H_5OH$/1 mol-rxn)[−277.0 kJ/mol $C_2H_5OH$] + (3 mol $O_2$/1 mol-rxn)[0 kJ/mol $O_2$]} = −1235.4 kJ/mol-rxn

100. g $C_2H_5OH$ (1 mol $C_2H_5OH$/46.07 g $C_2H_5OH$)(1 mol-rxn/1 mol $C_2H_5OH$)(−1235.4 kJ/mol-rxn) = −2680 kJ

The energy evolved as heat is 2680 kJ. This is more energy than all of the foods pictured except for the mixed nuts.

## Case Study: The Fuel Controversy–Alcohol and Gasoline

In the following, we assume water vapor, $H_2O(g)$, is formed upon oxidation.

1. Burning ethanol: $C_2H_5OH(\ell) + 3\ O_2(g) \rightarrow 2\ CO_2(g) + 3\ H_2O(g)$

   $\Delta_r H° = $ (2 mol $CO_2$/mol-rxn)[$\Delta_f H°(CO_2)$] + (3 mol $H_2O$/mol-rxn)[$\Delta_f H°(H_2O)$] − (1 mol $C_2H_5OH$/mol-rxn)[$\Delta_f H°(C_2H_5OH)$]

   $\Delta_r H° = $ (2 mol $CO_2$/mol-rxn)[−393.5 kJ/mol $CO_2$] + (3 mol $H_2O$/mol-rxn)[−241.8 kJ/mol $H_2O$] − (1 mol $C_2H_5OH$/mol-rxn)[−277.0 kJ/mol $C_2H_5OH$] = −1235.4 kJ/mol-rxn

   1 mol ethanol per 1 mol-rxn; therefore, $q$ per mol is −1235.4 kJ/mol

   $q$ per gram: −1235.4 kJ/mol (1 mol $C_2H_5OH$/46.07 g $C_2H_5OH$) = −26.80 kJ/g $C_2H_5OH$

   Burning octane: $C_8H_{18}(\ell) + 12.5\ O_2(g) \rightarrow 8\ CO_2(g) + 9\ H_2O(g)$

   $\Delta_r H° = $ (8 mol $CO_2$/mol-rxn)[$\Delta_f H°(CO_2)$] + (9 mol $H_2O$/mol-rxn)[$\Delta_f H°(H_2O)$] − (1 mol $C_8H_{18}$/mol-rxn)[$\Delta_f H°(C_8H_{18})$]

   $\Delta_r H° = $ (8 mol $CO_2$/mol-rxn)[−393.5 kJ/mol $CO_2$] + (9 mol $H_2O$/mol-rxn)[−241.8 kJ/mol $H_2O$] − (1 mol $C_8H_{18}$/mol-rxn)[−250.1 kJ/mol $C_8H_{18}$] = −5074.1 kJ/mol-rxn

   1 mol octane per mol-rxn; therefore, $q$ per mol is −5074.1 kJ/mol

   $q$ per gram: −5074.1 kJ/1 mol $C_8H_{18}$ (1 mol $C_8H_{18}$/114.2 g $C_8H_{18}$) = −44.43 kJ/g $C_8H_{18}$

2. For ethanol, per liter: $q = $ −26.80 kJ/g (785 g/L) = −2.10 × 10⁴ kJ/L

   For octane, per liter: $q = $ −44.43 kJ/g (699 g/L) = − 3.11 × 10⁴ kJ/L

   Octane produces almost 50% more energy per liter of fuel.

3. Mass of $CO_2$ per liter of ethanol = 1.000 L (785 g $C_2H_5OH$/L)(1 mol $C_2H_5OH$/46.07 g $C_2H_5OH$)(2 mol $CO_2$/1 mol $C_2H_5OH$)(44.01 g $CO_2$/1 mol $CO_2$) = 1.50 × 10³ g $CO_2$

   Mass of $CO_2$ per liter of octane = 1.000 L (699 g $C_8H_{18}$/L)(1 mol $C_8H_{18}$/114.2 g $C_8H_{18}$)(8 mol $CO_2$/1 mol $C_8H_{18}$)(44.01 g $CO_2$/1 mol $CO_2$) = 2.16 × 10³ g $CO_2$

4. Volume of ethanol needed to obtain 3.11 × 10⁴ kJ of energy from oxidation: 2.10 × 10⁴ kJ/L $C_2H_5OH$)($x$) = 3.11 × 10⁴ kJ (where $x$ is volume of ethanol)

   Volume of ethanol = $x$ = 1.48 L

   Mass of $CO_2$ produced by burning 1.48 L of ethanol = (1.50 × 10³ g $CO_2$/L $C_2H_5OH$)(1.48 L $C_2H_5OH$) = 2.22 × 10³ g $CO_2$

   To obtain the same amount of energy, slightly more $CO_2$ is produced by burning ethanol than by burning octane.

5. Your car will travel about 50% farther on a liter of octane, and it will produce slightly less $CO_2$ emissions, than if you burned 1.0 L of ethanol.

## Chapter 6
### Chapter Opening: Fireworks

1. Yellow light has a longer wavelength than blue light.

2. Blue light has a greater energy per photon than yellow light.

3. The energy of light emitted by atoms is determined by the energy levels of the electrons in an atom. See discussion in the text, Section 6.3.

### Case Study: What Makes the Colors in Fireworks?

1. Yellow light is from the 589 and 590 nm emissions.

2. Primary emission for Sr is red. This has a longer wavelength than yellow light.

3. $4\ Mg(s) + KClO_4(s) \rightarrow KCl(s) + 4\ MgO(s)$

## Chapter 7
### Chapter Opening: Rubies and Sapphires—Pretty Stones

1. Cr: $[Ar]3d^5 4s^1$; $Cr^{3+}$: $[Ar]3d^3$

2. $Cr^{2+}$ is paramagnetic with four unpaired electrons. $Cr^{3+}$ is paramagnetic with three unpaired electrons.

3. The radius of $Al^{3+}$ is 57 pm. The radius of $Cr^{3+}$ is thus only 7 pm larger than that of $Al^{3+}$.

4. $Fe^{2+}$: $[Ar]3d^6$; $Ti^{4+}$: $[Ar]$

## Case Study: Metals in Biochemistry and Medicine

1. Fe: $[Ar]3d^64s^2$; $Fe^{2+}$: $[Ar]3d^6$; $Fe^{3+}$: $[Ar]3d^5$

2. Both iron ions are paramagnetic.

3. Cu: $[Ar]3d^{10}4s^1$; $Cu^+$: $[Ar]3d^{10}$; $Cu^{2+}$: $[Ar]3d^9$; $Cu^{2+}$ is paramagnetic; $Cu^+$ is diamagnetic.

4. The slightly larger size of Cu compared to Fe is related to greater electron–electron repulsions.

5. $Fe^{2+}$ is larger than $Fe^{3+}$ and will fit less well into the structure. As a result, some distortion of the ring structure from planarity occurs.

# Chapter 8

## Chapter Opening: Chemical Bonding in DNA

1. Carbon and phosphorus (in phosphate) achieve the noble gas configuration by forming four bonds.

2. In each instance, there are four bonds to the element; VSEPR predicts that these atoms will have tetrahedral geometry with 109.5° angles.

3. Bond angles in these rings are 120°. To achieve this preferred bond angle, the rings must be planar.

4. Thymine and cytosine are polar molecules.

## Case Study: Hydroxyl Radicals, Atmospheric Chemistry, and Hair Dyes

1. 18 valence electrons

$$\text{H}-\ddot{\text{O}}-\ddot{\text{N}}=\ddot{\text{O}}$$

All atoms have a formal charge of zero. There are no equivalent resonance structures.

2. 30 valence electrons

All atoms have zero formal charge except for those indicated.

## Case Study: Ibuprofen, A Study in Green Chemistry

1. The Lewis structures for the key portions of the molecules where the reaction takes place are the following:

Bond broken: 1 C—O and 1 C≡O

$(1 \text{ mol C—O}/1 \text{ mol-rxn})(358 \text{ kJ/mol C—O}) +$
$(1 \text{ mol C≡O}/1 \text{ mol-rxn})(1046 \text{ kJ/mol C≡O})$
$= 1404 \text{ kJ/mol-rxn}$

Bonds formed: 1 C—C, 1 C=C, and 1 C—O

$(1 \text{ mol C—C}/1 \text{ mol-rxn})(346 \text{ kJ/mol C—C}) +$
$(1 \text{ mol C=O}/1 \text{ mol-rxn})(745 \text{ kJ/mol C=O}) +$
$(1 \text{ mol C—O}/1 \text{ mol-rxn})(358 \text{ kJ/mol C—O})$
$= 1449 \text{ kJ/mol-rxn}$

$\Delta_r H° \approx 1404 \text{ kJ/mol-rxn} - 1449 \text{ kJ/mol-rxn}$
$= -45 \text{ kJ/mol-rxn}$

The reaction is thus predicted to be exothermic.

2. All of the atoms in ibuprofen have a formal charge of zero.

3. The most polar bond in the molecule is the O—H bond.

4. The molecule is not symmetrical and so is polar.

5. The shortest bond in the molecule is the O—H bond.

6. The C=O bond has the highest bond order. The C=C bonds in the ring have an order of 1.5.

7. Yes, there are 120° bond angles present: the bond angles around the C atoms in the ring and those around the C atom in the $-CO_2H$ group are all 120°. There are no 180° angles in this molecule.

8. There is one acid group in ibuprofen ($-CO_2H$), therefore 1 mol of ibuprofen will react with 1 mol of NaOH.

   200. mg ibuprofen (1 g/1000 mg)(1 mol ibuprofen/206.3 g ibuprofen)(1 mol NaOH/ 1 mol ibuprofen)(1 L/0.0259 mol NaOH) (1000 mL/1 L) = 37.4 mL

   Therefore 37.4 mL of the NaOH solution would be required.

# Chapter 9

## Chapter Opening: The Noble Gases: Not So Inert

1. $XeF_2$ is linear. The electron-pair geometry is trigonal-bipyramidal. Three lone pairs are located in the equatorial plane, and the two F atoms are located in the axial positions. This symmetrical structure will not have a dipole.

2. The Xe atom is $sp^3d$ hybridized. Xe—F bonds: overlap of Xe $sp^3d$ orbitals with F $2p$ orbital. 3 lone pairs in Xe $sp^3d$ orbitals.

**3.** This 36-electron molecule has a bent molecular structure.

## Case Study: Green Chemistry, Safe Dyes, and Molecular Orbitals

**1.** $C_8H_4BrNO$

**2.** The energy per photon is inversely proportional to wavelength. The light absorbed by butter yellow has a smaller wavelength than that absorbed by nitrated butter yellow; therefore butter yellow absorbs higher energy light than does nitrated butter yellow.

**3.** Tyrian purple: 9

Nitrated butter yellow: 8

## Chapter 10
### Chapter Opening: The Food of the Gods

**1.** The only structural difference between theobromine and caffeine occurs on the N in the six-member ring that is between the two C=O groups. In theobromine, there is an H atom attached to this N. In caffeine, there is a $CH_3$ group attached.

**2.** 5.00 g sample (2.16 g theobromine/100 g sample) = 0.108 g theobromine

### Case Study: An Awakening with L-DOPA

**1.** L-DOPA is chiral. Its chiral center is indicated in the following structural formula.

**2.** Dopamine is not chiral. Epinephrine is chiral. Its chiral center is indicated in the following structural formula.

**3.** 5.0 g L-DOPA (1 mol L-DOPA/197.2 g L-DOPA) = 0.025 mol L-DOPA

## Case Study: Green Adhesives

**1.** Structural formulas:

phenol          urea          formaldehyde

**2.** The electron-pair and molecular geometries are both trigonal-planar. The C—H σ bonds are each formed by the overlap of an $sp^2$ hybrid orbital on the C atom with the $1s$ orbital of the H atom. The σ bond between the C and O is formed by the overlap of an $sp^2$ hybrid orbital on the C with an $sp^2$ hybrid orbital on the O. The π bond between the C and O is formed by the overlap of a $2p$ orbital on C with a $2p$ orbital on O.

**3.** Similarity: Both nylon-6,6 and proteins are polyamides.

Differences:

1. In proteins there is one direction for the amide linkage: CONH. In nylon-6,6 two orientations are present: CONH and NHCO.

2. In proteins there is only one C between the amide linkages. In nylon-6,6 there are four or six carbons between amide linkages.

3. Proteins have numerous R groups that can be attached to the carbon in between the amide groups, whereas nylon-6,6 has only hydrogen atoms attached to the carbons in between the amide groups.

4. Proteins are chiral, whereas nylon-6,6 is not.

## Chapter 11
### Chapter Opening: The Atmosphere and Altitude Sickness

**1.** $P(O_2)$ at 3000 m is 70% of 0.21 atm, the value of $P(O_2)$ at sea level. Thus, $P(O_2)$ at 3000 m = 0.21 atm × 0.70 = 0.15 atm (110 mm Hg). At the top of Everest, $P(O_2)$ = 0.21 atm × 0.29 = 0.061 atm (46 mm Hg).

**2.** Blood saturation levels (estimated from table): at 3000 m, >95%; at top of Everest, 75%.

### Case Study: What to Do with All of that $CO_2$? More on Green Chemistry

**1.** $9.1 \times 10^9$ g C (1 mol C/12.0 g C) (1 mol $CO_2$/1 mol C)(44.0 g $CO_2$/1 mol $CO_2$) = $3.3 \times 10^{10}$ g $CO_2$

2. $1.0 \times 10^6$ g $CO_2$ (1 mol $CO_2$/44.0 g $CO_2$) (1 mol $(NH_4)_2CO_3$/1 mol $CO_2$) (96.1 g $(NH_4)_2CO_3$/1 mol $(NH_4)_2CO_3$) = $2.2 \times 10^6$ g $(NH_4)_2CO_3$

## Chapter 12
### Case Study: Methane Hydrates

1. One $CH_4$ molecule is contained in a clathrate cage that has 12 faces, 20 apexes, and 30 edges; each edge is an O—H—O unit, so there are 30 hydrogen bonds.

2. $164$ m$^3$ = $1.64 \times 10^5$ L of $CH_4$. Use the ideal gas law to calculate $n$ ($n = 7.32 \times 10^3$ mol $CH_4$). Using $\Delta_f H°$ values, calculate the enthalpy change for the combustion of 1.00 mole of $CH_4$ to form $CO_2(g)$ and $H_2O(g)$ ($\Delta_r H° = -802$ kJ/mol). $\Delta_r H°$ for 164 m$^3$ of $CH_4$ = $(-802$ kJ/mol$)$ $(7.32 \times 10^3$ mol$)$ = $-5.87 \times 10^6$ kJ.

### Case Study: A Pet Food Catastrophe

1. % N in melamine = $84/126 \times 100 = 67\%$

   % N in cyanuric acid = $42/129 \times 100 = 33\%$

   Both of these compounds have a greater percentage of nitrogen than the average protein.

2. 454 g sample (0.14 g melamine/1,000,000 g sample) = $6.4 \times 10^{-5}$ g melamine = 0.064 mg melamine = 64 $\mu$g melamine

## Chapter 13
### Chapter Opening: Lithium and "Green Cars"

1. 73,000,000 metric tons $Li_2CO_3$ (13.88 metric tons Li/73.89 metric tons $Li_2CO_3$) = $1.4 \times 10^7$ metric tons Li (= 14 million metric tons Li)

2. The unit cell for lithium metal is body-centered cubic. (There are atoms at each of the corners of a cube and one atom embedded in the middle of the cube.)

3. 351 pm (1 m/$10^{12}$ pm) (100 cm/1 m) = $3.51 \times 10^{-8}$ cm

   $V$ of unit cell = $(3.51 \times 10^{-8}$ cm$)^3$ = $4.32 \times 10^{-23}$ cm$^3$

   Mass of unit cell = 6.941 g Li/mol (1 mol/$6.022 \times 10^{23}$ atoms)(2 atoms/unit cell) = $2.305 \times 10^{-23}$ g/unit cell

   Density = mass/volume = $2.305 \times 10^{-23}$ g/$4.32 \times 10^{-23}$ cm$^3$ = 0.533 g/cm$^3$

4. One method is to carry out the following gas-forming reaction:

   $Li_2CO_3(aq) + 2 HCl(aq) \rightarrow 2 LiCl(aq) + H_2O(\ell) + CO_2(g)$

### Case Study: High-Strength Steel and Unit Cells

1. Ferrite has a body-centered cubic unit cell.

2. Austenite has a face-centered cubic unit unit cell of iron atoms with a carbon atom embedded in the body of the cell.

3. The face-centered unit cell of austenite transforms into a body-centered unit cell, but this unit cell is not cubic because it is longer in one dimension than the other two (this is called a *body-centered tetragonal unit cell*). The carbon atoms remain embedded in the lattice.

### Case Study: Graphene—The Hottest New Network Solid

1. We want to know the distance $x$ in the diagram of the hexagon. You know the interior angles in a hexagon are all 120°. To find $x$, we can find the distance $y$ in the figure and then double it ($x = 2y$). The angle bounded by the side of the hexagon and $y$ is 30°, and, from geometry, cos 30° = $y$/(hexagon side) so $y$ = (cos 30°) (139 pm) = (0.866)(139 pm) = 120. pm. Finally, $x = 241$ pm.

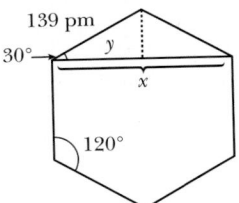

2. 1.0 $\mu$m (1 m/$10^6$ $\mu$m) ($10^{12}$ pm/1 m) (1 $C_6$-ring/241 pm) = $4.1 \times 10^3$ $C_6$-rings

3. The thickness would be approximately 150 pm. This corresponds to the diameter of a carbon atom, found by multiplying the radius of a carbon atom (given in Figure 7.6) by 2 and rounding off to two significant figures.

## Chapter 14
### Chapter Opening: Survival at Sea

$\Pi = cRT = (1.15$ mol/L$)(0.082057$ L atm/mol $\cdot$ K$)(298$ K$) = 28.1$ atm

### Case Study: Exploding Lakes and Diet Coke

1. $PV = nRT$

   4.0 atm(0.025 L) = $n$(0.08206 L $\cdot$ atm/mol $\cdot$ K) 298 K; $n = 4.1 \times 10^{-3}$ mol

2. $P_1 V_1 = P_2 V_2$

   4.0 atm(0.025 L) = $3.7 \times 10^{-4}$ atm ($V_2$); $V_2 = 270$ L

   The gas expanded by a factor of 11,000 (= 270 L/0.025 L).

3. Solubility of $CO_2 = k_H P_g = 0.034$ mol/kg · bar $(3.7 \times 10^{-4}$ bar$) = 1.3 \times 10^{-5}$ mol/kg

4. Before opening: Solubility of $CO_2$ before opening $= k_H P_g = 0.034$ mol/kg · bar $(4.0$ bar$)$ $= 0.14$ mol/kg

   Assume the density of the solution is 1.0 g/cm$^3$, therefore 1.0 L corresponds to 1.0 kg. The amount of $CO_2$ dissolved is 0.14 mol.

   After opening: Solubility of $CO_2 = 1.3 \times 10^{-5}$ mol/kg as calculated in part 3 above. The amount of $CO_2$ in 1.0 kg is $1.3 \times 10^{-5}$ mol.

   Mass of $CO_2$ released $= (0.14$ mol $CO_2 -$ $1.3 \times 10^{-5}$ mol $CO_2)(44.01$ g $CO_2/1$ mol $CO_2)$ $= 6.0$ g $CO_2$

## Chapter 15

### Chapter Opening: Where Did the Indicator Go?

See the answer to Study Question 75 for this chapter in Appendix R.

### Case Study: Enzymes—Nature's Catalysts

1. To decompose an equivalent amount of $H_2O_2$ catalytically would take $1.0 \times 10^{-7}$ years; this is equivalent to 3.2 seconds.

2.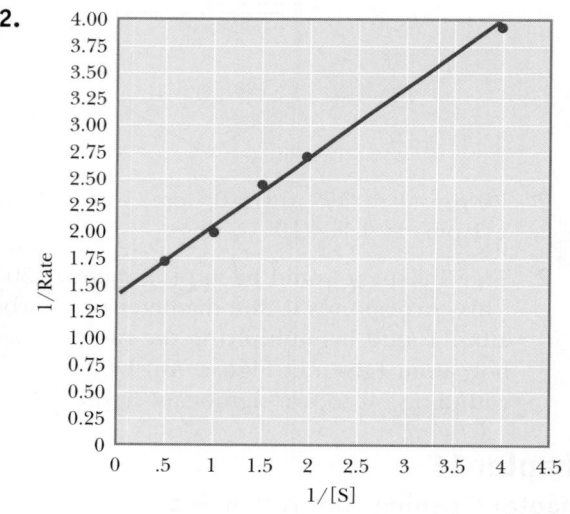

| [S] | 1/[S] | Rate | 1/Rate |
|------|-------|-------|--------|
| 2.50 | 0.400 | 0.588 | 1.70 |
| 1.00 | 1.00 | 0.500 | 2.00 |
| 0.714 | 1.40 | 0.417 | 2.40 |
| 0.526 | 1.90 | 0.370 | 2.70 |
| 0.250 | 4.00 | 0.256 | 3.91 |

From the graph, we obtain a value of 1/Rate = 1.47 when 1/[S] = 0. From this, $R_{max} = 0.68$ mmol/min.

## Chapter 16

### Chapter Opening: Dynamic and Reversible

1. Endothermic. Raising the temperature (adding energy as heat) leads to conversion of reactants to products.

2. Apply LeChatelier's Principle: Increasing the concentration of $Cl^-$ by adding HCl results in a shift to the right to produce more $[CoCl_4]^{2-}$. Decreasing the concentration of $Cl^-$ by addition of water results in a shift to the left and the formation of more $[Co(H_2O)_6]^{2+}$.

3. The various stresses applied have caused the system to adjust in either direction. (Better evidence: Show that when heating and cooling the system is *repeated several times* the system cycles back and forth between the two colors.)

### Case Study: Applying Equilibrium Concepts— The Haber–Bosch Ammonia Process

1. (a) Oxidize part of the $NH_3$ to $HNO_3$, then react $NH_3$ and $HNO_3$ (an acid–base reaction) to form $NH_4NO_3$.

   $4\,NH_3 + 5O_2 \rightarrow 4\,NO_2 + 6\,H_2O$

   $2\,NO_2 + H_2O \rightarrow HNO_3 + HNO_2$

   $HNO_3 + NH_3 \rightarrow NH_4NO_3$

   (b) $\Delta_r H° = (1$ mol $(NH_2)_2CO$/mol-rxn$)$ $[\Delta_f H°((NH_2)_2CO)] + (1$ mol $H_2O$/mol-rxn$)$ $[\Delta_f H°(H_2O)] - (2$ mol $NH_3$/mol-rxn$)$ $[\Delta_f H°(NH_3)] - (1$ mol $CO_2$/mol-rxn$)$ $[\Delta_f H°(CO_2)]$

   $\Delta_r H° = (1$ mol $(NH_2)_2CO$/mol-rxn$)$ $(-333.1$ kJ/mol$) + (1$ mol $H_2O$/mol-rxn$)$ $(-241.8$ kJ/mol$) - (2$ mol $NH_3$/mol-rxn$)$ $(-45.90$ kJ/mol$) - (1$ mol $CO_2$/mol-rxn$)$ $(-393.5$ kJ/mol$)$

   $\Delta_r H° = -89.6$ kJ/mol-rxn.

   The reaction as written is exothermic, so the equilibrium will be more favorable for product formation at a low temperature. The reaction converts three moles of gaseous reactants to one mole of gaseous products; thus, high pressure will be more favorable to product formation.

2. (a) For $CH_4(g) + H_2O(g) \rightarrow CO(g) + 3\,H_2(g)$

   $\Delta_r H° = (1$ mol $CO$/mol-rxn$)[\Delta_f H°(CO)] -$ $(1$ mol $CH_4$/mol-rxn$)[\Delta_f H°(CH_4)] - (1$ mol $H_2O$/mol-rxn$)[\Delta_f H°(H_2O)]$

   $\Delta_r H° = (1$ mol $CO$/mol-rxn$)(-110.5$ kJ/mol$)$ $- (1$ mol $CH_4$/mol-rxn$)(-74.87$ kJ/mol$) -$ $(1$ mol $H_2O$/mol-rxn$)(-241.8$ kJ/mol$) =$ $206.2$ kJ/mol-rxn (endothermic)

For $CO(g) + H_2O(g) \rightarrow CO_2(g) + H_2(g)$

$\Delta_r H° = (1 \text{ mol } CO_2/\text{mol-rxn})[\Delta_f H°(CO_2)] -$ $(1 \text{ mol } CO/\text{mol-rxn})[\Delta_f H°(CO)] - (1 \text{ mol}$ $H_2O/\text{mol-rxn})[\Delta_f H°(H_2O)]$

$\Delta_r H° = (1 \text{ mol } CO_2/\text{mol-rxn})(-393.5 \text{ kJ/mol})$ $- (1 \text{ mol } CO/\text{mol-rxn})(-110.5 \text{ kJ/mol}) -$ $(1 \text{ mol } H_2O/\text{mol-rxn})(-241.8 \text{ kJ/mol}) =$ $-41.2 \text{ kJ/mol-rxn (exothermic)}$

(b) (15 billion kg = $1.5 \times 10^{13}$ g)

Add the two equations:
$CH_4(g) + 2 H_2O(g) \rightarrow CO_2(g) + 4 H_2(g)$

$CH_4$ required = $(1.5 \times 10^{13} \text{ g } NH_3)(1 \text{ mol}$ $NH_3/17.03 \text{ g } NH_3)(3 \text{ mol } H_2/2 \text{ mol } NH_3)$ $(1 \text{ mol } CH_4/4 \text{ mol } H_2)(16.04 \text{ g } CH_4/1 \text{ mol}$ $CH_4) = 5.3 \times 10^{12} \text{ g } CH_4$

$CO_2$ formed = $(1.5 \times 10^{13} \text{ g } NH_3)(1 \text{ mol}$ $NH_3/17.03 \text{ g } NH_3)(3 \text{ mol } H_2/2 \text{ mol } NH_3)$ $(1 \text{ mol } CO_2/4 \text{ mol } H_2)(44.01 \text{ g } CO_2/1 \text{ mol}$ $CO_2) = 1.5 \times 10^{13} \text{ g } CO_2$

# Chapter 17

## Chapter Opening: Aspirin is More Than 100 Years Old!

1. Aspirin, with a smaller $pK_a$, is a stronger acid than acetic acid.

2. The acidic hydrogen is the H on the $-CO_2H$ (carboxylic acid) functional group.

3. $C_6H_4(CO_2CH_3)CO_2H + H_2O \rightarrow$
$\qquad C_6H_4(CO_2CH_3)CO_2^- + H_3O^+$

## Case Study: Would You Like Some Belladonna Juice in Your Drink?

1. $(100. \text{ mg } C_{17}H_{23}NO_3)(1 \text{ g}/1000 \text{ mg})(1 \text{ mol}$ $C_{17}H_{23}NO_3/289.4 \text{ g } C_{17}H_{23}NO_3) = 3.46 \times 10^{-4}$ $\text{mol } C_{17}H_{23}NO_3$

2. The proton will attach to the N.

3. The $pK_a$ of protonated atropine (4.35) is less than that of the ammonium ($pK_a = 9.26$), methylammonium ($pK_a = 10.70$), and anilinium ($pK_a = 4.60$) ions.

4. The site of chirality is a carbon atom with four different groups attached; this is the carbon atom that has the $-CH_2OH$ group attached.

# Chapter 18

## Chapter Opening: Nature's Acids

1. (a) $H_2C_2O_4(aq) + 2 NaOH(aq) \rightarrow$
$\qquad Na_2C_2O_4(aq) + 2 H_2O(\ell)$

28 g rhubarb (1.2 g $H_2C_2O_4$/100 g rhubarb) (1 mol $H_2C_2O_4$/90.04 g $H_2C_2O_4$)(2 mol NaOH/1 mol $H_2C_2O_4$)(1 L/0.25 mol NaOH)(1000 mL/1 L) = 30. mL

(b) $Ca^{2+}(aq) + H_2C_2O_4(aq) + 2 H_2O(\ell) \rightarrow$
$\qquad CaC_2O_4(s) + 2 H_3O^+(aq)$

28 g rhubarb (1.2 g $H_2C_2O_4$/100 g rhubarb) (1 mol $H_2C_2O_4$/90.04 g $H_2C_2O_4$)(1 mol $CaC_2O_4$/1 mol $H_2C_2O_4$)(128.1 $CaC_2O_4$/ 1 mol $CaC_2O_4$) = 0.48 g $CaC_2O_4$

2. $CaC_2O_4(s) \rightleftharpoons Ca^{2+}(aq) + C_2O_4^{2-}(aq)$

$K_{sp} = 4 \times 10^{-9} = [Ca^{2+}][C_2O_4^{2-}]$

Let $x$ = solubility of $CaC_2O_4$

$4 \times 10^{-9} = x^2$

$x = 6 \times 10^{-5} \text{ mol/L}$

Solubility in g/L = $6 \times 10^{-5}$ mol/L (128.1 g $CaC_2O_4$/1 mol $CaC_2O_4$) = 0.008 g/L

## Case Study: Take a Deep Breath!

1. $pH = pK_a + \log[HPO_4^{2-}]/[H_2PO_4^-]$

$7.4 = 7.20 + \log[HPO_4^{2-}]/[H_2PO_4^-]$

$[HPO_4^{2-}]/[H_2PO_4^-] = 1.6$

2. Assign $x = [HPO_4^{2-}]$, then $[H_2PO_4^-] = (0.020 - x)$

$1.6 = x/(0.020 - x); x = 0.012$

$[HPO_4^{2-}] = x = 0.012 \text{ mol/L}$

$[H_2PO_4^-] = 0.020 - x = 0.008 \text{ mol/L}$

## Case Study: Chemical Equilibria in the Oceans

For both of these compounds, the chemical equilibrium is:

$CaCO_3(s) \rightleftharpoons Ca^{2+}(aq) + CO_3^{2-}(aq)$

$K_{sp} = [Ca^{2+}][CO_3^{2-}]$ and the solubility (in mol/L) is equal to $(K_{sp})^{1/2}$.

Aragonite:

Solubility (in g/L) = $[(6.0 \times 10^{-9})^{1/2}$ mol $CaCO_3$/L](100.1 g $CaCO_3$/1 mol $CaCO_3$) = $7.8 \times 10^{-3}$ g $CaCO_3$/L

Calcite:

Solubility (in g/L) = $[(3.4 \times 10^{-9})^{1/2}$ mol $CaCO_3$/L](100.1 g $CaCO_3$/1 mol $CaCO_3$) = $5.8 \times 10^{-3}$ g $CaCO_3$/L

Aragonite is $7.8 \times 10^{-3}$ g/L/$5.8 \times 10^{-3}$ g/L = 1.3 times more soluble than calcite.

# Chapter 19
## Chapter Opening: Hydrogen for the Future?

1. $\Delta_r H° = (2 \text{ mol } H_2/\text{mol-rxn})\Delta_f H°[H_2(g)] +$
   $(1 \text{ mol } O_2/\text{mol-rxn})\Delta_f H°[O_2(g)] -$
   $(2 \text{ mol } H_2O/\text{mol-rxn})\Delta_f H°[H_2O(\ell)]$
   $= (2 \text{ mol } H_2/\text{mol-rxn})[0 \text{ kJ/mol } H_2] +$
   $(1 \text{ mol } O_2/\text{mol-rxn})[0 \text{ kJ/mol } O_2] -$
   $(2 \text{ mol } H_2O/\text{mol-rxn})[-285.83 \text{ kJ/mol } H_2O]$
   $= +571.66 \text{ kJ/mol-rxn}$

   $\Delta_r S° = (2 \text{ mol } H_2/\text{mol-rxn})S°[H_2(g)] +$
   $(1 \text{ mol } O_2/\text{mol-rxn})S°[O_2(g)] -$
   $(2 \text{ mol } H_2O/\text{mol-rxn})S°[H_2O(\ell)]$
   $= (2 \text{ mol } H_2/\text{mol-rxn})[130.7 \text{ J/K} \cdot \text{mol } H_2] +$
   $(1 \text{ mol } O_2/\text{mol-rxn})[205.07 \text{ J/K} \cdot \text{mol } O_2] -$
   $(2 \text{ mol } H_2O/\text{mol-rxn})[69.95 \text{ J/K} \cdot \text{mol } H_2O]$
   $= +326.6 \text{ J/K} \cdot \text{mol-rxn} =$
   $+0.3266 \text{ kJ/K} \cdot \text{mol-rxn}$

   $\Delta_r G° = \Delta_r H° - T\Delta_r S°$
   $= 571.66 \text{ kJ/mol-rxn} - 298.15 \text{ K}(0.3266 \text{ kJ/K} \cdot \text{mol-rxn}) = +474.29 \text{ kJ/mol-rxn}$

2. $\Delta_r H° = (3 \text{ mol } H_2/\text{mol-rxn})\Delta_f H°[H_2(g)] +$
   $(1 \text{ mol } CO/\text{mol-rxn})\Delta_f H°[CO(g)] -$
   $\{(1 \text{ mol } CH_4/\text{mol-rxn})\Delta_f H°[CH_4(g)] +$
   $(1 \text{ mol } H_2O/\text{mol-rxn})\Delta_f H°[H_2O(g)]\}$
   $= (3 \text{ mol } H_2/\text{mol-rxn})[0 \text{ kJ/mol } H_2] +$
   $(1 \text{ mol } CO/\text{mol-rxn})[-110.525 \text{ kJ/mol } CO] -$
   $\{(1 \text{ mol } CH_4/\text{mol-rxn})[-74.87 \text{ kJ/mol } CH_4] +$
   $(1 \text{ mol } H_2O/\text{mol-rxn})[-241.83 \text{ kJ/mol } H_2O]\}$
   $= +206.18 \text{ kJ/mol-rxn}$

   $\Delta_r S° = (3 \text{ mol } H_2/\text{mol-rxn})S°[H_2(g)] +$
   $(1 \text{ mol } CO/\text{mol-rxn})S°[CO(g)] -$
   $\{(1 \text{ mol } CH_4/\text{mol-rxn})S°[CH_4(g)] +$
   $(1 \text{ mol } H_2O/\text{mol-rxn})S°[H_2O(g)]\}$
   $= (3 \text{ mol } H_2/\text{mol-rxn})[130.7 \text{ J/K} \cdot \text{mol } H_2] +$
   $(1 \text{ mol } CO/\text{mol-rxn})[197.674 \text{ J/K} \cdot \text{mol } CO] -$
   $\{(1 \text{ mol } CH_4/\text{mol-rxn})[186.26 \text{ J/K} \cdot \text{mol } CH_4] +$
   $(1 \text{ mol } H_2O/\text{mol-rxn})[188.84 \text{ J/K} \cdot \text{mol } H_2O]\}$
   $= +214.7 \text{ J/K} \cdot \text{mol-rxn} =$
   $+0.2147 \text{ kJ/K} \cdot \text{mol-rxn}$

   $\Delta_r G° = \Delta_r H° - T\Delta_r S° = 206.18 \text{ kJ/mol-rxn} -$
   $298.15 \text{ K}(0.2147 \text{ kJ/K} \cdot \text{mol-rxn})$
   $= +142.17 \text{ kJ/mol-rxn}$

## Case Study: Thermodynamics and Living Things

1. Creatine phosphate $+ H_2O \rightarrow$ creatine $+ HP_i$
   $$\Delta G° = -43.3 \text{ kJ/mol}$$

   Adenosine $+ HP_i \rightarrow$ adenosine monophosphate $+ H_2O$
   $$\Delta G° = +9.2 \text{ kJ/mol}$$

   Net reaction (sum of the two reactions):

   Creatine phosphate $+$ adenosine $\rightarrow$
   creatine $+$ adenosine monophosphate

   For this, $\Delta G° = -43.3 \text{ kJ/mol} + 9.2 \text{ kJ/mol} = -34.1 \text{ kJ/mol}$. The negative value indicates that the transfer of phosphate from creatine phosphate to adenosine is product-favored.

2. $\Delta G°' = \Delta G° + RT \ln[C][H_3O^+]/[A][B] =$
   $\Delta G° + (8.31 \times 10^{-3} \text{ kJ/mol} \cdot \text{K})(298 \text{ K})$
   $\ln[1][1 \times 10^{-7}]/[1][1]$

   $\Delta G°' = \Delta G° - 39.9 \text{ kJ/mol}$

# Chapter 20
## Chapter Opening: Battery Power

1. (a) The oxidation number of cobalt in $CoO_2$ is $+4$ and in $LiCoO_2$ is $+3$.

   (b) Cobalt(IV) is reduced in this reaction, so $CoO_2$ is the cathode, and Li is the anode.

   (c) Lithium in the battery is elemental Li in a carbon matrix. Elemental Li reacts readily with water (◄ page 324).

2. (a) (1 hour) $(3600 \text{ s}/1 \text{ hour})(7.5 \text{ C/s})(1 \text{ mol } e^-/96,485 \text{ C}) = 0.28 \text{ mol } e^-$

   (b) $(0.28 \text{ mol } e^-)(1 \text{ mol Li}/1 \text{ mol } e^-)(6.941 \text{ g Li}/1 \text{ mol Li}) = 1.9 \text{ g Li}$

## Case Study: Manganese in the Oceans

1. Cathode reaction: $Mn^{3+} + e^- \rightarrow Mn^{2+}$

   Anode reaction: $Mn^{3+} + 2 H_2O \rightarrow MnO_2 + 4 H^+ + e^-$

   Net reaction: $2 Mn^{3+} + 2 H_2O \rightarrow MnO_2 + Mn^{2+} + 4 H^+$

   $E°_{cell} = E°(\text{cathode}) - E°(\text{anode}) = 1.50 \text{ V} - 0.95 \text{ V} = 0.55 \text{ V}$

   The positive value associated with disproportionation (the net reaction) is positive, indicating a product-favored reaction.

2. (a) $MnO_2 + HS^- + 3 H^+ \rightarrow Mn^{2+} + S + 2 H_2O$

   (b) $2 Mn^{2+} + O_2 + 2 H_2O \rightarrow 2 MnO_2 + 4 H^+$

3. Cathode reaction: $O_2 + 4 H^+ + 4 e^- \rightarrow 2 H_2O$ $(E° = 1.229 \text{ V})$

   Anode reaction: $Mn^{2+} + 2 H_2O \rightarrow MnO_2 + 4 H^+ + 2 e^-$ $(E° = 1.23 \text{ V, from Appendix M})$

   $E°_{cell} = E°(\text{cathode}) - E°(\text{anode}) = 1.229 \text{ V} - 1.23 \text{ V} = 0 \text{ V}.$

# Chapter 21

## Chapter Opening: Carbon and Silicon

1. $CH_4(g) + 2 H_2O(\ell) \rightarrow CO_2(g) + 4 H_2(g)$

   $SiH_4(g) + 2 H_2O(\ell) \rightarrow SiO_2(s) + 4 H_2(g)$

2. For $CH_4$:

   $\Delta_rG° = (1 \text{ mol } CO_2/\text{mol-rxn})\Delta_fG°[CO_2(g)] + (4 \text{ mol } H_2/\text{mol-rxn})\Delta_fG°[H_2(g)] - \{(1 \text{ mol } CH_4/\text{mol-rxn})\Delta_fG°[CH_4(g)] + (2 \text{ mol } H_2O/\text{mol-rxn})\Delta_fG°[H_2O(\ell)]\}$

   $\Delta_rG° = (1 \text{ mol } CO_2/\text{mol-rxn})(-394.359 \text{ kJ/mol } CO_2) + (4 \text{ mol } H_2/\text{mol-rxn})(0 \text{ kJ/mol } H_2) - \{(1 \text{ mol } CH_4/\text{mol-rxn})(-50.8 \text{ kJ/mol } CH_4) + (2 \text{ mol } H_2O/\text{mol-rxn})(-237.15 \text{ kJ/mol } H_2O)\}$
   $= 130.7 \text{ kJ/mol-rxn}$

   For $SiH_4$:

   $\Delta_rG° = (1 \text{ mol } SiO_2/\text{mol-rxn})\Delta_fG°[SiO_2(s)] + (4 \text{ mol } H_2/\text{mol-rxn})\Delta_fG°[H_2(g)] - \{(1 \text{ mol } SiH_4/\text{mol-rxn})\Delta_fG°[SiH_4(g)] + (2 \text{ mol } H_2O/\text{mol-rxn})\Delta_fG°[H_2O(\ell)]\}$

   $\Delta_rG° = (1 \text{ mol } SiO_2/\text{mol-rxn})(-856.97 \text{ kJ/mol } SiO_2) + (4 \text{ mol } H_2/\text{mol-rxn})(0 \text{ kJ/mol } H_2) - \{(1 \text{ mol } SiH_4/\text{mol-rxn})(56.84 \text{ kJ/mol } SiH_4) + (2 \text{ mol } H_2O/\text{mol-rxn})(-237.15 \text{ kJ/mol } H_2O)\}$
   $= -439.51 \text{ kJ/mol-rxn}$

   The reaction involving $SiH_4$ is product-favored at equilibrium, whereas the reaction involving $CH_4$ is reactant-favored at equilibrium.

3. Electronegativities: C 2.5, Si 1.9, H 2.2. From this we conclude that the polarities of C—H and Si—H bonds are in the opposite directions. In $SiH_4$, the H has a slight negative charge, and in $CH_4$ the H has a slight positive charge.

4. General observation from these examples: Carbon often bonds to other atoms via double bonds, whereas Si does not. We would not expect $H_2Si{=}SiH_2$ to exist as a molecular species; instead a polymeric structure $-(SiH_2SiH_2)_n-$ is predicted.

## Case Study: Hard Water

1. For $Mg^{2+}$: (50. mg)(1 mmol $Mg^{2+}$/24.31 mg)(1 mmol CaO/mmol $Mg^{2+}$)(56.08 mg CaO/1 mmol CaO) = 120 mg CaO

   For $Ca^{2+}$: (150 mg)(1 mmol $Ca^{2+}$/40.08 mg)(1 mmol CaO/mmol $Ca^{2+}$)(56.08 mg CaO/1 mmol CaO) = 210 mg CaO

   Total CaO = 120 mg + 210 mg = 330 mg (two significant figures)

   We get 2 mol $CaCO_3$ per mole $Ca^{2+}$ and 1 mol each of $CaCO_3$ and $MgCO_3$ per mole $Mg^{2+}$

   $CaCO_3$ from $Ca^{2+}$ reaction: (0.15 g $Ca^{2+}$)(1 mol/40.08 g $Ca^{2+}$)(2 mol $CaCO_3$/1 mol $Ca^{2+}$)(100.1 g $CaCO_3$/1 mol $CaCO_3$) = 0.75 g

   $CaCO_3$ from $Mg^{2+}$ reaction: (0.050 g $Mg^{2+}$)(1 mol/24.31 g $Mg^{2+}$)(1 mol $CaCO_3$/1 mol $Mg^{2+}$)(100.1 g $CaCO_3$/1 mol $CaCO_3$) = 0.21 g

   $MgCO_3$ from $Mg^{2+}$ reaction: (0.050 g $Mg^{2+}$)(1 mol/24.31 g $Mg^{2+}$)(1 mol $MgCO_3$/1 mol $Mg^{2+}$)(84.31 g $MgCO_3$/1 mol $MgCO_3$) = 0.17 g

   Total mass of solids = 0.75 g + 0.21 g + 0.17 g = 1.1 g (two significant figures)

2. $CaCO_3(s) + 2 CH_3CO_2H(aq) \rightarrow Ca(CH_3CO_2H)_2(aq) + H_2O(\ell) + CO_2(g)$

   This is a gas-forming reaction.

## Case Study: Lead, Beethoven, and a Mystery Solved

1. 50 ppb is 50 g in $1 \times 10^9$ g of blood. Assume the density of blood is 1.0 g/mL. In $1.0 \times 10^3$ mL (i.e., 1.0 L) of blood, there will be $50 \times 10^{-6}$ g of Pb. From this:

   $(50 \times 10^{-6} \text{ g})(1 \text{ mol Pb}/207.2 \text{ g Pb})(6.022 \times 10^{23} \text{ atoms Pb/mol Pb}) = 1.5 \times 10^{17}$ atoms Pb

2. (750 mL wine)(1.0 g wine/mL wine)(2000 g Pb/1,000,000 g wine) = 1.5 g Pb

## Case Study: A Healthy Saltwater Aquarium and the Nitrogen Cycle

1. $2 NH_4^+(aq) + 4 OH^-(aq) + 3 O_2(aq) \rightarrow 2 NO_2^-(aq) + 6 H_2O(\ell)$

2. Reduction half-reaction: $2 NO_3^-(aq) + 6 H_2O(\ell) + 10 e^- \rightarrow N_2(g) + 12 OH^-(aq)$

   Oxidation half-reaction: $CH_3OH(aq) + 6 OH^-(aq) \rightarrow CO_2(aq) + 5 H_2O(\ell) + 6 e^-$

   Net: $6 NO_3^-(aq) + 5 CH_3OH \rightarrow 3 N_2(g) + 5 CO_2(aq) + 6 OH^-(aq) + 7 H_2O(\ell)$

3. $HCO_3^-$ is the predominant species. Recall that when acid and base concentrations are equal, $pH = pK_a$. If $H_2CO_3$ and $HCO_3^-$ are present in equal concentrations, the pH would be about 6.4. If $HCO_3^-$ and $CO_3^{2-}$ are present in equal concentrations, the pH would be 10.2. For the pH to be about 8 (in a salt water aquarium), $[HCO_3^-]$ would have to be higher than either of the other carbonate species.

4. Concentration of N in ppm (mg N/L) =
$[(1.7 \times 10^4 \text{ kg NO}_3^-)(10^6 \text{ mg NO}_3^-/\text{kg NO}_3^-)$
$(14.0 \text{ mg N}/62.0 \text{ mg NO}_3^-)]/(2.2 \times 10^7 \text{ L}) =$
$1.7 \times 10^2 \text{ mg/L} = 1.7 \times 10^2 \text{ ppm}$

Concentration of $NO_3^-$ in ppm (mg/L) =
$(1.7 \times 10^4 \text{ kg})(10^6 \text{ mg/kg})/(2.2 \times 10^7 \text{ L}) =$
770 mg/L

Concentration of $NO_3^-$ in mol/L =
$[(1.7 \times 10^4 \text{ kg})(10^3 \text{ g/kg})(1 \text{ mol}/62.0 \text{ g})]/$
$(2.2 \times 10^7 \text{ L}) = 0.012 \text{ mol/L}$

## Chapter 22

### Chapter Opening: Memory Metal

1. Define length of the side of the cube as $x$, then the length of the diagonal across the cube is $x\sqrt{3}$. This is set equal to:
$2 r_{Ti} + 2 r_{Ni}$, i.e., $x\sqrt{3} = 2 r_{Ti} + 2 r_{Ni} = 540$ pm;
$x = 312$ pm ($a = b = c = 3.12 \times 10^{-8}$ cm)

2. Calculated density:

   Mass of one unit cell is the mass of one Ti and one Ni atom = (47.87 g/mol)(1 mol/$6.022 \times 10^{23}$ atoms Ti) + (58.69 g/mol)(1 mol/$6.022 \times 10^{23}$ atoms Ti) = $1.77 \times 10^{-22}$ g

   Volume of the unit cell is $x^3 =$
   $(3.12 \times 10^{-8} \text{ cm})^3 = 3.04 \times 10^{-23}$ cm$^3$

   Calculated density = $1.77 \times 10^{-22}$ g/
   $3.04 \times 10^{-23}$ cm$^3$ = 5.82 g/cm$^3$

   The agreement is not very good, probably because atoms don't pack together as tightly as is assumed.

3. As free atoms, both Ti and Ni are paramagnetic.

### Case Study: Accidental Discovery of a Chemotherapy Drug

1. First-order kinetics: $\ln[x/x_o] = - kt$

   $\ln[x/10 \text{ mg}] =$
   $- 7.6 \times 10^{-5} \text{ s}^{-1}[24 \text{ h} \times 3600 \text{ s/h}]$

   $x/10 \text{ mg} = 1.4 \times 10^{-3}$; $x = 1.4 \times 10^{-2}$ mg remain

### Case Study: Ferrocene—The Beginning of a Chemical Revolution

1. $Fe^{2+}$ in ferrocene has an electron configuration [Ar] $3d^6$ and is present in the low-spin state.

2. Cr(0). Cr(0) in this compound is assumed to have an electron configuration [Ar] $3d^6$, is present in the low-spin state, and so is diamagnetic.

3. Both are in accordance with the 18-electron rule.

4. Select oxidizing agents from Table 20.1 (page 917) based on the northeast–southwest rule (above $E° = 0.400$ v). Common oxidizing agents include the halogens $H_2O_2$ and $MnO_4^-$. $Cl_2$ is a sufficiently strong oxidizing agent to carry out this oxidation.

5. $NiCl_2 + 2 \text{ Na}[C_5H_5] \rightarrow Ni(\eta\text{-}C_5H_5)_2 + 2 \text{ NaCl}$. Nickelocene is predicted to have two unpaired electrons ($Ni^{2+}$, with a $d^8$ configuration, in an octahedral environment.)

## Chapter 23

### Chapter Opening: A Primordial Nuclear Reactor

1. $^{235}$U: 92 protons, $235 - 92 = 143$ neutrons

   $^{238}$U: 92 protons, 146 neutrons

2. (a) $^{238}\text{U} + {}^1_0\text{n} \rightarrow {}^{239}\text{U}$

   (b) $^{239}\text{U} \rightarrow {}^{239}\text{Np} + {}^0_{-1}\beta$

   $^{239}\text{Np} \rightarrow {}^{239}\text{Pu} + {}^0_{-1}\beta$

   (c) $^{239}\text{Pu} \rightarrow {}^{235}\text{U} + {}^4_2\alpha$

### Case Study: Nuclear Medicine and Hyperthyroidism

1. $^{131}\text{I} \rightarrow {}^{131}\text{Xe} + {}^0_{-1}\beta$

2. Calculate the fraction ($= f$) of each remaining after 7 days

   For $^{123}$I: $k = 0.693/t_{\frac{1}{2}} = 0.693/13.3 \text{ h} = 0.0521 \text{ h}^{-1}$

   $\ln(f) = - 0.0521 \text{ h}^{-1}[7 \text{ d}(24 \text{ h/d})]$

   $f = 1.6 \times 10^{-4}$

   For $^{131}$I: $k = 0.693/t_{\frac{1}{2}} = 0.693/8.04 \text{ d} = 0.0862 \text{ d}^{-1}$

   $\ln(f) = - 0.0862 \text{ d}^{-1}(7 \text{ d})$

   $f = 0.55$

   Ratio of amounts remaining, $[^{131}\text{I}]/[^{123}\text{I}]$
   $= 0.55/(1.6 \times 10^{-4}) = 3400$

   The amount of $^{131}$I isotope is 3400 times greater than the amount of $^{123}$I.

# O Answers to Check Your Understanding Questions

## Let's Review

**LR 1** 0.154 nm $(1 \text{ m}/10^9 \text{ nm})(10^{12} \text{ pm}/1 \text{ m}) = 154$ pm

0.154 nm $(1 \text{ m}/10^9 \text{ nm})(100 \text{ cm}/1 \text{ m}) = 1.54 \times 10^{-8}$ cm

**LR 2** Student A: average $= -0.1$ °C; percent error
$= \{[(-0.1 + 273.15) \text{ K} - 273.15 \text{ K}]/273.15 \text{ K}\} \times 100\%$
$= -0.04\%$

Student B: average $= +0.01$ °C; percent error
$= \{[(0.01 + 273.15) \text{ K} - 273.15 \text{ K}]/273.15 \text{ K}\} \times 100\%$
$= 0.004\%$

Student B has the smaller error.

**LR 3** $x = 3.9 \times 10^5$. The difference between 110.7 and 64 is 47. Dividing 47 by 0.056 and 0.00216 gives an answer with two significant figures.

**LR 4** $(19,320 \text{ kg/m}^3)(10^3 \text{ g/1 kg})(1 \text{ m}^3/10^6 \text{ cm}^3)$
$= 19.32 \text{ g/cm}^3$

**LR 5** Change all dimensions to centimeters: 7.6 m
$= 760$ cm; 2.74 m $= 274$ cm; 0.13 mm $= 0.013$ cm.

Volume of paint $= (760 \text{ cm})(274 \text{ cm})(0.013 \text{ cm})$
$= 2.7 \times 10^3 \text{ cm}^3$

Volume (L) $= (2.7 \times 10^3 \text{ cm}^3)(1 \text{ L}/10^3 \text{ cm}^3) = 2.7$ L

Mass $= (2.7 \times 10^3 \text{ cm}^3)(0.914 \text{ g/cm}^3) = 2.5 \times 10^3$ g

## Chapter 2

**2.1** (1) Mass number with 26 protons and 30 neutrons is 56
(2) $(59.930788 \text{ u})(1.661 \times 10^{-24} \text{ g/u}) = 9.955 \times 10^{-23}$ g
(3) $^{64}$Zn has 30 protons, 30 electrons, and $(64 - 30)$
$= 34$ neutrons.

**2.2** Use Equation 2.2 for the calculation.

Atomic mass $= (34.96885)(75.77/100) + (36.96590)$
$(24.23/100) = 35.45$. (Accuracy is limited by the value of the percent abundance to four significant figures.)

**2.3** Use Equation 2.2 for the calculation. Let $x =$ percent abundance of $^{20}$Ne and $y =$ percent abundance of $^{22}$Ne.

$20.1797 \text{ u} = (x/100)(19.992435 \text{ u}) + (0.27/100)$
$(20.993843 \text{ u}) + (y/100)(21.991383 \text{ u})$

Because all the percent abundances must sum to 100%, $y = 100 - x - 0.27 = 99.73 - x$.

$20.1797 \text{ u} = (x/100)(19.992435 \text{ u}) + 0.27/100)$
$(20.993843 \text{ u}) + [(99.73 - x)/100](21.991383 \text{ u})$

$x = 90.5$; therefore the percent abundance of $^{20}$Ne $=$ 90.5% and the percent abundance of $^{22}$Ne $= 9.2\%$.

**2.4** (a) (1) NaF: 1 Na$^+$ and 1 F$^-$ ion. (2) Cu(NO$_3$)$_2$:
1 Cu$^{2+}$ and 2 NO$_3^-$ ions. (3) NaCH$_3$CO$_2$: 1 Na$^+$
and 1 CH$_3$CO$_2^-$ ion.
(b) FeCl$_2$, FeCl$_3$

**2.5** Na$_2$S, Na$_3$PO$_4$, BaS, Ba$_3$(PO$_4$)$_2$

**2.6** $(2.6 \times 10^{24} \text{ atoms})(1.000 \text{ mol}/6.022 \times 10^{23}$
atoms$)(197.0 \text{ g Au}/1.000 \text{ mol}) = 850$ g Au

Volume $= (850 \text{ g Au})(1.00 \text{ cm}^3/19.32 \text{ g}) = 44 \text{ cm}^3$

Volume $= 44 \text{ cm}^3 = (\text{thickness})(\text{area}) = (0.10 \text{ cm})(\text{area})$

Area $= 440 \text{ cm}^2$

Length $=$ width $= \sqrt{440 \text{ cm}^2} = 21$ cm

**2.7** Molar mass H$_3$C$_6$H$_5$O$_7$ = 8(1.01) + 6(12.01) +
7(16.00) = 192.14 g/mol

$(454 \text{ g H}_3\text{C}_6\text{H}_5\text{O}_7)(1 \text{ mol H}_3\text{C}_6\text{H}_5\text{O}_7/192.14 \text{ g}$
H$_3$C$_6$H$_5$O$_7$) $= 2.36$ mol H$_3$C$_6$H$_5$O$_7$

$(2.36 \text{ mol H}_3\text{C}_6\text{H}_5\text{O}_7)(6.022 \times 10^{23} \text{ molecules}/1 \text{ mol})$
$= 1.42 \times 10^{24}$ molecules H$_3$C$_6$H$_5$O$_7$

$(1.42 \times 10^{24} \text{ molecules H}_3\text{C}_6\text{H}_5\text{O}_7)(6 \text{ atoms C}/1 \text{ mole-}$
cule H$_3$C$_6$H$_5$O$_7$) $= 8.54 \times 10^{24}$ atoms C

**2.8** (1) 1.00 mol (NH$_4$)$_2$CO$_3$ (molar mass 96.09 g/mol)
has 28.0 g of N (29.2%), 8.06 g of H (8.39%),
12.0 g of C (12.5%), and 48.0 g of O (50.0%)
(2) 454 g C$_8$H$_{18}$ (1 mol C$_8$H$_{18}$/114.2 g)(8 mol C/1 mol
C$_8$H$_{18}$)(12.01 g C/1 mol C) $= 382$ g C

**2.9** (1) C$_5$H$_4$
(2) C$_2$H$_4$O$_2$
(3) $(88.17 \text{ g C})(1 \text{ mol C}/12.011 \text{ g C}) = 7.341$ mol C
$(11.83 \text{ g H})(1 \text{ mol H}/1.008 \text{ g H}) = 11.74$ mol H
11.74 mol H/7.341 mol C $= 1.6$ mol H/1 mol C
$= (8/5)$; (mol H/1 mol C) $= 8$ mol H/5 mol C

The empirical formula is C$_5$H$_8$. The molar mass,
68.11 g/mol, closely matches this formula, so C$_5$H$_8$
is also the molecular formula.
(4) $(78.90 \text{ g C})(1 \text{ mol C}/12.011 \text{ g C}) = 6.569$ mol C
$(10.59 \text{ g H})(1 \text{ mol H}/1.008 \text{ g H}) = 10.51$ mol H
$(10.51 \text{ g O})(1 \text{ mol O}/16.00 \text{ g O}) = 0.6569$ mol O
10.51 mol H/0.6569 mol O $= 16$ mol H/1 mol O
6.569 mol C/0.6569 mol O $= 10$ mol C/1 mol O

The empirical formula is C$_{10}$H$_{16}$O.

**2.10**  (1.25 g Ga)(1 mol Ga/69.72 g Ga) = 0.0179 mol Ga

1.68 g product − 1.25 g Ga = 0.43 g O

(0.43 g O)(1 mol O/16.00 g O) = 0.027 mol O

Mole ratio = 0.027 mol O/0.0179 mol Ga

= 1.5 mol O/1.0 mol Ga = 3.0 mol O/2.0 mol Ga

Empirical formula = $Ga_2O_3$

**2.11**  (0.586 g K)(1 mol K/39.10 g K) = 0.0150 mol K

(0.480 g O)(1 mol O/16.00 g O) = 0.0300 mol O

The ratio of moles K to moles O atoms is 1:2; the empirical formula is $KO_2$.

**2.12**  Mass of water lost on heating is 0.235 g − 0.128 g = 0.107 g; 0.128 g $NiCl_2$ remain

(0.107 g $H_2O$)(1 mol $H_2O$/18.016 g $H_2O$) = 0.00594 mol $H_2O$

(0.128 g $NiCl_2$)(1 mol $NiCl_2$/129.6 g $NiCl_2$) = 0.000988 mol $NiCl_2$

Mole ratio = 0.00594 mol $H_2O$/0.000988 mol $NiCl_2$ = 6.01: Therefore $x = 6$

The formula for the hydrate is $NiCl_2 \cdot 6 H_2O$.

# Chapter 3

**3.1**  (a) $2 C_4H_{10}(g) + 13 O_2(g) \longrightarrow$
$$8 CO_2(g) + 10 H_2O(g)$$
(b) $2 Pb(C_2H_5)_4(\ell) + 27 O_2(g) \longrightarrow$
$$2 PbO(s) + 16 CO_2(g) + 20 H_2O(g)$$

**3.2**  (a) $LiNO_3$ is soluble and gives $Li^+(aq)$ and $NO_3^-(aq)$ ions.
(b) $CaCl_2$ is soluble and gives $Ca^{2+}(aq)$ and $Cl^-(aq)$ ions.
(c) CuO is not water soluble.
(d) $NaCH_3CO_2$ is soluble and gives $Na^+(aq)$ and $CH_3CO_2^-(aq)$ ions.

**3.3**  (a) $Na_2CO_3(aq) + CuCl_2(aq) \longrightarrow$
$$2 NaCl(aq) + CuCO_3(s)$$
(b) No reaction; no insoluble compound is produced.
(c) $NiCl_2(aq) + 2 KOH(aq) \longrightarrow$
$$Ni(OH)_2(s) + 2 KCl(aq)$$

**3.4**  (a) $3 CaCl_2(aq) + 2 Na_3PO_4(aq) \longrightarrow$
$$Ca_3(PO_4)_2(s) + 6 NaCl(aq)$$
$3 Ca^{2+}(aq) + 2 PO_4^{3-}(aq) \longrightarrow Ca_3(PO_4)_2(s)$
(b) $FeCl_3(aq) + 3 KOH(aq) \longrightarrow$
$$Fe(OH)_3(s) + 3 KCl(aq)$$
$Fe^{3+}(aq) + 3 OH^-(aq) \longrightarrow Fe(OH)_3(s)$
(c) $Pb(NO_3)_2(aq) + 2 KCl(aq) \longrightarrow$
$$PbCl_2(s) + 2 KNO_3(aq)$$
$Pb^{2+}(aq) + 2 Cl^-(aq) \longrightarrow PbCl_2(s)$

**3.5**  (a) $H_3PO_4(aq) + H_2O(\ell) \rightleftharpoons$
$$H_3O^+(aq) + H_2PO_4^-(aq)$$
(b) Acting as an acid:
$H_2PO_4^-(aq) + H_2O(\ell) \rightleftharpoons$
$$HPO_4^{2-}(aq) + H_3O^+(\ell)$$
Acting as a base:
$H_2PO_4^-(aq) + H_2O(\ell) \rightleftharpoons$
$$H_3PO_4(aq) + OH^-(aq)$$
Because $H_2PO_4^-(aq)$ can react as a Brønsted acid and as a base, it is said to be amphiprotic.

**3.6**  $Mg(OH)_2(s) + 2 HCl(aq) \longrightarrow$
$$MgCl_2(aq) + 2 H_2O(\ell)$$
Net ionic equation: $Mg(OH)_2(s) + 2 H_3O^+(aq)$
$$\longrightarrow Mg^{2+}(aq) + 4 H_2O(\ell)$$

**3.7**  $BaCO_3(s) + 2 HNO_3(aq) \longrightarrow$
$$Ba(NO_3)_2(aq) + CO_2(g) + H_2O(\ell)$$
Barium carbonate and nitric acid produce barium nitrate, carbon dioxide, and water.

**3.8**  (a) Fe in $Fe_2O_3$, +3; (b) S in $H_2SO_4$, +6;
(c) C in $CO_3^{2-}$, +4; (d) N in $NO_2^+$, +5

**3.9**  Dichromate ion is the oxidizing agent and is reduced. (Cr with a +6 oxidation number is reduced to $Cr^{3+}$ with a +3 oxidation number.) Ethanol is the reducing agent and is oxidized. (The C atoms in ethanol have an oxidation number of −2. The oxidation number is 0 in acetic acid.)

**3.10**  (a) Gas-forming reaction:
$CuCO_3(s) + H_2SO_4(aq) \longrightarrow$
$$CuSO_4(aq) + H_2O(\ell) + CO_2(g)$$
Net ionic equation:
$CuCO_3(s) + 2 H_3O^+(aq) \longrightarrow$
$$Cu^{2+}(aq) + 3 H_2O(\ell) + CO_2(g)$$
(b) Oxidation–reduction: $4 Ga(s) + 3 O_2(g) \longrightarrow$
$$2 Ga_2O_3(s)$$
(c) Acid–base reaction:
$Ba(OH)_2(aq) + 2 HNO_3(aq) \longrightarrow$
$$Ba(NO_3)_2(aq) + 2 H_2O(\ell)$$
Net ionic equation:
$OH^-(aq) + H_3O^+(aq) \longrightarrow 2 H_2O(\ell)$
(d) Precipitation reaction:
$CuCl_2(aq) + (NH_4)_2S(aq) \longrightarrow$
$$CuS(s) + 2 NH_4Cl(aq)$$
Net ionic equation:
$Cu^{2+}(aq) + S^{2-}(aq) \longrightarrow CuS(s)$

# Chapter 4

**4.1**  (454 g $C_3H_8$)(1 mol $C_3H_8$/44.10 g $C_3H_8$) = 10.3 mol $C_3H_8$

10.3 mol $C_3H_8$ (5 mol $O_2$/1 mol $C_3H_8$)(32.00 g $O_2$/1 mol $O_2$) = 1650 g $O_2$

(10.3 mol $C_3H_8$)(3 mol $CO_2$/1 mol $C_3H_8$)(44.01 g $CO_2$/1 mol $CO_2$) = 1360 g $CO_2$

(10.3 mol $C_3H_8$)(4 mol $H_2O$/1 mol $C_3H_8$)(18.02 g $H_2O$/1 mol $H_2O$) = 742 g $H_2O$

**4.2**  (a) Amount Al = (50.0 g Al)(1 mol Al/26.98 g Al) = 1.85 mol Al

Amount $Fe_2O_3$ = (50.0 g $Fe_2O_3$)(1 mol $Fe_2O_3$/159.7 g $Fe_2O_3$) = 0.313 mol $Fe_2O_3$

Mol Al/mol $Fe_2O_3$ = 1.85/0.313 = 5.92

This is more than the 2:1 ratio required, so the limiting reactant is $Fe_2O_3$.
(b) Mass Fe = (0.313 mol $Fe_2O_3$)(2 mol Fe/1 mol $Fe_2O_3$)(55.85 g Fe/1 mol Fe) = 35.0 g Fe

**4.3**  (0.143 g $O_2$)(1 mol $O_2$/32.00 g $O_2$)(3 mol $TiO_2$/3 mol $O_2$)(79.87 g $TiO_2$/1 mol $TiO_2$) = 0.357 g $TiO_2$

Percent $TiO_2$ in sample = (0.357 g/2.367 g)(100%)
$$= 15.1\%$$

**4.4** $(1.612 \text{ g CO}_2)(1 \text{ mol CO}_2/44.010 \text{ g CO}_2)(1 \text{ mol C}/$
$1 \text{ mol CO}_2) = 0.03663 \text{ mol C}$

$(0.7425 \text{ g H}_2\text{O})(1 \text{ mol H}_2\text{O}/18.015 \text{ g H}_2\text{O})(2 \text{ mol H}/$
$1 \text{ mol H}_2\text{O}) = 0.08243 \text{ mol H}$

$0.08243 \text{ mol H}/0.03663 \text{ mol} = 2.250 \text{ H}/1 \text{ C} = 9 \text{ H}/4 \text{ C}$

The empirical formula is $C_4H_9$, which has a molar mass of 57 g/mol. This is one half of the measured value of molar mass, so the molecular formula is $C_8H_{18}$.

**4.5** $(0.240 \text{ g CO}_2)(1 \text{ mol CO}_2/44.01 \text{ g CO}_2)(1 \text{ mol C}/$
$1 \text{ mol CO}_2)(12.01 \text{ g C}/1 \text{ mol C}) = 0.06549 \text{ g C}$

$(0.0982 \text{ g H}_2\text{O})(1 \text{ mol H}_2\text{O}/18.02 \text{ g H}_2\text{O})(2 \text{ mol H}/$
$1 \text{ mol H}_2\text{O})(1.008 \text{ g H}/1 \text{ mol H}) = 0.01099 \text{ g H}$

Mass O (by difference) =
$0.1342 \text{ g} - 0.06549 \text{ g} - 0.01099 \text{ g} = 0.0577 \text{ g}$

Amount C = $0.06549 \text{ g}(1 \text{ mol C}/12.01 \text{ g C})$
$= 0.00545 \text{ mol C}$

Amount H = $0.01099 \text{ g H}(1 \text{ mol H}/1.008 \text{ g H})$
$= 0.01090 \text{ mol H}$

Amount O = $0.0577 \text{ g O}(1 \text{ mol O}/16.00 \text{ g O})$
$= 0.00361 \text{ mol O}$

To find a whole-number ratio, divide each value by 0.00361; this gives 1.51 mol C : 3.02 mol H : 1 mol O. Multiply each value by 2, and round off to 3 mol C : 6 mol H : 2 mol O. The empirical formula is $C_3H_6O_2$; given the molar mass of 74.1, this is also the molecular formula.

**4.6** $(26.3 \text{ g})(1 \text{ mol NaHCO}_3/84.01 \text{ g NaHCO}_3)$
$= 0.313 \text{ mol NaHCO}_3$

$0.313 \text{ mol NaHCO}_3/0.200 \text{ L} = 1.57 \text{ M}$

Ion concentrations: $[\text{Na}^+] = [\text{HCO}_3^-] = 1.57 \text{ M}$

**4.7** $(2.00 \text{ M})(V_{conc}) = (1.00 \text{ M})(0.250 \text{ L}); V_{conc} = 0.125 \text{ L}$

To prepare the solution, measure accurately 125 mL of 2.00 M NaOH into a 250-mL volumetric flask, and add water to give a total volume of 250 mL.

**4.8** (a) pH = $-\log (2.6 \times 10^{-2}) = 1.59$
(b) $-\log [\text{H}^+] = 3.80; [\text{H}^+] = 1.6 \times 10^{-4} \text{ M}$

**4.9** HCl is the limiting reagent.

$(0.350 \text{ mol HCl}/1 \text{ L})(0.0750 \text{ L})(1 \text{ mol CO}_2/$
$2 \text{ mol HCl})(44.01 \text{ g CO}_2/1 \text{ mol CO}_2) = 0.578 \text{ g CO}_2$

**4.10** $(0.953 \text{ mol NaOH}/1 \text{ L})(0.02833 \text{ L NaOH})$
$= 0.0270 \text{ mol NaOH}$

$(0.0270 \text{ mol NaOH})(1 \text{ mol CH}_3\text{CO}_2\text{H}/1 \text{ mol NaOH})$
$= 0.0270 \text{ mol CH}_3\text{CO}_2\text{H}$

$(0.0270 \text{ mol CH}_3\text{CO}_2\text{H})(60.05 \text{ g/mol})$
$= 1.62 \text{ g CH}_3\text{CO}_2\text{H}$

$0.0270 \text{ mol CH}_3\text{CO}_2\text{H}/0.0250 \text{ L} = 1.08 \text{ M}$

**4.11** $(0.100 \text{ mol HCl}/1 \text{ L})(0.02967 \text{ L}) = 0.00297 \text{ mol HCl}$

$(0.00297 \text{ mol HCl})(1 \text{ mol NaOH}/1 \text{ mol HCl})$
$= 0.00297 \text{ mol NaOH}$

$0.00297 \text{ mol NaOH}/0.02500 \text{ L} = 0.119 \text{ M NaOH}$

**4.12** Moles acid = moles base = $(0.323 \text{ mol/L})(0.03008 \text{ L})$
$= 9.716 \times 10^{-3} \text{ mol}$

Molar mass = $0.856 \text{ g acid}/9.716 \times 10^{-3} \text{ mol acid}$
$= 88.1 \text{ g/mol}$

**4.13** $(0.196 \text{ mol Na}_2\text{S}_2\text{O}_3/1 \text{ L})(0.02030 \text{ L})$
$= 0.00398 \text{ mol Na}_2\text{S}_2\text{O}_3$

$(0.00398 \text{ mol Na}_2\text{S}_2\text{O}_3)(1 \text{ mol I}_2/2 \text{ mol Na}_2\text{S}_2\text{O}_3)$
$= 0.00199 \text{ mol I}_2$

$0.00199 \text{ mol I}_2$ is in excess and was not used in the reaction with ascorbic acid.

$\text{I}_2$ originally added = $(0.0520 \text{ mol I}_2/1 \text{ L})(0.05000 \text{ L})$
$= 0.00260 \text{ mol I}_2$

$\text{I}_2$ used in reaction with ascorbic acid
$= 0.00260 \text{ mol} - 0.00199 \text{ mol} = 6.1 \times 10^{-4} \text{ mol I}_2$

$(6.1 \times 10^{-4} \text{ mol I}_2)(1 \text{ mol C}_6\text{H}_8\text{O}_6/1 \text{ mol I}_2)$
$(176.1 \text{ g}/1 \text{ mol}) = 0.11 \text{ g C}_6\text{H}_8\text{O}_6$

**4.14** A Beer's Law plot of the calibration data was constructed by plotting concentration of $\text{Cu}^{2+}$ along the x-axis and the absorbance along the y-axis. The equation for the best-fit line is $y = 13.0x + 0.011$.

Substituting the absorbance for the solution of unknown concentration yields

$0.418 = 13.0x + 0.011$

$x = 0.0315$

Thus the concentration of $\text{Cu}^{2+}$ in the solution of unknown concentration is 0.0315 M.

## Chapter 5

**5.1** $C = 59.8 \text{ J}/[(25.0 \text{ g})(1.00 \text{ K})] = 2.39 \text{ J/g} \cdot \text{K}$

**5.2** $(15.5 \text{ g})(C_{metal})(18.9 \text{ °C} - 100.0 \text{ °C}) + (55.5 \text{ g})$
$(4.184 \text{ J/g} \cdot \text{K})(18.9 \text{ °C} - 16.5 \text{ °C}) = 0$

$C_{metal} = 0.44 \text{ J/g} \cdot \text{K}$

**5.3** $1.00 \text{ L}(1000 \text{ mL}/1 \text{ L})(0.7849 \text{ g/cm}^3) = 785 \text{ g}$

Heat liquid from 25.0 °C to 78.3 °C.

$\Delta T = 78.3 \text{ °C} - 25.0 \text{ °C} = 53.3 \text{ °C} = 53.3 \text{ K}$
$q = (2.44 \text{ J/g} \cdot \text{K})(785 \text{ g})(53.3 \text{ K})$
$= 1.02 \times 10^5 \text{ J} = 102 \text{ kJ}$

Boil the liquid.
$q = 38.56 \text{ kJ/mol} (785 \text{ g})(1 \text{ mol}/46.08 \text{ g})$
$= 657 \text{ kJ}$

Total = $102 \text{ kJ} + 657 \text{ kJ} = 759 \text{ kJ}$

**5.4** Energy transferred as heat from tea + energy as heat expended to melt ice = 0.

$(250 \text{ g})(4.2 \text{ J/g} \cdot \text{K})(273.2 \text{ K} - 291.4 \text{ K}) +$
$x \text{ g}(333 \text{ J/g}) = 0$

$x = 57 \text{ g}$

57 g of ice melts with energy supplied by cooling 250 g of tea from 18.2 °C (291.4 K) to 0 °C (273.2 K).

Mass of ice remaining = mass of ice initially − mass of ice melted

Mass of ice remaining = $75 \text{ g} - 57 \text{ g} = 18 \text{ g}$

**5.5** $(15.0 \text{ g C}_2\text{H}_6)(1 \text{ mol C}_2\text{H}_6/30.07 \text{ g C}_2\text{H}_6) = 0.499 \text{ mol}$
$\text{C}_2\text{H}_6$

$\Delta H° = 0.499 \text{ mol C}_2\text{H}_6(1 \text{ mol-rxn}/2 \text{ mol C}_2\text{H}_6)$
$(-2857.3 \text{ kJ/mol-rxn})$

$= -713 \text{ kJ}$

**5.6** Mass of final solution = 400. g

$\Delta T = 27.78\ °C - 25.10\ °C = 2.68\ °C = 2.68\ K$

Amount of HCl used = amount of NaOH used = $C \times V = (0.400\ mol/L) \times 0.200\ L = 0.0800\ mol$

Energy transferred as heat by acid–base reaction + energy gained as heat to warm solution = 0

$q_{rxn} + (4.20\ J/g \cdot K)(400.\ g)(2.68\ K) = 0$

$q_{rxn} = -4.50 \times 10^3\ J$

This represents the energy transferred as heat in the reaction of 0.0800 mol HCl.

Energy transferred as heat per mole = $\Delta_r H$ = $-4.50\ kJ/0.0800\ mol\ HCl = -56.3\ kJ/mol\ HCl$

**5.7** (a) Energy evolved as heat in reaction + energy as heat absorbed by $H_2O$ + energy as heat absorbed by bomb = 0

$q_{rxn} + (1.50 \times 10^3\ g)(4.20\ J/g \cdot K)(27.32\ °C - 25.00\ °C) + (837\ J/K)(27.32\ °C - 25.00\ °C) = 0$

$q_{rxn} = -16,600\ J$ (energy as heat evolved in burning 1.0 g sucrose)

(b) Energy evolved as heat per mole = $(-16.6\ kJ/g$ sucrose$)(342.3\ g$ sucrose$/1\ mol$ sucrose$) = -5670\ kJ/mol$ sucrose

**5.8** $C(s) + O_2(g) \longrightarrow CO_2(g) \qquad \Delta_r H_1° = -393.5\ kJ$

$2\ [S(s) + O_2(g) \longrightarrow SO_2(g)]$
$\Delta_r H° = 2\ \Delta_r H_2° = 2(-296.8) = -593.6\ kJ$

$CO_2(g) + 2\ SO_2(g) \longrightarrow CS_2(g) + 3\ O_2(g)$
$\Delta_r H° = -\Delta_r H_3° = +1103.9\ kJ$

Net: $C(s) + 2\ S(s) \longrightarrow CS_2(g)$
$\Delta_r H°_{net} = -393.5\ kJ + -593.6\ kJ + 1103.9\ kJ$
$= +116.8\ kJ$

**5.9** $\Delta_r H° = (6\ mol\ CO_2/mol\text{-}rxn)\Delta_f H°[CO_2(g)] + (3\ mol\ H_2O/mol\text{-}rxn)\Delta_f H°[H_2O(\ell)] - \{(1\ mol\ C_6H_6/1\ mol\text{-}rxn)\Delta_f H°[C_6H_6(\ell)] + (15\frac{1}{2}\ mol\ O_2/mol\text{-}rxn)\Delta_f H°[O_2(g)]\}$

$= (6\ mol/mol\text{-}rxn)(-393.5\ kJ/mol) + (3\ mol/mol\text{-}rxn)(-285.8\ J/mol) - (1\ mol/mol\text{-}rxn)(+49.0\ kJ/mol) - 0$

$= -3267.4\ kJ/mol\text{-}rxn$

## Chapter 6

**6.1** (a) Highest frequency, violet; lowest frequency, red
(b) The frequency of a microwave oven, 2.45 GHz, is higher than the FM radio frequency, 91.7 MHz.
(c) The wavelength of x-rays is shorter than the wavelength of ultraviolet light.

**6.2** (a) $E$ (per atom) = $-Rhc/n^2$
$= (-2.179 \times 10^{-18})/(3^2)\ J/atom$
$= -2.421 \times 10^{-19}\ J/atom$
(b) $E$ (per mol) = $(-2.421 \times 10^{-19}\ J/atom)$
$(6.022 \times 10^{23}\ atoms/mol)$
$(1\ kJ/10^3\ J)$
$= -145.8\ kJ/mol$

**6.3** The least energetic line is from the electron transition from $n = 2$ to $n = 1$.

$\Delta E = -Rhc[1/1^2 - 1/2^2]$
$= -(2.179 \times 10^{-18}\ J/atom)(3/4)$
$= -1.634 \times 10^{-18}\ J/atom$

The photon emitted thus has $E_{photon} = 1.634 \times 10^{-18}\ J$

$\nu = E_{photon}/h$
$= (1.634 \times 10^{-18}\ J)/(6.626 \times 10^{-34}\ J \cdot s)$
$= 2.466 \times 10^{15}\ s^{-1}$

$\lambda = c/\nu = (2.998 \times 10^8\ m/s^{-1})/(2.466 \times 10^{15}\ s^{-1})$
$= 1.216 \times 10^{-7}\ m$ (or 121.6 nm)

**6.4** First, calculate the velocity of the neutron:
$v = [2E/m]^{1/2} = [2(6.21 \times 10^{-21}\ kg \cdot m^2\ s^{-2})/(1.675 \times 10^{-27}\ kg)]^{1/2}$
$= 2720\ m \cdot s^{-1}$

Use this value in the de Broglie equation:
$\lambda = h/mv = (6.626 \times 10^{-34}\ kg \cdot m^2\ s^{-2} \cdot s)/(1.675 \times 10^{-27}\ kg)(2720\ m\ s^{-1})$
$= 1.45 \times 10^{-10}\ m = 0.145\ nm$

## Chapter 7

**7.1** (a) chlorine (Cl)
(b) $1s^2 2s^2 2p^6 3s^2 3p^3$

$$[Ne]\ \boxed{\uparrow\downarrow}_{3s}\quad \boxed{\uparrow\ \uparrow\ \uparrow}_{3p}$$

**7.2** Calcium has two valence electrons in the $4s$ subshell. Quantum numbers for these two electrons are $n = 4$, $\ell = 0$, $m_\ell = 0$, and $m_s = \pm1/2$

**7.3** Obtain the answers from Table 7.3.

**7.4**

$V^{2+}$  [Ar]  $\boxed{\uparrow|\uparrow|\uparrow|\ |\ }_{3d}$  $\boxed{\ }_{4s}$

$V^{3+}$  [Ar]  $\boxed{\uparrow|\uparrow|\ |\ |\ }_{3d}$  $\boxed{\ }_{4s}$

$Co^{3+}$  [Ar]  $\boxed{\uparrow\downarrow|\uparrow|\uparrow|\uparrow|\uparrow}_{3d}$  $\boxed{\ }_{4s}$

All three ions are paramagnetic with three, two, and four unpaired electrons, respectively.

**7.5** (a) Increasing atomic radius: C < B < Al
(b) Increasing ionization energy: Al < B < C
(c) Carbon is predicted to have the more negative electron attachment enthalpy.

## Chapter 8

**8.1**

$$\left[\begin{array}{c} H \\ | \\ H-N-H \\ | \\ H \end{array}\right]^+ \quad :C\equiv O: \quad [:N\equiv O:]^+ \quad \left[\begin{array}{c} :\ddot{O}: \\ | \\ :\ddot{O}-S-\ddot{O}: \\ | \\ :\ddot{O}: \end{array}\right]^{2-}$$

**8.2**

$$H-\underset{\underset{H}{|}}{\overset{\overset{H}{|}}{C}}-\ddot{O}-H \qquad H-\underset{\underset{H}{|}}{N}-\ddot{O}-H$$

methanol            hydroxylamine

**8.3** (a) $CN^-$ : formal charge on C is $-1$; formal charge on N is 0.

(b) $SO_3^{2-}$: formal charge on S is $+1$; formal charge on each O is $-1$.

**8.4** Resonance structures for the $HCO_3^-$ ion:

$$\left[ \ddot{O}=\overset{|}{\underset{\underset{\ddot{O}-H}{|}}{C}}-\ddot{\ddot{O}}: \right]^- \longleftrightarrow \left[ :\ddot{\ddot{O}}-\overset{|}{\underset{\underset{\ddot{O}-H}{|}}{C}}=\ddot{O} \right]^-$$

(a) No. Three resonance structures are needed in the description of $CO_3^{2-}$; only two are needed to describe $HCO_3^-$.

(b) In each resonance structure: carbon's formal charge is 0; the oxygen of the $-OH$ group and the double-bonded oxygen have a formal charge of zero; the singly bonded oxygen has a formal charge of $-1$. The average formal charge on the latter two oxygen atoms is $-\frac{1}{2}$. In the carbonate ion, each of the three oxygen atoms has an average formal charge of $-\frac{2}{3}$.

(c) $H^+$ would be expected to add to one of the oxygens with a negative formal charge; that is, one of the oxygens with formal charge of $-\frac{1}{2}$ in this structure.

**8.5** $\left[ :\ddot{F}-\overset{..}{\underset{..}{Cl}}-\ddot{F}: \right]^+$ $ClF_2^+$, 2 bond pairs and 2 lone pairs.

$\left[ :\ddot{F}-\overset{..}{\underset{..}{\ddot{Cl}}}-\ddot{F}: \right]^-$ $ClF_2^-$, 2 bond pairs and 3 lone pairs.

**8.6** Tetrahedral geometry around carbon. The Cl—C—Cl bond angle will be close to $109.5°$.

**8.7** For each species, the electron-pair geometry and the molecular shape are the same. $BF_3$: trigonal-planar; $BF_4^-$: tetrahedral. Adding $F^-$ to $BF_3$ adds an electron pair to the central atom and changes the shape.

**8.8** The electron-pair geometry around I is trigonal-bipyramidal. The molecular geometry of the ion is linear.

$$\left[ :\overset{\overset{\textstyle :\ddot{Cl}:}{|}}{\underset{\underset{\textstyle :\ddot{Cl}:}{|}}{\ddot{I}}}< \right]^-$$

**8.9** (a) In $PO_4^{3-}$, there is tetrahedral electron-pair geometry. The molecular geometry is also tetrahedral.

$$\left[ \overset{\overset{\textstyle :\ddot{O}:}{|}}{\underset{\underset{\textstyle :\ddot{O}:}{|}}{:\ddot{O}-P-\ddot{O}:}} \right]^{3-} \qquad \overset{\overset{\textstyle O}{\|}}{\underset{\underset{\textstyle O}{}}{O-P\overset{\text{\tiny '''}}{-}O}}$$

(b) In $SO_3^{2-}$, there is tetrahedral electron-pair geometry. The molecular geometry is trigonal-pyramidal.

$$\left[ :\ddot{O}-\overset{|}{\underset{\underset{\textstyle :\ddot{O}:}{|}}{\ddot{S}}}-\ddot{O}: \right]^{2-} \qquad O-\overset{\overset{\textstyle ..}{S}}{\underset{\underset{\textstyle O}{}}{\text{\tiny '''}O}}$$

(c) In $IF_5$, there is octahedral electron-pair geometry. The molecular geometry is square-pyramidal.

$$:\overset{\textstyle :\ddot{F}:}{\underset{\underset{\textstyle :\ddot{F}:}{}}{\ddot{F}\diagdown\overset{|}{I}\diagup\ddot{F}:}} \qquad \overset{\textstyle F}{\underset{\underset{\textstyle F}{}}{F\diagdown\overset{|}{I}\diagup F}}$$

**8.10** (a) The H atom is the positive pole in each case. H—F ($\Delta\chi = 1.8$) is more polar than H—I ($\Delta\chi = 0.5$).

(b) The B atom is the positive pole in each case. B—F ($\Delta\chi = 2.0$) is more polar than B—C ($\Delta\chi = 0.5$).

(c) C—Si ($\Delta\chi = 0.6$) is more polar than C—S ($\Delta\chi = 0.1$). In C—Si, C is the negative pole, and Si is the positive pole. In C—S, S is the negative pole, and C the positive pole.

**8.11** 16 valence electrons

$$\left[ :S\equiv C-\ddot{N}: \right]^- \longleftrightarrow \left[ :\ddot{S}=C=\ddot{N}: \right]^- \longleftrightarrow \left[ :\ddot{S}-C\equiv N: \right]^-$$

Formal charges  $+$   0   $2-$         0   0   $-$         $-$   0   0

Formal charge considerations favor the middle structure because it has less formal charge than the left structure and, unlike the right structure, it has the negative formal charge on the most electronegative atom in the ion.

Bond polarity: For the C–N bond, $\Delta\chi = 0.5$, so this bond is polar and should have a partially positive C and a partially negative N. For the C–S bond, $\Delta\chi = 0.1$, so this bond should be only slightly polar with a partially positive C and a partially negative S. Comparison of formal charge and bond polarity: The bonding in $SCN^-$ will be closest to the middle resonance structure with a smaller contribution of the resonance structure on the right. From this we conclude that both N and S will have a negative formal charge, with N having the more negative value. The polarities of the C–N and C–S bonds match this description, with N and S being the negative end of each polar bond.

**8.12** (a) $BFCl_2$, polar, negative side is the F atom because F is the most electronegative atom in the molecule.

$$\overset{\overset{\textstyle F}{|}}{\underset{\underset{\textstyle Cl\quad\quad Cl}{}}{B}} \big\uparrow +$$

(b) $NH_2Cl$, polar, negative side is the Cl atom.

$$\overset{\delta-}{Cl}\diagdown\overset{..}{\underset{\underset{\textstyle H\,\delta+}{}}{N}}\overset{\text{\tiny ''''}}{-}H\,\delta+$$

(c) $SCl_2$, polar, Cl atoms are on the negative side.

$$Cl\diagup\overset{\overset{\textstyle ..}{S}}{\underset{\underset{\textstyle \delta-}{\delta+}}{}}\diagdown\underset{\delta-}{Cl} \big\downarrow$$

**8.13** (a)

$$:\!\overset{..}{O}\!:$$
$$|$$
$$:\!\overset{..}{Cl}\!-\!S\!-\!\overset{..}{Cl}\!:$$

Formal charges: $S = +1$, $O = -1$, $Cl = 0$

(b) Geometry: trigonal-pyramidal. The molecule is polar. The positive charge is on sulfur, the negative charge on oxygen.

**8.14** $CH_4(g) + 2\,O_2(g) \longrightarrow CO_2(g) + 2\,H_2O(g)$

Break 4 C—H bonds and 2 O=O bonds:
$(4\text{ mol})(413\text{ kJ/mol}) + (2\text{ mol})(498\text{ kJ/mol}) = 2648\text{ kJ}$

Make 2 C=O bonds and 4 H—O bonds:
$(2\text{ mol})(745\text{ kJ/mol}) + (4\text{ mol})(463\text{ kJ/mol}) = 3342\text{ kJ}$

$\Delta_r H° = 2648\text{ kJ} - 3342\text{ kJ} = -694\text{ kJ/mol-rxn}$
(value calculated using enthalpies of formation
$= -802\text{ kJ/mol-rxn}$)

# Chapter 9

**9.1** This molecule has a tetrahedral electron-pair geometry and also a tetrahedral molecular shape. The carbon is $sp^3$ hybridized. The C—H bond arises from overlap of a carbon $sp^3$ orbital and the hydrogen $1s$ orbital. The C—Cl bonds each arise from overlap of a carbon $sp^3$ orbital and a chlorine $3p$ orbital.

**9.2** The carbon and nitrogen atoms in $CH_3NH_2$ are $sp^3$ hybridized. The C—H bonds arise from overlap of carbon $sp^3$ orbitals and hydrogen $1s$ orbitals. The bond between C and N is formed by overlap of $sp^3$ orbitals from these atoms. Overlap of nitrogen $sp^3$ and hydrogen $1s$ orbitals gives the two N—H bonds, and there is a lone pair in the remaining $sp^3$ orbital on nitrogen.

**9.3** This molecule has a trigonal-bipyramidal electron-pair geometry and a linear molecular shape. The xenon is $sp^3d$ hybridized. The Xe—F bonds each arise from the overlap of one of the axial $sp^3d$ hybrid orbitals on Xe with a $2p$ orbital on the F. The three lone pairs around Xe are in the equatorial $sp^3d$ hybrid orbitals.

**9.4** (a) $BH_4^-$, tetrahedral electron-pair geometry, $sp^3$
(b) $SF_5^-$, octahedral electron-pair geometry, $sp^3d^2$
(c) $OSF_4$, trigonal-bipyramidal electron-pair geometry, $sp^3d$
(d) $ClF_3$, trigonal-bipyramidal electron-pair geometry, $sp^3d$
(e) $BCl_3$, trigonal-planar electron-pair geometry, $sp^2$
(f) $XeO_6^{4-}$, octahedral electron-pair geometry, $sp^3d^2$

**9.5** The two $CH_3$ carbon atoms are $sp^3$ hybridized, and the center carbon atom is $sp^2$ hybridized. For each of the carbon atoms in the methyl groups, the $sp^3$ orbitals overlap with hydrogen $1s$ orbitals to form the three C—H bonds, and the fourth $sp^3$ orbital overlaps with an $sp^2$ orbital on the central carbon atom, forming a carbon–carbon sigma bond. Overlap of an $sp^2$ orbital on the central carbon and an oxygen $sp^2$ orbital gives the sigma bond between these elements. The $\pi$ bond between carbon and oxygen arises by overlap of a $p$ orbital from each element.

**9.6** $H_2^+$: $(\sigma_{1s})^1$ The ion has a bond order of ½ and is expected to exist. A bond order of ½ is predicted for $He_2^+$ and $H_2^-$, both of which are predicted to have electron configurations $(\sigma_{1s})^2(\sigma^*_{1s})^1$.

**9.7** $Li_2^-$ is predicted to have an electron configuration $(\sigma_{1s})^2(\sigma^*_{1s})^2(\sigma_{2s})^2(\sigma^*_{2s})^1$ and a bond order of ½, the positive value implying that the ion might exist.

**9.8** $O_2^+$: [core electrons] $(\sigma_{2s})^2(\sigma^*_{2s})^2(\sigma_{2p})^2(\pi_{2p})^4(\pi^*_{2p})^1$. The bond order is 2.5. The ion is paramagnetic with one unpaired electron.

# Chapter 10

**10.1** (a) Isomers of $C_7H_{16}$

$CH_3CH_2CH_2CH_2CH_2CH_2CH_3$    heptane

$$\underset{\displaystyle CH_3CH_2CH_2CH_2\underset{\displaystyle |}{\overset{\displaystyle |}{C}H}CH_3}{\overset{\displaystyle CH_3}{}}$$    2-methylhexane

$$\underset{}{\overset{\displaystyle CH_3}{CH_3CH_2CH_2CHCH_2CH_3}}$$    3-methylhexane

$$CH_3CH_2\overset{\displaystyle CH_3}{\underset{\displaystyle CH_3}{CHCH}}CH_3$$    2,3-dimethylpentane

$$CH_3CH_2CH_2\overset{\displaystyle CH_3}{\underset{\displaystyle CH_3}{C}}CH_3$$    2,2-dimethylpentane

$$CH_3CH_2\overset{\displaystyle CH_3}{\underset{\displaystyle CH_3}{C}}CH_2CH_3$$    3,3-dimethylpentane

$$CH_3\overset{\displaystyle CH_3}{\underset{\displaystyle CH_3}{CH}}CH_2CHCH_3$$    2,4-dimethylpentane

3-Ethylpentane is pictured on page 446.

$$\overset{\displaystyle H_3C\quad CH_3}{\underset{\displaystyle CH_3}{CH_3C-CHCH_3}}$$    2,2,3-trimethylbutane

(b) Two isomers, 3-methylhexane and 2,3-dimethylpentane, are chiral.

**10.2** The names accompany the structures in the answer to Check Your Understanding 10.1.

**10.3** Isomers of $C_6H_{12}$ in which the longest chain has six C atoms:

Names (in order, top to bottom): 1-hexene, *cis*-2-hexene, *trans*-2-hexene, *cis*-3-hexene, *trans*-3-hexene. None of these isomers is chiral.

**10.4** (a)

bromoethane

(b)

2,3-dibromobutane

**10.5** 1,4-diaminobenzene

**10.6** $CH_3CH_2CH_2CH_2OH$     1-butanol

    2-butanol

    2-methyl-1-propanol

    2-methyl-2-propanol

**10.7** (a) $CH_3CH_2CH_2OH$: 1-propanol, has an alcohol (—OH) group

$CH_3CO_2H$: ethanoic acid (acetic acid), has a carboxylic acid (—$CO_2H$) group

$CH_3CH_2NH_2$: ethylamine, has an amino (—$NH_2$) group

(b) 1-propyl ethanoate (propyl acetate)

(c) Oxidation of this primary alcohol first gives propanal, $CH_3CH_2CHO$. Further oxidation gives propanoic acid, $CH_3CH_2CO_2H$.

(d) *N*-ethylacetamide, $CH_3CONHCH_2CH_3$

(e) The amine is protonated by hydrochloric acid, forming ethylammonium chloride, $[CH_3CH_2NH_3]Cl$.

**10.8** Kevlar is a condensation polymer, prepared by the reaction of terephthalic acid and 1,4-diaminobenzene.

$$n\,H_2NC_6H_4NH_2 + n\,HO_2CC_6H_4CO_2H \rightarrow$$
$$-(HNC_6H_4NHCOC_6H_4CO)_n^- + 2n\,H_2O$$

# Chapter 11

**11.1** 0.83 bar (0.82 atm) > 75 kPa (0.74 atm) > 0.63 atm > 250 mm Hg (0.33 atm)

**11.2** $V_2 = P_1V_1/P_2 = (745\text{ mm Hg})(65.0\text{ L})/$
$\qquad\qquad\qquad [0.70(745\text{ mm Hg})] = 93\text{ L}$

**11.3** $V_1 = 45\text{ L}$ and $T_1 = 298\text{ K}$; $V_2 = ?$ and $T_2 = 263\text{ K}$
$V_2 = V_1(T_2/T_1) = (45\text{ L})(263\text{ K}/298\text{ K}) = 40.\text{ L}$

**11.4** $V_2 = V_1(P_1/P_2)(T_2/T_1)$
$\quad = (22\text{ L})(150\text{ atm}/0.993\text{ atm})(295\text{ K}/304\text{ K})$
$\quad = 3200\text{ L}$

At 5.0 L per balloon, there is sufficient He to fill 640 balloons.

**11.5** 44.8 L of $O_2$ is required; 44.8 L of $H_2O(g)$ and 22.4 L of $CO_2(g)$ are produced.

**11.6** $PV = nRT$

$(750/760\text{ atm})(V) =$
$\qquad (1300\text{ mol})(0.08206\text{ L}\cdot\text{atm}/\text{mol}\cdot\text{K})(296\text{ K})$

$V = 3.2 \times 10^4\text{ L}$

**11.7** $d = PM/RT$; $M = dRT/P$
$M = (5.02\text{ g/L})(0.082057\text{ L}\cdot\text{atm}/\text{mol}\cdot\text{K})$
$\qquad (288.2\text{ K})/(745/760\text{ atm}) = 121\text{ g/mol}$

**11.8** $PV = (m/M)RT$; $M = mRT/PV$
$M = (0.105\text{ g})(0.082057\text{ L}\cdot\text{atm}/\text{mol}\cdot\text{K})$
$\qquad (296.2\text{ K})/[(561/760)\text{ atm }(0.125\text{ L})] = 27.7\text{ g/mol}$

**11.9** $n(N_2) = PV/RT = (1.10\text{ atm})(25.0\text{ L})/$
$\qquad (0.082057\text{ L}\cdot\text{atm}/\text{mol}\cdot\text{K})(298.2\text{ K}) = 1.12\text{ mol }N_2$

1.12 mol $N_2$ (2 mol Na/3 mol $N_2$)
$\qquad\qquad (22.99\text{ g Na}/1\text{ mol Na}) = 17.2\text{ g Na}$

**11.10** $n(H_2) = PV/RT$
$\quad = (542/760\text{ atm})(355\text{ L})/$
$\qquad\qquad (0.08206\text{ L}\cdot\text{atm}/\text{mol}\cdot\text{K})(298.2\text{ K})$

$n(H_2) = 10.3\text{ mol}$
$n(NH_3) = (10.3\text{ mol }H_2)(2\text{ mol }NH_3/3\text{ mol }H_2)$
$\qquad\qquad = 6.90\text{ mol }NH_3$
$P(125\text{ L}) = (6.90\text{ mol})(0.082057\text{ L}\cdot\text{atm}/\text{mol}\cdot\text{K})$
$\qquad\qquad\qquad (298.2\text{ K})$

$P(NH_3) = 1.35\text{ atm}$

**11.11** $P_{halothane}$ (5.00 L)

$\quad$ = (0.0760 mol)(0.08206 L · atm/mol · K) (298.2 K)

$\quad P_{halothane}$ = 0.372 atm (or 283 mm Hg)

$\quad P_{oxygen}$ (5.00 L)

$\quad$ = (0.734 mol)(0.08206 L · atm/mol · K)(298.2 K)

$\quad P_{oxygen}$ = 3.59 atm (or 2730 mm Hg)

$\quad P_{total} = P_{halothane} + P_{oxygen}$

$\quad$ = 283 mm Hg + 2730 mm Hg = 3010 mm Hg

**11.12** For He: Use Equation 11.9, with $M = 4.00 \times 10^{-3}$ kg/mol, $T = 298$ K, and $R = 8.314$ J/mol · K to calculate the rms speed of 1360 m/s. A similar calculation for $N_2$, with $M = 28.01 \times 10^{-3}$ kg/mol, gives an rms speed of 515 m/s.

**11.13** The molar mass of $CH_4$ is 16.0 g/mol.

$$\frac{\text{Rate for } CH_4}{\text{Rate for unknown}} = \frac{n \text{ molecules/1.50 min}}{n \text{ molecules/4.73 min}} = \sqrt{\frac{M_{unknown}}{16.0}}$$

$\quad M_{unknown}$ = 159 g/mol

## Chapter 12

**12.1** Because $F^-$ is the smaller ion, water molecules can approach more closely and interact more strongly. Thus, $F^-$ should have the more negative enthalpy of hydration.

**12.2**

$$H_3C-O\overset{\displaystyle H}{\diagdown}$$
$$H-O\diagdown$$
$$\qquad\quad CH_3$$

Hydrogen bonding in methanol entails the attraction of the hydrogen atom bearing a partial positive charge ($\delta^+$) on one molecule to the oxygen atom bearing a partial negative charge ($\delta^-$) on a second molecule. The strong attractive force of hydrogen bonding will cause the boiling point and the enthalpy of vaporization of methanol to be quite high.

**12.3** Water is a polar solvent, while hexane and $CCl_4$ are nonpolar. London dispersion forces are the primary forces of attraction between all pairs of dissimilar solvents. For mixtures of water with the other solvents, dipole–induced dipole forces will also be important.

**12.4** (a) $O_2$: induced dipole–induced dipole forces only.

(b) $CH_3OH$: strong hydrogen bonding (dipole–dipole forces) as well as induced dipole–induced dipole forces.

(c) Forces between water molecules: strong hydrogen bonding and induced dipole–induced dipole forces. Between $N_2$ and $H_2O$: dipole-induced dipole forces and induced dipole–induced dipole forces.

$\quad$ Relative strengths: a < forces between $N_2$ and $H_2O$ in c < b < forces between water molecules in c.

**12.5** (1.00 × 10³ g)(1 mol/32.04 g)(35.2 kJ/mol)

$$= 1.10 \times 10^3 \text{ kJ}$$

**12.6** (a) At 40 °C, the vapor pressure of ethanol is about 120 mm Hg.

(b) The equilibrium vapor pressure of ethanol at 60 °C is about 320 mm Hg. At 60 °C and 600 mm Hg, ethanol is a liquid. If vapor is present, it will condense to a liquid.

## Chapter 13

**13.1** (a) The strategy to solve this problem is given in Example 13.1.

$\quad$ Step 1. Mass of the unit cell

$\quad$ = (197.0 g/mol)(1 mol/6.022 × 10²³ atom)

$\qquad\qquad\qquad\qquad\qquad$ (4 atoms/unit cell)

$\quad$ = 1.309 × 10⁻²¹ g/unit cell

$\quad$ Step 2. Volume of unit cell

$\quad$ = (1.309 × 10⁻²¹ g/unit cell)(1 cm³/19.32 g)

$\quad$ = 6.773 × 10⁻²³ cm³/unit cell

$\quad$ Step 3. Length of side of unit cell

$\quad$ = [6.773 × 10⁻²³ cm³/unit cell]$^{1/3}$

$\quad$ = 4.076 × 10⁻⁸ cm

$\quad$ Step 4. Calculate the radius from the edge dimension.

$\quad$ Diagonal distance = 4.076 × 10⁻⁸ cm (2$^{1/2}$) = 4 ($r_{Au}$)

$\quad r_{Au}$ = 1.441 × 10⁻⁸ cm ( = 144.1 pm)

(b) To verify a body-centered cubic structure, calculate the mass contained in the unit cell. If the structure is bcc, then the mass will be the mass of 2 Fe atoms. (Other possibilities: fcc − mass of 4 Fe; primitive cubic − mass of 1 Fe atom). This calculation uses the four steps from the previous exercise in reverse order.

$\quad$ Step 1. Use radius of Fe to calculate cell dimensions. In a body-centered cube, atoms touch across the diagonal of the cube.

$\quad$ Diagonal distance = side dimension ($\sqrt{3}$) = 4 $r_{Fe}$

$\quad$ Side dimension of cube = 4 (1.26 × 10⁻⁸ cm)/($\sqrt{3}$) = 2.910 × 10⁻⁸ cm

$\quad$ Step 2. Calculate unit cell volume

$\quad$ Unit cell volume = (2.910 × 10⁻⁸ cm)³

$\quad$ = 2.464 × 10⁻²³ cm³

$\quad$ Step 3. Combine unit cell volume and density to find the mass of the unit cell.

$\quad$ Mass of unit cell = 2.464 × 10⁻²³ cm³(7.8740 g/cm³)

$\quad$ = 1.940 × 10⁻²² g

$\quad$ Step 4. Calculate the mass of 2 Fe atoms, and compare this to the answer from step 3.

$\quad$ Mass of 2 Fe atoms

$\quad$ = 55.85 g/mol (1 mol/6.022 × 10²³ atoms)

$\qquad\qquad\qquad\qquad\qquad\qquad$ (2 atoms)

$\quad$ = 1.85 × 10⁻²² g.

$\quad$ This is a fairly good match, and clearly much better than the two other possibilities, primitive and fcc.

**13.2** $M_2X$. In a face-centered cubic unit cell, there are four anions and eight tetrahedral holes in which to place metal ions. All of the tetrahedral holes are inside the unit cell, so the ratio of atoms in the unit cell is 2 : 1.

**13.3** We need to calculate the mass and volume of the unit cell from the information given. The density of KCl will then be mass/volume. Select units so the density is calculated as $g/cm^3$

Step 1. Mass: The unit cell contains 4 $K^+$ ions and 4 $Cl^-$ ions

Unit cell mass = $(39.10 \text{ g/mol})(1 \text{ mol}/6.022 \times 10^{23} K^+ \text{ ions})(4 K^+ \text{ ions}) + (35.45 \text{ g/mol})(1 \text{ mol}/6.022 \times 10^{23} Cl^- \text{ ions})(4 Cl^- \text{ ions})$

$= 2.355 \times 10^{-22}$ g $+ 2.597 \times 10^{-22}$ g

$= 4.952 \times 10^{-22}$ g

Step 2. Volume: Assuming $K^+$ and $Cl^-$ ions touch along one edge of the cube, the side dimension = $2 r_{K^+} + 2 r_{Cl^-}$. The volume of the cube is the cube of this value. (Convert the ionic radius from pm to cm.)

$V = [2(1.33 \times 10^{-8}$ cm$) + 2(1.81 \times 10^{-8}$ cm$)]^3$

$= 2.477 \times 10^{-22}$ cm$^3$

Step 3. Density = mass/volume

$= 4.952 \times 10^{-22}$ g$/2.477 \times 10^{-22}$ cm$^3)$

$= 2.00$ g/cm$^3$

## Chapter 14

**14.1** (a) 10.0 g sucrose = 0.0292 mol; 250. g $H_2O$ = 13.9 mol

$X_{sucrose} = (0.0292 \text{ mol})/(0.0292 \text{ mol} + 13.9 \text{ mol})$
$= 0.00210$

$c_{sucrose} = (0.0292 \text{ mol sucrose})/(0.250 \text{ kg solvent})$
$= 0.117 \ m$

Weight % sucrose =
$(10.0 \text{ g sucrose}/260 \text{ g soln})(100\%) = 3.85\%$

(b) $1.08 \times 10^4$ ppm =
$1.08 \times 10^4$ mg $Na^+$ per 1000 g soln

$= (1.08 \times 10^4$ mg $Na^+/1000$ g soln$)$
$(1050$ g soln$/1$ L$)$

$= 1.13 \times 10^4$ mg $Na^+$/L

$= 11.3$ g $Na^+$/L

$(11.3$ g $Na^+$/L$)(58.44$ g NaCl$/23.0$ g $Na^+) =$
28.8 g NaCl/L

**14.2** $\Delta_{soln}H° = \Delta_f H°[NaOH(aq)] - \Delta_f H°[NaOH(s)]$
$= -469.2$ kJ/mol $- (-425.9$ kJ/mol$)$
$= -43.3$ kJ/mol

**14.3** Solubility of $CO_2 = k_H P_g = 0.034$ mol/kg · bar $\times$ 0.33 bar $= 1.1 \times 10^{-2}$ mol/kg

**14.4** The solution contains sucrose $[(10.0 \text{ g})(1 \text{ mol}/342.3 \text{ g})$
$= 0.0292$ mol$]$ in water $[(225 \text{ g})(1 \text{ mol}/18.02 \text{ g})$
$= 12.5$ mol$]$.

$X_{water} = (12.5$ mol $H_2O)/(12.5$ mol $+ 0.0292$ mol$)$
$= 0.998$

$P_{water} = X_{water}P°_{water} = 0.998(149.4$ mm Hg$)$
$= 149$ mm Hg

**14.5** $c_{glycol} = \Delta T_{bp}/K_{bp} = 1.0 °C/(0.512 °C/m)$
$= 2.0 \ m = 2.0$ mol/kg

$mass_{glycol} = (2.0 \text{ mol/kg})(0.125 \text{ kg})(62.07 \text{ g/mol}) = 15$ g

**14.6** $c_{glycol} = (525 \text{ g})(1 \text{ mol}/62.07 \text{ g})/(3.00 \text{ kg}) = 2.82 \ m$

$\Delta T_{fp} = K_{fp} \times m = (-1.86 °C/m)(2.82 \ m) = -5.24 °C$

You will be protected only to about $-5 °C$ and not to $-25 °C$.

**14.7** $c$ (mol/L) = 0.033 g bradykinin (1 mol bradykinin/1060 g bradykinin)/0.0500 L = $6.2 \times 10^{-4}$ M

$\Pi = cRT$
$= (6.2 \times 10^{-4}$ mol/L$)(0.082057$ L·atm/mol·K$)(293$ K$)$
$= 0.015$ atm

**14.8** $\Delta T_{fp} = 5.265 °C - 5.50 °C = -0.24 °C$

$\Delta T_{fp} = K_{fp} \times m_{solute}$

$m_{solute} = -0.24 °C/-5.12 °C/m = 0.046$ mol/kg

$n_{solute} = (0.046$ mol solute/kg benzene$)$
$(0.02346$ kg benzene$) = 0.0011$ mol solute

$M = 0.448$ g$/0.0011$ mol $= 4.2 \times 10^2$ g/mol

$M(\text{compound})/M(\text{empirical formula})$
$= 4.2 \times 10^2$ g/mol$/104.1$ g/mol $= 4.0$

Molecular formula = $(C_2H_5)_8Al_4F_4$

**14.9** $c$ (mol/L) = $\Pi/RT$ = $[(1.86$ mm Hg$)(1$ atm$/760$ mm Hg$)]/[(0.08206$ L · atm/mol · K$)(298$ K$)]$
$= 1.00 \times 10^{-4}$ M

$(1.00 \times 10^{-4}$ mol/L$)(0.100$ L$) = 1.00 \times 10^{-5}$ mol

Molar mass = $1.40$ g$/1.00 \times 10^{-5}$ mol
$= 1.4 \times 10^5$ g/mol

(Assuming the polymer is composed of $CH_2$ units, the polymer is about 10,000 units long.)

**14.10** $c_{NaCl} = (25.0 \text{ g NaCl})(1 \text{ mol}/58.44 \text{ g})/(0.525 \text{ kg})$
$= 0.815 \ m$

$\Delta T_{fp} = K_{fp} \times m \times i = (-1.86 °C/m)(0.815 \ m)(1.85)$
$= -2.80 °C$

## Chapter 15

**15.1** $-\frac{1}{2} (\Delta[NOCl]/\Delta t) = \frac{1}{2}(\Delta[NO]/\Delta t) = \Delta[Cl_2]/\Delta t$

**15.2** For the first 2 hours:

$-\Delta[\text{sucrose}]/\Delta t = -[(0.033 - 0.050)$ mol/L$]/(2.0$ h$)$
$= 0.0085$ mol/L · h

For the last 2 hours:

$-\Delta[\text{sucrose}]/\Delta t = -[(0.010 - 0.015)$ mol/L$]/(2.0$ h$)$
$= 0.0025$ mol/L · h

Instantaneous rate at 4 hours = 0.0045 mol/L · h. (Calculated from the slope of a line tangent to the curve at the defined concentration.)

**15.3** Compare experiments 1 and 2: Doubling $[O_2]$ causes the rate to double, so the rate is first order in $[O_2]$. Compare experiments 2 and 4: Doubling $[NO]$ causes the rate to increase by a factor of 4, so the rate is second order in $[NO]$. Thus, the rate law is

Rate $= -(1/2)(\Delta[NO]/\Delta t) = k[NO]^2[O_2]$

Notice that stoichiometry requires the factor of $(1/2)$ in the reaction rate expression.

Using the data in experiment 1 to determine $k$:
$(1/2)0.028 \text{ mol/L} \cdot \text{s} = k[0.020 \text{ mol/L}]^2[0.010 \text{ mol/L}]$
$k = 3.5 \times 10^3 \text{ L}^2/\text{mol}^2 \cdot \text{s}$

**15.4** Rate $= k[Pt(NH_3)_2Cl_2] = (0.27 \text{ h}^{-1})(0.020 \text{ mol/L})$
$= 0.0054 \text{ mol/L} \cdot \text{h}$

**15.5** $\ln ([\text{sucrose}]/[\text{sucrose}]_o) = -kt$
$\ln ([\text{sucrose}]/[0.010]) = -(0.21 \text{ h}^{-1})(5.0 \text{ h})$
$[\text{sucrose}] = 0.0035 \text{ mol/L}$

**15.6** (a) The fraction remaining is $[CH_3N_2CH_3]/[CH_3N_2CH_3]_o$.

$\ln ([CH_3N_2CH_3]/[CH_3N_2CH_3]_o)$
$\qquad = -(3.6 \times 10^{-4} \text{ s}^{-1})(150 \text{ s})$
$[CH_3N_2CH_3]/[CH_3N_2CH_3]_o = 0.95$

(b) After the reaction is 99% complete $[CH_3N_2CH_3]/[CH_3N_2CH_3]_o = 0.010$
$\ln (0.010) = -(3.6 \times 10^{-4} \text{ s}^{-1})(t)$
$t = 1.3 \times 10^4 \text{ s} (210 \text{ min})$

**15.7** $1/[HI] - 1/[HI]_o = kt$
$1/[HI] - 1/[0.010 \text{ M}] = (30. \text{ L/mol} \cdot \text{min})(12 \text{ min})$
$[HI] = 0.0022 \text{ M}$

**15.8** $(0.060 \text{ M}/0.24 \text{ M}) = 0.25$; thus $\frac{1}{4}$ of the original material remains and two half-lives have transpired.
$t_{1/2} = 141 \text{ min}.$
$k = \ln2/t_{1/2} = (\ln 2)/141 \text{ min} = 4.9 \times 10^{-3} \text{ min}^{-1}$
Initial rate $= k[H_2O_2]_0$
$= 4.9 \times 10^{-3} \text{ min}^{-1} (0.24 \text{ mol/L})$
$= 1.2 \times 10^{-3} \text{ mol/L} \cdot \text{min}$

**15.9** (a) For $^{241}Am$, $t_{1/2} = 0.693/k = 0.693/(0.0016 \text{ y}^{-1})$
$= 430 \text{ y}$

For $^{125}I$, $t_{1/2} = 0.693/(0.011 \text{ d}^{-1}) = 63 \text{ d}$
(b) $^{125}I$ decays much faster.
(c) $\ln [(n)/(1.6 \times 10^{15} \text{ atoms})] = -(0.011 \text{ d}^{-1})(2.0 \text{ d})$
$n/1.6 \times 10^{15} \text{ atoms} = 0.978$; $n = 1.57 \times 10^{15} \text{ atoms}$

Since the answer should have two significant figures, we should round this off to $1.6 \times 10^{15}$ atoms. The approximately 2% that has decayed is not discernable within the limits of accuracy of the data presented.

**15.10** An Arrhenius plot was constructed by plotting $\ln k$ on the $y$-axis and $1/T$ on the $x$-axis. Using Microsoft Excel, the equation of the best-fit line is $y = -22336x + 27.304$.

$E_a = -R \cdot \text{(slope)}$
$= -(0.0083145 \text{ kJ/mol} \cdot \text{K})(-22336 \text{ K})$
$= 1.9 \times 10^2 \text{ kJ/mol}$

**15.11** $\ln (k_2/k_1) = (-E_a/R)(1/T_2 - 1/T_1)$
$\ln [(1.00 \times 10^4)/(4.5 \times 10^3)]$
$= -(E_a/8.3145 \times 10^{-3} \text{ kJ/mol} \cdot \text{K})(1/283 \text{ K} - 1/274 \text{ K})$
$E_a = 57 \text{ kJ/mol}$

**15.12** All three steps are bimolecular.
For step 3: Rate $= k[N_2O][H_2]$.
There are two intermediates, $N_2O_2(g)$ and $N_2O(g)$.
When the three equations are added, $N_2O_2$ (a product in the first step and a reactant in the second step) and $N_2O$ (a product in the second step and a reactant in the third step) cancel, leaving the net equation:
$2 \text{ NO}(g) + 2 \text{ H}_2(g) \longrightarrow \text{N}_2(g) + 2 \text{ H}_2\text{O}(g).$

**15.13** (a) $2 \text{ NH}_3(aq) + \text{OCl}^-(aq) \longrightarrow$
$\qquad \text{N}_2\text{H}_4(aq) + \text{Cl}^-(aq) + \text{H}_2\text{O}(\ell)$
(b) The second step is the rate-determining step.
(c) Rate $= k[NH_2Cl][NH_3]$
(d) $NH_2Cl$, $N_2H_5^+$, and $OH^-$ are intermediates.

**15.14** Overall reaction: $2 \text{ NO}_2\text{Cl}(g) \longrightarrow 2 \text{ NO}_2(g) + \text{Cl}_2(g)$
Rate $= k'[NO_2Cl]^2/[NO_2]$ (where $k' = k_1k_2/k_{-1}$)
Increasing $[NO_2]$ causes the reaction rate to decrease.

# Chapter 16

**16.1** (a) $K = [CO]^2/[CO_2]$
(b) $K = [Cu^{2+}][NH_3]^4/[Cu(NH_3)_4{}^{2+}]$
(c) $K = [H_3O^+][CH_3CO_2^-]/[CH_3CO_2H]$

**16.2** (a) $Q = [2.18]/[0.97] = 2.2$. The system is not at equilibrium; $Q < K$. To reach equilibrium, [isobutane] will increase and [butane] will decrease.
(b) $Q = [2.60]/[0.75] = 3.5$. The system is not at equilibrium; $Q > K$. To reach equilibrium, [butane] will increase and [isobutane] will decrease.

**16.3** (a)

| Equation | $C_6H_{10}I_2$ | $\rightleftharpoons$ $C_6H_{10}$ | + $I_2$ |
|---|---|---|---|
| Initial (M) | 0.050 | 0 | 0 |
| Change (M) | $-0.035$ | $+0.035$ | $+0.035$ |
| Equilibrium (M) | 0.015 | 0.035 | 0.035 |

(b) $K = (0.035)(0.035)/(0.015) = 0.082$

**16.4**

| Equation | $PCl_5(g)$ | $\rightleftharpoons$ $PCl_3(g)$ | + $Cl_2(g)$ |
|---|---|---|---|
| Initial (atm) | 2.000 | 0 | 0 |
| Change (atm) | $-x$ | $+x$ | $+x$ |
| Equilibrium (atm) | $2.000 - x$ | $x$ | $x$ |

The partial pressure of $Cl_2$ at equilibrium is 0.814 atm, so $x = 0.814$ atm.

$P(PCl_5) = 2.000 \text{ atm} - 0.814 \text{ atm} = 1.186 \text{ atm}$
$P(PCl_3) = P(Cl_2) = 0.814 \text{ atm}$
$K_p = (0.814)(0.814)/1.186 = 0.559$

**16.5**

| Equation | $H_2$ | + | $I_2$ | ⇌ | 2 HI |
|---|---|---|---|---|---|
| Initial (M) | $6.00 \times 10^{-3}$ | | $6.00 \times 10^{-3}$ | | 0 |
| Change (M) | $-x$ | | $-x$ | | $+2x$ |
| Equilibrium (M) | $0.00600 - x$ | | $0.00600 - x$ | | $+2x$ |

$$K_c = 33 = \frac{(2x)^2}{(0.00600 - x)^2}$$

$x = 0.0045$ M, so $[H_2] = [I_2] = 0.0015$ M and [HI] $= 0.0090$ M.

**16.6**

| Equation | $PCl_5(g)$ | ⇌ | $PCl_3(g)$ | + | $Cl_2(g)$ |
|---|---|---|---|---|---|
| Initial (M) | 0.1000 | | 0 | | 0 |
| Change (M) | $-x$ | | $+x$ | | $+x$ |
| Equilibrium (M) | $0.1000 - x$ | | $x$ | | $x$ |

$K_c = [PCl_3][Cl_2]/[PCl_5]$

$33.3 = x^2/0.1000 - x$

We cannot use the simplifying assumption in this case ($K$ is $> 1$ and $100 \cdot K > 0.1000$), so we must solve using the quadratic formula.

$x^2 + 33.3x - 3.33 = 0$

Using the quadratic formula, $x = 0.0997$ (the other root, $x = -33.4$, is not possible because it leads to negative concentrations).

$[PCl_3] = [Cl_2] = 0.0997$ M

$[PCl_5] = 0.1000$ M $- 0.0997$ M $= 0.0003$ M

**16.7** (a) $K' = K^2 = (2.5 \times 10^{-29})^2 = 6.3 \times 10^{-58}$
(b) $K'' = 1/K^2 = 1/(6.3 \times 10^{-58}) = 1.6 \times 10^{57}$

**16.8**

| Equation | Butane | ⇌ | Isobutane |
|---|---|---|---|
| Initial (M) | 0.20 | | 0.50 |
| After adding 2.0 M more isobutane | 0.20 | | 2.00 + 0.50 |
| Change (M) | $+x$ | | $-x$ |
| Equilibrium (M) | $0.20 + x$ | | $2.50 - x$ |

$$K = \frac{[\text{isobutane}]}{[\text{butane}]} = \frac{(2.50 - x)}{(0.20 + x)} = 2.50$$

Solving for $x$ gives $x = 0.57$ M. Therefore, [isobutane] $= 2.50 - 0.57 = 1.93$ M and [butane] $= 0.20 + 0.57 = 0.77$ M.

## Chapter 17

**17.1** $[H_3O^+] = 4.0 \times 10^{-3}$ M; $[OH^-] = K_w/[H_3O^+]$ $= 2.5 \times 10^{-12}$ M

**17.2** (a) pH $= 7$
(b) pH $< 7$ ($NH_4^+$ is an acid)
(c) pH $< 7$ $[Al(H_2O)_6]^{3+}$ is an acid
(d) pH $> 7$ ($HPO_4^{2-}$ is a stronger base than it is an acid)

**17.3** (a) $NH_4^+$ is a stronger acid than $HCO_3^-$. $CO_3^{2-}$, the conjugate base of $HCO_3^-$, is a stronger base than $NH_3$, the conjugate base of $NH_4^+$.
(b) Reactant-favored; the reactants are the weaker acid and base.
(c) Reactant-favored; the reactants are the weaker acid and base, so reaction lies to the left.

**17.4** From the pH, we can calculate $[H_3O^+] = 1.9 \times 10^{-3}$ M. Also, $[\text{butanoate}^-] = [H_3O^+] = 1.9 \times 10^{-3}$ M. Use these values along with [butanoic acid] to calculate $K_a$.
$K_a = [1.9 \times 10^{-3}][1.9 \times 10^{-3}]/(0.055 - 1.9 \times 10^{-3})$
$= 6.8 \times 10^{-5}$

**17.5** $K_a = 1.8 \times 10^{-5} = [x][x]/(0.10 - x)$
$x = [H_3O^+] = [CH_3CO_2^-] = 1.3 \times 10^{-3}$ M;
$[CH_3CO_2H] = 0.099$ M; pH $= 2.87$

**17.6** $HF(aq) + H_2O(\ell) \rightleftharpoons H_3O^+(aq) + F^-(aq)$
$K_a = 7.2 \times 10^{-4} = [x][x]/(0.00150 - x)$

The $x$ in the denominator cannot be dropped. This equation must be solved with the quadratic formula or by successive approximations. Because this problem follows the section dealing with the method of successive approximations, that method will be used here.

$7.2 \times 10^{-4} = x^2/(0.00150);\ x = 1.0 \times 10^{-3}$
$7.2 \times 10^{-4} = x^2/(0.00150 - 1.0 \times 10^{-3});\ x = 6.0 \times 10^{-4}$
$7.2 \times 10^{-4} = x^2/(0.00150 - 6.0 \times 10^{-4});\ x = 8.0 \times 10^{-4}$
$7.2 \times 10^{-4} = x^2/(0.00150 - 8.0 \times 10^{-4});\ x = 7.1 \times 10^{-4}$
$7.2 \times 10^{-4} = x^2/(0.00150 - 7.1 \times 10^{-4});\ x = 7.5 \times 10^{-4}$
$7.2 \times 10^{-4} = x^2/(0.00150 - 7.5 \times 10^{-4});\ x = 7.3 \times 10^{-4}$
$7.2 \times 10^{-4} = x^2/(0.00150 - 7.3 \times 10^{-4});\ x = 7.4 \times 10^{-4}$
$7.2 \times 10^{-4} = x^2/(0.00150 - 7.4 \times 10^{-4});\ x = 7.4 \times 10^{-4}$

The result has converged to two significant figures.
$[H_3O^+] = [F^-] = 7.4 \times 10^{-4}$ M
$[HF] = 0.00150$ M $- 7.4\ 10^{-4}$ M $= 7.6 \times 10^{-4}$ M

**17.7** $OCl^-(aq) + H_2O(\ell) \rightleftharpoons HOCl(aq) + OH^-(aq)$
$K_b = 2.9 \times 10^{-7} = [x][x]/(0.015 - x)$
$x = [OH^-] = [HOCl] = 6.6 \times 10^{-5}$ M
pOH $= 4.18$; pH $= 9.82$

**17.8** Equivalent amounts of acid and base react to form water, $CH_3CO_2^-$ and $Na^+$. Acetate ion hydrolyzes to a small extent, giving $CH_3CO_2H$ and $OH^-$. We need to determine $[CH_3CO_2^-]$ and then solve a weak base equilibrium problem to determine $[OH^-]$.

Amount $CH_3CO_2^-$ = moles base $= 0.12$ mol/L $\times 0.015$ L $= 1.8 \times 10^{-3}$ mol

Total volume $= 0.030$ L, so $[CH_3CO_2^-] =$ $(1.8 \times 10^{-3}$ mol$)/0.030$ L $= 0.060$ M

$CH_3CO_2^-(aq) + H_2O(\ell) \rightleftharpoons$
$CH_3CO_2H(aq) + OH^-(aq)$

$K_b = 5.6 \times 10^{-10} = [x][x]/(0.060 - x)$
$x = [OH^-] = [CH_3CO_2H] = 5.8 \times 10^{-6}$ M
pOH $= 5.24$; pH $= 8.76$

**17.9** $H_2C_2O_4(aq) + H_2O(\ell) \rightleftharpoons$
$$H_3O^+(aq) + HC_2O_4^-(aq)$$

$K_{a1} = 5.9 \times 10^{-2} = [x][x]/(0.10 - x)$

The $x$ in the denominator cannot be dropped. This equation must be solved with the quadratic formula or by successive approximations.

$x = [H_3O^+] = [HC_2O_4^-] = 5.3 \times 10^{-2}$ M

pH = 1.28

$K_{a2} = [H_3O^+][C_2O_4^{2-}]/[HC_2O_4^-]$; because $[H_3O^+]$
$= [HC_2O_4^-]$

$[C_2O_4^{2-}] = K_{a2} = 6.4 \times 10^{-5}$ M

## Chapter 18

**18.1** pH of 0.30 M $HCO_2H$:

$K_a = [H_3O^+][HCO_2^-]/[HCO_2H]$

$1.8 \times 10^{-4} = [x][x]/[0.30 - x]$

$x = 7.3 \times 10^{-3}$ M; pH = 2.13

pH of 0.30 M formic acid + 0.10 M $NaHCO_2$

$K_a = [H_3O^+][HCO_2^-]/[HCO_2H]$

$1.8 \times 10^{-4} = [x][0.10 + x]/(0.30 - x)$

$x = 5.4 \times 10^{-4}$ M; pH = 3.27

**18.2**

| Equation | $HCO_2H + H_2O \rightleftharpoons H_3O^+ + HCO_2^-$ | | |
|---|---|---|---|
| Initial (M) | 0.50 | 0 | 0.70 |
| Change (M) | $-x$ | $+x$ | $+x$ |
| Equilibrium (M) | $0.50 - x$ | $x$ | $0.70 + x$ |

$K_a = 1.8 \times 10^{-4} = (x)(0.70 + x)/(0.50 - x)$

The value of $x$ will be insignificant compared to 0.50 M and 0.70 M.

$1.8 \times 10^{-4} = (x)(0.70)/(0.50)$

$x = [H_3O^+] = 1.3 \times 10^{-4}$ M

pH = $-\log[H_3O^+] = 3.89$

**18.3** $(15.0 \text{ g } NaHCO_3)(1 \text{ mol}/84.01 \text{ g}) = 0.179$ mol $NaHCO_3$, and $(18.0 \text{ g } Na_2CO_3)(1 \text{ mol}/106.0 \text{ g})$
$= 0.170$ mol $Na_2CO_3$

pH = $pK_a + \log \{[\text{base}]/[\text{acid}]\}$

pH = $-\log (4.8 \times 10^{-11}) + \log \{[0.170]/[0.179]\}$

pH = $10.32 - 0.02 = 10.30$

**18.4** pH = $pK_a + \log \{[\text{base}]/[\text{acid}]\}$

$5.00 = -\log (1.8 \times 10^{-5}) + \log \{[\text{base}]/[\text{acid}]\}$

$5.00 = 4.74 + \log \{[\text{base}]/[\text{acid}]\}$

$[\text{base}]/[\text{acid}] = 1.8$

To prepare this buffer solution, the ratio [base]/[acid] must equal 1.8. For example, you can dissolve 1.8 mol (148 g) of $NaCH_3CO_2$ and 1.0 mol (60.05 g) of $CH_3CO_2H$ in enough water to make 1.0 L of solution.

**18.5** Initial pH (before adding acid):

pH = $pK_a + \log \{[\text{base}]/[\text{acid}]\}$

$= -\log (1.8 \times 10^{-4}) + \log \{[0.70]/[0.50]\}$

$= 3.74 + 0.15 = 3.89$

After adding acid, the added HCl will react with the weak base (formate ion) and form more formic acid. The net effect is to change the ratio of [base]/[acid] in the buffer solution.

Initial amount $HCO_2H$ = 0.50 mol/L × 0.500 L
$= 0.25$ mol

Initial amount $HCO_2^-$ = 0.70 mol/L × 0.50 L
$= 0.35$ mol

Amount HCl added = 1.0 mol/L × 0.010 L
$= 0.010$ mol

Amount $HCO_2H$ after HCl addition
$= 0.25$ mol + 0.010 mol = 0.26 mol

Amount $HCO_2^-$ after HCl addition
$= 0.35$ mol − 0.010 mol = 0.34 mol

pH = $pK_a + \log \{[\text{base}]/[\text{acid}]\}$

pH = $-\log (1.8 \times 10^{-4}) + \log \{[0.34]/[0.26]\}$

pH = $3.74 + 0.12 = 3.86$

**18.6** 35.0 mL base will partially neutralize the acid.

Initial amount $CH_3CO_2H$
$= (0.100 \text{ mol/L})(0.1000 \text{ L}) = 0.0100$ mol

Amount NaOH added
$= (0.100 \text{ mol/L})(0.0350 \text{ L}) = 0.00350$ mol

Amount $CH_3CO_2H$ after reaction
$= 0.0100 - 0.00350 = 0.0065$ mol

Amount $CH_3CO_2^-$ after reaction = 0.0035 mol

$[CH_3CO_2H]$ after reaction = 0.0065 mol/0.1350 L
$= 0.048$ M

$[CH_3CO_2^-]$ after reaction = 0.00350 mol/0.1350 L
$= 0.0259$ M

$K_a = [H_3O^+][CH_3CO_2^-]/[CH_3CO_2H]$

$1.8 \times 10^{-5} = [x][0.0259 + x]/[0.048 - x]$

$x = [H_3O^+] = 3.3 \times 10^{-5}$ M; pH = 4.48

**18.7** 75.0 mL acid will partially neutralize the base.

Initial amount $NH_3$ = $(0.100 \text{ mol/L})(0.1000 \text{ L})$
$= 0.0100$ mol

Amount HCl added = $(0.100 \text{ mol/L})(0.0750 \text{ L})$
$= 0.00750$ mol

Amount $NH_3$ after reaction = $0.0100 - 0.00750$
$= 0.0025$ mol

Amount $NH_4^+$ after reaction = 0.00750 mol

Solve using the Henderson–Hasselbach equation; use $K_a$ for the weak acid $NH_4^+$:

pH = $pK_a + \log \{[\text{base}]/[\text{acid}]\}$

pH = $-\log (5.6 \times 10^{-10}) + \log \{[0.0025]/[0.00750]\}$

pH = $9.25 - 0.48 = 8.77$

**18.8** $BaF_2(s) \rightleftharpoons Ba^{2+}(aq) + 2 F^-(aq)$

$[F^-] = 2[Ba^{2+}] = 2(3.6 \times 10^{-3} M) = 7.2 \times 10^{-3} M$

$K_{sp} = [Ba^{2+}][F^-]^2 = (3.6 \times 10^{-3})(7.2 \times 10^{-3})^2$
$= 1.9 \times 10^{-7}$

**18.9** $AgCN(s) \rightleftharpoons Ag^+(aq) + CN^-(aq)$

$K_{sp} = [Ag^+][CN^-]$

Let $x$ = solubility of AgCN in mol/L

$6.0 \times 10^{-17} = x^2$

$x = 7.7 \times 10^{-9}$ mol/L

$(7.7 \times 10^{-9}$ mol AgCN/L$)(133.9$ g AgCN/1 mol AgCN$) = 1.0 \times 10^{-6}$ g/L

**18.10** $Ca(OH)_2(s) \rightleftharpoons Ca^{2+}(aq) + 2 OH^-(aq)$

$K_{sp} = [Ca^{2+}][OH^-]^2; K_{sp} = 5.5 \times 10^{-5}$

$5.5 \times 10^{-5} = [x][2x]^2$ (where $x$ = solubility in mol/L)

$x = 2.4 \times 10^{-2}$ mol/L

Solubility in g/L =
$(2.4 \times 10^{-2}$ mol/L$)(74.1$ g/mol$) = 1.8$ g/L

**18.11** (a) In pure water:

$K_{sp} = [Ba^{2+}][SO_4^{2-}]; 1.1 \times 10^{-10} = [x][x];$

$x = 1.0 \times 10^{-5}$ mol/L

(b) In 0.010 M $Ba(NO_3)_2$, which furnishes 0.010 M $Ba^{2+}$ in solution:

$K_{sp} = [Ba^{2+}][SO_4^{2-}]$
$1.1 \times 10^{-10} = [0.010 + x][x]$
$x = 1.1 \times 10^{-8}$ mol/L

**18.12** (a) In pure water:

$K_{sp} = [Zn^{2+}][CN^-]^2; 8.0 \times 10^{-12} = [x][2x]^2 = 4x^3$

Solubility $= x = 1.3 \times 10^{-4}$ mol/L

(b) In 0.10 M $Zn(NO_3)_2$, which furnishes 0.10 M $Zn^{2+}$ in solution:

$K_{sp} = [Zn^{2+}][CN^-]^2; 8.0 \times 10^{-12} = [0.10 + x][2x]^2$

Solubility $= x = 4.5 \times 10^{-6}$ mol/L

**18.13** When $[Pb^{2+}] = 1.1 \times 10^{-3}$ M, $[I^-] = 2.2 \times 10^{-3}$ M.

$Q = [Pb^{2+}][I^-]^2 = [1.1 \times 10^{-3}][2.2 \times 10^{-3}]^2$
$= 5.3 \times 10^{-9}$

This value is less than $K_{sp}$, which means that the system has not yet reached equilibrium and more $PbI_2$ will dissolve.

**18.14** $K_{sp} = [Pb^{2+}][I^-]^2$. Let $x$ be the concentration of $I^-$ required at equilibrium.

$9.8 \times 10^{-9} = [0.050][x]^2$

$x = [I^-] = 4.4 \times 10^{-5}$ mol/L. A concentration greater than this value will result in precipitation of $PbI_2$.

Let $x$ be the concentration of $Pb^{2+}$ in solution, in equilibrium with 0.0015 M $I^-$.

$9.8 \times 10^{-9} = [x][1.5 \times 10^{-3}]^2$

$x = [Pb^{2+}] = 4.4 \times 10^{-3}$ M

**18.15** First, determine the concentrations of $Ag^+$ and $Cl^-$; then calculate $Q$, and see whether it is greater than or less than $K_{sp}$. Concentrations are calculated using the final volume, 105.0 mL, in the equation $C_{dil} \times V_{dil} = C_{conc} \times V_{conc}$.

$[Ag^+](0.1050$ L$) = (0.0010$ mol/L$)(0.1000$ L$)$

$[Ag^+] = 9.5 \times 10^{-4}$ M

$[Cl^-](0.1050$ L$) = (0.025$ M$)(0.0050$ L$)$

$[Cl^-] = 1.2 \times 10^{-3}$ M

$Q = [Ag^+][Cl^-] = [9.5 \times 10^{-4}][1.2 \times 10^{-3}]$
$= 1.1 \times 10^{-6}$

Because $Q > K_{sp}$, precipitation occurs.

**18.16**

| Equation | $Ag(NH_3)_2^+ \rightleftharpoons$ | $Ag^+ +$ | $2 NH_3$ |
|---|---|---|---|
| Initial (M) | 0.0050 | 0 | $1.00 - 2(0.0050)$ |
| Change | $-x$ | $+x$ | $+2x$ |
| Equilibrium (M) | $0.0050 - x$ | $x$ | $0.99 + 2x$ |

$K = 1/K_f = 1/1.1 \times 10^7 = [x][0.99]^2/0.0050$
$x = [Ag^+] = 4.6 \times 10^{-10}$ mol/L

**18.17** $Cu(OH)_2(s) \rightleftharpoons Cu^{2+}(aq) + 2 OH^-(aq)$

$K_{sp} = [Cu^{2+}][OH^-]^2$

$Cu^{2+}(aq) + 4 NH_3(aq) \rightleftharpoons Cu(NH_3)_4^{2+}(aq)$

$K_{form} = [Cu(NH_3)_4^{2+}]/[Cu^{2+}][NH_3]^4$

Net: $Cu(OH)_2(s) + 4 NH_3(aq) \rightleftharpoons Cu(NH_3)_4^{2+}(aq) + 2 OH^-(aq)$

$K_{net} = K_{sp} \times K_f = (2.2 \times 10^{-20})(2.1 \times 10^{13})$
$= 4.6 \times 10^{-7}$

# Chapter 19

**19.1** (a) $O_3$; larger molecules generally have higher entropies than smaller molecules.
(b) $SnCl_4(g)$; gases have higher entropies than liquids.

**19.2** (a) $\Delta_r S° = \Sigma n S°(products) - \Sigma n S°(reactants)$

$\Delta_r S° = (1$ mol/mol-rxn$) S°[NH_4Cl(aq)])$
$\qquad - (1$ mol/mol-rxn$) S°[NH_4Cl(s)]$

$\Delta_r S° = (1$ mol/mol-rxn$)(169.9$ J/mol · K$)$
$\qquad - (1$ mol/mol-rxn$)(94.85$ J/mol · K$)$

$= 75.1$ J/K · mol-rxn

A gain in entropy for the formation of a mixture (solution) is expected.

(b) $\Delta_r S° = (2$ mol $CO_2$/mol-rxn$) S°(CO_2) + (3$ mol $H_2O$/mol-rxn$) S°(H_2O) - [(1$ mol $C_2H_5OH$/mol-rxn$) S°(C_2H_5OH) + (3$ mol $O_2$/mol-rxn$) S°(O_2)]$

$\Delta_r S° = (2$ mol/mol-rxn$)(213.74$ J/mol · K$)$
$\qquad + (3$ mol/mol-rxn$)(188.84$ J/mol · K$)$
$\qquad - [(1$ mol/mol-rxn$)(282.70$ J/mol · K$)$
$\qquad + (3$ mol/mol-rxn$)(205.07$ J/mol · K$)]$

$\Delta_r S° = +96.09$ J/K · mol-rxn

An increase in entropy is expected because there is a increase in the number of moles of gases.

**19.3** $\Delta S°$(system) $= \Delta_r S°$
$$= \Sigma n S°\text{(products)} - \Sigma n S°\text{(reactants)}$$

$\Delta_r S° = $ (2 mol HCl/mol-rxn) $S°[\text{HCl(g)}]$
  $-$ {(1 mol H$_2$/mol-rxn) $S°[\text{H}_2\text{(g)}]$
  $+$ (1 mol Cl$_2$/mol-rxn) $S°[\text{Cl}_2\text{(g)}]$}

  $=$ (2 mol HCl/mol-rxn)(186.2 J/K $\cdot$ mol HCl)
  $-$ {(1 mol H$_2$/mol-rxn)(130.7 J/K $\cdot$ mol H$_2$)
  $+$ (1 mol Cl$_2$/mol-rxn) (223.08 J/K $\cdot$ mol Cl$_2$(g)}

  $=$ 18.6 J/K $\cdot$ mol-rxn

$\Delta_r H° = \Sigma n \Delta_f H°\text{(products)} - \Sigma n \Delta_f H°\text{(reactants)}$

$\Delta_r H° = $ (2 mol HCl/mol-rxn) $\Delta_f H°[\text{HCl(g)}]$
  $-$ {(1 mol H$_2$/mol-rxn) $\Delta_f H°[\text{H}_2\text{(g)}]$
  $+$ (1 mol Cl$_2$/mol-rxn) $\Delta_f H°[\text{Cl}_2\text{(g)}]$}

  $=$ (2 mol HCl/mol-rxn)($-$92.31 kJ/mol HCl)
  $-$ {(1 mol H$_2$/mol-rxn)(0 kJ/mol H$_2$)
  $+$ (1 mol Cl$_2$/mol-rxn) (0 kJ/mol Cl$_2$(g)}

  $=$ $-$184.62 kJ/mol-rxn

Both $\Delta_r H°$ ($<$ 0) and $\Delta_r S°$ ($>$ 0) are favorable, so this reaction is predicted to be spontaneous under standard conditions.

$\Delta S°$(surroundings) $= -\Delta_r H°/T$
$= -(-184.62\text{ kJ/mol-rxn})/298.15\text{ K}$
$= 0.61922$ kJ/K $\cdot$ mol-rxn $= 619.22$ J/K $\cdot$ mol-rxn

$\Delta S°$(universe) $= \Delta S°$(system) $+ \Delta S°$(surroundings)
$=$ 18.6 J/K $\cdot$ mol-rxn $+$ 619.22 J/K $\cdot$ mol-rxn
$=$ 637.8 J/K $\cdot$ mol-rxn

$\Delta S°$(universe) $> 0$, so the reaction is spontaneous under standard conditions.

**19.4** For the reaction N$_2$(g) + 3 H$_2$(g) $\longrightarrow$ 2 NH$_3$(g):

$\Delta_r H° = $ (2 mol/mol-rxn) $\Delta_f H°$ for NH$_3$(g)
$=$ (2 mol/mol-rxn)($-$45.90 kJ/mol)
$=$ $-$91.80 kJ/mol-rxn

$\Delta_r S° = $ (2 mol/mol-rxn) $S°$(NH$_3$) $-$ [(1 mol/mol-rxn)
$S°$(N$_2$) $+$ (3 mol/mol-rxn) $S°$(H$_2$)]

$\Delta_r S° = $ (2 mol/mol-rxn)(192.77 J/ mol $\cdot$ K)
  $-$ [(1 mol/mol-rxn)(191.56 J/mol $\cdot$ K)
  $+$ (3 mol/mol-rxn)(130.7 J/mol $\cdot$ K)]

$\Delta_r S° = $ $-$198.1 J/K $\cdot$ mol-rxn ($=$ 0.1981 kJ/K $\cdot$ mol-rxn)

$\Delta_r G° = \Delta_r H° - T\Delta_r S° = $
$-$91.80 kJ/mol-rxn $-$ (298 K)($-$0.1981 kJ/K $\cdot$ mol-rxn)

$\Delta_r G° = $ $-$32.8 kJ/mol-rxn

**19.5** SO$_2$(g) + ½ O$_2$(g) $\longrightarrow$ SO$_3$(g)

$\Delta_r G° = \Sigma n \Delta_f G°\text{(products)} - \Sigma n \Delta_f G°\text{(reactants)}$

$\Delta_r G° = $ (1 mol/mol-rxn)$\Delta_f G°[\text{SO}_3\text{(g)}]$
  $-$ {(1 mol/mol-rxn)$\Delta_f G°[\text{SO}_2\text{(g)}]$
  $+$ (0.5 mol/mol-rxn)$\Delta_f G°[\text{O}_2\text{(g)}]$}

$\Delta_r G° = $ $-$371.04 kJ/mol-rxn
  $-$ ($-$300.13 kJ/mol-rxn $+$ 0 kJ/mol-rxn)

  $=$ $-$70.91 kJ/mol-rxn

**19.6** HgO(s) $\longrightarrow$ Hg($\ell$) + ½ O$_2$(g); determine the temperature at which $\Delta_r G° = \Delta_r H° - T\Delta_r S° = 0$. $T$ is the unknown in this problem.

$\Delta_r H° = [-\Delta_f H°$ for HgO(s)] $=$ 90.83 kJ/mol-rxn

$\Delta_r S° = S°[\text{Hg}(\ell)] + \frac{1}{2} S°(\text{O}_2) - S°[\text{HgO(s)}]$

$\Delta_r S° = $ (1 mol/mol-rxn)(76.02 J/mol $\cdot$ K)
  $+$ [(0.5 mol/mol-rxn)(205.07 J/mol $\cdot$ K)
  $-$ (1 mol/mol-rxn)(70.29 J/mol $\cdot$ K)]
  $=$ 108.26 J/K $\cdot$ mol-rxn

$\Delta_r H° - T(\Delta_r S°) = 0$
$=$ 90,830 J/mol-rxn $- T$(108.26 J/K $\cdot$ mol-rxn)

$T =$ 839 K (566 °C)

**19.7** CaCO$_3$(s) $\rightleftharpoons$ CaO(s) + CO$_2$(g)

$\Delta_r G° = \Sigma\ n \Delta_f G°\text{(products)} - \Sigma\ n \Delta_f G°\text{(reactants)}$

$\Delta_r G° = \Delta_f G°(\text{CaO}) + \Delta_f G°(\text{CO}_2) - \Delta_f G°(\text{CaCO}_3)$

$\Delta_r G° = $ (1 mol CaO/mol-rxn)($-$603.42 kJ/mol CaO)
  $+$ (1 mol CO$_2$/mol-rxn)($-$394.359 kJ/mol CO$_2$)
  $-$ (1 mol CaCO$_3$/mol-rxn)
    ($-$1129.16 kJ/mol CaCO$_3$)

$\Delta_r G° = $ 131.38 kJ/mol-rxn

$\Delta_r G° = -RT \ln K$

131,380 J/mol-rxn
  $= -$(8.3145 J/mol-rxn $\cdot$ K)(298 K)(ln $K$)

$K_p = 9.37 \times 10^{-24}$

**19.8** C(s) + CO$_2$(g) $\rightleftharpoons$ 2 CO(g)

$\Delta_r G° = \Sigma\ n \Delta_f G°\text{(products)} - \Sigma\ n \Delta_f G°\text{(reactants)}$

$\Delta_r G° = 2\ \Delta_f G°(\text{CO}) - \Delta_f G°(\text{CO}_2)$

$\Delta_r G° = $ (2 mol/mol-rxn)($-$137.17 kJ/mol)
  $-$ (1 mol/mol-rxn)($-$394.36 kJ/mol)

$\Delta_r G° = $ 120.02 kJ/mol-rxn

$\Delta_r G° = -RT \ln K$

120,020 J/mol-rxn
  $= -$(8.3145 J/mol-rxn $\cdot$ K)(298 K)(ln $K$)

$K = 9.18 \times 10^{-22}$

# Chapter 20

**20.1** Oxidation half-reaction: Al(s) $\longrightarrow$ Al$^{3+}$(aq) + 3 e$^-$
Reduction half-reaction: 2 H$^+$(aq) + 2 e$^-$ $\longrightarrow$ H$_2$(g)
Overall reaction: 2 Al(s) + 6 H$^+$(aq) $\longrightarrow$
  2 Al$^{3+}$(aq) + 3 H$_2$(g)

Al is the reducing agent and is oxidized; H$^+$(aq) is the oxidizing agent and is reduced.

**20.2** (1) 2 VO$^{2+}$(aq) + Zn(s) + 4 H$^+$(aq) $\longrightarrow$
  Zn$^{2+}$(aq) + 2 V$^{3+}$(aq) + 2 H$_2$O($\ell$)
  2 V$^{3+}$(aq) + Zn(s) $\longrightarrow$ 2 V$^{2+}$(aq) + Zn$^{2+}$(aq)
(2) Oxidation (Fe$^{2+}$, the reducing agent, is oxidized):
  Fe$^{2+}$(aq) $\longrightarrow$ Fe$^{3+}$(aq) + e$^-$
  Reduction (MnO$_4^-$, the oxidizing agent, is reduced)
  MnO$_4^-$(aq) + 8 H$^+$(aq) + 5 e$^-$ $\longrightarrow$
    Mn$^{2+}$(aq) + 4 H$_2$O($\ell$)
  Overall reaction:
  MnO$_4^-$(aq) + 8 H$^+$(aq) + 5 Fe$^{2+}$(aq) $\longrightarrow$
    Mn$^{2+}$(aq) + 5 Fe$^{3+}$(aq) + 4 H$_2$O($\ell$)

**20.3** (a) Oxidation half-reaction:

$$Al(s) + 3\ OH^-(aq) \longrightarrow Al(OH)_3(s) + 3\ e^-$$

Reduction half-reaction:

$$S(s) + H_2O(\ell) + 2\ e^- \longrightarrow HS^-(aq) + OH^-(aq)$$

Overall reaction:

$$2\ Al(s) + 3\ S(s) + 3\ H_2O(\ell) + 3\ OH^-(aq) \longrightarrow$$
$$2\ Al(OH)_3(s) + 3\ HS^-(aq)$$

(b) Aluminum is the reducing agent and is oxidized; sulfur is the oxidizing agent and is reduced.

**20.4** Construct two half-cells, the first with a silver electrode and a solution containing $Ag^+(aq)$, and the second with a nickel electrode and a solution containing $Ni^{2+}(aq)$. Connect the two half-cells with a salt bridge. When the electrodes are connected through an external circuit, electrons will flow from the anode (the nickel electrode) to the cathode (the silver electrode). The overall cell reaction is $Ni(s) + 2\ Ag^+(aq) \longrightarrow$ $Ni^{2+}(aq) + 2\ Ag(s)$. To maintain electrical neutrality in the two half-cells, negative ions will flow from the $Ag\,|\,Ag^+$ half-cell to the $Ni\,|\,Ni^{2+}$ half-cell, and positive ions will flow in the opposite direction.

**20.5** (a) Using Appendix M, the order determined for these metals from least strong reducing agent to strongest reducing agent is Hg < Pb < Sn. (The further down the table, the stronger the metal is as a reducing agent.)

(b) $F_2$, $Cl_2$, and $Br_2$ all can oxidize mercury to mercury(II); Hg is located "southeast" of them on the table. $I_2$ cannot oxidize mercury to mercury(II); mercury is located "northeast" rather than "southeast" of it.

**20.6** Overall reaction: $2\ Al(s) + 3\ Fe^{2+}(aq) \longrightarrow$
$$2\ Al^{3+}(aq) + 3\ Fe(s)$$

$(E°_{cell} = 1.22\ \text{V}, n = 6)$

$E_{cell} = E°_{cell} - (0.0257/n)\ \ln\ \{[Al^{3+}]^2/[Fe^{2+}]^3\}$

$= 1.22 - (0.0257/6)\ \ln\ \{[0.025]^2/[0.50]^3\}$

$= 1.22\ \text{V} - (-0.023)\ \text{V} = 1.24\ \text{V}$

**20.7** Overall reaction: $Fe(s) + 2\ H^+(aq) \longrightarrow$
$$Fe^{2+}(aq) + H_2(g)$$

$(E°_{cell} = 0.44\ \text{V}, n = 2)$

$E_{cell} = E°_{cell} - (0.0257/n)\ \ln\ \{[Fe^{2+}]P_{H_2}/[H^+]^2\}$

$= 0.44 - (0.0257/2)\ \ln\ \{[0.024]1.0/[0.056]^2\}$

$= 0.44\ \text{V} - 0.026\ \text{V} = 0.41\ \text{V}$

**20.8** $\Delta_r G° = -nFE°$
$= -(2\ \text{mol e}^-)(96{,}500\ \text{C/mol e}^-)$
$$(-0.76\ \text{V})(1\ \text{J}/1\ \text{C} \cdot \text{V})$$
$= 146{,}680\ \text{J} = 150\ \text{kJ}$

The negative value of $E°$ and the positive value of $\Delta G°$ both indicate a reactant-favored reaction.

**20.9** $E°_{cell} = E°_{cathode} - E°_{anode} = 0.799\ \text{V} - 0.855\ \text{V}$
$= -0.056\ \text{V}; n = 2$

$E° = (0.0257/n)\ \ln\ K$

$-0.056 = (0.0257/2)\ \ln\ K$

$K = 0.013$

**20.10** Cathode: $2\ H_2O(\ell) + 2\ e^- \longrightarrow 2\ OH^-(aq) + H_2(g)$

$E°_{cathode} = -0.83\ \text{V}$

Anode: $4\ OH^-(aq) \longrightarrow O_2(g) + 2\ H_2O(\ell) + 4\ e^-$

$E°_{anode} = 0.40\ \text{V}$

Overall: $2\ H_2O(\ell) \longrightarrow 2\ H_2(g) + O_2(g)$

$E°_{cell} = E°_{cathode} - E°_{anode} = -0.83\ \text{V} - 0.40\ \text{V} = -1.23\ \text{V}$

The minimum voltage needed to cause this reaction to occur is 1.23 V.

**20.11** (1) $O_2$ is formed at the anode, by the reaction

$$2\ H_2O(\ell) \longrightarrow 4\ H^+(aq) + O_2(g) + 4\ e^-.$$

(0.445 A)(45 min)(60 s/min)(1 C/1 A · s)(1 mol $e^-$/96,500 C)(1 mol $O_2$/4 mol $e^-$)(32 g $O_2$/1 mol $O_2$) = 0.10 g $O_2$

(2) The cathode reaction (electrolysis of molten NaCl) is

$$Na^+(\text{melt}) + e^- \longrightarrow Na(\ell).$$

$(25 \times 10^3\ \text{A})(60\ \text{min})(60\ \text{s/min})(1\ \text{C}/1\ \text{A} \cdot \text{s})$
$(1\ \text{mol e}^-/96{,}500\ \text{C})(1\ \text{mol Na/mol e}^-)(23\ \text{g Na/}$
$1\ \text{mol Na}) = 21{,}450\ \text{g Na} = 21\ \text{kg}$

# Chapter 21

**21.1** (a) $2\ Na(s) + Br_2(\ell) \longrightarrow 2\ NaBr(s)$
(b) $Ca(s) + Se(s) \longrightarrow CaSe(s)$
(c) $2\ Pb(s) + O_2(g) \longrightarrow 2\ PbO(s)$

Lead(II) oxide, a red compound commonly called *litharge*, is the most widely used inorganic lead compound. Maroon-colored lead(IV) oxide is the product of lead oxidation in lead-acid storage batteries (Chapter 20). Other oxides such as $Pb_3O_4$ also exist.

(d) $2\ Al(s) + 3\ Cl_2(g) \longrightarrow 2\ AlCl_3(s)$

**21.2** (a) $H_2Te$
(b) $Na_3AsO_4$
(c) $SeCl_6$
(d) $HBrO_4$

**21.3** (a) $NH_4^+$ (ammonium ion)
(b) $O_2^{2-}$ (peroxide ion)
(c) $N_2H_4$ (hydrazine)
(d) $NF_3$ (nitrogen trifluoride)

**21.4** (a) In $Na_2Cl$, chlorine would have the unlikely charge of 2− (to balance the two positive charges of the two $Na^+$ ions).
(b) This compound would require either the calcium ion to have the formula $Ca^+$ or the acetate ion to have the formula $CH_3CO_2^{2-}$. In all of its compounds, calcium occurs as the $Ca^{2+}$ ion. The acetate ion, formed from acetic acid by loss of $H^+$, has a 1− charge.
(c) In $Mg_2O$, the magnesium ions would need to have the incorrect charge of 1+ to balance charge of the $O^{2-}$ ion or else the oxygen would need to have the incorrect charge of 4− to balance the charge of the two $Mg^{2+}$ ions. Neither of these possiblities is acceptable.

# Chapter 22

**22.1** (a) $Co(NH_3)_3Cl_3$
(b) $Fe(H_2NCH_2CH_2NH_2)_2Br_2 = Fe(en)_2Br_2$

**22.2** (a) (i) $K_3[Co(NO_2)_6]$: a complex of cobalt(III) with a coordination number of 6
(ii) $Mn(NH_3)_4Cl_2$: a complex of manganese(II) with a coordination number of 6
(b) $NH_4[Co(edta)]$: a complex of cobalt(III) with a co-ordination number of 6

**22.3** (a) hexaaquanickel(II) sulfate
(b) dicyanobis(ethylenediamine)chromium(III) chloride
(c) potassium amminetrichloroplatinate(II)
(d) potassium dichlorocuprate(I)

**22.4** (a) Geometric isomers are possible (with the $NH_3$ ligands in *cis* and *trans* positions).
(b) Only a single structure is possible.
(c) Only a single structure is possible.
(d) This compound is chiral; there are two optical isomers.
(e) Only a single structure is possible.
(f) Two structural isomers are possible based on coordination of the $NO_2^-$ ligand through oxygen or nitrogen.

**22.5** (a) $[Ru(H_2O)_6]^{2+}$: an octahedral complex of ruthenium(II) ($d^6$). A low-spin complex has no unpaired electrons and is diamagnetic. A high-spin complex has four unpaired electrons and is paramagnetic.

$$\begin{array}{cc} \underline{\uparrow} \quad \underline{\uparrow} \\ d_{x^2-y^2} \quad d_{z^2} \end{array} \qquad \begin{array}{cc} \underline{\phantom{\uparrow}} \quad \underline{\phantom{\uparrow}} \\ d_{x^2-y^2} \quad d_{z^2} \end{array}$$

$$\begin{array}{ccc} \underline{\uparrow\downarrow} \quad \underline{\uparrow} \quad \underline{\uparrow} \\ d_{xy} \quad d_{xz} \quad d_{yz} \end{array} \qquad \begin{array}{ccc} \underline{\uparrow\downarrow} \quad \underline{\uparrow\downarrow} \quad \underline{\uparrow\downarrow} \\ d_{xy} \quad d_{xz} \quad d_{yz} \end{array}$$
high-spin $Ru^{2+}$    low-spin $Ru^{2+}$

(b) $[Ni(NH_3)_6]^{2+}$: an octahedral complex of nickel(II) ($d^8$). Only one electron configuration is possible; it has two unpaired electrons and is paramagnetic.

$$\begin{array}{cc} \underline{\uparrow} \quad \underline{\uparrow} \\ d_{x^2-y^2} \quad d_{z^2} \end{array}$$

$$\begin{array}{ccc} \underline{\uparrow\downarrow} \quad \underline{\uparrow\downarrow} \quad \underline{\uparrow\downarrow} \\ d_{xy} \quad d_{xz} \quad d_{yz} \end{array}$$
$Ni^{2+}$ion ($d^8$)

**22.6** (1) A wavelength of 500 nm corresponds to green light being absorbed. The complex ion will appear magenta.
(2) The complex appears yellow because blue light is being absorbed. The high energy of blue light indicates that $\Delta_o$ is large and the complex is therefore low spin.

**22.7** (a) The $C_5H_5^-$ ligand is an anion (6 $\pi$ electrons), $C_6H_6$ is a neutral ligand (6 $\pi$ electrons), so Mn must be +1 (6 valence electrons). There is a total of 18 valence electrons.
(b) The ligands in this complex all are neutral, so the Mo atom must have no charge. The $C_6H_6$ ligand contributes six electrons, each CO contributes two electrons for a total of six, and Mo has six valence electrons. The total is 18 electrons.

# Chapter 23

**23.1** (a) Emission of six $\alpha$ particles leads to a decrease of 24 in the mass number and a decrease of 12 in the atomic number. Emission of four $\beta$ particles increases the atomic number by 4 but doesn't affect the mass. The final product of this process has a mass number of $232 - 24 = 208$ and an atomic number of $90 - 12 + 4 = 82$, identifying it as $^{208}_{82}Pb$.

(b) Step 1: $^{232}_{90}Th \longrightarrow {}^{228}_{88}Ra + {}^{4}_{2}\alpha$
Step 2: $^{228}_{88}Ra \longrightarrow {}^{228}_{89}Ac + {}^{0}_{-1}\beta$
Step 3: $^{228}_{89}Ac \longrightarrow {}^{228}_{90}Th + {}^{0}_{-1}\beta$

**23.2** (a) $^{0}_{+1}\beta$    (b) $^{41}_{19}K$    (c) $^{0}_{-1}\beta$    (d) $^{22}_{10}Ne$

**23.3** (a) $^{32}_{14}Si \longrightarrow {}^{32}_{15}P + {}^{0}_{-1}\beta$
(b) $^{45}_{22}Ti \longrightarrow {}^{45}_{21}Sc + {}^{0}_{+1}\beta$ or
$^{45}_{22}Ti + {}^{0}_{-1}e \longrightarrow {}^{45}_{21}Sc$
(c) $^{239}_{94}Pu \longrightarrow \alpha + {}^{235}_{92}U$
(d) $^{42}_{19}K \longrightarrow {}^{42}_{20}Ca + {}^{0}_{-1}\beta$

**23.4** $\Delta m = 0.03435$ g/mol
$\Delta E = (3.435 \times 10^{-5} \text{ kg/mol})(2.998 \times 10^8 \text{ m/s})^2$
$= 3.087 \times 10^{12}$ J/mol $(= 3.087 \times 10^9$ kJ/mol$)$
$E_b = 5.146 \times 10^8$ kJ/mol nucleons

**23.5** (a) 49.2 years is exactly four half-lives; quantity remaining $= 1.5$ mg$(1/2)^4 = 0.094$ mg
(b) Three half-lives, 36.9 years
(c) 1% is between six half-lives, 73.8 years (1/64 remains), and seven half-lives, 86.1 years (1/128 remains). [Using the integrated first-order rate equation with $[R]/[R]_0 = 0.010$ and $k = (\ln 2)/t_{1/2} = 0.0564$ y$^{-1}$, the amount of time is calculated to be 81.7 years.]

**23.6** (a) $\ln([A]/[A_o]) = -kt$
$\ln([3.18 \times 10^3]/[3.35 \times 10^3]) = -k(2.00 \text{ d})$
$k = 0.0260$ d$^{-1}$
$t_{1/2} = 0.693/k = 0.693/(0.0260 \text{ d}^{-1}) = 26.7$ d
(b) $k = 0.693/t_{1/2} = 0.693/200$ y $= 3.47 \times 10^{-3}$ y$^{-1}$
$\ln([A]/[A_o]) = -kt$
$\ln([3.00 \times 10^3]/[6.50 \times 10^{12}]) =$
$\qquad\qquad\qquad\qquad -(3.47 \times 10^{-3} \text{ y}^{-1})t$
$\ln(4.62 \times 10^{-10}) = -(3.47 \times 10^{-3} \text{ y}^{-1})t$
$t = 6190$ y

**23.7** $\ln([A]/[A_o]) = -kt$
$\ln([9.32]/[13.4]) = -(1.21 \times 10^{-4} \text{ y}^{-1})t$
$t = 3.00 \times 10^3$ y
This compares quite well with the estimated date.

**23.8** $^{98}_{42}Mo + {}^{1}_{0}n \rightarrow {}^{99}_{42}Mo + \gamma$
$^{99}_{42}Mo \rightarrow {}^{99}_{43}Tc + {}^{0}_{-1}\beta$

**23.9** $4.17 \times 10^{-5}(0.0100$ g $Pb^{2+}) = 4.17 \times 10^{-7}$ g $Pb^{2+}$
Solubility $= [4.17 \times 10^{-7}$ g $Pb^{2+}$ (1 mol $Pb^{2+}$/207.2 g Pb)(1 mol $PbCrO_4$/1 mol $Pb^{2+}$)]/0.01000 L $= 2.01 \times 10^{-7}$ mol $PbCrO_4$/L

# P   Answers to Review & Check Questions

## Chapter 1

### Section 1.4

1.   (b) Na
2.   (d) silicon

### Section 1.5

1.   (d) water
2.   (c) potassium

### Section 1.6

1.   (c) gasoline burns in air
2.   (b) polypropylene $<$ water $<$ soda bottle plastic
3.   (d) volume $= 13.6 \text{ cm}^3$

### Section 1.7

(b) The campfire wood burns.

### Section 1.8

1.   (d) 1.0 g of water vapor at 100 °C
2.   (a) A mixture of $H_2$ and $O_2$ has lower chemical potential energy than $H_2O$.

### Let's Review

### Section 1

1.   (b) $-196$ °C
2.   (c) $0.16 \text{ cm}^3$
3.   (a) 0.750 L
4.   (c) 1.9 L
5.   (a) $5.59 \times 10^3$ mg
6.   (d) $2 \times 10^{-8}$ g/L
7.   (c) 1050 kJ

### Section 2

1.   (c) 0.03 g
2.   (b) Student B

### Section 3

1.   (c) 3
2.   (a) 1
3.   (b) 10.32 g
4.   (c) $0.65 \text{ cm}^2$

### Section 4

1.   (a) $23.3 \text{ km}^2$
2.   (c) $2.8 \times 10^{17}$ km

### Section 5

1.   (a) 2.4
2.   (d) 78 g

### Section 6

(c) 130 m

## Chapter 2

### Section 2.2

1.   (b) 30 neutrons
2.   (c) Na

### Section 2.3

(d) $^{109}_{47}\text{Ag}$, 48.161%

### Section 2.4

1.   (a) $^{63}\text{Cu}$
2.   (b) 40%

## Section 2.5

1.    (a) Ge
2.    (a) Si
3.    (c) O
4.    (c) allotropes

## Section 2.6

(b) $C_3H_7NO_2S$

## Section 2.7

1.    (b) 2+
2.    (a) loses 3 electrons
3.    (b) ammonium sulfide
4.    (a) $Ba(CH_3CO_2)_2$
5.    (a) vanadium(III) oxide
6.    (a) MgO

## Section 2.8

1.    (a) $O_2F_2$
2.    (b) nitrogen pentaoxide, $N_2O_5$
3.    (c) dinitrogen tetrafluoride
4.    (b) tetraphosphorus decaoxide

## Section 2.9

1.    (c) 164.09 g/mol
2.    (b) 4.0 g $H_2$
3.    (c) 0.40 mol Ca
4.    (d) 30 g HF
5.    (a) $6.0 \times 10^{23}$ atoms O

## Section 2.10

1.    (d) butane, $C_4H_{10}$
2.    (a) benzene, $C_6H_6$
3.    (b) $C_6H_{12}O_6$
4.    (b) $C_5H_6O$, $C_{10}H_{12}O_2$

## Section 2.11

(d) $MgSO_4 \cdot 3H_2O$

# Chapter 3

## Section 3.1

1.    (b) 2, 3, 1
2.    (c) 12,000

## Section 3.2

(b) 9 $O_2$, 8 $H_2O$

## Section 3.3

(d) All chemical equilibria are product-favored.

## Section 3.4

1.    (a) $Ba(NO_3)_2$
2.    (b) $Ca^{2+}$ and 2 $NO_3^-$
3.    (b) acetic acid

## Section 3.5

1.    (b) $Ag_2S$
2.    (d) 1, 2, 3, and 4
3.    (c) $2\,Ag^+(aq) + CO_3{}^{2-}(aq) \rightarrow Ag_2CO_3(s)$

## Section 3.6

1.    (d) $H_2SO_4$
2.    (d) $PO_4{}^{3-}$
3.    (c) $CH_3CO_2H(aq) + OH^-(aq) \rightarrow$
$$H_2O(\ell) + CH_3CO_2{}^-(aq)$$
4.    (b) BaO

## Section 3.7

(b) $Na_2CO_3$

## Section 3.8

1.    (c) +6
2.    (c) 2 and 4
3.    (c) $KMnO_4$

## Section 3.9

(c) acid–base and precipitation

# Chapter 4

## Section 4.1

1.    (b) 0.60 moles $Cl_2$
2.    (a) 0.60 g Mg

## Section 4.2

(b) $O_2$

## Section 4.3

1. (c) 41.8 g
2. (c) 32.5%

## Section 4.4

(c) $C_4H_4O$

## Section 4.5

1. (c) 0.080 M
2. (b) 0.010 M
3. (b) 15 mL of 0.20 M KOH

## Section 4.6

1. (a) 0.10 M HCl
2. (c) 1.301

## Section 4.7

1. (a) acidic
2. (a) 80.0 mL

## Section 4.8

(b) A is reduced to half the original value.

# Chapter 5

## Section 5.1

(a) melting of ice at 0 °C

## Section 5.2

1. (b) warming 2.0 g of copper by 10 °C
2. (c) 20 g of water at 20 °C + 10 g of water at 30 °C

## Section 5.3

1. (a) Raising the temperature of 100 g of water by 1.0 °C
2. (b) All of the ice melts; liquid water is at a temperature between 0 °C and 10 °C.

## Section 5.4

1. (b) 2 and 4
2. (c) $2\ C(s) + O_2(g) \rightarrow 2\ CO(g)$

## Section 5.5

1. (c) 90.8 kJ
2. (b) −425 kJ

## Section 5.6

1. (b) endothermic
2. (b) The calculated value of $\Delta_{solution}H°$ will be too small.

## Section 5.7

1. (d) $Al(s) + 3/2\ Cl_2(g) \rightarrow AlCl_3(s)$
2. (c) $1/2\ \Delta_r H_1° - \Delta_r H_2° + 1/2\ \Delta_r H_3°$

# Chapter 6

## Section 6.1

(d) microwaves from a microwave oven

## Section 6.2

1. (a) $3.9 \times 10^5$ J/mol
2. (a) UVB

## Section 6.3

1. (d) from $n = 6$ to $n = 2$
2. (b) from $n = 4$ to $n = 2$

## Section 6.4

(b) Wavelength will be shorter.

## Section 6.5

1. (b) $4p$
2. (d) 16
3. (c) both $n$ and $\ell$

## Section 6.6

1. (d) $3f$
2. (b) $n = 4, \ell = 1, m_\ell = 0$
3. (c) 2

# Chapter 7

## Section 7.1

(d) 98

## Section 7.2

(a) $4s$

(b) $6s$

(c) $5s$

## Section 7.3

1.    (c) $3d^{10}4s^24p^4$
2.    (c) Ni

## Section 7.4

1.    (d) $Fe^{2+}$
2.    (c) $Co^{3+}$

## Section 7.5

1.    (d) $S^{2-} > Cl^- > K^+$
2.    (c) N highest, Si lowest

## Section 7.6

1.    (a) MgCl
2.    (d) $S^{3-}$

# Chapter 8

## Section 8.1

(c) $SiBr_4$

## Section 8.2

1.    (a) Sulfur has three single bonds to oxygen and a lone pair.
2.    (c) $O_3$
3.    (b) $OCN^-$

## Section 8.3

(c) $+1$

## Section 8.4

1.    (b) $SO_2$ and $SO_3$
2.    (b) Formal charge on each N is $+1$, formal charge on each oxygen is $-1/2$.

## Section 8.5

1.    (b) $SF_4$, $SF_5^+$, $SF_6$
2.    (d) 3

## Section 8.6

1.    (a) $PCl_3$
2.    (c) square pyramidal
3.    (c) $120°$
4.    (a) linear, $180°$ angle

## Section 8.7

1.    (d) Al—Cl
2.    (c) The I—Cl bond is polar with I being the positive end.
3.    (a) $:N{\equiv}N{-}\ddot{\underset{..}{O}}:$

## Section 8.8

1.    (a) HF
2.    (a) $BCl_3$

## Section 8.9

1.    (d) $H_2NOH$
2.    (a) $CN^-$
3.    (b) $-206$ kJ/mol-rxn

# Chapter 9

## Section 9.2

1.    (b) $sp^3d$
2.    (a) boron $sp^3$ + fluorine $2p$
3.    (c) The hybridization of I in $ICl_4^-$ is $sp^3$.
4.    (d) $p$ on atom A with $p$ on atom B
5.    (b) The nitrogens are attached by one $\sigma$ and two $\pi$ bonds.

## Section 9.3

1.    (b) 2.5
2.    (b) $\pi^*_{2p}$
3.    (c) $C_2$
4.    (a) $O_2^+$

# Chapter 10

## Section 10.1

1.    (c) b and c
2.    (a) a and b
3.    (c) 2

## Section 10.2

1.    (c) 2,5-dimethylheptane
2.    (c) The compound is an isomer of hexane, is not chiral, and is named 2,2-dimethylbutane.

3.  **(i)** (c) only 3

    **(ii)** (c) 1 and 2

4.  (a)

$$Br-\overset{\overset{\displaystyle CH_3}{|}}{\underset{\underset{\displaystyle CH_3}{|}}{C}}-\overset{\overset{\displaystyle CH_2CH_3}{|}}{\underset{\underset{\displaystyle H}{|}}{C}}-H$$

5.  (c) 3

## Section 10.3

1.  (d) more than 4

2.  (a) 2-propanol

3.  (a) $sp^3$

4.  (d) NaOH

## Section 10.4

1.  (d) 1 aldehyde and 2 ketones

2.  (b) 2-butanone

3.  (d) 120°, $sp^2$ hybridized

4.  (c) ethyl ethanoate

## Section 10.5

(c) $CH_2=\overset{\overset{\displaystyle CO_2H}{|}}{CH}$

# Chapter 11

## Section 11.1

1.  (b) 16 kPa

2.  (b) 7.8 m

## Section 11.2

1.  (b) 463 mL

2.  (d) 120. °C

3.  (d) none of the above (pressure = 0.458 atm)

## Section 11.3

1.  (e) Xe

2.  (b) B

3.  (b) D

## Section 11.4

1.  (d) 0.88 g

2.  (a) 0.18 mol

## Section 11.5

(c) 40. mm Hg $C_2H_2$ and 100. mm Hg $O_2$

## Section 11.6

(a) A = Xe, B = $O_2$, C = Ne, D = He

## Section 11.7

(c) rms for $HCl$/rms for $NH_3$ = 0.68

## Section 11.8

(a) 18.0 atm

# Chapter 12

## Section 12.2

(b) $AlCl_3$

## Section 12.3

1.  (b) $CH_3OH$

2.  (a) $H_2O$

## Section 12.4

1.  (d) $I_2$

2.  (d) octane, $C_8H_{18}$

## Section 12.5

(a) He < $SO_2$ < $CH_3OH$

## Section 12.6

1.  (b) All the water evaporates.

2.  (a) 29.1 kJ/mol

# Chapter 13

## Section 13.1

1.  (b) body-centered cubic

2.  (a) 0.858 g/cm$^3$

## Section 13.2

1.  (c) face-centered cubic

2.  (c) 3.21 g/cm$^3$

## Section 13.3

(a) 1800 nm, infrared

## Section 13.4

1.    (d) NaF

2.    (c) $Na^+(g) + Cl^-(g) \rightarrow NaCl(s)$

3.    (c) $-287$ kJ/mol

## Section 13.5

1.    (c) buckyballs ($C_{60}$)

2.    (b) an amorphous solid

## Section 13.6

1.    (a) NaCl

2.    (b) 15 g

## Section 13.7

1.    (d) Supercritical $CO_2$ can be obtained at 25 °C if a high enough pressure is applied.

2.    (b) At 66 K and 0.50 atm $N_2$ is a gas.

# Chapter 14

## Section 14.1

1.    (b) 0.063

      (b) 3.7

2.    (a) weight percent

## Section 14.2

      (c) $-23.55$ kJ/mol

## Section 14.3

      (b) 0.097 mol

## Section 14.4

1.    (b) $Na_2SO_4$ < sugar < KBr < $C_2H_4(OH)_2$

2.    (d) naphthalene, $C_{10}H_8$

3.    (c) 1.0 g propylene glycol, $C_3H_6(OH)_2$

4.    (c) 122 g/mol

## Section 14.5

      (b) 40 million atoms

# Chapter 15

## Section 15.1

1.    (b) The rate of disappearance of NO(g) is twice the rate of disappearance of $O_2$(g).

2.    (c) $0.6 \times 10^{-5}$ mol/L · min

## Section 15.2

      (e) all of the above

## Section 15.3

      (b) $1.24 \times 10^{-5}$ mol/L·s

## Section 15.4

1.    (b) between 6 and 7

2.    (d) A graph of $\ln[SO_2Cl_2]$ vs. time gives a straight line.

3.    (b) second order

## Section 15.5

1.    (c) $\ln k$ vs. 1/T

2.    (b) A higher proportion of reactant molecules exceeds the activation energy.

## Section 15.6

1.    (b) This reaction might occur in a single elementary step.

2.    (c) Rate = $k[A]^2[B]$

# Chapter 16

## Section 16.1

      (a) More $CaCO_3$ would precipitate.

## Section 16.2

1.    (b) $K = [SO_2]^2[O_2]/[SO_3]^2$

2.    (b) No, it is not at equilibrium, and the reaction proceeds further to the right.

## Section 16.3

      (b) $6.1 \times 10^{-4}$

## Section 16.4

      (b) 0.011 M

## Section 16.5

(c) $K_p = 2.7 \times 10^{33}$

## Section 16.6

1. (b) shift right
2. (a) shift left
3. (a) exothermic

# Chapter 17

## Section 17.1

(c) $H_2CO_3$, $CH_3CO_2H$, $H_3PO_4$

## Section 17.2

1. (c) amphiprotic
2. (b) base
3. (b) acid = $HNO_3$ and conjugate base = $NO_3^-$
   (a) base = $NH_3$ and conjugate acid = $NH_4^+$
4. (c) $HF/F^-$ and $CH_3CO_2H/CH_3CO_2^-$

## Section 17.3

1. (b) 11.08
2. (a) $4.8 \times 10^{-5}$ M
3. (d) $1.4 \times 10^{-4}$ M

## Section 17.4

1. (a) HF
2. (c) HCN
3. (a) $C_6H_5CO_2H$
4. (b) 9.25
5. (c) 10.15

## Section 17.5

1. (b) decrease
2. (a) increase

## Section 17.6

1. (b) product-favored
2. (b) right

## Section 17.7

1. (a) acidic
2. (a) acidic
3. (b) basic

## Section 17.8

1. (b) $6.3 \times 10^{-6}$ M
2. (a) $2.3 \times 10^{-5}$
3. (b) pH = 8.37, $[Na^+]$ = 0.10 M, $[CHO_2^-]$ = 0.10 M, $[OH^-]$ = $2.4 \times 10^{-6}$ M
4. (c) greater than 7

## Section 17.9

(c) 10.16

## Section 17.10

1. (a) $H_2SeO_4$
2. (b) $[Fe(H_2O)_6]^{3+}$
3. (a) HOCl

## Section 17.11

1. (b) $BCl_3$
2. (c) Brønsted base and (d) Lewis base

# Chapter 18

## Section 18.1

(b) 5.05

## Section 18.2

1. (a) 0.20 M HCN and 0.10 M KCN
2. (d) 18 mL
3. (b) 9.25
4. (c) 1/1.8

## Section 18.3

1. (b) 1.48
2. (d) 11.29
3. (c) methyl red

## Section 18.4

1. (b) $K_{sp} = [Ag^+]^2[CO_3^{2-}]$
2. (a) AgCl
   (b) $Ca(OH)_2$
   (c) $Ca(OH)_2$
3. (b) $1.6 \times 10^{-4}$ M
4. (a) $1.0 \times 10^{-7}$ M
5. (a) $FeCO_3$

## Section 18.5

(b) no

## Section 18.6

(b) $1.9 \times 10^{-36}$ M

## Section 18.7

(c) $1.1 \times 10^{5}$

# Chapter 19

## Section 19.1

1. (b) toward equilibrium
2. (b) false
3. (b) sometimes spontaneous

## Section 19.2

1. (c) $> 0$
2. (c) dispersed
3. (b) 3.19 J/K

## Section 19.3

1. (b) increases
2. (c) $2.5 \times 10^{-23}$ J/K

## Section 19.4

1. (c) $NaCl(s) < H_2O(\ell) < NH_3(g)$
2. (c) $\Delta_r S° > 0$
3. (a) $-326.6$ J/K·mol-rxn

## Section 19.5

1. (b) $-121.6$ J/K·mol-rxn
2. (d) 1320 J/K·mol-rxn
3. (b) at higher temperatures

## Section 19.6

1. (d) less, less
2. (a) product-favored at equilibrium
3. (b) false

## Section 19.7

1. (c) $-2155$ kJ/mol-rxn
2. (a) $-225$ kJ/mol-rxn
3. (c) 23 kJ/mol-rxn

# Chapter 20

## Section 20.1

1. (a) CuS
2. (d) $4 H^+ + 3 e^- + NO_3^- \rightarrow NO + 2 H_2O$
3. (b) $12 OH^- + Br_2 \rightarrow 2 BrO_3^- + 6 H_2O + 10 e^-$

## Section 20.2

1. (b) Electrons transfer from Cd to Ni.
2. (a) Cd is the anode and is negative.
3. (b) $NO_3^-$ ions move from the Ni half-cell to the Cd half-cell, and $K^+$ ions move from the Cd half-cell to the Ni half-cell.

## Section 20.3

1. (b) Lead(IV) oxide is reduced.
2. (b) Sulfuric acid is consumed.

## Section 20.4

1. (a) 1.562 V
2. (d) Mg
3. (a) ii and iv

## Section 20.5

(a) 0.47 V

## Section 20.6

(b) $6.3 \times 10^{16}$

## Section 20.7

(d) $Ag^+$

## Section 20.8

(d) 1450 seconds

# Chapter 21

## Section 21.2

1. (d) $Ca_2O_3$
2. (d) tetraphosphorus decaoxide
3. (b) $+3$
4. (d) $+5$

## Section 21.3

1. (a) neon
2. (c) the high temperature reaction of methane and water

## Section 21.4

1. (c) high melting point (>400 °C)
2. (a) $Li^+$
3. (c) two $Na^+$ ions and one $O_2^{2-}$ ion

## Section 21.5

1. (c) gypsum, $CaSO_4 \cdot 2H_2O$
2. (c) converting slaked lime, $Ca(OH)_2$, to lime

## Section 21.6

1. (c) third
2. (d) dissolve in acid and in base

## Section 21.7

1. (c) $SiO_2$
2. (c) +4

## Section 21.8

1. (c) between 2 and 3
2. (b) Solutions of ammonia are acidic.
3. (c) +3

## Section 21.9

1. (c) +3
2. (d) All electrons in $O_2$ are paired.

## Section 21.10

1. (b) $Cl_2$
2. (c) $F_2$ is prepared industrially by electrolysis of aqueous NaF.

## Chapter 22

## Section 22.1

1. (e) +7
2. (b) Atomic radii that are similar to the 5th period transition elements.

## Section 22.2

1. (b) Copper is reduced; sulfur is oxidized.
2. (b) iron oxide

## Section 22.3

1. (b) 6
2. (d) +3
3. (b) $Na_4[Fe(C_2O_4)_3]$
4. (b) pentaamminehydroxochromium(III) chloride

## Section 22.4

1. (b) $Ni(H_2O)_4(C_2O_4)$
2. (b) $Fe(en)_2(CN)_2$
3. (b) There are two geometric isomers, one of which has an optical isomer.
4. (d) 3

## Section 22.5

1. (b) high-spin $[Mn(NH_3)_6]^{2+}$
2. (a) square-planar $[PtCl_4]^{2-}$

## Section 22.6

(c) $[CrF_6]^{3-}$

## Section 22.7

(d) the anion in Zeise's salt, $[Pt(\eta^2\text{-}C_2H_4)Cl_3]^-$

## Chapter 23

## Section 23.2

1. (a) alpha radiation
2. (b) 7 $\alpha$ and 4 $\beta$
3. (c) $^{90}_{38}Sr \rightarrow ^{90}_{39}Y + \beta$

## Section 23.3

(c) $^{56}_{26}Fe$

## Section 23.4

1. (a) 20%
2. (d) 1/32

## Section 23.5

(c) electrons

## Section 23.6

(a) $^{93}_{37}Rb$

# Q Answers to Selected Interchapter Study Questions

## The Chemistry of Fuels and Energy Resources

1. (a) From methane: $H_2O(g) + CH_4(g) \rightarrow$
$$3 H_2(g) + CO(g)$$

   100. g $CH_4$(1 mol $CH_4$/16.043 g)
   (3 mol $H_2$/mol $CH_4$)(2.016 g $H_2$/1 mol $H_2$)
   = 37.7 g of $H_2$ produced

   (b) From petroleum: $H_2O(g) + CH_2(\ell) \rightarrow$
$$2 H_2(g) + CO\ (g)$$

   100. g $CH_2$(1 mol $CH_2$/14.026 g $CH_2$)
   (2 mol $H_2$/1 mol $CH_2$)(2.016 g $H_2$/1 mol $H_2$)
   = 28.7 g $H_2$ produced

   (c) From coal: $H_2O(g) + C(s) \rightarrow H_2(g) + CO(g)$

   100. g C(1 mol C/12.011 g C)(1 mol $H_2$/mole C)
   (2.016 g $H_2$/1 mol $H_2$) = 16.8 g $H_2$ produced

3. 70. lb (453.6 g/lb)(33 kJ/g) = $1.0 \times 10^6$ kJ

5. Assume burning oil produces 43 kJ/g (the value for crude petroleum in Table 1)

   7.0 gal(3.785 L/gal)(1000 $cm^3$/L)(0.8 g/$cm^3$)
   (43 kJ/g) = $0.9 \times 10^6$ kJ. Uncertainty in the numbers is one significant figure. This value is close to the value for the energy obtained by burning from 70 kg of coal (calculated in Question 3.)

7. (a) Isooctane: $C_8H_{18}(\ell) + 25/2\ O_2(g) \rightarrow$
$$8\ CO_2(g) + 9\ H_2O(\ell)$$

   $\Delta_rH° =$ (8 mol $CO_2$/1 mol-rxn)$\Delta_fH°[CO_2(g)]$
   + (9 mol $H_2O$/1 mol-rxn)$\Delta_fH°[H_2O(\ell)]$
   − {(1 mol $C_8H_{18}$/1 mol-rxn)$\Delta_fH°[C_8H_{18}(\ell)]$
   + 25/2 mol $O_2$/1 mol-rxn)$\Delta_fH°[O_2(g)]$}
   = (8 mol $CO_2$/1 mol-rxn)(−393.509 kJ/mol $CO_2$)
   + (9 mol $H_2O$/1 mol-rxn)(−285.83 kJ/mol $H_2O$)
   − {(1 mol $C_8H_{18}$/1 mol-rxn)(−259.3 kJ/mol $C_8H_{18}$)
   + 25/2 mol $O_2$/1 mol-rxn)(0 kJ/mol $O_2$)}
   = −5461.2 kJ/mol-rxn
   −5461.2 kJ/mol-rxn (1 mol-rxn/1 mol $C_8H_{18}$)
   (1 mol $C_8H_{18}$/114.230 g $C_8H_{18}$)(1000 g/1 kg)
   = −47,809 kJ/kg $C_8H_{18}$

   Ethanol: $C_2H_5OH(\ell) + 3\ O_2(g) \rightarrow$
$$2\ CO_2(g) + 3\ H_2O(\ell)$$

   $\Delta_rH° =$ (2 mol $CO_2$/1 mol-rxn)$\Delta_fH°[CO_2(g)]$
   + (3 mol $H_2O$/1 mol-rxn)$\Delta_fH°[H_2O(\ell)]$
   − {(1 mol $C_2H_5OH$/1 mol-rxn)$\Delta_fH°[C_2H_5OH(\ell)]$
   + 3 mol $O_2$/1 mol-rxn)$\Delta_fH°[O_2(g)]$}
   = (2 mol $CO_2$/1 mol-rxn)(−393.509 kJ/mol $CO_2$)
   + (3 mol $H_2O$/1 mol-rxn)(−285.83 kJ/mol $H_2O$)
   − {(1 mol $C_2H_5OH$/1 mol-rxn)(−277.0 kJ/mol
   $C_2H_5OH$) + 3 mol $O_2$/1 mol-rxn)(0 kJ/mol $O_2$)} =
   −1367.5 kJ/mol-rxn
   −1367.5 kJ/mol-rxn (1 mol-rxn/1 mol $C_2H_5OH$)
   (1 mol $C_2H_5OH$/46.069 g $C_2H_5OH$)(1000 g/1 kg) =
   −29,684 kJ/kg $C_2H_5OH$

   Isooctane releases more energy per kilogram.

   (b) Isooctane: 1.00 kg $C_8H_{18}$ (1000 g/1 kg)(1 mol
   $C_8H_{18}$/114.230 g $C_8H_{18}$)(8 mol $CO_2$/1 mol $C_8H_{18}$)
   = 70.0 mol $CO_2$

   Ethanol: 1.00 kg $C_2H_5OH$ (1000 g/1 kg)(1 mol
   $C_2H_5OH$/46.069 g $C_2H_5OH$)(2 mol $CO_2$/1 mol
   $C_2H_5OH$) = 43.4 mol $CO_2$

   Ethanol produces less $CO_2$ per kilogram.

   (c) On the basis of this simplistic comparison, there is not a clear winner. Isooctane releases more energy per kilogram but also releases more $CO_2$ per kilogram.

9. The factor for converting kW-h to kJ is 1 kW-h = 3600 kJ

   (940 kW-h/yr)(3600 kJ/kW-h) = $3.4 \times 10^6$ kJ/yr
   (940 kW-h/yr) (1 yr/12 months)($0.08/kW-h) = $ 6.3

11. First, calculate $\Delta_rH°$ for the reaction $CH_3OH(\ell)$ +
   1.5 $O_2(g) \rightarrow CO_2(g) + 2\ H_2O(\ell)$, using enthalpies of formation ($\Delta_rH°$ = −726.8 kJ/mol-rxn). Use molar mass and density to calculate energy per liter
   [−726.8 kJ/mol-rxn (1 mol-rxn/32.04 g)(787 g/L) =
   −17.9 × $10^3$ kJ/L]. Then use the kW-h to kJ conversion factor from Question 9 to obtain the answer
   [(17.9 × $10^3$ kJ/L)(1 kW-h/3600 kJ) = 4.96 kW-h/L].

13. Area of parking lot = 325 m × 50.0 m = $1.63 \times 10^4\ m^2$
   $2.6 \times 10^7$ J/$m^2$($1.63 \times 10^4\ m^2$) = $4.2 \times 10^{11}$ J

15. Energy per gallon of gas = (48.0 kJ/g)(0.737 g/$cm^3$)
   (1000 $cm^3$/L)(3.785 L/gal) = $1.34 \times 10^5$ kJ/gal

   Energy to travel 1 mile = 1.00 mile (1 gal/55.0 mile)
   ($1.34 \times 10^5$ kJ/gal) = 2430 kJ

# Milestones in the Development of Chemistry and the Modern View of Atoms and Molecules

1.  Atoms are not solid, hard, or impenetrable. They do have mass (an important aspect of Dalton's hypothesis), and we now know that atoms are in rapid motion at all temperatures above absolute zero (the kinetic-molecular theory).

3.  mass $e$/mass $p = 9.109383 \times 10^{-28}$ g/$1.672622 \times 10^{-24}$ g $= 5.446170 \times 10^{-4}$. (Mass of $p$ and $e$ obtained from Table 2.1, page 53.) The proton is 1,834 times more massive than an electron. Thomson's estimate was off by a factor of about 2.

# The Chemistry of Life: Biochemistry

1.  (a)

    $$H-\underset{\underset{\displaystyle H-\underset{\displaystyle CH_3}{\overset{\displaystyle |}{C}}-CH_3}{\overset{\displaystyle |}{\underset{\displaystyle |}{}}}{\overset{\displaystyle H}{\overset{|}{N}}}-\overset{\overset{\displaystyle H}{|}}{C}-\overset{\displaystyle :O:}{\overset{\|}{C}}-O-H$$

    (b)

    The zwitterionic form.

    (c) The zwitterionic form is the predominant form at physiological pH.

3.

5.

7.  (a) The structure of ribose is given in Figure 12.
    (b)

    Adenosine

    (c)        Adenosine-5'-monophosphate

9.  The sequences differ in the positions of attachments of the phosphate to deoxyribose on adjacent units. Consider the A-T attachments. In ATGC, the phosphate links the 3' position on A to the 5' position on T. In CGTA, the phosphate links the 5' position on A to the 3' position on T.

11. (a) 5'-GAATCGCGT-3'
    (b) 5'-GAAUCGCGU-3'
    (c) 5'-UUC-3', 5'-CGA-3', and 5'-ACG-3'
    (d) glutamic acid, serine, and arginine

13. (a) In transcription, a strand of RNA complementary to the segment of DNA is constructed.
    (b) In translation, an amino acid sequence is constructed based on the information in a mRNA sequence.

15. The four-ring structure present in all steroids is given in Figure 17a.

17. (a) false     (b) true     (c) true     (d) true

19. (a) $6\ CO_2(g) + 6\ H_2O(\ell) \rightarrow C_6H_{12}O_6(s) + 6\ O_2(g)$

$\Delta_r H° = \Sigma n\Delta_f H°(\text{products}) -$
$$\Sigma n\Delta_f H°(\text{reactants})$$

$\Delta_r H° = (1 \text{ mol } C_6H_{12}O_6/\text{mol-rxn})$
$[\Delta_f H°(C_6H_{12}O_6)] - (6 \text{ mol } H_2O/\text{mol-rxn})$
$[\Delta_f H°(H_2O)] - (6 \text{ mol } CO_2/\text{mol-rxn})$
$[\Delta_f H°(CO_2)]$

$\Delta_r H° = (1 \text{ mol } C_6H_{12}O_6/\text{mol-rxn})$
$(-1273.3 \text{ kJ/mol } C_6H_{12}O_6) - (6 \text{ mol } H_2O/\text{mol-rxn})$
$(-285.8 \text{ kJ/mol } H_2O) - (6 \text{ mol } CO_2/\text{mol-rxn})$
$(-393.5 \text{ kJ/mol } CO_2)$

$\Delta_r H° = +2,803 \text{ kJ/mol-rxn}$

(b) $(2803 \text{ kJ/mol})(1 \text{ mol}/6.022 \times 10^{23} \text{ molecules})$
$(1000 \text{ J}/1 \text{ kJ}) = 4.655 \times 10^{-18} \text{ J/molecule}$

(c) $\lambda = 650 \text{ nm }(1 \text{ m}/10^9 \text{ nm}) = 6.50 \times 10^{-7} \text{ m}$

$E = hc/\lambda = (6.626 \times 10^{-34} \text{ J} \cdot \text{s})$
$(3.00 \times 10^8 \text{ m} \cdot \text{s}^{-1})/(6.50 \times 10^{-7} \text{ m})$
$= 3.06 \times 10^{-19} \text{ J}$

(d) The energy per photon is less than the amount required per molecule of glucose; therefore, multiple photons must be absorbed.

# The Chemistry of Modern Materials

1. Figure 14b: $5.0 \text{ mm}/1 \text{ mm} = 5$; magnification is $5\times$

   Figure 14c: $5.0 \text{ mm}/20 \text{ } \mu\text{m} = 5.0 \text{ mm}/(20 \times 10^{-3} \text{ mm})$
   $= 250$; magnification is $250\times$

   Figure 14d: $5.0 \text{ mm}/500 \text{ nm} = 5.0 \text{ mm}/(5 \times 10^{-4} \text{ mm})$
   $= 10,000$; magnification $= 10,000\times$

3. The amount of light falling on a single solar cell
   $= 925 \text{ W/m}^2 [(1 \text{ m}^2/10^4 \text{ cm}^2)(1.0 \text{ cm}^2/\text{cell})$
   $= 0.093 \text{ W/cell.}]$ Using the conversion factor 1 W
   $= 1 \text{ J/s}$, the energy incident on the cell is
   $(0.093 \text{ W/cell})(1 \text{ J/W} \cdot \text{s})(60 \text{ sec/min})$
   $= 5.6 \text{ J/(min} \cdot \text{cell)}$. At 25% efficiency, the energy absorbed for each cell is 1.4 J/min.

5. Pewter consists of 91% Sn, 7.5% Sb, and 1.5% Cu. The densities of these elements (from www.ptable.com and converted to units of g/cm³) are 7.310 g/cm³ for Sn, 6.697 g/cm³ for Sb, and 8.920 g/cm³ for Cu.

   Density of pewter $= 0.91(7.310 \text{ g/cm}^3) + 0.075$
   $(6.697 \text{ g/cm}^3) + 0.015(8.920 \text{ g/cm}^3) = 7.3 \text{ g/cm}^3$

7. Density of aerogel (from Question 6) $= 0.0019 \text{ g/cm}^3$

   Volume $= 180 \text{ cm} \times 150 \text{ cm} \times 0.20 \text{ cm}$
   $= 5.4 \times 10^3 \text{ cm}^3$

   Mass aerogel needed $= 5.4 \times 10^3 \text{ cm}^3 (0.0019 \text{ g/cm}^3)$
   $= 10. \text{ g}$

# The Chemistry of the Environment

1. $[Na^+] = 0.460 \text{ mol/L}$, $[Cl^-] = 0.550 \text{ mol/L}$; a larger amount of chloride than sodium ion is present in a sample of seawater.

3. The amount of NaCl is limited by the amount of sodium present. From a 1.0-L sample of seawater, a maximum of 0.460 mol NaCl could be obtained. The mass of this amount of NaCl is 26.9 g [(0.460 mol/L) (1.00 L)(58.43 g NaCl/1 mol NaCl) = 26.9 g].

5. For gases, ppm refers to numbers of particles, and hence to mole fractions (see footnote to Table 1). Gas pressure exerted is directly proportional to mole fraction. Thus, 40,000 ppm water vapor would exert a pressure of 40,000/1,000,000 of one atmosphere, or 30.4 mm Hg (0.040 × 760 mm Hg). This would be the case at a little over 29 °C, at 100% humidity.

7. The concentration of $Mg^{2+}$ in seawater is 52 mmol/L (Table 2). Assuming that all this is converted to Mg metal, one would expect to obtain 1.3 g from 1.0 L of seawater [0.052 mol (24.31 g/mol) = 1.3 g]. To obtain 100 kg of Mg, 79,000 L of seawater [100. kg (1000 g/kg)(1 L/1.3 g) = 7.9 × 10⁴ L] would be needed.

9. (a) Only 92% of the ice is submerged, and the water displaced by ice (the volume of ice under the surface of water) is 23 cm³ (0.92 × 25 cm³ = 23 cm³). Thus, the liquid level in the graduated cylinder will be 123 mL.

   (b) Melting 25 cm³ of ice will produce 23 mL of liquid water [25 cm³ ice (0.92 g $H_2O$/cm³ ice) (1.0 cm³ liquid $H_2O$/g $H_2O$) = 23 cm³ liquid $H_2O$]. The water level will be 123 mL (the same as in (a); that is, the water level won't rise as the ice melts).

# R Answers to Selected Study Questions

## Chapter 1

**1.1** (a) C, carbon
(b) K, potassium
(c) Cl, chlorine
(d) P, phosphorus
(e) Mg, magnesium
(f) Ni, nickel

**1.3** (a) Ba, barium
(b) Ti, titanium
(c) Cr, chromium
(d) Pb, lead
(e) As, arsenic
(f) Zn, zinc

**1.5** (a) Na (element) and NaCl (compound)
(b) Sugar (compound) and carbon (element)
(c) Gold (element) and gold chloride (compound)

**1.7** (a) Physical property
(b) Chemical property
(c) Chemical property
(d) Physical property
(e) Physical property
(f) Physical property

**1.9** (a) Physical (colorless liquid) and chemical (burns in air)
(b) Physical (shiny metal, orange liquid) and chemical (reacts with bromine)

**1.11** Mechanical energy is used to move the lever, which in turn moves gears. The device produces electrical energy and radiant energy.

**1.13** (a) Kinetic energy
(b) Potential energy
(c) Potential energy
(d) Potential energy

**1.15** (a) Qualitative: blue-green color, solid physical state
Quantitative: density = 2.65 g/cm³ and mass = 2.5 g
(b) Density, physical state, and color are intensive properties, whereas mass is an extensive property.
(c) Volume = 0.94 cm³

**1.17** Observation c is a chemical property.

**1.19** Calcium, Ca; fluorine, F
The crystals are cubic in shape because the atoms are arranged in cubic structures.

**1.21** Heterogeneous mixture
The iron can be separated from the sand using a magnet.

**1.23** Physical changes: a, b, d
Chemical changes: c

**1.25** The macroscopic view is the photograph of NaCl, and the particulate view is the drawing of the ions in a cubic arrangement. The structure of the compound at the particulate level determines the properties that are observed at the macroscopic level.

**1.27** The density of the plastic is less than that of CCl₄, so the plastic will float on the liquid CCl₄. Aluminum is more dense than CCl₄, so aluminum will sink when placed in CCl₄.

**1.29** (a) Mixture
(b) Mixture
(c) Element
(d) Compound

**1.31**

**1.33** The three liquids will form three separate layers with hexane on the top, water in the middle, and perfluorohexane on the bottom. The HDPE will float at the interface of the hexane and water layers. The PVC will float at the interface of the water and perfluorohexane layers. The Teflon will sink to the bottom of the cylinder.

**1.35** HDPE will float in ethylene glycol, water, acetic acid, and glycerol.

**1.37** The sample's density and melting point could be compared to those of pure silver.

**1.39** If too much sugar is excreted, the density of the urine would be higher than normal. If too much water is excreted, the density would be lower than normal.

**1.41** (a) Solid potassium metal reacts with liquid water to produce gaseous hydrogen and a homogeneous mixture (solution) of potassium hydroxide in liquid water.

(b) The reaction is a chemical change.

(c) The reactants are potassium and water. The products are hydrogen gas and a water (aqueous) solution of potassium hydroxide. Heat and light are also evolved.

(d) Among the qualitative observations are (i) the reaction is violent, and (ii) heat and light (a purple flame) are produced.

**1.43** The balloons containing helium and neon will float in air.

**1.45** Physical change

# Let's Review: The Tools of Quantitative Chemistry

**1** 298 K

**3** (a) 289 K
(b) 97 °C
(c) 310 K ($3.1 \times 10^2$ K)

**5** 42,195 m; 26.219 miles

**7** 5.3 cm²; $5.3 \times 10^{-4}$ m²

**9** 250. cm³; 0.250 L, $2.50 \times 10^{-4}$ m³; 0.250 dm³

**11** $2.52 \times 10^3$ g

**13** 555 g

**15** (c) zinc

**17** $5.0 \times 10^6$ J

**19** 170 kcal is equivalent to 710 kJ, which is considerably greater than 280 kJ.

**21** (a) Method A with all data included:
average = 2.4 g/cm³

Method B with all data included:
average = 3.480 g/cm³

For B, the 5.811 g/cm³ data point can be excluded because it is more than twice as large as all other points for Method B. Using only the first three points, average = 2.703 g/cm³

(b) Method A: error = 0.3 g/cm³ or about 10%

Method B: error = 0.001 g/cm³ or about 0.04%

(c) Method A: standard deviation = 0.2 g/cm³

Method B (including all data points):
standard deviation = 1.554 g/cm³

Method B (excluding the 5.811 g/cm³ data point):
standard deviation = 0.002 g/cm³

(d) Method B's average value is both more precise and more accurate so long as the 5.811 g/cm³ data point is excluded.

**23** (a) $5.4 \times 10^{-2}$ g, two significant figures
(b) $5.462 \times 10^3$ g, four significant figures
(c) $7.92 \times 10^{-4}$ g, three significant figures
(d) $1.6 \times 10^3$ mL, two significant figures

**25** (a) $9.44 \times 10^{-3}$
(b) 5694
(c) 11.9
(d) 0.122

**27**

Popcorn kernels

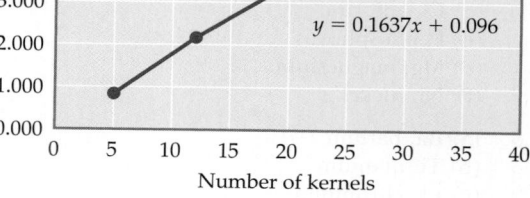

Slope: 0.1637 g/kernel
The slope represents the average mass of a popcorn kernel.
Mass of 20 popcorn kernels = 3.370 g
There are 127 kernels in a sample with a mass of 20.88 g.

**29** (a) $y = -4.00x + 20.00$
(b) $y = -4.00$

**31** $C = 0.0823$

**33** $T = 295$

**35** 0.197 nm; 197 pm

**37** (a) $7.5 \times 10^{-6}$ m; (b) $7.5 \times 10^3$ nm; (c) $7.5 \times 10^6$ pm

**39** 50. mg procaine hydrochloride

**41** The volume of the marbles is 99 mL − 61 mL = 38 mL. This yields a density of 2.5 g/cm³.

**43** (a) 0.178 nm³; $1.78 \times 10^{-22}$ cm³
(b) $3.87 \times 10^{-22}$ g
(c) $9.68 \times 10^{-23}$ g

**45** Your normal body temperature (about 98.6 °F) is 37 °C. As this is higher than gallium's melting point, the metal will melt in your hand.

**47** (a) 15%
(b) $3.63 \times 10^3$ kernels

**49** $8.0 \times 10^4$ kg of sodium fluoride per year

**51** 245 g sulfuric acid

**53** (a) 272 mL ice
(b) The ice cannot be contained in the can.

**55** 7.99 g/cm³

**57** (a) 8.7 g/cm$^3$

(b) The metal is probably cadmium, but the calculated density is close to that of cobalt, nickel, and copper. Further testing should be done on the metal.

**59** 0.0927 cm

**61** (a) $1.143 \times 10^{21}$ atoms; 76.4% of the lattice is filled with atoms; 23.6% of the lattice is open space.

Atoms are spheres. When spheres are packed together, they touch only at certain points, therefore leaving spaces in the structure.

(b) Four atoms

**63** Al, aluminum

**65**

When absorbance = 0.635, concentration = $2.55 \times 10^{-3}$ g/L = $2.55 \times 10^{-3}$ mg/mL

**67** Average = 5.24%, standard deviation = 0.05%

Seven of the ten values fall within the region $5.19 \le x \le 5.29$

# Chapter 2

**2.1** Atoms contain the following fundamental particles: protons (+1 charge), neutrons (zero charge), and electrons (−1 charge). Protons and neutrons are in the nucleus of an atom. Electrons are the least massive of the three particles.

**2.3** The electron cloud would extend around $1 \times 10^{-13}$ cm = 1 fm.

**2.5** (a) $^{27}_{12}Mg$
(b) $^{48}_{22}Ti$
(c) $^{62}_{30}Zn$

**2.7**

| Element | Electrons | Protons | Neutrons |
|---------|-----------|---------|----------|
| $^{24}Mg$ | 12 | 12 | 12 |
| $^{119}Sn$ | 50 | 50 | 69 |
| $^{232}Th$ | 90 | 90 | 142 |
| $^{13}C$ | 6 | 6 | 7 |
| $^{63}Cu$ | 29 | 29 | 34 |
| $^{205}Bi$ | 83 | 83 | 122 |

**2.9** $^{16}O/^{12}C = 1.3329$

**2.11** $^{57}_{27}Co$, $^{58}_{27}Co$, $^{60}_{27}Co$

**2.13** Protium: one proton, one electron
Deuterium: one proton, one neutron, one electron
Tritium: one proton, two neutrons, one electron

**2.15** $^{205}Tl$ is more abundant than $^{203}Tl$. The atomic mass of thallium is closer to 205 than to 203.

**2.17** $(0.0750)(6.015121) + (0.9250)(7.016003) = 6.94$

**2.19** (c), about 50%. Actual percent $^{107}Ag = 51.839\%$

**2.21** $^{69}Ga$, 60.12%; $^{71}Ga$, 39.88%

**2.23**

| | Symbol | Atomic No. | Atomic Mass | Group | Period | |
|---|--------|-----------|-------------|-------|--------|---|
| Titanium | Ti | 22 | 47.867 | 4B(IUPAC 4) | 4 | Metal |
| Thallium | Tl | 81 | 204.3833 | 3A(IUPAC 13) | 6 | Metal |

**2.25** Eight elements: periods 2 and 3. 18 elements: periods 4 and 5. 32 elements: period 6.

**2.27** (a) Nonmetals: C, Cl
(b) Main group elements: C, Ca, Cl, Cs
(c) Lanthanides: Ce
(d) Transition elements: Cr, Co, Cd, Ce, Cm, Cu, Cf
(e) Actinides: Cm, Cf
(f) Gases: Cl

**2.29** Metals: Na, Ni, Np
Metalloids: None in this list
Nonmetals: N, Ne

**2.31** Molecular formula: $H_2SO_4$.
Structural formula:

$$O\!-\!\overset{\displaystyle O}{\underset{\displaystyle O-H}{S}}\!-\!O\!-\!H$$

The structure is not flat. The O atoms are arranged around the sulfur at the corners of a tetrahedron. The hydrogen atoms are connected to two of the oxygen atoms.

**2.33** Molecular formula for asparagine, $C_4H_8N_2O_3$
Structural formula:

**2.35** (a) $Mg^{2+}$
(b) $Zn^{2+}$
(c) $Ni^{2+}$
(d) $Ga^{3+}$

**2.37** (a) $Ba^{2+}$
(b) $Ti^{4+}$

(c) $PO_4^{3-}$
(d) $HCO_3^-$
(e) $S^{2-}$
(f) $ClO_4^-$
(g) $Co^{2+}$
(h) $SO_4^{2-}$

**2.39** K loses one electron per atom to form a $K^+$ ion. It has the same number of electrons as an Ar atom.

**2.41** $Ba^{2+}$ and $Br^-$ ions. The compound's formula is $BaBr_2$.

**2.43** (a) Two $K^+$ ions and one $S^{2-}$ ion
(b) One $Co^{2+}$ ion and one $SO_4^{2-}$ ion
(c) One $K^+$ ion and one $MnO_4^-$ ion
(d) Three $NH_4^+$ ions and one $PO_4^{3-}$ ion
(e) One $Ca^{2+}$ ion and two $ClO^-$ ions
(f) One $Na^+$ ion and one $CH_3CO_2^-$ ion

**2.45** $Co^{2+}$ gives CoO and $Co^{3+}$ gives $Co_2O_3$.

**2.47** (a) $AlCl_2$ should be $AlCl_3$ (based on an $Al^{3+}$ ion and three $Cl^-$ ions).
(b) $KF_2$ should be KF (based on a $K^+$ ion and an $F^-$ ion).
(c) $Ga_2O_3$ is correct.
(d) MgS is correct.

**2.49** (a) Potassium sulfide
(b) Cobalt(II) sulfate
(c) Ammonium phosphate
(d) Calcium hypochlorite

**2.51** (a) $(NH_4)_2CO_3$
(b) $CaI_2$
(c) $CuBr_2$
(d) $AlPO_4$
(e) $AgCH_3CO_2$

**2.53** Compounds with $Na^+$: $Na_2CO_3$ (sodium carbonate) and NaI (sodium iodide). Compounds with $Ba^{2+}$: $BaCO_3$ (barium carbonate) and $BaI_2$ (barium iodide).

**2.55** The force of attraction is stronger in NaF than in NaI because the distance between ion centers is smaller in NaF (235 pm) than in NaI (322 pm).

**2.57** (a) Nitrogen trifluoride
(b) Hydrogen iodide
(c) Boron triiodide
(d) Phosphorus pentafluoride

**2.59** (a) $SCl_2$
(b) $N_2O_5$
(c) $SiCl_4$
(d) $B_2O_3$

**2.61** (a) 67 g Al
(b) 0.0698 g Fe
(c) 0.60 g Ca
(d) $1.32 \times 10^4$ g Ne

**2.63** (a) 1.9998 mol Cu
(b) 0.0017 mol Li
(c) $2.1 \times 10^{-5}$ mol Am
(d) 0.250 mol Al

**2.65** Of these elements, He has the smallest molar mass, and Fe has the largest molar mass. Therefore, 1.0 g of

He has the largest number of atoms in these samples, and 1.0 g of Fe has the smallest number of atoms.

**2.67** 0.02 mol H < 0.0597 mol P < 0.0996 mol Ca < 0.259 mol O

**2.69** (a) 159.7 g/mol
(b) 117.2 g/mol
(c) 176.1 g/mol

**2.71** (a) 290.8 g/mol
(b) 249.7 g/mol

**2.73** (a) 1.53 g
(b) 4.60 g
(c) 4.60 g
(d) 1.48 g

**2.75** Amount of $SO_3$ = 12.5 mol
Number of molecules = $7.52 \times 10^{24}$ molecules
Number of S atoms = $7.52 \times 10^{24}$ atoms
Number of O atoms = $2.26 \times 10^{25}$ atoms

**2.77** $4 \times 10^{21}$ molecules

**2.79** (a) 86.60% Pb and 13.40% S
(b) 81.71% C and 18.29% H
(c) 79.96% C, 9.394% H, and 10.65% O

**2.81** 66.46% copper in CuS. 15.0 g of CuS is needed to obtain 10.0 g of Cu.

**2.83** $C_4H_6O_4$

**2.85** (a) CH, 26.0 g/mol; $C_2H_2$
(b) CHO, 116.1 g/mol; $C_4H_4O_4$
(c) $CH_2$, 112.2 g/mol, $C_8H_{16}$

**2.87** Empirical formula, CH; molecular formula, $C_2H_2$

**2.89** Empirical formula, $C_3H_4$; molecular formula, $C_9H_{12}$

**2.91** Empirical and molecular formulas are both $C_8H_8O_3$

**2.93** $XeF_2$

**2.95** $ZnI_2$

**2.97**

| Symbol | $^{58}$Ni | $^{33}$S | $^{20}$Ne | $^{55}$Mn |
|---|---|---|---|---|
| Protons | 28 | 16 | 10 | 25 |
| Neutrons | 30 | 17 | 10 | 30 |
| Electrons | 28 | 16 | 10 | 25 |
| Name | Nickel | Sulfur | Neon | Manganese |

**2.99**

| S | N |
|---|---|
| B | I |

**2.101** (a) $1.0552 \times 10^{-22}$ g for 1 Cu atom
(b) $6.286 \times 10^{-22}$ dollars for 1 Cu atom

**2.103** (a) Strontium
(b) Zirconium

(c) Carbon

(d) Arsenic

(e) Iodine

(f) Magnesium

(g) Krypton

(h) Sulfur

(i) Germanium or arsenic

**2.105** (a) 0.25 mol U

(b) 0.50 mol Na

(c) 10 atoms of Fe

**2.107** 40.157 g $H_2$ (b) < 103.0 g C (c) < 182 g Al (f) < 210 g Si (d) < 212.0 g Na (e) < 351 g Fe (a) < 650 g $Cl_2$ (g)

**2.109** (a) Atomic mass of O = 15.873 u; Avogadro's number = $5.9802 \times 10^{23}$ particles per mole

(b) Atomic mass of H = 1.00798 u; Avogadro's number = $6.0279 \times 10^{23}$ particles per mole

**2.111** $(NH_4)_2CO_3$, $(NH_4)_2SO_4$, $NiCO_3$, $NiSO_4$

**2.113** All of these compounds have one atom of some element plus three Cl atoms. The highest mass percent of chlorine will occur in the compound having the lightest central element. Here, that element is B, so $BCl_3$ should have the highest mass percent of Cl (90.77%).

**2.115** The molar mass of adenine ($C_5H_5N_5$) is 135.13 g/mol. $3.0 \times 10^{23}$ molecules represents 67 g. Thus, $3.0 \times 10^{23}$ molecules of adenine has a larger mass than 40.0 g of the compound.

**2.117** $1.7 \times 10^{21}$ molecules of water

**2.119** 245.75 g/mol. Mass percent: 25.86% Cu, 22.80% N, 5.742% H, 13.05% S, and 32.55% O. In 10.5 g of compound there are 2.72 g Cu and 0.770 g $H_2O$.

**2.121** Empirical formula of malic acid: $C_4H_6O_5$

**2.123** $Fe_2(CO)_9$

**2.125** (a) $C_7H_5NO_3S$

(b) $6.82 \times 10^{-4}$ mol saccharin

(c) 21.9 mg S

**2.127** (a) NaClO, ionic

(b) $BI_3$

(c) $Al(ClO_4)_3$, ionic

(d) $Ca(CH_3CO_2)_2$, ionic

(e) $KMnO_4$, ionic

(f) $(NH_4)_2SO_3$, ionic

(g) $KH_2PO_4$, ionic

(h) $S_2Cl_2$

(i) $ClF_3$

(j) $PF_3$

**2.129** (a) Empirical formula = molecular formula = $CF_2O_2$

(b) Empirical formula = $C_5H_4$; molecular formula = $C_{10}H_8$

**2.131** Empirical formula and molecular formula = $C_5H_{14}N_2$

**2.133** $C_9H_7MnO_3$

**2.135** 68.42% Cr; $1.2 \times 10^3$ kg $Cr_2O_3$

**2.137** Empirical formula = $ICl_3$; molecular formula = $I_2Cl_6$

**2.139** 7.35 kg of iron

**2.141** (d) $Na_2MoO_4$

**2.143** $5.52 \times 10^{-4}$ mol $C_{21}H_{15}Bi_3O_{12}$; 0.346 g Bi

**2.145** The molar mass of the compound is 154 g/mol. The unknown element is carbon.

**2.147** $n = 2.19 \times 10^3$

**2.149** (a) $2.3 \times 10^{14}$ $g/cm^3$

(b) $3.34 \times 10^{-3}$ $g/cm^3$

(c) The nucleus is much more dense than the space occupied by the electrons.

**2.151** (a) 0.0130 mol Ni

(b) $NiF_2$

(c) Nickel(II) fluoride

**2.153** Formula is $MgSO_4 \cdot 7\ H_2O$

**2.155** Volume = 3.0 $cm^3$; length of side = 1.4 cm

**2.157** (c) The calculated mole ratio is 0.78 mol $H_2O$ per mol $CaCl_2$. The student should heat the crucible again and then reweigh it. More water might be driven off.

**2.159** (a) $m/Z = 50$ is $^{12}C^1H_3^{35}Cl^+$; $m/Z = 52$ is $^{12}C^1H_3^{37}Cl^+$ The height of the line at $m/Z = 52$ is about 1/3 the height of the line at $m/Z = 50$ because the abundance of $^{37}Cl$ is about 1/3 that of $^{35}Cl$.

(b) $^{13}C^1H_3^{35}Cl^+$ (a small portion of this peak is also due to $^{12}C^2H^1H_2^{35}Cl^+$)

**2.161** Required data: density of iron (d), molar mass of iron (b), Avogadro's number (c)

$$1.00\ cm^3 \left( \frac{7.87\ g}{1\ cm^3} \right) \left( \frac{1\ mol}{55.85\ g} \right) \left( \frac{6.02 \times 10^{23}\ atoms}{1\ mol} \right) = 8.49 \times 10^{22}\ atoms\ Fe$$

**2.163** (a) Barium would be more reactive than calcium, so a more vigorous evolution of hydrogen should occur.

(b) Reactivity increases on descending the periodic table, at least for Groups 1A and 2A.

**2.165** When words are written with the pink, hydrated compound, the words are not visible. However, when heated, the hydrated salt loses water to form anhydrous $CoCl_2$, which is deep blue. The words are then visible.

## Applying Chemical Principles: Argon—An Amazing Discovery

**1.** 162.18 $cm^3$

**3.** % Abundance $^{40}Ar$ = 99.600%
Atomic mass of $^{40}Ar$ = 39.963 u

# Chapter 3

**3.1** (a) $2 Al(s) + Fe_2O_3(s) \rightarrow 2 Fe(\ell) + Al_2O_3(s)$
So much energy is released as heat in this reaction that the iron formed is in the liquid state.
(b) $C(s) + H_2O(g) \rightarrow CO(g) + H_2(g)$
(c) $SiCl_4(\ell) + 2 Mg(s) \rightarrow Si(s) + 2 MgCl_2(s)$

**3.3** (a) $4 Cr(s) + 3 O_2(g) \rightarrow 2 Cr_2O_3(s)$
(b) $Cu_2S(s) + O_2(g) \rightarrow 2 Cu(s) + SO_2(g)$
(c) $C_6H_5CH_3(\ell) + 9 O_2(g) \rightarrow 4 H_2O(\ell) + 7 CO_2(g)$

**3.5** (a) $Fe_2O_3(s) + 3 Mg(s) \rightarrow 3 MgO(s) + 2 Fe(s)$
Reactants = iron(III) oxide, magnesium
Products = magnesium oxide, iron
(b) $AlCl_3(s) + 3 NaOH(aq) \rightarrow$
$Al(OH)_3(s) + 3 NaCl(aq)$
Reactants = aluminum chloride, sodium hydroxide
Products = aluminum hydroxide, sodium chloride
(c) $2 NaNO_3(s) + H_2SO_4(aq) \rightarrow$
$Na_2SO_4(s) + 2 HNO_3(aq)$
Reactants = sodium nitrate, sulfuric acid
Products = sodium sulfate, nitric acid
(d) $NiCO_3(s) + 2 HNO_3(aq) \rightarrow$
$Ni(NO_3)_2(aq) + CO_2(g) + H_2O(\ell)$
Reactants = nickel(II) carbonate, nitric acid
Products = nickel(II) nitrate, carbon dioxide, water

**3.7** The reaction involving HCl is more product-favored at equilibrium.

**3.9** Electrolytes are compounds whose aqueous solutions conduct electricity. Given an aqueous solution containing a strong electrolyte and another aqueous solution containing a weak electrolyte at the same concentration, the solution containing the strong electrolyte (such as NaCl) will conduct electricity much better than the one containing the weak electrolyte (such as acetic acid).

**3.11** (a) $CuCl_2$
(b) $AgNO_3$
(c) All are water-soluble.

**3.13** (a) $K^+$ and $OH^-$ ions
(b) $K^+$ and $SO_4^{2-}$ ions
(c) $Li^+$ and $NO_3^-$ ions
(d) $NH_4^+$ and $SO_4^{2-}$ ions

**3.15** (a) Soluble, $Na^+$ and $CO_3^{2-}$ ions
(b) Soluble, $Cu^{2+}$ and $SO_4^{2-}$ ions
(c) Insoluble
(d) Soluble, $Ba^{2+}$ and $Br^-$ ions

**3.17** $CdCl_2(aq) + 2 NaOH(aq) \rightarrow$
$Cd(OH)_2(s) + 2 NaCl(aq)$
$Cd^{2+}(aq) + 2 OH^-(aq) \rightarrow Cd(OH)_2(s)$

**3.19** (a) $NiCl_2(aq) + (NH_4)_2S(aq) \rightarrow NiS(s) + 2 NH_4Cl(aq)$
$Ni^{2+}(aq) + S^{2-}(aq) \rightarrow NiS(s)$
(b) $3 Mn(NO_3)_2(aq) + 2 Na_3PO_4(aq) \rightarrow$
$Mn_3(PO_4)_2(s) + 6 NaNO_3(aq)$
$3 Mn^{2+}(aq) + 2 PO_4^{3-}(aq) \rightarrow Mn_3(PO_4)_2(s)$

**3.21** $HNO_3(aq) + H_2O(\ell) \rightarrow H_3O^+(aq) + NO_3^-(aq)$

**3.23** $H_2C_2O_4(aq) + H_2O(\ell) \rightarrow H_3O^+(aq) + HC_2O_4^-(aq)$
$HC_2O_4^-(aq) + H_2O(\ell) \rightarrow H_3O^+(aq) + C_2O_4^{2-}(aq)$

**3.25** $MgO(s) + H_2O(\ell) \rightarrow Mg(OH)_2(s)$

**3.27** (a) Acetic acid reacts with magnesium hydroxide to give magnesium acetate and water.
$2 CH_3CO_2H(aq) + Mg(OH)_2(s) \rightarrow$
$Mg(CH_3CO_2)_2(aq) + 2 H_2O(\ell)$
(b) Perchloric acid reacts with ammonia to give ammonium perchlorate
$HClO_4(aq) + NH_3(aq) \rightarrow NH_4ClO_4(aq)$

**3.29** $Ba(OH)_2(aq) + 2 HNO_3(aq) \rightarrow$
$Ba(NO_3)_2(aq) + 2 H_2O(\ell)$

**3.31** $HNO_3(aq) + H_2O(\ell) \rightleftharpoons H_3O^+(aq) + NO_3^-(aq)$
Brønsted acids: $HNO_3(aq)$ and $H_3O^+(aq)$
Brønsted bases: $H_2O(\ell)$ and $NO_3^-(aq)$
$HNO_3$ is a strong acid; therefore, this reaction is product-favored at equilibrium.

**3.33** $H_2O(\ell) + HBr(aq) \rightleftharpoons H_3O^+(aq) + Br^-(aq)$
Water accepts $H^+$ from HBr(aq)
$H_2O(\ell) + NH_3(aq) \rightleftharpoons OH^-(aq) + NH_4^+(aq)$
Water donates $H^+$ to $NH_3(aq)$

**3.35** (a) $(NH_4)_2CO_3(aq) + Cu(NO_3)_2(aq) \rightarrow$
$CuCO_3(s) + 2 NH_4NO_3(aq)$
$CO_3^{2-}(aq) + Cu^{2+}(aq) \rightarrow CuCO_3(s)$
(b) $Pb(OH)_2(s) + 2 HCl(aq) \rightarrow PbCl_2(s) + 2 H_2O(\ell)$
$Pb(OH)_2(s) + 2 H_3O^+(aq) + 2 Cl^-(aq) \rightarrow$
$PbCl_2(s) + 4 H_2O(\ell)$
(c) $BaCO_3(s) + 2 HCl(aq) \rightarrow$
$BaCl_2(aq) + H_2O(\ell) + CO_2(g)$
$BaCO_3(s) + 2 H_3O^+(aq) \rightarrow$
$Ba^{2+}(aq) + 3 H_2O(\ell) + CO_2(g)$
(d) $2 CH_3CO_2H(aq) + Ni(OH)_2(s) \rightarrow$
$Ni(CH_3CO_2)_2(aq) + 2 H_2O(\ell)$
$2 CH_3CO_2H(aq) + Ni(OH)_2(s) \rightarrow$
$Ni^{2+}(aq) + 2 CH_3CO_2^-(aq) + 2 H_2O(\ell)$

**3.37** (a) $AgNO_3(aq) + KI(aq) \rightarrow AgI(s) + KNO_3(aq)$
$Ag^+(aq) + I^-(aq) \rightarrow AgI(s)$
(b) $Ba(OH)_2(aq) + 2 HNO_3(aq) \rightarrow$
$Ba(NO_3)_2(aq) + 2 H_2O(\ell)$
$OH^-(aq) + H_3O^+(aq) \rightarrow 2 H_2O(\ell)$
(c) $2 Na_3PO_4(aq) + 3 Ni(NO_3)_2(aq) \rightarrow$
$Ni_3(PO_4)_2(s) + 6 NaNO_3(aq)$
$2 PO_4^{3-}(aq) + 3 Ni^{2+}(aq) \rightarrow Ni_3(PO_4)_2(s)$

**3.39** (a) $HNO_2(aq) + OH^-(aq) \rightarrow NO_2^-(aq) + H_2O(\ell)$
(b) $Ca(OH)_2(s) + 2 H_3O^+(aq) \rightarrow$
$Ca^{2+}(aq) + 4 H_2O(\ell)$

**3.41** $FeCO_3(s) + 2\ HNO_3(aq) \rightarrow$
$$Fe(NO_3)_2(aq) + CO_2(g) + H_2O(\ell)$$

Iron(II) carbonate reacts with nitric acid to give iron(II) nitrate, carbon dioxide, and water.

**3.43** $(NH_4)_2S(aq) + 2\ HBr(aq) \rightarrow 2\ NH_4Br(aq) + H_2S(g)$

Ammonium sulfide reacts with hydrobromic acid to give ammonium bromide and hydrogen sulfide.

**3.45** (a) Br = +5 and O = −2
(b) C = +3 each and O = −2
(c) F = −1
(d) Ca = +2 and H = −1
(e) H = +1, Si = +4, and O = −2
(f) H = +1, S = +6, and O = −2

**3.47** (a) Oxidation–reduction
Zn is oxidized from 0 to +2, and N in $NO_3^-$ is reduced from +5 to +4 in $NO_2$.
(b) Acid–base reaction
(c) Oxidation–reduction
Calcium is oxidized from 0 to +2 in $Ca(OH)_2$, and H is reduced from +1 in $H_2O$ to 0 in $H_2$.

**3.49** (a) $O_2$ is the oxidizing agent (as it always is), so $C_2H_4$ is the reducing agent. In this process, $C_2H_4$ is oxidized, and $O_2$ is reduced.
(b) Si is oxidized from 0 in Si to +4 in $SiCl_4$. $Cl_2$ is reduced from 0 in $Cl_2$ to −1 in $Cl^-$. Si is the reducing agent, and $Cl_2$ is the oxidizing agent.

**3.51** (a) Acid–base
$$Ba(OH)_2(aq) + 2\ HCl(aq) \rightarrow$$
$$BaCl_2(aq) + 2\ H_2O(\ell)$$
(b) Gas-forming
$$2\ HNO_3(aq) + CoCO_3(s) \rightarrow$$
$$Co(NO_3)_2(aq) + H_2O(\ell) + CO_2(g)$$
(c) Precipitation
$$2\ Na_3PO_4(aq) + 3\ Cu(NO_3)_2(aq) \rightarrow$$
$$Cu_3(PO_4)_2(s) + 6\ NaNO_3(aq)$$

**3.53** (a) Precipitation
$$MnCl_2(aq) + Na_2S(aq) \rightarrow MnS(s) + 2\ NaCl(aq)$$
$$Mn^{2+}(aq) + S^{2-}(aq) \rightarrow MnS(s)$$
(b) Precipitation
$$K_2CO_3(aq) + ZnCl_2(aq) \rightarrow ZnCO_3(s) + 2\ KCl(aq)$$
$$CO_3^{2-}(aq) + Zn^{2+}(aq) \rightarrow ZnCO_3(s)$$

**3.55** (a) $CuCl_2(aq) + H_2S(aq) \rightarrow$
$$CuS(s) + 2\ HCl(aq)\ \text{precipitation}$$
(b) $H_3PO_4(aq) + 3\ KOH(aq) \rightarrow$
$$3\ H_2O(\ell) + K_3PO_4(aq)$$
acid–base
(c) $Ca(s) + 2\ HBr(aq) \rightarrow H_2(g) + CaBr_2(aq)$
oxidation–reduction and gas-forming
(d) $MgCl_2(aq) + 2\ NaOH(aq) \rightarrow$
$$Mg(OH)_2(s) + 2\ NaCl(aq)$$
precipitation

**3.57** (a) $Ca(OH)_2(s) + 2\ HBr(aq) \rightarrow$
$$2\ H_2O(\ell) + CaBr_2(aq)$$
(b) $MgCO_3(s) + 2\ HNO_3(aq) \rightarrow$
$$Mg(NO_3)_2(aq) + CO_2(g) + H_2O(\ell)$$
(c) $BaCl_2(aq) + Na_2SO_4(aq) \rightarrow$
$$BaSO_4(s) + 2\ NaCl(aq)$$
(d) $NH_3(g) + H_2O(\ell) \rightarrow NH_4^+(aq) + OH^-(aq)$

**3.59** (a) $CO_2(g) + 2\ NH_3(g) \rightarrow NH_2CONH_2(s) + H_2O(\ell)$
(b) $UO_2(s) + 4\ HF(aq) \rightarrow UF_4(s) + 2\ H_2O(\ell)$
$$UF_4(s) + F_2(g) \rightarrow UF_6(s)$$
(c) $TiO_2(s) + 2\ Cl_2(g) + 2\ C(s) \rightarrow TiCl_4(\ell) + 2\ CO(g)$
$$TiCl_4(\ell) + 2\ Mg(s) \rightarrow Ti(s) + 2\ MgCl_2(s)$$

**3.61** (a) NaBr, KBr, or other alkali metal bromides; Group 2A bromides; other metal bromides except AgBr, $Hg_2Br_2$, and $PbBr_2$
(b) $Al(OH)_3$ and transition metal hydroxides
(c) Alkaline earth carbonates ($CaCO_3$) or transition metal carbonates ($NiCO_3$)
(d) Metal nitrates are generally water-soluble [e.g., $NaNO_3$, $Ni(NO_3)_2$].
(e) $CH_3CO_2H$, other acids containing the $-CO_2H$ group

**3.63** Water soluble: $Cu(NO_3)_2$, $CuCl_2$. Water-insoluble: $CuCO_3$, $Cu_3(PO_4)_2$

**3.65** $2\ H_3O^+(aq) + Mg(OH)_2(s) \rightarrow 4\ H_2O(\ell) + Mg^{2+}(aq)$
Spectator ion, $NO_3^-$. Acid–base reaction.

**3.67** (a) $Cl_2$ is reduced (to $Cl^-$) and $Br^-$ is oxidized (to $Br_2$).
(b) $Cl_2$ is the oxidizing agent and $Br^-$ is the reducing agent.

**3.69** (a) $MgCO_3(s) + 2\ H_3O^+(aq) \rightarrow$
$$CO_2(g) + Mg^{2+}(aq) + 3\ H_2O(\ell)$$
Chloride ion ($Cl^-$) is the spectator ion.
(b) Gas-forming reaction

**3.71** (a) $H_2O$, $NH_3$, $NH_4^+$, and $OH^-$ (and a trace of $H_3O^+$)
weak Brønsted base
(b) $H_2O$, $CH_3CO_2H$, $CH_3CO_2^-$, and $H_3O^+$ (and a trace of $OH^-$)
weak Brønsted acid
(c) $H_2O$, $Na^+$, and $OH^-$ (and a trace of $H_3O^+$)
strong Brønsted base
(d) $H_2O$, $H_3O^+$, and $Br^-$ (and a trace of $OH^-$)
strong Brønsted acid

**3.73** (a) $K_2CO_3(aq) + 2\ HClO_4(aq) \rightarrow$
$$2\ KClO_4(aq) + CO_2(g) + H_2O(\ell)$$

gas-forming

Potassium carbonate and perchloric acid react to form potassium perchlorate, carbon dioxide, and water

$$CO_3^{2-}(aq) + 2\ H_3O^+(aq) \rightarrow CO_2(g) + 3\ H_2O(\ell)$$

(b) $FeCl_2(aq) + (NH_4)_2S(aq) \rightarrow$
$$FeS(s) + 2\ NH_4Cl(aq)$$

precipitation

Iron(II) chloride and ammonium sulfide react to form iron(II) sulfide and ammonium chloride

$$Fe^{2+}(aq) + S^{2-}(aq) \rightarrow FeS(s)$$

(c) $Fe(NO_3)_2(aq) + Na_2CO_3(aq) \rightarrow$
$$FeCO_3(s) + 2\ NaNO_3(aq)$$

precipitation

Iron(II) nitrate and sodium carbonate react to form iron(II) carbonate and sodium nitrate

$$Fe^{2+}(aq) + CO_3^{2-}(aq) \rightarrow FeCO_3(s)$$

(d) $3\ NaOH(aq) + FeCl_3(aq) \rightarrow$
$$3\ NaCl(aq) + Fe(OH)_3(s)$$

precipitation

Sodium hydroxide and iron(III) chloride react to form sodium chloride and iron(III) hydroxide

$$3\ OH^-(aq) + Fe^{3+}(aq) \rightarrow Fe(OH)_3(s)$$

**3.75** (a) $NaOH$
(b) $MgCl_2$
(c) $KI$
(d) $NH_4Cl$

**3.77** (a) $NH_3$
(b) $CH_3CO_2H$, $HF$

**3.79** $2\ H_3O^+(aq) + S^{2-}(aq) \rightarrow H_2S(g) + 2\ H_2O(\ell)$
$H_2S(g) + Pb^{2+}(aq) + 2\ H_2O(\ell) \rightarrow$
$$PbS(s) + 2\ H_3O^+(aq)$$

**3.81** (a) Reactants: $Na(+1)$, $I(-1)$, $H(+1)$, $S(+6)$, $O(-2)$, $Mn(+4)$

Products: $Na(+1)$, $S(+6)$, $O(-2)$, $Mn(+2)$, $I(0)$, $H(+1)$

(b) The oxidizing agent is $MnO_2$, and $NaI$ is oxidized. The reducing agent is $NaI$, and $MnO_2$ is reduced.
(c) Based on the picture, the reaction is product-favored.
(d) Sodium iodide, sulfuric acid, and manganese(IV) oxide react to form sodium sulfate, manganese(II) sulfate, and water.

**3.83** Among the reactions that could be used are the following:

$MgCO_3(s) + 2\ HCl(aq) \rightarrow$
$$MgCl_2(aq) + CO_2(g) + H_2O(\ell)$$

$MgS(s) + 2\ HCl(aq) \rightarrow MgCl_2(aq) + H_2S(g)$

$MgSO_3(s) + 2\ HCl(aq) \rightarrow$
$$MgCl_2(aq) + SO_2(g) + H_2O(\ell)$$

In each case, the resulting solution could be evaporated to obtain the desired magnesium chloride.

**3.85** The $Ag^+$ was reduced (to silver metal), and the glucose was oxidized (to $C_6H_{12}O_7$). The $Ag^+$ is the oxidizing agent, and the glucose is the reducing agent.

**3.87** Weak electrolyte test: Compare the conductivity of a solution of lactic acid and that of an equal concentration of a strong acid. The conductivity of the lactic acid solution should be significantly less.

Reversible reaction: The fact that lactic acid is an electrolyte indicates that the reaction proceeds in the forward direction. To test whether the ionization is reversible, one could prepare a solution containing as much lactic acid as it will hold and then add a strong acid (to provide $H_3O^+$). If the reaction proceeds in the reverse direction, this will cause some lactic acid to precipitate.

**3.89** (a) Several precipitation reactions are possible:

i. $BaCl_2(aq) + H_2SO_4(aq) \rightarrow$
$$BaSO_4(s) + 2\ HCl(aq)$$

ii. $BaCl_2(aq) + Na_2SO_4(aq) \rightarrow$
$$BaSO_4(s) + 2\ NaCl(aq)$$

iii. $Ba(OH)_2(aq) + H_2SO_4(aq) \rightarrow$
$$BaSO_4(s) + 2\ H_2O(\ell)$$

(b) Gas-forming reaction:
$BaCO_3(s) + H_2SO_4(aq) \rightarrow$
$$BaSO_4(s) + CO_2(g) + H_2O(\ell)$$

**3.91** $NiC_8H_{14}N_4O_4$

**3.93** (a) Reactants: As: $+3$; S: $-2$; N: $+5$

Products: As: $+5$; S: $0$; N: $+2$

(b) $Ag_3AsO_4$

## Applying Chemical Principles: Superconductors

**1.** In this case, because you know that Cu has an implied subscript of 1, divide the number of moles of each element determined by the number of moles of Cu. $x = 0.15$; Formula $= La_{1.85}Ba_{0.15}CuO_4$

**3.** One formula unit of the compound contains two $Cu^{2+}$ ions and one $Cu^{3+}$ ion.

**5.** $0.011$ g $O_2$

## Chapter 4

**4.1** $4.5$ mol $O_2$; $310$ g $Al_2O_3$

**4.3** $22.7$ g $Br_2$; $25.3$ g $Al_2Br_6$

**4.5** (a) $CO_2$, carbon dioxide, and $H_2O$, water
(b) $CH_4(g) + 2\ O_2(g) \rightarrow CO_2(g) + 2\ H_2O(\ell)$
(c) $102$ g $O_2$
(d) $128$ g products

**4.7**

| Equation | $2 PbS(s)$ | $+ 3 O_2(g)$ | $\rightarrow 2 PbO(s)$ | $+ 2 SO_2(g)$ |
|---|---|---|---|---|
| Initial (mol) | 2.50 | 3.75 | 0 | 0 |
| Change (mol) | $-2.50$ | $-\frac{3}{2}(2.50)$ $= -3.75$ | $+\frac{2}{2}(2.50)$ $= +2.50$ | $+\frac{2}{2}(2.50)$ $= +2.50$ |
| Final (mol) | 0 | 0 | 2.50 | 2.50 |

The amounts table shows that 2.50 mol of PbS requires $\frac{3}{2}(2.50) = 3.75$ mol of $O_2$ and produces 2.50 mol of PbO and 2.50 mol of $SO_2$.

**4.9** (a) Balanced equation: $4 Cr(s) + 3 O_2(g) \rightarrow 2 Cr_2O_3(s)$
(b) 0.175 g of Cr is equivalent to 0.00337 mol

| Equation | $4 Cr(s)$ | $+ 3 O_2(g)$ | $\rightarrow$ | $2 Cr_2O_3(s)$ |
|---|---|---|---|---|
| Initial (mol) | 0.00337 | 0.00252 mol | | 0 |
| Change (mol) | $-0.00337$ | $-\frac{3}{4}(0.00337)$ $= -0.00252$ | | $\frac{2}{4}(0.00337)$ $= +0.00168$ |
| Final (mol) | 0 | 0 | | 0.00168 |

The 0.00168 mol $Cr_2O_3$ produced corresponds to 0.256 g $Cr_2O_3$.
(c) 0.081 g $O_2$

**4.11** 0.11 mol of $Na_2SO_4$ and 0.62 mol of C are mixed. Sodium sulfate is the limiting reactant. Therefore, 0.11 mol of $Na_2S$ is formed, or 8.2 g.

**4.13** $F_2$ is the limiting reactant.

**4.15** (a) $CH_4$ is the limiting reactant.
(b) 375 g $H_2$
(c) Excess $H_2O$ = 1390 g

**4.17** (a) $2 C_6H_{14}(\ell) + 19 O_2(g) \rightarrow 12 CO_2(g) + 14 H_2O(g)$
(b) $O_2$ is the limiting reactant. Products are 187 g of $CO_2$ and 89.2 g of $H_2O$.
(c) 154 g of hexane remains
(d)

| Equation | $2 C_6H_{14}(\ell)$ | $+ 19 O_2(g)$ | $\rightarrow 12 CO_2(g)$ | $+ 14 H_2O(g)$ |
|---|---|---|---|---|
| Initial (mol) | 2.49 | 6.72 | 0 | 0 |
| Change (mol) | $-0.707$ | $-6.72$ | $+4.24$ | $+4.95$ |
| Final (mol) | 1.78 | 0 | 4.24 | 4.95 |

**4.19** $(332 \text{ g}/407 \text{ g})100\% = 81.6\%$

**4.21** (a) 14.3 g $Cu(NH_3)_4SO_4$
(b) 88.3% yield

**4.23** 91.9% hydrate

**4.25** 84.3% $CaCO_3$

**4.27** 1.467% $Tl_2SO_4$

**4.29** Empirical formula = CH

**4.31** Empirical formula = $CH_2$; molecular formula = $C_5H_{10}$

**4.33** Empirical formula = $CH_3O$; molecular formula = $C_2H_6O_2$

**4.35** $Ni(CO)_4$

**4.37** $[Na_2CO_3]$ = 0.254 M; $[Na^+]$ = 0.508 M; $[CO_3^{2-}]$ = 0.254 M

**4.39** 0.494 g $KMnO_4$

**4.41** $5.08 \times 10^3$ mL

**4.43** (a) 0.50 M $NH_4^+$ and 0.25 M $SO_4^{2-}$
(b) 0.246 M $Na^+$ and 0.123 M $CO_3^{2-}$
(c) 0.056 M $H_3O^+$ and 0.056 M $NO_3^-$

**4.45** A mass of 1.06 g of $Na_2CO_3$ is required. After weighing out this quantity of $Na_2CO_3$, transfer it to a 500.-mL volumetric flask. Rinse any solid from the neck of the flask while filling the flask with distilled water. Dissolve the solute in water. Add water until the bottom of the meniscus of the water is at the top of the scribed mark on the neck of the flask. Thoroughly mix the solution.

**4.47** 0.0750 M

**4.49** Method (a) is correct. Method (b) gives an acid concentration of 0.15 M.

**4.51** 0.00340 M

**4.53** $[H_3O^+] = 10^{-pH} = 4.0 \times 10^{-4}$ M; the solution is acidic.

**4.55** $HNO_3$ is a strong acid, so $[H_3O^+]$ = 0.0013 M. pH = 2.89.

**4.57**

| | pH | $[H_3O^+]$ | Acidic/Basic |
|---|---|---|---|
| (a) | 1.00 | 0.10 M | Acidic |
| (b) | 10.50 | $3.2 \times 10^{-11}$ M | Basic |
| (c) | 4.89 | $1.3 \times 10^{-5}$ M | Acidic |
| (d) | 7.64 | $2.3 \times 10^{-8}$ M | Basic |

**4.59** 268 mL

**4.61** 210 g NaOH and 190 g $Cl_2$

**4.63** 174 mL of $Na_2S_2O_3$ solution

**4.65** $1.50 \times 10^3$ mL of $Pb(NO_3)_2$ solution

**4.67** 44.6 mL

**4.69** 1.052 M HCl

**4.71** 104 g/mol

**4.73** 12.8% Fe

**4.75**

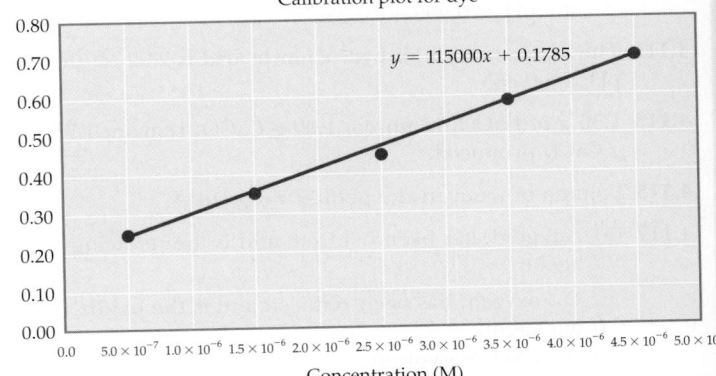

Calibration plot for dye

$y = 115000x + 0.1785$

(a) Slope = $1.2 \times 10^5$ $M^{-1}$; y-intercept = 0.18 M
(b) $3.0 \times 10^{-6}$ M

**4.77** (a) Products = $CO_2(g)$ and $H_2O(g)$
(b) $2 C_6H_6(\ell) + 15 O_2(g) \rightarrow 12 CO_2(g) + 6 H_2O(g)$
(c) 49.28 g $O_2$
(d) 65.32 g products (= sum of $C_6H_6$ mass and $O_2$ mass)

**4.79** 0.28 g arginine, 0.21 g ornithine

**4.81** (a) Titanium(IV) chloride, water, titanium(IV) oxide, hydrogen chloride
(b) 4.60 g $H_2O$
(c) 10.2 $TiO_2$, 18.6 g HCl

**4.83** 8.33 g $NaN_3$

**4.85** Mass percent saccharin = 75.92%

**4.87** $SiH_4$

**4.89** $C_3H_2O$

**4.91** 1.85 kg $H_2SO_4$

**4.93** The calculated molar mass of the metal is $1.2 \times 10^2$ g/mol. The metal is probably tin (118.67 g/mol).

**4.95** 479 kg $Cl_2$

**4.97** 66.5 kg CaO

**4.99** 1.27 g $C_4H_8$ (44.4%) and 1.59 g $C_4H_{10}$ (55.6%)

**4.101** 62.2% $Cu_2S$ and 26.8% CuS

**4.103** (a) $MgCO_3(s) + 2 H_3O^+(aq) \rightarrow$
$CO_2(g) + Mg^{2+}(aq) + 2 H_2O(\ell)$
(b) Gas-forming reaction
(c) 0.15 g

**4.105** 15.0 g of $NaHCO_3$ require 1190 mL of 0.15 M acetic acid. Therefore, acetic acid is the limiting reactant. (Conversely, 125 mL of 0.15 M acetic acid requires only 1.58 g of $NaHCO_3$.) 1.54 g of $NaCH_3CO_2$ produced.

**4.107** 3.13 g $Na_2S_2O_3$, 96.8%

**4.109** (a) pH = 0.979
(b) $[H_3O^+]$ = 0.0028 M; the solution is acidic.
(c) $[H_3O^+] = 2.1 \times 10^{-10}$ M; the solution is basic.
(d) The new solution's concentration is 0.102 M HCl; the pH = 0.990

**4.111** The concentration of hydrochloric acid is 2.92 M; the pH is −0.465

**4.113** 1.56 g of $CaCO_3$ required; 1.00 g $CaCO_3$ remain; 1.73 g $CaCl_2$ produced.

**4.115** Volume of water in the pool = $7.6 \times 10^4$ L

**4.117** (a) Au, gold, has been oxidized and is the reducing agent.
$O_2$, oxygen, has been reduced and is the oxidizing agent.
(b) 26 L NaCN solution

**4.119** % Atom economy = 49.81%

**4.121** The concentration of $Na_2CO_3$ in the first solution prepared is 0.0275 M, in the second solution prepared the concentration of $Na_2CO_3$ is 0.00110 M.

**4.123** (a) First reaction: oxidizing agent = $Cu^{2+}$ and reducing agent = $I^-$
Second reaction: oxidizing agent = $I_3^-$ and reducing agent = $S_2O_3^{2-}$
(b) 67.3% copper

**4.125** $x = 6$; $Cr(NH_3)_6Cl_3$.

**4.127** 11.48% 2,4-D

**4.129** 3.3 mol $H_2O$/mol $CaCl_2$

**4.131** (a) Slope = $2.06 \times 10^5$; y-intercept = 0.024
(b) $1.20 \times 10^{-4}$ g/L
(c) 0.413 mg $PO_4^{3-}$

**4.133** The total mass of the beakers and products after reaction is equal to the total mass before the reaction (167.170 g) because no gases were produced in the reaction and there is conservation of mass in chemical reactions.

**4.135** The balanced chemical equation indicates that the stoichiometric ratio of HCl to Zn is 2 mol HCl/1 mol Zn. In each reaction, there is 0.100 mol of HCl present. In reaction 1, there is 0.107 mol of Zn present. This gives a 0.93 mol HCl/mol Zn ratio, indicating that HCl is the limiting reactant. In reaction 2, there is 0.050 mol of Zn, giving a 2.0 mol HCl/mol Zn ratio. This indicates that the two reactants are present in exactly the correct stoichiometric ratio. In reaction 3, there is 0.020 mol of Zn, giving a 5.0 mol HCl/mol Zn ratio. This indicates that the HCl is present in excess and that the zinc is the limiting reactant.

**4.137** If both students base their calculations on the amount of HCl solution pipeted into the flask (20 mL), then the second student's result will be (e), the same as the first student's. However, if the HCl concentration is calculated using the diluted solution volume, student 1 will use a volume of 40 mL, and student 2 will use a volume of 80 mL in the calculation. The second student's result will be (c), half that of the first student's.

**4.139** (a) % Atom economy = 44.15%
(b) Theoretical yield of maleic anhydride = $1.26 \times 10^3$ g; % yield = 77.4%
The theoretical yield of carbon dioxide from 1.00 kg of benzene is 1.13 kg.

## Applying Chemical Principles: Antacids

**1.** $NaHCO_3$, $KHCO_3$, and $CaCO_3$

**3.** (a) $Mg(OH)_2(s) + 2 HCl(aq) \rightarrow MgCl_2(aq) + 2 H_2O(\ell)$
(b) 110. mg $Mg(OH)_2$

**5.** Rolaids neutralizes the greatest quantity of acid.

# Chapter 5

**5.1** The system is the part of the universe being studied. The surroundings are everything else in the universe that can exchange matter and/or energy with the system. A system and its surroundings are said to be in thermal equilibrium if they can exchange energy with each other but are at the same temperature; therefore, there is no net transfer of energy as heat from one to the other.

**5.3** (a) Exothermic
(b) Endothermic
(c) Endothermic
(d) Endothermic

**5.5** $0.140 \, J/g \cdot K$

**5.7** $2.44 \, kJ$

**5.9** $32.8 \, °C$

**5.11** $20.7 \, °C$

**5.13** $47.8 \, °C$

**5.15** $0.40 \, J/g \cdot K$

**5.17** $330 \, kJ$

**5.19** $49.3 \, kJ$

**5.21** $273 \, J$

**5.23** $9.97 \times 10^5 \, J$

**5.25** Reaction is exothermic because $\Delta_r H°$ is negative. The heat evolved is $2.38 \, kJ$.

**5.27** $-3.3 \times 10^4 \, kJ$

**5.29** $\Delta H = -56 \, kJ/mol \, CsOH$

**5.31** $0.52 \, J/g \cdot K$

**5.33** $\Delta_r H = +23 \, kJ/mol\text{-rxn}$

**5.35** $-297 \, kJ/mol \, SO_2$

**5.37** $-3.09 \times 10^3 \, kJ/mol \, C_6H_5CO_2H$

**5.39** $0.236 \, J/g \cdot K$

**5.41** (a) $\Delta_r H° = -126 \, kJ/mol\text{-rxn}$
(b)

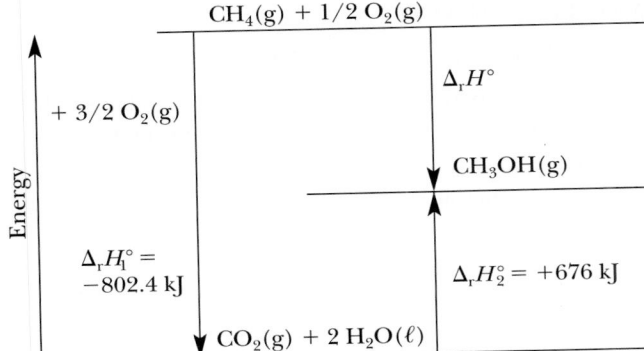

**5.43** $\Delta_r H° = +90.3 \, kJ/mol\text{-rxn}$

**5.45** $C(s) + 2 \, H_2(g) + 1/2 \, O_2(g) \rightarrow CH_3OH(\ell)$
$\Delta_f H° = -238.4 \, kJ/mol$

**5.47** (a) $2 \, Cr(s) + 3/2 \, O_2(g) \rightarrow Cr_2O_3(s)$
$\Delta_f H° = -1134.7 \, kJ/mol$
(b) $2.4 \, g$ is equivalent to $0.046 \, mol$ of Cr. This will produce $26 \, kJ$ of energy transferred as heat.

**5.49** (a) $\Delta H° = -24 \, kJ$ for $1.0 \, g$ of phosphorus
(b) $\Delta H° = -18 \, kJ$ for $0.20 \, mol$ NO
(c) $\Delta H° = -16.9 \, kJ$ for the formation of $2.40 \, g$ of $NaCl(s)$
(d) $\Delta H° = -1.8 \times 10^3 \, kJ$ for the oxidation of $250 \, g$ of iron

**5.51** (a) $\Delta_r H° = -906.2 \, kJ$
(b) The heat evolved is $133 \, kJ$ for the oxidation of $10.0 \, g$ of $NH_3$

**5.53** (a) $\Delta_r H° = +161.6 \, kJ/mol\text{-rxn}$; the reaction is endothermic.
(b)

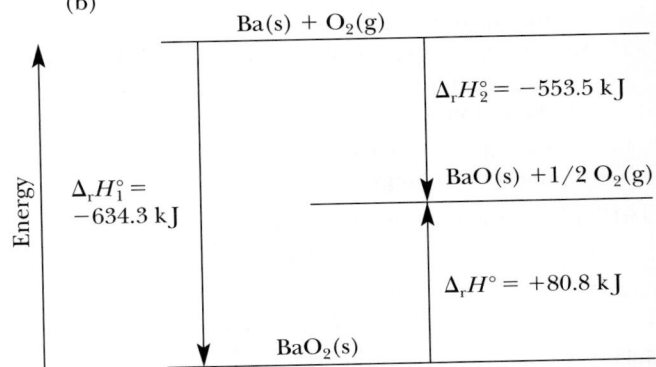

**5.55** $\Delta_f H° = +77.7 \, kJ/mol$ for naphthalene

**5.57** (a) Exothermic: a process in which energy is transferred as heat from a system to its surroundings. (The combustion of methane is exothermic.)

Endothermic: a process in which energy is transferred as heat from the surroundings to the system. (Ice melting is endothermic.)

(b) System: the object or collection of objects being studied. (A chemical reaction—the system—taking place inside a calorimeter—the surroundings.)

Surroundings: everything outside the system that can exchange mass or energy with the system. (The calorimeter and everything outside the calorimeter comprise the surroundings.)

(c) Specific heat capacity: the quantity of energy that must be transferred as heat to raise the temperature of 1 gram of a substance 1 kelvin. (The specific heat capacity of water is $4.184 \, J/g \cdot K$.)

(d) State function: a quantity that is characterized by changes that do not depend on the path chosen to go from the initial state to the final state. (Enthalpy and internal energy are state functions.)

(e) Standard state: the most stable form of a substance in the physical state that exists at a pressure of 1 bar and at a specified temperature. (The standard state of carbon at 25 °C is graphite.)

(f) Enthalpy change, $\Delta H$: the energy transferred as heat at constant pressure. (The enthalpy change for melting ice at 0 °C is $6.00 \, kJ/mol$.)

(g) Standard enthalpy of formation: the enthalpy change for the formation of 1 mol of a compound in its standard state directly from the component elements in their standard states. ($\Delta_f H°$ for liquid water is $-285.83$ kJ/mol.)

**5.59** (a) System: reaction between methane and oxygen

Surroundings: the furnace and the rest of the universe. Energy is transferred as heat from the system to the surroundings.

(b) System: water drops

Surroundings: skin and the rest of the universe

Energy is transferred as heat from the surroundings to the system

(c) System: water

Surroundings: freezer and the rest of the universe

Energy is transferred as heat from the system to the surroundings

(d) System: reaction of aluminum and iron(III) oxide

Surroundings: flask, laboratory bench, and rest of the universe

Energy is transferred as heat from the system to the surroundings.

**5.61** Standard state of oxygen is gas, $O_2(g)$.

$O_2(g) \rightarrow 2 O(g)$, $\Delta_r H° = +498.34$ kJ/mol-rxn, endothermic

$3/2 O_2(g) \rightarrow O_3(g)$, $\Delta_r H° = +142.67$ kJ/mol-rxn

**5.63** (a) Energy is transferred as heat from the surroundings to the system and as work done by the system.

(b) Energy is transferred as heat from the surroundings to the system and as work done by the system.

**5.65** $\Delta H° = -0.627$ kJ

**5.67** $C_{Ag} = 0.24$ J/g · K

**5.69** Mass of ice melted = 75.4 g

**5.71** Final temperature = 278 K (5 °C)

**5.73** (a) When summed, the following equations give the balanced equation for the formation of $B_2H_6(g)$ from the elements.

| | |
|---|---|
| $2 B(s) + 3/2 O_2(g) \rightarrow B_2O_3(s)$ | $\Delta_r H° = -1271.9$ kJ |
| $3 H_2(g) + 3/2 O_2(g) \rightarrow 3 H_2O(g)$ | $\Delta_r H° = -725.4$ kJ |
| $B_2O_3(s) + 3 H_2O(g) \rightarrow B_2H_6(g) + 3 O_2(g)$ | $\Delta_r H° = +2032.9$ kJ |
| $2 B(s) + 3 H_2(g) \rightarrow B_2H_6(g)$ | $\Delta_r H° = +35.6$ kJ |

(b) The enthalpy of formation of $B_2H_6(g)$ is $+35.6$ kJ/mol.

(c)

(d) The formation of $B_2H_6(g)$ is endothermic.

**5.75** (a) $\Delta_r H° = +131.31$ kJ

(b) Endothermic

(c) $1.0932 \times 10^7$ kJ

**5.77** Assuming $CO_2(g)$ and $H_2O(\ell)$ are the products of combustion:

$\Delta_r H°$ for isooctane is $-5461.3$ kJ/mol or $-47.81$ kJ per gram.

$\Delta_r H°$ for liquid methanol is $-726.77$ kJ/mol or $-22.682$ kJ per gram.

**5.79** (a) Adding the equations as they are given in the question results in the desired equation for the formation of $SrCO_3(s)$. The calculated $\Delta_r H° = -1220.$ kJ/mol.

(b)

**5.81** $\Delta_r H° = -305.3$ kJ

**5.83** $C_{Pb} = 0.121$ J/g · K

**5.85** $\Delta_r H = -69$ kJ/mol AgCl

**5.87** 36.0 kJ evolved per mol of $NH_4NO_3$

**5.89** The standard enthalpy change, $\Delta_r H°$, is $-352.88$ kJ. The quantity of magnesium needed is 0.43 g.

**5.91** (a) Exothermic

(b) Exothermic

**5.93** The enthalpy change for each of the three reactions below is known or can be measured by calorimetry. The three equations sum to give the enthalpy of formation of $CaSO_4(s)$.

$Ca(s) + 1/2\ O_2(g) \rightarrow CaO(s)$    $\Delta_rH° = \Delta_fH° = -635.09$ kJ

$1/8\ S_8(s) + 3/2\ O_2(g) \rightarrow SO_3(g)$    $\Delta_rH° = \Delta_fH° = -395.77$ kJ

$CaO(s) + SO_3(g) \rightarrow CaSO_4(s)$    $\Delta_rH° = -402.7$ kJ

$Ca(s) + 1/8\ S_8(s) + 2\ O_2(g) \rightarrow CaSO_4(s)$    $\Delta_rH° = \Delta_fH° = -1433.6$ kJ

**5.95**

| Metal | Molar Heat Capacity (J/mol · K) |
|---|---|
| Al | 24.2 |
| Fe | 25.1 |
| Cu | 24.5 |
| Au | 25.4 |

All the metals have a molar heat capacity of $24.8 \pm 0.5$ J/mol · K. Therefore, assuming the molar heat capacity of Ag is 24.8 J/mol · K, its specific heat capacity is 0.230 J/g · K. This is very close to the experimental value of 0.236 J/g · K.

**5.97** 120 g of $CH_4$ required (assuming $H_2O(g)$ as product)

**5.99** $1.6 \times 10^{11}$ kJ released to the surroundings. This is equivalent to $3.8 \times 10^4$ tons of dynamite.

**5.101** (a)

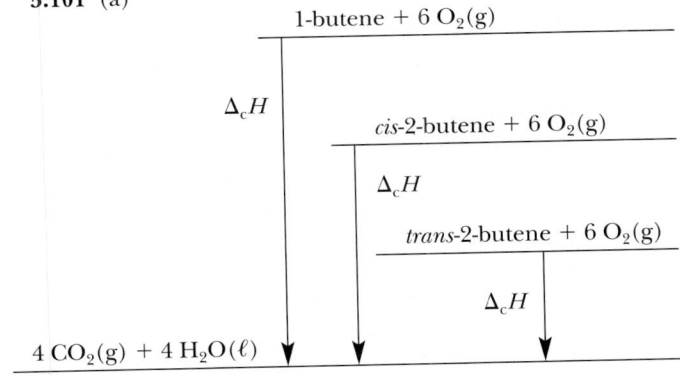

(b) *cis*-2-butene: $\Delta_fH° = -7.6$ kJ/mol

   *trans*-2-butene: $\Delta_fH° = -10.8$ kJ/mol

   1-butene: $\Delta_fH° = -0.6$ kJ/mol

(c)

(d) $-3.4$ kJ/mol-rxn

**5.103** (a) $-726$ kJ/mol Mg

(b) 25.0 °C

**5.105** (a) Methane

(b) Methane

(c) $-279$ kJ

(d) $CH_4(g) + 1/2\ O_2(g) \rightarrow CH_3OH(\ell)$

**5.107** (a) Metal heated = 100.0 g of Al; metal cooled = 50.0 g of Au; final temperature = 26 °C

(b) Metal heated = 50.0 g of Zn; metal cooled = 50.0 g of Al; final temperature = 21 °C

**5.109** $w = -(1.0\ L \cdot atm)(0.36\ L - 0\ L) = -0.36\ L\ atm = -36$ J

Thus, 36 J of work is done by the system on the surroundings.

## Applying Chemical Principles: Gunpowder

**1.** (a) $\Delta_rH° = -567.9$ kJ/mol-rxn

(b) $\Delta H° = -2.10$ kJ

**3.** (a) $4\ C_3H_5N_3O_9(\ell) \rightarrow 12\ CO_2(g) + 6\ N_2(g) + 10\ H_2O(g) + O_2(g)$

(b) $\Delta_fH° = -3.70 \times 10^2$ kJ/mol

# Chapter 6

**6.1** (a) Microwaves

(b) Red light

(c) Infrared

**6.3** (a) Green light has a higher frequency than amber light

(b) $5.04 \times 10^{14}$ s$^{-1}$

**6.5** Frequency = $6.0 \times 10^{14}$ s$^{-1}$; energy per photon = $4.0 \times 10^{-19}$ J; energy per mol of photons = $2.4 \times 10^5$ J

**6.7** Frequency = $7.5676 \times 10^{14}$ s$^{-1}$; energy per photon = $5.0144 \times 10^{-19}$ J; 302 kJ/mol of photons

**6.9** In order of increasing energy: FM station < microwaves < yellow light < x-rays

**6.11** Light with a wavelength as long as 600 nm would be sufficient. This is in the visible region.

**6.13** (a) The light of shortest wavelength has a wavelength of 253.652 nm.

(b) Frequency = $1.18190 \times 10^{15}$ s$^{-1}$. Energy per photon = $7.83139 \times 10^{-19}$ J/photon.

(c) The lines at 404 nm (violet) and 436 nm (blue) are in the visible region of the spectrum.

**6.15** The color is violet. $n_{initial} = 6$ and $n_{final} = 2$

**6.17** (a) 10 lines possible

(b) Highest frequency (highest energy), $n = 5$ to $n = 1$

(c) Longest wavelength (lowest energy), $n = 5$ to $n = 4$

**6.19** (a) $n = 3$ to $n = 2$

(b) $n = 4$ to $n = 1$. The energy levels are progressively closer at higher levels, so the energy difference from $n = 4$ to $n = 1$ is greater than from $n = 5$ to $n = 2$.

**6.21** Wavelength = 102.6 nm and frequency = $2.923 \times 10^{15}$ $s^{-1}$. Light with these properties is in the ultraviolet region.

**6.23** Wavelength = 0.29 nm

**6.25** The wavelength is $2.2 \times 10^{-25}$ nm. (Calculated from $\lambda = h/m \cdot v$, where $m$ is the ball's mass in kg and $v$ is the velocity.) To have a wavelength of $5.6 \times 10^{-3}$ nm, the ball would have to travel at $1.2 \times 10^{-21}$ m/s.

**6.27** (a) $n = 4$, $\ell = 0, 1, 2, 3$
(b) When $\ell = 2$, $m_\ell = -2, -1, 0, 1, 2$
(c) For a 4s orbital, $n = 4$, $\ell = 0$, and $m_\ell = 0$
(d) For a 4f orbital, $n = 4$, $\ell = 3$, and $m_\ell = -3, -2, -1, 0, 1, 2, 3$

**6.29** Set 1: $n = 4$, $\ell = 1$, and $m_\ell = -1$
Set 2: $n = 4$, $\ell = 1$, and $m_\ell = 0$
Set 3: $n = 4$, $\ell = 1$, and $m_\ell = +1$

**6.31** Four subshells. (The number of subshells in a shell is always equal to $n$.)

**6.33** (a) $\ell$ must have a value no greater than $n - 1$.
(b) When $\ell = 0$, $m_\ell$ can only equal 0.
(c) When $\ell = 0$, $m_\ell$ can only equal 0.

**6.35** (a) None. The quantum number set is not possible. When $\ell = 0$, $m_\ell$ can only equal 0.
(b) 3 orbitals
(c) 11 orbitals
(d) 1 orbital

**6.37** (a) $m_s = 0$ is not possible. $m_s$ may only have values of $\pm1/2$.
One possible set of quantum numbers: $n = 4$, $\ell = 2$, $m_\ell = 0$, $m_s = +1/2$
(b) $m_\ell$ cannot equal $-3$ in this case. If $\ell = 1$, $m_\ell$ can only be $-1$, 0, or 1.
One possible set of quantum numbers: $n = 3$, $\ell = 1$, $m_\ell = -1$, $m_s = -1/2$
(c) $\ell = 3$ is not possible in this case. The maximum value of $\ell$ is $n - 1$.
One possible set of quantum numbers: $n = 3$, $\ell = 2$, $m_\ell = -1$, $m_s = +1/2$

**6.39** 2d and 3f orbitals cannot exist. The $n = 2$ shell consists only of s and p subshells. The $n = 3$ shell consists only of s, p, and d subshells.

**6.41** (a) For 2p: $n = 2$, $\ell = 1$, and $m_\ell = -1, 0$, or $+1$
(b) For 3d: $n = 3$, $\ell = 2$, and $m_\ell = -2, -1, 0, +1$, or $+2$
(c) For 4f: $n = 4$, $\ell = 3$, and $m_\ell = -3, -2, -1, 0, +1, +2$, or $+3$

**6.43** 4d

**6.45** (a) 2s has 0 nodal surfaces that pass through the nucleus ($\ell = 0$).
(b) 5d has 2 nodal surfaces that pass through the nucleus ($\ell = 2$).
(c) 5f has three nodal surfaces that pass through the nucleus ($\ell = 3$).

**6.47** (a) Correct
(b) Incorrect. The intensity of a light beam is independent of frequency and is related to the number of photons of light with a certain energy.
(c) Correct

**6.49** Considering only angular nodes (nodal surfaces that pass through the nucleus):

s orbital — 0 nodal surfaces through the nucleus
p orbitals — 1 nodal surface or plane passing through the nucleus
d orbitals — 2 nodal surfaces or planes passing through the nucleus
f orbitals — 3 nodal surfaces or planes passing through the nucleus

**6.51**

| $\ell$ Value | Orbital Type |
|---|---|
| 3 | f |
| 0 | s |
| 1 | p |
| 2 | d |

**6.53** Considering only angular nodes (nodal surfaces that pass through the nucleus):

| Orbital Type | Number of Orbitals in a Given Subshell | Number of Nodal Surfaces |
|---|---|---|
| s | 1 | 0 |
| p | 3 | 1 |
| d | 5 | 2 |
| f | 7 | 3 |

**6.55** (a) Green light
(b) Red light has a wavelength of 680 nm, and green light has a wavelength of 500 nm.
(c) Green light has a higher frequency than red light.

**6.57** (a) Wavelength = 0.35 m
(b) Energy = 0.34 J/mol
(c) Violet light (with $\lambda = 420$ nm) has an energy of 280 kJ/mol of photons.
(d) Violet light has an energy (per mol of photons) that is 840,000 times greater than a mole of photons from a cell phone.

**6.59** The ionization energy for $He^+$ is 5248 kJ/mol. This is four times the ionization energy for the H atom.

**6.61** $1s < 2s = 2p < 3s = 3p = 3d < 4s$
In the H atom orbitals in the same shell (e.g., 2s and 2p) have the same energy.

**6.63** Frequency = $2.836 \times 10^{20}$ $s^{-1}$ and wavelength = $1.057 \times 10^{-12}$ m

**6.65** 260 s or 4.3 min

**6.67** (a) Size and energy
(b) $\ell$
(c) More
(d) 7 (when $\ell = 3$ these are $f$ orbitals)
(e) One orbital
(f) (Left to right) $d$, $s$, and $p$
(g) $\ell = 0, 1, 2, 3, 4$
(h) 16 orbitals (1$s$, 3$p$, 5$d$, and 7$f$) ($= n^2$)
(i) Paramagnetic

**6.69** (a) Drawing (a) is a ferromagnetic solid, (b) is a diamagnetic solid, and (c) is a paramagnetic solid.
(b) Substance (a) would be most strongly attracted to a magnet, whereas (b) would be least strongly attracted.

**6.71** The pickle glows because it was made by soaking a cucumber in brine, a concentrated solution of NaCl. The sodium atoms in the pickle are excited by the electric current and release energy as yellow light as they return to the ground state. Excited sodium atoms are the source of the yellow light you see in fireworks and in certain kinds of street lighting.

**6.73** (a) $\lambda = 0.0005$ cm $= 5$ $\mu$m
(b) The left side is the higher energy side, and the right side is the lower energy side.
(c) The interaction with O—H requires more energy.

**6.75** (c)

**6.77** An experiment can be done that shows that the electron can behave as a particle, and another experiment can be done to show that it has wave properties. (However, no single experiment shows both properties of the electron.) The modern view of atomic structure is based on the wave properties of the electron.

**6.79** (a) and (b)

**6.81** Radiation with a wavelength of 93.8 nm is sufficient to raise the electron to the $n = 6$ quantum level (see Figure 6.10). There should be 15 emission lines involving transitions from $n = 6$ to lower energy levels. (There are five lines for transitions from $n = 6$ to lower levels, four lines for $n = 5$ to lower levels, three for $n = 4$ to lower levels, two lines for $n = 3$ to lower levels, and one line for $n = 2$ to $n = 1$.) Wavelengths for many of the lines are given in Figure 6.10. For example, there will be an emission involving an electron moving from $n = 6$ to $n = 2$ with a wavelength of 410.2 nm.

**6.83** (a) Group 7B (IUPAC Group 7); Period 5
(b) $n = 5$, $\ell = 0$, $m_\ell = 0$, $m_s = +1/2$
(c) $\lambda = 8.79 \times 10^{-12}$ m; $\nu = 3.41 \times 10^{19}$ s$^{-1}$
(d) (i) $HTcO_4(aq) + NaOH(aq) \rightarrow$
$\qquad H_2O(\ell) + NaTcO_4(aq)$
(ii) $8.5 \times 10^{-3}$ g NaTcO$_4$ produced;
$1.8 \times 10^{-3}$ g NaOH needed
(e) 0.28 mg NaTcO$_4$; 0.00015 M

## Applying Chemical Principles: Chemistry of the Sun

1.  $\nu = 5.102 \times 10^{14}$ s$^{-1}$

3.  For $\lambda = 589.00$ nm, $E = 3.3726 \times 10^{-19}$ J
For $\lambda = 589.59$ nm, $E = 3.3692 \times 10^{-19}$ J
$\Delta E = 3.4 \times 10^{-22}$ J

5.  Balmer series: G', F, C (as marked on the spectrum)

# Chapter 7

**7.1** (a) Phosphorus: $1s^2 2s^2 2p^6 3s^2 3p^3$

The element is in the third period in Group 5A. Therefore, it has five electrons in the third shell.
(b) Chlorine: $1s^2 2s^2 2p^6 3s^2 3p^5$

The element is in the third period and in Group 7A. Therefore, it has seven electrons in the third shell.

**7.3** (a) Chromium: $1s^2 2s^2 2p^6 3s^2 3p^6 3d^5 4s^1$
(b) Iron: $1s^2 2s^2 2p^6 3s^2 3p^6 3d^6 4s^2$

**7.5** (a) Arsenic: $1s^2 2s^2 2p^6 3s^2 3p^6 3d^{10} 4s^2 4p^3$; [Ar]$3d^{10} 4s^2 4p^3$
(b) Krypton: $1s^2 2s^2 2p^6 3s^2 3p^6 3d^{10} 4s^2 4p^6$;
[Ar]$3d^{10} 4s^2 4p^6 =$ [Kr]

**7.7** (a) Tantalum: This is the third element in the transition series in the sixth period. Therefore, it has a core equivalent to Xe plus two 6$s$ electrons, 14 4$f$ electrons, and three electrons in 5$d$: [Xe]$4f^{14} 5d^3 6s^2$
(b) Platinum: This is the eighth element in the transition series in the sixth period. Therefore, it is predicted to have a core equivalent to Xe plus two 6$s$ electrons, 14 4$f$ electrons, and eight electrons in 5$d$: [Xe]$4f^{14} 5d^8 6s^2$. In reality, its actual configuration (Table 7.3) is [Xe]$4f^{14} 5d^9 6s^1$.

**7.9** Americium: [Rn]$5f^7 7s^2$ (see Table 7.3)

**7.11** (a) 2
(b) 1
(c) None (because $\ell$ cannot equal $n$)

**7.13** Magnesium: $1s^2 2s^2 2p^6 3s^2$

[Ne] ⇅
$\qquad$ 3$s$

Quantum numbers for the two electrons in the 3$s$ orbital:
$n = 3$, $\ell = 0$, $m_\ell = 0$, and $m_s = +1/2$
$n = 3$, $\ell = 0$, $m_\ell = 0$, and $m_s = -1/2$

**7.15** Gallium: $1s^2 2s^2 2p^6 3s^2 3p^6 3d^{10} 4s^2 4p^1$

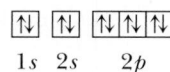
$$3d \qquad 4s \qquad 4p$$

Quantum numbers for the $4p$ electron:

$n = 4$, $\ell = 1$, $m_\ell = -1, 0,$ or $+1$, and $m_s = +\frac{1}{2}$ or $-\frac{1}{2}$

**7.17** (a) $Mg^{2+}$ ion

$$1s \quad 2s \qquad 2p$$

(b) $K^+$ ion

$$1s \quad 2s \qquad 2p \qquad 3s \qquad 3p$$

(c) $Cl^-$ ion (Note that both $Cl^-$ and $K^+$ have the same configuration; both are equivalent to Ar.)

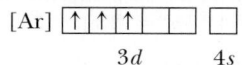
$$1s \quad 2s \qquad 2p \qquad 3s \qquad 3p$$

(d) $O^{2-}$ ion

$$1s \quad 2s \qquad 2p$$

**7.19** (a) V (paramagnetic; three unpaired electrons)

$$[Ar] \qquad 3d \qquad 4s$$

(b) $V^{2+}$ ion (paramagnetic, three unpaired electrons)

$$[Ar] \qquad 3d \qquad 4s$$

(c) $V^{5+}$ ion. This ion has an electron configuration equivalent to argon, [Ar]. It is diamagnetic with no unpaired electrons.

**7.21** (a) Manganese

$$[Ar] \qquad 3d \qquad 4s$$

(b) $Mn^{4+}$

$$[Ar] \qquad 3d \qquad 4s$$

(c) The $4^+$ ion is paramagnetic to the extent of three unpaired electrons.

(d) 3

**7.23** Increasing size: C < B < Al < Na < K

**7.25** (a) $Cl^-$
(b) Al
(c) In

**7.27** (c)

**7.29** (a) Largest radius, Na
(b) Most negative electron attachment enthalpy: O
(c) Ionization energy: Na < Mg < P < O

**7.31** (a) Increasing ionization energy: S < O < F. S is less than O because the IE decreases down a group. F is greater than O because IE generally increases across a period.
(b) Largest IE: O. IE decreases down a group.
(c) Most negative electron attachment enthalpy: Cl. Electron attachment enthalpy becomes more negative across the periodic table and on ascending a group.
(d) Largest size: $O^{2-}$. Negative ions are larger than their corresponding neutral atoms. $F^-$ is thus larger than F. $O^{2-}$ and $F^-$ are isoelectronic, but the $O^{2-}$ ion has only eight protons in its nucleus to attract the 10 electrons, whereas the $F^-$ has nine protons, making the $O^{2-}$ ion larger.

**7.33** Uranium configuration: $[Rn]5f^3 6d^1 7s^2$

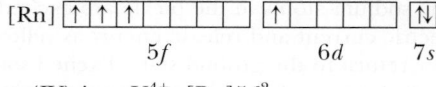
$$5f \qquad\qquad 6d \qquad 7s$$

Uranium(IV) ion, $U^{4+}$: $[Rn]5f^2$

$$5f \qquad\qquad 6d \qquad 7s$$

Both U and $U^{4+}$ are paramagnetic.

**7.35** (a) Atomic number = 20
(b) Total number of $s$ electrons = 8
(c) Total number of $p$ electrons = 12
(d) Total number of $d$ electrons = 0
(e) The element is Ca, calcium, a metal.

**7.37** (a) Valid. Possible elements are Li and Be.
(b) Not valid. The maximum value of $\ell$ is $(n - 1)$.
(c) Valid. Possible elements are B through Ne.
(d) Valid. Possible elements are Y through Cd.

**7.39** (a) Neodymium, Nd: $[Xe]4f^4 6s^2$ (Table 7.3)

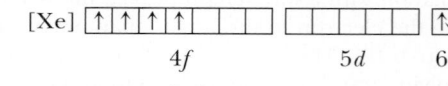
$$4f \qquad\qquad 5d \qquad 6s$$

Iron, Fe: $[Ar]3d^6 4s^2$

$$3d \qquad 4s$$

Boron, B: $[He]2s^2 2p^1$

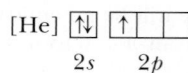
$$2s \quad 2p$$

(b) All three elements have unpaired electrons and so should be paramagnetic.
(c) Neodymium(III) ion, $Nd^{3+}$: $[Xe]4f^3$

$$4f \qquad\qquad 5d \qquad 6s$$

Iron(III) ion, $Fe^{3+}$: $[Ar]3d^5$

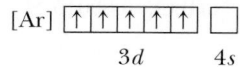
$$3d \qquad 4s$$

Both neodymium(III) and iron(III) have unpaired electrons and are paramagnetic.

**7.41** K < Ca < Si < P

**7.43** (a) Metal
(b) B
(c) A
(d) A
(e) $Rb_2Se$

**7.45** $In^{4+}$: Indium has three outer shell electrons and so is unlikely to form a $4^+$ ion.

$Fe^{6+}$: Although iron has eight electrons in its $3d$ and $4s$ orbitals, ions with a $6^+$ charge are highly unlikely. The ionization energy is too large.

$Sn^{5+}$: Tin has four outer shell electrons and so is unlikely to form a $5^+$ ion.

**7.47** (a) Se
(b) $Br^-$
(c) Na
(d) N
(e) $N^{3-}$

**7.49** (a) Na
(b) C
(c) Na < Al < B < C

**7.51** (a) Cobalt
(b) Paramagnetic
(c) Four unpaired electrons

**7.53** (a) 0.421 g
(b) Paramagnetic; two unpaired electrons
(c) 99.8 mg; the nickel powder is paramagnetic and will stick to a magnet.

**7.55** Li has three electrons ($1s^2 2s^1$) and $Li^+$ has only two electrons ($1s^2$). The ion is smaller than the atom because there are only two electrons to be held by three protons in the ion. Also, an electron in a larger orbital has been removed. Fluorine atoms have nine electrons and nine protons ($1s^2 2s^2 2p^5$). The anion, $F^-$, has one additional electron, which means that 10 electrons must be held by only nine protons, and so the ion is larger than the atom.

**7.57** Element 1 comes from Group 4A (IUPAC Group 14). The first two IEs correspond to removing electrons from a $p$ subshell. With the third IE, there is a fairly large jump in IE corresponding to removing an electron from an $s$ subshell. The fourth electron removed comes from the same $s$ subshell and therefore does not increase the IE by as much. None of the IEs are large enough to correspond to removing an electron from a lower energy level.

Element 2 comes from Group 3A (IUPAC Group 13). There is a large change in IE between the third and fourth IEs. The first three IEs correspond to removing electrons from the same energy level. The large jump at the fourth IE corresponds to having to remove the electron from a lower energy level.

**7.59** Most stable: (d). The two electrons are in separate orbitals, following Hund's rule, and are of the same spin.

Least stable: (a). In this case the electrons violate both Hund's rule and the Pauli exclusion principle.

**7.61** K $(1s^2 2s^2 2p^6 3s^2 3p^6 4s^1) \rightarrow$ K$^+ (1s^2 2s^2 2p^6 3s^2 3p^6)$
K$^+ (1s^2 2s^2 2p^6 3s^2 3p^6) \rightarrow$ K$^{2+} (1s^2 2s^2 2p^6 3s^2 3p^5)$

The first ionization is for the removal of an electron from the valence shell of electrons. The second electron, however, is removed from the $3p$ subshell. This subshell is significantly lower in energy than the $4s$ subshell, and considerably more energy is required to remove this second electron.

**7.63** (a) In going from one element to the next across the period, the effective nuclear charge increases slightly and the attraction between the nucleus and the electrons increases.
(b) The size of fourth period transition elements, for example, is a reflection of the size of the $4s$ orbital. As $d$ electrons are added across the series, protons are added to the nucleus. Adding protons should lead to a decreased atom size, but the effect of the protons is balanced by repulsions of the $3d$ electrons and $4s$ electrons, and the atom size is changed little.

**7.65** Among the arguments for a compound composed of $Mg^{2+}$ and $O^{2-}$ are the following:
(a) Chemical experience suggests that all Group 2A elements form $2^+$ cations, and that oxygen is typically the $O^{2-}$ ion in its compounds.
(b) Other alkaline earth elements form oxides such as BeO, CaO, and BaO.

A possible experiment is to measure the melting point of the compound. An ionic compound such as NaF (with ions having $1^+$ and $1^-$ charges) melts at 990 °C, whereas a compound analogous to MgO, CaO, melts at a much higher temperature (2580 °C).

**7.67** (a) The effective nuclear charge increases, causing the valence orbital energies to become more negative on moving across the period.
(b) As the valence orbital energies become more negative, it is increasingly difficult to remove an electron from the atom, and the IE increases. Toward the end of the period, the orbital energies have become so negative that removing an electron requires significant energy. Instead, the effective nuclear charge has reached the point that the atom forms a negative ion, in line with the more negative electron attachment enthalpy for elements on the right side of the periodic table.
(c) The valence orbital energies are in the order:

Li (−520.0 kJ) < Be (−899.3 kJ) > B (−800.8 kJ) < C (−1029 kJ)

This means it is more difficult to remove an electron from Be than from either Li or B. The energy is more negative for C than for B, so it is more difficult to remove an electron from C than from B.

**7.69** The size declines across this series of elements while their mass increases. Thus, the mass per volume, the density, increases.

**7.71** (a) Element 113: $[Rn]5f^{14}6d^{10}7s^27p^1$
Element 115: $[Rn]5f^{14}6d^{10}7s^27p^3$
(b) Element 113 is in Group 3A (with elements such as boron and aluminum), and element 115 is in Group 5A (with elements such as nitrogen and phosphorus).
(c) Americium ($Z = 95$) + argon ($Z = 18$) = element 113

**7.73** (a) Sulfur electron configuration

1s  2s    2p    3s    3p

(b) $n = 3$, $\ell = 1$, $m_\ell = 1$, and $m_s = +1/2$
(c) S has the smallest ionization energy and O has the smallest radius.
(d) S is smaller than the $S^{2-}$ ion.
(e) 584 g $SCl_2$
(f) 10.0 g of $SCl_2$ is the limiting reactant, and 11.6 g of $SOCl_2$ can be produced.
(g) $\Delta_f H°[SCl_2(g)] = -17.6$ kJ/mol

**7.75** (a) Z* for F is 5.20; Z* for Ne is 5.85. The effective nuclear charge increases from O to F to Ne. As the effective nuclear charge increases, the atomic radius decreases, and the first ionization energy increases.
(b) Z* for a 3d electron in Mn is 5.6; for a 4s electron it is only 3.6. The effective nuclear charge experienced by a 4s electron is much smaller than that experienced by a 3d electron. A 4s electron in Mn is thus more easily removed.

## Applying Chemical Principles: The Not-So-Rare Earths

**1.** (a) $Sm^{3+}$: $[Xe]4f^5$
(b) 4 Sm(s) + 3 $O_2$(g) → 2 $Sm_2O_3$(s)

**3.** (a) [Xe] ↑↑↑↑↑↑↑ | ↑ | | | | | ↑↓
        4f            5d      6s
(b) The most common oxidation state is +3, corresponding to the loss of the two 6s and one 5d electrons. The electron configuration of $Gd^{3+}$ is $[Xe]4f^7$.

**5.** $\nu = 4.90 \times 10^{14}$ s$^{-1}$; $E = 3.25 \times 10^{-19}$ J/photon

## Chapter 8

**8.1.** (a) Group 6A, six valence electrons
(b) Group 3A, three valence electrons
(c) Group 1A, one valence electron
(d) Group 2A, two valence electrons
(e) Group 7A, seven valence electrons
(f) Group 6A, six valence electrons

**8.3** Group 4A, four bonds
Group 5A, three bonds (for a neutral compound)
Group 6A, two bonds (for a neutral compound)
Group 7A, one (for a neutral compound)

**8.5** (a) $NF_3$, 26 valence electrons

:F—N—F:
     |
    :F:

(b) $ClO_3^-$, 26 valence electrons

[ :O—Cl—O: ]⁻
       |
      :O:

(c) HOBr, 14 valence electrons

H—Ö—Br:

(d) $SO_3^{2-}$, 26 valence electrons

[ :O—S—O: ]²⁻
      |
     :O:

**8.7** (a) $CHClF_2$, 26 valence electrons

        H
        |
:Cl—C—F:
        |
       :F:

(b) $CH_3CO_2H$, 24 valence electrons

    H  :O:
    |   ||
H—C—C—Ö—H
    |
    H

(c) $CH_3CN$, 16 valence electrons

    H
    |
H—C—C≡N:
    |
    H

(d) $H_2CCCH_2$, 16 valence electrons

   H      H
   |      |
H—C=C=C—H

**8.9** (a) $SO_2$, 18 valence electrons

:O—S=O: ⟷ O=S—O:

(b) $HNO_2$, 18 valence electrons

H—Ö—N=Ö

(c) $SCN^-$, 16 valence electrons

[ S=C=N ]⁻ ⟷ [ :S≡C—N: ]⁻ ⟷ [ :S—C≡N: ]⁻

**8.11** (a) $BrF_3$, 28 valence electrons

    :F:
    |
:Br—F:
    |
    :F:

(b) $I_3^-$, 22 valence electrons

(c) $XeO_2F_2$, 34 valence electrons

$$:\ddot{F}:$$
$$|$$
$$:\ddot{O}-Xe-\ddot{O}:$$
$$|$$
$$:\ddot{F}:$$

(d) $XeF_3^{+}$, 28 valence electrons

$$:\ddot{F}:$$
$$|$$
$$:Xe-\ddot{F}:$$
$$|$$
$$:\ddot{F}:$$

**8.13** (a) N = 0; H = 0
(b) P = +1; O = −1
(c) B = −1; H = 0
(d) All are zero.

**8.15** (a) N = +1; O = 0
(b) The central N is 0. The singly bonded O atom is −1, and the doubly bonded O atom is 0.

$$\left[:\ddot{O}-\ddot{N}=\ddot{O}\right]^{-} \longleftrightarrow \left[\ddot{O}=\ddot{N}-\ddot{O}:\right]^{-}$$

(c) N and F are both 0.
(d) The central N atom is +1, one of the O atoms is −1, and the other two O atoms and the H atom are all 0.

$$\overset{0}{H-\ddot{O}}-\overset{+1}{N}=\overset{0}{\ddot{O}}$$
$$|$$
$$\underset{-1}{:\ddot{O}:}$$

**8.17** (a) Electron-pair geometry around N is tetrahedral. Molecular geometry is trigonal-pyramidal.

$$:\ddot{C}l-\overset{}{N}-H$$
$$|$$
$$H$$

(b) Electron-pair geometry around O is tetrahedral. Molecular geometry is bent.

$$:\ddot{C}l-\ddot{O}-\ddot{C}l:$$

(c) Electron-pair geometry around C is linear. Molecular geometry is linear.

$$\left[\ddot{S}=C=\ddot{N}\right]^{-}$$

(d) Electron-pair geometry around O is tetrahedral. The molecular geometry is bent.

$$H-\ddot{O}-\ddot{F}:$$

**8.19** (a) Electron-pair geometry around C is linear. Molecular geometry is linear.

$$\ddot{O}=C=\ddot{O}$$

(b) Electron-pair geometry around N is trigonal-planar. Molecular geometry is bent.

$$\left[:\ddot{O}-\ddot{N}=\ddot{O}\right]^{-}$$

(c) Electron-pair geometry around O is trigonal-planar. Molecular geometry is bent.

$$\ddot{O}=\ddot{O}-\ddot{O}:$$

(d) Electron-pair geometry around Cl atom is tetrahedral. Molecular geometry is bent.

$$\left[:\ddot{O}-\ddot{C}l-\ddot{O}:\right]^{-}$$

All have two atoms attached to the central atom. As the bond and lone pairs vary, the electron-pair geometries vary from linear to tetrahedral, and the molecular geometries vary from linear to bent.

**8.21** (a) Electron-pair geometry around Cl is trigonal-bipyramidal. Molecular geometry is linear.

$$\left[:\ddot{F}-\ddot{C}l-\ddot{F}:\right]^{-}$$

(b) Electron-pair geometry around Cl is trigonal-bipyramidal. Molecular geometry is T-shaped.

$$:\ddot{F}-\ddot{C}l-\ddot{F}:$$
$$|$$
$$:\ddot{F}:$$

(c) Electron-pair geometry around Cl is octahedral. Molecular geometry is square-planar.

$$\left[\begin{array}{c}:\ddot{F}:\\|\\:\ddot{F}-\ddot{C}l-\ddot{F}:\\|\\:\ddot{F}:\end{array}\right]^{-}$$

(d) Electron-pair geometry around Cl is octahedral. Molecular geometry is a square-pyramidal.

$$:\ddot{F}:$$
$$:F\diagdown|\diagup F:$$
$$Cl$$
$$:F\diagup\diagdown F:$$

**8.23** (a) Ideal O—S—O angle = 120°
(b) 120°
(c) 120°
(d) H—C—H = 109° and C—C—N angle = 180°

**8.25** 1 = 120°; 2 = 109°; 3 = 120°; 4 = 109°; 5 = 109°

The chain cannot be linear because the first two carbon atoms in the chain have bond angles of 109° and the final one has a bond angle of 120°. These bond angles do not lead to a linear chain.

**8.27**

| $\overrightarrow{C-O}$ | $\overrightarrow{C-N}$ |
|---|---|
| $+\delta \quad -\delta$ | $+\delta \quad -\delta$ |

CO is more polar

| $\overrightarrow{P-Cl}$ | $\overrightarrow{P-Br}$ |
|---|---|
| $+\delta \quad -\delta$ | $+\delta \quad -\delta$ |

PCl is more polar

| $\overrightarrow{B-O}$ | $\overrightarrow{B-S}$ |
|---|---|
| $+\delta \quad -\delta$ | $+\delta \quad -\delta$ |

BO is more polar

| $\overrightarrow{B-F}$ | $\overrightarrow{B-I}$ |
|---|---|
| $+\delta \quad -\delta$ | $+\delta \quad -\delta$ |

BF is more polar

**8.29** (a) CH and CO bonds are polar.
(b) The CO bond is most polar, and O is the most negative atom.

**8.31** (a) OH$^-$: The formal charge on O is $-1$ and on H it is 0.
(b) BH$_4^-$: Even though the formal charge on B is $-1$ and on H is 0, H is slightly more electronegative than B. The four H atoms are therefore more likely to bear the $-1$ charge of the ion. The BH bonds are polar with the H atom the negative end.
(c) The CH and CO bonds are all polar (but the C—C bond is not). The negative charge in the CO bonds lies on the O atoms.

**8.33** Structure C is most reasonable. The charges are as small as possible, and the negative charge resides on the more electronegative atom.

$$\overset{-2}{:}\!\ddot{\text{N}}\!\!-\!\!\overset{+1}{\text{N}}\!\!\equiv\!\!\overset{+1}{\text{O}}: \longleftrightarrow \overset{-1}{\ddot{\text{N}}}\!\!=\!\!\overset{+1}{\text{N}}\!\!=\!\!\overset{0}{\ddot{\text{O}}} \longleftrightarrow \overset{0}{:}\text{N}\!\!\equiv\!\!\overset{+1}{\text{N}}\!\!-\!\!\overset{-1}{\ddot{\text{O}}}:$$
$$\qquad\text{A}\qquad\qquad\qquad\text{B}\qquad\qquad\qquad\text{C}$$

**8.35** Lewis structures:

$$\left[\ddot{\text{O}}\!=\!\text{C}\!-\!\ddot{\text{O}}\!-\!\text{H}\right]^- \longleftrightarrow \left[:\!\ddot{\text{O}}\!-\!\text{C}\!-\!\ddot{\text{O}}\!-\!\text{H}\right]^-$$
$$\qquad\quad |\qquad\qquad\qquad\qquad\quad \|$$
$$\qquad\quad :\!\ddot{\text{O}}:\qquad\qquad\qquad\qquad :\!\ddot{\text{O}}:$$

$$\ddot{\text{O}}\!=\!\text{N}\!-\!\ddot{\text{O}}\!-\!\text{H} \longleftrightarrow :\!\ddot{\text{O}}\!-\!\text{N}\!-\!\ddot{\text{O}}\!-\!\text{H}$$
$$\quad |\qquad\qquad\qquad\qquad\qquad \|$$
$$\quad :\!\ddot{\text{O}}:\qquad\qquad\qquad\qquad\quad :\!\ddot{\text{O}}:$$

(a) These species are isoelectronic.
(b) Each has two major resonance structures.
(c) In HCO$_3^-$, the H, C, and O attached to the H all have a formal charge of 0. Each of the other oxygen atoms has a formal charge of $-1/2$.
In HNO$_3$, the same formal charges are present as in HCO$_3^-$ except that the central N has a formal charge of $+1$.
(d) HNO$_3$ is much more acidic than HCO$_3^-$. This is due, in part, to simple electrostatics. It is much easier to remove a positively charge species (H$^+$) from a neutral species (HNO$_3$) than from a negatively charged one (HCO$_3^-$).

**8.37** (a)
$$\left[\overset{-1}{:}\!\ddot{\text{O}}\!-\!\overset{0}{\text{N}}\!=\!\overset{0}{\ddot{\text{O}}}\right]^- \longleftrightarrow \left[\overset{0}{\ddot{\text{O}}}\!=\!\overset{0}{\text{N}}\!-\!\overset{-1}{\ddot{\text{O}}}:\right]^-$$

(b) If an H$^+$ ion were to attack NO$_2^-$, it would attach to an O atom because the O atoms bear the negative charge in this ion.

(c)
$$\text{H}\!-\!\ddot{\text{O}}\!-\!\text{N}\!=\!\ddot{\text{O}}: \longleftrightarrow :\!\ddot{\text{O}}\!-\!\text{N}\!=\!\ddot{\text{O}}\!-\!\text{H}$$

The structure on the left is strongly favored because all of the atoms have zero formal charge, whereas the structure on the right has a $-1$ formal charge on one oxygen and a $+1$ formal charge on the other.

**8.39** (i) The most polar bonds are in H$_2$O (because O and H have the largest difference in electronegativity).
(ii) Not polar: CO$_2$ and CCl$_4$
(iii) The F atom is more negatively charged.

**8.41** (a) BeCl$_2$, nonpolar linear molecule
(b) HBF$_2$, polar trigonal-planar molecule with F atoms on the negative end of the dipole and the H atom on the positive end.
(c) CH$_3$Cl, polar tetrahedral molecule. The Cl atom is on the negative end of the dipole and the three H atoms are on the positive side of the molecule.
(d) SO$_3$, a nonpolar trigonal-planar molecule

**8.43** (a) Two C—H bonds, bond order is 1; 1 C=O bond, bond order is 2.
(b) Three S—O single bonds, bond order is 1.
(c) Two nitrogen–oxygen double bonds, bond order is 2.
(d) One N=O double bond, bond order is 2; one N—Cl bond, bond order is 1.

**8.45** (a) B—Cl
(b) C—O
(c) P—O
(d) C=O

**8.47** NO bond orders: 2 in NO$_2^+$, 1.5 in NO$_2^-$; 1.33 in NO$_3^-$. The NO bond is longest in NO$_3^-$ and shortest in NO$_2^+$.

**8.49** The CO bond in carbon monoxide is a triple bond, so it is both shorter and stronger than the CO double bond in H$_2$CO.

**8.51** Using bond dissociation enthalpy data, $\Delta_r H^\circ \approx -44$ kJ/mol-rxn. Using $\Delta_f H^\circ$ data, $\Delta_r H^\circ = -45.9$ kJ/mol-rxn.

**8.53** $\Delta_r H = -126$ kJ

**8.55** O—F bond dissociation energy = 192 kJ/mol

**8.57**

| Element | Number of Valence Electrons |
|---------|------------------------------|
| Li | 1 |
| Ti | 4 |
| Zn | 2 |
| Si | 4 |
| Cl | 7 |

**8.59** SeF$_4$, BrF$_4^-$, XeF$_4$

**8.61**
$$\left[\text{H}\!-\!\text{C}\!-\!\ddot{\text{O}}:\right]^- \longleftrightarrow \left[\text{H}\!-\!\text{C}\!=\!\ddot{\text{O}}\right]^-$$
$$\quad\;\; \|\qquad\qquad\qquad\qquad\quad |$$
$$\quad :\ddot{\text{O}}:\qquad\qquad\qquad\qquad :\ddot{\text{O}}:$$

Bond order = 3/2

**8.63** To estimate the enthalpy change, we need bond dissociation enthalpies for the following bonds: O=O, H—H, and H—O.

$\Delta H$ to break bonds $\approx$ 498 kJ (for O=O) + 2 × 436 kJ (for H—H) = +1370 kJ

$\Delta H$ evolved when bonds are made $\approx$ 4 × 463 kJ (for O—H) = $-1852$ kJ

$\Delta_r H \approx -482$ kJ

**8.65** All the species in the series have 16 valence electrons and all are linear.

(a) $\ddot{O}=C=\ddot{O}$ $\longleftrightarrow$ $:\ddot{O}-C\equiv O:$ $\longleftrightarrow$ $:O\equiv C-\ddot{O}:$

(b)

$\left[\ddot{N}=N=\ddot{N}\right]^{-}$ $\longleftrightarrow$ $\left[:\ddot{N}-N\equiv N:\right]^{-}$ $\longleftrightarrow$ $\left[:N\equiv N-\ddot{N}:\right]^{-}$

(c)

$\left[\ddot{O}=C=\ddot{N}\right]^{-}$ $\longleftrightarrow$ $\left[:\ddot{O}-C\equiv N:\right]^{-}$ $\longleftrightarrow$ $\left[:O\equiv C-\ddot{N}:\right]^{-}$

**8.67** The N—O bonds in $NO_2^-$ have a bond order of 1.5, whereas in $NO_2^+$ the bond order is 2. The shorter bonds (110 pm) are the NO bonds with the higher bond order (in $NO_2^+$), whereas the longer bonds (124 pm) in $NO_2^-$ have a lower bond order.

**8.69** The F—Cl—F bond angle in $ClF_2^+$, which has a tetrahedral electron-pair geometry, is approximately 109°.

$$\left[:\ddot{F}-\ddot{Cl}-\ddot{F}:\right]^{+}$$

The $ClF_2^-$ ion has a trigonal-bipyramidal electron-pair geometry with F atoms in the axial positions and the lone pairs in the equatorial positions. Therefore, the F—C—F angle is 180°.

$$\left[:\ddot{F}-\ddot{Cl}-\ddot{F}:\right]^{-}$$

**8.71** An $H^+$ ion will attach to an O atom of $SO_3^{2-}$ and not to the S atom. The O atoms each have a formal charge of −1, whereas the S atom formal charge is +1.

$$\left[:\ddot{O}-S-\ddot{O}:\atop\quad:\ddot{O}:\right]^{2-}$$

**8.73** (a) Calculation from bond dissociation enthalpies: $\Delta_r H° = -1070$ kJ/mol-rxn; $\Delta H° = -535$ kJ/mol $CH_3OH$

(b) Calculation from thermochemical data: $\Delta_r H° = -1352.3$ kJ/mol-rxn; $\Delta H° = -676$ kJ/mol $CH_3OH$

**8.75** (a)

$$\left[:C\equiv N-\ddot{O}:\right]^{-} \longleftrightarrow \left[\ddot{C}=N=\ddot{O}\right]^{-} \longleftrightarrow \left[:\ddot{C}-N\equiv O:\right]^{-}$$
$$\begin{array}{ccc} -1\ \ +1\ \ -1 & \ -2\ \ +1\ \ \ 0 & -3\ \ +1\ \ +1 \end{array}$$

(b) The first resonance structure is the most reasonable because oxygen, the most electronegative atom, has a negative formal charge, and the unfavorable negative charge on the least electronegative atom, carbon, is smallest.

(c) This species is so unstable because carbon, the least electronegative element in the ion, has a negative formal charge. In addition, all three resonance structures have an unfavorable charge distribution.

**8.77**

$$:-\overset{F}{\underset{F}{X}\!e}\rangle 120° \qquad F-\overset{F}{\underset{F}{C}\!l}\rangle 120°$$

(a) $XeF_2$ has three lone pairs around the Xe atom. The electron-pair geometry is trigonal-bipyramidal. Because lone pairs require more space than bond pairs, it is better to place the lone pairs in the equator of the bipyramid where the angles between them are 120°.

(b) Like $XeF_2$, $ClF_3$ has a trigonal-bipyramidal electron-pair geometry, but with only two lone pairs around the Cl. These are again placed in the equatorial plane where the angle between them is 120°.

**8.79** (a) Angle 1 = 109°; angle 2 = 120°; angle 3 = 109°; angle 4 = 109°; and angle 5 = 109°

(b) The O—H bond is the most polar bond.

**8.81** $\Delta_r H = +146$ kJ $= 2\ (\Delta H_{C-N}) + \Delta H_{C=O} - [\Delta H_{N-N} + \Delta H_{C\equiv O}]$

**8.83** (a) Two C—H bonds and one O=O are broken and two O—C bonds and two H—O bonds are made in the reaction. $\Delta_r H = -318$ kJ. The reaction is exothermic.

(b) Both hydroxyacetone and acetone are polar.

(c) The O—H hydrogen atoms are the most positive in dihydroxyacetone.

**8.85** (a) The C=C bond is stronger than the C—C bond.

(b) The C—C single bond is longer than the C=C double bond.

(c) Ethylene is nonpolar, whereas acrolein is polar.

(d) The reaction is exothermic ($\Delta_r H = -45$ kJ).

**8.87** $\Delta_r H = -211$ kJ

**8.89** Methanol is a polar solvent. Methanol contains two bonds of significant polarity, the C—O bond and the O—H bond. The C—O—H atoms are in a bent configuration, leading to a polar molecule. Toluene contains only carbon and hydrogen atoms, which have similar electronegativites and which are arranged in tetrahedral or trigonal planar geometries, leading to a molecule that is largely nonpolar.

**8.91** (a)

$$H-\overset{H}{\underset{H}{C}}-\ddot{S}-\overset{H}{\underset{H}{C}}-H$$

The bond angles are all approximately 109°.

(b) The sulfur atom should have a slight partial negative charge, and the carbons should have slight partial positive charges. The molecule has a bent shape and is polar.

(c) $1.6 \times 10^{18}$ molecules

**8.93** (a) $P_4 + 6\ Cl_2 \rightarrow 4\ PCl_3$

(b) $\Delta_r H = -1206.9$ kJ/mol-rxn

(c) Bonds broken: 6 mol P—P, 6 mol Cl—Cl

Bonds formed: 12 mol P—Cl

$\Delta H_{P-Cl} = 322$ kJ/mol; the value in Table 8.9 is 326 kJ/mol

**8.95** (a) Odd electron molecules: BrO (13 electrons)

(b) $Br_2(g) \rightarrow 2\ Br(g)$    $\Delta_r H = +193\ kJ$
$2\ Br(g) + O_2(g) \rightarrow 2\ BrO(g)$    $\Delta_r H = +96\ kJ$
$BrO(g) + H_2O(g) \rightarrow HOBr(g) + OH(g)$
$\Delta_r H = 0\ kJ$

(c) $\Delta_f H\ [HOBr(g)] = -101\ kJ/mol$

(d) The reactions in part (b) are endothermic (or thermal-neutral for the third reaction), and the enthalpy of formation in part (c) is exothermic.

## Applying Chemical Principles: Linus Pauling and Electronegativity

**1.** Using average bond dissociation enthalpies:
$\chi_{Cl} - \chi_H = 0.98$
According to Figure 8.11, $\chi_{Cl} - \chi_H = 1.0$

**3.** $\chi_S = 2.55$

# Chapter 9

**9.1** The electron-pair and molecular geometry of $CHCl_3$ are both tetrahedral. Each C—Cl bond is formed by the overlap of an $sp^3$ hybrid orbital on the C atom with a $3p$ orbital on a Cl atom to form a sigma bond. A C—H sigma bond is formed by the overlap of an $sp^3$ hybrid orbital on the C atom with an H atom $1s$ orbital.

$$H—\overset{\displaystyle :\!\ddot{C}l:}{\underset{\displaystyle :\!\ddot{C}l:}{C}}—\ddot{C}l:$$

**9.3**
$$H—\overset{}{\underset{\displaystyle H}{\ddot{N}}}—\ddot{O}—H$$

Both the N and the O are $sp^3$ hybridized. One of the $sp^3$ orbitals on the N overlaps with one of the $sp^3$ hybrid orbitals on the O.

**9.5**
$$:\!\ddot{F}—\overset{\displaystyle \overset{..}{\underset{}{O}}:\!\!\parallel}{C}—\ddot{F}:$$

The electron-pair and molecular geometries are both trigonal-planar. The carbon atom is $sp^2$ hybridized. The $\sigma$ bond between the C and O is formed by the overlap of an $sp^2$ hybrid orbital on C with an $sp^2$ hybrid orbital on O. The $\pi$ bond is formed by the overlap of a $2p$ orbital on C with a $2p$ orbital on O.

**9.7**

| Electron-Pair Geometry | Molecular Geometry | Hybrid Orbital Set |
|---|---|---|
| (a) Trigonal-planar | Trigonal-planar | $sp^2$ |
| (b) Linear | Linear | $sp$ |
| (c) Tetrahedral | Tetrahedral | $sp^3$ |
| (d) Trigonal-planar | Trigonal-planar | $sp^2$ |

**9.9** (a) C, $sp^3$; O, $sp^3$

(b) $CH_3$, $sp^3$; middle C, $sp^2$; $CH_2$, $sp^2$

(c) $CH_2$, $sp^3$; $CO_2H$, $sp^2$; N, $sp^3$

**9.11** (a) Electron-pair geometry is octahedral. Molecular geometry is octahedral. Si: $sp^3d^2$

(b) Electron-pair geometry is trigonal-bipyramidal. Molecular geometry is seesaw. Se: $sp^3d$

(c) Electron-pair geometry is trigonal-bipyramidal. Molecular geometry is linear. I: $sp^3d$

(d) Electron-pair geometry is octahedral. Molecular geometry is square-planar. Xe: $sp^3d^2$

**9.13** There are 32 valence electrons in both $HPO_2F_2$ and its anion. Both have a tetrahedral molecular geometry, so the P atom in both is $sp^3$ hybridized.

**9.15** The C atom is $sp^2$ hybridized. Two of the $sp^2$ hybrid orbitals are used to form C—Cl $\sigma$ bonds, and the third is used to form the C—O $\sigma$ bond. The $p$ orbital not used in the C atom hybrid orbitals is used to form the CO pi bond.

**9.17** The electron-pair geometry around S is tetrahedral, and the molecular geometry is trigonal-pyramidal. The S atom is $sp^3$ hybridized.

**9.19**

*cis* isomer      *trans* isomer

**9.21** $H_2^+$ ion: $(\sigma_{1s})^1$. Bond order is 0.5. The bond in $H_2^+$ is weaker than in $H_2$ (bond order $=1$).

**9.23** MO diagram for $C_2^{2-}$ ion

$$\underline{\qquad} \; \sigma^*_{2p}$$
$$\underline{\qquad} \; \underline{\qquad} \; \pi^*_{2p}$$
$$\underline{\uparrow\downarrow} \; \sigma_{2p}$$
$$\underline{\uparrow\downarrow} \; \underline{\uparrow\downarrow} \; \pi_{2p}$$
$$\underline{\uparrow\downarrow} \; \sigma^*_{2s}$$
$$\underline{\uparrow\downarrow} \; \sigma_{2s}$$

The ion has 10 valence electrons (isoelectronic with $N_2$). There are one net $\sigma$ bond and two net $\pi$ bonds, for a bond order of 3. The bond order increases by 1 on going from $C_2$ to $C_2^{2-}$. The ion is not paramagnetic.

**9.25** $O_2$: (core electrons)$(\sigma_{2s})^2(\sigma^*_{2s})^2(\sigma_{2p})^2(\pi_{2p})^4(\pi^*_{2p})^2$
$O_2^{2-}$: (core electrons)$(\sigma_{2s})^2(\sigma^*_{2s})^2(\sigma_{2p})^2(\pi_{2p})^4(\pi^*_{2p})^4$
(a) $O_2$ is paramagnetic; $O_2^{2-}$ is diamagnetic.
(b) $O_2$ has one net $\sigma$ bond and one net $\pi$ bond. $O_2^{2-}$ has one net $\sigma$ bond.
(c) $O_2$ bond order = 2; $O_2^{2-}$ bond order = 1
(d) The bond length in $O_2$ is shorter than that in $O_2^{2-}$.

**9.27** Shortest, $N_2$; longest, $Li_2$

**9.29** (a) ClO has 13 valence electrons
$$[core](\sigma_s)^2(\sigma^*_s)^2(\pi_p)^4(\sigma_p)^2(\pi^*_p)^3$$
(b) $\pi^*_p$
(c) Diamagnetic
(d) There are net 1 $\sigma$ bond and 0.5 $\pi$ bonds; bond order is 1.5.

**9.31**

$$\left[ \begin{array}{c} :\ddot{F}: \\ | \\ :\ddot{F}{-}Al{-}\ddot{F}: \\ | \\ :\ddot{F}: \end{array} \right]^-$$

The electron pair and molecular geometries are both tetrahedral. The Al atom is $sp^3$ hybridized, so the Al—F bonds are formed by overlap of an Al $sp^3$ orbital with a $p$ orbital on each F atom. The formal charge on each of the fluorines is 0, and that on the Al is −1. This is not a reasonable charge distribution because the less electronegative atom, aluminum, has the negative charge.

**9.33**

| Molecule/Ion | O—S—O Angle | Hybrid Orbitals |
|---|---|---|
| $SO_2$ | 120° | $sp^2$ |
| $SO_3$ | 120° | $sp^2$ |
| $SO_3^{2-}$ | 109° | $sp^3$ |
| $SO_4^{2-}$ | 109° | $sp^3$ |

**9.35** $\left[:\ddot{O}{-}\dot{N}{=}\ddot{O}\right]^- \longleftrightarrow \left[\ddot{O}{=}\dot{N}{-}\ddot{O}:\right]^-$

The electron-pair geometry is trigonal-planar. The molecular geometry is bent (or angular). The O—N—O angle will be about 120°, the average N—O bond order is 3/2, and the N atom is $sp^2$ hybridized.

**9.37** The resonance structures of $N_2O$, with formal charges, are shown here.

$$\overset{-2 \quad +1 \quad +1}{:\ddot{N}{-}N{\equiv}O:} \longleftrightarrow \overset{-1 \quad +1 \quad 0}{\ddot{N}{=}N{=}\ddot{O}} \longleftrightarrow \overset{0 \quad +1 \quad -1}{:N{\equiv}N{-}\ddot{O}:}$$

$$\quad\;\; A \qquad\qquad\quad B \qquad\qquad\quad C$$

The central N atom is $sp$ hybridized in all structures. The two $sp$ hybrid orbitals on the central N atom are used to form N—N and N—O $\sigma$ bonds. The two $p$ orbitals not used in the N atom hybridization are used to form the required $\pi$ bonds.

**9.39** (a) All three have the formula $C_2H_4O$. They are usually referred to as structural isomers.
(b) *Ethylene oxide:* Both C atoms are $sp^3$ hybridized. *Acetaldehyde:* The $CH_3$ carbon atom has $sp^3$ hybridization, and the other C atom is $sp^2$ hybridized. *Vinyl alcohol:* Both C atoms are $sp^2$ hybridized.
(c) *Ethylene oxide:* 109° *Acetaldehyde:* 109° *Vinyl alcohol:* 120°
(d) All are polar.
(e) Acetaldehyde has the strongest CO bond, and vinyl alcohol has the strongest C—C bond.

**9.41** (a) $CH_3$ carbon atom: $sp^3$
C=N carbon atom: $sp^2$
N atom: $sp^2$
(b) C—N—O bond angle = 120°

**9.43** (a) C(1) = $sp^2$; O(2) = $sp^3$; N(3) = $sp^3$; C(4) = $sp^3$; P(5) = $sp^3$
(b) Angle A = 120°; angle B = 109°; angle C = 109°; angle D = 109°
(c) The P—O and O—H bonds are most polar ($\Delta\chi = 1.3$).

**9.45** (a) C=O bond is most polar.
(b) 18 $\sigma$ bonds and five $\pi$ bonds
(c)

*trans* isomer          *cis* isomer

(d) All C atoms are $sp^2$ hybridized.
(e) All bond angles are 120°.

**9.47** (a) The Sb in $SbF_5$ is $sp^3d$ hybridized, whereas it is $sp^3d^2$ hybridized in $SbF_6^-$.
(b) The molecular geometry of the $H_2F^+$ ion is bent or angular, and the F atom is $sp^3$ hybridized.

$$\left[ \ddot{F}{\cdots}H \atop \quad H \right]^-$$

**9.49** (a) The peroxide ion has a bond order of 1.

$$\left[:\ddot{O}-\ddot{O}:\right]^{2-}$$

(b) [Core electrons] $(\sigma_{2s})^2(\sigma^*_{2s})^2(\sigma_{2p})^2(\pi_{2p})^4(\pi^*_{2p})^4$
This configuration also leads to a bond order of 1.

(c) Both theories lead to a diamagnetic ion with a bond order of 1.

**9.51** Paramagnetic diatomic molecules: $B_2$ and $O_2$

Bond order of 1: $Li_2$, $B_2$, $F_2$; bond order of 2: $C_2$ and $O_2$; highest bond order: $N_2$

**9.53** CN has nine valence electrons.
[core electrons] $(\sigma_{2s})^2(\sigma^*_{2s})^2(\pi_{2p})^4(\sigma_{2p})^1$

(a) HOMO, $\sigma_{2p}$

(b, c) Bond order = 2.5 (0.5 $\sigma$ bond and 2 $\pi$ bonds)

(d) Paramagnetic

**9.55** (a) All C atoms are $sp^3$ hybridized.

(b) About 109°

(c) Polar

(d) The six-membered ring cannot be planar, owing to the tetrahedral C atoms of the ring. The bond angles are all 109°.

**9.57** (a) The geometry about the boron atom is trigonal-planar in $BF_3$ but tetrahedral in $H_3N-BF_3$.

(b) Boron is $sp^2$ hybridized in $BF_3$ but $sp^3$ hybridized in $H_3N-BF_3$.

(c) Yes

(d) The ammonia molecule is polar with the N atom partially negative. While the $BF_3$ molecule is non-polar overall, each of the B—F bonds is polarized such that the B has a partial positive charge. The partially negative N in $NH_3$ is attracted to the partially positive B in $BF_3$.

(e) One of the lone pairs on the oxygen of $H_2O$ can form a coordinate covalent bond with the B in $BF_3$. The resulting compound would be (the lone pairs on the F's not shown):

$$\begin{array}{ccc} & H & F \\ & | & | \\ H-&O-B&-F \\ & & | \\ & & F \end{array}$$

**9.59** (a) $NH_2^-$: electron-pair geometry = tetrahedral, molecular geometry = bent, hybridization of N = $sp^3$

$SO_3$: electron-pair geometry = molecular geometry = trigonal-planar, hybridization of S = $sp^2$

(b)

$$\left[\begin{array}{c} :\ddot{O}: \\ H_{\cdots} \quad | \\ H^{\blacktriangle}N-S^{\cdots\cdots}\ddot{O}: \\ \quad \ddot{O}: \end{array}\right]^-$$

The bond angles around the N and the S are all approximately 109°.

(c) The N does not undergo any change in its hybridization; the S changes from $sp^2$ to $sp^3$.

(d) The $SO_3$ is the acceptor of an electron pair in this reaction. The electrostatic potential map confirms this to be reasonable because the sulfur has a partial positive charge.

**9.61**

$$\left[\begin{array}{c} H \quad :\ddot{O}: \\ \quad | \quad\quad | \\ H-C-C-\ddot{O}: \\ \quad | \\ \quad H \end{array}\right]^- \longleftrightarrow \left[\begin{array}{c} H \quad :\ddot{O}: \\ \quad | \quad\quad \| \\ H-C-C=\ddot{O} \\ \quad | \\ \quad H \end{array}\right]^-$$

Hybridization of C in $-CO_2^-$ is $sp^2$

C—C bond: overlap of $sp^2$ hybrid orbital on the carbon of $-CO_2^-$ with $sp^3$ hybrid orbital on the other C.

C—O $\sigma$ bond of C=O double bond: overlap of $sp^2$ hybrid orbital on C with $sp^2$ hybrid orbital on O.

C—O $\pi$ bond of C=O double bond: overlap of $p$ orbital on C with $p$ orbital on O

C—O single bond: The Lewis structure by itself would make it appear this bond is formed by the overlap of an $sp^2$ hybrid orbital on C with an $sp^3$ hybrid orbital on O. In the resonance hybrid, however, this oxygen would also have $sp^2$ hybridization.

**9.63**

$$\ddot{O}=S-\ddot{O}: \longleftrightarrow :\ddot{O}-S=\ddot{O}$$

MO theory pictures one net $\sigma$ bond for each S—O linkage plus a contribution from $\pi$ bonding. The $\pi$ bonding in this molecule will be similar to that in $O_3$ discussed in the text. There will be two electrons in a $\pi$ bonding MO and two electrons in a $\pi$ non-bonding MO. This gives an overall bond order of 1 for the $\pi$ bonding in the entire molecule and therefore a net $\pi$ bond order of 0.5 for each S—O linkage. The total bond order for each S—O linkage is therefore 1.5 (1 from $\sigma$ bonding, 0.5 from $\pi$ bonding).

**9.65** A C atom may form, at most, four hybrid orbitals ($sp^3$). The minimum number is two, for example, the $sp$ hybrid orbitals used by carbon in CO. Carbon has only four valence orbitals, so it cannot form more than four hybrid orbitals.

**9.67** (a) C, $sp^2$; N (predicted based on Lewis structure), $sp^3$

(b) The amide or peptide link has two resonance structures (shown here with formal charges on the O and N atoms). Structure B is less favorable, owing to the separation of charge.

$$\begin{array}{cc} :\overset{0}{\ddot{O}}: & :\ddot{O}:^- \\ \| & | \\ R-C \quad \ddot{N}-H & R-C \quad \overset{+}{N}-H \\ \quad\quad | & \quad\quad\quad \| \\ A \quad R & B \quad R \end{array}$$

(c) The fact that the amide link is planar indicates that structure B has some importance and that the N of the peptide linkage is $sp^2$ hybridized.

The principal sites of positive charge are the nitrogen in the amide linkage and the hydrogen of the —O—H group. The principal regions of negative charge are oxygen atoms and the nitrogen of the free —$NH_2$ group.

**9.69** MO theory is better to use when explaining or understanding the effect of adding energy to molecules. A molecule can absorb energy and an electron can thus be promoted to a higher level. Using MO theory, one can see how this can occur. Additionally, MO theory is a better model to use to predict whether a molecule is paramagnetic.

**9.71** Lowest energy = orbital C < orbital B < orbital A = highest energy

**9.73** B surrounded by three electron pairs: electron-pair geometry = molecular geometry = trigonal planar; hybridization = $sp^2$; formal charge = 0

B surrounded by four electron pairs; electron-pair geometry = molecular geometry = tetrahedral; hybridization = $sp^3$; formal charge = $-1$

**9.75** HF has a bond order of 1. $HF_2^-$ has a bond order of 1 for the entire three-center-four-electron bond and thus a 0.5 bond order per H—F linkage. It should therefore be easier to break the bond in $HF_2^-$, leading to a smaller bond enthalpy for $HF_2^-$ than for HF.

**9.77** (a) $BrF_5$
(b) square pyramidal molecular geometry; $sp^3d^2$ hybridization
(c) The square pyramidal structure is polar, so this is consistent with a dipole moment being present for the molecule.

**9.79** (a) empirical formula = $Br_2O$

$$:\ddot{Br}—\ddot{O}—\ddot{Br}:$$

The O should have $sp^3$ hybrid orbitals.
(b) 13 valence electrons; $(\sigma_s)^2(\sigma^*_s)^2(\pi_p)^4(\sigma_p)^2(\pi^*_p)^3$
$HOMO = \pi^*_p$

## Applying Chemical Principles: Probing Molecules with Photoelectron Spectroscopy

**1.** Metal

**3.** $\sigma_{2p}$

**5.** The 15.6 eV and 16.7 eV ejected electrons came from bonding orbitals. Removing an electron from a bonding orbital weakens the bond and thus results in a longer bond length. The 18.6 eV ejected electron comes from an antibonding orbital.

# Chapter 10

**10.1** Heptane

**10.3** $C_5H_{12}$ and $C_{14}H_{30}$ are alkanes.

**10.5** 3-Ethyl-2-methylhexane

CH₃—CH—CH—CH₂—CH₂—CH₃ with CH₃ and CH₂CH₃ substituents

2,3,3,4-Tetramethylpentane

CH₃—CH—C—CH—CH₃ with CH₃, CH₃, CH₃, and CH₃ substituents

Other possibilities include 2,2,3,4-tetramethylpentane, 3-ethyl-2,2-dimethylpentane, 3-ethyl-2,3-dimethylpentane, and 3-ethyl-2,4-dimethylpentane.

**10.7** 2,3-Dimethylbutane

**10.9** (a) 2,3-Dimethylhexane

CH₃—CH—CH—CH₂—CH₂—CH₃ with two CH₃ substituents

(b) 2,3-Dimethyloctane

CH₃—CH—CH—CH₂—CH₂—CH₂—CH₂—CH₃ with two CH₃ substituents

(c) 3-Ethylheptane

CH₃—CH₂—CH—CH₂—CH₂—CH₂—CH₃ with CH₂CH₃ substituent

(d) 3-Ethyl-2-methylhexane

CH₃—CH—CH—CH₂—CH₂—CH₃ with CH₂CH₃ and CH₃ substituents

**10.11**

H₃C—C(H)(CH₃)—CH₂CH₂CH₂CH₂CH₃   2-methylheptane

CH₃CH₂CH₂—C(H)(CH₃)—CH₂CH₂CH₃   4-methylheptane

CH₃CH₂—C*(H)(CH₃)—CH₂CH₂CH₂CH₃   3-methylheptane. The C atom with an asterisk is chiral.

**10.13** Chair form of cyclohexane:

Axial hydrogens are shown in red; equatorial hydrogens are shown in blue.

**10.15**

CH₃CH₂CH₂—C(H)(CH₂CH₃)—CH₂CH₂CH₃   4-ethylheptane. The compound is not chiral.

CH₃CH₂—C(H)(CH₂CH₃)—CH₂CH₂CH₂CH₃   3-ethylheptane. Not chiral.

**10.17** $C_4H_{10}$, butane: a low-molar-mass fuel gas at room temperature and pressure. Slightly soluble in water.

$C_{12}H_{26}$, dodecane: a colorless liquid at room temperature. Expected to be insoluble in water but quite soluble in nonpolar solvents.

**10.19**

H₃C, CH₃ CH—CH₂CH₃    *cis*-4-methyl-2-hexene

C=C with H, H   *(structure)*

*cis*-4-methyl-2-hexene

*(structure)* *trans*-4-methyl-2-hexene

**10.21** (a)

1-pentene

2-methyl-2-butene

2-methyl-1-butene

*cis*-2-pentene

3-methyl-1-butene

*trans*-2-pentene

(b) H₂C—CH₂ / H₂C, CH₂ / CH₂

cyclopentane

**10.23** (a) 1,2-Dibromopropane, CH₃CHBrCH₂Br

(b) Pentane, C₅H₁₂

**10.25** The three alkenes are 1-butene, *cis*-2-butene, and *trans*-2-butene. The reaction with 1-butene is shown below:

C=C (H, H / H, CH₂CH₃) + HBr ⟶ CH₃CHCH₂CH₃ (with Br)

**10.27** Four isomers are possible.

*cis*-1-chloropropene

2-chloropropene

*trans*-1-chloropropene

3-chloro-1-propene

**10.29**

Hydrogenation is often carried out in the presence of a metal catalyst (Pt, Pd, Rh). Hydrogenation is often carried out in the food industry to convert liquid oils to solids and to make them less susceptible to spoilage.

**10.31**

*m*-dichlorobenzene          *p*-bromotoluene

**10.33**

⟶ CH₃CH₂Cl/AlCl₃ ⟶ ethylbenzene

**10.35**

CH₃Cl/AlCl₃ ⟶ 1,2,4-trimethylbenzene

**10.37** (a) 1-Propanol, primary

(b) 1-Butanol, primary

(c) 2-Methyl-2-propanol, tertiary

(d) 2-Methyl-2-butanol, tertiary

**10.39** (a) Ethylamine, CH₃CH₂NH₂

(b) Dipropylamine, (CH₃CH₂CH₂)₂NH

CH₃CH₂CH₂—N—CH₂CH₂CH₃ (H)

(c) Butyldimethylamine

CH₃CH₂CH₂CH₂—N—CH₃ (CH₃)

(d) Triethylamine

CH₃CH₂—N—CH₂CH₃ (CH₂CH₃)

**10.41** (a) 1-Butanol, CH₃CH₂CH₂CH₂OH

(b) 2-Butanol

CH₃CH₂—C—CH₃ (OH / H)

(c) 2-Methyl-1-propanol

$$CH_3-\underset{\underset{CH_3}{|}}{\overset{\overset{H}{|}}{C}}-CH_2OH$$

(d) 2-Methyl-2-propanol

$$CH_3-\underset{\underset{CH_3}{|}}{\overset{\overset{OH}{|}}{C}}-CH_3$$

**10.43** (a) $C_6H_5NH_2(aq) + HCl(aq) \rightarrow (C_6H_5NH_3)Cl(aq)$
(b) $(CH_3)_3N(aq) + H_2SO_4(aq) \rightarrow$
$\qquad\qquad\qquad [(CH_3)_3NH]HSO_4(aq)$

**10.45** (a)

$$CH_3CH_2CH_2-\underset{\underset{CH_3}{|}}{\overset{\overset{CH_3}{|}\;\;\overset{O}{\|}}{CH}}-C-OH$$

(b)

$$CH_3CH_2-\underset{\underset{CH_3}{|}}{\overset{\overset{CH_3}{|}\;\;\overset{O}{\|}}{CH}}-C-CH_3$$

(c)

$$OH-\overset{O}{\overset{\|}{C}}-CH_2CH_2-\overset{O}{\overset{\|}{C}}-OH$$

(d)

$$NH_2CH_2CH_2-\overset{O}{\overset{\|}{C}}-OH$$

**10.47**

$$CH_3-\overset{O}{\overset{\|}{C}}-CH_2CH_2CH_3$$

$$H-\overset{O}{\overset{\|}{C}}-CH_2CH_2CH_2CH_2CH_3$$

$$CH_3CH_2CH_2CH_2-\overset{O}{\overset{\|}{C}}-OH$$

**10.49** (a) Acid, 3-methylpentanoic acid
(b) Ester, methyl propanoate
(c) Ester, butyl acetate (or butyl ethanoate)
(d) Acid, p-bromobenzoic acid

**10.51** (a) Pentanoic acid

$$CH_3CH_2CH_2CH_2-\overset{O}{\overset{\|}{C}}-OH$$

(b) 2-Octanol

$$H_3C-\underset{\underset{H}{|}}{\overset{\overset{OH}{|}}{C}}-CH_2CH_2CH_2CH_2CH_2CH_3$$

**10.53** Step 1: Oxidize 1-propanol to propanoic acid.

$$CH_3CH_2-\underset{\underset{H}{|}}{\overset{\overset{H}{|}}{C}}-OH \xrightarrow{\text{oxidizing agent}} CH_3CH_2-\overset{O}{\overset{\|}{C}}-OH$$

Step 2: Combine propanoic acid and 1-propanol.

$$CH_3CH_2-\overset{O}{\overset{\|}{C}}-OH + CH_3CH_2-\underset{\underset{H}{|}}{\overset{\overset{H}{|}}{C}}-OH \xrightarrow{-H_2O}$$

$$CH_3CH_2-\overset{O}{\overset{\|}{C}}-O-CH_2CH_2CH_3$$

**10.55** Sodium acetate, $NaCH_3CO_2$, and 1-butanol, $CH_3CH_2CH_2CH_2OH$

**10.57** (a) Trigonal-planar
(b) 120°
(c) The molecule is chiral. There are four different groups around the carbon atom marked 2.
(d) The acidic H atom is the H attached to the $CO_2H$ (carboxyl) group.

**10.59**

$$CH_3CH_2CH_2\overset{O}{\overset{\|}{C}}NHCH_3$$

This compound is an amide.

$$CH_3CH_2CH_2CO_2H + CH_3NH_2 \rightarrow$$
$$CH_3CH_2CH_2CONHCH_3 + H_2O$$

**10.61** (a) Alcohol; (b) amide; (c) acid; (d) ester

**10.63** (a) Prepare polyvinyl acetate (PVA) from vinylacetate.

(b) Three units of PVA:

(c) Hydrolysis of polyvinyl acetate will yield polyvinyl alcohol.

**10.65** Illustrated here is a segment of a copolymer composed of two units of 1,1–dichloroethylene and two units of chloroethylene.

**10.67**

(a)

*cis* isomer     *trans* isomer

(b)

**10.69**

cyclohexane     methylcyclopentane

$CH_3CH{=}CHCH_2CH_2CH_3$

2-hexene
Other isomers are possible by
moving the double bond and
with a branched chain.

The three structures shown above are not chiral, but some chiral isomers do exist.

**10.71**

**10.73** (a)

(b)

**10.75**

$n\ HOCH_2CH_2OH + n\ HO{-}\overset{O}{\underset{}{C}}{-}\bigcirc{-}\overset{O}{\underset{}{C}}{-}OH \longrightarrow$

**10.77** (a) 2, 3-Dimethylpentane

(b) 3, 3-Diethylpentane

(c) 3-Ethyl-2-methylpentane

(d) 3-Ethylhexane

**10.79**

1,1-Dichloropropane

1,2-Dichloropropane

1,3-Dichloropropane

2,2-Dichloropropane

**10.81**

1,2,3-trimethylbenzene   1,2,4-trimethylbenzene   1,3,5-trimethylbenzene

**10.83** Replace the carboxylic acid group with an H atom.

**10.85** (a)

butane (not chiral)

(b)

**10.87**

(a)

$$H_2C-O-\overset{\overset{\displaystyle O}{\|}}{C}(CH_2)_{10}CH_3$$
$$HC-O-\overset{\overset{\displaystyle O}{\|}}{C}(CH_2)_{10}CH_3$$
$$H_2C-O-\overset{\overset{\displaystyle O}{\|}}{C}(CH_2)_{10}CH_3$$

(b)

$$H_2C-O-\overset{\overset{\displaystyle O}{\|}}{C}(CH_2)_{10}CH_3$$
$$HC-O-\overset{\overset{\displaystyle O}{\|}}{C}(CH_2)_{10}CH_3 \;+\; 3\,NaOH \longrightarrow$$
$$H_2C-O-\overset{\overset{\displaystyle O}{\|}}{C}(CH_2)_{10}CH_3$$

$$H_2C-OH$$
$$HC-OH \;+\; 3\left[\,CH_3(CH_2)_{10}\overset{\overset{\displaystyle O}{\|}}{C}O^-\,\right]Na^+$$
$$H_2C-OH$$

$$H_2C-O-\overset{\overset{\displaystyle O}{\|}}{C}(CH_2)_{10}CH_3$$
$$HC-O-\overset{\overset{\displaystyle O}{\|}}{C}(CH_2)_{10}CH_3 \;+\; 3\,CH_3OH \longrightarrow$$
$$H_2C-O-\overset{\overset{\displaystyle O}{\|}}{C}(CH_2)_{10}CH_3$$

$$H_2C-OH$$
$$HC-OH \;+\; 3\;CH_3(CH_2)_{10}\overset{\overset{\displaystyle O}{\|}}{C}OCH_2$$
$$H_2C-OH$$

**10.89**

add $H_2$ →

oxidize →

polymerize →

$CH_3CO_2H$ →

**10.91** (a)

2-bromopropane

(b)

2-methyl-2-butanol

(c)

The product is the same for parts (b) and (c).

**10.93** Compound (b), acetaldehyde, and (c), ethanol, produce acetic acid when oxidized.

**10.95** Cyclohexene, a cyclic alkene, will add $Br_2$ readily (to give $C_6H_{10}Br_2$).

Benzene, however, needs much more stringent conditions to react with bromine; then $Br_2$ will substitute for H atoms on benzene and not add to the ring.

**10.97** (a) The compound is either propanone, a ketone, or propanal, an aldehyde.

propanone
(a ketone)

propanal
(an aldehyde)

(b) The ketone will not undergo oxidation, but the aldehyde will be oxidized to the acid, $CH_3CH_2CO_2H$. Thus, the unknown is likely propanal.

(c) Propanoic acid

**10.99** 2-Propanol will react with an oxidizing agent such as $KMnO_4$ (to give the ketone), whereas methyl ethyl ether ($CH_3OC_2H_5$) will not react. In addition, the alcohol should be more soluble in water than the ether.

**10.101**

X = 3,3-dimethyl-1-pentene

↓ +H₂O

Y = 3,3-dimethyl-2-pentanol

oxidizing agent →

3,3-dimethyl-2-pentanone

**10.103**

methane — four single bonds

formaldehyde — one double bond and two single bonds

allene — two double bonds

H—C≡C—H  acetylene — one single bond and one triple bond

**10.105** (a) Cross-linking makes the material very rigid and inflexible.
   (b) The OH groups give the polymer a high affinity for water.
   (c) Hydrogen bonding allows the chains to form coils and sheets with high tensile strength.

**10.107** (a) Ethane enthalpy of combustion = −47.51 kJ/g
   Ethanol enthalpy of combustion = −26.82 kJ/g
   (b) The enthalpy change for the combustion of ethanol is less negative than for ethane, so partially oxidizing ethane to form ethanol decreases the amount of energy per gram available from the combustion of the substance.

**10.109** (a) Empirical formula, CHO
   (b) Molecular formula, $C_4H_4O_4$
   (c)

   (d) All four C atoms are $sp^2$ hybridized.
   (e) 120°

## Applying Chemical Principles: Biodiesel— An Attractive Fuel for the Future?

**1.** $C_{13}H_{27}CO_2CH_3(\ell) + 43/2\ O_2(g) \rightarrow$
$$15\ CO_2(g) + 15\ H_2O(g)$$

**3.** Hexadecane ($\Delta H° = −9951.2$ kJ/mol) provides more energy per mole of fuel than methyl myristate ($\Delta H° = −8759.1$ kJ/mol).

Hexadecane ($\Delta H° = −3.4 \times 10^4$ kJ/L) also provides more energy per liter of fuel than methyl myristate ($\Delta H° = −3.1 \times 10^4$ kJ/L).

## Chapter 11

**11.1** (a) 0.58 atm
   (b) 0.59 bar
   (c) 59 kPa

**11.3** (a) 0.754 bar
   (b) 650 kPa
   (c) 934 kPa

**11.5** $2.70 \times 10^2$ mm Hg

**11.7** 3.7 L

**11.9** 250 mm Hg

**11.11** $3.2 \times 10^2$ mm Hg

**11.13** 9.72 atm

**11.15** (a) 75 mL $O_2$
   (b) 150 mL $NO_2$

**11.17** 0.919 atm

**11.19** $V$ = 2.9 L

**11.21** $1.9 \times 10^6$ g He

**11.23** $3.7 \times 10^{-4}$ g/L

**11.25** 34.0 g/mol

**11.27** 57.5 g/mol

**11.29** Molar mass = 74.9 g/mol; $B_6H_{10}$

**11.31** 0.039 mol $H_2$; 0.096 atm; 73 mm Hg

**11.33** 170 g $NaN_3$

**11.35** 1.7 atm $O_2$

**11.37** 4.1 atm $H_2$; 1.6 atm Ar; total pressure = 5.7 atm

**11.39** (a) 0.30 mol halothane/1 mol $O_2$
   (b) $3.0 \times 10^2$ g halothane

**11.41** (a) $CO_2$ has the higher kinetic energy.
   (b) The root mean square speed of the $H_2$ molecules is greater than the root mean square speed of the $CO_2$ molecules.
   (c) The number of $CO_2$ molecules is greater than the number of $H_2$ molecules $[n(CO_2) = 1.8n(H_2)]$.
   (d) The mass of $CO_2$ is greater than the mass of $H_2$.

**11.43** Average speed of $CO_2$ molecule $= 3.65 \times 10^4$ cm/s

**11.45** Average speed increases (and molar mass decreases) in the order $CH_2F_2 < Ar < N_2 < CH_4$.

**11.47** (a) $F_2$ (38 g/mol) effuses faster than $CO_2$ (44 g/mol).
(b) $N_2$ (28 g/mol) effuses faster than $O_2$ (32 g/mol).
(c) $C_2H_4$ (28.1 g/mol) effuses faster than $C_2H_6$ (30.1 g/mol).
(d) $CFCl_3$ (137 g/mol) effuses faster than $C_2Cl_2F_4$ (171 g/mol).

**11.49** 36 g/mol

**11.51** $P$ from the van der Waals equation $= 26.0$ atm
$P$ from the ideal gas law $= 30.6$ atm

**11.53** (a) Standard atmosphere: 1 atm; 760 mm Hg; 101.325 kPa; 1.013 bar
(b) $N_2$ partial pressure: 0.780 atm; 593 mm Hg; 79.1 kPa; 0.791 bar
(c) $H_2$ pressure: 131 atm; $9.98 \times 10^4$ mm Hg; $1.33 \times 10^4$ kPa; 133 bar
(d) Air: 0.333 atm; 253 mm Hg; 33.7 kPa; 0.337 bar

**11.55** $T = 290.$ K or 17 °C

**11.57** $2\ C_4H_9SH(g) + 15\ O_2(g) \rightarrow$
$$8\ CO_2(g) + 10\ H_2O(g) + 2\ SO_2(g)$$
Total pressure $= 37.3$ mm Hg. Partial pressures: $CO_2 = 14.9$ mm Hg, $H_2O = 18.6$ mm Hg, and $SO_2 = 3.73$ mm Hg.

**11.59** 4 mol

**11.61** Ni is the limiting reactant; 1.31 g $Ni(CO)_4$

**11.63** (a, b) Sample 4 (He) has the largest number of molecules and sample 3 ($H_2$ at 27 °C and 760 mm Hg) has the fewest number of molecules.
(c) Sample 2 (Ar)

**11.65** 8.54 g $Fe(CO)_5$

**11.67** $S_2F_{10}$

**11.69** (a) 28.7 g/mol $\simeq$ 29 g/mol
(b) $X$ of $O_2 = 0.17$ and $X$ of $N_2 = 0.83$

**11.71** Molar mass $= 86.4$ g/mol. The gas is probably $ClO_2F$.

**11.73** (d) is not correct. The rate of effusion is really inversely proportional to the square root of a gas's molar mass.

**11.75** $1.3 \times 10^2$ g/mol

**11.77** $n(He) = 0.0128$ mol

**11.79** Weight percent $KClO_3 = 69.1\%$

**11.81** (a) $NO_2 < O_2 < NO$
(b) $P(O_2) = 75$ mm Hg
(c) $P(NO_2) = 150$ mm Hg

**11.83** $P(NH_3) = 69$ mm Hg and $P(F_2) = 51$ mm Hg
Pressure after reaction $= 17$ mm Hg

**11.85** At 20 °C, there is $7.8 \times 10^{-3}$ g $H_2O$/L. At 0 °C, there is $4.6 \times 10^{-3}$ g $H_2O$/L.

**11.87** The mixture contains 0.22 g $CO_2$ and 0.77 g CO.
$P(CO_2) = 0.22$ atm; $P(O_2) = 0.12$ atm; $P(CO) = 1.22$ atm

**11.89** The formula of the iron compound is $Fe(CO)_5$.

**11.91** (a) $P(B_2H_6) = 0.0160$ atm
(b) $P(H_2) = 0.0320$ atm, so $P_{total} = 0.0480$ atm

**11.93** Amount of $Na_2CO_3 = 0.00424$ mol
Amount of $NaHCO_3 = 0.00951$ mol
Amount of $CO_2$ produced $= 0.0138$ mol
Volume of $CO_2$ produced $= 0.343$ L

**11.95** Decomposition of 1 mol of $Cu(NO_3)_2$ should give 2 mol $NO_2$ and ½ mol of $O_2$. Total actual amount $= 4.72 \times 10^{-3}$ mol of gas.
(a) Average molar mass $= 41.3$ g/mol
(b) Mole fractions: $X(NO_2) = 0.666$ and $X(O_2) = 0.334$
(c) Amount of each gas: $3.13 \times 10^{-3}$ mol $NO_2$ and $1.57 \times 10^{-3}$ mol $O_2$. The ratio of these amounts is 1.99 mol $NO_2$/mol $O_2$. This is different from the 4 mol $NO_2$/mol $O_2$ ratio expected from the reaction.
(d) If some $NO_2$ molecules combine to form $N_2O_4$, the apparent mole fraction of $NO_2$ would be smaller than expected ($= 0.8$). As this is the case, it is apparent that some $N_2O_4$ has been formed (as is observed in the experiment).

**11.97** (a) M $= 138$ g/mol; the unknown compound is $P_2F_4$.
(b) M $= 1.4 \times 10^2$ g/mol; this is consistent with the result obtained in part (a).

**11.99** (a) 10.0 g of $O_2$ represents more molecules than 10.0 g of $CO_2$. Therefore, $O_2$ has the greater partial pressure.
(b) The average speed of the $O_2$ molecules is greater than the average speed of the $CO_2$ molecules.
(c) The gases are at the same temperature and so have the same average kinetic energy.

**11.101** (a) $P(C_2H_2) > P(CO)$
(b) There are more molecules in the $C_2H_2$ container than in the CO container.

**11.103** (a) Not a gas. A gas would expand to an infinite volume.
(b) Not a gas. A density of 8.2 g/mL is typical of a solid.
(c) Insufficient information
(d) Gas

**11.105** (a) There are more molecules of $H_2$ than atoms of He.
(b) The mass of He is greater than the mass of $H_2$.

**11.107** The speed of gas molecules is related to the square root of the absolute temperature, so a doubling of the temperature will lead to an increase of about $(2)^{1/2}$ or 1.4.

## Applying Chemical Principles: The Goodyear Blimp

**1.** 0.164 g/L

**3.** Mass of passengers + ballast = $5.75 \times 10^5$ g = 575 kg

## Chapter 12

**12.1** (a) Dipole–dipole interactions (and hydrogen bonds)
(b) Induced dipole–induced dipole forces
(c) Dipole–dipole interactions (and hydrogen bonds)

**12.3** (a) Induced dipole–induced dipole forces
(b) Induced dipole–induced dipole forces
(c) Dipole–dipole forces
(d) Dipole–dipole forces (and hydrogen bonding)

**12.5** The predicted order of increasing strength is $CH_4 < Ne < CO < CCl_4$. In this case, prediction agrees with reality. The boiling points are Ne $(-246 °C) < CO (-192 °C) < CH_4$ $(-162 °C) < CCl_4 (77 °C)$.

**12.7** (c) HF; (d) acetic acid; (f) $CH_3OH$

**12.9** (a) LiCl. The $Li^+$ ion is smaller than $Cs^+$ (Figure 7.12), which makes the ion–ion forces of attraction stronger in LiCl.
(b) $Mg(NO_3)_2$. The $Mg^{2+}$ ion is smaller than the $Na^+$ ion (Figure 7.12), and the magnesium ion has a 2+ charge (as opposed to 1+ for sodium). Both of these effects lead to stronger ion–ion forces of attraction in magnesium nitrate.
(c) $NiCl_2$. The nickel(II) ion has a larger charge than $Rb^+$ and is considerably smaller. Both effects mean that there are stronger ion–ion forces of attraction in nickel(II) chloride.

**12.11** $q = +90.1$ kJ

**12.13** (a) Water vapor pressure is about 150 mm Hg at 60 °C. (Appendix G gives a value of 149.4 mm Hg at 60 °C.)
(b) 600 mm Hg at about 93 °C
(c) At 70 °C, ethanol has a vapor pressure of about 520 mm Hg, whereas that of water is about 225 mm Hg.

**12.15** At 30 °C, the vapor pressure of ether is about 590 mm Hg. (This pressure requires 0.23 g of ether in the vapor phase at the given conditions, so there is sufficient ether in the flask.) At 0 °C, the vapor pressure is about 160 mm Hg, so some ether condenses when the temperature declines.

**12.17** (a) $O_2$ $(-183 °C)$ (bp of $N_2 = -196 °C$)
(b) $SO_2$ $(-10 °C)$ ($CO_2$ sublimes at $-78 °C$)
(c) HF $(+19.7 °C)$ (HI, $-35.6 °C$)
(d) $GeH_4$ $(-90.0 °C)$ ($SiH_4$, $-111.8 °C$)

**12.19** (a) $CS_2$, about 620 mm Hg; $CH_3NO_2$, about 80 mm Hg
(b) $CS_2$, induced dipole–induced dipole forces; $CH_3NO_2$, dipole–dipole forces
(c) $CS_2$, about 46 °C; $CH_3NO_2$, about 100 °C
(d) About 39 °C
(e) About 34 °C

**12.21** (a) 80.1 °C
(b) At about 48 °C, the liquid has a vapor pressure of 250 mm Hg.
The vapor pressure is 650 mm Hg at 75 °C.
(c) 33.5 kJ/mol (from slope of plot)

**12.23** No, CO cannot be liquefied at room temperature because the critical temperature is lower than room temperature.

**12.25** The layer of molecules on the surface of a liquid is harder to break through than the bulk liquid. The energy needed to break through this skin is the surface tension. An application of surface tension is that it is possible to float a paperclip on the surface of water, but if the paperclip breaks through the surface, it will sink. Surface tension results from intermolecular forces because molecules in the interior of a liquid interact through intermolecular forces with molecules all around them, but molecules on the surface have intermolecular forces only with molecules at or below the surface layer and thus feel a net inward force of attraction.

**12.27** This phenomenon results from capillary action. The water is attracted to —OH groups in the paper. As a result of these adhesive forces, some water molecules begin to move up the paper. Other water molecules remain in contact with these water molecules by means of cohesive forces. A stream of water molecules thus moves up the paper.

**12.29** $Ar < CO_2 < CH_3OH$

**12.31** $Li^+$ ions are smaller than $Cs^+$ ions (78 pm and 165 pm, respectively; see Figure 7.12). Thus, there will be a stronger attractive force between $Li^+$ ion and water molecules than between $Cs^+$ ions and water molecules.

**12.33** (a) 350 mm Hg
(b) Ethanol (lower vapor pressure at every temperature)
(c) 84 °C
(d) $CS_2$, 46 °C; $C_2H_5OH$, 78 °C; $C_7H_{16}$, 99 °C
(e) $CS_2$, gas; $C_2H_5OH$, gas; $C_7H_{16}$, liquid

**12.35** Molar enthalpy of vaporization increases with increasing intermolecular forces: $C_2H_6$ (14.69 kJ/mol; induced dipole) < HCl (16.15 kJ/mol; dipole) < $CH_3OH$ (35.21 kJ/mol, hydrogen bonds). (The molar enthalpies of vaporization here are given at the boiling point of the liquid.)

**12.37** $5.49 \times 10^{19}$ atoms/m$^3$

**12.39** (a) 70.3 °C

(b)

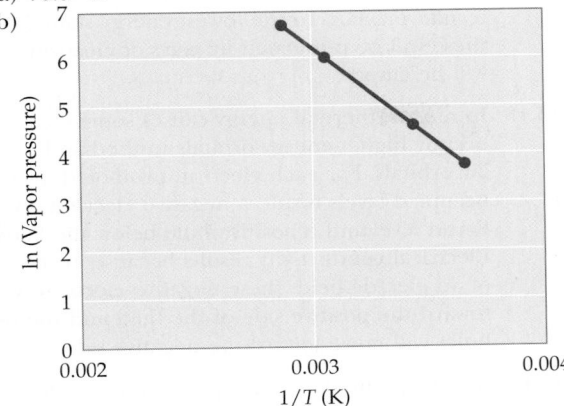

Using the equation for the straight line in the plot

$$\ln P = -3885\,(1/T) + 17.949$$

we calculate that $T = 312.6$ K (39.5 °C) when $P = 250$ mm Hg. When $P = 650$ mm Hg, $T = 338.7$ K (65.5 °C).

(c) Calculated $\Delta_{vap}H = 32.3$ kJ/mol

**12.41** (a) When the can is inverted in cold water, the water vapor pressure in the can, which was approximately 760 mm Hg, drops rapidly—say, to 9 mm Hg at 10 °C. This creates a partial vacuum in the can, and the can is crushed because of the difference in pressure inside the can and the pressure of the atmosphere pressing down on the outside of the can.

(b)

 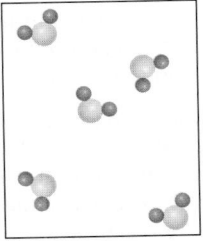

Before heating      After heating

**12.43** Acetone and water can interact by hydrogen bonding.

**12.45** Ethylene glycol's viscosity will be greater than ethanol's, owing to the greater hydrogen-bonding capacity of glycol.

**12.47** (a) Water has two OH bonds and two lone pairs, whereas the O atom of ethanol has only one OH bond (and two lone pairs). More extensive hydrogen bonding is likely for water.

(b) Water and ethanol interact extensively through hydrogen bonding, so the volume is expected to be slightly smaller than the sum of the two volumes.

**12.49** Two pieces of evidence for $H_2O(\ell)$ having considerable intermolecular attractive forces:

(a) Based on the boiling points of the Group 6A hydrides (Figure 12.6), the boiling point of water should be approximately −80 °C. The actual boiling point of 100 °C reflects the significant hydrogen bonding that occurs.

(b) Liquid water has a specific heat capacity that is higher than almost any other liquid. This reflects the fact that a relatively larger amount of energy is necessary to overcome intermolecular forces and raise the temperature of the liquid.

**12.51** (a) HI, hydrogen iodide

(b) The large iodine atom in HI leads to a significant polarizability for the molecule and thus to a large dispersion force.

(c) The dipole moment of HCl (1.07 D, Table 8.7) is larger than for HI (0.38 D).

(d) HI. See part (b).

**12.53** A gas can be liquefied at or below its critical temperature. The critical temperature for $CF_4$ (−45.7 °C) is below room temperature (25 °C), so it cannot be liquefied at room temperature.

**12.55** Hydrogen bonding is most likely at the O—H group at the "right" end of the molecule, and at the C=O and N—H groups in the amide group (—NH—CO—).

**12.57** Boiling point, enthalpy of vaporization, volatility, surface tension

**12.59** The more branching in the hydrocarbons, the lower the boiling point. This implies weaker induced dipole–induced dipole forces. Greater branching results in a more compact shape with less surface area available for contact and therefore smaller induced dipole–induced dipole forces.

**12.61** $F_2 < Cl_2 < Br_2 < I_2$
$He < Ne < Ar < Kr < Xe$

Molar mass and boiling point correlate with these orders.

**12.63** The boiling point of the water in the pressure cooker is 121 °C.

**12.65** Using the equation of the line from Question 12.64, $P = 9.8$ atm.

**12.67** (a) There will be water in the tube in equilibrium with its vapor, but almost all of the water will be present as liquid water.

(b) 760. mm Hg

(c) 10.4 cm$^3$

(d) 0.0233 g $H_2O$

## Applying Chemical Principles: Chromatography

1.  (a) The 1,5-pentanediol is most attracted to the mobile phase. The primary attractive force is hydrogen bonding. Dipole–dipole forces and dispersion forces are also present.
    (b) The propyl ethyl ether is most attracted to the stationary phase by dispersion forces but there are also some dipole–induced dipole interactions.
    (c) The molecules will elute in the following order (first to last): 1,5-pentanediol, 1-pentanol, and propyl ethyl ether.

## Chapter 13

**13.1** Two possible unit cells are illustrated here. The simplest formula is $AB_8$.

 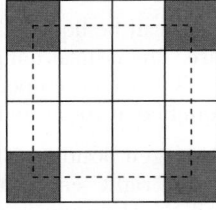

**13.3** $Ca^{2+}$ ions at eight corners = 1 net $Ca^{2+}$ ion

$O^{2-}$ ions in six faces = 3 net $O^{2-}$ ions

$Ti^{4+}$ ion in center of unit cell = 1 net $Ti^{4+}$ ion

Formula = $CaTiO_3$

**13.5** (a) There are eight $O^{2-}$ ions at the corners and one in the center for a net of two $O^{2-}$ ions per unit cell. There are four Cu ions in the interior in tetrahedral holes. The ratio of ions is $Cu_2O$.
    (b) The oxidation number of copper must be +1.

**13.7** Calcium atom radius = 197 pm

**13.9** There are three ways the edge dimensions can be calculated:
    (a) Calculate mass of unit cell ($= 1.103 \times 10^{-21}$ g/uc)

    Calculate volume of unit cell from mass ($= 3.53 \times 10^{-22}$ cm$^3$/uc)

    Calculate edge length from volume (= 707 pm)
    (b) Assume $I^-$ ions touch along the cell diagonal (◄ Check Your Understanding 13.1) and use $I^-$ radius to find the edge length. Radius $I^-$ = 220 pm

    Edge = $4(220 \text{ pm})/2^{1/2}$ = 622 pm
    (c) Assume the $I^-$ and $K^+$ ions touch along the cell edge (page 593)

    Edge = $2 \times I^-$ radius + $2 \times K^+$ radius = 706 pm

    Methods (a) and (c) agree. It is apparent that the sizes of the ions are such that the $I^-$ ions cannot touch along the cell diagonal.

**13.11** The 1000 2s orbitals will combine to form 1000 molecular orbitals. In the lowest energy state, 500 of these will be populated by pairs of electrons, and 500 will be empty.

**13.13** In metals, thermal energy causes some electrons to occupy higher-energy orbitals in the band of molecular orbitals. For each electron promoted, two singly occupied levels result: a negative electron above the Fermi level and a positive hole below the Fermi level. Electrical conductivity results because in the presence of an electric field, these negative electrons will move toward the positive side of the field and the positive holes will move toward the negative side.

**13.15** In carbon the band gap is too large for electrons to move up in energy from the valence band to the conduction band, whereas in silicon the band gap is small enough to permit this.

**13.17** An intrinsic semiconductor is one that naturally can have electrons move across the band gap, whereas an extrinsic semiconductor requires the addition of dopants in order for it to conduct.

**13.19** Increasing lattice energy: RbI < LiI < LiF < CaO

**13.21** As the ion–ion distance decreases, the force of attraction between ions increases. This should make the lattice more stable, and more energy should be required to melt the compound.

**13.23** $\Delta_f H° = -607$ kJ/mol

**13.25** (a) Eight C atoms per unit cell. There are eight corners (= 1 net C atom), six faces (= 3 net C atoms), and four internal C atoms
    (b) Face-centered cubic (fcc) with C atoms in the tetrahedral holes

**13.27** Type of solid: particles, forces of attraction
    (a) Metallic: metal atoms, metallic bonding
    (b) Ionic: ions, ion–ion interactions
    (c) Molecular: molecules, covalent bonds within the molecules and intermolecular forces between the molecules
    (d) Network: extended network of covalently bonded atoms, covalent bonds
    (e) Amorphous: covalently bonded networks with no long-range regularity, covalent bonds

**13.29** Substance: type of solid, particles, forces, property
    (a) Gallium arsenide: network, covalently bonded atoms, covalent bonds, semiconductor
    (b) Polystyrene: amorphous, covalent bonds within the polymer molecules and dispersion forces between the polymer molecules, thermal insulator
    (c) Silicon carbide: network, covalently bonded atoms, covalent bonds, very hard material
    (d) Perovskite: ionic, $Ca^{2+}$ and $TiO_3^{2-}$ ions, ion–ion interactions, high melting point

**13.31** $q$ (for fusion) = $-1.97$ kJ; $q$ (for melting) = $+1.97$ kJ

**13.33** (a) The density of liquid $CO_2$ is less than that of solid $CO_2$.

(b) $CO_2$ is a gas at 5 atm and 0 °C.

(c) Critical temperature = 31 °C, so $CO_2$ cannot be liquefied at 45 °C.

**13.35** $q$ (to heat the liquid) = $9.4 \times 10^2$ kJ

$q$ (to vaporize $NH_3$) = $1.6 \times 10^4$ kJ

$q$ (to heat the vapor) = $8.8 \times 10^2$ kJ

$q_{total}$ = $1.8 \times 10^4$ kJ

**13.37** $O_2$ phase diagram. (i) Note the slight positive slope of the solid–liquid equilibrium line. It indicates that the density of solid $O_2$ is greater than that of liquid $O_2$. (ii) Using the diagram here, the vapor pressure of $O_2$ at 77 K is between 150 and 200 mm Hg.

**13.39** Radius of silver = 145 pm

**13.41** $1.356 \times 10^{-8}$ cm (literature value is $1.357 \times 10^{-8}$ cm)

**13.43** Mass of 1 $CaF_2$ unit calculated from crystal data = $1.2963 \times 10^{-22}$ g. Divide molar mass of $CaF_2$ (78.077 g/mol) by mass of 1 $CaF_2$ to obtain Avogadro's number. Calculated value = $6.0230 \times 10^{23}$ $CaF_2$/mol.

**13.45** Diagram A leads to a surface coverage of 78.5%. Diagram B leads to 90.7% coverage.

**13.47** (a) The lattice can be described as an fcc lattice of Si atoms with Si atoms in one half of the tetrahedral holes.

(b) There are eight Si atoms in the unit cell.

Mass of unit cell = $3.731 \times 10^{-22}$ g

Volume of unit cell = $1.602 \times 10^{-22}$ cm³

Density = 2.329 g/cm³ (which is the same as the literature value)

In the Si unit cell we cannot assume the atoms touch along the edge or along the face diagonal. Instead, we know that the Si atoms in the tetrahedral holes are bonded to the Si atoms at the corner.

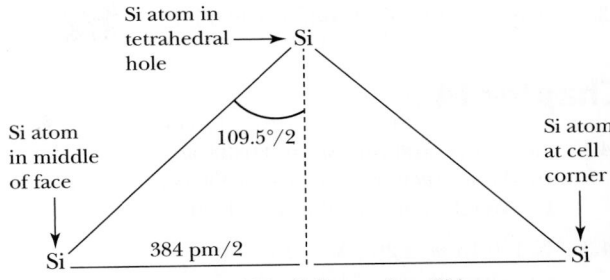

Distance = 1/2 (cell diagonal) = 384 pm

Distance across cell face diagonal = 768 pm

Sin (109.5°/2) = 0.817 = (384 pm/2)/(Si-Si distance)

Distance from Si in tetrahedral hole to face or corner Si = 235 pm

Si radius = 118 pm

Table 7.8 gives Si radius as 117 pm

**13.49** (a) $Mg^{2+}$ ions are in ⅛ of the eight possible tetrahedral holes, and $Al^{3+}$ ions are in ½ of the four available octahedral holes.

(b) $Fe^{2+}$ ions are in ⅛ of the eight possible tetrahedral holes, and $Cr^{3+}$ ions are in ½ of the four available octahedral holes.

**13.51** $8.5 \times 10^2$ nm

**13.53** Germanium has a smaller band gap, so it has a higher conductivity.

**13.55** Because boron is electron deficient in comparison to carbon, this is a p-type semiconductor.

**13.57** Lead sulfide has the same structure as sodium chloride, not the same structure as ZnS. There are four $Pb^{2+}$ ions and four $S^{2-}$ ions per unit cell, a 1:1 ratio that matches the compound formula.

**13.59** (a) $BBr_3(g) + PBr_3(g) + 3 H_2(g) \rightarrow BP(s) + 6 HBr(g)$

(b) If B atoms are in an fcc lattice, then the P atoms must be in ½ of the tetrahedral holes. (In this way it resembles Si in Question 13.47.)

(c) Unit cell volume = $1.092 \times 10^{-22}$ cm³

Unit cell mass = $2.775 \times 10^{-22}$ g

Density = 2.54 g/cm³

(d) The solution to this problem is identical to Question 13.47. In the BP lattice, the cell face diagonal is 676 pm. Therefore, the calculated BP distance is 207 pm.

**13.61** Assuming the spheres are packed in an identical way, the water levels are the same. A face-centered cubic lattice, for example, uses 74% of the available space, regardless of the sphere size.

## Applying Chemical Principles: Tin Disease

**1.** β-Tin has four atoms in the unit cell. α-Tin has eight atoms in the unit cell.

**3.** The length of each side is 649.0 pm.

## Chapter 14

**14.1** (a) Concentration $(m)$ = 0.0434 $m$
(b) Mole fraction of acid = 0.000781
(c) Weight percent of acid = 0.509%

**14.3** NaI: 0.15 $m$; 2.2%; $X$ = $2.7 \times 10^{-3}$
$CH_3CH_2OH$: 1.1 $m$; 5.0%; $X$ = 0.020
$C_{12}H_{22}O_{11}$: 0.15 $m$; 4.9%; $X$ = $2.7 \times 10^{-3}$

**14.5** 2.65 g $Na_2CO_3$; $X(Na_2CO_3)$ = $3.59 \times 10^{-3}$

**14.7** 220 g glycerol; 5.7 $m$

**14.9** 16.2 $m$; 37.1%

**14.11** Molality = $2.6 \times 10^{-5}$ $m$ (assuming that 1 kg of seawater is equivalent to 1 kg of solvent)

**14.13** (b) and (c)

**14.15** $\Delta_{soln}H°$ for LiCl = −36.9 kJ/mol. This is an exothermic enthalpy of solution, as compared with the very slightly endothermic value for NaCl.

**14.17** Above about 40 °C the solubility increases with temperature; therefore, add more NaCl and raise the temperature.

**14.19** $2 \times 10^{-3}$ g $O_2$

**14.21** 1130 mm Hg or 1.49 bar

**14.23** 35.0 mm Hg

**14.25** $X(H_2O)$ = 0.869; 16.7 mol glycol; 1040 g glycol

**14.27** Calculated boiling point = 84.2 °C

**14.29** $\Delta T_{bp}$ = 0.808 °C; solution boiling point = 62.51 °C

**14.31** Molality = 8.60 $m$; 28.4%

**14.33** Molality = 0.195 $m$; $\Delta T_{fp}$ = fp = −0.362 °C

**14.35** (a) $\Delta T_{fp}$ = −0.348 °C; fp = −0.348 °C
(b) $\Delta T_{bp}$ = +0.0959 °C; bp = 100.0959 °C
(c) Π = 4.58 atm

The osmotic pressure is large and can be measured with a small experimental error.

**14.37** Molar mass = $6.0 \times 10^3$ g/mol

**14.39** Molar mass = 360 g/mol; $C_{20}H_{16}Fe_2$

**14.41** Molar mass = 150 g/mol

**14.43** Molar mass = 170 g/mol

**14.45** Freezing point = −24.6 °C

**14.47** 0.08 $m$ $CaCl_2$ < 0.1 $m$ NaCl < 0.04 $m$ $Na_2SO_4$ < 0.1 sugar

**14.49** (a) $BaCl_2(aq)$ + $Na_2SO_4(aq)$ →
$$BaSO_4(s) + 2 NaCl(aq)$$
(b) Initially, the $BaSO_4$ particles form a colloidal suspension.
(c) Over time, the particles of $BaSO_4(s)$ grow and precipitate.

**14.51** Molar mass = 110 g/mol

**14.53** (a) Increase in vapor pressure of water
0.20 $m$ $Na_2SO_4$ < 0.50 $m$ sugar < 0.20 $m$ KBr < 0.35 $m$ ethylene glycol
(b) Increase in boiling point
0.35 $m$ ethylene glycol < 0.20 $m$ KBr < 0.50 $m$ sugar < 0.20 $m$ $Na_2SO_4$

**14.55** (a) 0.456 mol DMG and 11.4 mol ethanol; $X$(DMG) = 0.0385
(b) 0.869 $m$
(c) VP ethanol over the solution at 78.4 °C = 730.7 mm Hg
(d) bp = 79.5 °C

**14.57** For ammonia: 23 $m$; $X(NH_3)$ = 0.29; 28%

**14.59** 0.592 g $Na_2SO_4$

**14.61** (a) 0.20 $m$ KBr; (b) 0.10 $m$ $Na_2CO_3$

**14.63** Freezing point = −11 °C

**14.65** $4.0 \times 10^2$ g/mol

**14.67** $4.7 \times 10^{-4}$ mol/kg

**14.69** (a) Molar mass = $4.9 \times 10^4$ g/mol
(b) $\Delta T_{fp}$ = $-3.8 \times 10^{-4}$ °C

**14.71** $\Delta_{soln}H°$ [$Li_2SO_4$] = −28.0 kJ/mol
$\Delta_{soln}H°$ [LiCl] = −36.9 kJ/mol
$\Delta_{soln}H°$ [$K_2SO_4$] = +23.7 kJ/mol
$\Delta_{soln}H°$ [KCl] = +17.2 kJ/mol

Both lithium compounds have exothermic enthalpies of solution, whereas both potassium compounds have endothermic values. Consistent with this is the fact that lithium salts (LiCl) are often more water-soluble than potassium salts (KCl) (see Figure 14.11).

**14.73** $X$(benzene in solution) = 0.67 and $X$(toluene in solution) = 0.33

$$P_{total} = P_{toluene} + P_{benzene} = 7.3 \text{ mm Hg} + 50. \text{ mm Hg} = 57 \text{ mm Hg}$$

$$X(\text{toluene in vapor}) = \frac{7.3 \text{ mm Hg}}{57 \text{ mm Hg}} = 0.13$$

$$X(\text{benzene in vapor}) = \frac{50. \text{ mm Hg}}{57 \text{ mm Hg}} = 0.87$$

**14.75** $i$ = 1.7. That is, there is 1.7 mol of ions in solution per mole of compound.

**14.77** (a) Calculate the number of moles of ions in $10^6$ g $H_2O$: 550. mol $Cl^-$; 470. mol $Na^+$; 53.1 mol $Mg^{2+}$; 9.42 mol $SO_4^{2-}$; 10.3 mol $Ca^{2+}$; 9.72 mol $K^+$; 0.84 mol $Br^-$. Total moles of ions = $1.103 \times 10^3$ per $10^6$ g water. This gives $\Delta T_{fp}$ of $-2.05$ °C.
(b) $\Pi = 27.0$ atm. This means that a minimum pressure of 27 atm would have to be used in a reverse osmosis device.

**14.79** (a) $i = 2.06$
(b) There are approximately two particles in solution, so $H^+ + HSO_4^-$ best represents $H_2SO_4$ in aqueous solution.

**14.81** Mass of $N_2O$ = 0.53 g; concentration = $1.1 \times 10^3$ ppm

**14.83** The best method would be to shine a laser through the liquid and look for the Tyndall effect. Some other properties of colloids that could be utilized are that the dispersed material in a colloid will either not crystallize or crystallize only with difficulty and will either not diffuse across a membrane or do so much more slowly than a true solute.

**14.85** The calculated molality at the freezing point of benzene is 0.47 $m$, whereas it is 0.99 $m$ at the boiling point. A higher molality at the higher temperature indicates more molecules are dissolved. Therefore, assuming benzoic acid forms dimers like acetic acid (Figure 12.7), dimer formation is more prevalent at the lower temperature. In this process two molecules become one entity, lowering the number of separate species in solution and lowering the molality.

**14.87** Molar mass in benzene = $1.20 \times 10^2$ g/mol; molar mass in water = 62.4 g/mol. The actual molar mass of acetic acid is 60.1 g/mol. In benzene, the molecules of acetic acid form "dimers." That is, two molecules form a single unit through hydrogen bonding. See Figure 12.7 on page 556.

**14.89** (a) Molar mass = 97.6 g/mol; empirical formula, $BF_2$, and molecular formula, $B_2F_4$
(b)

**14.91** The strength of the interactions goes inversely with the size of the ion. Thus, $Be^{2+}$ is most strongly hydrated, and $Ca^{2+}$ is least strongly hydrated.

**14.93** Colligative properties depend on the number of ions or molecules in solution. Each mole of $CaCl_2$ provides 1.5 times as many ions as each mole of NaCl.

**14.95** Benzene is a nonpolar solvent. Thus, ionic substances such as $NaNO_3$ and $NH_4Cl$ will certainly not dissolve. However, naphthalene is also nonpolar and resembles benzene in its structure; it should dissolve very well. (A chemical handbook gives a solubility of 33 g naphthalene per 100 g benzene.) Diethyl ether is weakly polar but is miscible to some extent with benzene.

Water is a polar solvent. The ionic compounds, $NaNO_3$ and $NH_4Cl$, are both soluble in water ($NaNO_3$ solubility (at 25 °C) = 91 g per 100 g water; $NH_4Cl$ solubility (at 25 °C) = 40 g per 100 g water. The slightly polar compound diethyl ether is soluble to a small extent in water (about 6 g per 100 g water at 25 °C). Nonpolar naphthalene is not soluble in water (solubility at 25 °C = 0.003 g per 100 g water).

**14.97** The C—C and C—H bonds in hydrocarbons are nonpolar or weakly polar and tend to make such dispersions hydrophobic (water-hating). The C—O and O—H bonds in starch present opportunities for hydrogen bonding with water. Hence, starch is expected to be more hydrophilic.

**14.99** [NaCl] = 1.0 M and $[KNO_3]$ = 0.88 M. The $KNO_3$ solution has a higher solvent concentration, so solvent will flow from the $KNO_3$ solution to the NaCl solution.

**14.101** (a) $X(C_2H_5OH)$ = 0.051; $X(H_2O)$ = 0.949
(b) $P(C_2H_5OH)$ over mixture = 38 mm Hg; $P°(H_2O)$ calculated by linear interpolation using the vapor pressures at 78 °C and 79 °C = 334.2 mm Hg; $P(H_2O)$ over mixture = 317 mm Hg
(c) $X(C_2H_5OH)$ = 0.11; $X(H_2O)$ = 0.89
(d) The mole fraction of ethanol increased from 0.051 to 0.11, a factor of 2.2 times. Weight percent of $C_2H_5OH$ = 24%

**14.103** The molality of the 5.00% NaCl solution is 0.901 $m$. Assuming no dissociation, this leads to $\Delta T_{fp}$(calculated) = $-1.68$ °C and $i$ = 1.82. The molality of the 5.00% $Na_2SO_4$ solution is 0.371 $m$, $\Delta T_{fp}$(calculated) = $-0.689$ °C, and $i$ = 1.97. These values are consistent with the trends seen in Table 14.4. As the concentration of the ionic solute increases, the value of $i$ continues to decrease for both solutes, and rate of decrease is falling for both solutes. In the case of NaCl, this value is leveling off quite a bit. In the case of $Na_2SO_4$, it is continuing to decrease by significant amounts. Interestingly, the value of $i$ for $Na_2SO_4$ has now fallen below 2 and is getting closer to that for NaCl.

**14.105** This does not lend credence to this story. The reported lowest temperature for a NaCl solution corresponds to a temperature of 2.372 °F. The temperature of 0 °F is still below this.

## Applying Chemical Principles: Distillation

1. $X(hexane)$ = 0.59

3. Mass percent (hexane) = 18%

# Chapter 15

**15.1** (a) $-\dfrac{1}{2}\dfrac{\Delta[O_3]}{\Delta t} = \dfrac{1}{3}\dfrac{\Delta[O_2]}{\Delta t}$

(b) $-\dfrac{1}{2}\dfrac{\Delta[HOF]}{\Delta t} = \dfrac{1}{2}\dfrac{\Delta[HF]}{\Delta t} = \dfrac{\Delta[O_2]}{\Delta t}$

**15.3** $\dfrac{1}{3}\dfrac{\Delta[O_2]}{\Delta t} = -\dfrac{1}{2}\dfrac{\Delta[O_3]}{\Delta t}$ or $\dfrac{\Delta[O_2]}{\Delta t} = -\dfrac{2}{3}\dfrac{\Delta[O_2]}{\Delta t}$

so $\Delta[O_3]/\Delta t = -1.0 \times 10^{-3}$ mol/L · s.

**15.5** (a) The graph of [B] (product concentration) versus time shows [B] increasing from zero. The line is curved, indicating the rate changes with time; thus the rate depends on concentration. Rates for the four 10-s intervals are as follows: 0–10 s, 0.0326 mol/L · s; from 10–20 s, 0.0246 mol/L · s; 20–30 s, 0.0178 mol/L · s; 30–40 s, 0.0140 mol/L · s.

(b) $-\dfrac{\Delta[A]}{\Delta t} = \dfrac{1}{2}\dfrac{\Delta[B]}{\Delta t}$ throughout the reaction

In the interval 10–20 s, $\dfrac{\Delta[A]}{\Delta t} = -0.0123 \dfrac{mol}{L \cdot s}$

(c) Instantaneous rate when [B] = 0.750 mol/L

$= \dfrac{\Delta[B]}{\Delta t} = 0.0163 \dfrac{mol}{L \cdot s}$

**15.7** The reaction is second order in A, first order in B, and third order overall.

**15.9** (a) Rate = $k[NO_2][O_3]$
(b) If $[NO_2]$ is tripled, the rate triples.
(c) If $[O_3]$ is halved, the rate is halved.

**15.11** (a) The reaction is second order in [NO] and first order in $[O_2]$.

(b) Rate = $1/2 \dfrac{-\Delta[NO]}{\Delta t} = k[NO]^2[O_2]$

(c) $k = 13$ L²/mol² · s

(d) Rate = $1.4 \times 10^{-5}$ mol/L · s

(e) When $-\Delta[NO]/\Delta t = 1.0 \times 10^{-4}$ mol/L · s, $\Delta[O_2]/\Delta t = 5.0 \times 10^{-5}$ mol/L · s and $\Delta[NO_2]/\Delta t = 1.0 \times 10^{-4}$ mol/L · s.

**15.13** (a) Rate = $-(1/2)\Delta[NO]/\Delta t = k[NO]^2[O_2]$
(b) 25. L²/mol² · h
(c) Rate = $8.5 \times 10^{-9}$ mol/L · h

**15.15** $k = 3.73 \times 10^{-3}$ min⁻¹

**15.17** $5.0 \times 10^2$ min

**15.19** (a) 153 min
(b) 1790 min

**15.21** 97 s

**15.23** 39 s

**15.25** (a) $t_{1/2}$ = 10,000 s (b) 34,000 s

**15.27** 1.87 g azomethane remains, 0.063 g $N_2$ formed

**15.29** Fraction of $^{64}$Cu remaining = 0.030

**15.31** The straight line obtained in a graph of $\ln[N_2O]$ versus time indicates a first-order reaction.

$k = (-\text{slope}) = 0.0127$ min⁻¹

The rate when $[N_2O]$ = 0.035 mol/L is $4.4 \times 10^{-4}$ mol/L · min.

**15.33** The graph of $1/[NO_2]$ versus time gives a straight line, indicating the reaction is second order with respect to $[NO_2]$ (see Table 15.1 on page 686). The slope of the line is $k$, so $k = 1.1$ L/mol · s.

**15.35** $-\Delta[C_2F_4]/\Delta t = k[C_2F_4]^2 = (0.04$ L/mol · s$)[C_2F_4]^2$

**15.37** Activation energy = 102 kJ/mol

**15.39** $k = 0.3$ s⁻¹

**15.41**

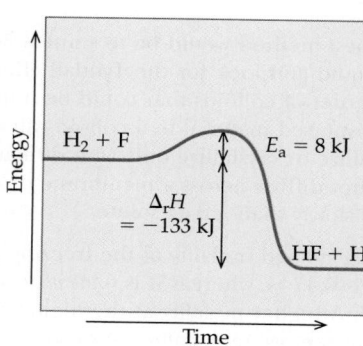

**15.43** (a) Rate = $k[NO_3][NO]$
(b) Rate = $k[Cl][H_2]$
(c) Rate = $k[(CH_3)_3CBr]$

**15.45** (a) The second step; (b) Rate = $k[O_3][O]$

**15.47** (a) $NO_2$ is a reactant in the first step and a product in the second step. CO is a reactant in the second step. $NO_3$ is an intermediate, and $CO_2$ is a product. NO is a product.
(b) Reaction coordinate diagram

**15.49** Doubling the concentration of A will increase the rate by a factor of 4 because the concentration of A appears in the rate law as $[A]^2$. Halving the concentration of B will halve the rate The net result is that the rate of the reaction will double.

**15.51** After measuring pH as a function of time, one could then calculate pOH and then $[OH^-]$. Finally, a plot of $1/[OH^-]$ versus time would give a straight line with a slope equal to $k$.

**15.53** 72 s represents two half-lives, so $t_{1/2} = 36$ s.

**15.55** (a) A plot of $1/[C_2F_4]$ versus time indicates the reaction is second order with respect to $[C_2F_4]$. The rate law is Rate $= k[C_2F_4]^2$.
(b) The rate constant ($=$ slope of the line) is about 0.045 L/mol · s. (The graph does not allow a very accurate calculation.)
(c) Using $k = 0.045$ L/mol · s, the concentration after 600 s is 0.03 M (to one significant figure).
(d) Time $= 2000$ s [using $k$ from part (b)].

**15.57** (a) A plot of $1/[NH_4NCO]$ versus time is linear, so the reaction is second order with respect to $NH_4NCO$.
(b) Slope $= k = 0.0109$ L/mol · min.
(c) $t_{1/2} = 200.$ min
(d) $[NH_4NCO] = 0.0997$ mol/L

**15.59** Mechanism 2

**15.61** $k = 0.0176$ h$^{-1}$ and $t_{1/2} = 39.3$ h

**15.63** (a) After 125 min, 0.251 g remains. After 145, 0.144 g remains.
(b) Time $= 43.9$ min
(c) Fraction remaining $= 0.016$

**15.65** The rate equation for the slow step is Rate $= k[O_3][O]$. The equilibrium constant, $K$, for step 1 is $K = [O_2][O]/[O_3]$. Solving this for $[O]$, we have $[O] = K[O_3]/[O_2]$. Substituting the expression for $[O]$ into the rate equation we find
Rate $= k[O_3]\{K[O_3]/[O_2]\} = kK[O_3]^2/[O_2]$

**15.67** The slope of the ln $k$ versus $1/T$ plot is $-6370$. From slope $= -E_a/R$, we derive $E_a = 53.0$ kJ/mol.

**15.69** Estimated time at 90 °C $= 4.76$ min

**15.71** After 30 min (one half-life), $P_{HOF} = 50.0$ mm Hg and $P_{total} = 125.0$ mm Hg. After 45 min, $P_{HOF} = 35.4$ mm Hg and $P_{total} = 132$ mm Hg.

**15.73** (a) Reaction is first order in $NO_2NH_2$ and $-1$ for $H_3O^+$. In a buffered solution, $[H_3O]^+$ is constant, so the reaction has an apparent order of 1.
(b, c) Mechanism 3
In step 1, $K = k_4/k_4'$ $= [NO_2NH^-][H_3O^+]/[NO_2NH_2]$
Rearrange this and substitute into the rate law for the slow step.
Rate $= k_5[NO_2NH^-] = k_5K[NO_2NH_2]/[H_3O^+]$
This is the same as the experimental rate law, where the overall rate constant $k = k_5K$.
(d) Addition of OH$^-$ ions will shift the equilibrium in step 1 (by reacting with $H_3O^+$) to produce a larger concentration of $NO_2NH^-$, the reactant in the rate-determining step.

**15.75** (a) Average rate for $t = 0$ to $t = 15$ is about $4.7 \times 10^{-5}$ M/s. For $t = 100$ s to 125 s, the average rate is about $1.6 \times 10^{-5}$ M/s. The rate slows because the rate of the reaction is dependent on the concentration of reactant and this concentration is declining with time.
(b) Instantaneous rate at 50 s is about $2.7 \times 10^{-5}$ M/s.
(c) A plot of ln (concentration) versus time is a straight line with an equation of $y = -0.010x - 5.2984$. The slope, which is equal to $-k$, is $-0.010$, so $k = 0.010$ s$^{-1}$.
(d) From the data the half-life is 69.3 s, and the same value comes from the relation $t_{1/2} = \ln 2/k$.

**15.77** A plot of 1/Rate versus 1/[S] gives the equation
$1/\text{Rate} = 94 \, (1/[S]) + 7.5 \times 10^4$
so Rate$_{max} = 1/(7.5 \times 10^4)$ $= 1.3 \times 10^{-5}$ M min$^{-1}$.

**15.79** The finely divided rhodium metal will have a significantly greater surface area than the small block of metal. This leads to a large increase in the number of reaction sites and vastly increases the reaction rate.

**15.81** (a) False. The reaction may occur in a single step but this does not have to be true.
(b) True
(c) False. Raising the temperature increases the value of $k$.
(d) False. Temperature has no effect on the value of $E_a$.
(e) False. If the concentrations of both reactants are doubled, the rate will increase by a factor of 4.
(f) True

**15.83** (a) True
(b) True
(c) False. As a reaction proceeds, the reactant concentration decreases and the rate decreases.
(d) False. It is possible to have a one-step mechanism for a third-order reaction if the slow, rate-determining step is termolecular.

**15.85** (a) Decrease (d) No change
(b) Increase (e) No change
(c) No change (f) No change

**15.87** (a) There are three mechanistic steps.
(b) The overall reaction is exothermic.

## Applying Chemical Principles: Kinetics and Mechanisms: A 70-Year-Old Mystery Solved

1. (a) 207 kJ/mol photons
(b) 792 nm

3. The probability of three particles colliding simultaneously with the correct geometry for a successful reaction is low.

# Chapter 16

**16.1**  (a) $K = \dfrac{[H_2O]^2[O_2]}{[H_2O_2]^2}$

(b) $K = \dfrac{[CO_2]}{[CO][O_2]^{1/2}}$

(c) $K = \dfrac{[CO]^2}{[CO_2]}$

(d) $K = \dfrac{[CO_2]}{[CO]}$

**16.3**  $Q = (2.0 \times 10^{-8})^2/(0.020) = 2.0 \times 10^{-14}$
$Q < K$, so the reaction proceeds to the right.

**16.5**  $Q = 1.0 \times 10^3$, so $Q > K$ and the reaction is not at equilibrium. It proceeds to the left to convert products to reactants.

**16.7**  $K = 1.2$

**16.9**  (a) $K = 0.025$
(b) $K = 0.025$
(c) The amount of solid does not affect the equilibrium.

**16.11**  (a) $[COCl_2] = 0.00308$ M; $[CO] = 0.0071$ M
(b) $K = 140$

**16.13**  [isobutane] = 0.024 M; [butane] = 0.010 M

**16.15**  $[I_2] = 6.14 \times 10^{-3}$ M; $[I] = 4.79 \times 10^{-3}$ M

**16.17**  $[COBr_2] = 0.107$ M; $[CO] = [Br_2] = 0.143$ M
57.1% of the $COBr_2$ has decomposed.

**16.19**  (b)

**16.21**  (e) $K_2 = 1/(K_1)^2$

**16.23**  $K = 13.7$

**16.25**  (a) Equilibrium shifts to the right
(b) Equilibrium shifts to the left
(c) Equilibrium shifts to the right
(d) Equilibrium shifts to the left

**16.27**  Equilibrium concentrations are the same under both circumstances: [butane] = 1.1 M and [isobutane] = 2.9 M.

**16.29**  $K = 3.9 \times 10^{-4}$

**16.31**  For decomposition of $COCl_2$, $K = 1/(K$ for $COCl_2$ formation$) = 1/(6.5 \times 10^{11}) = 1.5 \times 10^{-12}$

**16.33**  $K = 4$

**16.35**  $Q$ is less than $K$, so the system shifts to form more isobutane.

At equilibrium, [butane] = 0.86 M and [isobutane] = 2.14 M.

**16.37**  The second equation has been reversed and multiplied by 2.
(c) $K_2 = 1/K_1^2$

**16.39**  (a) No change   (d) Shifts right
(b) Shifts left   (e) Shifts right
(c) No change

**16.41**  (a) The equilibrium will shift to the left on adding more $Cl_2$.
(b) $K$ is calculated (from the quantities of reactants and products at equilibrium) to be 0.0470. After $Cl_2$ is added, the concentrations are: $[PCl_5] = 0.0199$ M, $[PCl_3] = 0.0231$ M, and $[Cl_2] = 0.0403$ M.

**16.43**  $K_p = 0.215$

**16.45**  (a) Fraction dissociated = 0.15
(b) Fraction dissociated = 0.189. If the pressure decreases, the equilibrium shifts to the right, increasing the fraction of $N_2O_4$ dissociated.

**16.47**  $[NH_3] = 0.67$ M; $[N_2] = 0.57$ M; $[H_2] = 1.7$ M; $P_{total} = 180$ atm

**16.49**  (a) $[NH_3] = [H_2S] = 0.013$ M
(b) $[NH_3] = 0.027$ M and $[H_2S] = 0.0067$ M

**16.51**  $P(NO_2) = 0.37$ atm and $P(N_2O_4) = 0.96$ atm; $P$(total) = 1.33 atm

**16.53**  (a) $K_p = K_c = 56$. Because 2 mol of reactant gases gives 2 mol of product gases, $\Delta n$ does not change and $K_p = K_c$ (◀ page 726).
(b, c) Initial $P(H_2) = P(I_2) = 2.6$ atm and $P_{total} = 5.2$ atm

At equilibrium, $P(H_2) = P(I_2) = 0.54$ atm and $P(HI) = 4.1$ atm. Therefore, $P_{total} = 5.2$ atm. The initial total pressure and the equilibrium total pressure are the same owing to the reaction stoichiometry. Percent dissociation = 69%

**16.55**  $P(CO) = 0.0010$ atm

**16.57**  $1.7 \times 10^{18}$ O atoms

**16.59**  Glycerin concentration should be 1.7 M

**16.61**  (a) $K_p = 0.20$
(b) When initial $[N_2O_4] = 1.00$ atm, the equilibrium pressures are $[N_2O_4] = 0.80$ atm and $[NO_2] = 0.40$ atm. When initial $[N_2O_4] = 0.10$ atm, the equilibrium pressures are $[N_2O_4] = 0.050$ atm and $[NO_2] = 0.10$ atm. The percent dissociation is now 50.%. This is in accord with Le Chatelier's principle: If the initial pressure of the reactant is smaller, the equilibrium shifts to the right, increasing the fraction of the reactant dissociated. [This might be clearer if you imagine beginning with the equilibrium system in the case when the initial pressure of $N_2O_4$ was 1.00 atm and then increasing the volume tenfold (obtaining the same equilibrium system as starting with 0.10 atm $N_2O_4$). Le Chatelier's principle predicts a shift in the direction that has a greater number of gas molecules. See also Question 16.45.]

**16.63** (a) The flask containing $(H_3N)B(CH_3)_3$ will have the largest partial pressure of $B(CH_3)_3$.
(b) $P[B(CH_3)_3] = P(NH_3) = 2.1$ and $P[(H_3N)B(CH_3)_3] = 1.0$ atm

$P_{total} = 5.2$ atm

Percent dissociation = 69%

**16.65** (a) As more KSCN is added, Le Chatelier's principle predicts more of the red complex ion $[Fe(H_2O)_5(SCN)]^+$ will form.
(b) Adding $Ag^+$ ions leads to a precipitate of AgSCN, thus removing $SCN^-$ ions from solution. The equilibrium shifts left, dropping the concentration of the red complex ion.

**16.67** (a) False. The magnitude of $K$ is always dependent on temperature.
(b) True
(c) False. The equilibrium constant for a reaction is the reciprocal of the value of $K$ for its reverse.
(d) True
(e) False. $\Delta n = 1$, so $K_p = K_c(RT)$

**16.69** (a) Product-favored, $K >> 1$
(b) Reactant-favored, $K << 1$
(c) Product-favored, $K >> 1$

**16.71** Begin with an equilibrium system containing $^{14}N_2$, $H_2$, and $^{14}NH_3$. Introduce some $^{15}N_2$ and allow the system to equilibrate. The presence of $^{15}NH_3$ indicates that the forward reaction has occurred. In addition, the presence of $^{15}N^{14}N$ indicates that the reverse reaction has occurred. Further evidence of the reverse reaction occurring could be obtained by carrying out another trial in which $^{15}NH_3$ is added to the initial equilibrium mixture. The presence of $^{15}N^{14}N$ or $^{15}N_2$ indicates that the reverse reaction is occurring. (A similar set of experiments could be run using $^2H$ instead of $^{15}N$.)

## Applying Chemical Principles: Trivalent Carbon

1. (a) Concentration (molality) = $-0.542$ °C/$-5.12$ °C/$m$ = 0.106 mol dimer/kg benzene
Amount dimer = (0.106 mol dimer/kg benzene)(0.0100 kg benzene) = $1.06 \times 10^{-3}$ mol dimer
Molar mass of dimer = 0.503 g/$1.06 \times 10^{-3}$ mol = 475 g/mol
(b) Each molecule of the dimer that decomposes produces two monomer particles, increasing the total number of moles of particles in solution. When the mass of the dimer is divided by the moles of particles, the calculated molar mass is too low.

3. [Monomer] = 0.0045 M, [dimer] = 0.0503 M

5. (b) Triphenylmethyl radical

# Chapter 17

**17.1** (a) $CN^-$, cyanide ion
(b) $SO_4^{2-}$, sulfate ion
(c) $F^-$, fluoride ion

**17.3** (a) $H_3O^+(aq) + NO_3^-(aq)$; $H_3O^+(aq)$ is the conjugate acid of $H_2O$, and $NO_3^-(aq)$ is the conjugate base of $HNO_3$.
(b) $H_3O^+(aq) + SO_4^{2-}(aq)$; $H_3O^+(aq)$ is the conjugate acid of $H_2O$, and $SO_4^{2-}(aq)$ is the conjugate base of $HSO_4^-$.
(c) $H_2O + HF$; $H_2O$ is the conjugate base of $H_3O^+$, and HF is the conjugate acid of $F^-$.

**17.5** Brønsted acid: $HC_2O_4^-(aq) + H_2O(\ell) \rightleftharpoons H_3O^+(aq) + C_2O_4^{2-}(aq)$

Brønsted base: $HC_2O_4^-(aq) + H_2O(\ell) \rightleftharpoons H_2C_2O_4(aq) + OH^-(aq)$

**17.7**

| | Acid (A) | Base (B) | Conjugate Base of A | Conjugate Acid of B |
|---|---|---|---|---|
| (a) | $HCO_2H$ | $H_2O$ | $HCO_2^-$ | $H_3O^+$ |
| (b) | $H_2S$ | $NH_3$ | $HS^-$ | $NH_4^+$ |
| (c) | $HSO_4^-$ | $OH^-$ | $SO_4^{2-}$ | $H_2O$ |

**17.9** $[H_3O^+] = 1.8 \times 10^{-4}$ M; acidic

**17.11** HCl is a strong acid, so $[H_3O^+]$ = concentration of the acid. $[H_3O^+] = 0.0075$ M and $[OH^-] = 1.3 \times 10^{-12}$ M. pH = 2.12.

**17.13** $Ba(OH)_2$ is a strong base, so $[OH^-] = 2 \times$ concentration of the base.
$[OH^-] = 3.0 \times 10^{-3}$ M; pOH = 2.52; and pH = 11.48

**17.15** (a) The strongest acid is $HCO_2H$ (largest $K_a$) and the weakest acid is $C_6H_5OH$ (smallest $K_a$).
(b) The strongest acid ($HCO_2H$) has the weakest conjugate base.
(c) The weakest acid ($C_6H_5OH$) has the strongest conjugate base.

**17.17** (c) HClO, the weakest acid in this list (Table 17.3), has the strongest conjugate base.

**17.19** $CO_3^{2-}(aq) + H_2O(\ell) \rightarrow HCO_3^-(aq) + OH^-(aq)$

**17.21** Highest pH, $Na_2S$; lowest pH, $AlCl_3$ (which gives the weak acid $[Al(H_2O)_6]^{3+}$ in solution)

**17.23** $pK_a = 4.19$

**17.25** $K_a = 3.0 \times 10^{-10}$; in Table 17.3, this acid falls between hexaaquairon(II) ion and the hydrogen carbonate ion.

**17.27** 2-Chlorobenzoic acid is the stronger acid; it has the smaller $pK_a$ value.

**17.29** $K_b = 7.1 \times 10^{-12}$

**17.31** $K_b = 6.3 \times 10^{-5}$

**17.33** $CH_3CO_2H(aq) + HCO_3^-(aq) \rightleftharpoons$
$$CH_3CO_2^-(aq) + H_2CO_3(aq)$$
Equilibrium lies predominantly to the right because $CH_3CO_2H$ is a stronger acid than $H_2CO_3$.

**17.35** (a) Left; $NH_3$ and HBr are the stronger base and acid, respectively.
(b) Left; $PO_4^{3-}$ and $CH_3CO_2H$ are the stronger base and acid, respectively.
(c) Right; $[Fe(H_2O)_6]^{3+}$ and $HCO_3^-$ are the stronger acid and base, respectively.

**17.37** (a) $OH^-(aq) + HPO_4^{2-}(aq) \rightleftharpoons$
$$H_2O(\ell) + PO_4^{3-}(aq)$$
(b) $OH^-$ is a stronger base than $PO_4^{3-}$, so the equilibrium will lie to the right.

**17.39** (a) $CH_3CO_2H(aq) + HPO_4^{2-}(aq) \rightleftharpoons$
$$CH_3CO_2^-(aq) + H_2PO_4^-(aq)$$
(b) $CH_3CO_2H$ is a stronger acid than $H_2PO_4^-$, so the equilibrium will lie to the right.

**17.41** (a) $2.1 \times 10^{-3}$ M; (b) $K_a = 3.5 \times 10^{-4}$

**17.43** $K_b = 6.6 \times 10^{-9}$

**17.45** (a) $[H_3O^+] = 1.6 \times 10^{-4}$ M
(b) Moderately weak; $K_a = 1.1 \times 10^{-5}$

**17.47** $[CH_3CO_2^-] = [H_3O^+] = 1.9 \times 10^{-3}$ M and $[CH_3CO_2H] = 0.20$ M

**17.49** $[H_3O^+] = [CN^-] = 3.2 \times 10^{-6}$ M; $[HCN] = 0.025$ M; pH = 5.50

**17.51** $[NH_4^+] = [OH^-] = 1.6 \times 10^{-3}$ M; $[NH_3] = 0.15$ M; pH = 11.22

**17.53** $[OH^-] = 0.010$ M; pH = 12.01; pOH = 1.99

**17.55** pH = 3.25

**17.57** $[H_3O^+] = 1.1 \times 10^{-5}$ M; pH = 4.98

**17.59** $[HCN] = [OH^-] = 3.3 \times 10^{-3}$ M; $[H_3O^+] = 3.0 \times 10^{-12}$ M; $[Na^+] = 0.441$ M

**17.61** $[H_3O^+] = 1.5 \times 10^{-9}$ M; pH = 8.81

**17.63** (a) The reaction produces acetate ion, the conjugate base of acetic acid. The solution is weakly basic. pH is greater than 7.
(b) The reaction produces $NH_4^+$, the conjugate acid of $NH_3$. The solution is weakly acidic. pH is less than 7.
(c) The reaction mixes equal molar amounts of strong base and strong acid. The solution will be neutral. pH will be 7.

**17.65** (a) pH = 1.17; (b) $[SO_3^{2-}] = 6.2 \times 10^{-8}$ M

**17.67** (a) $[OH^-] = [N_2H_5^+] = 9.2 \times 10^{-5}$ M; $[N_2H_6^{2+}] = 8.9 \times 10^{-16}$ M
(b) pH = 9.96

**17.69** HOCN should be a stronger acid than HCN because the H atom in HOCN is attached to the more electronegative O atom. The electron attachment enthalpy of OCN is thus more negative than that of CN, thus stabilizing the conjugate base that forms and making the ionization of HOCN more product-favored.

**17.71** The S atom is surrounded by four highly electronegative O atoms. These help stabilize the conjugate base that needs to form so that the negative charge is more readily accepted.

**17.73** (a) Lewis base
(b) Lewis acid
(c) Lewis base (owing to lone pair of electrons on the N atom)

**17.75** CO is a Lewis base in its reactions with transition metal atoms. It donates a lone pair of electrons on the C atom.

**17.77** pH = 2.671

**17.79** Both $Ba(OH)_2$ and $Sr(OH)_2$ dissolve completely in water to provide $M^{2+}$ and $OH^-$ ions. 2.50 g $Sr(OH)_2$ in 1.00 L of water gives $[Sr^{2+}] = 0.021$ M and $[OH^-] = 0.041$ M. The concentration of $OH^-$ is reflected in a pH of 12.61.

**17.81** $H_2S(aq) + CH_3CO_2^-(aq) \rightleftharpoons$
$$CH_3CO_2H(aq) + HS^-(aq)$$
The equilibrium lies to the left and favors the reactants.

**17.83** $[X^-] = [H_3O^+] = 3.0 \times 10^{-3}$ M; [HX] = 0.007 M; pH = 2.52

**17.85** $K_a = 1.4 \times 10^{-5}$; $pK_a = 4.86$

**17.87** pH = 5.84

**17.89** (a) Ethylamine is a stronger base than ethanolamine.
(b) For ethylamine, the pH of the solution is 11.82.

**17.91** pH = 7.66

**17.93** Acidic: $NaHSO_4$, $NH_4Br$, $FeCl_3$
Neutral: $KClO_4$, $NaNO_3$, LiBr
Basic: $Na_2CO_3$, $(NH_4)_2S$, $Na_2HPO_4$
Highest pH: $(NH_4)_2S$, lowest pH: $NaHSO_4$

**17.95** $K_{net} = K_{a1} \times K_{a2} = 3.8 \times 10^{-6}$

**17.97** For the reaction $HCO_2H(aq) + OH^-(aq) \rightarrow$ $H_2O(\ell) + HCO_2^-(aq)$, $K_{net} =$ $K_a$ (for $HCO_2H$) $\times [1/K_w] = 1.8 \times 10^{10}$

**17.99** To double the percent ionization, you must dilute 100 mL of solution to 400 mL.

**17.101** $H_2O > H_2C_2O_4 > HC_2O_4^- = H_3O^+ > C_2O_4^{2-} > OH^-$

**17.103** Measure the pH of 0.1 M solutions of the three bases. The solution containing the strongest base will have the highest pH. The solution having the weakest base will have the lowest pH.

**17.105** The possible cation–anion combinations are NaCl (neutral), NaOH (basic), $NH_4Cl$ (acidic), $NH_4OH$ (basic), HCl (acidic), and $H_2O$ (neutral).
A = $H^+$ solution; B = $NH_4^+$ solution; C = $Na^+$ solution; Y = $Cl^-$ solution; Z = $OH^-$ solution

**17.107** $K_a = 3.0 \times 10^{-5}$

**17.109** (a) Aniline is both a Brønsted and a Lewis base. As a proton acceptor it gives $C_6H_5NH_3^+$. The N atom can also donate an electron pair to give a Lewis acid–base adduct, $F_3B \leftarrow NH_2C_6H_5$.
(b) pH = 7.97

**17.111** Water can both accept a proton (a Brønsted base) and donate a lone pair (a Lewis base). Water can also donate a proton (Brønsted acid), but it cannot accept a pair of electrons (and act as a Lewis acid).

**17.113** (a) HOCl is the strongest acid (smallest $pK_a$ and largest $K_a$), and HOI is the weakest acid.
(b) Cl is more electronegative than Br or I, so the $OCl^-$ anion is more stable than the other two oxoanions.

**17.115** (a) $HClO_4 + H_2SO_4 \rightleftharpoons ClO_4^- + H_3SO_4^+$
(b) The O atoms on sulfuric acid have lone pairs of electrons that can be used to bind to an $H^+$ ion.

$$H-\overset{\displaystyle :\ddot{O}:}{\underset{\displaystyle :\ddot{O}:}{\ddot{O}-S-\ddot{O}}}-H$$

**17.117** (a) $\left[:\ddot{I}-\ddot{I}-\ddot{I}:\right]^-$
(b) $I^-(aq)$ [Lewis base] $+ I_2(aq)$ [Lewis acid] $\rightarrow$ $I_3^-(aq)$

**17.119** (a) For the weak acid HA, the concentrations at equilibrium are $[HA] = C_0 - \alpha C_0$, $[H_3O^+] = [A^-] = \alpha C_0$. Putting these into the usual expression for $K_a$ we have $K_a = \alpha^2 C_0/(1-\alpha)$.
(b) For 0.10 M $NH_4^+$, $\alpha = 7.5 \times 10^{-5}$ (reflecting the fact that $NH_4^+$ is a much weaker acid than acetic acid).

**17.121** (a) Add the three equations.
$NH_4^+(aq) + H_2O(\ell) \rightleftharpoons NH_3(aq) + H_3O^+(aq)$
$K_1 = K_w/K_b$
$CN^-(aq) + H_2O(\ell) \rightleftharpoons HCN(aq) + OH^-(aq)$
$K_2 = K_w/K_a$
$H_3O^+(aq) + OH^-(aq) \rightleftharpoons 2 H_2O(\ell)\ K_3 = 1/K_w$
$NH_4^+(aq) + CN^-(aq) \rightleftharpoons NH_3(aq) + HCN(aq)$
$K_{net} = K_1K_2K_3 = K_w/K_aK_b$
(b) The salts $NH_4CN$, $NH_4CH_3CO_2$, and $NH_4F$ have $K_{net}$ values of 1.4, $3.1 \times 10^{-5}$, and $7.7 \times 10^{-7}$, respectively. Only in the case of $NH_4CN$ is the base (the cyanide ion) strong enough to remove a proton from the ammonium ion and produce a significant concentration of products.
(c) $NH_4CN$: basic, $K_b$ of $CN^- > K_a$ of $NH_4^+$
$NH_4CH_3CO_2$: neutral, $K_b$ of $CH_3CO_2^- = K_a$ of $NH_4^+$
$NH_4F$: acidic, $K_b$ of $F^-$ is less than $K_a$ of $NH_4^+$

## Applying Chemical Principles: The Leveling Effect, Nonaqueous Solvents, and Superacids

**1.** $HClO_4$ ($K = 5 \times 10^{-6}$) > $H_2SO_4$ ($K = 2 \times 10^{-7}$) > HCl ($K = 2 \times 10^{-9}$)

**3.** $NH_2^-(aq) + H_2O(\ell) \rightleftharpoons NH_3(aq) + OH^-(aq)$
The reaction is product-favored at equilibrium.

**5.** (a) $2 NH_3 \rightleftharpoons NH_4^+ + NH_2^-$
(b) The strongest acid is $NH_4^+$; the strongest base is $NH_2^-$.
(c) HCl is a stronger acid than $NH_4^+$, so HCl will be completely ionized. The solution will be a strong conductor.
(d) $O^{2-} + NH_3 \rightleftharpoons OH^- + NH_2^-$
The reaction is product-favored at equilibrium.

## Chapter 18

**18.1** (a) Decrease pH; (b) increase pH; (c) no change in pH

**18.3** pH = 9.25

**18.5** pH = 4.38

**18.7** pH = 9.12; pH of buffer is lower than the pH of the original solution of $NH_3$(pH = 11.17).

**18.9** 4.7 g

**18.11** pH = 4.92

**18.13** (a) pH = 3.59; (b) $[HCO_2H]/[HCO_2^-] = 0.45$

**18.15** (b) $NH_3 + NH_4Cl$

**18.17** The buffer must have a ratio of 0.51 mol $NaH_2PO_4$ to 1 mol $Na_2HPO_4$. For example, dissolve 0.51 mol $NaH_2PO_4$ (61 g) and 1.0 mol $Na_2HPO_4$ (140 g) in some amount of water.

**18.19** (a) pH = 4.95; (b) pH = 5.05

**18.21** (a) pH = 9.55; (b) pH = 9.50

**18.23** (a) Original pH = 5.62
(b) $[Na^+] = 0.0323$ M, $[OH^-] = 1.5 \times 10^{-3}$ M, $[H_3O^+] = 6.5 \times 10^{-12}$ M, and $[C_6H_5O^-] = 0.0308$ M
(c) pH = 11.19

**18.25** (a) Original $NH_3$ concentration = 0.0154 M
(b) At the equivalence point $[H_3O^+] = 1.9 \times 10^{-6}$ M, $[OH^-] = 5.3 \times 10^{-9}$ M, $[NH_4^+] = 6.25 \times 10^{-3}$ M.
(c) pH at equivalence point = 5.73

**18.27** The titration curve begins at pH = 13.00 and drops slowly as HCl is added. Just before the equivalence point (when 30.0 mL of acid has been added), the curve falls steeply. The pH at the equivalence point is exactly 7. Just after the equivalence point, the curve flattens again and begins to approach the final pH of just over 1.0. The total volume at the equivalence point is 60.0 mL.

**18.29** (a) Starting pH = 11.12
  (b) pH at equivalence point = 5.28
  (c) pH at midpoint (half-neutralization point) = 9.25
  (d) Methyl red, bromcresol green
  (e)

| Acid (mL) | Added pH |
|-----------|----------|
| 5.00      | 9.85     |
| 15.0      | 9.08     |
| 20.0      | 8.65     |
| 22.0      | 8.39     |
| 30.0      | 2.04     |

**18.31** See Figure 18.10 on page 828.
  (a) Thymol blue or bromphenol blue
  (b) Phenolphthalein
  (c) Methyl red; thymol blue

**18.33** (a) Silver chloride, AgCl; lead(II) chloride, $PbCl_2$
  (b) Zinc carbonate, $ZnCO_3$; zinc sulfide, ZnS
  (c) Iron(II) carbonate, $FeCO_3$; iron(II) oxalate, $FeC_2O_4$

**18.35** (a) and (b) are soluble, (c) and (d) are insoluble.

**18.37** (a) $AgCN(s) \rightarrow Ag^+(aq) + CN^-(aq)$,
    $K_{sp} = [Ag^+][CN^-]$
  (b) $NiCO_3(s) \rightarrow Ni^{2+}(aq) + CO_3^{2-}(aq)$,
    $K_{sp} = [Ni^{2+}][CO_3^{2-}]$
  (c) $AuBr_3(s) \rightarrow Au^{3+}(aq) + 3 Br^-(aq)$,
    $K_{sp} = [Au^{3+}][Br^-]^3$

**18.39** $K_{sp} = (1.9 \times 10^{-3})^2 = 3.6 \times 10^{-6}$

**18.41** $K_{sp} = 4.37 \times 10^{-9}$

**18.43** $K_{sp} = 1.4 \times 10^{-15}$

**18.45** (a) $9.2 \times 10^{-9}$ M; (b) $2.2 \times 10^{-6}$ g/L

**18.47** (a) $2.4 \times 10^{-4}$ M; (b) 0.018 g/L

**18.49** Only $2.1 \times 10^{-4}$ g dissolves.

**18.51** (a) $PbCl_2$; (b) FeS; (c) $Fe(OH)_2$

**18.53** Solubility in pure water = $1.0 \times 10^{-6}$ mol/L; solubility in 0.010 M $SCN^-$ = $1.0 \times 10^{-10}$ mol/L

**18.55** (a) Solubility in pure water = $2.2 \times 10^{-6}$ mg/mL
  (b) Solubility in 0.020 M $AgNO_3$ = $1.0 \times 10^{-12}$ mg/mL

**18.57** (a) PbS
  (b) $Ag_2CO_3$
  (c) $Al(OH)_3$

**18.59** $Q < K_{sp}$, so no precipitate forms.

**18.61** $Q > K_{sp}$; $Zn(OH)_2$ will precipitate.

**18.63** $[OH^-]$ must exceed $1.0 \times 10^{-5}$ M.

**18.65** Using $K_{sp}$ for $Zn(OH)_2$ and $K_f$ for $[Zn(OH)_4]^{2-}$, $K_{net}$ for
$Zn(OH)_2(s) + 2 OH^-(aq) \rightleftharpoons [Zn(OH)_4]^{2-}(aq)$
is $1 \times 10^1$. This indicates that the reaction is definitely product-favored.

**18.67** $K_{net}$ for $AgCl(s) + 2 NH_3(aq) \rightleftharpoons [Ag(NH_3)_2]^+(aq) + Cl^-(aq)$ is $2.0 \times 10^{-3}$. When all the AgCl dissolves, $[Ag(NH_3)_2^+] = [Cl^-] = 0.050$ M. To achieve these concentrations, $[NH_3]$ must be 1.12 M. Therefore, the amount of $NH_3$ added must be $2 \times 0.050$ mol/L (to react with the AgCl) plus 1.12 mol/L (to achieve the proper equilibrium concentration). The total is 1.22 mol/L $NH_3$.

**18.69** (a) Solubility in pure water = $1.3 \times 10^{-5}$ mol/L or 0.0019 g/L.
  (b) $K_{net}$ for $AgCl(s) + 2 NH_3(aq) \rightleftharpoons [Ag(NH_3)_2]^+(aq) + Cl^-(aq)$ is $2.0 \times 10^{-3}$. When using 1.0 M $NH_3$, the concentrations of species in solution are $[Ag(NH_3)_2]^+ = [Cl^-] = 0.041$ M and so $[NH_3] = 1.0 - 2(0.041)$ M or about 0.9 M. The amount of AgCl dissolved is 0.041 mol/L or 5.88 g/L.

**18.71** (a) $NaBr(aq) + AgNO_3(aq) \rightarrow$
      $NaNO_3(aq) + AgBr(s)$
  (b) $2 KCl(aq) + Pb(NO_3)_2(aq) \rightarrow$
      $2 KNO_3(aq) + PbCl_2(s)$

**18.73** $Q > K_{sp}$, so $BaSO_4$ precipitates.

**18.75** $[H_3O^+] = 1.9 \times 10^{-10}$ M; pH = 9.73

**18.77** $BaCO_3 < Ag_2CO_3 < Na_2CO_3$

**18.79** Original pH = 8.62; dilution will not affect the pH.

**18.81** (a) 0.100 M acetic acid has a pH of 2.87. Adding sodium acetate slowly raises the pH.
  (b) Adding $NaNO_3$ to 0.100 M $HNO_3$ has no effect on the pH.
  (c) In part (a), adding the conjugate base of a weak acid creates a buffer solution. In part (b), $HNO_3$ is a strong acid, but its conjugate base ($NO_3^-$) is so weak that the base has no effect on the complete ionization of the acid.

**18.83** (a) pH = 4.13
  (b) 0.6 g of $C_6H_5CO_2H$
  (c) 8.2 mL of 2.0 M HCl should be added

**18.85** $K = 2.1 \times 10^6$; yes, AgI forms

**18.87** (a) $[F^-] = 1.3 \times 10^{-3}$ M
  (b) $[Ca^{2+}] = 2.9 \times 10^{-5}$ M

**18.89** (a) $PbSO_4$ will precipitate first.
  (b) $[Pb^{2+}] = 5.1 \times 10^{-6}$ M

**18.91** When $[CO_3^{2-}] = 0.050$ M, $[Ca^{2+}] = 6.8 \times 10^{-8}$ M. This means only $6.8 \times 10^{-4}$ % of the ions remain, or that essentially all of the calcium ions have been removed.

**18.93** (a) Add $H_2SO_4$, precipitating $BaSO_4$ and leaving $Na^+(aq)$ in solution.
  (b) Add HCl or another source of chloride ion. $PbCl_2$ will precipitate, but $NiCl_2$ is water-soluble.

**18.95** (a) $BaSO_4$ will precipitate first.
  (b) $[Ba^{2+}] = 1.8 \times 10^{-7}$ M

**18.97** (a) pH = 2.81
(b) pH at equivalence point = 8.72
(c) pH at the midpoint = $pK_a$ = 4.62
(d) Phenolphthalein
(e) After 10.0 mL, pH = 4.39.
After 20.0 mL, pH = 5.07.
After 30.0 mL, pH = 11.84.
(f) A plot of pH versus volume of NaOH added would begin at a pH of 2.81, rise slightly to the midpoint at pH = 4.62, and then begin to rise more steeply as the equivalence point is approached (when the volume of NaOH added is 27.0 mL). The pH rises vertically through the equivalence point, and then begins to level off above a pH of about 11.0.

**18.99** The $K_b$ value for ethylamine ($4.27 \times 10^{-4}$) is found in Appendix I.
(a) pH = 11.89
(b) Midpoint pH = 10.63
(c) pH = 10.15
(d) pH = 5.93 at the equivalence point
(e) pH = 2.13
(f) Titration curve

(g) Alizarin or bromcresol purple (see Figure 18.10)

**18.101** 110 mL NaOH

**18.103** Add dilute HCl, say 1 M HCl, to a solution of the salts. Both AgCl and $PbCl_2$ will precipitate, but $Cu^{2+}$ ions will stay in solution (as $CuCl_2$ is water-soluble). Decant off the copper-containing solution to leave a precipitate of white AgCl and $PbCl_2$. Lead(II) chloride ($K_{sp}$ = $1.7 \times 10^{-5}$) is much more soluble than AgCl ($K_{sp}$ = $1.8 \times 10^{-10}$). Warming the precipitates in water will dissolve the $PbCl_2$ and leave the AgCl as a white solid.

**18.105** $Cu(OH)_2$ will dissolve in a nonoxidizing acid such as HCl, whereas CuS will not.

**18.107** When $Ag_3PO_4$ dissolves slightly, it produces a small concentration of the phosphate ion, $PO_4^{3-}$. This ion is a strong base and hydrolyzes to $HPO_4^{2-}$. As this reaction removes the $PO_4^{3-}$ ion from equilibrium with $Ag_3PO_4$, the equilibrium shifts to the right, producing more $PO_4^{3-}$ and $Ag^+$ ions. Thus, $Ag_3PO_4$ dissolves to a greater extent than might be calculated from a $K_{sp}$ value (unless the $K_{sp}$ value was actually determined experimentally).

**18.109** (a) Base is added to increase the pH. The added base reacts with acetic acid to form more acetate ions in the mixture. Thus, the fraction of acid declines and the fraction of conjugate base rises (i.e., the ratio $[CH_3CO_2H]/[CH_3CO_2^-]$ decreases) as the pH rises.
(b) At pH = 4, acid predominates (85% acid and 15% acetate ions). At pH = 6, acetate ions predominate (95% acetate ions and 5% acid).
(c) At the point the lines cross, $[CH_3CO_2H]$ = $[CH_3CO_2^-]$. At this point pH = $pK_a$, so $pK_a$ for acetic acid is 4.74.

**18.111** (a) C—C—C angle, 120°; O—C=O, 120°; C—O—H, 109°; C—C—H, 120°
(b) Both the ring C atoms and the C in $CO_2H$ are $sp^2$ hybridized.
(c) $K_a$ = $1 \times 10^{-3}$
(d) 10%
(e) pH at half-way point = $pK_a$ = 3.0; pH at equivalence point = 7.3

## Applying Chemical Principles: Everything That Glitters

1. $2.9 \times 10^2$ mL

3. $[Au^+]$ = $1.1 \times 10^{-38}$ M. Yes, the conclusion is reasonable; less than one free $Au^+$ ion is present per liter of solution.

5. $2\ NaAu(CN)_2(aq) + Zn(s) \rightarrow 2\ Au(s) + Na_2Zn(CN)_4(aq)$

## Chapter 19

**19.1** (a) For a given substance at a given temperature, a gas always has a greater entropy than the liquid. Matter and energy are more dispersed.
(b) Liquid water at 50 °C
(c) Ruby
(d) One mole of $N_2$ at 1 bar

**19.3** (a) $\Delta_r S°$ = +12.7 J/K · mol-rxn. Entropy increases.
(b) $\Delta_r S°$ = −102.55 J/K · mol-rxn. Significant decrease in entropy.
(c) $\Delta_r S°$ = +93.3 J/K · mol-rxn. Entropy increases.
(d) $\Delta_r S°$ = −129.7 J/K · mol-rxn. The solution has a smaller entropy (with $H^+$ forming $H_3O^+$ and hydrogen bonding occurring) than HCl in the gaseous state.

**19.5** (a) $\Delta_r S°$ = +9.3 J/K · mol-rxn
(b) $\Delta_r S°$ = −293.97 J/K · mol-rxn

**19.7** (a) $\Delta_r S°$ = −507.3 J/K · mol-rxn; entropy declines as a gaseous reactant is incorporated in a solid compound.
(b) $\Delta_r S°$ = +313.25 J/K · mol-rxn; entropy increases as five molecules (three of them in the gas phase) form six molecules of products (all gases).

**19.9** $\Delta S°$(system) $= -134.18$ J/K · mol-rxn; $\Delta H°$(system) $= -662.75$ kJ/mol-rxn; $\Delta S°$(surroundings) $= +2222.9$ J/K · mol-rxn; $\Delta S°$(universe) $= +2088.7$ J/K · mol-rxn. The reaction is spontaneous under standard conditions.

**19.11** $\Delta S°$(system) $= +163.3$ J/K · mol-rxn; $\Delta H°$(system) $= +285.83$ kJ/mol-rxn; $\Delta S°$(surroundings) $= -958.68$ J/K · mol-rxn; $\Delta S°$(universe) $= -795.4$ J/K · mol-rxn

The reaction is not spontaneous because the overall entropy change in the universe is negative. The reaction is disfavored by energy dispersal.

**19.13** (a) Type 2. The reaction is enthalpy-favored but entropy-disfavored. It is more favorable at low temperatures.

(b) Type 4. This endothermic reaction is not favored by the enthalpy change nor is it favored by the entropy change. It is not spontaneous under standard conditions at any temperature.

**19.15** (a) $\Delta_r H° = -438$ kJ/mol-rxn; $\Delta_r S° = -201.7$ J/K · mol-rxn; $\Delta_r G° = -378$ kJ/mol-rxn. The reaction is product-favored at equilibrium and is enthalpy-driven.

(b) $\Delta_r H° = -86.61$ kJ/mol-rxn; $\Delta_r S° = -79.4$ J/K · mol-rxn; $\Delta_r G° = -62.9$ kJ/mol-rxn. The reaction is product-favored at equilibrium. The enthalpy change favors the reaction.

**19.17** (a) $\Delta_r H° = +116.7$ kJ/mol-rxn; $\Delta_r S° = +168.0$ J/K · mol-rxn; $\Delta_f G° = +66.6$ kJ/mol

(b) $\Delta_r H° = -425.93$ kJ/mol-rxn; $\Delta_r S° = -154.6$ J/K · mol-rxn; $\Delta_f G° = -379.82$ kJ/mol

(c) $\Delta_r H° = +17.51$ kJ/mol-rxn; $\Delta_r S° = +77.95$ J/K · mol-rxn; $\Delta_f G° = -5.73$ kJ/mol

The reactions in (b) and (c) are predicted to be spontaneous under standard conditions.

**19.19** (a) $\Delta_r G° = -817.54$ kJ/mol-rxn; product-favored
(b) $\Delta_r G° = +256.6$ kJ/mol-rxn; reactant-favored
(c) $\Delta_r G° = -1101.14$ kJ/mol-rxn; product-favored

**19.21** $\Delta_f G°$ [BaCO$_3$(s)] $= -1134.4$ kJ/mol

**19.23** (a) $\Delta_r H° = +66.2$ kJ/mol-rxn; $\Delta_r S° = -121.62$ J/K · mol-rxn; $\Delta_r G° = +102.5$ kJ/mol-rxn

Both the enthalpy and the entropy changes indicate the reaction is not spontaneous. There is no temperature at which it will become spontaneous. This is a case like that in the right panel in Figure 19.11 and is a Type 4 reaction (Table 19.1). As the temperature increases, the reaction becomes even more reactant-favored (the value of $\Delta_r G°$ becomes more positive).

(b) $\Delta_r H° = -221.05$ kJ/mol-rxn; $\Delta_r S° = +179.1$ J/K · mol-rxn; $\Delta_r G° = -283.99$ kJ/mol-rxn

The reaction is favored by both enthalpy and entropy and is product-favored at all temperatures. This is a case like that in the left panel in Figure 19.11 and is a Type 1 reaction. As the temperature increases, the reaction becomes even more product-favored (the value of $\Delta_r G°$ becomes more negative).

(c) $\Delta_r H° = -179.0$ kJ/mol-rxn; $\Delta_r S° = -160.2$ J/K · mol-rxn; $\Delta_r G° = -131.4$ kJ/mol-rxn

The reaction is favored by the enthalpy change but disfavored by the entropy change. The reaction becomes less product-favored as the temperature increases; it is a case like the line with a negative slope in the middle panel of Figure 19.11.

(d) $\Delta_r H° = +822.2$ kJ/mol-rxn; $\Delta_r S° = +181.28$ J/K · mol-rxn; $\Delta_r G° = +768.08$ kJ/mol-rxn

The reaction is not favored by the enthalpy change but favored by the entropy change. The reaction becomes more product-favored as the temperature increases; it is a case like the line with a positive slope in the middle panel of Figure 19.11.

**19.25** (a) $\Delta_r S° = +174.75$ J/K · mol-rxn; $\Delta_r H° = +116.94$ kJ/mol-rxn

(b) $\Delta_r G° = +64.87$ kJ/mol-rxn. The reaction is not spontaneous under standard conditions at 298 K.

(c) As the temperature increases, $\Delta_r S°$ becomes more important, so $\Delta_r G°$ can become negative at a sufficiently high temperature.

**19.27** $K = 6.8 \times 10^{-16}$. Note that $K$ is very small and that $\Delta G°$ is positive. Both indicate a process that is reactant-favored at equilibrium.

**19.29** $\Delta_r G° = -100.24$ kJ/mol-rxn and $K_p = 3.6 \times 10^{17}$. Both the free energy change and $K$ indicate a process that is product-favored at equilibrium.

**19.31** (a) HBr(g)
(b) NH$_4$Cl(aq)
(c) C$_2$H$_4$(g)
(d) NaCl(g)

**19.33** $\Delta_r G° = -98.9$ kJ/mol-rxn. The reaction is spontaneous under standard conditions and therefore product-favored at equilibrium. It is enthalpy-driven.

**19.35** $\Delta_r H° = -1428.66$ kJ/mol-rxn; $\Delta_r S° = +47.1$ J/K · mol-rxn; $\Delta S°$(universe) $= +4840$ J/K · mol-rxn. Combustion reactions are spontaneous, and this is confirmed by the sign of $\Delta S°$(universe).

**19.37** (a) The reaction occurs spontaneously and is product-favored. Therefore, $\Delta S°$(universe) is positive and $\Delta_r G°$ is negative. The reaction is likely to be exothermic, so $\Delta_r H°$ is negative, and $\Delta S°$(surroundings) is positive. $\Delta S°$(system) is expected to be negative because two moles of gas form one mole of solid. The calculated values are as follows:

$\Delta S°$(system) $= -284.2$ J/K · mol-rxn

$\Delta_r H° = -176.34$ kJ/mol-rxn

$\Delta S°$(surroundings) $= +591.45$ J/K · mol-rxn

$\Delta S°$(universe) $= +307.3$ J/K · mol-rxn

$\Delta_r G° = -91.64$ kJ/mol-rxn
(b) $K_p = 1.2 \times 10^{16}$

**19.39** $K_p = 1.3 \times 10^{29}$ at 298 K ($\Delta G° = -166.1$ kJ/mol-rxn). The reaction is already extremely product-favored at 298 K. A higher temperature would make the reaction less product-favored because $\Delta_r S°$ has a negative value ($-242.3$ J/K · mol-rxn).

**19.41** At the boiling point, $\Delta G° = 0 = \Delta H° - T\Delta S°$.

Here $\Delta S° = \Delta H°/T = 112$ J/K · mol-rxn at 351.15 K.

**19.43** $\Delta_r S°$ is $+137.2$ J/K · mol-rxn. A positive entropy change means that raising the temperature will increase the product favorability of the reaction (because $T\Delta S°$ will become more negative).

**19.45** The reaction is exothermic, so $\Delta_r H°$ should be negative. Also, a gas and an aqueous solution are formed, so $\Delta_r S°$ should be positive. The calculated values are $\Delta_r H° = -183.32$ kJ/mol-rxn (with a negative sign as expected) and $\Delta_r S° = -7.7$ J/K · mol-rxn

The entropy change is slightly negative, not positive as predicted. The reason for this is the negative entropy change upon dissolving NaOH. Apparently the $OH^-$ ions in water hydrogen-bond with water molecules, an effect that also leads to a small, negative entropy change.

**19.47** $\Delta_r H° = +126.03$ kJ/mol-rxn; $\Delta_r S° = +78.2$ J/K · mol-rxn; and $\Delta_r G° = +103$ kJ/mol-rxn. The reaction is not predicted to be spontaneous under standard conditions and therefore is not product-favored at equilibrium.

**19.49** $\Delta_r G°$ from $K$ value = 4.87 kJ/mol-rxn

$\Delta_r G°$ from free energies of formation = 4.73 kJ/mol-rxn

**19.51** $\Delta_r G° = -2.27$ kJ/mol-rxn

**19.53** (a) $\Delta_r G° = +141.82$ kJ/mol-rxn, so the reaction is not spontaneous.
(b) $\Delta_r H° = +197.86$ kJ/mol-rxn; $\Delta_r S° = +187.95$ J/K · mol-rxn

$T = \Delta_r H°/\Delta_r S° = 1052.7$ K or 779.6 °C
(c) $\Delta_r G°$ at 1500 °C (1773 K) = $-135.4$ kJ/mol-rxn

$K_p$ at 1500 °C = $1 \times 10^4$

**19.55** $\Delta_r S° = -459.0$ J/K · mol-rxn; $\Delta_r H° = -793$ kJ/mol-rxn;

$\Delta_r G° = -657$ kJ/mol-rxn

The reaction is spontaneous under standard conditions and therefore product-favored at equilibrium. It is enthalpy-driven.

**19.57** (a) $\Delta_r G°$ at 80.0 °C = $+0.14$ kJ/mol-rxn

$\Delta_r G°$ at 110.0 °C = $-0.12$ kJ/mol-rxn

Rhombic sulfur is more stable than monoclinic sulfur at 80 °C, but the reverse is true at 110 °C.
(b) $T = 370$ K or about 96 °C. This is the temperature at which the two forms are at equilibrium under standard conditions.

**19.59** $\Delta_r G°$ at 298 K = 22.64 kJ/mol; reaction is not product-favored at equilibrium.

It does become product-favored above 469 K (196 °C).

**19.61** $\Delta_f G°$ [HI(g)] = $-10.9$ kJ/mol

**19.63** (a) $\Delta_r G° = +194.8$ kJ/mol-rxn and $K = 6.68 \times 10^{-11}$
(b) The reaction is not spontaneous under standard conditions at 727 °C; it is reactant-favored at equilibrium.
(c) Keep the pressure of CO as low as possible (by removing it during the course of the reaction).

**19.65** $K_p = P_{Hg(g)}$ at any temperature

$K_p = 1$ at 620.3 K or 347.2 °C when $P_{Hg(g)} = 1.000$ bar

$T$ when $P_{Hg(g)} = (1/760)$ bar is 398.3 K or 125.2 °C.

**19.67** (a) True
(b) False. Whether an exothermic system is spontaneous also depends on the entropy change for the system.
(c) False. Reactions with $+ \Delta_r H°$ and $+ \Delta_r S°$ are spontaneous at higher temperatures.
(d) True

**19.69** Dissolving a solid such as NaCl in water is a spontaneous process. Thus, $\Delta G° < 0$. If $\Delta H° = 0$, then the only way the free energy change can be negative is if $\Delta S°$ is positive. Generally the entropy change is the important factor in forming a solution.

**19.71** $2 C_2H_6(g) + 7 O_2(g) \rightarrow 4 CO_2(g) + 6 H_2O(g)$
(a) Not only is this an exothermic combustion reaction, but there is also an increase in the number of molecules of gases from reactants to products. Therefore, we would predict a positive value for $\Delta S°$ for both the system and the surroundings and thus for the universe as well.
(b) The exothermic reaction has $\Delta_r H° < 0$. Combined with a positive $\Delta S°$(system), the value of $\Delta_r G°$ is negative.
(c) The value of $K_p$ is likely to be much greater than 1. Further, because $\Delta S°$(system) is positive, the value of $K_p$ will be even larger at a higher temperature. (See the left panel of Figure 19.11.)

**19.73** Reaction 1: $\Delta_r S_1° = -80.7$ J/K · mol-rxn

Reaction 2: $\Delta_r S_2° = -161.60$ J/K · mol-rxn

Reaction 3: $\Delta_r S_3° = -242.3$ J/K · mol-rxn

$\Delta_r S_1° + \Delta_r S_2° = \Delta_r S_3°$; entropy is a state function.

**19.75** (a) $\Delta_r H° = -352.88$ kJ/mol-rxn and $\Delta_r S° = +21.31$ J/K · mol-rxn. Therefore, at 298 K, $\Delta_r G° = -359.23$ kJ/mol-rxn.
(b) 4.84 g of Mg is required.

**19.77** (a) $N_2H_4(\ell) + O_2(g) \rightarrow 2\ H_2O(\ell) + N_2(g)$

$O_2$ is the oxidizing agent and $N_2H_4$ is the reducing agent.

(b) $\Delta_rH° = -622.29$ kJ/mol-rxn and $\Delta_rS° = +4.87$ J/K · mol-rxn. Therefore, at 298 K, $\Delta_rG° = -623.77$ kJ/mol-rxn.

(c) 0.0027 K

(d) 7.5 mol $O_2$

(e) $4.8 \times 10^3$ g solution

(f) 7.5 mol $N_2(g)$ occupies 170 L at 273 K and 1.0 atm of pressure.

**19.79** Iodine dissolves readily, so the process is spontaneous and $\Delta G°$ must be less than zero. Because $\Delta H° = 0$, the process is entropy-driven.

**19.81** $CH_3OH(g) \rightarrow C(s,\ graphite) + 2\ H_2(g) + 1/2\ O_2(g)$

(a) The spontaneity increases as temperature increases.

(b) There is no temperature between 400 K and 1000 K at which the decomposition is spontaneous.

**19.83** (a, b)

| Temperature (K) | $\Delta_rG°$ (kJ/mol) | $K$ |
|---|---|---|
| 298.0 K | −32.74 | $5.5 \times 10^5$ |
| 800.0 K | +72.9 | $2 \times 10^{-5}$ |
| 1300. K | +184.0 | $4.0 \times 10^{-8}$ |

(c) The largest mole fraction of $NH_3$ in an equilibrium mixture will be at 298 K.

## Applying Chemical Principles: Are Diamonds Forever?

1. C(diamond) → C(graphite)

(a) $\Delta_rG° = -2.900$ kJ/mol-rxn; $K = 3.22$

(b) $\Delta_rH° = -1.8$ kJ/mol-rxn; $\Delta_rS° = 3.2$ J/K · mol-rxn = 0.0032 kJ/K · mol; $\Delta_rG° = -5.0$ kJ/mol-rxn; $K = 1.8$

Though still favoring graphite, the equilibrium has shifted more toward diamond.

(c) Greater pressures favor the formation of diamond, which is more dense than graphite.

(d) The rate of reaction is negligibly slow at room temperature.

# Chapter 20

**20.1** (a) $Cr(s) \rightarrow Cr^{3+}(aq) + 3\ e^-$

Cr is a reducing agent; this is an oxidation reaction.

(b) $AsH_3(g) \rightarrow As(s) + 3\ H^+(aq) + 3\ e^-$

$AsH_3$ is a reducing agent; this is an oxidation reaction.

(c) $VO_3^-(aq) + 6\ H^+(aq) + 3\ e^- \rightarrow$
$$V^{2+}(aq) + 3\ H_2O(\ell)$$

$VO_3^-(aq)$ is an oxidizing agent; this is a reduction reaction.

(d) $2\ Ag(s) + 2\ OH^-(aq) \rightarrow$
$$Ag_2O(s) + H_2O(\ell) + 2e^-$$

Silver is a reducing agent; this is an oxidation reaction.

**20.3** (a) $Ag(s) \rightarrow Ag^+(aq) + e^-$

$e^- + NO_3^-(aq) + 2\ H^+(aq) \rightarrow NO_2(g) + H_2O(\ell)$

$Ag(s) + NO_3^-(aq) + 2\ H^+(aq) \rightarrow$
$$Ag^+(aq) + NO_2(g) + H_2O(\ell)$$

(b) $2[MnO_4^-(aq) + 8\ H^+(aq) + 5\ e^- \rightarrow$
$$Mn^{2+}(aq) + 4\ H_2O(\ell)]$$

$5[HSO_3^-(aq) + H_2O(\ell) \rightarrow$
$$SO_4^{2-}(aq) + 3\ H^+(aq) + 2\ e^-]$$

$2\ MnO_4^-(aq) + H^+(aq) + 5\ HSO_3^-(aq) \rightarrow$
$$2\ Mn^{2+}(aq) + 3\ H_2O(\ell) + 5\ SO_4^{2-}(aq)$$

(c) $4[Zn(s) \rightarrow Zn^{2+}(aq) + 2\ e^-]$

$2\ NO_3^-(aq) + 10\ H^+(aq) + 8\ e^- \rightarrow$
$$N_2O(g) + 5\ H_2O(\ell)$$

$4\ Zn(s) + 2\ NO_3^-(aq) + 10\ H^+(aq) \rightarrow$
$$4\ Zn^{2+}(aq) + N_2O(g) + 5\ H_2O(\ell)$$

(d) $Cr(s) \rightarrow Cr^{3+}(aq) + 3\ e^-$

$3\ e^- + NO_3^-(aq) + 4\ H^+(aq) \rightarrow$
$$NO(g) + 2\ H_2O(\ell)$$

$Cr(s) + NO_3^-(aq) + 4\ H^+(aq) \rightarrow$
$$Cr^{3+}(aq) + NO(g) + 2\ H_2O(\ell)$$

**20.5** (a) $2[Al(s) + 4\ OH^-(aq) \rightarrow Al(OH)_4^-(aq) + 3\ e^-]$

$3[2\ H_2O(\ell) + 2\ e^- \rightarrow H_2(g) + 2\ OH^-(aq)]$

$2\ Al(s) + 2\ OH^-(aq) + 6\ H_2O(\ell) \rightarrow$
$$2\ Al(OH)_4^-(aq) + 3\ H_2(g)$$

(b) $2[CrO_4^{2-}(aq) + 4\ H_2O(\ell) + 3\ e^- \rightarrow$
$$Cr(OH)_3(s) + 5\ OH^-(aq)]$$

$3[SO_3^{2-}(aq) + 2\ OH^-(aq) \rightarrow$
$$SO_4^{2-}(aq) + H_2O(\ell) + 2\ e^-]$$

$2\ CrO_4^{2-}(aq) + 3\ SO_3^{2-}(aq) + 5\ H_2O(\ell) \rightarrow$
$$2\ Cr(OH)_3(s) + 3\ SO_4^{2-}(aq) + 4\ OH^-(aq)$$

(c) $Zn(s) + 4\ OH^-(aq) \rightarrow [Zn(OH)_4]^{2-}(aq) + 2\ e^-$
$Cu(OH)_2(s) + 2\ e^- \rightarrow Cu(s) + 2\ OH^-(aq)$

$Zn(s) + 2\ OH^-(aq) + Cu(OH)_2(s) \rightarrow$
$[Zn(OH)_4]^{2-}(aq) + Cu(s)$

(d) $3[HS^-(aq) + OH^-(aq) \rightarrow S(s) + H_2O(\ell) + 2\ e^-]$
$ClO_3^-(aq) + 3\ H_2O(\ell) + 6\ e^- \rightarrow$
$Cl^-(aq) + 6\ OH^-(aq)$

$3\ HS^-(aq) + ClO_3^-(aq) \rightarrow$
$3\ S(s) + Cl^-(aq) + 3\ OH^-(aq)$

**20.7** Electrons flow from the Cr electrode to the Fe electrode. Negative ions move via the salt bridge from the $Fe/Fe^{2+}$ half-cell to the $Cr/Cr^{3+}$ half-cell (and positive ions move in the opposite direction).

Anode (oxidation): $Cr(s) \rightarrow Cr^{3+}(aq) + 3\ e^-$
Cathode (reduction): $Fe^{2+}(aq) + 2\ e^- \rightarrow Fe(s)$

**20.9** (a) Oxidation: $Fe(s) \rightarrow Fe^{2+}(aq) + 2\ e^-$
Reduction: $O_2(g) + 4\ H^+(aq) + 4\ e^- \rightarrow 2\ H_2O(\ell)$
Overall: $2\ Fe(s) + O_2(g) + 4\ H^+(aq) \rightarrow$
$2\ Fe^{2+}(aq) + 2\ H_2O(\ell)$

(b) Anode, oxidation: $Fe(s) \rightarrow Fe^{2+}(aq) + 2\ e^-$
Cathode, reduction: $O_2(g) + 4\ H^+(aq) + 4\ e^- \rightarrow$
$2\ H_2O(\ell)$

(c) Electrons flow from the negative anode (Fe) to the positive cathode (site of the $O_2$ half-reaction). Negative ions move through the salt bridge from the cathode compartment in which the $O_2$ reduction occurs to the anode compartment in which Fe oxidation occurs (and positive ions move in the opposite direction).

**20.11** (a) All are primary batteries, not rechargeable.
(b) Dry cells and alkaline batteries have Zn anodes and are primary batteries. Ni-Cd batteries have a cadmium anode and are rechargeable.
(c) Dry cells have an acidic environment, whereas the environment is alkaline for alkaline and Ni-Cd cells.

**20.13** (a) $E°_{cell} = -1.298$ V; not product-favored
(b) $E°_{cell} = -0.51$ V; not product-favored
(c) $E°_{cell} = -1.023$ V; not product-favored
(d) $E°_{cell} = +0.028$ V; product-favored

**20.15** (a) $Sn^{2+}(aq) + 2\ Ag(s) \rightarrow Sn(s) + 2\ Ag^+(aq)$
$E°_{cell} = -0.94$ V; not product-favored
(b) $3\ Sn^{4+}(aq) + 2\ Al(s) \rightarrow 3\ Sn^{2+}(aq) + 2\ Al^{3+}(aq)$
$E°_{cell} = +1.81$ V; product-favored
(c) $2\ ClO_3^-(aq) + 10\ Ce^{3+}(aq) + 12\ H^+(aq) \rightarrow$
$Cl_2(aq) + 10\ Ce^{4+}(aq) + 6\ H_2O(\ell)$
$E°_{cell} = -0.14$ V; not product-favored
(d) $3\ Cu(s) + 2\ NO_3^-(aq) + 8\ H^+(aq) \rightarrow$
$3\ Cu^{2+}(aq) + 2\ NO(g) + 4\ H_2O(\ell)$
$E°_{cell} = +0.62$ V; product-favored

**20.17** (a) Al
(b) Zn and Al
(c) $Fe^{2+}(aq) + Sn(s) \rightarrow Fe(s) + Sn^{2+}(aq)$;
reactant-favored
(d) $Zn^{2+}(aq) + Sn(s) \rightarrow Zn(s) + Sn^{2+}(aq)$;
reactant-favored

**20.19** Best reducing agent, Cr(s) (Use Appendix M.)

**20.21** $Ag^+$

**20.23** See Example 20.5
(a) $F_2$, most readily reduced
(b) $F_2$ and $Cl_2$

**20.25** $E°_{cell} = +0.3923$ V. When $[Zn(OH)_4^{2-}] = [OH^-] = 0.025$ M and $P(H_2) = 1.0$ bar, $E_{cell} = 0.345$ V.

**20.27** $E°_{cell} = +1.563$ V and $E_{cell} = +1.58$ V

**20.29** $E°_{cell} = +1.563$ V. When $E_{cell} = 1.48$ V, $n = 2$, and $[Zn^{2+}] = 1.0$ M, the concentration of $Ag^+ = 0.040$ M.

**20.31** (a) $\Delta_r G° = -29.0$ kJ; $K = 1 \times 10^5$
(b) $\Delta_r G° = +89$ kJ; $K = 3 \times 10^{-16}$

**20.33** $E°_{cell}$ for $AgBr(s) \rightarrow Ag^+(aq) + Br^-(aq)$ is $-0.7281$.
$K_{sp} = 4.9 \times 10^{-13}$

**20.35** $K_{formation} = 2 \times 10^{25}$

**20.37** See Figure 20.19. Electrons from the battery or other source enter the cathode where they are transferred to $Na^+$ ions, reducing the ions to Na metal. Chloride ions move toward the positively charged anode where an electron is transferred from each $Cl^-$ ion, and $Cl_2$ gas is formed.

**20.39** $O_2$ from the oxidation of water is more likely than $F_2$. See Example 20.10.

**20.41** See Example 20.10.
(a) Cathode: $2\ H_2O(\ell) + 2\ e^- \rightarrow H_2(g) + 2\ OH^-(aq)$
(b) Anode: $2\ Br^-(aq) \rightarrow Br_2(\ell) + 2\ e^-$

**20.43** Mass of Ni $= 0.0334$ g

**20.45** Time $= 2300$ s or 38 min

**20.47** Time $= 250$ h

**20.49** (a) $UO_2^+(aq) + 4\ H^+(aq) + e^- \rightarrow$
$U^{4+}(aq) + 2\ H_2O(\ell)$
(b) $ClO_3^-(aq) + 6\ H^+(aq) + 6\ e^- \rightarrow$
$Cl^-(aq) + 3\ H_2O(\ell)$
(c) $N_2H_4(aq) + 4\ OH^-(aq) \rightarrow$
$N_2(g) + 4\ H_2O(\ell) + 4\ e^-$
(d) $ClO^-(aq) + H_2O(\ell) + 2\ e^- \rightarrow$
$Cl^-(aq) + 2\ OH^-(aq)$

**20.51** (a, c) The electrode at the right is a magnesium anode. (Magnesium metal supplies electrons and is oxidized to $Mg^{2+}$ ions.) Electrons pass through the wire to the silver cathode, where $Ag^+$ ions are reduced to silver metal. Nitrate ions move via the salt bridge from the $AgNO_3$ solution to the $Mg(NO_3)_2$ solution (and $Na^+$ ions move in the opposite direction). A salt bridge is needed to maintain electrical neutrality in each half-cell and to complete the electrical circuit.

   (b) Anode: $Mg(s) \rightarrow Mg^{2+}(aq) + 2\ e^-$

   Cathode: $Ag^+(aq) + e^- \rightarrow Ag(s)$

   Net reaction: $Mg(s) + 2\ Ag^+(aq) \rightarrow$
   $$Mg^{2+}(aq) + 2\ Ag(s)$$

**20.53** (a) For 1.7 V:

   Use chromium as the anode to reduce $Ag^+(aq)$ to $Ag(s)$ at the cathode. The cell potential is +1.71 V.

   (b) For 0.5 V:

   (i) Use copper as the anode to reduce silver ions to silver metal at the cathode. The cell potential is +0.46 V.

   (ii) Use silver as the anode to reduce chlorine to chloride ions. The cell potential would be +0.56 V. (In practice, this setup is not likely to work well because the product would be insoluble silver chloride.)

**20.55** (a) $Zn^{2+}(aq)$    (c) $Zn(s)$

   (b) $Au^+(aq)$    (d) $Au(s)$

   (e) Yes, $Sn(s)$ will reduce $Cu^{2+}$.

   (f) No, $Ag(s)$ can only reduce $Au^+(aq)$.

   (g) $Cu^{2+}$, $Ag^+$ and $Au^+$

   (h) $Ag^+(aq)$ can oxidize Cu, Sn, Co, and Zn.

**20.57** (a) The cathode is the site of reduction, so the half-reaction must be $2\ H^+(aq) + 2\ e^- \rightarrow H_2(g)$. This is the case with the following half-reactions: $Cr^{3+}(aq)|Cr(s)$, $Fe^{2+}(aq)|Fe(s)$, and $Mg^{2+}(aq)|Mg(s)$.

   (b) Choosing from the half-cells in part (a), the reaction of $Mg(s)$ and $H^+(aq)$ would produce the most positive potential (2.37 V), and the reaction of $H_2$ with $Cu^{2+}$ would produce the least positive potential (+0.337 V).

**20.59** $8.1 \times 10^5$ g Al

**20.61** (a) $E°_{anode} = -0.268$ V

   (b) $K_{sp} = 2 \times 10^{-5}$

**20.63** $\Delta_r G° = -409$ kJ

**20.65** 6700 kWh; 820 kg Na; 1300 kg $Cl_2$

**20.67** $Ru^{2+}$, $Ru(NO_3)_2$

**20.69** $9.5 \times 10^6$ g $Cl_2$ per day

**20.71** Anode: $2\ H_2O(\ell) \rightarrow O_2(g) + 4\ H^+(aq) + 4\ e^-$
   Cathode: $Cu^{2+}(aq) + 2\ e^- \rightarrow Cu(s)$

**20.73** The rate of the reaction with $H_2O$ is more rapid than the rate of the reaction with $NO_3^-$.
   Products formed at anode: $O_2(g)$ and $H^+(aq)$
   Anode half-reaction: $2\ H_2O(\ell) \rightarrow$
   $$O_2(g) + 4\ H^+(aq) + 4\ e^-$$

**20.75** Under standard conditions, the spontaneous reaction is $Hg^{2+}(aq) + 2\ Fe^{2+}(aq) \rightarrow Hg(\ell) + 2\ Fe^{3+}(aq)$ with $E° = 0.084$ V.

   Under the conditions present, $E = -0.244$ V. The reaction is not spontaneous in the same direction as under standard conditions but in the opposite direction: $Hg(\ell) + 2\ Fe^{3+}(aq) \rightarrow Hg^{2+}(aq) + 2\ Fe^{2+}(aq)$. Under these conditions, the anode for the spontaneous reaction is the $Hg(\ell)|Hg^{2+}(aq, 0.020\ M)$ electrode and the measured voltage will be 0.244 V.

**20.77** $E° = 0.771$ V. When $[H^+] = 1.0 \times 10^{-7}$ M, $E = 1.185$ V. The reaction is more favorable at a lower $[H^+]$ (higher pH). The reaction is thus less favorable at lower pH.

**20.79** (a) See Figure 20.5

   In this case, both electrodes are made of silver metal. On one side, the solution contains $1.0 \times 10^{-5}$ M $Ag^+$ and on the other the solution contains 1.0 M $Ag^+$. The cathode is the electrode on the side that has the 1.0 M $Ag^+$ solution [half-reaction: $Ag^+(aq) + e^- \rightarrow Ag(s)$], and the anode is the electrode on the side that has the $1.0 \times 10^{-5}$ M $Ag^+$ solution [half-reaction: $Ag(s) \rightarrow Ag^+(aq) + e^-$]. Connecting the two electrodes is a wire. Electrons flow through the wire from the anode to the cathode. A salt bridge also connects the two compartments.

   (b) $E = 0.30$ V

**20.81** (a) $K = 3.4 \times 10^{-10}$; reactant-favored at equilibrium

   (b) $K = 3.0$; product-favored at equilibrium

**20.83** (a) $\Delta_r G° = -3.6 \times 10^2$ kJ/mol-rxn

   (b) $\Delta_r G° = -79$ kJ/mol-rxn

**20.85** (a) $2[Ag^+(aq) + e^- \rightarrow Ag(s)]$

   $C_6H_5CHO(aq) + H_2O(\ell) \rightarrow$
   $$C_6H_5CO_2H(aq) + 2\ H^+(aq) + 2\ e^-$$
   $\overline{\phantom{xxxxxxxxxxxxxxxxxxxxxxxxxxxxxxx}}$
   $2Ag^+(aq) + C_6H_5CHO(aq) + H_2O(\ell) \rightarrow$
   $$C_6H_5CO_2H(aq) + 2\ H^+(aq) + 2\ Ag(s)$$

   (b) $3[CH_3CH_2OH(aq) + H_2O(\ell) \rightarrow$
   $$CH_3CO_2H(aq) + 4\ H^+(aq) + 4\ e^-]$$
   $2[Cr_2O_7^{2-}(aq) + 14\ H^+(aq) + 6\ e^- \rightarrow$
   $$2\ Cr^{3+}(aq) + 7\ H_2O(\ell)]$$
   $\overline{\phantom{xxxxxxxxxxxxxxxxxxxxxxxxxxxxxxx}}$
   $3\ CH_3CH_2OH(aq) +$
   $2\ Cr_2O_7^{2-}(aq) + 16\ H^+(aq) \rightarrow$
   $$3\ CH_3CO_2H(aq) + 4\ Cr^{3+}(aq) + 11\ H_2O(\ell)$$

**20.87** (a) 0.974 kJ/g

   (b) 0.60 kJ/g

   (c) The silver-zinc battery produces more energy per gram of reactants.

**20.89** (a) $2\ NO_3^-(aq) + 3\ Mn^{2+}(aq) + 2\ H_2O(\ell) \rightarrow$
   $$2\ NO(g) + 3\ MnO_2(s) + 4\ H^+(aq)$$
   $3\ MnO_2(s) + 4\ H^+(aq) + 2\ NH_4^+(aq) \rightarrow$
   $$N_2(g) + 3\ Mn^{2+}(aq) + 6\ H_2O(\ell)$$

   (b) $E°$ for reduction of $NO_3^-$ with $Mn^{2+}$ is $-0.27$ V. $E°$ for oxidation of $NH_4^+$ with $MnO_2$ is $+1.50$ V.

**20.91** (a) $Fe^{2+}(aq) + 2 e^- \rightarrow Fe(s)$
$2[Fe^{2+}(aq) \rightarrow Fe^{3+}(aq) + e^-]$
$3 Fe^{2+}(aq) \rightarrow Fe(s) + 2 Fe^{3+}(aq)$
(b) $E°_{cell} = -1.21$ V; not product-favored
(c) $K = 1 \times 10^{-41}$

**20.93** (a)

(b) Anode: $Cd(s) \rightarrow Cd^{2+}(aq) + 2 e^-$
Cathode: $Ni^{2+}(aq) + 2 e^- \rightarrow Ni(s)$
Net: $Cd(s) + Ni^{2+}(aq) \rightarrow Cd^{2+}(aq) + Ni(s)$
(c) The anode is negative and the cathode is positive.
(d) $E°_{cell} = E°_{cathode} - E°_{anode} =$
$(-0.25$ V$) - (-0.40$ V$) = +0.15$ V
(e) Electrons flow from anode (Cd) to cathode (Ni).
(f) Positive ions move from the anode compartment to the cathode compartment. Anions move in the opposite direction.
(g) $K = 1 \times 10^5$
(h) $E_{cell} = 0.21$ V; yes, the net reaction is still the same.
(i) 480 h

**20.95** 0.054 g Au

**20.97** $I^-$ is the strongest reducing agent of the three halide ions. Iodide ion reduces $Cu^{2+}$ to $Cu^+$, forming insoluble $CuI(s)$.
$2 Cu^{2+}(aq) + 4 I^-(aq) \rightarrow 2 CuI(s) + I_2(aq)$

**20.99** (a) 92 g HF required; 230 g $CF_3SO_2F$ and 9.3 g $H_2$ isolated
(b) $H_2$ is produced at the cathode.
(c) 48 kWh

**20.101** 290 h

**20.103** (a) 3.6 mol glucose and 22 mol $O_2$
(b) 86 mol electrons
(c) 96 amps
(d) 96 watts

## Applying Chemical Principles: Sacrifice!

1. An insulator will prevent the flow of electrons from the zinc to copper, preventing zinc from keeping the copper reduced.

3. (e) chromium

5. (a) $Cu(OH)_2(s) + 2 e^- \rightarrow Cu(s) + 2 OH^-(aq)$
(b) $Zn(s) + 2 OH^-(aq) \rightarrow Zn(OH)_2(s) + 2 e^-$
(c) $Cu(OH)_2(s) + Zn(s) \rightarrow Cu(s) + Zn(OH)_2(s)$
(d) $E = 0.89$ V

# Chapter 21

**21.1** $4 Li(s) + O_2(g) \rightarrow 2 Li_2O(s)$
$Li_2O(s) + H_2O(\ell) \rightarrow 2 LiOH(aq)$
$2 Ca(s) + O_2(g) \rightarrow 2 CaO(s)$
$CaO(s) + H_2O(\ell) \rightarrow Ca(OH)_2(s)$

**21.3** These are the elements of Group 3A: boron, B; aluminum, Al; gallium, Ga; indium, In; and thallium, Tl.

**21.5** $2 Na(s) + Cl_2(g) \rightarrow 2 NaCl(s)$
The reaction is exothermic and the product is ionic. See Figure 1.2.

**21.7** The product, NaCl, is a colorless solid and is soluble in water. Other alkali metal chlorides have similar properties.

**21.9** Calcium will not exist in the earth's crust because the metal reacts with water.

**21.11** Increasing basicity: $CO_2 < SiO_2 < SnO_2$

**21.13** (a) $2 Na(s) + Br_2(\ell) \rightarrow 2 NaBr(s)$
(b) $2 Mg(s) + O_2(g) \rightarrow 2 MgO(s)$
(c) $2 Al(s) + 3 F_2(g) \rightarrow 2 AlF_3(s)$
(d) $C(s) + O_2(g) \rightarrow CO_2(g)$

**21.15** $2 H_2(g) + O_2(g) \rightarrow 2 H_2O(g)$
$H_2(g) + Cl_2(g) \rightarrow 2 HCl(g)$
$3 H_2(g) + N_2(g) \rightarrow 2 NH_3(g)$

**21.17** $CH_4(g) + H_2O(g) \rightarrow CO(g) + 3 H_2(g)$
$\Delta_rH° = +206.2$ kJ; $\Delta_rS° = +214.7$ J/K; $\Delta_rG° = +142.2$ kJ (at 298 K).

**21.19** Step 1: $2 SO_2(g) + 4 H_2O(\ell) + 2 I_2(s) \rightarrow$
$2 H_2SO_4(\ell) + 4 HI(g)$
Step 2: $2 H_2SO_4(\ell) \rightarrow$
$2 H_2O(\ell) + 2 SO_2(g) + O_2(g)$
Step 3: $4 HI(g) \rightarrow 2 H_2(g) + 2 I_2(g)$
Net: $2 H_2O(\ell) \rightarrow 2 H_2(g) + O_2(g)$

**21.21** $2 Na(s) + F_2(g) \rightarrow 2 NaF(s)$
$2 Na(s) + Cl_2(g) \rightarrow 2 NaCl(s)$
$2 Na(s) + Br_2(\ell) \rightarrow 2 NaBr(s)$
$2 Na(s) + I_2(s) \rightarrow 2 NaI(s)$
The alkali metal halides are white, crystalline solids. They have high melting and boiling points, and they are soluble in water.

**21.23** (a) $2 Cl^-(aq) + 2 H_2O(\ell) \rightarrow$
$Cl_2(g) + H_2(g) + 2 OH^-(aq)$
(b) If this were the only process used to produce chlorine, the mass of $Cl_2$ reported for industrial production would be 0.88 times the mass of NaOH produced (2 mol NaCl, 117 g, would yield 2 mol NaOH, 80 g, and 1 mol $Cl_2$, 70 g). The amounts quoted indicate a $Cl_2$ to NaOH mass ratio 0.96. Chlorine is presumably also prepared by other routes than this one.

**21.25** $2\ Mg(s) + O_2(g) \rightarrow 2\ MgO(s)$

$3\ Mg(s) + N_2(g) \rightarrow Mg_3N_2(s)$

**21.27** $CaCO_3$ is used in agriculture to neutralize acidic soil, to prepare CaO for use in mortar, and in steel production.

$CaCO_3(s) + H_2O(\ell) + CO_2(g) \rightarrow$
$Ca^{2+}(aq) + 2\ HCO_3^-(aq)$

**21.29** $1.4 \times 10^6$ g $SO_2$

**21.31**

$B_3O_6{}^{3-}$

$B_2O_5{}^{4-}$

**21.33** (a) $2\ B_5H_9(g) + 12\ O_2(g) \rightarrow 5\ B_2O_3(s) + 9\ H_2O(g)$

(b) Enthalpy of combustion of $B_5H_9 = -4341.2$ kJ/mol. This is more than double the enthalpy of combustion of $B_2H_6$.

(c) Enthalpy of combustion of $C_2H_6(g)$ [to give $CO_2(g)$ and $H_2O(g)$] $= -1428.7$ kJ/mol. $C_2H_6$ produces 47.5 kJ/g, whereas diborane produces much more (73.7 kJ/g).

**21.35** $2\ Al(s) + 6\ HCl(aq) \rightarrow$
$2\ Al^{3+}(aq) + 6\ Cl^-(aq) + 3\ H_2(g)$

$2\ Al(s) + 3\ Cl_2(g) \rightarrow 2\ AlCl_3(s)$

$4\ Al(s) + 3\ O_2(g) \rightarrow 2\ Al_2O_3(s)$

**21.37** $2\ Al(s) + 2\ OH^-(aq) + 6\ H_2O(\ell) \rightarrow$
$2\ Al(OH)_4^-(aq) + 3\ H_2(g)$

Volume of $H_2$ obtained from 13.2 g Al = 18.4 L

**21.39** $Al_2O_3(s) + 3\ H_2SO_4(aq) \rightarrow Al_2(SO_4)_3(s) + 3\ H_2O(\ell)$

Mass of $H_2SO_4$ required = 860 g and mass of $Al_2O_3$ required = 298 g.

**21.41** Pyroxenes have as their basic structural unit an extended chain of linked $SiO_4$ tetrahedra. The ratio of Si to O is 1:3.

**21.43** This structure has a six-member ring of Si atoms with O atom bridges. Each Si also has two O atoms attached. The basic unit is $SiO_3{}^{2-}$, and the overall charge is $-12$ in $[(SiO_3)_6]^{-12}$. (Electron lone pairs are omitted in the following structure.)

**21.45** Consider the general decomposition reaction:

$N_xO_y \rightarrow {}^x/_2\ N_2 + {}^y/_2\ O_2$

The value of $\Delta G°$ can be obtained for all $N_xO_y$ molecules because $\Delta_rG° = -\Delta_fG°$. These data show that the decomposition reaction is spontaneous for all of the nitrogen oxides. All are unstable with respect to decomposition to the elements.

| Compound | $-\Delta_fG°$ (kJ/mol) |
|---|---|
| NO(g) | $-86.58$ |
| $NO_2$ | $-51.23$ |
| $N_2O$ | $-104.20$ |
| $N_2O_4$ | $-97.73$ |

**21.47** $\Delta_rH° = -114.4$ kJ/mol-rxn; exothermic $\Delta_rG° = -70.7$ kJ/mol-rxn, product-favored at equilibrium

**21.49** (a) $N_2H_4(aq) + O_2(g) \rightarrow N_2(g) + 2\ H_2O(\ell)$

(b) $1.32 \times 10^3$ g

**21.51** (a) Oxidation number = $+3$

(b) Diphosphorous acid ($H_4P_2O_5$) should be a diprotic acid (losing the two H atoms attached to O atoms).

**21.53** (a) $3.5 \times 10^3$ kg $SO_2$

(b) $4.1 \times 10^3$ kg $Ca(OH)_2$

**21.55**

disulfide ion

**21.57** $E°_{cell} = E°_{cathode} - E°_{anode} = +1.44\ V - (+1.51\ V) = -0.07\ V$

The reaction is not product-favored under standard conditions.

**21.59** $Cl_2(aq) + 2\ Br^-(aq) \rightarrow 2\ Cl^-(aq) + Br_2(\ell)$

$Cl_2$ is the oxidizing agent, $Br^-$ is the reducing agent; $E°_{cell} = 0.28$ V.

**21.61** The reaction consumes $4.32 \times 10^8$ C to produce $8.51 \times 10^4$ g $F_2$.

**21.63**

| Element | Appearance | State |
|---|---|---|
| Na, Mg, Al | Silvery metal | Solids |
| Si | Black, shiny metalloid | Solid |
| P | White, red, and black allotropes; nonmetal | Solid |
| S | Yellow nonmetal | Solid |
| Cl | Pale green nonmetal | Gas |
| Ar | Colorless nonmetal | Gas |

**21.65** (a) $2\,K(s) + Cl_2(g) \rightarrow 2\,KCl(s)$

$Ca(s) + Cl_2(g) \rightarrow CaCl_2(s)$

$2\,Ga(s) + 3\,Cl_2(g) \rightarrow 2\,GaCl_3(s)$

$Ge(s) + 2\,Cl_2(g) \rightarrow GeCl_4(\ell)$

$2\,As(s) + 3\,Cl_2(g) \rightarrow 2\,AsCl_3(\ell)$

(AsCl$_5$ has been prepared but is not stable.)

(b) KCl and CaCl$_2$ are ionic; the other products are covalent.

(c) The electron-pair and molecular geometries of GaCl$_3$ are both trigonal-planar; the electron-pair geometry of AsCl$_3$ is tetrahedral, and its molecular geometry is trigonal-pyramidal.

**21.67** (a) $2\,KClO_3(s) \rightarrow 2\,KCl(s) + 3\,O_2(g)$

(b) $2\,H_2S(g) + 3\,O_2(g) \rightarrow 2\,H_2O(g) + 2\,SO_2(g)$

(c) $2\,Na(s) + O_2(g) \rightarrow Na_2O_2(s)$

(d) $P_4(s) + 3\,KOH(aq) + 3\,H_2O(\ell) \rightarrow$
    $\qquad PH_3(g) + 3\,KH_2PO_2(aq)$

(e) $NH_4NO_3(s) \rightarrow N_2O(g) + 2\,H_2O(g)$

(f) $2\,In(s) + 3\,Br_2(\ell) \rightarrow 2\,InBr_3(s)$

(g) $SnCl_4(\ell) + 2\,H_2O(\ell) \rightarrow SnO_2(s) + 4\,HCl(aq)$

**21.69** $1.4 \times 10^5$ metric tons

**21.71** Mg: $\quad \Delta_r G° = +64.9$ kJ

Ca: $\quad \Delta_r G° = +131.40$ kJ

Ba: $\quad \Delta_r G° = +219.4$ kJ

Relative tendency to decompose:
MgCO$_3$ > CaCO$_3$ > BaCO$_3$

**21.73** (a) $\Delta_f G°$ should be more negative than $(-95.1$ kJ$) \times n$.

(b) Ba, Pb, Ti

**21.75** O—F bond energy = 190 kJ/mol

**21.77** (a) N$_2$O$_4$ is the oxidizing agent (N is reduced from +4 to 0 in N$_2$), and H$_2$NN(CH$_3$)$_2$ is the reducing agent.

(b) $1.3 \times 10^4$ kg N$_2$O$_4$ is required. Product masses: $5.7 \times 10^3$ kg N$_2$; $4.9 \times 10^3$ kg H$_2$O; $6.0 \times 10^3$ kg CO$_2$.

**21.79** $\Delta_r H° = -257.78$ kJ. This reaction is entropy-disfavored, however, with $\Delta_r S° = -963$ J/K because of the decrease in the number of moles of gases. Combining these values gives $\Delta_r G° = +29.19$ kJ, indicating that under standard conditions at 298 K the reaction is not spontaneous. (The reaction has a favorable $\Delta_r G°$ at temperatures less than 268 K, indicating that further research on this system might be worthwhile. Note that at that temperature water is a solid.)

**21.81** A = B$_2$H$_6$; B = B$_4$H$_{10}$; C = B$_5$H$_{11}$; D = B$_5$H$_9$; E = B$_{10}$H$_{14}$

**21.83** 48.6 kiloamps

**21.85**

The ring is not expected to be planar because a tetrahedral electron-pair geometry is predicted for each atom in the ring.

**21.87** $\Delta_r G° = -834.28$ kJ/mol-rxn, therefore the reaction is product-favored at equilibrium at 298 K.

$\Delta_r S° = -149.9$ J/K · mol-rxn at 298 K. Because this is negative, the reaction will be less product-favored at high temperatures.

**21.89** (a) $2\,CH_3Cl(g) + Si(s) \rightarrow (CH_3)_2SiCl_2(\ell)$

(b) 0.823 atm

(c) 12.2 g

**21.91** $5\,N_2H_5^+(aq) + 4\,IO_3^-(aq) \rightarrow$
    $\qquad 5\,N_2(g) + 2\,I_2(aq) + H^+(aq) + 12\,H_2O(\ell)$

$E°_{net} = 1.43$ V

**21.93** (a) Br$_2$O$_3$

(b) The structure of Br$_2$O is reasonably well known. Several possible structures for Br$_2$O$_3$ can be imagined, but experiment confirms the structure below.

**21.95** (a) The NO bond with a length of 114.2 pm is a double bond. The other two NO bonds (with a length of 121 pm) have a bond order of 1.5 (as there are two resonance structures involving these bonds).

(b) $K = 1.90$; $\Delta_r S° = 141$ J/K · mol-rxn

(c) $\Delta_f H° = 82.9$ kJ/mol

**21.97** The flask contains a fixed number of moles of gas at the given pressure and temperature. One could burn the mixture because only the H$_2$ will combust; the argon is untouched. Cooling the gases from combustion would remove water (the combustion product of H$_2$) and leave only Ar in the gas phase. Measuring its pressure in a calibrated volume at a known temperature would allow one to calculate the amount of Ar that was in the original mixture.

**21.99** Generally, a sodium fire can be extinguished by smothering it with sand. The worst choice is to use water (which reacts violently with sodium to give $H_2$ gas and NaOH).

**21.101** Nitrogen is a relatively unreactive gas, so it will not participate in any reaction typical of hydrogen or oxygen. The most obvious property of $H_2$ is that it burns, so attempting to burn a small sample of the gas would immediately confirm or deny the presence of $H_2$. If $O_2$ is present, it can be detected by allowing it to react as an oxidizing agent. There are many reactions known with low-valent metals, especially transition metal ions in solution, that can be detected by color changes.

**21.103** 3.5 kW-h

**21.105** The reducing ability of the Group 3A metals declines considerably on descending the group, with the largest drop occurring on going from Al to Ga. The reducing ability of gallium and indium are similar, but another large change is observed on going to thallium. In fact, thallium is most stable in the +1 oxidation state. This same tendency for elements to be more stable with lower oxidation numbers is seen in Groups 4A (Ge and Pb) and 5A (Bi).

## Applying Chemical Principles: Van Arkel Triangles and Bonding

1.
 (a) CuZn is metallic.
 (b) GaAs and BP are semiconductors. As and B are metalloids; Ga and P are not. In both compounds, only one element is a metalloid.
 (c) $Mg_3N_2$ and $SrBr_2$ are ionic. Both are composed of a metal combined with a nonmetal.
 (d) Covalent bonding
 (e) $SBr_2$ and $C_3N_4$ are covalent. Both elements in the compounds are nonmetallic.

## Chapter 22

**22.1**
 (a) $Cr^{3+}$: $[Ar]3d^3$, paramagnetic
 (b) $V^{2+}$: $[Ar]3d^3$, paramagnetic
 (c) $Ni^{2+}$: $[Ar]3d^8$, paramagnetic
 (d) $Cu^+$: $[Ar]3d^{10}$, diamagnetic

**22.3**
 (a) $Fe^{3+}$: $[Ar]3d^5$, isoelectronic with $Mn^{2+}$
 (b) $Zn^{2+}$: $[Ar]3d^{10}$, isoelectronic with $Cu^+$
 (c) $Fe^{2+}$: $[Ar]3d^6$, isoelectronic with $Co^{3+}$
 (d) $Cr^{3+}$: $[Ar]3d^3$, isoelectronic with $V^{2+}$

**22.5**
 (a) $Cr_2O_3(s) + 2\, Al(s) \rightarrow Al_2O_3(s) + 2\, Cr(s)$
 (b) $TiCl_4(\ell) + 2\, Mg(s) \rightarrow Ti(s) + 2\, MgCl_2(s)$
 (c) $2\,[Ag(CN)_2]^-(aq) + Zn(s) \rightarrow$
 $2\, Ag(s) + [Zn(CN)_4]^{2-}(aq)$
 (d) $3\, Mn_3O_4(s) + 8\, Al(s) \rightarrow 9\, Mn(s) + 4\, Al_2O_3(s)$

**22.7** Monodentate: $CH_3NH_2$, $CH_3CN$, $N_3^-$, $Br^-$
 Bidentate: en, phen (see Figure 22.14)

**22.9** (a) $Mn^{2+}$; (b) $Co^{3+}$; (c) $Co^{3+}$; (d) $Cr^{2+}$

**22.11** $[Ni(en)(NH_3)_3(H_2O)]^{2+}$

**22.13** (a) $Ni(en)_2Cl_2$ (en = $H_2NCH_2CH_2NH_2$)
 (b) $K_2[PtCl_4]$
 (c) $K[Cu(CN)_2]$
 (d) $[Fe(NH_3)_4(H_2O)_2]^{2+}$

**22.15** (a) Diaquabis(oxalato)nickelate(II) ion
 (b) Dibromobis(ethylenediamine)cobalt(III) ion
 (c) Amminechlorobis(ethylenediamine)cobalt(III) ion
 (d) Diammineoxalatoplatinum(II)

**22.17** (a) $[Fe(H_2O)_5OH]^{2+}$
 (b) Potassium tetracyanonickelate(II)
 (c) Potassium diaquabis(oxalato)chromate(III)
 (d) $(NH_4)_2[PtCl_4]$

**22.19**

Only one structure possible. (N—N is the bidentate ethylenediamine ligand.)

**22.21** (a) $Fe^{2+}$ is a chiral center.
 (b) $Co^{3+}$ is not a chiral center.
 (c) $Co^{3+}$ is not a chiral center.
 (d) No. Square-planar complexes are never chiral.

**22.23** (a) $[Mn(CN)_6]^{4-}$: $d^5$, low-spin $Mn^{2+}$ complex is paramagnetic (one unpaired electron).

$$\underline{\uparrow\downarrow} \quad \underline{\uparrow\downarrow} \quad \underline{\uparrow}$$

 (b) $[Co(NH_3)_6]^{3+}$: $d^6$, low-spin $Co^{3+}$ complex is diamagnetic.

$$\underline{\uparrow\downarrow} \quad \underline{\uparrow\downarrow} \quad \underline{\uparrow\downarrow}$$

 (c) $[Fe(H_2O)_6]^{3+}$: $d^5$, low-spin $Fe^{3+}$ complex is paramagnetic [one unpaired electron; same as part (a)].

 (d) $[Cr(en)_3]^{2+}$: $d^4$, $Cr^{2+}$ complex is paramagnetic (two unpaired electrons).

$$\underline{\uparrow\downarrow} \quad \underline{\uparrow} \quad \underline{\uparrow}$$

**22.25** (a) $Fe^{2+}$, $d^6$, paramagnetic, four unpaired electrons
(b) $Co^{2+}$, $d^7$, paramagnetic, three unpaired electrons
(c) $Mn^{2+}$, $d^5$, paramagnetic, five unpaired electrons
(d) $Zn^{2+}$, $d^{10}$, diamagnetic, zero unpaired electrons

**22.27** (a) 6
(b) Octahedral
(c) +2
(d) Four unpaired electrons (high spin)
(e) Paramagnetic

**22.29** With four ligands, complexes of the $d^8$ $Ni^{2+}$ ion can be either tetrahedral or square-planar. The $CN^-$ ligand is at one end of the spectrochemical series and leads to a large ligand field splitting, whereas $Cl^-$ is at the opposite end and often leads to complexes with small orbital splitting. With ligands such as $CN^-$ the complex will be square-planar (and for a $d^8$ ion it will be diamagnetic). With a weak field ligand ($Cl^-$) the complex will be tetrahedral and, for the $d^8$ ion, two electrons will be unpaired, giving a paramagnetic complex.

**22.31** The light absorbed is in the green region of the spectrum (page 1043). Therefore, the light transmitted—which is the color of the solution—is magenta.

**22.33** (a) The $Mn^+$ ion in this complex has six $d$ electrons. Each CO contributes two electrons, giving a total of 18 for the complex ion.
(b) The $C_5H_5^-$ ligand contributes six electrons, CO and $PR_3$ each contribute two electrons, for a total of 10 electrons for the ligands. The cobalt is effectively a $Co^+$ ion and contributes eight $d$ electrons. The total is 18 electrons.
(c) The $C_5H_5^-$ ligand contributes six electrons, each CO contributes two electrons, for a total of 12 electrons for the ligands. The manganese is effectively a $Mn^+$ ion and contributes six $d$ electrons. The total is 18 electrons.

**22.35** Determine the magnetic properties of the complex. Square-planar $Ni^{2+}$ ($d^8$) complexes are diamagnetic, whereas tetrahedral complexes are paramagnetic.

**22.37** $Fe^{2+}$ has a $d^6$ configuration. Low-spin octahedral complexes are diamagnetic, whereas high-spin octahedral complexes of this ion have four unpaired electrons and are paramagnetic.

**22.39** Square-planar complexes most often arise from $d^8$ transition metal ions. Therefore, it is likely that $[Ni(CN)_4]^{2-}$ ($Ni^{2+}$) and $[Pt(CN)_4]^{2-}$ ($Pt^{2+}$) are square planar. (See also Study Question 22.29.)

**22.41** Two geometric isomers are possible.

**22.43** Absorbing at 425 nm means the complex is absorbing light in the blue-violet end of the spectrum. Therefore, red and green light are transmitted, and the complex appears yellow (see Figure 22.27).

**22.45** (a) $Mn^{2+}$; (b) 6; (c) octahedral; (d) 5; (e) paramagnetic; (f) *cis* and *trans* isomers exist.

**22.47** Name: tetraamminedichlorocobalt(III) chloride

*cis*      *trans*

**22.49** $[Co(en)_2(H_2O)Cl]^{2+}$

**22.51**

*mer*    *fac*

*trans* chlorides    *cis* chlorides

**22.53**

$H_2O$ and $NH_3$ *cis*, chiral

$H_2O$ *cis* and $NH_3$ *trans*, not chiral

$H_2O$ *trans* and $NH_3$ *cis*, not chiral

**22.55** In $[Mn(H_2O)_6]^{2+}$ and $[Mn(CN)_6]^{4-}$, Mn has an oxidation number of +2 (Mn is a $d^5$ ion).

$[Mn(H_2O)_6]^{2+}$ paramagnetic, 5 unpaired $e^-$

$[Mn(CN)_6]^{4-}$ paramagnetic, 1 unpaired $e^-$

This shows that $\Delta_o$ for $CN^-$ is greater than for $H_2O$.

**22.57** (a) Ammonium tetrachlorocuprate(II)

(b) Hexacarbonylmolybdenum(0)

(c) $[Cr(H_2O)_4Cl_2]Cl$

(d) $[Co(H_2O)(NH_2CH_2CH_2NH_2)_2(SCN)](NO_3)_2$

**22.59** (a) The light absorbed is in the orange region of the spectrum (page 1043). Therefore, the light transmitted (the color of the solution) is blue or cyan.

(b) Using the cobalt(III) complexes in Table 22.3 as a guide, we might place $CO_3^{2-}$ between $F^-$ and the oxalato ion, $C_2O_4^{2-}$.

(c) $\Delta_o$ is small, so the complex should be high spin and paramagnetic.

**22.61**

$N\ \ O = H_2N-CH_2-CO_2^-$

enantiometric pair

enantiometric pair

enantiometric pair

**22.63** (a) In complexes such as $M(PR_3)Cl_2$ the metal is $Ni^{2+}$ or $Pd^{2+}$, both of which are $d^8$ metal ions. If an $Ni^{2+}$ complex is paramagnetic it must be tetrahedral, whereas the $Pd^{2+}$ must be square planar. (A $d^8$ metal complex cannot be diamagnetic if it has a tetrahedral structure.)

Tetrahedral $Ni^{2+}$ complex, paramagnetic

Square-planar $Pd^{2+}$ complex, diamagnetic

(b) A tetrahedral $Ni^{2+}$ complex cannot have isomers, whereas a square-planar complex of the type $M(PR_3)_2Cl_2$ can have *cis* and *trans* isomers. (See page 1035.)

**22.65** A, dark violet isomer: $[Co(NH_3)_5Br]SO_4$

B, violet-red isomer: $[Co(NH_3)_5(SO_4)]Br$

$[Co(NH_3)_5Br]SO_4(aq) + BaCl_2(aq) \rightarrow$
$\qquad [Co(NH_3)_5Br]Cl_2(aq) + BaSO_4(s)$

**22.67** (a) There is $5.41 \times 10^{-4}$ mol of $UO_2(NO_3)_2$, and this provides $5.41 \times 10^{-4}$ mol of $U^{n+}$ ions on reduction by Zn. The $5.41 \times 10^{-4}$ mol $U^{n+}$ requires $2.16 \times 10^{-4}$ mol $MnO_4^-$ to reach the equivalence point. This is a ratio of 5 mol of $U^{n+}$ ions to 2 mol $MnO_4^-$ ions. The 2 mol $MnO_4^-$ ions require 10 mol of $e^-$ (to go to $Mn^{2+}$ ions), so 5 mol of $U^{n+}$ ions provide 10 mol $e^-$ (on going to 5 $UO_2^{2+}$ ions, with a uranium oxidation number of +6). This means the $U^{n+}$ ion must be $U^{4+}$.

(b) $Zn(s) \rightarrow Zn^{2+}(aq) + 2\ e^-$

$UO_2^{2+}(aq) + 4\ H^+(aq) + 2\ e^- \rightarrow$
$\qquad U^{4+}(aq) + 2\ H_2O(\ell)$

___

$UO_2^{2+}(aq) + 4\ H^+(aq) + Zn(s) \rightarrow$
$\qquad U^{4+}(aq) + 2\ H_2O(\ell) + Zn^{2+}(aq)$

(c) $5[U^{4+}(aq) + 2\ H_2O(\ell) \rightarrow$
$\qquad UO_2^{2+}(aq) + 4\ H^+(aq) + 2\ e^-]$

$2[MnO_4^-(aq) + 8\ H^+(aq) + 5\ e^- \rightarrow$
$\qquad Mn^{2+}(aq) + 4\ H_2O(\ell)]$

___

$5\ U^{4+}(aq) + 2\ MnO_4^-(aq) + 2\ H_2O(\ell) \rightarrow$
$\qquad 5\ UO_2^{2+}(aq) + 4\ H^+(aq) + 2\ Mn^{2+}(aq)$

**22.69**

| Ion | $K_{formation}$ (ammine complexes) |
|-----|-----|
| $Co^{2+}$ | $1.3 \times 10^5$ |
| $Ni^{2+}$ | $5.5 \times 10^8$ |
| $Cu^{2+}$ | $2.1 \times 10^{13}$ |
| $Zn^{2+}$ | $2.9 \times 10^9$ |

The data for these hexaammine complexes do, indeed, verify the Irving-Williams series. In the book *Chemistry of the Elements* (N. N. Greenwood and A. Earnshaw: 2nd edition, p. 908, Oxford, England, Butterworth-Heinemann, 1997), it is stated: "the stabilities of corresponding complexes of the bivalent ions of the first transition series, irrespective of the particular ligand involved, usually vary in the Irving-Williams order, . . . , which is the reverse of the order for the cation radius. These observations are consistent with the view that, at least for metals in oxidation states +2 and +3, the coordinate bond is largely electrostatic. This was a major factor in the acceptance of the crystal field theory."

**22.71** Wilkinson's catalyst and the EAN rule.

*Step 1: Rhodium-containing reactant.* Each $PR_3$ ligand donates two electrons as does the $Cl^-$ ligand. The $Rh^+$ ion has 8 $d$ electrons. Total electrons = 16.

*Step 1: Rhodium-containing product.* Assuming that the H ligand is $H^-$, each donates two electrons, as do $Cl^-$ and the two $PR_3$ ligands. The metal center is $Rh^{3+}$, a $d^6$ metal ion. Total electrons = 18.

*Step 2:* The product has 16 electrons because one $PR_3$ ligand has been dissociated.

*Step 3:* The product has 18 electrons. The two-electron donor ligand $CH_2CH_2$ has replaced the dissociated $PR_3$ ligand.

*Step 4:* The product has 16 electrons. There are three anionic, two-electron donor ligands ($Cl^-$, $H^-$, and $CH_3CH_2^-$), two two-electron donor $PR_3$ ligands, and an $Rh^{3+}$ ion ($d^6$).

*Step 5:* The product has 14 electrons. It is an $Rh^+$ complex ($d^8$) with two $PR_3$ ligands (two electrons each) and one $Cl^-$ (two electrons). (It is likely a solvent molecule fills the vacant site here to give a transient, 16-electron complex.)

*Step 6:* The product is once again the active, 16-electron catalyst.

## Applying Chemical Principles: Green Catalysts

1.  Coordination number = 5

3.  Dentate

5.  Square-planar

# Chapter 23

**23.1**  Each answer is in the format: person(s); experiment; significance.
   (a) Becquerel; potassium uranyl sulfate caused an image to appear on a photographic plate; this opened up a new area of study.
   (b) Marie and Pierre Curie; separated these elements from pitchblende; discovery of new elements based on radioactivity.
   (c) Rutherford; bombarded $^{14}N$ with $\alpha$ particles and found protons and $^{17}O$ among products; human-caused transmutation of one element into another.
   (d) Fermi; absorption of a neutron by a nucleus with subsequent release of a $\gamma$ ray; production of more nuclei and the use of this process to produce many of the radioisotopes used in medicine.
   (e) Hahn and Strassman, experiment explained by Meitner; bombarded a sample of uranium with neutrons and detected barium in products; nuclear fission is used in atomic bombs and in nuclear energy plants.

**23.3**  Binding energy per nucleon is determined by first calculating the mass defect for an isotope, converting the mass defect to binding energy (using $E = mc^2$) and then dividing the binding energy by the mass number of the nucleus.

**23.5**  Nuclear reactions are carried out in a laboratory by hitting a nucleus with a particle. Various particles have been used: $\alpha$ particles, protons, neutrons, and the nuclei of other atoms. In producing transuranium elements, this last method is used; the particles are usually accelerated to high energy in a particle accelerator.

**23.7**  While an organism lives, the percentage of carbon that is $^{14}C$ in the organism will equal the percentage in the atmosphere. When the organism dies, it no longer replenishes the $^{14}C$. By measuring the activity of $^{14}C$ in the organism, comparing it to the ambient $^{14}C$ activity, and using first-order kinetics, it is possible to determine how long ago the organism stopped taking in $^{14}C$ (died). Limitations: (1) The method assumes that the amount of $^{14}C$ in the atmosphere has remained constant, whereas it has varied by as much as 10%. (2) $^{14}C$ dating cannot be used to date an object less than 100 or more than about 40,000 years old. (3) The accuracy of $^{14}C$ dating is about $\pm100$ years.

**23.9**  A radioactive decay series occurs when a radioactive isotope decays to form another radioactive isotope. The series continues until a nonradioactive isotope is formed. Uranium ore contains radium and polonium because these elements are formed in the radioactive decay series of uranium.

**23.11**  (a) $^{56}_{28}Ni$; (b) $^{1}_{0}n$; (c) $^{32}_{15}P$; (d) $^{97}_{43}Tc$; (e) $^{0}_{-1}\beta$; (f) $^{0}_{1}e$ (positron)

**23.13**  (a) $^{0}_{-1}\beta$; (b) $^{87}_{37}Rb$; (c) $^{4}_{2}\alpha$; (d) $^{226}_{88}Ra$; (e) $^{0}_{-1}\beta$; (f) $^{24}_{11}Na$

**23.15**  $^{235}_{92}U \rightarrow ^{231}_{90}Th + ^{4}_{2}\alpha$
$^{231}_{90}Th \rightarrow ^{231}_{91}Pa + ^{0}_{-1}\beta$
$^{231}_{91}Pa \rightarrow ^{227}_{89}Ac + ^{4}_{2}\alpha$
$^{227}_{89}Ac \rightarrow ^{227}_{90}Th + ^{0}_{-1}\beta$
$^{227}_{90}Th \rightarrow ^{223}_{88}Ra + ^{4}_{2}\alpha$
$^{223}_{88}Ra \rightarrow ^{219}_{86}Rn + ^{4}_{2}\alpha$
$^{219}_{86}Rn \rightarrow ^{215}_{84}Po + ^{4}_{2}\alpha$
$^{215}_{84}Po \rightarrow ^{211}_{82}Pb + ^{4}_{2}\alpha$
$^{211}_{82}Pb \rightarrow ^{211}_{83}Bi + ^{0}_{-1}\beta$
$^{211}_{83}Bi \rightarrow ^{211}_{84}Po + ^{0}_{-1}\beta$
$^{211}_{84}Po \rightarrow ^{207}_{82}Pb + ^{4}_{2}\alpha$

**23.17**  (a) $^{198}_{79}Au \rightarrow ^{198}_{80}Hg + ^{0}_{-1}\beta$
(b) $^{222}_{86}Rn \rightarrow ^{218}_{84}Po + ^{4}_{2}\alpha$
(c) $^{137}_{55}Cs \rightarrow ^{137}_{56}Ba + ^{0}_{-1}\beta$
(d) $^{110}_{49}In \rightarrow ^{110}_{48}Cd + ^{0}_{1}e$

**23.19** (a) $^{80}_{35}$Br has a high neutron/proton ratio of 45/35. Beta decay will allow the ratio to decrease: $^{80}_{35}$Br → $^{80}_{36}$Kr + $^{0}_{-1}\beta$.

(b) Alpha decay is likely: $^{240}_{98}$Cf → $^{236}_{96}$Cm + $^{4}_{2}\alpha$

(c) Cobalt-61 has a high $n/p$ ratio, so beta decay is likely: $^{61}_{27}$Co → $^{61}_{28}$Kr + $^{0}_{-1}\beta$

(d) Carbon-11 has only five neutrons, so K-capture or positron emission may occur:
$^{11}_{6}$C + $^{0}_{-1}$e → $^{11}_{5}$B
$^{11}_{6}$C → $^{11}_{5}$B + $^{0}_{1}$e

**23.21** Generally beta decay will occur when the $n/p$ ratio is high, whereas positron emission will occur when the $n/p$ ratio is low.

(a) Beta decay: $^{20}_{9}$F → $^{20}_{10}$Ne + $^{0}_{-1}\beta$
$^{3}_{1}$H → $^{3}_{2}$He + $^{0}_{-1}\beta$

(b) Positron emission
$^{22}_{11}$Na → $^{22}_{10}$Ne + $^{0}_{1}\beta$

**23.23** Binding energy per mole of nucleons for $^{11}$B = $6.70 \times 10^8$ kJ

Binding energy per mole of nucleons for $^{10}$B = $6.26 \times 10^8$ kJ

**23.25** $8.256 \times 10^8$ kJ/mol nucleons

**23.27** $7.700 \times 10^8$ kJ/mol nucleons

**23.29** 0.781 micrograms

**23.31** (a) $^{131}_{53}$I → $^{131}_{54}$Xe + $^{0}_{-1}\beta$
(b) 0.075 micrograms

**23.33** $9.5 \times 10^{-4}$ mg

**23.35** (a) $^{222}_{86}$Rn → $^{218}_{84}$Po + $^{4}_{2}\alpha$
(b) Time = 8.87 d

**23.37** (a) 15.8 y; (b) 88%

**23.39** $^{239}_{94}$Pu + $^{4}_{2}\alpha$ → $^{240}_{95}$Am + $^{1}_{1}$H + 2 $^{1}_{0}$n

**23.41** $^{48}_{20}$Ca + $^{242}_{94}$Pu → $^{287}_{114}$Uuq + 3 $^{1}_{0}$n

**23.43** (a) $^{115}_{48}$Cd; (b) $^{7}_{4}$Be; (c) $^{4}_{2}\alpha$; (d) $^{63}_{29}$Cu

**23.45** $^{10}_{5}$B + $^{1}_{0}$n → $^{7}_{3}$Li + $^{4}_{2}\alpha$

**23.47** Time = $4.4 \times 10^{10}$ y

**23.49** If $t_{1/2}$ = 14.28 d, then $k = 4.854 \times 10^{-2}$ d$^{-1}$. If the original disintegration rate is $3.2 \times 10^6$ dpm, then (from the integrated first order rate equation), the rate after 365 d is 0.065 dpm. The plot will resemble Figure 23.5.

**23.51** (a) $^{238}_{92}$U + $^{1}_{0}$n → $^{239}_{92}$U + $\gamma$
(b) $^{239}_{92}$U → $^{239}_{93}$Np + $^{0}_{-1}\beta$
(c) $^{239}_{93}$Np → $^{239}_{94}$Pu + $^{0}_{-1}\beta$
(d) $^{239}_{94}$Pu + $^{1}_{0}$n → 2 $^{1}_{0}$n + energy + other nuclei

**23.53** About 2700 years old

**23.55** Plot ln(activity) versus time. The slope of the plot is $-k$, the rate constant for decay. Here, $k = 0.0050$ d$^{-1}$, so $t_{1/2}$ = 140 d.

**23.57** Time = $1.9 \times 10^9$ y

**23.59** Energy obtained from 1.000 lb (452.6 g) of $^{235}$U = $4.1 \times 10^{10}$ kJ

Mass of coal required = $1.6 \times 10^3$ ton (or about 3 million pounds of coal)

**23.61** 27 fish tagged fish out of 5250 fish caught represents 0.51% of the fish in the lake. Therefore, 1000 fish put into the lake represent 0.51% of the fish in the lake, or 0.51% of 190,000 fish.

**23.63** (a) The mass decreases by 4 units (with an $^{4}_{2}\alpha$ emission) or is unchanged (with a $^{0}_{-1}\beta$ emission), so the only masses possible are 4 units apart.

(b) $^{232}$Th series, $m = 4n$; $^{235}$U series $m = 4n + 3$

(c) $^{226}$Ra and $^{210}$Bi, $4n + 2$ series; $^{215}$At, $4n + 3$ series; $^{228}$Th, $4n$ series

(d) Each series is headed by a long-lived isotope (in the order of $10^9$ years, the age of the Earth). The $4n + 1$ series is missing because there is no long-lived isotope in this series. Over geologic time, all the members of this series have decayed completely.

**23.65** (a) $^{231}$Pa isotope belongs to the $^{235}$U decay series (see Question 23.63b).

(b) $^{235}_{92}$U → $^{231}_{90}$Th + $^{4}_{2}\alpha$
$^{231}_{90}$Th → $^{231}_{91}$Pa + $^{0}_{-1}\beta$

(c) Pa-231 is present to the extent of 1 part per million. Therefore, 1 million grams of pitchblende need to be used to obtain 1 g of Pa-231.

(d) $^{231}_{91}$Pa → $^{227}_{89}$Ac + $^{4}_{2}\alpha$

**23.67** Pitchblende contains $^{238}_{92}$U and $^{235}_{92}$U. Thus, both radium and polonium isotopes must belong to either the $4n + 2$ or $4n + 3$ decay series. Furthermore, the isotopes must have sufficiently long half-lives in order to survive the separation and isolation process. These criteria are satisfied by $^{226}$Ra and $^{210}$Po.

# Applying Chemical Principles: The Age of Meteorites

**1.** $^{87}_{37}$Rb → $^{87}_{38}$Sr + $^{0}_{-1}\beta$

**3.** $k = 1.42 \times 10^{-11}$ y$^{-1}$

**5.** Age of meteorite = $2.80 \times 10^9$ y

# Index/Glossary

**electrostatic force(s)** Forces of attraction or repulsion caused by electric charges, 76
electrostatic potential surface, 378
**element(s)** Matter that is composed of only one kind of atom, 10
abundances of, 961, 962t
  in Earth's crust, 62t
  in solar system, *103*
atomic number of, 52
atomic weight of, 55
attachment enthalpy values of, A-18
*d*-block, 1017
diatomic molecules of, *64*
early definitions of, 336
*f*-block, 1017
ionization energies of, A-18
isotopes of, 54–55
main group, *60*, 61
  chemistry of, 960–1015
molar mass of, 80
monatomic ions of, charges on, 70
names of, 10–11
oxidation number of zero, 139
*p*-block, 308
  molecular orbitals involving, 421, 423
physical states of, 549
*s*-block, 307
sources of, *1023*
specific heat capacity of, 212t
standard enthalpy of formation of, 234
standard enthalpy of vaporization of, 567t
symbol for, 52–53
synthesis of, 1076
transition, *60*, 61, 66. *See also* transition elements.
transuranium, 1076, 1077
**elementary step** A simple event in which some chemical transformation occurs; one of a sequence of events that form the reaction mechanism, 698
rate equation for, 699
elephants, frontalin in, 443
eluent, 581
Empedocles, 335
**empirical formula** A molecular formula showing the simplest possible ratio of atoms in a molecule, 87
determination by combustion analysis, 169–172
relation to molecular formula, 88
emulsifying agent, 645
**emulsion** A colloidal dispersion of one liquid in another, 644t
**enantiomers** A stereoisomeric pair consisting of a chiral compound and its mirror image isomer, 441
of α-amino acids, 493
end point. *See* **equivalence point.**
endocytosis, 503
**endothermic process** A thermodynamic process in which energy as heat flows into a system from its surroundings, 211, 860
enthalpy change of, 224
in metabolism, 504
**energy** The capacity to do work and transfer heat, 209–211, A-7. *See also* **enthalpy** *and* **heat** *entries.*
activation. *See* **activation energy.**
alternate sources of, 256, 262
binding, 1067–1070
color of photons and, 272
conversion of forms of, *17*, 18
density, in batteries vs. gasoline, 912t
direction of transfer, 210
dispersal of, 861, 862
in food, 29, 208
internal, 220
ionization. *See* **ionization energy.**

lattice, 599
law of conservation of, 18, 209
levels in hydrogen atom, 274
mass equivalence of, 1068
nuclear, 1079
quantization of, 274, 281, 865
relation to frequency of radiation, 270
sources for human activity, 209
state changes and, 216–219
units of, A-7
energy level diagram, 230
energy resources and usage, 254–267
**enthalpy (H)** The sum of the internal energy of the system and the product of its pressure and volume, 222
bond dissociation, 383–387
effect on acid strength, 788
**enthalpy change (ΔH)** The energy as heat transferred at constant pressure, 222, 860
for chemical reactions, 224–226
sign conventions for, 222
as state function, 222
enthalpy of formation, standard molar, 233
values of, A-26
**enthalpy of fusion (Δ_fusH)** The energy as heat required to convert one mole of a substance from a solid to a liquid at constant temperature, 602, 604t, A-14t
enthalpy of hydration, 551
of alkali metals, 972
**enthalpy of solution (Δ_solnH)** The amount of energy as heat involved in the process of solution formation, 623–626
measurement of, 625
enthalpy of solvation, 551
**enthalpy of sublimation (Δ_sublimationH)** The energy as heat required to convert one mole of a substance from a solid to a gas, 605
**enthalpy of vaporization (Δ_vapH)** The quantity of energy as heat required to convert 1 mol of a liquid to a gas at constant temperature, 566, 567t, A-14t
intermolecular forces and, 552, 554t
of nonpolar substances, 560t, 567t
relation to vapor pressure, 570
**entropy (S)** A measure of the dispersal of energy in a system, 861
effect on acid strength, 788
molecular structure and, 867
physical state and, 867
second law of thermodynamics and, 870
solution process and, 621–622
standard molar, 866
statistical basis of, 862–864
entropy change (ΔS), for universe, system, and surroundings, 870
of reaction, 868
environment, chemistry of, 946–959
**enzyme(s)** A biological catalyst, 495, 675
catalysis by, 702
enzyme cofactors, 500
ephedrine, structure of 105
epichlorohydrin, structure of, 477
Epicurus, 335
epinephrine, 464
structure of, 397
epoxy copolymer, 477
Epsom salt, 96
formula of, 107
equation(s), Arrhenius, 693
Balmer, 273
Beer–Lambert law, 191
Bohr, 274, 331
boiling point elevation, 632

Boltzmann, 864
bond order, 382, 419
Boyle's law, 512
buffer solution pH, 812
Celsius–Kelvin scale conversion, 27
Charles's law, 514
chemical, 16, 111–113
Clausius–Clapeyron, 570
Coulomb's law, 76
Dalton's law, 525
de Broglie, 278
dilution, 176
Einstein's, 1068
electronegativity, 399
enthalpy of formation, 234
entropy, 861
entropy change of reaction, 868
equilibrium constant expression, 723
equilibrium constant of electrochemical cell, 927
first law of thermodynamics, 220
formal charge, 354
free energy change at nonequilibrium conditions, 876
freezing point depression, 634
general gas law, 515
Gibbs free energy, 874
Graham's law, 533
half-life, 686
  for radioactive decay, 1072
heat and temperature change, 212
Henderson–Hasselbalch, 813
Henry's law, 626
Hess's law, 230
ideal gas law, 518
integrated rate, 681–689
ion pair energy, 598
ionization constants, for acids and bases, 765
  for water, 761
$K_a$ and $K_b$, 768
kinetic energy, 529
molarity, 173
mole fraction, 618
Nernst, 921
net ionic, 126
  of strong acid–strong base reactions, 132
nuclear reactions, 1060
osmotic pressure, 636
pH, 178, 763
  of buffer solution, 812
$pK_a$, 768
Planck's, 269–272
pressure–volume work, 221
quadratic, 735, A-4
Raoult's law, 630
rate, 669, 676. *See also* **rate equation(s).**
rms speed, 530
Schrödinger, 281
second law of thermodynamics, 870
speed of a wave, 267
standard free energy change of reaction, 876
standard potential, 915, 918
straight line, 41
van der Waals, 535
equatorial position, in cyclohexane structure, 449
  in trigonal-bipyramidal molecular geometry, 368
**equilibrium** A condition in which the forward and reverse reaction rates in a physical or chemical system are equal, 116–119
chemical, 720–755. *See also* chemical equilibrium.

## PHYSICAL AND CHEMICAL CONSTANTS

Avogadro's number     $N = 6.0221415 \times 10^{23}/mol$
Electronic charge      $e = 1.60217653 \times 10^{-19}$ C
Faraday's constant     $F = 9.6485338 \times 10^{4}$ C/mol electrons
Gas constant          $R = 8.314472$ J/K $\cdot$ mol
                      $= 0.082057$ L $\cdot$ atm/K $\cdot$ mol

$\pi$                    $\pi = 3.1415926536$
Planck's constant    $h = 6.6260693 \times 10^{-34}$ J $\cdot$ sec
Speed of light       $c = 2.99792458 \times 10^{8}$ m/sec
(in a vacuum)

## USEFUL CONVERSION FACTORS AND RELATIONSHIPS

### Length
**SI unit: Meter (m)**
1 kilometer $= 1000$ meters
           $= 0.62137$ mile
1 meter $= 100$ centimeters
1 centimeter $= 10$ millimeters
1 nanometer $= 1.00 \times 10^{-9}$ meter
1 picometer $= 1.00 \times 10^{-12}$ meter
1 inch $= 2.54$ centimeter (exactly)
1 Ångstrom $= 1.00 \times 10^{-10}$ meter

### Mass
**SI unit: Kilogram (kg)**
1 kilogram $= 1000$ grams
1 gram $= 1000$ milligrams
1 pound $= 453.59237$ grams $= 16$ ounces
1 ton $= 2000$ pounds

### Volume
**SI unit: Cubic meter (m³)**
1 liter (L) $= 1.00 \times 10^{-3}$ m³
           $= 1000$ cm³
           $= 1.056710$ quarts
1 gallon $= 4.00$ quarts

### Energy
**SI unit: Joule (J)**
1 joule $= 1$ kg $\cdot$ m²/s²
           $= 0.23901$ calorie
           $= 1$ C $\times$ 1 V
1 calorie $= 4.184$ joules

### Pressure
**SI unit: Pascal (Pa)**
1 pascal $= 1$ N/m²
           $= 1$ kg/m $\cdot$ s²
1 atmosphere $= 101.325$ kilopascals
           $= 760$ mm Hg $= 760$ torr
           $= 14.70$ lb/in²
           $= 1.01325$ bar
1 bar $= 10^{5}$ Pa (exactly)

### Temperature
**SI unit: kelvin (K)**
0 K $= -273.15$ °C
K $=$ °C $+ 273.15$°C
? °C $= (5$ °C/9 °F)(°F $- 32$ °F)
? °F $= (9$ °F/5 °C)(°C) $+ 32$ °F

## LOCATION OF USEFUL TABLES AND FIGURES

### Atomic and Molecular Properties

| | |
|---|---|
| Atomic electron configurations | Table 7.3 |
| Atomic radii | Figures 7.6, 7.9 |
| Bond dissociation enthalpies | Table 8.9 |
| Bond lengths | Table 8.8 |
| Electron Attachment Enthalpy | Figure 7.11, Appendix F |
| Electronegativity | Figure 8.11 |
| Elements and their unit cells | Figure 13.5 |
| Hybrid orbitals | Figure 9.3 |
| Ionic radii | Figure 7.12 |
| Ionization energies | Figure 7.10, Table 7.5 |

### Thermodynamic Properties

| | |
|---|---|
| Enthalpy, free energy, entropy | Appendix L |
| Lattice energies | Table 13.2 |
| Specific heat capacities | Appendix D |

### Acids, Bases and Salts

| | |
|---|---|
| Common acids and bases | Table 3.1 |
| Formation constants | Appendix K |
| Ionization constants for weak acids and bases | Table 17.3, Appendix H, I |
| Names and composition of polyatomic ions | Table 2.4 |
| Solubility guidelines | Figure 3.10 |
| Solubility constants | Appendix J |

### Miscellaneous

| | |
|---|---|
| Charges on common monatomic cations and anions | Figure 2.18 |
| Common polymers | Table 10.12 |
| Oxidizing and reducing agents | Table 3.3 |
| Selected alkanes | Table 10.2 |
| Standard reduction potentials | Table 20.1, Appendix M |